About the Cover

The cover image illustrates a Seifert surface, named for German mathematician Herbert Seifert. The boundary of a Seifert surface is a simple knot called a trefoil. You could make a trefoil by joining together the two loose ends of a common overhand knot, resulting in a knotted loop.

Meet the Artist

The cover art was generated by Paul Nylander, a mechanical engineer with strong programming and mathematical skills that he uses to design complex engineering systems. Nylander says that he always enjoyed science and art as a hobby. When he was in high school, he had some aptitude for math, but programming was difficult for him. However, he became much more interested in programming when he began studying computer graphics. Most of Nylander's artwork is created in Mathematica, POV-Ray, and C++.

You can find a short bio and description of his work at: http://virtualmathmuseum.org/mathart/ArtGalleryNylander/Nylanderindex.html.

Cover: Seifert. By Daniel Erdely and Paul Nylander (bugman123.com)

GLENCOE

GEOMETRY

McGraw Hill Education

mheducation.com/prek-12

Send all inquiries to:
McGraw-Hill Education
8787 Orion Place
Columbus, OH 43240

ISBN: 978-0-07-898490-7 *(Teacher Edition, Vol. 1)*
MHID: 0-07-898490-4 *(Teacher Edition, Vol. 1)*
ISBN: 978-0-07-898493-8 *(Teacher Edition, Vol. 2)*
MHID: 0-07-898493-9 *(Teacher Edition, Vol. 2)*
ISBN: 978-0-07-903994-1 *(Student Edition)*
MHID: 0-07-903994-4 *(Student Edition)*

Printed in the United States of America.

3 4 5 6 7 8 9 QVS 22 21 20 19 18 17

STEM

McGraw-Hill is committed to providing instructional materials in Science, Technology, Engineering, and Mathematics (STEM) that give all students a solid foundation, one that prepares them for college and careers in the 21st century.

Contents in Brief

SUGGESTED PACING GUIDE

Each chapter includes multiple days for review and assessment.

Chapter 0	5 days
Chapter 1	16 days
Chapter 2	17 days
Chapter 3	12 days
Chapter 4	12 days
Chapter 5	12 days
Chapter 6	9 days
Chapter 7	9 days
Chapter 8	14 days
Chapter 9	11 days
Chapter 10	12 days
Chapter 11	13 days
Chapter 12	10 days
Total	**152 days**

Authors

Our lead authors ensure that the Macmillan/McGraw-Hill and Glencoe/McGraw-Hill mathematics programs are truly vertically aligned by beginning with the end in mind — success in Algebra 1 and beyond. By "backmapping" the content from the high school programs, all of our mathematics programs are well articulated in their scope and sequence.

LEAD AUTHORS

John A. Carter, Ph.D.

Mathematics Teacher
WINNETKA, ILLINOIS

Areas of Expertise:
Using technology and manipulatives to visualize concepts; mathematics achievement of English-language learners

Gilbert J. Cuevas, Ph.D.

Professor of Mathematics Education, Texas State University—San Marcos
SAN MARCOS, TEXAS

Areas of Expertise:
Applying concepts and skills in mathematically rich contexts; mathematical representations; use of technology in the development of geometric thinking

Roger Day, Ph.D., NBCT

Mathematics Department Chairperson, Pontiac Township High School
PONTIAC, ILLINOIS

Areas of Expertise:
Understanding and applying probability and statistics; mathematics teacher education

In Memoriam

Carol Malloy, Ph.D.

Dr. Carol Malloy was a fervent supporter of mathematics education. She was a Professor at the University of North Carolina, Chapel Hill, NCTM Board of Directors member, President of the Benjamin Banneker Association (BBA), and 2013 BBA Lifetime Achievement Award for Mathematics winner. She joined McGraw-Hill in 1996. Her influence significantly improved our programs' focus on real-world problem solving and equity. We will miss her inspiration and passion for education.

PROGRAM AUTHOR

In Memoriam

Jerry Cummins

Jerry Cummins was a passionate and enthusiastic mathematics educator who taught math and computer science in the Chicago area for 32 years. Mr. Cummins was on the forefront of graphing technology usage in the classroom. His influence greatly improved the integration of technology within our programs. In 1997, Mr. Cummins received the Distinguished Life Achievement Award from the Illinois Council of Teachers of Mathematics. He also served as the President of the National Council of Supervisors of Mathematics from 1999-2001. We will miss his exuberance and devotion to education.

CONTRIBUTING AUTHORS

Dinah Zike FOLDABLES

Educational Consultant
Dinah-Might Activities, Inc.
SAN ANTONIO, TEXAS

Jay McTighe

Educational Author and Consultant
COLUMBIA, MARYLAND

Consultants and Reviewers

These professionals were instrumental in providing valuable input and suggestions for improving the effectiveness of the mathematics instruction.

LEAD CONSULTANT

Viken Hovsepian
Professor of Mathematics
Rio Hondo College
WHITTIER, CALIFORNIA

CONSULTANTS

MATHEMATICAL CONTENT

Lead Consultant
Viken Hovsepian
Professor of Mathematics
Rio Hondo College
WHITTIER, CALIFORNIA

Grant A. Fraser, Ph.D.
Professor of Mathematics
California State University, Los Angeles
LOS ANGELES, CALIFORNIA

Arthur K. Wayman, Ph.D.
Professor of Mathematics Emeritus
California State University, Long Beach
LONG BEACH, CALIFORNIA

GIFTED AND TALENTED

Shelbi K. Cole
Research Assistant
University of Connecticut
STORRS, CONNECTICUT

COLLEGE READINESS

Robert Lee Kimball, Jr.
Department Head, Math and Physics
Wake Technical Community College
RALEIGH, NORTH CAROLINA

DIFFERENTIATION FOR ENGLISH-LANGUAGE LEARNERS

Susana Davidenko
State University of New York
CORTLAND, NEW YORK

Alfredo Gómez
Mathematics/ESL Teacher
George W. Fowler High School
SYRACUSE, NEW YORK

GRAPHING CALCULATOR

Ruth M. Casey
T^3 National Instructor
FRANKFORT, KENTUCKY

MATHEMATICAL FLUENCY

Robert M. Capraro
Associate Professor
Texas A&M University
COLLEGE STATION, TEXAS

PRE-AP

Dixie Ross
Lead Teacher for Advanced Placement Mathematics
Pflugerville High School
PFLUGERVILLE, TEXAS

READING AND WRITING

ReLeah Cossett Lent
Author and Educational Consultant
MORGANTON, GEORGIA

Lynn T. Havens
Director of Project CRISS
KALISPELL, MONTANA

REVIEWERS

Corey Andreasen
Mathematics Teacher
North High School
SHEBOYGAN, MICHIGAN

Mark B. Baetz
Mathematics Coordinating Teacher
Salem City Schools
SALEM, VIRGINIA

Kathryn Ballin
Mathematics Supervisor
Newark Public Schools
NEWARK, NEW JERSEY

Kevin C. Barhorst
Mathematics Department Chair
Independence High School
COLUMBUS, OHIO

Brenda S. Berg
Mathematics Teacher
Carbondale Community High School
CARBONDALE, ILLINOIS

Sheryl Pernell Clayton
Mathematics Teacher
Hume Fogg Magnet School
NASHVILLE, TENNESSEE

Bob Coleman
Mathematics Teacher
Cobb Middle School
TALLAHASSEE, FLORIDA

Jane E. Cotts
Mathematics Teacher
O'Fallon Township High School
O'FALLON, ILLINOIS

Michael D. Cuddy
Mathematics Instructor
Zypherhills High School
ZYPHERHILLS, FLORIDA

Melissa M. Dalton, NBCT
Mathematics Instructor
Rural Retreat High School
RURAL RETREAT, VIRGINIA

Trina Louise Davis
Teacher
Fort Mill High School
FORT MILL, SOUTH CAROLINA

Tina S. Dohm
Mathematics Teacher
Naperville Central High School
NAPERVILLE, ILLINOIS

Laurie L.E. Ferrari
Teacher
L'Anse Creuse High School—North
MACOMB, MICHIGAN

Patricia R. Frazier
Mathematics Department Chair/Instructor
Celina High School
CELINA, OHIO

Steve Freshour
Mathematics Teacher
Parkersburg South High School
PARKERSBURG, WEST VIRGINIA

Shirley D. Glover
Mathematics Teacher
TC Roberson High School
ASHEVILLE, NORTH CAROLINA

Caroline W. Greenough
Mathematics Teacher
Cape Fear Academy
WILMINGTON, NORTH CAROLINA

Michelle Hanneman
Mathematics Teacher
Moore High School
MOORE, OKLAHOMA

Theresalynn Haynes
Mathematics Teacher
Glenbard East High School
LOMBARD, ILLINOIS

Sandra Hester
Mathematics Teacher/AIG Specialist
North Henderson High School
HENDERSONVILLE, NORTH CAROLINA

Jacob K. Holloway
Mathematics Teacher
Capitol Heights Junior High School
MONTGOMERY, ALABAMA

Robert Hopp
Mathematics Teacher
Harrison High School
HARRISON, MICHIGAN

Eileen Howanitz
Mathematics Teacher/Department Chairperson
Valley View High School
ARCHBALD, PENNSYLVANIA

Charles R. Howard, NBCT
Mathematics Teacher
Tuscola High School
WAYNESVILLE, NORTH CAROLINA

Sue Hvizdos
Mathematics Department Chairperson
Wheeling Park High School
WHEELING, WEST VIRGINIA

Elaine Keller
Mathematics Teacher
Mathematics Curriculum Director K–12
Northwest Local Schools
CANAL FULTON, OHIO

Sheila A. Kotter
Mathematics Educator
River Ridge High School
NEW PORT RICHEY, FLORIDA

Frank Lear
Mathematics Department Chair
Cleveland High School
CLEVELAND, TENNESSEE

Jennifer Lewis
Mathematics Teacher
Triad High School
TROY, ILLINOIS

Catherine McCarthy
Mathematics Teacher
Glen Ridge High School
GLEN RIDGE, NEW JERSEY

Jacqueline Palmquist
Mathematics Department Chair
Waubonsie Valley High School
AURORA, ILLINOIS

Thom Schacher
Mathematics Teacher
Otsego High School
OTSEGO, MICHIGAN

Laurie Shappee
Teacher/Mathematics Coordinator
Larson Middle School
TROY, MICHIGAN

Jennifer J. Southers
Mathematics Teacher
Hillcrest High School
SIMPSONVILLE, SOUTH CAROLINA

Sue Steinbeck
Mathematics Department Chair
Parkersburg High School
PARKERSBURG, WEST VIRGINIA

Kathleen D. Van Sise
Mathematics Teacher
Mandarin High School
JACKSONVILLE, FLORIDA

Karen Wiedman
Mathematics Teacher
Taylorville High School
TAYLORVILLE, ILLINOIS

Solutions That Work

Glencoe High School Math Series is about connecting math content, rigor, and adaptive instruction for student success.

Glencoe High School Math Series provides you the flexibility to meet your classroom needs. As you build teacher-student relationships and a classroom environment that encourages learning, this program provides a flexible print and digital solution that allows you to:

- **Personalize learning** for all students with differentiated instruction and math content that meets rigorous standards.
- **Engage students** in a variety of ways with projects, activities, and resources that make math come to life and enable students to connect math to their world.
- **Drive success** on state assessments with dynamic digital tools that support and inform instructional decisions.

"Great...easy textbook to use, good online resources, and many examples, including great exit ticket ideas and warm up questions."

--High School Teacher

Hero Images/Getty Images

Rigor in Instruction

Glencoe High School Math Series is about connecting math content and rigor. Rigor is built-in throughout the entire program with a strong focus on promoting conceptual understanding and encouraging students to think critically.

Performance Tasks

A Performance Task is available for each chapter that enables students to practice persevering through a rich, multi-step task. The Performance Tasks are previewed at the beginning of the chapter. Students will learn concepts and skills as they work through each lesson that will help them to finish the task at the end of the chapter.

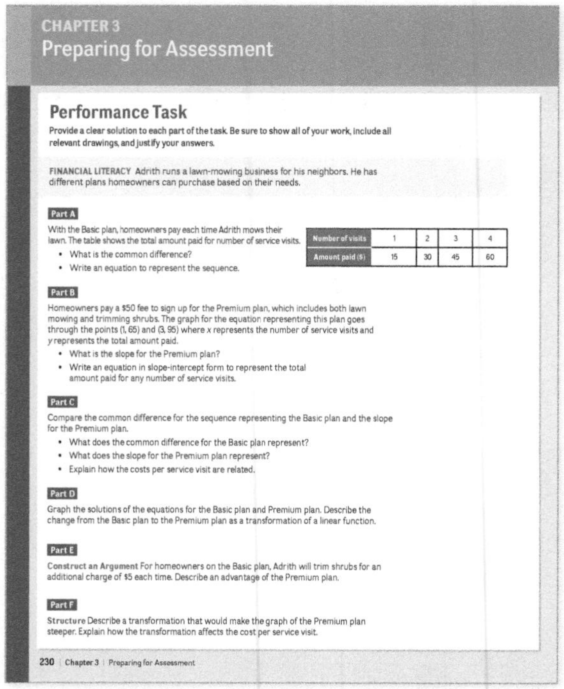
CHAPTER 3
Preparing for Assessment

Performance Task

Provide a clear solution to each part of the task. Be sure to show all of your work, include all relevant drawings, and justify your answers.

FINANCIAL LITERACY Adrith runs a lawn-mowing business for his neighbors. He has different plans homeowners can purchase based on their needs.

Part A

With the Basic plan, homeowners pay each time Adrith mows their lawn. The table shows the total amount paid for number of service visits.

Number of visits	1	2	3	4
Amount paid ($)	15	30	45	60

- What is the common difference?
- Write an equation to represent the sequence.

Part B

Homeowners pay a $50 fee to sign up for the Premium plan, which includes both lawn mowing and trimming shrubs. The graph for the equation representing this plan goes through the points (1, 65) and (3, 95) where x represents the number of service visits and y represents the total amount paid.

- What is the slope for the Premium plan?
- Write an equation in slope-intercept form to represent the total amount paid for any number of service visits.

Part C

Compare the common difference for the sequence representing the Basic plan and the slope for the Premium plan.

- What does the common difference for the Basic plan represent?
- What does the slope for the Premium plan represent?
- Explain how the costs per service visit are related.

Part D

Graph the solutions of the equations for the Basic plan and Premium plan. Describe the change from the Basic plan to the Premium plan as a transformation of a linear function.

Part E

Construct an Argument For homeowners on the Basic plan, Adrith will trim shrubs for an additional charge of $5 each time. Describe an advantage of the Premium plan.

Part F

Structure Describe a transformation that would make the graph of the Premium plan steeper. Explain how the transformation affects the cost per service visit.

230 | Chapter 3 | Preparing for Assessment

Multi-Step Questions

Multi-step questions allow students to practice reasoning, modeling, and looking for structure in different situations. These questions are incorporated into the Preparing for Assessment page at the end of each lesson and can also be found online in eAssessment.

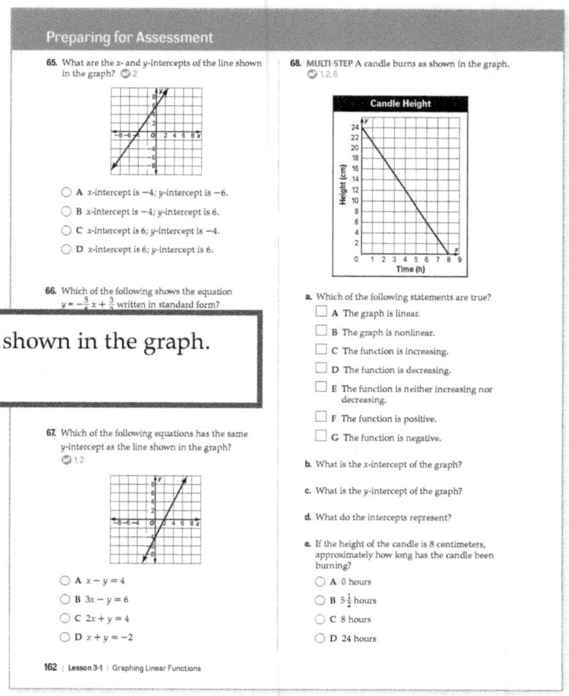
Preparing for Assessment

65. What are the x- and y-intercepts of the line shown in the graph? MP 2

- A x-intercept is −4; y-intercept is −6.
- B x-intercept is −4; y-intercept is 6.
- C x-intercept is 6; y-intercept is −4.
- D x-intercept is 6; y-intercept is 6.

66. Which of the following shows the equation $y = -\frac{5}{}x + \frac{3}{}$ written in standard form?

67. Which of the following equations has the same y-intercept as the line shown in the graph? MP 1, 2

- A $x - y = 4$
- B $3x - y = 6$
- C $2x + y = 4$
- D $x + y = -2$

68. MULTI-STEP A candle burns as shown in the graph. MP 1, 2, 8

a. Which of the following statements are true?
- A The graph is linear.
- B The graph is nonlinear.
- C The function is increasing.
- D The function is decreasing.
- E The function is neither increasing nor decreasing.
- F The function is positive.
- G The function is negative.

b. What is the x-intercept of the graph?

c. What is the y-intercept of the graph?

d. What do the intercepts represent?

e. If the height of the candle is 8 centimeters, approximately how long has the candle been burning?
- A 0 hours
- B $5\frac{1}{2}$ hours
- C 8 hours
- D 24 hours

162 | Lesson 3-1 | Graphing Linear Functions

68. MULTI-STEP A candle burns as shown in the graph.
MP 1, 2, 8

Standards for Mathematical Practice

The Standards for Mathematical Practice describe how students should approach mathematics. The goal of the practice standards is to instill in all students the abilities to be mathematically literate and to create a positive disposition for the importance of using math effectively.

You can use the following tools to incorporate the practices into your teaching.

- Mathematical Practice Study Tips located in the margins of the student edition.
- Look for the MP icon to see which practice is being taught.
- Mathematical Practice Strategies show you how to incorporate the practices in each chapter.

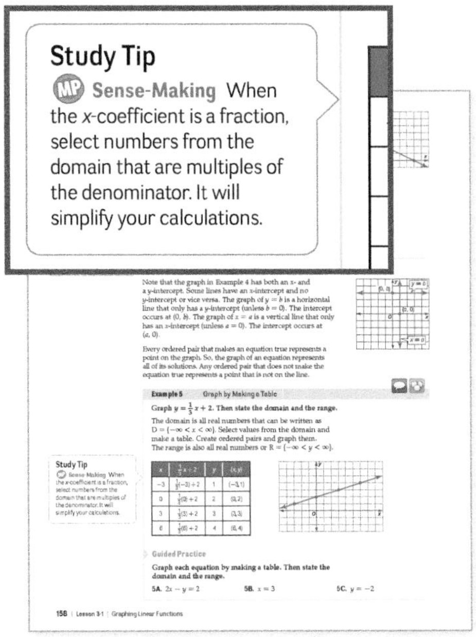

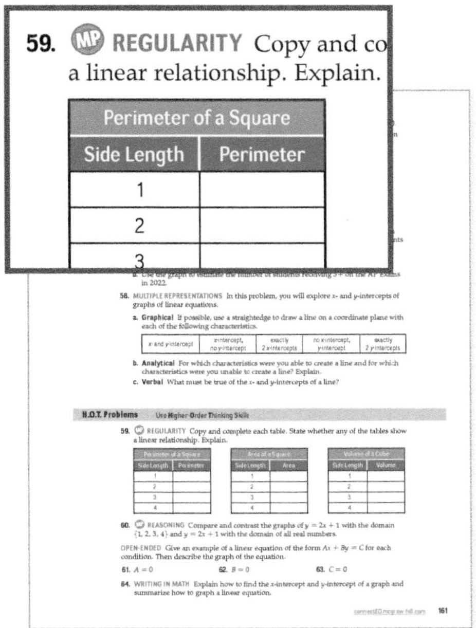

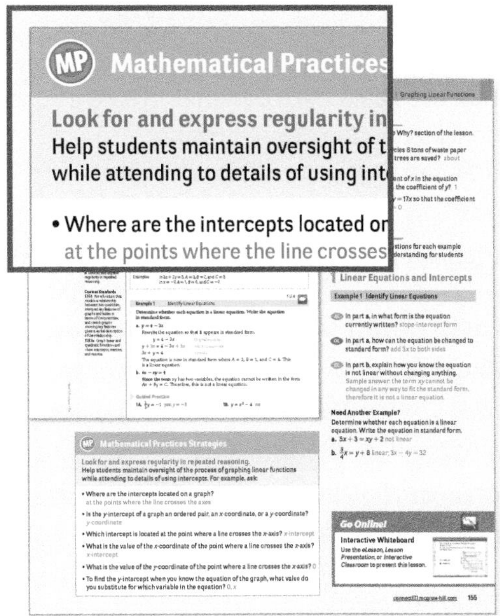

Interactive Student Guide

Working together, the Student Edition and *Interactive Student Guide* (ISG) promote a deep understanding of the content to ensure student success. Topics from the ISG correspond to the lessons within the Student Edition and point-of-use references are located in the margins of the Teacher Edition.

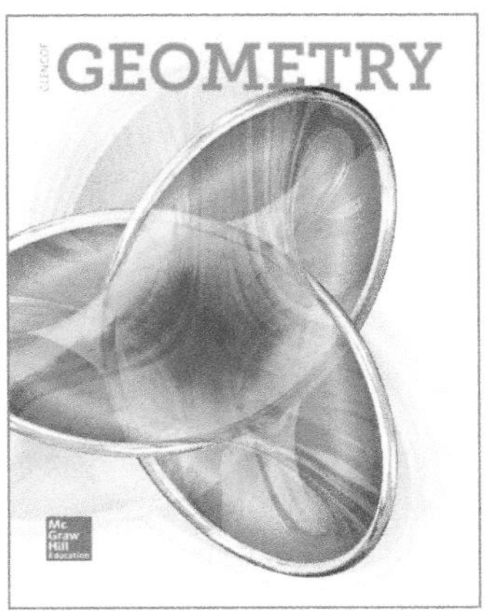

+

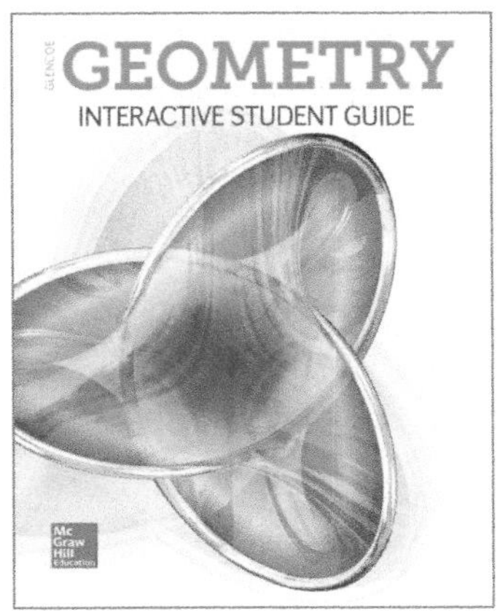

Understanding by Design

What should students know and be able to do? Understanding by Design can be used to help teachers identify learning goals, develop revealing assessments of student understanding, and plan effective and engaging learning activities.

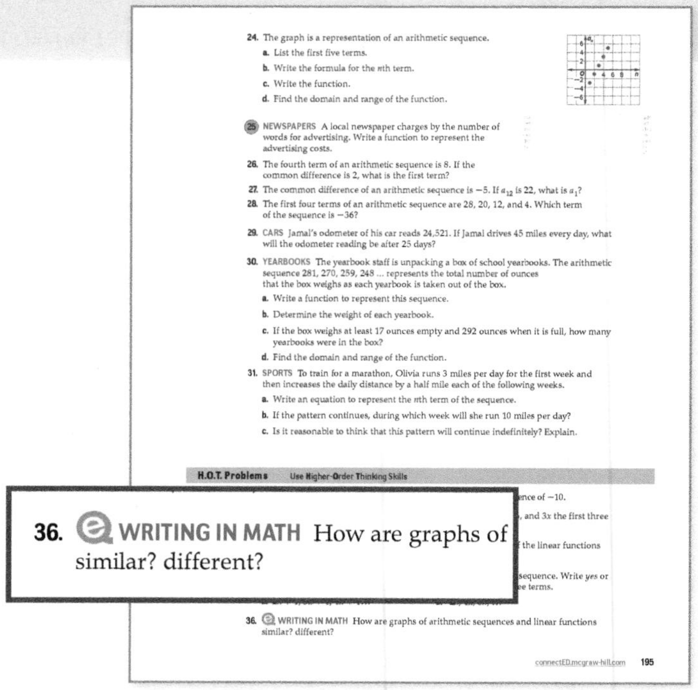

24. The graph is a representation of an arithmetic sequence.
 a. List the first five terms.
 b. Write the formula for the nth term.
 c. Write the function.
 d. Find the domain and range of the function.

25. NEWSPAPERS A local newspaper charges by the number of words for advertising. Write a function to represent the advertising costs.

26. The fourth term of an arithmetic sequence is 8. If the common difference is 2, what is the first term?

27. The common difference of an arithmetic sequence is −5. If a_{12} is 22, what is a_1?

28. The first four terms of an arithmetic sequence are 28, 20, 12, and 4. Which term of the sequence is −36?

29. CARS Jamal's odometer of his car reads 24,521. If Jamal drives 45 miles every day, what will the odometer reading be after 25 days?

30. YEARBOOKS The yearbook staff is unpacking a box of school yearbooks. The arithmetic sequence 281, 270, 259, 248 ... represents the total number of ounces that the box weighs as each yearbook is taken out of the box.
 a. Write a function to represent this sequence.
 b. Determine the weight of each yearbook.
 c. If the box weighs at least 17 ounces empty and 292 ounces when it is full, how many yearbooks were in the box?
 d. Find the domain and range of the function.

31. SPORTS To train for a marathon, Olivia runs 3 miles per day for the first week and then increases the daily distance by a half mile each of the following weeks.
 a. Write an equation to represent the nth term of the sequence.
 b. If the pattern continues, during which week will she run 10 miles per day?
 c. Is it reasonable to think that this pattern will continue indefinitely? Explain.

H.O.T. Problems Use Higher-Order Thinking Skills

36. WRITING IN MATH How are graphs of similar? different?

36. WRITING IN MATH How are graphs of arithmetic sequences and linear functions similar? different?

connectED.mcgraw-hill.com 195

Backward Design

Understanding by Design (UbD) is a framework that uses backward design to create a coherent curriculum by considering the desired results first and then planning instruction.

The backward design process guided the development of Glencoe Algebra 1, Glencoe Geometry, and Glencoe Algebra 2.

Identifying Desired Results

The first step in developing an effective curriculum using the UbD framework is to consider the goals. What should students know and be able to do?

Glencoe High School Math Series addresses the big ideas of algebra and focuses student attention on Essential Questions, which are located within each chapter of the Student and Teacher Editions.

An Essential Question is provided at the beginning of each chapter. These thought provoking questions can be used as:

- a discussion starter for your class; throughout the discussion identify what the students already know and what they would like to know about the topic. Revisit these notes throughout the chapter.
- a benchmark of understanding; post these questions in a prominent place and have students expand upon their initial response as their understanding of the subject material grows.

Follow-up Essential Questions can be found throughout each chapter. These questions challenge students to apply specific knowledge to a broader context, thus deepening their understanding.

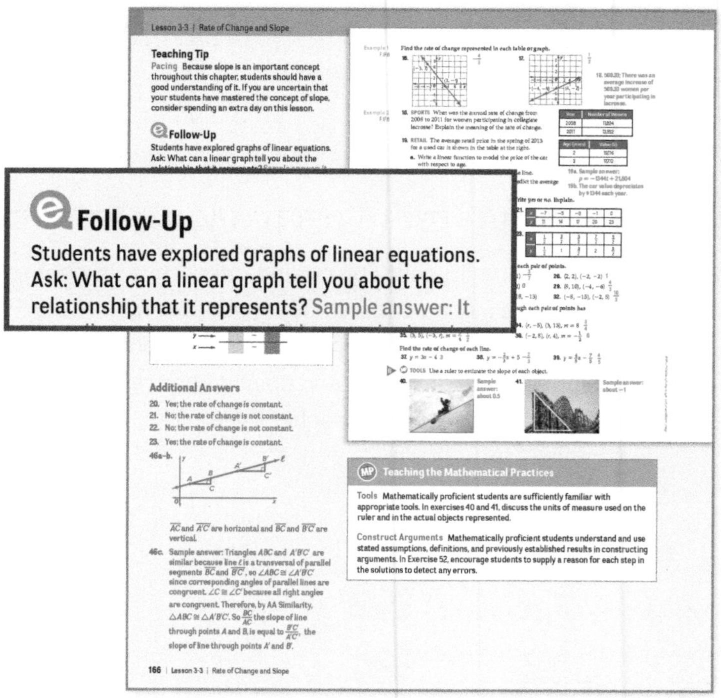

Lesson 3-3 | Rate of Change and Slope

Teaching Tip

Pacing Because slope is an important concept throughout this chapter, students should have a good understanding of it. If you are uncertain that your students have mastered the concept of slope, consider spending an extra day on this lesson.

Follow-Up

Students have explored graphs of linear equations. Ask: What can a linear graph tell you about the relationship that it represents? Sample answer: It

Find the rate of change represented in each table or graph.

18. SPORTS What was the annual rate of change from 2008 to 2011 for women participating in collegiate lacrosse? Explain the meaning of the rate of change.

19. RETAIL The average retail price in the spring of 2013 for a used car is shown in the table at the right.
 a. Write a linear function to model the price of the car with respect to age.

Find the rate of change of each line.

TOOLS Use a ruler to estimate the slope of each object.

Additional Answers

20. Yes; the rate of change is constant.
21. No; the rate of change is not constant.
22. No; the rate of change is not constant.
23. Yes; the rate of change is constant.

$\overline{AC}$ and $\overline{A'C'}$ are horizontal and $\overline{BC}$ and $\overline{B'C'}$ are vertical.

46c. Sample answer: Triangles ABC and $A'B'C'$ are similar because line ℓ is a transversal of parallel segments $\overline{BC}$ and $\overline{B'C'}$, so $\angle ABC \cong \angle A'B'C'$ since corresponding angles of parallel lines are congruent. $\angle C \cong \angle C'$ because all right angles are congruent. Therefore, by AA Similarity, $\triangle ABC \cong \triangle A'B'C'$. So $\frac{BC}{AC}$ the slope of line through points A and B, is equal to $\frac{B'C'}{A'C'}$, the slope of line through points A' and B'.

166 | Lesson 3-3 | Rate of Change and Slope

Teaching the Mathematical Practices

Tools Mathematically proficient students are sufficiently familiar with appropriate tools. In exercises 40 and 41, discuss the units of measure used on the ruler and in the actual objects represented.

Construct Arguments Mathematically proficient students understand and use stated assumptions, definitions, and previously established results in constructing arguments. In Exercise 52, encourage students to supply a reason for each step in the solutions to detect any errors.

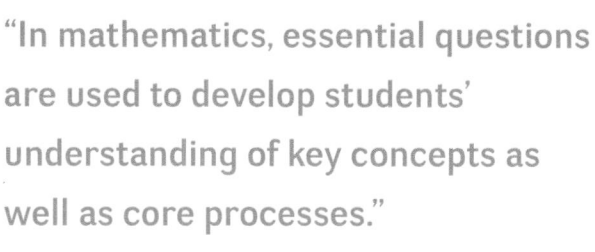

“In mathematics, essential questions are used to develop students’ understanding of key concepts as well as core processes.”

— **JAY MCTIGHE,** co-author of *Understanding by Design*

Determine Acceptable Evidence

A variety of assessment opportunities are available that enable students to show evidence of their understanding.

- Practice and Problem Solving and H.O.T. Problems allow students to explain, interpret, and apply mathematical concepts.
- Mid-Chapter Quizzes and Chapter Tests offer more traditional methods of assessment.
- McGraw-Hill eAssessment can also be used to customize and create assessments.

Plan Learning Experiences and Instruction

There are numerous performance activities available throughout the program, including:

- Algebra Labs that offer students hands-on learning experiences, and
- Graphing Technology Labs that use graphing calculators to aid student understanding.

You can also visit **connectED.mcgraw-hill.com** to choose from an extensive collection of resources to use when planning instruction, such as presentation tools, chapter projects, editable worksheets, digital animations, and eTools.

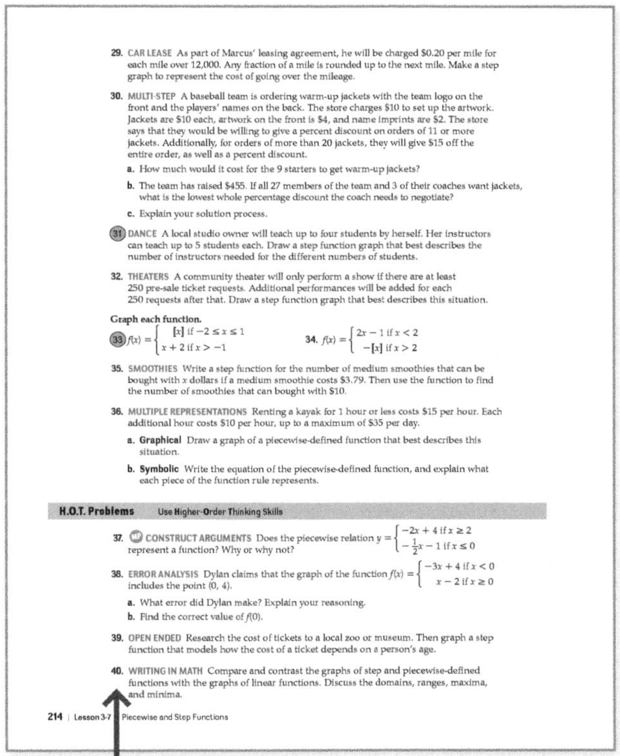

29. CAR LEASE As part of Marcus’ leasing agreement, he will be charged $0.20 per mile for each mile over 12,000. Any fraction of a mile is rounded up to the next mile. Make a step graph to represent the cost of going over the mileage.

30. MULTI-STEP A baseball team is ordering warm-up jackets with the team logo on the front and the players’ names on the back. The store charges $10 to set up the artwork. Jackets are $10 each, artwork on the front is $4, and name imprints are $2. The store says that they would be willing to give a percent discount on orders of 11 or more jackets. Additionally, for orders of more than 20 jackets, they will give $15 off the entire order, as well as a percent discount.
    a. How much would it cost for the 9 starters to get warm-up jackets?
    b. The team has raised $455. If all 27 members of the team and 3 of their coaches want jackets, what is the lowest whole percentage discount the coach needs to negotiate?
    c. Explain your solution process.

31. DANCE A local studio owner will teach up to four students by herself. Her instructors can teach up to 5 students each. Draw a step function graph that best describes the number of instructors needed for the different numbers of students.

32. THEATERS A community theater will only perform a show if there are at least 250 pre-sale ticket requests. Additional performances will be added for each 250 requests after that. Draw a step function graph that best describes this situation.

Graph each function.

33. $f(x) = \begin{cases} [\![x]\!] \text{ if } -2 \le x \le 1 \\ x + 2 \text{ if } x > -1 \end{cases}$

34. $f(x) = \begin{cases} 2x - 1 \text{ if } x < 2 \\ -[\![x]\!] \text{ if } x > 2 \end{cases}$

35. SMOOTHIES Write a step function for the number of medium smoothies that can be bought with x dollars if a medium smoothie costs $3.79. Then use the function to find the number of smoothies that can bought with $10.

36. MULTIPLE REPRESENTATIONS Renting a kayak for 1 hour or less costs $15 per hour. Each additional hour costs $10 per hour, up to a maximum of $35 per day.
    a. **Graphical** Draw a graph of a piecewise-defined function that best describes this situation.
    b. **Symbolic** Write the equation of the piecewise-defined function, and explain what each piece of the function rule represents.

H.O.T. Problems Use Higher-Order Thinking Skills

37. CONSTRUCT ARGUMENTS Does the piecewise relation $y = \begin{cases} -2x + 4 \text{ if } x \ge 2 \\ -\frac{1}{2}x - 1 \text{ if } x \le 0 \end{cases}$ represent a function? Why or why not?

38. ERROR ANALYSIS Dylan claims that the graph of the function $f(x) = \begin{cases} -3x + 4 \text{ if } x < 0 \\ x - 2 \text{ if } x \ge 0 \end{cases}$ includes the point (0, 4).
    a. What error did Dylan make? Explain your reasoning.
    b. Find the correct value of $f(0)$.

39. OPEN ENDED Research the cost of tickets to a local zoo or museum. Then graph a step function that models how the cost of a ticket depends on a person’s age.

40. WRITING IN MATH Compare and contrast the graphs of step and piecewise-defined functions with the graphs of linear functions. Discuss the domains, ranges, maxima, and minima.

214 | Lesson 3-7 | Piecewise and Step Functions

40. WRITING IN MATH Compare and contr
functions with the graphs of linear fu
and minima.

Built-In Differentiated Instruction

Approximately 43% of teachers feel their classes are so mixed in terms of students' learning abilities that they can't teach them effectively.

The **Glencoe High School Math Series** fully supports the 3-tier RtI model with print and digital resources to diagnose students, identify areas of need, and conduct short, frequent assessments for accurate data-driven decision making. Every lesson provides easy-to-use resources that consider the needs of all students.

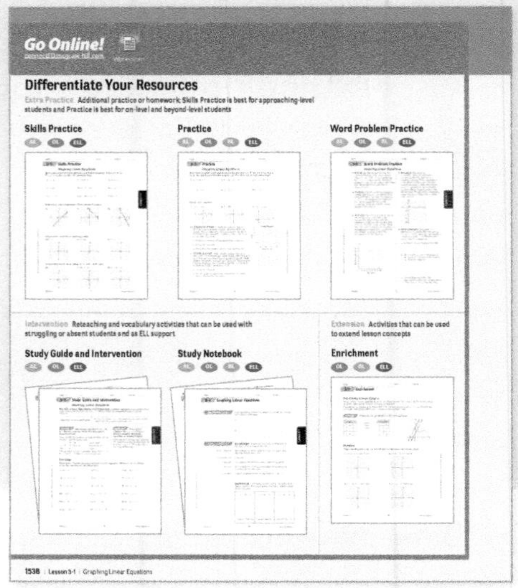

RtI: Response to Intervention

TIER 1: Daily Intervention

OL On grade level

Core instruction targets on-level students. Comprehensive instructional materials help you personalize instruction for every student.

- Diagnostic Teaching
- Options for Differentiated Instruction
- Leveled Exercise Sets, Resources, and Technology
- Data-Driven Decision Making

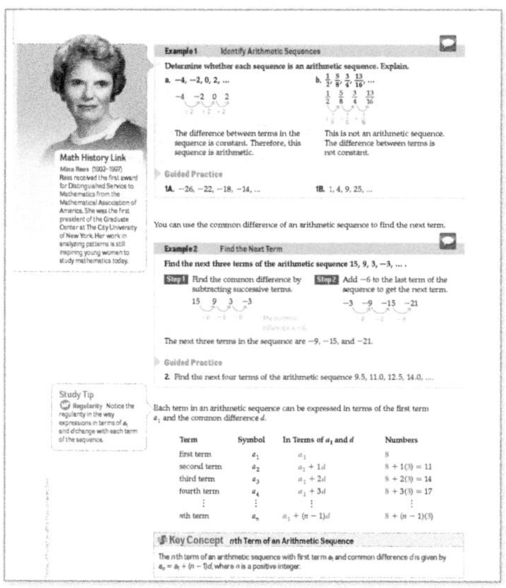

BL Beyond grade level

At every step, resources and assignments are available for advanced learners.

- Higher-Order Thinking Questions
- Differentiated Homework Options
- Enrichment Masters
- Differentiated Instruction: Extension

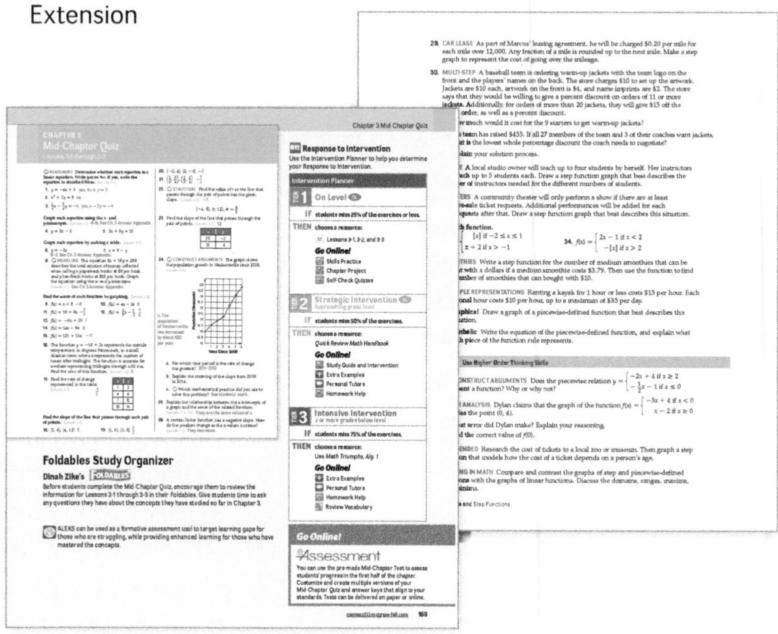

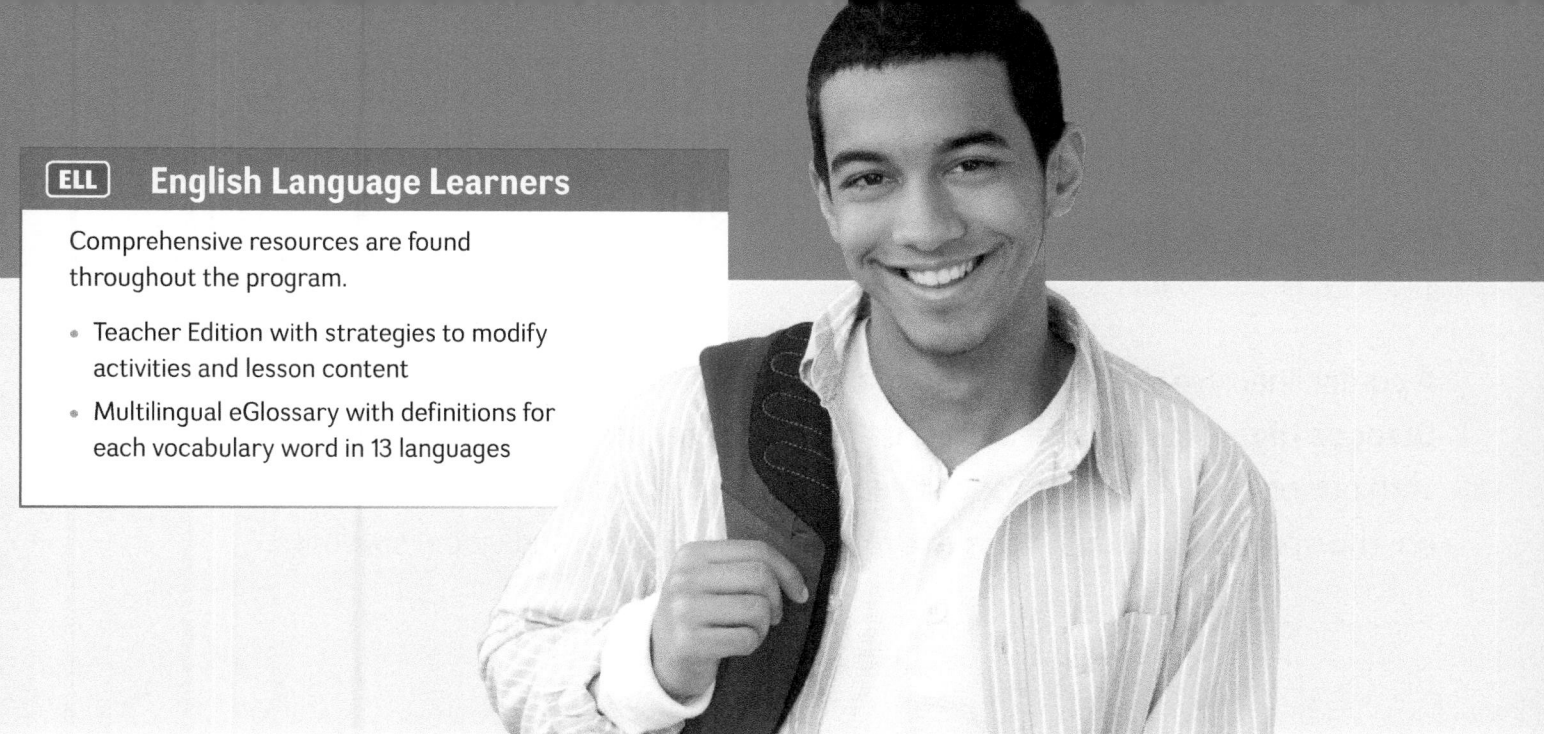

ELL English Language Learners

Comprehensive resources are found throughout the program.

- Teacher Edition with strategies to modify activities and lesson content
- Multilingual eGlossary with definitions for each vocabulary word in 13 languages

TIER 2: Strategic Intervention

AL Approaching grade level

You can choose from a myriad of intervention tips and ancillary materials to support struggling learners.

- Using Manipulatives
- Alternate Teaching Strategies
- Online resources, including animations, examples, and Personal Tutors

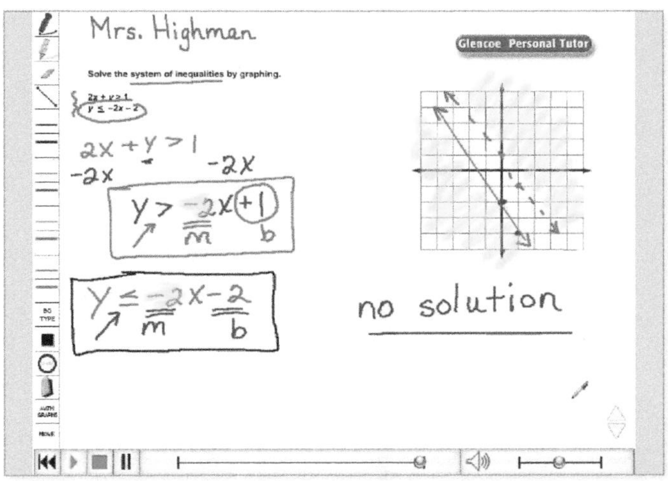

TIER 3: Intensive Intervention

AL Significantly below grade level

For students who are far below grade level, **Math Triumphs** provides step-by-step instruction, vocabulary support, and meaningful practice.

(t to b): KidStock/Blend Images/Getty Images, Brand X Pictures/Stockbyte/Getty Images

Assessment Tools that Inform Instruction

A comprehensive variety of print and online assessment options are built into **Glencoe High School Math Series**. Using traditional assessment combined with our online test generator and reporting system, you can use data to make on-the-spot instructional decisions for the entire class or individual students.

Chapter Assessment Resources

Prebuilt assessment resources are provided with every chapter to quickly print and deliver on demand. As an added feature, most are available in editable Word documents to allow for maximum flexibility and customization:

- Chapter Quizzes
- Mid-Chapter Tests
- Vocabulary Tests
- Extended Response Tests
- Standardized Tests

The personalized study resources your students need today – to master state assessments tomorrow.

eAssessment

With a simple, intuitive interface that enables teachers to create customized assessments and homework, web-based eAssessment means easy, anytime access via a secure online test center. Manage your content, create and assign quizzes and tests that can be assigned online or in traditional format. The reporting system enables you to see performance at both a class and a student level which allows you to modify instruction or provide targeted support to improve student achievement.

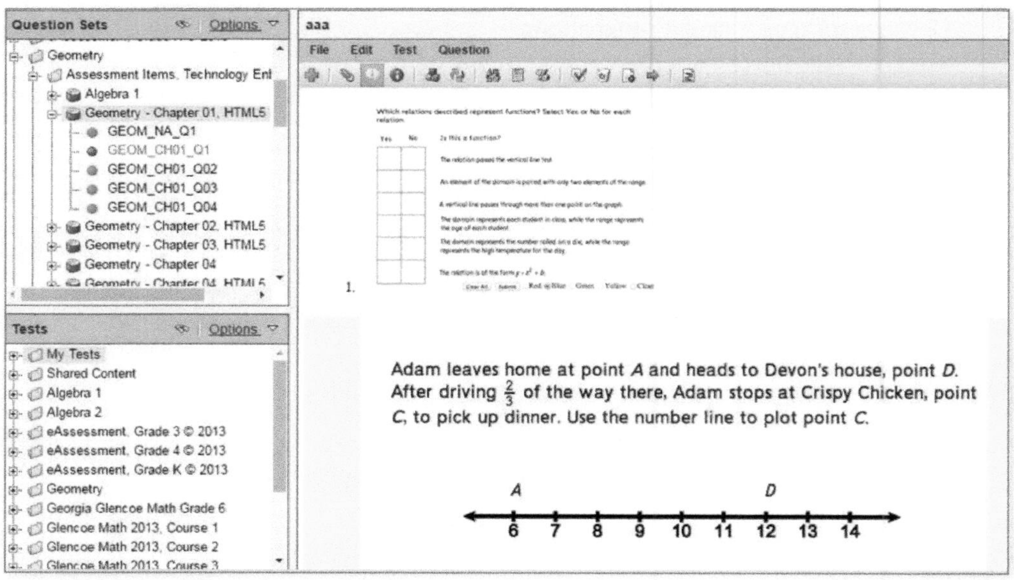

Help students learn faster, study more efficiently, and retain more knowledge.

LEARNSMART®

Using this robust, online personalized study resource, students have a modernized study partner to practice for high-stakes testing. By following a personalized study plan, each student will see the course topics they have mastered or which they need to revisit. Learning resources are tagged to questions to ensure students have multiple opportunities to refresh their content knowledge. Advanced reporting enables you to maximize your instructional time leading up to end of course or end of year assessments.

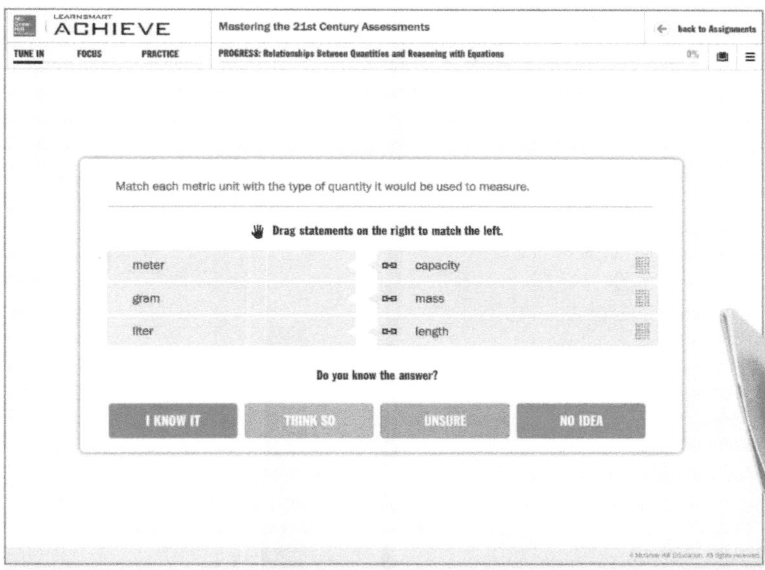

Bill Cheyrou/Alamy

ALEKS®

Differentiating instruction can be a challenge. It's ***ALEKS***® to the rescue! This online resource uses adaptive questioning to provide each student with a personalized learning path.

Support each student's unique needs

- Knowledge checks identify what a student knows and where there are gaps
- Personalized instruction allows students to progress at their own pace
- Robust Reporting tools provide instructionally-actionable data
- Targeted instruction on Ready to Learn topics build learning momentum and confidence
- Open-response environment ensures students demonstrate understanding–no guessing!

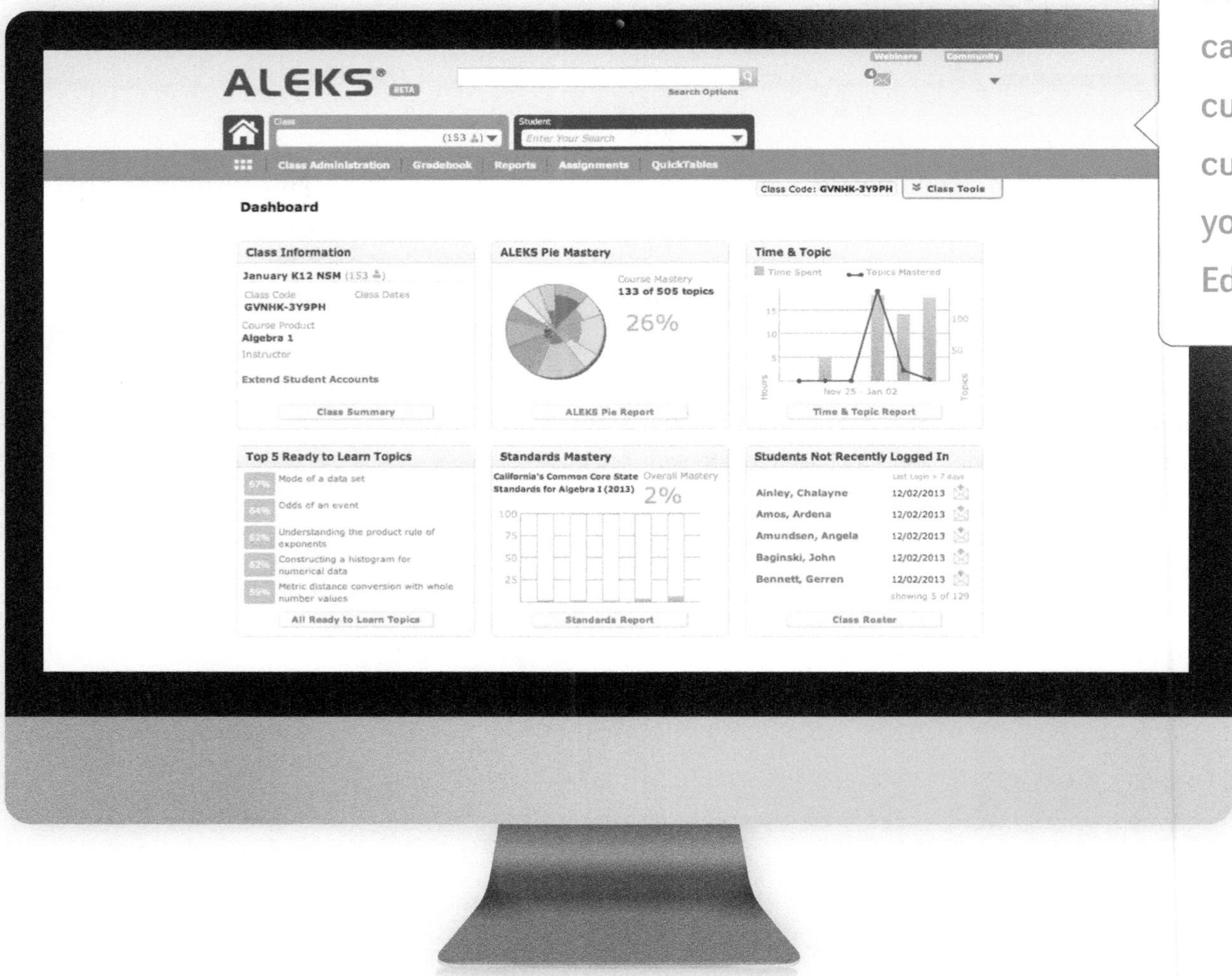

Learn how ***ALEKS*** can enhance your current math curriculum. Contact your McGraw-Hill Education rep today.

Use ConnectED as Your Portal

Nearly 84% of teachers say that they only spend half of their time teaching, as opposed to disciplining or doing administrative work.

ConnectED is a time-saving online portal that has all of your digital program resources in one place. Through this portal, you can access the complete Student Edition and Teacher Edition, digital animations and tutorials, editable worksheets, presentation tools, and assessment resources.

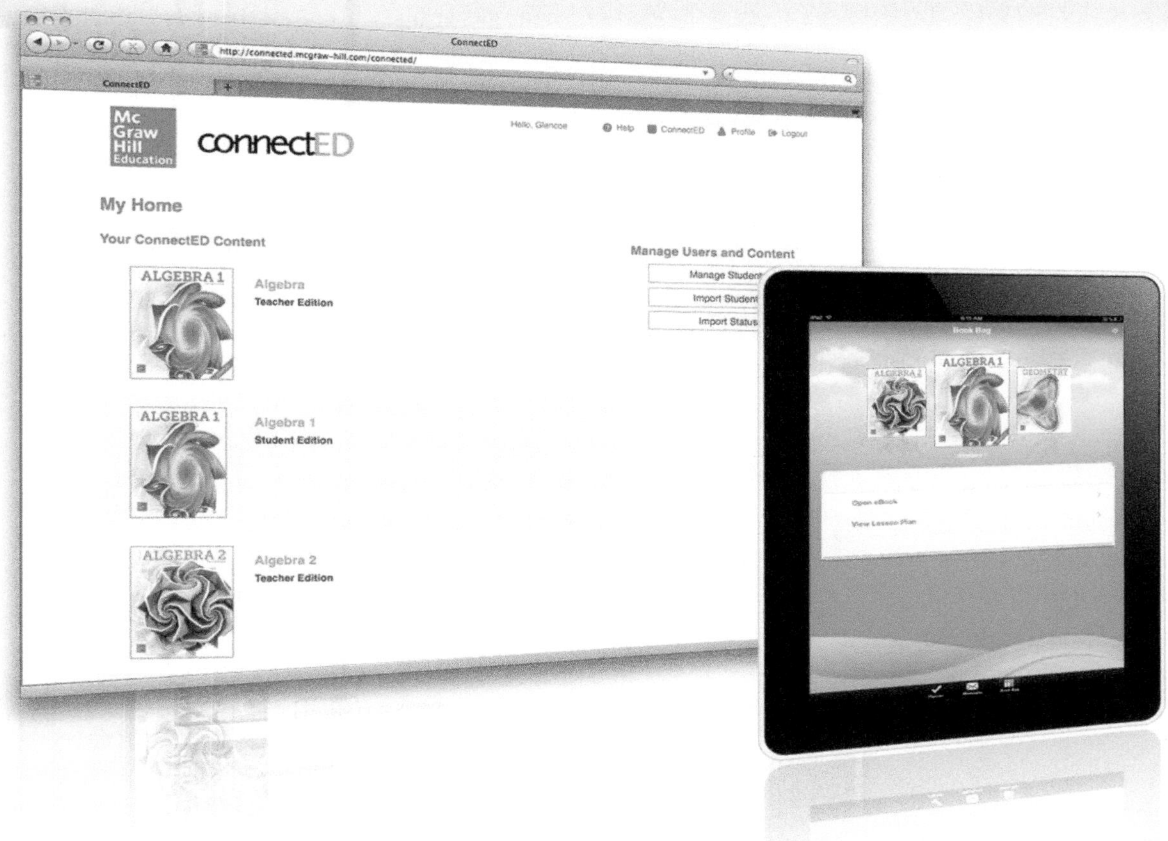

With ConnectED Mobile you can browse through your course content on the go. The app includes a powerful eBook engine where you can download, view, and interact with your books.

connectED allows you to:

- build lesson plans with easy-to-find print and digital resources
- search for activities to meet a variety of learning modalities
- teach with technology by providing virtual manipulatives, lesson animations, whole-class presentations, and more
- personalize instruction with print and digital resources
- provide students with anywhere, anytime access to student resources and tools, including eBooks, tutorials, animations, and the eGlossary
- access eAssessment, which allows you to assign online assessments, track student progress, generate reports, and differentiate instruction

Digital Tools to Enhance Learning Opportunities

Today's students have an unprecedented access to and appetite for technology and new media. They perceive technology as their friend and rely on it to study, work, play, relax, and communicate.

Your students are accustomed to the role that computers play in today's world. They may well be the first generation whose primary educational tool is a computer or a cell phone. The eStudentEdition allows your students to access their math curriculum anytime, anywhere. Along with your teacher edition, ***Glencoe Geometry*** provides a blended instructional solution for your next-generation students.

Investigate

Sketchpad Discover concepts using The Geometer's Sketchpad®.

Vocabulary tools include fun Vocabulary Review Games.

Tools enhance understanding through exploration.

Go Online!

Look for the *Go Online!* feature in your Teacher Edition to easily find digital tools to engage students and personalize instruction.

- Each chapter includes a curated list of differentiated resources as well as featured interactive whiteboard resources with suggested pacing.
- Each lesson includes a list of digital resources with implementation tips and suggested pacing.

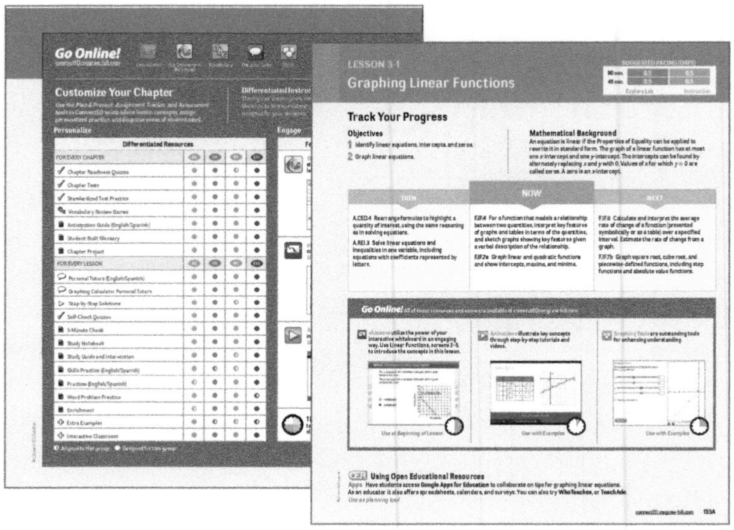

The Geometer's Sketchpad

The Geometer's Sketchpad is proven to increase engagement, understanding, and achievement. This premier digital learning tool makes math come alive by giving students a tangible, visual way to see the math in action through dynamic model manipulation of lines, shapes, and functions.

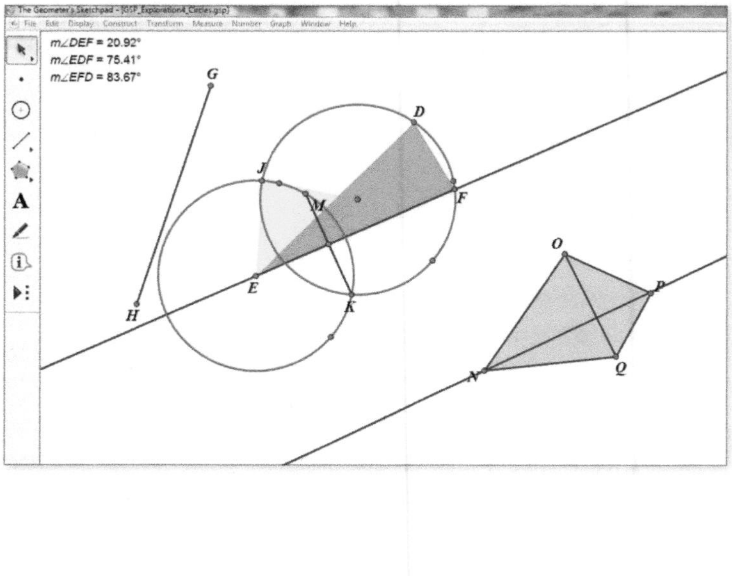

Learn

LearnSmart
Topic based online assessment

Animations
illustrate key concepts through step-by-step tutorials and videos.

Tutors
See and hear a teacher explain how to solve problems.

Calculator Resources
provides other calculator keystrokes for each Graphing Technology Lab.

Practice

Self-Check Practice
allows students to check their understanding and send results to their teacher.

eBook
Interactive learning experience with links directly to assets

eToolkit

eToolkit enables students to use virtual manipulatives to extend learning beyond the classroom by modifying concrete models in a real-time, interactive format focused on problem-based learning.

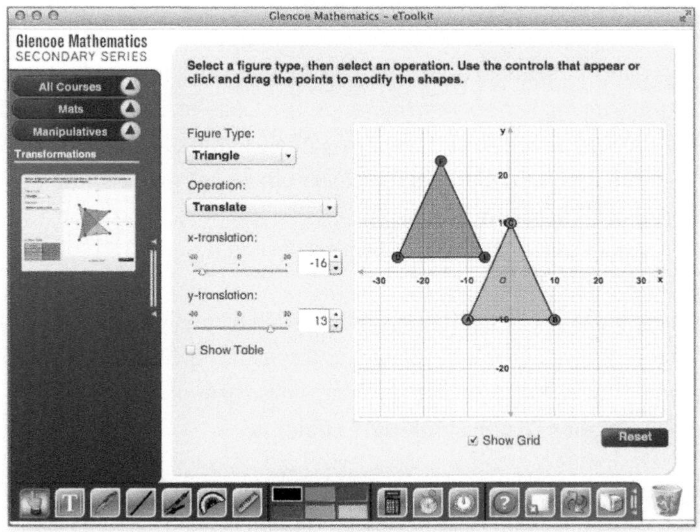

Interactive Student Guide

Interactive Student Guide is a dynamic digital resource to help you and your students meet the increasing demands for rigor.

You can be empowered to teach confidently knowing every lesson includes standards-aligned content and emphasizes the Standards for Mathematical Practice. This guide works together with the student edition to ensure that students can reflect on comprehension and application, use mathematics in real-world applications, and internalize concepts to develop "second nature" recall.

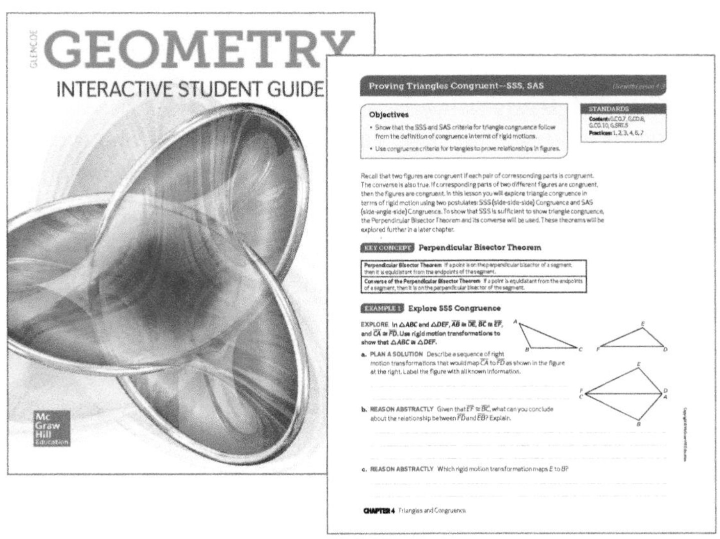

21st Century Skills

The U.S. Department of Labor estimates that 90% of 21st-century skilled workforce jobs will require post-secondary education. To be competitive in tomorrow's global workforce, American students must be prepared to succeed in college.

A strong high school curriculum is a good predictor of college readiness (Adelman, 2006). Students who take at least three years of college-preparatory mathematics using programs like ***Glencoe Algebra 1***, ***Glencoe Geometry***, and ***Glencoe Algebra 2*** are less likely to need remedial courses in college than students who do not (Abraham & Creech, 2002).

College Readiness

David Conley at the University of Oregon developed the following criteria for college readiness.

Key Content Knowledge

Glencoe High School Math Series is aligned to rigorous state and national standards, including the *NCTM Principles & Standards for School Mathematics,* the College Board Standards for College Success, and the American Diploma Project's Benchmarks. Correlations to these standards can be found at **connectED.mcgraw-hill.com.**

Habits of Mind

These include critical thinking skills such as analysis, interpretation, problem solving, and reasoning. Students can hone critical higher-order thinking skills through the use of **H.O.T. (Higher Order Thinking) Problems.**

Contextual Skills

These are practical skills like understanding the admissions process and financial aid, placement testing, and communicating with professors. Throughout each Glencoe mathematics program, students are required to write, explain, justify, prove, and analyze.

Academic Behaviors

These include general skills such as reading comprehension, time management, note-taking, and metacognition. Reading Math tips and Vocabulary Links help students with reading comprehension. Study Notebooks and Anticipation Guides help students build note-taking skills and aid with metacognition.

Developing STEM Careers

With **Glencoe High School Math Series**, you can unleash your students' curiosity about the world around them and prepare them for exciting STEM (**S**cience, **T**echnology, **E**ngineering, and **M**ath) careers.

Examples

Examples are relevant, connecting in-class experiences to the world beyond the classroom.

Real-World Careers

Real-World Careers are engaging, providing information on exciting careers.

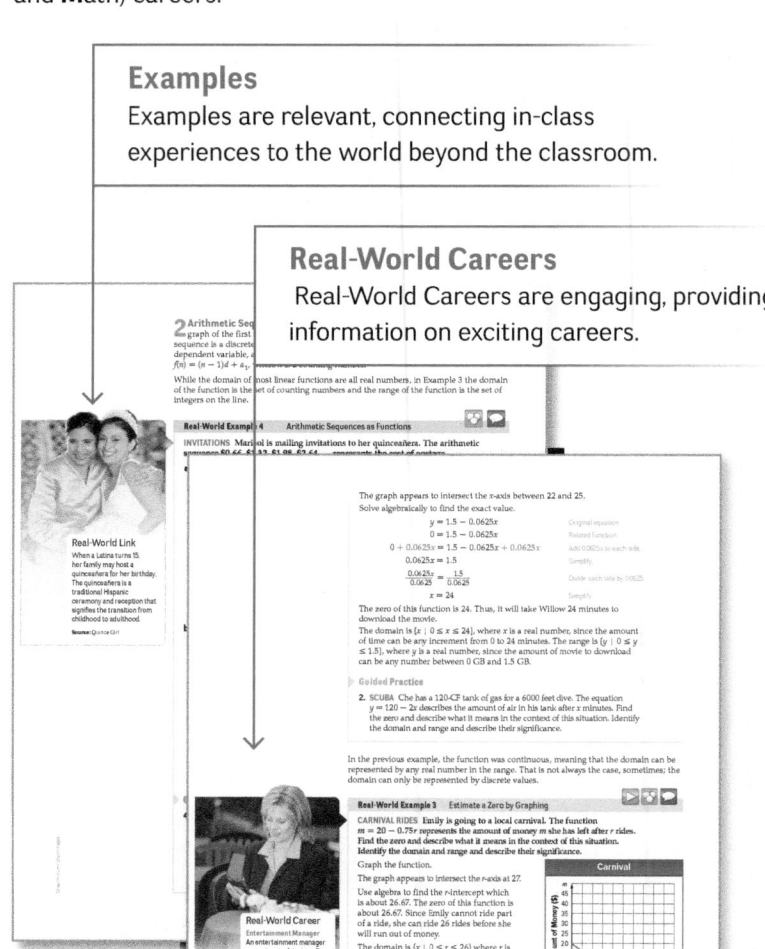

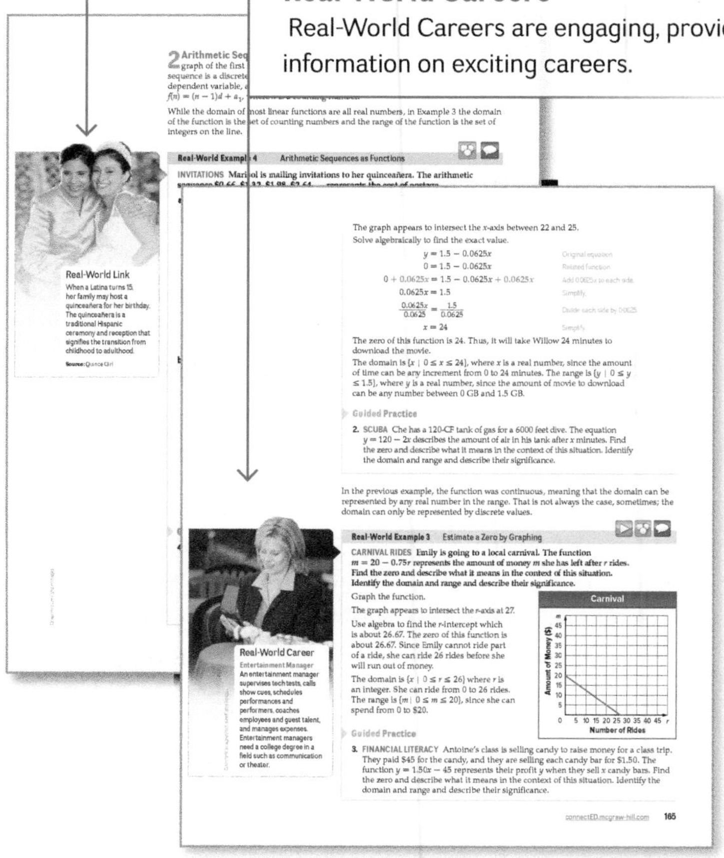

(l to r) DreamPictures/Blend Images, Comstock Images/Stockbyte/Getty Images

"The current and future health of America's 21st Century Economy depends directly on how broadly and deeply Americans reach a new level of literacy–'21st Century Literacy'–that includes strong academic skills, thinking, reasoning, teamwork skills, and proficiency in using technology."

–21st Century Workforce Commission National Alliance of Business

Developing 21st Century Skills

The Partnership for 21st Century Skills identifies the following key student elements of a 21st century education.

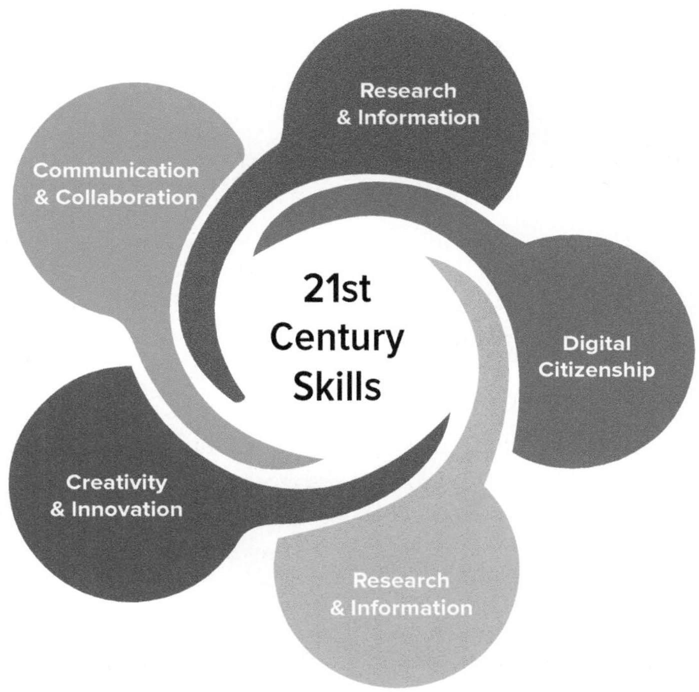

Core Subjects and 21st Century Themes

Glencoe High School Math Series has been aligned to rigorous state and national standards, *NCTM Principles & Standards for School Mathematics*, and the American Diploma Project's Benchmarks. Throughout each program, students solve problems that incorporate 21st century themes, such as financial literacy.

Learning and Innovation Skills

Students who are prepared for increasingly complex life and work environments are creative and innovative critical thinkers, problem solvers, effective communicators, and know how to work collaboratively. Throughout each **Glencoe High School Math Series**, students are required to write, explain, justify, prove, and analyze. Students use critical thinking skills through the use of H.O.T. (Higher Order Thinking) Problems and are encouraged to work collaboratively in labs.

Information, Media, and Technology Skills

Students use technology, including graphing calculators and the Internet, to develop 21st century mathematics knowledge and skills throughout each program.

21st Century Assessments

Glencoe High School Math Series offers a variety of frequent and meaningful assessments built right into the curriculum structure and teacher support materials. These programs include both traditional and nontraditional methods of assessment, including quizzes and tests, performance tasks, and open-ended assessments. Digital assessment solutions offer additional options for creating, customizing, administering, and instantly grading assessments.

(t to b): Creatas/PunchStock, Szekely Katalin/Shutterstock.com

Professional Development

McGraw-Hill Education recognizes that learning is a lifelong endeavor. To ensure student and teacher success, we have built in resources to the Glencoe High School Math Series featuring best practices, implementation support, alternative teaching practices, and much more.

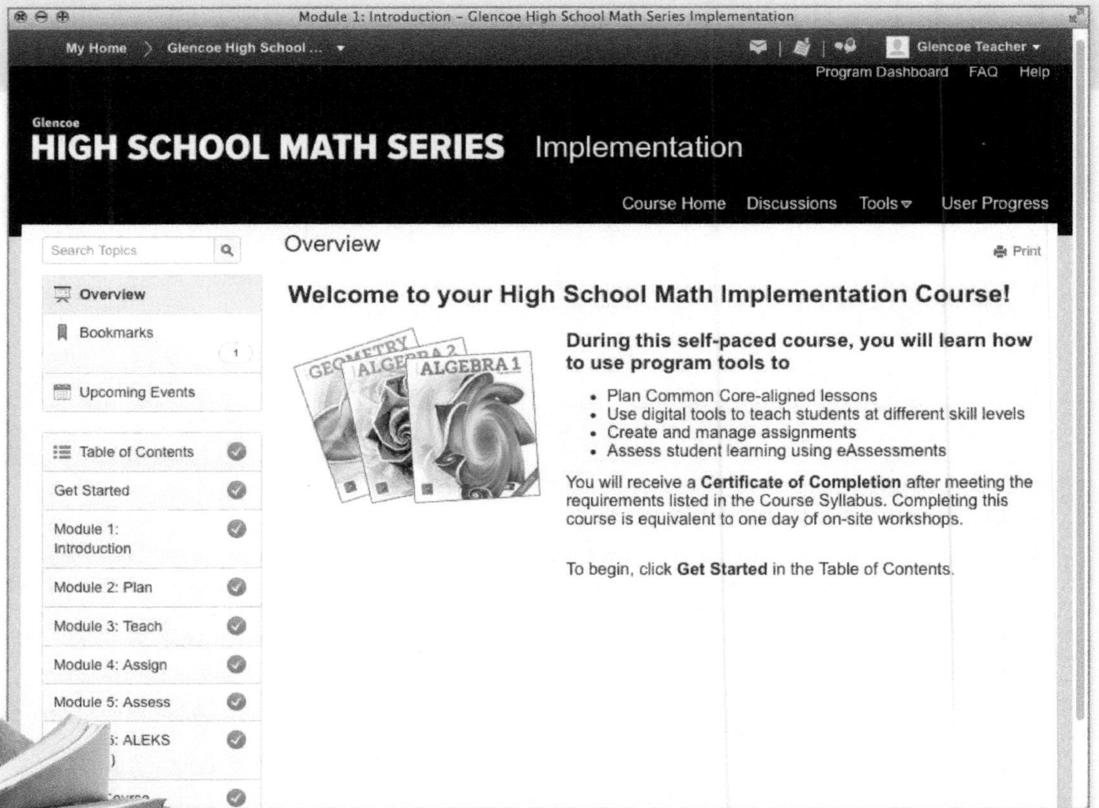

Content Standards, Traditional Geometry Pathway, Correlated to *Glencoe Geometry*

Lessons in which the standard is the primary focus are indicated in **bold**.

Standards	Student Edition Lesson(s)	Student Edition Page(s)
Geometry		
Congruence G-CO		
Experiment with transformations in the plane. 1. Know precise definitions of angle, circle, perpendicular line, parallel line, and line segment, based on the undefined notions of point, line, distance along a line, and distance around a circular arc.	**1-1, 1-2, 1-3, 1-4, 1-5, 2-7, 9-1**	**5-12, 14-25, 26-35, 36-44, 46-54, 169-176, 643-651**
2. Represent transformations in the plane using, e.g., transparencies and geometry software; describe transformations as functions that take points in the plane as inputs and give other points as outputs. Compare transformations that preserve distance and angle to those that do not (e.g., translation versus horizontal stretch).	**1-7, Extend 1-7, Explore 3-1, 3-1, Explore 3-2, 3-2, Explore 3-3, 3-3, Explore 3-4, 3-4, 7-1**	**67-73, 74-75, 219-220, 221-229, 230-231, 232-238, 239, 240-246, 248, 249-258, 492-501**
3. Given a rectangle, parallelogram, trapezoid, or regular polygon, describe the rotations and reflections that carry it onto itself.	**3-5**	**259-265**
4. Develop definitions of rotations, reflections, and translations in terms of angles, circles, perpendicular lines, parallel lines, and line segments.	**3-1, 3-2, 3-3**	**221-229, 232-238, 240-246**
5. Given a geometric figure and a rotation, reflection, or translation, draw the transformed figure using, e.g., graph paper, tracing paper, or geometry software. Specify a sequence of transformations that will carry a given figure onto another.	**Explore 3-1, 3-1, Explore 3-2, 3-2, Explore 3-3, 3-3, Explore 3-4, 3-4**	**219-220, 221-229, 230-231, 232-238, 239, 240-246, 248, 249-258**
Understand congruence in terms of rigid motions. 6. Use geometric descriptions of rigid motions to transform figures and to predict the effect of a given rigid motion on a given figure; given two figures, use the definition of congruence in terms of rigid motions to decide if they are congruent.	**Explore 3-1, 3-1, Explore 3-2, 3-2, Explore 3-3, 3-3**	**219-220, 221-229, 230-231, 232-238, 239, 240-246**
7. Use the definition of congruence in terms of rigid motions to show that two triangles are congruent if and only if corresponding pairs of sides and corresponding pairs of angles are congruent.	**4-2**	**291-299**
8. Explain how the criteria for triangle congruence (ASA, SAS, and SSS) follow from the definition of congruence in terms of rigid motions.	**4-3, 4-4**	**300-308, 311-318**

Standards	Student Edition Lesson(s)	Student Edition Page(s)
Prove geometric theorems. 9. Prove theorems about lines and angles.	**2-5, 2-6, 2-7, 2-9**	**152-158, 159-167, 169-176, 186-193**
10. Prove theorems about triangles.	**4-1, 4-5, 4-6, 4-7, 5-1, 5-2, 5-3, 5-4, 5-5, 5-6, 7-5, Explore 8-2**	**282-290, 319-324, 325-333, 334-340, 354-363, 365-373, 374-381, 385-392, 394-400, 401-410, 534-543, 574**
11. Prove theorems about parallelograms.	**6-2, 6-3, 6-4, 6-5**	**433-441, 443-451, 453-459, 460-468**
Make geometric constructions. 12. Make formal geometric constructions with a variety of tools and methods (compass and straightedge, string, reflective devices, paper folding, dynamic geometric software, etc.).	**1-2, 1-3, 1-4, Extend 1-5, Extend 1-6, 2-5, Explore 2-7, 2-9, 2-10, 3-1, Explore 3-3, Extend 3-5, Explore 4-1, 4-3, Extend 4-3, 4-4, 4-6, Explore 5-1, Explore 5-2, Explore 5-5, Explore 6-3, 6-3, 6-4, 6-5, 7-5, 9-3, 9-5, Extend 9-5**	**14-25, 26-35, 36-44, 55, 66, 152-158, 168, 186-193, 194-203, 239, 266-267, 281, 300-308, 309, 311-318, 325-333, 353, 364, 393, 442, 443-451, 453-459, 460-468, 534-543, 661-668, 678-685, 686**
13. Construct an equilateral triangle, a square, and a regular hexagon inscribed in a circle.	**Extend 9-5**	**686**
Similarity, Right Triangles, and Trigonometry G-SRT		
Understand similarity in terms of similarity transformations. 1. Verify experimentally the properties of dilations given by a center and a scale factor: a. A dilation takes a line not passing through the center of the dilation to a parallel line, and leaves a line passing through the center unchanged.	**Explore 7-1, 7-1**	**491, 492-501**
b. The dilation of a line segment is longer or shorter in the ratio given by the scale factor.	**Explore 7-1, 7-1**	**491, 492-501**
2. Given two figures, use the definition of similarity in terms of similarity transformations to decide if they are similar; explain using similarity transformations the meaning of similarity for triangles as the equality of all corresponding pairs of angles and the proportionality of all corresponding pairs of sides.	**7-2, 7-3, 7-4**	**502-510, 511-520, 521-530**
3. Use the properties of similarity transformations to establish the AA criterion for two triangles to be similar.	**7-2, 7-3**	**502-510, 511-520**

Standards	Student Edition Lesson(s)	Student Edition Page(s)
Prove theorems involving similarity. 4. Prove theorems about triangles.	7-3, 7-4, 7-5, 7-6, 8-1	511-520, 521-530, 534-543, 544-551, 565-573
5. Use congruence and similarity criteria for triangles to solve problems and to prove relationships in geometric figures.	4-2, 4-3, Extend 4-3, 4-4, 4-5, 7-3, 7-4, 7-5, 7-6, 8-1	291-299, 300-308, 309, 311-318, 319-324, 511-520, 521-530, 534-543, 544-551, 565-573
Define trigonometric ratios and solve problems involving right triangles. 6. Understand that by similarity, side ratios in right triangles are properties of the angles in the triangle, leading to definitions of trigonometric ratios for acute angles.	8-3, Explore 8-4, 8-4, Extend 8-4	586-594, 595, 596-605, 606
7. Explain and use the relationship between the sine and cosine of complementary angles.	8-4	596-606
8. Use trigonometric ratios and the Pythagorean Theorem to solve right triangles in applied problems. ★	8-2, 8-4, 8-5, 8-6, 8-7	575-583, 596-606, 608-615, 616-623, 624-629
Apply trigonometry to general triangles. 9. (+) Derive the formula $A = \frac{1}{2} ab \sin (C)$ for the area of a triangle by drawing an auxiliary line from a vertex perpendicular to the opposite side.	8-6	616-623
10. (+) Prove the Laws of Sines and Cosines and use them to solve problems.	8-6, 8-7	616-623, 624-629
11. (+) Understand and apply the Law of Sines and the Law of Cosines to find unknown measurements in right and non-right triangles (e.g., surveying problems, resultant forces).	8-6, 8-7	616-623, 624-629
Circles G-C		
Understand and apply theorems about circles. 1. Prove that all circles are similar.	9-1	643-651
2. Identify and describe relationships among inscribed angles, radii, and chords.	9-2, 9-3, 9-4, 9-5, 9-6	652-660, 661-668, 669-676, 678-685, 687-695
3. Construct the inscribed and circumscribed circles of a triangle, and prove properties of angles for a quadrilateral inscribed in a circle.	9-4, Extend 9-5	669-676, 686
4. (+) Construct a tangent line from a point outside a given circle to the circle.	9-5	678-685
Find arc lengths and areas of sectors of circles. 5. Derive using similarity the fact that the length of the arc intercepted by an angle is proportional to the radius, and define the radian measure of the angle as the constant of proportionality; derive the formula for the area of a sector.	9-2, 10-3	652-660, 743-749

★ **Mathematical Modeling Standards**
(+) **Advanced Mathematics Standards**

Correlations

Standards	Student Edition Lesson(s)	Student Edition Page(s)
Expressing Geometric Properties with Equations G-GPE		
Translate between the geometric description and the equation for a conic section. 1. Derive the equation of a circle of given center and radius using the Pythagorean Theorem; complete the square to find the center and radius of a circle given by an equation.	**9-7**	**696-702**
2. Derive the equation of a parabola given a focus and directrix.	**9-8**	**703-710**
Use coordinates to prove simple geometric theorems algebraically. 4. Use coordinates to prove simple geometric theorems algebraically.	**4-7, 6-2 6-3, 6-4, 6-5, 6-6, 9-7**	**334-340, 433-441, 443-451, 453-459, 453-459, 460-468, 469-478, 696-702**
5. Prove the slope criteria for parallel and perpendicular lines and use them to solve geometric problems (e.g., find the equation of a line parallel or perpendicular to a given line that passes through a given point).	**Explore 2-8, 2-8, Extend 2-8, Extend 7-4**	**177, 178-184, 185, 531-532**
6. Find the point on a directed line segment between two given points that partitions the segment in a given ratio.	**1-3**	**26-35**
7. Use coordinates to compute perimeters of polygons and areas of triangles and rectangles, e.g., using the distance formula. ★	**1-6, 10-1**	**56-65, 725-732**
Geometric Measurement and Dimension G-GMD		
Explain volume formulas and use them to solve problems. 1. Give an informal argument for the formulas for the circumference of a circle, area of a circle, volume of a cylinder, pyramid, and cone.	**9-1, 10-3, 10-5, 11-2, 11-3, 11-6**	**643-651, 743-749,** 763-769, **802-809, 810-816,** 834-840
3. Use volume formulas for cylinders, pyramids, cones, and spheres to solve problems. ★	**1-8, 11-2, 11-3, 11-4**	**76-83, 802-809, 810-816, 818-825**
Visualize relationships between two-dimensional and three-dimensional objects. 4. Identify the shapes of two-dimensional cross-sections of three-dimensional objects, and identify three-dimensional objects generated by rotations of two-dimensional objects.	**11-1**	**797-801**
Modeling with Geometry G-MG		
Apply geometric concepts in modeling situations. 1. Use geometric shapes, their measures, and their properties to describe objects (e.g., modeling a tree trunk or a human torso as a cylinder). ★	**Throughout the text; for example, Extend 1-1, 1-8, 1-9, 6-1, 10-5, 10-6**	13, 76-83, 84-90, 423-431, 763-769, 770-781
2. Apply concepts of density based on area and volume in modeling situations (e.g., persons per square mile, BTUs per cubic foot). ★	**11-7**	**841-846**
3. Apply geometric methods to solve problems (e.g., designing an object or structure to satisfy physical constraints or minimize cost; working with typographic grid systems based on ratios). ★	**2-4, 2-10, 5-1, 5-2, 5-5, 6-6, 8-2, 9-3, 10-2, 10-4, 10-6, 11-2, 11-4**	141-150, 194-203, 354-363, 365-373, 394-400, 469-478, 575-583, 661-668, 735-742, 752-760, 770-781, 802-809, 818-825

★ **Mathematical Modeling Standards**

Standards	Student Edition Lesson(s)	Student Edition Page(s)
Statistics and Probability		
Conditional Probability and the Rules of Probability S-CP		
Understand independence and conditional probability and use them to interpret data. 1. Describe events as subsets of a sample space (the set of outcomes) using characteristics (or categories) of the outcomes, or as unions, intersections, or complements of other events ("or," "and," "not").	**12-2,** 12-5, 12-6	**866-871,** 889-896, 897-902
2. Understand that two events *A* and *B* are independent if the probability of *A* and *B* occurring together is the product of their probabilities, and use this characterization to determine if they are independent.	**12-5**	**889-896**
3. Understand the conditional probability of *A* given *B* as $\frac{P(A \text{ and } B)}{P(B)}$, and interpret independence of *A* and *B* as saying that the conditional probability of *A* given *B* is the same as the probability of *A*, and the conditional probability of *B* given *A* is the same as the probability of *B*.	**12-7**	**903-908**
4. Construct and interpret two-way frequency tables of data when two categories are associated with each object being classified. Use the two-way table as a sample space to decide if events are independent and to approximate conditional probabilities.	**12-8**	**909-915**
5. Recognize and explain the concepts of conditional probability and independence in everyday language and everyday situations.	**12-7**	**903-908**
Use the rules of probability to compute probabilities of compound events in a uniform probability model. 6. Find the conditional probability of *A* given *B* as the fraction of *B*'s outcomes that also belong to *A*, and interpret the answer in terms of the model.	12-7, **12-8**	903-908, **909-915**
7. Apply the Addition Rule, $P(A \text{ or } B) = P(A) + P(B) - P(A \text{ and } B)$, and interpret the answer in terms of the model.	**12-6**	**897-902**

Standards	Student Edition Lesson(s)	Student Edition Page(s)
8. (+) Apply the general Multiplication Rule in a uniform probability model, $P(A \text{ and } B) = P(A)P(B\|A) = P(B)P(A\|B)$, and interpret the answer in terms of the model.	**12-5**	**889-896**
9. (+) Use permutations and combinations to compute probabilities of compound events and solve problems.	**12-3**	**872-880**
Using Probability to Make Decisions S-MD		
Use probability to evaluate outcomes of decisions. 6. (+) Use probabilities to make fair decisions (e.g., drawing by lots, using a random number generator).	0-3	P8-P9
7. (+) Analyze decisions and strategies using probability concepts (e.g., product testing, medical testing, pulling a hockey goalie at the end of a game).	0-3, 12-4, 12-5	P8-P9, 881-887, 889-896

(+) **Advanced Mathematics Standards**

Standards for Mathematical Practice

Glencoe Geometry exhibits these practices throughout the entire program. All of the Standards for Mathematical Practice are covered in each chapter. The MP icon notes specific areas of coverage.

Mathematical Practices	Student Edition Lessons
1. Make sense of problems and persevere in solving them.	Throughout the text, for example: 1-7, 2-8, 2-9, 3-4, 4-1, 4-3, 5-1, 5-3, 5-5, 5-6, 6-6, 7-1, 7-2, 7-4, 7-5, 7-6, 8-2, 8-3, 8-4, 8-5, 8-6, 8-7, 9-1, 9-5, 9-8, 10-1, 10-3, 10-4, 10-5, 10-6, 11-2, 11-3, 11-4, Extend 11-4, 11-7, 12-1, 12-2, 12-3, 12-4, 12-5, 12-6
2. Reason abstractly and quantitatively.	Throughout the text, for example: 1-6, 1-7, 1-8, 2-4, 2-5, 2-10, 3-4, 4-5, Explore 5-4, 5-4, 5-5, 6-3, 6-5, 6-6, 7-4, 8-4, 9-5, 9-7, 9-8, 10-6, 11-1, 12-1, 12-2, 12-4, 12-7, 1 2-8
3. Construct viable arguments and critique the reasoning of others.	Throughout the text, for example: 1-1, 2-1, 2-2, 2-3, 2-4, 2-5, 2-6, 2-9, 3-4, 4-1, 4-2, 4-3, Extend 4-3, 4-4, 4-5, 4-6, 4-7, 5-1, 5-2, 5-3, 5-4, 5-6, 6-1, 6-2, 6-3, 6-4, 6-5, 7-3, 7-4, Extend 7-4, 7-5, 7-6, 8-1, 9-3, 9-4, 10-5, 11-5, 12-6
4. Model with mathematics.	Throughout the text, for example: 1-1, 1-9, 2-8, 2-10, 3-4, 3-5, Explore 4-1, 5-5, 6-1, 6-2, 7-3, 7-4, Explore 8-2, 8-2, Extend 8-2, 8-5, 8-6, 8-7, 9-1, 9-2, 9-3, 9-8, 10-5, Explore 11-1, 11-1, 11-7, 12-2, 12-3, 12-5, 12-7, 12-8
5. Use appropriate tools strategically.	Throughout the text, for example: 1-4, 1-5, Extend 1-5, Extend 1-6, Extend 1-7, 1-10, Explore 2-7, Explore 2-8, 3-1, 3-2, Explore 3-3, 3-3, Explore 3-4, Extend 3-5, Explore 4-1, Extend 4-3, Explore 5-1, Explore 5-2, Explore 5-5, Extend 6-1, Explore 6-3, 6-4, Explore 7-1, 7-1, Explore 8-4, 8-4, Extend 8-4, 8-6, 8-7, Extend 9-5, Explore 10-4, 11-7, 12-7
6. Attend to precision.	Throughout the text, for example: 1-1, Extend 1-1, 1-2, 1-3, 1-4, 1-5, 1-6, 1-8, 1-10, 2-6, 3-5, 4-7, 5-2, Explore 5-4, 6-2, 7-2, 8-7, 9-2, 10-3, 10-4, 10-6, 11-4, Extend 11-4, 12-8
7. Look for and make use of structure.	Throughout the text, for example: 1-3, 2-8, Explore 3-1, Explore 3-2, 3-2, 3-3, 4-7, 5-1, 6-1, 7-4, 8-1, 8-3, 9-4, 9-7, 9-8, 10-1, 11-2, 11-3, 12-8
8. Look for and express regularity in repeated reasoning.	Throughout the text, for example: 1-6, Extend 2-8, 3-5, 4-1, 5-3, 6-2, Extend 7-6, 8-4, 9-4, 11-6, 12-3

CHAPTER 0
Preparing for Geometry

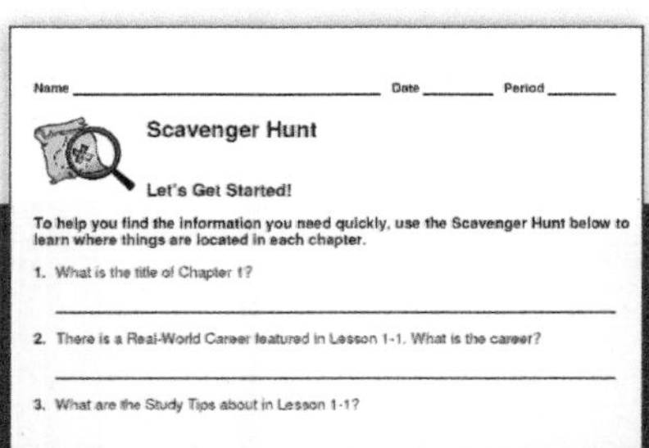
Name ______________ Date ______ Period ______

Scavenger Hunt

Let's Get Started!

To help you find the information you need quickly, use the Scavenger Hunt below to learn where things are located in each chapter.

1. What is the title of Chapter 1?

2. There is a Real-World Career featured in Lesson 1-1. What is the career?

3. What are the Study Tips about in Lesson 1-1?

Worksheets help to explain key concepts, let you practice your skills, and offer opportunities for extending the lessons. Find them in the Resources in ConnectED.

Go Online!
connectED.mcgraw-hill.com

CHAPTER 1
Tools of Geometry

ASSESSMENT

UpperCut Images/Alamy Stock Photo

Go Online!
connectED.mcgraw-hill.com

Geometer's Sketchpad® allows you to interact with geometry in a visual way. Investigate geometric concepts with sketches in ConnectED.

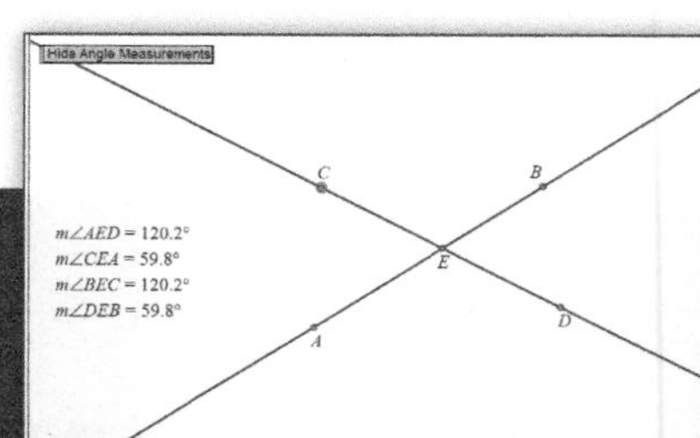

CHAPTER 2

Logical Arguments and Line Relationships

ASSESSMENT

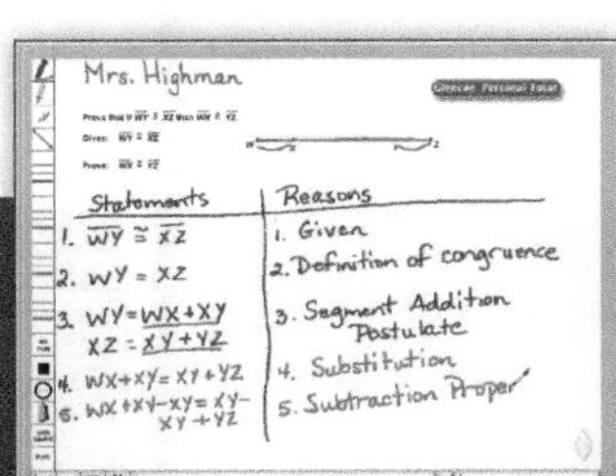

Watch as a real teacher solves a problem, pause to work ahead, or rewind to watch again. A **Personal Tutor** for each example is just a click away in ConnectED.

Go Online!
connectED.mcgraw-hill.com

CHAPTER 3

Rigid Transformations and Symmetry

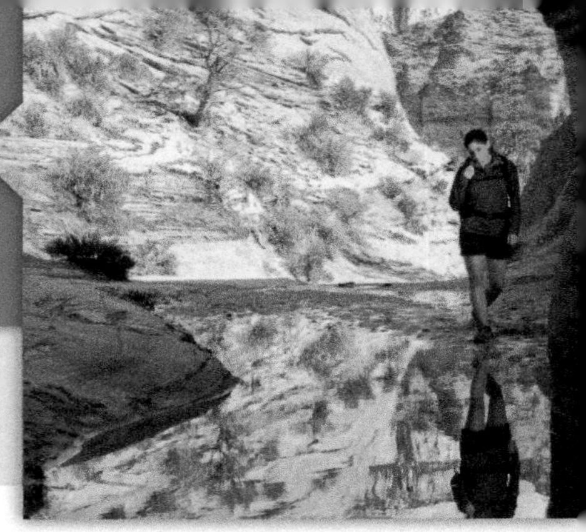

ASSESSMENT

Michael DeYoung/Blend Images

Go Online!
connectED.mcgraw-hill.com

With the **Geometry Tools** in ConnectED, you can explore the effects of transformations on geometric figures.

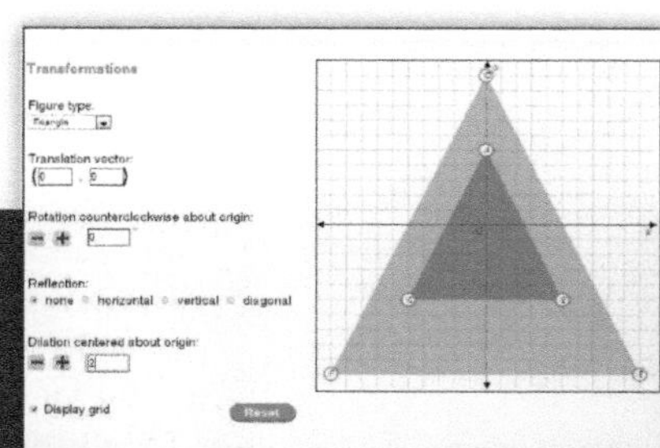

CHAPTER 4

Triangles and Congruence

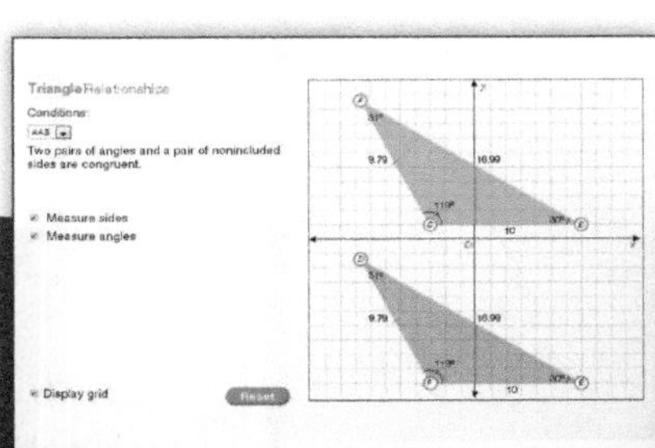

With the **Graphing Tools** in ConnectED, explore when two triangles are congruent and when they are not.

Go Online!
connectED.mcgraw-hill.com

CHAPTER 5
Relationships in Triangles

ASSESSMENT

Go Online!
connectED.mcgraw-hill.com

Animations demonstrate Key Concepts and topics from the chapter. Click to watch animations in ConnectED.

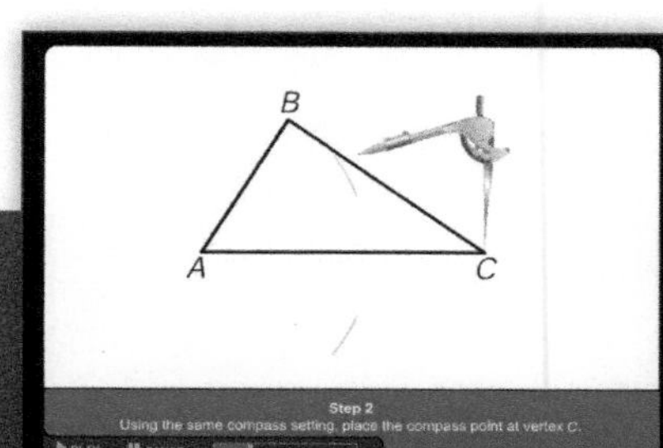

CHAPTER 6
Quadrilaterals

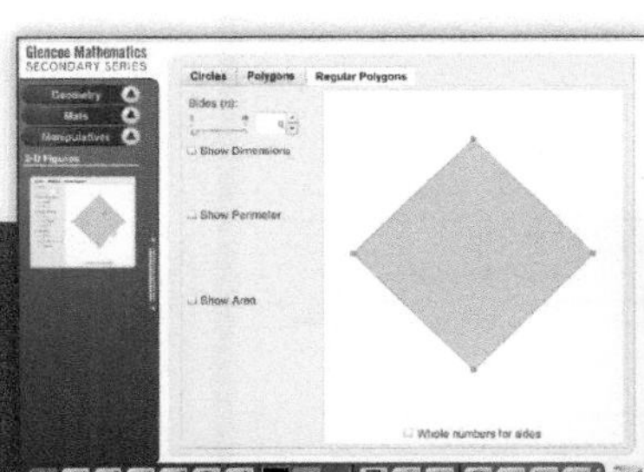

Create, change, and investigate quadrilaterals using the 2-D Figures tool in the eToolkit. Find these **virtual manipulatives** in ConnectED.

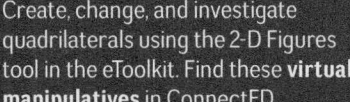

Go Online!
connectED.mcgraw-hill.com

CHAPTER 7
Similarity

Go Online!
connectED.mcgraw-hill.com

Worksheets help to explain key concepts, let you practice your skills, and offer opportunities for extending the lessons. Find them in the Resources in ConnectED.

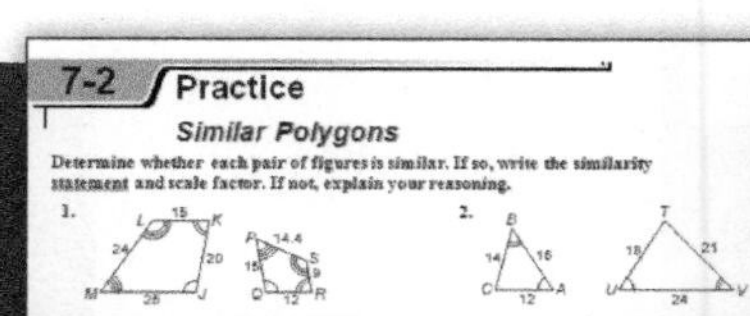
7-2 Practice
Similar Polygons
Determine whether each pair of figures is similar. If so, write the similarity statement and scale factor. If not, explain your reasoning.
1.
2.

CHAPTER 8

Right Triangles and Trigonometry

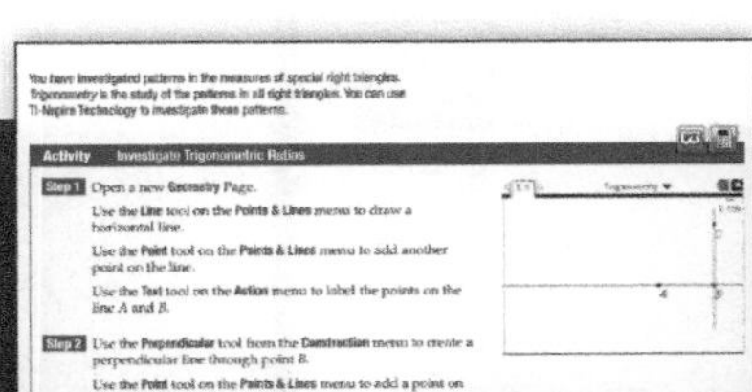

Using a graphing calculator allows you to quickly visualize concepts. **Graphing Calculator Keystrokes** help you navigate your calculator. Find the keystrokes for your calculator in the Resources in ConnectED.

Go Online!
connectED.mcgraw-hill.com

CHAPTER 9
Circles

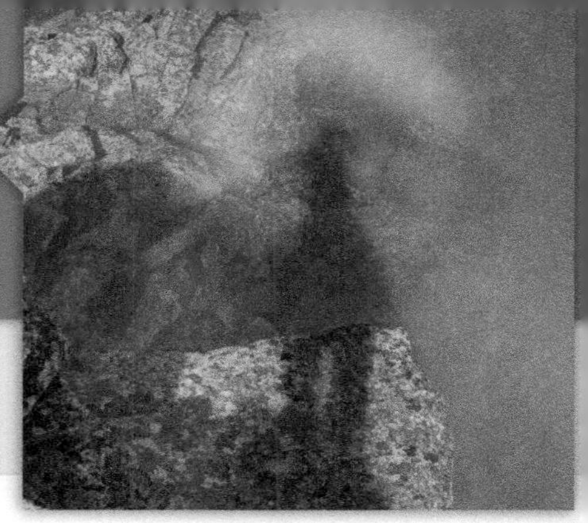

ASSESSMENT

Go Online!
connectED.mcgraw-hill.com

Tap into the power of your graphing calculator with Graphing Calculator Easy Files™. Practice vocabulary in English or Spanish with Lesson Vocabulary Review Files. Or review with a 5-Minute Check. Ask your teacher to assign them to you in ConnectED.

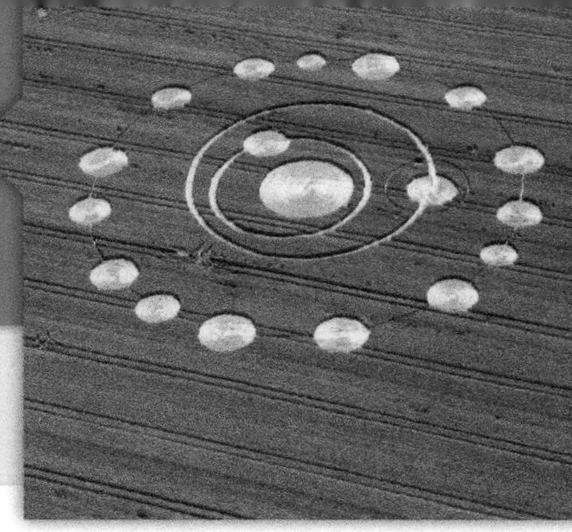

CHAPTER 10
Extending Area

ASSESSMENT

Joze Pojbic/iStockphoto/Getty Images

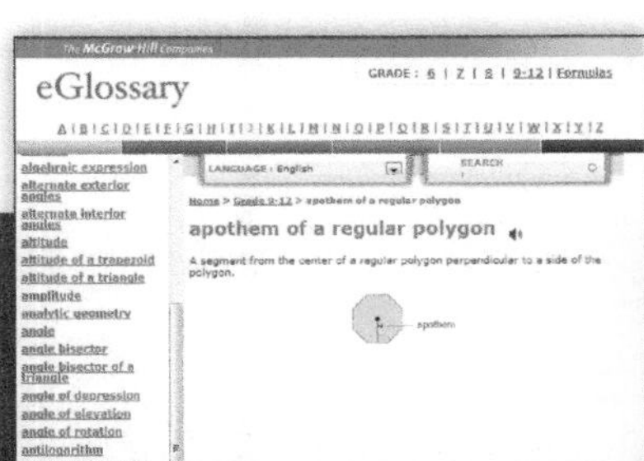

Vocabulary is important to learning the key concepts in this chapter. Find all the terms with animations, English pronunciations, and translations into 13 languages in the eGlossary in ConnectED.

Go Online!
connectED.mcgraw-hill.com

CHAPTER 11
Extending Volume

Norman Pogson/Alamy Stock Photo

Go Online!
connectED.mcgraw-hill.com

Visualize and interact with three-dimensional figures as you study this chapter. Find the **Virtual Manipulatives** in the eToolkit in ConnectED.

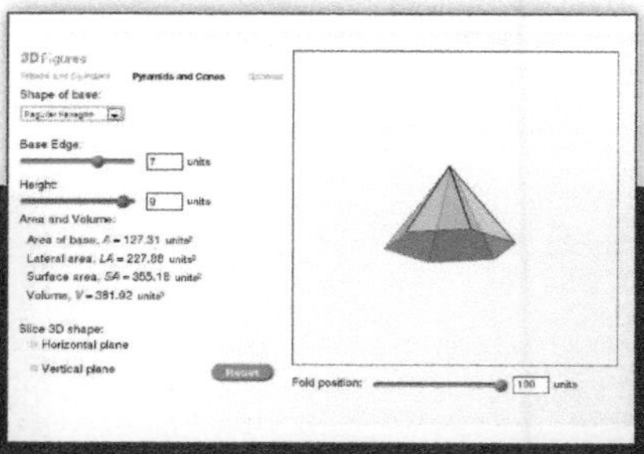

CHAPTER 12
Probability

ASSESSMENT

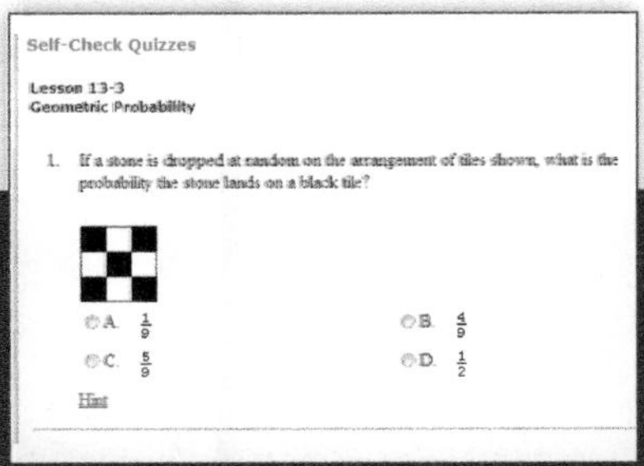

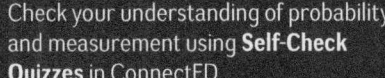

Check your understanding of probability and measurement using **Self-Check Quizzes** in ConnectED.

Go Online!
connectED.mcgraw-hill.com

Student Handbook

Built-In Workbook

Reference

Standards for Mathematical Practice

Glencoe Geometry exhibits these practices throughout the entire program. All of the Standards for Mathematical Practice will be covered in each chapter. The MP icon notes specific areas of coverage.

Mathematical Practices	What does it mean?
1. Make sense of problems and persevere in solving them.	Solving a mathematical problem takes time. Use a logical process to make sense of problems, understand that there may be more than one way to solve a problem, and alter the process if needed.
2. Reason abstractly and quantitatively.	You can start with a concrete or real-world context and then represent it with abstract numbers or symbols (decontextualize), find a solution, then refer back to the context to check that the solution makes sense (contextualize).
3. Construct viable arguments and critique the reasoning of others.	Sound mathematical arguments require a logical progression of statements and reasons. Mathematically proficient students can clearly communicate their thoughts and defend them.
4. Model with mathematics.	Modeling links classroom mathematics and statistics to everyday life, work, and decision-making. High school students at this level are expected to apply key takeaways from earlier grades to high-school level problems.
5. Use appropriate tools strategically.	Certain tools, including estimation and virtual tools are more appropriate than others. You should understand the benefits and limitations of each tool.
6. Attend to precision.	Precision in mathematics is more than accurate calculations. It is also the ability to communicate with the language of mathematics. In high school mathematics, precise language makes for effective communication and serves as a tool for understanding and solving problems.
7. Look for and make use of structure.	Mathematics is based on a well-defined structure. Mathematically proficient students look for that structure to find easier ways to solve problems.
8. Look for and express regularity in repeated reasoning.	Mathematics has been described as the study of patterns. Recognizing a pattern can lead to results more quickly and efficiently.

Folding Instructions

The following pages offer step-by-step instructions to make the Foldables® study guides.

Layered-Look Book

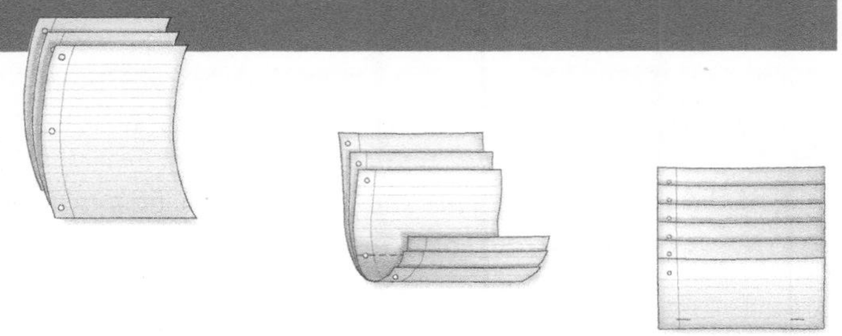

1. Collect three sheets of paper and layer them about 1 cm apart vertically. Keep the edges level.
2. Fold up the bottom edges of the paper to form 6 equal tabs.
3. Fold the papers and crease well to hold the tabs in place. Staple along the fold. Label each tab.

Shutter-Fold and Four-Door Books

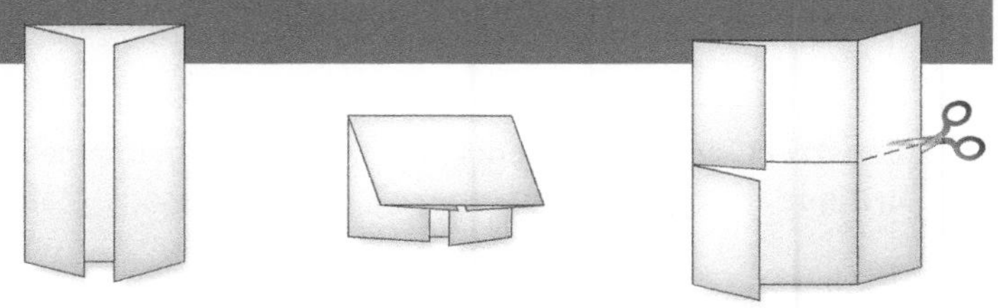

1. Find the middle of a horizontal sheet of paper. Fold both edges to the middle and crease the folds. Stop here if making a shutter-fold book. For a four-door book, complete the steps below.
2. Fold the folded paper in half, from top to bottom.
3. Unfold and cut along the fold lines to make four tabs. Label each tab.

Concept-Map Book

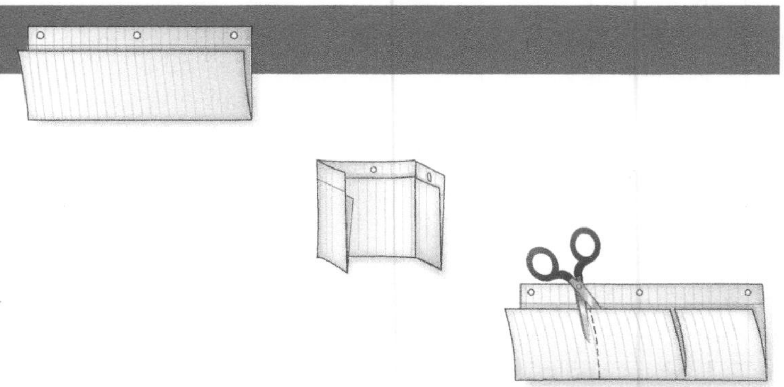

1. Fold a horizontal sheet of paper from top to bottom. Make the top edge about 2 cm shorter than the bottom edge.
2. Fold width-wise into thirds.
3. Unfold and cut only the top layer along both folds to make three tabs. Label the top and each tab.

Vocabulary Book

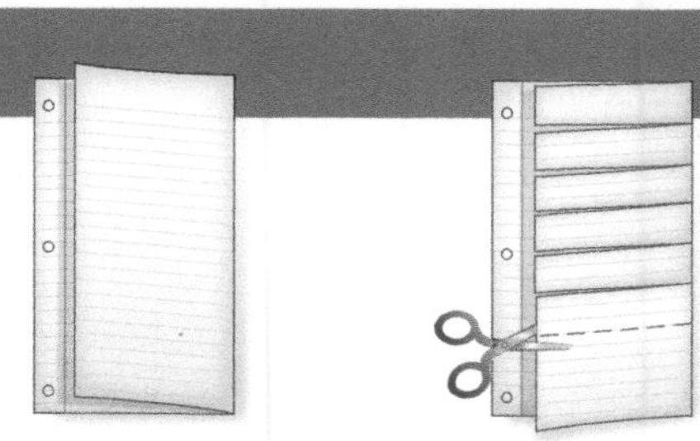

1. Fold a vertical sheet of notebook paper in half.
2. Cut along every third line of only the top layer to form tabs. Label each tab.

Pocket Book

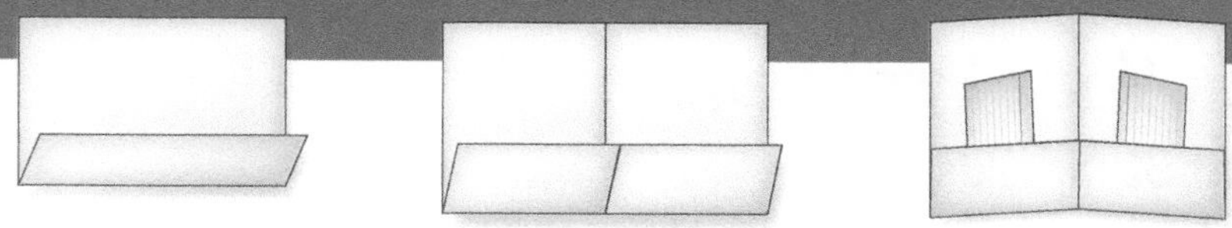

1. Fold the bottom of a horizontal sheet of paper up about 3 cm.
2. If making a two-pocket book, fold in half. If making a three-pocket book, fold in thirds.
3. Unfold once and dot with glue or staple to make pockets. Label each pocket.

Bound Book

1. Fold several sheets of paper in half to find the middle. Hold all but one sheet together and make a 3-cm cut at the fold line on each side of the paper.
2. On the final page, cut along the fold line to within 3-cm of each edge.
3. Slip the first few sheets through the cut in the final sheet to make a multi-page book.

Top-Tab Book

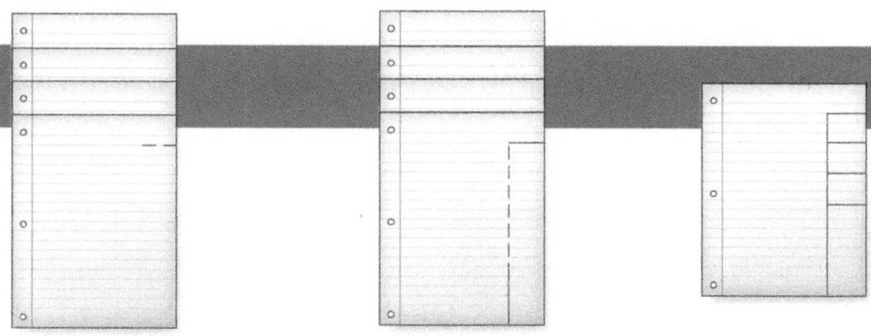

1. Layer multiple sheets of paper so that about 2–3 cm of each can be seen.
2. Make a 2–3-cm horizontal cut through all pages a short distance (3 cm) from the top edge of the top sheet.
3. Make a vertical cut up from the bottom to meet the horizontal cut.
4. Place the sheets on top of an uncut sheet and align the tops and sides of all sheets. Label each tab.

Accordion Book

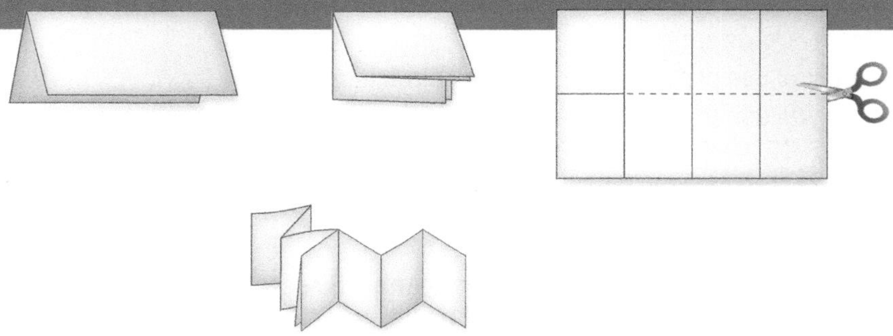

1. Fold a sheet of paper in half. Fold in half and in half again to form eight sections.
2. Cut along the long fold line, stopping before you reach the last two sections.
3. Refold the paper into an accordion book. You may want to glue the double pages together.

CHAPTER 7
Similarity

SUGGESTED PACING (DAYS)

	Instruction	Review & Assess
90 min.	4	1
45 min.	7	2

Track Your Progress

Content Standards

This chapter focuses on content from the **Similarity, Right Triangles**, and **Trigonometry and Congruence** domains.

THEN	NOW	NEXT
G.CO.11 Prove theorems about parallelograms. **G.CO.12** Make formal geometric constructions with a variety of tools and methods. **G.GPE.4** Use coordinates to prove simple geometric theorems algebraically. **G.MG.3** Apply geometric methods to solve problems.	**G.SRT.2** Given two figures, use the definition of similarity in terms of similarity transformations to decide if they are similar. **G.SRT.3** Use the properties of similarity transformations to establish the AA criterion for two triangles to be similar. **G.SRT.4** Prove theorems about triangles. **G.SRT.5** Use congruence and similarity criteria for triangles to solve problems.	**G.SRT.6** Understand that by similarity, side ratios in right triangles are properties of the angles in the triangle, leading to definitions of trigonometric ratios for acute angles. **G.SRT.8** Use trigonometric ratios and the Pythagorean Theorem to solve right triangles in applied problems. **G.SRT.10** Prove the Laws of Sines and Cosines and use them to solve problems.

Standards for Mathematical Practice

All of the Standards for Mathematical Practice will be covered in this chapter. The MP icon notes specific areas of coverage.

MP Teaching the Mathematical Practices
Help students develop the mathematical practices by asking questions like these.

Questioning Strategies

As students approach problems in this chapter, help them develop mathematical practices by asking:

Sense-Making
- Can you solve real-world problems using the properties of similar polygons?
- Can you solve real-world problems using the properties of similar triangles?

Reasoning
- How can you use proportions to identify similar polygons?
- How do you identify similarity transformations?

Construct Arguments
- How do you use proportional parts within triangles?
- How do you use proportional parts with parallel lines?

Using Tools
- How do the AA Similarity Postulate and the SSS and SAS Similarity Theorems help you to identify similar triangles?
- In what ways can you apply the Triangle Angle Bisector Theorem?

Precision
- How do you verify similarity after a similarity transformation?

Go Online!

StudySync: SMP Modeling Videos

These demonstrate how to apply the Standards for Mathematical Practice to collaborate, discuss, and solve real-world math problems.

Go Online!

connectED.mcgraw-hill.com

LearnSmart | The Geometer's Sketchpad | Vocabulary | Tutor | Tools | Calculator Resources | Check | Watch

Customize Your Chapter

Use the *Plan & Present*, *Assignment Tracker*, and *Assessment* tools in ConnectED to introduce lesson concepts, assign personalized practice, and diagnose areas of student need.

Differentiated Instruction

Throughout the program, look for the icons to find specialized content designed for your students.

- **AL** Approaching Level
- **OL** On Level
- **BL** Beyond Level
- **ELL** English Language Learners

Personalize

Differentiated Resources				
FOR EVERY CHAPTER	AL	OL	BL	ELL
Chapter Readiness Quizzes	●	●	◐	●
Chapter Tests	●	●	●	●
Standardized Test Practice	●	●	●	●
Vocabulary Review Games	●	●	◐	●
Anticipation Guide (English/Spanish)	●	●	◐	●
Student-Built Glossary	●	●	◐	●
Chapter Project	◐	●	◐	●
FOR EVERY LESSON	AL	OL	BL	ELL
Personal Tutors (English/Spanish)	●	●	◐	●
Graphing Calculator Personal Tutors	●	●	●	●
Step-by-Step Solutions	●	●	◐	●
Self-Check Quizzes	●	●	●	●
5-Minute Check	●	●	●	●
Study Notebook	●	●	●	●
Study Guide and Intervention	●	●		●
Skills Practice (English/Spanish)	●	◐		●
Practice (English/Spanish)	◐	●	●	●
Word Problem Practice	◐	●	●	◐
Enrichment		●	●	●
Extra Examples	●	◐		◐
Interactive Classroom	●	●	●	●

◐ Aligned to this group ● Designed for this group

Engage

Featured IWB Resources

The Geometer's Sketchpad provides students with a tangible, visual way to learn. *Use with Lessons 7-1 through 7-6.*

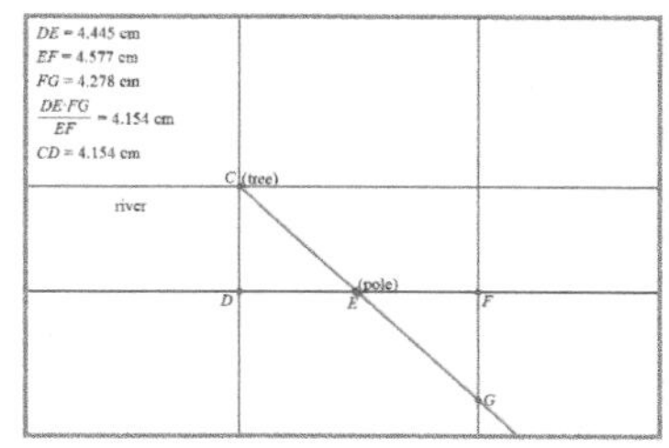

eLessons engage students and help build conceptual understanding of big ideas. *Use with Lessons 7-2 through 7-4.*

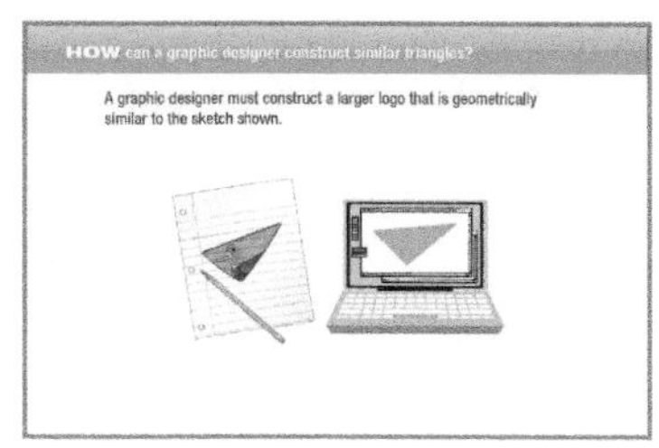

Geometry Tools provide students with tools to explore triangle congruence and similarity. *Use with Lesson 7-3 and 7-5.*

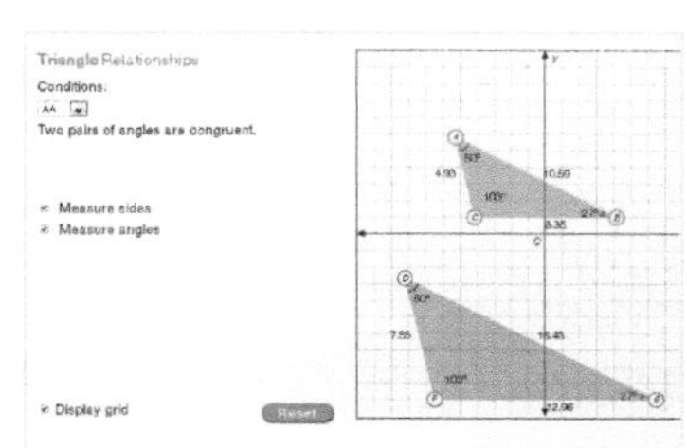

Time Management How long will it take to use these resources? Look for the clock in each lesson interleaf.

Introduce the Chapter

Mathematical Background

A ratio is a comparison of two quantities and can be used to solve problems involving similar figures. Similar figures are related by a scale factor that is the ratio of the lengths of two corresponding sides. Similar triangles can be used to measure distances indirectly. If two figures are similar, there is a relationship between the perimeters of similar polygons and the altitudes, medians, and bisectors of similar triangles.

Essential Questions

At the end of this chapter, students should be able to answer the Essential Questions.

- How can two objects be similar? **Sample answers: Two objects could have similar designs, patterns, shapes, sizes, or colors.**
- How does similarity in mathematics compare to similarity in everyday life? **Sample answer: In mathematics, similarity has a more specific definition: objects or figures can only be similar if they have the same shape.**

Apply Math to the Real World

SPORTS In this activity, students will use what they know about triangles to model the path a ball takes when it bounces. Have students complete this activity individually or in small groups. MP 1

CHAPTER 7

Similarity

THEN

You learned about angles of polygons, including quadrilaterals, and applied them to real-world applications.

NOW

In this chapter you will:

- Identify dilations.
- Identify similar polygons.
- Identify AA, SSS, and SAS similarity and the parts of similar triangles.
- Use parallel lines and proportional parts.

MP WHY

SPORTS Triangles can be used in sports to describe the path of a ball, such as a bounce pass from one person to another.

Use the Mathematical Practices to complete the activity.

1. **Sense-Making** What sports involve a bounce pass? Can you think of sports where the ball is struck, follows a path to the ground or playing surface, and then bounces up?
2. **Apply Math** Write a problem involving a bounce path and two triangles.
3. **Modeling** Use the Geometry Tool in ConnectED to model the triangles in the problem you created.

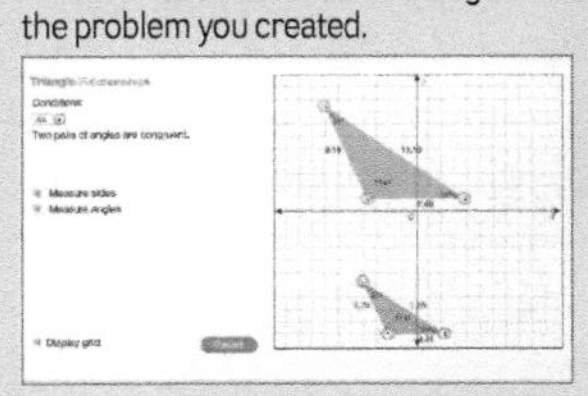

4. **Reasoning** What can you do to make your problem more realistic? What other forces are at play in the real world when a ball is bounced or struck?

ALEKS®

Your Student Success Tool ALEKS is an adaptive, personalized learning environment that identifies precisely what each student knows and is ready to learn—ensuring student success at all levels.

- **Formative Assessment:** Dynamic, detailed reports monitor students' progress toward standards mastery.
- **Automatic Differentiation:** Strengthen prerequisite skills and target individual learning gaps.
- **Personalized Instruction:** Supplement in-class instruction with personalized assessment and learning opportunities.

Go Online!

Chapter Project

Model Makers Students use what they have learned about similarities and proportional parts to complete a project. This chapter project addresses business literacy, as well as several specific skills identified as being essential to student success by the Framework for 21st Century Learning. MP 1, 3, 4, 6

Go Online to Guide Your Learning

Explore & Explain

Transformation Tool

Use the **Transformation** tool to explore similarity transformations discussed in Lesson 7-2.

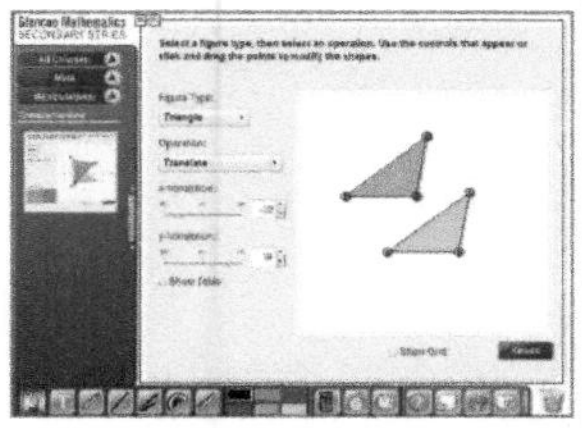

The Geometer's Sketchpad

Use the **The Geometer's Sketchpad** to discover principles of similarity and develop the definition of similar polygons, to explore the results of cutting through a triangle with a line parallel to a side, and to explore how to use similar triangles to find a distance that cannot be measured directly.

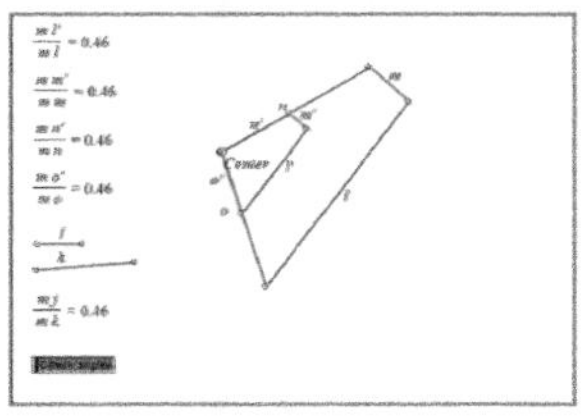

eBook

Interactive Student Guide

Before starting the chapter, answer the **Chapter Focus** preview questions. Check your answers as you complete each lesson. At the end of the chapter, try the **Performance Task**.

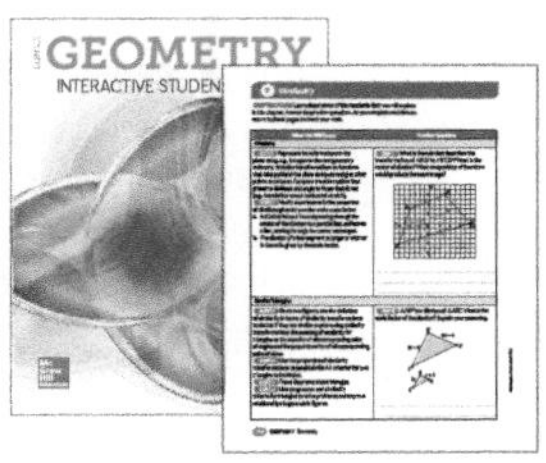

Organize

Foldables

Get organized! Create this Similarity Foldable before you start the chapter to help you organize your notes about dilations, similar polygons, similar triangles, parallel lines, and proportional parts.

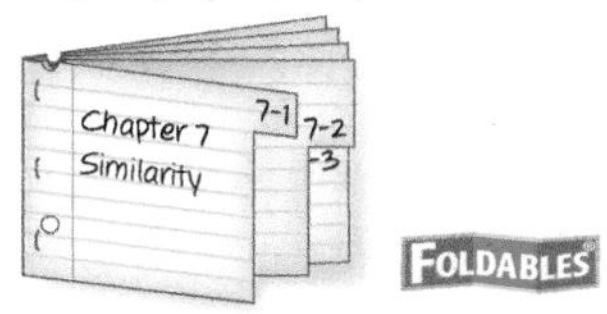

Collaborate

Chapter Project

In the **Model Makers** project, you will use what you have learned about similarities and proportional parts to complete a business project.

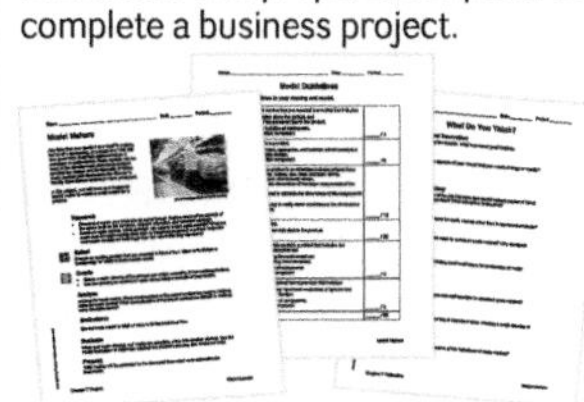

Focus

LEARNSMART

Need help studying? Complete the **Similarity, Proof, and Trigonometry** domain in LearnSmart to review for the chapter test.

ALEKS

You can use the **Similarities and Transformations** topic in ALEKS to explore what you know about relationships in triangles and what you are ready to learn.*

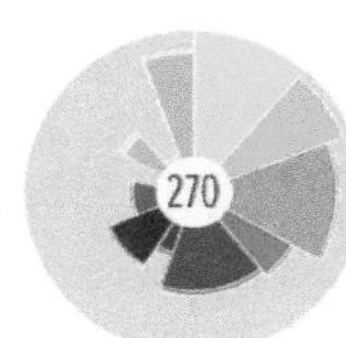

* Ask your teacher if this is part of your program.

Dinah Zike's FOLDABLES

Focus Students write notes about each lesson in this chapter.

Teach Have students make and label the Foldable as illustrated.

Students use their Foldables for notes, problem solving, and descriptions. As students read and work through each lesson of this chapter, have them record their questions. As students learn more about proportions and similarity, encourage students to answer their own questions. Self-questioning is a strategy that helps students stay focused during reading.

When to Use It Use the appropriate tabs as students cover each lesson in this chapter. Students can add to the vocabulary tab during each lesson.

Go Online!

Choosing Foldables

How do you know which Foldables strategy to use? In this video, you will learn best practices to use when choosing Foldables. MP 1

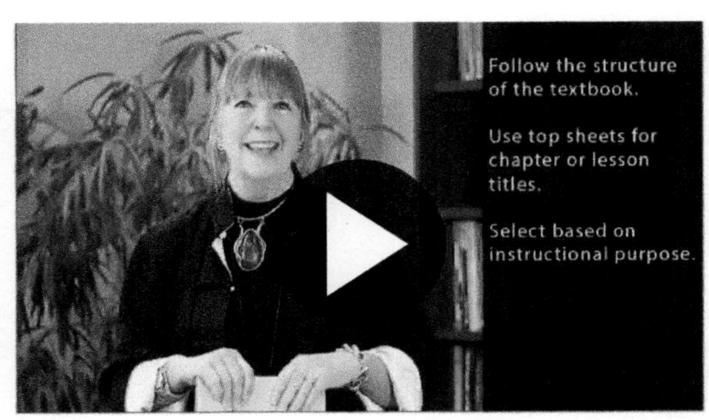

Follow the structure of the textbook.
Use top sheets for chapter or lesson titles.
Select based on instructional purpose.

Get Ready for the Chapter

RtI Response to Intervention

Use the Concept Check results and the Intervention Planner chart to help you determine your Response to Intervention.

Intervention Planner

TIER 1 On Level OL

IF students miss 25% of the exercises or less,

THEN choose a resource:

Go Online!

- Skills Practice, Chapter 1
- Chapter Project
- Self-Check Quizzes

TIER 2 Approaching Level AL

IF students miss 50% of the exercises,

THEN choose a resource:

Go Online!

- Study Guide and Intervention, Ch. 1
- Extra Examples
- Personal Tutors
- Homework Help
- *Quick Review Math Handbook*

TIER 3 Intensive Intervention

IF students miss 75% of the exercises,

THEN Use *Math Triumphs, Geometry*

Go Online!

- Extra Examples
- Personal Tutors
- Homework Help
- Review Vocabulary

Go Online! for Vocabulary Review Games and key vocabulary in 13 languages.

Get Ready for the Chapter

Connecting Concepts

Concept Check

Review the concepts used in this chapter by answering the questions below.

1. Given the equation $\frac{x+9}{2} = \frac{3x-1}{8}$, what would be the first step to solve? **cross-multiplication**
2. Given the equation $3(4x - 3) = 5(2x + 11)$, what rule would you apply to begin solving? **Distributive Property**

In the figure, $\overrightarrow{QP}$ and $\overrightarrow{QR}$ are opposite rays and $\overrightarrow{QT}$ bisects $\angle SQR$.

3. How can you express $m\angle SQR$ in terms of $m\angle TQR$? **$m\angle SQR$ is twice $m\angle TQR$.**

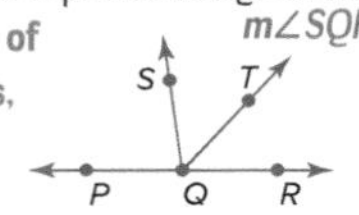

6. By definition of angle bisectors, $m\angle SQT = \frac{1}{2}$ $m\angle SQR$.

4. Justify your answer. **An angle bisector divides an angle into two congruent angles.**
5. If $m\angle SQR = 6x + 8$ and $m\angle TQR = 4x - 14$, what mathematical method would you apply first to solve the equation? **substitution**
6. What do you know about $m\angle SQT$ in relation to $m\angle SQR$? How?
7. Knowing the value of x, how can you determine $m\angle SQT$? **The value of x is known and value of $m\angle TQR$ in terms of x is known. Substitute and solve.**

Performance Task Review

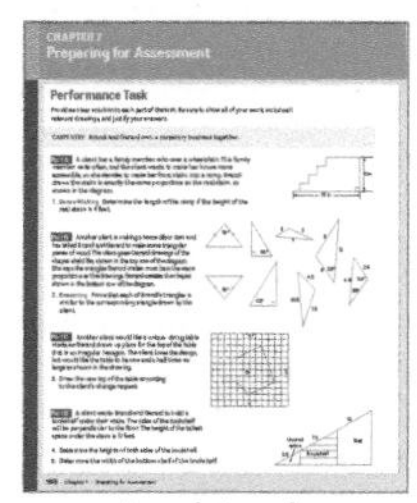

You can use the concepts and skills in the chapter to design projects for a carpentry business. Understanding similarities will help you finish the Performance Task at the end of the chapter.

MP In this Performance Task you will:

- make sense of problems and persevere in solving them
- model with mathematics
- attend to precision

New Vocabulary

English		Español
dilation	p. 492	homotecia
similar polygons	p. 502	polígonos semejantes
similarity transformation	p. 502	transformación de semejanza
scale factor	p. 504	factor de escala
midsegment of a triangle	p. 535	segmento medio de un triángulo

Review Vocabulary

altitude altura a segment drawn from a vertex of a triangle perpendicular to the line containing the other side

angle bisector bisectriz de un ángulo a ray that divides an angle into two congruent angles

median mediana a segment drawn from a vertex of a triangle to the midpoint of the opposite side

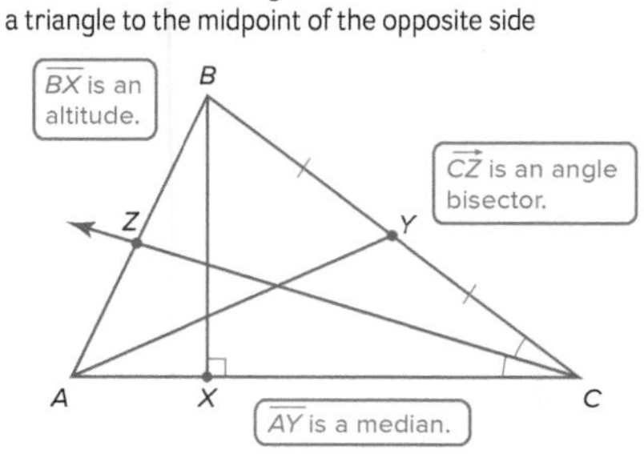

Key Vocabulary ELL

Introduce the key vocabulary in the chapter using the routine below.

Define The scale factor is the ratio of the lengths of the corresponding sides of two similar polygons.

Example In the diagram, $\triangle DFG \sim \triangle JHK$.

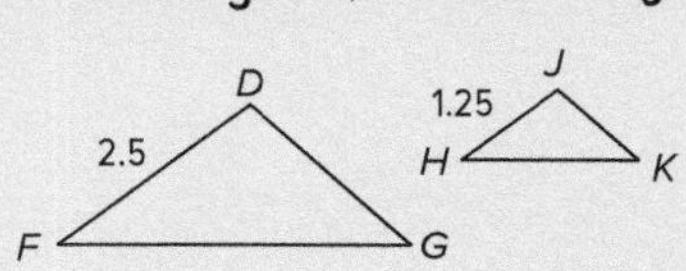

Ask What is the scale factor of $\triangle DFG$ to $\triangle JHK$? $\frac{2.5}{1.25}$ or 2 What is the scale factor of $\triangle JHK$ to $\triangle DFG$? $\frac{1.25}{2.5}$ or $\frac{1}{2}$

LESSON 7-1

Dilations

SUGGESTED PACING (DAYS)

	Explore	Instruction	Extend
90 min.	.25	0.5	.25
45 min.	0.5	1.0	0.5

Track Your Progress

Objectives

1 Draw dilations.

2 Draw dilations in the coordinate plane.

Mathematical Background

A dilation is a transformation that changes the size of a figure by a scale factor. If the scale factor is 1, then the dilation is a congruence transformation. If the scale factor is not 1, then the dilation is a similarity transformation.

THEN

G.SRT.1 Verify experimentally the properties of dilations given by a center and a scale factor.

NOW

G.CO.2 Represent transformations in the plane using, e.g., transparencies and geometry software; describe transformations as functions that take points in the plane as inputs and give other points as outputs. Compare transformations that preserve distance and angle to those that do not (e.g., translation versus horizontal stretch).

NEXT

G.SRT.2 Given two figures, use the definition of similarity in terms of similarity transformations to decide if they are similar; explain using similarity transformations the meaning of similarity for triangles as the equality of all corresponding pairs of angles and the proportionality of all corresponding pairs of sides.

G.SRT.3 Use the properties of similarity transformations to establish the AA criterion for two triangles to be similar.

Go Online! All of these resources and more are available at connectED.mcgraw-hill.com

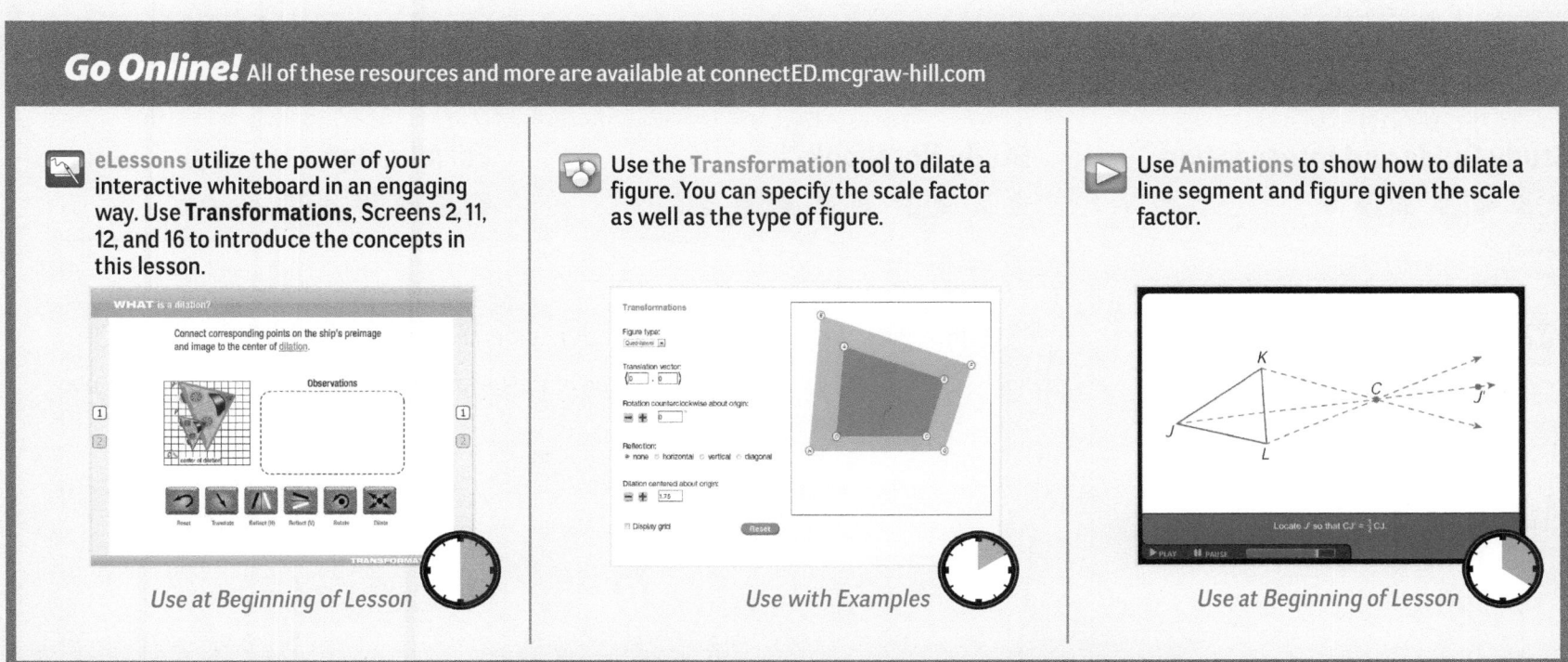

eLessons utilize the power of your interactive whiteboard in an engaging way. Use **Transformations**, Screens 2, 11, 12, and 16 to introduce the concepts in this lesson.

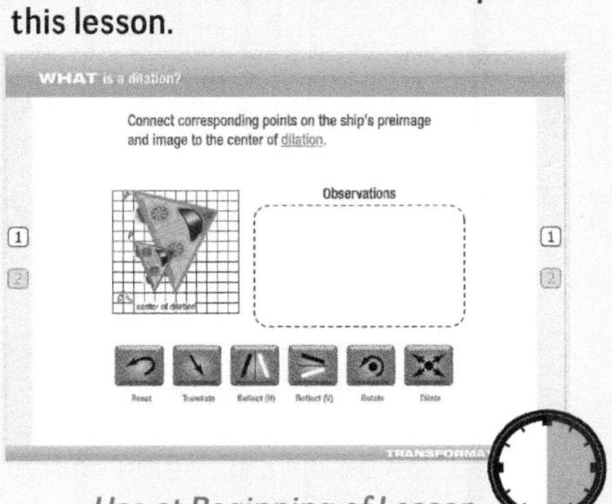

Use at Beginning of Lesson

Use the Transformation tool to dilate a figure. You can specify the scale factor as well as the type of figure.

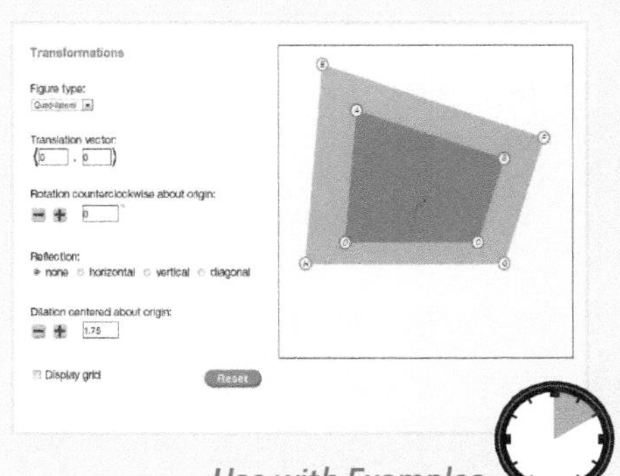

Use with Examples

Use Animations to show how to dilate a line segment and figure given the scale factor.

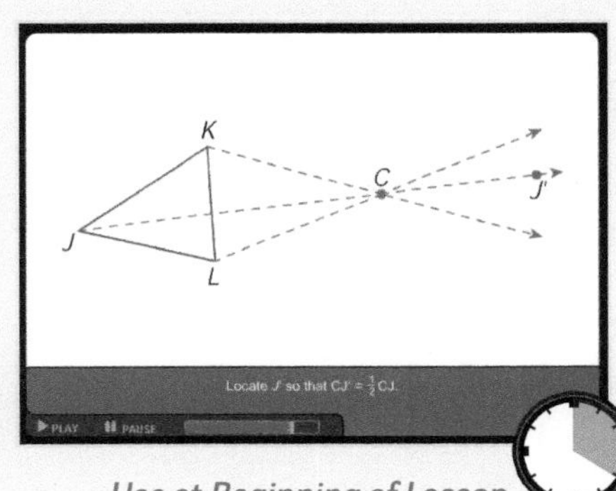

Use at Beginning of Lesson

OER Using Open Educational Resources

Video Sharing Have students work in groups to create a video lesson on **Knowmia Teach** demonstrating what they have learned about dilations and other transformations. Then post students' videos online so students can review them before taking the assessment. *Use as homework*

Go Online!
connectED.mcgraw-hill.com

Worksheets

Differentiate Your Resources

Extra Practice Additional practice or homework; Skills Practice is best for approaching-level students and Practice is best for on-level and beyond-level students

Skills Practice

AL OL ELL

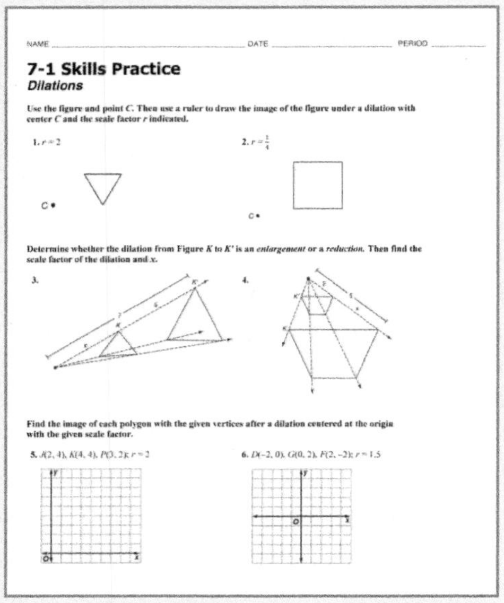
7-1 Skills Practice
Dilations

Practice

AL OL BL ELL

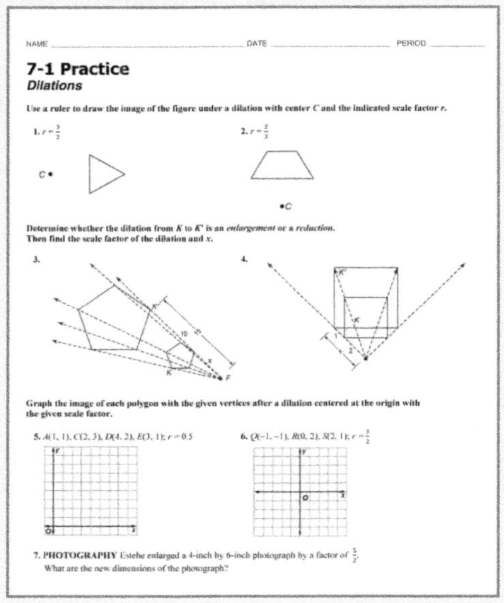
7-1 Practice
Dilations

Word Problem Practice

AL OL BL ELL

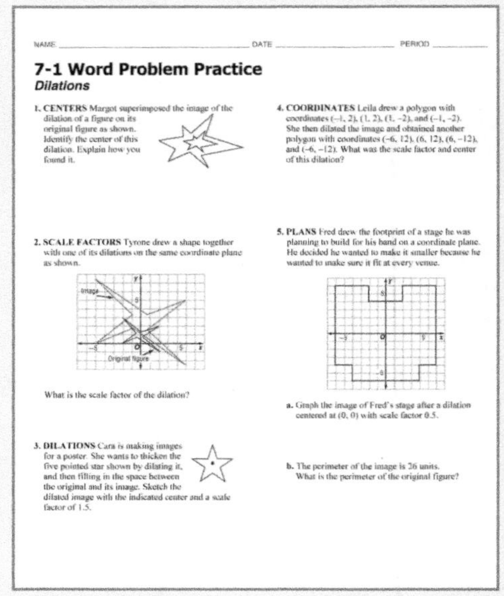
7-1 Word Problem Practice
Dilations

Intervention Reteaching and vocabulary activities that can be used with struggling or absent students and as ELL support

Study Guide and Intervention

AL OL ELL

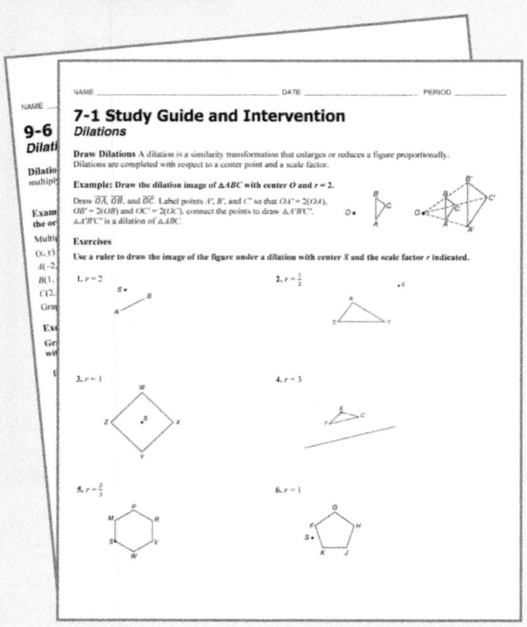
7-1 Study Guide and Intervention
Dilations

Study Notebook

AL OL BL ELL

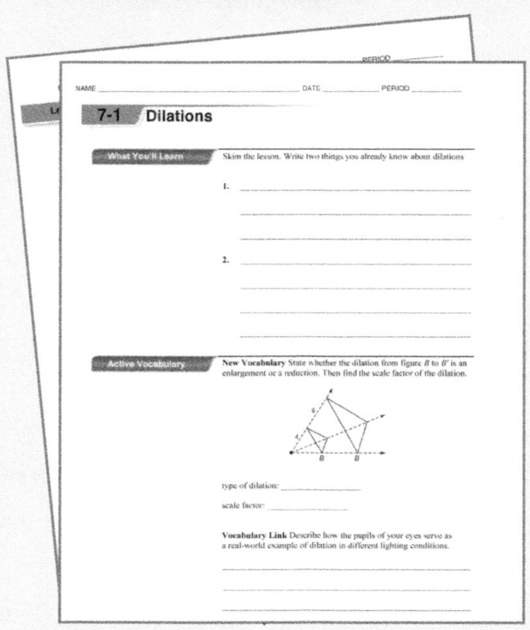
7-1 Dilations

Extension Activities that can be used to extend lesson concepts

Enrichment

OL BL ELL

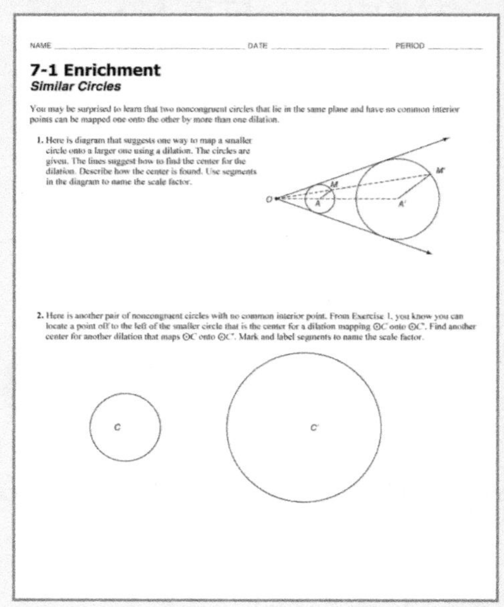
7-1 Enrichment
Similar Circles

EXPLORE 7-1
Graphing Technology Lab
Dilations

You can use TI-Nspire Technology to explore properties of dilations.

Mathematical Practices
MP 5 Use appropriate tools strategically.

Content Standards
G.SRT.1 Understand similarity in terms of similarity transformations. Verify experimentally the properties of dilations given by a center and a scale factor:
a. A dilation takes a line not passing through the center of the dilation to a parallel line, and leaves a line passing through the center unchanged.
b. The dilation of a line segment is longer or shorter in the ratio given by the scale factor.

Activity 1 Dilation of a Triangle

Work cooperatively. Dilate a triangle by a scale factor of 1.5.

Step 1 Add a new **Geometry** page. Then, from the **Points & Lines** menu, use the **Point** tool to add a point and label it *X*.

Step 2 From the **Shapes** menu, select **Triangle** and specify three points. Label the points *A*, *B*, and *C*.

Step 3 From the **Actions** menu, use the **Text** tool to separately add the text *Scale Factor* and *1.5* to the page.

Step 4 From the **Transformation** menu, select **Dilation**. Then select point *X*, △*ABC*, and the text *1.5*.

Step 5 Label the points on the image *A′*, *B′*, and *C′*.

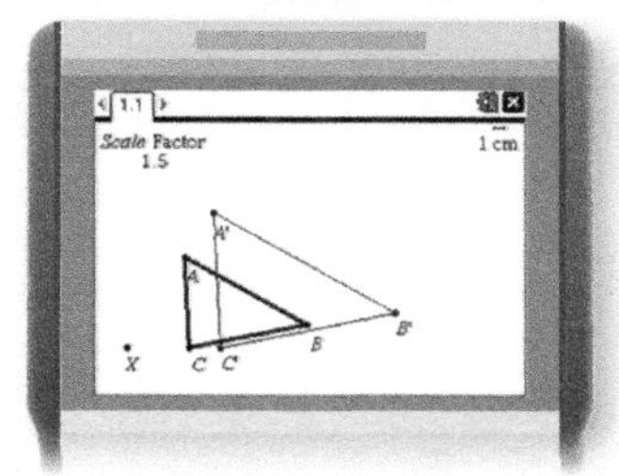

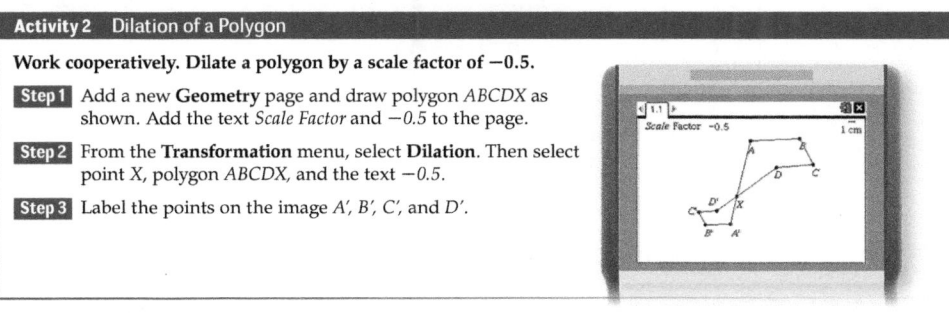

Analyze the Results Work cooperatively. 1–3. See margin.

1. Using the **Slope** tool on the **Measurement** menu, describe the effect of the dilation on $\overline{AB}$. That is, how are the lines through $\overline{AB}$ and $\overline{A'B'}$ related?
2. What is the effect of the dilation on the line passing through side $\overline{CA}$?
3. What is the effect of the dilation on the line passing through side $\overline{CB}$?

Activity 2 Dilation of a Polygon

Work cooperatively. Dilate a polygon by a scale factor of −0.5.

Step 1 Add a new **Geometry** page and draw polygon *ABCDX* as shown. Add the text *Scale Factor* and *−0.5* to the page.

Step 2 From the **Transformation** menu, select **Dilation**. Then select point *X*, polygon *ABCDX*, and the text *−0.5*.

Step 3 Label the points on the image *A′*, *B′*, *C′*, and *D′*.

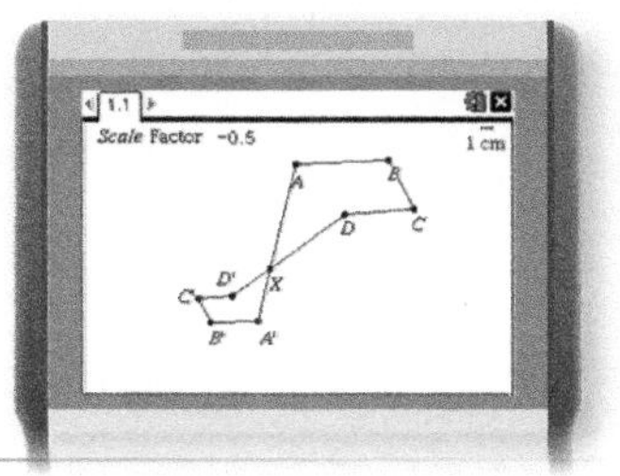

Model and Analyze Work cooperatively. 4–6. See margin.

4. Analyze the effect of the dilation in Activity 2 on sides that contain the center of the dilation.
5. Analyze the effect of a dilation of trapezoid *ABCD* shown with a scale factor of 0.75 and the center of the dilation at *A*.
6. **MAKE A CONJECTURE** Describe the effect of a dilation on segments that pass through the center of a dilation and segments that do not pass through the center of a dilation.

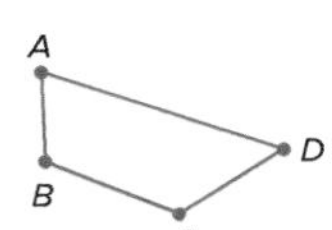

Additional Answers

1. The dilation maps $\overline{AB}$ to $\overline{A'B'}$, which are parallel segments.
2. The dilation maps $\overline{CA}$ to $\overline{C'A'}$, which are parallel segments.
3. The dilation maps $\overline{CB}$ to $\overline{C'B'}$, which are parallel segments.
4. The original line segment and dilated segment are part of the same line.
5. The new trapezoid *A′B′C′D′* is 75% the size of trapezoid *ABCD* and is oriented so that *A* and *A′* coincide.
6. Sample answer: Segments that do not pass through the center of the dilation are mapped onto parallel segments. Segments that pass through the center of a dilation are mapped onto segments that are part of the same line.

Launch

Objective Use graphing technology to explore the properties of dilations.

Materials
- TI-Nspire technology

Teaching Tips
- Explain to students that their measurements will not be the same as the measurements on the screen.
- When dilating the figures, it is important that the display confirms the selection prior to pressing ENTER.
- If the transformation causes the figure to move off the screen, move the cursor to a blank place on the screen and hold down on the center of the touchpad until the hand closes. Drag until the figure is on the screen.
- To use the **Slope** tool on the **Measurement** menu, students will need to place a line segment on top of the side of the triangle.

Alternative Method
The activities presented in this lesson can also be completed using Geometer's Sketchpad software or Cabri Jr. on a TI-84.

Teach

Working in Cooperative Groups Divide the class into pairs. Work through Activity 1 as a class. Then ask students to work with their partners to complete Activity 2. ELL

Go Online!

Graphing Calculators
Students can use the Graphing Calculator Personal Tutors to review the use of the graphing calculator to represent functions. They can also use the Other Calculator Keystrokes, which cover lab content for students with calculators other than the TI-84 Plus.

Launch

Have students read the Why? section of the lesson. Ask:

- If you enlarge the entire photo shown, will it decrease the empty space at the top of the photo? No, because the entire photo is enlarged by the same amount.
- What is the relationship between the original photo and the reduced photo? They are the same shape, but different sizes.
- How can you prove that a dilated figure is the same shape as the original figure? Prove that their corresponding angles are congruent and the measures of their corresponding sides are proportional.

Teach

Ask the scaffolded questions for each example to build conceptual understanding for students at all levels.

1 Draw Dilations

Example 1 Draw a Dilation

AL Can the dilated image be either bigger or smaller than the original image? Explain. Yes; If the scale factor is greater than 1, it will be bigger. If the scale factor is less than 1, it will be smaller.

OL For a dilation, what would happen if the scale factor k were 1? If the scale factor were 1, the dilation would map the image onto itself.

BL What scale factor would result in a dilated image that is 25% smaller than the original image? $\frac{3}{4}$

Go Online!

Interactive Whiteboard

Use the *eLesson*, *Lesson Presentation*, or *Interactive Classroom* to present this lesson.

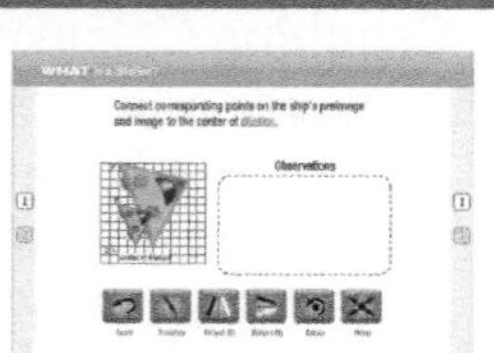

LESSON 1

Dilations

:·Then	:·Now	:·Why?
You identified dilations and verified them as similarity transformations.	1 Draw dilations. 2 Draw dilations in the coordinate plane.	Charles can resize his photos before uploading them to a social networking site. Scaling down the size or enlarging the size of the original photo is an example of a *dilation*.

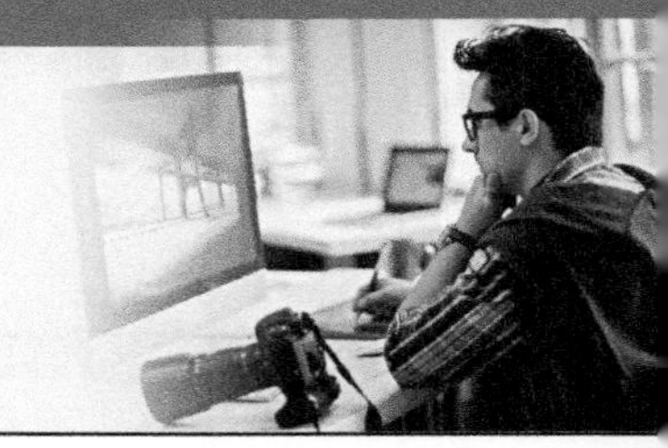

New Vocabulary
dilation

Mathematical Practices
1 Make sense of problems and persevere in solving them.
5 Use appropriate tools strategically.

Content Standards
G.CO.2 Represent transformations in the plane using, e.g., transparencies and geometry software; describe transformations as functions that take points in the plane as inputs and give other points as outputs. Compare transformations that preserve distance and angle to those that do not (e.g., translation versus horizontal stretch).
G.SRT.1 Understand similarity in terms of similarity transformations. Verify experimentally the properties of dilations given by a center and a scale factor:
a. A dilation takes a line not passing through the center of the dilation to a parallel line, and leaves a line passing through the center unchanged.
b. The dilation of a line segment is longer or shorter in the ratio given by the scale factor.

1 Draw Dilations A **dilation** or *scaling* is a similarity transformation that enlarges or reduces a figure proportionally with respect to a *center* point and a *scale* factor.

Key Concept Dilation

A dilation with center C and positive scale factor k, $k \neq 1$, is a function that maps a point P in a figure to its image such that

- if point P and C coincide, then the image and preimage are the same point, or
- if point P is not the center of dilation, then P' lies on $\overrightarrow{CP}$ and $CP' = k(CP)$.

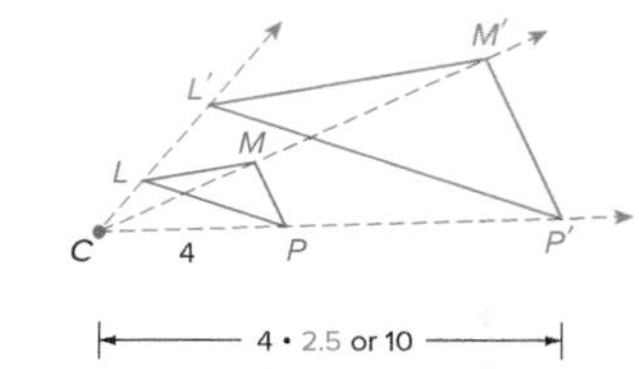

$\triangle L'M'P'$ is the image of $\triangle LMP$ under a dilation with center C and scale factor 2.5.

G.CO.2

Example 1 Draw a Dilation

Copy $\triangle ABC$ and point D. Then use a ruler to draw the image of $\triangle ABC$ under a dilation with center D and scale factor $\frac{1}{2}$.

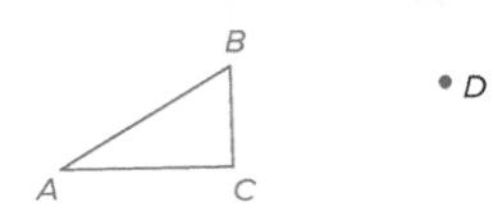

Step 1 Draw rays from D though each vertex.

Step 2 Locate A' on $\overrightarrow{DA}$ such that $DA' = \frac{1}{2}DA$.

Step 3 Locate B' on $\overrightarrow{DB}$ and C' on $\overrightarrow{DC}$ in the same way. Then draw $\triangle A'B'C'$.

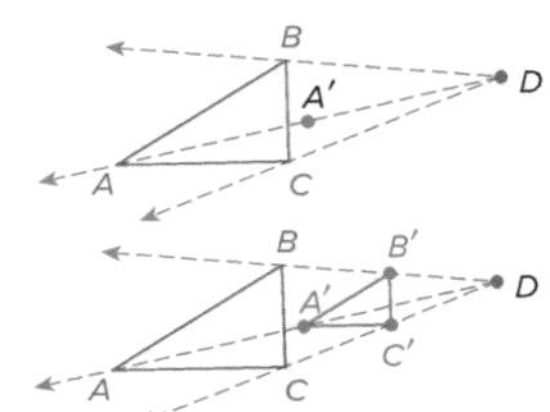

Guided Practice 1A, 1B. See Ch. 7 Answer Appendix.

Copy the figure and point J. Then use a ruler to draw the image of the figure under a dilation with center J and the scale factor k indicated.

1A. $k = \frac{3}{2}$

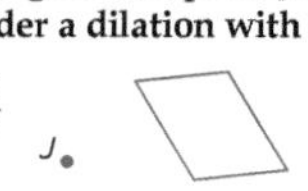

1B. $k = 0.75$

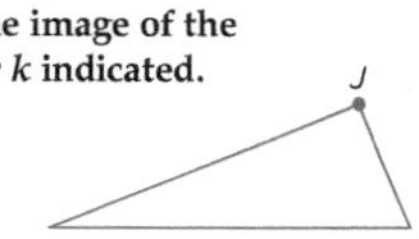

MP Mathematical Practices Strategies

Look for and make use of structure.
Help students understand dilations. Ask them questions to help them think through the concepts. For example:

- Look at the diagram in the Key Concept box. Explain why it makes sense that $CP' = k(CP)$. Sample answer: The distance CP is multiplied by the factor of dilation k, so $CP' = kCP$.
- If you have dilated a figure to 3 times its original size, what do you know about the lengths of the sides compared to its original? They will be three times as long.
- A figure is dilated by a scale factor of 2.5. If the figure was also dilated by a scale factor of 2.5 about a different center, how would the areas of the two figures compare? They are the same.
- Does the location of the center of dilation change the shape of the dilated figure? No, if you dilate a figure properly it does not matter where the center is; the dilated figure will have the same shape.

If $k > 1$, then the dilation is an *enlargement*. If $0 < k < 1$, then the dilation is a *reduction*. A dilation with a scale factor of 1 is called an *isometry dilation*. It produces an image that coincides with the preimage. The two figures are congruent.

G.SRT.1

Real-World Example 2 Find the Scale Factor of a Dilation

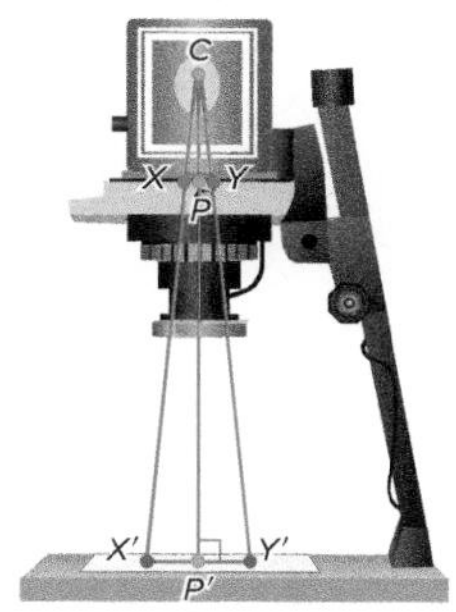

PHOTOGRAPHY **To create different-sized prints, you can adjust the distance between a film negative and the enlarged print by using a photographic enlarger. Suppose the distance between the light source C and the negative is 45 millimeters (CP). To what distance PP' should you adjust the enlarger to create a 22.75-centimeter wide print ($X'Y'$) from a 35-millimeter wide negative (XY)?**

Understand This problem involves a dilation. The center of dilation is C, $XY = 35$ mm, $X'Y' = 22.75$ cm or 227.5 mm, and $CP = 45$ mm. You are asked to find PP'.

Plan Find the scale factor of the dilation from the preimage XY to the image $X'Y'$. Use the scale factor to find CP' and then use CP and CP' to find PP'.

Solve The scale factor k of the enlargement is the ratio of a length on the image to a corresponding length on the preimage.

$k = \frac{\text{image length}}{\text{preimage length}} = \frac{X'Y'}{XY}$ Scale factor of image; image $= X'Y'$, preimage $= XY$

$= \frac{227.5}{35}$ or 6.5 Divide.

Use this scale factor of 6.5 to find CP'.

$CP' = k(CP)$ Definition of dilation

$= 6.5(45)$ $k = 6.5$ and $CP = 45$

$= 292.5$ Multiply.

Use CP' and CP to find PP'.

$CP + PP' = CP'$ Segment addition

$45 + PP' = 292.5$ $CP = 45$ and $CP' = 292.5$

$PP' = 247.5$ Subtract 45 from each side.

So the enlarger should be adjusted so that the distance from the negative to the enlarged print (PP') is 247.5 millimeters or 24.75 centimeters.

Check $k = \frac{\text{distance from } C \text{ to } P'}{\text{distance from } C \text{ to } P}$

$= \frac{CP'}{CP} = \frac{292.5}{45}$ or 6.5 ✓

Because the dilation is an enlargement, the scale factor should be greater than 1. Because $6.5 > 1$, the scale factor found is reasonable.

Problem-Solving Tip

MP **Perseverance** To prevent calculations errors, estimate the answer to a problem before solving. In Example 2, estimate the scale factor of the dilation to be about $\frac{240}{40}$ or 6. Then CP' would be about $6 \cdot 50$ or 300 and PP' about $300 - 50$ or 250 millimeters, which is 25 centimeters. A measure of 24.75 centimeters is close to this estimate, so the answer is reasonable.

Differentiated Instruction AL OL BL ELL

Auditory/Musical Learners Students can relate dilations to music by how loud or soft a sound is. A harmonica's sound is magnified or dilated with a scale factor of r greater than 1 when a great force is used to create a musical note. The sound is much softer when the same note is produced with half the force. They can also correlate drawing a breath through the harmonica with a negative scale factor and exhaling into the harmonica with a positive scale factor.

Need Another Example?

Copy trapezoid *PQRS* and point *C*. Then use a ruler to draw the image of trapezoid *PQRS* under a dilation with center *C* and scale factor 3.

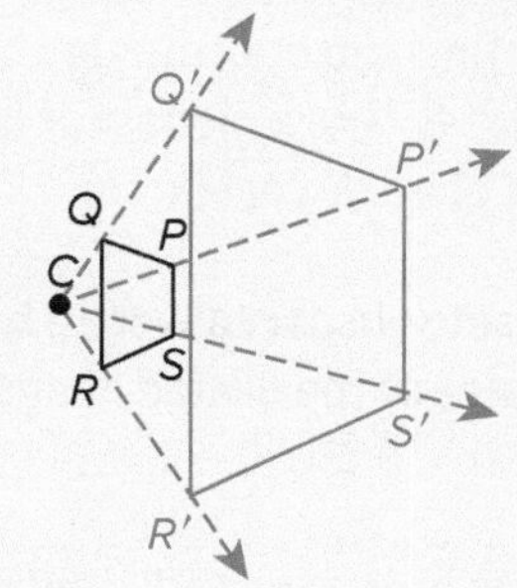

Example 2 Find the Scale Factor of a Dilation

AL What does it mean to enlarge something? What clue does the name "photographic enlarger" give us about the scale factor of the dilation? to make it bigger; It tells us that the scale factor will be greater than 1.

OL To what distance PP' to the nearest millimeter should you adjust the enlarger to create a print that is 6 inches wide? 151 mm

BL If PP' is 240 millimeters, what will be the width of the enlarged print to the nearest millimeter? 222 mm

Need Another Example?

Puppets To create the illusion of a "life-sized" image, puppeteers sometimes use a light source to show an enlarged image of a puppet projected on a screen or wall. Suppose that the distance between a light source L and the puppet is 24 inches (LP). To what distance PP' should you place the puppet from the screen to create a 49.5-inch tall shadow ($I'M'$) from a 9 inch puppet?

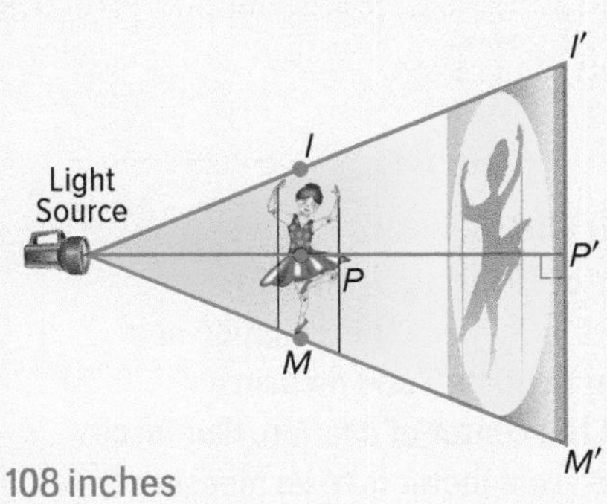

9 feet or 108 inches

2 Dilations in the Coordinate Plane

Example 3 Dilations in the Coordinate Plane

AL How do you find the coordinates of a dilated image? Multiply the scale factor by the coordinates of each vertex.

OL If the scale factor in part **a** were 0.5, what would the coordinates of the dilated image be? $J'(-1, 2)$, $K'(-1, -1)$, $L'(-2, -1)$, $M'(-2, 1)$

BL If the figure in part **a** were dilated so that the coordinates of the image are $J'(-1.5, 3)$, $K'(-1.5, -1.5)$, $L'(-3, -1.5)$, and $M'(-3, 1.5)$, what is the scale factor be? $\frac{3}{4}$

Need Another Example?

Graph the image of each polygon with the given vertices after a dilation at the indicated center with the given scale factor.

a. $E(-8, 4)$, $F(-4, 8)$, $G(8, 4)$, and $H(-4, -8)$; origin; $k = \frac{1}{4}$

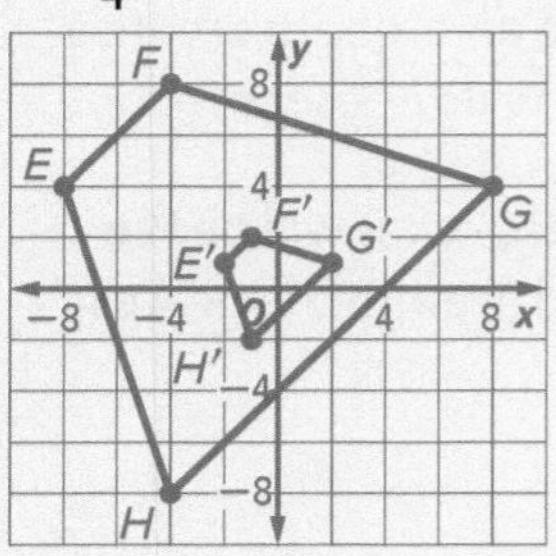

b. $A(-2, -4)$, $B(3, 2)$, $C(0, 4)$; $(1, 2)$; 1.5

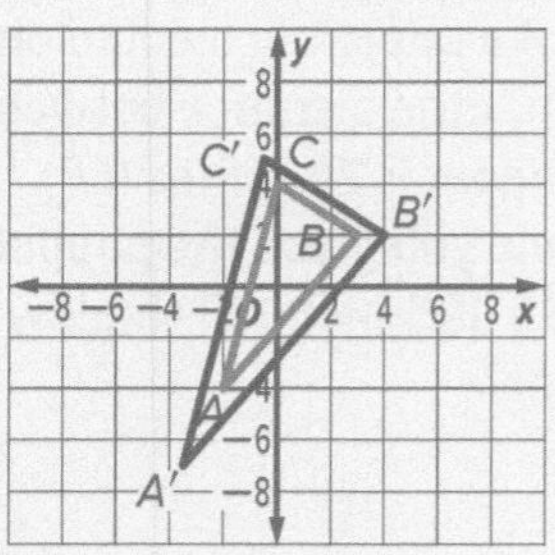

Watch Out!

Center of Dilation Watch for students who begin their dilation at a point on the figure and measure beyond the center of dilation. Reinforce that the scale factor is to be measured beginning at the center of dilation.

Guided Practice

2. Determine whether the dilation from Figure Q to Q' is an *enlargement* or a *reduction*. Then find the scale factor of the dilation and x. enlargement; 3; 10

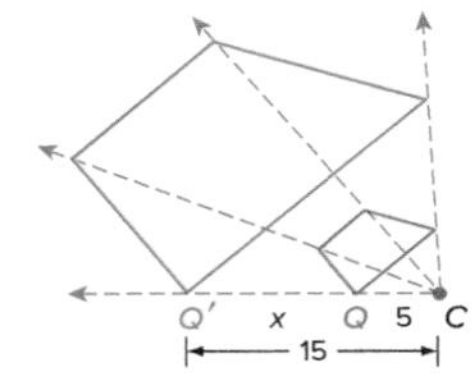

2 Dilations in the Coordinate Plane You can use the following rules to find the image of a figure after a dilation centered at the origin.

Study Tip ELL
Negative Scale Factors Dilations can also have negative scale factors. You will investigate this type of dilation in Exercise 40.

Key Concept Dilations in the Coordinate Plane

Words To find the coordinates of an image after a dilation centered at the origin, multiply the x- and y-coordinates of each point on the preimage by the scale factor of the dilation, k.

Symbols $(x, y) \rightarrow (kx, ky)$

Example

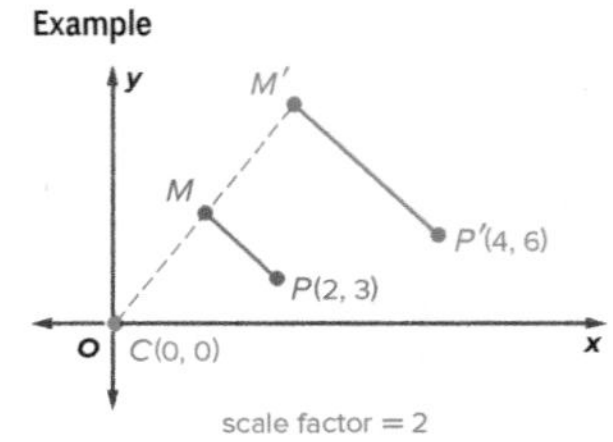

Go Online!

Investigate dilations by using the Geometry Tools in ConnectED.

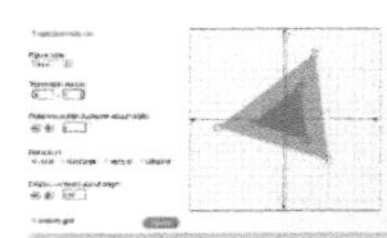

G.SRT.1

Example 3 Dilations in the Coordinate Plane

Graph the image of each polygon with the given vertices after a dilation at the indicated center with the given scale factor.

a. $J(-2, 4)$, $K(-2, -2)$, $L(-4, -2)$, $M(-4, 2)$; origin; $k = 2.5$

The distance from (0, 0) to J' should be 2.5 times longer than the distance from (0, 0) to J. To find the coordinates of the image, multiply the x- and y-coordinates of each vertex by the scale factor, 2.5.

$(x, y) \rightarrow (2.5x, 2.5y)$
$J(-2, 4) \rightarrow J'(-5, 10)$
$K(-2, -2) \rightarrow K'(-5, -5)$
$L(-4, -2) \rightarrow L'(-10, -5)$
$M(-4, 2) \rightarrow M'(-10, 5)$

Graph $JKLM$ and its image $J'K'L'M'$.

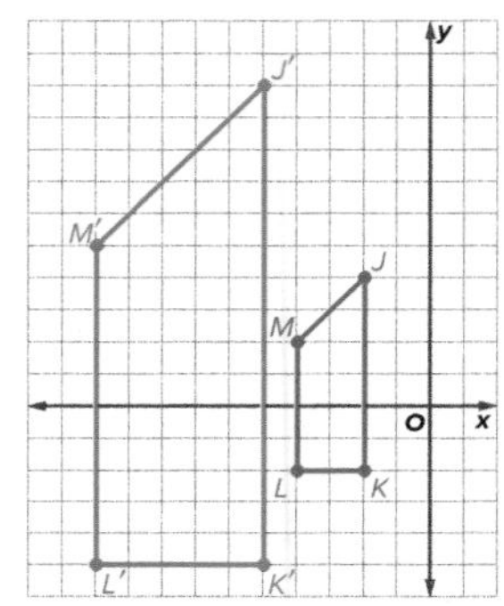

Differentiated Instruction OL BL

Extension Ask students to discuss what they know about the definition of congruence in terms of rigid transformations. How do they think figures that are dilated, or dilated and then transformed using a rigid transformation, could be related? Are they congruent? Explain why or why not. No, the figures are not congruent because the sides are not congruent. They are the same shape, but not necessarily the same size.

b. $B(-1, -1)$, $C(-4, -1)$, $D(-4, -3)$, $E(-1, -3)$; $(1, 1)$; $k = 2$

First, graph $BCDE$ and label the center of dilation A.

Plot the distance from A to B. Then double this distance to locate B'. B is 2 units left and 2 units down from A. So B' must be 4 units to the left and 4 units down from A. Continue on in this manner to locate each vertex of the image.

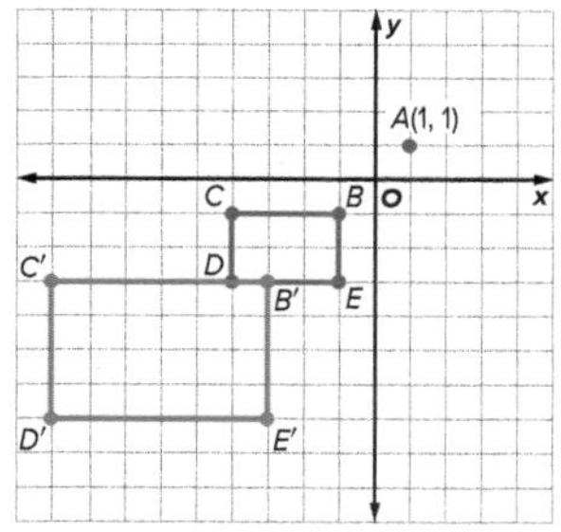

Guided Practice 3A–3B. See margin.

3A. $Q(0, 6)$, $R(-6, -3)$, $S(6, -3)$; origin; $k = \frac{1}{3}$

3B. $F(-5, -3)$, $G(-6, -1)$, $H(-1, -1)$, $J(-2, -3)$; $(1, -1)$; $k = 1$

G.SRT.1

Example 4 Compositions of Dilations

Graph $QRST$ and its images after a composition of dilations centered at the origin with scale factor 2 and scale factor 1.5, given $Q(1, 1)$, $R(1, 3)$, $S(3, 3)$, and $T(4, 1)$.

Step 1 Multiply the x- and y-coordinates of each vertex by the scale factor of the first dilation.

$(x, y) \rightarrow (2x, 2y)$

$Q(1, 1) \rightarrow Q'(2, 2)$

$R(1, 3) \rightarrow R'(2, 6)$

$S(3, 3) \rightarrow S'(6, 6)$

$T(4, 1) \rightarrow T'(8, 2)$

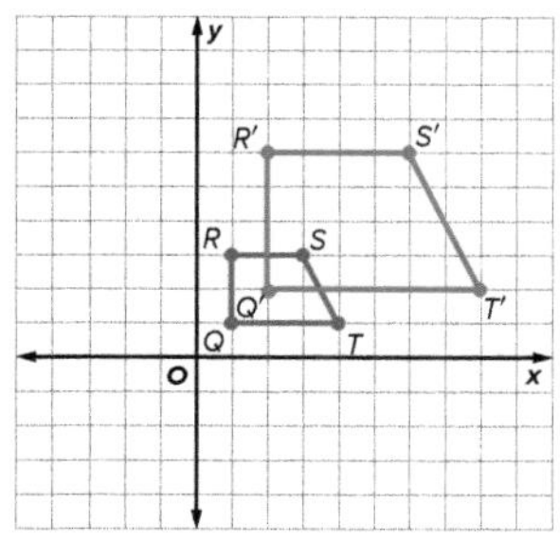

Step 2 Multiply the x- and y-coordinates of $Q'R'S'T'$ by the scale factor of the second dilation.

$(x, y) \rightarrow (1.5x, 1.5y)$

$Q'(2, 2) \rightarrow Q''(3, 3)$

$R'(2, 6) \rightarrow R''(3, 9)$

$S'(6, 6) \rightarrow S''(9, 9)$

$T'(8, 2) \rightarrow T''(12, 3)$

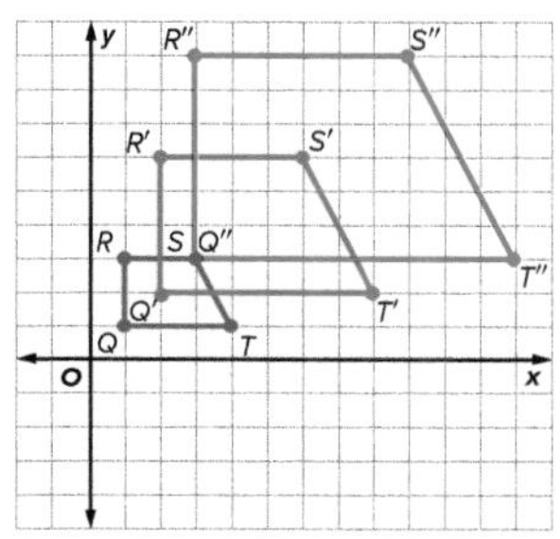

Guided Practice

Graph each figure and its images after the indicated transformations with the given center. 4A–4B. See margin.

4A. $A(-5, 2)$, $B(-1, 8)$, $C(2, 4)$; dilation: 2; dilation: $\frac{1}{3}$; center $(0, 0)$

4B. $J(-2, 1)$, $K(-2, 6)$, $L(-4, 6)$, $M(-4, 1)$; dilation: $\frac{1}{2}$, reflection: x-axis, center $(1, 2)$

Example 4 Compositions of Dilations

AL **What do you think it means to have a composition of dilations?** Sample answer: to apply a dilation to a figure and then to apply a dilation to the transformed figure one or more times

OL **What do you think compositions of dilations can be used for?** Sample answer: to create a piece of art where each figure looks like it is behind the other

BL **Do you think you could perform a composition of dilations with two different centers? Explain.** Yes; sample answer: Just like any other composition of transformations, you would evaluate the first dilation at one center, then find the dilation of the transformed figure with a different center.

Need Another Example?

Graph $ABCD$ and its images after a composition of dilations centered at the origin with scale factor $\frac{1}{2}$ and scale factor $\frac{1}{5}$, given $A(7, 8)$, $B(-5, 6)$, $C(-7, -5)$, and $D(6, -4)$. Sample Answer:

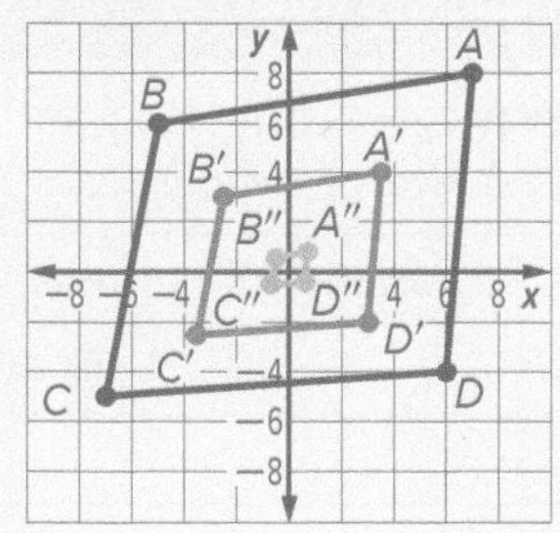

Additional Answers (Guided Practice)

3A.

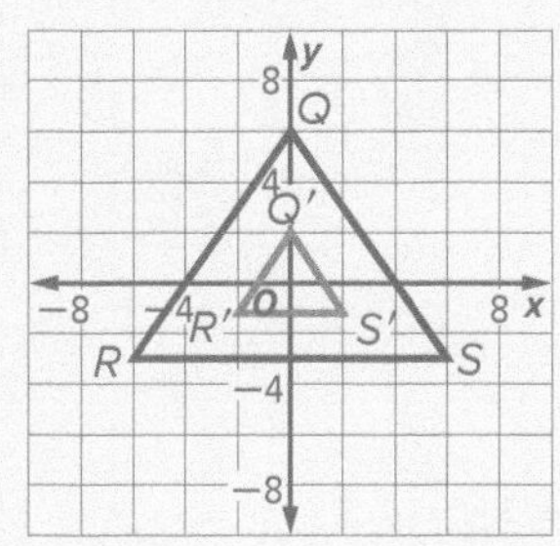

3B.

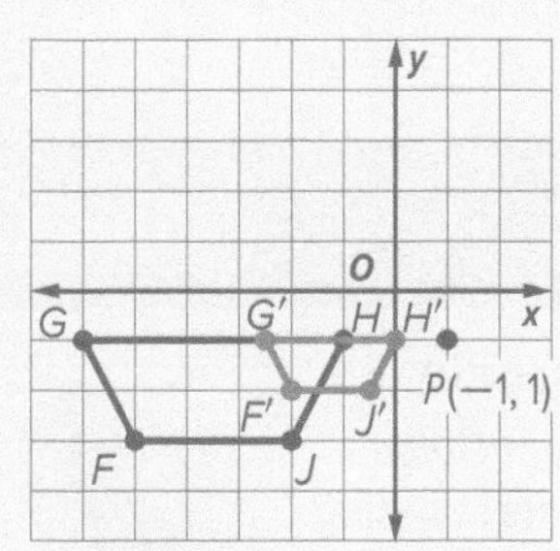

4A.

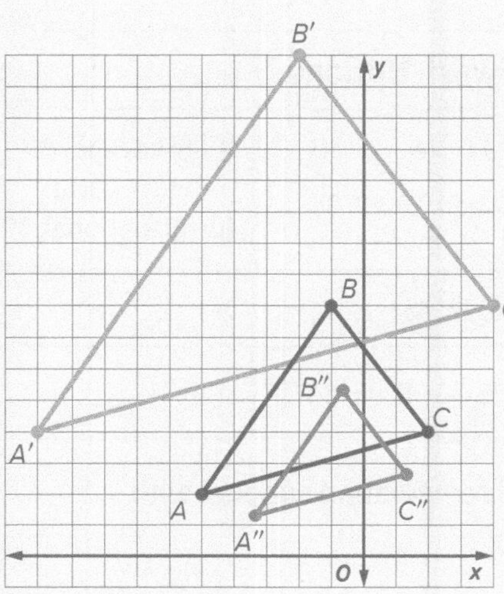

4B.

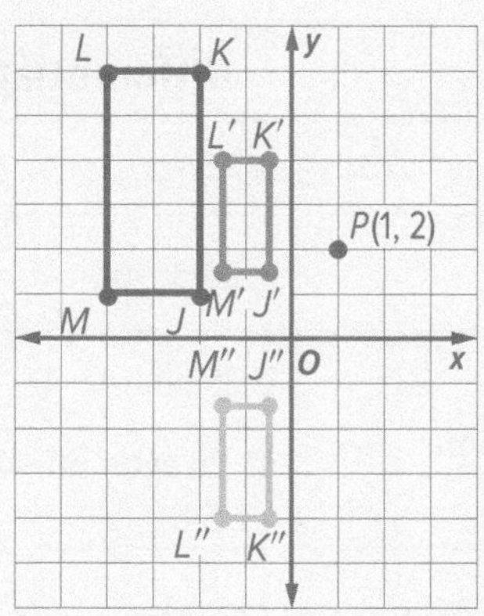

Practice

Formative Assessment Use Exercises 1–10 to assess students' understanding of the concepts in this lesson.

The Practice and Problem Solving exercises assess the content taught in the lesson. The Preparing for Assessment page is meant to be used as preparation for end-of-course assessments.

MP Teaching the Mathematical Practices

Tools Mathematically proficient students consider the available tools when solving a mathematical problem. In Exercises 11–14, encourage students to use tracing paper or patty paper and a ruler.

Extra Practice

See page R7 for extra exercises for students who are approaching level or for on-level students who need additional reinforcement.

Levels of Complexity Chart

The levels of the exercises progress from 1 to 3, with Level 1 indicating the lowest level of complexity.

Exercises	9–32	33–39, 50–54	40–49
C Level 3			●
B Level 2		●	
Level 1	●		

Additional Answers

1.

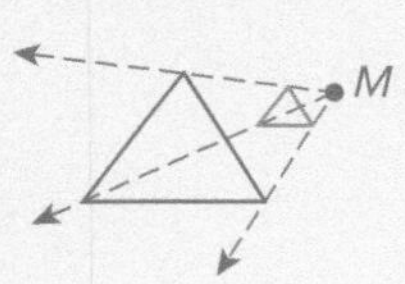

2.

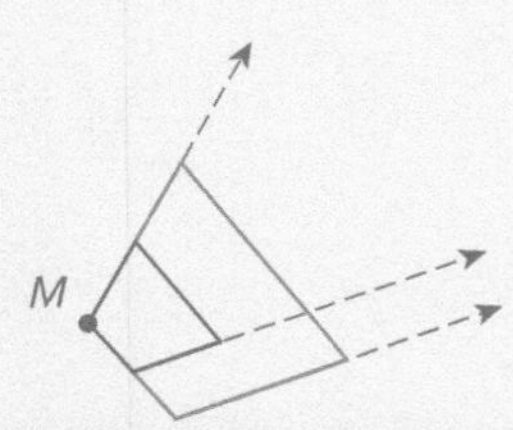

Go Online! eBook

Interactive Student Guide

Use the *Interactive Student Guide* to deepen conceptual understanding.
· Dilations

Go Online! for a Self-Check Quiz

Check Your Understanding

○ = Step-by-Step Solutions begin on page R13.

Example 1 G.CO.2

Copy the figure and point M. Then use a ruler to draw the image of the figure under a dilation with center M and the scale factor k indicated. **1–2. See margin.**

1. $k = \frac{1}{4}$

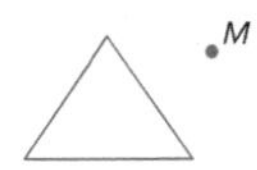

2. $k = 2$

Example 2 G.SRT.1

3 Determine whether the dilation from Figure B to B' is an *enlargement* or a *reduction*. Then find the scale factor of the dilation and x. **enlargement; $\frac{4}{3}$; 2**

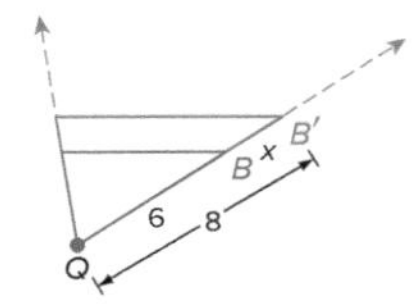

4. **BIOLOGY** Under a microscope, a single-celled organism 200 microns in length appears to be 50 millimeters long. If 1 millimeter = 1000 microns, what magnification setting (scale factor) was used? Explain your reasoning.
250×; The organism's length in millimeters is 200 ÷ 1000 or 0.2 mm. The scale factor of the dilation is $\frac{50}{0.2}$ or 250.

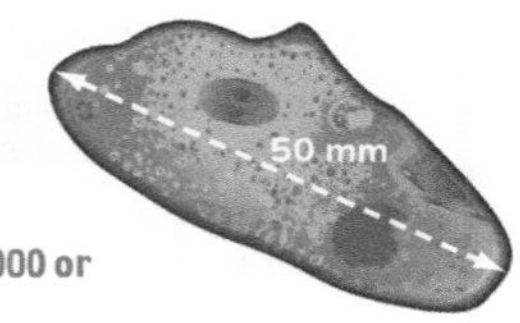

Example 3 G.SRT.1

Graph the image of each polygon with the given vertices after a dilation at the indicated center with the given scale factor. **5–8. See margin.**

5. $W(0, 0)$, $X(6, 6)$, $Y(6, 0)$; origin; $k = 1.5$

6. $Q(-4, 4)$, $R(-4, -4)$, $S(4, -4)$, $T(4, 4)$; origin; $k = \frac{1}{2}$

7. $A(-1, 4)$, $B(2, 4)$, $C(3, 2)$, $D(-2, 2)$; $(-4, -3)$; $k = 2$

8. $J(-2, 0)$, $K(2, 4)$, $L(8, 0)$, $M(2, -4)$; $(-2, 0)$; $k = \frac{3}{4}$

Example 4 G.SRT.1

Graph each figure and its image after the indicated transformations with the given center. **9–10. See margin.**

9. $C(-7, -3)$, $D(-7, 6)$, $E(1, 3)$; dilation: $\frac{1}{2}$; dilation: 4; center (0, 0)

10. $W(4, 4)$, $X(1, -3)$, $Y(6, -6)$, $Z(13, 4)$; dilation: $\frac{1}{3}$, reflection: y-axis, center (1, 1)

11–14. See Ch. 7 Answer Appendix.

Practice and Problem Solving

Extra Practice is on page R7.

Example 1 G.CO.2

MP TOOLS Copy the figure and point S. Then use a ruler to draw the image of the figure under a dilation with center S and the scale factor k indicated.

11. $k = \frac{5}{2}$

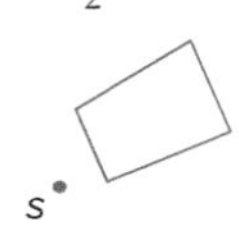

12. $k = 3$

13. $k = 0.8$

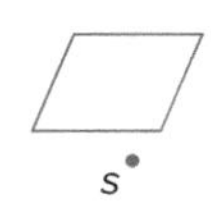

14. $k = \frac{1}{3}$

Differentiated Homework Options

Levels	AL Basic	OL Core	BL Advanced
Exercises	9–26, 38–54	9–27 odd, 28, 29–35 odd, 36, 38–54	40–49 (optional: 50–54)
2-Day Option	9–25 odd, 42–47	9–26, 42–45	
	10–26 even, 38–41, 48–54	27–36, 38–41, 46–54	

You can use ALEKS to provide additional remediation support with personalized instruction and practice.

Example 2
G.SRT.1

Determine whether the dilation from figure W to W' is an *enlargement* or a *reduction*. Then find the scale factor of the dilation and x.

15.

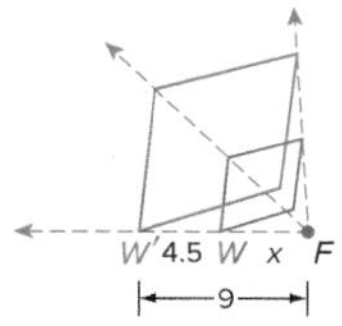

enlargement; 2; 4.5

16.

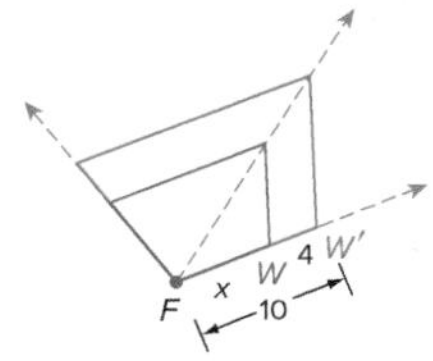

enlargement; $\frac{5}{3}$; 6

17.

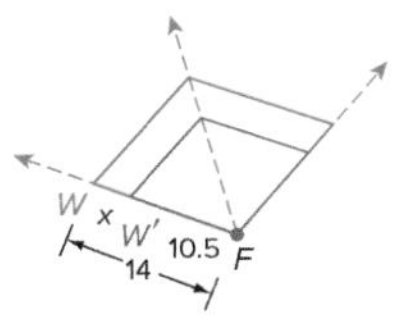

reduction; $\frac{3}{4}$; 3.5

18.

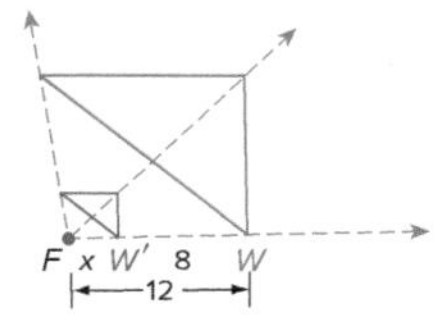

reduction; $\frac{1}{3}$; 4

INSECTS When viewed under a microscope, each insect has the measurement given on the picture. Given the actual measure of each insect, what magnification was used? Explain your reasoning.

19.

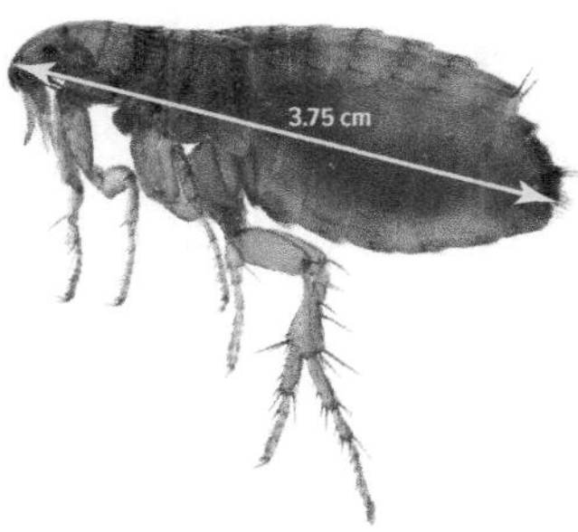

20.

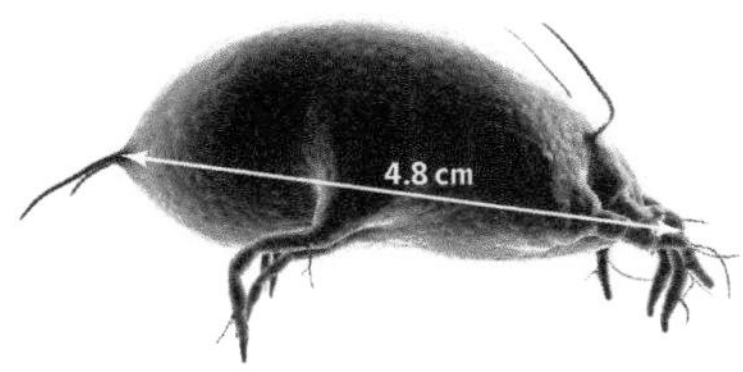

19. 15×; The insect's image length in millimeters is 3.75 • 10 or 37.5 mm. The scale factor of the dilation is $\frac{37.5}{2.5}$ or 15.

20. 96×; The insect's image length in millimeters is 4.8 • 10 or 48 mm. The scale factor of the dilation is $\frac{48}{0.5}$ or 96.

Example 3
G.SRT.1

MP SENSE-MAKING Graph the image of each polygon with the given vertices after a dilation at the indicated center with the given scale factor. 21–26. See Ch. 7 Answer Appendix.

21. $J(-8, 0)$, $K(-4, 4)$, $L(-2, 0)$; origin; $k = 0.5$

22. $S(0, 0)$, $T(-4, 0)$, $V(-8, -8)$; origin; $k = 1.25$

23. $A(9, 9)$, $B(3, 3)$, $C(6, 0)$; origin; $k = \frac{1}{3}$

24. $D(4, 4)$, $F(0, 0)$, $G(8, 0)$; origin; $k = 0.75$

25. $M(-2, 0)$, $P(0, 2)$, $Q(2, 0)$, $R(0, -2)$; $(-4, -4)$; $k = 2.5$

26. $W(2, 2)$, $X(2, 0)$, $Y(0, 1)$, $Z(1, 2)$; $(4, -2)$; $k = 3$

MP Teaching the Mathematical Practices

Sense-Making Mathematically proficient students start by explaining the meaning of a problem to themselves and looking for entry points to its solution. They plan a solution pathway rather than simply jumping into a solution attempt. In Exercises 21–26, encourage students to make a plan to solve each problem first.

Additional Answers

5.

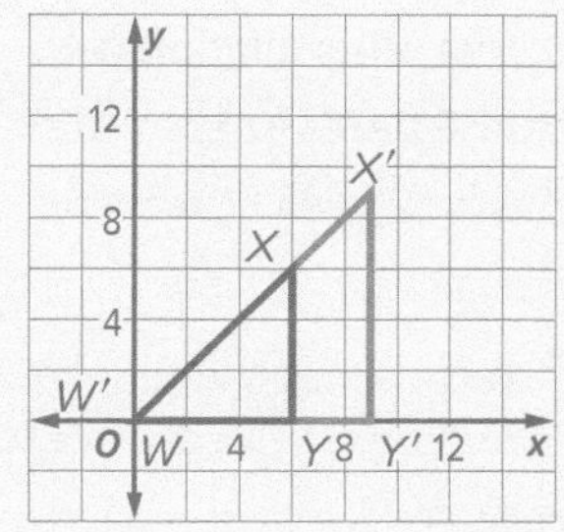

6.

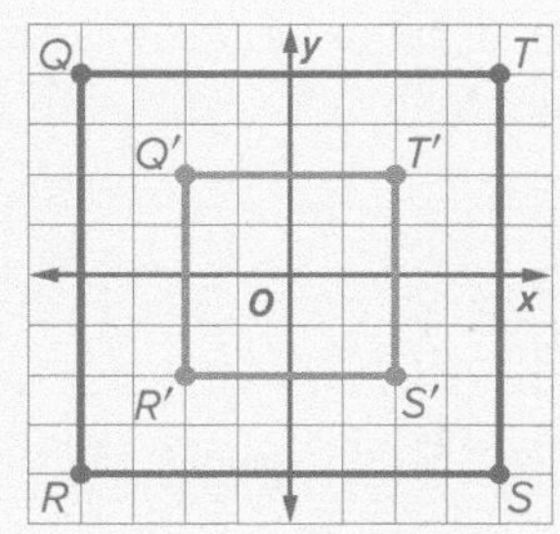

7.

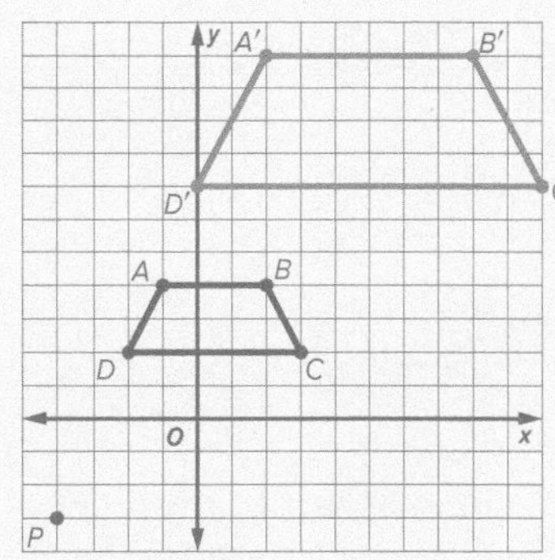

8.

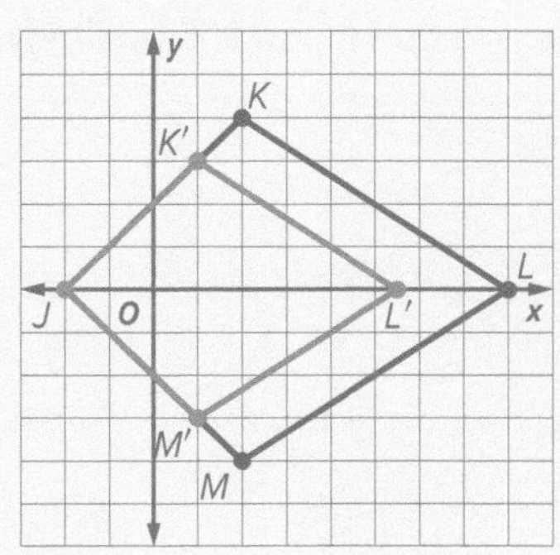

9.

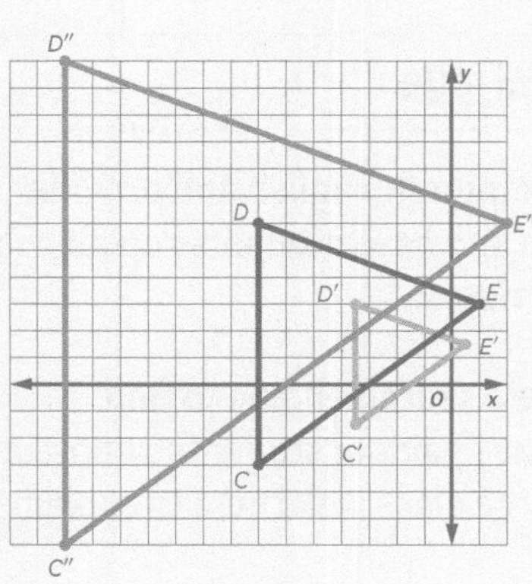

10.

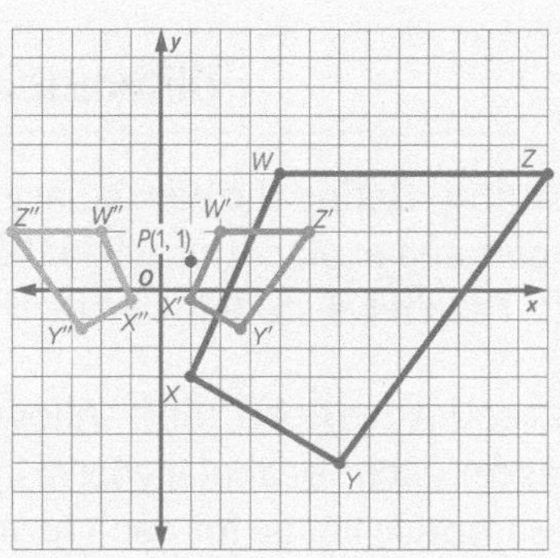

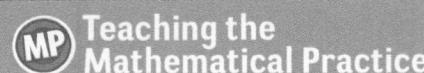

MP Teaching the Mathematical Practices

Perseverance Mathematically proficient students check their answers to problems using a different method, and they continually ask themselves, "does this make sense?" Encourage students to use alternative methods of problem solving.

Additional Answers

33d. surface area: 4 times greater after dilation with scale factor 2; $\frac{1}{4}$ as great after dilation with scale factor $\frac{1}{2}$. Volume: 8 times greater after dilation with scale factor 2; $\frac{1}{8}$ as great after dilation with scale factor $\frac{1}{2}$.

33e. The surface area of the preimage would be multiplied by r^2. The volume of the preimage would be multiplied by r^3.

35a.

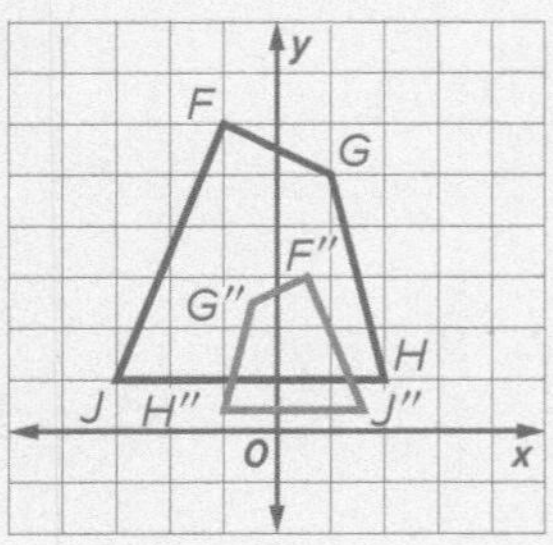

35b.

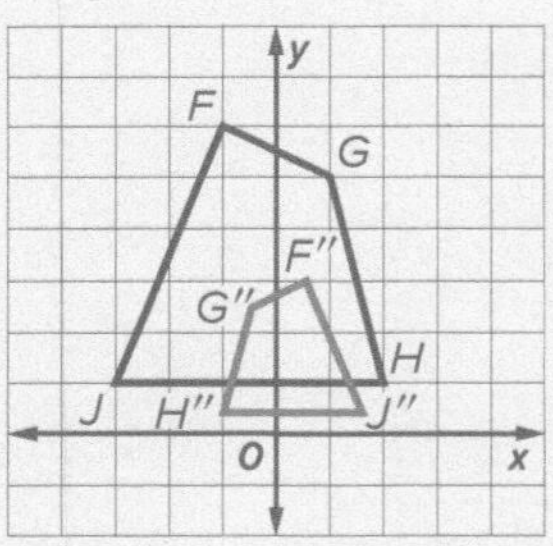

35d. Sometimes; sample answer: For the order of a composition of a dilation centered at the origin and a reflection to be unimportant, the line of reflection must contain the origin, or must be of the form $y = mx$.

Example 4
G.CO.2

Graph each figure and its images after the indicated transformations with the given center.

27. dilation: $\frac{1}{3}$; dilation: 2; center (0, 0)

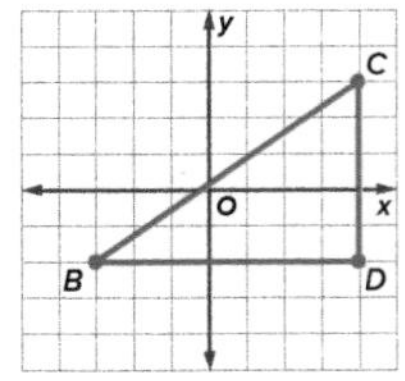

28. dilation: $\frac{1}{2}$; dilation: 2; center (0, 0)

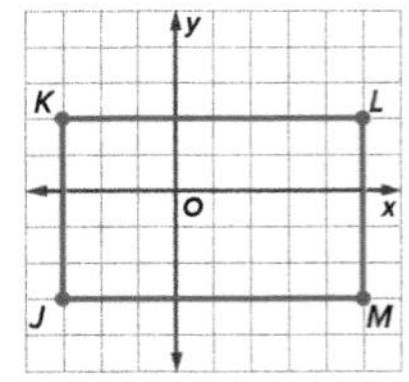

29. dilation: 2; dilation: $\frac{3}{2}$; center (1, 1)

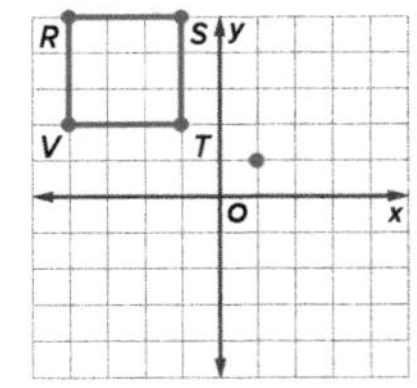

27–32. See Ch. 7 Answer Appendix.

30. dilation: $\frac{1}{2}$; dilation: 3; center (−2, 0)

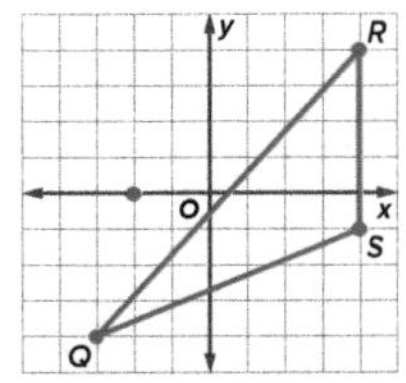

31. dilation: $\frac{1}{2}$; reflection: y-axis; center (0, 0)

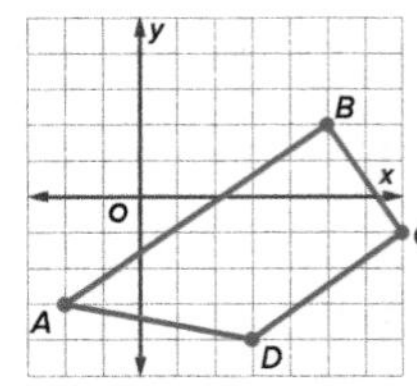

32. dilation: 3; rotation: 180°; center (−2, −2)

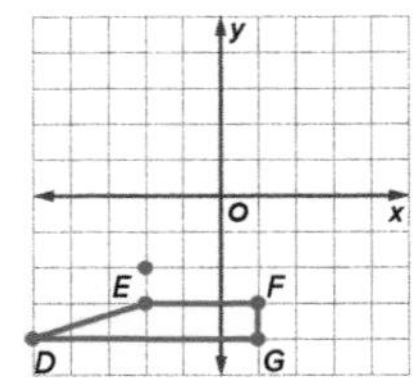

33 **CHANGING DIMENSIONS** A three-dimensional figure can also undergo a dilation. Consider the rectangular prism shown.

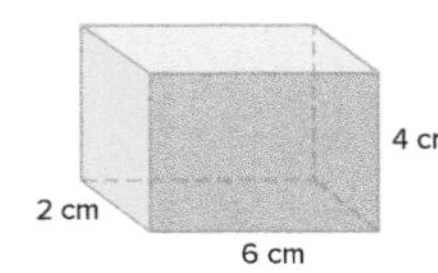

33a. surface area: 88 cm^2; volume: 48 cm^3

33b. surface area: 352 cm^2; volume: 384 cm^3

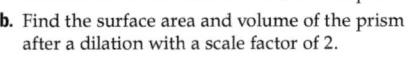

a. Find the surface area and volume of the prism.

b. Find the surface area and volume of the prism after a dilation with a scale factor of 2.

c. Find the surface area and volume of the prism after a dilation with a scale factor of $\frac{1}{2}$. surface area: 22 cm^2; volume: 6 cm^3

d. How many times as great is the surface area and volume of the image as the preimage after each dilation? See margin.

e. Make a conjecture as to the effect a dilation with a positive scale factor *r* would have on the surface area and volume of a prism. See margin.

34. **PHOTOGRAPHY AND ART** To make a scale drawing of a photograph, students overlay a $\frac{1}{4}$-inch grid on a 5-inch by 7-inch high contrast photo, overlay a $\frac{1}{2}$-inch grid on a 10-inch by 14-inch piece of drawing paper, and then sketch the image in each square of the photo to the corresponding square on the drawing paper.

a. What is the scale factor of the dilation? 2:1

b. To create an image that is 10 times as large as the original, what size grids are needed? 2.5 in.

c. What would be the area of a grid drawing of a 5-inch by 7-inch photo that used 2-inch grids? 2240 in^2

Differentiated Instruction ELL

Beginning Define the vocabulary words in the chapter in English and provide examples and explanations. Say the terms out loud and have students repeat the words. Then have students write the word in their notes.

Advanced/Advanced High Allow students to use a search engine to find images for each vocabulary term in the chapter. Have pairs of students choose a representative image for each term to share with the class. Ask them to explain why their image represents the term.

35. COORDINATE GEOMETRY Refer to the graph of *FGHJ*. **a, b, d. See margin.**

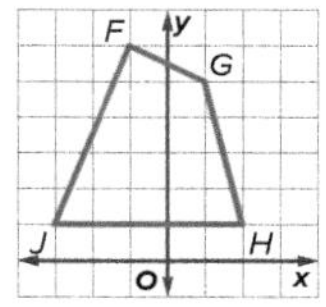

a. Dilate *FGHJ* by a scale factor of $\frac{1}{2}$ centered at the origin, and then reflect the dilated image in the *y*-axis.

b. Complete the composition of transformations in part **a** in reverse order.

c. Does the order of the transformations affect the final image? **no**

d. Will the order of a composition of a dilation and a reflection *always*, *sometimes*, or *never* affect the dilated image? Explain your reasoning.

36. MP **PERSEVERANCE** Refer to the graph of $\triangle DEF$. **a–c. See margin.**

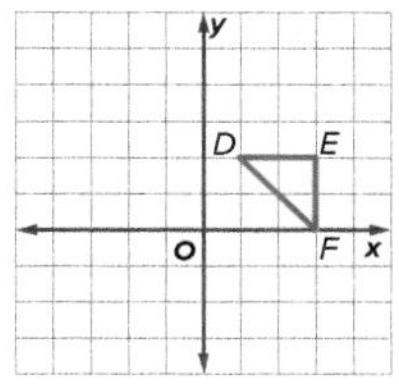

a. Graph the dilation of $\triangle DEF$ centered at point *D* with a scale factor of 3.

b. Describe the dilation as a composition of transformations including a dilation with a scale factor of 3 centered at the origin.

c. If a figure is dilated by a scale factor of 3 with a center of dilation (*x*, *y*), what composition of transformations, including a dilation with a scale factor of 3 centered at the origin, will produce the same final image?

37. HEALTH A coronary artery may be dilated with a balloon catheter as shown. The cross section of the middle of the balloon is a circle.

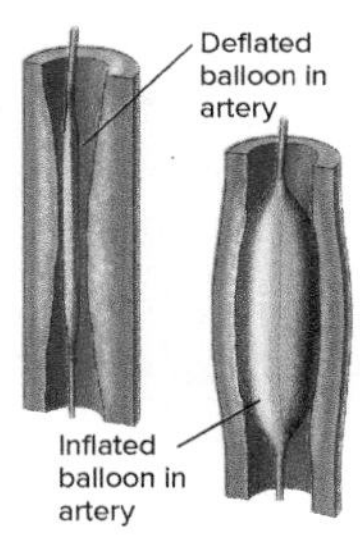

a. A surgeon inflates a balloon catheter in a patient's coronary artery, dilating the balloon from a diameter of 1.5 millimeters to 2 millimeters. Find the scale factor of this dilation. $1\frac{1}{3}$

b. Find the cross-sectional area of the balloon before and after the dilation. $1.77\ mm^2$; $3.14\ mm^2$

40d. Sample answer: A dilation centered at the origin with a scale factor of $-k$ can be described as a dilation centered at the origin with a scale factor of k and a rotation 180° about the origin.

Each figure shows a preimage and its image after a dilation centered at point *P*. Copy each figure, locate point *P*, and estimate the scale factor. 38–39. See margin.

38.

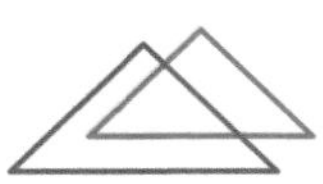

39.

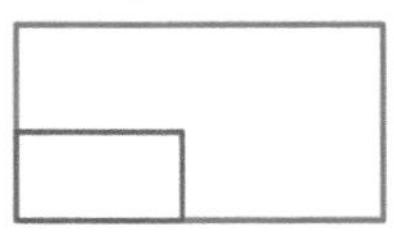

40b. Sample answer: Each of the coordinates is multiplied by the negative scale factor.

40. MULTIPLE REPRESENTATIONS In this problem, you will investigate dilations centered at the origin with negative scale factors. **a. and d. See margin.**

a. Geometric Draw $\triangle ABC$ with points $A(-2, 0)$, $B(2, -4)$, and $C(4, 2)$. Then draw the image of $\triangle ABC$ after a dilation centered at the origin with a scale factor of -2. Repeat the dilation with scale factors of $-\frac{1}{2}$ and -3. Record the coordinates for each dilation.

b. Verbal Make a conjecture about the function relationship for a dilation centered at the origin with a negative scale factor.

c. Analytical Write the function rule for a dilation centered at the origin with a scale factor of $-k$. $(x, y) \rightarrow (-kx, -ky)$

d. Verbal Describe a dilation centered at the origin with a negative scale factor as a composition of transformations.

40a.

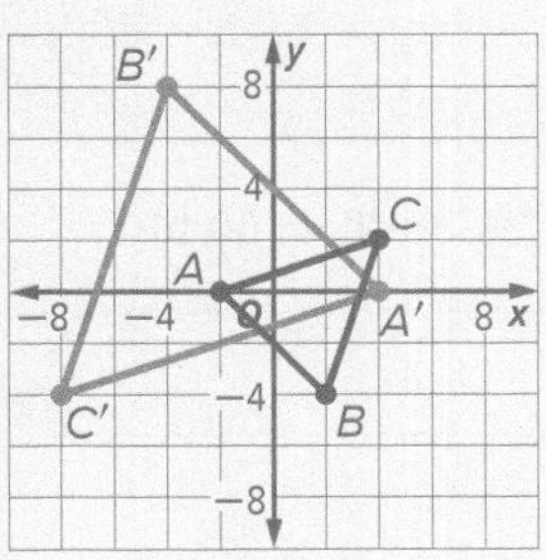

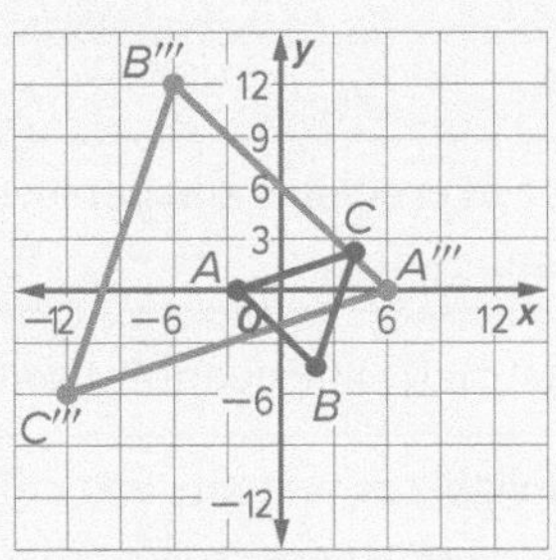

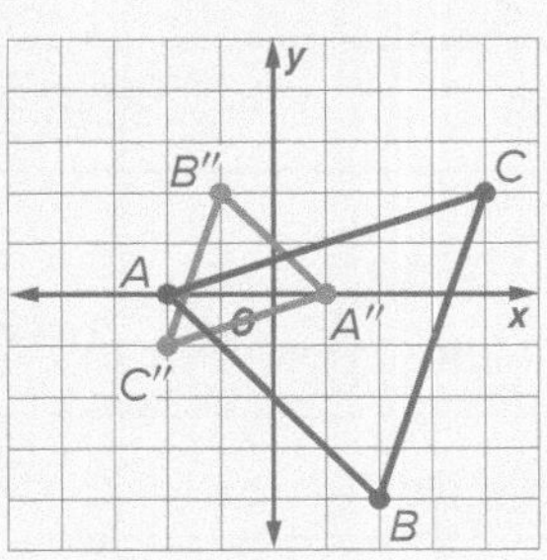

	Coordinates		
Scale Factor	**A**	**B**	**C**
-2	(4, 0)	(−4, 8)	(−8, −4)
$-\frac{1}{2}$	(1, 0)	(−1, 2)	(−2, −1)
-3	(6, 0)	(−6, 12)	(−12, −6)

MP Teaching the Mathematical Practices

Construct Arguments Mathematically proficient students understand and use stated assumptions and definitions in constructing arguments. They make conjectures and build a logical progression of statements to explore the truth of their conjectures. In Exercise 47, encourage students to draw diagrams of each transformation.

Additional Answers

36a.

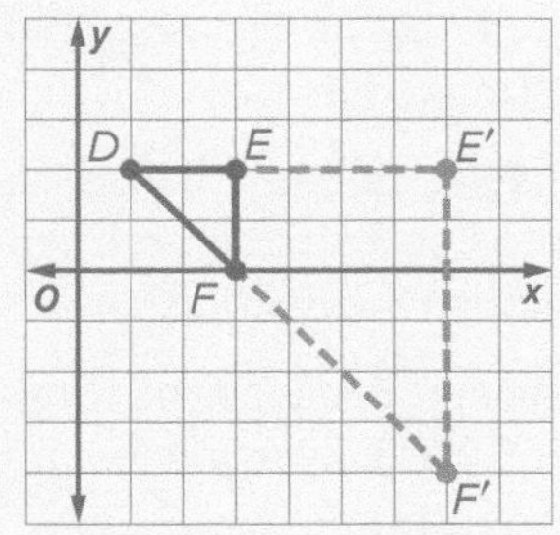

36b. the composition of a dilation with scale factor 3 centered at the origin and a translation along ⟨−2, −4⟩

36c. the composition of a dilation with a scale factor of 3 centered at the origin and a translation along ⟨−2*x*, −2*y*⟩

38.

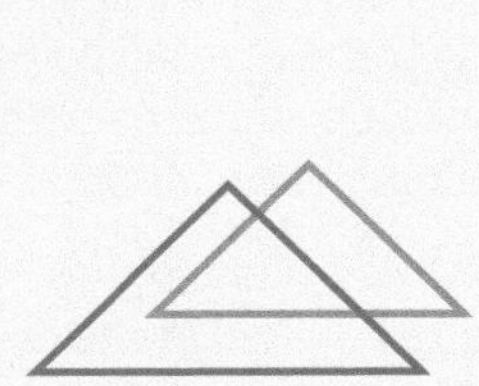

$\frac{4}{5}$

39.

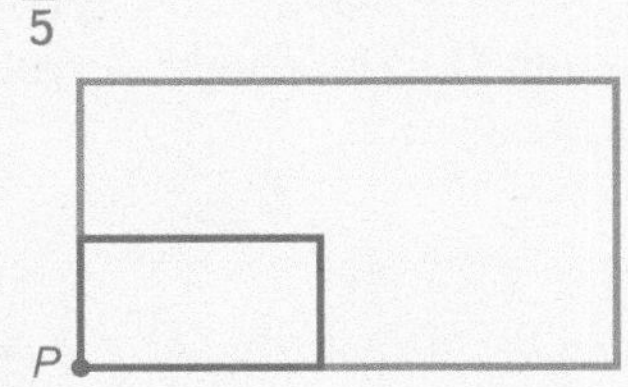

$\frac{11}{5}$

Assess

Ticket Out the Door Students should measure an object in the room and apply a dilation to reduce the object and make a model with poster board and/or construction paper. Have students turn in their models before they leave the classroom.

Additional Answers

41. The submitted image is distorted because it was not reduced proportionally. Divide the width of the submitted photo by the width of the original photo to determine that the scale factor is 0.6. Multiply the original height of the photo by the scale factor to find the height of the image that should be submitted is 2.7 in. Becca should submit an image sized to 1.8 in. by 2.7 in.

47a. Always; sample answer: Because a dilation of 1 maps an image onto itself, all four vertices will remain invariant under the dilation.

47b. Always; sample answer: Because the rotation is centered at *B*, point *B* will always remain invariant under the rotation.

47c. Sometimes: sample answer: If one of the vertices is on the *x*-axis, then that point will remain invariant under reflection. If two vertices are on the *x*-axis, then the two vertices located on the *x*-axis will remain invariant under reflection.

47d. Never; when a figure is translated, all points move an equal distance. Therefore, no points can remain invariant under translation.

47e. Sometimes; sample answer: If one of the vertices of the triangle is located at the origin, then that vertex would remain invariant under the dilation. If none of the points on $\triangle XYZ$ are located at the origin, then no points will remain invariant under the dilation.

Go Online!

eSolutions Manual

Create worksheets, answer keys, and solutions handouts for your assignments.

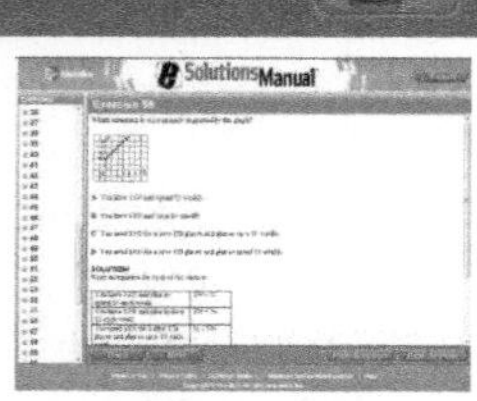

41. **PHOTOGRAPHY** Becca took this photo for the school newspaper. The original picture was too large to fit in the space she had within the article, so she used her computer to reduce the width and height to fit the space exactly. Why did the newspaper's editor reject her image? What are the dimensions of the photo she resubmits? Explain. **See margin.**

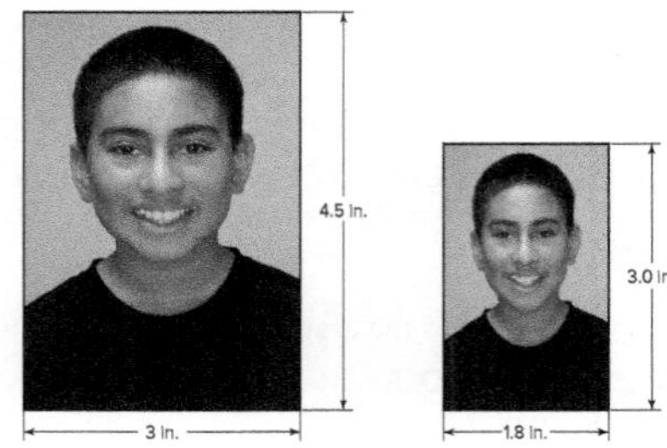

42. Describe the dilation from AB to $A'B'$ and $A'B'$ to $A''B''$ in the triangles shown. **$\overline{AB}$ is dilated by 1.75 to $\overline{A'B'}$. Then $\overline{A'B'}$ is dilated by 0.25 to $\overline{A''B''}$.**

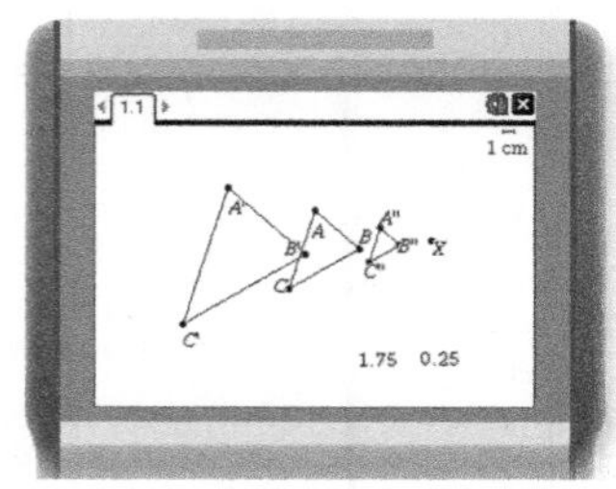

43-44. See Ch. 7 Answer Appendix for graphs.

***WXYZ* has vertices $W(6, 2)$, $X(3, 7)$, $Y(-1, 4)$, and $Z(4, -2)$.**

43. Graph *WXYZ* and find the perimeter of the figure. **≈23.1**

44. Graph the image of *WXYZ* after a dilation of $\frac{1}{2}$ centered at the origin. Find the perimeter of the dilated image and compare it to the perimeter of *WXYZ*. **≈11.6; The perimeter of the dilated figure is half of the perimeter of *WXYZ*.**

G.CO.2, G.SRT.1

H.O.T. Problems Use Higher-Order Thinking Skills

45. **CHALLENGE** Find the equation for the dilated image of the line $y = 4x - 2$ if the dilation is centered at the origin with a scale factor of 1.5. **$y = 4x - 3$**

46. **WRITING IN MATH** Are parallel lines (parallelism) and collinear points (collinearity) preserved under all transformations? Explain. **See Ch. 7 Answer Appendix.**

47. MP **CONSTRUCT ARGUMENTS** Determine whether invariant points are *sometimes*, *always*, or *never* maintained for the transformations described below. If so, describe the invariant point(s). If not, explain why invariant points are not possible. **a–e. See margin.**

a. dilation of *ABCD* with scale factor 1

b. rotation of $\overline{AB}$ 74° about *B*

c. reflection of $\triangle MNP$ in the *x*-axis

d. translation of *PQRS* along $\langle 7, 3 \rangle$

e. dilation of $\triangle XYZ$ centered at the origin with scale factor 2

48. **OPEN-ENDED** Graph a triangle. Dilate the triangle so that its area is four times the area of the original triangle. State the scale factor and center of your dilation. **See Ch. 7 Answer Appendix.**

49. **WRITING IN MATH** Can you use transformations to create congruent figures, similar figures, and equal figures? Explain. **See Ch. 7 Answer Appendix.**

Caroline Schiff/Blend Images/Getty Images

MP Standards for Mathematical Practice

Emphasis On	Exercises
1 Make sense of problems and persevere in solving them.	1-3, 15-18, 21-26, 36, 38-40, 45, 50, 51
2 Reason abstractly and quantitatively.	46, 48, 49
3 Construct viable arguments and critique the reasoning of others.	47
4 Model with mathematics.	3, 19, 20, 34, 37, 41
5 Use appropriate tools strategically.	11-14, 42
6 Attend to precision.	5-10, 27-32, 43, 44, 54
7 Look for and make use of structure.	33, 35, 50-53

Preparing for Assessment

50. Point A has coordinates $A(2, 1)$. What is the distance between point A and its final image after a reflection in the y-axis and a dilation centered at the origin with a scale factor of 2? Round to the nearest tenth. MP 1, 7 G.CO.2 **6.1**

51. Zariah drew $\triangle JKL$ on a coordinate plane and then applied a composition of two transformations to produce $\triangle MNP$.

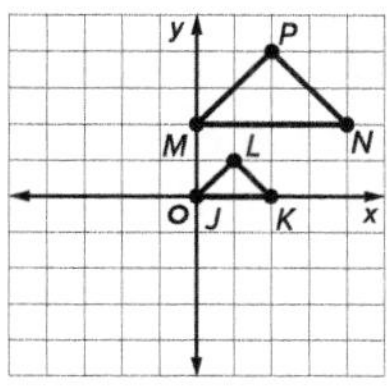

Which statement appears to be true? MP 1, 7 G.CO.2 **B**

- ○ **A** $\triangle JKL \cong \triangle MNP$
- ○ **B** The transformations included a dilation with a scale factor of 2.
- ○ **C** Zariah used only rigid motions.
- ○ **D** The area of $\triangle MNP$ is 2 times the area of $\triangle JKL$.

52. Theo plots the point $A(1, 3)$. Then he translates it along $\langle -2, -1 \rangle$ and dilates the image using a dilation centered at the origin with a scale factor of 3. What are the coordinates of the final image? MP 7 G.CO.2 **E**

- ○ **A** (2, 5)
- ○ **B** (−1, 2)
- ○ **C** (1, 8)
- ○ **D** (−6, −3)
- ○ **E** (−3, 6)

53. $\overline{JK}$ has endpoints $J(2, 4)$ and $K(6, 2)$. Maria dilates the segment using a dilation centered at the origin with a scale factor of $\frac{1}{2}$ and then reflects the image in the x-axis. What is the midpoint of the final image? MP 7 G.CO.2 **A**

- ○ **A** (2, −1.5)
- ○ **B** (−2, 1.5)
- ○ **C** (2, 1.5)
- ○ **D** (1.5, 2)

54. MULTI-STEP Point P is (−4, 3). It is translated along $\langle 7, -1 \rangle$ and then dilated by a factor of 3.5. MP 6 G.CO.2

a. Which formula is used to find the coordinates of the translated point in Step 1? **B**

- ○ **A** $(x + 7, y + 7)$
- ○ **B** $(x + 7, y - 1)$
- ○ **C** $(x + 1, y - 7)$
- ○ **D** $(x + 7, y + 1)$

b. Which formula is used to find the coordinates of the dilated point in Step 2? **C**

- ○ **A** $(x + 3.5, y + 3.5)$
- ○ **B** $(x - 3.5, y - 3.5)$
- ○ **C** $(3.5x, 3.5y)$
- ○ **D** $\left(\frac{x}{3.5}, \frac{y}{3.5}\right)$

c. What are the coordinates of the final point? **A**

- ○ **A** (10.5, 7)
- ○ **B** (−14, 10.5)
- ○ **C** (3, 2)
- ○ **D** (7, 10.5)

d. What are the coordinates of point $Q(9, -3)$ after these transformations? **D**

- ○ **A** (16, −4)
- ○ **B** (31.5, −10.5)
- ○ **C** (−3, 9)
- ○ **D** (56, −7)

e. The final image of a point under these transformations is (14, 3.5). What are the coordinates of the point? **B**

- ○ **A** (4, 1)
- ○ **B** (−3, 2)
- ○ **C** (7, 2.5)
- ○ **D** (1, 2)

Follow-Up

Students have explored transformations and symmetry.

Ask:

- How are dilations related to the concepts of symmetry and transformations? Sample answer: A dilation is a similarity transformation as it enlarges or reduces a figure proportionally. A dilation by a scale factor of 1 or −1 is also a congruence transformation.

Preparing for Assessment

Exercises 50–54 require students to use the skills they will need on standardized assessments. Exercises are dual-coded with content standards and mathematical practice standards.

Dual Coding

Exercises	Content Standards	MP Mathematical Practices
50	G.CO.2	1, 7
51	G.CO.2	1, 7
52	G.CO.2	7
53	G.CO.2	7
54	G.CO.2	6

Diagnose Student Errors

Survey student responses for each item. Class trends may indicate common errors and misconceptions.

51.

- A Forgot the definition of triangle congruence
- B CORRECT
- C Did not understand that rigid motions produce congruent figures
- D Assumed that a dilation with a scale factor of 2 doubles the area

52.

- A Added 3 to each coordinate to perform the dilation
- B Did not perform the dilation
- C Reversed the order of the transformations
- D Applied the dilation to (−2, −1)
- E CORRECT

53.

- A CORRECT
- B Reflected in the y-axis
- C Did not perform the reflection
- D Reflected in the line $y = x$

Go Online!

Quizzes

Students can use *Self-Check Quizzes* to check their understanding of this lesson and have the results sent to you. You can also give the *Chapter Quiz*, which covers the content in Lesson 7-1.

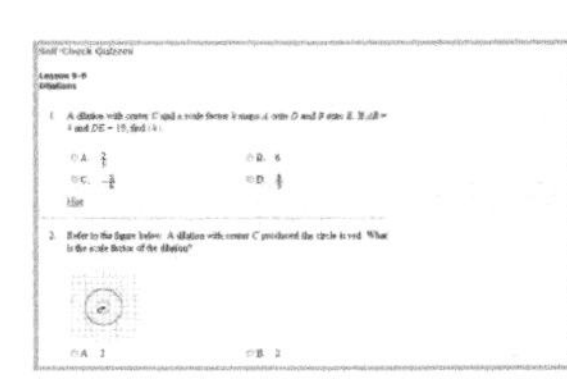

Similar Polygons

SUGGESTED PACING (DAYS)

90 min.	0.5
45 min.	1
	Instruction

Track Your Progress

Objectives

1. Use the definition of similarity to identify similar polygons.
2. Solve problems by using the properties of similar polygons.

Mathematical Background

Two polygons are similar if there is a similarity transformation or combination of a similarity transformation and one or more rigid transformations that maps one polygon onto the other. Similarity transformations are dilations and the rigid motions (translations, reflections, and rotations).

THEN	NOW	NEXT
G.CO.2 Represent transformations in the plane using, e.g., transparencies and geometry software; describe transformations as functions that take points in the plane as inputs and give other points as outputs. Compare transformations that preserve distance and angle to those that do not (e.g., translation versus horizontal stretch). **G.SRT.1** Verify experimentally the properties of dilations given by a center and a scale factor.	**G.SRT.2** Given two figures, use the definition of similarity in terms of similarity transformations to decide if they are similar; explain using similarity transformations the meaning of similarity for triangles as the equality of all corresponding pairs of angles and the proportionality of all corresponding pairs of sides.	**G.SRT.3** Use the properties of similarity transformations to establish the AA criterion for two triangles to be similar. **G.SRT.4** Prove theorems about triangles. **G.SRT.5** Use congruence and similarity criteria for triangles to solve problems and to prove relationships in geometric figures.

Go Online! All of these resources and more are available at connectED.mcgraw-hill.com

eLessons utilize the power of your interactive whiteboard in an engaging way. Use **Similarity Using Transformations**, Screens 4–5, to introduce the concepts in this lesson.

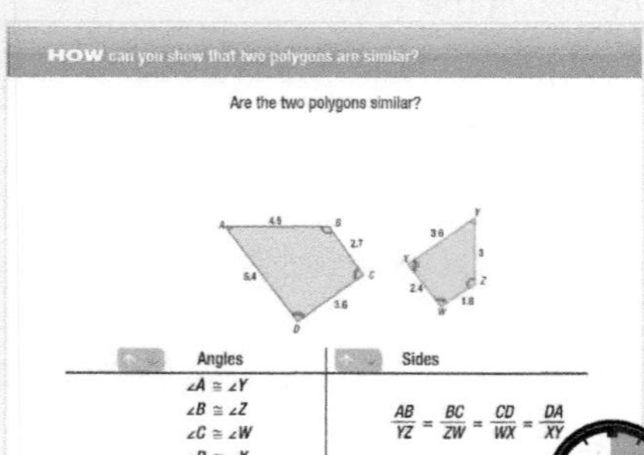

Use at Beginning of Lesson

Use **Animations** to show how to determine the scale factor of similar polygons.

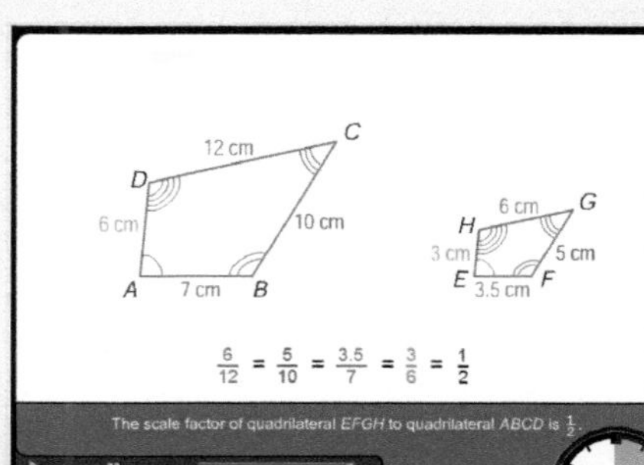

Use at Beginning of Lesson

Use **The Geometer's Sketchpad** to discover principles of similarity and to develop the definition of similar polygons.

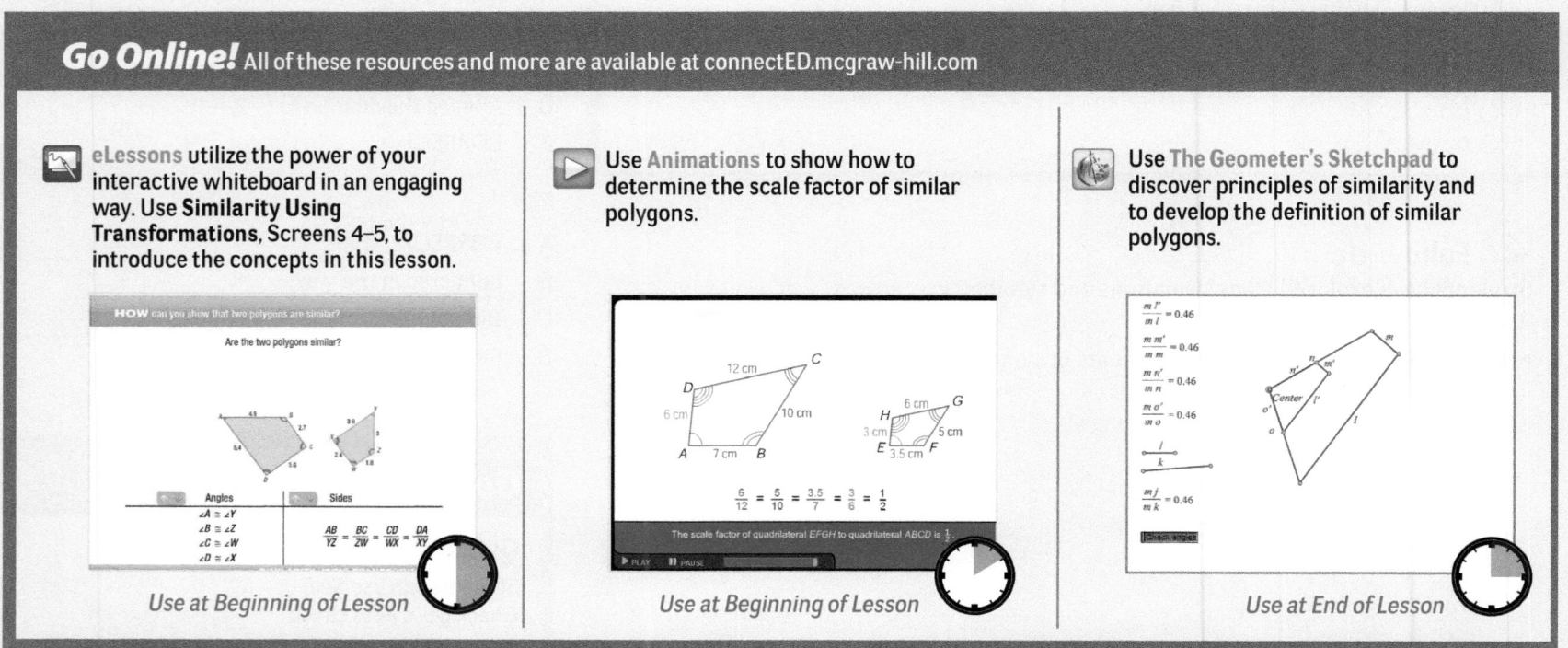

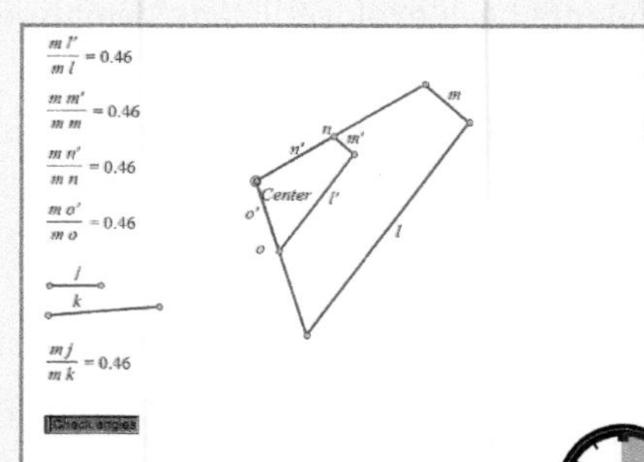

Use at End of Lesson

OER Using Open Educational Resources

Games Have students play the *Scale Factor X* game on **mathplayground.com** to practice finding scale factors and ratios. *Use as homework or classwork*

Go Online!
connectED.mcgraw-hill.com

Worksheets

Differentiate Your Resources

Extra Practice Additional practice or homework; Skills Practice is best for approaching-level students and Practice is best for on-level and beyond-level students

Skills Practice

AL OL ELL

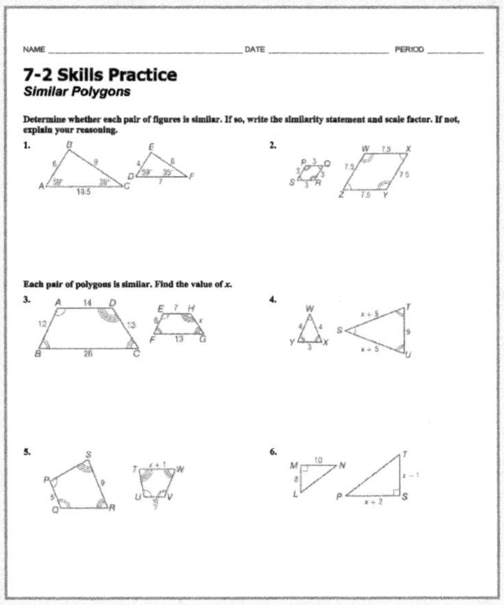

Practice

AL OL BL ELL

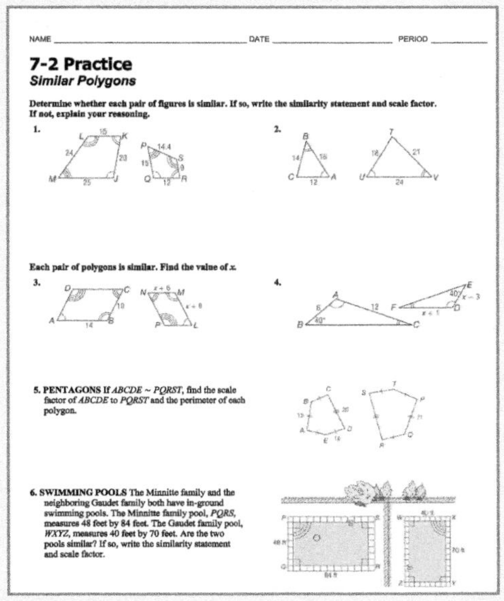

Word Problem Practice

AL OL BL ELL

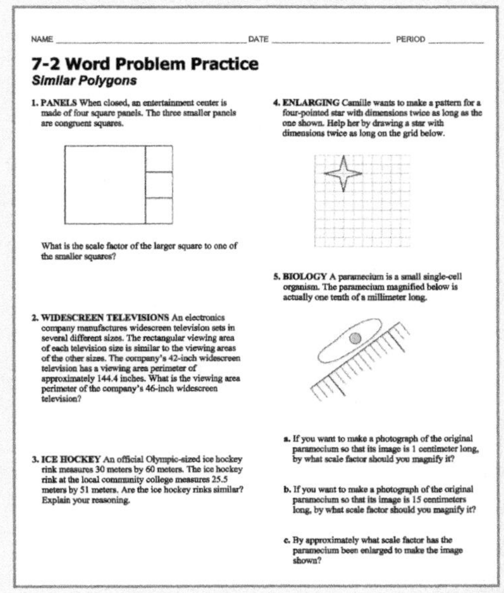

Intervention Reteaching and vocabulary activities that can be used with struggling or absent students and as ELL support

Study Guide and Intervention

AL OL ELL

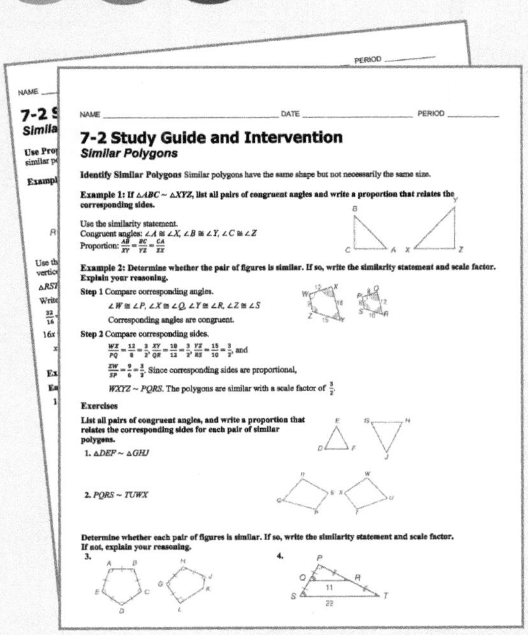

Study Notebook

AL OL BL ELL

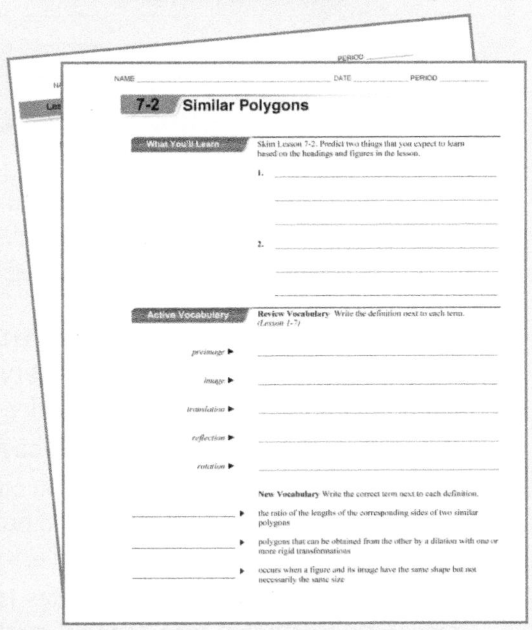

Extension Activities that can be used to extend lesson concepts

Enrichment

OL BL ELL

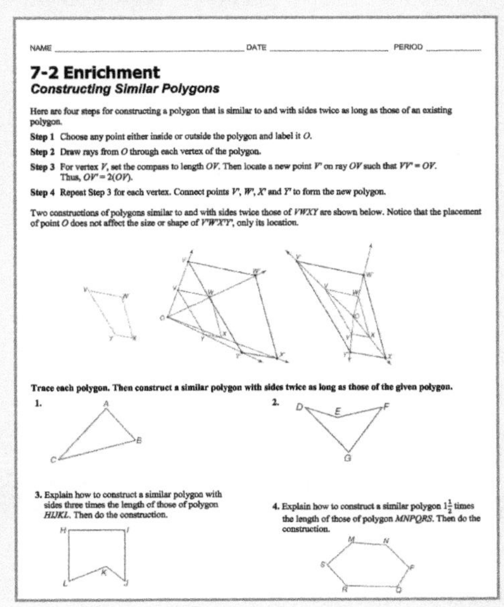

Launch

Have students read the Why? section of the lesson. Ask:

- In what direction has the picture been stretched? lengthwise
- Why is the photo distorted when it is made to fit the screen? The screen is wider than it is tall.
- What other ways could the picture be used to fit the screen without distorting it? Sample answer: Multiple copies of the picture could be tiled.

Teach

Ask the scaffolded questions for each example to build conceptual understanding for students at all levels.

1 Identify Similar Polygons

Example 1 Determine Whether Polygons Are Similar

AL Do the polygons in part **a** appear to be similar? why or why not? Yes; they have the same shape but different sizes.

OL What are the coordinate rules for the transformations that are used in part **a**? Dilation: $(x, y) \rightarrow (0.5x, 0.5y)$; translation: $(x, y) \rightarrow (x-4, y-2)$

BL What is another way to map *JKLM* to *PQRS*? Dilate *JKLM* using a dilation centered at (10, 4) with scale factor 0.5, then translate along $[-9, -4]$.

LESSON 2

Similar Polygons

Then

- You drew the image of a figure after a dilation.

Now

1. Use the definition of similarity to identify similar polygons.
2. Solve problems by using the properties of similar polygons.

Why?

- People often customize their computer desktops using photos, centering the images at their original size or stretching them to fit the screen. This second method distorts the image because the original and new images are not geometrically similar.

New Vocabulary
similar polygons
similarity transformation
scale factor

Mathematical Practices
1 Make sense of problems and persevere in solving them.
6 Attend to precision.

Content Standards
G.SRT.2 Given two figures, use the definition of similarity in terms of similarity transformations to decide if they are similar; explain using similarity transformations the meaning of similarity for triangles as the equality of all corresponding pairs of angles and the proportionality of all corresponding pairs of sides.

1 Identify Similar Polygons Two polygons are **similar polygons** if one can be obtained from the other by a dilation or by a dilation with one or more rigid transformations. A dilation is a type of similarity transformation. A **similarity transformation** occurs when a figure and its image have the same shape but not necessarily the same size.

G.SRT.2

Example 1 Determine Whether Polygons Are Similar

Determine whether the given polygons are similar. Explain.

a. *JKLM* and *PQRS*

First dilate polygon *JKLM* so that its image is the same size as polygon *PQRS*.

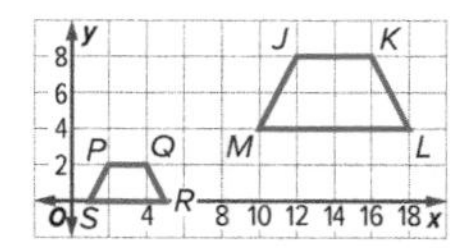

Dilate polygon *JKLM* using a dilation centered at the origin with scale factor 0.5.

The image of polygon *JKLM* is polygon *J′K′L′M′*.

Now translate polygon *J′K′L′M′* so that vertex *J′* maps to vertex *P*.

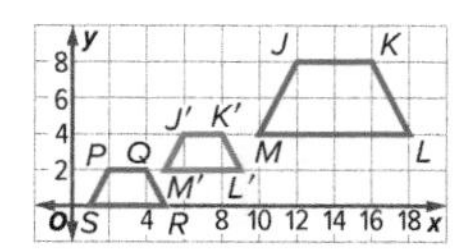

A translation along the vector $\langle -4, -2 \rangle$ maps polygon *J′K′L′M′* to polygon *PQRS*.

Polygon *JKLM* and polygon *PQRS* are similar because one polygon can be obtained from the other polygon by a similarity transformation followed by a rigid transformation.

b. *ABCD* and *EFGH*

Polygon *ABCD* and polygon *EFGH* do not have the same shape.

The polygons are not similar because there is no similarity transformation and no combination of similarity transformation and rigid transformations that will map one polygon onto the other.

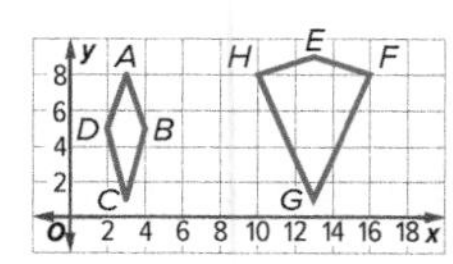

MP Mathematical Practices Strategies

Attend to precision.
Help students communicate precisely to others by focusing on the new terminology in this lesson. Use the terminology in conjunction with vocabulary students already know. For example, ask:

- For what types of transformations are the preimage and the image similar but not necessarily congruent? For what types are the preimage and the image congruent? dilation; translation, reflection, rotation
- Which transformation do you use if you need to change the size of a figure? dilation
- If two figures are congruent, can you conclude that they are similar? Why? Yes; if the figures are congruent, one can be mapped onto the other using rigid motions, and rigid motions are similarity transformations.
- If two polygons have different shapes, is it possible to find similarity transformations that map one to the other? Why? No; all similarity transformations preserve the shape of a figure, so no sequence of similarity transformations can map one polygon to the other.

Go Online!

Interactive Whiteboard
Use the *eLesson, Lesson Presentation,* or *Interactive Classroom* to present this lesson.

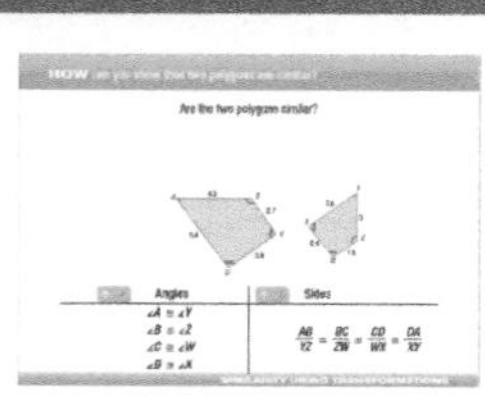

1A. Yes; map *ABCD* to *PQRS* using a dilation centered at the origin with scale factor 0.5 followed by a translation along ⟨11, 3⟩.

1B. Yes; map △*JKL* to △*XYZ* using a dilation centered at the origin with scale factor 2 followed by a reflection across the *y*-axis

Guided Practice

Determine whether the given polygons are similar. Explain.

1A. *ABCD* and *PQRS*

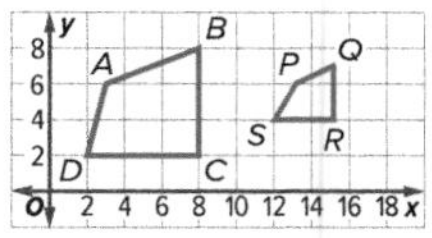

1B. △*JKL* and △*XYZ*

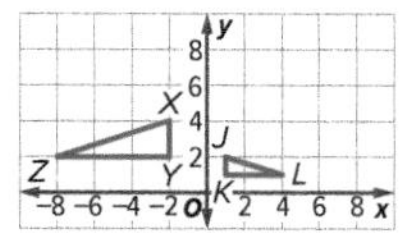

2 Use Properties of Similar Polygons

When two polygons are similar, there are important relationships among the polygons' angles and sides.

Key Concept Similar Polygons

Two polygons are similar if and only if their corresponding angles are congruent and corresponding side lengths are proportional.

Example In the diagram below, *ABCD* is similar to *WXYZ*.

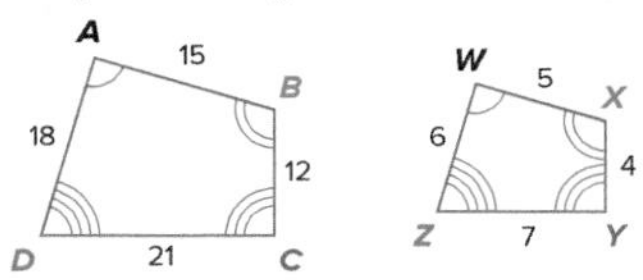

Corresponding angles

$\angle A \cong \angle W$, $\angle B \cong \angle X$, $\angle C \cong \angle Y$, and $\angle D \cong \angle Z$

Corresponding sides

$\frac{AB}{WX} = \frac{BC}{XY} = \frac{CD}{YZ} = \frac{DA}{ZW} = \frac{3}{1}$

Symbols $ABCD \sim WXYZ$

As with congruence statements, the order of vertices in a similarity statement like $ABCD \sim WXYZ$ is important. It identifies the corresponding angles and sides.

Watch Out!

Proportions There are many equivalent ways to write a proportion. When you check your answer to a problem like Example 2, be sure to consider different ways to write the proportion.

G.SRT.2

Example 2 Use a Similarity Statement

If $\triangle FGH \sim \triangle JKL$, list all pairs of congruent angles, and write a proportion that relates the corresponding sides.

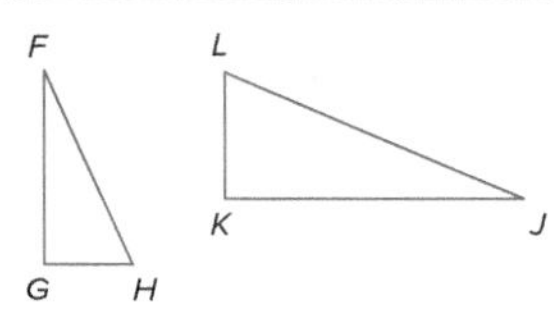

Use the similarity statement.

$\triangle FGH \sim \triangle JKL$

Congruent angles: $\angle F \cong \angle J$, $\angle G \cong \angle K$, $\angle H \cong \angle L$

Proportion: $\frac{FG}{JK} = \frac{GH}{KL} = \frac{HF}{LJ}$

Guided Practice

See Ch. 7 Answer Appendix.

2. In the diagram, $NPQR \sim UVST$. List all pairs of congruent angles, and write a proportion that relates the corresponding sides.

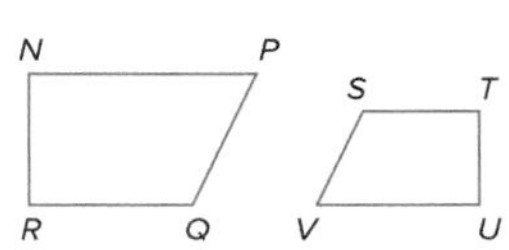

Need Another Example?

If $\triangle ABC \sim \triangle RST$, list all pairs of congruent angles and write a proportion that relates the corresponding sides.

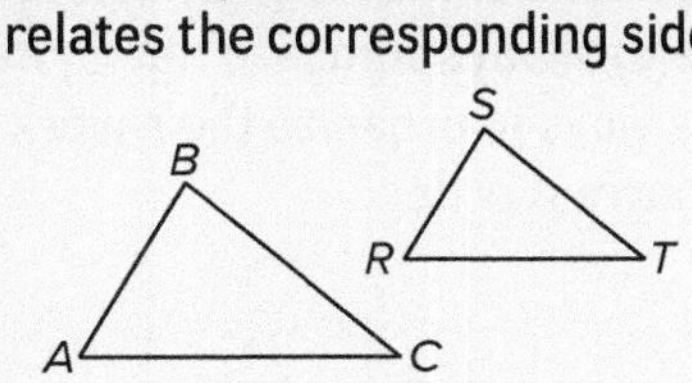

Congruent angles: $\angle A \cong \angle R$, $\angle B \cong \angle S$, $\angle C \cong \angle T$;

Proportion: $\frac{AB}{RS} = \frac{BC}{ST} = \frac{AC}{RT}$

Need Another Example?

Determine whether the given polygons are similar. Explain.

a. *ABCD* and *EFGH*

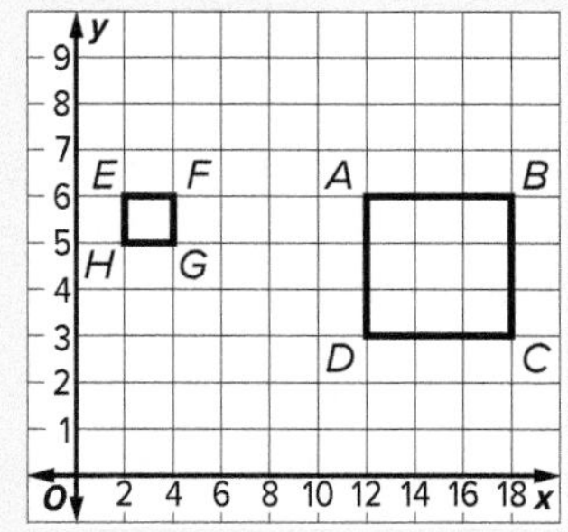

Yes; map *ABCD* to *EFGH* using a dilation centered at the origin with scale factor $\frac{1}{3}$ followed by a translation along [−2, 4].

b. △*PQR* and △*STU*

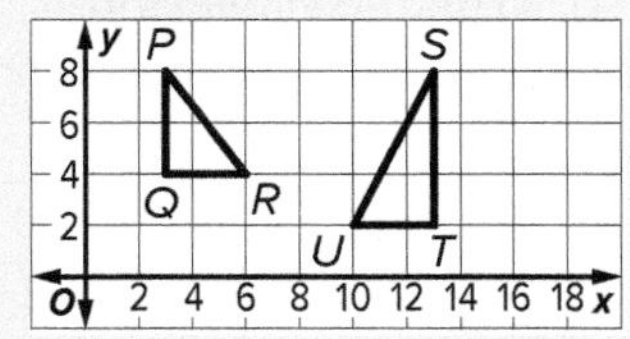

No; the triangles do not have the same shape, so there are no similarity transformations that will map one to the other.

2 Use Properties of Similar Polygons

Example 2 Use a Similarity Statement

AL What does it mean if two triangles are similar? The two triangles have congruent corresponding angles and proportional corresponding sides.

OL What are the advantages of using the similarity statement to write the proportion instead of the drawing? Explain. Sample answer: If you use the drawing, you may confuse the order of the vertices, but if you use the similarity statement it is easy to see which vertices correspond.

BL Why do you think the proportion of the sides of two similar polygons is important? Sample answer: We can use the proportion to find lengths.

Example 3 Identify Similar Polygons

AL What does the scale factor between two similar polygons tell us? the ratio of the lengths of all corresponding sides

OL If rectangle *PQRS* has side lengths $QR = 4.8$ and $RS = 6$, is *PQRS* similar to *ABCD*? If so, what is the scale factor? yes; $\frac{3}{5}$

BL A rectangle similar to *ABCD* has length 25 inches. What is the rectangle's width? 20 in.

Need Another Example?

Menus Tan is designing a new menu for the restaurant where he works. Determine whether the following sizes for the new menu are similar to the original menu. If so, write the similarity statement and scale factor. Explain your reasoning.

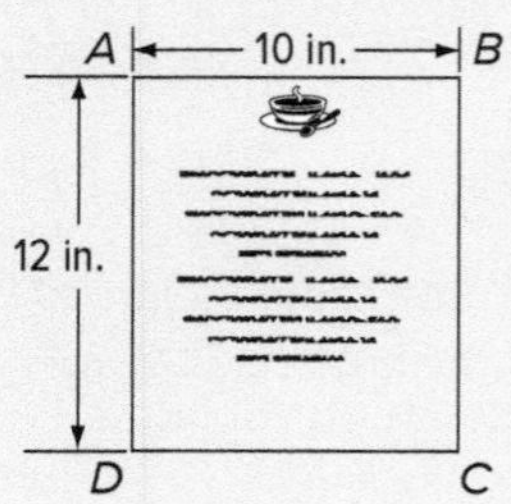

a.

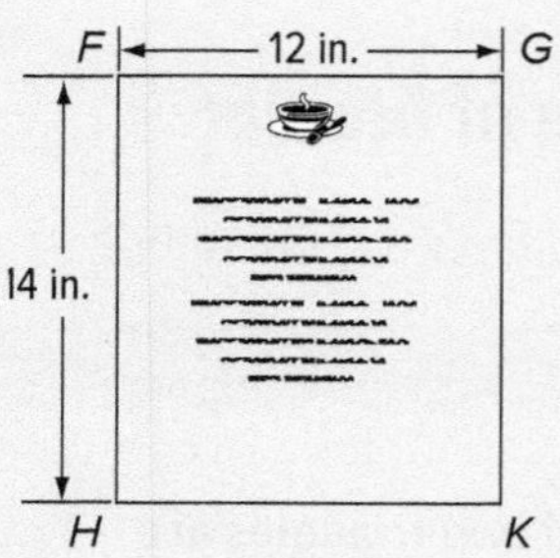

No, because $\frac{AB}{FG} \neq \frac{AD}{FH}$.

b.

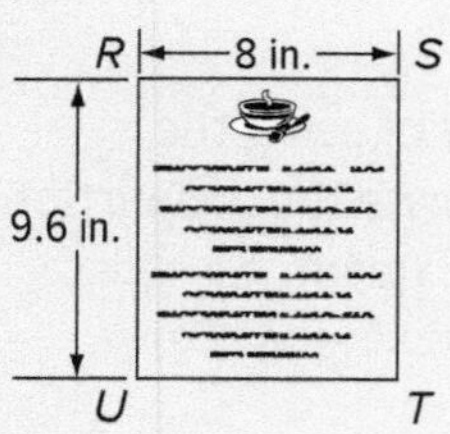

Yes, because $\frac{AB}{RS} = \frac{AD}{RU} = \frac{5}{4}$.

Go Online!

Discover the principles of similarity with a Geometer's Sketchpad® sketch in ConnectED. Discuss your findings with a partner. Ask for clarification as you need it.

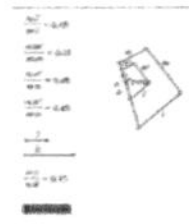

The ratio of the lengths of the corresponding sides of two similar polygons is called the **scale factor**. The scale factor depends on the order of comparison.

In the diagram, $\triangle ABC \sim \triangle XYZ$.

The scale factor from $\triangle XYZ$ to $\triangle ABC$ is $\frac{6}{3}$ or 2.

The scale factor from $\triangle ABC$ to $\triangle XYZ$ is $\frac{3}{6}$ or $\frac{1}{2}$.

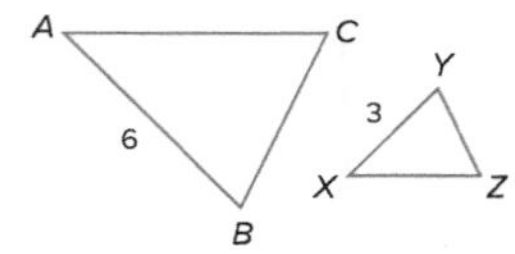

G.SRT.2

Real-World Example 3 Identify Similar Polygons

PHOTO EDITING **Kuma wants to use the rectangular photo shown as the background for her computer's desktop, but she needs to resize it. Determine whether the following rectangular images are similar. If so, write the similarity statement and scale factor. Explain your reasoning.**

a.

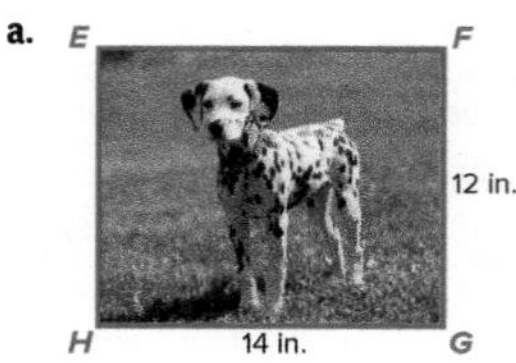

b.

a. **Step 1** Compare corresponding angles.

Because all angles of a rectangle are right angles and right angles are congruent, corresponding angles are congruent.

Step 2 Compare corresponding sides.

$\frac{DC}{HG} = \frac{10}{14}$ or $\frac{5}{7}$ $\qquad \frac{BC}{FG} = \frac{8}{12}$ or $\frac{2}{3}$ $\qquad \frac{5}{7} \neq \frac{2}{3}$

Because corresponding sides are not proportional, $ABCD \nsim EFGH$. So the photos are not similar.

b. **Step 1** Because *ABCD* and *JKLM* are both rectangles, corresponding angles are congruent.

Step 2 Compare corresponding sides.

$\frac{DC}{ML} = \frac{10}{15}$ or $\frac{2}{3}$ $\qquad \frac{BC}{KL} = \frac{8}{12}$ or $\frac{2}{3}$ $\qquad \frac{2}{3} = \frac{2}{3}$

Because corresponding sides are proportional, $ABCD \sim JKLM$. So the rectangles are similar with a scale factor from *JKLM* to *ABCD* of $\frac{2}{3}$.

Reading Math

Similarity Symbol The symbol $\nsim$ is read as *is not similar to*.

Guided Practice

3. Determine whether the triangles shown are similar. If so, write the similarity statement and scale factor. Explain your reasoning.

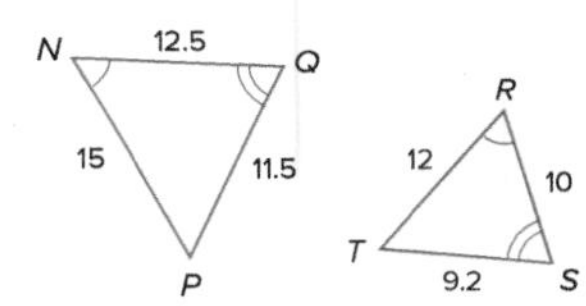

3. Yes; $\triangle NQP \sim \triangle RST$, since $\angle N \cong \angle R$, $\angle Q \cong \angle S$, and $\angle P \cong \angle T$ by the Third Angles Theorem, and $\frac{NQ}{RS} = \frac{QP}{ST} = \frac{PN}{TR}$. The scale factor from $\triangle RST$ to $\triangle NQP$ is $\frac{5}{4}$.

Stockbyte/Getty Images

Differentiated Instruction AL OL BL

Visual/Spatial Learners Show students how to be consistent when analyzing figures for similarity. For example, they may choose to always compare the figure on the left to the figure on the right. Show students ways to organize their work so that they reference corresponding vertices in the correct order.

G.SRT.2

Example 4 Use Similar Figures to Find Missing Measures

In the diagram, $ACDF \sim VWYZ$.

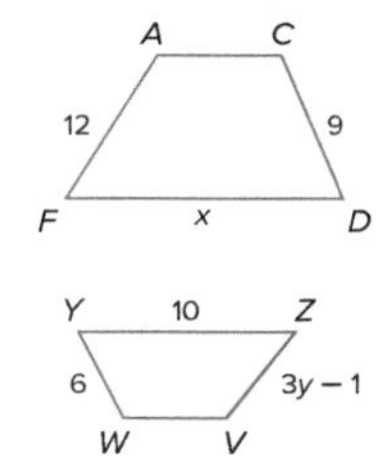

a. Find x.

Use the corresponding side lengths to write a proportion.

$\frac{CD}{WY} = \frac{DF}{YZ}$ Similarity proportion

$\frac{9}{6} = \frac{x}{10}$ $CD = 9$, $WY = 6$, $DF = x$, $YZ = 10$

$9(10) = 6(x)$ Cross Products Property

$90 = 6x$ Multiply.

$15 = x$ Divide each side by 6.

b. Find y.

Use the corresponding side lengths to write a proportion.

$\frac{CD}{WY} = \frac{FA}{ZV}$ Similarity proportion

$\frac{9}{6} = \frac{12}{3y - 1}$ $CD = 9$, $WY = 6$, $FA = 12$, $ZV = 3y - 1$

$9(3y - 1) = 6(12)$ Cross Products Property

$27y - 9 = 72$ Multiply.

$27y = 81$ Add 9 to each side.

$y = 3$ Divide each side by 27.

Study Tip

MP Sense-Making When only two congruent angles of a triangle are given, remember that you can use the Third Angles Theorem to establish that the remaining corresponding angles are also congruent.

Guided Practice

Find the value of each variable if $\triangle JLM \sim \triangle QST$.

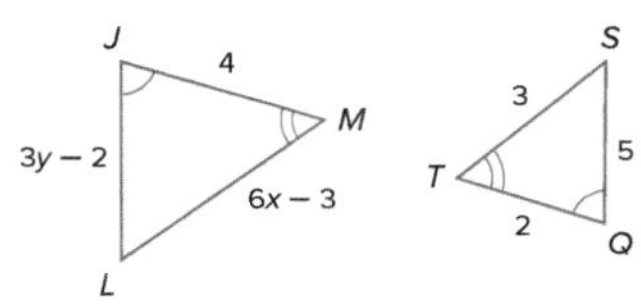

4A. x 1.5

4B. y 4

In similar polygons, the ratio of any two corresponding lengths is proportional to the scale factor between them. This leads to the following theorem about the perimeters of two similar polygons.

Theorem 7.1 Perimeters of Similar Polygons

If two polygons are similar, then their perimeters are proportional to the scale factor between them.

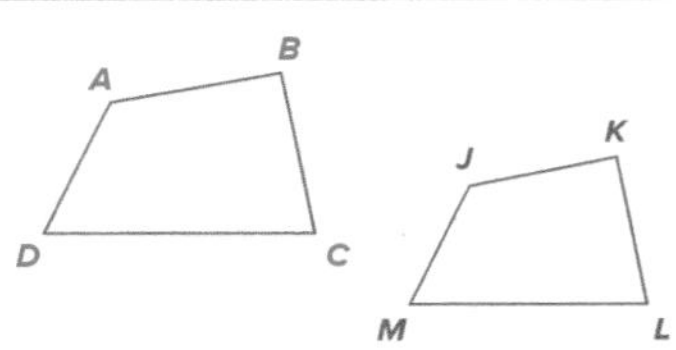

Example If $ABCD \sim JKLM$, then

$$\frac{AB + BC + CD + DA}{JK + KL + LM + MJ} = \frac{AB}{JK} = \frac{BC}{KL} = \frac{CD}{LM} = \frac{DA}{MJ}$$

Example 4 Use Similar Figures to Find Missing Measures

AL What is the scale factor of $ACDF$ to $VWYZ$? $\frac{3}{2}$

OL If $AC = 11$ and $VW = z$, what is z? $7\frac{1}{3}$

BL If the perimeter of $ACDF$ is 46, what is VW? $6\frac{2}{3}$

Need Another Example?

The two polygons are similar.

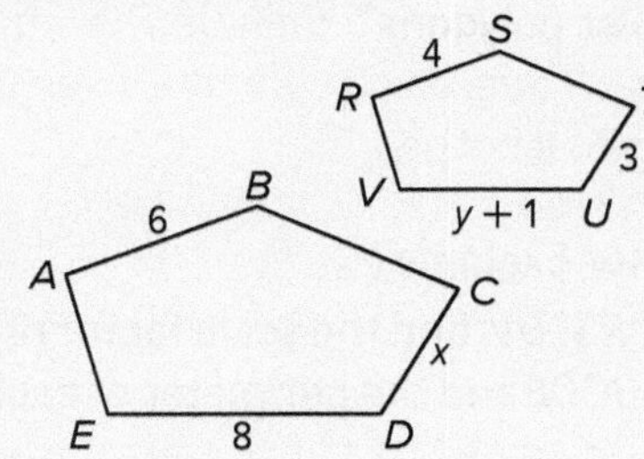

a. Find x. $\frac{9}{2}$

b. Find y. $\frac{13}{3}$

Teaching Tip

Vary Colors When identifying corresponding parts, use different colors to circle letters of congruent angles.

Follow-Up

Students have explored dilations and similar polygons.

Ask:

- **How can you determine whether two objects are similar?** Sample answer: You can determine whether there is a dilation or combination of a dilation and one or more rigid transformations that map one figure onto the other. You can also compare corresponding angle measures to see if they are congruent and corresponding side lengths to see if they are proportional.

Example 5 Use a Scale Factor to Find Perimeter

AL Why is the scale factor greater than 1? *ABCDE* is larger than *PQRST*.

OL How can we check our solution? Sample answer: Use the scale factor to find *ST*, then find the perimeter of *PQRST*.

BL Do you think you could use the scale factor as we did in the example to compare the areas of similar polygons? Sample answer: No; The area is in square units and the scale factor applies to lengths.

Need Another Example?

If *ABCDE* ~ *RSTUV*, find the scale factor of from *RSTUV* to *ABCDE* and the perimeter of each polygon.

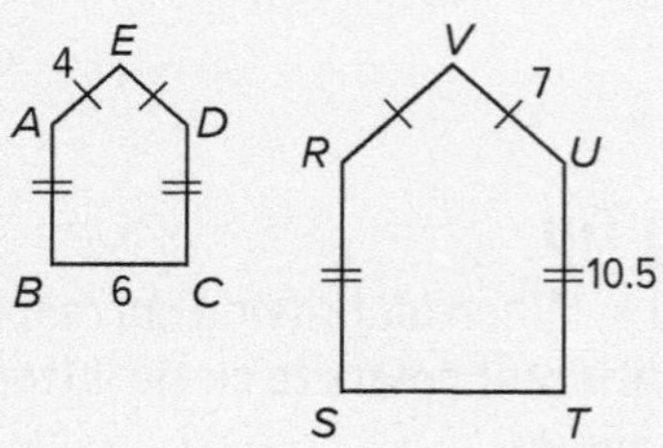

scale factor: $\frac{4}{7}$; perimeter of *ABCDE*: 26; perimeter of *RSTUV*: 45.5

G.SRT2

Example 5 Use a Scale Factor to Find Perimeter

If *ABCDE* ~ *PQRST*, find the scale factor of *ABCDE* to *PQRST* and the perimeter of each polygon.

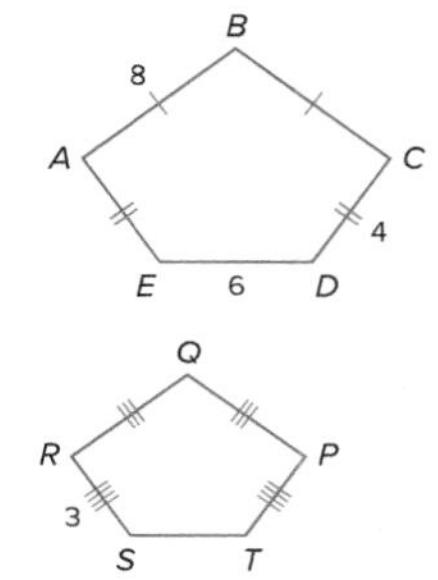

The scale factor from *PQRST* to *ABCDE* is $\frac{CD}{RS}$ or $\frac{4}{3}$.

Because $\overline{BC} \cong \overline{AB}$ and $\overline{AE} \cong \overline{CD}$, the perimeter of *ABCDE* is 8 + 8 + 4 + 6 + 4 or 30.

Use the perimeter of *ABCDE* and the scale factor to write a proportion. Let *x* represent the perimeter of *PQRST*.

$\frac{4}{3} = \frac{\text{perimeter of } ABCDE}{\text{perimeter of } PQRST}$	Theorem 7.1
$\frac{4}{3} = \frac{30}{x}$	Substitution
$(3)(30) = 4x$	Cross Products Property
$22.5 = x$	Solve.

So, the perimeter of *PQRST* is 22.5.

Watch Out!

Perimeter Remember that perimeter is the distance around a figure. Be sure to find the sum of all side lengths when finding the perimeter of a polygon. You may need to use other markings or geometric principles to find the length of unmarked sides.

Guided Practice

5. If *MNPQ* ~ *XYZW*, find the scale factor from *XYZW* to *MNPQ* and the perimeter of each polygon.

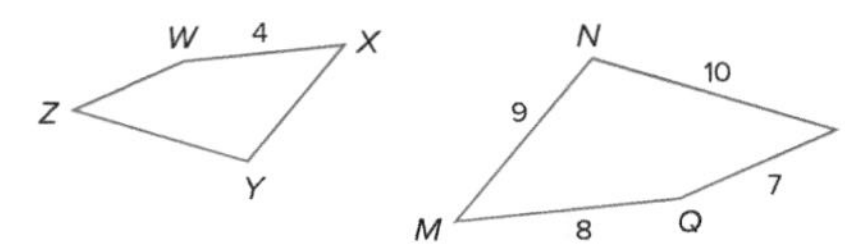

5. scale factor = 2; perimeter of *MNPQ* = 34, perimeter of *XYZW* = 17

Check Your Understanding ◯ = Step-by-Step Solutions begin on page R13.

Go Online! for a Self-Check Quiz

Example 1 G.SRT2

Determine whether the given polygons are similar. Explain.

1. *DEFG* and *JKLM*

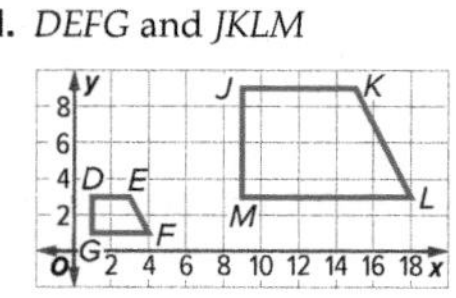

2. *ABCD* and *RSTU*

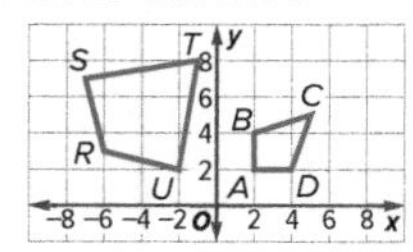

1. Yes; map *DEFG* to *JKLM* using a dilation centered at the origin with scale factor 3 followed by a translation along (6, 0).

2. No; the polygons do not have the same shape, so there are no similarity transformations that will map one to the other.

Example 2 G.SRT2

List all pairs of congruent angles, and write a proportion that relates the corresponding sides for each pair of similar polygons.

3. △*ABC* ~ △*ZYX*

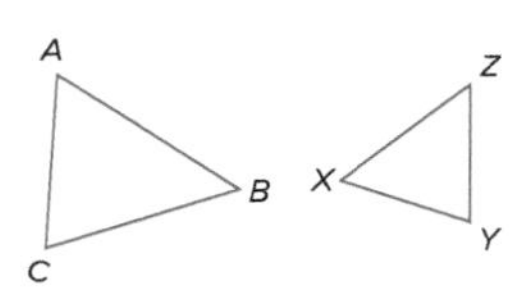

4. *JKLM* ~ *TSRQ*

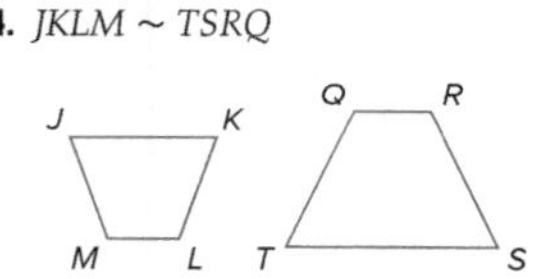

3. ∠*A* ≅ ∠*Z*, ∠*B* ≅ ∠*Y*, ∠*C* ≅ ∠*X*; $\frac{AC}{ZX} = \frac{BC}{YX} = \frac{AB}{ZY}$

4. ∠*J* ≅ ∠*T*, ∠*K* ≅ ∠*S*, ∠*M* ≅ ∠*Q*; ∠*L* ≅ ∠*R*; $\frac{JM}{TQ} = \frac{ML}{QR} = \frac{KL}{SR} = \frac{JK}{TS}$

Differentiated Instruction ELL

Beginning Help students access text by working through Examples using an interactive whiteboard. Point out each part of the similar polygons, identify the ones that are being used in each step of the solution, and give an explanation using short phrases.

Intermediate Provide students with a study guide to make it accessible to all students. Paraphrasing content helps students make connections more easily. The Study Guide and Intervention worksheets on ConnectED offer concise explanations with examples.

Example 3
G.SRT.2

Determine whether each pair of figures is similar. If so, write the similarity statement and scale factor. If not, explain your reasoning.

5.

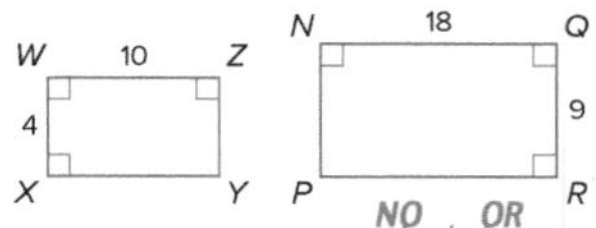

no; $\frac{NQ}{WZ} \neq \frac{QR}{WX}$

6.

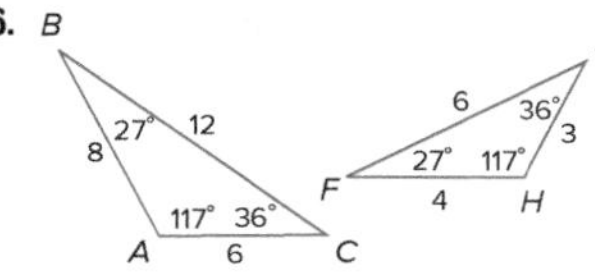

6. Yes; $\triangle ABC \sim \triangle HFJ$ since $\angle A \cong \angle H$, $\angle B \cong \angle F$, $\angle C \cong \angle J$ and $\frac{AB}{HF} = \frac{BC}{FJ} = \frac{CA}{JH}$; scale factor: $\frac{2}{1}$.

Example 4
G.SRT.2

Each pair of polygons is similar. Find the value of x.

7. 6

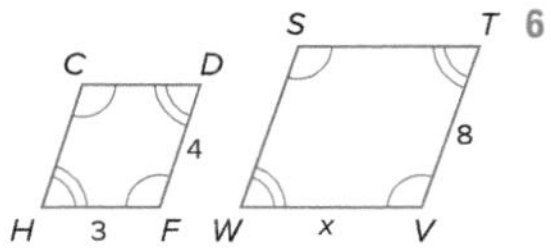

8. 16

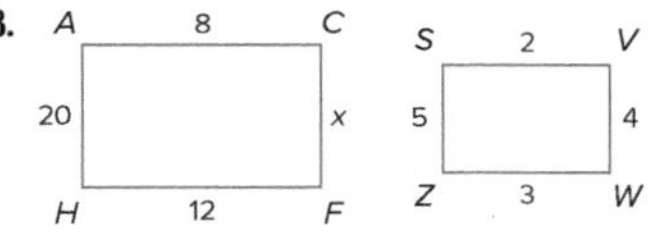

Example 5
G.SRT.2

9. DESIGN On the blueprint of the apartment shown, the balcony measures 1 inch wide by 1.75 inches long. If the actual length of the balcony is 7 feet, what is the perimeter of the balcony? 22 ft

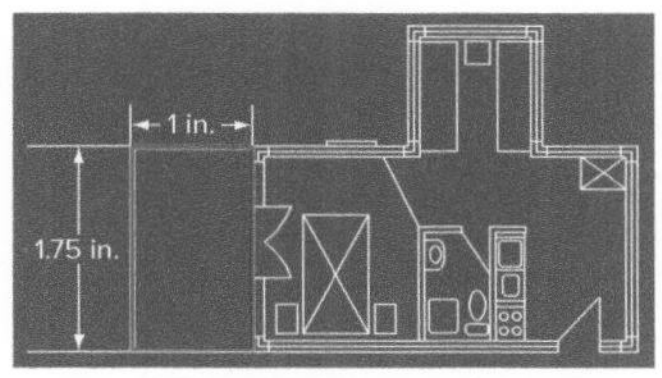

Practice and Problem Solving

Extra Practice is on page R7.

Example 1
G.SRT.2

Determine whether the given polygons are similar. Explain.

10. $\triangle GHJ$ and $\triangle KLM$

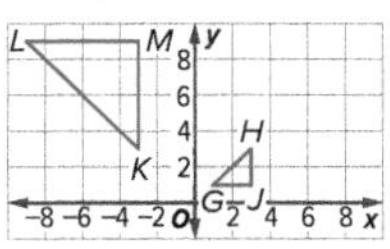

11. $PQRS$ and $WXYZ$

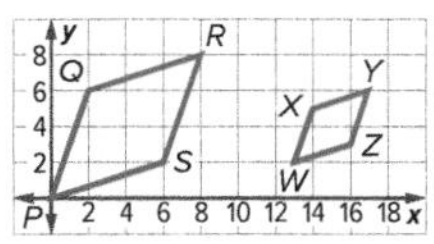

10. Yes; map $\triangle GHJ$ to $\triangle KLM$ using a dilation centered at the origin with scale factor 3 followed by a counterclockwise rotation of 90° about the origin.

11. Yes; map $PQRS$ to $WXYZ$ using a dilation centered at the origin with scale factor 0.5 followed by a translation along (13, 2).

Example 2
G.SRT.2

List all pairs of congruent angles, and write a proportion that relates the corresponding sides for each pair of similar polygons.

12. $\triangle CHF \sim \triangle YWS$

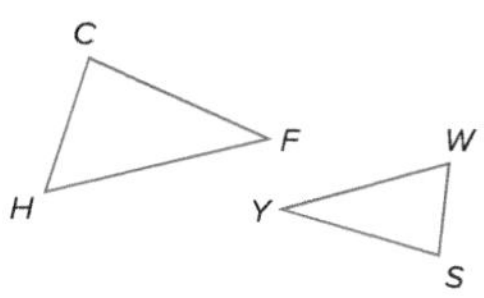

12. $\angle C \cong \angle Y$, $\angle H \cong \angle W$, $\angle F \cong \angle S$; $\frac{CH}{YW} = \frac{HF}{WS} = \frac{FC}{SY}$

13. $JHFM \sim PQST$

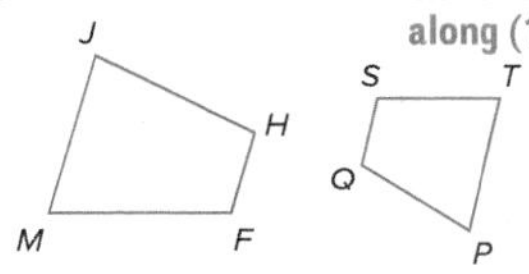

13. $\angle J \cong \angle P$, $\angle F \cong \angle S$, $\angle M \cong \angle T$, $\angle H \cong \angle Q$; $\frac{PQ}{JH} = \frac{TS}{MF} = \frac{SQ}{FH} = \frac{TP}{MJ}$

Example 3
G.SRT.2

MP CONSTRUCT ARGUMENTS Determine whether each pair of figures is similar. If so, write the similarity statement and scale factor. If not, explain your reasoning.

14. no; $\angle L \not\cong \angle W$

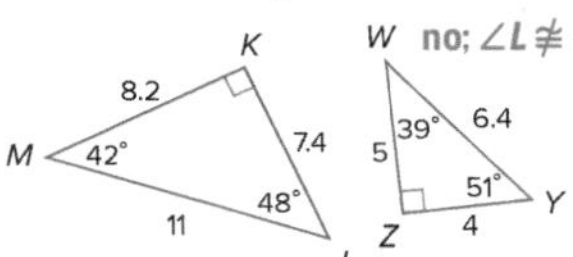

15

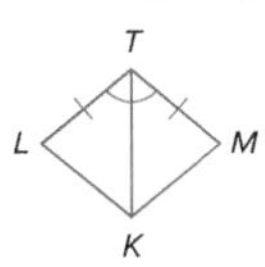

Yes; $\triangle LTK \sim \triangle MTK$ because $\triangle LTK \cong \triangle MTK$; scale factor: 1.

Differentiated Homework Options

Levels	AL Basic	OL Core	BL Advanced
Exercises	10–26, 35–43	11–29 odd, 30–33, 35–43	31–37 (optional: 38–43)
2-Day Option	11–25 odd, 38–43	10–29	
	10–26 even, 35–37	30–33, 35–43	

You can use ALEKS to provide additional remediation support with personalized instruction and practice.

Practice

Formative Assessment Use Exercises 1–9 to assess students' understanding of the concepts in this lesson.

The Practice and Problem Solving exercises assess the content taught in the lesson. The Preparing for Assessment page is meant to be used as preparation for end-of-course assessments.

MP Teaching the Mathematical Practices

Construct Arguments Mathematically proficient students understand and use stated assumptions and definitions in constructing arguments. In Exercises 14 and 15, encourage students to redraw the figures so the orientation of each is the same. This may help students explain whether the figures are similar.

Levels of Complexity Chart

The levels of the exercises progress from 1 to 3, with Level 1 indicating the lowest level of complexity.

Exercises	10–26	27–30, 38–43	31–37
Level 3			●
Level 2		●	
Level 1	●		

Extra Practice

See page R7 for extra exercises for students who are approaching level or for on-level students who need additional reinforcement.

Teaching the Mathematical Practices

Regularity Mathematically proficient students maintain oversight of the process, while attending to the details. They continually evaluate the reasonableness of their intermediate results. Encourage students to write a similarity statement for Exercises 18–21. Have them check that the statement matches the information in the given figure.

16. **GAMES** The dimensions of a hockey rink are 200 feet by 85 feet. Are the hockey rink and the air hockey table shown similar? Explain your reasoning.

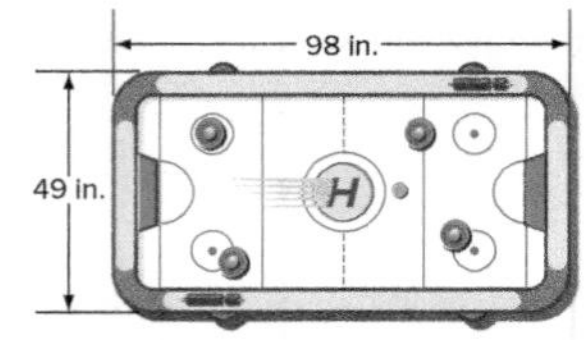

No; sample answer: The ratio of the lengths of the hockey rink and air hockey table is about 2 and the ratio of the widths is about 1.7.

17. **COMPUTERS** The dimensions of a 17-inch flat panel computer screen are approximately $13\frac{1}{4}$ by $10\frac{3}{4}$ inches. The dimensions of a 19-inch flat panel computer screen are approximately $14\frac{1}{2}$ by 12 inches. To the nearest tenth, are the computer screens similar? Explain your reasoning. Yes; sample answer: The ratio of the longer dimensions of the screens is approximately 1.1 and the ratio of the shorter dimensions of the screens is 1.1.

Example 4 G.SRT.2

MP REGULARITY **Each pair of polygons is similar. Find the value of x.**

18. 7

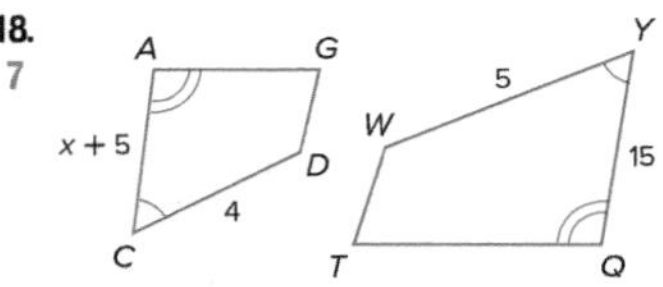

19. 5

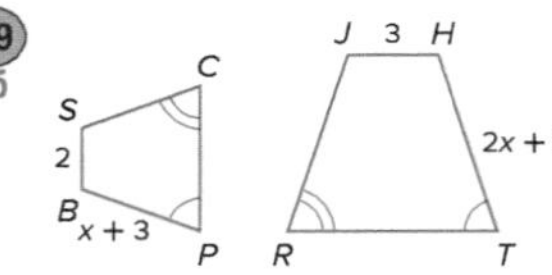

20. 2

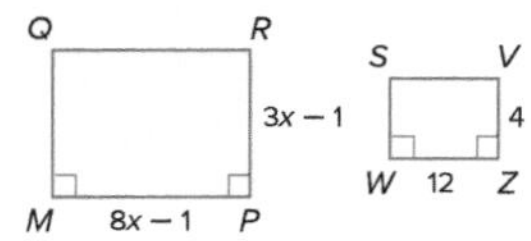

21. 3

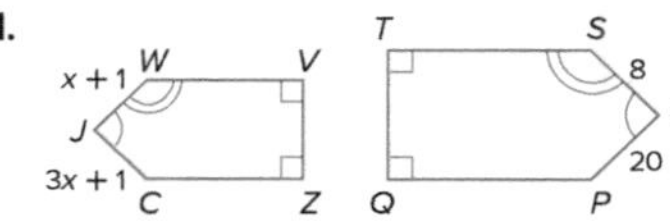

Example 5 G.SRT.2

22. Rectangle $ABCD$ has a width of 8 yards and a length of 20 yards. Rectangle $QRST$, which is similar to rectangle $ABCD$, has a length of 40 yards. Find the scale factor of rectangle $ABCD$ to rectangle $QRST$ and the perimeter of each rectangle. 1:2; perimeter of $ABCD$ = 56 yd, perimeter of $QRST$ = 112 yd

Find the perimeter of the given triangle.

23. $\triangle DEF$, if $\triangle ABC \sim \triangle DEF$, $AB = 5$, $BC = 6$, $AC = 7$, and and $DE = 3$ 10.8

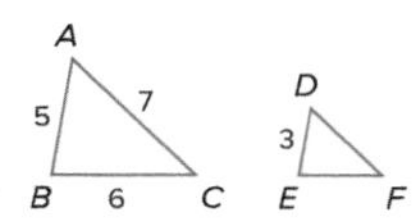

24. $\triangle WZX$, if $\triangle WZX \sim \triangle SRT$, $ST = 6$, $WX = 5$, and the perimeter of $\triangle SRT = 15$ 12.5

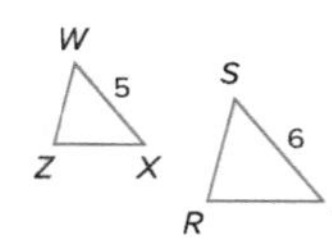

25. $\triangle CBH$, if $\triangle CBH \sim \triangle FEH$, $ADEG$ is a parallelogram, $CH = 7$, $FH = 10$, $FE = 11$, and $EH = 6$ 18.9

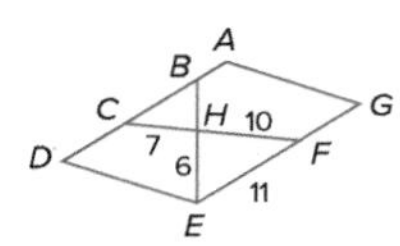

26. $\triangle DEF$, if $\triangle DEF \sim \triangle CBF$, perimeter of $\triangle CBF = 27$, $DF = 6$, $FC = 8$ 20.25

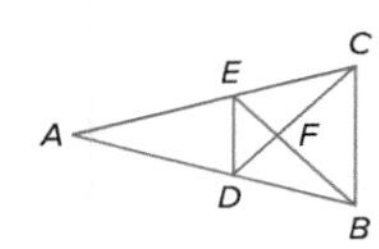

B **27.** Two similar rectangles have a scale factor of 2 : 4. The perimeter of the large rectangle is 80 meters. Find the perimeter of the small rectangle. 40 m

28. Two similar rectangles have a scale factor of 3 : 2. The perimeter of the small rectangle is 50 feet. Find the perimeter of the large rectangle. 75 ft

MP Standards for Mathematical Practice

Emphasis On	Exercises
1 Make sense of problems and persevere in solving them.	7, 8, 22–28, 34, 37–41
2 Reason abstractly and quantitatively.	1–6, 10–13, 31–33, 36
3 Construct viable arguments and critique the reasoning of others.	14, 15. 29, 35
4 Model with mathematics.	9, 16, 17, 30, 42, 43
8 Look for and express regularity in repeated reasoning.	18–21

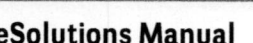

Go Online!

eSolutions Manual

Create worksheets, answer keys, and solutions handouts for your assignments.

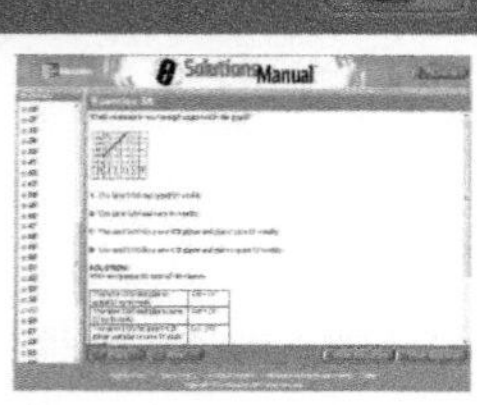

29. PROOF Write a paragraph proof of Theorem 7.1.

Given: $\triangle ABC \sim \triangle DEF$ and $\frac{AB}{DE} = \frac{m}{n}$

Prove: $\frac{\text{perimeter of } \triangle ABC}{\text{perimeter of } \triangle DEF} = \frac{m}{n}$ See margin.

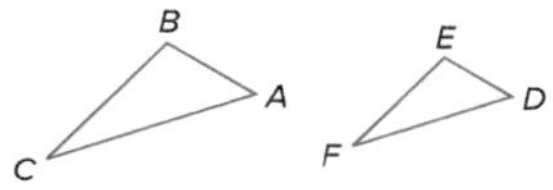

30. PHOTOS You are enlarging the photo shown at the right for your school yearbook. If the dimensions of the original photo are $2\frac{1}{3}$ inches by $1\frac{2}{3}$ inches and the scale factor of the old photo to the new photo is 2:3, what are the dimensions of the new photo? $3\frac{1}{2}$ in. by $2\frac{1}{2}$ in.

31. CHANGING DIMENSIONS Rectangle *QRST* is similar to rectangle *JKLM* with sides in a ratio of 4:1.

a. What is the ratio of the areas of the two rectangles? 16:1

b. Suppose the dimension of each rectangle is tripled. What is the new ratio of the sides of the rectangles? 4:1

c. What is the ratio of the areas of these larger rectangles? 16:1

d. Suppose only one pair of corresponding dimensions of each rectangle is doubled. What is the new ratio of the sides of the rectangles? 4:1

32. CHANGING DIMENSIONS In the figure shown, $\triangle FGH \sim \triangle XYZ$.

a. Show that the perimeters of $\triangle FGH$ and $\triangle XYZ$ have the same ratio as their corresponding sides.

b. If 6 units are added to the lengths of each side, are the new triangles similar? Explain.

32a. $\frac{a}{3a} = \frac{b}{3b} = \frac{c}{3c} = \frac{a+b+c}{3(a+b+c)} = \frac{1}{3}$

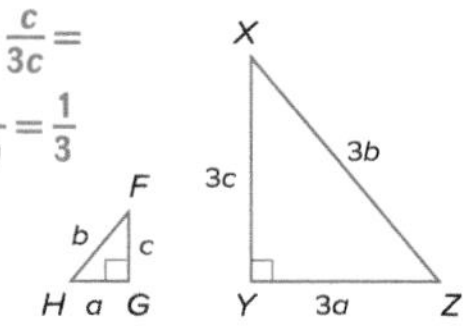

No; the sides are no longer proportional.

33. MULTIPLE REPRESENTATIONS In this problem, you will investigate similarity in squares.

a. **Geometric** Draw three different-sized squares. Label them *ABCD*, *PQRS*, and *WXYZ*. Measure and label each square with its side length. See margin.

b. **Tabular** Calculate and record in a table the ratios of corresponding sides for each pair of squares: *ABCD* and *PQRS*, *PQRS* and *WXYZ*, and *WXYZ* and *ABCD*. Is each pair of squares similar? See margin.

c. **Verbal** Make a conjecture about the similarity of all squares. Sample answer: All squares are similar.

G.SRT2

H.O.T. Problems — Use Higher-Order Thinking Skills

34. CHALLENGE For what value(s) of *x* is *BEFA* ~ *EDCB*? 4

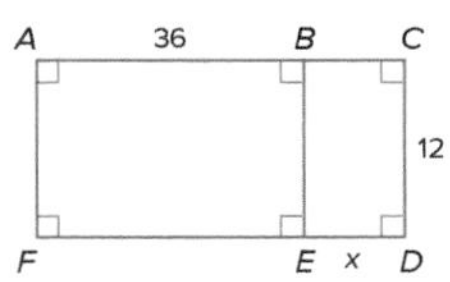

35. OPEN-ENDED Find a counterexample for the following statement.

All rectangles are similar. See margin.

36. REASONING Draw two regular pentagons of different sizes. Are the pentagons similar? Will any two regular polygons with the same number of sides be similar? Explain. See margin.

37. WRITING IN MATH How can you describe the relationship between two figures? See margin.

Exercise Alert

Ruler Exercise 33 requires the use of a ruler.

Assess

Crystal Ball Ask students to predict how today's lesson about similar polygons helped them prepare for tomorrow's lesson about similar triangles. What may be the same? What may be different?

Additional Answers

29. Given: $\triangle ABC \sim \triangle DEF$ and $\frac{AB}{DE} = \frac{m}{n}$

Prove: $\frac{\text{perimeter of } \triangle ABC}{\text{perimeter of } \triangle DEF} = \frac{m}{n}$

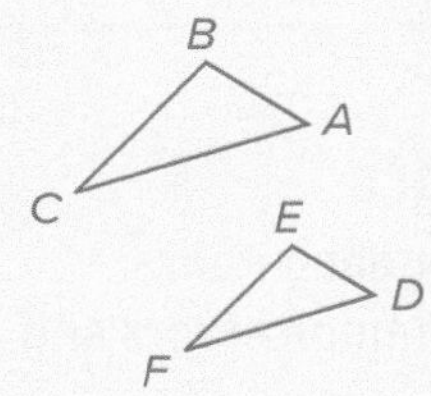

Proof: Because $\triangle ABC \sim \triangle DEF$, $\frac{AB}{DE} = \frac{BC}{EF} = \frac{AC}{DF}$. So $\frac{AB}{DE} = \frac{BC}{EF} = \frac{AC}{DF} = \frac{m}{n}$. Cross products yield $AB = DE\left(\frac{m}{n}\right)$, $BC = EF\left(\frac{m}{n}\right)$, and $AC = DF\left(\frac{m}{n}\right)$. Using substitution, the perimeter of $\triangle ABC = DE\left(\frac{m}{n}\right) + EF\left(\frac{m}{n}\right) + DF\left(\frac{m}{n}\right)$, or $\frac{m}{n}(DE + EF + DF)$. The ratio of the two perimeters $= \frac{\frac{m}{n}(DE + EF + DF)}{DE + EF + DF}$ or $\frac{m}{n}$.

33a. Sample answer:

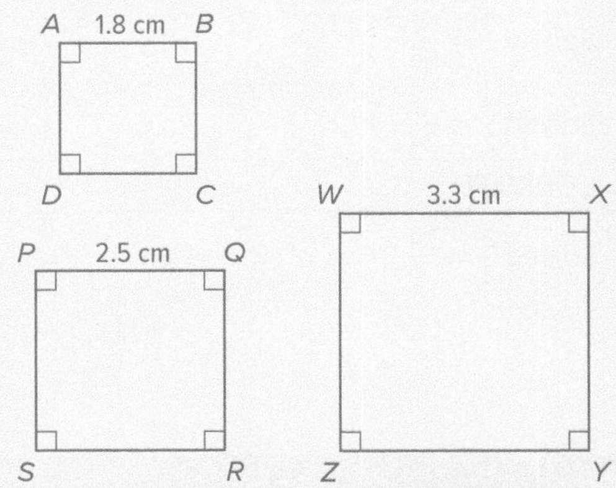

33b.

ABCD and *PQRS*		*PQRS* and *WXYZ*		*WXYZ* and *ABCD*	
AB:*PQ*	0.72	*PQ*:*WX*	0.76	*WX*:*AB*	1.8
BC:*QR*	0.72	*QR*:*XY*	0.76	*XY*:*BC*	1.8
CD:*RS*	0.72	*RS*:*YZ*	0.76	*YZ*:*CD*	1.8
AD:*SP*	0.72	*SP*:*ZW*	0.76	*ZW*:*DA*	1.8

ABCD is similar to *PQRS*; *PQRS* is similar to *WXYZ*; *WXYZ* is similar to *ABCD*.

35. Sample answer:

36.

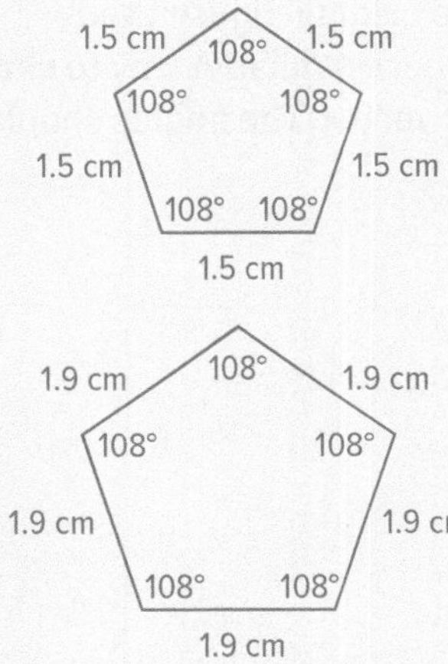

Yes; yes; sample answer: The pentagons are similar because their corresponding angles are congruent and their corresponding sides are proportional. All of the angles and sides in a regular polygon are congruent. The angles will be congruent regardless of the size of the figure, and since all of the sides are congruent the ratios of the sides of one regular figure to a second regular figure with the same number of sides will all be the same. Therefore, all regular polygons with the same number of sides are similar.

37. Sample answer: The figures could be described as congruent if they are the same size and shape, similar if their corresponding angles are congruent and their corresponding sides are proportional, and equal if they are the same exact figure.

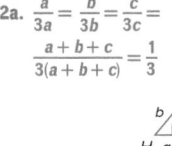

Preparing for Assessment

Exercises 38–43 require students to use the skills they will need on standardized assessments. Exercises are dual-coded with content standards and mathematical practice standards.

Dual Coding		
Items	Content Standards	MP Mathematical Practices
38	G.SRT.2	1
39	G.SRT.2	1
40	G.SRT.2	1
41	G.SRT.2	1
42	G.SRT.2	4
43	G.SRT.2	4

Diagnose Student Errors

Survey student responses for each item. Class trends may indicate common errors and misconceptions.

39.

A	Solved $\frac{3}{4} = \frac{x}{12}$
B	Solved $\frac{3}{4} = \frac{12}{x}$
C	Solved $\frac{3}{4} = \frac{x}{24}$
D	CORRECT

42.

A	Solved $\frac{3}{2} = \frac{x}{36}$
B	Solved $\frac{3}{2} = \frac{x}{24}$
C	CORRECT
D	Solved $\frac{3}{2} = \frac{24}{x}$

Preparing for Assessment

38. In the figure, $JKLM \sim PQRS$. What is the perimeter of $PQRS$? MP 1 G.SRT.2 **D**

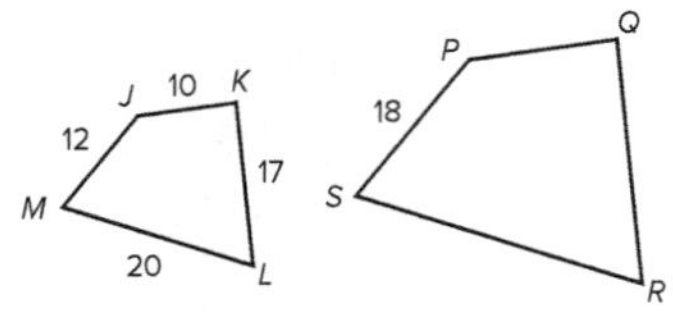

○ A 18
○ B 39.3
○ C 59
○ D 88.5

39. Braden drew two rectangles, *RSTU* and *VWXY*, so that $RSTU \sim VWXY$. The ratio of the perimeter of *RSTU* to the perimeter of *VWXY* is $\frac{3}{4}$. Given that the length of *RSTU* is 24 and the width of *RSTU* is 12, what is the length of *VWXY*? MP 1 G.SRT.2 **D**

○ A 9
○ B 16
○ C 18
○ D 32

40. In the figure, $\triangle ABC \sim \triangle DEF$.

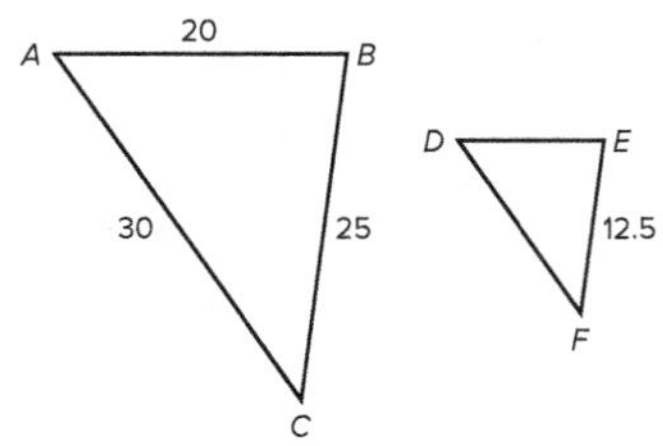

What is the perimeter of $\triangle DEF$? MP 1 G.SRT.2 **37.5**

perimeter = ☐

41. Two similar rectangles have a scale factor of 3 : 5. The perimeter of the larger rectangle is 65 meters. What is the perimeter in meters of the smaller rectangle? MP 1 G.SRT.2 **39**

perimeter = ☐

42. An architect is designing two triangular support structures for a roof. The support structures must be similar. The architect designs them so that $\triangle KLM \sim \triangle PQR$, as shown. She wants the ratio of the perimeter of $\triangle KLM$ to the perimeter of $\triangle PQR$ to be $\frac{3}{2}$.

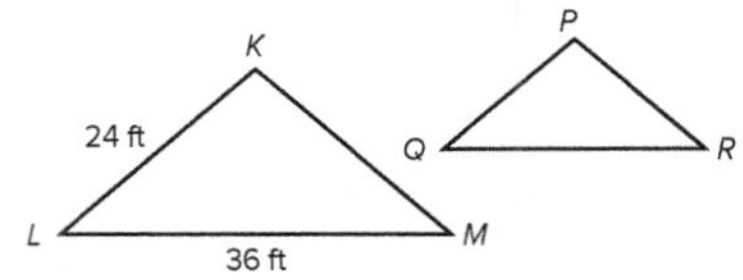

What length should the architect use for $\overline{QR}$? MP 4 G.SRT.2 **C**

○ A 54 ft
○ B 36 ft
○ C 24 ft
○ D 16 ft

43. **MULTI-STEP** Yasmina uses a coordinate plane to design jewelry to sell at a craft fair. The figure shows the design for a pair of earrings that will be based on polygon *DEFG*. MP 4 G.SRT.2

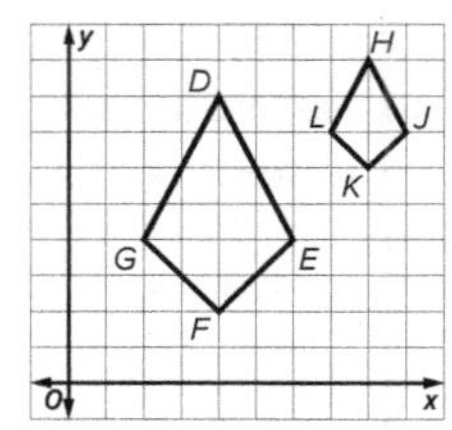

a. Yasmina decides to base the earrings on polygon *HJKL* instead. Use transformations to explain why polygons *DEFG* and *HJKL* are similar.

b. Write a similarity statement for the polygons.

c. Write a proportion that shows how the sides of the polygons are related.

d. Suppose the perimeter of polygon *DEFG* is 6.2 centimeters. What is the perimeter of polygon *HJKL*? Explain how you know.

43a–d. See margin.

Differentiated Instruction OL BL

Extension Have students use a word processing program and experiment with different polygons that the program provides. After they choose a shape, have them generate a figure that is similar. They can copy the original figure then change the figure's scale, which will make the second figure similar. A way to check for similarity is to superimpose the two polygons at any vertex. The angles should be identical.

Go Online!

Quizzes

Students can use *Self-Check Quizzes* to check their understanding of this lesson and have the results sent to you. You can also give the *Chapter Quiz*, which covers the content in Lessons 7-1 and 7-2.

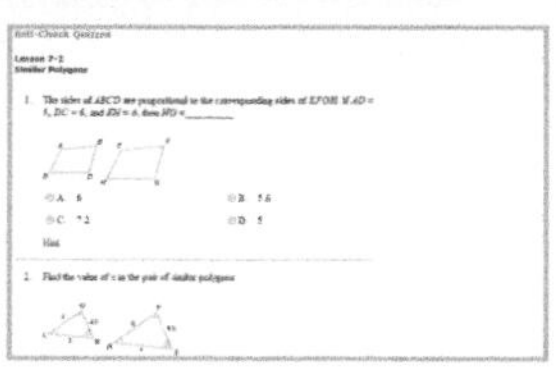

43a. Map *DEFG* to *HJKL* using a dilation centered at the origin with scale factor 0.5, followed by a translation along ⟨6, 5⟩.

43b. $DEFG \sim HJKL$

43c. $\frac{DE}{HJ} = \frac{EF}{JK} = \frac{FG}{KL} = \frac{GD}{LH}$

43d. 3.1 cm; because the scale factor of the dilation is 0.5, the perimeter of *HJKL* is 0.5 times the perimeter of *DEFG*.

LESSON 7-3

Similar Triangles: AA Similarity

SUGGESTED PACING (DAYS)

	Instruction	Extend Lab
90 min.	0.5	.25
45 min.	1	0.5

Track Your Progress

Objectives

1. Use the AA similarity criterion to prove triangles similar.
2. Solve problems by using the properties of similar triangles.

Mathematical Background

Triangles can be proved similar without knowing the measures of every angle and side. The AA similarity criterion, stated as the AA Similarity Postulate, establishes that two triangles are similar if two pairs of their angles are congruent. The properties of similar triangles can be used in indirect measurement, which can be useful in solving real-world problems.

THEN

G.CO.2 Represent transformations in the plane using, e.g., transparencies and geometry software; describe transformations as functions that take points in the plane as inputs and give other points as outputs. Compare transformations that preserve distance and angle to those that do not (e.g., translation versus horizontal stretch).

G.SRT.1 Verify experimentally the properties of dilations given by a center and a scale factor.

NOW

G.SRT.3 Use the properties of similarity transformations to establish the AA criterion for two triangles to be similar.

G.SRT.5 Use congruence and similarity criteria for triangles to solve problems and to prove relationships in geometric figures.

NEXT

G.GPE.5 Prove the slope criteria for parallel and perpendicular lines and use them to solve geometric problems (e.g., find the equation of a line parallel or perpendicular to a given line that passes through a given point).

Go Online! All of these resources and more are available at connectED.mcgraw-hill.com

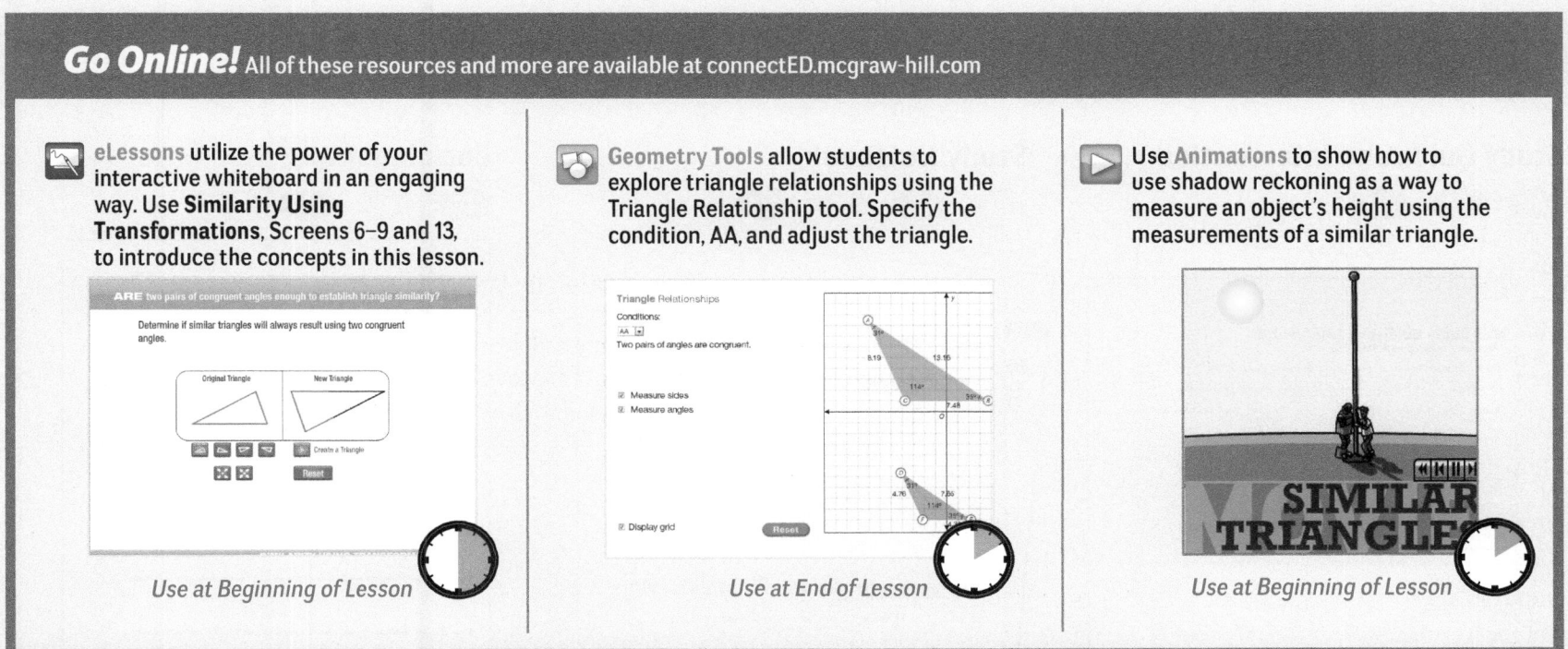

eLessons utilize the power of your interactive whiteboard in an engaging way. Use **Similarity Using Transformations**, Screens 6–9 and 13, to introduce the concepts in this lesson.

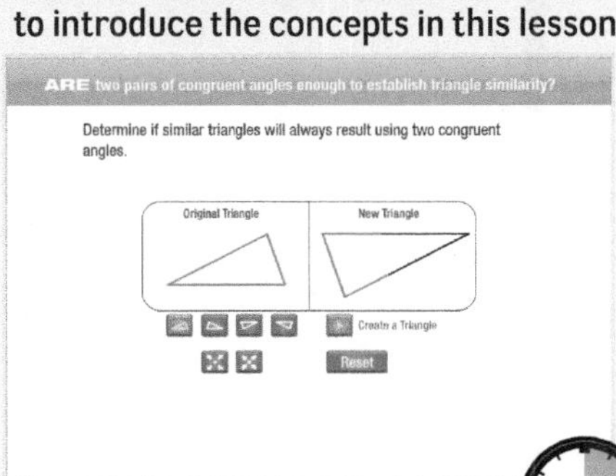

Use at Beginning of Lesson

Geometry Tools allow students to explore triangle relationships using the Triangle Relationship tool. Specify the condition, AA, and adjust the triangle.

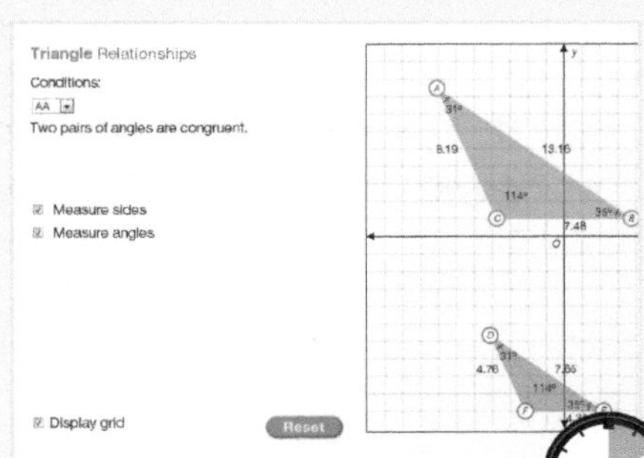

Use at End of Lesson

Use **Animations** to show how to use shadow reckoning as a way to measure an object's height using the measurements of a similar triangle.

Use at Beginning of Lesson

OER Using Open Educational Resources

Submitting Assignments Communicate with students and parents using **DropBox**. Dropbox is a free cloud service that allows you to set up a folder for each student. *Use as organization tool*

Go Online!

connectED.mcgraw-hill.com

Worksheets

Differentiate Your Resources

Extra Practice Additional practice or homework; Skills Practice is best for approaching-level students and Practice is best for on-level and beyond-level students

Skills Practice

AL OL ELL

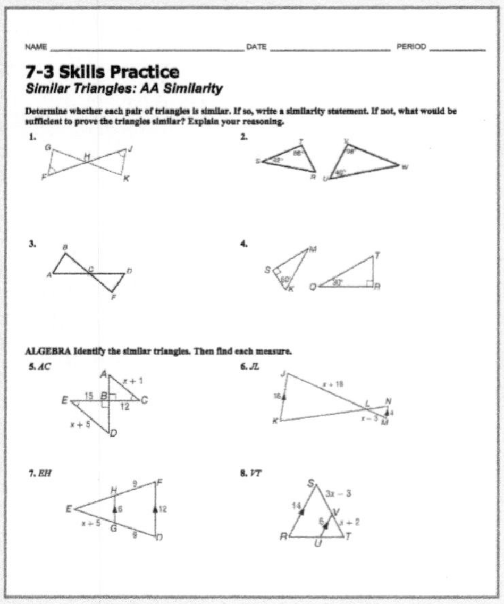

Practice

AL OL BL ELL

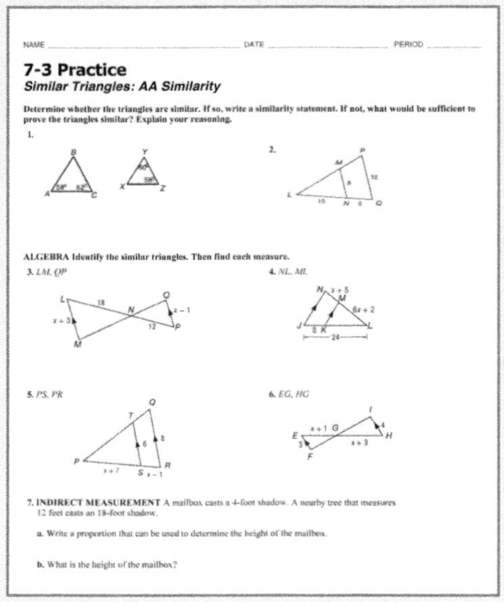

Word Problem Practice

AL OL BL ELL

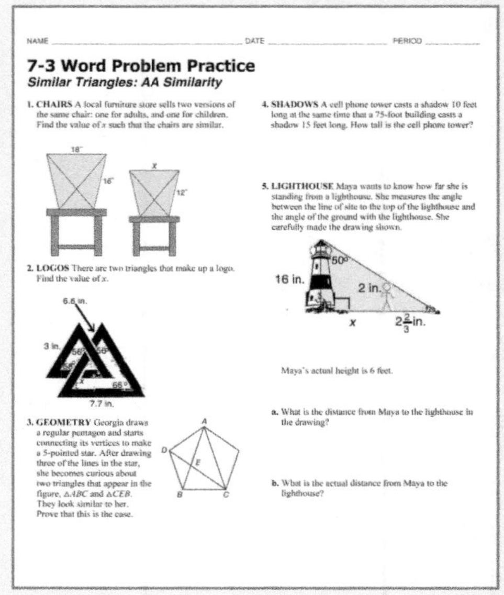

Intervention Reteaching and vocabulary activities that can be used with struggling or absent students and as ELL support

Study Guide and Intervention

AL OL ELL

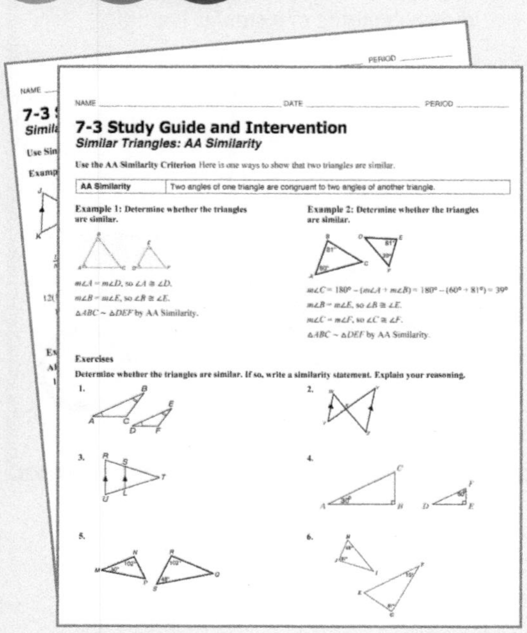

Study Notebook

AL OL BL ELL

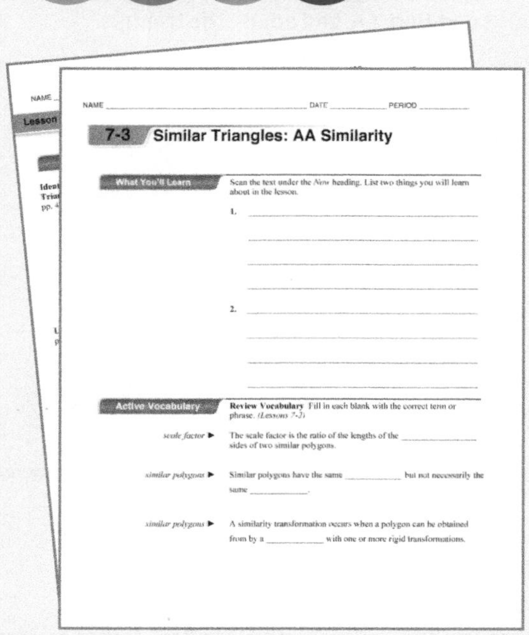

Extension Activities that can be used to extend lesson concepts

Enrichment

OL BL ELL

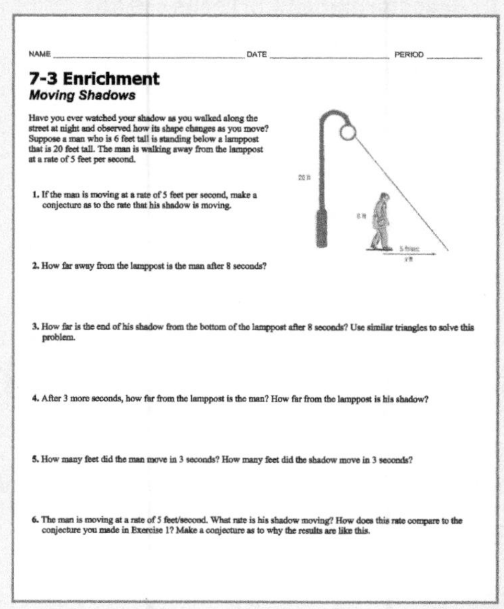

LESSON 3

Similar Triangles: AA Similarity

Then

- You used the properties of similarity to compare polygons.

Now

1. Use the AA similarity criterion to prove triangles similar.
2. Solve problems by using the properties of similar triangles.

Why?

- Julian wants to draw a similar version of his lacrosse club's logo on a poster. He first draws a line at the bottom of the poster. Next, he uses a cutout of the original triangle to copy the two bottom angles. Finally, he extends the non-common sides of the two angles.

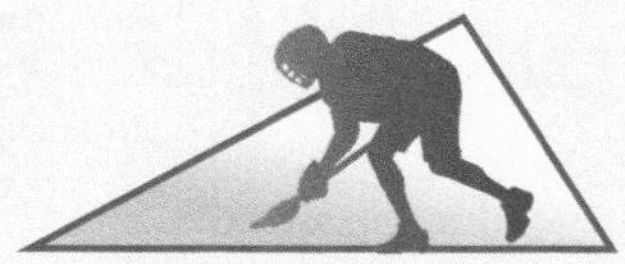

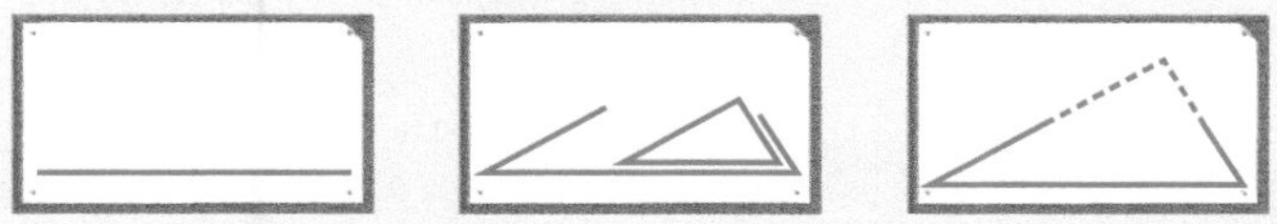

New Vocabulary
similar triangles

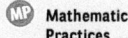

Mathematical Practices
3 Construct viable arguments and critique the reasoning of others.
4 Model with mathematics.

Content Standards
G.SRT.2 Given two figures, use the definition of similarity transformations to decide if they are similar; explain using similarity transformations the meaning of similarity for triangles as the equality of all corresponding pairs of angles and the proportionality of all corresponding pairs of sides.
G.SRT.3 Use the properties of similarity transformations to establish the AA criterion for two triangles to be similar.
G.SRT.5 Use congruence and similarity criteria for triangles to solve problems and to prove relationships in geometric figures.

1 Use the AA Similarity Criterion

Two triangles are **similar triangles** if there exists a composition of similarity transformations and rigid transformations that maps one triangle onto the other triangle. You can prove that two triangles are similar by showing that all corresponding angles are congruent and all corresponding sides are proportional. There are also shortcuts to proving triangle similarity.

Consider $\triangle ABC$ and $\triangle DEF$ in which $\angle A \cong \angle D$ and $\angle B \cong \angle E$. To prove that the triangles are similar, we must show that there is a similarity transformation or a combination of a similarity transformation and one or more rigid transformations that maps one triangle onto the other.

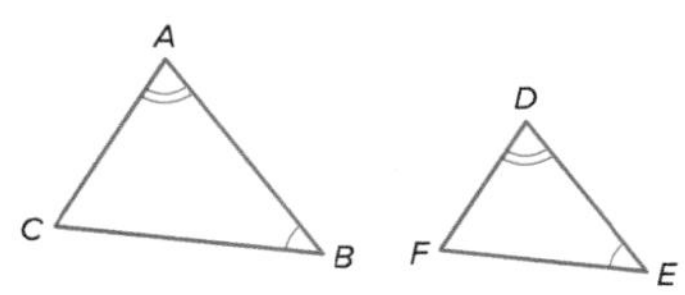

The Third Angles Theorem allows us to conclude that $\angle C \cong \angle F$.

To analyze the sides of the triangles, translate $\triangle DEF$ so that $\angle E'$ coincides with $\angle B$.

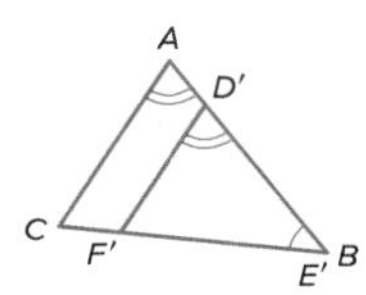

Dilations preserve angle measures, so $\angle D \cong \angle D'$, $\angle E \cong \angle E'$, and $\angle F \cong \angle F'$. By substitution, $\angle A \cong \angle D'$, $\angle B \cong \angle E'$, and $\angle C \cong \angle F'$. Notice that because $\angle B \cong \angle E'$, D' lies on $\overline{AB}$ and F' lies on $\overline{CE}$. Suppose we perform a dilation of $\triangle D'E'F'$ with respect to the center B. We would like to move D' to A. The scale factor which will accomplish this is $\frac{AB}{D'B}$.

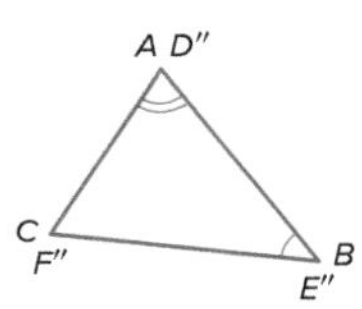

Launch

Have students read the Why? section of the lesson. Ask:

- **How do the angles of the two triangles compare?** They are congruent.
- **Is the new triangle congruent to the original one?** No, the side lengths are not the same.
- **Julian copied two angles from the original triangle. Is the third angle the same in each triangle? Why?** Yes, because the sum of the angle measures is 180.

Mathematical Practices Strategies

Construct viable arguments and critique the reasoning of others.
Help students develop an understanding of the definition of similarity transformations so they can explain the meaning of similarity. For example, ask:

- **How does a dilation affect a figure and how does that differ from other transformations?** Rotations, reflections, and translations do not alter the size of a figure. Dilations can increase or decrease the size of the figure.
- **Explain whether all similarity transformations lead to congruent figures.** A dilation can change the size of a figure, so the image would not be congruent to the preimage.
- **Why are corresponding sides important?** To prove that figures are similar, you must show that corresponding sides are proportional.

Go Online!

Interactive Whiteboard
Use the *eLesson*, *Lesson Presentation*, or *Interactive Classroom* to present this lesson.

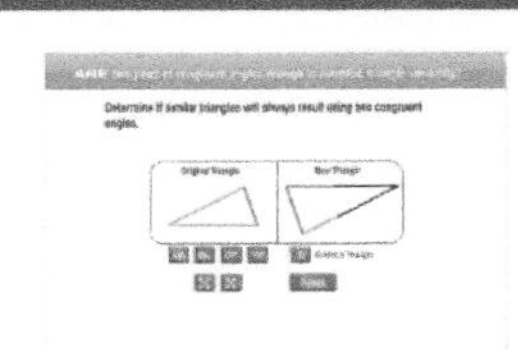

Teach

Ask the scaffolded questions for each example to build conceptual understanding for students at all levels.

1 Use the AA Similarity Criterion

Example 1 Use the AA Similarity Postulate

AL **In part b, how do we know that $\angle R \cong \angle W$?** If two parallel lines are cut by a transversal, then opposite interior angles are congruent.

OL **In part b, is there another way to show that $\triangle LJK \sim \triangle MQP$? If so, explain.** Yes; we could also find $m\angle Q$ to show that they are similar.

BL **If we increase *RX* and decrease *WT*, will the triangles still be similar? Explain.** Yes; because we do not use the ratio of the sides to determine similarity, they would still be similar.

Need Another Example?

Determine whether the triangles are similar. If so, write a similarity statement. Explain your reasoning.

a.

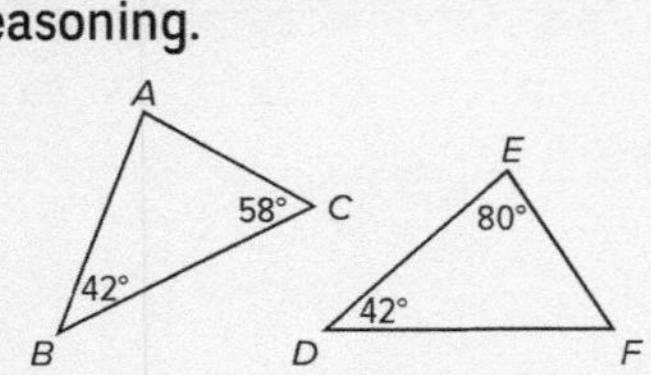

By the Triangle Sum Theorem, $m\angle A = 80$. Because $\angle A \cong \angle E$ and $\angle B \cong \angle D$, $\triangle ABC \sim \triangle EDF$ by AA Similarity.

b.

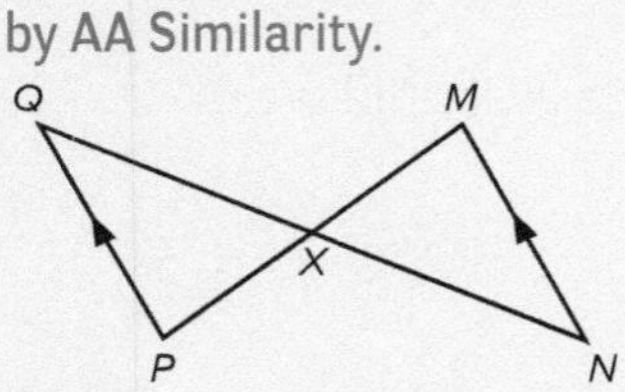

By the Vertical Angles Theorem, $\angle QXP \cong \angle NXM$, and because $\overline{PQ} \parallel \overline{MN}$, $\angle Q \cong \angle N$. Therefore, $\triangle QXP \sim \triangle NXM$ by AA Similarity.

Go Online!

How do you know whether two triangles are similar? Investigate by using the Geometry Tools in ConnectED. ELL

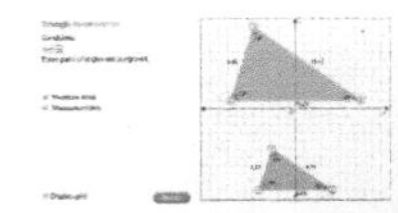

To check that *F* maps to *C*, recall that $\angle A \cong \angle D$. Angles are preserved by dilations and so this means that $\overline{D'F'}$ must map to $\overline{AC}$. This is proved by contradiction. If the dilation mapped *F′* to a point other than *C*, then there would be segments from *A* to two different points on $\overleftrightarrow{BC}$ that form the same angle with $\overline{AB}$. This is not possible, so $\overline{D'F'}$ must map to $\overline{AC}$.

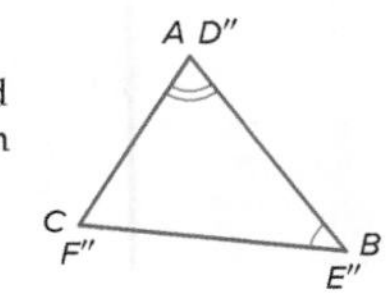

Because we have found a combination of a similarity transformation and a rigid transformation that maps $\triangle DEF$ onto $\triangle ABC$, the two triangles are similar.

This demonstrates the Angle-Angle Similarity Postulate.

Postulate 7.1 Angle-Angle (AA) Similarity

If two angles of one triangle are congruent to two angles of another triangle, then the triangles are similar.

Example If $\angle A \cong \angle F$ and $\angle B \cong \angle G$, then $\triangle ABC \sim \triangle FGH$.

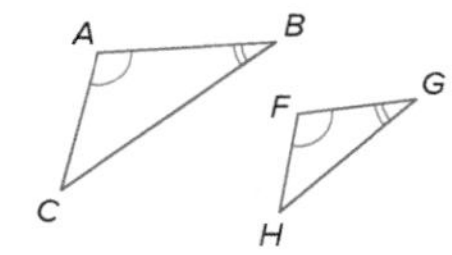

You can use Angle-Angle Similarity to determine that two triangles are similar. To determine which angles of two triangles correspond, begin by comparing the angles with the greatest measures, then the angles with the next greatest measures, and finish by comparing the angles with the least measures.

G.SRT.2

Example 1 Use the AA Similarity Postulate

Determine whether the triangles are similar. If so, write a similarity statement. Explain your reasoning.

a.

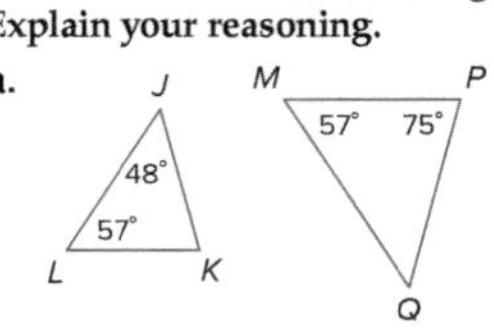

Since $m\angle L = m\angle M$, $\angle L \cong \angle M$. By the Triangle Sum Theorem, $57 + 48 + m\angle K = 180$, so $m\angle K = 75$. Since $m\angle P = 75$, $\angle K \cong \angle P$. So, $\triangle LJK \sim \triangle MQP$ by AA Similarity.

b.

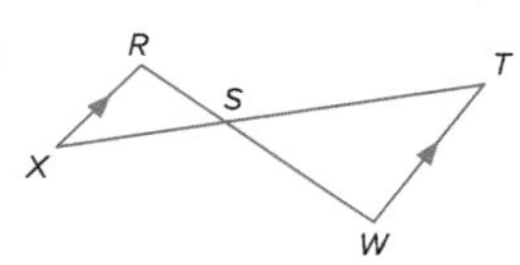

$\angle RSX \cong \angle WST$ by the Vertical Angles Theorem. Since $\overline{RX} \parallel \overline{TW}$, $\angle R \cong \angle W$. So, $\triangle RSX \sim \triangle WST$ by AA Similarity.

Study Tip
MP Sense-Making It is helpful to redraw similar triangles so that the corresponding side lengths have the same orientation.

1A. Yes. Using the Triangle Sum Theorem, you find that the missing angle for $\triangle ABC$ is 66°. These triangles are similar by AA Similarity Theorem.

1B. No. The triangles do not have two pairs of congruent angles.

c.

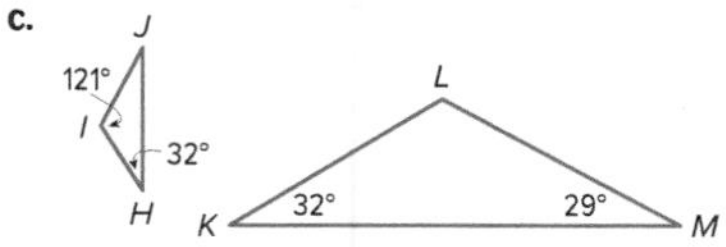

$180° - (121° + 32°) = 27°$

Two angles not are congruent.

So, $\triangle HIJ \nsim \triangle KLM$.

d.

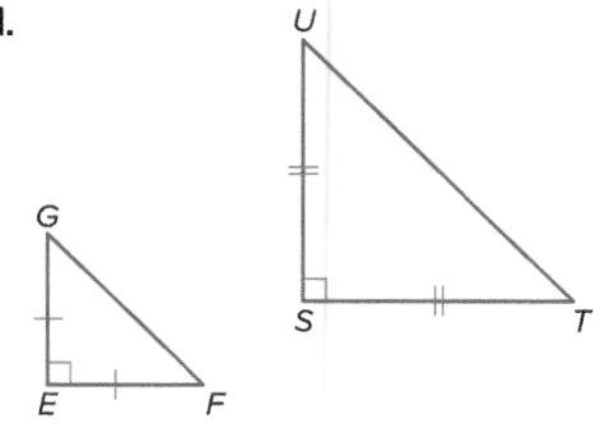

By the Isosceles Triangle Theorem, $\angle F \cong \angle G$.

$\frac{180° - 90°}{2} = 45°$.

Because both of these triangles are Isosceles Right triangles, we know that the unknown angles are 45°. Two pairs of angles are congruent. $\triangle EFG \sim \triangle STU$ by the AA Similarity Theorem.

1A.

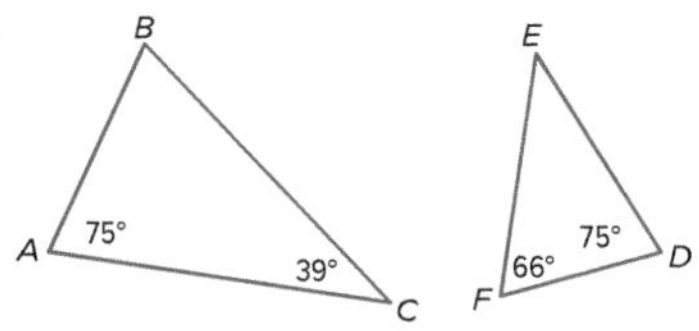

1B.

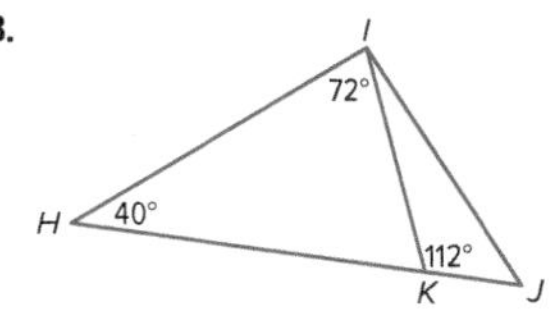

You can decide whether the information you have is sufficient to prove that two triangles are similar.

Study Tip
Identifying Nonexamples Sometimes test questions require you to find a nonexample, as in this case. You must check each option until you find a valid nonexample. If you would like to check your answer, confirm that each additional option is correct.

G.SRT2

Example 2 Identify Sufficient Conditions

In the figure, $\angle LNM$ is a right angle. Which of the following would not be sufficient to prove that $\triangle LNM \sim \triangle MNO$?

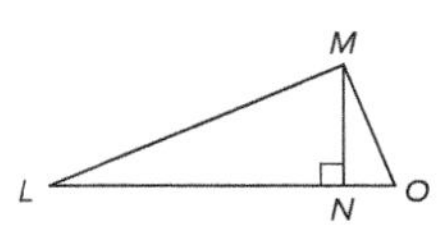

A $\angle LMN \cong \angle MON$

B $\angle LNM \cong \angle MNO$

C $m\angle MLN = 28°$ and $m\angle OMN = 28°$

D $m\angle LMN = 52°$ and $m\angle MON = 52°$

$\angle LNM$ and $\angle MNO$ form a straight angle, and $\angle LNM$ is a right angle, so $\angle MNO$ is a also a right angle. All right angles are congruent, so $\angle LNM \cong \angle MNO$. Check each answer choice until you find one that does not supply a sufficient additional condition to prove that $\triangle LNM \sim \triangle MNO$.

Choices A, C, and D: You only need to identify one more pair of congruent angles to use AA. Each of these choices has at least one more congruent pair of angles.

Choice B: This choice restates the pair of right angles you know are congruent. It does not give sufficient information to prove the triangles are similar.

Differentiated Instruction AL OL BL ELL

Interpersonal Learners Give students identical triangles. Have students choose a partner. Ask each pair of students to create geometric art using similarity transformation sequences. Write the steps and give them to other students to see if they can recreate the art by following the sequence of transformations and similar triangles.

Example 2 Sufficient Conditions

AL If you only know the lengths of the sides of two triangles, can you prove similarity using AA? Explain. Sample answer: No, you need to be able to find two pairs of congruent angles.

OL Why is the given information not sufficient to prove that the triangles are congruent? We can conclude that one pair of corresponding angles are congruent, but two are needed to prove the triangles are congruent by AA Similarity.

BL Would knowing that the vertex angles of two isosceles triangles are congruent be sufficient to prove that the triangles are similar by using the AA Similarity Postulate? Explain. Yes; suppose that the vertex angles measure $x°$. Then the base angles in both triangles would each measure $\left(\frac{(180° - x)}{2}\right)^{\circ}$. Thus the base angles are congruent and the triangles are similar.

Need Another Example?

$\triangle QRS$ and $\triangle WXY$ are isosceles triangles. Which of the following is an incorrect statement? Which of the following would not be sufficient to prove that $\triangle QRS \sim \triangle WXY$? B

A $\triangle QRS \cong \triangle WXY$

B $\angle QRS \cong \angle WXY$

C $\angle QRS$ and $\angle WXY$ are the vertex angles and $\angle QRS \cong \angle WXY$.

D $\angle QRS$ and $\angle WXY$ are base angles and $\angle QRS \cong \angle WXY$.

Watch Out!

Angles The AA Similarity Postulate is a simple way to prove Triangle Similarity, but you still have to be careful and check your work. Finding all three angles is a good way to check your work.

2 Use Similar Triangles

Example 3 Parts of Similar Triangles

AL **How can we check our solutions?** Sample answer: Substitute *BE* and *AD* into the appropriate proportions and make sure the proportions are true.

OL **If *A* is moved so that *AC* and *AD* are longer but *CD* remains the same, would the triangles still be similar? Explain.** Yes; AA Similarity would still apply.

BL **If two triangles with parallel bases share a common vertex, do you think the triangles will always be similar?** Sample answer: No; a common vertex and parallel bases is not a criteria for similarity. You cannot assume that the angles with the common vertex are vertical angles.

Need Another Example?

Algebra Given $\overline{RS} \parallel \overline{UT}$, $RS = 4$, $RQ = x + 3$, $QT = 2x + 10$, $UT = 10$. Find *RQ* and *QT*. 8; 20

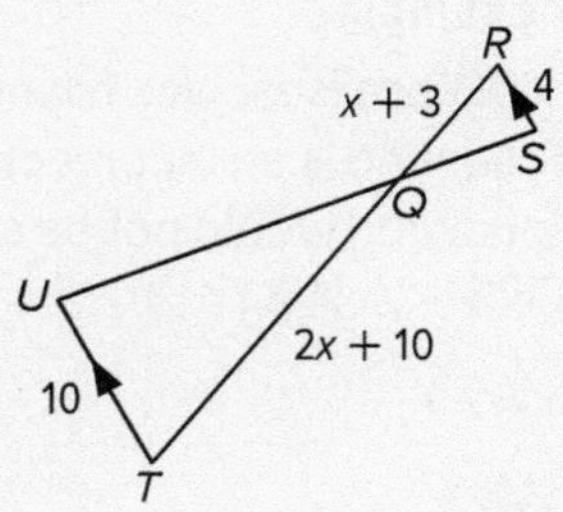

Guided Practice

2. If $\triangle JKL$ and $\triangle FGH$ are two triangles such that $\angle J \cong \angle F$, which of the following would be sufficient information to prove that the triangles are congruent? H

F $\angle G \cong \angle F$ **G** $\angle G \cong \angle L$ **H** $\angle G \cong \angle K$ **J** $\angle G \cong \angle F$

2 Use Similar Triangles Like the congruence of triangles, similarity of triangles is reflexive, symmetric, and transitive.

Theorem 7.2 Properties of Similarity

Reflexive Property of Similarity	$\triangle ABC \sim \triangle ABC$
Symmetric Property of Similarity	If $\triangle ABC \sim \triangle DEF$, then $\triangle DEF \sim \triangle ABC$.
Transitive Property of Similarity	If $\triangle ABC \sim \triangle DEF$, and $\triangle DEF \sim \triangle XYZ$, then $\triangle ABC \sim \triangle XYZ$.

You will prove Theorem 7.2 in Exercise 25.

G.SRT.2

Example 3 Parts of Similar Triangles

Find *BE* and *AD*.

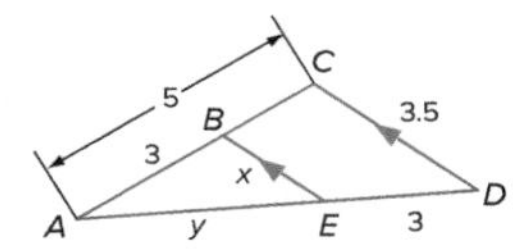

Since $\overline{BE} \parallel \overline{CD}$, $\angle ABE \cong \angle BCD$, and $\angle AEB \cong \angle EDC$ because they are corresponding angles. By AA Similarity, $\triangle ABE \sim \triangle ACD$.

$\frac{AB}{AC} = \frac{BE}{CD}$	Definition of Similar Polygons
$\frac{3}{5} = \frac{x}{3.5}$	$AC = 5$, $CD = 3.5$, $AB = 3$, $BE = x$
$3.5 \cdot 3 = 5 \cdot x$	Cross Products Property
$2.1 = x$	

BE is 2.1.

$\frac{AC}{AB} = \frac{AD}{AE}$	Definition of Similar Polygons
$\frac{5}{3} = \frac{y+3}{y}$	$AC = 5$, $AB = 3$, $AD = y + 3$, $AE = y$
$5 \cdot y = 3(y + 3)$	Cross Products Property
$5y = 3y + 9$	Distributive Property
$2y = 9$	Subtract 3*y* from each side.
$y = 4.5$	*AD* is $y + 3$ or 7.5.

Study Tip

Proportions An additional proportion that is true for Example 3 is $\frac{AC}{CD} = \frac{AB}{BE}$.

Guided Practice

Find each measure.

3A. *QP* and *MP* 3; 8

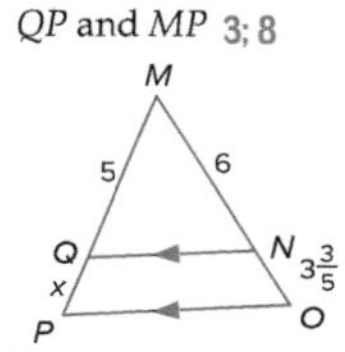

3B. *WR* and *RT* 8; 10

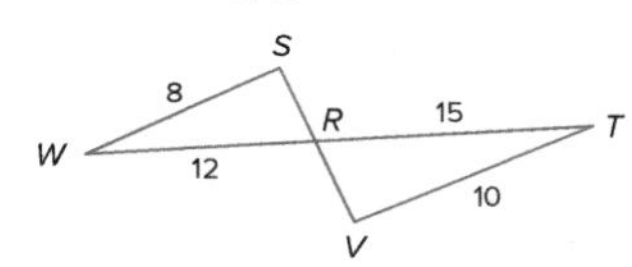

When you can represent real-world situations with similar triangles, you can use proportions and the properties of the triangles to find measurements. This is called indirect measurement.

Real-World Example 4 Indirect Measurement

ROLLER COASTERS Hallie is estimating the height of the Superman roller coaster in Mitchellville, Maryland. She is 5 feet 3 inches tall and her shadow is 3 feet long. If the length of the shadow of the roller coaster is 40 feet, how tall is the roller coaster?

Understand Make a sketch of the situation. Hallie's height of 5 feet 3 inches is equivalent to 5.25 feet.

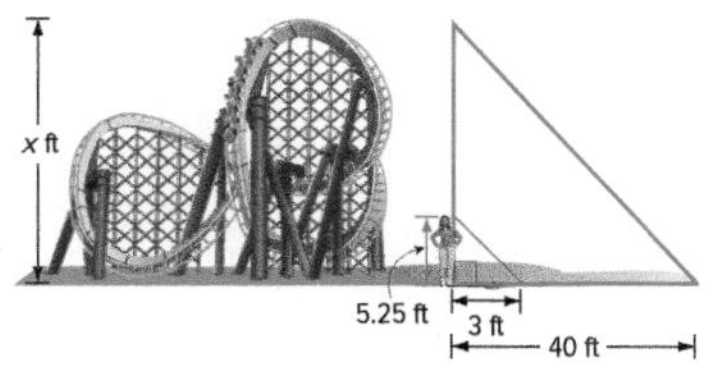

Plan In shadow problems, you can assume that the angles formed by the Sun's rays with any two objects are congruent and that the two objects form the sides of two right triangles.

Because two pairs of angles are congruent, the right triangles are similar by the AA Similarity Postulate. Write a proportion.

$$\frac{\text{Hallie's height}}{\text{coaster's height}} = \frac{\text{Hallie's shadow length}}{\text{coaster's shadow length}}$$

Solve Using the proportion, substitute the known values and let x represent roller coaster's height.

$\frac{5.25}{x} = \frac{3}{40}$	Substitution
$3 \cdot x = 40(5.25)$	Cross Products Property
$3x = 210$	Simplify.
$x = 70$	Divide each side by 3.

The roller coaster is 70 feet tall.

Check The roller coaster's shadow length is $\frac{40 \text{ ft}}{3 \text{ ft}}$ or about 13.3 times Hallie's shadow length. Check to see that the roller coaster's height is about 13.3 times Hallie's height. $\frac{70 \text{ ft}}{5.25 \text{ ft}} \approx 13.3$ ✓

Problem-Solving Tip

Reasonable Answers When you have solved a problem, check your answer for reasonableness. In this example, Hallie's shadow is a little more than half her height. The coaster's shadow is also a little more than half of the height. Therefore, the answer is reasonable.

Guided Practice

4. **BUILDINGS** Adam is standing next to the Palmetto Building in Columbia, South Carolina. He is 6 feet tall and the length of his shadow is 9 feet. If the length of the shadow of the building is 322.5 feet, how tall is the building? 215 ft

Example 4 Indirect Measurement

AL How do we know that this measurement is an approximation? Sample answer: It would not be possible to measure the exact length of the shadows, so the measurement is an approximation.

OL If the length of the shadow were 34 feet, about how tall would the roller coaster be? 59.5 ft

BL Why does indirect measurement make sense in a situation like this one? Sample answer: It would not be possible to measure the height of a roller coaster with a measuring device like a tape measure, so it is necessary to find a way to estimate the height.

Need Another Example?

Skyscrapers Josh wanted to measure the height of the Willis Tower in Chicago. He used a 12-foot light pole and measured its shadow at 1:00 P.M. The length of the shadow was 2 feet. Then he measured the length of Willis Tower's shadow and it was 242 feet at the same time. What is the height of the Willis Tower?

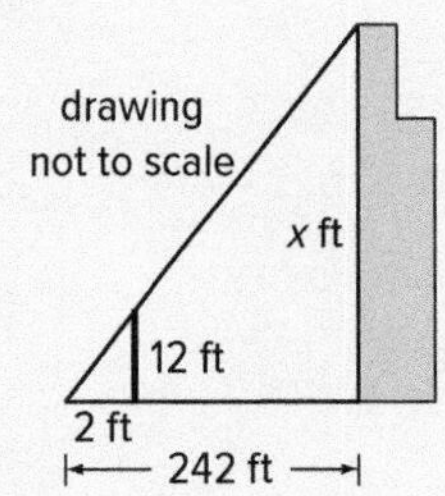

1452 ft (actual height: 1450 feet)

Practice

Formative Assessment Use Exercises 1–8 to assess students' understanding of the concepts in this lesson.

Practice and Problem Solving exercises assess the content taught in the lesson. The Preparing for Assessment page is meant to be used as preparation for end-of-course assessments.

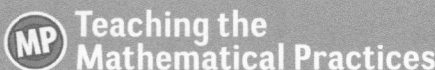

MP Teaching the Mathematical Practices

Structure Mathematically proficient students look closely to discern a pattern or structure. They also can step back for an overview and shift perspective. In Exercises 6–7, it may be helpful to some students to draw the similar triangles in the same orientation.

Extra Practice

See page R7 for extra exercises for students who are approaching level or for on-level students who need additional reinforcement.

Additional Answer

10. No; $\overline{BC}$ needs to be parallel to $\overline{DF}$ for $\triangle DAF \sim \triangle BAC$ by AA Similarity.

Check Your Understanding

◯ = Step-by-Step Solutions begin on page R13.

Go Online! for a Self-Check Quiz

Examples 1 G.SRT.2, G.SRT.5

Determine whether the triangles are similar, using the AA Similarity Theorem. If so, write a similarity statement.

1. 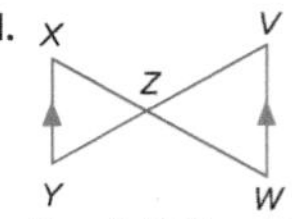

Yes; $\triangle YXZ \sim \triangle VWZ$ by AA Similarity.

2. 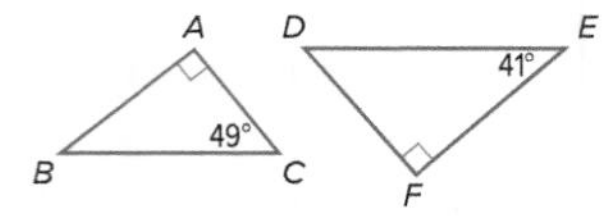

Yes; $\triangle ABC \sim \triangle FED$ by AA Similarity.

3. 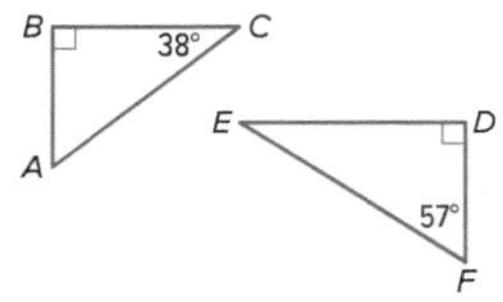

3. No; the angles are not congruent.

4. 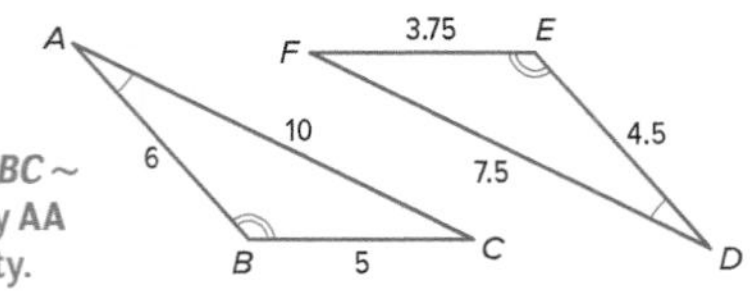

Yes; $\triangle ABC \sim \triangle FED$ by AA Similarity.

Example 2 G.SRT.2

5. **MULTIPLE CHOICE** In the figure, $\overline{AB}$ intersects $\overline{DE}$ at point *C*. Which additional information would be enough to prove that $\triangle ADC \sim \triangle BEC$? **C**

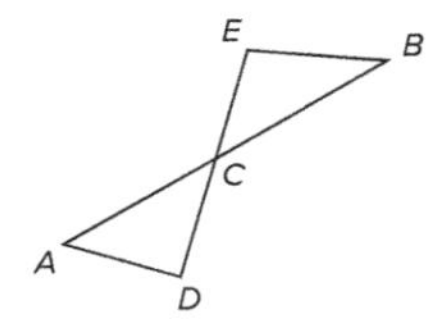

A $\angle DAC$ and $\angle ECB$ are congruent.

B $\overline{AC}$ and $\overline{BC}$ are congruent.

C $\overline{AD}$ and $\overline{EB}$ are parallel.

D $\angle CBE$ is a right angle.

Example 3 G.SRT.2

MP STRUCTURE Identify the similar triangles. Find each measure.

6. *XZ* $\triangle XYZ \sim \triangle JKL$; 6.25

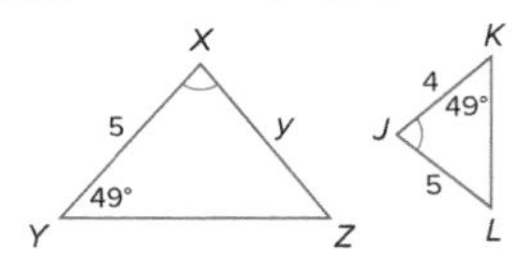

7. *VS* $\triangle QVS \sim \triangle RTS$; 20

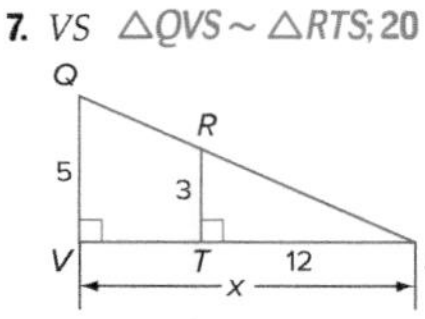

9. Yes; $\triangle ACE \sim \triangle BCD$ by AA Similarity.
10. See margin.
11. Yes; $\triangle TUV \sim \triangle VXW$ by AA Similarity.

Example 4 G.SRT.2

8. **COMMUNICATION** A cell phone tower casts a 100-foot shadow. At the same time, a 4-foot, 6-inch post near the tower casts a shadow of 3 feet 4 inches. Find the height of the tower. **135 ft**

Practice and Problem Solving

Extra Practice is on page R7.

Examples 1, 2 G.SRT.2, G.SRT.5

Determine whether the triangles are similar. If so, write a similarity statement. Explain your reasoning.

9. $\triangle ACE$, $\triangle BCD$

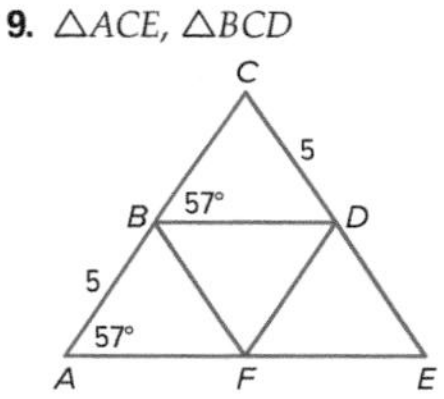

10. 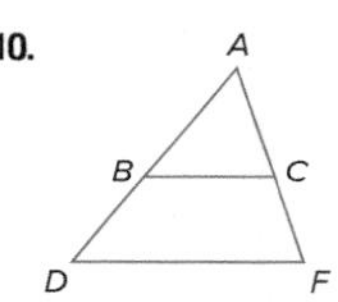

11. 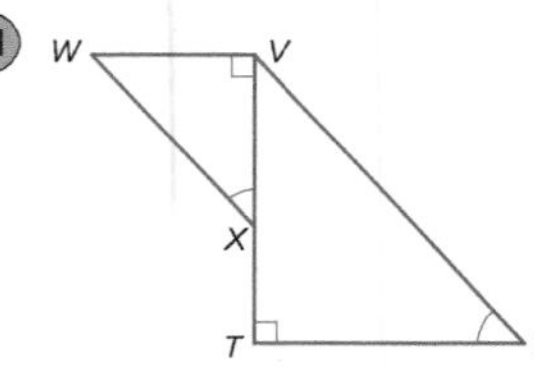

Differentiated Homework Options

Levels	AL Basic	OL Core	BL Advanced
Exercises	9–24, 37, 39–44	9–21 odd, 22–25, 27, 29, 31–33, 35, 37, 39–44	33–39 (Optional: 34–44)
2-Day Option	9–23 odd, 40–44	9–24, 40–44	
	10–24 even, 37, 39	25–37, 39–40	

You can use ALEKS to provide additional remediation support with personalized instruction and practice.

Examples 1–3 G.SRT.2, G.SRT.5 **Determine whether the triangles are similar. If so, write a similarity statement. Explain your reasoning.**

12. Yes; $\triangle MLJ \sim \triangle PKJ$ by AA Similarity.
13–14. See margin.

12.

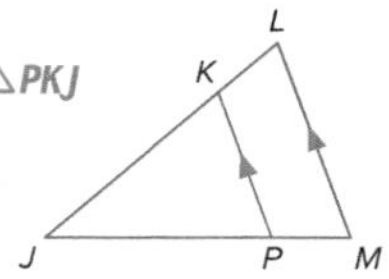

13.

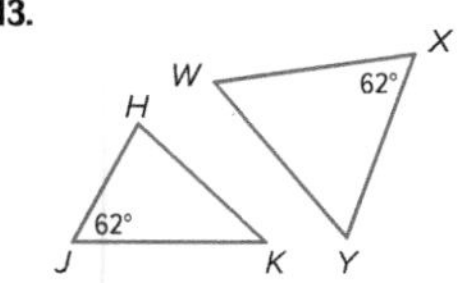

14.

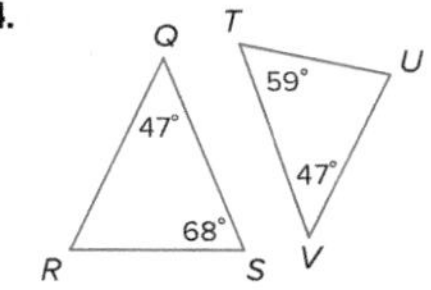

15. MP **MODELING** Scientists are studying eyes and how light is refracted by the lens of the eyes to create two similar triangles. Prove that the triangles are similar using similarity transformations and the relationship between the angles and sides of the triangles.

15. Reflect or rotate one triangle about the shared vertex *B*, then dilate one triangle to show the triangles are similar.

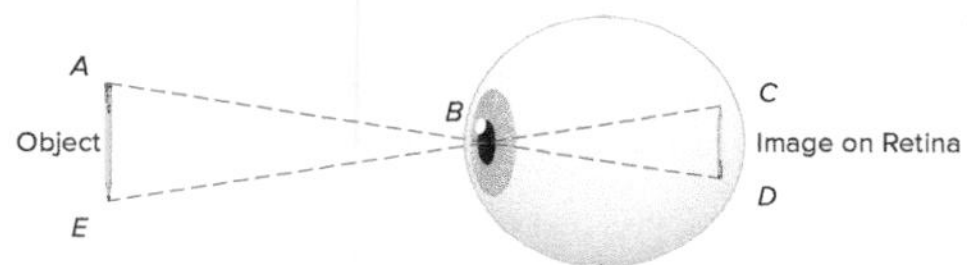

Example 4 G.SRT.2 **ALGEBRA Identify the similar triangles. Then find each measure.**

16. *EG* $\triangle DEC \sim \triangle GEF$; 4

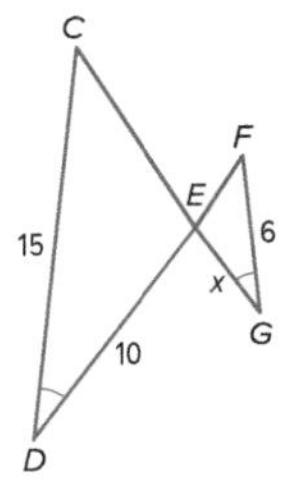

17. *ST* $\triangle QRS \sim \triangle QPT$; 5

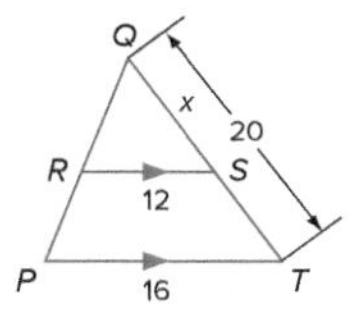

18. *WZ*, *UZ* $\triangle WUZ \sim \triangle YUW$; 30, 18

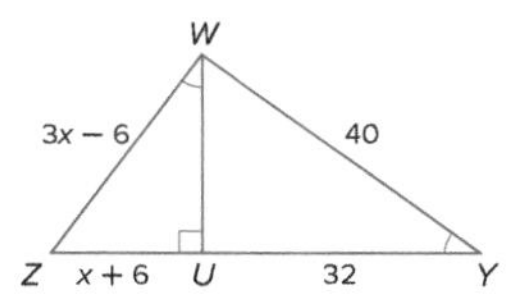

19. *HJ*, *HK* $\triangle HJK \sim \triangle NQP$; 15, 10

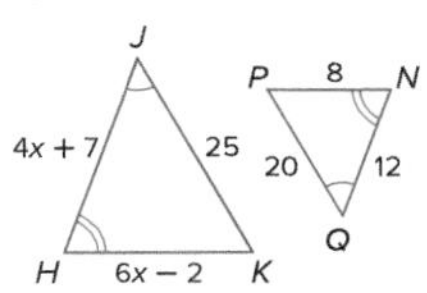

20. *EB* $\triangle ABE \sim \triangle DCE$; 6

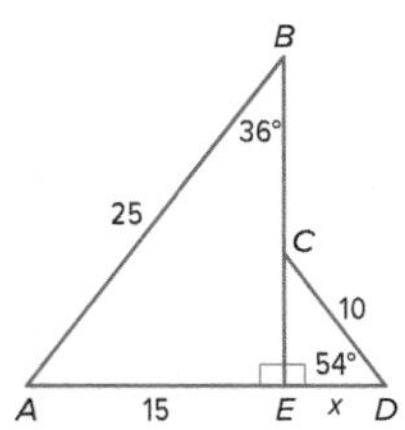

21. *GD*, *DH* $\triangle GHJ \sim \triangle GDH$; 14, 20

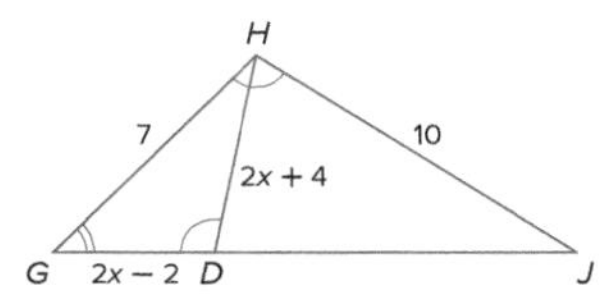

Example 5 G.SRT.2

22. **STATUES** Mei is standing next to a statue in the park. If Mei is 5 feet tall, her shadow is 3 feet long, and the statue's shadow is $10\frac{1}{2}$ feet long, how tall is the statue? $17\frac{1}{2}$ ft

23. **SPORTS** When Alonzo, who is 5′11″ tall, stands next to a basketball goal, his shadow is 2′ long, and the basketball goal's shadow is 4′4″ long. About how tall is the basketball goal? 12.8 ft

24. **BIRDWATCHING** Taylor sees the nest of a rare bird near the top of a tree. He wants to report its position to the local conservation group. Taylor is 6 feet tall and casts a 3.5-foot shadow. The tree with the nest casts a shadow 6 feet long. About how far above the ground is the nest? about 10.3 feet

B **25.** **PROOF** Write a two-column proof for each part of Theorem 7.2. See margin.

Teaching the Mathematical Practices

Modeling Mathematically proficient students can apply the mathematics they know to solve problems arising in everyday life. In Exercises 15 and 30, encourage students to use the five-step problem solving plan.

Levels of Complexity Chart

The levels of the exercises progress from 1 to 3, with Level 1 indicating the lowest level of complexity.

Exercises	9–24	25–32, 40–44	33–39
C Level 3			●
B Level 2		●	
Level 1	●		

Additional Answers

13. No; not enough information is given to determine that the triangles are similar.

14. No; the angles of the triangles are not congruent, so the triangles are not similar.

25.

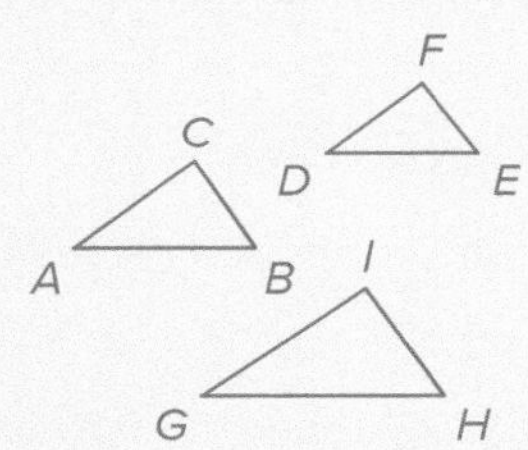

Reflexive Property of Similarity

Given: $\triangle ABC$

Prove: $\triangle ABC \sim \triangle ABC$

Proof: Statements (Reasons)

1. $\triangle ABC$ (Given)
2. $\angle A \cong \angle A$, $\angle B \cong \angle B$ (Refl. Prop.)
3. $\triangle ABC \sim \triangle ABC$ (AA Similarity)

Symmetric Property of Similarity

Given: $\triangle ABC \sim \triangle DEF$

Prove: $\triangle DEF \sim \triangle ABC$

Proof: Statements (Reasons)

1. $\triangle ABC \sim \triangle DEF$ (Given)
2. $\angle A \cong \angle D$, $\angle B \cong \angle E$ (Def. of ~ polygons)
3. $\angle D \cong \angle A$, $\angle E \cong \angle B$ (Symm. Prop.)
4. $\triangle DEF \sim \triangle ABC$ (AA Similarity)

Transitive Property of Similarity

Given: $\triangle ABC \sim \triangle DEF$ and $\triangle DEF \sim \triangle GHI$

Prove: $\triangle ABC \sim \triangle GHI$

Proof: Statements (Reasons)

1. $\triangle ABC \sim \triangle DEF$, $\triangle DEF \sim \triangle GHI$ (Given)
2. $\angle A \cong \angle D$, $\angle B \cong \angle E$, $\angle D \cong \angle G$, $\angle E \cong \angle H$ (Def. of ~ polygons)
3. $\angle A \cong \angle G$, $\angle B \cong \angle H$ (Trans. Prop.)
4. $\triangle ABC \sim \triangle GHI$ (AA Similarity)

Go Online! eBook

Interactive Student Guide
Use the *Interactive Student Guide* to deepen conceptual understanding.
· Similar Triangles

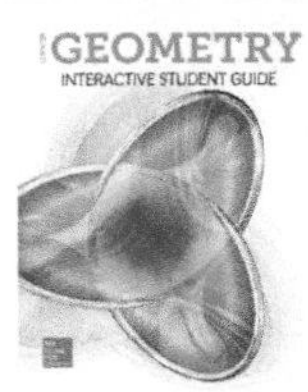

Additional Answers

26. Proof:

Statements (Reasons)

1. $ABCD$ is a trapezoid. (Given)
2. $\overline{AB} \parallel \overline{DC}$ (Def. of trap.)
3. $\angle BDC \cong \angle ABD$, $\angle BAC \cong \angle DCA$ (Alt. Int. ∠ Thm.)
4. $\triangle DCP \sim \triangle BAP$ (AA Similarity)
5. $\frac{DP}{PB} = \frac{CP}{PA}$ (Corr. sides of ~ △s are proportional.)

27. Proof:

Statements (Reasons)

1. $\triangle XYZ$ and $\triangle ABC$ are right triangles. (Given)
2. $\angle XYZ$ and $\angle ABC$ are right angles. (Def. of rt. △)
3. $\angle XYZ \cong \angle ABC$ (All rt. ∠s are ≅.)
4. $\angle Z = \angle C$ (Given)
5. $\triangle YXZ \sim \triangle BAC$ (AA Similarity)

PROOF Write a two-column proof. 26–27. See margin.

26. **Given:** $ABCD$ is a trapezoid.
Prove: $\frac{DP}{PB} = \frac{CP}{PA}$

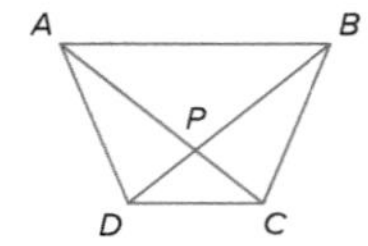

27. **Given:** $\triangle XYZ$ and $\triangle ABC$ are right triangles; $\angle Z = \angle C$.
Prove: $\triangle YXZ \sim \triangle BAC$

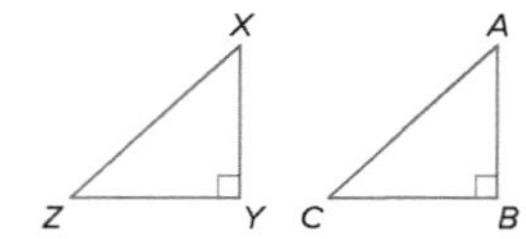

COORDINATE GEOMETRY $\triangle XYZ$ and $\triangle WYV$ have vertices $X(-1, -9)$, $Y(5, 3)$, $Z(-1, 6)$, $W(1, -5)$, and $V(1, 5)$.

28. Graph the triangles, and prove that $\triangle XYZ \sim \triangle WYV$. See Ch. 7 Answer Appendix.

29 Find the ratio of the perimeters of the two triangles. $\frac{3}{2}$

30. MP **MODELING** When Luis's dad threw a bounce pass to him, the angles formed by the basketball's path were congruent. The ball landed $\frac{2}{3}$ of the way between them before it bounced back up. If Luis's dad released the ball 40 inches above the floor, at what height did Luis catch the ball? 20 in.

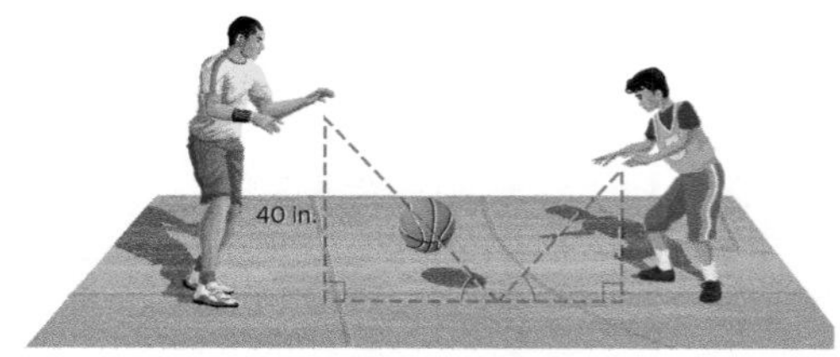

31. **BILLIARDS** When a ball is deflected off a smooth surface, the angles formed by the path are congruent. Booker hit the orange ball and it followed the path from A to B to C as shown below. What was the total distance traveled by the ball from the time Booker hit it until it came to rest at the end of the table? about 61 in.

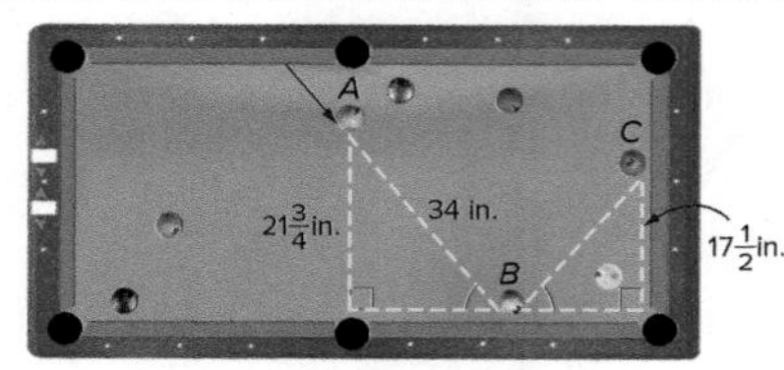

32. If possible, describe a similarity transformation or a combination of a similarity transformation and a rigid transformation that could be used to demonstrate that the triangles are similar.
$\frac{D'E'}{DE} = \frac{5.5}{2.2}$ or 2.5, $\frac{E'F'}{EF} = \frac{5}{2}$ or 2.5, and $\frac{D'F'}{DF} = \frac{2.5}{1}$ or 2.5, so a dilation with scale factor of 2.5 followed by a translation demonstrates that $\triangle DEF \sim \triangle D'E'F'$.

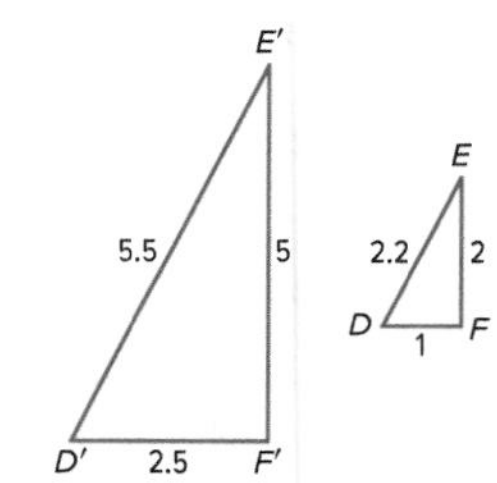

Additional Answers

35a. Sample answer:

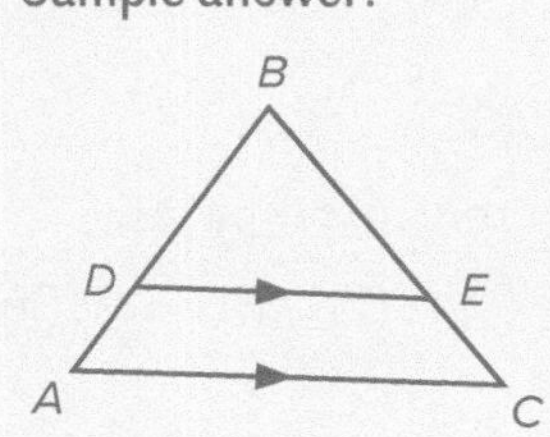

35b. Sample answer:

Lengths		Ratios	
AD	0.9 cm	$\frac{AD}{DB}$	$\frac{1}{2}$
DB	1.8 cm		
CE	1.1 cm	$\frac{CE}{EB}$	$\frac{1}{2}$
EB	2.2 cm		

33. CHANGING DIMENSIONS Assume that $\triangle ABC \sim \triangle JKL$.

a. If the lengths of the sides of $\triangle JKL$ are half the lengths of the corresponding sides of $\triangle ABC$, and the perimeter of $\triangle ABC$ is 40 inches, what is the perimeter of $\triangle JKL$? How is the perimeter related to the scale factor from $\triangle ABC$ to $\triangle JKL$? 20 in; The ratio of the perimeters is the scale factor.

b. If the lengths of the sides of $\triangle ABC$ are three times the lengths of the corresponding sides of $\triangle JKL$, and the perimeter of $\triangle ABC$ is 21 inches, what is the perimeter of $\triangle JKL$? How is the perimeter related to the scale factor from $\triangle ABC$ to $\triangle JKL$? 7 in; The ratio of the perimeters is the scale factor.

34. MEDICINE Certain medical treatments involve laser beams that contact and penetrate the skin. Refer to the diagram at the right.

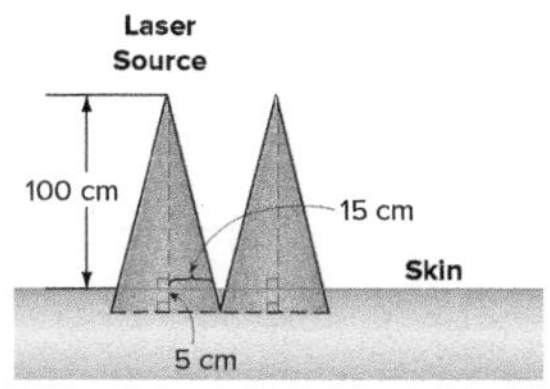

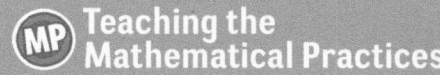

a. What needs to be true for the triangles formed by the edges of the laser beams and the surface of the skin to be similar to triangles formed by the edges of the laser beams and the treated area beneath the skin? The surface of the skin and the treated area beneath the skin are parallel.

b. What needs to be true for the triangles formed by the edges of the two laser beams and the surface of the skin to be similar to each other? The segment with endpoints at the sources is parallel to the surface of the skin.

c. If all of the triangles are similar, how far apart should the laser sources be placed to ensure that the areas treated by each source do not overlap or leave an area untreated? 31.5 cm

35. MULTIPLE REPRESENTATIONS In this problem, you will explore proportional parts of triangles.

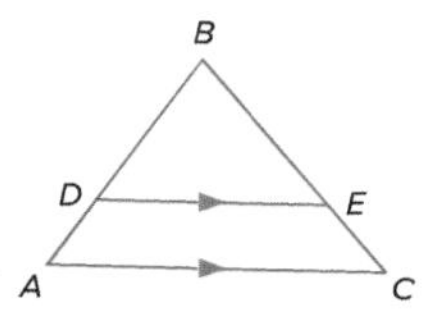

a. **Geometric** Draw $\triangle ABC$ with $\overline{DE}$ parallel to $\overline{AC}$ as shown at the right. See margin.

b. **Tabular** Measure and record the lengths AD, DB, CE, and EB and the ratios $\frac{AD}{DB}$ and $\frac{CE}{EB}$ in a table. See margin.

c. **Verbal** Make a conjecture about the segments created by a line parallel to one side of a triangle and intersecting the other two sides. Sample answer: The segments created by a line || to one side of a $\triangle$ and intersecting the other two sides are proportional.

G.SRT.2, G.SRT.3, G.SRT.5

H.O.T. Problems Use Higher-Order Thinking Skills

36. WRITING IN MATH Explain why the AA Postulate requires that only two pairs of corresponding angles rather than three are shown to be congruent in order to prove that two triangles are similar. See margin.

37. CHALLENGE $\overline{YW}$ is an altitude of $\triangle XYZ$. Can you prove that $\triangle WXY$ and $\triangle WYZ$ are similar triangles? Explain. See margin.

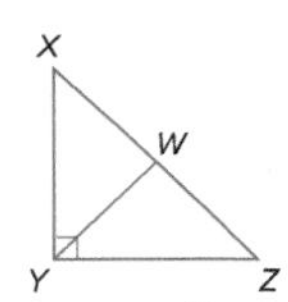

38. REASONING In a pair of similar triangles, the sides of one triangle measure 3, 3.25, and 4.75 4.5 units, The sides of the second triangle measure $x - 0.46$, x, and $x + 2.76$ units. Find the value of x. 5.98

39. OPEN-ENDED Draw a triangle that is similar to $\triangle ABC$ shown. Explain how you know your triangle is similar to $\triangle ABC$. See margin.

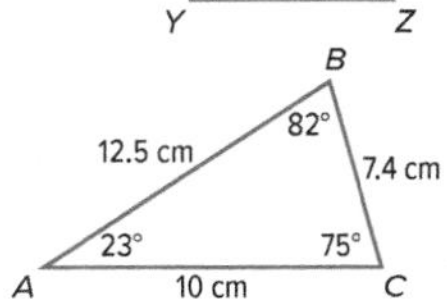

Additional Answers

36. Sample answer: The Third Angles Theorem ensures that if two pairs of corresponding angles in two triangles are congruent, then the third pair of angles is also congruent.

37. Yes; Because it is an altitude, $\overline{YW} \perp \overline{XZ}$. So $\angle XWY$ and $\angle ZWY$ are right angles. It is given that $\angle XYZ$ is a right angle. Thus $\angle XWY \cong \angle XYZ$ and $\angle XYZ \cong \angle ZWY$ because all right angles are congruent. $\angle WXY \cong \angle YXZ$ by the Reflexive property. So $\triangle WXY \sim \triangle YXZ$ by AA Similarity. $\angle XZY \cong \angle YZW$ by the Reflexive property. So $\triangle YXZ \sim \triangle WYZ$ by AA Similarity. Therefore $\triangle WXY \sim \triangle WYZ$ by the Transitive property.

39. Sample answer:

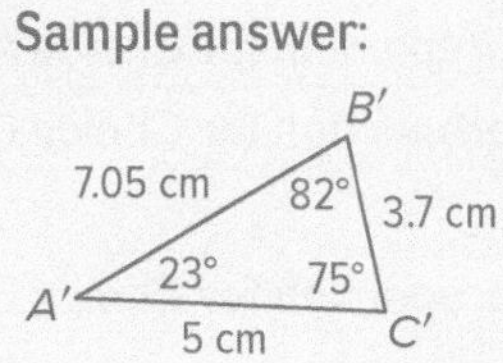

$\triangle A'B'C' \sim \triangle ABC$ because the measures of each side have a scale factor of 0.5 and the measures of corresponding angles are equal.

Exercise Alert

Ruler Exercise 35 requires the use of a ruler.

Protractor and Ruler Exercise 39 requires the use of a protractor and a ruler.

Teaching the Mathematical Practices

Reasoning Mathematically proficient students make sense of quantities and their relationships in problem situations. In Exercise 38, encourage students to draw a diagram representing the similar triangles described in the exercise.

Assess

Ticket Out the Door Ask students to explain how similar triangles can be used to find the height of a tall tree. Have them tell you on their way out the door.

Standards for Mathematical Practice

Emphasis On	Exercises
1 Make sense of problems and persevere in solving them.	1-4, 9-14, 33, 35, 37, 41
2 Reason abstractly and quantitatively.	5, 16-21, 32, 36, 38, 39
3 Construct viable arguments and critique the reasoning of others.	25-27, 43, 44
4 Model with mathematics.	8, 15, 22–24, 28, 30, 31, 34, 40, 42
7 Look for and make use of structure.	6, 7, 28, 29
8 Look for and express regularity in repeated reasoning.	45

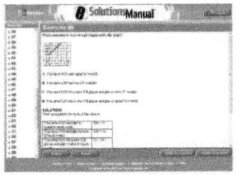

Preparing for Assessment

Exercises 40–44 require students to use the skills they will need on standardized assessments. Exercises are dual-coded with content standards and mathematical practice standards.

Dual Coding		
Items	Content Standards	MP Mathematical Practices
40	G.SRT.5	4
41	G.SRT.5	1
42	G.SRT.5	4
43	G.SRT.2, G.SRT.5	3
44	G.SRT.2, G.SRT.5	3

Diagnose Student Errors

Survey student responses for each item. Class trends may indicate common errors and misconceptions.

42.

A	Used 5.6 feet instead of 5.5 for Sonia's height
B	CORRECT
C	Did not use correct proportion
D	Solved $\frac{x}{10} = \frac{2}{5.5}$

43a.

A	Related incorrect segments to write proportion
B	Related incorrect segments to write proportion
C	Transposed measures in proportion
D	CORRECT

Preparing for Assessment

40. The ladder of a slide is perpendicular to the ground. The slide slopes downward at an angle of 58 degrees. What angles cannot be used to prove that $\triangle JKL \sim \triangle JMN$ by AA Similarity? MP 4 G.SRT.5 C

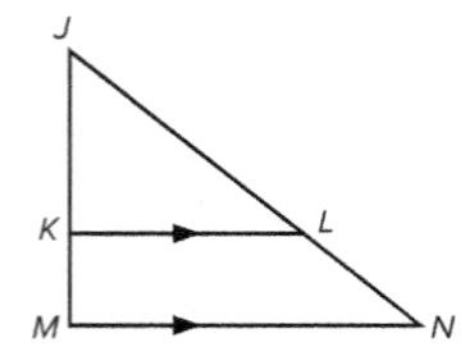

- A $\angle KJL \cong \angle MJN$ and $\angle JKL \cong \angle JMN$
- B $\angle KLJ \cong \angle MNJ$ and $\angle JKL \cong \angle JMN$
- C $\angle KLJ \cong \angle NLK$ and $\angle JKL \cong \angle MKL$
- D $\angle KLJ \cong \angle MNJ$ and $\angle KJL \cong \angle MJN$

41. $\triangle JKL \sim \triangle PQR$, the measure of angle P is 34°, and the measure of angle R is 72°. The measure of angle K is given by the expression $(7x + 32)$°. What is the value of x? MP 1 G.SRT.5 6

42. Sonia is 5 feet 6 inches tall. She wants to estimate the height of a palm tree near her school. She measures her shadow and the palm tree's shadow and then sets up the sketch shown below.

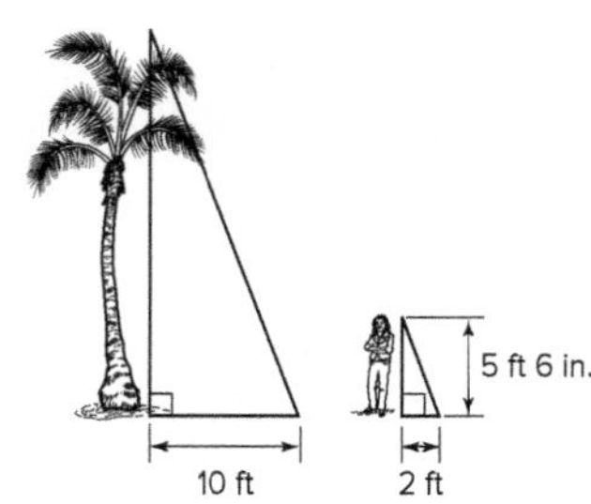

Which of the following is the best estimate of the height of the palm tree? MP 4 G.SRT.5 B

- A 28 ft
- B 27.5 ft
- C 13.5 ft
- D 3.6 ft

43. In the figure below, $\overline{EB} \parallel \overline{DC}$. MP 3 G.SRT.2, G.SRT.5

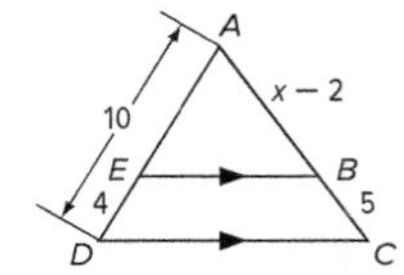

a. Which proportion correctly represents the situation? D

- A $\frac{x-2}{6} = \frac{4}{10}$
- B $\frac{6}{x-2} = \frac{4}{10}$
- C $\frac{x-2}{6} = \frac{4}{5}$
- D $\frac{6}{x-2} = \frac{4}{5}$

b. Find the value of x and the measure of $\overline{AB}$. C

- A $x = 4.4$, $AB = 2.4$
- B $x = 6.8$, $AB = 4.8$
- C $x = 9.5$, $AB = 7.5$
- D $x = 17$, $AB = 15$

44. MULTI-STEP These two triangles are similar and $\angle F \cong \angle R$. MP 3 G.SRT.2, G.SRT.5

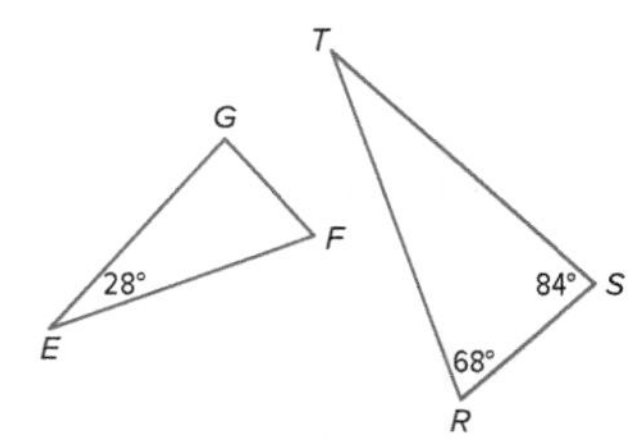

a What is the measure of angle F? B

- A 28°
- B 68°
- C 74°
- D 96°

b Which of the following are true? Select all that apply. B, D, E, F

- A $\angle G \cong \angle T$
- B $\angle T \cong \angle E$
- C $\triangle EFG \sim \triangle RST$
- D $\triangle EFG \sim \triangle TRS$
- E $\triangle FEG$ is a dilation of $\triangle RTS$.
- F $\triangle RTS$ is a dilation of $\triangle FEG$.

43b.

A	Solved the proportion for Choice A in part a.
B	Solved the proportion for Choice C in part a.
C	CORRECT
D	Solved the proportion for Choice B in part a.

Go Online!

Quizzes

Students can use *Self-Check Quizzes* to check their understanding of this lesson and have the results sent to you. You can also give the *Chapter Quiz*, which covers the content in Lessons 7-3 and 7-4.

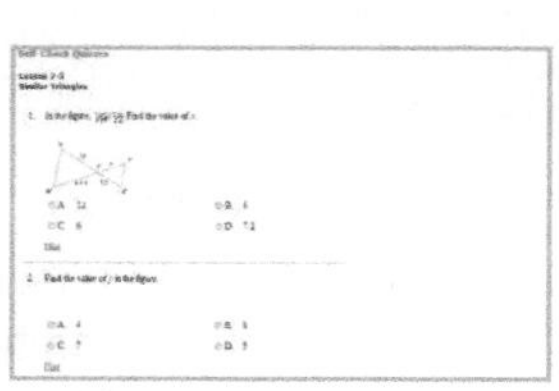

LESSON 7-4
Similar Triangles: SSS and SAS Similarity

SUGGESTED PACING (DAYS)

	Instruction		Extend
90 min.	0.5	.25	
45 min.	1.0		0.5

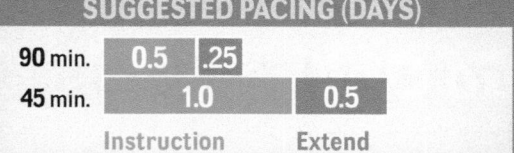

Track Your Progress

Objectives

1. Use the SSS similarity criterion to prove triangles are similar.
2. Use the SAS similarity criterion to prove triangles are similar.

Mathematical Background

You can use the SSS or the SAS similarity criteria to prove that two triangles are similar. For SSS, if all three pairs of corresponding side lengths are proportional, then the triangles are similar. For SAS, if the lengths of two sides of one triangle are proportional to the corresponding sides of another triangle and their included angles are congruent, then the triangles are similar.

THEN	NOW	NEXT
G.SRT.3 Use the properties of similarity transformations to establish the AA criterion for two triangles to be similar.	**G.SRT.2** Given two figures, use the definition of similarity in terms of similarity transformations to decide if they are similar; explain using similarity transformations the meaning of similarity for triangles as the equality of all corresponding pairs of angles and the proportionality of all corresponding pairs of sides. **G.SRT.4** Prove theorems about similarity. **G.SRT.5** Use congruence and similarity criteria for triangles to solve problems and to prove relationships in geometric figures.	**G.SRT.6** Understand that by similarity, side ratios in right triangles are properties of the angles in the triangle, leading to definitions of trigonometric ratios for acute angles. **G.SRT.8** Use trigonometric ratios and the Pythagorean Theorem to solve right triangles in applied problems.

Go Online! All of these resources and more are available at connectED.mcgraw-hill.com

eLessons utilize the power of your interactive whiteboard in an engaging way. Use **Similarity Using Transformations**, Screens 10–12 and 14–15, to introduce the concepts in this lesson.

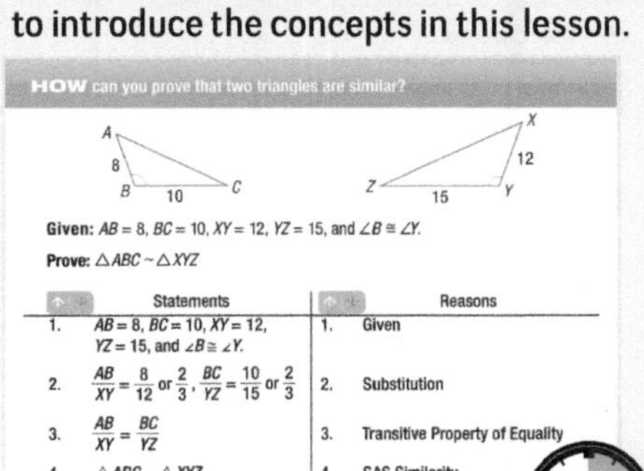

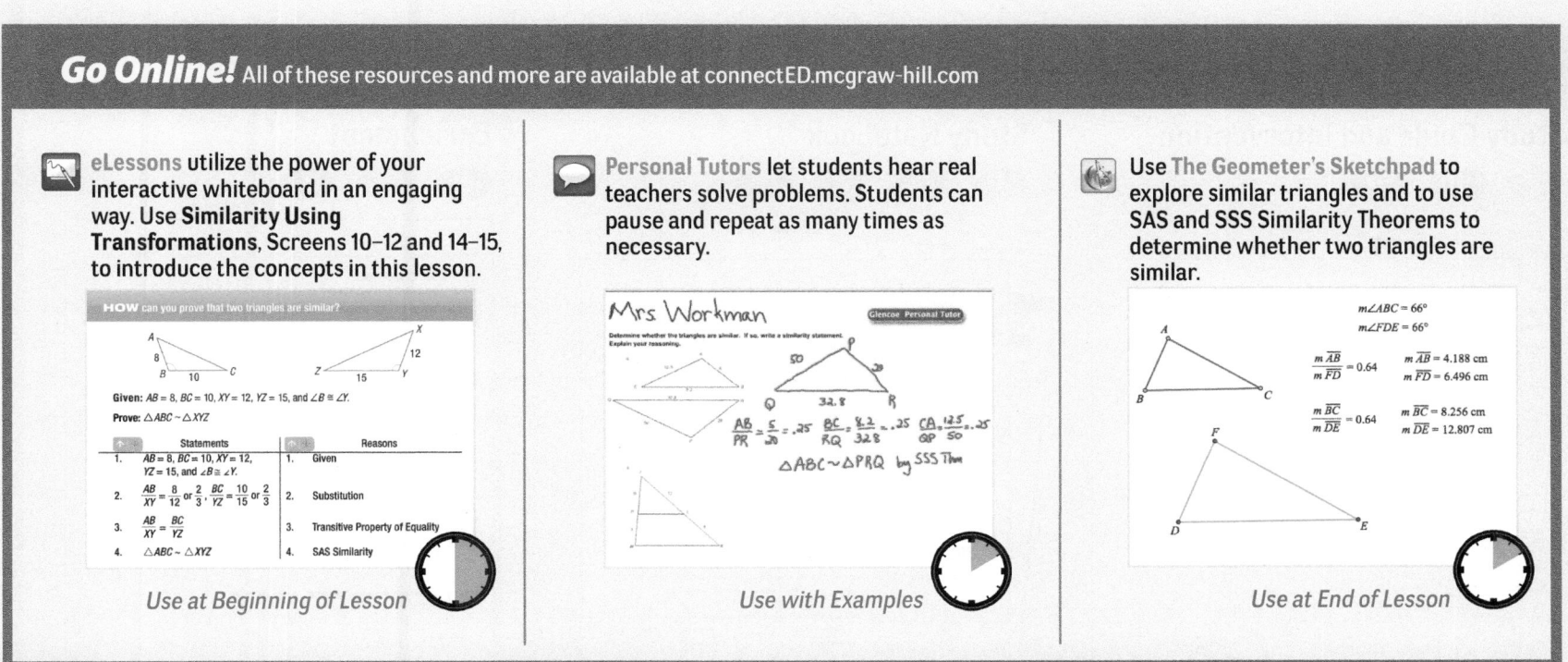

Use at Beginning of Lesson

Personal Tutors let students hear real teachers solve problems. Students can pause and repeat as many times as necessary.

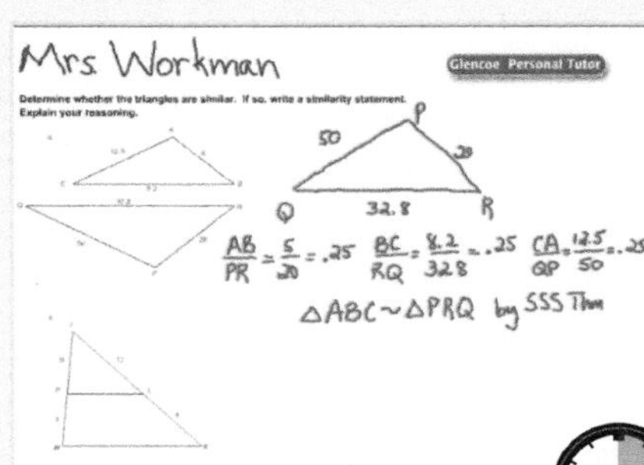

Use with Examples

Use The Geometer's Sketchpad to explore similar triangles and to use SAS and SSS Similarity Theorems to determine whether two triangles are similar.

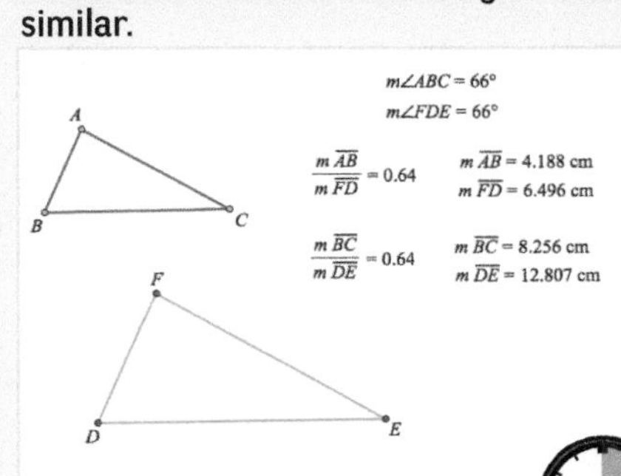

Use at End of Lesson

OER Using Open Educational Resources

Submitting Assignments Communicate with students and parents using **DropBox**. Dropbox is a free cloud service that allows you to set up a folder for each student. *Use as organization tool*

Go Online!
connectED.mcgraw-hill.com
Worksheets

Differentiate Your Resources

Extra Practice Additional practice or homework; Skills Practice is best for approaching-level students and Practice is best for on-level and beyond-level students

Skills Practice

AL OL ELL

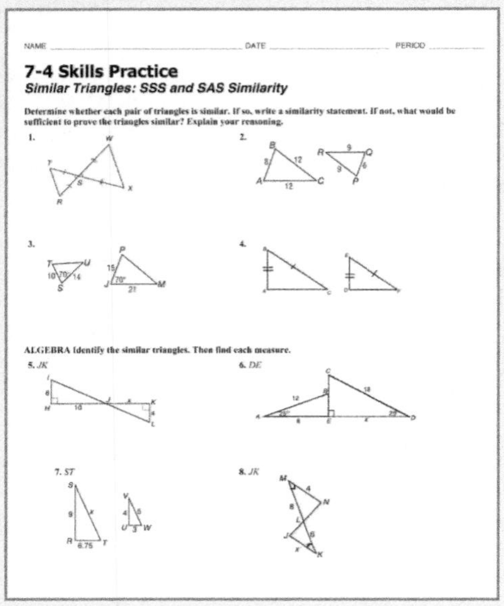
7-4 Skills Practice
Similar Triangles: SSS and SAS Similarity

Practice

AL OL BL ELL

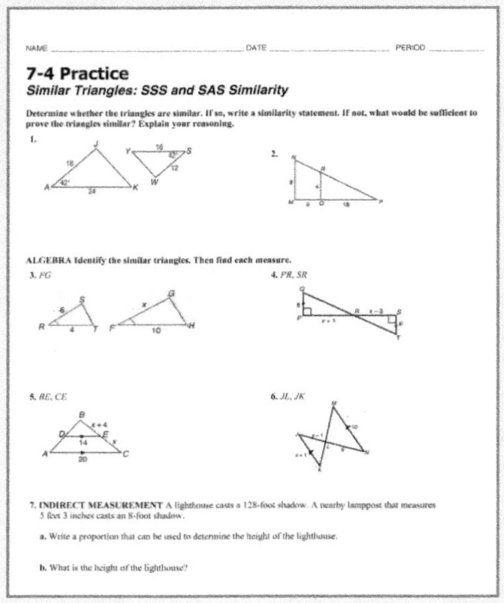
7-4 Practice
Similar Triangles: SSS and SAS Similarity

Word Problem Practice

AL OL BL ELL

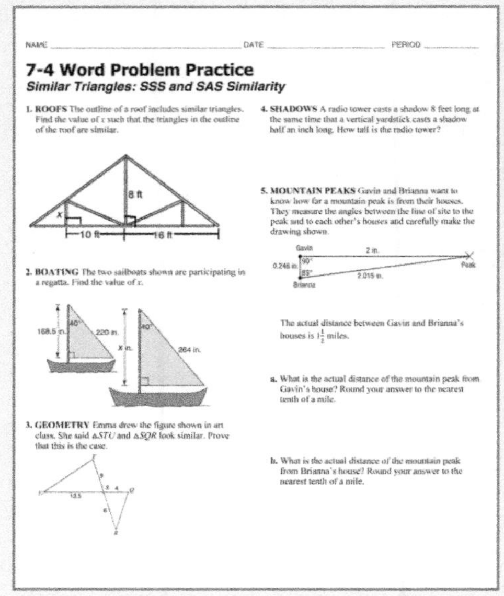
7-4 Word Problem Practice
Similar Triangles: SSS and SAS Similarity

Intervention Reteaching and vocabulary activities that can be used with struggling or absent students and as ELL support

Study Guide and Intervention

AL OL ELL

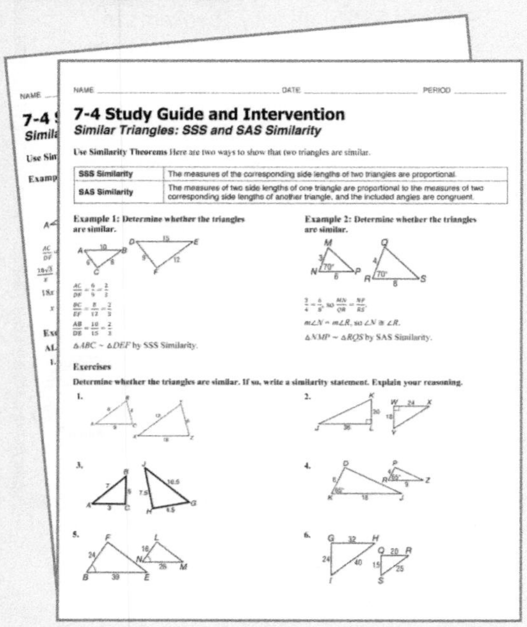
7-4 Study Guide and Intervention
Similar Triangles: SSS and SAS Similarity

Study Notebook

AL OL BL ELL

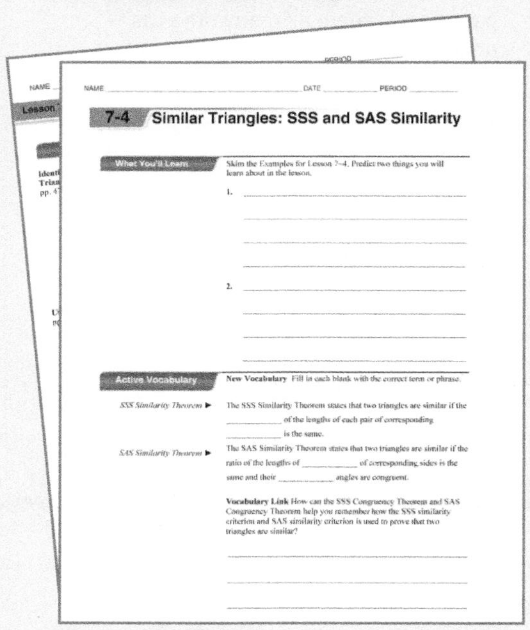
7-4 Similar Triangles: SSS and SAS Similarity

Extension Activities that can be used to extend lesson concepts

Enrichment

OL BL ELL

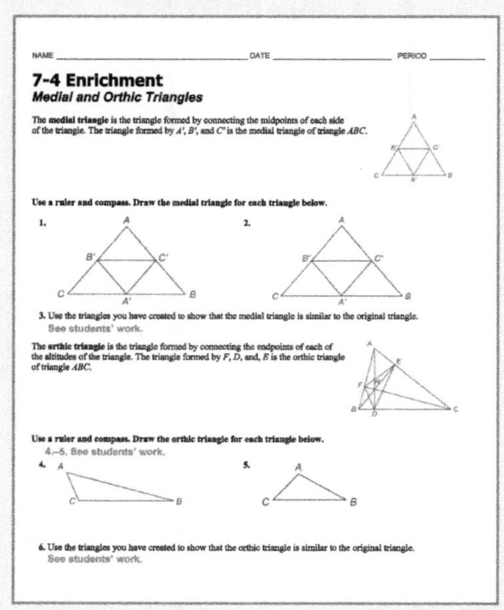
7-4 Enrichment
Medial and Orthic Triangles

LESSON 4

Similar Triangles: SSS and SAS Similarity

Then

- You used the AA Similarity Postulate to prove triangles are similar.

Now

1. Use the SSS similarity criterion to prove triangles are similar.
2. Use the SAS similarity criterion to prove triangles are similar.

Why?

- The sports store where Miguel works sells 2-person tents and larger 6-person tents with ends shaped like isosceles triangles. Miguel sets up a display with a 2-person tent so that the angle formed at the top of the tent between the two equal-length sides is 65°. If he sets up a 6-person tent so that the angle formed at the top of the tent between the two equal-length sides is 65° are the triangles in the tents similar?

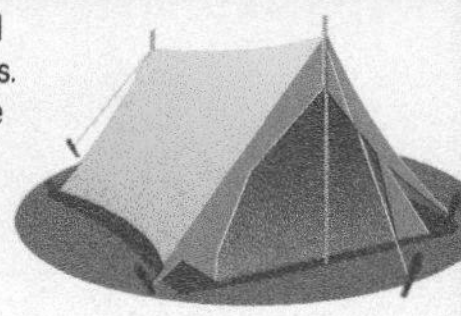

MP Mathematical Practice Standards

1 Make sense of problems and persevere in solving them.
2 Reason abstractly and quantitatively.
3 Construct viable arguments and critique the reasoning of others.
4 Model with mathematics.

Content Standards
G.SRT.2 Given two figures, use the definition of similarity in terms of similarity transformations to decide if they are similar; explain using similarity transformations the meaning of similarity for triangles as the equality of all corresponding pairs of angles and the proportionality of all corresponding pairs of sides.
G.SRT.4 Prove theorems about similarity.
G.SRT.5 Use congruence and similarity for triangles to solve problems and to prove relationships in geometric figures.

1 SSS Similarity You can use the AA Similarity Postulate to prove other statements about triangle similarity. The SSS Similarity Theorem states that two triangles are similar if the ratio of the lengths of each pair of corresponding sides is the same.

G.SRT.4

Theorem 7.3 SSS Triangle Similarity

Side-Side-Side (SSS) Similarity
If the corresponding side lengths of two triangles are proportional, then the triangles are similar.

Example If $\frac{JK}{MP} = \frac{KL}{PQ} = \frac{LJ}{QM}$, then $\triangle JKL \sim \triangle MPQ$.

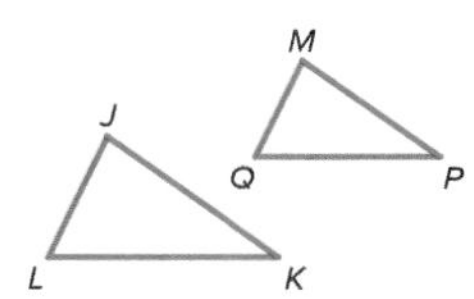

Proof Theorem 7.3

Given: $\frac{AB}{FG} = \frac{BC}{GH} = \frac{AC}{FH}$

Prove: $\triangle ABC \sim \triangle FGH$

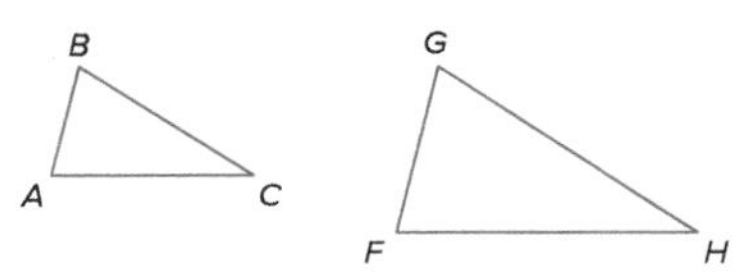

Paragraph Proof:

Locate J on $\overline{FG}$ so that $JG = AB$.
Draw $\overline{JK}$ so that $\overline{JK} \parallel \overline{FH}$.
Label $\angle GJK$ as $\angle 1$.

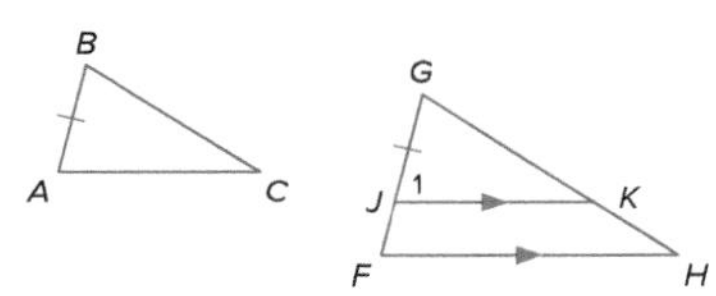

Because $\angle G \cong \angle G$ by the Reflexive Property and $\angle 1 \cong \angle F$ by the Corresponding Angles Postulate, $\triangle GJK \sim \triangle GFH$ by the AA Similarity Postulate.

By the definition of similar polygons, $\frac{JG}{FG} = \frac{GK}{GH} = \frac{JK}{FH}$. By substitution, $\frac{AB}{FG} = \frac{GK}{GH} = \frac{JK}{FH}$.

(continued on the next page)

Launch

Have students read the Why? section of the lesson. Ask:

- How do the sides of the two triangles represented by the front edges of the tent compare? They are proportional.
- How do the included angles of the two triangles compare? They are congruent.
- Is the triangle in the 6-person tent congruent to the triangle in the 2-person tent? Explain. No, the side lengths are not the same.

MP Mathematical Practices Strategies

Reason abstractly and quantitatively.
Help students understand the SSS and SAS Similarity Theorems by asking them to determine if various pairs of triangles are similar. For example, ask:

- Why are some pairs of triangles not similar? They do not meet the criteria of either similarity theorem or of the AA Similarity Postulate.
- Why do you think there is no AAS Similarity Theorem? The AA Similarity Postulate proves that triangles with two pairs of congruent angles are similar. An AAS Similarity Theorem would add an unnecessary criterion to meet.

Go Online!

Interactive Whiteboard
Use the *eLesson, Lesson Presentation,* or *Interactive Classroom* to present this lesson.

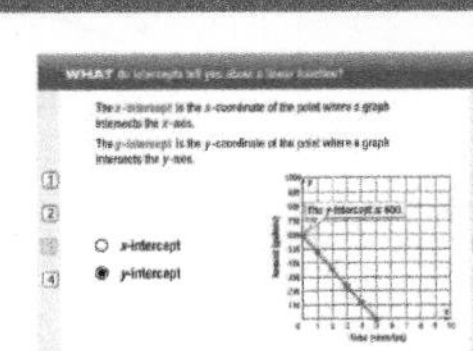

Teach

Ask the scaffolded questions for each example to build conceptual understanding for students at all levels.

1 SSS Similarity

Example 1 Use the SSS Theorem

AL What does the Reflexive Property state? An angle measure or length is equal to itself.

OL How can you tell which sides of two triangles are corresponding? Use the lengths. The longest sides correspond, the next longest sides correspond, and the shortest sides correspond.

BL How are the SSS Similarity Theorem and the SSS Congruence Postulate similar and how are they different? Both the Similarity Theorem and the Congruence Postulate involve the relationship between the correspond sides of two triangles. The Similarity Theorem involves proportional sides; and the Congruence Postulate involves congruent sides.

Need Another Example?

Determine whether the triangles are similar. If so, write a similarity statement. Explain your reasoning.

a.

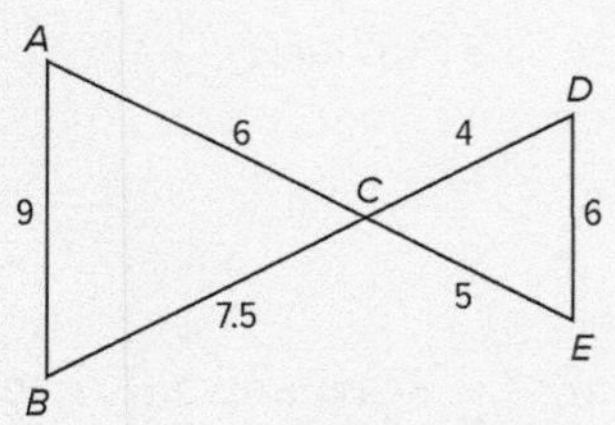

$\triangle ABC \sim \triangle DEC$ by the SSS Similarity Theorem.

b.

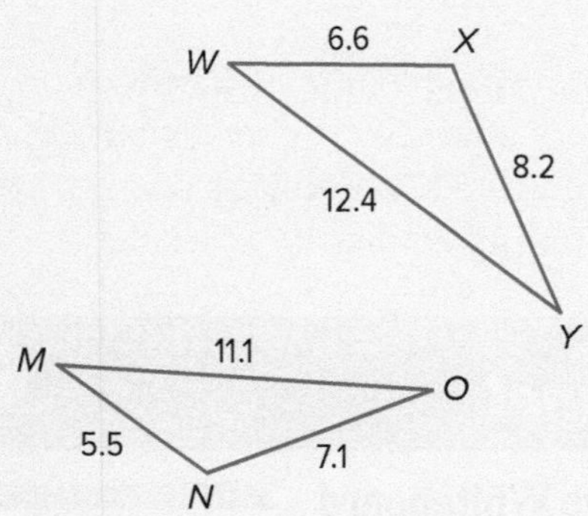

The sides are not proportional, so $\triangle MNO \nsim \triangle WXY$.

Go Online!

How do you know whether two triangles are similar? Investigate by using the **Geometry Tools** in ConnectED. ELL

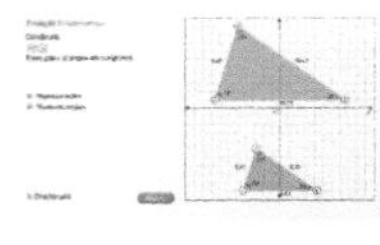

Because we are also given that $\frac{AB}{FG} = \frac{BC}{GH} = \frac{AC}{FH}$, we can say that $\frac{GK}{GH} = \frac{BC}{GH}$ and $\frac{JK}{FH} = \frac{AC}{FH}$. This means that $GK = BC$ and $JK = AC$, so $\overline{GK} \cong \overline{BC}$ and $\overline{JK} \cong \overline{AC}$.

By SSS, $\triangle ABC \cong \triangle JGK$.

By CPCTC, $\angle B \cong \angle G$ and $\angle A \cong \angle 1$. Because $\angle 1 \cong \angle F$, $\angle A \cong \angle F$ by the Transitive Property. By AA Similarity, $\triangle ABC \sim \triangle FGH$.

G.SRT.5

Example 1 Use the SAS Similarity Theorem

Determine whether the triangles are similar. If so, write a similarity statement. Explain your reasoning.

a.

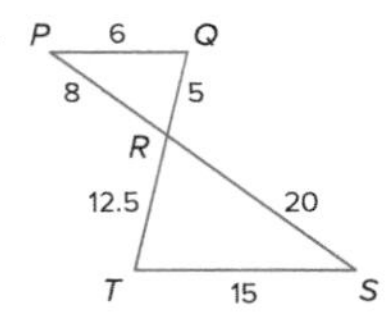

$\frac{PR}{SR} = \frac{8}{20}$ or $\frac{2}{5}$, $\frac{PQ}{ST} = \frac{6}{15}$ or $\frac{2}{5}$, and $\frac{QR}{TR} = \frac{5}{12.5} = \frac{50}{125}$ or $\frac{2}{5}$. So, $\triangle PQR \sim \triangle STR$ by the SSS Similarity Theorem.

b.

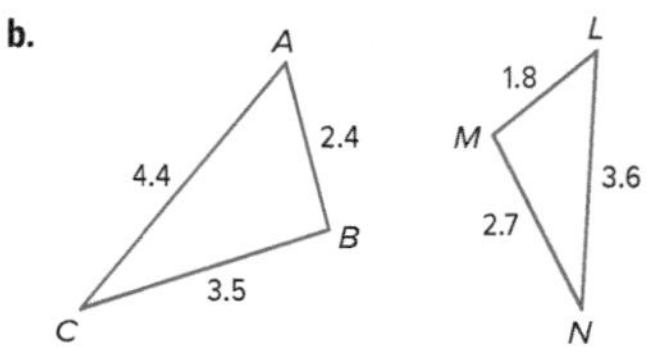

$\frac{AB}{LM} = \frac{2.4}{1.8}$ or $\frac{4}{3}$, $\frac{BC}{MN} = \frac{3.5}{2.7}$ or $\frac{35}{27}$, $\frac{AC}{LN} = \frac{4.4}{3.6}$ or $\frac{11}{9}$.

The sides are not proportional, so $\triangle ABC \nsim \triangle LMN$.

Guided Practice

1A.

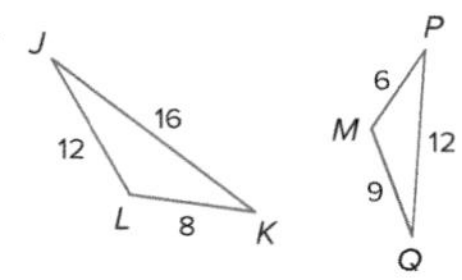

1B.

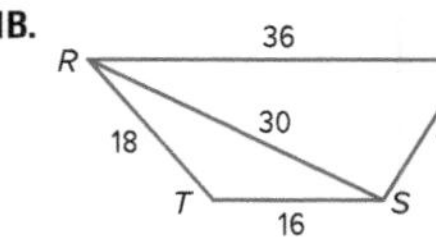

1A. Yes; $\triangle JLK \sim \triangle QMP$ by SSS Similarity since $\frac{JL}{QM} = \frac{LK}{MP} = \frac{JK}{QP} = \frac{4}{3}$.

1B. No; $\frac{RT}{RS} \neq \frac{RS}{RQ}$, so the corresponding side lengths are not proportional.

The SSS Similarity Theorem allows you to analyze triangles on the coordinate plane.

G.SRT.5

Example 2 Analyze Triangles on the Coordinate Plane

Determine whether $\triangle ABC$ with vertices $A(-2, 1)$, $B(3, -1)$, and $C(1, 4)$ is similar to $\triangle XYZ$ with vertices $X(-2, 4)$, $Y(2, -6)$, and $Z(-8, -2)$. Explain your reasoning.

Use the Distance Formula to find the measures of the sides.

$AB = \sqrt{(-2-(3))^2 + (-1-(1))^2} = \sqrt{(-5)^2 + (-2)^2}$ or $\sqrt{29}$

$BC = \sqrt{(3-1)^2 + (-1-4)^2} = \sqrt{(2)^2 + ((-5))^2}$ or $\sqrt{29}$

$AC = \sqrt{(-2-1)^2 + (1-4)^2} = \sqrt{(-3)^2 + (-3)^2}$ or $3\sqrt{2}$

Watch Out!

Congruent Angles The SAS Similarity Theorem can be used only if the angle is between the two corresponding sides of each triangle.

$XY = \sqrt{(-2-2)^2 + (4-(-6))^2} = \sqrt{(-4)^2 + 10^2}$ or $2\sqrt{29}$

$YZ = \sqrt{(2-(-8))^2 + (-6-(-2))^2} = \sqrt{(10)^2 + (-4)^2}$ or $2\sqrt{29}$

$XZ = \sqrt{(-2-(-8))^2 + (4-(-2))^2} = \sqrt{6^2 + 6^2}$ or $6\sqrt{2}$

$\frac{AB}{XY} = \frac{\sqrt{29}}{2\sqrt{29}}$ or $\frac{1}{2}$ $\frac{BC}{YZ} = \frac{\sqrt{29}}{2\sqrt{29}}$ or $\frac{1}{2}$ $\frac{AC}{XZ} = \frac{3\sqrt{2}}{6\sqrt{2}}$ or $\frac{1}{2}$

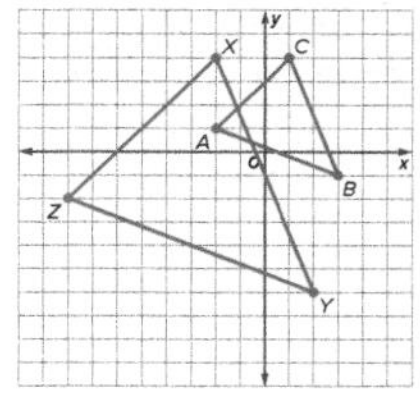

Because the side measures are proportional, $\triangle ABC$ is similar to $\triangle XYZ$ by SSS Similarity.

Guided Practice

Determine whether the triangles are similar.

2A. $\triangle MNO$ with $M(5, 2)$, $N(3, -8)$, and $O(0, -2)$ and $\triangle PQR$ with $P(11, 5)$, $Q(7, -15)$, and $R(1, -3)$

2B. $\triangle FGH$ with $F(1, 10)$, $G(3, -5)$, and $H(7, 5)$ and $\triangle JKL$ with $J(2, 7)$, $K(3, -1)$, and $L(5, 4)$

2A. $\triangle MNO \sim \triangle PQR$ by SSS Similarity since $\frac{MN}{PQ} = \frac{NO}{QR} = \frac{MO}{PR} = 2$

2B. $\triangle FGH \nsim \triangle JKL$

2 SSS Similarity

The SAS Triangle Similarity Theorem states that two triangles are similar if the ratio of the lengths of two pairs of corresponding sides is the same and their included angles are congruent.

Theorem 7.4 SAS Triangle Similarity

Side-Angle-Side (SAS) Similarity
If the lengths of two sides of one triangle are proportional to the lengths of two corresponding sides of another triangle and the included angles are congruent, then the triangles are similar.

Example If $\frac{RS}{XY} = \frac{ST}{YZ}$ and $\angle S \cong \angle Y$, then $\triangle RST \sim \triangle XYZ$.

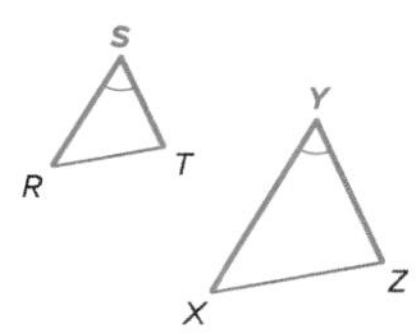

You will prove Theorem 7.4 in Exercise 28.

G.SRT2

Example 3 Use the SAS Similarity Theorem

Determine whether the triangles are similar. If so, write a similarity statement. Explain your reasoning.

a.

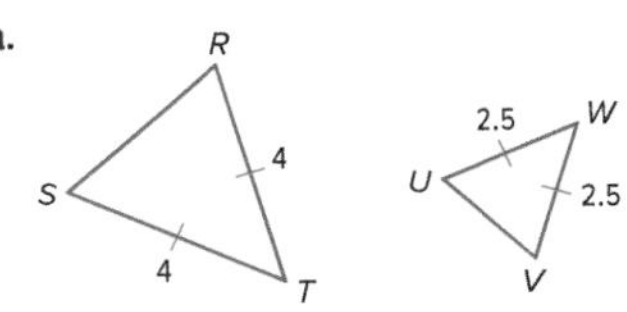

$\frac{RT}{UW} = \frac{4}{2.5}$ or 1.6 $\frac{VW}{ST} = \frac{4}{2.5}$ or 1.6

The lengths of the two pairs of sides are proportional. However we don't know that the lengths of the third pair of sides are proportional or that the included angles are congruent. There is not enough information to prove that the triangles are congruent.

Example 2 Analyze Triangles on the Coordinate Plane

AL **Why is it necessary to find the lengths of all three sides of each triangle?** To apply the SSS Similarity Theorem, all 3 pairs of sides must be proportional.

OL **In part a, could you prove that the triangles are similar by comparing the ratios $\frac{XY}{AB'}$, $\frac{YZ}{BC'}$, and $\frac{XZ}{AC'}$? Explain.** Yes; comparing these ratios would still show that the sides are proportional.

BL **In part a, how could you show that the triangles are similar using a dilation?** Sample answer: Dilate $\triangle ABC$ using a scale factor of 2. Then translate $\triangle A'B'C'$ so that it coincides with $\triangle XYZ$.

Need Another Example?

Determine whether $\triangle DEF$ with vertices $D(-4, 0)$, $E(6, -1)$, and $F(3, 3)$ is similar to $\triangle LMN$ with vertices $L(-3, -5)$, $M(15, -7)$, and $N(11, -1)$. Explain your reasoning. The sides are not proportional, so $\triangle DEF \nsim \triangle LMN$.

2 SAS Similarity

Example 3 Use the SAS Similarity Theorem

AL **How many pieces of information do you need to apply the SSS or SAS Similarity Theorems?** 3; 3 pairs of proportional sides for SSS or two pairs of proportional sides and the included angle for SAS

OL **If we were given $m\angle T = 37$, what would need to be true to conclude that $\triangle RST \sim \triangle UVW$?** $m\angle V = 37$

BL **Why does knowing that the triangles are isosceles not allow you to conclude that $\angle R \cong \angle U$ and $\angle S \cong \angle V$ and the triangles are congruent by AA Similarity?** The isosceles Triangle Theorem allows you to conclude that $\angle R \cong \angle S$ and $\angle U \cong \angle V$, but not that $\angle R \cong \angle U$ and $\angle S \cong \angle V$.

Differentiated Instruction AL OL BL ELL

Interpersonal Learners Have students choose a partner. Ask each pair of students to measure the height of the school building by using their own shadows and similar triangles.

Need Another Example?

Determine whether the triangles are similar. If so, write a similarity statement. Explain your reasoning.

a.

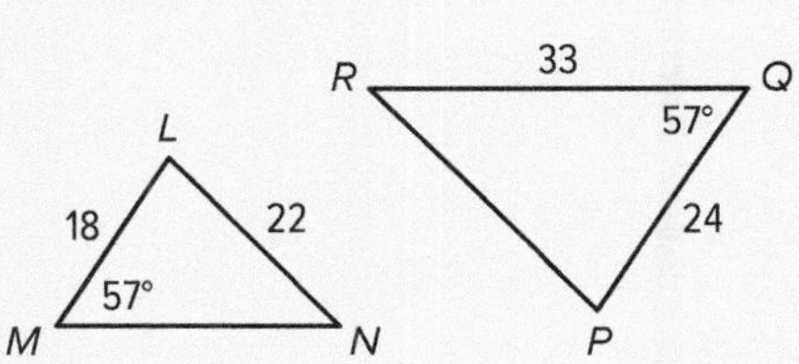

$\triangle LMN \sim \triangle PQR$ by SAS Similarity Theorem

b.

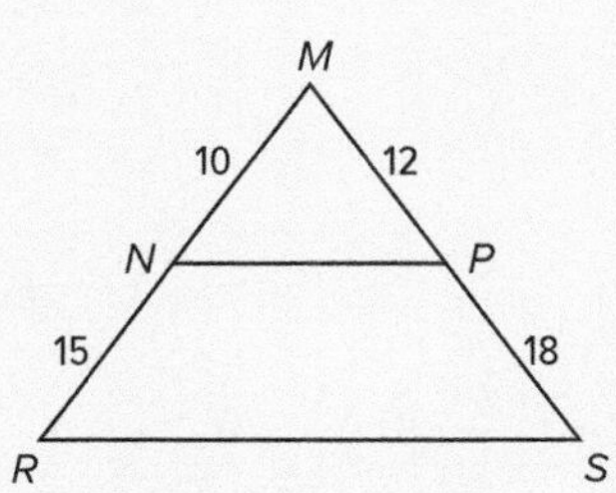

$\triangle MNO \sim \triangle MRS$ by the SAS Similarity Theorem.

Example 4 Analyze Triangles on the Coordinate Plane

AL **Why is it only necessary to find the lengths of two sides of each triangle?** To apply the SAS Similarity Theorem, two pairs of sides must be proportional and the included angles must be congruent.

OL **Could you prove that the triangles are similar by comparing the ratios $\frac{EC}{BC}$ and $\frac{DC}{AC}$? Explain.** Yes; comparing these ratios would still show that the sides are proportional.

BL **How could you show that the triangles are similar using a dilation?** Sample answer: Dilate $\triangle CDE$ using a scale factor of 1.5 and a center of C. $\triangle C'D'E'$ will coincide with $\triangle CAB$.

Need Another Example?

Determine whether $\triangle WUV$ with vertices $W(-2, 5)$, $U(2, -6)$, and $V(3, 5)$ is similar to $\triangle WXY$ with vertices $X(10, -28)$, and $Y(13, 5)$. Explain your reasoning.

$\triangle WUV \sim \triangle WXY$ by SAS Similarity

Teaching Tip

MP Modeling Finding the missing lengths of triangles using similarity relationships is useful to architects when they make their scale drawings. Encourage students to investigate scale drawings in architecture.

3A. Yes; $\triangle TWZ \sim \triangle YWX$ by SAS Similarity since $\angle W \cong \angle W$ and $\frac{TW}{YW} = \frac{WZ}{WX} = \frac{1}{2}$.

3B. Yes; $\triangle EFG \sim \triangle EHJ$ by SAS Similarity Theorem since $\angle E \cong \angle E$ and $\frac{EF}{EH} = \frac{EG}{EJ} = \frac{3}{2}$.

b.

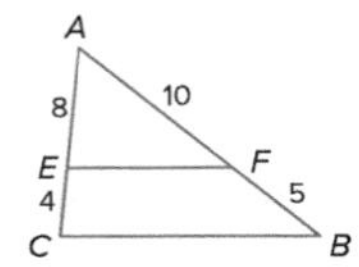

By the Reflexive Property, $\angle A \cong \angle A$.

$\frac{AF}{AB} = \frac{10}{10+5} = \frac{10}{15}$ or $\frac{2}{3}$ and $\frac{AE}{AC} = \frac{8}{8+4} = \frac{8}{12}$ or $\frac{2}{3}$.

Because the lengths of the sides that include $\angle A$ are proportional, $\triangle AEF \sim \triangle ACB$ by the SAS Similarity Theorem.

Guided Practice

3A.

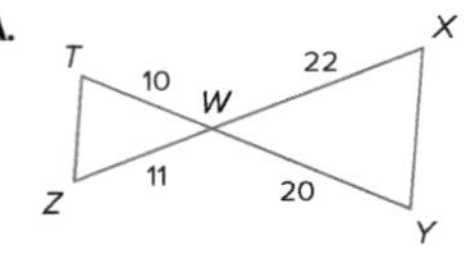

3B.

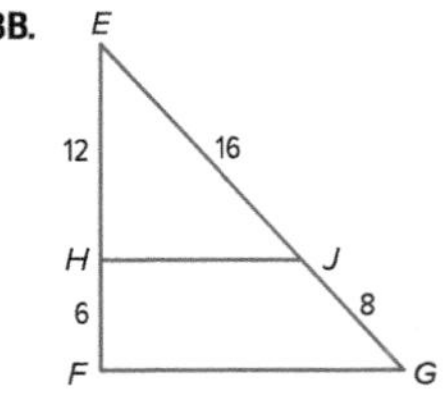

You can also use the SSS Similarity Theorem to analyze triangles on the coordinate plane.

G.SRT.5

Example 4 Analyze Triangles on the Coordinate Plane

Determine whether $\triangle ABC$ with vertices $A(-2, 7)$, $B(-2, -8)$, and $C(4, 4)$ is similar to $\triangle DEC$ with vertices $D(0, 6)$, and $E(0, -4)$. Explain your reasoning.

$\angle ACB$ $\angle DCE$ by the Reflexive Property. Use the distance formula to find the measures of the sides for which $\angle C$ is the included angle.

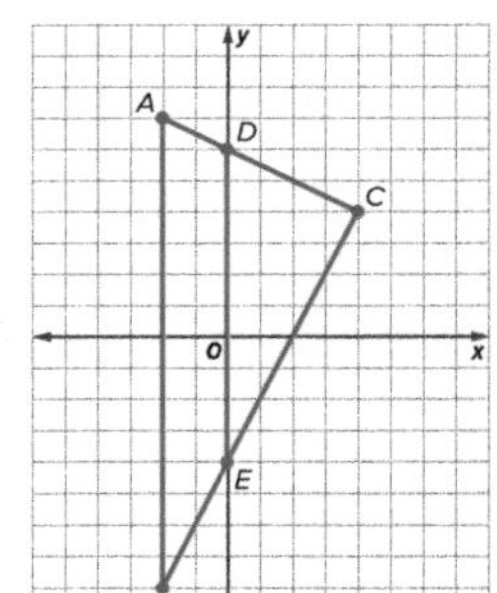

$AC = \sqrt{(-2-4)^2 + (7-4)^2} = \sqrt{(-6)^2 + 3^2}$ or $3\sqrt{5}$

$BC = \sqrt{(-2-4)^2 + (-8-4)^2} = \sqrt{(-6)^2 + (-(12))^2}$ or $6\sqrt{5}$

$DC = \sqrt{(0-4)^2 + (6-4)^2} = \sqrt{(-4)^2 + 2^2}$ or $2\sqrt{5}$

$EC = \sqrt{(0-4)^2 + (-4-4)^2} = \sqrt{(-4)^2 + (-(8))^2}$ or $4\sqrt{5}$

$\frac{BC}{EC} = \frac{6\sqrt{5}}{4\sqrt{5}}$ or 1.5 $\quad \frac{AC}{DC} = \frac{3\sqrt{5}}{2\sqrt{5}}$ or 1.5

Because two pairs of side measures are proportional and the included angles are congruent, $\triangle ABC$ is similar to $\triangle DEC$ by SAS Similarity.

Study Tip

Using Diagrams Marking a diagram as you identify the corresponding congruent and proportional parts of triangles can help you verify that the similarity criteria are met.

Guided Practice

Determine whether the triangles are similar.

4A. $\triangle PQR$ with $P(1, 5)$, $Q(7, -2)$, and $R(3, -3)$ and $\triangle STR$ with $S(2, 5)$, and $T(6, -2)$

4B. $\triangle EFG$ with $E(-1, 1)$, $F(2, -5)$, and $G(4, 2)$ and $\triangle ABG$ with $A(-6, 0)$, and $B(0, -12)$

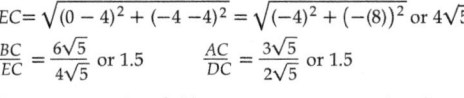

4A. $\triangle PQR \nsim \triangle STR$

4B. $\triangle EFG \sim \triangle ABG$ by SAS Similarity since $\angle EGF \cong \angle AGB$ and $\frac{EG}{AG} = \frac{FG}{BG} = 2$

Once you have established that two triangles are similar, you can write and solve a proportion to find an unknown measurement.

G.SRT.5

Real-World Example 5 Indirect Measurement

ECOLOGY A park volunteer is doing an inventory of the trees in the park, noting the species and height of each tree. He stands so that his shadow coincides with the tree's shadow. He is 5 feet 9 inches tall and his shadow is 12 feet long. If the length of the tree's shadow is 17.2 feet, how tall is the tree?

Understand Make a sketch of the situation. 5 feet 9 inches is equivalent to 5.75 feet. If the tree's shadow is 17.2 feet, the length of the tree's shadow behind the volunteer is 5.2 feet.

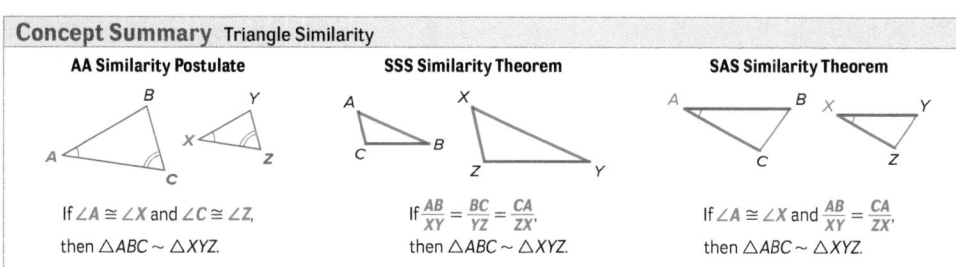

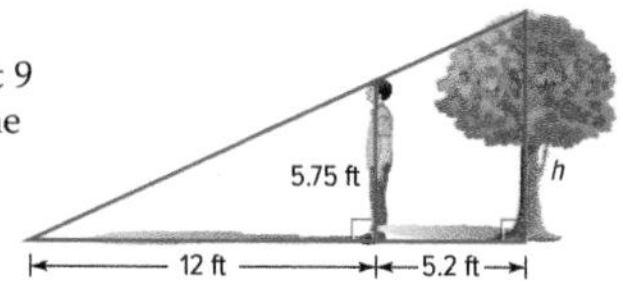

> **Study Tip**
> **MP Structure** Proportions must have corresponding parts such as height to length. This demonstrates the corresponding sides that are proportional.

Plan In shadow problems, you can assume that the angles formed by the Sun's rays with any two objects are congruent and that the objects form the sides of two right triangles. Because two corresponding pairs of sides are proportional, the triangles are similar by the SAS Similarity Theorem.

$$\frac{\text{volunteer's height}}{\text{tree's height}} = \frac{\text{volunteer's shadow length}}{\text{tree's shadow length}}$$

Solve Substitute the known values and let h = tree's height.

$$\frac{5.75}{h} = \frac{12}{17.2}$$

$$12 \cdot h = (5.75)(17.2)$$

$$12h = 98.9$$

$$h \approx 8.2$$

The tree is about 8.2 feet tall.

Check The tree's shadow length is $\frac{17.2}{12} \approx 1.4$ times the volunteer's shadow length. Check to see that the tree's height is about 1.4 times the volunteer's height. $\frac{8.2}{5.75} \approx 1.4$.

Guided Practice

5. **MEASUREMENT** Connor is standing next to the flagpole at his school and wants to use his shadow to help measure the pole. The length of his shadow is 8 feet when the flagpole's shadow is 50 feet. How high is the flagpole to the nearest foot? 36 ft

In addition to the definition of similar triangles, you now know three methods for proving that triangles are similar.

Concept Summary Triangle Similarity

AA Similarity Postulate

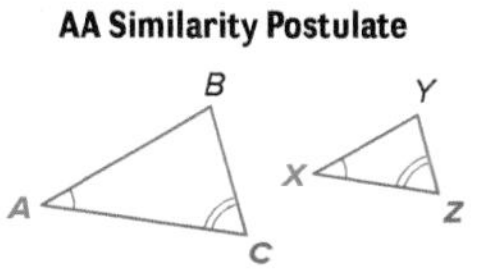

If $\angle A \cong \angle X$ and $\angle C \cong \angle Z$, then $\triangle ABC \sim \triangle XYZ$.

SSS Similarity Theorem

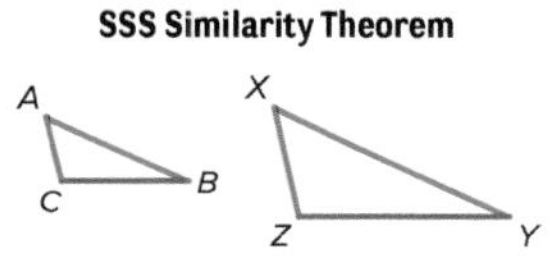

If $\frac{AB}{XY} = \frac{BC}{YZ} = \frac{CA}{ZX}$, then $\triangle ABC \sim \triangle XYZ$.

SAS Similarity Theorem

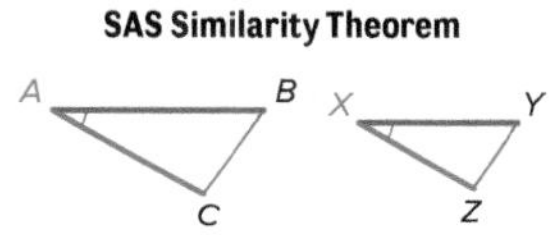

If $\angle A \cong \angle X$ and $\frac{AB}{XY} = \frac{CA}{ZX}$, then $\triangle ABC \sim \triangle XYZ$.

Differentiated Instruction OL BL

Extension Have students draw a right triangle on a coordinate plane and label each vertex with an ordered pair. Then have them draw another right triangle that is larger and proportional to it. Students should write a paragraph proof to show that the two right triangles are similar. See students' work. Students can use the fact that all right angles are congruent to apply SAS Similarity.

Example 5 Indirect Measurement

AL How do we know that this measurement is an approximation? Sample answer: It would not be possible to measure the exact length of the shadows, so the measurement is an approximation.

OL If the length of the tree's shadow were 30 feet, how tall would the tree be? about 14.4 feet

BL Why does indirect measurement make sense in this situation? Sample answer: Without current technology like lasers, it would not be possible to measure the height of a tree with measuring devices like tape measures. So it is necessary to estimate the height.

Need Another Example?

Joaquin wants to measure the height of a building obstructing his view of the lake. He stands so that the tip of his shadow coincides with the tip of the building's shadow. He is 5 feet 6 inches tall, and his shadow is 18 feet long at the same time that the building's shadow is 360 feet long. About how tall is the building?

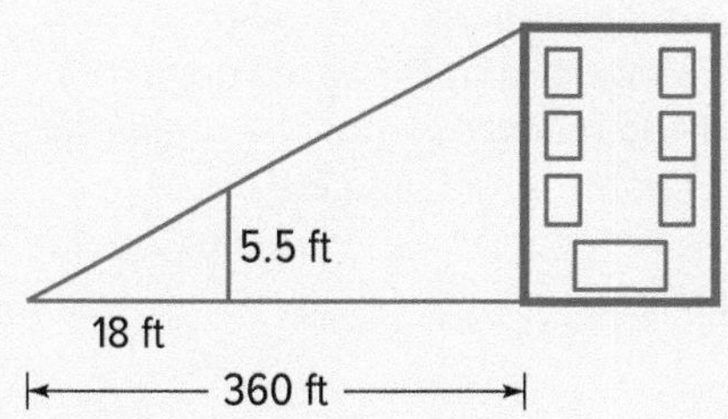

110 feet

Teaching the Mathematical Practices

MP Modeling Measuring distances that otherwise would not be measurable, like the width of a lake, is a good use of triangle similarity theorems. Encourage students to investigate how indirect measurement is used to measure distances.

Essential Question

How do you use the SSS or the SAS similarity criterion to show that two triangles are similar? To use the SSS criterion, show that all three pairs of corresponding sides are proportional. To use the SAS criterion, show that two pairs of corresponding sides are proportional and that their included angles are congruent.

Practice

Formative Assessment Use Exercises 1–8 to assess students' understanding of the concepts in this lesson.

The Practice and Problem Solving exercises assess the content taught in the lesson. The Preparing for Assessment page is meant to be used as preparation for end-of-course assessments.

Extra Practice

See page R7 for extra exercises for students who are approaching level or for on-level students who need additional reinforcement.

Additional Answers

13. No; there is not enough information to determine. If $JH = 3$ and $WY = 24$, then $\triangle JHK \sim \triangle XWY$ by SSS Similarity.

16. No; there is not enough information to determine. If the third pair of sides were known to be proportional, the triangles would be similar by SSS Similarity. If the included angles were congruent, the triangles would be similar by SAS Similarity.

17. No; there is not enough information to determine. If sides $\overline{AF}$ and $\overline{DF}$ were known to be proportional, the triangles would be similar by SAS Similarity. If either $\angle C$ and $\angle B$ or $\angle A$ and $\angle D$ were congruent, the triangles would be similar by AA Similarity.

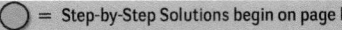

Check Your Understanding ◯ = Step-by-Step Solutions begin on page R13.

Go Online! for a Self-Check Quiz

Examples 1, 3 G.SRT.2 **Determine whether the triangles are similar. If so, write a similarity statement. Explain your reasoning.**

1. 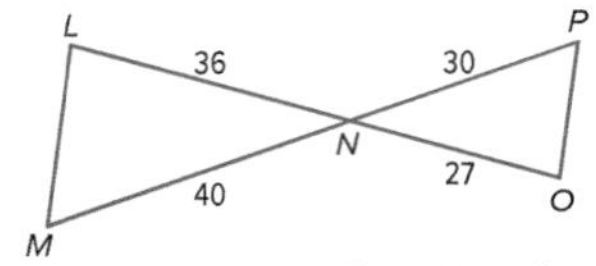

Yes; $\triangle LMN \sim \triangle OPN$ by SAS Similarity.

2. 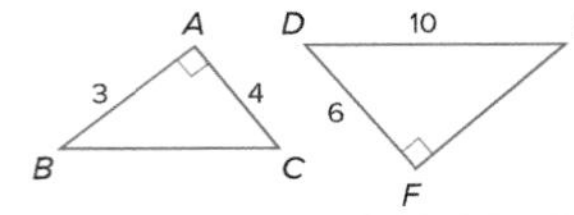

Yes; $\triangle BAC \sim \triangle DFE$ by SAS Similarity.

3. 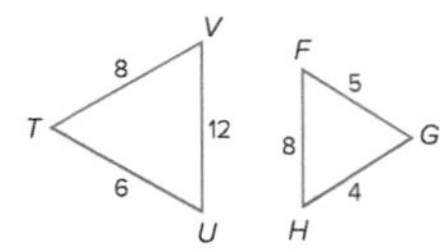

3. No; corresponding sides are not proportional.

4. 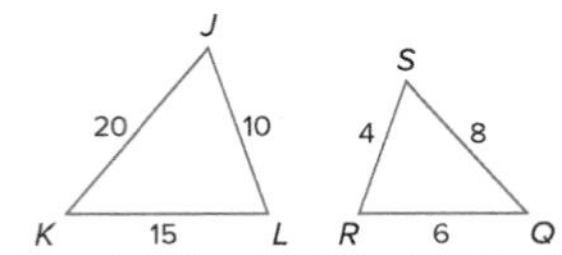

Yes; $\triangle JLK \sim \triangle SRQ$ by SSS Similarity.

Examples 2, 4 **Determine whether the triangles are similar.**

5. $\triangle LMN$ with $L(10, -2)$, $M(-2, 4)$, and $N(6, -4)$ and $\triangle PQR$ with $P(-1, 5)$, $Q(2, -1)$, and $R(-3, 3)$

6. $\triangle ABC$ with $A(2, -2)$, $B(5, -4)$, and $C(-3, -3)$ and $\triangle ADE$ with $D(8, -6)$, and $E(-8, -4)$

5. $\triangle LMN \nsim \triangle PQR$ 6. $\triangle ABC \sim \triangle ADE$ by SAS Similarity since $\angle BAC \cong \angle DAE$ and $\frac{AB}{AD} = \frac{AC}{AE} = \frac{1}{2}$.

7. In the figure, $\frac{AB}{DE} = \frac{BC}{EF}$. Determine whether the given information is sufficient to prove that $\triangle ABC \sim \triangle DEF$. Explain.

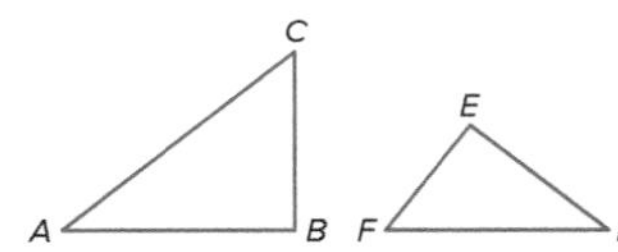

a. $\angle C \cong \angle C$ No; need congruent included angles.

b. $\frac{AB}{DE} = \frac{AC}{DF}$ Yes; SSS Similarity.

c. $\angle B \cong \angle E$ Yes; SAS Similarity.

d. $\angle A \cong \angle D$ No; need congruent included angles.

Example 5 G.SRT.5

8. **SPORTS** The goalpost at the North High School football field casts a shadow 50 feet long. The distance from the post to the shadow of the crossbar is 16 feet. If the crossbar is 10 feet above the ground, how tall is the goalpost? 31.25 ft

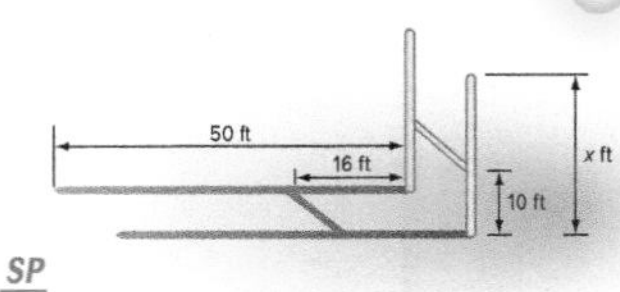

9. Yes; $\triangle XUZ \sim \triangle WUY$ by SSS Similarity. 10. No; $\frac{QS}{TR} = \frac{SP}{RS}$
11. Yes; $\triangle CBA \sim \triangle DBF$ by SAS Similarity.

Practice and Problem Solving Extra Practice is on page R7.

Examples 1, 3 G.SRT.2, G.SRT.5 **Determine whether the triangles are similar. If so, write a similarity statement. If not, what would be sufficient to prove the triangles similar? Explain your reasoning.**

9. 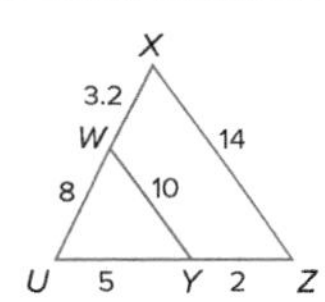

10. 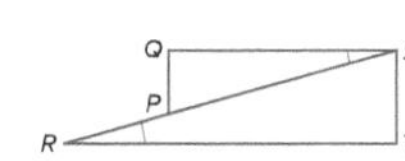

(11) 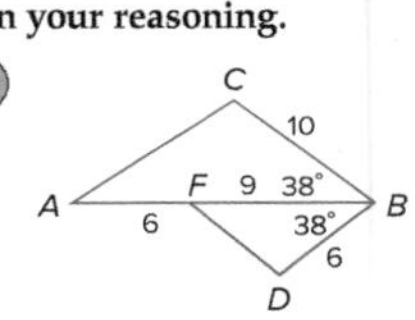

Homework Options

Use this chart to customize assignments for your students.

Differentiated Homework Options			
Levels	AL Basic	OL Core	BL Advanced
Exercises	9–26, 38–48	9–25 odd, 38–44	35–48
2-Day Option	9–25 odd, 45–48	9–26	
	10–26 even, 38–44	27–34, 38–48	

You can use ALEKS to provide additional remediation support with personalized instruction and practice.

Go Online! eBook

Interactive Student Guide

Use the *Interactive Student Guide* to deepen conceptual understanding.
- Graphing Linear Functions
- Modeling: Linear Functions

Examples 1, 3 G.SRT.2, G.SRT.5 **Determine whether the triangles are similar. If so, write a similarity statement. If not, what would be sufficient to prove the triangles similar? Explain your reasoning.**

12. Yes; $\triangle ABC \sim \triangle DCE$ by SAS Similarity
13. See margin.
14. Yes; $\triangle RST \sim \triangle YXW$ by SSS Similarity

12.

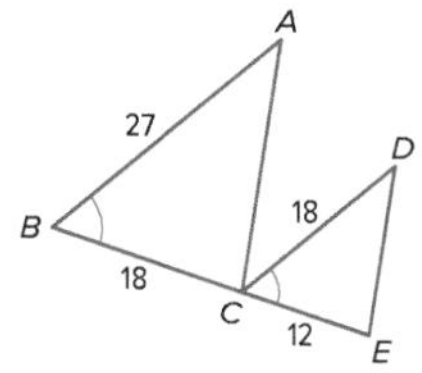

13.

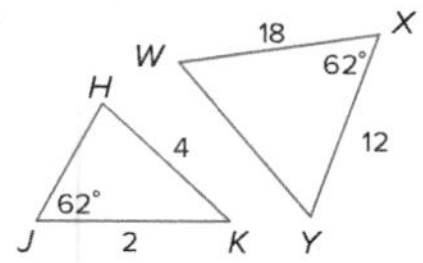

14.

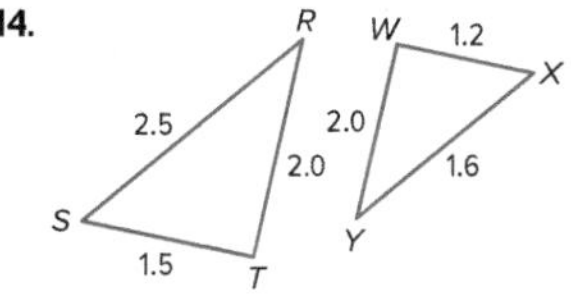

15.

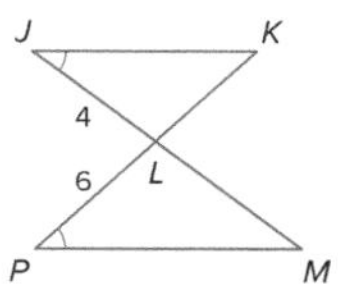

Yes; $\triangle JLK \sim \triangle PLM$ by AA Similarity.

16.

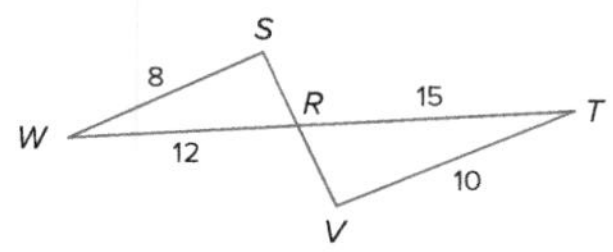

See margin.

17.

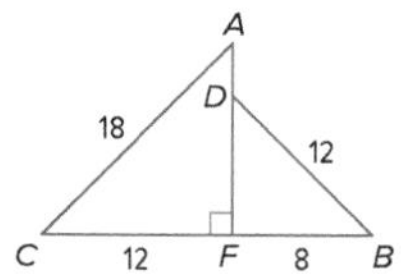

See margin.

Determine whether the triangles are similar. 18–25. See margin.

Example 2 G.SRT.5

18. $\triangle LMN$ with $L(-6, -2)$, $M(2, 4)$, and $N(8, -4)$ and $\triangle PQR$ with $P(3, 1)$, $Q(-1, -2)$, and $R(-2, 2)$

19. $\triangle DEF$ with $D(3, -1)$, $E(-1, 4)$, and $F(2, -3)$ and $\triangle GHI$ with $G(-3, 9)$, $H(12, -3)$, and $I(-9, 6)$

20. $\triangle RST$ with $R(1.5, -1.0)$, $S(-3.5, 1.0)$, and $T(3.0, -2.5)$ and $\triangle UVW$ with $U(-2.0, 3.0)$, $V(2.0, 6.0)$, and $W(-5.0, 5.0)$

21. $\triangle JKL$ with $J(1.2, -2.0)$, $K(-3.2, 4.0)$, and $L(3.6, -2.4)$ and $\triangle MNO$ with $M(-0.3, 0.5)$, $N(0.8, -1.0)$, and $O(0.9, -0.6)$

Example 4 G.SRT.5

22. $\triangle ABC$ with $A(-2, 4)$, $B(3, -4)$, and $C(1, -6)$ and $\triangle ADE$ with $D(8, -12)$, and $E(4, -16)$

23. $\triangle FGH$ with $F(5, 5)$, $G(20, -7)$, and $H(5, -10)$ and $\triangle FJK$ with $J(10, 1)$, and $K(5, 0)$

24. $\triangle BCD$ with $B(1.7, -1.0)$, $C(3.3, 0.6)$, and $D(-1.5, -1.8)$ and $\triangle BFG$ with $F(2.1, -0.6)$, and $G(0.9, -1.2)$

25. $\triangle MNP$ with $M(2.5, -1.2)$, $N(2.5, -0.4)$, and $P(3.1, -2.3)$ and $\triangle MRT$ with $R(2.5, 0.4)$, and $T(4.3, -4.5)$

Example 5

26. **FORESTRY** A hypsometer, as shown, can be used to estimate the height of a tree. Bartolo looks through the straw to the top of the tree and obtains the readings given. Find the height of the tree. 10.75 m

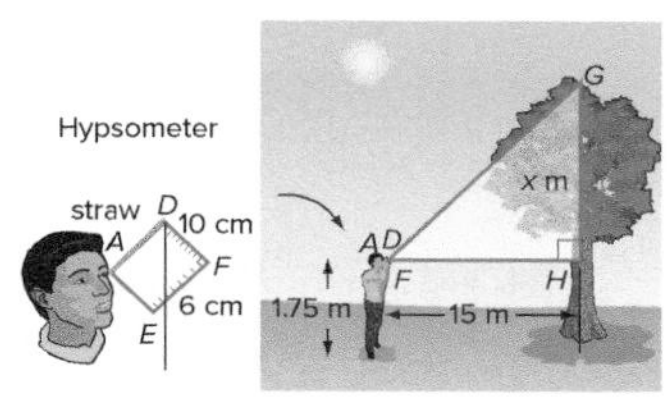

B **27.** **Given:** $\triangle XYZ$ and $\triangle ABC$ are right triangles; $\frac{XY}{AB} = \frac{YZ}{BC}$ 27, 28. See margin.

Prove: $\triangle YXZ \sim \triangle BAC$

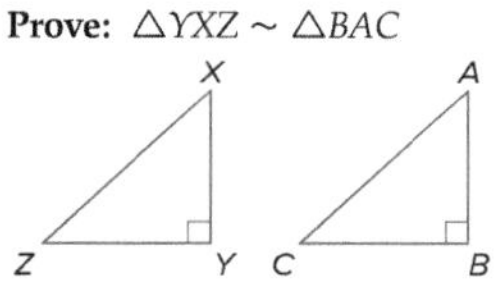

28. **PROOF** Write a two-column proof for Theorem 7.4.

28. Given: $\angle B \cong \angle E$, $\overline{QP} \parallel \overline{BC}$, $\overline{QP} \cong \overline{EF}$, $\frac{AB}{DE} = \frac{BC}{EF}$

Prove: $\triangle ABC \sim \triangle DEF$

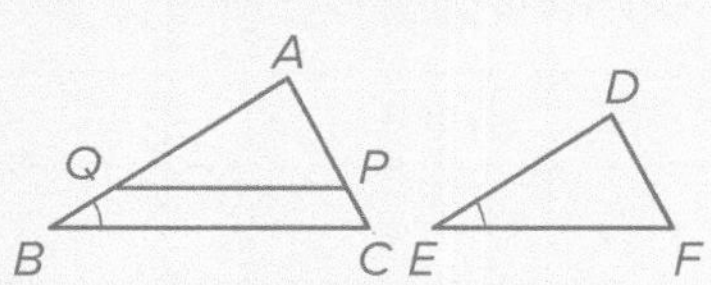

Proof: Statements (Reasons)

1. $\angle B \cong \angle E$, $\overline{QP} \parallel \overline{BC}$, $\overline{QP} \cong \overline{EF}$, $\frac{AB}{DE} = \frac{BC}{EF}$ (Given)
2. $\angle APQ \cong \angle C$, $\angle AQP \cong \angle B$ (Corr. ∠s Post.)
3. $\angle AQP \cong \angle E$ (Trans. Prop.)
4. $\triangle ABC \sim \triangle AQP$ (AA Similarity)
5. $\frac{AB}{AQ} = \frac{BC}{QP}$ (Def. of ~ △s)
6. $AB \cdot QP = AQ \cdot BC$; $AB \cdot EF = DE \cdot BC$ (Cross products)
7. $QP = EF$ (Def. of ≅ segs.)
8. $AB \cdot EF = AQ \cdot BC$ (Subst.)
9. $AQ \cdot BC = DE \cdot BC$ (Subst.)
10. $AQ = DE$ (Div. Prop.)
11. $\overline{AQ} \cong \overline{DE}$ (Def. of ≅ segs.)
12. $\triangle AQP \cong \triangle DEF$ (SAS)
13. $\angle APQ \cong \angle F$ (CPCTC)
14. $\angle C \cong \angle F$ (Trans. Prop.)
15. $\triangle ABC \sim \triangle DEF$ (AA Similarity)

Teaching the Mathematical Practices

Modeling Mathematically proficient students can apply the mathematics they know to solve problems arising in everyday life. In Exercise 26, encourage students to use the four-step problem solving plan.

Levels of Complexity Chart

The levels of the exercises progress from 1 to 3, with Level 1 indicating the lowest level of complexity.

Exercises	9–26	27–34, 45–48	35–44
C Level 3			●
B Level 2		●	
Level 1	●		

Additional Answers

18. $\triangle LMN \sim \triangle PQR$ by SSS Similarity since $\frac{LM}{PQ} = \frac{MN}{QR} = \frac{LN}{PR} = 2$
19. $\triangle DEF \sim \triangle GHI$ by SSS Similarity since $\frac{DE}{GH} = \frac{EF}{HI} = \frac{DF}{GI} = \frac{1}{3}$
20. $\triangle RST \not\sim \triangle UVW$
21. $\triangle JKL \sim \triangle MNO$ by SSS Similarity since $\frac{JK}{MN} = \frac{KL}{NO} = \frac{JL}{MO} = 4$
22. $\triangle ABC \sim \triangle ADE$ by SAS Similarity since $\angle BAC \cong \angle DAE$ and $\frac{AB}{AD} = \frac{BC}{DE} = \frac{1}{2}$
23. $\triangle FGH \sim \triangle FJK$ by SAS Similarity since $\angle GFH \cong \angle JFK$ and $\frac{FG}{FJ} = \frac{FH}{FK} = 3$
24. $\triangle BCD \sim \triangle BFG$ by SAS Similarity since $\angle CBD \cong \angle FBG$ and $\frac{BC}{BF} = \frac{BD}{BG} = 4$
25. $\triangle MNP \not\sim \triangle MRT$
27. **Proof:**

Statements (Reasons)

1. $\triangle XYZ$ and $\triangle ABC$ are right triangles. (Given)
2. $\angle XYZ$ and $\angle ABC$ are right angles. (Def. of rt. △)
3. $\angle XYZ \cong \angle ABC$ (All rt. ∠s are ≅.)
4. $\frac{XY}{AB} = \frac{YZ}{BC}$ (Given)
5. $\triangle YXZ \sim \triangle BAC$ (SAS Similarity)

Go Online!

The most up-to-date resources available for your program can be found at connectED.mcgraw-hill.com.

Additional Answers

31. Proof:

Statements (Reasons)

1. $\triangle ABC$ and $\triangle DEF$ are right triangles. (Given)
2. $\angle B$ and $\angle E$ are right angles. (Def. of rt. triangle)
3. $\angle B \cong \angle E$ (All rt. angles are congruent.)
4. $DE = \frac{2}{3}AB$, $EF = \frac{2}{3}BC$ (Given)
5. $\frac{DE}{AB} = \frac{2}{3}$, $\frac{EF}{BC} = \frac{2}{3}$ (Div. Prop. of =)
6. $\frac{DE}{AB} = \frac{EF}{BC}$ (Substitution)
7. $\triangle ABC \sim \triangle DEF$ (SAS Similarity Theorem)
8. $\frac{DF}{AC} = \frac{DE}{AB}$ (Corr. sides of ~ triangles are proportional.)

33a.

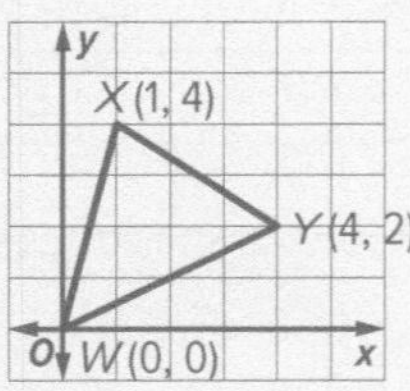

33c. Use the distance formula to find the side lengths of the preimage triangle and of the image triangle. Then find the ratio of the side lengths for each pair of corresponding sides. Use coordinates $W'(0, 0)$, $X'(2, 8)$, and $Y'(8, 4)$ for the image triangle.

$WX = \sqrt{(1-0)^2 + (4-0)^2} = \sqrt{17}$

$W'X' = \sqrt{(2-0)^2 + (8-0)^2} = \sqrt{68}$ or $2\sqrt{17}$

So, $\frac{W'X'}{WX} = \frac{2\sqrt{17}}{\sqrt{17}}$ or 2.

$XY = \sqrt{(4-1)^2 + (2-4)^2} = \sqrt{13}$

$X'Y' = \sqrt{(8-2)^2 + (4-8)^2} = \sqrt{52}$ or $2\sqrt{13}$

So, $\frac{X'Y'}{XY} = \frac{2\sqrt{13}}{\sqrt{13}} = 2.$

$WX = \sqrt{(2-0)^2 + (4-0)^2} = \sqrt{20} =$ or $2\sqrt{5}$

$W'X' = \sqrt{(4-0)^2 + (8-0)^2} = \sqrt{80}$ or $4\sqrt{5}$

So, $\frac{W'X'}{WX} = \frac{4\sqrt{5}}{2\sqrt{5}} = 2.$

Because all three pairs of corresponding sides have a ratio of 2 to 1, the triangles are similar by the SSS Similarity Theorem.

33d. The ratio of the perimeters is 2:1. Because the corresponding sides have a ratio of 2:1, the ratio will not change if you add the sides to find the perimeter.

MP STRUCTURE **Identify the similar triangles. Find each measure.**

29. KL $\triangle XYZ \sim \triangle JKL$; 12

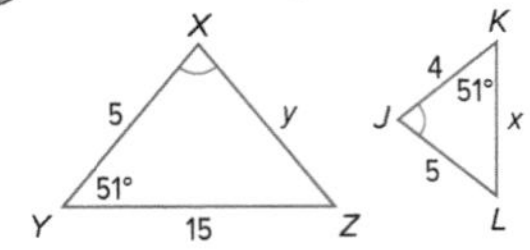

30. GH $\triangle FHK \sim \triangle FGJ$; $\frac{50}{3}$

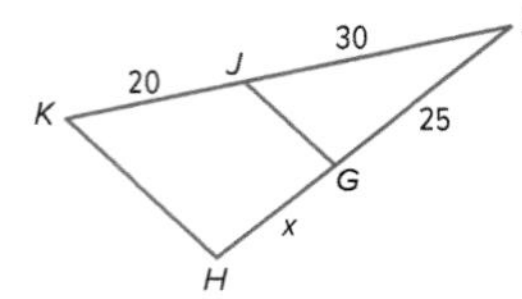

PROOF **Write a two-column proof.** See margin.

31. Given: $\triangle ABC$ and $\triangle DEF$ are right triangles; $DE = \frac{2}{3}AB$, $EF = \frac{2}{3}BC$

Prove: $\frac{DF}{AC} = \frac{DE}{AB}$

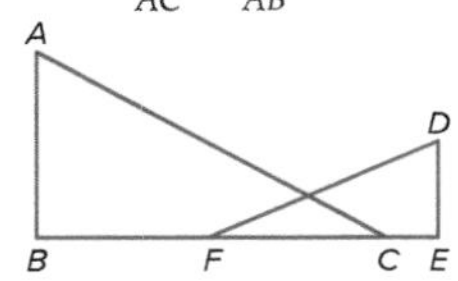

34. $\angle C \cong \angle C'$, since all rt. ∠s are ≅. Line ℓ is a transversal of || segments $\overline{BC}$ and $\overline{B'C'}$, so $\angle ABC \cong \angle A'B'C'$ since corresponding ∠s of || lines are ≅. Therefore, by AA Similarity, $\triangle ABC \sim \triangle A'B'C'$. So $\frac{BC}{AC}$, the slope of line ℓ through points A and B, is equal to $\frac{B'C'}{A'C'}$, the slope of line ℓ through points A′ and B′.

32. RIDES The Power Tower ride at Cedar Point amusement park is casting a shadow that is about 76 feet long. Addy is 5 feet 7 inches tall and her shadow is about 17 inches long.

a. About how tall is the Power Tower? 300 ft

b. If the shadow of the Valravn roller coaster is about 56.5 feet long, about how tall is the Valravn? 223 ft

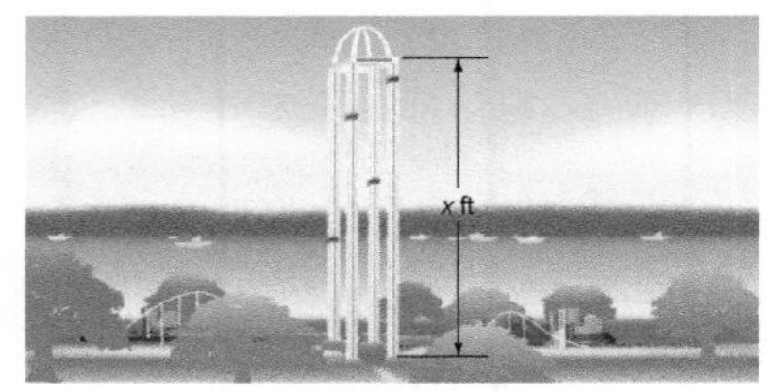

33. $\triangle WXY$ has coordinates $W(0, 0)$, $X(1, 4)$, and $Y(4, 2)$.

a. Graph the triangle. See margin.

b. $\triangle WXY$ is dilated in the coordinate plane with a scale factor of 2 and center (0, 0). What are the coordinates of the image triangle, $\triangle W'X'Y'$? $W'(0, 0)$, $X'(2, 8)$, and $Y'(8, 4)$

c. Use SSS Similarity to prove that $\triangle WXY \sim \triangle W'X'Y'$. See margin.

d. Find the ratio of the perimeters of the two triangles. Justify your reasoning. See margin.

34. REASONING Use similar triangles to show that the slope of the line through any two points on that line is constant. That is, if points A, B, A′ and B′ are on line ℓ, use similar triangles to show that the slope of the line from A to B is equal to the slope of the line from A′ to B′.

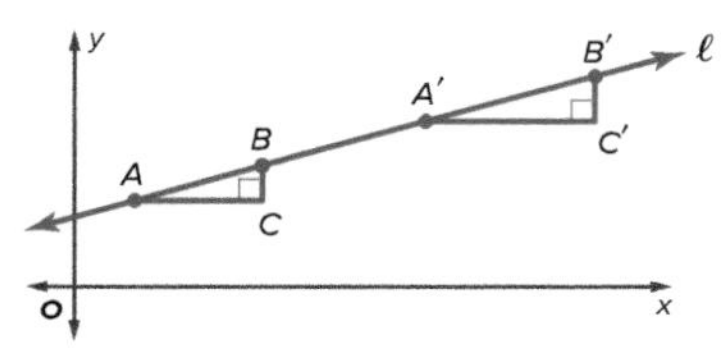

36a. Sample answer:

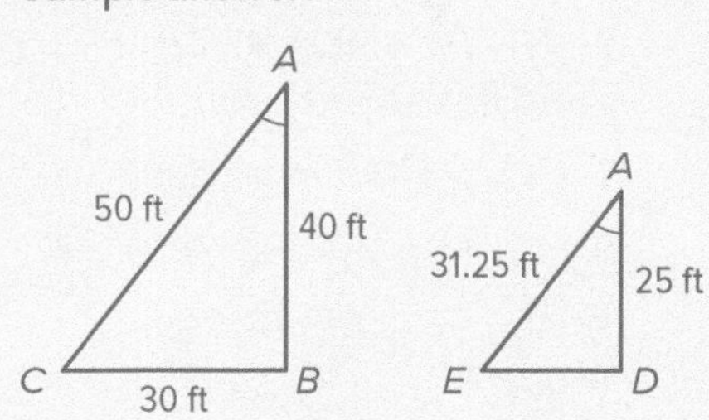

37a. Sample answer:

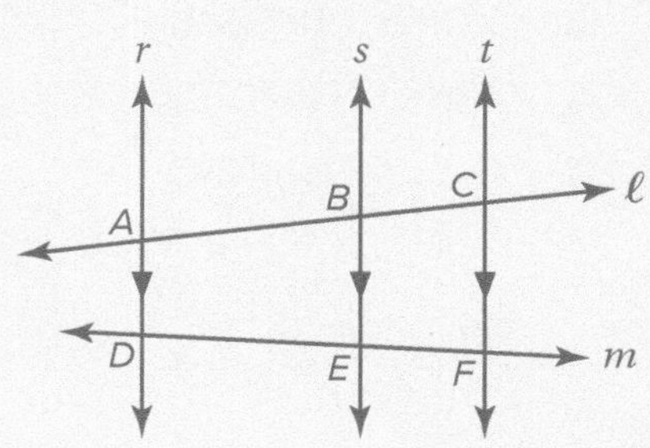

37b. Sample answer:

Lengths		Ratios	
AB	13 mm	$\frac{AB}{BC}$	1.625
BC	8 mm		
DE	12 mm	$\frac{DE}{EF}$	1.714
EF	7 mm		

37c. Sample answer: If three parallel lines intersect two transversals, then they divide the transversals proportionally.

35. Assume that $\triangle ABC \sim \triangle JKL$.

a. If the lengths of the sides of $\triangle JKL$ are half the length of the sides of $\triangle ABC$, and the area of $\triangle ABC$ is 40 square inches, what is the area of $\triangle JKL$? How is the area related to the scale factor of $\triangle ABC$ to $\triangle JKL$?

b. If the lengths of the sides of $\triangle ABC$ are three times the length of the sides of $\triangle JKL$, and the area of $\triangle ABC$ is 63 square inches, what is the area of $\triangle JKL$? How is the area related to the scale factor of $\triangle ABC$ to $\triangle JKL$?

35a. 10 in^2; The ratio of the areas is the square of the scale factor.

35b. 7 in^2; The ratio of the areas is the square of the scale factor.

36. ARCHITECTURAL DESIGN A-frame houses feature steeply-angled sides that begin at or near the foundation line and meet at the top in the shape of the letter A. Jessica is designing an A-frame house that will be 40 feet tall and the base of the house will be 60 feet long. She will build a second floor balcony around the outside of the house, 15 feet above the ground. The left side of the house will be 50 feet long and the balcony will intersect the side 18.75 feet from the bottom. The height of the house bisects the base of the house and the balcony.

a. Draw a diagram to model the side of the house. See margin.

b. Calculate the total length of the balcony. 37.5 feet

37. MULTIPLE REPRESENTATION In this problem, you will explore proportional parts of parallel lines.

a. Geometric Draw parallel lines r, s, and t with transversals l and m intersecting all three lines, as shown at the right.

b. Tabular Measure and record the lengths AB, BC, DE, EF, and the ratios $\frac{AB}{BC}$ and $\frac{DE}{EF}$.

c. Verbal Make a conjecture about the segments created by transversals intersecting parallel lines. 37a–c. See margin.

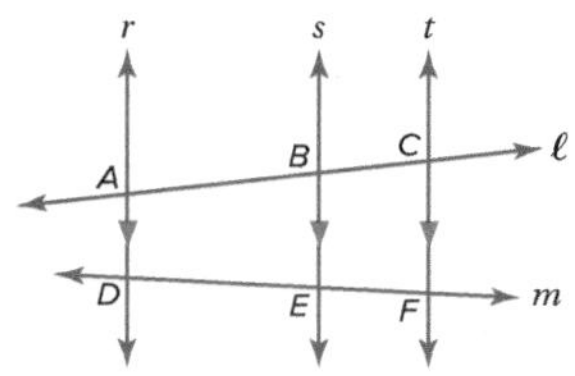

G.SRT.2, G.SRT.4, G.SRT.5

H.O.T. Problems Use Higher-Order Thinking Skills

38. WRITING IN MATH Compare and contrast the AA Similarity Postulate, the SSS Similarity Theorem, and the SAS Similarity Theorem. See margin.

39. REASONING Explain how you know $\triangle EFG \sim \triangle DBC$. Find EG and DB. See Ch. 7 Answer Appendix.

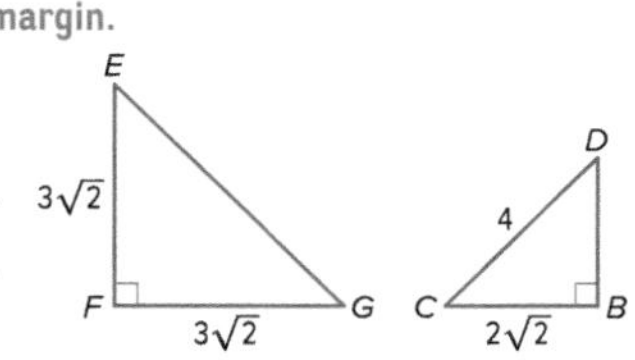

40. MP **REASONING** A triangle has sides that measure 3 inches, 4 inches, and 5 inches. Each side length is increased by x inches. Is the new triangle similar to the original triangle? Justify your reasoning. See Ch. 7 Answer Appendix.

41. OPEN-ENDED Draw a triangle that is similar to $\triangle ABC$ shown. Explain how you know that it is similar. See Ch. 7 Answer Appendix.

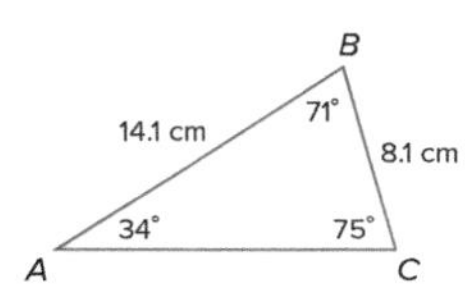

42. e **WRITING IN MATH** How can you choose an appropriate scale for a model or drawing? See Ch 7. Answer Appendix.

43. REASONING Explain how to determine whether $\triangle KLM \sim \triangle OPN$. Then, if possible, find KL and OP. See margin.

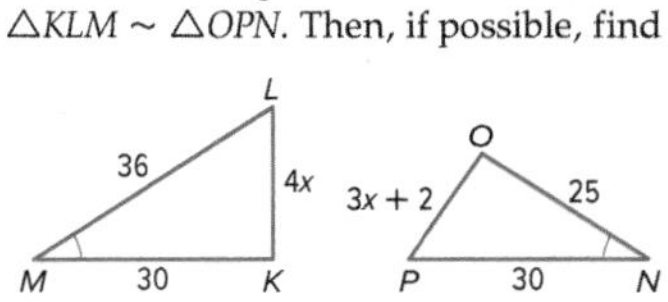

44. OPEN-ENDED Create a real-world problem that uses similar triangles to find the height of a tall object. Answers will vary.

MP Standards for Mathematical Practice

Emphasis On	Exercises
1 Make sense of problems.	18–25, 28–30, 33, 35, 41, 42
2 Reason abstractly.	1–7, 9–17, 34, 38–40, 43, 45–47
3 Construct viable arguments.	26, 27, 31, 45
4 Model with mathematics.	8, 26, 32, 36, 44, 48
6 Attend to precision.	37

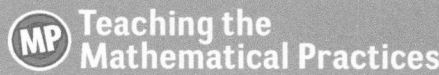

Exercise Alert

Protractor and Ruler Exercise 41 requires the use of a protractor and a ruler.

MP Teaching the Mathematical Practices

Reasoning Mathematically proficient students make sense of quantities and their relationships in problem situations. In Exercise 40, encourage students to draw a diagram representing the similar triangles described in the exercise.

Assess

Ticket Out the Door Make several copies of several pairs of triangles that are similar by either the SSS or SAS Similarity theorems. Include pairs of triangles that are not similar. As students leave the room, ask them to justify why the pairs of triangle are similar or not similar.

Additional Answers

38. Sample answer: The AA Similarity Postulate, SSS Similarity Theorem, and SAS Similarity Theorem are all tests that can be used to determine whether two triangles are similar. The AA Similarity Postulate is used when two pairs of congruent angles on two triangles are given. The SSS Similarity Theorem is used when the corresponding side lengths of two triangles are given. The SAS Similarity Theorem is used when two proportional side lengths and the included angle on two triangles are given.

43. Sample answer: Since one pair of corresponding angles are congruent, compare the ratios of the sides for which the angle is an including angle, or $\frac{KM}{ON} = \frac{30}{25} = \frac{6}{5}$; $\frac{LM}{PN} = \frac{36}{30} = \frac{6}{5}$. Since $\frac{KM}{ON} = \frac{LM}{PN}$, the SAS Similarity Theorem applies. To find KL, solve the proportion $\frac{KL}{OP} = \frac{6}{5}$; $\frac{4x}{3x+2} = \frac{6}{5}$, $x = 6$; $KL = 24$, $OP = 20$.

Go Online!

eSolutions Manual

Create worksheets, answer keys, and solutions handouts for your assignments.

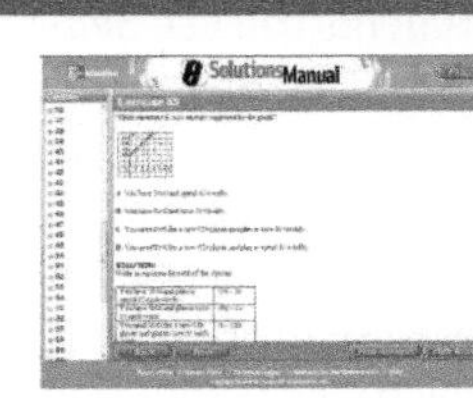

Preparing for Assessment

Exercises 45–48 require students to use the skills they will need on standardized assessments. Exercises are dual-coded with content standards and mathematical practice standards.

Dual Coding		
Items	Content Standards	MP Mathematical Practices
45a, b, c	G.SRT.2	2, 3
46	G.SRT.3	2
47	G.SRT.2	2
48	G.SRT.2	4

Diagnose Student Errors

Survey student responses for each item. Class trends may indicate common errors and misconceptions.

45.

A–C	Did not match up the vertices correctly.
D	CORRECT

47.

A	Did not recognize an SAS condition for proving similarity
B	Did not recognize an AA condition for proving similarity
C	Chose information that does not guarantee similarity
D	CORRECT
E	Included information that does not guarantee similarity

48.

A	Multiplied 1.8 by 2
B	CORRECT
C	Added the lengths of the shadows
D	Set up proportion incorrectly

Go Online!

Quizzes

Students can use *Self-Check Quizzes* to check their understanding of this lesson and have the results sent to you. You can also give the *Chapter Quiz*, which covers the content in Lessons 7-3 and 7-4.

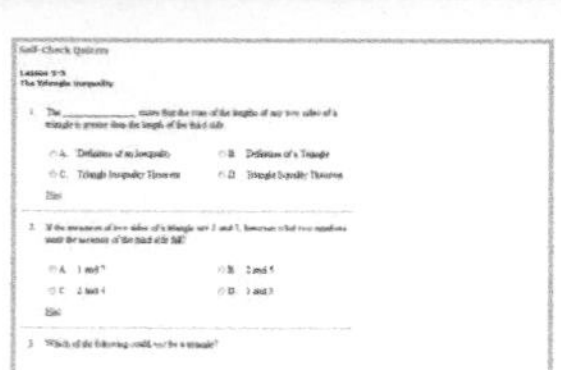

Preparing for Assessment

45. MULTI-STEP

a. In the figure, $\frac{AB}{DE} = \frac{BC}{EF}$. Which additional information would be sufficient to prove that the triangles are similar? Select all that apply. MP 2 G.SRT.2 **C**

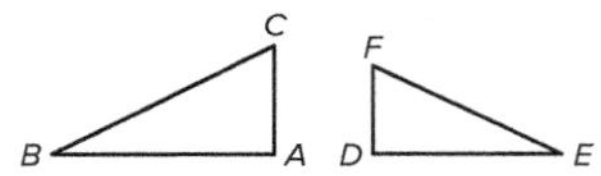

- ☐ A $\angle C \cong \angle F$
- ☐ B $\frac{AB}{DE} = \frac{BC}{EF}$
- ☐ C $\angle B \cong \angle E$
- ☐ D $\angle A \cong \angle D$

b. If the information you chose in part **a** is true, which of the following is a similarity statement for the two triangles? MP 2 **D**

- ○ A $\triangle ABC \sim \triangle FED$
- ○ B $\triangle ABC \sim \triangle EDF$
- ○ C $\triangle ABC \sim \triangle DFE$
- ○ D $\triangle ABC \sim \triangle DEF$

c. Which of the following statements can be proved true because they are corresponding parts of similar triangles? Select all that apply. MP 3 **B, D, E**

- ☐ A $\angle C \cong \angle D$
- ☐ B $\frac{AC}{FD} = \frac{BC}{EF}$
- ☐ C $\frac{AB}{DF} = \frac{BC}{EF}$
- ☐ D $\angle B \cong \angle E$
- ☐ E $\angle A \cong \angle D$
- ☐ F $\frac{AB}{EF} = \frac{BC}{DE}$

46. In the figure, $VT = 8\sqrt{3}$ and $RT = 10\sqrt{3}$. Determine whether the triangles are similar. If so, write a similarity statement. If not, what additional information would be sufficient to prove the triangles similar? Explain your reasoning. MP 2 G.SRT.3 **See margin.**

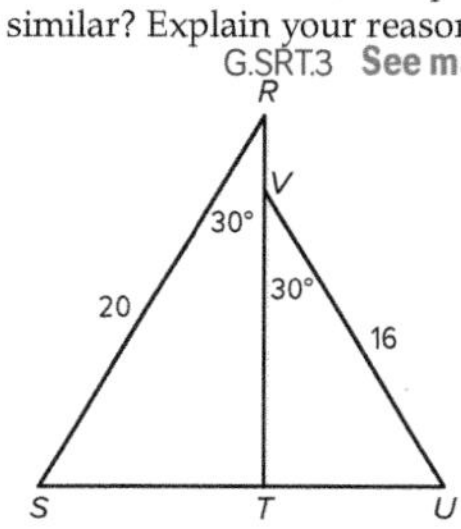

47. In the figure, $\angle P \cong \angle S$.

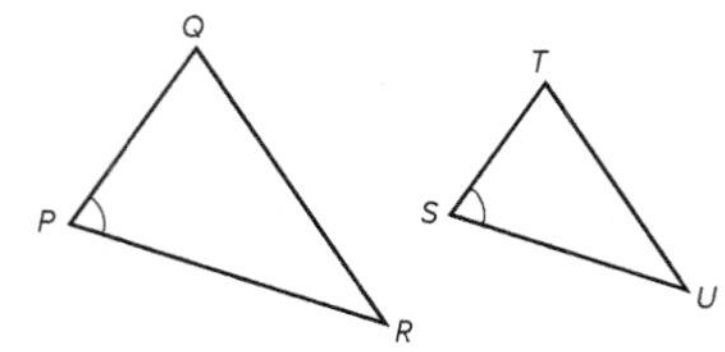

Which of the following additional pieces of information would allow you to prove that $\triangle PQR \sim \triangle STU$? MP 2 G.SRT.2 **D**

I. $\angle Q \cong \angle T$

II. $PQ = 8$, $ST = 6$, $PR = 12$, $SU = 9$

III. $\overline{QR} \cong \overline{TU}$

- ○ A I only
- ○ B II only
- ○ C III only
- ○ D I and II only
- ○ E I, II, and III

48. Michelle's dog is 35 centimeters tall. She wants to estimate the height of the street sign on the corner. She measures her dog's shadow and the street sign's shadow and then draws the sketch shown below.

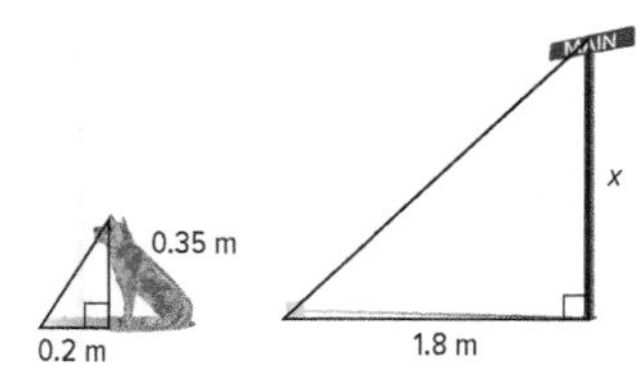

Which of the following is the best estimate of the height of the street sign? MP 4 G.SRT.2 **B**

- ○ A 3.6 m
- ○ B 3.15 m
- ○ C 2.0 m
- ○ D 1.03 m

Additional Answer

46. The triangles are similar by SAS Similarity Theorem. Since $\angle SRT$ and $\angle UVT = 30°$, $\angle SRT \cong \angle UVT$. Find the ratio of the sides including this angle. $\frac{10\sqrt{3}}{8\sqrt{3}} = \frac{5}{4} = \frac{20}{16}$. So, $\frac{RT}{VT} = \frac{RS}{VU}$ and the triangles are similar by SAS. The similarity statement is $\triangle RST \sim \triangle VUT$.

EXTEND 7-4

Geometry Lab

Proofs of Perpendicular and Parallel Lines

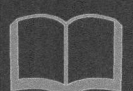

You have learned that two straight lines that are neither horizontal nor vertical are perpendicular if and only if the product of their slopes is −1. In this activity, you will use similar triangles to prove the first half of this theorem: if two straight lines are perpendicular, then the products of their slopes is −1.

Mathematical Practices

MP **3** Construct viable arguments and critique the reasoning of others.

Content Standards

G.GPE.5 Prove the slope criteria for parallel and perpendicular lines and use them to solve geometric problems (e.g., find the equation of a line parallel or perpendicular to a given line that passes through a given point).

Activity 1 Perpendicular Lines

Given: Slope of $\overleftrightarrow{AC} = m_1$, slope of $\overleftrightarrow{CE} = m_2$, and $\overleftrightarrow{AC} \perp \overleftrightarrow{CE}$

Prove: $m_1 m_2 = -1$

Step 1 On a coordinate plane, construct $\overleftrightarrow{AC} \perp \overleftrightarrow{CE}$ and transversal $\overleftrightarrow{BD}$ parallel to the *x*-axis through *C*. Then construct a right triangle $\triangle ABC$ such that $\overline{AC}$ is the hypotenuse and a right triangle $\triangle EDC$ such that $\overline{CE}$ is the hypotenuse. The legs of both triangles should be parallel to the *x*-and *y*-axes, as shown.

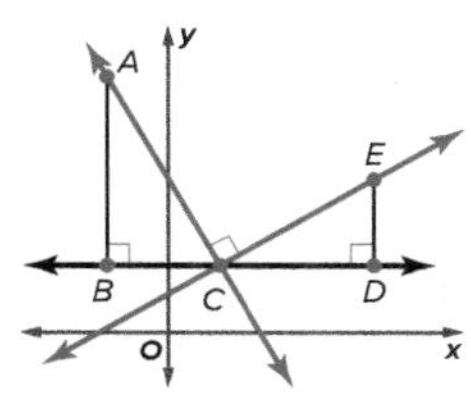

Step 2 Find the slopes of $\overleftrightarrow{AC}$ and $\overleftrightarrow{CE}$.

Slope of $\overleftrightarrow{AC}$

$m_1 = \frac{\text{rise}}{\text{run}}$ Slope Formula

$= \frac{-AB}{BC}$ or $-\frac{AB}{BC}$ rise = −AB, run = BC

Slope of $\overleftrightarrow{CE}$

$m_2 = \frac{\text{rise}}{\text{run}}$ Slope Formula

$= \frac{DE}{CD}$ rise = DE, run = CD

Step 3 Show that $\triangle ABC \sim \triangle CDE$.

Because $\triangle ACB$ is a right triangle with right angle *B*, $\angle BAC$ is complementary to $\angle ACB$. It is given that $\overleftrightarrow{AC} \perp \overleftrightarrow{CE}$, so we know that $\angle ACE$ is a right angle.

By construction, $\angle BCD$ is a straight angle. So, $\angle ECD$ is complementary to $\angle ACB$. Because angles complementary to the same angle are congruent, $\angle BAC \cong \angle ECD$.

Because right angles are congruent, $\angle B \cong \angle D$. Therefore, by AA Similarity, $\triangle ABC \sim \triangle CDE$.

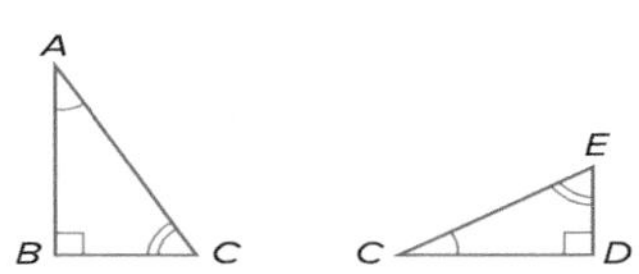

Step 4 Use the fact that $\triangle ABC \sim \triangle CDE$ to show that $m_1 m_2 = -1$.

Because $m_1 = -\frac{AB}{BC}$ and $m_2 = \frac{DE}{CD}$, $m_1 m_2 = \left(-\frac{AB}{BC}\right)\left(\frac{DE}{CD}\right)$. Because two similar polygons have proportional sides, $\frac{AB}{BC} = \frac{CD}{DE}$. Therefore, by substitution, $m_1 m_2 = \left(-\frac{CD}{DE}\right)\left(\frac{DE}{CD}\right)$ or −1.

Launch

Objective Use similar triangles to prove the slope criteria for perpendicular and parallel lines.

Materials for Each Group

- compass
- straightedge

Teaching Tip

Ask students what techniques (AA, SSS, SAS Similarity) they have learned thus far that could be used to prove that two triangles are similar.

Teach ELL

Working in Cooperative Groups Arrange students in groups of two, mixing abilities. Then have students complete the activity.

Practice Have students complete Exercises 1 and 2.

Focus on Mathematical Content

Finding Slope In Activity 1, the slope of $\overleftrightarrow{AC}$ is negative because it is the *rise* from *A* to *B* in the *negative* direction over the *run* from *B* to *C* in the *positive* direction.

Assess

Formative Assessment

Use Exercises 1 and 2 to assess whether students understand how to prove the slope criteria for perpendicular and parallel lines.

Additional Answer

1. Proof: The slope of $\overleftrightarrow{CE} = m_1 = \frac{DE}{CD}$, and the slope of $\overleftrightarrow{AC} = m_2 = -\frac{AB}{BC}$.

$m_1 m_2 = -1$	Given
$\left(\frac{DE}{CD}\right)\left(-\frac{AB}{BC}\right) = -1$	Substitution
$\left(\frac{DE}{CD}\right)\left(-\frac{AB}{BC}\right)\left(-\frac{BC}{AB}\right) = -1\left(-\frac{BC}{AB}\right)$	Multiply.
$\frac{DE}{CD} = \frac{BC}{AB}$	Simplify.

Because $\angle B$ and $\angle D$ are right angles, $\angle B \cong \angle D$. By SAS Similarity, $\triangle ABC \sim \triangle CDE$. Because $\angle B$ is a right angle, $\angle BAC$ and $\angle BCA$ are complementary. Because $\triangle ABC \sim \triangle CDE$, $\angle BAC \cong \angle DCE$. By substitution, $\angle DCE$ and $\angle BCA$ are complementary. By definition of complementary, $m\angle DCE + m\angle BCA = 90$. Because $\angle BCD$ is a straight angle, by angle addition $m\angle DCE + m\angle ACE + m\angle BCA = 180$ or $(m\angle DCE + m\angle BCA) + m\angle ACE = 180$. By substitution, $90 + m\angle ACE = 180$, so $m\angle ACE = 90$. By definition, $\angle ACE$ is a right angle. Because $\overleftrightarrow{CE}$ and $\overleftrightarrow{AC}$ intersect to form right $\angle ACE$, $\overleftrightarrow{CE} \perp \overleftrightarrow{AC}$.

2. Proof: The slope of $\overleftrightarrow{FG} = m_1 = \frac{GH}{FH}$, and the slope of $\overleftrightarrow{JK} = m_2 = \frac{KL}{LJ}$. Because $\overleftrightarrow{FG} \parallel \overleftrightarrow{JK}$, $\angle GFH \cong \angle KJL$ by the Corresponding Angles Postulate. Because right angles are congruent, $\angle GHF \cong \triangle KLJ$. Therefore, by AA Similarity, $\triangle FHG \sim \triangle JLK$. Because the corresponding sides of similar triangles are proportional, $\frac{GH}{KL} = \frac{HF}{LJ}$. This ratio can be rewritten as $\frac{GH}{HF} = \frac{KL}{LJ}$. Because $m_1 = \frac{GH}{HF}$ and $m_2 = \frac{KL}{LJ}$, by substitution, $m_1 = m_2$.

EXTEND 7-4

Geometry Lab

Proofs of Perpendicular and Parallel Lines *Continued*

Model Work cooperatively.

1. **PROOF** Use the diagram from Activity 1 to prove the second half of the theorem.

Given: Slope of $\overleftrightarrow{CE} = m_1$, slope of $\overleftrightarrow{AC} = m_2$, and $m_1 m_2 = -1$; $\triangle ABC$ is a right triangle with right angle B. $\triangle CDE$ is a right triangle with right angle D.

Prove: $\overleftrightarrow{CE} \perp \overleftrightarrow{AC}$ See margin.

You can also use similar triangles to prove that two distinct nonvertical lines are parallel if and only if they have the same slope. In this activity, you will prove the first half of the biconditional.

Activity 1 Parallel Lines

Given: Slope of $\overleftrightarrow{FG} = m_1$, slope of $\overleftrightarrow{JK} = m_2$, and $m_1 = m_2$. $\triangle FHG$ is a right triangle with right angle H. $\triangle JLK$ is a right triangle with right angle L.

Prove: $\overleftrightarrow{FG} \parallel \overleftrightarrow{JK}$

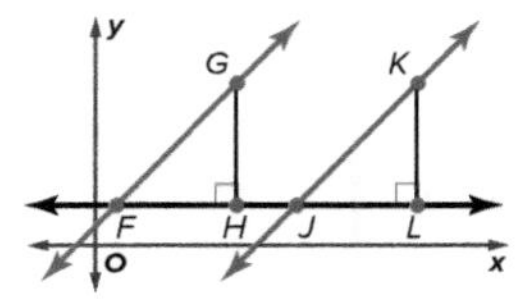

Step 1 On a coordinate plane, construct $\overleftrightarrow{FG}$ and $\overleftrightarrow{JK}$, right $\triangle FHG$, and right $\triangle JLK$. Then draw horizontal transversal $\overleftrightarrow{FL}$, as shown.

Step 2 Find the slopes of $\overleftrightarrow{FG}$ and $\overleftrightarrow{JK}$.

Slope of $\overleftrightarrow{FG}$		Slope of $\overleftrightarrow{JK}$	
$m_1 = \frac{\text{rise}}{\text{run}}$	Slope Formula	$m_2 = \frac{\text{rise}}{\text{run}}$	Slope Formula
$= \frac{GH}{HF}$	rise = GH, run = HF	$= \frac{KL}{LJ}$	rise = KL, run = LJ

Step 3 Show that $\triangle FHG \sim \triangle JLK$.

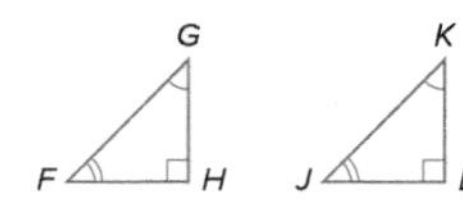

It is given that $m_1 = m_2$. By substitution, $\frac{GH}{HF} = \frac{KL}{LJ}$. This ratio can be rewritten as $\frac{GH}{KL} = \frac{HF}{LJ}$, so two pairs of corresponding sides are proportional. Because $\angle H$ and $\angle L$ are right angles, $\angle H \cong \angle L$.

Therefore, by SAS Similarity, $\triangle FHG \sim \triangle JLK$.

Step 4 Use the fact that $\triangle FHG \sim \triangle JLK$ to prove that $\overleftrightarrow{FG} \parallel \overleftrightarrow{JK}$.

Corresponding angles in similar triangles are congruent, so $\angle GFH \cong \angle KJL$. Notice that these are corresponding angles formed when $\overleftrightarrow{FG}$ and $\overleftrightarrow{JK}$ are cut by transversal $\overleftrightarrow{FL}$. Thus, by the Converse of the Corresponding Angles Postulate, $\overleftrightarrow{FG} \parallel \overleftrightarrow{JK}$.

Model Work cooperatively.

2. **PROOF** Use the diagram from Activity 2 to prove the second half of the theorem.

Given: Slope of $\overleftrightarrow{FG} = m_1$, slope of $\overleftrightarrow{JK} = m_2$, and $\overleftrightarrow{FG} \parallel \overleftrightarrow{JK}$

Prove: $m_1 = m_2$ See margin.

CHAPTER 7
Mid-Chapter Quiz
Lessons 7-1 through 7-4

Dilate the figure with the given vertices after a dilation at the indicated center with the given scale factor. Name the coordinates of the image. (Lesson 7-1)

1. $A(1, 4)$, $B(6, 8)$, $C(4, 9)$; center $(3, 6)$; $k = 0.5$ $A'(2, 5)$, $B'(4.5, 7)$, $C'(3.5, 7.5)$
2. $P(-3, 2)$, $Q(-3, 6)$, $R(-6, 1)$; center $(0, 0)$; $k = 3$ $P'(-9, 6)$, $Q'(-9, 18)$, $R'(-18, 3)$
3. $X(-1, -1)$, $Y(3, 3)$, $Z(2, -2)$; center $(1, -1)$; $k = 2$ $X'(-3, 1)$, $Y'(5, 7)$, $Z'(3, -3)$
4. **BUSINESS** A graphic designer has designed a 40 centimeter by 40 centimeter logo for a business with a circle with a radius of 5 centimeters at the center. They now need to reduce the logo to a 2 centimeter by 2 centimeter size to fit on business cards. (Lesson 7-1)
   a. What will the scale factor of the dilation be? 0.05
   b. What will the diameter of the circle be on the business card? 0.5 cm
5. **BIOLOGY** Mary studies red blood cells under a microscope to diagnose leukemia. The microscope is attached to a large screen on the wall where the picture is enlarged. If a red blood cell image is 15.04 centimeters on the screen and 0.00000752 meters in real life, how many times has the microscope amplified the image? (Lesson 7-1) 20,000 times

Each pair of polygons is similar. Find the value of x. (Lesson 7-2)

6. 22.5

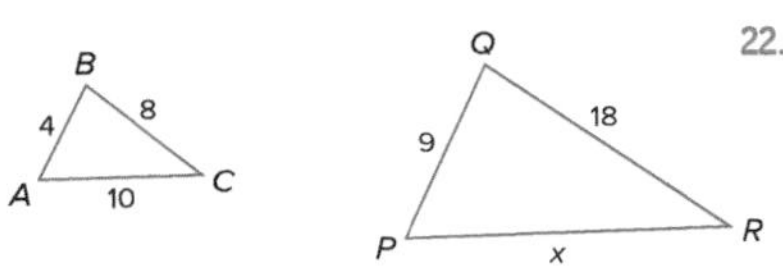

7. 3.4

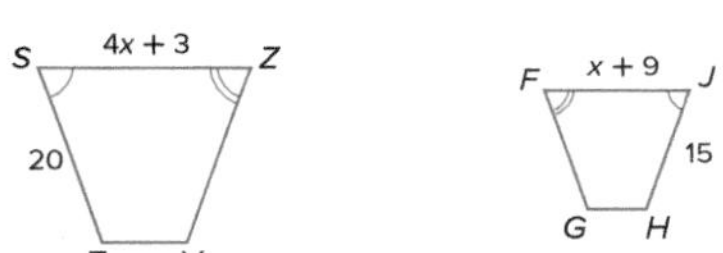

8. **MULTIPLE CHOICE** Two similar polygons have a scale factor of 3 : 5. The perimeter of the larger polygon is 120 feet. What is the perimeter of the smaller polygon? (Lesson 7-2) B

   A 68 ft **C** 192 ft
   B 72 ft **D** 200 ft

Determine whether the triangles are similar. If so, write a similarity statement. If not, what would be sufficient to prove the triangles similar? Explain your reasoning. (Lesson 7-3) 9. Yes; $\triangle YXZ \sim \triangle QRZ$ by AA Similarity.

9.

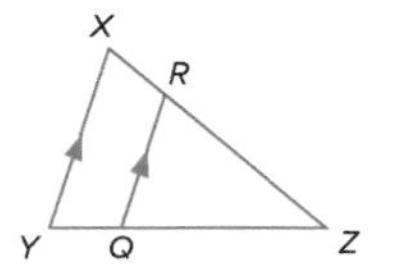

10.

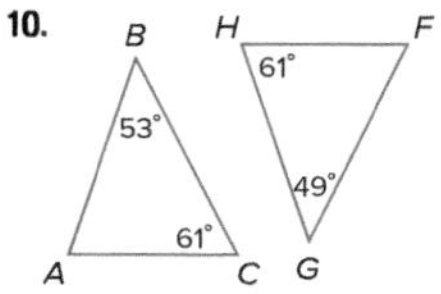

10. No; the missing $\angle$s of the $\triangle$s can never be $\cong$, so the $\triangle$s can never be $\sim$.

ALGEBRA Identify the similar triangles. Find the value of x in each case. (Lesson 7-3)

11. SR $\triangle JKL \sim \triangle RST$; 4

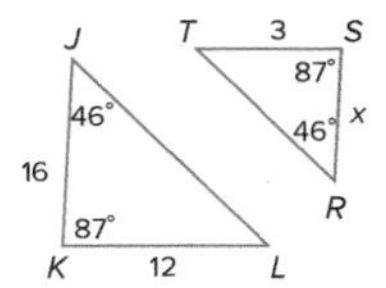

12. AF $\triangle ABC \sim \triangle AFD$; 10.8

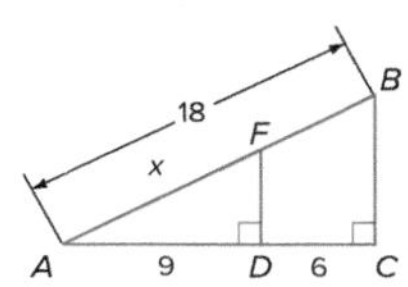

13. Is $\triangle TWZ$ similar to $\triangle YWX$? Explain your reasoning. (Lesson 7-4)

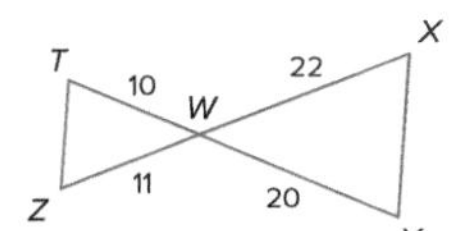

$\triangle TWZ \sim \triangle YWX$ by SAS Similarity, because $\angle W \cong \angle W$ and $\frac{TW}{YW} = \frac{WZ}{WX} = \frac{1}{2}$.

14. **TENNIS** Justin is playing tennis. When serving, he stands 12 feet away from the net, which is 3 feet tall. The ball is served from a height of 7.5 feet. Justin thinks the ball travels about 21.4 feet before it hits the ground 8 feet from the net on the opposite side. (Lesson 7-4)
    a. How far does the ball travel before it reaches the net? Round your answer to the nearest tenth if necessary. 12.8 feet
    b. What assumptions did you make to solve for the distance the ball travels? See margin.
    c. What mathematical practice did you use to solve this problem? See students' work.

Foldables Study Organizer

Dinah Zike's FOLDABLES®

Before students complete the Mid-Chapter Quiz, encourage them to review the information for Lessons 7-1 through 7-4 in their Foldables. Ask students to share the items they have added to their Foldables that have been helpful as they study Chapter 7.

ALEKS can be used as a formative assessment tool to target learning gaps for those who are struggling, while providing enhanced learning for those who have mastered the concepts.

Additional Answer

14b. Sample answer: I assumed that the ball traveled in a straight line, and barely passed over the net. I assumed that the angle between the net at the ground was a 90° angle, and I assumed that the angle between Justin and the ground was a 90° angle.

RtI Response to Intervention

Use the Intervention Planner to help you determine your Response to Intervention.

Intervention Planner

TIER 1 On Level OL

IF students miss 25% of the exercises or less,

THEN choose a resource:

SE Lessons 7-1, 7-2, 7-3, and 7-4

Go Online!
- Skills Practice
- Chapter Project
- Self-Check Quizzes

TIER 2 Strategic Intervention AL
Approaching grade level

IF students miss 50% of the exercises,

THEN choose a resource:

Quick Review Math Handbook

Go Online!
- Study Guide and Intervention
- Extra Examples
- Personal Tutors
- Homework Help

TIER 3 Intensive Intervention
2 or more grades below level

IF students miss 75% of the exercises,

THEN choose a resource:

Use *Math Triumphs, Geometry*

Go Online!
- Extra Examples
- Personal Tutors
- Homework Help
- Review Vocabulary

Go Online!

eAssessment

You can use the premade Mid-Chapter Test to assess students' progress in the first half of the chapter. Customize and create multiple versions of your Mid-Chapter Quiz and answer keys that align to your standards. Tests can be delivered on paper or online.

LESSON 7-5

Parallel Lines and Proportional Parts

SUGGESTED PACING (DAYS)

	Instruction
90 min.	0.5
45 min.	1.0

Track Your Progress

Objectives

1. Use proportional parts within triangles.
2. Use proportional parts with parallel lines.

Mathematical Background

If a line is parallel to one side of a triangle and intersects the other two sides in two distinct points, then it separates these sides into segments of proportional lengths. A *midsegment* is a segment with endpoints that are the midpoints of two sides of the triangle. The midsegment is parallel to one side of the triangle.

THEN

G.SRT.2 Given two figures, use the definition of similarity in terms of similarity transformations to decide if they are similar; explain using similarity transformations the meaning of similarity for triangles as the equality of all corresponding pairs of angles and the proportionality of all corresponding pairs of sides.

NOW

G.SRT.4 Prove theorems about triangles. *Theorems include: a line parallel to one side of a triangle divides the other two proportionally, and conversely; the Pythagorean Theorem proved using triangle similarity.*

G.SRT.5 Use congruence and similarity criteria for triangles to solve problems and to prove relationships in geometric figures.

G.CO.12 Make formal geometric constructions with a variety of tools and methods (compass and straightedge, string, reflective devices, paper folding, dynamic geometric software, etc.)

NEXT

G.SRT.5 Use congruence and similarity criteria for triangles to solve problems and to prove relationships in geometric figures.

Go Online! All of these resources and more are available at connectED.mcgraw-hill.com

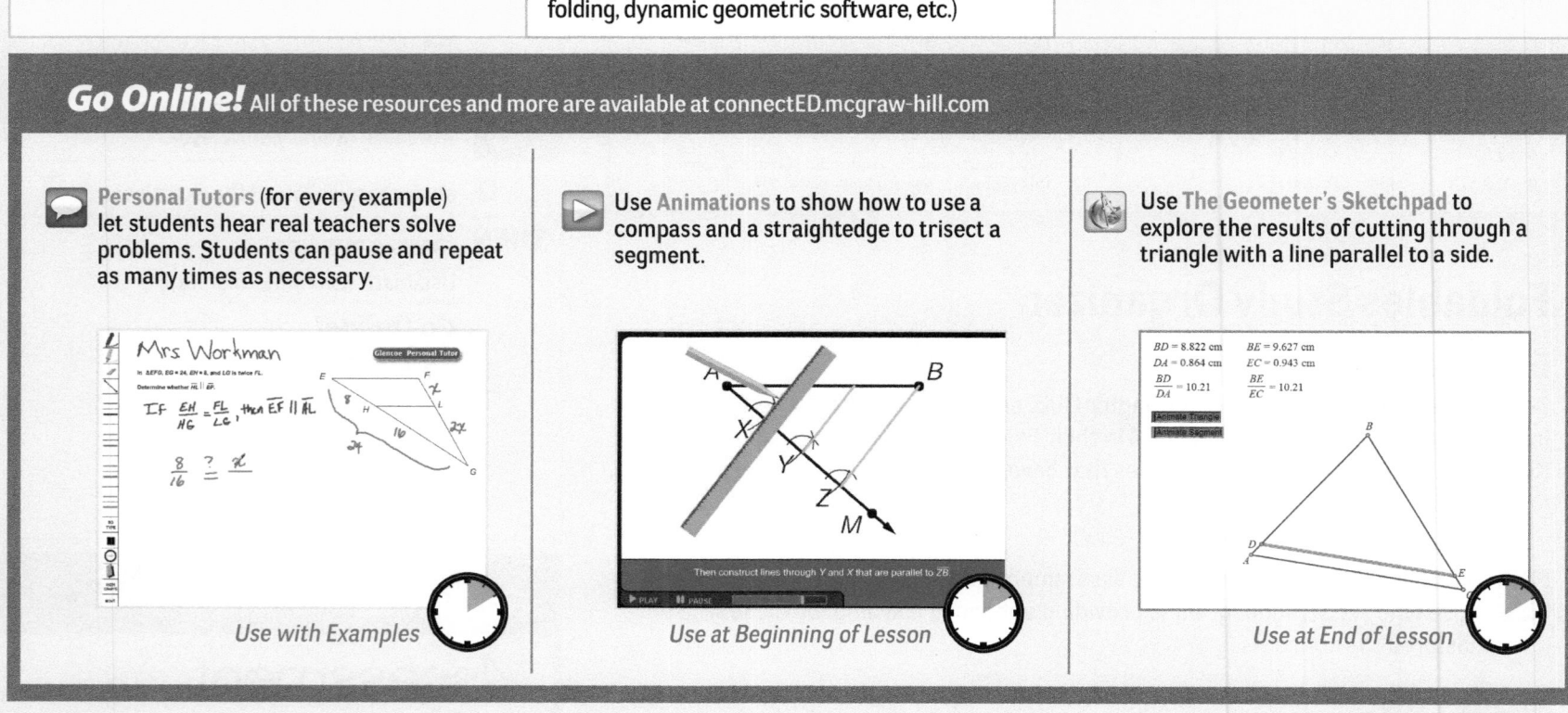

Personal Tutors (for every example) let students hear real teachers solve problems. Students can pause and repeat as many times as necessary.

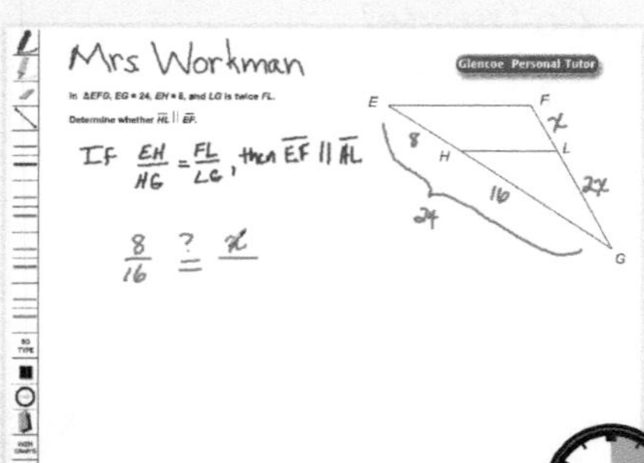

Use with Examples

Use **Animations** to show how to use a compass and a straightedge to trisect a segment.

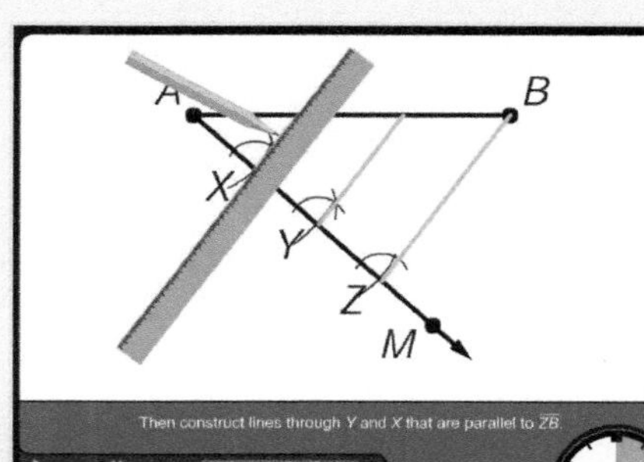

Use at Beginning of Lesson

Use **The Geometer's Sketchpad** to explore the results of cutting through a triangle with a line parallel to a side.

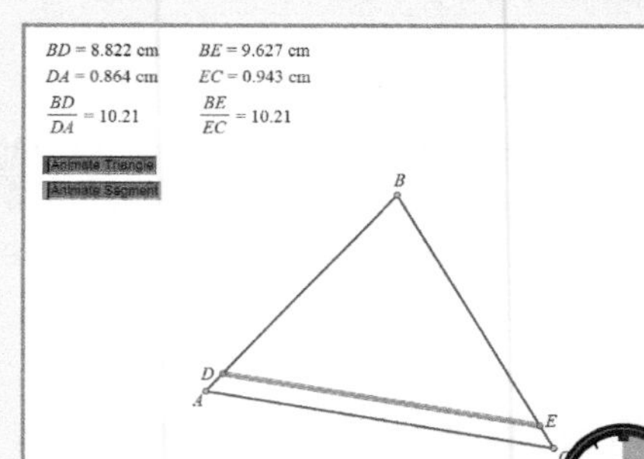

Use at End of Lesson

Using Open Educational Resources

Video Sharing If you are worried about offensive or distracting advertisements detracting from your lesson, use **SafeShare** to view YouTube videos. **SafeShare** filters out any distractions or advertisements. If you are unable to access SafeShare, try **KidsTube**, **MathATube**, **SchoolTube**, or **TeacherTube**. *Use as professional development*

Go Online!
connectED.mcgraw-hill.com

Worksheets

Differentiate Your Resources

Extra Practice Additional practice or homework; Skills Practice is best for approaching-level students and Practice is best for on-level and beyond-level students

Skills Practice

AL OL ELL

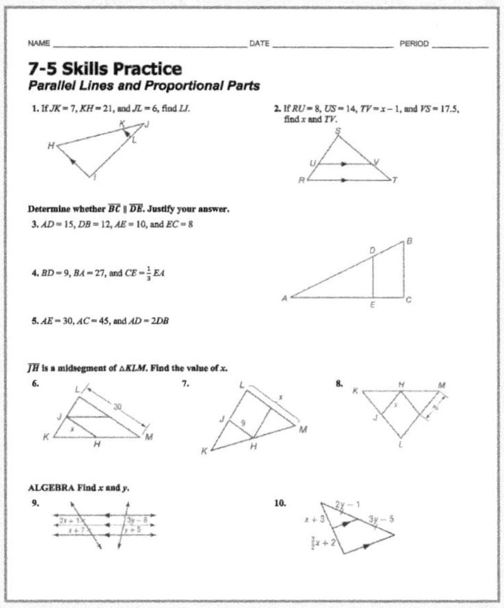
NAME ______ DATE ______ PERIOD ______

7-5 Skills Practice

Parallel Lines and Proportional Parts

Practice

AL OL BL ELL

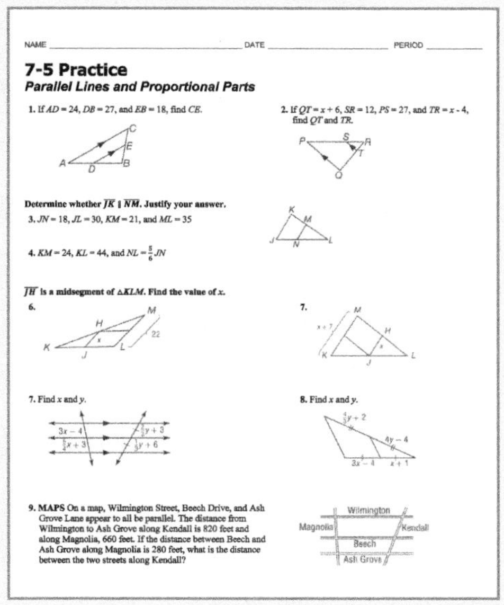
NAME ______ DATE ______ PERIOD ______

7-5 Practice

Parallel Lines and Proportional Parts

Word Problem Practice

AL OL BL ELL

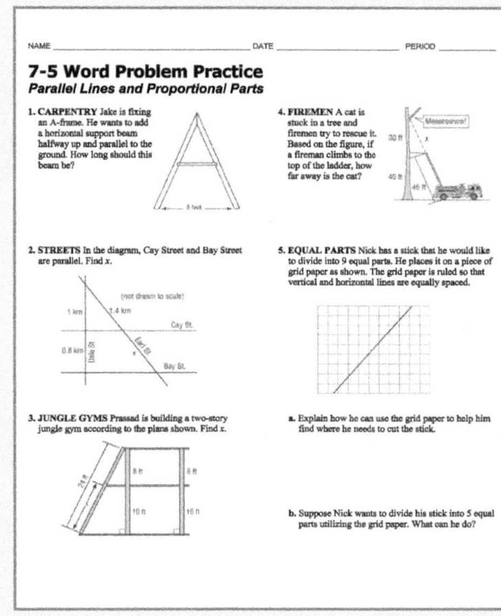
NAME ______ DATE ______ PERIOD ______

7-5 Word Problem Practice

Parallel Lines and Proportional Parts

Intervention Reteaching and vocabulary activities that can be used with struggling or absent students and as ELL support

Study Guide and Intervention

AL OL ELL

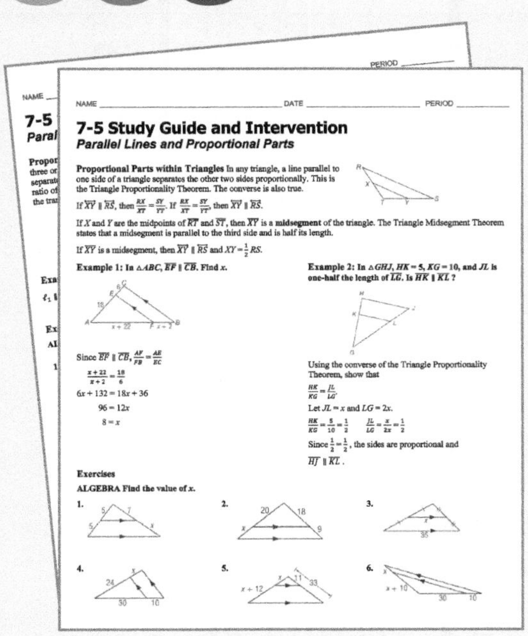
NAME ______ DATE ______ PERIOD ______

7-5 Study Guide and Intervention

Parallel Lines and Proportional Parts

Study Notebook

AL OL BL ELL

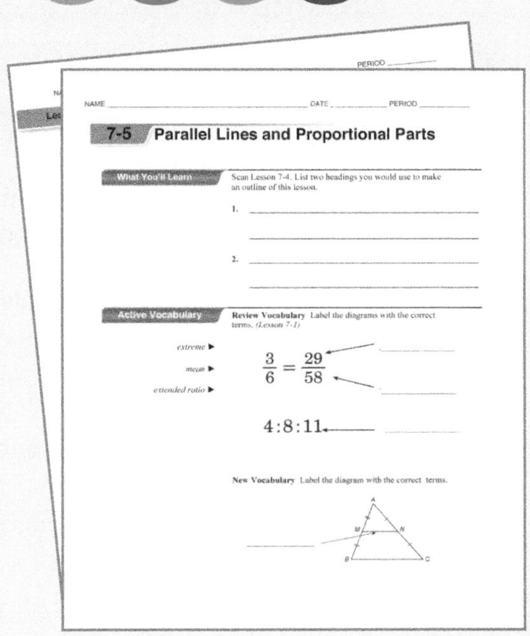
NAME ______ DATE ______ PERIOD ______

7-5 Parallel Lines and Proportional Parts

What You'll Learn

Active Vocabulary

Extension Activities that can be used to extend lesson concepts

Enrichment

OL BL ELL

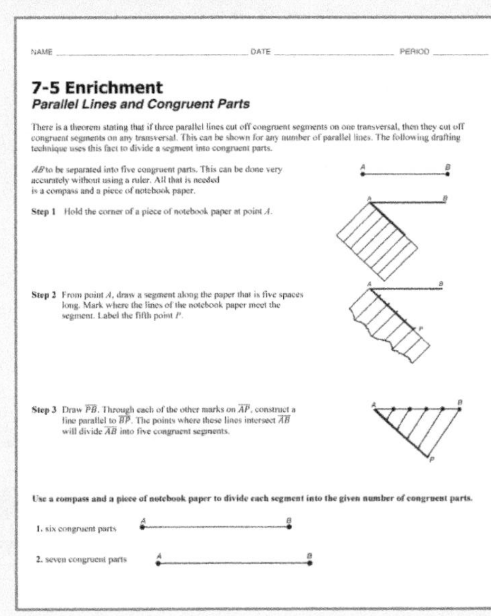
NAME ______ DATE ______ PERIOD ______

7-5 Enrichment

Parallel Lines and Congruent Parts

Launch

Have students read the Why? section of the lesson. Ask:

- Describe the distance between two parallel lines. It is always the same.
- Why does the distance between the train tracks appear to get smaller? Sample answer: The lines in the picture get closer together.
- Are the lines in the picture formed by the train tracks parallel? yes

Teach

Ask the scaffolded questions for each example to build conceptual understanding for students at all levels.

1 Proportional Parts Within Triangles

Example 1 Find the Length of a Side

AL What is one similarity statement for these triangles? Sample answer: $\triangle PST \sim \triangle PRQ$

OL Could you use *ST* and *RQ* with the Triangle Proportionality Theorem? No; The Triangle Proportionality Theorem only applies to the nonparallel sides.

BL If *S* and *T* are moved toward *P*, and *R* and *Q* remain stationary, how will the proportion change? The proportion will stay the same. The ratios of *PS* to *SR* and *PT* to *TQ* will decrease.

Need Another Example?
In $\triangle RST$, $\overline{RT} \parallel \overline{VU}$, $SV = 3$, $VR = 8$, and $UT = 12$. Find *SU*.

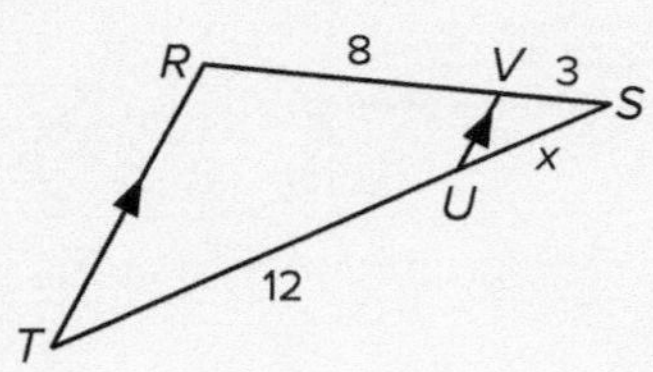

$4\frac{1}{2}$

Go Online!

Interactive Whiteboard
Use the *eLesson*, *Lesson Presentation*, or *Interactive Classroom* to present this lesson.

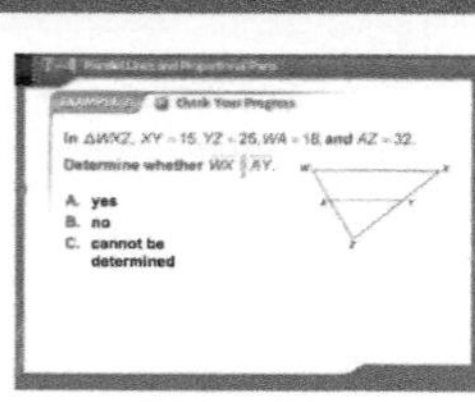

LESSON 5

Parallel Lines and Proportional Parts

Then
- You used proportions to solve problems between similar triangles.

Now
- 1 Use proportional parts within triangles.
- 2 Use proportional parts with parallel lines.

Why?
- Photographers have many techniques at their disposal that can be used to add interest to a photograph. One such technique is the use of a vanishing point perspective, in which an image with parallel lines, such as train tracks, is photographed so that the lines appear to converge at a point on the horizon.

New Vocabulary
midsegment of a triangle

Mathematical Practices
1 Make sense of problems and persevere in solving them.
3 Construct viable arguments and critique the reasoning of others.

Content Standards
G.SRT.4 Prove theorems about triangles.
G.SRT.5 Use congruence and similarity criteria for triangles to solve problems and to prove relationships in geometric figures.
G.CO.12 Make formal geometric constructions with a variety of tools and methods (compass and straightedge, string, reflective devices, paper folding, dynamic geometric software, etc.).

1 Proportional Parts Within Triangles When a triangle contains a line that is parallel to one of its sides, the two triangles formed can be proved similar using the Angle-Angle Similarity Postulate. Because the triangles are similar, their sides are proportional.

Theorem 7.5 Triangle Proportionality Theorem

If a line is parallel to one side of a triangle and intersects the other two sides, then it divides the sides into segments of proportional lengths.

Example If $\overline{BE} \parallel \overline{CD}$, then $\frac{AB}{BC} = \frac{AE}{ED}$.

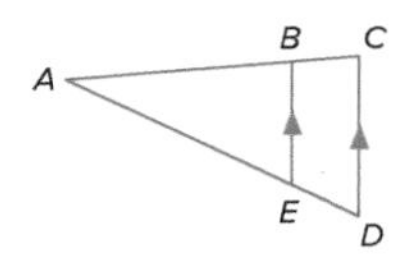

You will prove Theorem 7.5 in Exercise 30.

G.SRT.4

Example 1 Find the Length of a Side

In $\triangle PQR$, $\overline{ST} \parallel \overline{RQ}$. If $PT = 7.5$, $TQ = 3$, and $SR = 2.5$, find PS.

Use the Triangle Proportionality Theorem.

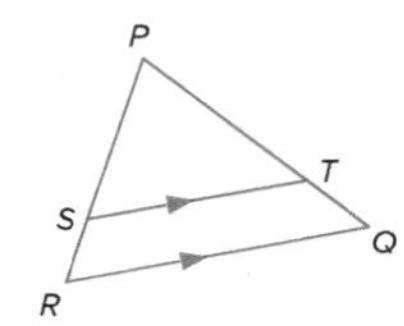

$\frac{PS}{SR} = \frac{PT}{TQ}$	Triangle Proportionality Theorem
$\frac{PS}{2.5} = \frac{7.5}{3}$	Substitute.
$PS \cdot 3 = (2.5)(7.5)$	Cross Products Property
$3PS = 18.75$	Multiply.
$PS = 6.25$	Divide each side by 3.

Guided Practice

1. If $PS = 12.5$, $SR = 5$, and $PT = 15$, find TQ. 6

MP Mathematical Practices Strategies

Look for and make use of structure.
Help students understand proportionality. Ask them questions to help them think through the concept. For example:

- How can you use proportionality to solve problems? Look through the examples in this lesson if you need help. You can write proportions to represent the relationships among the side lengths, substitute the known numbers, and solve for the unknown values.
- Are the lengths of two parallel segments that have their endpoints on two other parallel lines proportional? Yes; in fact, they are the same.
- Are the lengths of two parallel segments that have their endpoints on two intersecting lines proportional? yes
- What is a midsegment of a triangle? a segment that joins the midpoints of two sides
- What relationships do you know about the midsegment of a triangle? A midsegment of a triangle will be parallel to the third side of the triangle, and will be one half its length.

Math History Link

Galileo Galilei (1564–1642) Galileo was born in Pisa, Italy. He studied philosophy, astronomy, and mathematics. Galileo made essential contributions to all three disciplines.

Source: *Encyclopaedia Britannica*

The converse of Theorem 7.5 can be proven using the proportional parts of a triangle.

Theorem 7.6 Converse of Triangle Proportionality Theorem

If a line intersects two sides of a triangle and separates the sides into proportional corresponding segments, then the line is parallel to the third side of the triangle.

Example If $\frac{AE}{EB} = \frac{CD}{DB}$, then $\overline{AC} \parallel \overline{ED}$.

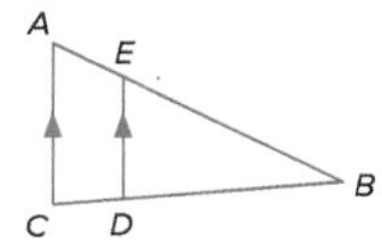

You will prove Theorem 7.6 in Exercise 31.

G.SRT.5

Example 2 Determine if Lines Are Parallel

In $\triangle DEF$, $EH = 3$, $HF = 9$, and DG is one-third the length of $\overline{GF}$. Is $\overline{DE} \parallel \overline{GH}$?

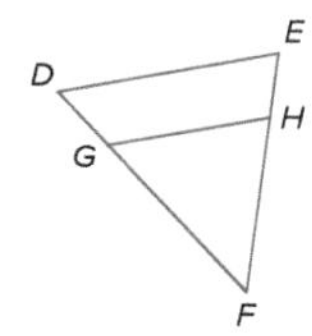

Using the converse of the Triangle Proportionality Theorem, in order to show that $\overline{DE} \parallel \overline{GH}$, we must show that $\frac{DG}{GF} = \frac{EH}{HF}$.

Find and simplify each ratio. Let $DG = x$.
Because DG is one-third of GF, $GF = 3x$.

$\frac{DG}{GF} = \frac{x}{3x}$ or $\frac{1}{3}$ $\qquad$ $\frac{EH}{HF} = \frac{3}{9}$ or $\frac{1}{3}$

Because $\frac{1}{3} = \frac{1}{3}$, the sides are proportional, so $\overline{DE} \parallel \overline{GH}$.

Guided Practice

2. DG is half the length of $\overline{GF}$, $EH = 6$, and $HF = 10$. Is $\overline{DE} \parallel \overline{GH}$? **no**

Study Tip ELL
MP Sense-Making The three midsegments of a triangle form the *midsegment triangle.*

A **midsegment of a triangle** is a segment with endpoints that are the midpoints of two sides of the triangle. Every triangle has three midsegments. The midsegments of $\triangle ABC$ are $\overline{RP}$, $\overline{PQ}$, and $\overline{RQ}$.

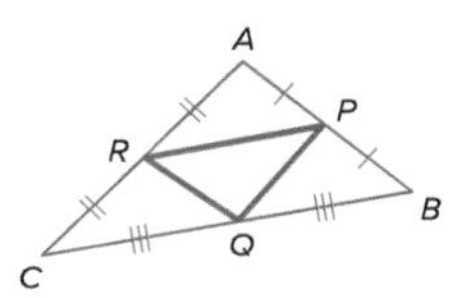

A special case of the Triangle Proportionality Theorem is the Triangle Midsegment Theorem. The Triangle Midsegment Theorem is similar to the Trapezoid Midsegment Theorem, which states that the midsegment of a trapezoid is parallel to the bases and its length is one half the sum of the measures of the bases.

Theorem 7.7 Triangle Midsegment Theorem

A midsegment of a triangle is parallel to one side of the triangle, and its length is one half the length of that side.

Example If J and K are midpoints of $\overline{FH}$ and $\overline{HG}$, respectively, then $\overline{JK} \parallel \overline{FG}$ and $JK = \frac{1}{2}FG$.

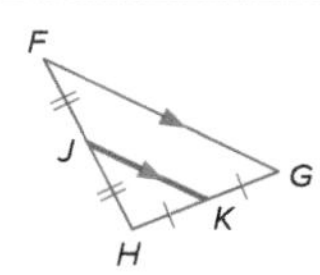

You will prove Theorem 7.7 in Exercise 32.

Example 2 Determine if Lines Are Parallel

AL **Could we write the proportion in a different way? If so, how?** Yes; Sample answer: $\frac{FG}{GD} = \frac{FH}{HE}$

OL **If we used x for GF and $\frac{1}{3}x$ for DG, would the result be the same?** Yes, as long as DG is 3 times GF.

BL **If $EH = 2$, $HF = 7$, and $GF = DG + 10$, can we show that $\overline{DE}$ is parallel to $\overline{GH}$?** No; the variables need to cancel out in order to prove that the ratios are equal.

Need Another Example?

In $\triangle DEF$, $DH = 18$, $HE = 36$, and $DG = \frac{1}{2}GF$. Is $\overline{GH} \parallel \overline{FE}$?

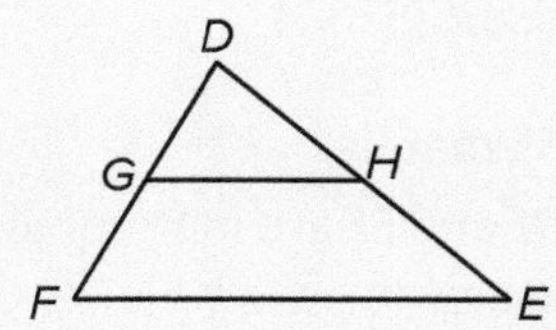

Yes; from the given information, $\frac{DG}{GH} = \frac{DH}{HE}$. Because the segments have proportional lengths, $\overline{GH} \parallel \overline{FE}$.

Watch Out!

Proportional Lengths When students use the Triangle Proportionality Theorem, direct them to write a proportion. Remind them that if they are finding the length of an entire side of a triangle, then they must use the entire side of the similar triangle.

Example 3 Use the Triangle Midsegment Theorem

AL What points do X, Y, and Z represent? the midpoints of the sides

OL If $RS = 22$, what is YZ? 11

BL What is $m\angle XZS$? 124

Need Another Example?
In the figure, $\overline{DE}$ and $\overline{EF}$ are midsegments of $\triangle ABC$. Find each measure.

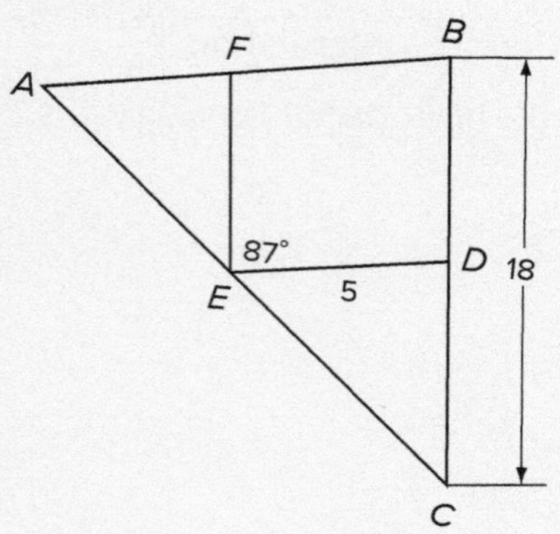

a. AB 10
b. FE 9
c. $m\angle AFE$ 87

G.SRT.5, G.CO.10

Example 3 Use the Triangle Midsegment Theorem

In the figure, $\overline{XY}$ and $\overline{XZ}$ are midsegments of $\triangle RST$. Find each measure.

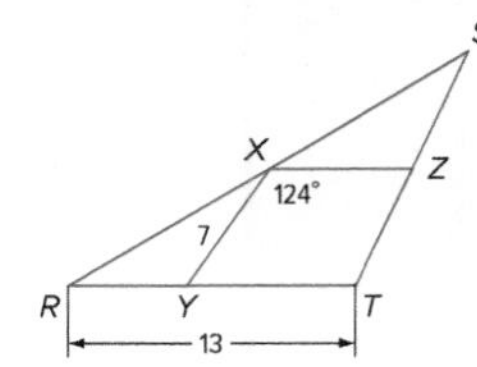

a. XZ

$XZ = \frac{1}{2}RT$ Triangle Midsegment Theorem

$XZ = \frac{1}{2}(13)$ Substitution

$XZ = 6.5$ Simplify.

b. ST

$XY = \frac{1}{2}ST$ Triangle Midsegment Theorem

$7 = \frac{1}{2}ST$ Substitution

$14 = ST$ Multiply each side by 2.

c. $m\angle RYX$

By the Triangle Midsegment Theorem, $\overline{XZ} \parallel \overline{RT}$.

$\angle RYX \cong \angle YXZ$ Alternate Interior Angles Theorem

$m\angle RYX = m\angle YXZ$ Definition of congruence

$m\angle RYX = 124$ Substitution

Guided Practice

Find each measure.

3A. DE 7.5

3B. DB 9.2

3C. $m\angle FED$ 82

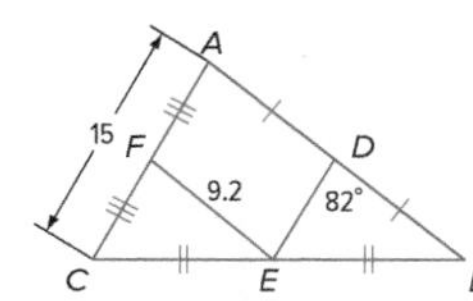

2 Proportional Parts with Parallel Lines

Another special case of the Triangle Proportionality Theorem involves three or more parallel lines cut by two transversals. Notice that if transversals a and b are extended, they form triangles with the parallel lines.

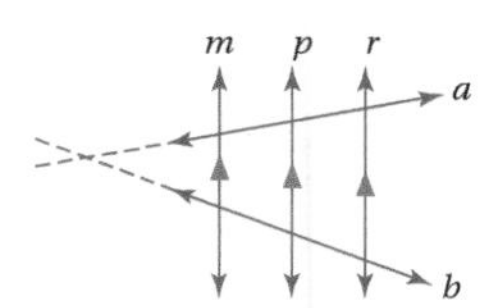

Study Tip ELL
Other Proportions
Two other proportions can be written for the example in Corollary 7.1.
$\frac{AB}{EF} = \frac{BC}{FG}$ and $\frac{AC}{BC} = \frac{EG}{FG}$

Corollary 7.1 Proportional Parts of Parallel Lines

If three or more parallel lines intersect two transversals, then they cut off the transversals proportionally.

Example If $\overline{AE} \parallel \overline{BF} \parallel \overline{CG}$, then $\frac{AB}{BC} = \frac{EF}{FG}$.

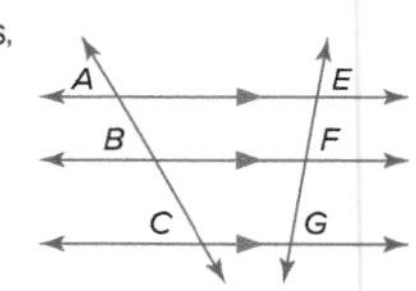

You will prove Corollary 7.1 in Exercise 28.

Real-World Link

To make a two-dimensional drawing appear three-dimensional, an artist provides several perceptual cues.

- *size* - faraway items look smaller
- *clarity* - closer objects appear more in focus
- *detail* - nearby objects have texture, while distant ones are roughly outlined

Source: Center for Media Literacy

G.SRT.5

Real-World Example 4 Use Proportional Segments of Transversals

ART **Megan is drawing a hallway in one-point perspective. She uses the guidelines shown to draw two windows on the left wall. If segments $\overline{AD}$, $\overline{BC}$, $\overline{WZ}$, and $\overline{XY}$ are all parallel, $AB = 8$ centimeters, $DC = 9$ centimeters, and $ZY = 5$ centimeters, find WX.**

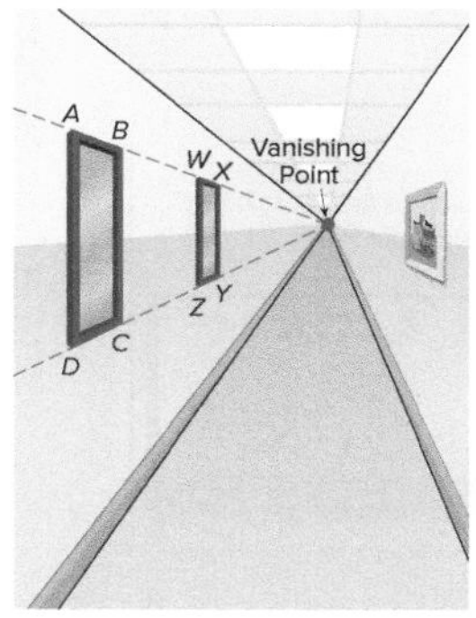

By Corollary 7.1, if $\overline{AD} \parallel \overline{BC} \parallel \overline{WZ} \parallel \overline{XY}$, then $\frac{AB}{WX} = \frac{DC}{ZY}$.

$\frac{AB}{WX} = \frac{DC}{ZY}$ Corollary 7.1

$\frac{8}{WX} = \frac{9}{5}$ Substitute.

$WX \cdot 9 = 8 \cdot 5$ Cross Products Property

$9WX = 40$ Simplify.

$WX = \frac{40}{9}$ Divide each side by 4.

The distance between W and X should be $\frac{40}{9}$ or about 4.4 centimeters.

CHECK The ratio of DC to ZY is 9 to 5, which is about 10 to 5 or 2 to 1. The ratio of AB to WX is 8 to 4.4 or about 8 to 4 or 2 to 1 as well, so the answer is reasonable. ✓

Guided Practice

4. REAL ESTATE *Frontage* is the measurement of a property's boundary that runs along the side of a particular feature such as a street, lake, ocean, or river. Find the ocean frontage for Lot A to the nearest tenth of a yard. **82.9 yd**

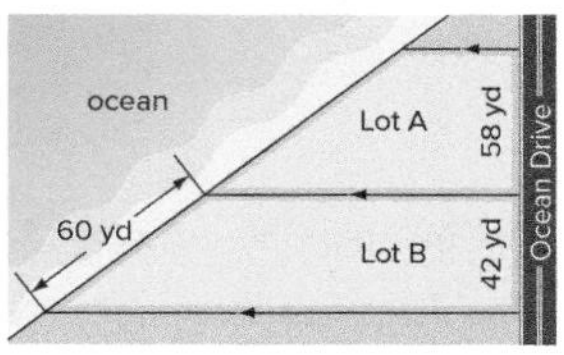

If the scale factor of the proportional segments is 1, then they separate the transversals into congruent parts.

Corollary 7.2 **Congruent Parts of Parallel Lines**

If three or more parallel lines cut off congruent segments on one transversal, then they cut off congruent segments on every transversal.

Example If $\overline{AE} \parallel \overline{BF} \parallel \overline{CG}$, and $\overline{AB} \cong \overline{BC}$, then $\overline{EF} \cong \overline{FG}$.

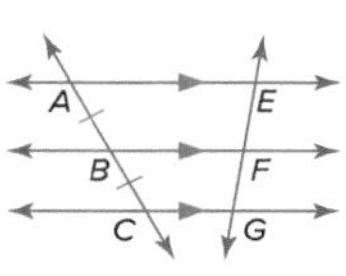

You will prove Corollary 7.2 in Exercise 29.

2 Proportional Parts with Parallel Lines

Example 4 Use Proportional Segments of Transversals

AL In this situation, what are the transversals? $\overline{AX}$ and $\overline{DY}$

OL What figures does the vanishing point create? similar triangles

BL If $DY = 22$ centimeters, what is BW? about 7.1 cm

Need Another Example?

Maps In the figure, Larch, Maple, and Nuthatch Streets are all parallel. The figure shows the distances between city blocks. Find x.

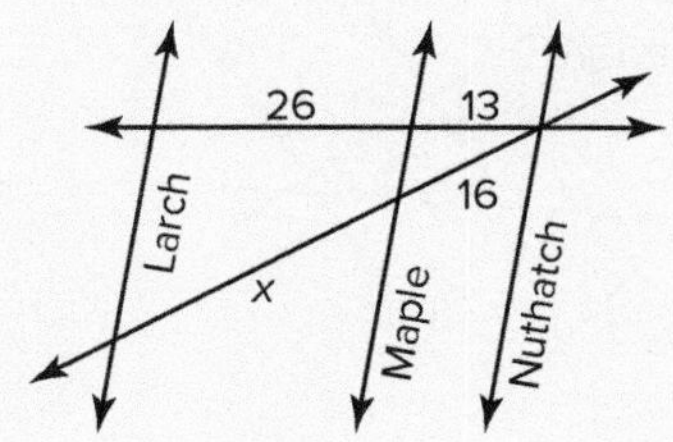

32

Differentiated Instruction OL BL

Visual Learners Artistically talented students can further investigate the mathematics of vanishing points (see p. 537, Example 4). Have students create a drawing that uses a vanishing point and discuss the mathematics involved.

Example 5 Use Congruent Segments of Transversals

AL **Does Corollary 7.2 address the relationships between the parallel segments?** no; only the transversals

OL **How can we check our solution?** Substitute the values of x and y and confirm that $JK = KL$ and $MP = PQ$.

BL **If we extended $\overline{JL}$ and $\overline{MQ}$ until they intersect, how many pairs of congruent triangles would be formed?** 3

Need Another Example?

Find x and y.

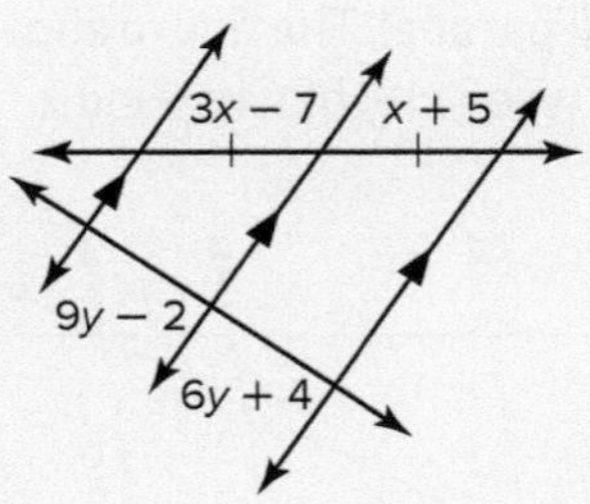

$x = 6$; $y = 2$

> **Watch Out!**
>
> **Answering Questions** Be careful to answer the question that is asked. In Example 5, you find the values of x and y, not the lengths of the line segments.

Go Online!

Log into ConnectED to watch an Animation of the trisecting a segment construction. Pause and continue to follow along using your tools.

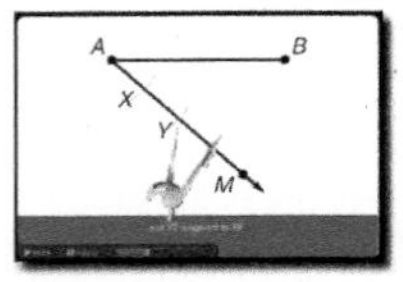

G.SRT.5

Real-World Example 5 Use Congruent Segments of Transversals

ALGEBRA Find x and y.

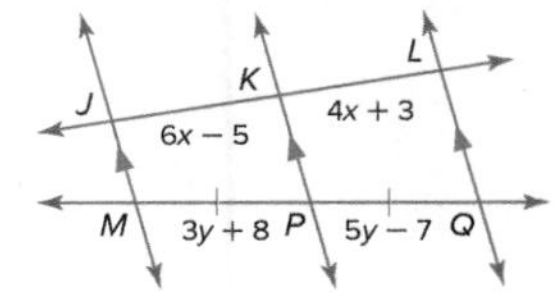

Because $\overleftrightarrow{JM} \parallel \overleftrightarrow{KP} \parallel \overleftrightarrow{LQ}$ and $\overline{MP} \cong \overline{PQ}$, then $\overline{JK} \cong \overline{KL}$ by Corollary 7.2.

$JK = KL$	Definition of congruence
$6x - 5 = 4x + 3$	Substitution
$2x - 5 = 3$	Subtract 4x from each side.
$2x = 8$	Add 5 to each side.
$x = 4$	Divide each side by 2.
$MP = PQ$	Definition of congruence
$3y + 8 = 5y - 7$	Substitution
$8 = 2y - 7$	Subtract 3y from each side.
$15 = 2y$	Add 7 to each side.
$7.5 = y$	Divide each side by 2.

Guided Practice

5A. $\frac{5}{3}$

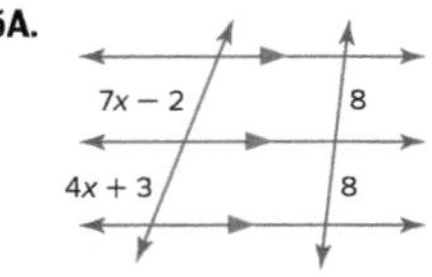

5B. 6

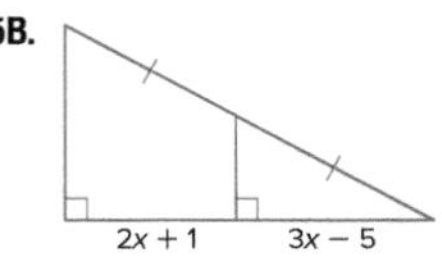

It is possible to separate a segment into two congruent parts by constructing the perpendicular bisector of a segment. However, a segment cannot be separated into three congruent parts by constructing perpendicular bisectors. To do this, you must use parallel lines and Corollary 7.2.

Construction Trisect a Segment

Draw a segment $\overline{AB}$. Then use Corollary 7.2 to trisect $\overline{AB}$.

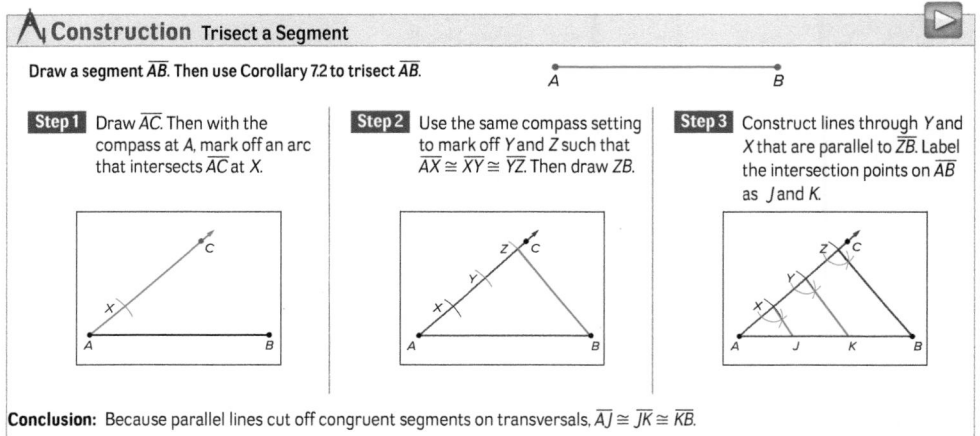

Step 1 Draw $\overline{AC}$. Then with the compass at A, mark off an arc that intersects $\overline{AC}$ at X.

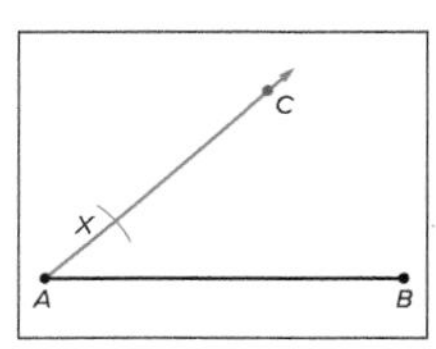

Step 2 Use the same compass setting to mark off Y and Z such that $\overline{AX} \cong \overline{XY} \cong \overline{YZ}$. Then draw ZB.

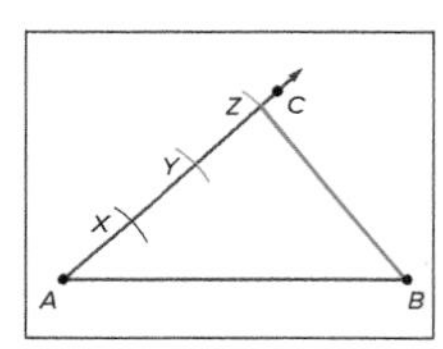

Step 3 Construct lines through Y and X that are parallel to $\overline{ZB}$. Label the intersection points on $\overline{AB}$ as J and K.

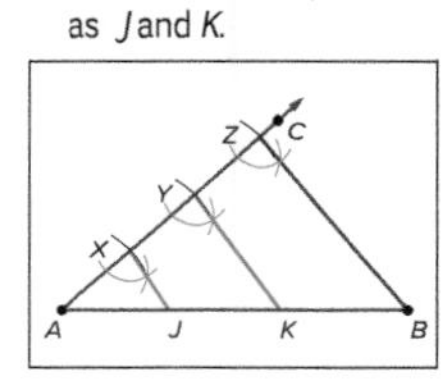

Conclusion: Because parallel lines cut off congruent segments on transversals, $\overline{AJ} \cong \overline{JK} \cong \overline{KB}$.

Differentiated Instruction AL OL BL

Kinesthetic Learners Have students use string, masking tape, and a tiled floor to mark off congruent segments on parallel lines made with masking tape on the floor. Use the string to show that if three or more parallel lines form congruent segments on one transversal, they form congruent segments on another transversal.

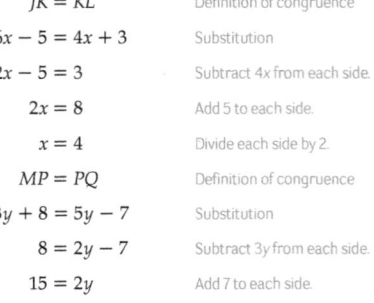

Check Your Understanding ◯ = Step-by-Step Solutions begin on page R13.

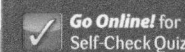

Go Online! for a Self-Check Quiz

Example 1 G.SRT.5

1. If $XM = 4$, $XN = 6$, and $NZ = 9$, find XY. 10

2. If $XN = 6$, $XM = 2$, and $XY = 10$, find NZ. 24

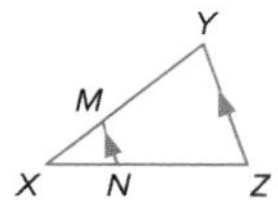

Example 2 G.SRT.4

3. In $\triangle ABC$, $BC = 15$, $BE = 6$, $DC = 12$, and $AD = 8$. Determine whether $\overline{DE} \parallel \overline{AB}$. Justify your answer.

3. Yes; $\frac{AD}{DC} = \frac{BE}{EC} = \frac{2}{3}$, so $\overline{DE} \parallel \overline{AB}$.

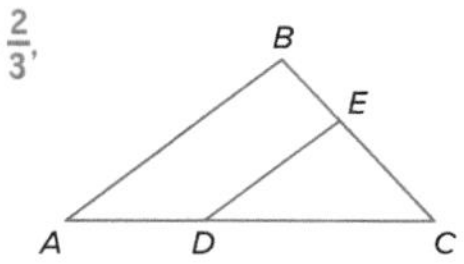

4. In $\triangle JKL$, $JK = 15$, $JM = 5$, $LK = 13$, and $PK = 9$. Determine whether $\overline{JL} \parallel \overline{MP}$. Justify your answer. no; $\frac{1}{2} \neq \frac{4}{9}$

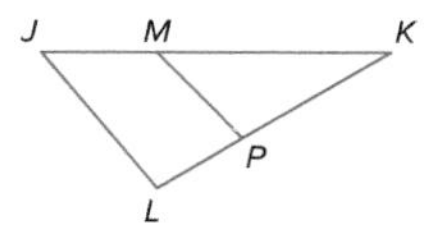

Example 3 G.SRT.5

$\overline{JH}$ is a midsegment of $\triangle KLM$. Find the value of x.

5. 11

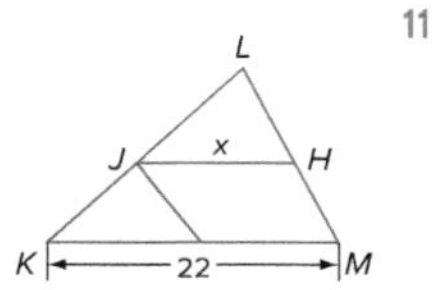

6. 10

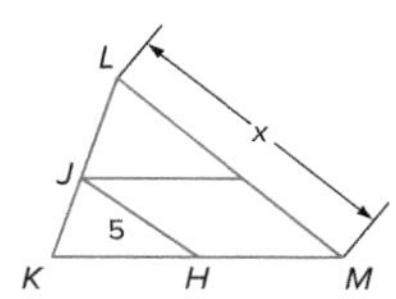

Example 4 G.SRT.5

7. MAPS Refer to the map at the right. 3rd Avenue and 5th Avenue are parallel. If the distance from 3rd Avenue to City Mall along State Street is 3201 feet, find the distance between 5th Avenue and City Mall along Union Street. Round to the nearest tenth. 2360.3 ft

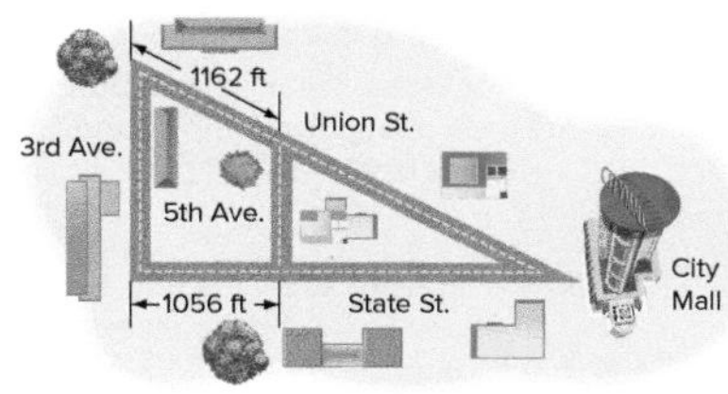

Example 5 G.SRT.5

ALGEBRA Find x and y.

8. $x = 5$; $y = 8$

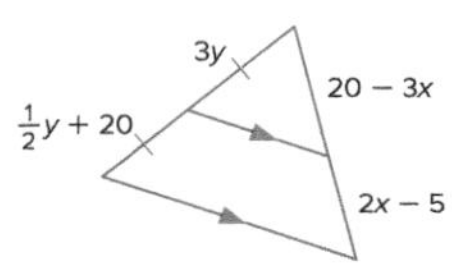

9. $x = 20$; $y = 2$

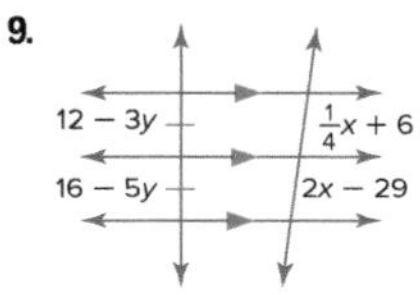

Practice and Problem Solving

Extra Practice is on page R7.

Example 1 G.SRT.5

10. If $AB = 6$, $BC = 4$, and $AE = 9$, find ED. 6

11 If $AB = 12$, $AC = 16$, and $ED = 5$, find AE. 15

12. If $AC = 14$, $BC = 8$, and $AD = 21$, find ED. 12

13. If $AD = 27$, $AB = 8$, and $AE = 12$, find BC. 10

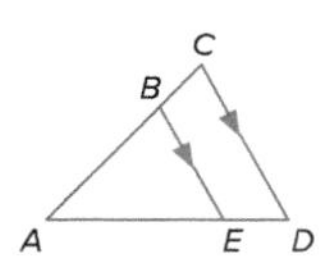

Practice

Formative Assessment Use Exercises 1–9 to assess students' understanding of the concepts in this lesson.

The Practice and Problem Solving exercises assess the content taught in the lesson. The Preparing for Assessment page is meant to be used as preparation for end-of-course assessments.

Extra Practice

See page R7 for extra exercises for students who are approaching level or for on-level students who need additional reinforcement.

Levels of Complexity Chart

The levels of the exercises progress from 1 to 3, with Level 1 indicating the lowest level of complexity.

Exercises	10–25	26–42, 53–59	43–52
Level 3			●
Level 2		●	
Level 1	●		

Differentiated Homework Options

Levels	AL Basic	OL Core	BL Advanced
Exercises	10–25, 48, 49, 51–59	11–47 odd, 48, 49, 51–59	26–59
2-Day Option	11–25 odd, 53–59	10–25, 53–59	
	10–24 even, 48, 49, 51, 52	26–49, 51, 52	

You can use ALEKS to provide additional remediation support with personalized instruction and practice.

Go Online! eBook

Interactive Student Guide
Use the *Interactive Student Guide* to deepen conceptual understanding.
· Parallel Lines and Proportional Parts

Teaching the Mathematical Practices

Modeling Mathematically proficient students can apply the mathematics they know to solve problems arising in everyday life. In Exercise 22, encourage students to analyze the given diagram to identify information important to solving the problem.

Additional Answers

28–30. Sample answers given.

28. Given: $\overline{AD} \parallel \overline{BE} \parallel \overline{CF}$

Prove: $\frac{AB}{BC} = \frac{DE}{EF}$

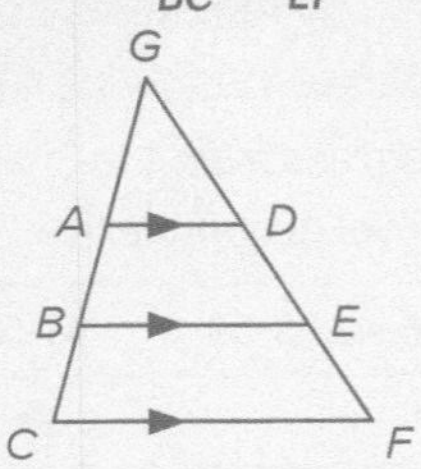

Proof:

In $\triangle GBE$, $\overline{AD} \parallel \overline{BE}$. By the Triangle Proportionality Theorem, AB and DE are proportional. In $\triangle GCF$, $\overline{BE} \parallel \overline{CF}$. By the Triangle Proportionality Theorem, BC and EF are proportional. Therefore, $\frac{AB}{BC} = \frac{DE}{EF}$.

29. Given: $\overline{AD} \parallel \overline{BE} \parallel \overline{CF}$, $\overline{AB} \cong \overline{BC}$

Prove: $\overline{DE} \cong \overline{EF}$

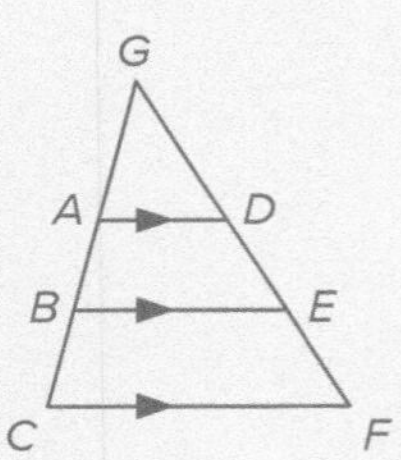

Proof:

From Corollary 7.1, $\frac{AB}{BC} = \frac{DE}{EF}$.
Because $\overline{AB} \cong \overline{BC}$, $AB = BC$ by definition of congruence. Therefore, $\frac{AB}{BC} = 1$. By substitution, $1 = \frac{DE}{EF}$. Thus, $DE = EF$. By definition of congruence, $\overline{DE} \cong \overline{EF}$.

Example 2 G.SRT.4

Determine whether $\overline{VY} \parallel \overline{ZW}$. Justify your answer.

14. $ZX = 18$, $ZV = 6$, $WX = 24$, and $YX = 16$

15. $VX = 7.5$, $ZX = 24$, $WY = 27.5$, and $WX = 40$

16. $ZV = 8$, $VX = 2$, and $YX = \frac{1}{2}WY$

17. $WX = 31$, $YX = 21$, and $ZX = 4ZV$

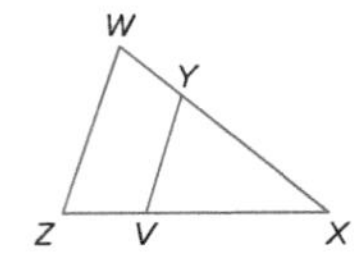

14. yes; $\frac{ZV}{VX} = \frac{WY}{YX} = \frac{1}{2}$
15. yes; $\frac{ZV}{VX} = \frac{WY}{YX} = \frac{11}{5}$
16. no; $\frac{ZV}{VX} \neq \frac{WY}{YX}$
17. no; $\frac{ZV}{VX} \neq \frac{WY}{YX}$

Example 3 G.SRT.5

$\overline{JH}$, $\overline{JP}$, and $\overline{PH}$ are midsegments of $\triangle KLM$. Find the value of x.

18. 57

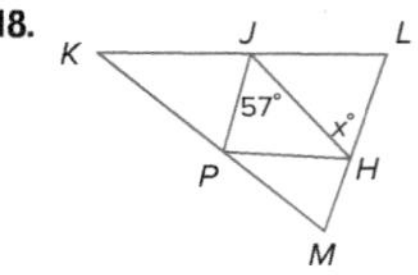

19 60

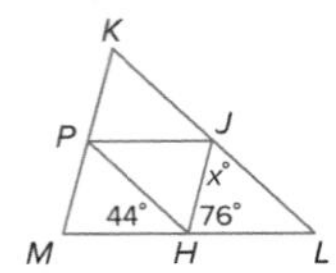

20. 50

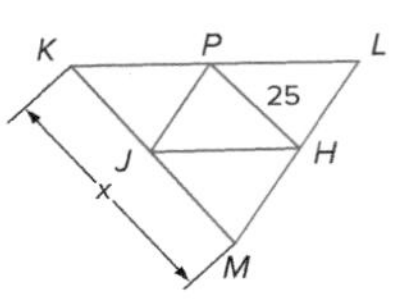

21. 1.35

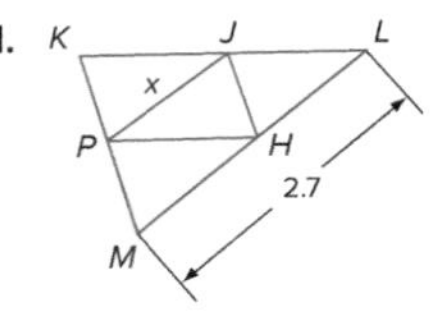

Example 4 G.SRT.5

22. **MODELING** In Charleston, South Carolina, Logan Street is parallel to both King Street and Smith Street between Beaufain Street and Queen Street. What is the distance from Smith to Logan along Beaufain? Round to the nearest foot. about 891 ft

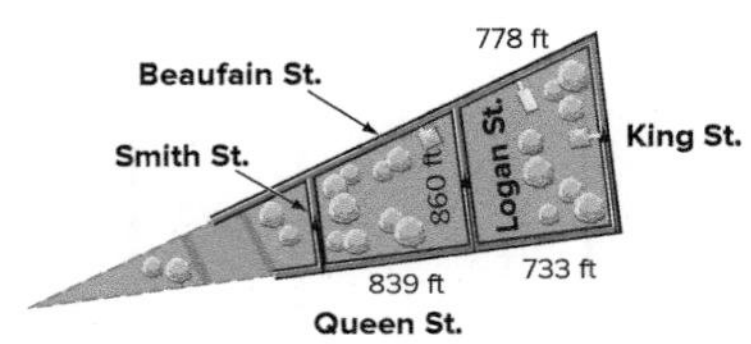

23. **ART** Tonisha drew the line of dancers shown below for her perspective project in art class. Each of the dancers is parallel. Find the lower distance between the first two dancers. 1.2 in.

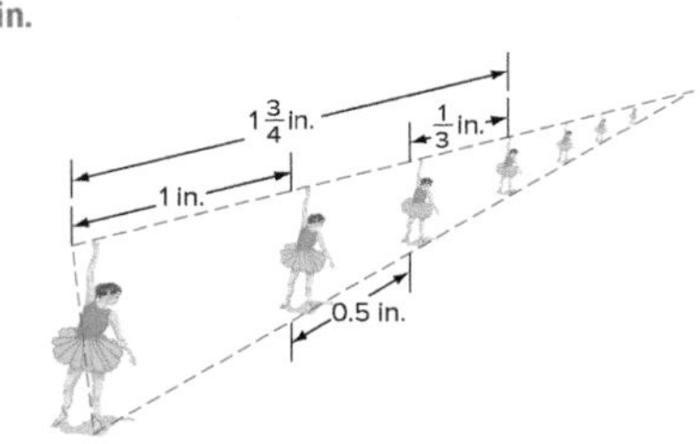

Example 5 G.SRT.5

ALGEBRA Find x and y.

24. $x = 2$; $y = 5$

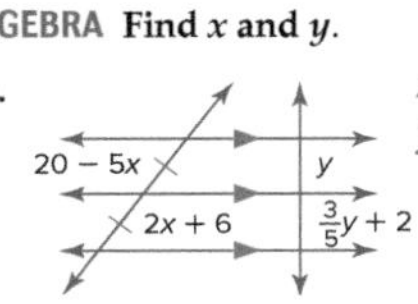

25. $x = 18$; $y = 3$

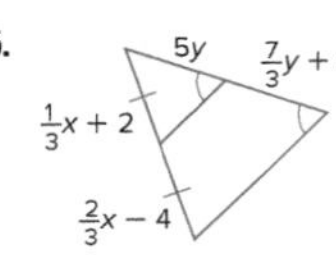

30. Given: $\overline{BD} \parallel \overline{AE}$

Prove: $\frac{BA}{CB} = \frac{DE}{CD}$

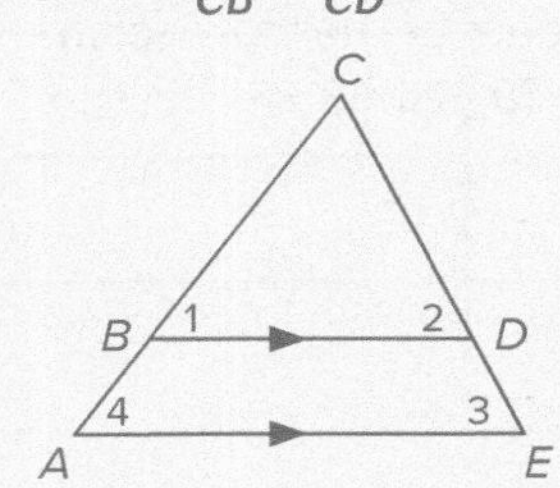

Proof: $\overline{BD} \parallel \overline{AE}$, $\angle 4 \cong \angle 1$ and $\angle 3 \cong \angle 2$ because they are corresponding angles. By AA Similarity, $\triangle ACE \sim \triangle BCD$. From the definition of similar polygons, $\frac{CA}{CB} = \frac{CE}{CD}$. By the Segment Addition Postulate, $CA = BA + CB$ and $CE = DE + CD$. By substitution, $\frac{BA + CB}{CB} = \frac{DE + CD}{CD}$. Rewriting as a sum, $\frac{BA}{CB} + \frac{CB}{CB} = \frac{DE}{CD} + \frac{CD}{CD}$. From simplifying, $\frac{BA}{CB} + 1 = \frac{DE}{CD} + 1$. Thus, $\frac{BA}{CB} = \frac{DE}{CD}$ by subtracting one from each side.

B **ALGEBRA** Find x and y.

26. 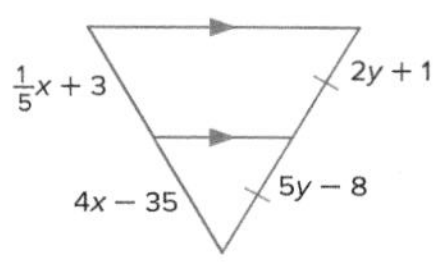

$x = 10$; $y = 3$

27. 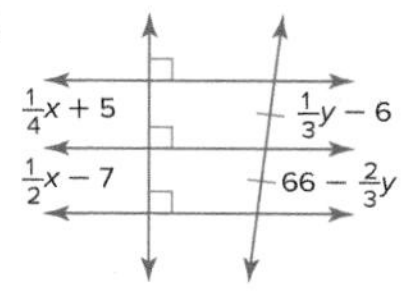

$x = 48$; $y = 72$

CONSTRUCT ARGUMENTS Write a paragraph proof. 28–30. See margin.

28. Corollary 7.1 **29.** Corollary 7.2 **30.** Theorem 7.5

CONSTRUCT ARGUMENTS Write a two-column proof. 31–32. See margin.

31. Theorem 7.6 **32.** Theorem 7.7

Refer to $\triangle QRS$.

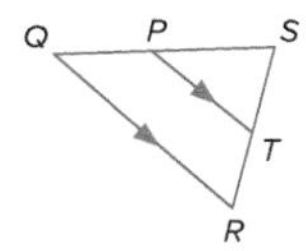

33. If $ST = 8$, $TR = 4$, and $PT = 6$, find QR. 9

34. If $SP = 4$, $PT = 6$, and $QR = 12$, find SQ. 8

35. If $CE = t - 2$, $EB = t + 1$, $CD = 2$, and $CA = 10$, find t and CE. 3, 1

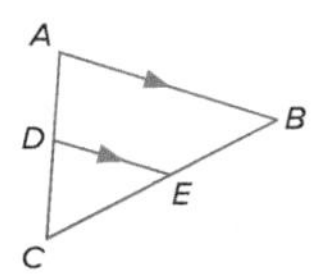

36. If $WX = 7$, $WY = a$, $WV = 6$, and $VZ = a - 9$, find WY. 21

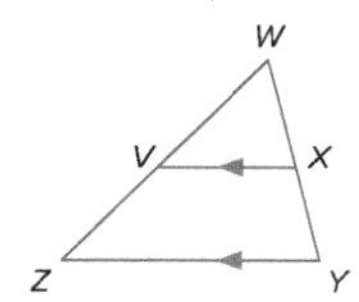

37. If $QR = 2$, $XW = 12$, $QW = 15$, and $ST = 5$, find RS and WV. 8, 7.5

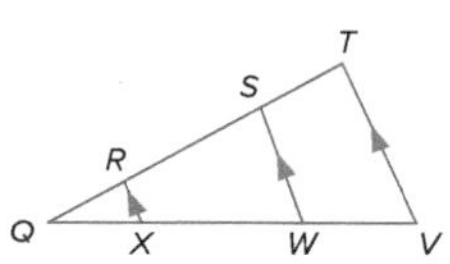

38. If $LK = 4$, $MP = 3$, $PQ = 6$, $KJ = 2$, $RS = 6$, and $LP = 2$, find ML, QR, QK, and JH. 2, 3, 6, 4

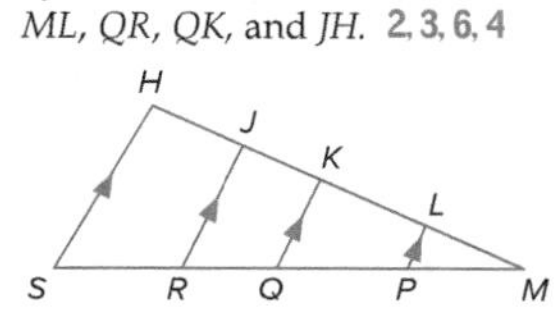

39. **DRAWING TOOLS** The golden ratio is found widely in art, architecture, and nature. The golden ratio is 1.618:1. A Fibonacci gauge is made of two pairs of wooden segments that are pinned so $\overline{AE} \parallel \overline{BG}$ and $\overline{FD} \parallel \overline{AC}$. As the sides of the gauge are moved, the ratio of EC to ED is always the golden ratio. Explain why this gauge works.
See Ch. 7 Answer Appendix.

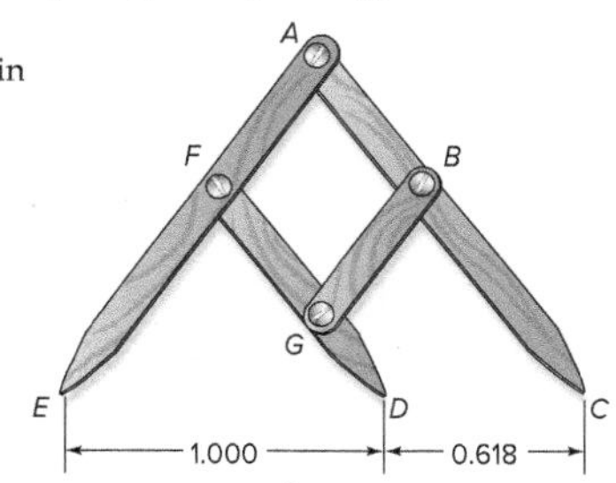

Determine the value of x so that $\overline{BC} \parallel \overline{DF}$.

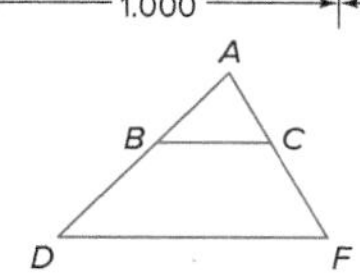

40. $AB = x + 5$, $BD = 12$, $AC = 3x + 1$, and $CF = 15$ 3

41. $AC = 15$, $BD = 3x - 2$, $CF = 3x + 2$, and $AB = 12$ 6

Differentiated Instruction OL BL

Extension A town's water tower is at location A. The borders of the town form a triangle using points B, C, and the water tower. Point D is halfway between the water tower and point B. Point E is halfway between the water tower and point C. The distance from D to E is 18.9 miles. What is the distance from point C to point B?
37.8 miles

Additional Answers

31. **Given:** $\frac{DB}{AD} = \frac{EC}{AE}$

Prove: $\overline{DE} \parallel \overline{BC}$

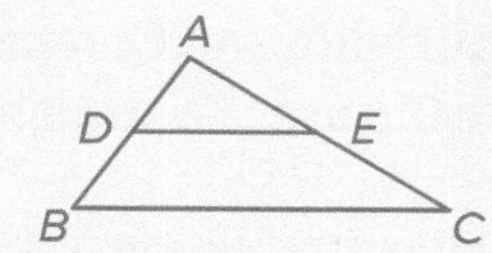

Proof:

Statements (Reasons)

1. $\frac{DB}{AD} = \frac{EC}{AE}$ (Given)
2. $\frac{AD}{AD} + \frac{DB}{AD} = \frac{AE}{AE} + \frac{EC}{AE}$ (Add. Prop.)
3. $\frac{AD + DB}{AD} = \frac{AE + EC}{AE}$ (Subst.)
4. $AB = AD + DB$, $AC = AE + EC$ (Seg. Add. Post.)
5. $\frac{AB}{AD} = \frac{AC}{AE}$ (Subst.)
6. $\angle A \cong \angle A$ (Refl. Prop.)
7. $\triangle ADE \sim \triangle ABC$ (SAS Similarity)
8. $\angle ADE \cong \angle ABC$ (Def. of $\sim$ polygons)
9. $\overline{DE} \parallel \overline{BC}$ (If corr. ∠s are ≅, then the lines are ∥.)

32. **Given:** D is the midpoint of $\overline{AB}$.
E is the midpoint of $\overline{AC}$.

Prove: $\overline{DE} \parallel \overline{BC}$; $DE = \frac{1}{2}BC$

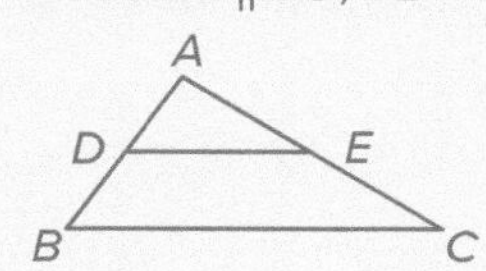

Proof:

Statements (Reasons)

1. D is the midpoint of $\overline{AB}$; E is the midpoint of $\overline{AC}$. (Given)
2. $\overline{AD} \cong \overline{DB}$, $\overline{AE} \cong \overline{EC}$ (Midpoint Thm.)
3. $AD = DB$, $AE = EC$ (Def. of ≅ segs.)
4. $AB = AD + DB$, $AC = AE + EC$ (Seg. Add. Post.)
5. $AB = AD + AD$, $AC = AE + AE$ (Subst.)
6. $AB = 2AD$, $AC = 2AE$ (Subst.)
7. $\frac{AB}{AD} = 2$, $\frac{AC}{AE} = 2$ (Div. Prop.)
8. $\frac{AB}{AD} = \frac{AC}{AE}$ (Trans. Prop.)
9. $\angle A \cong \angle A$ (Refl. Prop.)
10. $\triangle ADE \sim \triangle ABC$ (SAS Similarity)
11. $\angle ADE \cong \angle ABC$ (Def. of $\sim$ polygons)
12. $\overline{DE} \parallel \overline{BC}$ (If corr. ∠s are ≅, the lines are parallel.)
13. $\frac{BC}{DE} = \frac{AB}{AD}$ (Def. of $\sim$ polygons)
14. $\frac{BC}{DE} = 2$ (Substitution Prop.)
15. $2DE = BC$ (Mult. Prop.)
16. $DE = \frac{1}{2}BC$ (Division Prop.)

Exercise Alert

Straightedge and Compass Exercises 44–47 require the use of a straightedge and a compass.

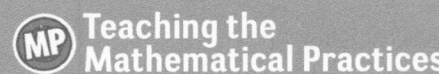

MP Teaching the Mathematical Practices

Critique Arguments Mathematically proficient students can distinguish correct logic from flawed reasoning. In Exercise 48, students should use the figure to judge the reasonableness of their answers. Sebastian reversed the role of the two parallel segments from Theorem 7.7, and he should see that $\overline{JL}$ is longer than $\overline{MP}$.

Assess

Name the Math Have students explain the Triangle Proportionality Theorem using triangle similarity properties.

Additional Answer

42.

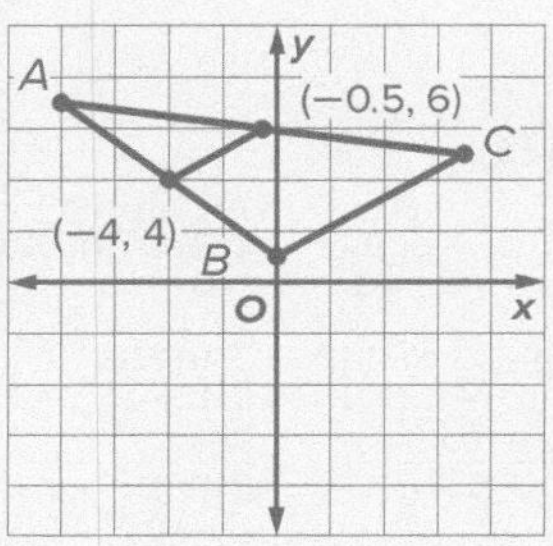

The endpoints of the midsegment are (−4, 4) and (−0.5, 6). Sample answer: The segment is parallel to $\overline{BC}$ because the slopes are both $\frac{4}{7}$ and the segment length is half of $\overline{BC}$. Thus, the segment is the midsegment of $\triangle ABC$.

42. COORDINATE GEOMETRY $\triangle ABC$ has vertices $A(-8, 7)$, $B(0, 1)$, and $C(7, 5)$. Draw $\triangle ABC$. Determine the coordinates of the midsegment of $\triangle ABC$ that is parallel to $\overline{BC}$. Justify your answer. See margin.

B **43. HOUSES** Refer to the diagram of the gable at the right. Each piece of siding is a uniform width. Find the lengths of $\overline{FG}$, $\overline{EH}$, and $\overline{DJ}$. 8.75 ft, 17.5 ft, 26.25 ft

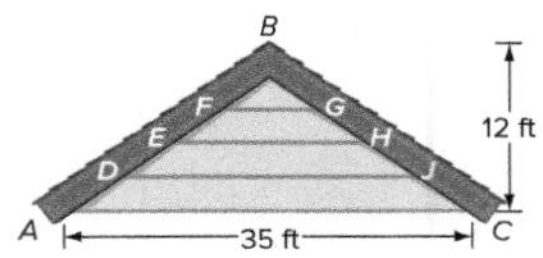

CONSTRUCTIONS **Construct each segment as directed.** 44–46. See Ch. 7 Answer Appendix.

44. a segment separated into five congruent segments

45. a segment separated into two segments in which their lengths have a ratio of 1 to 3

46. a segment 3 inches long, separated into four congruent segments

47. MULTIPLE REPRESENTATIONS In this problem, you will explore angle bisectors and proportions.

a. Geometric Draw three triangles: one acute, one right, and one obtuse. Label one triangle ABC and draw angle bisector $\overrightarrow{BD}$. Label the second MNP with angle bisector $\overrightarrow{NQ}$ and the third WXY with angle bisector $\overrightarrow{XZ}$. See Ch. 7 Answer Appendix.

b. Tabular Copy and complete the table at the right with the appropriate values.

c. Verbal Make a conjecture about the segments of a triangle created by an angle bisector.

47c. Sample answer: The proportion of the segments created by the angle bisector of a triangle is equal to the proportion of their respective consecutive sides.

Triangle	Length		Ratio	
ABC	AD	1.1 cm	$\frac{AD}{CD}$	1.0
	CD	1.1 cm		
	AB	2.0 cm	$\frac{AB}{CB}$	1.0
	CB	2.0 cm		
MNP	MQ	1.4 cm	$\frac{MQ}{PQ}$	0.8
	PQ	1.7 cm		
	MN	1.6 cm	$\frac{MN}{PN}$	0.8
	PN	2.0 cm		
WXY	WZ	0.8 cm	$\frac{WZ}{YZ}$	0.7
	YZ	1.2 cm		
	WX	2.0 cm	$\frac{WX}{YX}$	0.7
	YX	2.9 cm		

G.SRT.4, G.SRT.5

H.O.T. Problems Use Higher-Order Thinking Skills

48. MP CRITIQUE ARGUMENTS Jacob and Sebastian are finding the value of x in $\triangle JHL$. Jacob says that MP is one half of JL, so x is 4.5. Sebastian says that JL is one half of MP, so x is 18. Is either of them correct? Explain.

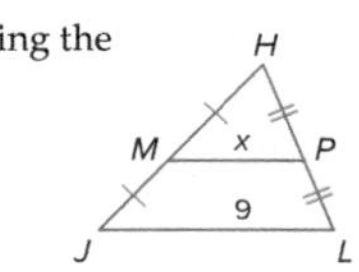

48. Jacob; sample answer: $\overline{MP}$ is the midsegment, so $MP = \frac{1}{2}JL$.

52. Both theorems deal with a parallel line inside the triangle. The Midsegment Theorem is a special case of the Converse of the Proportionality Theorem.

49. MP REASONING In $\triangle ABC$, $AF = FB$ and $AH = HC$. If D is $\frac{3}{4}$ of the way from A to B and E is $\frac{3}{4}$ of the way from A to C, is DE *always*, *sometimes*, or *never* $\frac{3}{4}$ of BC? Explain. See Ch. 7 Answer Appendix.

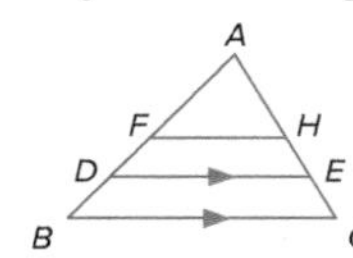

50. CHALLENGE Write a two-column proof.

Given: $AB = 4$, $BC = 4$, and $CD = DE$

Prove: $\overline{BD} \parallel \overline{AE}$ See Ch. 7 Answer Appendix.

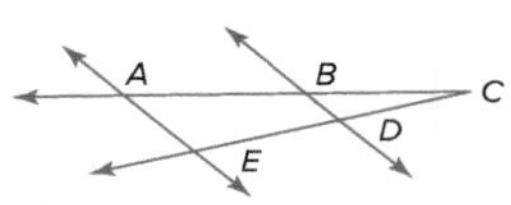

51. OPEN-ENDED Draw three segments, a, b, and c, of all different lengths. Draw a fourth segment, d, such that $\frac{a}{b} = \frac{c}{d}$. See Ch. 7 Answer Appendix.

52. WRITING IN MATH Compare the Triangle Proportionality Theorem and the Triangle Midsegment Theorem.

MP Standards for Mathematical Practice

Emphasis On	Exercises
1 Make sense of problems and persevere in solving them.	8, 9, 24–27, 33–38, 42, 43, 50, 53–57, 58
2 Reason abstractly and quantitatively.	1–6, 10–21, 40, 41, 51, 52, 56
3 Construct viable arguments and critique the reasoning of others.	28–32, 48, 49, 54, 56
4 Model with mathematics.	7, 22, 23, 39
5 Use appropriate tools strategically.	44–47
6 Attend to precision.	53, 55, 58, 59

Go Online!

eSolutions Manual

Create worksheets, answer keys, and solutions handouts for your assignments.

Preparing for Assessment

53. $\overline{RS}$ is a midsegment of $\triangle XYZ$.

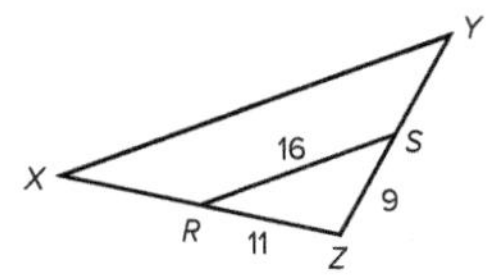

What is the perimeter of $\triangle XYZ$? MP 6 G.SRT.4 **B**

- ○ A 88
- ○ B 72
- ○ C 56
- ○ D 52
- ○ E 36

54. In $\triangle ABC$, P is the midpoint of $\overline{AB}$ and Q is the midpoint of $\overline{BC}$. Which of the following statements is not necessarily true? MP 3 G.SRT.5 **D**

- ○ A $\overline{PQ} \parallel \overline{AC}$
- ○ B $PQ = \frac{1}{2}AC$
- ○ C $BQ = QC$
- ○ D $BP = BQ$

55. In $\triangle FGH$, $\overleftrightarrow{JK}$ is parallel to $\overline{GH}$.

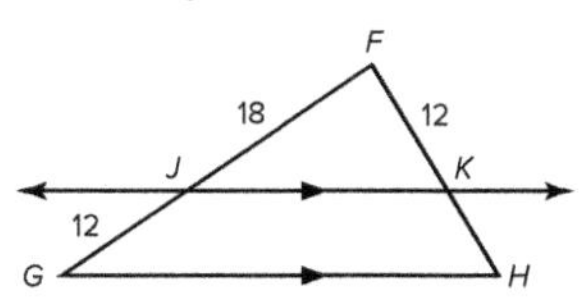

What is the length of $\overline{FH}$? MP 6 G.SRT.5 **C**

- ○ A 8
- ○ B 18
- ○ C 20
- ○ D 24

56. In $\triangle RST$, X is the midpoint of $\overline{RS}$ and Y is the midpoint of $\overline{RT}$. Given that $XY = 3z + 2$ and $ST = 7z - 1$, what is the value of z? MP 2, 3 G.SRT.5 **5**

57. If the vertices of $\triangle JKL$ are (0, 0), (0, 10), and (10, 10), what is the area of $\triangle JKL$ in square units? MP 1 G.SRT.5 **50**

58. **MULTI-STEP** First, Second, and Third Streets are parallel in a town. Waller Avenue is perpendicular to these streets, and Shaw Road runs at an angle to them. What is the distance along Waller Avenue from First Street to Third Street? MP 1, 6 G.SRT.5

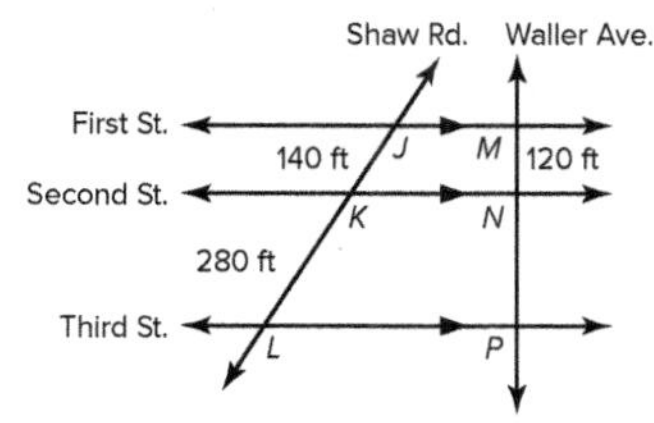

a. Which theorem can you use to solve this problem? **the Proportional Parts of Parallel Lines Theorem**

b. Which proportion is correct, and is helpful for solving this problem? **C**

- ○ A $\frac{KN}{JM} = \frac{KL}{JK}$
- ○ B $\frac{JK}{JM} = \frac{KN}{MN}$
- ○ C $\frac{JK}{KL} = \frac{MN}{NP}$
- ○ D $\frac{KN}{NP} = \frac{KL}{LP}$

c. What is NP? **240 ft**

d. What is the distance from First Street to Third Street? **120 ft + 240 ft = 360 ft**

59. In the figure, $\overleftrightarrow{BC} \parallel \overleftrightarrow{DE}$. $AD = 10$; $AB = 6$ and $BC = 4$. Find DE. MP 6 G.SRT.4 $\frac{20}{3}$

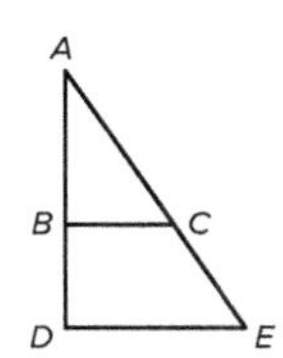

Preparing for Assessment

Exercises 53–59 require students to use the skills they will need on standardized assessments. Exercises are dual-coded with content standards and mathematical practice standards.

Dual Coding

Exercises	Content Standards	MP Mathematical Practices
53	G.SRT.4	6
54	G.SRT.5	3
55	G.SRT.5	6
56	G.SRT.5	2, 3
57	G.SRT.5	1
58	G.SRT.5	1, 6
59	G.SRT.4	6

Diagnose Student Errors

Survey student responses for each item. Class trends may indicate common errors and misconceptions.

53.

A	Included *RS* in the perimeter
B	CORRECT
C	Used 16 for the length of $\overline{XY}$
D	Did not include *XR* or *YS* in the perimeter
E	Found perimeter of $\triangle RSZ$

54.

A	Did not recognize part of the Triangle Midsegment Theorem
B	Did not recognize part of the Triangle Midsegment Theorem
C	Did not recognize a consequence of *Q* being the midpoint of $\overline{BC}$
D	CORRECT

55.

A	Found the length of $\overline{KH}$
B	Subtracted 6 from *FK* to find $KH = 6$
C	CORRECT
D	Assumed $\overline{FK} \cong \overline{KH}$

58b.

A	Used segments on parallel lines
B	Did not use the proportion in the Theorem
C	CORRECT
D	Used segments on parallel lines and on other lines

Go Online!

Quizzes

Students can use *Self-Check Quizzes* to check their understanding of this lesson and have the results sent to you. You can also give the *Chapter Quiz*, which covers the content in Lesson 7-5.

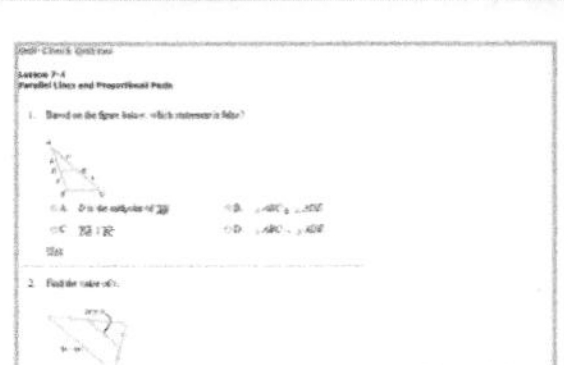

LESSON 7-6
Parts of Similar Triangles

SUGGESTED PACING (DAYS)

	Instruction		Extend Lab
90 min.	0.5	0.5	
45 min.	1.0		0.5

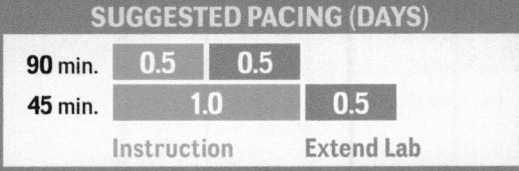

Track Your Progress

Objectives

1. Recognize and use proportional relationships of corresponding segments of similar triangles.
2. Use the Triangle Angle Bisector Theorem.

Mathematical Background

If two triangles are similar, then the perimeters and altitudes are proportional to the measures of corresponding sides. This relationship holds true for angle bisectors and medians as well.

THEN

G.CO.10 Prove theorems about triangles. Theorems include: measures of interior angles of a triangle sum to 180°; base angles of isosceles triangles are congruent; the segment joining midpoints of two sides of a triangle is parallel to the third side and half the length; the medians of a triangle meet at a point.

NOW

G.SRT.4 Prove theorems about triangles. *Theorems include: a line parallel to one side of a triangle divides the other two proportionally, and conversely; the Pythagorean Theorem proved using triangle similarity.*

G.SRT.5 Use congruence and similarity criteria for triangles to solve problems and to prove relationships in geometric figures.

NEXT

G.SRT.5 Use congruence and similarity criteria for triangles to solve problems and to prove relationships in geometric figures.

Go Online! All of these resources and more are available at connectED.mcgraw-hill.com

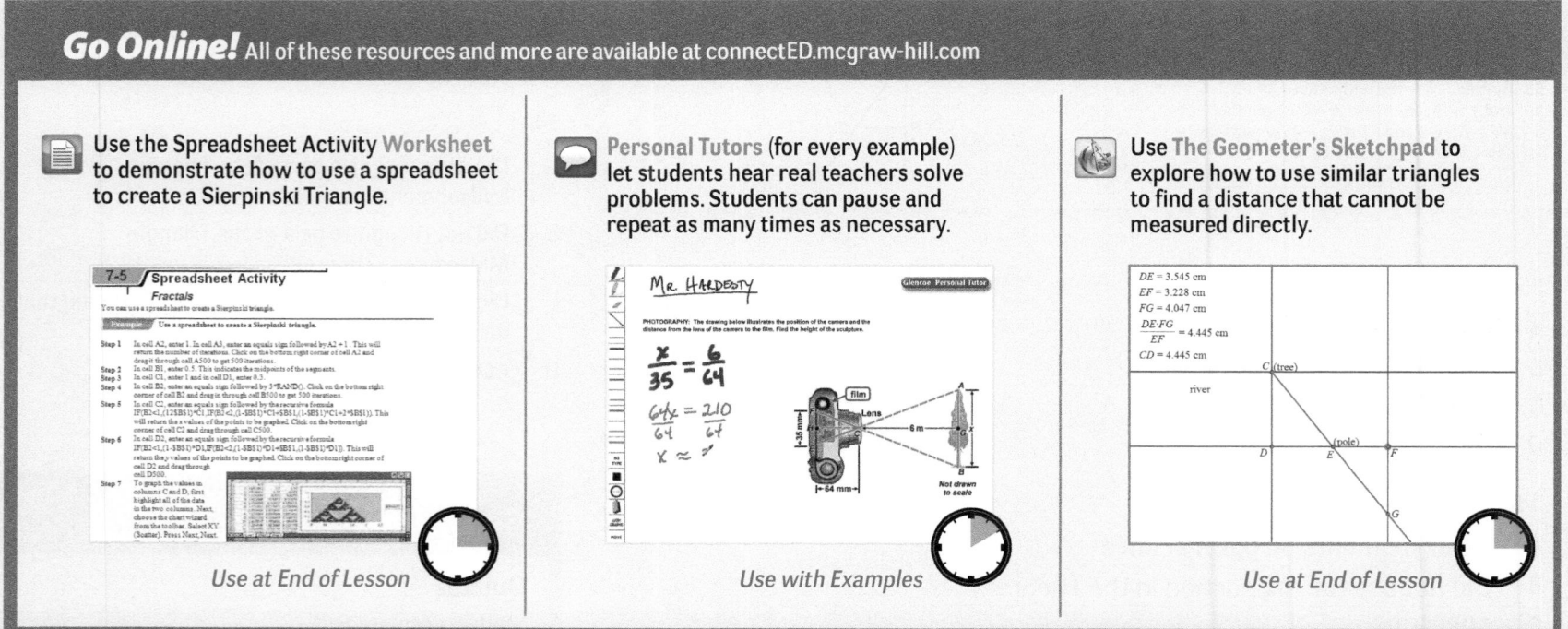

Use the Spreadsheet Activity Worksheet to demonstrate how to use a spreadsheet to create a Sierpinski Triangle.

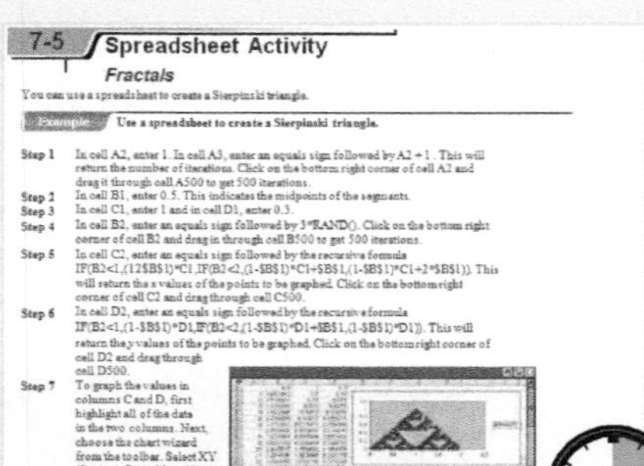

Use at End of Lesson

Personal Tutors (for every example) let students hear real teachers solve problems. Students can pause and repeat as many times as necessary.

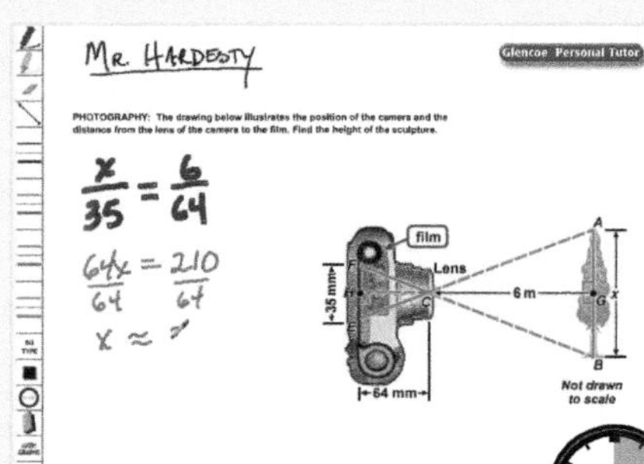

Use with Examples

Use The Geometer's Sketchpad to explore how to use similar triangles to find a distance that cannot be measured directly.

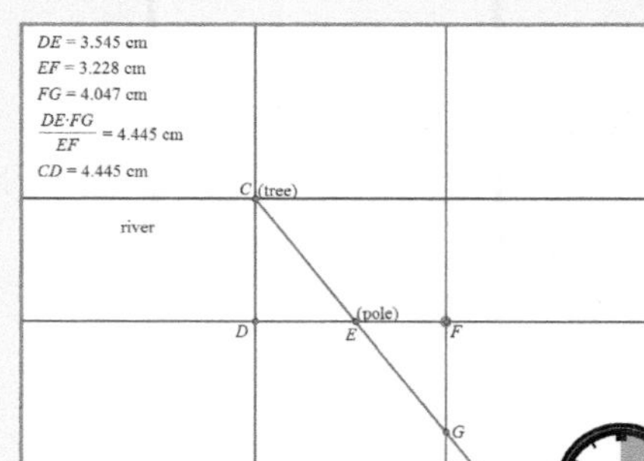

Use at End of Lesson

Using Open Educational Resources

Mnemonic Devices Have students work individually to write a song or a poem using **Rhymes.net** to help them remember the relationships between special segments of similar triangles. Have students volunteer to perform their mnemonic device in front of the class. *Use as homework*

Go Online!
connectED.mcgraw-hill.com

Worksheets

Differentiate Your Resources

Extra Practice Additional practice or homework; Skills Practice is best for approaching-level students and Practice is best for on-level and beyond-level students

Skills Practice

AL OL ELL

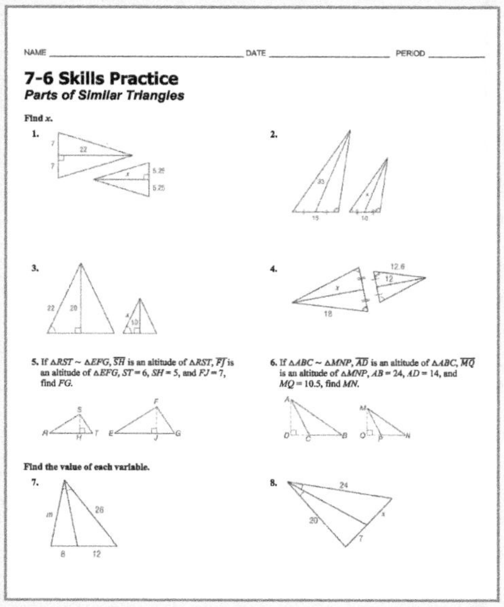
7-6 Skills Practice
Parts of Similar Triangles

Practice

AL OL BL ELL

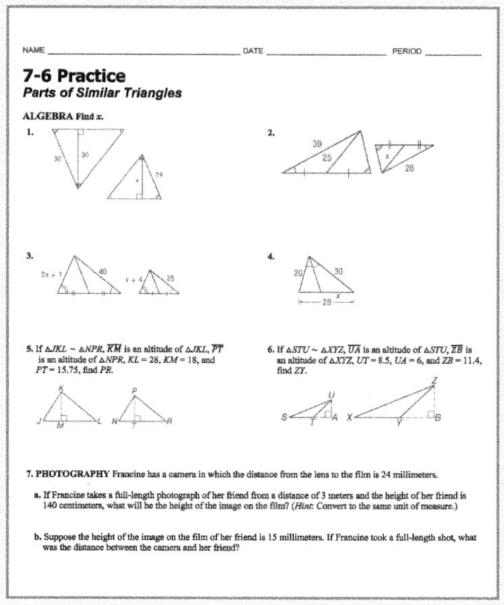
7-6 Practice
Parts of Similar Triangles

Word Problem Practice

AL OL BL ELL

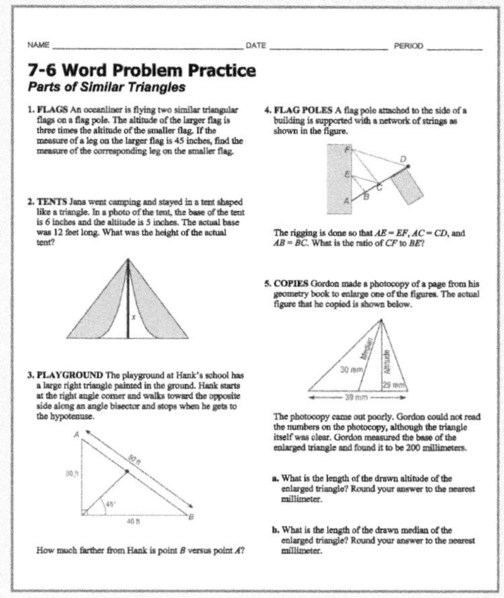
7-6 Word Problem Practice
Parts of Similar Triangles

Intervention Reteaching and vocabulary activities that can be used with struggling or absent students and as ELL support

Study Guide and Intervention

AL OL ELL

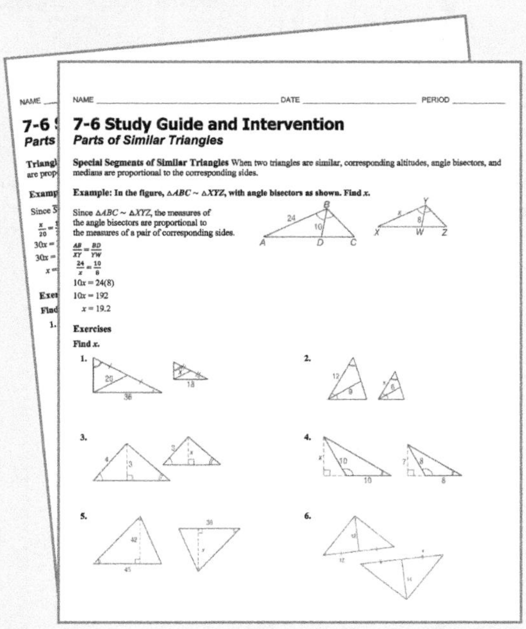
7-6 Study Guide and Intervention
Parts of Similar Triangles

Study Notebook

AL OL BL ELL

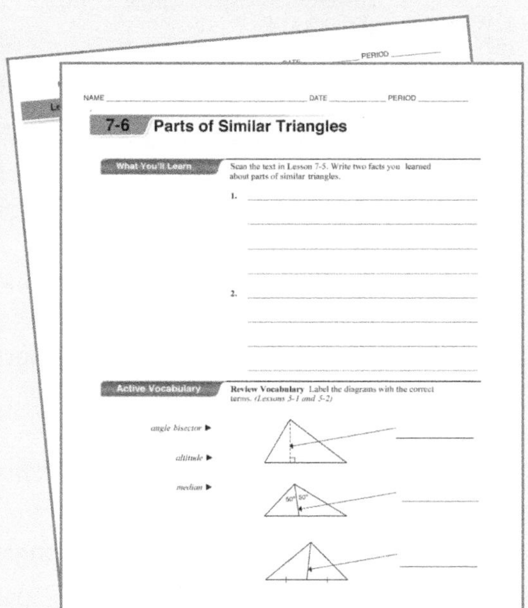
7-6 Parts of Similar Triangles

Extension Activities that can be used to extend lesson concepts

Enrichment

OL BL ELL

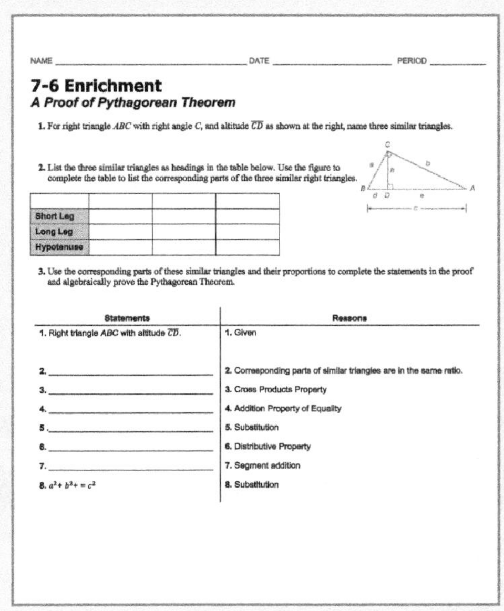
7-6 Enrichment
A Proof of Pythagorean Theorem

Launch

Have students read the Why? section of the lesson. Ask:

- What is the "Rule of Thumb" used to measure? It estimates distance to an object.
- What are some other ways to approximate distances? Sample answer: Count the number of steps.
- Would the ratio of a person's arm length to the distance between the person's eyes be less than or greater than 1? greater than 1

Go Online!

Interactive Whiteboard

Use the *eLesson*, *Lesson Presentation*, or *Interactive Classroom* to present this lesson.

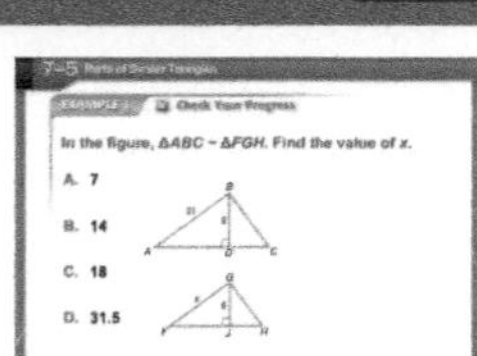

LESSON 6

Parts of Similar Triangles

Then

- You learned that corresponding sides of similar polygons are proportional.

Now

1. Recognize and use proportional relationships of corresponding angle bisectors, altitudes, and medians of similar triangles.
2. Use the Triangle Bisector Theorem.

Why?

- The "Rule of Thumb" uses the average ratio of a person's arm length to the distance between his or her eyes and the altitudes of similar triangles to estimate the distance between a person and an object of approximately known width.

Mathematical Practices

1 Make sense of problems and persevere in solving them.

3 Construct viable arguments and critique the reasoning of others.

Content Standards

G.SRT.4 Prove theorems about triangles.

G.SRT.5 Use congruence and similarity criteria for triangles to solve problems and to prove relationships in geometric figures.

1 Special Segments of Similar Triangles You learned in Lesson 7-2 that the corresponding side lengths of similar polygons, such as triangles, are proportional. This concept can be extended to other segments in triangles.

Theorems Special Segments of Similar Triangles

7.8 If two triangles are similar, the lengths of corresponding altitudes are proportional to the lengths of corresponding sides.

Abbreviation *~△s have corr. altitudes proportional to corr. sides.*

Example If $\triangle ABC \sim \triangle FGH$, then $\frac{AD}{FJ} = \frac{AB}{FG}$.

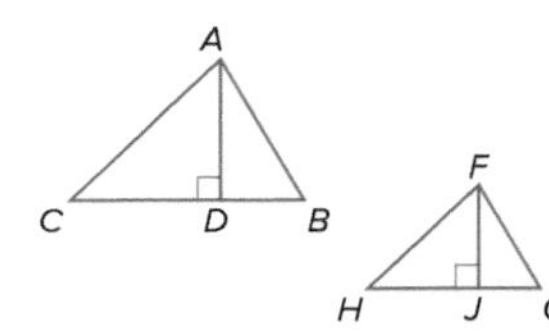

7.9 If two triangles are similar, the lengths of corresponding angle bisectors are proportional to the lengths of corresponding sides.

Abbreviation *~△s have corr. ∠ bisectors proportional to corr. sides.*

Example If $\triangle KLM \sim \triangle QRS$, then $\frac{LP}{RT} = \frac{LM}{RS}$.

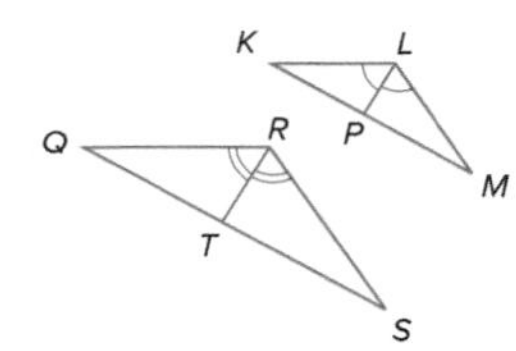

7.10 If two triangles are similar, the lengths of corresponding medians are proportional to the lengths of corresponding sides.

Abbreviation *~△s have corr. medians proportional to corr. sides.*

Example If $\triangle ABC \sim \triangle WXY$, then $\frac{CD}{YZ} = \frac{AB}{WX}$.

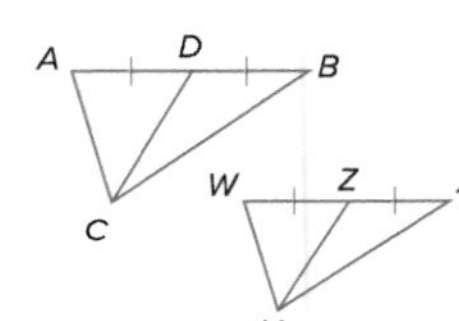

You will prove Theorems 7.9 and 7.10 in Exercises 18 and 19, respectively.

MP Mathematical Practices Strategies

Reason abstractly and quantitatively.

Ask students questions to help them understand and remember the different parts of similar triangles that will help them to determine congruence or similarity. For example:

- What is an altitude of a triangle? An altitude of a triangle is a segment from a vertex to the line containing the opposite side and perpendicular to the line containing that side.
- Will similar triangles always have congruent corresponding altitudes? No; the corresponding attitudes of two similar triangles will not be congruent unless the triangles are congruent.
- What is the bisector of an angle? The bisector of an angle is a line that divides the angle into two congruent angles.
- Will similar triangles always have congruent angles? yes
- What is the median of a triangle? A median of a triangle is a segment with endpoints that are a vertex of a triangle and the midpoint of the opposite side.
- Will similar triangles always have congruent corresponding medians? No; the corresponding medians of two similar triangles will not be congruent unless the triangles are congruent.

Real-World Career

Athletic Trainer Athletic trainers help prevent and treat sports injuries. They ensure that protective equipment is used properly and that people understand safe practices that prevent injury. An athletic trainer must have a bachelor's degree to be certified. Most also have master's degrees. Refer to Exercise 29.

Proof Theorem 7.8

Given: $\triangle FGH \sim \triangle KLM$
$\overline{FJ}$ and $\overline{KP}$ are altitudes.

Prove: $\frac{FJ}{KP} = \frac{HF}{MK}$

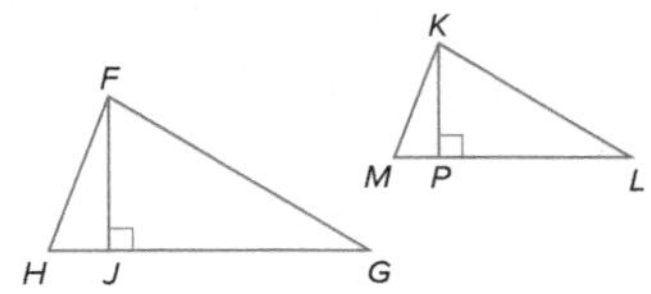

Paragraph Proof:
Because $\triangle FGH \sim \triangle KLM$, $\angle H \cong \angle M$. $\angle FJH \cong \angle KPM$ because they are both right angles created by the altitudes drawn to the opposite sides and all right angles are congruent.

Thus $\triangle HFJ \sim \triangle MKP$ by AA Similarity. So $\frac{FJ}{KP} = \frac{HF}{MK}$ by the definition of similar polygons.

Because the corresponding altitudes are chosen at random, we need not prove Theorem 7.8 for every pair of altitudes.

You can use special segments in similar triangles to find missing measures.

G.SRT.5

Example 1 Use Special Segments in Similar Triangles

In the figure, $\triangle ABC \sim \triangle FDG$. Find the value of x.

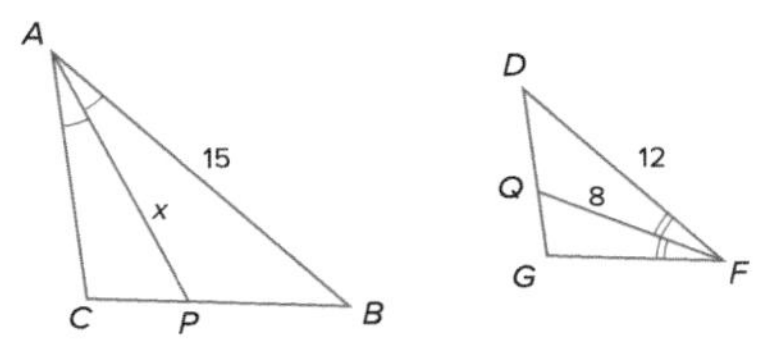

$\overline{AP}$ and $\overline{FQ}$ are corresponding angle bisectors and $\overline{AB}$ and $\overline{FD}$ are corresponding sides of similar triangles ABC and FDG.

$\frac{AP}{FQ} = \frac{AB}{FD}$	~△s have corr. ∠ bisectors proportional to the corr. sides.
$\frac{x}{8} = \frac{15}{12}$	Substitution
$8 \cdot 15 = x \cdot 12$	Cross Products Property
$120 = 12x$	Simplify.
$10 = x$	Divide each side by 12.

Study Tip

MP Sense-Making Example 1 could also have been solved by first finding the scale factor between $\triangle ABC$ and $\triangle FDG$. The ratio of the angle bisector in $\triangle ABC$ to the angle bisector in $\triangle FDG$ would then be equal to this scale factor.

Guided Practice

Find the value of x.

1A.

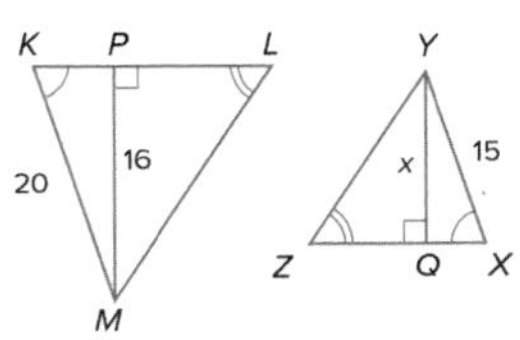

12

1B.

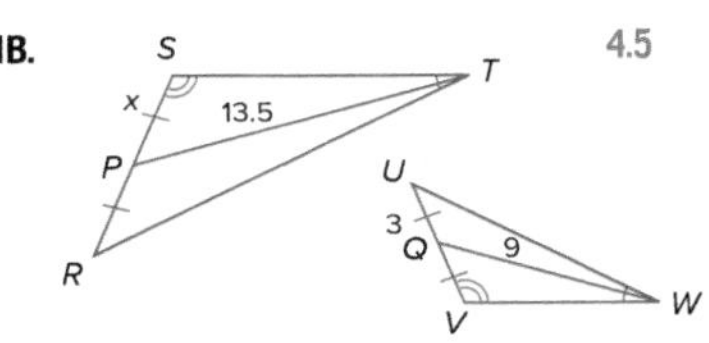

4.5

Teach

Ask the scaffolded questions for each example to build conceptual understanding for students at all levels.

1 Special Segments of Similar Triangles

Example 1 Use Special Segments in Similar Triangles

AL Would the relationship be the same if $\overline{AP}$ and $\overline{FQ}$ were medians instead of angle bisectors? yes

OL If $GF = 6$, what is CA? 7.5

BL Do you think perpendicular bisectors would divide similar triangles proportionally? Sample answer: Perpendicular bisectors only intersect the opposite vertex in special cases, but the segments produced would still be proportional for similar triangles.

Need Another Example?

In the figure, $\triangle LJK \sim \triangle SQR$. Find the value of x. 7.5

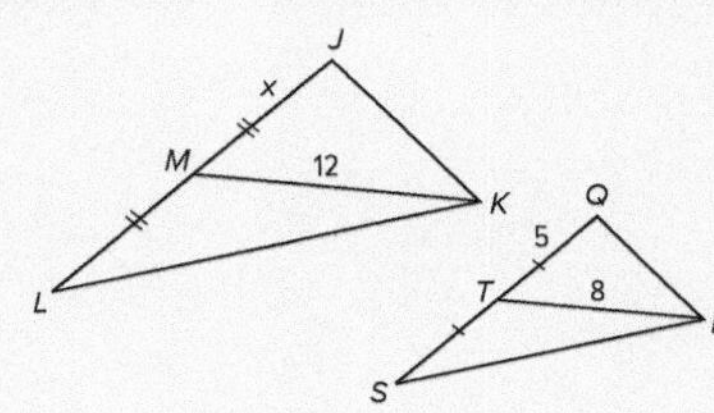

Watch Out!

Rotate Similar triangles may be oriented differently. Be sure to carefully look at markings on the figures to determine congruent angles and corresponding sides.

Example 2 Use Similar Triangles to Solve Problems

AL Why do we multiply 5.5 by 4 to find *DF*? Because the car is about 5.5 feet wide and it appears to jump about 4 car widths.

OL If the car appeared to jump about 5 car widths, what is the approximate distance from Liliana's thumb to the car? about 275 feet

BL If Liliana is about 250 feet from the car, how many car widths would you expect it to jump? About $4\frac{1}{2}$

Need Another Example?

Estimating Distance Sanjay's arm is about 9 times longer than the distance between his eyes. He sights a statue across the park that is 10 feet wide. If the statue appears to move 4 widths when he switches eyes, estimate the distance from Sanjay's thumb to the statue. 360 feet

Real-World Link

Hold your outstretched hand horizontal at arm's length with your palm facing you; for each hand width the sun is above the horizon, there is one remaining hour of sunlight.

Source: Sail Island Channels

G.SRT.5

Real-World Example 2 Use Similar Triangles to Solve Problems

ESTIMATING DISTANCES Liliana holds her arm straight out in front of her with her elbow straight and her thumb pointing up. Closing one eye, she aligns one edge of her thumb with a car she is sighting. Next she switches eyes without moving her head or her arm. The car appears to jump 4 car widths. If Liliana's arm is about 10 times longer than the distance between her eyes, and the car is about 5.5 feet wide, estimate the distance from Liliana's thumb to the car.

Understand Make a diagram labeling the given distances and the distance you need to find as x. Label the vertices of the triangles formed.

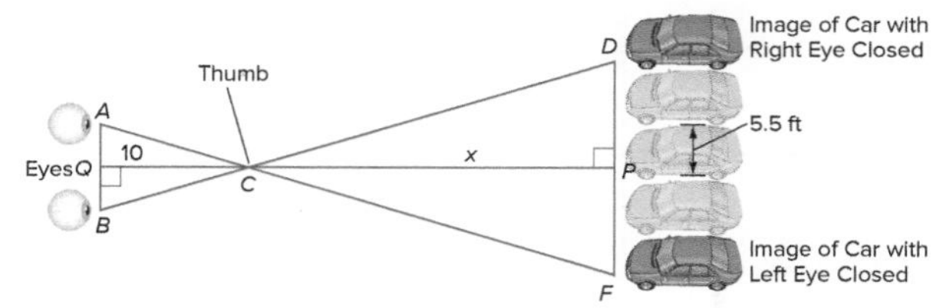

We assume that if Liliana's thumb is straight out in front of her, then $\overline{QC}$ is an altitude of $\triangle ABC$. Likewise, $\overline{PC}$ is the corresponding altitude. We assume that $\overline{AB} \parallel \overline{DF}$.

Plan Because $\overline{AB} \parallel \overline{DF}$, $\angle BAC \cong \angle DFC$ and $\angle CBA \cong \angle CDF$ by the Alternate Interior Angles Theorem. Therefore $\triangle ABC \sim \triangle FDC$ by AA Similarity. Write a proportion and solve for x.

Solve

$\frac{PC}{QC} = \frac{AB}{DF}$ Theorem 7.8

$\frac{10}{x} = \frac{1}{5.5 \cdot 4}$ Substitution

$\frac{10}{x} = \frac{1}{22}$ Simplify.

$10 \cdot 22 = x \cdot 1$ Cross Products Property

$220 = x$ Simplify.

So the estimated distance to the car is 220 feet.

Check The ratio of Liliana's arm length to the width between her eyes is 10 to 1. The ratio of the distance to the car to the distance the image of the car jumped is 220 to 22 or 10 to 1. ✓

Creating a diagram allows us to compare the corresponding angles and thus determine that the triangles are similar.

Go Online!

Watch Personal Tutor videos to hear descriptions of using similar triangles to solve problems. Try describing how to solve a problem for a partner. Have them ask you questions to help your understanding.

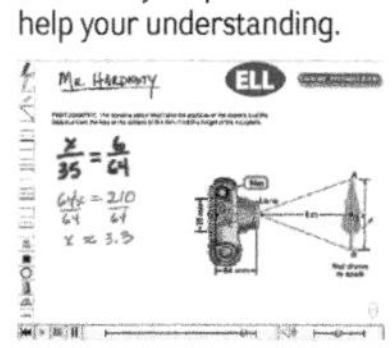

Guided Practice

2. Suppose Liliana stands at the back of her classroom and sights a clock on the wall at the front of the room. If the clock is 30 centimeters wide and appears to move 3 clock widths when she switches eyes, estimate the distance from Liliana's thumb to the clock. 900 cm or 9 m

Differentiated Instruction AL OL BL

Visual Learners A common error is to believe that the corresponding angles of two similar triangles have the same ratio as the corresponding sides. Emphasize that the corresponding angles of two similar triangles must be congruent.

2 Triangle Angle Bisector Theorem
An angle bisector of a triangle also divides the side opposite the angle proportionally.

Study Tip ELL
Proportions Another proportion that could be written using the Triangle Angle Bisector Theorem is $\frac{KM}{KJ} = \frac{LM}{LJ}$.

Theorem 7.11 Triangle Angle Bisector

An angle bisector in a triangle separates the opposite side into two segments that are proportional to the lengths of the other two sides.

Example If $\overline{JM}$ is an angle bisector of $\triangle JKL$,
then $\frac{KM}{LM} = \frac{KJ}{LJ}$. ← segments with vertex K ← segments with vertex L

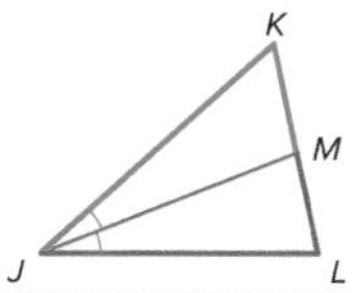

You will prove Theorem 7.11 in Exercise 25.

G.SRT.5

Example 3 Use the Triangle Angle Bisector Theorem

Find x.

Because $\overline{RT}$ is an angle bisector of $\triangle QRS$, you can use the Triangle Angle Bisector Theorem to write a proportion.

$\frac{QT}{ST} = \frac{QR}{SR}$ Triangle Angle Bisector Theorem

$\frac{x}{18 - x} = \frac{6}{14}$ Substitution

$(18 - x)(6) = x \cdot 14$ Cross Products Property

$108 - 6x = 14x$ Simplify.

$108 = 20x$ Add $6x$ to each side.

$5.4 = x$ Divide each side by 20.

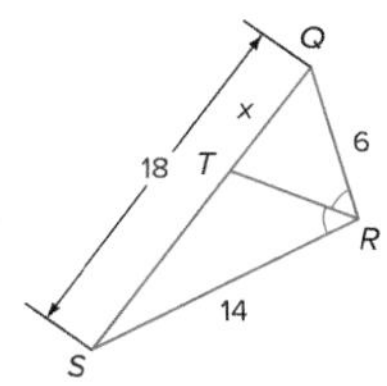

Guided Practice

Find the value of x.

3A. $8\frac{2}{3}$

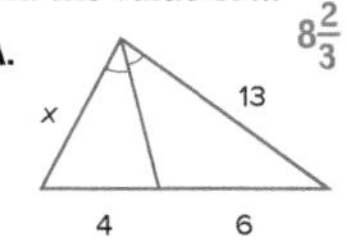

3B. 11.2

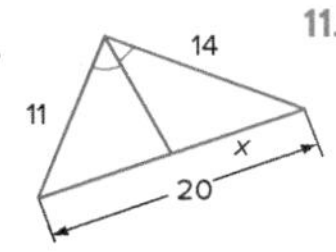

Check Your Understanding ○ = Step-by-Step Solutions begin on page R13.

Go Online! for a Self-Check Quiz

Example 1 G.SRT.5

Find x.

1 8

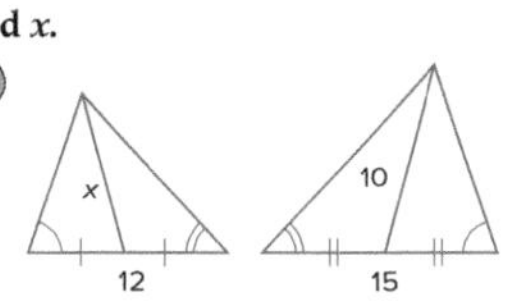

2. 12

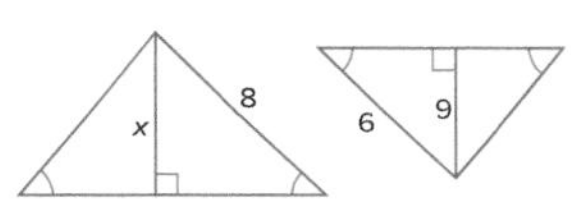

Example 2 G.SRT.5

3. VISION A cat that is 10 inches tall forms a retinal image that is 7 millimeters tall. If $\triangle ABE \sim \triangle DBC$ and the distance from the pupil to the retina is 25 millimeters, how far away from your pupil is the cat? 35.7 in.

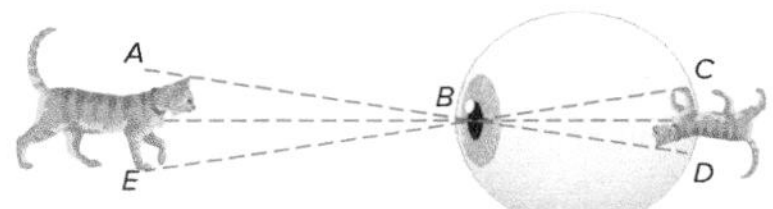

2 Triangle Angle Bisector Theorem

Example 3 Use the Triangle Angle Bisector Theorem

AL Does this prove that $\triangle QRT \sim \triangle SRT$? No; The Triangle Angle Bisector Theorem is not related to similarity.

OL What is another proportion you can write to solve this example? $\frac{QT}{QR} = \frac{ST}{SR}$

BL Give a counterexample to show that not all altitudes separate a triangle proportionally. Sample answer: In a right triangle, two of the altitudes are legs, so they do not separate the triangle at all.

Need Another Example?
Find x.

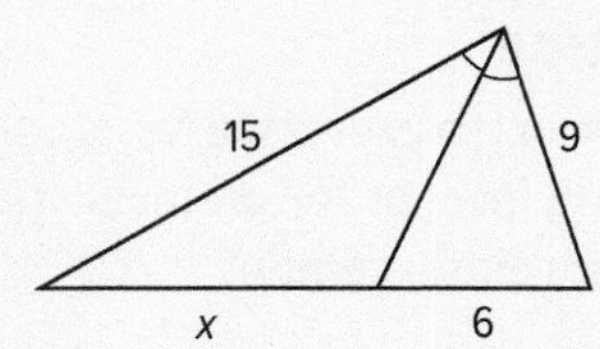

10

Go Online! eBook

Interactive Student Guide
Use the *Interactive Student Guide* to deepen conceptual understanding.
· Parts of Similar Triangles

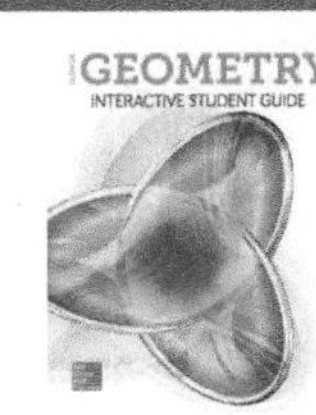

Practice

Formative Assessment Use Exercises 1–5 to assess students' understanding of the concepts in this lesson.

The Practice and Problem Solving exercises assess the content taught in the lesson. The Preparing for Assessment page is meant to be used as preparation for end-of-course assessments.

MP Teaching the Mathematical Practices

Sense-Making Mathematically proficient students start by explaining the meaning of a problem to themselves and looking for entry points to its solution. They plan a solution pathway rather than simply jumping into a solution attempt. In Exercises 11–14, encourage students to make a plan to solve each problem first.

Extra Practice

See page R7 for extra exercises for students who are approaching level or for on-level students who need additional reinforcement.

Levels of Complexity Chart

The levels of the exercises progress from 1 to 3, with Level 1 indicating the lowest level of complexity.

Exercises	6–16	17–28, 36–40	29–35
C Level 3			●
B Level 2		●	
Level 1	●		

Example 3 G.SRT.5 **Find the value of each variable.**

4. 6

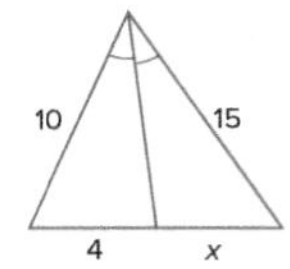

5. 20

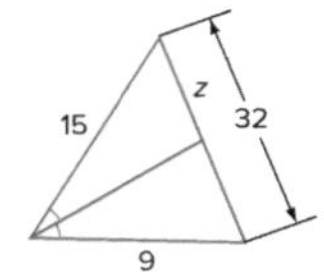

Practice and Problem Solving Extra Practice is on page R7.

Example 1 G.SRT.5 **Find** x.

6. 28

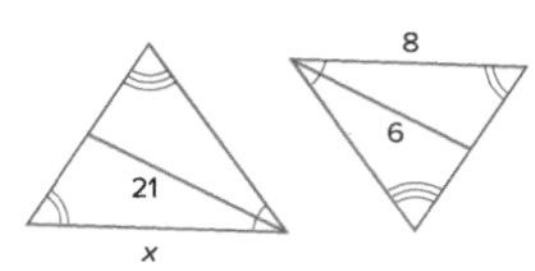

7. 8.5

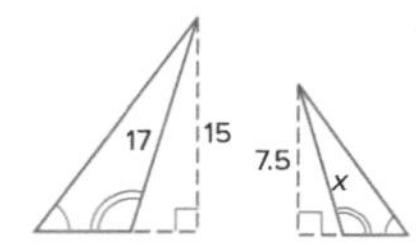

8. 9

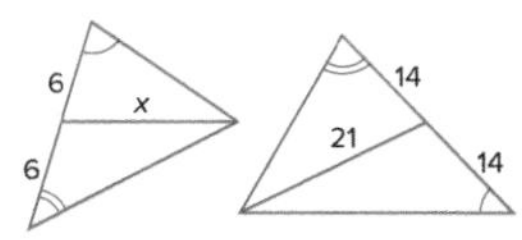

9. 18

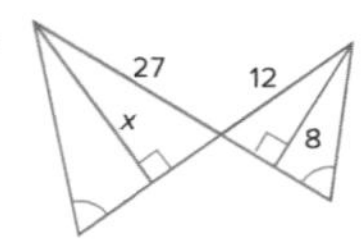

Example 2 G.SRT.5

10. ROADWAYS The intersection of the two roads shown forms two similar triangles. If AC is 382 feet, MP is 248 feet, and the gas station is 50 feet from the intersection, how far from the intersection is the bank? about 77 ft

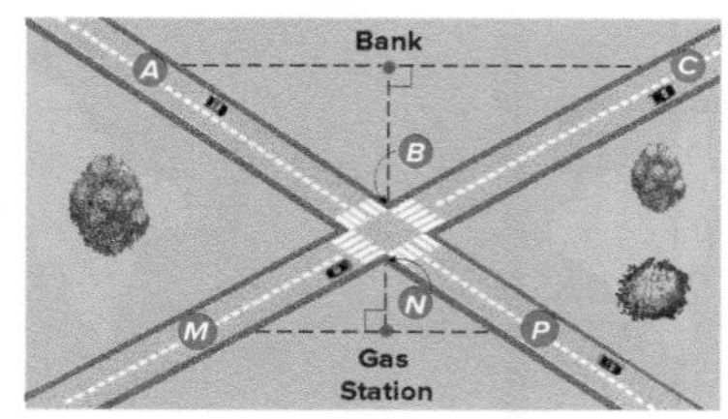

Example 3 G.SRT.5 MP SENSE-MAKING **Find the value of each variable.**

11. 18

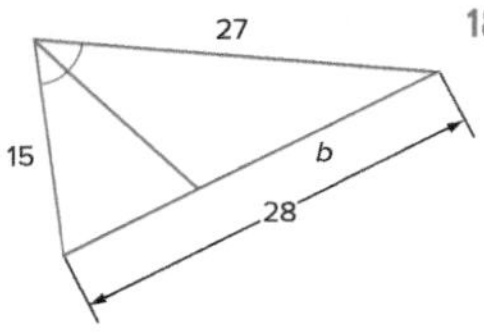

12. 12

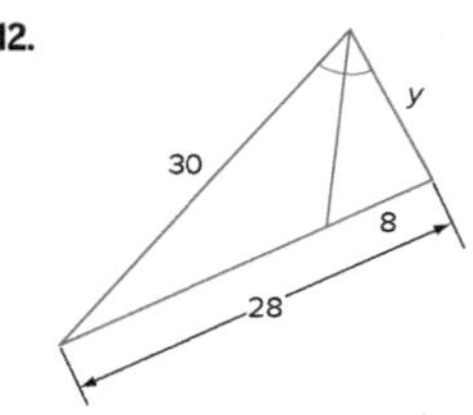

13. 15

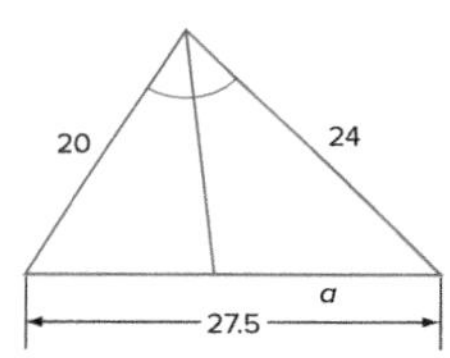

14. 11

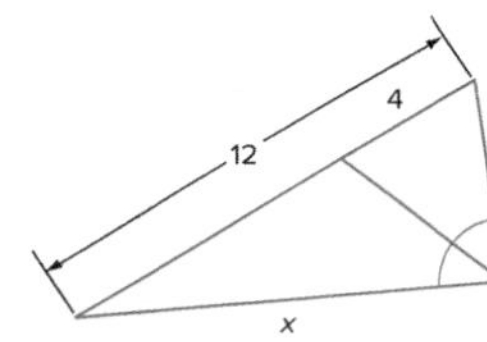

Differentiated Homework Options

Levels	AL Basic	OL Core	BL Advanced
Exercises	6–16, 31, 32, 34–40	7–23 odd, 24, 25, 27, 29–32, 34–40	29–35 (optional: 36–40)
2-Day Option	7–15 odd, 36–40	6–16, 36–40	
	6–16 even, 31, 32, 34, 35	17–32, 34, 35	

You can use ALEKS to provide additional remediation support with personalized instruction and practice.

Go Online!

The most up-to-date resources available for your program can be found at connectED.mcgraw-hill.com.

15 **ALGEBRA** If $\overline{AB}$ and $\overline{JK}$ are altitudes, $\triangle DAC \sim \triangle MJL$, $AB = 9$, $AD = 4x - 8$, $JK = 21$, and $JM = 5x + 3$, find x. 5

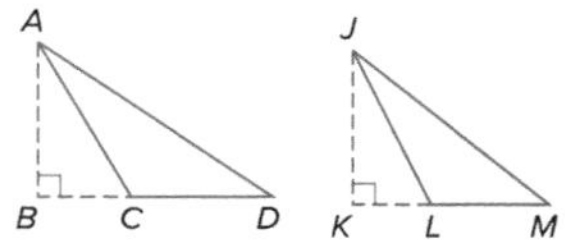

16. **ALGEBRA** If $\overline{NQ}$ and $\overline{VX}$ are medians, $\triangle PNR \sim \triangle WVY$, $NQ = 8$, $PR = 12$, $WY = 7x - 1$, and $VX = 4x + 2$, find x. 4

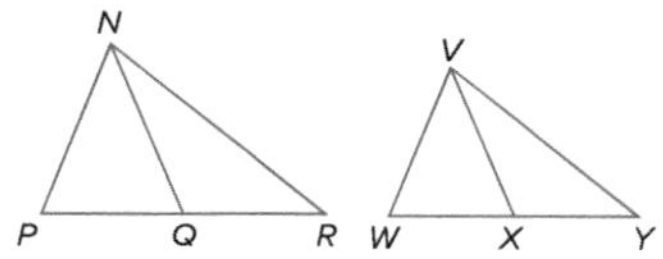

B **17.** If $\triangle SRY \sim \triangle WXQ$, $\overline{RT}$ is an altitude of $\triangle SRY$, $\overline{XV}$ is an altitude of $\triangle WXQ$, $RT = 5$, $RQ = 4$, $QY = 6$, and $YX = 2$, find XV. 4

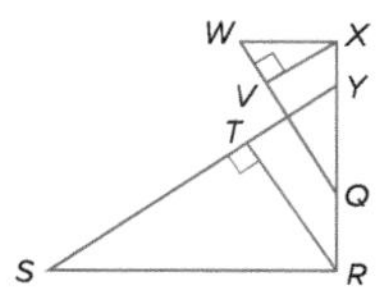

18. **PROOF** Write a paragraph proof of Theorem 7.9. See margin.

19. **PROOF** Write a two-column proof of Theorem 7.10. See margin.

ALGEBRA Find x.

20. 7

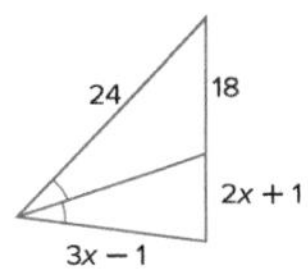

21. 3

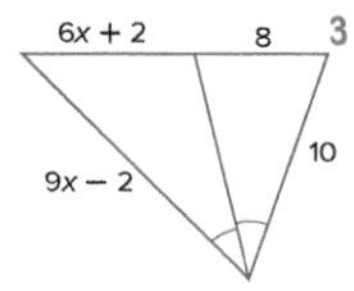

22. 3.1

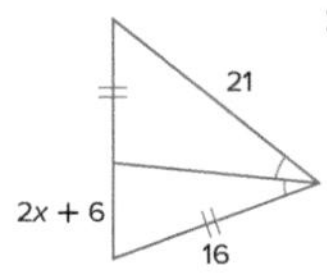

23. 70

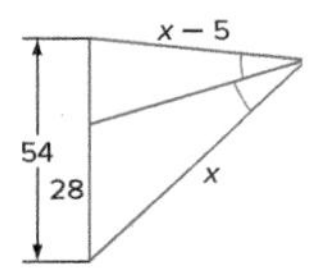

24. Right fielder; Sample answer: Since the hit bisects the triangle, the sides opposite the angle are proportional to the other two sides, or $\frac{CH}{RH} = \frac{BC}{BR}$. Substituting, $\frac{CH}{RH} = \frac{202}{197} = 1.03$. Because $\frac{CH}{RH}$ is slightly greater than 1, $\overline{CH}$ is slightly longer than $\overline{RH}$. Therefore, the right fielder is closer to the hit.

24. **SPORTS** Consider the triangle formed by the path between a batter, center fielder, and right fielder as shown. If the batter gets a hit that bisects the triangle at $\angle B$, is the center fielder or the right fielder closer to the ball? Explain your reasoning.

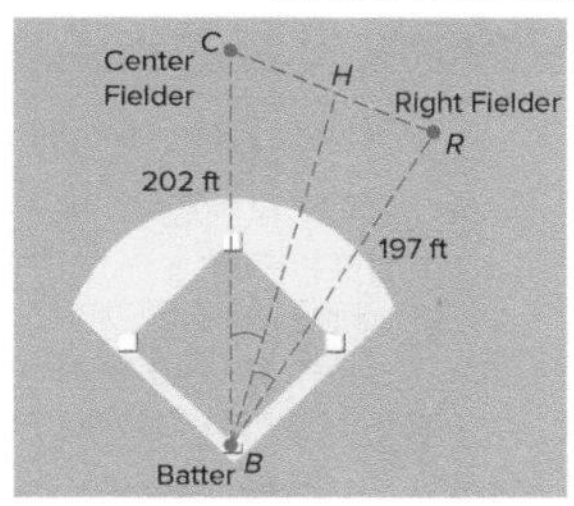

MP **CONSTRUCT ARGUMENTS** Write a two-column proof. 25–26. See Ch. 7 Answer Appendix.

25. Theorem 7.11

Given: $\overline{CD}$ bisects $\angle ACB$.
By construction, $\overline{AE} \parallel \overline{CD}$.

Prove: $\frac{AD}{DB} = \frac{AC}{BC}$

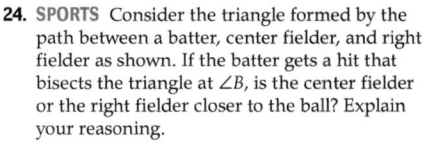

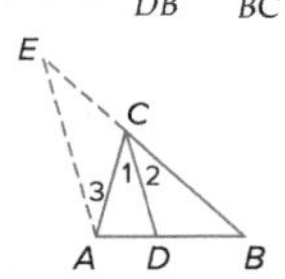

26. **Given:** $\angle H$ is a right angle.
L, K, and M are midpoints.

Prove: $\angle LKM$ is a right angle.

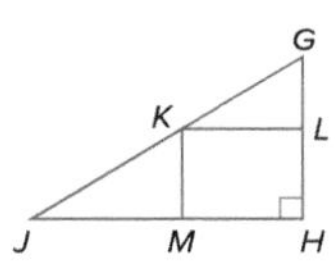

Differentiated Instruction OL BL

Extension Arrange students in groups of three or four, mixing abilities. Students should make a scale drawing of the perimeter of their school. Have the groups measure the perimeter of the school by counting how many paces it takes to walk the perimeter. Next, have them use a ratio of the number of paces to the number of units that they will be using for their drawing.

MP Teaching the Mathematical Practices

Construct Arguments Mathematically proficient students understand and use stated assumptions and definitions in constructing arguments. They make conjectures and build a logical progression of statements to explore the truth of their conjectures. In Exercises 25–26, encourage students to plan their proofs first.

Additional Answers

18. **Given:** $\triangle RTS \sim \triangle EGF$, $\overline{TA}$ and $\overline{GB}$ are angle bisectors.

Prove: $\frac{TA}{GB} = \frac{RT}{EG}$

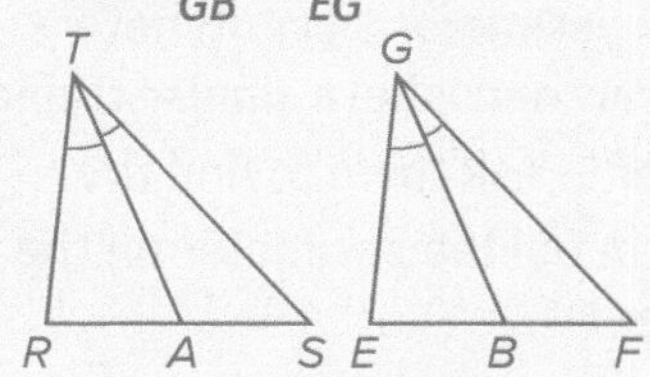

Proof: Because corresponding angles of similar triangles are congruent, $\angle R \cong \angle E$ and $\angle RTS \cong \angle EGF$. Because $\angle RTS$ and $\angle EGF$ are bisected, we know that $\frac{1}{2}m\angle RTS = \frac{1}{2}m\angle EGF$ or $m\angle RTA = m\angle EGB$. This makes $\angle RTA \cong \angle EGB$ and $\triangle RTA \sim \triangle EGB$ by AA Similarity. Thus, $\frac{TA}{GB} = \frac{RT}{EG}$.

19. **Given:** $\triangle ABC \sim \triangle RST$
$\overline{AD}$ is a median of $\triangle ABC$.
$\overline{RU}$ is a median of $\triangle RST$.

Prove: $\frac{AD}{RU} = \frac{AB}{RS}$

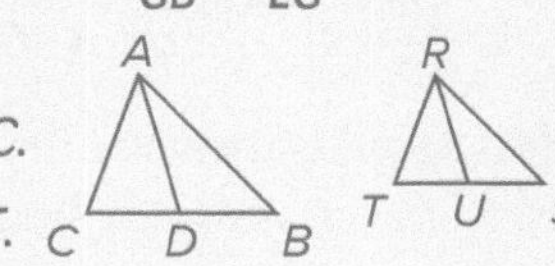

Proof:

Statements (Reasons)

1. $\triangle ABC \sim \triangle RST$; $\overline{AD}$ is a median of $\triangle ABC$; $\overline{RU}$ is a median of $\triangle RST$. (Given)
2. $CD = DB$; $TU = US$ (Def. of median)
3. $\frac{AB}{RS} = \frac{CB}{TS}$ (Def. of ~ ⚠s)
4. $CB = CD + DB$; $TS = TU + US$ (Seg. Add. Post.)
5. $\frac{AB}{RS} = \frac{CD + DB}{TU + US}$ (Subst.)
6. $\frac{AB}{RS} = \frac{DB + DB}{US + US}$ or $\frac{2(DB)}{2(US)}$ (Subst.)
7. $\frac{AB}{RS} = \frac{DB}{US}$ (Subst.)
8. $\angle B \cong \angle S$ (Def. of ~ ⚠s)
9. $\triangle ABD \sim \triangle RSU$ (SAS Similarity)
10. $\frac{AD}{RU} = \frac{AB}{RS}$ (Def. of ~ ⚠s)

Watch Out!

Error Analysis In Exercise 31, students should remember that in the Angle Bisector Theorem, each ratio compares the corresponding sides of the two triangles. Traci wrote each ratio to compare the two sides of one triangle at a time.

Exercise Alert

Ruler Exercise 34 requires the use of a ruler.

Assess

Ticket Out the Door Have students draw and label a triangle with perimeter 24 centimeters. Then ask them to draw and label a similar triangle with a scale factor of $\frac{2}{3}$. Ask them to find the perimeter. Have them tell the perimeter on the way out of the classroom. 16 cm

Additional Answers

32.

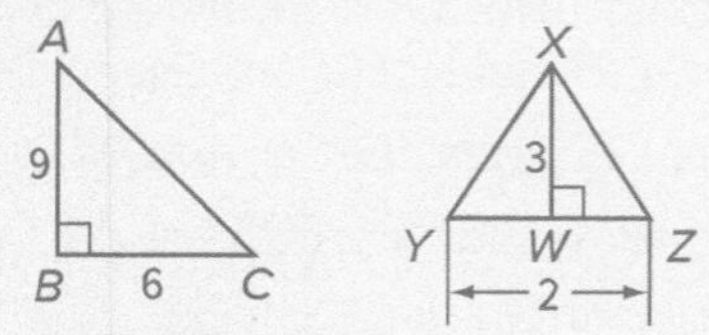

$\frac{AB}{BC} = \frac{XW}{YZ}$, but $\triangle ABC \nsim \triangle XYZ$.

34. Sample answer:

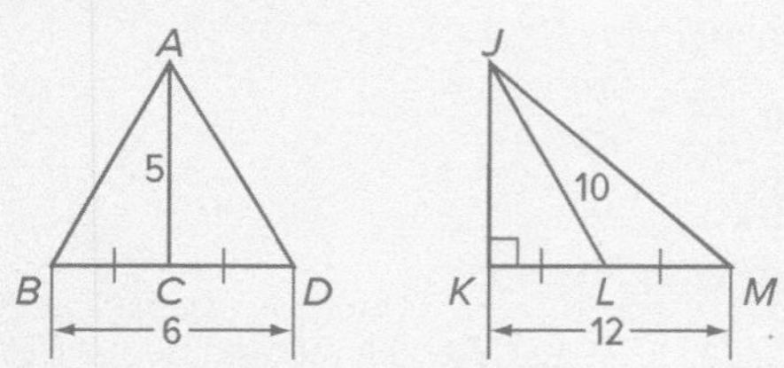

35. Both theorems have a segment that bisects an angle and have proportionate ratios. The Triangle Angle Bisector Theorem pertains to one triangle, while Theorem 7.9 pertains to similar triangles. Unlike the Triangle Angle Bisector Theorem, which separates the opposite side into segments that have the same ratio as the other two sides, Theorem 7.9 relates the angle bisector to the measures of the sides.

PROOF Write a two-column proof. 27–28. See Ch. 7 Answer Appendix.

27. Given: $\triangle QTS \sim \triangle XWZ$, $\overline{TR}$ and $\overline{WY}$ are angle bisectors.
Prove: $\frac{TR}{WY} = \frac{QT}{XW}$

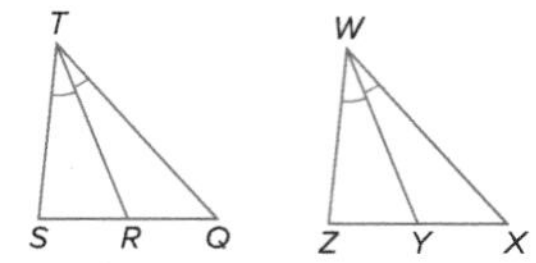

28. Given: $\overline{FD} \parallel \overline{BC}$, $\overline{BF} \parallel \overline{CD}$, $\overline{AC}$ bisects $\angle C$.
Prove: $\frac{DE}{EC} = \frac{BA}{AC}$

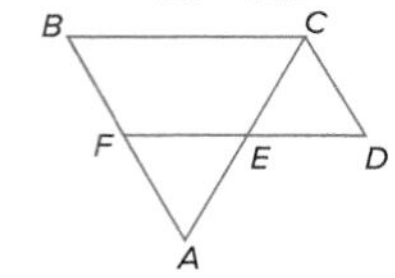

29. **SPORTS** During football practice, Trevor threw a pass to Ricardo as shown below. If Eli is farther from Trevor when he completes the pass to Ricardo and Craig and Eli move at the same speed, who will reach Ricardo to tackle him first? Craig

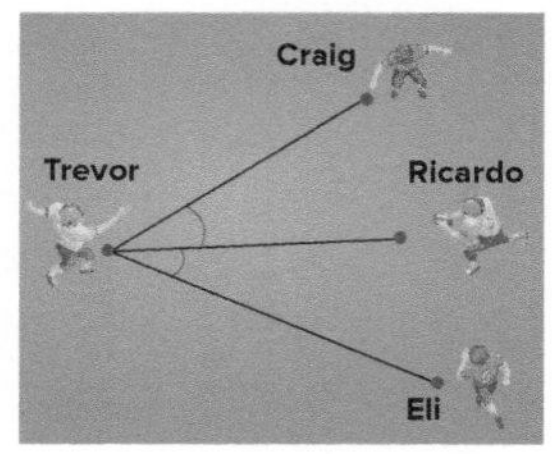

30. **SHELVING** In the bookshelf shown, the distance between each shelf is 13 inches and $\overline{AK}$ is a median of $\triangle ABC$. If EF is $3\frac{1}{3}$ inches, what is BK? 10 in.

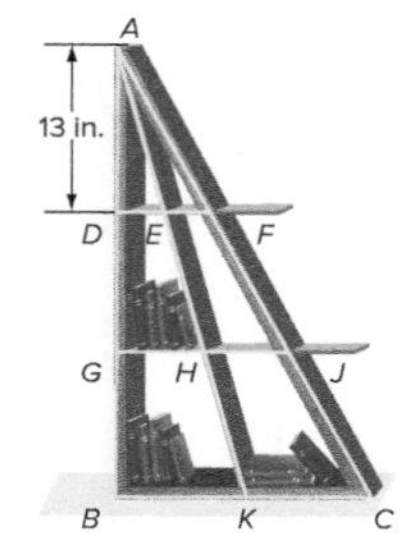

G.SRT.4, G.SRT.5

H.O.T. Problems Use Higher-Order Thinking Skills

31. **ERROR ANALYSIS** Chun and Traci are determining the value of x in the figure. Chun says to find x, solve the proportion $\frac{5}{8} = \frac{15}{x}$, but Traci says to find x, the proportion $\frac{5}{x} = \frac{8}{15}$ should be solved. Is either of them correct? Explain. Chun; by the Angle Bisector Theorem, the correct proportion is $\frac{5}{8} = \frac{15}{x}$.

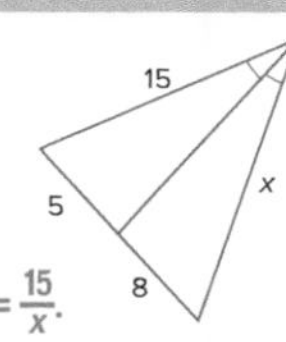

32. **CONSTRUCT ARGUMENTS** Find a counterexample to the following statement. Explain.

If the measure of an altitude and side of a triangle are proportional to the corresponding altitude and corresponding side of another triangle, then the triangles are similar. See margin.

33. **CHALLENGE** The perimeter of $\triangle PQR$ is 94 units. $\overline{QS}$ bisects $\angle PQR$. Find PS and RS. $PS = 18.4$, $RS = 24$

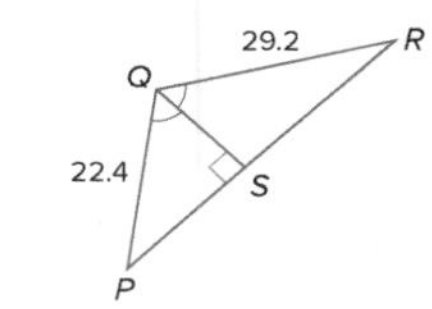

34. **OPEN-ENDED** Draw two triangles so that the measures of corresponding medians and a corresponding side are proportional, but the triangles are not similar. See margin.

35. **WRITING IN MATH** Compare and contrast Theorem 7.9 and the Triangle Angle Bisector Theorem. See margin.

Mathematical Practice Standards

Emphasis On	Exercises
1 Make sense of problems and persevere in solving them.	1, 2, 4–9, 11–17, 20–23, , 33, 39, 40
2 Reason abstractly and quantitatively.	34, 35, 38
3 Construct viable arguments and critique the reasoning of others.	18, 19, 25–28, 31, 32
4 Model with mathematics.	3, 10, 24, 29, 30
6 Attend to precision.	36, 40

Go Online!

eSolutions Manual

Create worksheets, answer keys, and solutions handouts for your assignments.

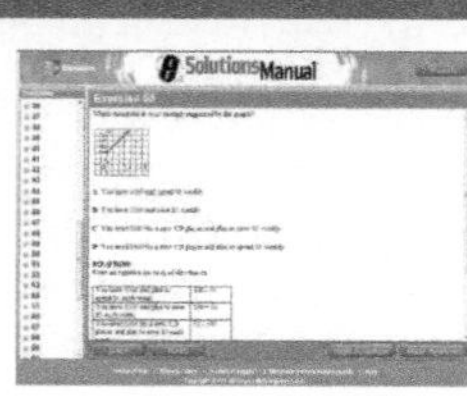

Preparing for Assessment

36. $\overline{MQ}$ is an angle bisector of $\triangle MNP$, as shown.

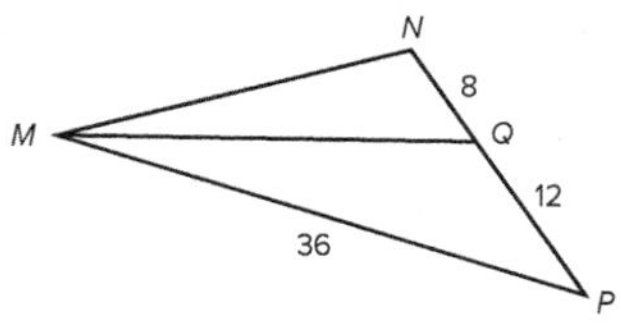

What is the perimeter of $\triangle MNP$? MP 1, 6 G.SRT.5 **C**

- ○ A 24
- ○ C 80
- ○ B 56
- ○ D 88

37. If $\triangle ABC \sim \triangle QRS$, what is the value of x? MP 1, 5 G.SRT.5 **D**

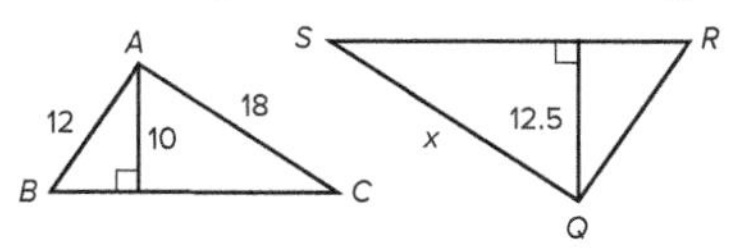

- ○ A 14.4
- ○ C 20.5
- ○ B 15
- ○ D 22.5

38. In $\triangle JKL$, $\overline{LJ}$ is 1.5 times as long as $\overline{LM}$. MP 2 G.SRT.5

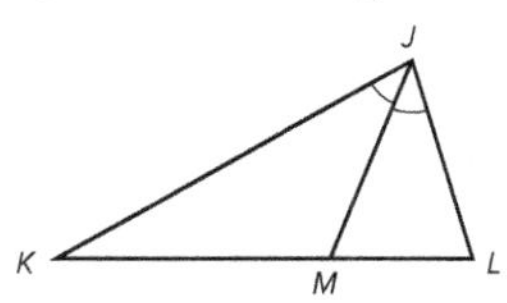

Which of the following statements must be true? **A**

I. $\overline{KJ}$ is 1.5 times as long as $\overline{KM}$.

II. $\overline{KM}$ is 1.5 times as long as $\overline{LM}$.

III. $\overline{KJ}$ is 1.5 times as long as $\overline{LJ}$.

- ☐ A I only
- ☐ B II only
- ☐ C III only
- ☐ D II and III only
- ☐ E I, II, and III

39. The measure of one of the base angles of an isosceles triangle is one third of the measure of the vertex angle. What is the measure of one of the base angles? MP 1 G.SRT.5 **36**

40. MULTI-STEP In the figure, $\triangle EFG \sim \triangle HJK$ and $\overline{EX}$ and $\overline{HY}$ are medians. MP 1, 2, 6 G.SRT.5

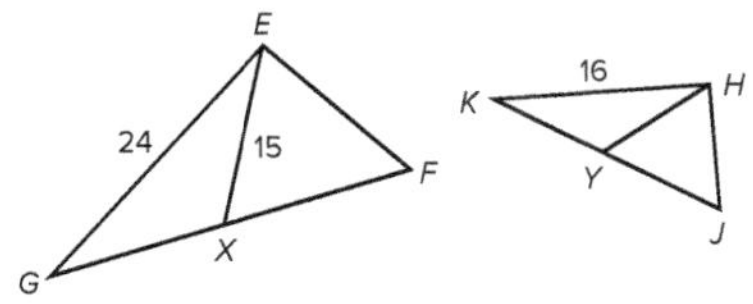

a. Which proportion could be used to find the length of $\overline{HY}$? **D**

- ○ A $\frac{EG}{GX} = \frac{KH}{KY}$
- ○ B $\frac{EG}{HY} = \frac{EX}{KH}$
- ○ C $\frac{EG}{EX} = \frac{HY}{KH}$
- ○ D $\frac{EG}{EX} = \frac{KH}{HY}$

b. Write three sets of similar triangles found in the diagram. **$\triangle GEX \sim \triangle KHY$, $\triangle FEX \sim \triangle JHY$, $\triangle JHK \sim \triangle FEG$**

c. What is the length of $\overline{HY}$? **B**

- ○ A 8
- ○ B 10
- ○ C 16
- ○ D 24

d. The perimeter of $\triangle EGX$ is 51. What is the length of $\overline{KY}$? **B**

- ○ A 12
- ○ B 8
- ○ C 10
- ○ D 6

Preparing for Assessment

Exercises 36–40 require students to use the skills they will need on standardized assessments. Exercises are dual-coded with content standards and mathematical practice standards.

Dual Coding

Exercises	Content Standards	MP Mathematical Practices
36	G.SRT.5	1, 6
37	G.SRT.5	1, 5
38	G.SRT.5	2
39	G.SRT.5	1
40	G.SRT.5	1, 2, 6

Diagnose Student Errors

Survey student responses for each item. Class trends may indicate common errors and misconceptions.

36.

A	Found the length of $\overline{MN}$
B	Did not include the length of $\overline{MN}$ in the perimeter
C	CORRECT
D	Added 24 to length of $\overline{NQ}$ to find length of $\overline{MN}$

37.

A	Solved $\frac{10}{12.5} = \frac{x}{18}$
B	Solved $\frac{10}{12.5} = \frac{12}{x}$
C	Added 8 to the length of the altitude in $\triangle QRS$
D	CORRECT

38.

A	CORRECT
B	Identified a relationship that is not equivalent to $\frac{LJ}{LM} = 1.5$
C	Identified a relationship that is not equivalent to $\frac{LJ}{LM} = 1.5$
D	Identified two relationships that are not equivalent to $\frac{LJ}{LM} = 1.5$
E	Identified two relationships that are not equivalent to $\frac{LJ}{LM} = 1.5$

Go Online!

Quizzes

Students can use *Self-Check Quizzes* to check their understanding of this lesson and have the results sent to you. You can also give the *Chapter Quiz*, which covers the content in Lessons 7-5 and 7-6.

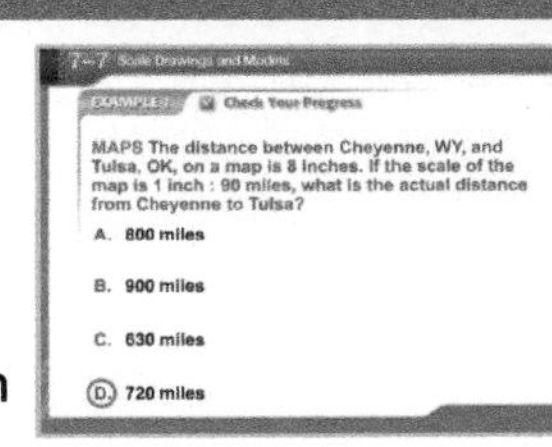

Launch

Objective
- Investigate iteration and draw fractals.
- Write recursive formulas.

Materials
- isometric dot paper

Easy to Make Manipulatives
Teaching Geometry with Manipulatives, template for:
- isometric dot paper, p. 7

Teaching Tip
Discuss with students how each stage is determined so that students understand the process. Every time each triangle is bisected to form one or more other triangles, it is one stage. Ask students to record the number of triangles at each stage so they can analyze the pattern in the numbers.

Teach ELL

Working in Cooperative Groups Arrange students in groups of four, mixing abilities. Tell one student in each group to collect the data by drawing the triangles while another student analyzes the data by counting the triangles and forming a sequence from the count. Tell a third student to find the perimeters of the triangles as the activity continues, and the fourth student to generate a sequence of numbers representing the perimeters of the triangles. This sequence should help them see that the perimeter approaches zero as the number of triangles increases. Have students complete Exercise 1.

Ask:
- Combine three copies of the Stage 4 Sierpinski Triangle. What stage of the Sierpinski Triangle is this? Stage 5

Practice Have students complete Analyze the Results 2–5.

EXTEND 7-6

Geometry Lab

Fractals

A **fractal** is a geometric figure that is created using iteration. **Iteration** is a process of repeating the same operation over and over again. Fractals are **self-similar**, which means that the smaller details of the shape have the same geometric characteristics as the original form.

Mathematical Practices

MP 8 Look for and express regularity in repeated reasoning.

Activity 1

Stage 0 Draw an equilateral triangle on isometric dot paper in which each side is 8 units long.

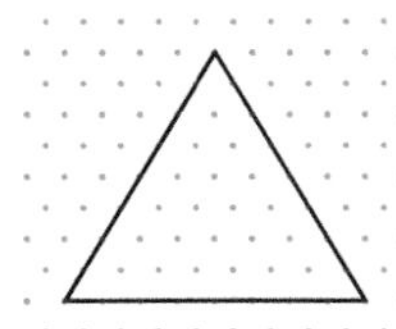

Stage 1 Connect the midpoints of the sides to form another triangle. Shade the center triangle.

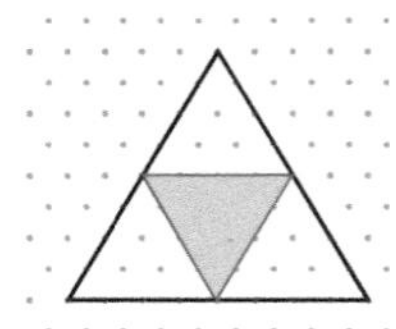

Stage 2 Repeat the process using the three unshaded triangles. Connect the midpoints of the sides to form three other triangles.

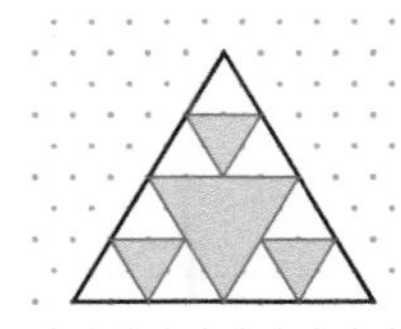

If you repeat this process indefinitely, the figure that results is called the Sierpinski Triangle.

Analyze the Results Work cooperatively.

1. If you continue the process, how many unshaded triangles will you have at Stage 3? 27
2. What is the perimeter of an unshaded triangle in Stage 4? 1.5 units
3. If you continue the process indefinitely, what will happen to the perimeters of the unshaded triangles? The perimeter will approach zero.
4. **CHALLENGE** Complete the proof below.

   Given: $\triangle KAP$ is equilateral. $D, F, M, B, C,$ and E are midpoints of $\overline{KA}, \overline{AP}, \overline{PK}, \overline{DA}, \overline{AF},$ and $\overline{FD}$, respectively.

   Prove: $\triangle BAC \sim \triangle KAP$

   See Ch. 7 Answer Appendix.

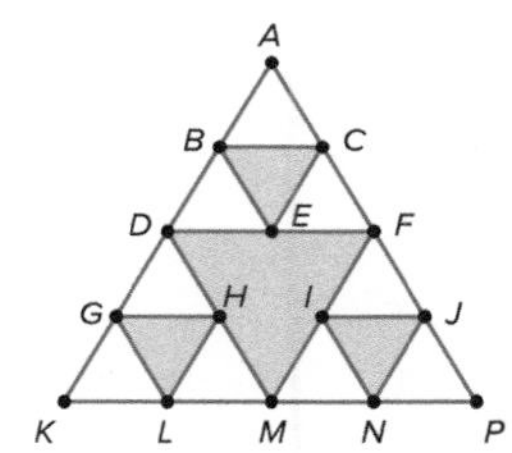

5. A *fractal tree* can be drawn by making two new branches from the endpoint of each original branch, each one third as long as the previous branch. See Ch. 7 Answer Appendix.
   a. Draw Stages 3 and 4 of a fractal tree. How many total branches do you have in Stages 1 through 4? (Do not count the stems.)
   b. Write an expression to predict the number of branches at each stage.

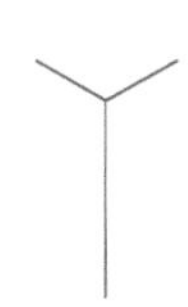

Stage 1

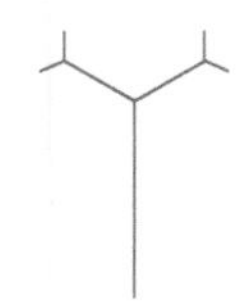

Stage 2

Assess

Formative Assessment
Use Analyze the Results 1–5 to assess whether students understand the meaning of fractals, iterations, self-similarity, and fractal trees.

Extending the Concept
Ask:
- Is a fractal tree self-similar? yes

From Concrete to Abstract
Use Analyze the Results 5b to extend what students observe in their drawings to an algebraic expression.

CHAPTER 7

Study Guide and Review

Go Online! for Vocabulary Review Games and key vocabulary in 13 languages

Study Guide

Key Concepts

Dilations (Lesson 7-1)

- Dilations enlarge or reduce figures proportionally.

Similar Polygons and Triangles (Lessons 7-2, 7-3, and 7-4)

- Two polygons are similar if and only if their corresponding angles are congruent and the measures of their corresponding sides are proportional.
- Two triangles are similar if:

  AA: Two angles of one triangle are congruent to two angles of the other triangle.

  SSS: The measures of the corresponding sides of the two triangles are proportional.

  SAS: The measures of two sides of one triangle are proportional to the measures of two corresponding sides of another triangle and their included angles are congruent.

Parallel Lines and Proportional Parts (Lesson 7-5)

- If a line is parallel to one side of a triangle and intersects the other two sides in two distinct points, then it separates these sides into segments of proportional length.
- A midsegment of a triangle is parallel to one side of the triangle and its length is one half the length of that side.

Parts of Similar Triangles (Lesson 7-6)

- Two triangles are similar when each of the following are proportional in measure:
  - their perimeters
  - their corresponding altitudes
  - their corresponding angle bisectors
  - their corresponding medians

FOLDABLES Study Organizer

Use your Foldable to review the chapter. Working with a partner can be helpful. Ask for clarification of concepts as needed.

Key Vocabulary

dilation (p. 511)	scale factor (p. 504)
enlargement (p. 511)	similar polygons (p. 503)
midsegment of a triangle (p. 535)	similarity transformation (p. 511)
reduction (p. 511)	

Vocabulary Check

Choose the letter of the word or phrase that best completes each statement.

a. scale factor	**f.** midsegment
b. AA Similarity Postulate	**g.** dilation
c. SSS Similarity Theorem	**h.** enlargement
d. SAS Similarity Theorem	**i.** reduction
e. Symmetric Property of Similarity	**j.** Transitive Property of Similarity

1. A(n) __?__ of a triangle has endpoints that are the midpoints of two sides of the triangle. f
2. If $\angle A \cong \angle X$ and $\angle C \cong \angle Z$, then $\triangle ABC \sim \triangle XYZ$ by the __?__. b
3. A(n) __?__ is an example of a similarity transformation. g
4. The ratio of the lengths of two corresponding sides of two similar polygons is the __?__. a
5. A dilation with a scale factor of $\frac{2}{5}$ will result in a(n) __?__. i
6. If $\angle A \cong \angle X$ and $\frac{AB}{XY} = \frac{AC}{XZ}$, then $\triangle ABC \sim \triangle XYZ$ by the __?__. d
7. If $\triangle ABC \sim \triangle DEF$ and $\triangle DEF \sim \triangle XYZ$, then $\triangle ABC \sim \triangle XYZ$ by the __?__. j

Concept Check

8. Explain whether two triangles must be similar if two sides of one triangle are proportional to the corresponding sides of the other triangle and an angle of one triangle is congruent to an angle of the other triangle. See margin.
9. A line segment connects the midpoints of two sides of a triangle. What conclusions that can be made about this line segment? See margin.

Answering the Essential Question

Before answering the Essential Question, have students review their answers to the *Building on the Essential Question* exercises found throughout the chapter.

- How can you determine whether two objects are similar? (p. 505)
- How do you use the SSS or the SAS similarity criterion to show that two triangles are similar? (p. 525)

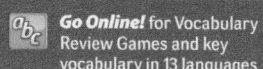

FOLDABLES Study Organizer

A completed Foldable for this chapter should include the Key Concepts related to proportions and similarity.

Key Vocabulary ELL

The page reference after each word denotes where that term was first introduced. If students have difficulty answering questions 1–7, remind them that they can use these page references to refresh their memories about the vocabulary terms.

Have students work together to match the correct terms to each sentence in the Vocabulary Check. Have students take turns saying each sentence aloud while the other student listens carefully.

You can use the detailed reports in ALEKS to automatically monitor students' progress and pinpoint remediation needs prior to the chapter test.

Additional Answers (Practice Test)

8. The angles must be included angles, otherwise the triangles may or may not be similar.
9. The line segment must be parallel to the third side and its length is one half the length of the third side.

Go Online!

Vocabulary Review

Students can use the *Vocabulary Review Games* to check their understanding of the vocabulary terms in this chapter. Students should refer to the *Student-Built Glossary* they have created as they went through the chapter to review important terms. You can also give a *Vocabulary Test* over the content of this chapter.

Lesson-by-Lesson Review

Intervention If the given examples are not sufficient to review the topics covered by the questions, remind students that the lesson references tell them where to review that topic in their textbook.

Two-Day Option Have students complete the Lesson-by-Lesson Review. Then you can use McGraw-Hill eAssessment to customize another review worksheet that practices all the objectives of this chapter or only the objectives on which your students need more help.

Additional Answers (Practice Test)

10.

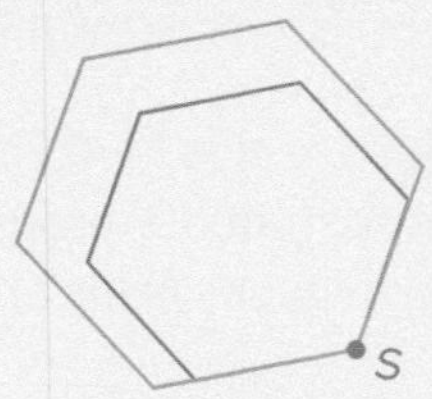

12. No, the polygons are not similar because the corresponding sides are not proportional.

13. Yes, the rectangles are similar because all of the corresponding angles are congruent and the corresponding sides are proportional in a 3:2 ratio.

CHAPTER 7

Study Guide and Review *Continued*

Lesson-by-Lesson Review

7-1 Dilations

G.CO.2, G.SRT.1

10. Copy the figure and point *S*. Then use a ruler to draw the image of the figure under a dilation with center *S* and scale factor $r = 1.25$. **See margin.**

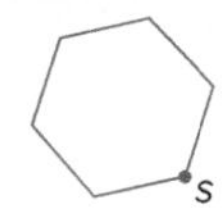

11. Determine whether the dilation from figure *W* to *W′* is an *enlargement* or a *reduction*. Then find the scale factor of the dilation and *x*. **reduction; 0.45; 8.25**

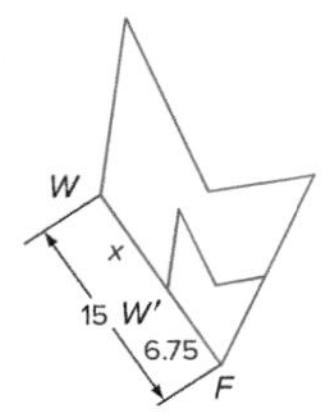

Example 1

Square *ABCD* has vertices *A*(0, 0), *B*(0, 8), *C*(8, 8), and *D*(8, 0). Find the image of *ABCD* after a dilation centered at the origin with a scale factor of 0.5.

Multiply the *x*- and *y*-coordinates of each vertex by the scale factor, 0.5.

(x, y)	→	$(0.5x, 0.5y)$
$A(0, 0)$	→	$A'(0, 0)$
$B(0, 8)$	→	$B'(0, 4)$
$C(8, 8)$	→	$C'(4, 4)$
$D(8, 0)$	→	$D'(4, 0)$

Graph *ABCD* and its image *A′B′C′D′*.

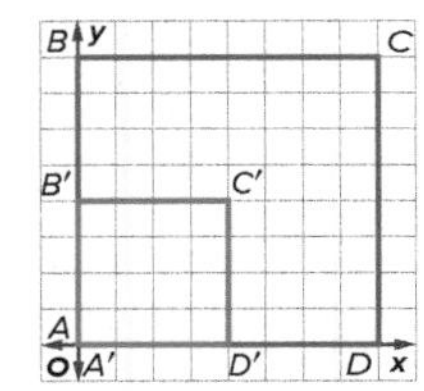

7-2 Similar Polygons

G.SRT.2, G.SRT.3, G.SRT.5, G.CO.8

Determine whether each pair of figures is similar. If so, write the similarity statement and scale factor. If not, explain your reasoning. 12–13. See margin.

12.

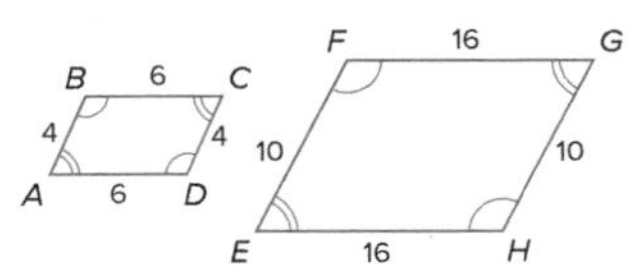

13.

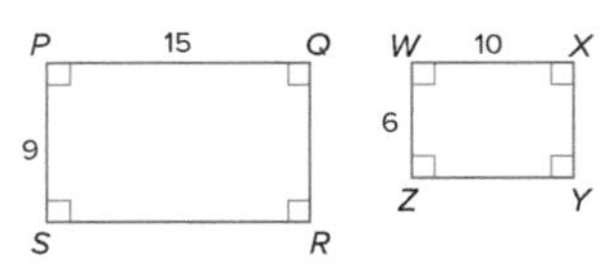

14. PHOTOS If the dimensions of a photo are 2 inches by 3 inches and the dimensions of a poster are 8 inches by 12 inches, are the photo and poster similar? Explain. **Yes; the ratios are the same.**

Example 2

Determine whether the pair of triangles is similar. If so, write the similarity statement and scale factor. If not, explain your reasoning.

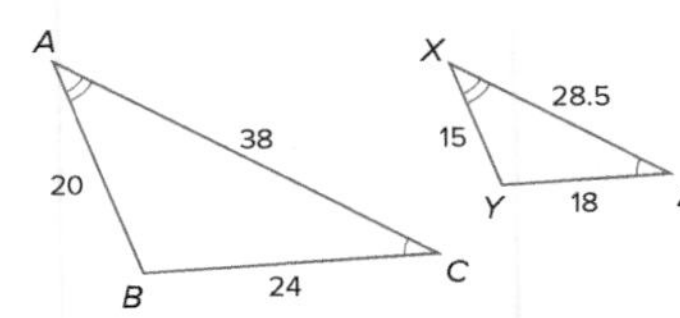

$\angle A \cong \angle X$ and $\angle C \cong \angle Z$, so by the Third Angle Theorem, $\angle B \cong \angle Y$. All of the corresponding angles are therefore congruent.

Similar polygons must also have proportional side lengths. Check the ratios of corresponding side lengths.

$\frac{AB}{XY} = \frac{20}{15}$ or $\frac{4}{3}$ $\quad \frac{BC}{YZ} = \frac{24}{18}$ or $\frac{4}{3}$ $\quad \frac{AC}{XZ} = \frac{38}{28.5}$ or $\frac{4}{3}$

Because corresponding sides are proportional, $\triangle ABC \sim \triangle XYZ$. So, the triangles are similar with a scale factor of $\frac{4}{3}$.

7-3 Similar Triangles: AA Similarity

G.SRT.2, G.SRT.3, G.SRT.4, G.SRT.5, G.CO.8

Determine whether the triangles are similar. If so, write a similarity statement. Explain your reasoning.

15.

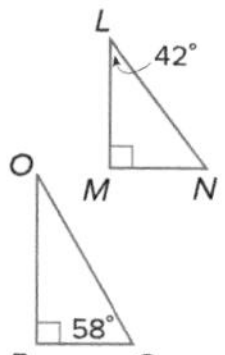

16.

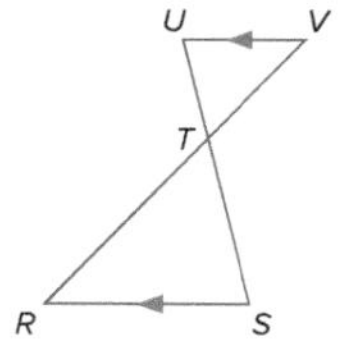

15–16. See margin.

17. **TREES** To estimate the height of a tree, Dave stands in the shadow of the tree so that his shadow and the tree's shadow end at the same point. Dave is 6 feet 4 inches tall and his shadow is 15 feet long. If he is standing 66 feet away from the tree, what is the height of the tree? **34.2 ft**

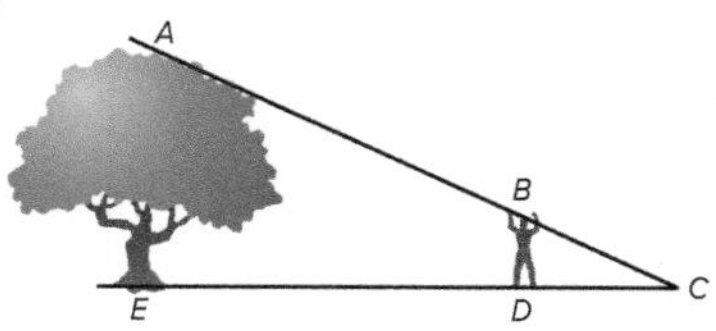

Example 3

Determine whether triangles *DEF* and *JKF* are similar. If so, write a similarity statement. Explain your reasoning.

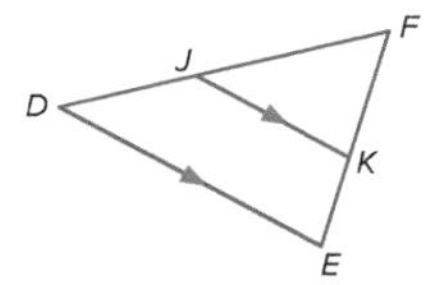

$\angle F \cong \angle F$ by the Reflexive Property.

Because $\overline{DE} \parallel \overline{JK}$, $\angle FJK \cong \angle FDE$ by the Corresponding Angles Postulate.

Because two angles of one triangle are congruent to two angles of the other triangle, $\triangle DEF \sim \triangle JKF$ by AA Similarity.

7-4 Similar Triangles: SSS and SAS Similarity

G.SRT.2, G.SRT.3, G.SRT.4, G.SRT.5

Determine whether the triangles are similar. If so, write a similarity statement. Explain your reasoning.

18.

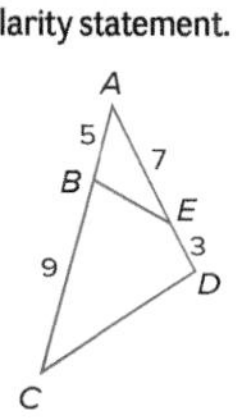

Yes, $\triangle ABE \sim \triangle ADC$ by the SAS ~ Thm.

19.

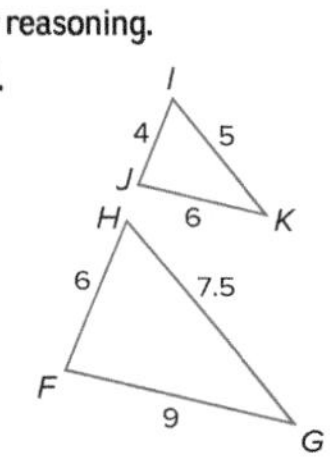

Yes, $\triangle IJK \sim \triangle HFG$ by the SSS ~ Thm.

Example 4

Determine whether triangles *WZX* and *XZY* are similar. If so, write a similarity statement. Explain your reasoning.

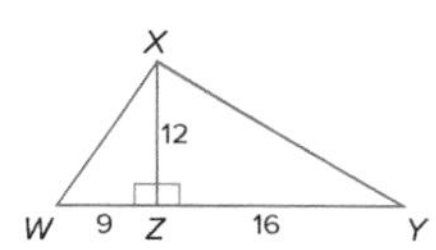

$\angle WZX \cong \angle XZY$ because they are both right angles. Now compare the ratios of the legs of the right triangles.

$$\frac{WZ}{XZ} = \frac{9}{12} = \frac{3}{4} \qquad \frac{XZ}{YZ} = \frac{12}{16} = \frac{3}{4}$$

Because two pairs of sides are proportional with the included angles congruent, $\triangle WZX \sim \triangle XZY$ by SAS Similarity.

Additional Answers (Practice Test)

15. The triangles are not similar.
16. Triangle *UVT* is similar to triangle *SRT* by the AA Similarity Postulate.

Go Online!

Anticipation Guide

Students should complete the *Chapter 7 Anticipation Guide*, and discuss how their responses have changed now that they have completed Chapter 7.

Before the Test

Have students complete the Study Notebook Tie it Together activity to review topics and skills presented in the chapter.

CHAPTER 7

Study Guide and Review *Continued*

7-5 Parallel Lines and Proportional Parts

G.SRT.4, G.SRT.5

Find x.

20. 96

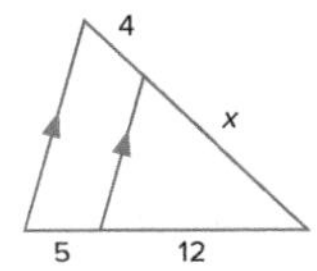

21. 22.5

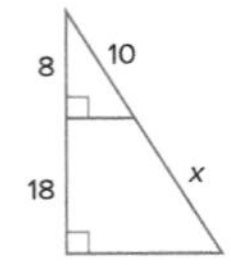

22. **STREETS** Find the distance along Broadway between 37th Street and 36th Street. 275 ft

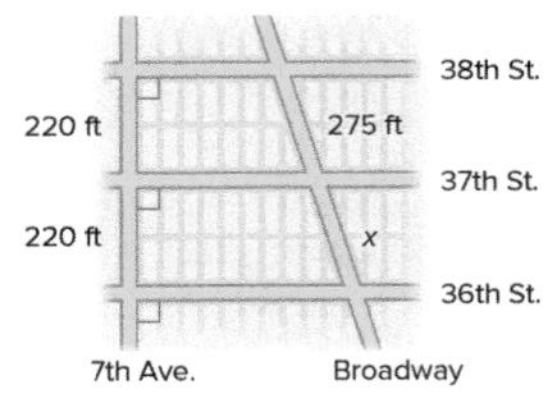

Example 5

ALGEBRA **Find x and y.**

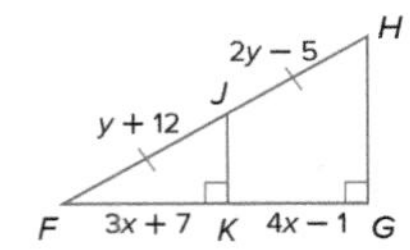

$FK = KG$

$3x + 7 = 4x - 1$

$-x = -8$

$x = 8$

$FJ = JH$	Definition of congruence
$y + 12 = 2y - 5$	Substitution
$-y = -17$	Subtract.
$y = 17$	Simplify.

7-6 Parts of Similar Triangles

G.SRT.4, G.SRT.5

Find the value of each variable.

23. 6

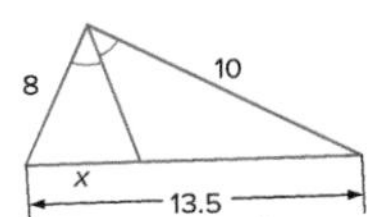

24. 19

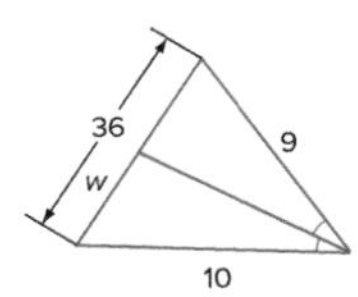

25. **MAPS** The scale given on a map of the state of Missouri indicates that 3 inches represents 50 miles. The cities of St. Louis, Springfield, and Kansas City form a triangle. If the measurements of the lengths of the sides of this triangle on the map are 15 inches, 10 inches, and 13 inches, find the perimeter of the actual triangle formed by these cities to the nearest mile. 633 mi

Example 6

Find x.

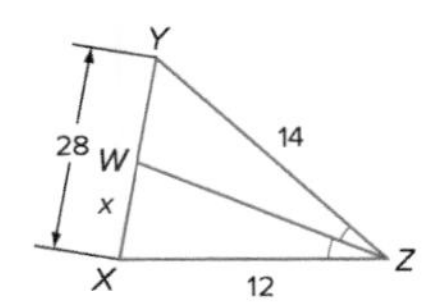

Use the Triangle Angle Bisector Theorem to write a proportion.

$\frac{WX}{YW} = \frac{XZ}{YZ}$	Triangle Angle Bisector Thm.
$\frac{x}{28 - x} = \frac{12}{14}$	Substitution
$(28 - x)(12) = x \cdot 14$	Cross Products Property
$336 - 12x = 14x$	Simplify.
$336 = 26x$	Add.
$12.9 = x$	Simplify.

Go Online!

eAssessment

Customize and create multiple versions of chapter tests and answer keys that align to your standards. Tests can be delivered on paper or online.

CHAPTER 7
Practice Test

Go Online! for another Chapter Test

Copy the figure and point M. Then use a ruler to draw the image of the figure under a dilation with center M and the scale factor r indicated. 1–2. See margin.

1. $r = 1.5$

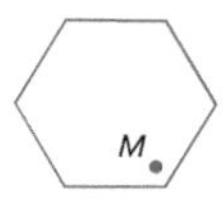

2. $r = \frac{1}{3}$

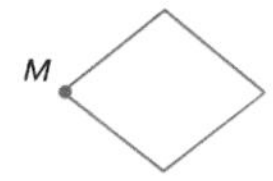

Determine whether each pair of figures is similar. If so, write the similarity statement and scale factor. If not, explain your reasoning.

3.

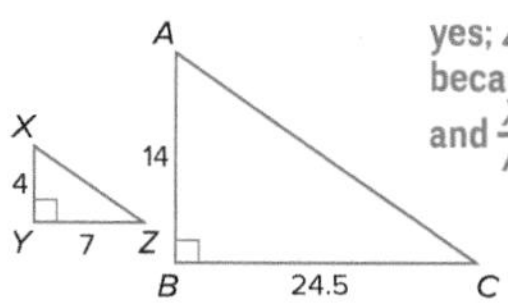

yes; $\triangle XYZ \sim \triangle ABC$ because $\angle Y \cong \angle B$ and $\frac{XY}{AB} = \frac{YZ}{BC}$; $\frac{2}{7}$

4.

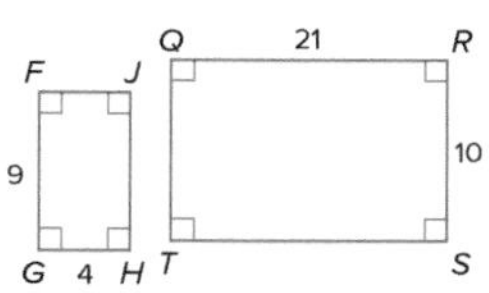

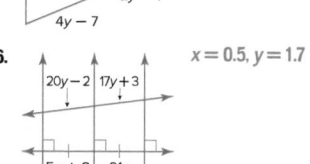

no; $\frac{FG}{QR} \neq \frac{GH}{RS}$

ALGEBRA Find x and y. Round to the nearest tenth if necessary.

5.

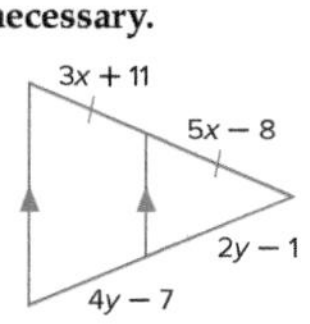

$x = 9.5, y = 3$

6.

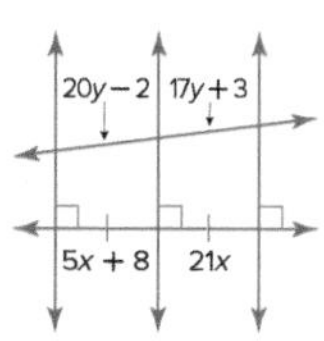

$x = 0.5, y = 1.7$

7. **ALGEBRA** Equilateral $\triangle MNP$ has perimeter $12a + 18b$. $\overline{QR}$ is a midsegment. What is QR? $2a + 3b$

8. **ALGEBRA** Right isosceles $\triangle ABC$ has hypotenuse with length h. $\overline{DE}$ is a midsegment with length $4x$ that is not parallel to the hypotenuse. What is the perimeter of $\triangle ABC$? $16x + h$

9. Determine whether the triangles are similar. If so, write a similarity statement. Explain your thinking.

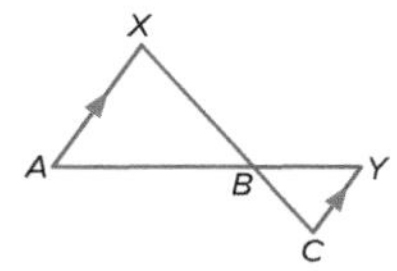

Yes; $\triangle ABX \sim \triangle YBC$ by AA Similarity

Find x.

10.

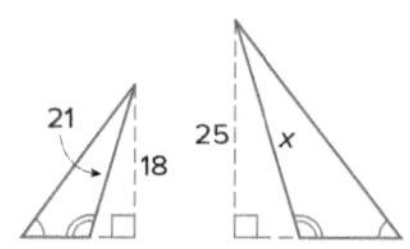

29.2

11.

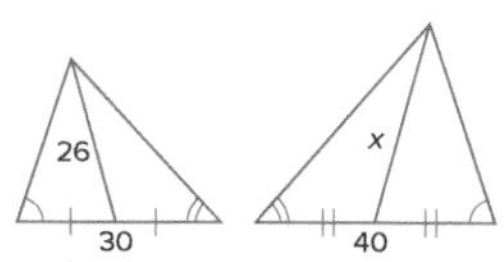

34.7

Determine whether the dilation from A to B is an *enlargement* or a *reduction*. Then find the scale factor of the dilation.

12.

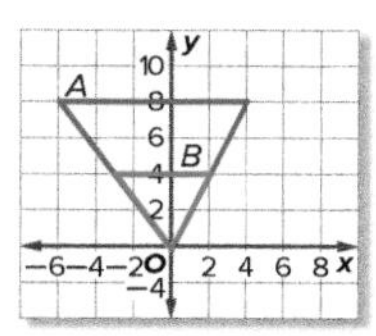

reduction; $\frac{1}{2}$

13.

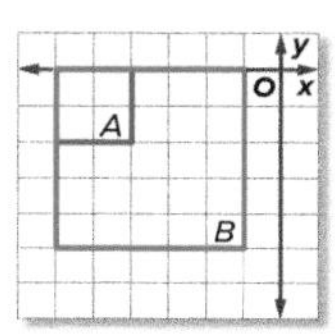

enlargement; $\frac{5}{2}$

14. **ALGEBRA** Identify the similar triangles. Find WZ and UZ.

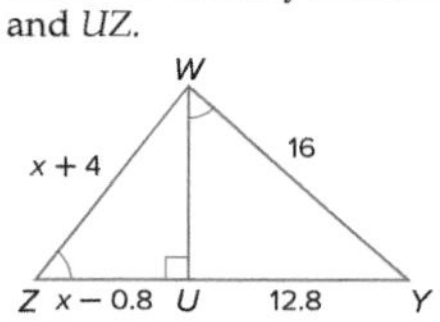

$\triangle WUZ \sim \triangle YUW$ by AA Similarity; 12, 7.2

RtI Response to Intervention

Use the Intervention Planner to help you determine your Response to Intervention.

Intervention Planner

TIER 1 On Level OL

IF students miss 25% of the exercises or less,

THEN choose a resource:

SE Lessons 7-1 through 7-6

Go Online!
- Skills Practice
- Chapter Project
- Self-Check Quizzes

TIER 2 Strategic Intervention AL
Approaching grade level

IF students miss 50% of the exercises,

THEN choose a resource:

Quick Review Math Handbook

Go Online!
- Study Guide and Intervention
- Extra Examples
- Personal Tutors
- Homework Help

TIER 3 Intensive Intervention
2 or more grades below level

IF students miss 75% of the exercises,

THEN choose a resource:

Use *Math Triumphs, Geometry*

Go Online!
- Extra Examples
- Personal Tutors
- Homework Help
- Review Vocabulary

Go Online!

Chapter Tests

You can use premade leveled *Chapter Tests* to differentiate assessment for your students. Students can also take self-checking *Chapter Tests* to plan and prepare for chapter assessments.

Form	Type	Level
1	MC	AL
2A	MC	OL
2B	FR	OL
2C	FR	OL
3	FR	BL
Vocabulary Test		
Extended-Response Test		

MC = multiple-choice questions
FR = free-response questions

Additional Answers

1.

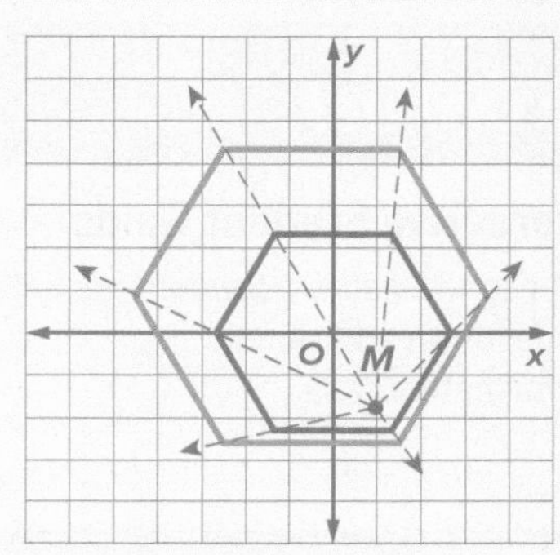

2.

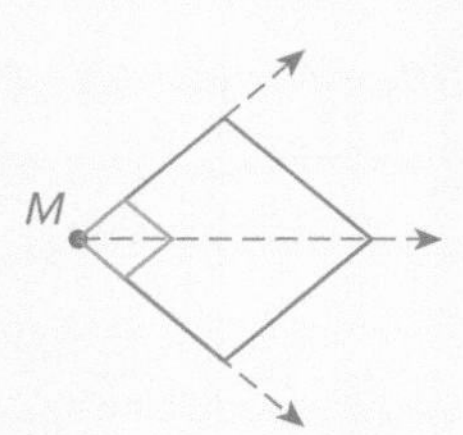

Launch

Objective Apply concepts and skills from this chapter in a real-world setting.

Teach

Ask:

- Where will the ramp start and stop? What units are used?
  Sample answer: It will start at the floor and stop at the top of the top step. Inches are used in the drawing, but feet are used in real life.
- What are the ways we prove triangles similar?
  Sample answer: Angle-Angle, Side-Side-Side, Side-Angle-Side
- If the client wants the table to be one and one half times bigger, by what factor should you multiply each coordinate? Sample answer: 1.5
- How many triangles do you see? We need to be sure the triangles in this figure are similar, or we will not have enough information to solve it. How can we tell they are similar?
  Sample answer: 3; Angle-Angle theorem, they all share one angle at the bottom left and they all also have a right angle in the bottom right.

The Performance Task focuses on the following content standards and standards for mathematical practice.

Dual Coding		
Parts	Content Standards	MP Mathematical Practices
A	G.CO.9, G.CO.10	1, 2, 4
B	G.CO.10, G.CO.12	1, 2, 3
C	G.CO.10	6
D	G.CO.10, G.MG.3	8

Go Online! eBook

Interactive Student Guide

Refer to *Interactive Student Guide* for an additional Performance Task.

CHAPTER 7

Preparing for Assessment

Performance Task

Provide a clear solution to each part of the task. Be sure to show all of your work, include all relevant drawings, and justify your answers.

CARPENTRY Brandi and Gerard own a carpentry business together.

Part A A client has a family member who uses a wheelchair. This family member visits often, and the client wants to make her house more accessible, so she decides to make her front stairs into a ramp. Brandi draws the stairs in exactly the same proportions as the real stairs, as shown in the diagram.

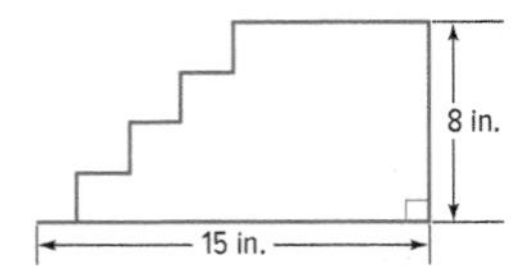

1. **Sense-Making** Determine the length of the ramp if the height of the real stairs is 4 feet.

Part B Another client is making a home décor item and has asked Brandi and Gerard to make some triangular pieces of wood. The client gives Gerard drawings of the shapes she'd like, shown in the top row of the diagram. She says the triangles Gerard makes must be in the same proportions as the drawings. Gerard creates the shapes shown in the bottom row of the diagram.

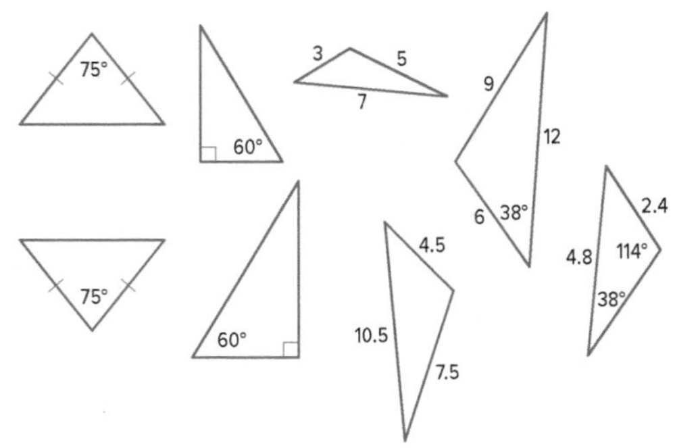

2. **Reasoning** Prove that each of Gerard's triangles is similar to the corresponding triangle drawn by the client.

Part C Another client would like a unique dining table made, so Brandi draws up plans for the top of the table that is an irregular hexagon. The client loves the design, but would like the table to be one and a half times as large as shown in the drawing.

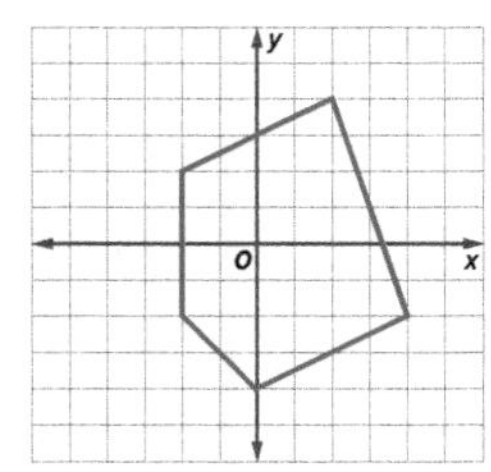

3. Draw the new top of the table according to the client's change request.

Part D A client wants Brandi and Gerard to build a bookshelf under their stairs. The sides of the bookshelf will be perpendicular to the floor. The height of the tallest space under the stairs is 12 feet.

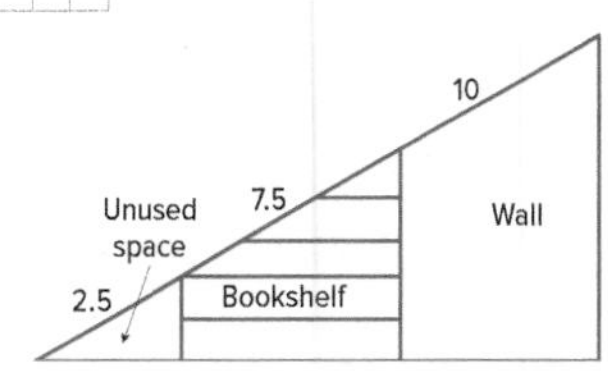

4. Determine the heights of both sides of the bookshelf.
5. Determine the width of the bottom shelf of the bookshelf.

Levels of Complexity Chart			
The levels of the exercises progress from 1 to 3, with Level 1 indicating the lowest level of complexity.			
Parts	Level 1	Level 2	Level 3
A	●		
B			●
C		●	
D			●

Part A
1. 8.5 feet

Part B
2. The first two are similar by AA or SAS. The second two by AA. The third two by SSS (a ratio of 1.5). The fourth by SAS.

Part C
3. The coordinates of the new vertices are: (–3, –3), (0, –6), (6, –3), (3, 6), and (–3, 3).

Part D
4. 1.5 feet and 6 feet
5. 6 feet

Test-Taking Strategy

Example

Read the problem. Identify what you need to know. Then use the information in the problem to solve.

In the triangle shown, $\angle MQN \cong \angle RQS$. Which of the following would not be sufficient to prove that $\triangle QMN \sim \triangle QRS$?

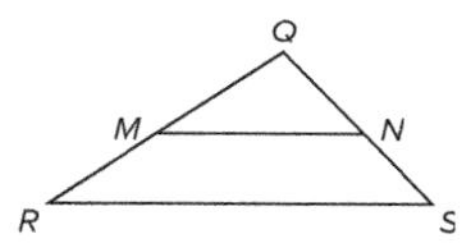

A $\angle QMN \cong \angle QRS$

B $\overline{MN} \parallel \overline{RS}$

C $\overline{QN} \cong \overline{NS}$

D $\frac{QM}{QR} = \frac{QN}{QS}$

Step 1 **What is the problem statement in the question? Are there any keywords that indicate this is a nonexample type question?**
The problem statement is that triangle *QMN* is similar to triangle *QRS*. The word "not" tells me this is a nonexample question.

Step 2 **Are any answer choices clearly incorrect? Are any in the wrong format? Do any have the wrong units?**
No, in this case no answers can be immediately eliminated because all of them appear to be the kind of statement that might prove similarity.

Step 3 **Which answer choice will you test first?**
The answer choices are not in any particular order, so I will start with choice A.

The correct answer is C.

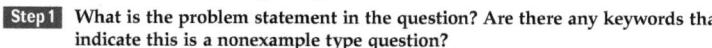

Test-Taking Tip

Identifying Nonexamples Multiple choice items sometimes ask you to determine which of the given answer choices is a nonexample. These types of problems require a different approach when solving them.

Apply the Strategy

Read the problem. Identify what you need to know. Then use the information in the problem to solve.

Consider the figure below.

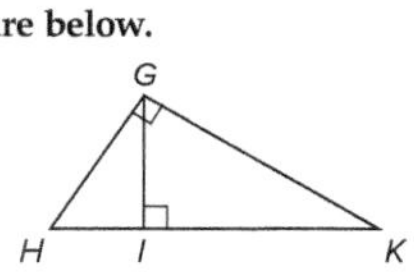

Which of the following is not sufficient to prove that $\triangle GIK \sim \triangle HIG$? C

A $\angle GKI \cong \angle HGI$

B $\frac{HI}{GI} = \frac{GI}{IK}$

C $\frac{GH}{GI} = \frac{GK}{HK}$

D $\angle IGK \cong \angle IHG$

Answer the questions below.

a. What is the problem statement in the question? Are there any keywords that indicate this is a nonexample type question? Triangle *GIK* is similar to triangle *HIK*; the word "not."

b. Are any answer choices clearly incorrect? no

c. Which answer choice will you test first? A

d. What is the correct answer? C

Test-Taking Strategy

Step 1 Read the problem and identify the problem statement. Look for keywords that indicate the question is a nonexample-type question.

Step 2 Look at the answer choices and identify any that can be eliminated because they are unreasonable.

Step 3 Work through the answer choices, testing them against the problem statement. Start with answer choices that are the most promising. If the answer choices are arranged in numerical order, start with one of the middle choices so that if it is wrong, you know which way you need to go.

Need Another Example?

In the triangle below, you know that $\angle EBF \cong \angle ABC$. Which of the following would *not* be sufficient to prove that $\triangle BFE \sim \triangle BCA$? C

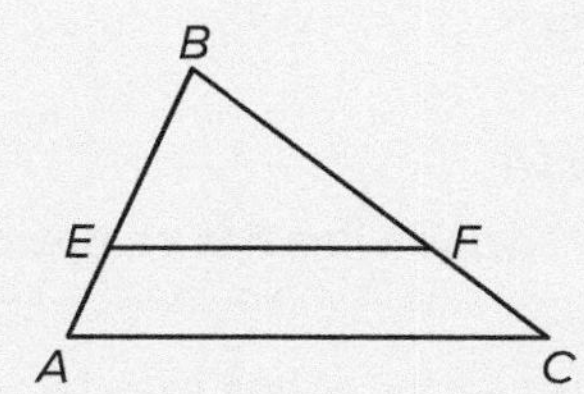

A $\angle BFE \cong \angle BCA$

B $\overline{EF} \parallel \overline{AC}$

C $\overline{BE} \cong \overline{EA}$

D $\frac{BF}{BC} = \frac{BE}{BA}$

a. What is the problem statement in the question? Are there any keywords that indicate this is a nonexample-type question? Triangle *BFE* is similar to triangle *BCA*. The word *not* is an indicator.

b. Are any answer choices clearly incorrect? no

c. Which answer choice will you test first? A, and then go down the list

d. What is the correct answer? C

Go Online!

The most up-to-date resources available for your program can be found at connectED.mcgraw-hill.com.

Diagnose Student Errors

Survey student responses for each item. Class trends may indicate common errors and misconceptions.

1.	A	Calculated $\frac{2}{3}CX$
	B	Assumed that the length of $\overline{CX}$ is $\frac{2}{3}$ the length of $\overline{JX}$
	C	Found the length of $\overline{JC}$
	D	CORRECT
2.	A	Solved $\frac{8}{20} = \frac{x}{12}$
	B	CORRECT
	C	Added 12 ft to length of $\overline{UX}$
	D	Found length of $\overline{RX}$
4.	A	CORRECT
	B	CORRECT
	C	Found the reciprocal of the scale factor
	D	Confused similarity and congruence
	E	CORRECT
5.	A	CORRECT
	B	Assumed given line has a slope of 3 rather than −3
	C	Found equation of line parallel to given line
	D	Assumed given line has a slope of 3 and found equation of line parallel to given line
7.	A	Found the length of $\overline{KM}$
	B	CORRECT
	C	Subtracted 3 cm from the length of $\overline{ML}$
	D	Solved $\frac{9}{12} = \frac{21}{x}$
8.	A	Found the measure of $\angle P$
	B	Divided 180 by 3
	C	Solved $3x + x = 180$
	D	CORRECT
9.	A	CORRECT
	B	Solved $\frac{y}{15} = \frac{42}{35}$
	C	Subtracted 20 from 42
	D	Found the length of $\overline{JH}$

Go Online!

Standardized Test Practice

Students can take self-checking tests in standardized format to plan and prepare for standardized assessments.

CHAPTER 7

Preparing for Assessment

Cumulative Review

Read each question. Then fill in the correct answer on the answer document provided by your teacher or on a sheet of paper.

1. Colin cuts out a triangle and locates the centroid C as shown in the figure.

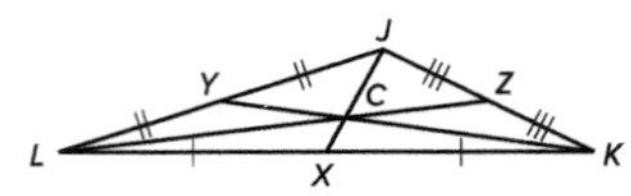

Given that $CX = 6$ inches, what is the length of $\overline{JX}$? G.CO.10 **D**

○ A 4 in. ○ C 12 in.

○ B 9 in. ○ D 18 in.

2. The figure shows one part of the support structure of a bridge. $\overline{RS}$ is parallel to $\overline{UV}$.

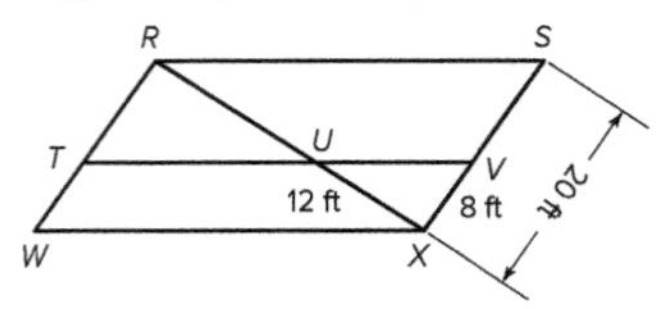

What is the length of $\overline{RU}$? G.SRT.5 **B**

○ A 4.8 ft ○ C 24 ft

○ B 18 ft ○ D 30 ft

3. Quadrilateral $ABCD$ is a parallelogram. What should be the value of x in order to guarantee that quadrilateral $ABCD$ is a rhombus? G.CO.11

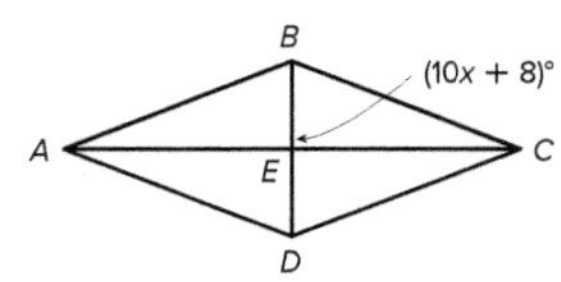

8.2

Test-Taking Tip

Question 3 Ask yourself what must be true about the diagonals of a parallelogram in order for the parallelogram to be a rhombus.

4. Dennis drew $\triangle PQR$ and then dilated it to create $\triangle XYZ$, as shown.

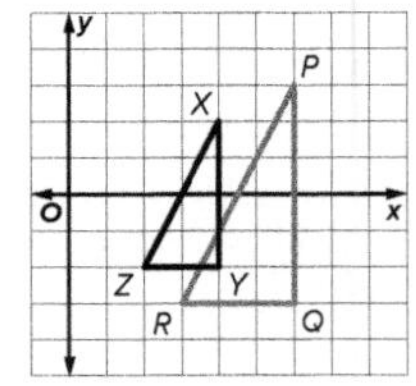

Select all of the true statements. G.SRT.2 **A, B, E**

☐ A The scale factor of the dilation is less than 1.

☐ B The scale factor of the dilation is $\frac{2}{3}$.

☐ C The scale factor of the dilation is $\frac{3}{2}$.

☐ D $\triangle PQR \cong \triangle XYZ$

☐ E $\triangle PQR \sim \triangle XYZ$

5. What is the equation of the line that passes through (3, 4) and is perpendicular to the line $3x + y = 3$? G.GPE.5 **A**

○ A $y = \frac{1}{3}x + 3$

○ B $y = -\frac{1}{3}x + 5$

○ C $y = -3x + 13$

○ D $y = 3x - 5$

6. In the figure, $ABCD \sim PQRS$. What is the perimeter of $ABCD$? G.SRT.2

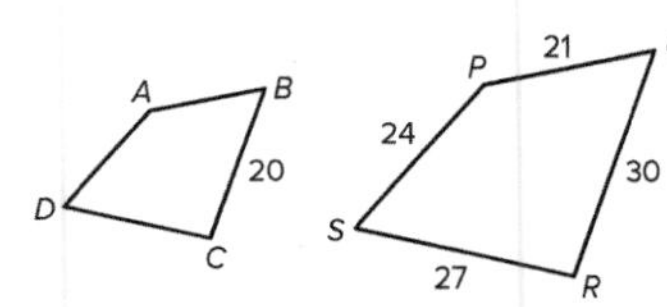

68

10.	A	Chose a distance that is possible in $\triangle CSL$, but not in $\triangle CPL$
	B	Chose a distance that is possible in $\triangle CSL$, but not in $\triangle CPL$
	C	CORRECT
	D	Chose a distance that is possible in $\triangle CPL$, but not in $\triangle CSL$
11.	A	Thought that showing how PQ and PM are related is sufficient
	B	Forgot that you need to know that included angles are congruent or the third pair of sides are proportional
	C	CORRECT
	D	Doesn't understand how to prove triangles similar
12.	A	Found the length of $\overline{ST}$
	B	CORRECT
	C	Found the value of x
	D	Solved $x + 3 = 3x - 5$ rather than $2(x + 3) = 3x - 5$

Go Online! for Standardized Test Practice

7. In $\triangle JKL$, $\overleftrightarrow{MN}$ is parallel to $\overline{KJ}$.

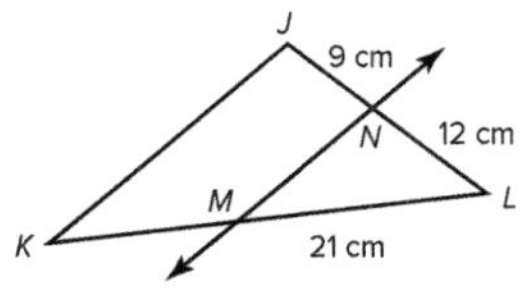

What is the length of $\overline{KL}$? G.SRT.5 B

A 15.75 cm C 39 cm

B 36.75 cm D 49 cm

8. In $\triangle PQR$, the measure of $\angle P$ is 3 times the measure of $\angle Q$.

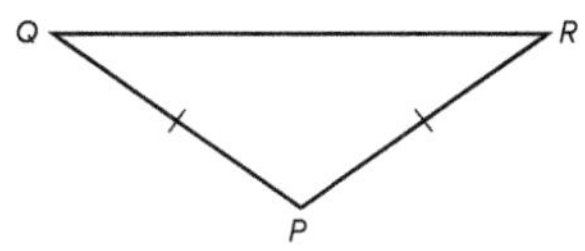

What is the measure of $\angle R$? G.CO.10 D

A 108 C 45

B 60 D 36

9. What is the value of y? G.SRT.5 A

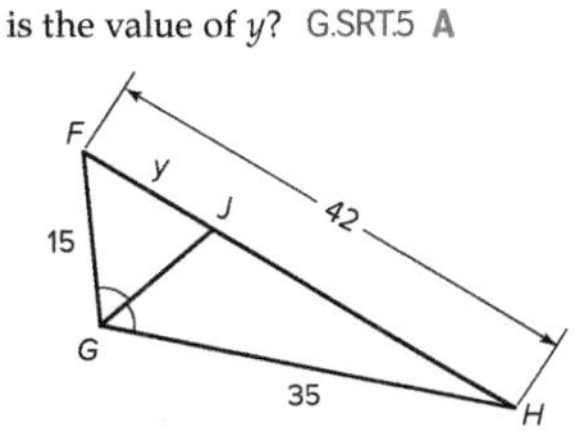

A 12.6 C 22

B 18 D 29.4

10. The figure shows the distances along several straight roads in Isabella's town. She drives the road directly from the library to city hall. G.CO.10

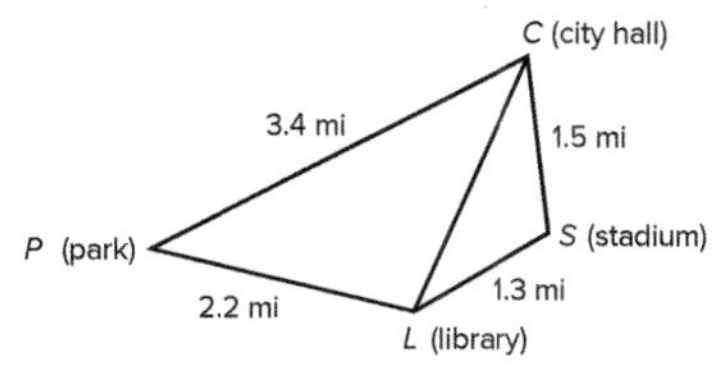

a. Which of the following is a possible distance Isabella might drive? C

A 0.9 mi C 1.5 mi

B 1.2 mi D 2.8 mi

b. MP What mathematical practice did you use to solve this problem? See students' work.

11. Which additional piece of information, if any, is sufficient to prove that $\triangle MNP \sim \triangle QRP$? G.SRT.3 C

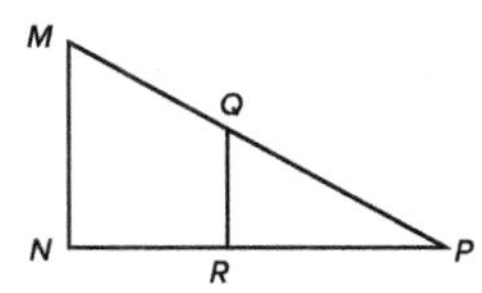

A Point Q is the midpoint of $\overline{MP}$.

B $\frac{MN}{MP} = \frac{RP}{QR}$

C $\overline{MN}$ is parallel to $\overline{QR}$.

D No additional information is needed.

12. $\overline{JK}$ is a midsegment of $\triangle RST$.

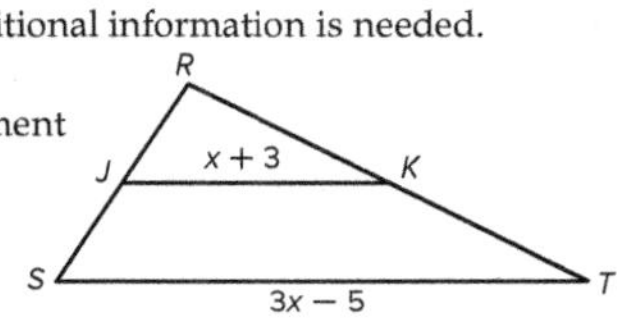

What is the length of $\overline{JK}$? G.SRT.4 B

A 28 C 11

B 14 D 7

Need Extra Help?

If you missed Question...	1	2	3	4	5	6	7	8	9	10	11	12
Go to Lesson...	5-2	7-3	6-5	7-2	2-8	7-2	7-5	4-6	7-6	5-5	7-3	7-5

Formative Assessment

You can use these pages to benchmark student progress.

Standardized Test Practice

Test Item Formats

In the Cumulative Review, students will encounter different formats for assessment questions to prepare them for standardized tests.

Question Type	Exercises
Multiple-Choice	1–2, 5, 7–9, 10a, 11, 12
Multiple Correct Answers	4
Short Response	3, 6
Extended Response	10b

Answer Sheet Practice

Have students simulate taking a standardized test by recording their answers on a practice recording sheet.

Homework Option

Get Ready for Chapter 8 Assign students the exercises on p. 564 as homework to assess whether they possess the prerequisite skills needed for the next chapter.

LEARNSMART®

Use LearnSmart as part of your test-preparation plan to measure student topic retention. You can create a student assignment in LearnSmart for additional practice on these topics.

- Understand Similarity in Terms of Similarity Transformations
- Prove Theorems Involving Similarity

Go Online!

eAssessment

Customize and create multiple versions of chapter tests and answer keys that align to your standards. Tests can be delivered on paper or online.

Lesson 7-1 (Guided Practice)

1A.

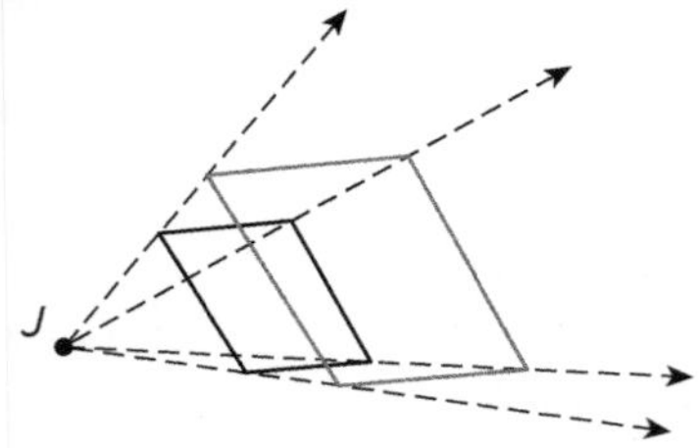

1B.

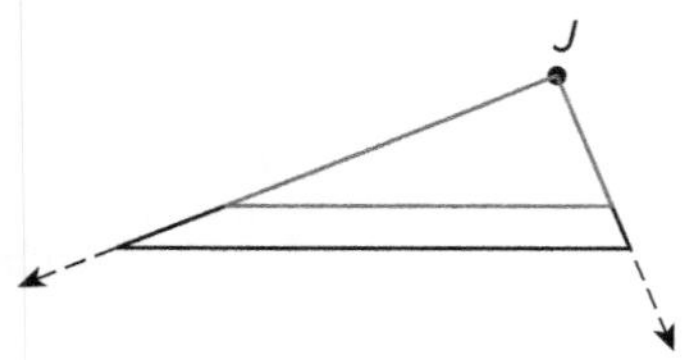

Lesson 7-1

11.

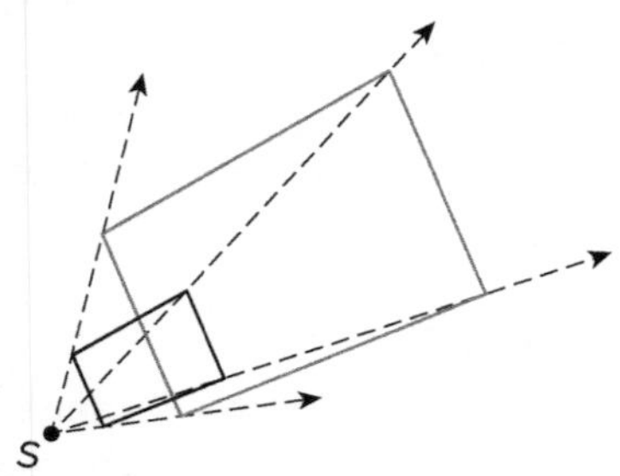

12.

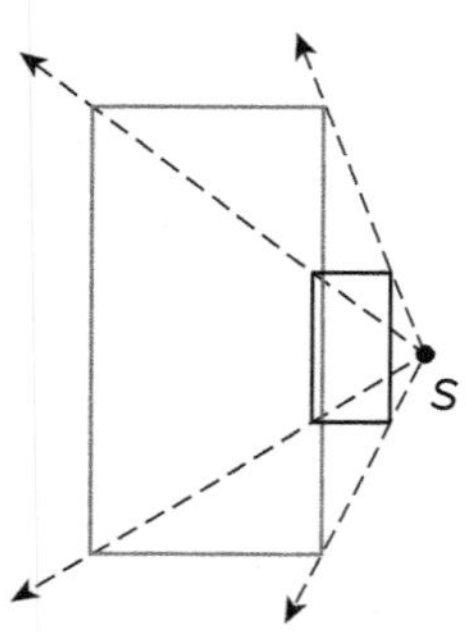

13.

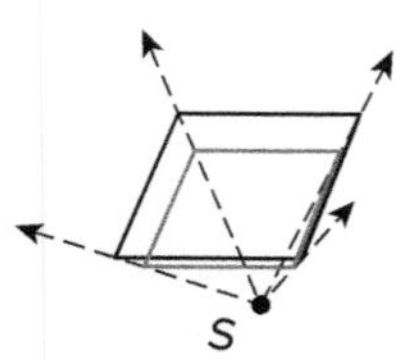

14.

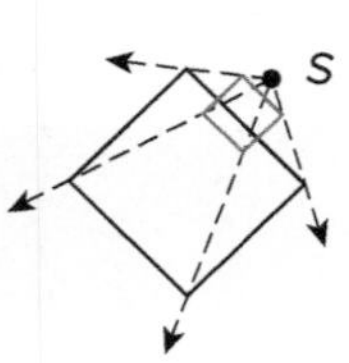

21.

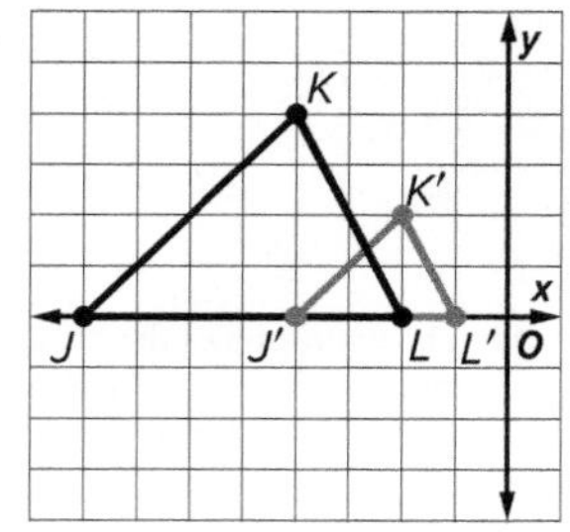

22.

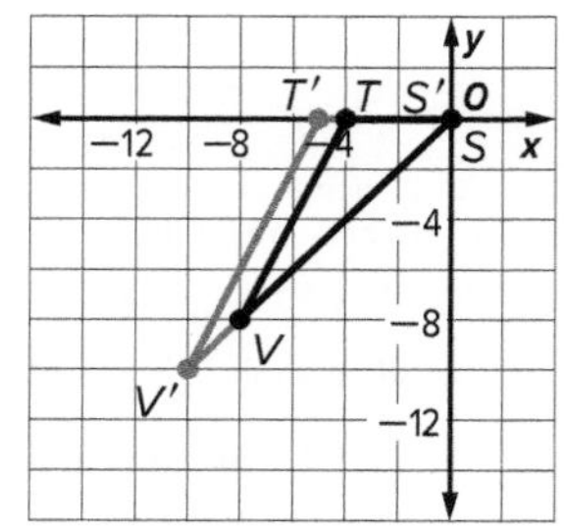

23.

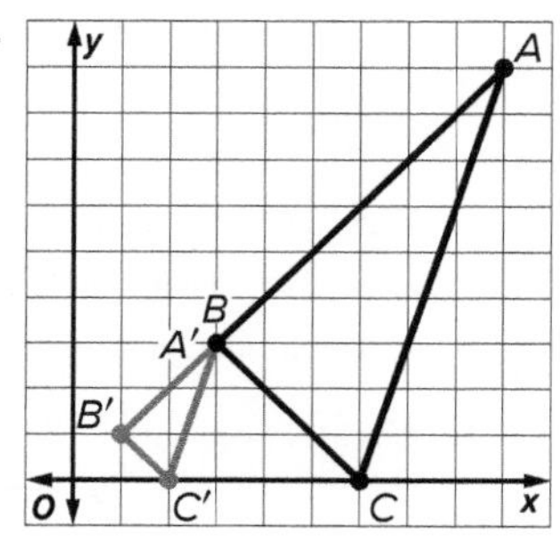

24.

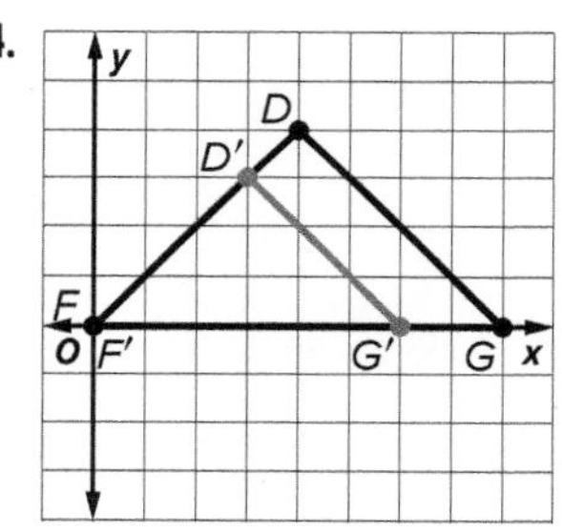

25.

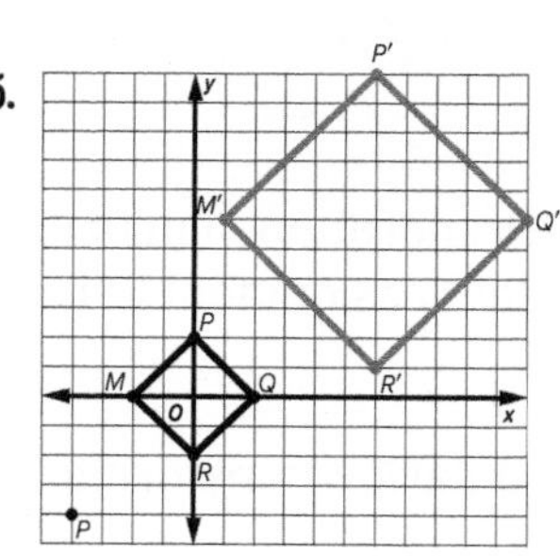

26.

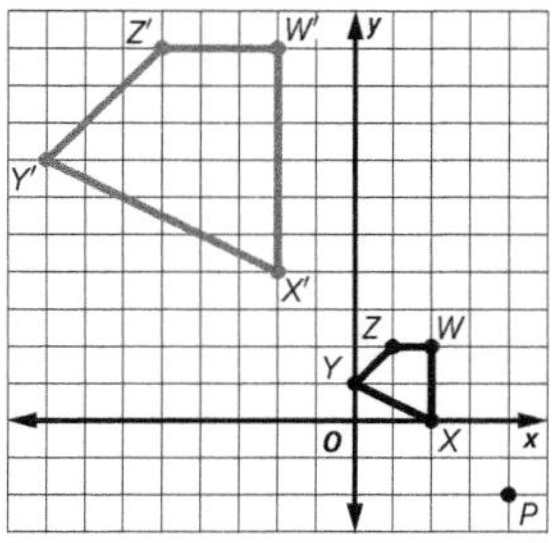

27.

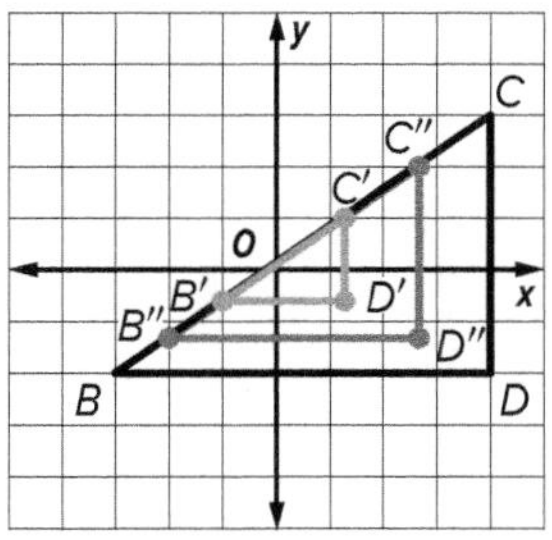

28.

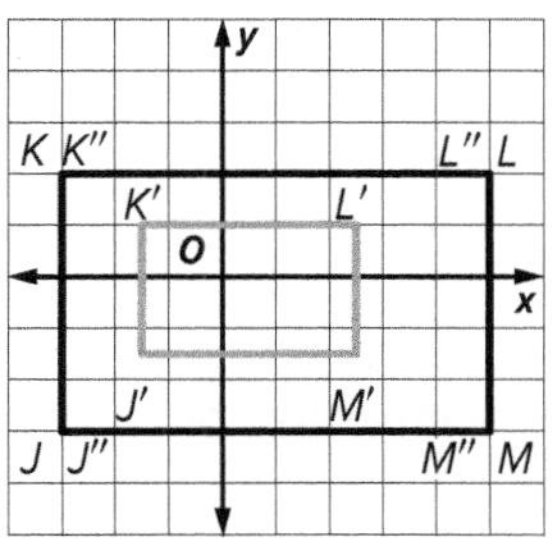

29.

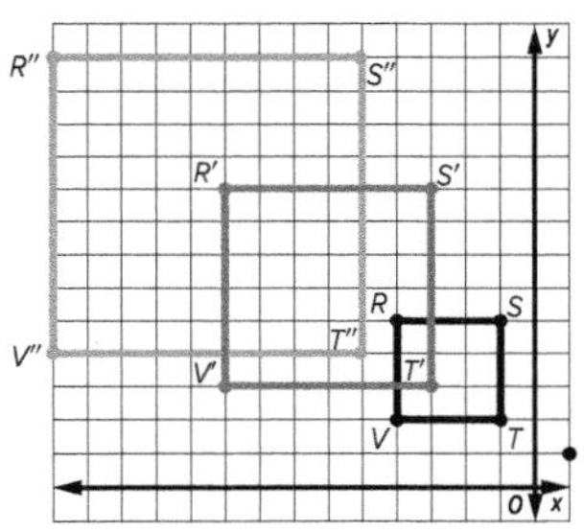

30.

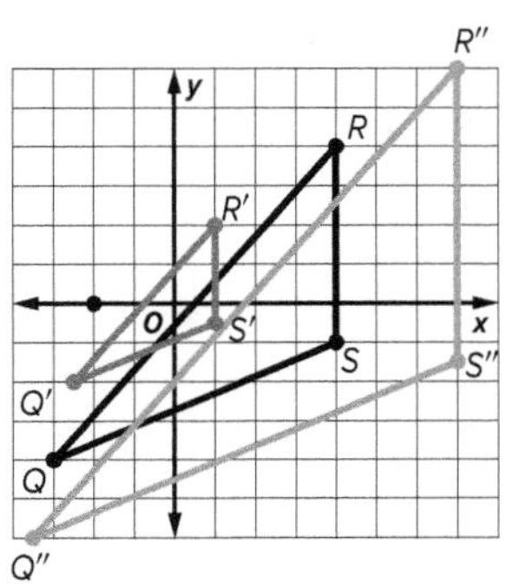

31.

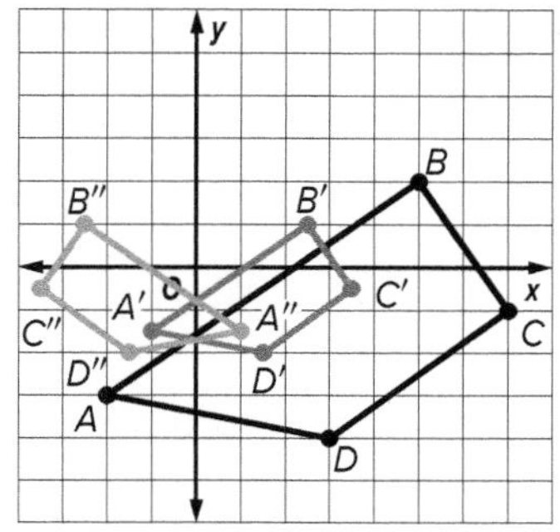

32.

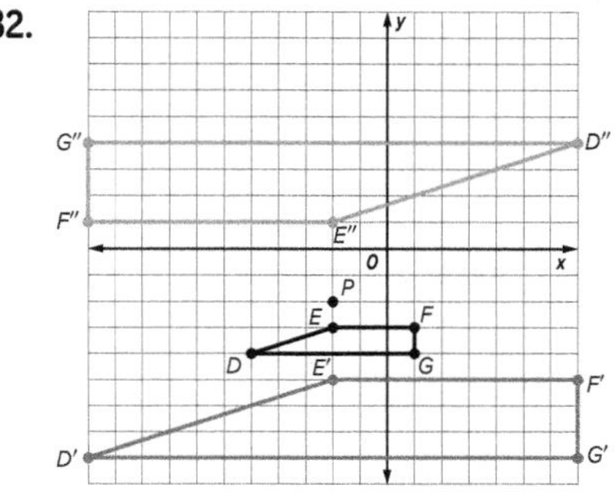

43.

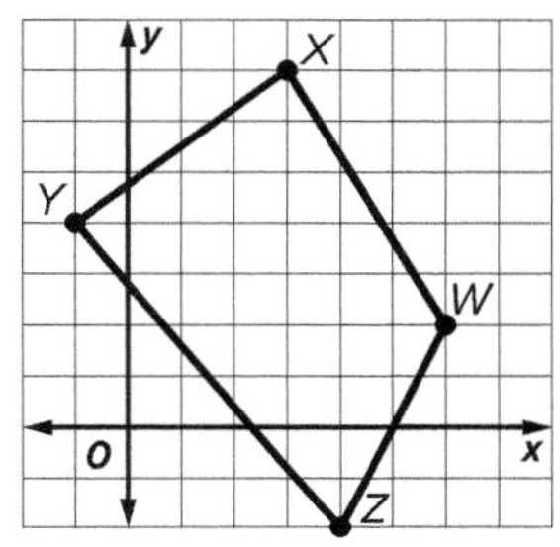

44.

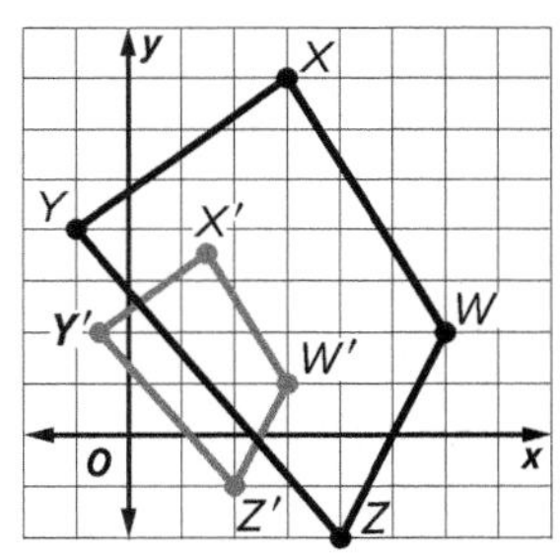

46. Sample answer: Yes; in translations, reflections, and rotations, congruent figures are formed, which means that sides that were parallel before transformation will be parallel after transformation and points that were collinear before transformation will still be collinear after transformation. Both parallel sides and collinear points are also preserved under dilations because a similar figure is formed, which has the same shape, but in a different proportion.

48. 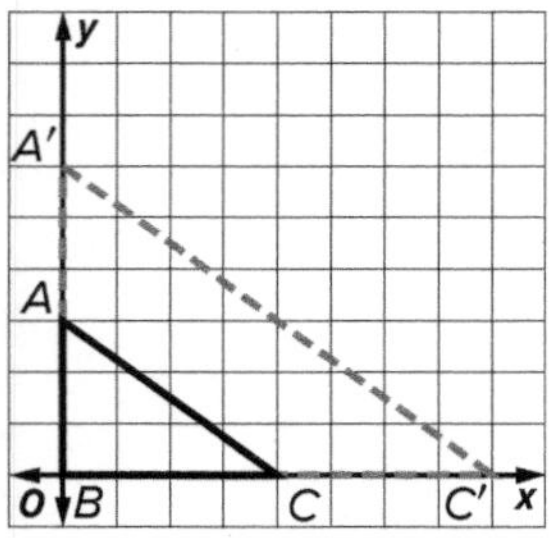

scale factor: 2, center of dilation: (0, 0)

49. Sample answer: Translations, reflections, and rotations produce congruent figures because the sides and angles of the preimage are congruent to the corresponding sides and angles of the image. Dilations produce similar figures, because the angles of the preimage and the image are congruent and the sides of the preimage are proportional to the corresponding sides of the image. A dilation with a scale factor of 1 produces an equal figure because the image is mapped onto its corresponding parts in the preimage.

Lesson 7-2 (Guided Practice)

2. Congruent angles: $\angle N \cong \angle U$, $\angle P \cong \angle V$, $\angle Q \cong \angle S$, $\angle R \cong \angle T$
Proportion: $\frac{NP}{UV} = \frac{PQ}{VS} = \frac{QR}{ST} = \frac{RN}{TU}$

Lesson 7-3

28. 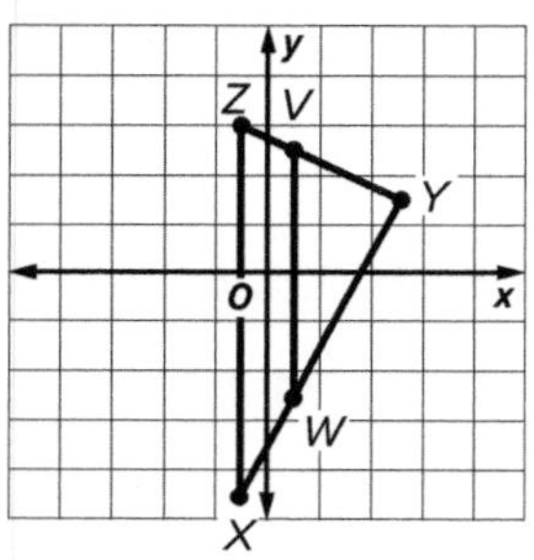

slope of $\overline{XZ} = \frac{-9-6}{-1-(-1)}$ or undefined
slope of $\overline{WV} = \frac{-5-5}{1-1}$ or undefined
$\overline{XZ} \parallel \overline{WV}$ because they have the same slope. Thus, $\angle YXZ \cong \angle YWV$ and $\angle YZX \cong \angle YVW$ by the Corresponding Angles Postulate. Therefore $\triangle XYZ \sim \triangle WYV$ by AA Similarity.

Lesson 7-4

39. Sample: $\triangle EFG$, $\triangle DBC$ are right triangles. Use the Pythagorean Theorem to find EG, or 6, and DB, or $2\sqrt{2}$. $\angle EFG \cong \angle DBC$ because all right angles are congruent and $\frac{EF}{DB} = \frac{FG}{BC} = \frac{3}{2}$. So $\triangle EFG \sim \triangle DBC$ by the SAS Similarity Theorem.

40. If the triangles are similar, then $\frac{3}{3+x} = \frac{4}{4+x} = \frac{5}{5+x}$.

$\frac{3}{3+x} = \frac{4}{4+x}$

$3(4+x) = 4(3+x)$

$12 + 3x = 12 + 4x$

$3x = 4x$

$x = 0$

If and only if $x = 0$, then the triangles are similar. So if the side lengths are increased by any nonzero amount, the triangles are not similar.

41. Sample answer:

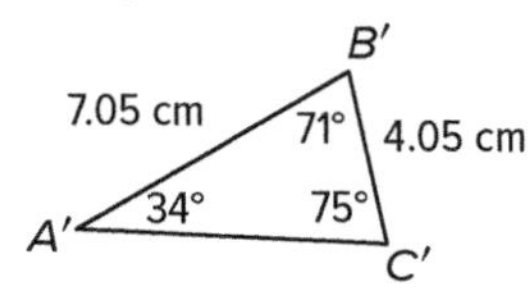

$\triangle A'B'C' \sim \triangle ABC$ because the measures of each side are half the measure of the corresponding side and the measures of corresponding angles are equal.

42. Sample answer: You could consider the amount of space that the actual object occupies and compare it to the amount of space that is available for the scale model or drawing. Then, you could determine the amount of detail that you want the scale model or drawing to have, and you could use these factors to choose an appropriate scale.

Lesson 7-5

39. Because $\overline{FD} \parallel \overline{AC}$, $\angle EFD \cong \angle EAC$. By the Reflexive Property of Congruence, $\angle AEC \cong \angle AEC$. Therefore, $\triangle EFD \sim \triangle EAC$ by AA Similarity Postulate. By the Triangle Proportionality Theorem, ED is proportional to EC. Because the segments stay parallel as the gauge is repositioned, ED remains proportional to EC.

44. Sample answer:

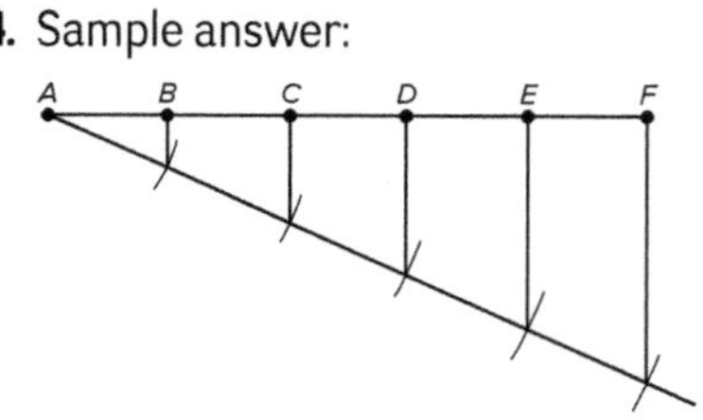

45. Sample answer:

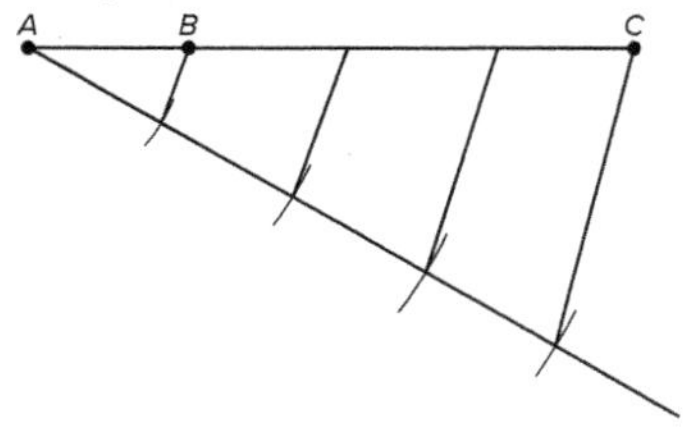

46. Sample answer:

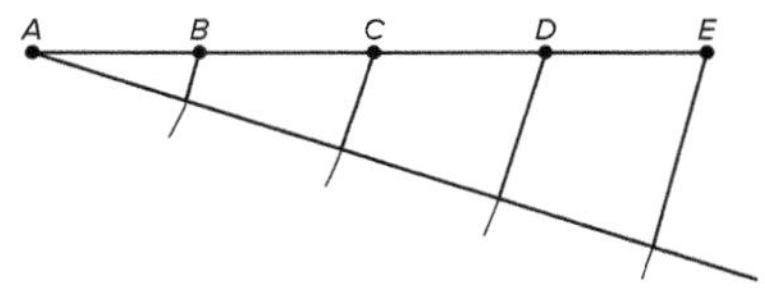

47a. Sample answer:

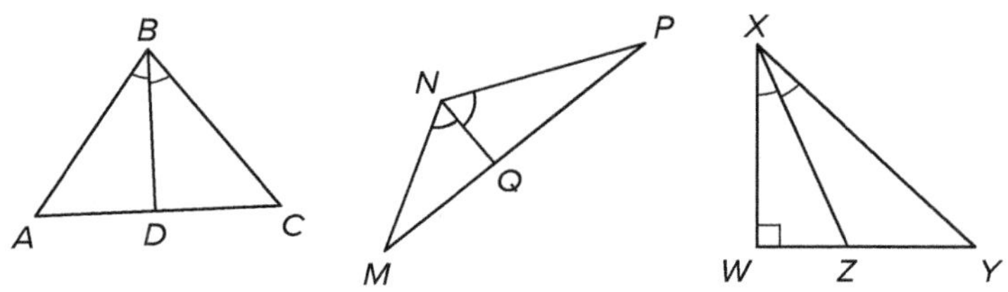

49. Always; sample answer: FH is a midsegment. Let $BC = x$, then $\overline{FH} = \frac{1}{2}x$. $FHCB$ is a trapezoid, so $DE = \frac{1}{2}(BC + FH) = \frac{1}{2}\left(x + \frac{1}{2}x\right) = \frac{1}{2}x + \frac{1}{4}x = \frac{3}{4}x$. Therefore, $DE = \frac{3}{4}BC$.

50. Proof:

Statements (Reasons)

1. $AB = 4$, $BC = 4$ (Given)
2. $AB = BC$ (Subst.)
3. $AB + BC = AC$ (Seg. Add. Post.)
4. $BC + BC = AC$ (Subst.)
5. $2BC = AC$ (Subst.)
6. $AC = 2BC$ (Symm. Prop).
7. $\frac{AC}{BC} = 2$ (Div. Prop.)
8. $ED = DC$ (Given)
9. $ED + DC = EC$ (Seg. Add. Post.)
10. $DC + DC = EC$ (Subst.)
11. $2DC = EC$ (Subst.)
12. $2 = \frac{EC}{DC}$ (Div. Prop.)
13. $\frac{AC}{BC} = \frac{EC}{DC}$ (Trans. Prop.)
14. $\angle C \cong \angle C$ (Reflexive Prop.)
15. $\triangle ACE \sim \triangle BCD$ (SAS Similarity)
16. $\angle CAE \cong \angle CBD$ (Def. of $\sim$ polygons)
17. $\overline{BD} \parallel \overline{AE}$ (If corr. ∠s are $\cong$, lines are $\parallel$.)

51.

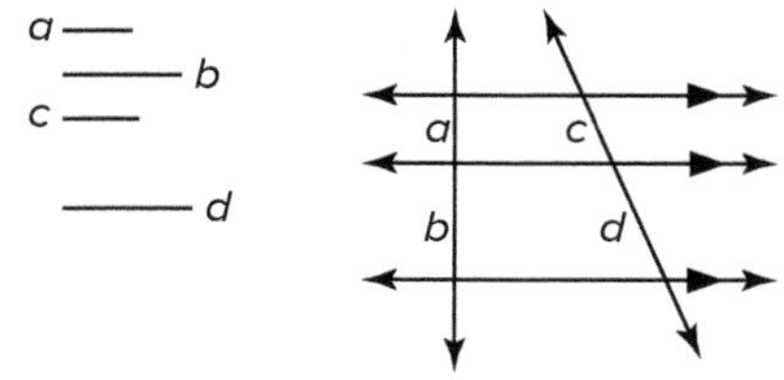

By Corollary 7.1, $\frac{a}{b} = \frac{c}{d}$.

Lesson 7-6

25. Proof:

Statements (Reasons)

1. $\overline{CD}$ bisects $\angle ACB$; By construction, $\overline{AE} \parallel \overline{CD}$. (Given)
2. $\frac{AD}{DB} = \frac{EC}{BC}$ ($\triangle$ Prop. Thm.)
3. $\angle 1 \cong \angle 2$ (Def. of $\angle$ Bisector)
4. $\angle 3 \cong \angle 1$ (Alt. Int. $\angle$ Thm.)
5. $\angle 2 \cong \angle E$ (Corr. ∠s Post.)
6. $\angle 3 \cong \angle E$ (Trans. Prop.)
7. $\overline{EC} \cong \overline{AC}$ (Conv. of Isos. $\triangle$ Thm.)
8. $EC = AC$ (Def. of $\cong$ segs.)
9. $\frac{AD}{DB} = \frac{AC}{BC}$ (Subst.)

26. Proof:

Statements (Reasons)

1. $\angle H$ is a right angle. L, K, and M are midpoints. (Given)
2. $\overline{JH} \parallel \overline{LK}$, $\overline{GH} \parallel \overline{KM}$ (Midsegment Thm.)
3. $\angle H \cong \angle GLK$ (Corr. ∠s Post.)
4. $\angle GLK \cong \angle LKM$ (Alt. Int. ∠s Thm.)
5. $\angle GLK$ is a right angle. (Subst.)
6. $\angle LKM$ is a right angle. (Subst.)

27. Proof:

Statements (Reasons)

1. $\triangle QTS \sim \triangle XWZ$, $\overline{TR}$ and $\overline{WY}$ are angle bisectors. (Given)
2. $\angle QTS \cong \angle XWZ$, $\angle Q \cong \angle X$ (Def of $\sim$ △s)
3. $\angle STR \cong \angle QTR$, $\angle ZWY \cong \angle XWY$ (Def. $\angle$ bisector)
4. $m\angle STQ = m\angle STR + m\angle QTR$, $m\angle ZWX = m\angle ZWY + m\angle XWY$ ($\angle$ Add. Post.)
5. $m\angle STQ = 2m\angle QTR$, $m\angle ZWX = 2m\angle XWY$ (Subst.)
6. $2m\angle QTR = 2m\angle XWY$ (Subst.)
7. $m\angle QTR = m\angle XWY$ (Div. Prop.)
8. $\angle QTR \cong \angle XWY$ (Def. of $\cong$ angles)
9. $\triangle QTR \sim \triangle XWY$ (AA Similarity)
10. $\frac{TR}{WY} = \frac{QT}{XW}$ (Def of $\sim$ △s)

28. **Proof:**

Statements (Reasons)

1. $\overline{FD} \parallel \overline{BC}$, $\overline{BF} \parallel \overline{CD}$, $\overline{AC}$ bisects $\angle BCD$. (Given)
2. $\angle BCE \cong \angle DCE$ (Def. $\angle$ bisector)
3. $\angle BCE \cong \angle AEF$ (Corr. ⦞ Post.)
4. $\angle AEF \cong \angle DEC$ (Vert. ⦞ are $\cong$)
5. $\angle BCE \cong \angle DEC$ (Trans. Prop.)
6. $\angle BAC \cong \angle DCE$ (Alt. Int ⦞ Thm.)
7. $\triangle DEC \sim \triangle BAC$ (AA Similarity)
8. $\frac{DE}{EC} = \frac{BA}{AC}$ (Def of $\sim$ ⧍)

Extend 7-6

4. **Given:** $\triangle KAP$ is equilateral. D, F, M, B, C, and E are midpoints of $\overline{KA}$, $\overline{AP}$, $\overline{PK}$, $\overline{DA}$, $\overline{AF}$, and $\overline{FD}$, respectively.

Prove: $\triangle BAC \sim \triangle KAP$

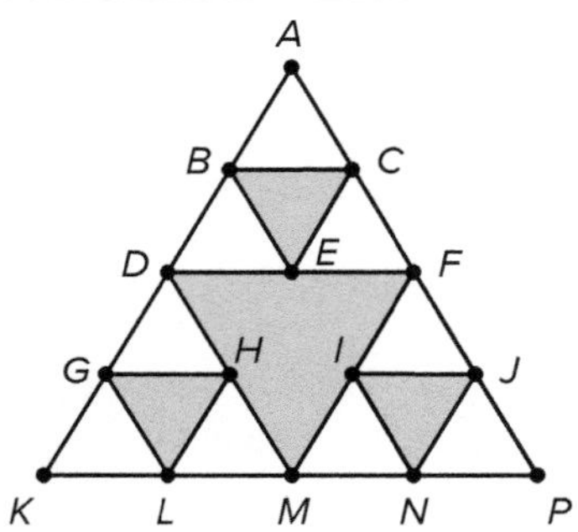

Proof:

Statements (Reasons)

1. $\triangle KAP$ is equilateral. D, F, M, B, C, and E are midpoints of $\overline{KA}$, $\overline{AP}$, $\overline{PK}$, $\overline{DA}$, $\overline{AF}$, and $\overline{FD}$, respectively. (Given)
2. $\overline{DF}$ is a midsegment of $\triangle KAP$; $\overline{BC}$ is a midsegment of $\triangle BAC$. (Def. of $\triangle$ midsegment)
3. $\overline{DF} \parallel \overline{KP}$, $\overline{BC} \parallel \overline{DF}$ ($\triangle$ Midsegment Thm.)
4. $\overline{KP} \parallel \overline{BC}$ (Two segs. $\parallel$ to the same seg. are $\parallel$.)
5. $\angle ABC \cong \angle AKP$ (Corr. ⦞ Post.)
6. $\angle A \cong \angle A$ (Refl. Prop.)
7. $\triangle BAC \sim \triangle KAP$ (AA Similarity)

5a. **Stage 1: 2, Stage 2: 6, Stage 3: 14, Stage 4: 30**

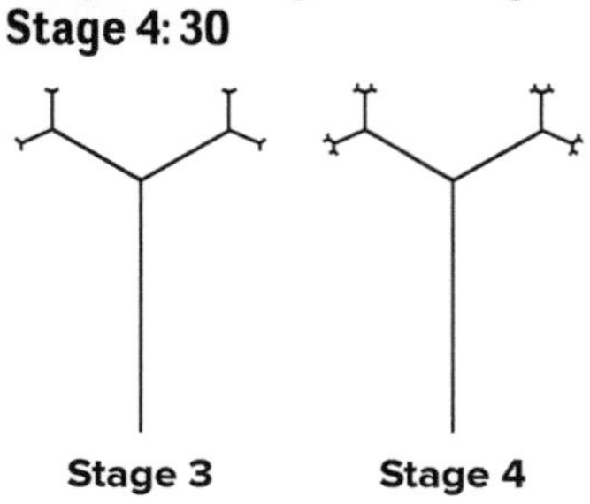

5b. At Stage n, the total number of branches is $2(2^n - 1)$.

Notes

CHAPTER 8
Right Triangles and Trigonometry

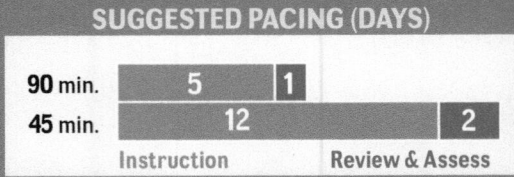

SUGGESTED PACING (DAYS)

	Instruction	Review & Assess
90 min.	5	1
45 min.	12	2

Track Your Progress

This chapter focuses on content from the Similarity, Right Triangles, and Trigonometry domain.

THEN

G.SRT.2 Given two figures, use the definition of similarity in terms of similarity transformations to decide if they are similar; explain using similarity transformations the meaning of similarity for triangles as the equality of all corresponding pairs of angles and the proportionality of all corresponding pairs of sides.

G.SRT.3 Use the properties of similarity transformations to establish the AA criterion for two triangles to be similar.

G.SRT.4 Prove theorems about triangles.

G.SRT.5 Use congruence and similarity criteria for triangles to solve problems and to prove relationships in geometric figures.

NOW

G.SRT.6 Understand that by similarity, side ratios in right triangles are properties of the angles in the triangle, leading to definitions of trigonometric ratios for acute angles.

G.SRT.8 Use trigonometric ratios and the Pythagorean Theorem to solve right triangles in applied problems.

G.SRT.10 Prove the Laws of Sines and Cosines and use them to solve problems.

G.SRT.11 Understand and apply the Law of Sines and the Law of Cosines to find unknown measurements in right and non-right triangles.

NEXT

G.C.2 Identify and describe relationships among inscribed angles, radii, and chords.

G.C.3 Construct the inscribed and circumscribed circles of a triangle, and prove properties of angles for a quadrilateral inscribed in a circle.

G.GPE.1 Derive the equation of a circle of given center and radius using the Pythagorean Theorem; complete the square to find the center and radius of a circle given by an equation.

G.GPE.2 Derive the equation of a parabola given a focus and directrix.

Standards for Mathematical Practice

All of the Standards for Mathematical Practice will be covered in this chapter. The MP icon notes specific areas of coverage.

MP Teaching the Mathematical Practices

Help students develop the mathematical practices by asking questions like these.

Questioning Strategies

As students approach problems in this chapter, help them develop mathematical practices by asking:

Sense-Making
- Can you solve real-world problems using the angles of elevation and depression?

Construct Arguments
- Can you use right triangles to find trigonometric ratios?
- How do you use trigonometric ratios to find the angle measures of right triangles?

Modeling
- How do you find the distance between two objects using angles of elevation and depression?

Precision
- How can you apply the properties of 45°—45°—90° triangles and 30°-60°-90° triangles to ensure precision in your work?

Go Online!

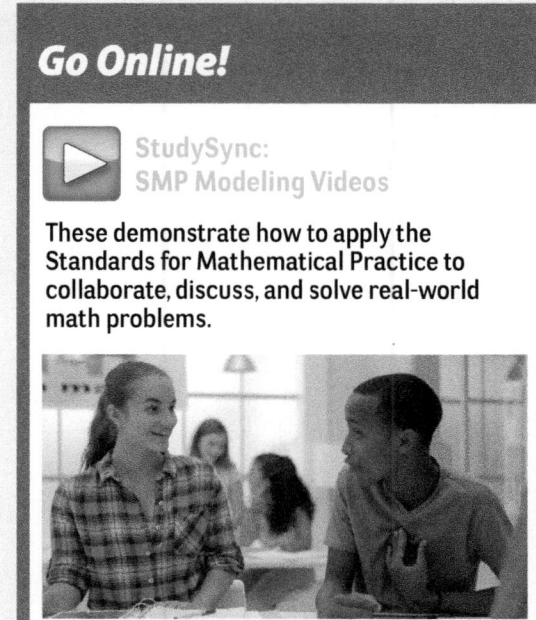

StudySync:
SMP Modeling Videos

These demonstrate how to apply the Standards for Mathematical Practice to collaborate, discuss, and solve real-world math problems.

Go Online!
connectED.mcgraw-hill.com

LearnSmart | The Geometer's Sketchpad | Vocabulary | Tutor | Tools | Calculator Resources | Check | Watch

Customize Your Chapter

Use the *Plan & Present, Assignment Tracker*, and *Assessment* tools in ConnectED to introduce lesson concepts, assign personalized practice, and diagnose areas of student need.

Differentiated Instruction

Throughout the program, look for the icons to find specialized content designed for your students.

- **AL** Approaching Level
- **OL** On Level
- **BL** Beyond Level
- **ELL** English Language Learners

Personalize

Differentiated Resources

FOR EVERY CHAPTER	AL	OL	BL	ELL
Chapter Readiness Quizzes	●	●	◐	●
Chapter Tests	●	●	●	●
Standardized Test Practice	●	●	●	●
Vocabulary Review Games	●	●	◐	●
Anticipation Guide (English/Spanish)	●	●	◐	●
Student-Built Glossary	●	●	◐	●
Chapter Project	◐	●	●	●
FOR EVERY LESSON	**AL**	**OL**	**BL**	**ELL**
Personal Tutors (English/Spanish)	●	●	◐	●
Graphing Calculator Personal Tutors	●	●	●	●
Step-by-Step Solutions	●	●	◐	●
Self-Check Quizzes	●	●	●	●
5-Minute Check	●	●	●	●
Study Notebook	●	●	●	●
Study Guide and Intervention	●	●		●
Skills Practice (English/Spanish)	●	◐		●
Practice (English/Spanish)	◐	●	●	●
Word Problem Practice	◐	●	●	◐
Enrichment		●	●	●
Extra Examples	●	◐		◐
Interactive Classroom	●	●	●	●

◐ Aligned to this group ● Designed for this group

Engage

Featured IWB Resources

The Geometer's Sketchpad provides students with a tangible, visual way to learn. *Use with Lessons 8-1 through 8-4.*

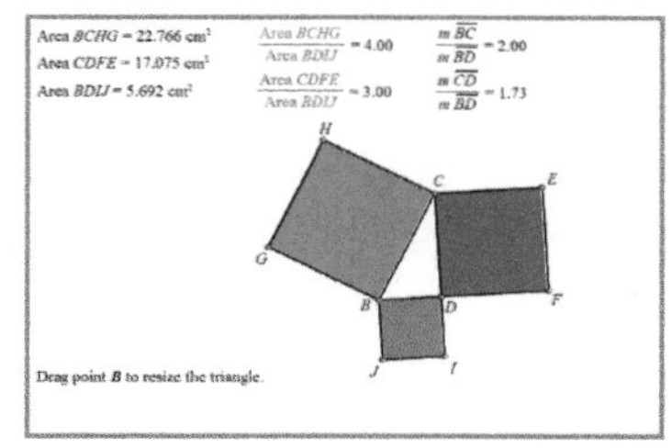

eLessons engage students and help build conceptual understanding of big ideas. *Use with Lessons 8-2 through 8-4.*

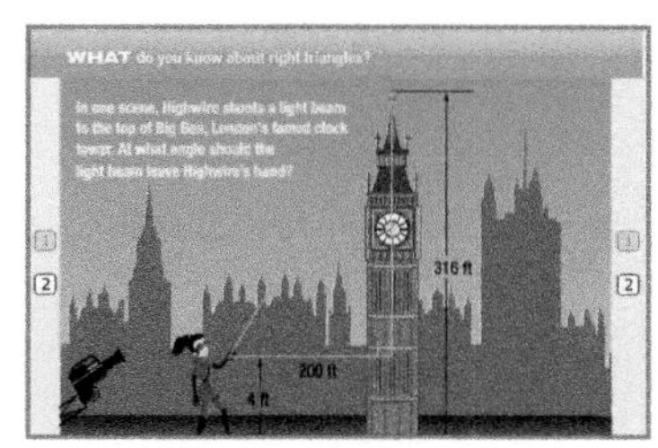

Animations help students make important connections through motion. *Use with Explore 8-2.*

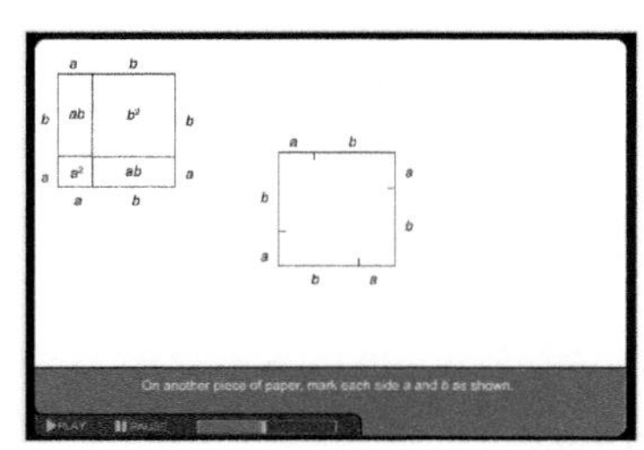

Time Management How long will it take to use these resources? Look for the clock in each lesson interleaf.

Introduce the Chapter

Mathematical Background

Similarity properties can be used to explore and justify conjectures about geometric figures. The Pythagorean Theorem is used to solve right triangles and prove that given measures form right triangles. Trigonometric ratios can be used to solve right triangles and meaningful problems, like angles of elevation and depression.

Essential Question

At the end of this chapter, students should be able to answer the Essential Question.

Why do we use mathematics to model real-world situations? Sample answers: to solve problems, understand phenomena, look for trends

Apply Math to the Real World

Event Planning In this activity, students use what they already know about right triangles to help plan the decorations for a dance or party. Have students complete this activity individually or in small groups. MP 1

Go Online!

Chapter Project

Surveyors Students use what they have learned about right triangles and trigonometry to complete a project. This chapter project addresses business literacy, as well as several specific skills identified as being essential to student success by the Framework for 21st Century Learning. MP 1, 3, 4, 8

CHAPTER 8

Right Triangles and Trigonometry

THEN

You solved proportions.

NOW

In this chapter, you will:

- Use the Pythagorean Theorem.
- Use properties of special right triangles.
- Use trigonometry to find missing measures of triangles.

MP WHY

EVENT PLANNING Properties of triangles and trigonometry can be used to determine the dimensions of decorations and supplies.

Use the Mathematical Practices to complete the activity.

1. **Sense-Making** How could right triangles be used to plan and build decorations for a special event?
2. **Apply Math** Write a problem using a right triangle to determine the dimensions of a decoration (i.e., a stand-up prop) or the length of a rope that suspends a decoration and is anchored to the ground, the wall, or other points.
3. **Modeling** Use the Ruler Grids mat and the protractor and line segment tools in ConnectED to model the right triangle for the problem you created, and determine side lengths.

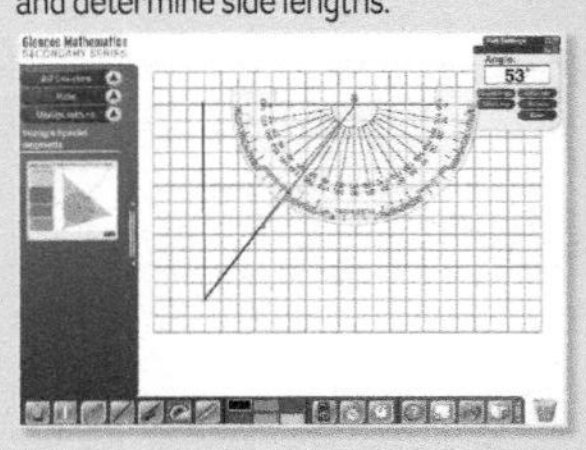

4. **Discuss** In what other ways could you use the properties of right triangles to plan for and place decorations?

RHIMAGE/Shutterstock.com

ALEKS®

Your Student Success Tool ALEKS is an adaptive, personalized learning environment that identifies precisely what each student knows and is ready to learn—ensuring student success at all levels.

- **Formative Assessment:** Dynamic, detailed reports monitor students' progress toward standards mastery.
- **Automatic Differentiation:** Strengthen prerequisite skills and target individual learning gaps.
- **Personalized Instruction:** Supplement in-class instruction with personalized assessment and learning opportunities.

Go Online to Guide Your Learning

Explore & Explain

Triangle Special Segments

Use the **Triangle Special Segments** tool with the protractor and ruler to explore the theorems discussed in Lesson 8-1 and to enhance understanding of other concepts contained in this chapter.

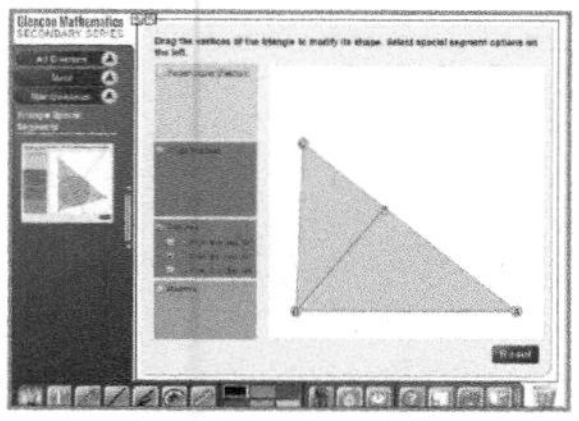

The Geometer's Sketchpad

Use the **The Geometer's Sketchpad** to provide a way to use squares and their areas to investigate the Pythagorean Theorem and to explore 30-60-90 triangles and the relationship among the side lengths and among areas. The Geometer's Sketchpad can also illustrate how to use the Law of Sines and the Law of Cosines, as discussed in Lessons 8-6 and 8-7.

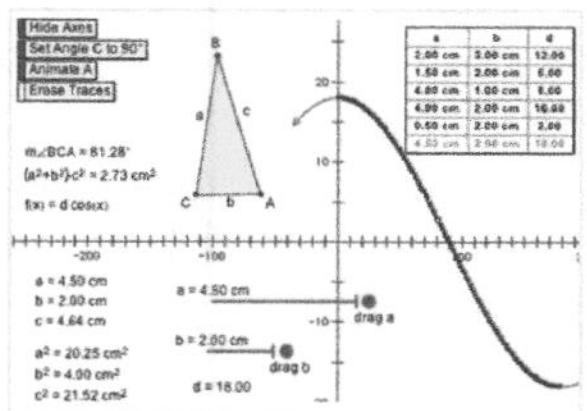

eBook

Interactive Student Guide

Before starting the chapter, answer the **Chapter Focus** preview questions. Check your answers as you complete each lesson. At the end of the chapter, try the **Performance Task**.

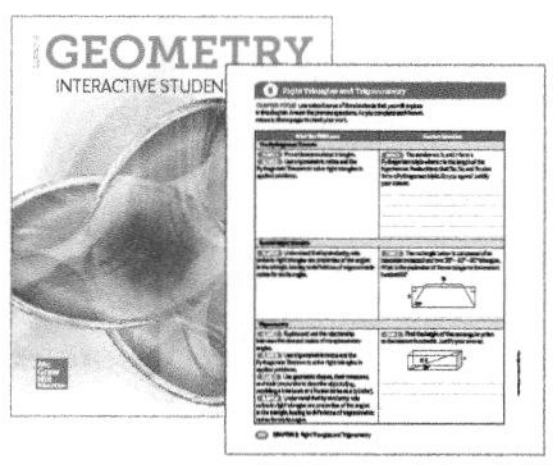

Organize

Foldables

Get organized! Create this **Right Triangles and Trigonometry Foldable** before you begin this chapter to help you organize your notes about right angles and trigonometry.

Collaborate

Chapter Project

In the **Surveyors** project, you will use what you have learned about right triangles and trigonometry to complete a business literacy project.

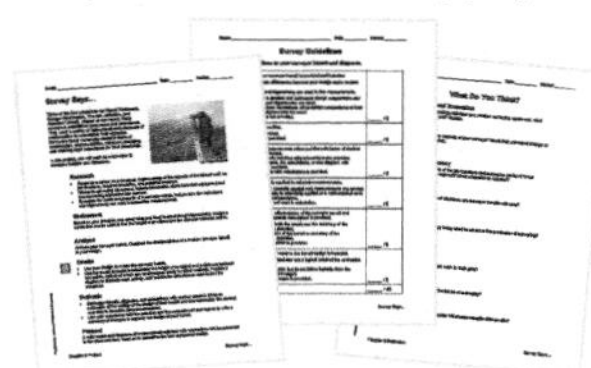

Focus

LEARNSMART

Need help studying? Complete the **Similarity, Proof, and Trigonometry** domain in LearnSmart to review for the chapter test.

ALEKS

You can use the **Triangles** topic in ALEKS to explore what you know about right triangles and trigonometry and what you are ready to learn.*

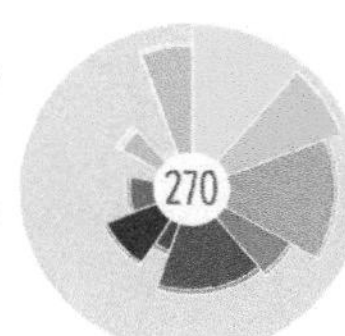

* Ask your teacher if this is part of your program.

Dinah Zike's FOLDABLES®

Focus Students use the Foldable journal to write about right triangles and trigonometry.

Teach Under the tabs of their Foldables, students take notes, define terms, solve problems, and write examples. On the front of each section, ask students to draw a visual to represent the information in a concise, easy-to-study format.

When to Use It Use the appropriate tabs as students cover each lesson in this chapter. Students can add to the vocabulary tab during each lesson.

Go Online!

Notebooking with Foldables

Save a tree! In this video, you will learn tips for decreasing the amount of paper used when creating notebooks with Foldables. MP 2, 5, 7

Get Ready for the Chapter

RtI Response to Intervention

Use the Concept Check results and the Intervention Planner chart to help you determine your Response to Intervention.

Intervention Planner

TIER 1 — On Level (OL)

IF students miss 25% of the exercises or less,

THEN choose a resource:

Go Online!

- Skills Practice, Chapter 1 and Chapter 3
- Chapter Project
- Self-Check Quizzes

TIER 2 — Approaching Level (AL)

IF students miss 50% of the exercises,

THEN choose a resource:

Go Online!

- Study Guide and Intervention, Ch. 1 and Ch. 3
- Extra Examples
- Personal Tutors
- Homework Help

Quick Review Math Handbook

TIER 3 — Intensive Intervention

IF students miss 75% of the exercises,

THEN Use *Math Triumphs, Geometry*

Go Online!

- Extra Examples
- Personal Tutors
- Homework Help
- Review Vocabulary

Get Ready for the Chapter

Go Online! for Vocabulary Review Games and key vocabulary in 13 languages.

Connecting Concepts

Concept Check

Review the concepts used in this chapter by answering the questions below.

1. What is the first step to simplify $\frac{6}{\sqrt{3}}$? **Multiply by $\frac{\sqrt{3}}{\sqrt{3}}$.**
2. Simplify $\frac{6\sqrt{3}}{3}$. $2\sqrt{3}$
3. Describe the Pythagorean Theorem.
4. Given the right triangle shown, what equation could you write to solve for x? $8^2 + 15^2 = x^2$

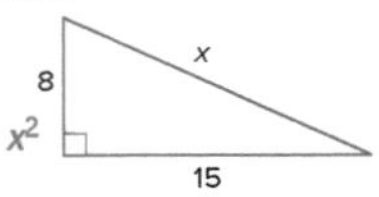

5. Describe how to solve the equation $289 = x^2$ for x? **Take the positive square root of each side.**
6. Anna is making a banner out of 4 congruent triangles as shown. She is planning to trim the perimeter with blue trim. Write an equation to solve for x. $x^2 = 10^2 + 14^2$

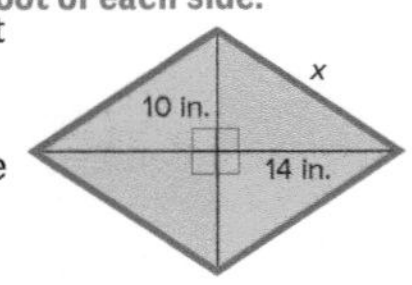

7. How much blue trim will Anna need in total? **68.8 in.**
8. Describe the steps needed to graph a line segment with endpoints $A(-4, 2)$ and $B(3, -2)$. **Plot points *A* and *B* and then connect the plotted points.**

3. If a triangle is a right triangle, then the square of the length of the hypotenuse is equal to the sum of the squares of the lengths of the legs.

Performance Task Review

You can use the concepts and skills in the chapter to solve problems related to navigation. Understanding right triangles and trigonometry will help you finish the Performance Task at the end of the chapter.

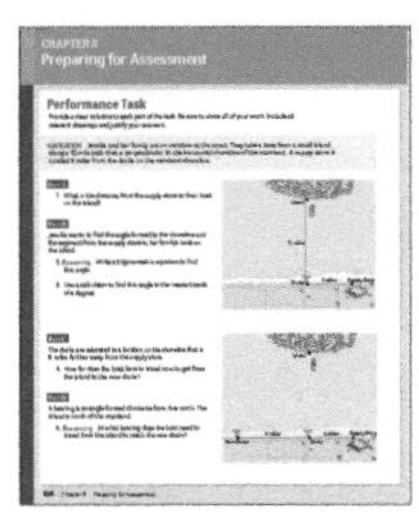

MP In this Performance Task you will:

- reason abstractly and quantitatively
- use appropriate tools strategically

New Vocabulary

English		Español
geometric mean	p. 565	media geométrica
Pythagorean triple	p. 576	triplete pitágorico
trigonometry	p. 596	trigonométria
trigonometric ratio	p. 596	razón trigonométrica
sine	p. 596	seno
cosine	p. 596	coseno
tangent	p. 596	tangente
inverse sine	p. 599	inverso del seno
inverse cosine	p. 599	inverso del coseno
inverse tangent	p. 599	inverse del tangente
angle of elevation	p. 608	ángulo de elevación
angle of depression	p. 608	ángulo de depresión
Law of Sines	p. 617	ley de los senos
solving a triangle	p. 617	resolver un triángulo
ambiguous case of the Law of Sines	p. 618	caso ambiguo de la ley de los senos
Law of Cosines	p. 624	ley do los cosenos

Review Vocabulary

altitude altura a segment drawn from a vertex of a triangle perpendicular to the line containing the other side

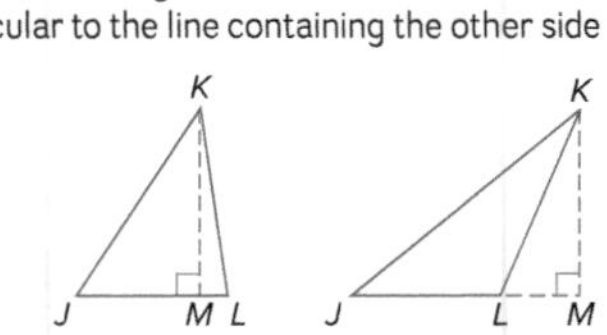

$\overline{KM}$ is an altitude of $\triangle JKL$.

Pythagorean Theorem Teorema de Pitágoras If a and b are the measures of the legs of a right triangle and c is the measure of the hypotenuse, then $a^2 + b^2 = c^2$.

Key Vocabulary ELL

Introduce the key vocabulary in the chapter using the routine below.

Define The geometric mean of two positive real numbers a and b is the number x such that $\frac{a}{x} = \frac{x}{b}$.

Example The geometric mean of 1 and 16 is 4, as $\frac{1}{4} = \frac{4}{16}$.

Ask Is the geometric mean the average of the two numbers? What are equivalent ways to show the relationship given by the geometric mean? no; $\frac{a}{x} = \frac{x}{b}$, $x^2 = ab$, $x = \sqrt{ab}$

LESSON 8-1

Geometric Mean

SUGGESTED PACING (DAYS)

	Instruction
90 min.	0.5
45 min.	1.0

Track Your Progress

Objectives

1 Find the geometric mean between two numbers.

2 Solve problems involving relationships between parts of a right triangle and the altitude to its hypotenuse.

Mathematical Background

The *geometric mean* between two numbers is the square root of their product. The geometric mean has a particular application for a right triangle.

Skills Trace

THEN	NOW	NEXT
G.SRT.A.3 Use the properties of similarity transformations to establish the AA criterion for two triangles to be similar.	**G.SRT.4** Prove theorems about triangles. **G.SRT.5** Use congruence and similarity criteria to solve problems and to prove relationships in geometric figures.	**G.SRT.10** Prove the Laws of Sines and Cosines and use them to solve problems.

Go Online! All of these resources and more are available at connectED.mcgraw-hill.com

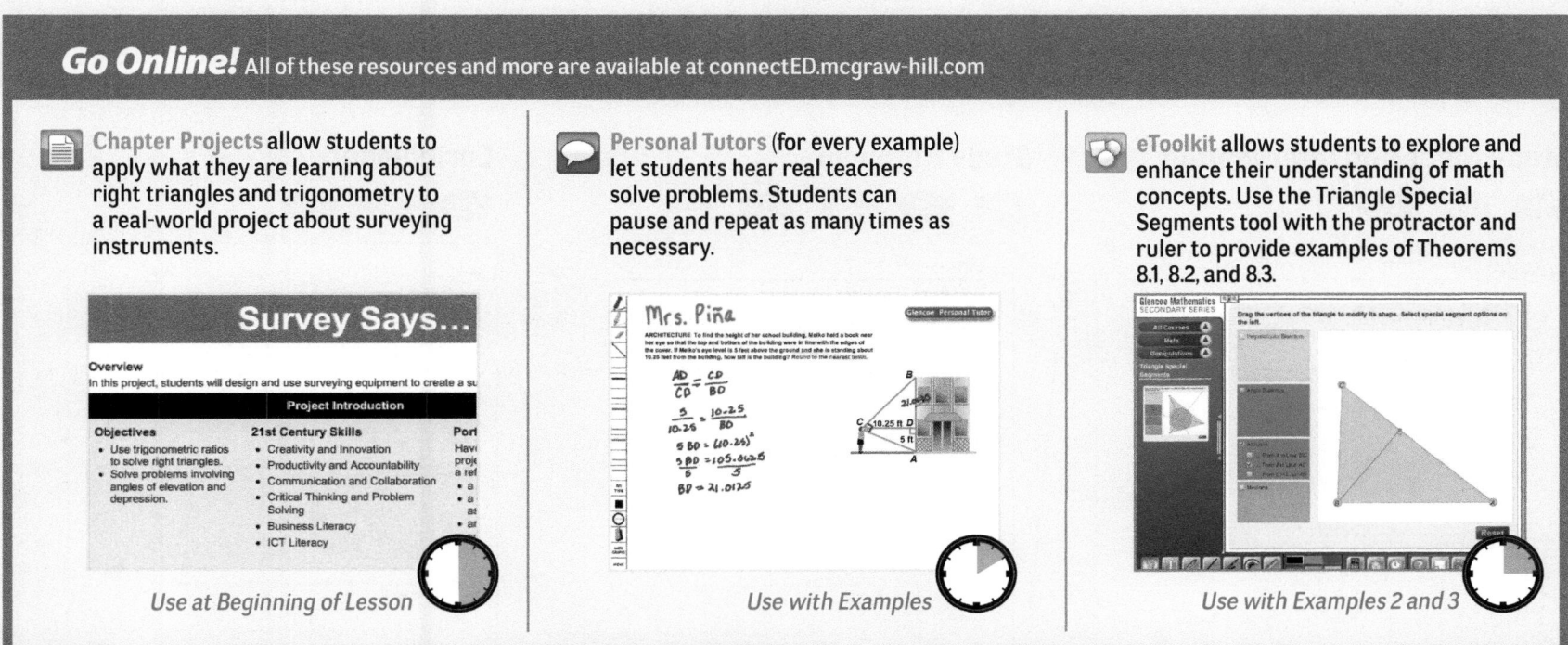

Chapter Projects allow students to apply what they are learning about right triangles and trigonometry to a real-world project about surveying instruments.

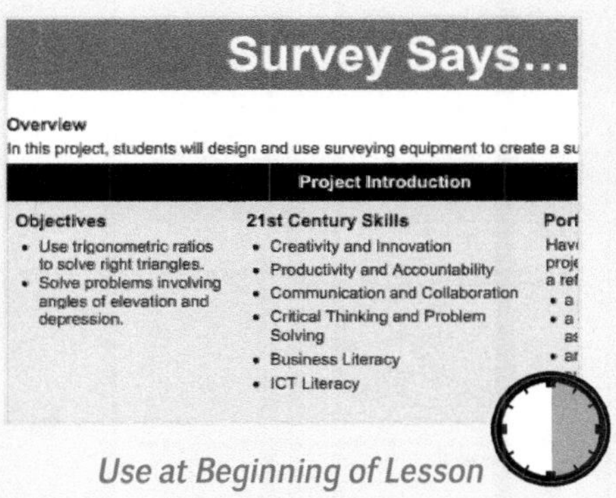

Use at Beginning of Lesson

Personal Tutors (for every example) let students hear real teachers solve problems. Students can pause and repeat as many times as necessary.

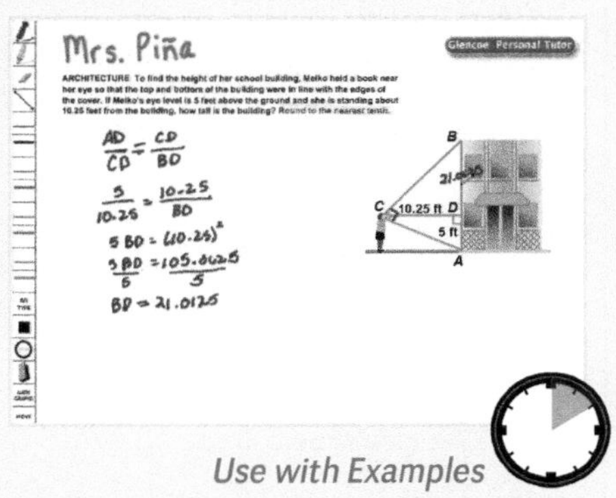

Use with Examples

eToolkit allows students to explore and enhance their understanding of math concepts. Use the Triangle Special Segments tool with the protractor and ruler to provide examples of Theorems 8.1, 8.2, and 8.3.

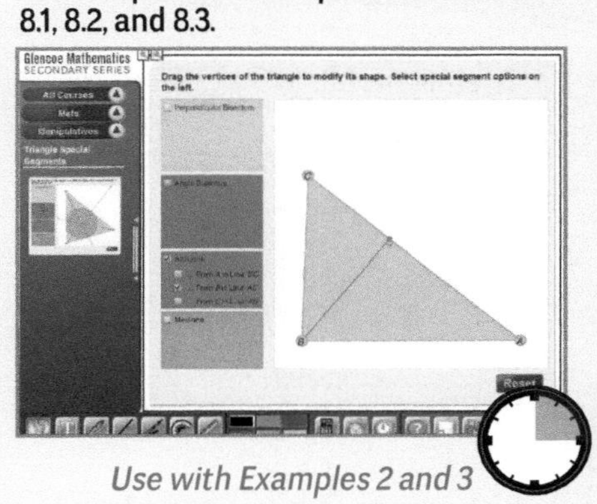

Use with Examples 2 and 3

Using Open Educational Resources

Collating Have students collect everything they learn about right triangles and trigonometry on **Livebinders** throughout this chapter. At the end of the chapter, students can create a portfolio to show their knowledge of the concepts. *Use as homework*

Go Online!
connectED.mcgraw-hill.com
Worksheets

Differentiate Your Resources

Extra Practice Additional practice or homework; Skills Practice is best for approaching-level students and Practice is best for on-level and beyond-level students

Skills Practice

AL OL ELL

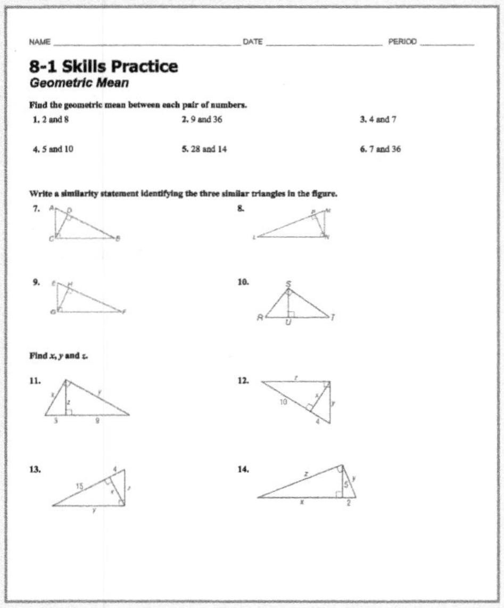
8-1 Skills Practice
Geometric Mean

Find the geometric mean between each pair of numbers.
1. 2 and 8 2. 9 and 36 3. 4 and 7
4. 5 and 10 5. 28 and 14 6. 7 and 36

Write a similarity statement identifying the three similar triangles in the figure.

Find x, y and z.

Practice

AL OL BL ELL

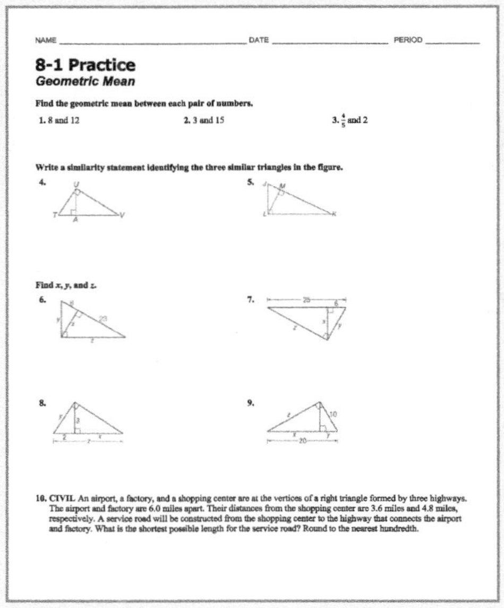
8-1 Practice
Geometric Mean

Find the geometric mean between each pair of numbers.
1. 8 and 12 2. 3 and 15 3. $\frac{4}{5}$ and 2

Write a similarity statement identifying the three similar triangles in the figure.

Find x, y, and z.

10. CIVIL An airport, a factory, and a shopping center are at the vertices of a right triangle formed by three highways. The airport and factory are 6.0 miles apart. Their distances from the shopping center are 3.6 miles and 4.8 miles, respectively. A service road will be constructed from the shopping center to the highway that connects the airport and factory. What is the shortest possible length for the service road? Round to the nearest hundredth.

Word Problem Practice

AL OL BL ELL

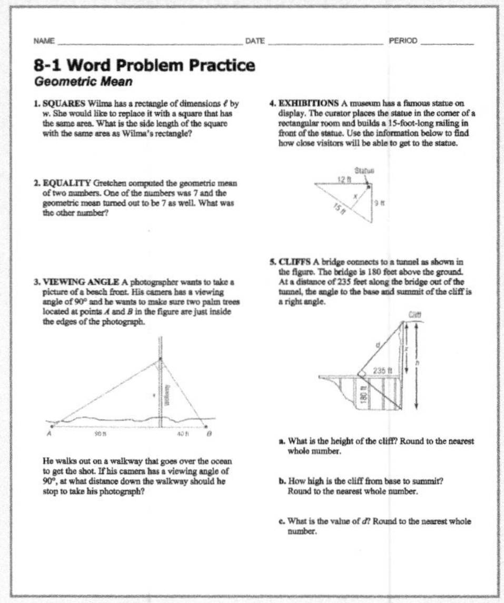
8-1 Word Problem Practice
Geometric Mean

1. SQUARES Wilma has a rectangle of dimensions ℓ by w. She would like to replace it with a square that has the same area. What is the side length of the square with the same area as Wilma's rectangle?

2. EQUALITY Gretchen computed the geometric mean of two numbers. One of the numbers was 7 and the geometric mean turned out to be 7 as well. What was the other number?

3. VIEWING ANGLE A photographer wants to take a picture of a beach front. His camera has a viewing angle of 90° and he wants to make sure two palm trees located at points A and B in the figure are just inside the edges of the photograph.

He walks out on a walkway that goes over the ocean to get the shot. If his camera has a viewing angle of 90°, at what distance down the walkway should he stop to take his photograph?

4. EXHIBITIONS A museum has a famous statue on display. The curator places the statue in the corner of a rectangular room and builds a 15-foot-long railing in front of the statue. Use the information below to find how close visitors will be able to get to the statue.

5. CLIFFS A bridge connects to a tunnel as shown in the figure. The bridge is 180 feet above the ground. At a distance of 235 feet along the bridge out of the tunnel, the angle to the base and summit of the cliff is a right angle.

a. What is the height of the cliff? Round to the nearest whole number.

b. How high is the cliff from base to summit? Round to the nearest whole number.

c. What is the value of d? Round to the nearest whole number.

Intervention Reteaching and vocabulary activities that can be used with struggling or absent students and as ELL support

Study Guide and Intervention

AL OL ELL

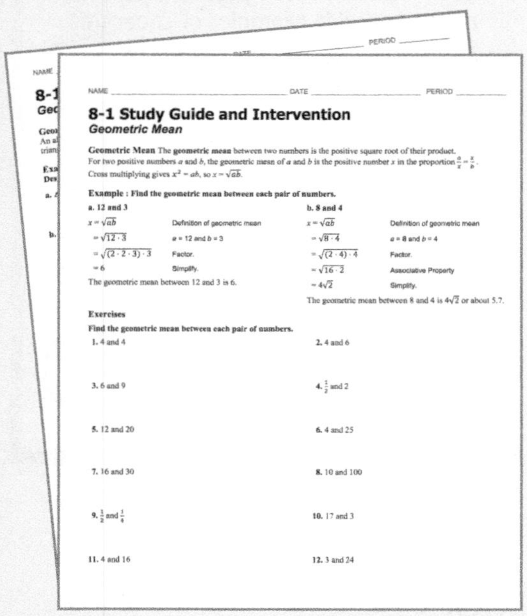
8-1 Study Guide and Intervention
Geometric Mean

Geometric Mean The geometric mean between two numbers is the positive square root of their product.

Exercises
Find the geometric mean between each pair of numbers.

Study Notebook

AL OL BL ELL

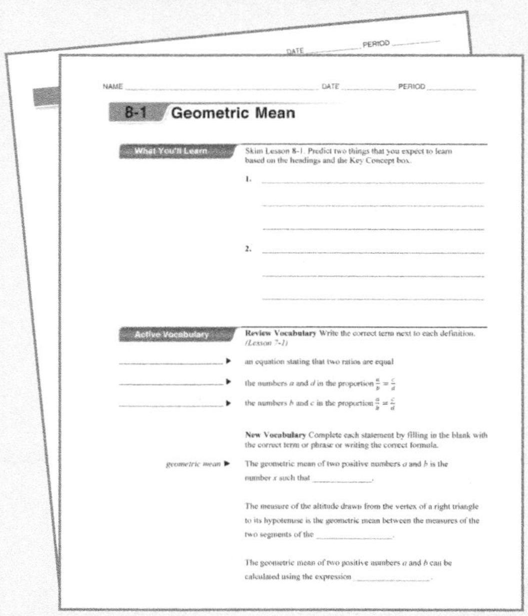
8-1 Geometric Mean

What You'll Learn
Active Vocabulary

Extension Activities that can be used to extend lesson concepts

Enrichment

OL BL ELL

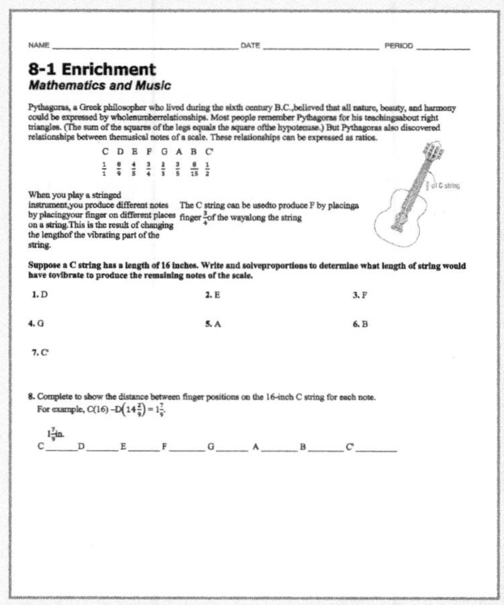
8-1 Enrichment
Mathematics and Music

Suppose a C string has a length of 16 inches. Write and solve proportions to determine what length of string would have to vibrate to produce the remaining notes of the scale.

LESSON 1

Geometric Mean

Then

- You used proportional relationships of corresponding angle bisectors, altitudes, and medians of similar triangles.

Now

1. Find the geometric mean between two numbers.
2. Solve problems involving relationships between parts of a right triangle and the altitude to its hypotenuse.

Why?

- Photographing very tall or very wide objects can be challenging. It can be difficult to include the entire object in your shot without distorting the image. If your camera is set for a vertical viewing angle of 90° and you know the height of the object you wish to photograph, you can use the geometric mean of the distance from the top of the object to your camera level and the distance from the bottom of the object to camera level.

New Vocabulary
geometric mean

Mathematical Practices
7 Look for and make use of structure.
3 Construct viable arguments and critique the reasoning of others.

Content Standards
G.SRT.4 Prove theorems about triagles.
G.SRT.5 Use congruence and similarity criteria for triangles to solve problems and prove relationships in geometric figures.

1 Geometric Mean

When the means of a proportion are the same number, that number is called the geometric mean of the extremes. The **geometric mean** between two numbers is the positive square root of their product.

$$\text{extreme} \rightarrow \frac{a}{x} = \frac{x}{b} \leftarrow \text{mean} \qquad (\text{mean} \rightarrow x,\ b \leftarrow \text{extreme})$$

Key Concept Geometric Mean

Words	The geometric mean of two positive numbers a and b is the number x such that $\frac{a}{x} = \frac{x}{b}$. So, $x^2 = ab$ and $x = \sqrt{ab}$.
Example	The geometric mean of $a = 9$ and $b = 4$ is 6, because $6 = \sqrt{9 \cdot 4}$.

G.SRT.5

Example 1 Geometric Mean

Find the geometric mean between 8 and 10.

$x = \sqrt{ab}$ — Definition of geometric mean
$= \sqrt{8 \cdot 10}$ — $a = 8$ and $b = 10$
$= \sqrt{(4 \cdot 2) \cdot (2 \cdot 5)}$ — Factor.
$= \sqrt{16 \cdot 5}$ — Associative Property
$= 4\sqrt{5}$ — Simplify.

The geometric mean between 8 and 10 is $4\sqrt{5}$ or about 8.9.

Guided Practice

Find the geometric mean between each pair of numbers.

1A. 5 and 45 15

1B. 12 and 15 $6\sqrt{5}$ or about 13.4

2 Geometric Means in Right Triangles

In a right triangle, an altitude drawn from the vertex of the right angle to the hypotenuse forms two additional right triangles. These three right triangles share a special relationship.

Mathematical Practices Strategies

Construct viable arguments and critique the reasoning of others.
Help students maintain oversight of the process of deriving and applying geometric means to find missing lengths in right triangles. For example, ask:

- When an altitude is drawn from the hypotenuse to the right angle of a triangle, how can you prove similarity between the triangles formed? AA Similarity Postulate
- When writing similarity statements for triangles formed by the hypotenuse, how can you ensure that you have the correct order? All of the triangles will have one right angle and one angle that is congruent to an acute angle in the original triangle, so you can use corresponding angles to determine the correct order.

Launch

Have students read the Why? section of the lesson. Ask:

- What is one possible problem when taking a picture of a very tall object? Sample statement: The image can be distorted.
- At what vertical viewing angle should the camera be set to use the geometric mean to photograph an object? 90°
- What measure do you need when using the geometric mean to photograph a very tall object? the height of the object

Teach

Ask the scaffolded questions for each example to build conceptual understanding for students at all levels.

1 Geometric Mean

Example 1 Geometric Mean

AL In this example, what values are the *extremes*? 8 and 10

OL What is the geometric mean between 8 and 13? $2\sqrt{26} \approx 10.2$

BL The geometric mean between two numbers is 10. Give an example of a pair of whole numbers that meet this criterion. Sample answer: 4 and 25

Need Another Example?
Find the geometric mean between 2 and 50. 10

Go Online!

Interactive Whiteboard
Use the *eLesson*, *Lesson Presentation*, or *Interactive Classroom* to present this lesson.

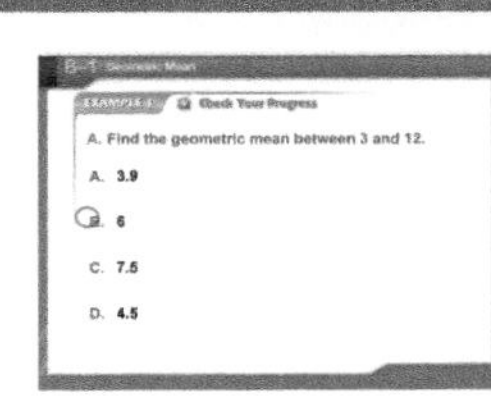

2 Geometric Means in Right Triangles

Example 2 Identify Similar Right Triangles

AL How can we prove that $\triangle FJG \sim \triangle FGH$? Explain. Because they are both right triangles and they share a common vertex and angle, they are similar by AA Similarity.

OL What are the altitudes of $\triangle FGH$? $\overline{GJ}$, $\overline{HG}$, and $\overline{FG}$

BL Will the altitude that divides a right triangle into three similar triangles always originate at the right angle and intersect the hypotenuse? Explain. Yes; since the two legs are also altitudes, the only altitude that will intersect the triangle in a place other than a vertex is the one that originates at the right angle and intersects the hypotenuse.

Need Another Example?

Write a similarity statement identifying the three similar triangles in the figure.

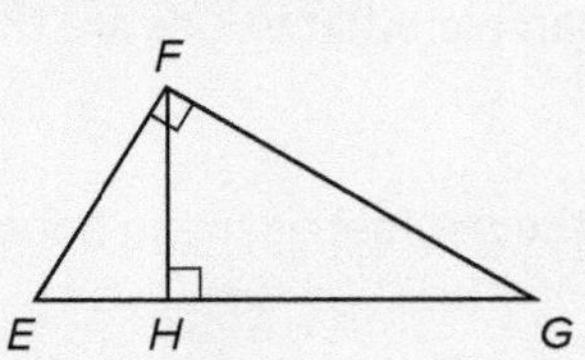

$\triangle EGF \sim \triangle EFH \sim \triangle FGH$

Watch Out!

Naming Triangles When writing similarity statements for triangles, be sure to name the vertices in the corresponding order in each triangle.

Review Vocabulary ELL

altitude (of a triangle) a segment from a vertex to the line containing the opposite side and perpendicular to the line containing that side

Theorem 8.1

If the altitude is drawn to the hypotenuse of a right triangle, then the two triangles formed are similar to the original triangle and to each other.

Example If $\overline{CD}$ is the altitude to hypotenuse $\overline{AB}$ of right $\triangle ABC$, then $\triangle ACD \sim \triangle ABC$, $\triangle CBD \sim \triangle ABC$, and $\triangle ACD \sim \triangle CBD$.

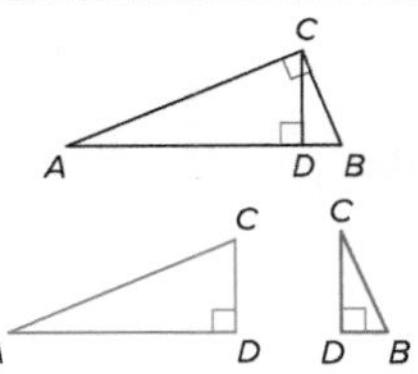

You will prove Theorem 8.1 in Exercise 39.

G.SRT.5

Example 2 Identify Similar Right Triangles

Write a similarity statement identifying the three similar right triangles in the figure.

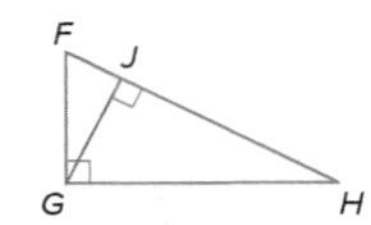

Separate the triangle into two triangles along the altitude. Then sketch the three triangles, reorienting the smaller ones so that their corresponding angles and sides are in the same positions as the original triangle.

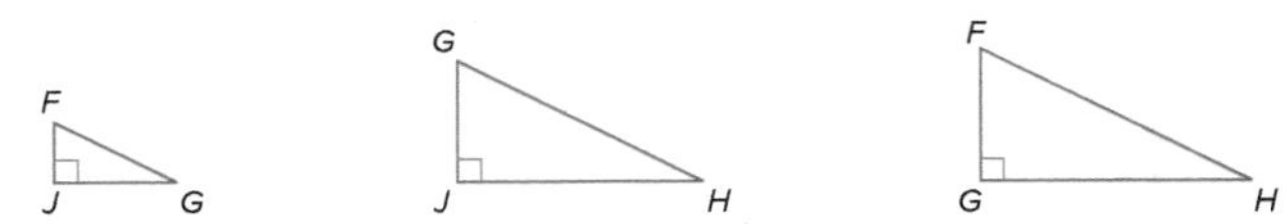

So by Theorem 8.1, $\triangle FJG \sim \triangle GJH \sim \triangle FGH$.

Study Tip

MP Sense-Making To reorient the right triangles in Example 2, first match up the right angles. Then match up the shorter sides.

Guided Practice

2A.

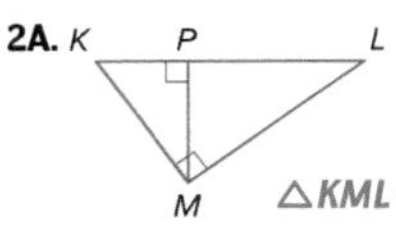

$\triangle KML \sim \triangle MPL \sim \triangle KPM$

2B.

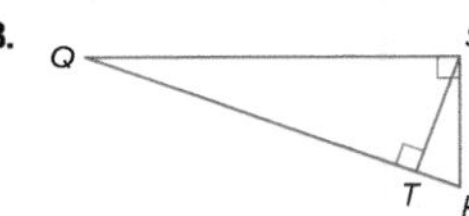

$\triangle STR \sim \triangle QTS \sim \triangle QSR$

From Theorem 8.1, you know that altitude $\overline{CD}$ drawn to the hypotenuse of right triangle ABC forms three similar triangles: $\triangle ACB \sim \triangle ADC \sim \triangle CDB$. By the definition of similar polygons, you can write the following proportions comparing the side lengths of these triangles.

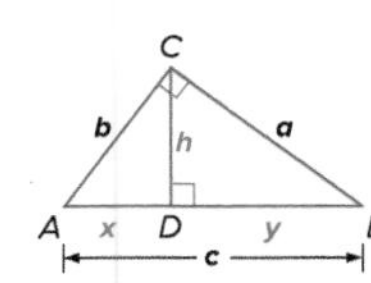

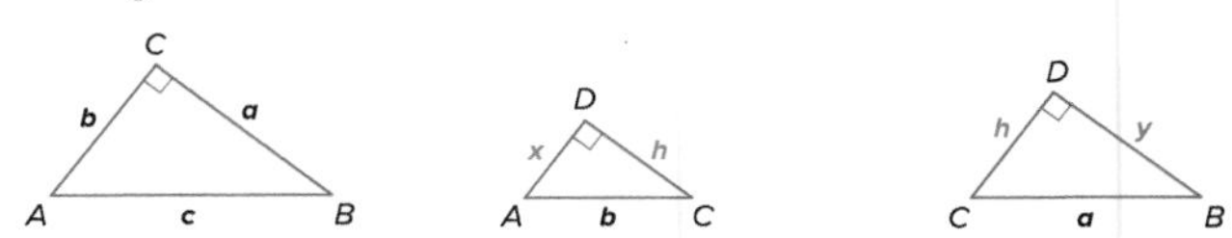

$\frac{\text{shorter leg}}{\text{longer leg}} = \frac{b}{a} = \frac{x}{h} = \frac{h}{y}$ $\quad \frac{\text{hypotenuse}}{\text{shorter leg}} = \frac{c}{b} = \frac{b}{x} = \frac{a}{h}$ $\quad \frac{\text{hypotenuse}}{\text{longer leg}} = \frac{c}{a} = \frac{b}{h} = \frac{a}{y}$

Notice that the circled relationships involve geometric means. This leads to the theorems at the top of the next page.

Differentiated Instruction AL OL BL ELL

Visual Learners Working in small groups, have students create a poster of terms from the chapter. Have them illustrate the term with an example and the formula related to the term. They can use this poster to study and review as they learn the material in this chapter.

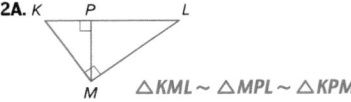

Theorems Right Triangle Geometric Mean Theorems

8.2 Geometric Mean (Altitude) Theorem The altitude drawn to the hypotenuse of a right triangle separates the hypotenuse into two segments. The length of this altitude is the geometric mean between the lengths of these two segments.

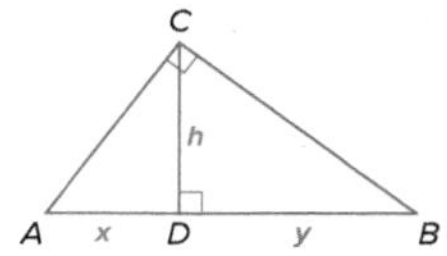

Example If $\overline{CD}$ is the altitude to hypotenuse $\overline{AB}$ of right $\triangle ABC$, then $\frac{x}{h} = \frac{h}{y}$ or $h = \sqrt{xy}$.

8.3 Geometric Mean (Leg) Theorem The altitude drawn to the hypotenuse of a right triangle separates the hypotenuse into two segments. The length of a leg of this triangle is the geometric mean between the length of the hypotenuse and the segment of the hypotenuse adjacent to that leg.

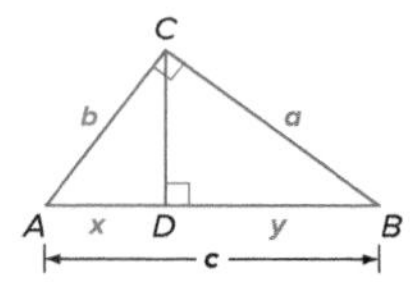

Example If $\overline{CD}$ is the altitude to hypotenuse $\overline{AB}$ of right $\triangle ABC$, then $\frac{c}{b} = \frac{b}{x}$ or $b = \sqrt{xc}$ and $\frac{c}{a} = \frac{a}{y}$ or $a = \sqrt{yc}$.

You will prove Theorems 8.2 and 8.3 in Exercises 40 and 41, respectively.

Go Online!

In Example 3, the value of x could also be found by solving the proportion $\frac{5}{x} = \frac{x}{20}$. Search proportions in ConnectED to find resources to review how to set up and solve proportions. ELL

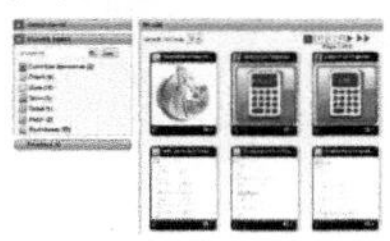

G.SRT.5

Example 3 Use Geometric Mean with Right Triangles

Find *x*, *y*, and *z*.

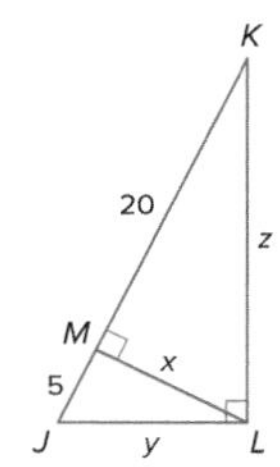

Since x is the measure of the altitude drawn to the hypotenuse of right $\triangle JKL$, x is the geometric mean of the lengths of the two segments that make up the hypotenuse, JM and MK.

$x = \sqrt{JM \cdot MK}$	Geometric Mean (Altitude) Theorem
$= \sqrt{5 \cdot 20}$	Substitution
$= \sqrt{100}$ or 10	Simplify.

Since y is the measure of leg $\overline{JL}$, y is the geometric mean of JM, the measure of the segment adjacent to this leg, and JK, the measure of the hypotenuse.

$y = \sqrt{JM \cdot JK}$	Geometric Mean (Leg) Theorem
$= \sqrt{5 \cdot (20 + 5)}$	Substitution
$= \sqrt{125}$ or about 11.2	Use a calculator to simplify.

Since z is the measure of leg $\overline{KL}$, z is the geometric mean of MK, the measure of the segment adjacent to $\overline{KL}$, and JK, the measure of the hypotenuse.

$z = \sqrt{MK \cdot JK}$	Geometric Mean (Leg) Theorem
$= \sqrt{20 \cdot (20 + 5)}$	Substitution
$= \sqrt{500}$ or about 22.4	Use a calculator to simplify.

Example 3 Use Geometric Mean with Right Triangles

AL Why are there three different geometric means we can write for the triangles formed by the altitude of a right triangle? because three similar triangles are formed

OL If $MJ = 2$ and $MK = 50$, what is x? 10

BL What proportion can you write to solve for z? $\frac{25}{z} = \frac{z}{20}$

Need Another Example?

Find c, d, and e.

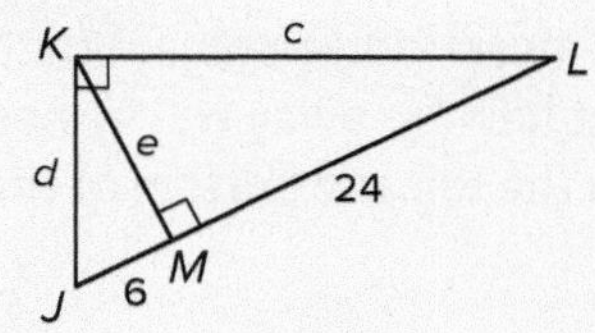

$c \approx 26.8$; $d \approx 13.4$; $e = 12$

Teaching Tip

Altitude The altitude drawn to the hypotenuse originates from the right angle. The other two altitudes of a right triangle are the legs.

Differentiated Instruction AL OL BL

Intrapersonal Learners Allow students to sit quietly and explore similarities and differences between Theorem 8.2 and 8.3. Encourage students to use the examples in the book or create their own to reinforce the concepts outlined in these two theorems. Ask students to think and write about why the formulas for geometric mean work for a right triangle with an altitude drawn to its hypotenuse.

Example 4 Indirect Measurement

AL Why does Zach need to use indirect measurement to estimate the height of the grandstand? Sample answer: Because it is not reasonable to measure the height of the grandstand using a measuring tool.

OL Suppose additional seating is added, and Zach wants to know the new height of the grandstand. He stands 15 feet from the grandstand to line up the top and bottom with his square. How tall is the new grandstand? about 45 ft

BL If Zach is measuring an object that is 35 feet tall, about how far away will he need to stand to line up the top and bottom of the object? about 13 ft

Need Another Example?

Kites Mrs. Alspach is making a kite for her son. She has to arrange two support rods so that they are perpendicular. The shorter rod is 27 inches long. If she places the short rod 7.25 inches from one end of the long rod in order to form two right angles with the kite fabric, what is the length of the long rod?

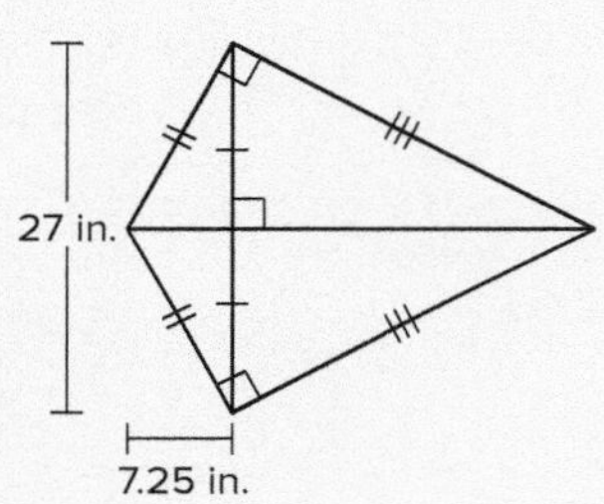

≈ 32.39 in.

Follow-Up

Students have explored the geometric mean.

Ask:

Why do we use the geometric mean to solve real-world problems? Sample answer: the geometric mean allows us to find the height of objects that are hard to measure using two measures that are easy to find.

3A. $x = 2\sqrt{66}$ or about 16.2, $y = 5\sqrt{33}$ or about 28.7, $z = 10\sqrt{2}$ or about 14.1

3B. $x = 16$, $y = 20$, $z = 15$

Guided Practice

Find x, y, and z.

3A.

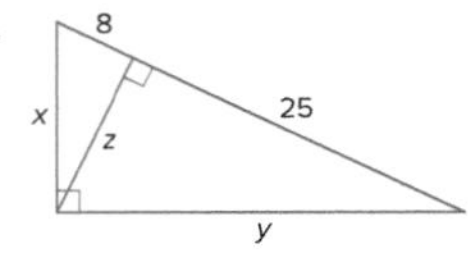

3B.

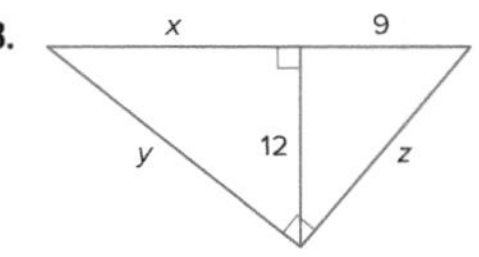

You can use geometric mean to measure height indirectly.

G.SRT.5

Real-World Career

Event Planner
Event planners organize events including choosing a location, arranging for food, and scheduling entertainment. They also coordinate services like transportation and photography.

Most of the skills required for event planning are acquired through on-the-job experience.

Real-World Example 4 Indirect Measurement

ADVERTISING **Zach wants to order a banner that will hang over the side of his high school baseball stadium grandstand and reach the ground.**

To find this height, he uses a cardboard square to line up the top and bottom of the grandstand. He measures his distance from the grandstand and from the ground to his eye level. Find the height of the grandstand to the nearest foot.

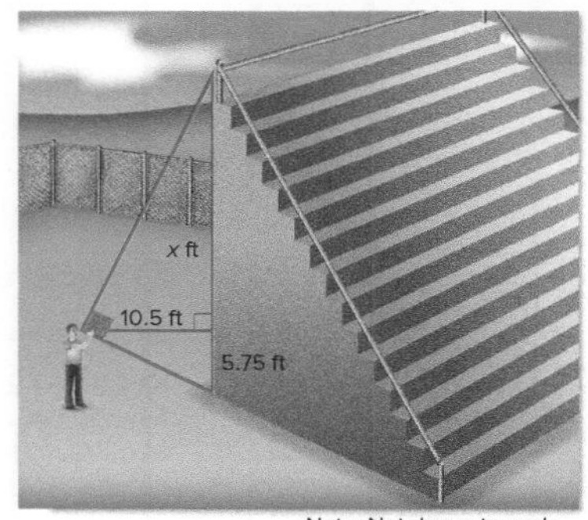

Note: Not drawn to scale.

The distance from Zach to the grandstand is the altitude to the hypotenuse of a right triangle. The length of this altitude is the geometric mean of the two segments that make up the hypotenuse. The shorter segment has the measure of 5.75 feet. Let the unknown measure be x feet.

$10.5 = \sqrt{5.75 \cdot x}$	Geometric Mean (Altitude) Theorem
$110.25 = 5.75x$	Square each side.
$19.17 \approx x$	Divide each side by 5.75.

The height of the grandstand is the total length of the hypotenuse, 5.75 + 19.17, or about 25 feet.

Guided Practice

4. **SPORTS** A community center needs to estimate the cost of installing a rock climbing wall by estimating the height of the wall. Sue holds a book up to her eyes so that the top and bottom of the wall are in line with the bottom edge and binding of the cover. If her eye level is 5 feet above the ground and she stands 11 feet from the wall, how high is the wall? Draw a diagram and explain your reasoning. **See margin.**

Additional Answer (Guided Practice)

4. 29.2 ft; the height of the rock wall is the total length of the hypotenuse, $5 + \frac{121}{5}$, or about 29.2 ft.

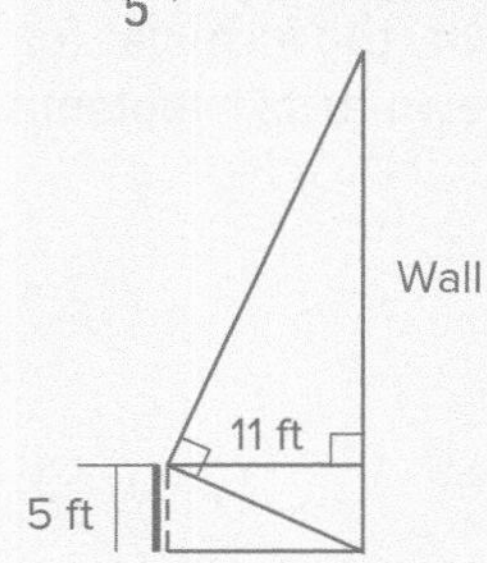

Check Your Understanding

◯ = Step-by-Step Solutions begin on page R13.

Go Online! for a Self-Check Quiz

Example 1 G.SRT.5

Find the geometric mean between each pair of numbers.

1. 5 and 20 10
2. 36 and 4 12
3. 40 and 15 $10\sqrt{6}$ or 24.5

Example 2 G.SRT.5

4. Write a similarity statement identifying the three similar triangles in the figure. $\triangle CFD \sim \triangle ECD \sim \triangle EFC$

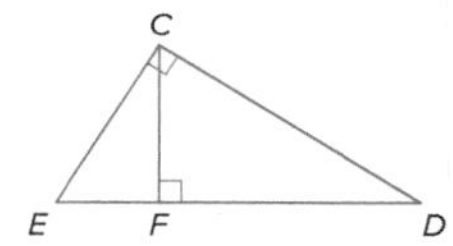

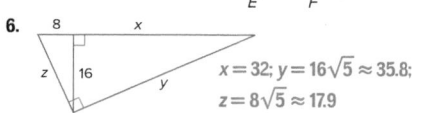

Example 3 G.SRT.5

Find *x*, *y*, and *z*. $x = 6$; $y = 3\sqrt{5} \approx 6.7$; $z = 6\sqrt{5} \approx 13.4$

5.

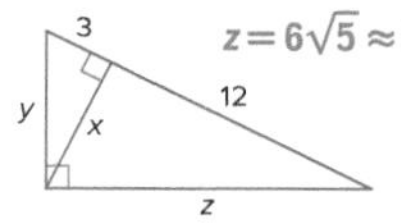

6.

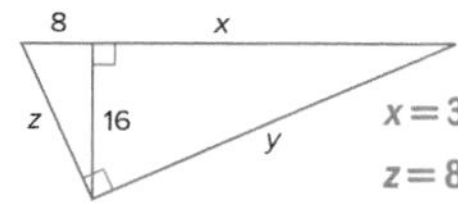

$x = 32$; $y = 16\sqrt{5} \approx 35.8$; $z = 8\sqrt{5} \approx 17.9$

Example 4 G.SRT.5

7. MP **MODELING** Corey is visiting the Jefferson Memorial with his family. He wants to estimate the height of the statue of Thomas Jefferson. Corey stands so that his line of vision to the top and base of the statue form a right angle as shown in the diagram. About how tall is the statue? 18 ft 11 in.

Note: Not drawn to scale.

Practice and Problem Solving

Extra Practice is on page R8.

Example 1 G.SRT.5

Find the geometric mean between each pair of numbers.

8. 81 and 4 18
9. 25 and 16 20
10. 20 and 25 $10\sqrt{5} \approx 22.4$
11. 36 and 24 $12\sqrt{6} \approx 29.4$
12. 12 and 2.4 $\frac{12\sqrt{5}}{5} \approx 5.4$
13. 18 and 1.5 $3\sqrt{3} \approx 5.2$

Example 2 G.SRT.5

Write a similarity statement identifying the three similar triangles in the figure.

14.

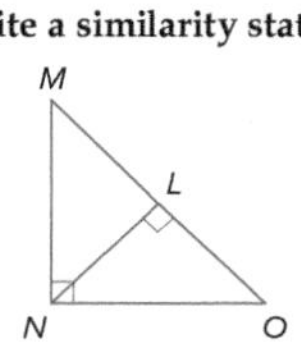

15.

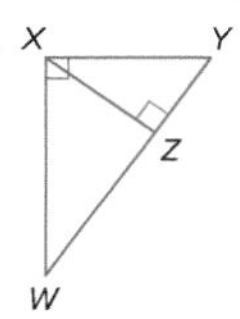

14. $\triangle MNO \sim \triangle NLO \sim \triangle MLN$
15. $\triangle WXY \sim \triangle XZY \sim \triangle WZX$
16. $\triangle QRS \sim \triangle RTS \sim \triangle QTR$
17. $\triangle HGF \sim \triangle HIG \sim \triangle GIF$

16.

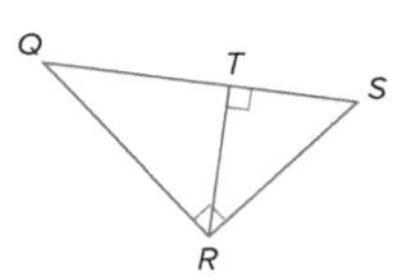

17.

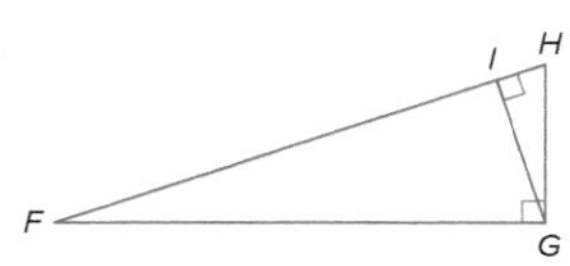

Differentiated Homework Options

Levels	AL Basic	OL Core	BL Advanced
Exercises	8–25, 49, 51–59	9–37 odd, 38, 39, 41, 42, 43–47 odd, 48, 49, 51–59	44–53, (optional: 54–59)
2-Day Option	9–25 odd, 54–59	8–25	
	8–24 even, 49, 51–53	26–49, 51–59	

You can use ALEKS to provide additional remediation support with personalized instruction and practice.

Practice

Formative Assessment Use Exercises 1–7 to assess students' understanding of the concepts in this lesson.

The Practice and Problem Solving exercises assess the content taught in the lesson. The Preparing for Assessment page is meant to be used as preparation for end-of-course assessments.

MP Teaching the Mathematical Practices

Modeling Mathematically proficient students can apply the mathematics they know to solve problems arising in everyday life. In Exercise 7, encourage students to use the diagrams given to identify information important to solving each problem.

Extra Practice

See page R8 for extra exercises for students who are approaching level or for on-level students who need additional reinforcement.

Levels of Complexity Chart

The levels of the exercises progress from 1 to 3, with Level 1 indicating the lowest level of complexity.

Exercises	8–25	26–43, 54–59	44–53
Level 3			●
Level 2		●	
Level 1	●		

MP Teaching the Mathematical Practices

Modeling Mathematically proficient students can apply the mathematics they know to solve problems arising in everyday life. In Exercises 24–25, encourage students to use the Pythagorean Theorem.

Additional Answers

39. Given: $\angle PQR$ is a right angle. $\overline{QS}$ is an altitude of $\triangle PQR$.

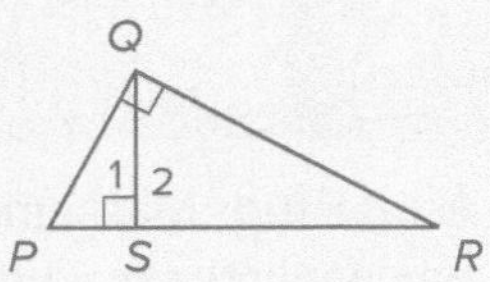

Prove: $\triangle PSQ \sim \triangle PQR$
$\triangle PQR \sim \triangle QSR$
$\triangle PSQ \sim \triangle QSR$

Proof:

Statements (Reasons)

1. $\angle PQR$ is a right angle. $\overline{QS}$ is an altitude of $\triangle PQR$. (Given)
2. $\overline{QS} \perp \overline{RP}$ (Definition of altitude)
3. $\angle 1$ and $\angle 2$ are right $\angle$s. (Definition of $\perp$ lines)
4. $\angle 1 \cong \angle PQR$; $\angle 2 \cong \angle PQR$ (All right $\angle$s are $\cong$.)
5. $\angle P \cong \angle P$; $\angle R \cong \angle R$ (Congruence of angles is reflexive.)
6. $\triangle PSQ \sim \triangle PQR$; $\triangle PQR \sim \triangle QSR$ (AA Similarity Statements 4 and 5)
7. $\triangle PSQ \sim \triangle QSR$ (Similarity of triangles is transitive.)

40. Given: $\triangle ADC$ is a right triangle. $\overline{DB}$ is an altitude of $\triangle ADC$.

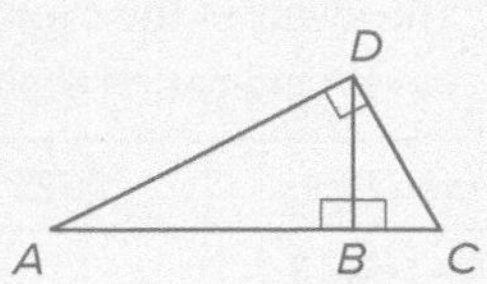

Prove: $\frac{AB}{DB} = \frac{DB}{CB}$

Proof: It is given that $\triangle ADC$ is a right triangle and $\overline{DB}$ is an altitude of $\triangle ADC$. $\angle ADC$ is a right angle by the definition of a right triangle. Therefore, $\triangle ADB \sim \triangle DCB$, because if the altitude is drawn from the vertex of the right angle to the hypotenuse of a right triangle, then the two triangles formed are similar to the given triangle and to each other. So $\frac{AB}{DB} = \frac{DB}{CB}$ by definition of similar triangles.

Example 3 G.SRT.5

Find x, y, and z.

18.

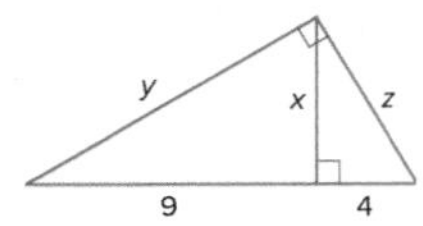

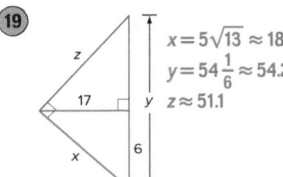

$x = 6$; $y = 3\sqrt{13} \approx 10.8$; $z = 2\sqrt{13} \approx 7.2$

19.

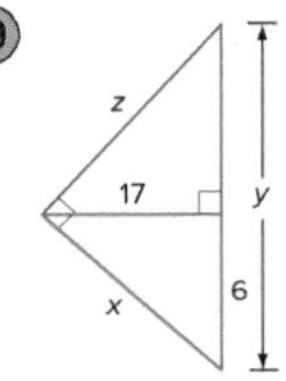

$x = 5\sqrt{13} \approx 18.0$; $y = 54\frac{1}{6} \approx 54.2$; $z \approx 51.1$

20.

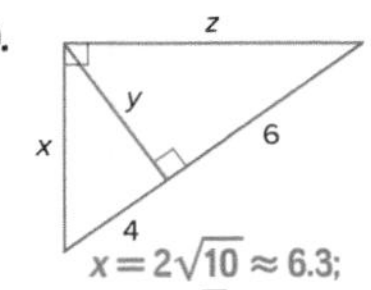

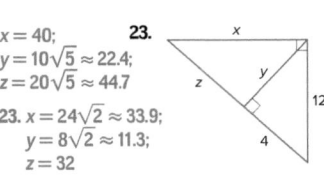

$x = 2\sqrt{10} \approx 6.3$; $y = 2\sqrt{6} \approx 4.9$; $z = 2\sqrt{15} \approx 7.7$

21.

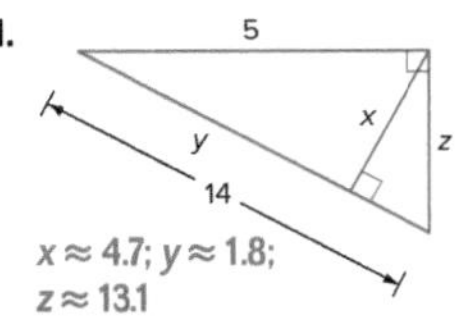

$x \approx 4.7$; $y \approx 1.8$; $z \approx 13.1$

22.

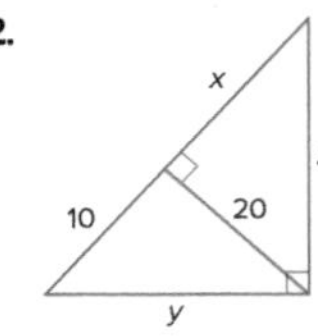

$x = 40$; $y = 10\sqrt{5} \approx 22.4$; $z = 20\sqrt{5} \approx 44.7$

23.

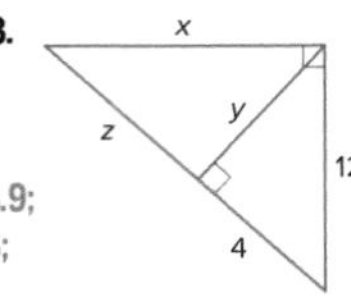

23. $x = 24\sqrt{2} \approx 33.9$; $y = 8\sqrt{2} \approx 11.3$; $z = 32$

Example 4 G.SRT.5

24. **MP MODELING** Evelina is hanging silver stars from the gym ceiling using string for the homecoming dance. She wants the ends of the strings where the stars will be attached to be 7 feet from the floor. Use the diagram to determine how long she should make the strings. 18 ft

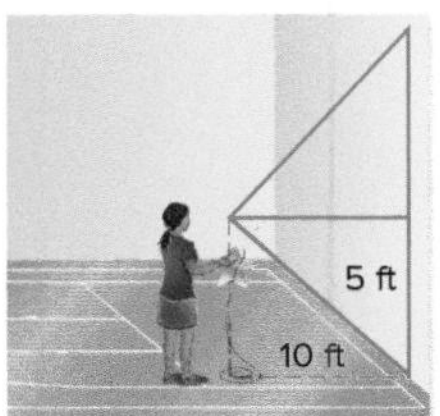

Note: Not drawn to scale.

25. **MP MODELING** Makayla is using a book to sight the top of a waterfall. Her eye level is 5 feet from the ground and she is a horizontal distance of 28 feet from the waterfall. Find the height of the waterfall to the nearest tenth of a foot. 161.8 ft

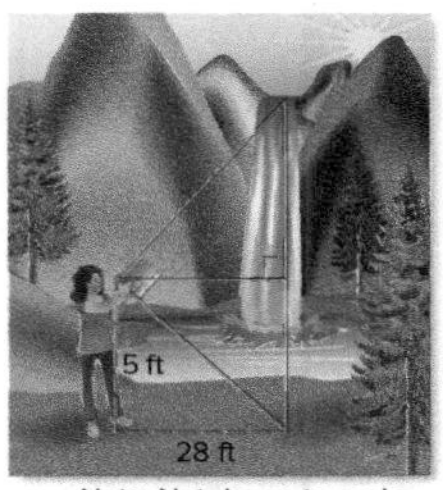

Note: Not drawn to scale.

B **Find the geometric mean between each pair of numbers.**

26. $\frac{1}{5}$ and 60 $2\sqrt{3}$ or 3.5

27. $\frac{3\sqrt{2}}{7}$ and $\frac{5\sqrt{2}}{7}$ $\frac{\sqrt{30}}{7}$ or 0.8

28. $\frac{3\sqrt{5}}{4}$ and $\frac{5\sqrt{5}}{4}$ $\frac{5\sqrt{3}}{4}$ or 2.2

Find x, y, and z.

29.

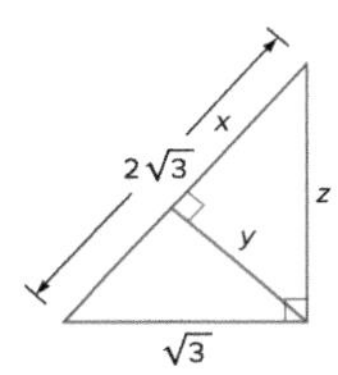

$x = \frac{3\sqrt{3}}{2} \approx 2.6$; $y = \frac{3}{2}$; $z = 3$

30.

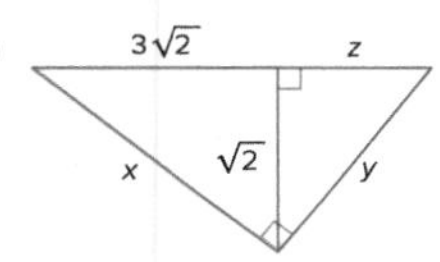

$x = 2\sqrt{5} \approx 4.5$; $y = \frac{2\sqrt{5}}{3} \approx 1.5$; $z = \frac{\sqrt{2}}{3} \approx 0.5$

31. **ALGEBRA** The geometric mean of a number and four times the number is 22. What is the number? 11

Go Online!

The most up-to-date resources available for your program can be found at connectED.mcgraw-hill.com.

Use similar triangles to find the value of x.

32. 

6.4 ft

33. 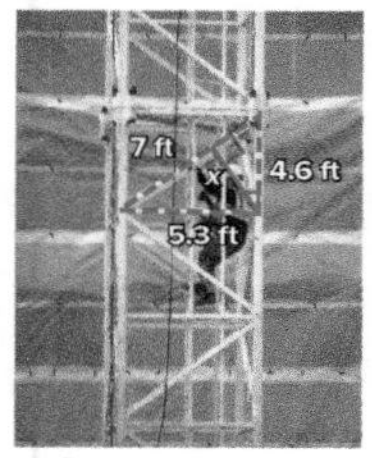

3.5 ft

34. 

13.75 ft

ALGEBRA Find the value of the variable.

35. 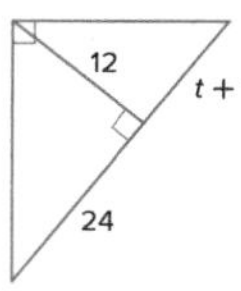

5

36. 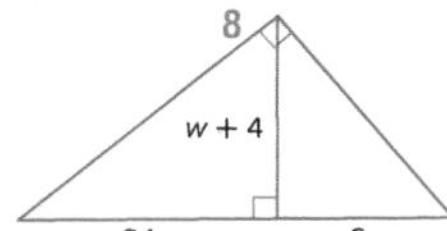

8

37. 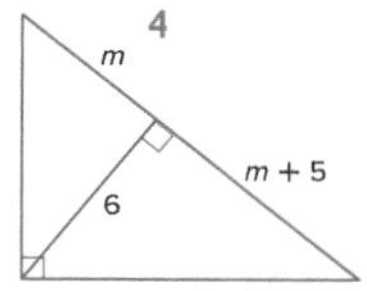

4

38. **CONSTRUCTION** A room-in-attic truss is a truss design that provides support while leaving an area that can be enclosed as living space. In the diagram, $\angle BCA$ and $\angle EGB$ are right angles, $\triangle BEF$ is isosceles, $\overline{CD}$ is an altitude of $\triangle ABC$, and $\overline{EG}$ is an altitude of $\triangle BEF$. If $DB = 5$ feet, $CD = 6$ feet 4 inches, $BF = 10$ feet 10 inches, and $EG = 4$ feet 6 inches, what is AE? about 20.07 ft

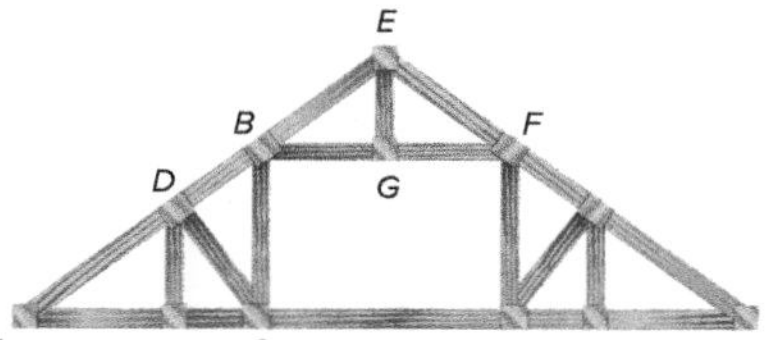

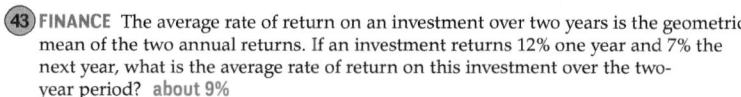

MP **CONSTRUCT ARGUMENTS** **Write a proof for each theorem.** 39–41. See margin.

39. Theorem 8.1
40. Theorem 8.2
41. Theorem 8.3

42. **TRUCKS** In photography, the angle formed by the top of the subject, the camera, and the bottom of the subject is called the viewing angle, as shown at the right. Natalie is taking a picture of Bigfoot #5, which is 15 feet 6 inches tall. She sets her camera on a tripod that is 5 feet above ground level. The vertical viewing angle of her camera is set for 90°.

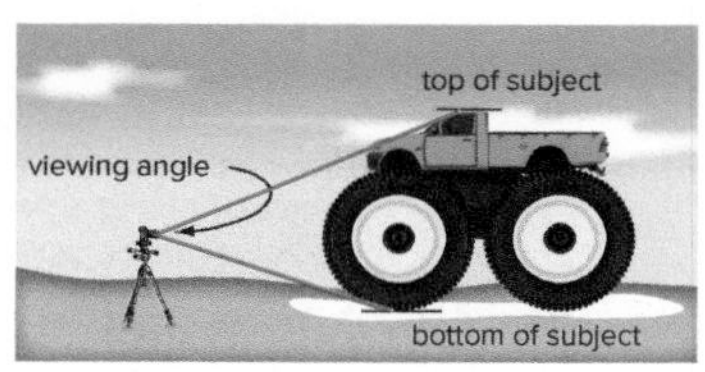

a. Sketch a diagram of this situation. See margin.
b. How far away from the truck should Natalie stand so that she perfectly frames the entire height of the truck in her shot? about 7.2 ft

43. **FINANCE** The average rate of return on an investment over two years is the geometric mean of the two annual returns. If an investment returns 12% one year and 7% the next year, what is the average rate of return on this investment over the two-year period? about 9%

Differentiated Instruction OL BL

Extension The word *mean* can be applied to geometry or statistics. In their own words, have the students compare and contrast the meaning of *mean* when applied to a triangle. Sample answer: The comparison is that the geometrical mean of a triangle and the statistical mean are comparing two or more numbers. The contrast is that the geometrical mean of a triangle uses different mathematical applications than the statistical mean.

Teaching Tip

Similar Triangles If students are uncertain about applying the geometric mean theorems, point out that they can write a similarity statement and a proportion of corresponding sides to find missing lengths.

MP Teaching the Mathematical Practices

Construct Arguments Mathematically proficient students understand and use stated assumptions and definitions in constructing arguments. They make conjectures and build a logical progression of statements to explore the truth of their conjectures. In Exercises 39–41, encourage students to draw diagrams of each theorem first.

Additional Answers

41. **Given:** $\angle ADC$ is a right angle. $\overline{DB}$ is an altitude of $\triangle ADC$.
Prove: $\frac{AB}{AD} = \frac{AD}{AC}$; $\frac{BC}{DC} = \frac{DC}{AC}$

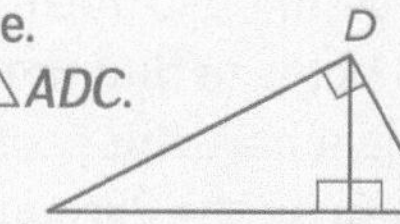

Proof:
<u>Statements (Reasons)</u>
1. $\angle ADC$ is a right angle. $\overline{DB}$ is an altitude of $\triangle ADC$ (Given)
2. $\triangle ADC$ is a right triangle. (Definition of right triangle)
3. $\triangle ABD \sim \triangle ADC$; $\triangle DBC \sim \triangle ADC$ (If the altitude is drawn from the vertex of the rt. ∠ to the hypotenuse of a rt. △, then the 2 △s formed are similar to the given △ and to each other.)
4. $\frac{AB}{AD} = \frac{AD}{AC}$; $\frac{BC}{DC} = \frac{DC}{AC}$ (Definition of similar triangles)

42a. 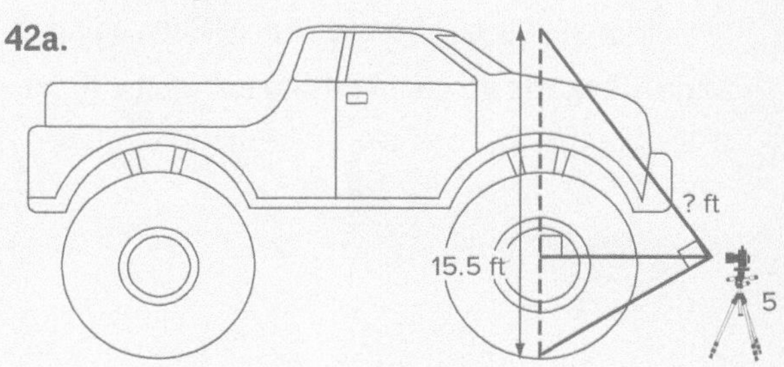

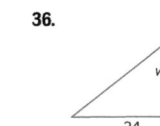

Watch Out!

Error Analysis Students should remember that proportions should compare similar parts of different triangles. In Exercise 49, Aiden uses segment lengths from only the smaller triangle.

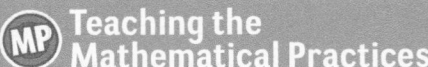

Teaching the Mathematical Practices

Reasoning Mathematically proficient students make sense of quantities and their relationships in problem situations. In Exercise 52, encourage students to review the definition of *orthocenter*.

Assess

Crystal Ball Have students describe how to find the geometric mean between numbers and how this helps to find the altitude of a triangle. Then explain how this process may connect to the next lesson on the Pythagorean Theorem.

Additional Answers

44. Using the Geometric Mean (Leg) Theorem, $a = \sqrt{yc}$ and $b = \sqrt{xc}$. Squaring both values, $a^2 = yc$ and $b^2 = xc$. The sum of the squares is $a^2 + b^2 = yc + xc$. Factoring the c on the right side of the equation, $a^2 + b^2 = c(y + x)$. By the Segment Addition Postulate, $c = y + x$. Substituting, $a^2 + b^2 = c(c)$ or $a^2 + b^2 = c^2$.

45. Never; Sample answer: The geometric mean of two consecutive integers is $\sqrt{x(x+1)}$, and the average of two consecutive integers is $\frac{x + (x+1)}{2}$. If you set the two expressions equal to each other, the equation has no solution.

Go Online!

eSolutions Manual

Create worksheets, answer keys, and solutions handouts for your assignments.

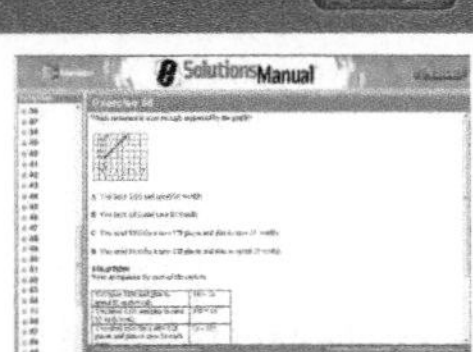

---

44. **PROOF** Derive the Pythagorean Theorem using the figure at the right and the Geometric Mean (Leg) Theorem. **See margin.**

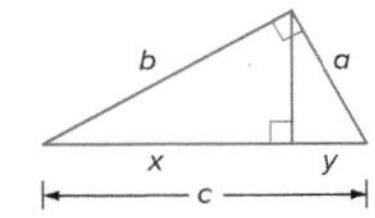

46. Always; sample answer: Since $\sqrt{ab}$ is equal to $\sqrt{a} \cdot \sqrt{b}$, the geometric mean for two perfect squares will always be the product of two positive integers, which is a positive integer.

47. Sometimes; sample answer: When the product of the two integers is a perfect square, the geometric mean will be a positive integer.

Determine whether each statement is *always*, *sometimes*, or *never* true. Explain your reasoning.

45. The geometric mean for consecutive positive integers is the mean of the two numbers. **See margin.**

46. The geometric mean for two perfect squares is a positive integer.

47. The geometric mean for two positive integers is another integer.

48. **MULTIPLE REPRESENTATIONS** In this problem, you will investigate geometric mean.

a. **Tabular** Copy and complete the table of five ordered pairs (x, y) such that $\sqrt{xy} = 8$.

x	y	$\sqrt{xy}$
2	32	8
4	16	8
8	8	8
16	4	8
32	2	8

b. **Graphical** Graph the ordered pairs from your table in a scatter plot.

c. **Verbal** Make a conjecture as to the type of graph that would be formed if you connected the points from your scatter plot. Do you think the graph of any set of ordered pairs that results in the same geometric mean would have the same general shape? Explain your reasoning. **b–c. See margin.**

G.SRT.4, G.SRT.5

H.O.T. Problems Use **H**igher-**O**rder **T**hinking Skills

49. Neither; sample answer: On the similar triangles created by the altitude, the leg that is x units long on the smaller triangle corresponds with the leg that is 8 units long on the larger triangle, so the correct proportion is $\frac{4}{x} = \frac{x}{8}$ and x is about 5.7.

51. Sample answer: 9 and 4, 8 and 8; In order for two whole numbers to result in a whole-number geometric mean, their product must be a perfect square.

49. **ERROR ANALYSIS** Aiden and Tia are finding the value of x in the triangle shown. Is either of them correct? Explain your reasoning.

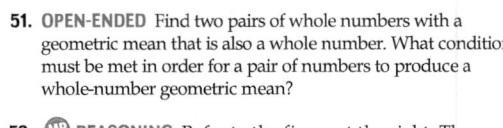

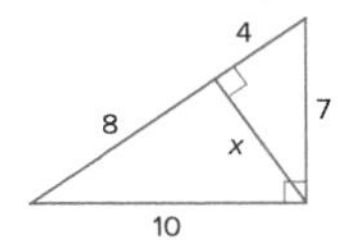

Aiden	Tia
$\frac{4}{x} = \frac{x}{7}$	$\frac{4}{x} = \frac{x}{10}$
$x \approx 5.3$	$x \approx 6.3$

50. **CHALLENGE** Refer to the figure at the right. Find x, y, and z. **$x = 5.2$, $y = 6.8$, $z = 11$**

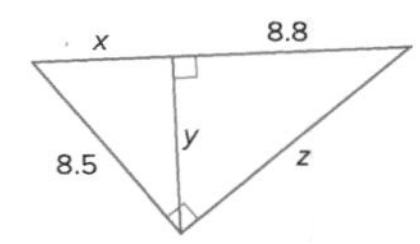

51. **OPEN-ENDED** Find two pairs of whole numbers with a geometric mean that is also a whole number. What condition must be met in order for a pair of numbers to produce a whole-number geometric mean?

52. **REASONING** Refer to the figure at the right. The orthocenter of $\triangle ABC$ is located 6.4 units from point D. Find BC. **10.0**

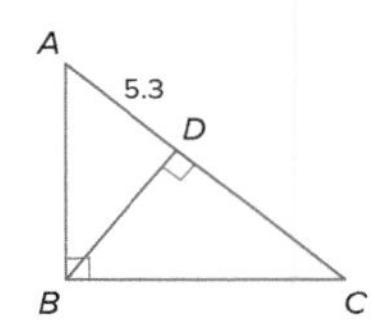

53. **WRITING IN MATH** Compare and contrast the arithmetic and geometric means of two numbers. When will the two means be equal? Justify your reasoning. **See Ch. 8 Answer Appendix.**

Standards for Mathematical Practice

Emphasis On	Exercises
1 Make sense of problems and persevere in solving them.	38, 42, 43
2 Reason abstractly and quantitatively.	50, 52
3 Construct viable arguments and critique the reasoning of others.	39–41, 44, 49, 53, 58
4 Model with mathematics.	7, 24, 25, 54, 57
7 Look for and make use of structure.	48, 51, 59

Preparing for Assessment

54. The figure shows the paths in a botanical garden.

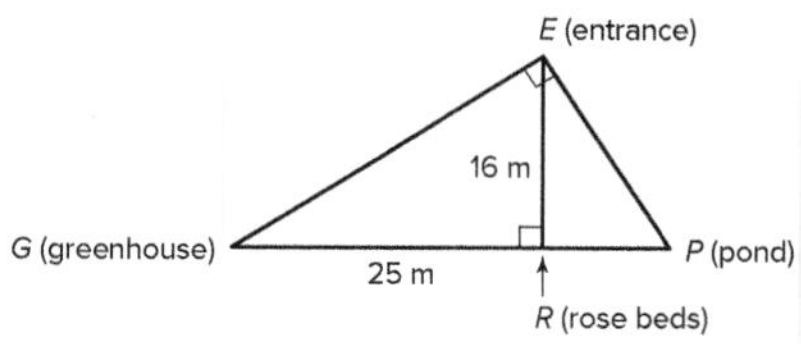

What is the distance from the greenhouse to the pond? MP 4 G.SRT.5 B

- ○ A 10.24 m
- ○ B 35.24 m
- ○ C 39.06 m
- ○ D 64.06 m

55. What is the area of $\triangle JKL$? MP 2 G.SRT.5 C

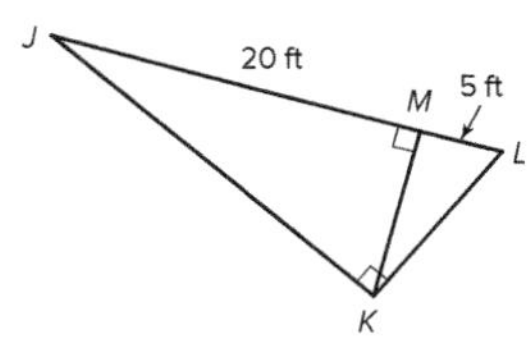

- ○ A 10 ft²
- ○ B 50 ft²
- ○ C 125 ft²
- ○ D 250 ft²

56. Which of the following is the best estimate of the length of $\overline{AB}$? MP 2 G.SRT.5 B

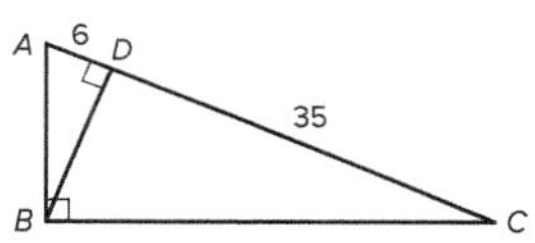

- ○ A 37.9
- ○ B 15.7
- ○ C 14.5
- ○ D 8.9

57. Zachary wants to estimate the height of a cliff. He stands 15 feet from the base of the cliff.

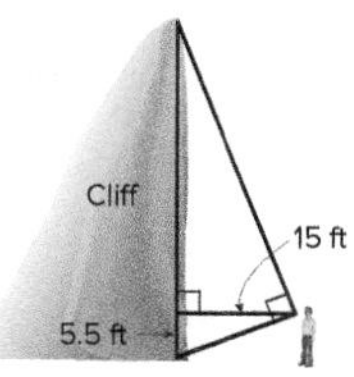

If his eye level is at 5.5 feet, which of the following is closest to the height of the cliff? MP 4 G.SRT.5 D

- ○ A 10.6 ft
- ○ B 17.5ft
- ○ C 40.9 ft
- ○ D 46.4 ft

58. In the figure, $\overline{AD}$ is perpendicular to $\overline{BC}$, and $\overline{AB}$ is perpendicular to $\overline{AC}$. What is BC? MP 3 G.SRT.4 D

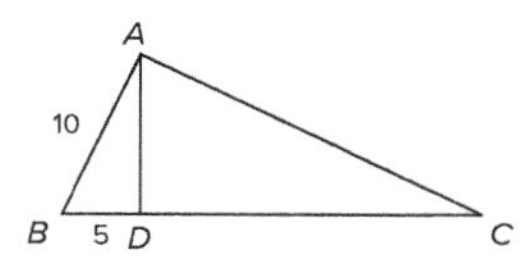

- ○ A $5\sqrt{3}$
- ○ B 15
- ○ C $10\sqrt{3}$
- ○ D 20

59. **MULTI-STEP** An altitude is drawn to the hypotenuse of a right triangle, separating the hypotenuse into two segments. The segments of the hypotenuse are in the ratio 4 : 9. MP 1, 7 G.SRT.5

a. What is the ratio of the length of the shorter segment of the hypotenuse to the length of the altitude?

2 : 3

b. Suppose the length of the altitude is 42 inches. What are the lengths of the hypotenuse segments?

28, 63

Preparing for Assessment

Exercises 54–59 require students to use the skills they will need on standardized assessments. Exercises are dual-coded with content standards and mathematical practice standards.

Dual Coding		
Items	Content Standards	MP Mathematical Practices
54	G.SRT.5	4
55	G.SRT.5	2
56	G.SRT.5	2
57	G.SRT.5	4
58	G.SRT.4	3
59	G.SRT.5	1, 7

Diagnose Student Errors

Survey student responses for each item. Class trends may indicate common errors and misconceptions.

54.

A	Found the distance from the pond to the rosebeds
B	CORRECT
C	Solved $25 = \sqrt{16x}$
D	Solved $25 = \sqrt{16x}$ and added to 25

55.

A	Found length of $\overline{MK}$
B	Calculated $\frac{1}{2}(20)(5)$
C	CORRECT
D	Omitted factor of $\frac{1}{2}$ in area formula

56.

A	Estimated length of $\overline{BC}$
B	CORRECT
C	Estimated length of $\overline{BD}$
D	Estimated length as $\sqrt{6} + \sqrt{41}$

57.

A	Calculated $\sqrt{5.5(5.5 + 15)}$
B	Calculated $\sqrt{15(15 + 5.5)}$
C	Found vertical height from eye level to top of cliff
D	CORRECT

58.

A	Found AD
B	Found DC
C	Found AC
D	CORRECT

48b.

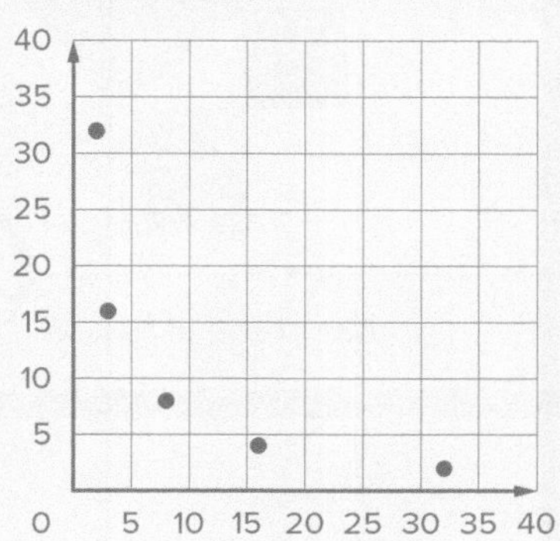

48c. hyperbola; yes; As x increases, y decreases, and as x decreases, y increases.

Go Online!

Quizzes

Students can use *Self-Check Quizzes* to check their understanding of this lesson and have the results sent to you. You can also give *Quiz 1*, which covers the content in Lessons 8-1 and 8-2.

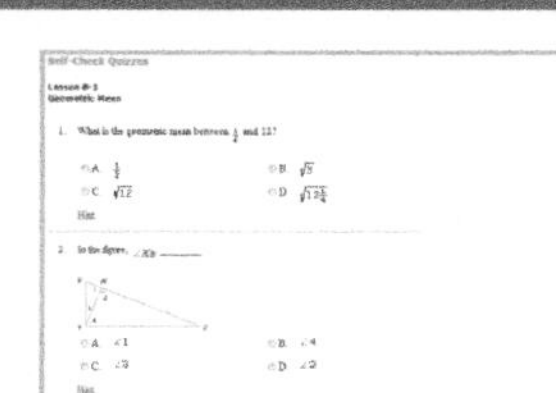

LESSON 8-2

The Pythagorean Theorem and Its Converse

SUGGESTED PACING (DAYS)

	Explore	Instruction	Extend
90 min.	.25	0.5	.25
45 min.	0.5	1.5	1

Track Your Progress

Objectives

1. Use the Pythagorean Theorem.
2. Use the Converse of the Pythagorean Theorem.

Mathematical Background

In a right triangle, the sum of the measures of the legs squared equals the square of the measure of the hypotenuse. A Pythagorean triple is a group of three whole numbers that satisfy the equation $a^2 + b^2 = c^2$.

Skills Trace

THEN

G.SRT.4 Prove theorems about triangles.

G.SRT.5 Use congruence and similarity criteria for triangles to solve problems and to prove relationships in geometric figures.

NOW

G.SRT.8 Use trigonometric ratios and the Pythagorean Theorem to solve right triangles in applied problems.

G.MG.3 Apply geometric methods to solve design problems.

NEXT

G.SRT.11 Understand and apply the Law of Sines and the Law of Cosines to find unknown measurements in right and non-right triangles.

Go Online! All of these resources and more are available at connectED.mcgraw-hill.com

Use a **Self-Check Quiz** to assess students' understanding of the Pythagorean Theorem and its converse.

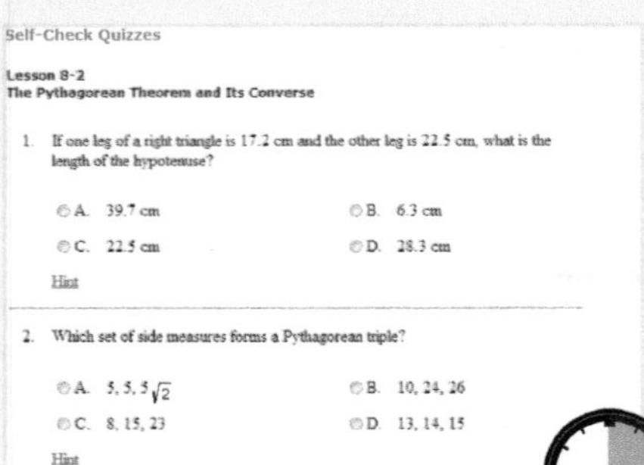

Use at End of Lesson

Personal Tutors (for every example) let students hear real teachers solve problems. Students can pause and repeat as many times as necessary.

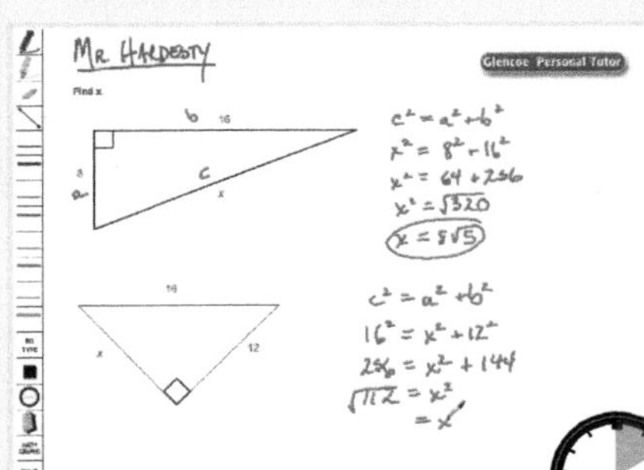

Use with Examples

Use **The Geometer's Sketchpad** to provide a way to use squares and their areas to investigate the Pythagorean Theorem.

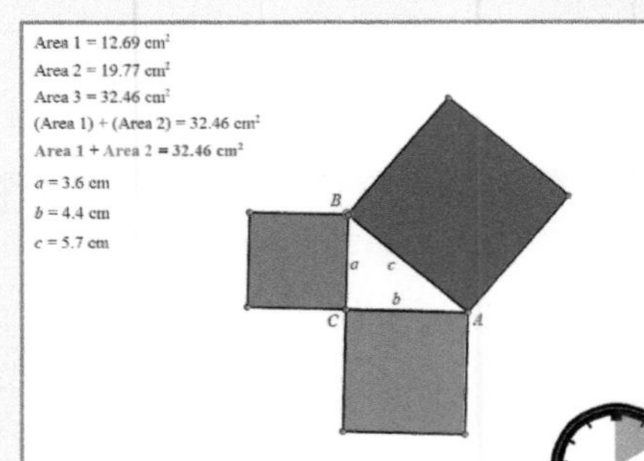

Use at End of Lesson

OER Using Open Educational Resources

Interactive Activity Have students use the **Pythagorean Relationships** activity on **Buzz Math** to review the Pythagorean Theorem and related concepts. *Use as review before assessment*

Go Online!

connectED.mcgraw-hill.com

Worksheets

Differentiate Your Resources

Extra Practice Additional practice or homework; Skills Practice is best for approaching-level students and Practice is best for on-level and beyond-level students

Skills Practice

AL OL ELL

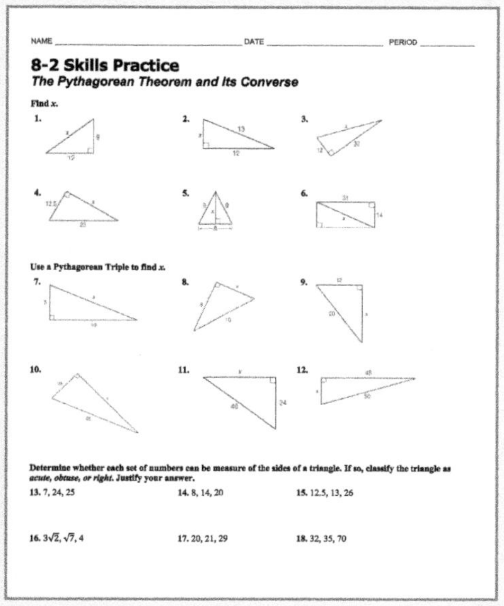
NAME ______ DATE ______ PERIOD ______

8-2 Skills Practice

The Pythagorean Theorem and Its Converse

Find *x*.

Use a Pythagorean Triple to find *x*.

Determine whether each set of numbers can be measure of the sides of a triangle. If so, classify the triangle as *acute*, *obtuse*, or *right*. Justify your answer.

Practice

AL OL BL ELL

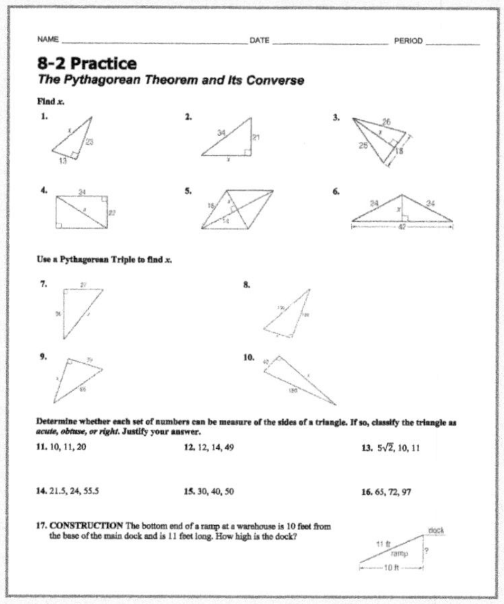
NAME ______ DATE ______ PERIOD ______

8-2 Practice

The Pythagorean Theorem and Its Converse

Find *x*.

Use a Pythagorean Triple to find *x*.

Determine whether each set of numbers can be measure of the sides of a triangle. If so, classify the triangle as *acute*, *obtuse*, or *right*. Justify your answer.

Word Problem Practice

AL OL BL ELL

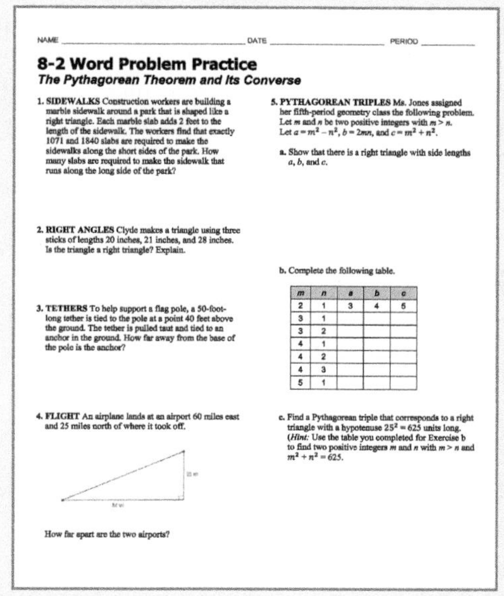
NAME ______ DATE ______ PERIOD ______

8-2 Word Problem Practice

The Pythagorean Theorem and Its Converse

How far apart are the two airports?

Intervention Reteaching and vocabulary activities that can be used with struggling or absent students and as ELL support

Study Guide and Intervention

AL OL ELL

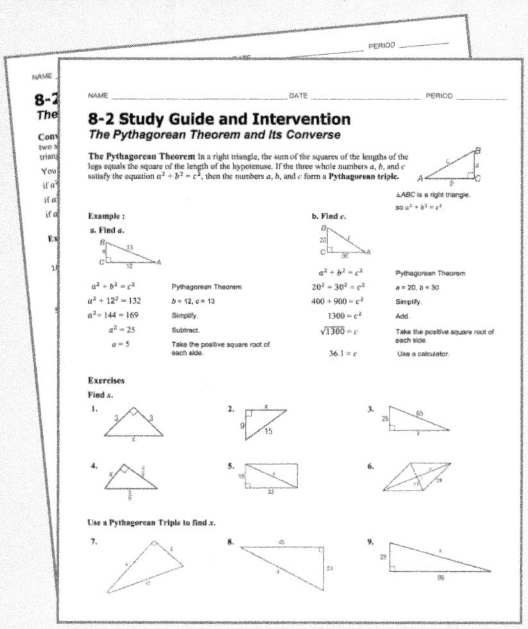
NAME ______ DATE ______ PERIOD ______

8-2 Study Guide and Intervention

The Pythagorean Theorem and Its Converse

Exercises

Use a Pythagorean Triple to find *x*.

Study Notebook

AL OL BL ELL

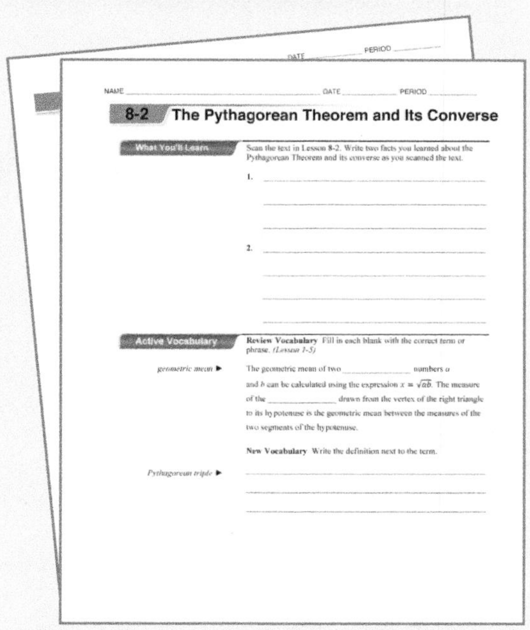
NAME ______ DATE ______ PERIOD ______

8-2 The Pythagorean Theorem and Its Converse

What You'll Learn

Active Vocabulary

Extension Activities that can be used to extend lesson concepts

Enrichment

OL BL ELL

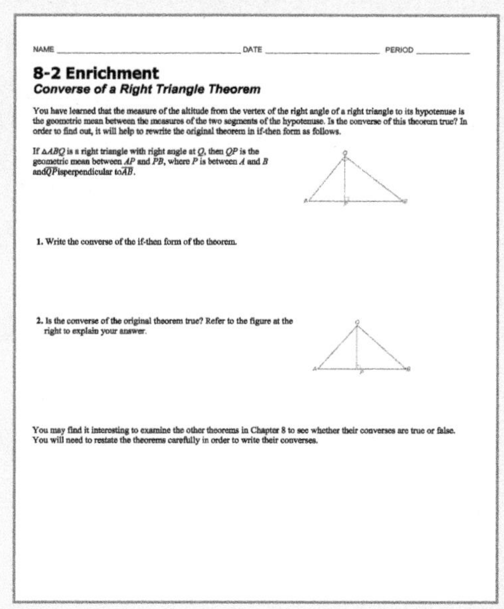
NAME ______ DATE ______ PERIOD ______

8-2 Enrichment

Converse of a Right Triangle Theorem

Launch

Objective Prove the Pythagorean Theorem by using diagrams without words.

Materials

- tracing paper
- ruler

Teaching Tip

In **Step 3**, have students use a ruler and a pencil to draw the lines that the creases make. Tell students that the key to this activity is making sure measures *a* and *b* are exactly the same on both sheets of paper. Without using a ruler, students may use one marked edge of the first paper to mark accurate lengths on the second paper.

Teach ELL

Work in Cooperative Pairs Model for the class each of the steps as they follow along.

Ask:

- How can you verify that the two pieces of paper have the same area? Sample answer: suggest that you could cut out the shaded triangles from the second piece of paper and arrange them over the shaded areas of the first piece of paper.

Practice Have students complete Exercises 1–3.

Assess

Formative Assessment

Ask students to summarize what they have learned about the Pythagorean Theorem.

From Concrete to Abstract

Have students draw a right triangle on paper and then trade with another student. Tell students to measure two of the sides, and then find the unknown side length. Ask them to check their answers by measuring the third side.

EXPLORE 8-2

Geometry Lab

Proofs Without Words

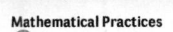

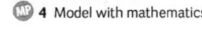

In Chapter 1, you learned that the Pythagorean Theorem relates the measures of the legs and the hypotenuse of a right triangle. You can prove the Pythagorean Theorem by using diagrams without words.

Mathematical Practices
MP 4 Model with mathematics

Content Standards
G.CO.10 Prove theorems about triangles.

Activity

Prove the Pythagorean Theorem by using paper and algebra.

Step 1

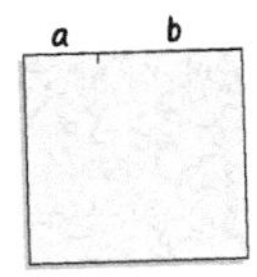

On a piece of tracing paper, mark one side *a* and *b* as shown above.

Step 2

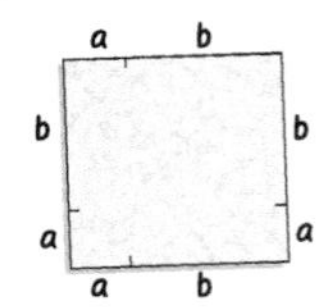

Copy these measures on each of the other sides.

Step 3

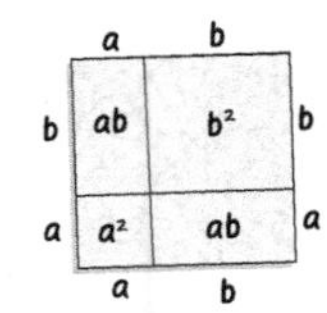

Fold the paper into four sections and label the area of each section.

Step 4

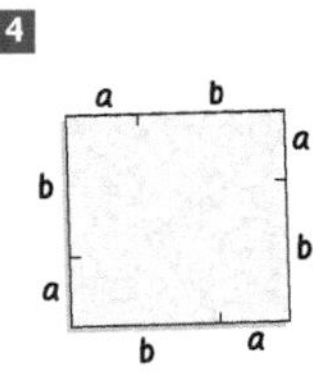

On another piece of tracing paper, mark each side *a* and *b* as shown above.

Step 5

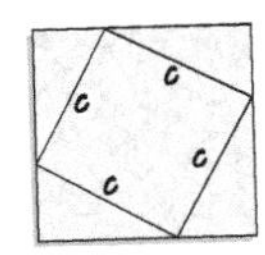

Connect the marks using a straightedge. Let *c* represent the length of each hypotenuse.

Step 6

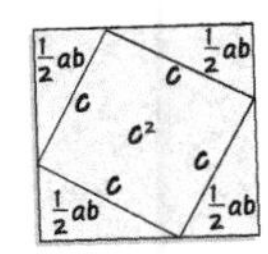

Label the area of each triangle $\frac{1}{2}ab$ and the area of each square c^2.

Step 7 Place the squares side by side and color the corresponding regions that have the same area. For example, $ab = \frac{1}{2}ab + \frac{1}{2}ab$. The parts that are not shaded tell us that $a^2 + b^2 = c^2$.

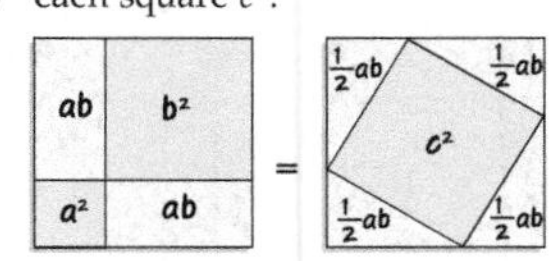

Analyze the Results Work cooperatively.

1. Use a ruler to measure *a*, *b*, and *c*. Do these measures confirm that $a^2 + b^2 = c^2$? yes
2. Repeat the activity with different *a* and *b* values. What do you notice? $a^2 + b^2 = c^2$
3. **WRITING IN MATH** Explain why the diagram at the right is an illustration of the Pythagorean Theorem. 3–4. See margin.
4. **CHALLENGE** Draw a geometric diagram to show that for any positive numbers *a* and *b*, $a + b > \sqrt{a^2 + b^2}$. Explain.

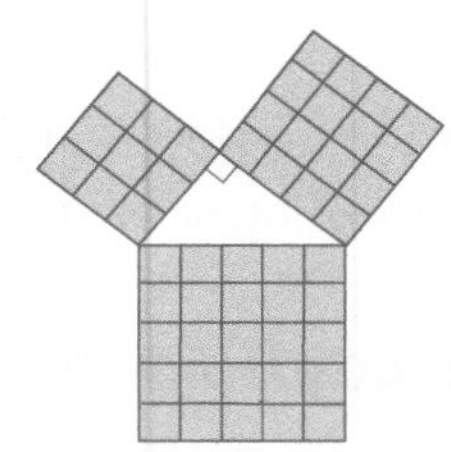

Additional Answers

3. Sample answer: The sum of the areas of the two smaller squares is equal to the area of the largest square.

4. 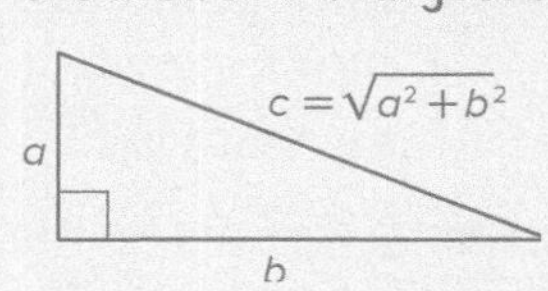

By the Triangle Inequality Theorem, $a + b > c$. Because $c = \sqrt{a^2 + b^2}$, by substitution, $a + b > \sqrt{a^2 + b^2}$.

LESSON 2

The Pythagorean Theorem and Its Converse

:: Then	:: Now	:: Why?
• You used the Pythagorean Theorem to develop the Distance Formula.	• **1** Use the Pythagorean Theorem. **2** Use the Converse of the Pythagorean Theorem.	• Tether lines are used to steady an inflatable snowman. Suppose you know the height at which the tether lines are attached to the snowman and how far away you want to anchor the tether in the ground. You can use the converse of the Pythagorean Theorem to adjust the lengths of the tethers to keep the snowman perpendicular to the ground.

New Vocabulary
Pythagorean triple

Mathematical Practices
1 Make sense of problems and persevere in solving them.
4 Model with mathematics.

Content Standards
G.SRT.8 Use trigonometric ratios and the pythagorean Theorem to solve right triangles in applied problems. ★
G.MG.3 Apply geometric methods to solve problems (e.g., designing an object or structure to satisfy physical constraints or minimize cost; working with typographic grid systems based on ratios). ★

1 The Pythagorean Theorem

The Pythagorean Theorem is perhaps one of the most famous theorems in mathematics. It relates the lengths of the hypotenuse (side opposite the right angle) and legs (sides adjacent to the right angle) of a right triangle.

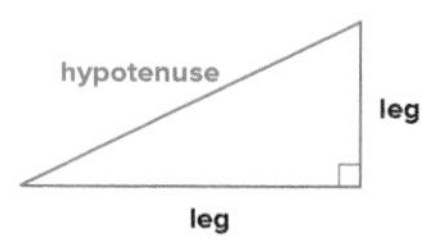

Theorem 8.4 Pythagorean Theorem

Words In a right triangle, the sum of the squares of the lengths of the legs is equal to the square of the length of the hypotenuse.

Symbols If $\triangle ABC$ is a right triangle with right angle C, then $a^2 + b^2 = c^2$.

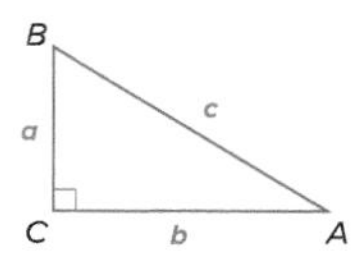

The geometric mean can be used to prove the Pythagorean Theorem.

Proof Pythagorean Theorem

Given: $\triangle ABC$ with right angle at C

Prove: $a^2 + b^2 = c^2$

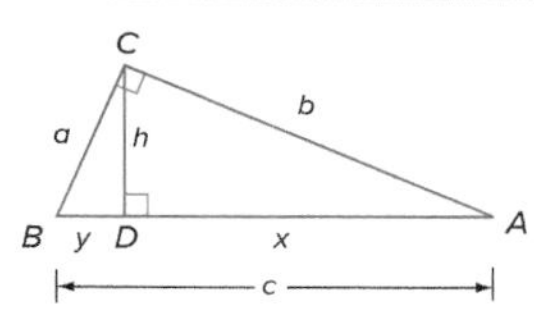

Proof:

Draw right triangle ABC so C is the right angle. Then draw the altitude from C to $\overline{AB}$. Let $AB = c$, $AC = b$, $BC = a$, $AD = x$, $DB = y$, and $CD = h$.
Two geometric means now exist.

$\frac{c}{a} = \frac{a}{y}$ and	$\frac{c}{b} = \frac{b}{x}$	Geometric Mean (Leg) Theorem
$a^2 = cy$	$b^2 = cx$	Cross products
$a^2 + b^2 = cy + cx$		Add the equations.
$a^2 + b^2 = c(y + x)$		Factor.
$a^2 + b^2 = c \cdot c$		Because $c = y + x$, substitute c for $(y + x)$.
$a^2 + b^2 = c^2$		Simplify.

MP Mathematical Practices Strategies

Make sense of problems and persevere in solving them.
Help students maintain oversight of the process of applying the Pythagorean Theorem, its converse, and the various Pythagorean inequalities. For example, ask:

- How can you verify the relationships between the altitude drawn from the right angle to the hypotenuse of a triangle and each segment of the hypotenuse? Because all of the triangles are similar, you can set up proportions relating similar segments, including the altitude and each segment of the hypotenuse. The proportions will verify that the altitude is the geometric mean of the segments of the hypotenuse.
- How can you determine whether a set of three numbers is a Pythagorean Triple? Sample answer: Let c equal the largest of the three numbers. Then, substitute the numbers into the Pythagorean Theorem and simplify to show that $a^2 + b^2 = c^2$.

Launch

Ask:

- What are tether lines used for? to steady a large object such as an inflatable snowman
- What type of triangle is formed by the snowman, the tether, and the ground? a right triangle
- What measurements do you need to find the length of the tether? the height at which it is attached to the snowman and the placement of the anchor

Go Online!

Interactive Whiteboard
Use the *eLesson*, *Lesson Presentation*, or *Interactive Classroom* to present this lesson.

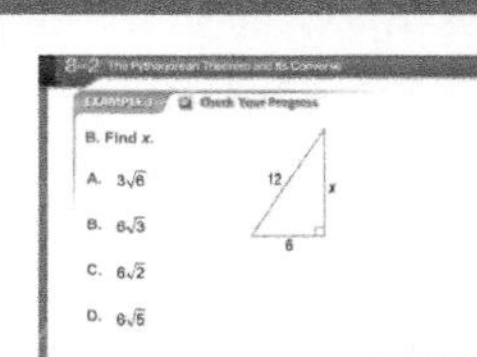

Teach

Ask the scaffolded questions for each example to build conceptual understanding for students at all levels.

1 The Pythagorean Theorem

Example 1 Find Missing Measures Using the Pythagorean Theorem

AL Which side of a right triangle is represented by the letter *c* in the Pythagorean Theorem? the hypotenuse

OL If the legs of a right triangle measure 8 and 15, what is the length of the hypotenuse? 17

BL If the hypotenuse of an isosceles right triangle measures 8 units, what are the lengths of the legs? $4\sqrt{2}$

Need Another Example?

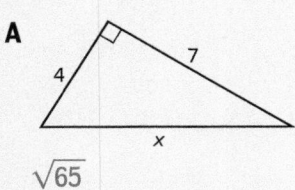

Find *x*.

A

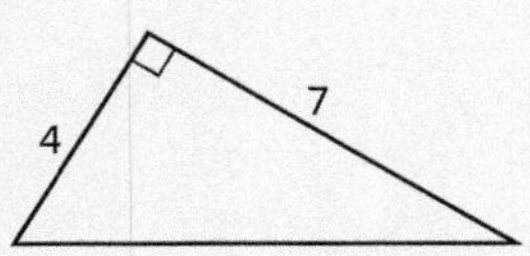

$\sqrt{65}$

B

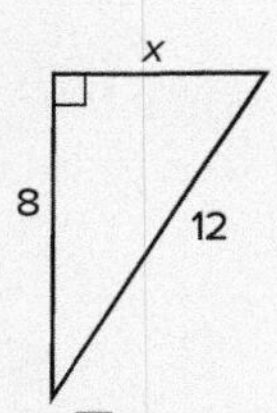

$4\sqrt{5}$

Watch Out!

Side Lengths Pythagorean Triples are not the only possible side lengths for a right triangle; they give the triangles where all the lengths are whole numbers, but the side lengths could be any real numbers.

You can use the Pythagorean Theorem to find the measure of any side of a right triangle given the lengths of the other two sides.

G.SRT.8

Example 1 Find Missing Measures Using the Pythagorean Theorem

Find x.

a.

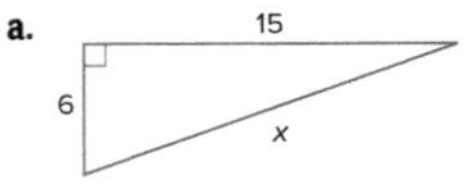

The side opposite the right angle is the hypotenuse, so $c = x$.

$a^2 + b^2 = c^2$ Pythagorean Theorem

$6^2 + 15^2 = x^2$ $a = 6$ and $b = 15$

$261 = x^2$ Simplify.

$\sqrt{261} = x$ Take the positive square root of each side.

$3\sqrt{29} = x$ Simplify.

Study Tip

Positive Square Root When finding the length of a side using the Pythagorean Theorem, use only the positive and not the negative square root, since length cannot be negative.

b.

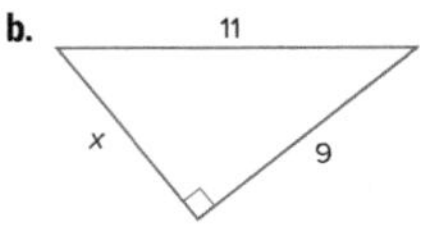

The hypotenuse is 11, so $c = 11$.

$a^2 + b^2 = c^2$ Pythagorean Theorem

$x^2 + 9^2 = 11^2$ $a = x$ and $b = 9$

$x^2 + 81 = 121$ Simplify.

$x^2 = 40$ Subtract 81 from each side.

$x = \sqrt{40}$ or $2\sqrt{10}$ Take the positive square root of each side and simplify.

Guided Practice

1A.

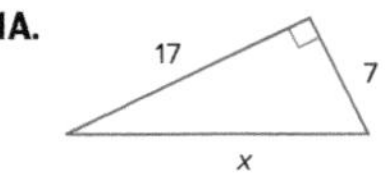

$13\sqrt{2}$

1B.

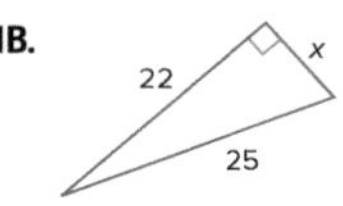

$\sqrt{141}$

A **Pythagorean triple** is a set of three nonzero whole numbers a, b, and c, such that $a^2 + b^2 = c^2$. One common Pythagorean triple is 3, 4, 5; that is, the sides of a right triangle are in the ratio 3:4:5. The most common Pythagorean triples are shown below in the first row. The triples below these are found by multiplying each number in the triple by the same factor.

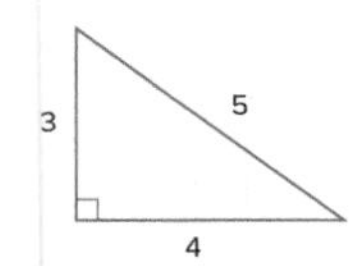

Study Tip

Pythagorean Triples If the measures of the sides of any right triangle are not whole numbers, the measures do not form a Pythagorean triple.

Key Concept Common Pythagorean Triples

3, 4, 5	5, 12, 13	8, 15, 17	7, 24, 25
6, 8, 10	10, 24, 26	16, 30, 34	14, 48, 50
9, 12, 15	15, 36, 39	24, 45, 51	21, 72, 75
$3x, 4x, 5x$	$5x, 12x, 13x$	$8x, 15x, 17x$	$7x, 24x, 25x$

The largest number in each triple is the length of the hypotenuse.

G.SRT.8

Example 2 Use a Pythagorean Triple

Use a Pythagorean triple to find x. Explain your reasoning.

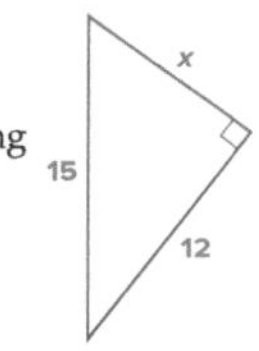

Notice that 15 and 12 are both multiples of 3, because $15 = 3 \cdot 5$ and $12 = 3 \cdot 4$. Because 3, 4, 5 is a Pythagorean triple, the missing leg length x is $3 \cdot 3$ or 9.

CHECK $12^2 + 9^2 \stackrel{?}{=} 15^2$ Pythagorean Theorem

$225 = 225$ ✓ Simplify.

Guided Practice

2A.

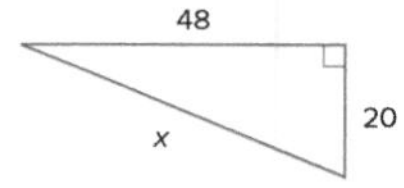

2B.

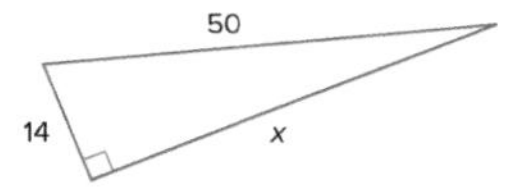

Reading Math

3-4-5 A right triangle with side lengths 3, 4, and 5 is called a *3-4-5 right triangle.*

2A. 52; $20 = 4 \cdot 5$ and $48 = 4 \cdot 12$. Because 5, 12, 13 is a Pythagorean triple, $x = 4 \cdot 13$ or 52.
2B. 48; $50 = 2 \cdot 25$ and $14 = 2 \cdot 7$. Because 7, 24, 25 is a Pythagorean triple, $x = 2 \cdot 24$ or 48.

The Pythagorean Theorem can be used to solve many real-world problems.

G.SRT.8

Example 3 Use the Pythagorean Theorem

Damon is locked out of his house. The only open window is on the second floor, which is 12 feet above the ground. He needs to borrow a ladder from his neighbor. If he must place the ladder 5 feet from the house to avoid some bushes, what length of ladder does Damon need?

A 7 feet **C** 13 feet

B 11 feet **D** 17 feet

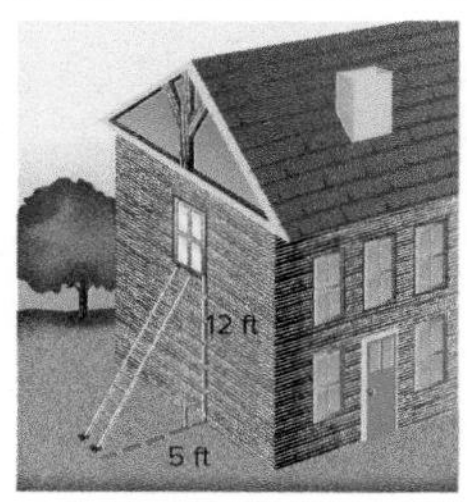

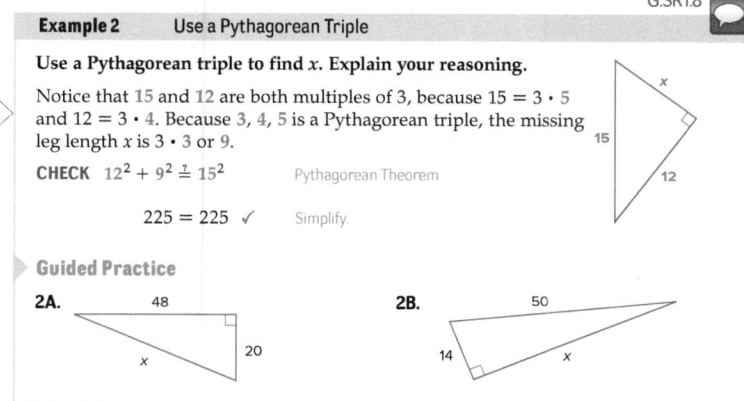

Note: Not drawn to scale.

Read the Item

The distance the ladder is from the house, the height the ladder reaches, and the length of the ladder itself make up the lengths of the sides of a right triangle. You need to find the length of the ladder, which is the hypotenuse.

Solve the Item

Method 1 Use a Pythagorean triple.

The lengths of the legs are 5 and 12. 5, 12, 13 is a Pythagorean triple, so the length of the ladder is 13 feet.

Method 2 Use the Pythagorean Theorem.

Let x represent the length of the ladder.

$5^2 + 12^2 = x^2$ Pythagorean Theorem

$169 = x^2$ Simplify.

$\sqrt{169} = x$ Take the positive square root of each side.

$13 = x$ Simplify.

So, the answer is choice C.

Study Tip

MP Sense-Making Because the hypotenuse of a right triangle is always the longest side, the length of the ladder in Example 3 must be greater than 5 or 12 feet. Because 7 and 11 feet are both less than 12 feet, choices A and B can be eliminated.

Differentiated Instruction AL OL

Visual/Spatial Learners Explain that many artists use right triangles in their works because they are so appealing to the eye. Right triangles can serve as guidelines to draw mountains in the background or to create vanishing points and perspective. Ask the students to construct one or more right triangles on a blank sheet of paper, find the lengths of the sides and then try to compose a picture using the triangles in an image or as a guide for an image. Examples could be a picture of a road vanishing in the distance or a house with right triangles as part of its roof.

Example 2 Use a Pythagorean Triple

AL What is a Pythagorean Triple? a set of three whole numbers that, when used as measures of the sides of a triangle, form a right triangle

OL If the hypotenuse of a right triangle measures 30 and a given leg measures 24, what is the measure of the other leg? 18

BL If the legs of a right triangle measure 24 and 45, what is the length of the hypotenuse? 51

Need Another Example?

Use a Pythagorean triple to find x. Explain your reasoning.

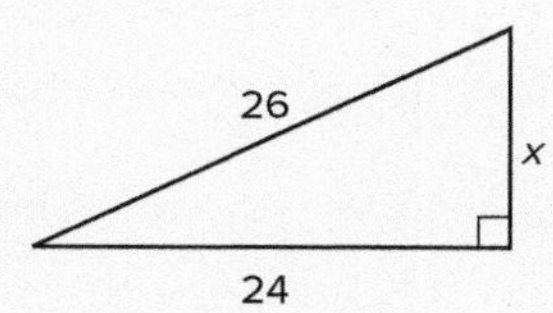

10; Because 24 and 26 are multiples of 2, $24 = 2 \cdot 12$ and $26 = 2 \cdot 13$. The missing leg is $2 \cdot 5 = 10$.

Example 3 Use the Pythagorean Theorem

AL How do we know that the ladder, the house, and the ground form a right triangle? Sample answer: Because the side of the house is perpendicular to the ground.

OL If Damon borrows a 15-foot ladder, how far from the house would he need to place the base in order for the top of the ladder to be at the window? 9 ft

BL Damon uses a 25-foot ladder placed 15 feet from the base of a house to reach a window. How tall is the base of the window? 20 ft

Need Another Example?

A 20-foot ladder is placed against a building to reach a window that is 16 feet above the ground. How many feet away from the building is the bottom of the ladder? C

A 3 **C** 12

B 4 **D** 15

MP Teaching the Mathematical Practices

Sense-Making Mathematically proficient students start by explaining the meaning of a problem to themselves and looking for entry points to its solution. Encourage students to analyze the answer choices and eliminate any unreasonable choices.

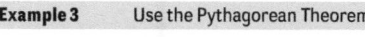

Go Online!

The Pythagorean Theorem and its converse are widely used in problems arising in everyday life, society, and the workplace. Ask your teacher a questions about it by sending a message in ConnectED. ELL

Guided Practice

3. The distance from the base of a ladder to a wall that it leans against should be at least one fourth of the ladder's total length. What is the maximum distance x up the wall that a 20-foot ladder will reach, to the nearest tenth? **B**

A 12 feet C 20.6 feet

B 19.4 feet D 30.6 feet

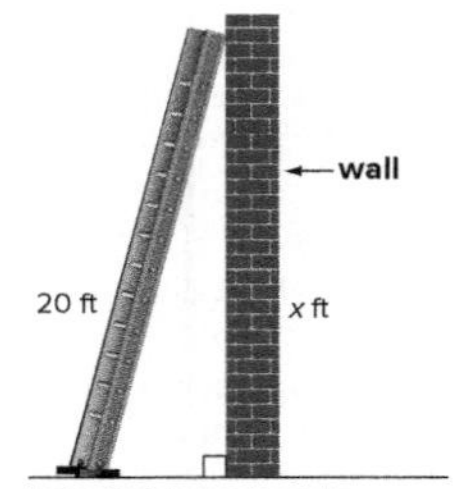

Note: Not drawn to scale.

2 Converse of the Pythagorean Theorem

The converse of the Pythagorean Theorem also holds. You can use this theorem to help you determine whether a triangle is a right triangle given the measures of all three sides.

Theorem 8.5 Converse of the Pythagorean Theorem

Words If the sum of the squares of the lengths of the shortest sides of a triangle is equal to the square of the length of the longest side, then the triangle is a right triangle.

Symbols If $a^2 + b^2 = c^2$, then $\triangle ABC$ is a right triangle.

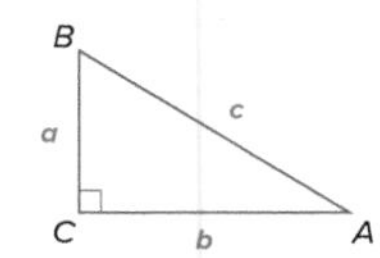

You will prove Theorem 8.5 in Exercise 35.

Study Tip ELL

Determining the Longest Side If the measures of any of the sides of a triangle are expressed as radicals, you may wish to use a calculator to determine which length is the longest.

You can also use side lengths to classify a triangle as acute or obtuse.

Theorem Pythagorean Inequality Theorems

8.6 If the square of the length of the longest side of a triangle is less than the sum of the squares of the lengths of the other two sides, then the triangle is an acute triangle.

Symbols If $c^2 < a^2 + b^2$, then $\triangle ABC$ is acute.

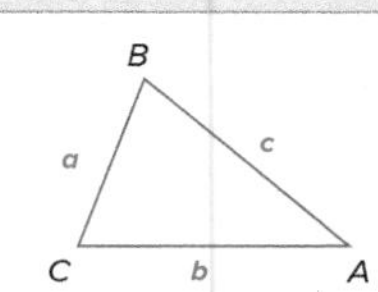

8.7 If the square of the length of the longest side of a triangle is greater than the sum of the squares of the lengths of the other two sides, then the triangle is an obtuse triangle.

Symbols If $c^2 > a^2 + b^2$, then $\triangle ABC$ is obtuse.

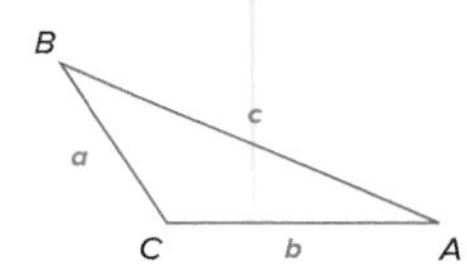

You will prove Theorems 8.6 and 8.7 in Exercises 36 and 37, respectively.

Differentiated Instruction ELL

Beginning Read the lesson opener aloud one sentence at a time. At the end of each sentence, ask students to say a word or phrase that describes important information from the sentence. Model recording information to prepare for solving the problem. Have students use your model to record information in their notes.

Intermediate Slowly read the lesson opener aloud. After each sentence or two, ask volunteers to identify the important information. Have students take notes.

Advanced Tell students to listen without taking notes while you read aloud. Then have them write down what they remember from your reading. Have them work in groups to compare notes and to discuss the problem and its solution.

Advanced High Have students practice active listening as you read aloud by taking notes. Then have students work in pairs to summarize the information and solve the problem. Have pairs share with the class.

G.SRT.8

Example 4 Classify Triangles

Determine whether each set of numbers can be the measures of the sides of a triangle. If so, classify the triangle as *acute*, *right*, or *obtuse*. Justify your answer.

a. 7, 14, 16

Step 1 Determine whether the measures can form a triangle using the Triangle Inequality Theorem.

$7 + 14 > 16$ ✓ $14 + 16 > 7$ ✓ $7 + 16 > 14$ ✓

The side lengths 7, 14, and 16 can form a triangle.

Step 2 Classify the triangle by comparing the square of the longest side to the sum of the squares of the other two sides.

$c^2 \stackrel{?}{=} a^2 + b^2$ Compare c^2 and $a^2 + b^2$.

$16^2 \stackrel{?}{=} 7^2 + 14^2$ Substitution

$256 > 245$ Simplify and compare.

Because $c^2 > a^2 + b^2$, the triangle is obtuse.

b. 9, 40, 41

Step 1 Determine whether the measures can form a triangle.

$9 + 40 > 41$ ✓ $40 + 41 > 9$ ✓ $9 + 41 > 40$ ✓

The side lengths 9, 40, and 41 can form a triangle.

Step 2 Classify the triangle.

$c^2 \stackrel{?}{=} a^2 + b^2$ Compare c^2 and $a^2 + b^2$.

$41^2 \stackrel{?}{=} 9^2 + 40^2$ Substitution

$1681 = 1681$ Simplify and compare.

Because $c^2 = a^2 + b^2$, the triangle is a right triangle.

Guided Practice

4A. 11, 60, 61 **4B.** $2\sqrt{3}, 4\sqrt{2}, 3\sqrt{5}$ **4C.** 6.2, 13.8, 20

Review Vocabulary

Triangle Inequality Theorem The sum of the lengths of any two sides of a triangle must be greater than the length of the third side.

4A. Yes; because $11 + 60 > 61$, $60 + 61 > 11$, and $11 + 61 > 60$; right, because $11^2 + 60^2 = 61^2$.

4B. Yes; because $2\sqrt{3} + 4\sqrt{2} > 3\sqrt{5}$, $2\sqrt{3} + 3\sqrt{5} > 4\sqrt{2}$, and $4\sqrt{2} + 3\sqrt{5} > 2\sqrt{3}$. Obtuse, because $(3\sqrt{5})^2 > (2\sqrt{3})^2 + (4\sqrt{2})^2$.

4C. No; because $6.2 + 13.8 \not> 20$, the side lengths cannot form a triangle.

Go Online! for a Self-Check Quiz

Check Your Understanding

○ = Step-by-Step Solutions begin on page R13.

Example 1 G.SRT.8

Find x.

1. 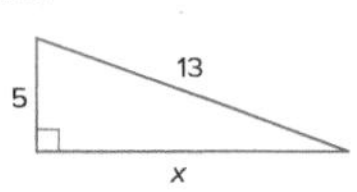

12

2. 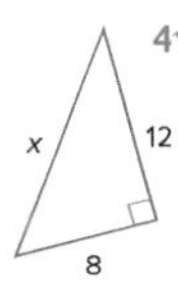

$4\sqrt{13} \approx 14.4$

3. 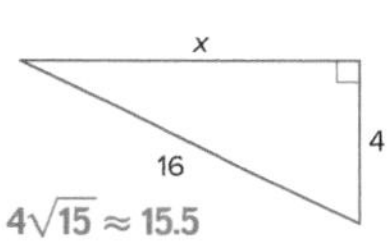

$4\sqrt{15} \approx 15.5$

Example 2 G.SRT.8

4. Use a Pythagorean triple to find x. Explain your reasoning.

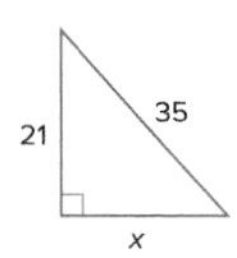

28; Because $35 = 7 \cdot 5$ and $21 = 7 \cdot 3$ and 3-4-5 is a Pythagorean triple, $x = 7 \cdot 4$ or 28.

2 Converse of the Pythagorean Theorem

Example 4 Classify Triangles

AL What is the definition of an acute triangle? an obtuse triangle? a triangle with three acute angles; a triangle with one obtuse and two acute angles

OL What is the largest whole number x such that 7, 14, x will create an acute triangle? 15

BL Give an example of three side lengths of a triangle that will form an acute triangle. Sample answer: 4, 5, 6

Need Another Example?

Determine whether each set of numbers can be the measures of the sides of a triangle. If so, classify the triangle as *acute*, *right*, or *obtuse*. Justify your answer.

a. 9, 12, and 15 The segments form the sides of a right triangle, because the measures form a Pythagorean triple.

b. 10, 11, and 13 The segments form the sides of an acute triangle because $13^2 < 10^2 + 11^2$.

Differentiated Instruction OL BL

Extension A baseball diamond is a square with 90-foot sides. What is the approximate distance the catcher must throw from home to second base? 127.3 ft

Go Online! eBook

Interactive Student Guide

Use the *Interactive Student Guide* to deepen conceptual understanding.

· The Pythagorean Theorem

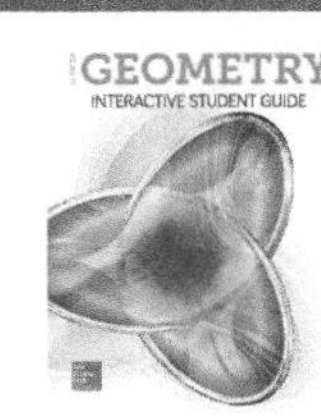

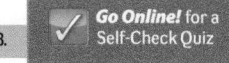

Practice

Formative Assessment Use Exercises 1–8 to assess students' understanding of the concepts in this lesson.

The Practice and Problem Solving exercises assess the content taught in the lesson. The Preparing for Assessment page is meant to be used as preparation for end-of-course assessments.

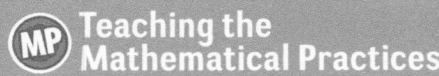

MP Teaching the Mathematical Practices

Perseverance Mathematically proficient students check their answers to problems using a different method, and they continually ask themselves, "does this make sense?" In Exercises 15–18, encourage students to check their work.

Additional Answers

6. yes; right
$39^2 \stackrel{?}{=} 15^2 + 36^2$
$1521 = 225 + 1296$

7. yes; obtuse
$26^2 \stackrel{?}{=} 16^2 + 18^2$
$676 > 256 + 324$

8. yes; acute
$24^2 \stackrel{?}{=} 15^2 + 20^2$
$576 < 225 + 400$

21. **yes; obtuse**
$21^2 \stackrel{?}{=} 7^2 + 15^2$
$441 > 49 + 225$

22. no; $23 > 10 + 12$

23. yes; right
$20.5^2 \stackrel{?}{=} 4.5^2 + 20^2$
$420.25 = 20.25 + 400$

24. no; $91 > 44 + 46$

25. yes; acute
$7.6^2 \stackrel{?}{=} 4.2^2 + 6.4^2$
$57.76 < 17.64 + 40.96$

26. yes; obtuse
$14^2 \stackrel{?}{=} 4^2 + 12^2$
$196 > 16 + 144$

30. **right;** $XY = \sqrt{8}$, $YZ = \sqrt{2}$, $XZ = \sqrt{10}$

31. acute; $XY = \sqrt{29}$, $YZ = \sqrt{20}$, $XZ = \sqrt{13}$;
$(\sqrt{29})^2 < (\sqrt{20})^2 + (\sqrt{13})^2$

32. obtuse; $XY = 5$, $YZ = 2$, $XZ = \sqrt{41}$;
$(\sqrt{41})^2 > 5^2 + 2^2$

33. right; $XY = 6$, $YZ = 10$, $XZ = 8$; $6^2 + 8^2 = 10^2$

Example 3 G.MG.3

5. **MULTIPLE CHOICE** The mainsail of a boat is shown. What is the length, in feet, of $\overline{LN}$? D

A 52.5 C 72.5
B 65 D 75

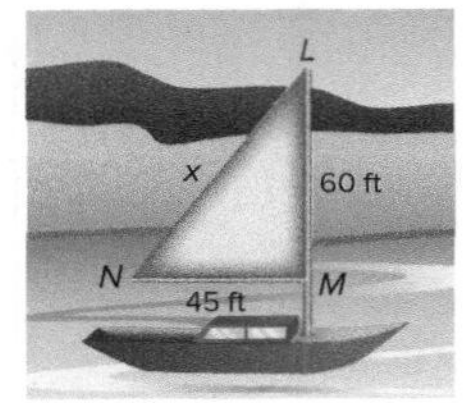

Example 4 G.SRT.8

Determine whether each set of numbers can be the measures of the sides of a triangle. If so, classify the triangle as *acute*, *obtuse*, or *right*. Justify your answer.

6. 15, 36, 39
7. 16, 18, 26
8. 15, 20, 24

6–8. See margin.

Practice and Problem Solving

Extra Practice is on page R8.

Example 1 G.SRT.8

Find x.

9. 20

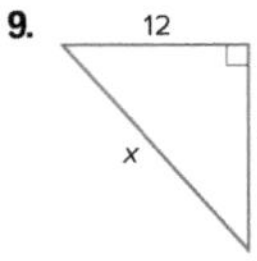

10. 12

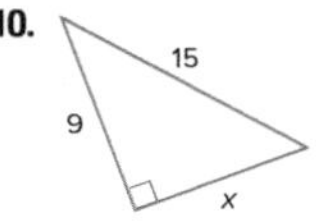

11. $\sqrt{21} \approx 4.6$

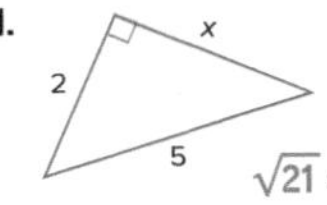

12. $33\sqrt{3} \approx 57.2$

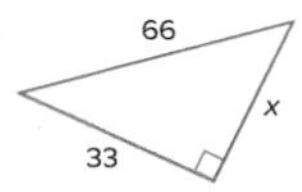

13. $\frac{\sqrt{10}}{5} \approx 0.6$

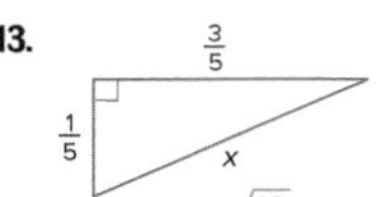

14. $\frac{4\sqrt{3}}{9} \approx 0.8$

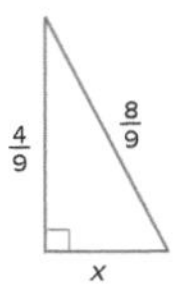

Example 2 G.SRT.8

MP **PERSEVERANCE** Use a Pythagorean Triple to find x.

15. 34

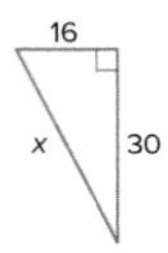

16. 50

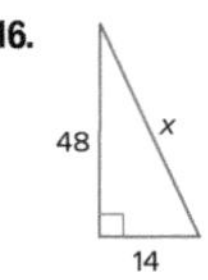

17. 70

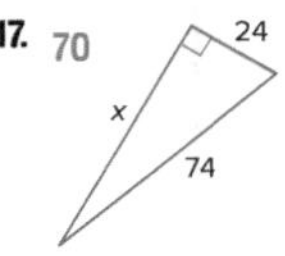

18. 30

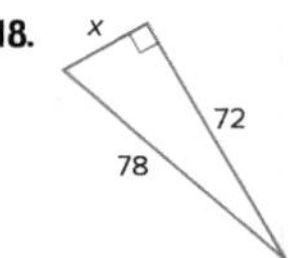

Example 3 G.MG.3

19. **BASKETBALL** The support for a basketball goal forms a right triangle as shown. What is the length x of the horizontal portion of the support? about 3 ft

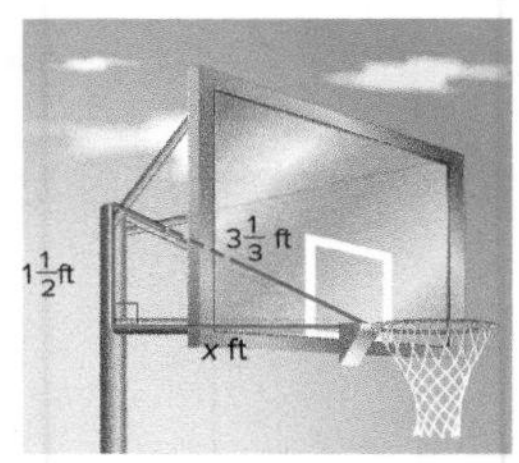

20. **DRIVING** The street that Khaliah usually uses to get to school is under construction. She has been taking the detour shown. If the construction starts at the point where Khaliah leaves her normal route and ends at the point where she reenters her normal route, about how long is the stretch of road under construction? about 2 mi

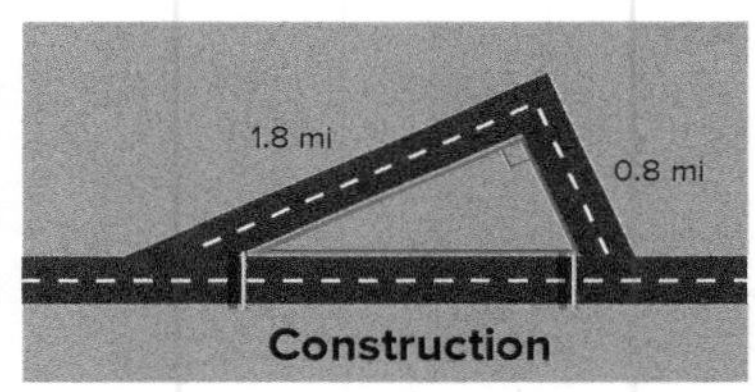

Differentiated Homework Options

Levels	AL Basic	OL Core	BL Advanced
Exercises	9–26, 50–59	9–33 odd, 34, 35–41 odd, 42–45, 47, 48, 50–58	35–52, (optional: 53–59)
2-Day Option	9–25 odd, 53–59	9–26	
	10–26 even, 50–52	27–48, 50–58	

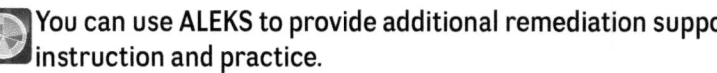

You can use ALEKS to provide additional remediation support with personalized instruction and practice.

Example 4 G.SRT.8 **Determine whether each set of numbers can be the measures of the sides of a triangle. If so, classify the triangle as *acute*, *obtuse*, or *right*. Justify your answer.** 21–26. See margin.

21. 7, 15, 21 **22.** 10, 12, 23 **23.** 4.5, 20, 20.5

24. 44, 46, 91 **25.** 4.2, 6.4, 7.6 **26.** 4, 12, 14

B **Find *x*.**

27.

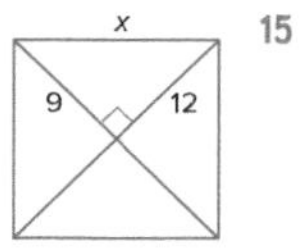

28.

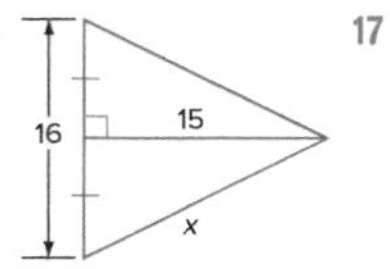

29.

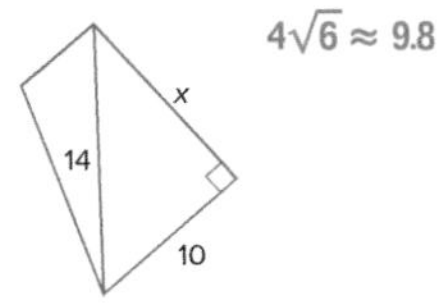

COORDINATE GEOMETRY Determine whether $\triangle XYZ$ is an *acute*, *right*, or *obtuse* triangle for the given vertices. Explain. 30–33. See margin.

30. $X(-3, -2)$, $Y(-1, 0)$, $Z(0, -1)$ **31.** $X(-7, -3)$, $Y(-2, -5)$, $Z(-4, -1)$

32. $X(1, 2)$, $Y(4, 6)$, $Z(6, 6)$ **33.** $X(3, 1)$, $Y(3, 7)$, $Z(11, 1)$

34. **JOGGING** Brett jogs in the park three times a week. Usually, he takes a $\frac{3}{4}$-mile path that cuts through the park. Today, the path is closed, so he is taking the orange route shown. How much farther will he jog on his alternate route than he would have if he had followed his normal path? 0.3 mi

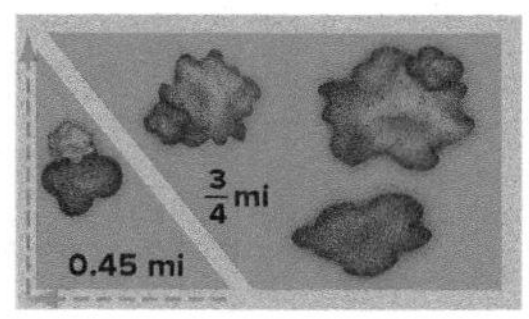

C **35.** **PROOF** Write a paragraph proof of Theorem 8.5. 35–36. See margin.

PROOF Write a two-column proof for each theorem.

36. Theorem 8.6 **37.** Theorem 8.7 See Ch. 8 Answer Appendix.

MP **SENSE-MAKING Find the perimeter and area of each figure.**

38. P = 48 units; A = 96 units²
39. P = 36 units; A = 60 units²
40. P = 32 units; A = 56 units²

38.

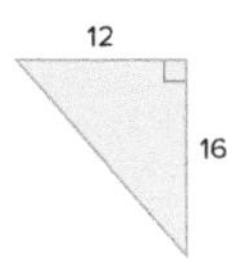

39.

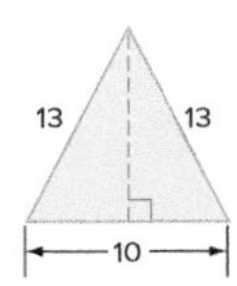

40.

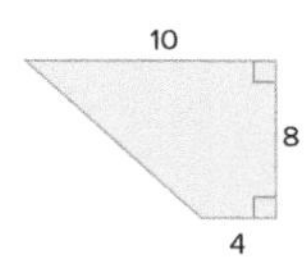

41. **ALGEBRA** The sides of a triangle have lengths x, $x + 5$, and 25. If the length of the longest side is 25, what value of x makes the triangle a right triangle? 15

42. **ALGEBRA** The sides of a triangle have lengths $2x$, 8, and 12. If the length of the longest side is $2x$, what values of x make the triangle acute? $6 < x < 2\sqrt{13}$

43. **TELEVISION** The screen aspect ratio, or the ratio of the width to the height, of a high-definition television is 16:9. The size of a television is given by the diagonal distance across the screen. If an HDTV is 41 inches wide, what is its screen size? ≈47 in.

MP Teaching the Mathematical Practices

Sense-Making Mathematically proficient students start by explaining the meaning of a problem to themselves and looking for entry points to its solution. They plan a solution pathway rather than simply jumping into a solution attempt. In Exercises 38–40, encourage students to use the Pythagorean Theorem to find the measures of the missing sides.

Levels of Complexity Chart

The levels of the exercises progress from 1 to 3, with Level 1 indicating the lowest level of complexity.

Exercises	9–26	27–34, 53–59	35–52
C Level 3			●
B Level 2		●	
Level 1	●		

Extra Practice

See page R8 for extra exercises for students who are approaching level or for on-level students who need additional reinforcement.

Additional Answers

35. **Given:** $\triangle ABC$ with sides of measure a, b, and c, where $c^2 = a^2 + b^2$

Prove: $\triangle ABC$ is a right triangle.

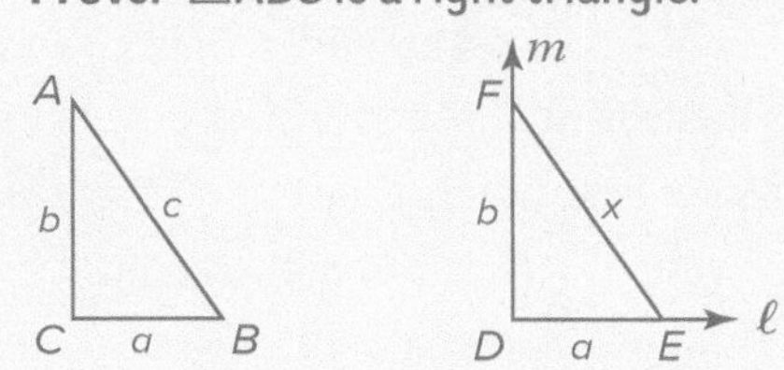

Proof: Draw $\overline{DE}$ on line ℓ with measure equal to a. At D, draw line $m \perp \overline{DE}$. Locate point F on m so that $DF = b$. Draw $\overline{FE}$ and call its measure x. Because $\triangle FED$ is a right triangle, $a^2 + b^2 = x^2$. But $a^2 + b^2 = c^2$, so $x^2 = c^2$ or $x = c$. Thus, $\triangle ABC \cong \triangle FED$ by SSS. This means $\angle C \cong \angle D$. Therefore, $\angle C$ must be a right angle, making $\triangle ABC$ a right triangle.

36. **Given:** In $\triangle ABC$, $c^2 < a^2 + b^2$ where c is the length of the longest side. In $\triangle PQR$, $\angle R$ is a right angle.

Prove: $\triangle ABC$ is an acute triangle.

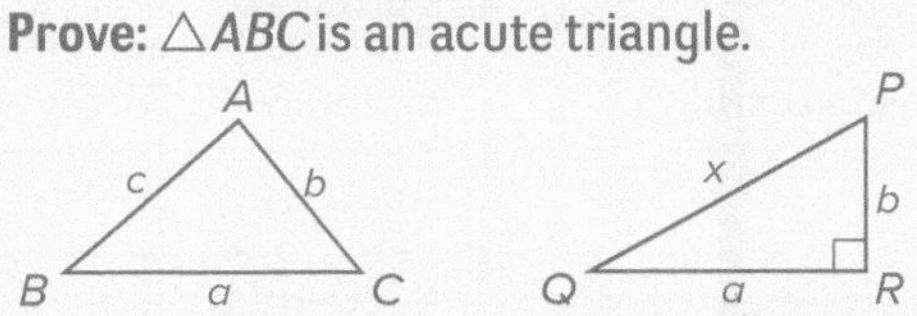

Proof:

Statements (Reasons)

1. In $\triangle ABC$, $c^2 < a^2 + b^2$ where c is the length of the longest side. In $\triangle PQR$, $\angle R$ is a right angle. (Given)
2. $a^2 + b^2 = x^2$ (Pythagorean Theorem)
3. $c^2 < x^2$ (Substitution Property)
4. $c < x$ (A property of square roots)
5. $m\angle R = 90°$ (Definition of a right angle)
6. $m\angle C < m\angle R$ (Converse of the Hinge Theorem)
7. $m\angle C < 90°$ (Substitution Property)
8. $\angle C$ is an acute angle. (Definition of an acute angle)
9. $\triangle ABC$ is an acute triangle. (Definition of an acute triangle)

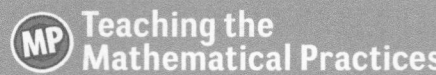

Teaching the Mathematical Practices

Arguments Mathematically proficient students understand and use stated assumptions and definitions in constructing arguments. They make conjectures and build a logical progression of statements to explore the truth of their conjectures. In Exercise 50, encourage students to start by finding examples or counterexamples.

Assess

Name the Math Ask students to recall how right triangles are modeled in suspension bridges, and have them demonstrate how a right triangle could model real-world objects.

Additional Answers

48a.

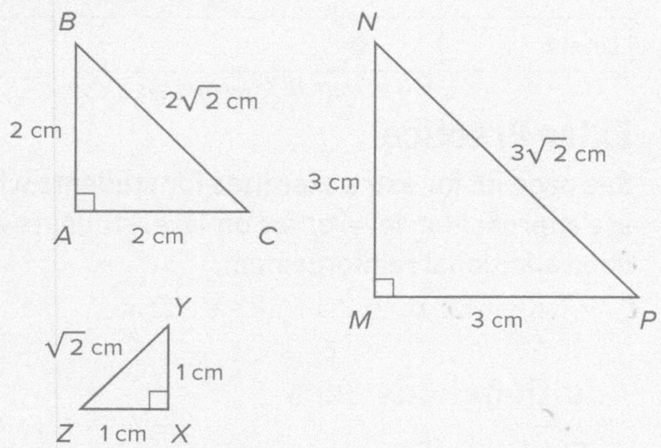

50. False; sample answer: A right triangle with legs measuring 3 in. and 4 in. has a hypotenuse of 5 in. and an area of $\frac{1}{2} \times 3 \times 4$ or 6 in². A right triangle with legs measuring 2 in. and $\sqrt{21}$ in. also has a hypotenuse of 5 in., but its area is $\frac{1}{2} \times 2 \times \sqrt{21}$ or $\sqrt{21}$ in², which is not equivalent to 6 in².

51. Right; sample answer: If you double or halve the side lengths, all three sides of the new triangles are proportional to the sides of the original triangle. Using the Side-Side-Side Similarity Theorem, you know that both of the new triangles are similar to the original triangle, so they are both right.

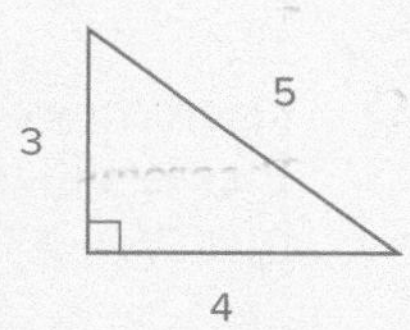

Go Online!

eSolutions Manual

Create worksheets, answer keys, and solutions handouts for your assignments.

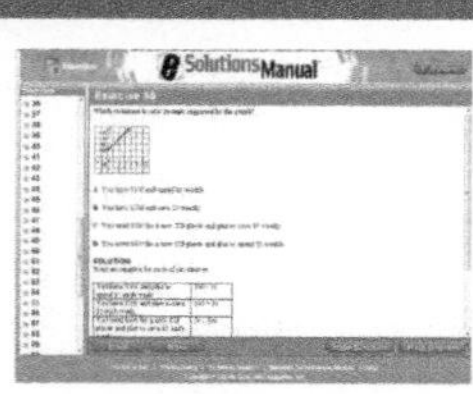

44. **PLAYGROUND** According to the *Handbook for Public Playground Safety*, the ratio of the vertical distance to the horizontal distance covered by a slide should not be more than about 4 to 7. If the horizontal distance allotted in a slide design is 14 feet, approximately how long should the slide be? **about 16 ft**

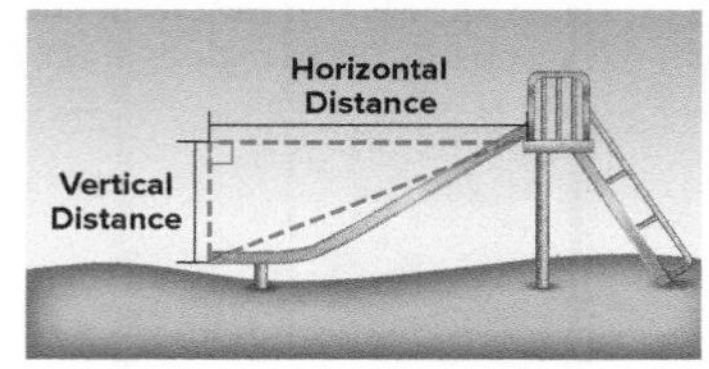

Find x.

45. **10**

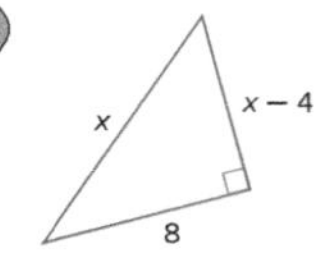

46. **15**

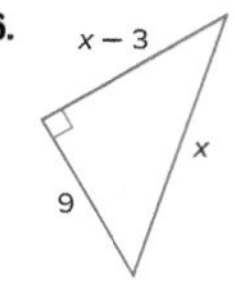

47. $\frac{1}{2}$

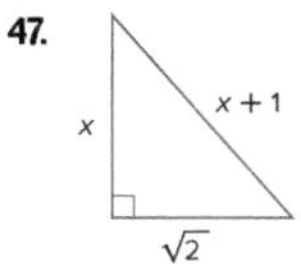

48. **MULTIPLE REPRESENTATIONS** In this problem, you will investigate special right triangles.
   a. **Geometric** Draw three different isosceles right triangles that have whole-number side lengths. Label the triangles *ABC*, *MNP*, and *XYZ* with the right angle located at vertices *A*, *M*, and *X*, respectively. Label the leg lengths of each side, and find the exact length of the hypotenuse. **See margin.**
   b. **Tabular** Copy and complete the table below.

Triangle	Length				Ratio	
ABC	*BC*	$2\sqrt{2}$	*AB*	2	$\frac{BC}{AB}$	$\sqrt{2}$
MNP	*NP*	$3\sqrt{2}$	*MN*	3	$\frac{NP}{MN}$	$\sqrt{2}$
XYZ	*YZ*	$\sqrt{2}$	*XY*	1	$\frac{YZ}{XY}$	$\sqrt{2}$

   c. **Verbal** Make a conjecture about the ratio of the hypotenuse to a leg of an isosceles right triangle. **Sample answer: The ratio of the hypotenuse to a leg of an isosceles right triangle is $\sqrt{2}$.**

G.SRT.8, G.MG.3

H.O.T. Problems Use **H**igher-**O**rder **T**hinking Skills

49. **CHALLENGE** Find the value of x in the figure at the right. **5.4**

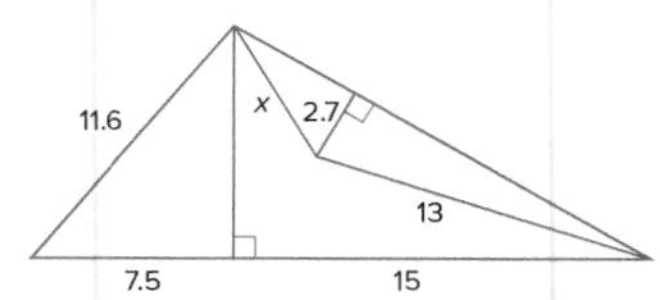

50. **ARGUMENTS** *True* or *false*? Any two right triangles with the same hypotenuse have the same area. Explain your reasoning. **See margin.**

51. **OPEN-ENDED** Draw a right triangle with side lengths that form a Pythagorean triple. If you double the length of each side, is the resulting triangle *acute*, *right*, or *obtuse*? if you halve the length of each side? Explain. **See margin.**

52. **WRITING IN MATH** Research *incommensurable magnitudes* and describe how this phrase relates to the use of irrational numbers in geometry. Include one example of an irrational number used in geometry. **See margin.**

Standards for Mathematical Practice

Emphasis On	Exercises
1 Make sense of problems and persevere in solving them.	15–18, 38–40, 53–58
2 Reason abstractly and quantitatively.	30–33, 41, 42, 49
3 Construct viable arguments and critique the reasoning of others.	35–37, 50, 51
4 Model with mathematics.	19, 20, 34, 43, 44, 53–56, 58
6 Attend to precision.	52, 57
8 Look for and express regularity in repeated reasoning.	48

Preparing for Assessment

53. Jessica has three wooden rods with the lengths shown below. She wants to place them together, if possible, to create a triangular picture frame.

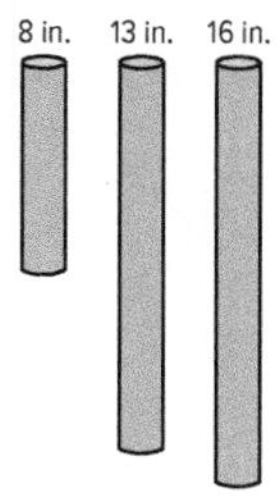

Which of the following is the best description of the frame Jessica can create? MP 1, 4 G.SRT.8, G.MG.3 **C**

- ○ A The frame will be an acute triangle.
- ○ B The frame will be a right triangle.
- ○ C The frame will be an obtuse triangle.
- ○ D The rods cannot be placed together to form a triangle.

54. Dontrell's school has a rectangular lawn with the dimensions shown. Students often walk along the diagonal of the lawn as a shortcut.

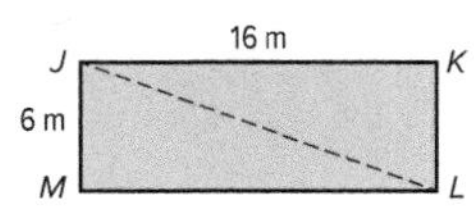

To the nearest tenth of a meter, how much shorter is it to walk directly from *J* to *L* rather than from *J* to *K* to *L*? MP 1, 4 G.SRT.8, G.MG.3 **A**

- ○ A 4.9 m
- ○ B 9.4 m
- ○ C 10.0 m
- ○ D 17.1 m

55. A square park has a diagonal walkway from one corner to another. If the walkway is 120 meters long, what is the approximate length of each side of the park in meters? MP 1, 4 G.MG.3, G.SRT.8 [85]

56. Lin wants to build a triangular vegetable bed with sides that are 7 feet, 8 feet, and 10 feet long. Which of the following best describes the vegetable bed? MP 1, 4 G.SRT.8, G.MG.3 **A**

- ○ A It will be an acute triangle.
- ○ B It will be a right triangle.
- ○ C It will be an obtuse triangle.
- ○ D Lin cannot form a triangle with these side lengths.

57. Which of the following is the best estimate of the perimeter of $\triangle RST$? MP 1, 6 G.SRT.8 **B**

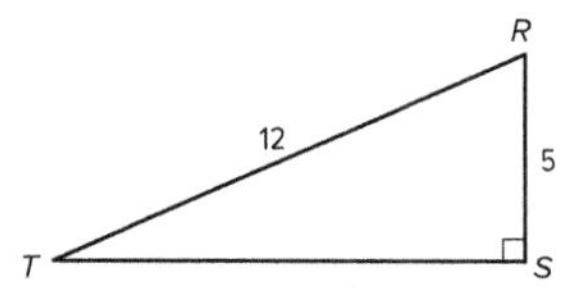

- ○ A 30.0
- ○ B 27.9
- ○ C 17.0
- ○ D 10.9

58. **MULTI-STEP** A gardener wishes to make a triangular garden. He has fence segments of length 8 feet, 14 feet, 15 feet, 17 feet, and 20 feet. MP 1, 4 G.SRT.8

a. What combination of fence lengths will make a right triangle? [8, 15, 17]

b. What combination of fence lengths will make an acute triangle? [Sample answer: 14, 15, 17]

c. What combinations of fence lengths will make an obtuse triangle? [Sample answer: 8, 14, 20]

59. A rhombus has a perimeter of 20 units. The length of one diagonal for the rhombus is 8. MP 1 G.SRT.8

a. Find the side length of the rhombus. [5]

b. Find the length of the other diagonal. [6]

Preparing for Assessment

Exercises 53–59 require students to use the skills they will need on future assessments. Exercises are dual-coded with content standards and mathematical practice standards.

Dual Coding		
Items	Content Standards	MP Mathematical Practices
53	G.SRT.8, G.MG.3	1, 4
54	G.SRT.8, G.MG.3	1, 4
55	G.SRT.8, G.MG.3	1, 4
56	G.SRT.8, G.MG.3	1, 4
57	G.SRT.8	1, 6
58	G.SRT.8	1, 4

Diagnose Student Errors

Survey student responses for each item. Class trends may indicate common errors and misconceptions.

53.

A	Incorrectly used the Pythagorean Inequality Theorems
B	Incorrectly used the Pythagorean Inequality Theorems
C	CORRECT
D	Incorrectly used the Triangle Inequality Theorems

54.

A	CORRECT
B	Used 16 m as the length of both legs
C	Subtracted lengths of legs of right triangle
D	Found the length of $\overline{JL}$

56.

A	CORRECT
B	Incorrectly used the Pythagorean Inequality Theorems
C	Incorrectly used the Pythagorean Inequality Theorems
D	Incorrectly used the Triangle Inequality Theorems

57.

A	Assumed the triangle is a 5-12-13 right triangle
B	CORRECT
C	Did not include $\overline{TS}$ in the perimeter
D	Found the length of $\overline{TS}$

52. Sample answer: Incommensurable magnitudes are magnitudes of the same kind that do not have a common unit of measure. Irrational numbers were invented to describe geometric relationships, such as ratios of incommensurable magnitudes that cannot be described using rational numbers. For example, to express the measures of the sides of a square with an area of 2 square units, the irrational number $\sqrt{2}$ is needed.

Go Online!

Quizzes

Students can use *Self-Check Quizzes* to check their understanding of this lesson and have the results sent to you. You can also give *Quiz 1*, which covers the content in Lessons 8-1 and 8-2.

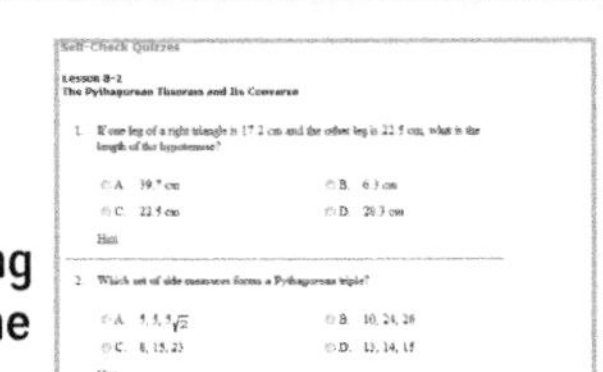

Launch

Objective Graph points in space and use the distance and midpoint formulas in space.

Materials for Each Student
- ruler

Teach ELL

Working in Cooperative Groups Have students of mixed abilities work in groups of three. In Activity 1, have students rotate in plotting the points in space.

If students have difficulty plotting points with the appropriate perspective, have them use a ruler to align each coordinate with the respective axis.

Practice Have students complete Exercises 1–5 and 10–14.

Additional Answers

1.
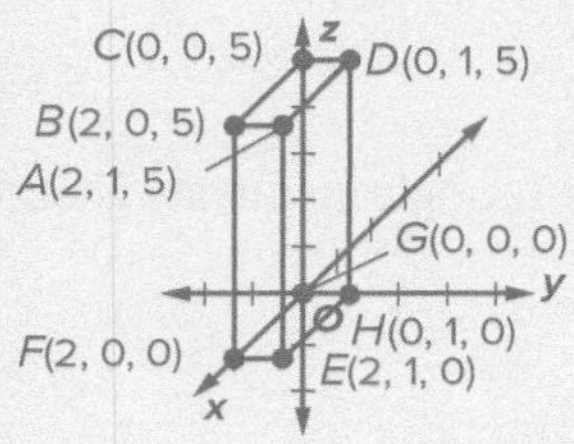

2.
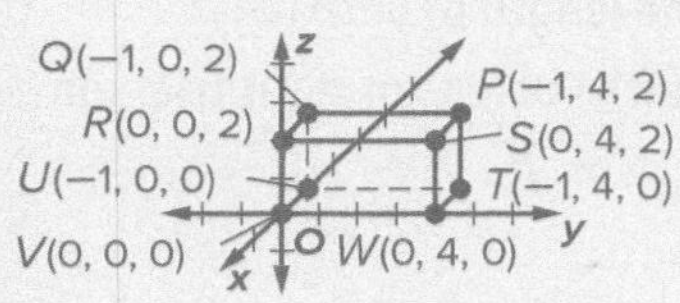

3.
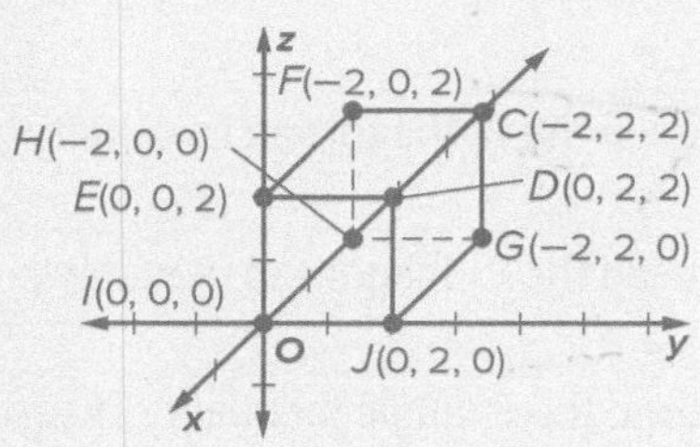

4.
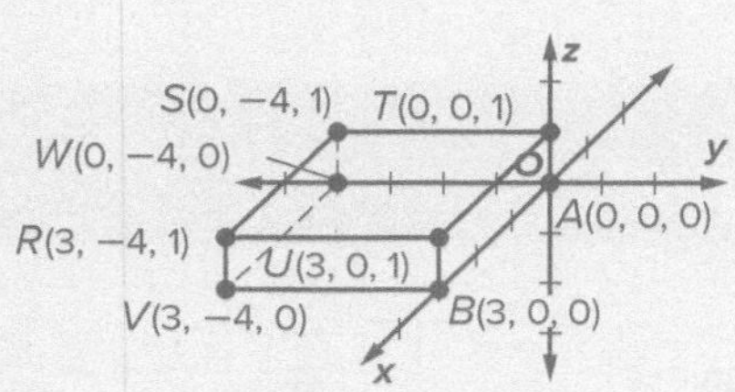

Geometry Lab

Coordinates in Space

You have used ordered pairs of two coordinates to describe the location of a point on the coordinate plane. Because space has three dimensions, a point requires three numbers, or coordinates, to describe its location in space.

A point in space is represented by an **ordered triple** of real numbers (x, y, z). In the figure at the right, the ordered triple (2, 3, 6) locates point P. Notice that a rectangular prism is used to show perspective.

Mathematical Practices
MP **4** Model with mathematics

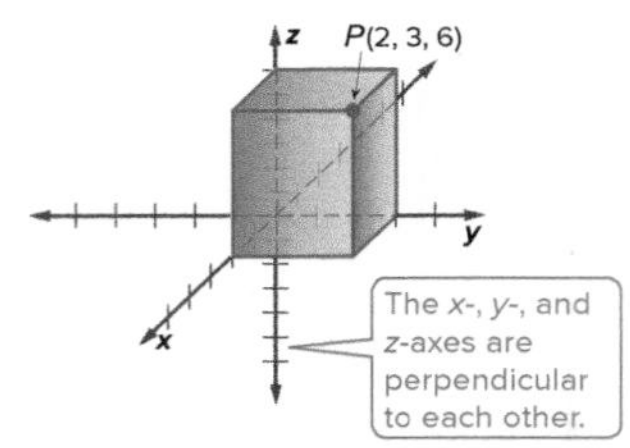

Activity 1 Graph a Rectangular Solid

Work cooperatively. Graph a rectangular solid that has two vertices, $L(4, -5, 2)$ and the origin. Label the coordinates of each vertex.

Step 1 Plot the x-coordinate first. Draw a segment from the origin 4 units in the positive direction.

Step 2 To plot the y-coordinate, draw a segment five units in the negative direction.

Step 3 Next, to plot the z-coordinate, draw a segment two units long in the positive direction.

Step 4 Label the coordinate L.

Step 5 Draw the rectangular prism and label each vertex: $L(4, -5, 2)$, $K(0, -5, 2)$, $J(0, 0, 2)$, $M(4, 0, 2)$ $Q(4, -5, 0)$, $P(0, -5, 0)$, $N(0, 0, 0)$, and $R(4, 0, 0)$.

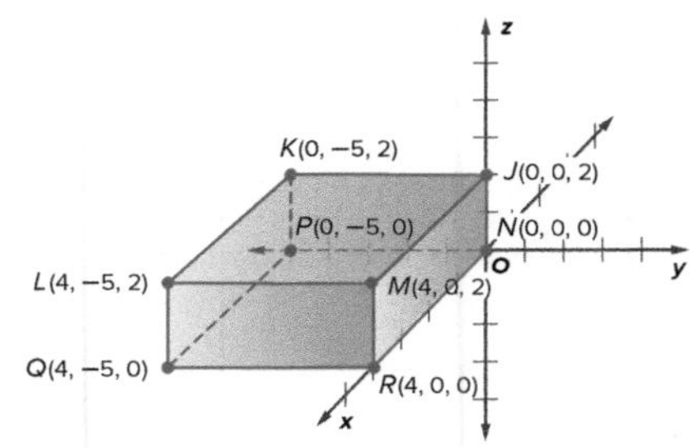

Finding the distance between points and the midpoint of a segment in space is similar to finding distance and a midpoint in the coordinate plane.

Key Concept Distance and Midpoint Formulas in Space

If A has coordinates $A(x_1, y_1, z_1)$ and B has coordinates $B(x_2, y_2, z_2)$, then

$AB = \sqrt{(x_2 - x_1)^2 + (y_2 - y_1)^2 + (z_2 - z_1)^2}$.

The midpoint M of $\overline{AB}$ has coordinates

$M\left(\frac{x_1 + x_2}{2}, \frac{y_1 + y_2}{2}, \frac{z_1 + z_2}{2}\right)$.

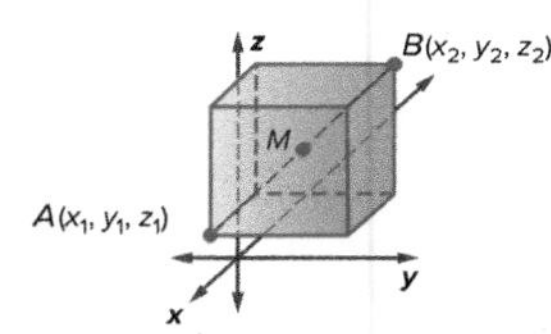

5.
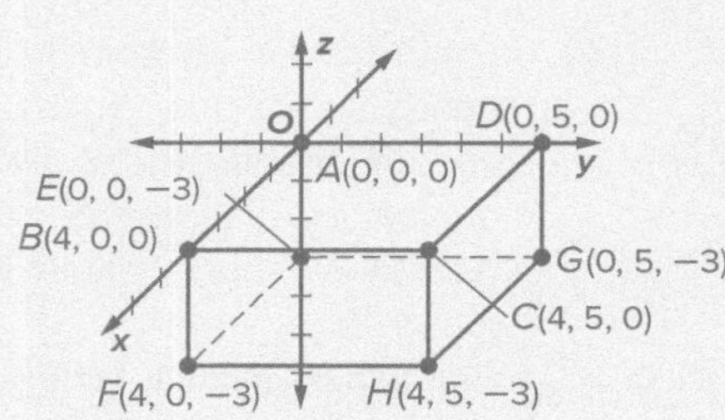

6.
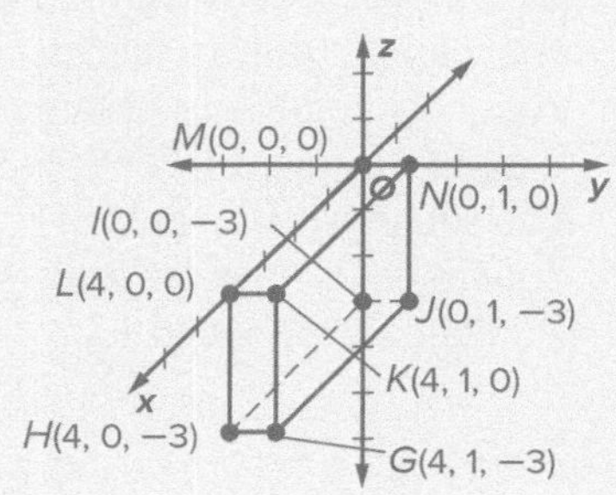

7.
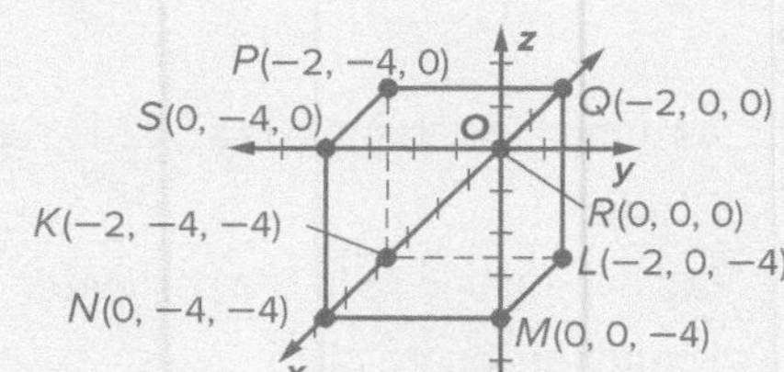

8.
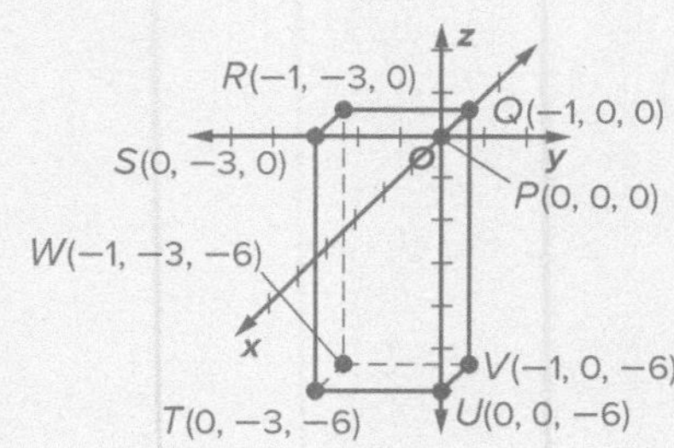

Activity 2 Distance and Midpoint Formulas in Space

Work cooperatively. Consider $J(2, 4, 9)$ and $K(-4, -5, 11)$.

a. Find JK.

$JK = \sqrt{(x_2 - x_1)^2 + (y_2 - y_1)^2 + (z_2 - z_1)^2}$ Distance Formula in Space

$= \sqrt{(-4 - 2)^2 + (-5 - 4)^2 + (11 - 9)^2}$ Substitution

$= \sqrt{121}$ Simplify.

$= 11$ Use a calculator.

b. Determine the coordinates of the midpoint M of $\overline{JK}$.

$M = \left(\frac{x_1 + x_2}{2}, \frac{y_1 + y_2}{2}, \frac{z_1 + z_2}{2}\right)$ Midpoint Formula in Space

$= \left(\frac{2 + (-4)}{2}, \frac{4 + (-5)}{2}, \frac{9 + 11}{2}\right)$ Substitution

$= \left(-1, -\frac{1}{2}, 10\right)$ Simplify.

Exercises

Work cooperatively. Graph a rectangular solid that contains the given point and the origin as vertices. Label the coordinates of each vertex. 1–9. See margin.

1. $A(2, 1, 5)$
2. $P(-1, 4, 2)$
3. $C(-2, 2, 2)$
4. $R(3, -4, 1)$
5. $P(4, 6, -3)$
6. $G(4, 1, -3)$
7. $K(-2, -4, -4)$
8. $W(-1, -3, -6)$
9. $W(3, 3, 4)$

Determine the distance between each pair of points. Then determine the coordinates of the midpoint M of the segment joining the pair of points. 10–19. See margin.

10. $D(0, 0, 0)$ and $E(1, 5, 7)$
11. $G(-3, -4, 6)$ and $H(5, -3, -5)$
12. $K(2, 2, 0)$ and $L(-2, -2, 0)$
13. $P(-2, -5, 8)$ and $Q(3, -2, -1)$
14. $A(4, 7, 9)$ and $B(-3, 8, -8)$
15. $W(-12, 8, 10)$ and $Z(-4, 1, -2)$
16. $F\left(\frac{3}{5}, 0, \frac{4}{5}\right)$ and $G(0, 3, 0)$
17. $G(1, -1, 6)$ and $H\left(\frac{1}{5}, -\frac{2}{5}, 2\right)$
18. $B(\sqrt{3}, 2, 2\sqrt{2})$ and $C(-2\sqrt{3}, 4, 4\sqrt{2})$
19. $S(6\sqrt{3}, 4, 4\sqrt{2})$ and $T(4\sqrt{3}, 5, \sqrt{2})$

20. **PROOF** Write a coordinate proof of the Distance Formula in Space. See margin.

Given: A has coordinates $A(x_1, y_1, z_1)$, and B has coordinates $B(x_2, y_2, z_2)$.

Prove: $AB = \sqrt{(x_2 - x_1)^2 + (y_2 - y_1)^2 + (z_2 - z_1)^2}$

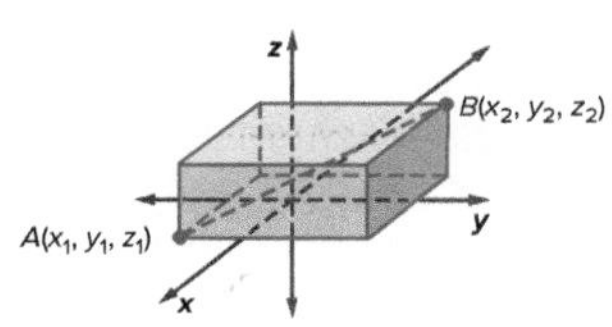

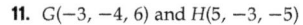

21. **WRITING IN MATH** Compare and contrast the Distance and Midpoint Formulas on the coordinate plane and in three-dimensional coordinate space. See margin.

9.

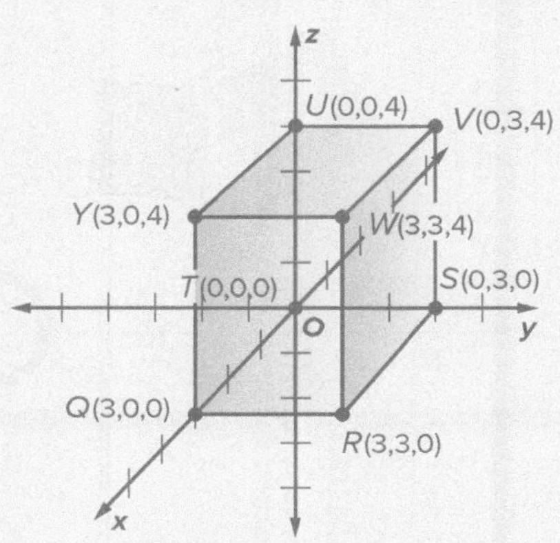

Assess

Formative Assessment

Use Exercises 6–9 and 15–21 to assess students' understanding of working in three dimensions.

From Concrete to Abstract

Have students compare the distance and midpoint formulas to the same formulas in the coordinate plane when the points have z-values equal to zero.

Extending the Concept

Have students explore how to use the coordinates of a rectangular solid to determine its volume.

Additional Answers

10. $DE = 5\sqrt{3}; \left(\frac{1}{2}, \frac{5}{2}, \frac{7}{2}\right)$
11. $GH = \sqrt{186}; \left(1, -\frac{7}{2}, \frac{1}{2}\right)$
12. $KL = 4\sqrt{2}; (0, 0, 0)$
13. $PQ = \sqrt{115}; \left(\frac{1}{2}, -\frac{7}{2}, \frac{7}{2}\right)$
14. $AB = \sqrt{339}; \left(\frac{1}{2}, \frac{15}{2}, \frac{1}{2}\right)$
15. $WZ = \sqrt{257}; \left(-8, \frac{9}{2}, 4\right)$
16. $FG = \sqrt{10}; \left(\frac{3}{10}, \frac{3}{2}, \frac{2}{5}\right)$
17. $GH = \sqrt{17}; \left(\frac{3}{5}, -\frac{7}{10}, 4\right)$
18. $BC = \sqrt{39}; \left(-\frac{\sqrt{3}}{2}, 3, 3\sqrt{2}\right)$
19. $ST = \sqrt{31}; \left(5\sqrt{3}, \frac{9}{2}, \frac{5\sqrt{2}}{2}\right)$
20.

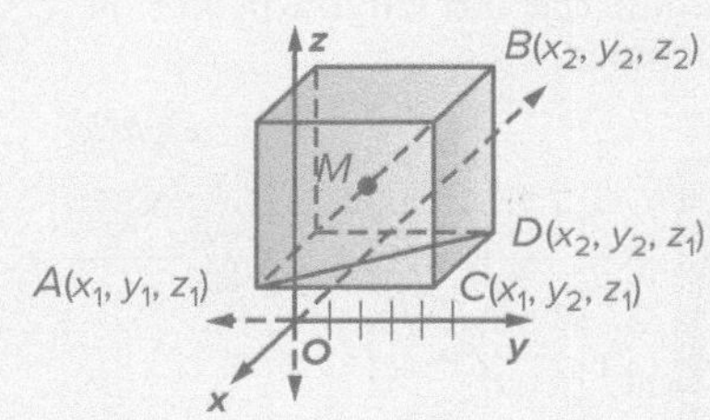

Proof: In $\triangle ACD$, $DC = (x_2 - x_1)$ and $AC = (y_2 - y_1)$. By the Pythagorean Theorem $(AD)^2 = (DC)^2 + (AC)^2$. Thus, $(AD)^2 = (x_2 - x_1)^2 + (y_2 - y_1)^2$. In $\triangle ADB$, $BD = (z_2 - z_1)$. By the Pythagorean Theorem, $(AB)^2 = (AD)^2 + (BD)^2$. Thus, $(AB)^2 = [(x_2 - x_1)^2 + (y_2 - y_1)^2] + (z_2 - z_1)^2$. Therefore, $AB = \sqrt{(x_2 - x_1)^2 + (y_2 - y_1)^2 + (z_2 - z_1)^2}$.

21. The formulas for the coordinate plane involve two coordinates and the formulas for three-dimensional space involve three coordinates. Both distance formulas involve the square root of the squares of the differences of the coordinates. Both midpoint formulas involve the averages of the coordinates.

LESSON 8-3

Special Right Triangles

SUGGESTED PACING (DAYS)

	Instruction
90 min.	0.5
45 min.	1.0

Track Your Progress

Objectives

1. Use the properties of 45°-45°-90° triangles.
2. Use the properties of 30°-60°-90° triangles.

Mathematical Background

A 45°-45°-90° triangle is the only type of isosceles right triangle. The hypotenuse is $\sqrt{2}$ times the length of a leg. A 30°-60°-90° triangle also has special properties. The measures of the sides are x, $x\sqrt{3}$, and $2x$. Knowing these properties can save valuable time when you are solving problems involving special right triangles.

Skills Trace

THEN	NOW	NEXT
G.SRT.8 Use trigonometric ratios and the Pythagorean Theorem to solve right triangles in applied problems.	**G.SRT.6** Understand that by similarity, side ratios in right triangles are properties of the angles in the triangle, leading to definitions of trigonometric ratios for acute angles.	**G.SRT.7** Explain and use the relationship between the sine and cosine of complementary angles.

Go Online! All of these resources and more are available at connectED.mcgraw-hill.com

Toolkit allows students to explore and enhance their understanding of math concepts. Use the Ruled Grids mat and the protractor and line segment tools to approximate the side lengths of special right triangles.

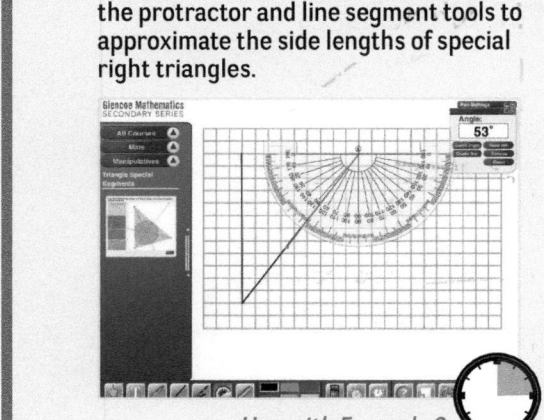

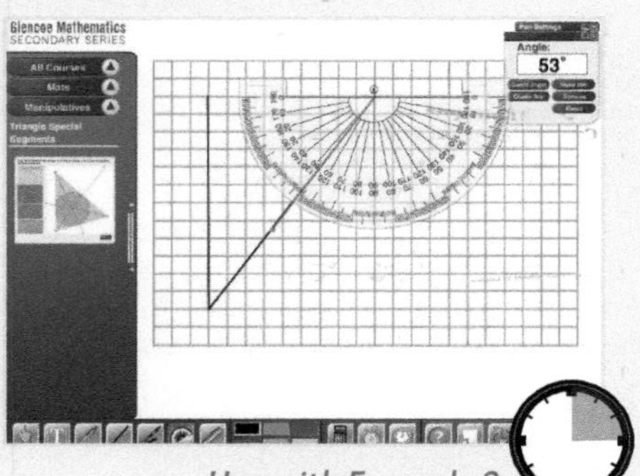

Use with Example 3

Personal Tutors (for every example) let students hear real teachers solve problems. Students can pause and repeat as many times as necessary.

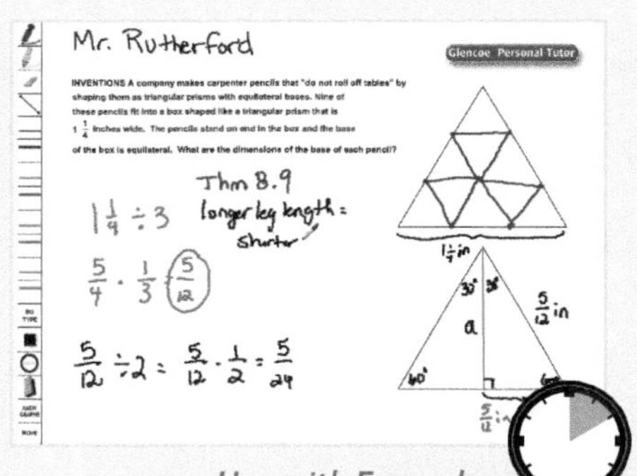

Use with Examples

Use **The Geometer's Sketchpad** to explore 30°-60°-90° triangles and discover a relationship among the side lengths and among areas.

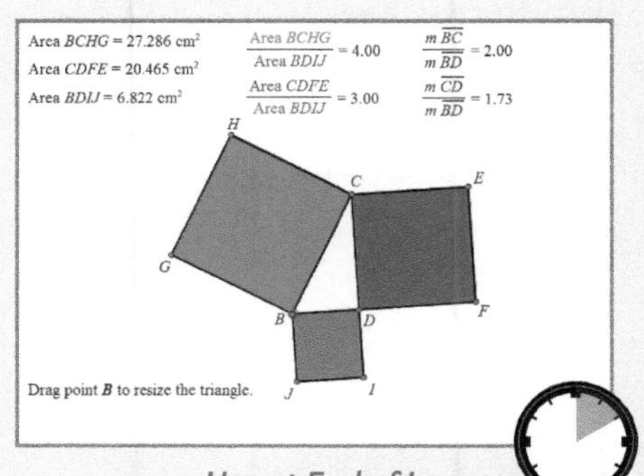

Use at End of Lesson

Using Open Educational Resources

Collaboration Have students work in pairs to write their own word problems involving special right triangles using **Boom Writer**. Boom Writer allows students to work together online in a safe environment. They can then trade their problems with another pair of students who will work the problems as homework. *Use as homework*

Go Online!
connectED.mcgraw-hill.com

Worksheets

Differentiate Your Resources

Extra Practice Additional practice or homework; Skills Practice is best for approaching-level students and Practice is best for on-level and beyond-level students

Skills Practice

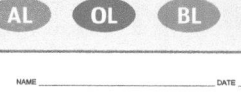

AL OL ELL

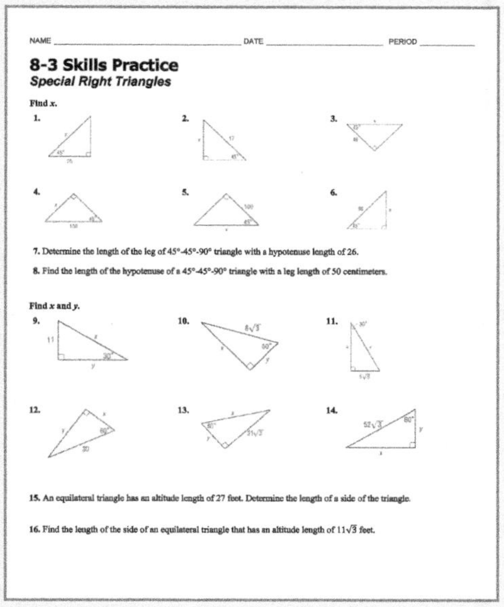
NAME ____ DATE ____ PERIOD ____

8-3 Skills Practice
Special Right Triangles

Find *x*.

7. Determine the length of the leg of 45°-45°-90° triangle with a hypotenuse length of 26.

8. Find the length of the hypotenuse of a 45°-45°-90° triangle with a leg length of 50 centimeters.

Find *x* and *y*.

15. An equilateral triangle has an altitude length of 27 feet. Determine the length of a side of the triangle.

16. Find the length of the side of an equilateral triangle that has an altitude length of $11\sqrt{3}$ feet.

Practice

AL OL BL ELL

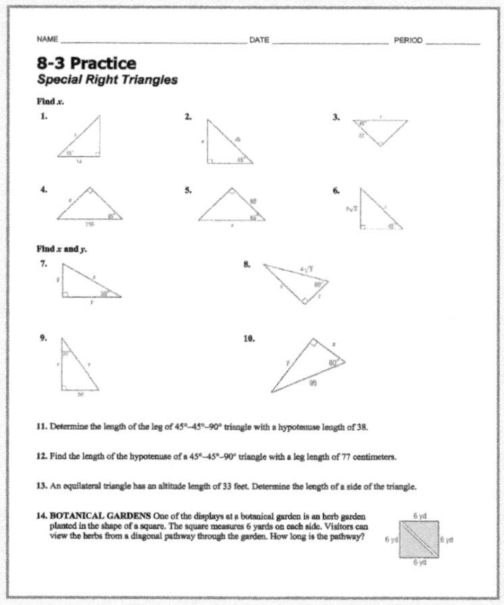
NAME ____ DATE ____ PERIOD ____

8-3 Practice
Special Right Triangles

Find *x*.

Find *x* and *y*.

11. Determine the length of the leg of 45°-45°-90° triangle with a hypotenuse length of 38.

12. Find the length of the hypotenuse of a 45°-45°-90° triangle with a leg length of 77 centimeters.

13. An equilateral triangle has an altitude length of 33 feet. Determine the length of a side of the triangle.

14. BOTANICAL GARDENS One of the displays at a botanical garden is an herb garden planted in the shape of a square. The square measures 6 yards on each side. Visitors can view the herbs from a diagonal pathway through the garden. How long is the pathway?

Word Problem Practice

AL OL BL ELL

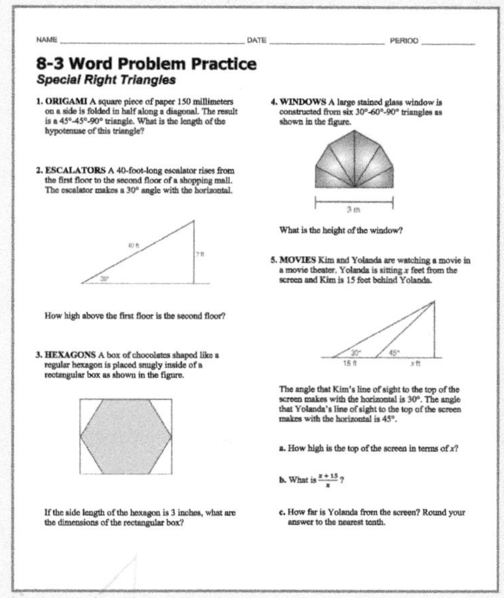
NAME ____ DATE ____ PERIOD ____

8-3 Word Problem Practice
Special Right Triangles

1. ORIGAMI A square piece of paper 150 millimeters on a side is folded in half along a diagonal. The result is a 45°-45°-90° triangle. What is the length of the hypotenuse of this triangle?

2. ESCALATORS A 40-foot-long escalator rises from the first floor to the second floor of a shopping mall. The escalator makes a 30° angle with the horizontal.

How high above the first floor is the second floor?

3. HEXAGONS A box of chocolates shaped like a regular hexagon is placed snugly inside of a rectangular box as shown in the figure.

If the side length of the hexagon is 3 inches, what are the dimensions of the rectangular box?

4. WINDOWS A large stained glass window is constructed from six 30°-60°-90° triangles as shown in the figure.

What is the height of the window?

5. MOVIES Kim and Yolanda are watching a movie in a movie theater. Yolanda is sitting *x* feet from the screen and Kim is 15 feet behind Yolanda.

The angle that Kim's line of sight to the top of the screen makes with the horizontal is 30°. The angle that Yolanda's line of sight to the top of the screen makes with the horizontal is 45°.

a. How high is the top of the screen in terms of *x*?

b. What is $\frac{x+15}{x}$?

c. How far is Yolanda from the screen? Round your answer to the nearest tenth.

Intervention Reteaching and vocabulary activities that can be used with struggling or absent students and as ELL support

Study Guide and Intervention

AL OL ELL

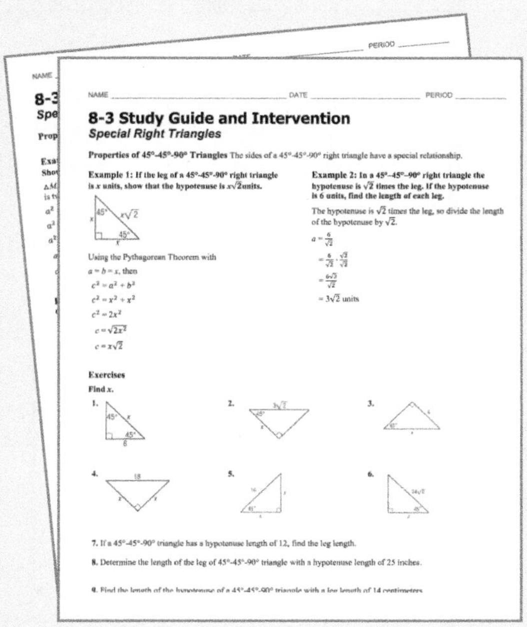
NAME ____ DATE ____ PERIOD ____

8-3 Study Guide and Intervention
Special Right Triangles

Properties of 45°-45°-90° Triangles The sides of a 45°-45°-90° right triangle have a special relationship.

Example 1: If the leg of a 45°-45°-90° right triangle is *x* units, show that the hypotenuse is $x\sqrt{2}$ units.

Using the Pythagorean Theorem with $a = b = x$, then

$c^2 = a^2 + b^2$

$c^2 = x^2 + x^2$

$c^2 = 2x^2$

$c = \sqrt{2x^2}$

$c = x\sqrt{2}$

Example 2: In a 45°-45°-90° right triangle the hypotenuse is $\sqrt{2}$ times the leg. If the hypotenuse is 6 units, find the length of each leg.

The hypotenuse is $\sqrt{2}$ times the leg, so divide the length of the hypotenuse by $\sqrt{2}$.

$a = \frac{6}{\sqrt{2}}$

$= \frac{6}{\sqrt{2}} \cdot \frac{\sqrt{2}}{\sqrt{2}}$

$= \frac{6\sqrt{2}}{2}$

$= 3\sqrt{2}$ units

Exercises

Find *x*.

7. If a 45°-45°-90° triangle has a hypotenuse length of 12, find the leg length.

8. Determine the length of the leg of 45°-45°-90° triangle with a hypotenuse length of 25 inches.

9. Find the length of the hypotenuse of a 45°-45°-90° triangle with a leg length of 14 centimeters.

Study Notebook

AL OL BL ELL

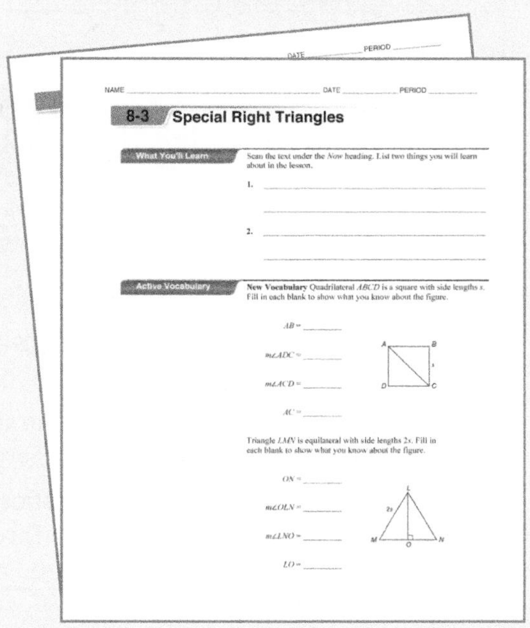
NAME ____ DATE ____ PERIOD ____

8-3 Special Right Triangles

What You'll Learn Scan the text under the *Now* heading. List two things you will learn about in the lesson.

1. ____

2. ____

Active Vocabulary **New Vocabulary** Quadrilateral *ABCD* is a square with side lengths *s*. Fill in each blank to show what you know about the figure.

AB = ____

m∠ADC = ____

m∠ACD = ____

AC = ____

Triangle *LMN* is equilateral with side lengths 2*s*. Fill in each blank to show what you know about the figure.

ON = ____

m∠OLN = ____

m∠LNO = ____

LO = ____

Extension Activities that can be used to extend lesson concepts

Enrichment

OL BL ELL

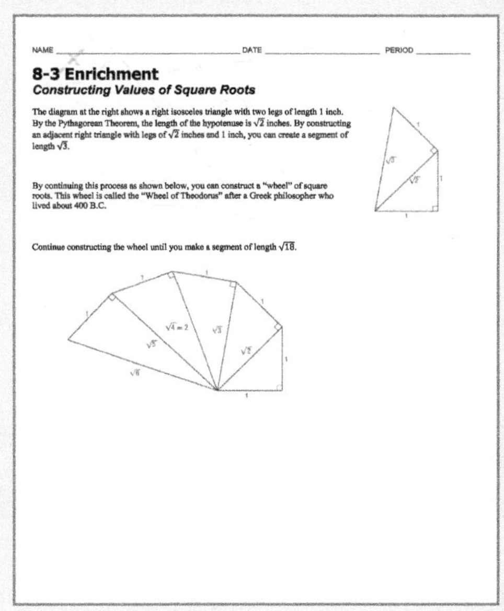
NAME ____ DATE ____ PERIOD ____

8-3 Enrichment
Constructing Values of Square Roots

The diagram at the right shows a right isosceles triangle with two legs of length 1 inch. By the Pythagorean Theorem, the length of the hypotenuse is $\sqrt{2}$ inches. By constructing an adjacent right triangle with legs of $\sqrt{2}$ inches and 1 inch, you can create a segment of length $\sqrt{3}$.

By continuing this process as shown below, you can construct a "wheel" of square roots. This wheel is called the "Wheel of Theodorus" after a Greek philosopher who lived about 400 B.C.

Continue constructing the wheel until you make a segment of length $\sqrt{18}$.

Launch

Have students read the Why? section of the lesson. Ask:

- What type of triangle is the highlighter? equilateral
- Describe the height of the triangle. It is the length of the segment that bisects the top angle and the bottom side of the triangle.
- What are the measures of the angles in the two triangles formed by the altitude of the triangle? 30, 60, 90

Teach

Ask the scaffolded questions for each example to build conceptual understanding for students at all levels.

1 Properties of 45°-45°-90° Triangles

Example 1 Find the Hypotenuse Length in a 45°-45°-90° Triangle

AL What is the relationship between the legs in a 45°-45°-90° triangle? They are congruent.

OL If a leg of a 45°-45°-90° triangle measures $6\sqrt{3}$, what is the length of the hypotenuse? $6\sqrt{6}$

BL If the hypotenuse of a 45°-45°-90° triangle measures $10\sqrt{3}$, what is the length of each leg? $5\sqrt{6}$

Need Another Example?

Find *x*.

a.

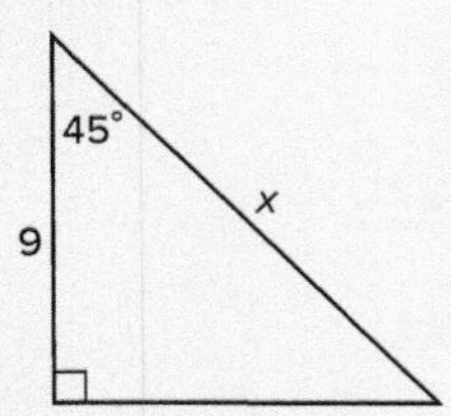

$9\sqrt{2}$

b.

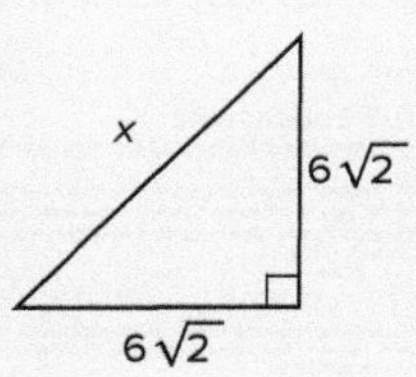

12

Go Online!

Interactive Whiteboard

Use the *eLesson, Lesson Presentation,* or *Interactive Classroom* to present this lesson.

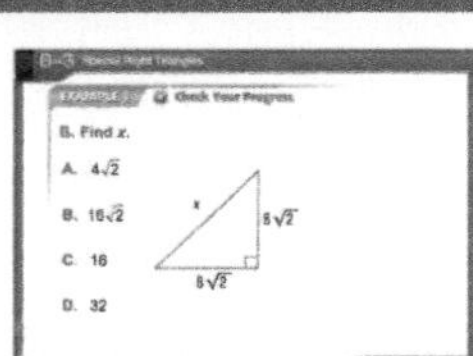

LESSON 3

Special Right Triangles

Then

- You used properties of isosceles and equilateral triangles.

Now

1. Use the properties of 45°-45°-90° triangles.
2. Use the properties of 30°-60°-90° triangles.

Why?

- As part of a packet for students attending a regional student council meeting, Lyndsay orders triangular highlighters. She wants to buy rectangular boxes for the highlighters and other items, but she is concerned that the highlighters will not fit in the box she has chosen. If she knows the length of a side of the highlighter, Lyndsay can use the properties of special right triangles to determine if it will fit in the box.

MP Mathematical Practices

1 Make sense of problems and persevere in solving them.

7 Look for and make use of structure.

Content Standards

G.SRT.6 Understand that by similarity, side ratios in right triangles are properties of the angles in the triangle, leading to definitions of trigonometric ratios for acute angles.

1 Properties of 45°-45°-90° Triangles The diagonal of a square forms two congruent isosceles right triangles. Because the base angles of an isosceles triangle are congruent, the measure of each acute angle is 90 ÷ 2 or 45. Such a triangle is also known as a 45°-45°-90° triangle.

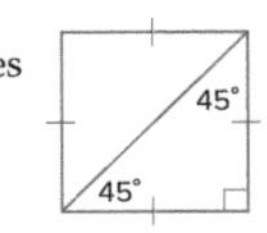

You can use the Pythagorean Theorem to find a relationship among the side lengths of a 45°-45°-90° right triangle.

$\ell^2 + \ell^2 = h^2$ Pythagorean Theorem

$2\ell^2 = h^2$ Simplify.

$\sqrt{2\ell^2} = \sqrt{h^2}$ Take the positive square root of each side.

$\ell\sqrt{2} = h$ Simplify.

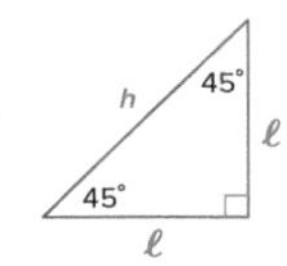

This algebraic proof verifies the following theorem.

Theorem 8.8 45°-45°-90° Triangle Theorem

In a 45°-45°-90° triangle, the legs ℓ are congruent and the length of the hypotenuse h is $\sqrt{2}$ times the length of a leg.

Symbols In a 45°-45°-90° triangle, $\ell = \ell$ and $h = \ell\sqrt{2}$.

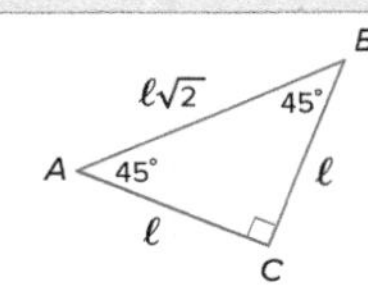

G.SRT.6

Example 1 Find the Hypotenuse Length in a 45°-45°-90° Triangle

Find *x*.

a.

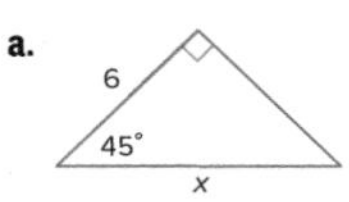

The acute angles of a right triangle are complementary, so the measure of the third angle is 90 − 45 or 45. Because this is a 45°-45°-90° triangle, use Theorem 8.8.

$h = \ell\sqrt{2}$ Theorem 8.8

$x = 6\sqrt{2}$ Substitution

b.

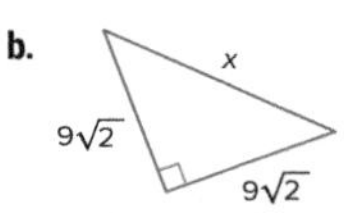

The legs of this right triangle have the same measure, so it is isosceles. Since this is a 45°-45°-90° triangle, use Theorem 8.8.

$h = \ell\sqrt{2}$ Theorem 8.8

$x = 9\sqrt{2} \cdot \sqrt{2}$ Substitution

$x = 9 \cdot 2$ or 18 $\quad \sqrt{2} \cdot \sqrt{2} = 2$

MP Mathematical Practices Strategies

Make sense of problems and persevere in solving them.
Help students express relationships between the lengths of sides in 30º-60º-90º or 45º-45º-90º triangles. For example, ask:

- Which is the shortest side in a 30º-60º-90º triangle? the side opposite the 30º angle
- What is the relationship between the shortest side and the hypotenuse in a 30º-60º-90º triangle? The hypotenuse is twice as long as the shortest side.
- How do you derive the side length ratios in a 45º-45º-90º triangle? Let the legs be 1 unit long, then use the Pythagorean Theorem to find the length of the hypotenuse.

Guided Practice

Find x.

1A. 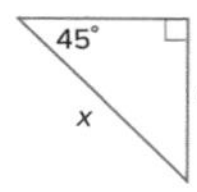

$4\sqrt{2}$

1B. 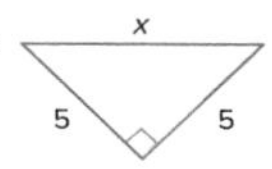

$5\sqrt{2}$

1C. 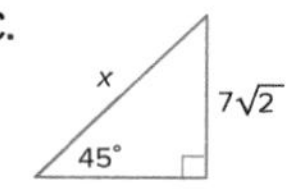

14

You can also work backward using Theorem 8.8 to find the lengths of the legs of a 45°-45°-90° triangle given the length of its hypotenuse.

G.SRT.6

Example 2 Find the Leg Lengths in a 45°-45°-90° Triangle

Find x.

The legs of this right triangle have the same measure, x, so it is a 45°-45°-90° triangle. Use Theorem 8.8 to find x.

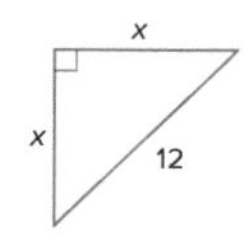

$h = \ell\sqrt{2}$	45°-45°-90° Triangle Theorem
$12 = x\sqrt{2}$	Substitution
$\frac{12}{\sqrt{2}} = x$	Divide each side by $\sqrt{2}$.
$\frac{12}{\sqrt{2}} \cdot \frac{\sqrt{2}}{\sqrt{2}} = x$	Rationalize the denominator.
$\frac{12\sqrt{2}}{2} = x$	Multiply.
$6\sqrt{2} = x$	Simplify.

Review Vocabulary

rationalizing the denominator a method used to eliminate radicals from the denominator of a fraction

Guided Practice

2A. 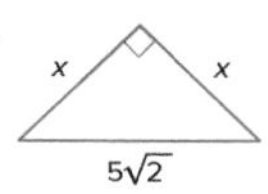

5

2B. 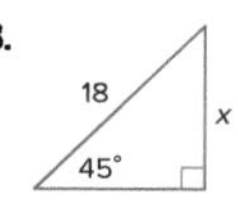

$9\sqrt{2}$

2 Properties of 30°-60°-90° Triangles

A 30°-60°-90° triangle is another *special* right triangle or right triangle with side lengths that share a special relationship. You can use an equilateral triangle to find this relationship.

Study Tip ELL

MP Sense-Making Notice that an altitude of an isosceles triangle is also a median of the triangle. In the figure at the right, $\overline{BD}$ bisects $\overline{AC}$.

When an altitude is drawn from any vertex of an equilateral triangle, two congruent 30°-60°-90° triangles are formed. In the figure shown, $\triangle ABD \cong \triangle CBD$, so $\overline{AD} \cong \overline{CD}$. If $AD = x$, then $CD = x$ and $AC = 2x$. Because $\triangle ABC$ is equilateral, $AB = 2x$ and $BC = 2x$.

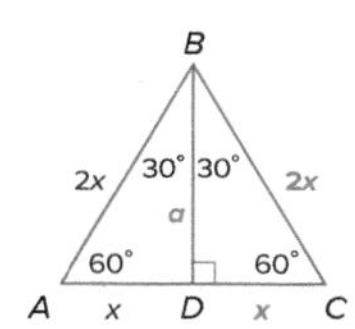

Use the Pythagorean Theorem to find a, the length of the altitude $\overline{BD}$, which is also the longer leg of $\triangle BDC$.

$a^2 + x^2 = (2x)^2$	Pythagorean Theorem
$a^2 + x^2 = 4x^2$	Simplify.
$a^2 = 3x^2$	Subtract x^2 from each side.
$a = \sqrt{3x^2}$	Take the positive square root of each side.
$a = x\sqrt{3}$	Simplify.

Example 2 Find the Leg Lengths in a 45°-45°-90° Triangle

AL Why do we need to rationalize the denominator in the fourth step? Sample answer: because you shouldn't leave square roots in the denominator of a fraction

OL What is the leg length of a 45°-45°-90° triangle if the hypotenuse is $4\sqrt{3}$? $2\sqrt{6}$

BL What is the leg length of a 45°-45°-90° triangle if the hypotenuse is $10\sqrt{6}$? $10\sqrt{3}$

Need Another Example?

Find a.

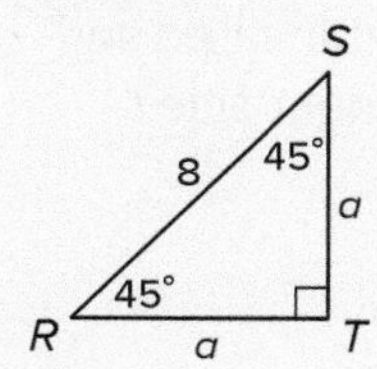

$a = 4\sqrt{2}$

Differentiated Instruction OL BL

Logical/Mathematical Learners Suggest that students close their books and divide a piece of paper into two columns. At the top of one column, ask them to draw a square with diagonal d and side x. At the top of the other column, ask students to draw an equilateral triangle with one altitude and tell them to label both sides of the segment that the altitude divides with an x. Then have students systematically use the Pythagorean Theorem to determine the side relationships of the 45°-45°-90° and 30°-60°-90° triangles in these two figures.

2 Properties of 30°-60°-90° Triangles

Example 3 Find Lengths in a 30°-60°-90° Triangle

AL In a 30°-60°-90° triangle, how do we know which is the shorter leg? The shorter leg is opposite the 30° angle.

OL In a 30°-60°-90° triangle, if we are given any side length, can we find the other two? Explain. Yes; Sample answer: Regardless of the side length you are given, you can find the other two because they are all related to the given side length.

BL Write the equation for the shorter side s and hypotenuse h in terms of the longer side ℓ.

$s = \frac{\ell\sqrt{3}}{3}, h = \frac{2\ell\sqrt{3}}{3}$

Need Another Example?

Find x and y.

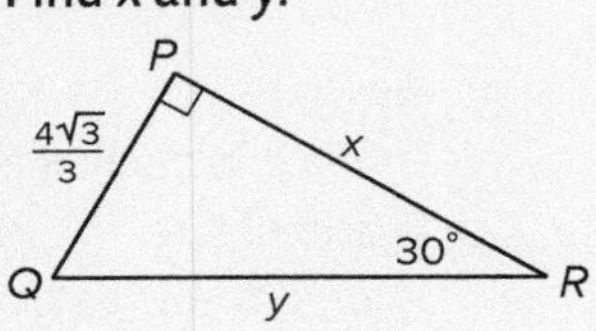

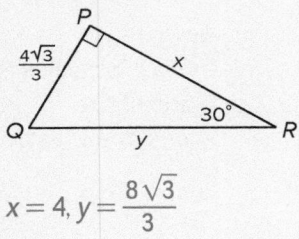

$x = 4, y = \frac{8\sqrt{3}}{3}$

Watch Out!

Fractions When giving side lengths of special triangles, be sure to rationalize the denominator.

Study Tip ELL

Use Ratios The lengths of the sides of a 30°-60°-90° triangle are in a ratio of 1 to $\sqrt{3}$ to 2 or 1 : $\sqrt{3}$: 2.

This algebraic proof verifies the following theorem.

Theorem 8.9 30°-60°-90° Triangle Theorem

In a 30°-60°-90° triangle, the length of the hypotenuse h is 2 times the length of the shorter leg s, and the length of the longer leg ℓ is $\sqrt{3}$ times the length of the shorter leg.

Symbols In a 30°-60°-90° triangle, $h = 2s$ and $\ell = s\sqrt{3}$.

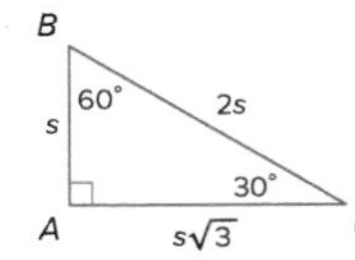

Remember, the shortest side of a triangle is opposite the smallest angle. So the shorter leg in a 30°-60°-90° triangle is opposite the 30° angle, and the longer leg is opposite the 60° angle.

G.SRT.6

Go Online!

Discover the special relationships among the lengths of the sides of 30°-60° right triangles and why they hold with a **Geometer's Sketchpad®** sketch in ConnectED. Discuss your findings with a partner. Ask for clarification as you need it. ELL

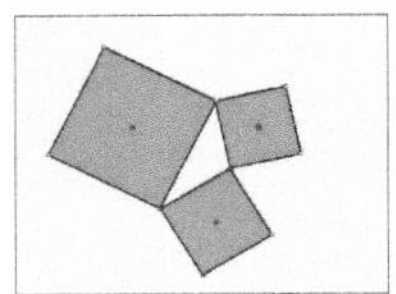

Example 3 Find Lengths in a 30°-60°-90° Triangle

Find x and y.

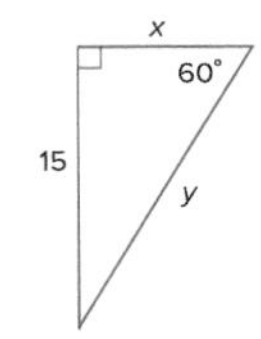

The acute angles of a right triangle are complementary, so the measure of the third angle in this triangle is 90 − 60 or 30. This is a 30°-60°-90° triangle.

Use Theorem 8.9 to find x, the length of the shorter side.

$\ell = s\sqrt{3}$	Theorem 8.9
$15 = x\sqrt{3}$	Substitution
$\frac{15}{\sqrt{3}} = x$	Divide each side by $\sqrt{3}$.
$\frac{15}{\sqrt{3}} \cdot \frac{\sqrt{3}}{\sqrt{3}} = x$	Rationalize the denominator.
$\frac{15\sqrt{3}}{\sqrt{3} \cdot \sqrt{3}} = x$	Multiply.
$\frac{15\sqrt{3}}{3} = x$	$\sqrt{3} \cdot \sqrt{3} = 3$
$5\sqrt{3} = x$	Simplify.

Now use Theorem 8.9 to find y, the length of the hypotenuse.

$h = 2s$	Theorem 8.9
$y = 2(5\sqrt{3})$ or $10\sqrt{3}$	Substitution

Guided Practice

Find x and y.

3A.

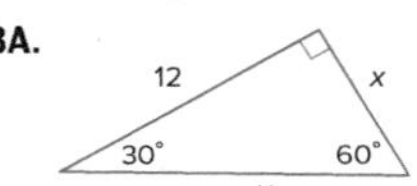

3B.

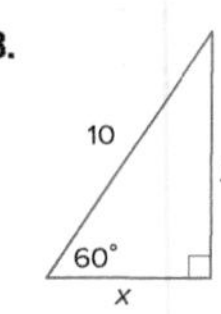

3C.

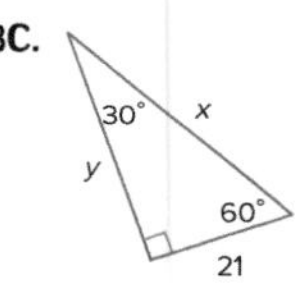

3A. $x = 4\sqrt{3}$; $y = 8\sqrt{3}$
3B. $x = 5$; $y = 5\sqrt{3}$
3C. $x = 42$; $y = 21\sqrt{3}$

G.SRT.6

Real-World Example 4 Use Properties of Special Right Triangles

INVENTIONS A company makes crayons that "do not roll off tables" by shaping them as triangular prisms with equilateral bases. Sixteen of these crayons fit into a box shaped like a triangular prism that is $1\frac{1}{2}$ inches wide. The crayons stand on end in the box and the base of the box is equilateral. What are the dimensions of each crayon?

Understand You know that 16 crayons with equilateral triangular bases fit into a prism. You need to find the base length and height of each crayon.

Plan Guess and check to determine the arrangement of 16 crayons that would stack to fill the box. Find the width of one crayon and use the 30°-60°-90° Triangle Theorem to find its altitude.

Solve Make a guess that 4 equilateral crayons will fit across the base of the box. A sketch shows that the total number of crayons it takes to fill the box using 4 crayons across the base is 16. ✓

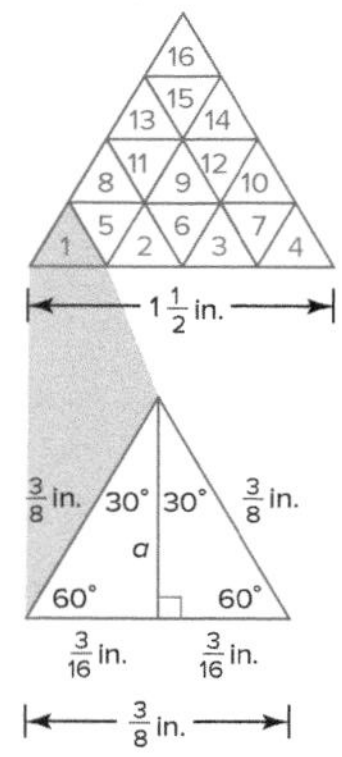

The width of the box is $1\frac{1}{2}$ inches, so the width of one crayon is $1\frac{1}{2} \div 4$ or $\frac{3}{8}$ inch.

Draw an equilateral triangle representing one crayon. Its altitude forms the longer leg of two 30°-60°-90° triangles. Use Theorem 8.9 to find the approximate length of the altitude a.

longer leg length = shorter leg length $\cdot \sqrt{3}$

$$a = \frac{3}{16} \cdot \sqrt{3} \text{ or about } 0.3$$

Each crayon is $\frac{3}{8}$ or about 0.4 inch by about 0.3 inch.

Check Find the height of the box using the 30°-60°-90° Triangle Theorem. Then divide by four, since the box is four crayons high. The result is a crayon height of about 0.3 inch. ✓

Guided Practice

4. **FURNITURE** The top of the aquarium coffee table shown is an isosceles right triangle. The table's longest side, $\overline{AC}$, measures 107 centimeters. What is the distance from vertex B to side $\overline{AC}$? What are the lengths of the other two sides? 53.5 cm; 75.7 cm

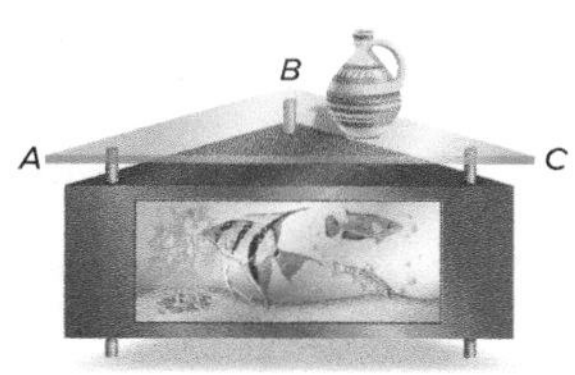

Problem-Solving Tip

Guess and Check In Example 4, suppose your first guess had been that the box was 5 crayons wide.

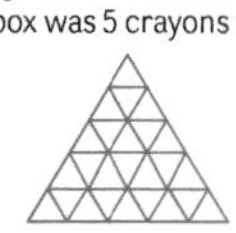

The sketch of this possibility reveals that this leads to a stack of 25, not 16 crayons.

Example 4 Use Properties of Special Right Triangles

AL **What do we know about the angle measures of the crayons from the given information?** Because they are equilateral triangle bases, each angle of the crayon measures 60°.

OL **If the base of the box for jumbo "no roll" crayons is 4 inches, what are the dimensions of each jumbo "no roll" crayon?** Each crayon has a base that measures 1 inch and a height that measures $\frac{\sqrt{3}}{2}$, or about 0.87 inch.

BL **If you had sixteen isosceles right triangle crayons, what shape box would you use? Explain.** Sample answer: a rectangle; If they are isosceles right triangles, two crayons can be placed so that their legs form a square. The box would fit four pairs of crayons across and two pairs up.

Need Another Example?

Quilting A quilt has the design shown in the figure, in which a square is divided into 8 isosceles right triangles. If the length of one side of the square is 3 inches, what are the dimensions of each triangle?

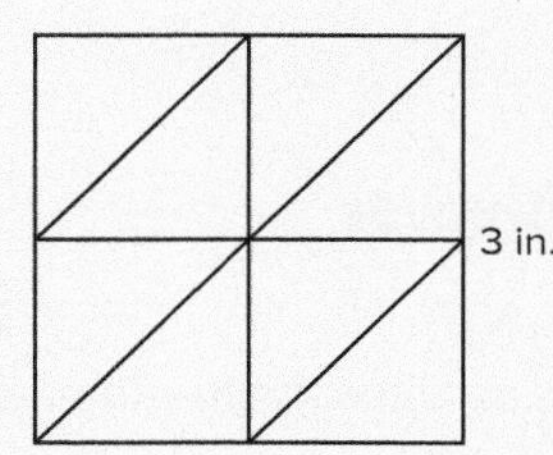

side length = 1.5 in.; hypotenuse = $1.5\sqrt{2}$

Teaching Tip

Common Misconceptions Advise students that a common mistake that can be made is to assume that the longer leg of a 30°-60°-90° triangle is twice the length of the shorter leg. Demonstrate that this cannot be true by providing one or more counterexamples.

Practice

Formative Assessment Use Exercises 1–7 to assess students' understanding of the concepts in this lesson.

The Practice and Problem Solving exercises assess the content taught in the lesson. The Preparing for Assessment page is meant to be used as preparation for end-of-course assessments.

MP Teaching the Mathematical Practices

Sense-Making Mathematically proficient students start by explaining the meaning of a problem to themselves and looking for entry points to its solution. They plan a solution pathway rather than simply jumping into a solution attempt. In Exercises 8–13, encourage students to analyze each figure to determine which special right triangle to use.

Extra Practice

See page R8 for extra exercises for students who are approaching level or for on-level students who need additional reinforcement.

Additional Answer

7. Yes; Sample answer: The height of the triangle is about $3\frac{1}{2}$ in., so since the height of the plaque is less than the diameter of the opening, it will fit.

Check Your Understanding

○ = Step-by-Step Solutions begin on page R13.

Go Online! for a Self-Check Quiz

Examples 1-2 G.SRT.6 **Find x.**

1.

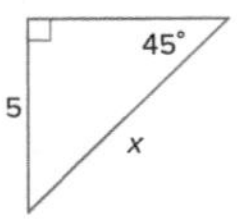

$5\sqrt{2}$

2.

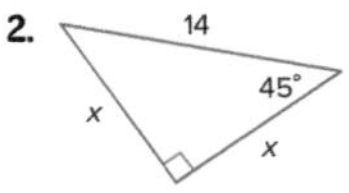

$7\sqrt{2}$

3.

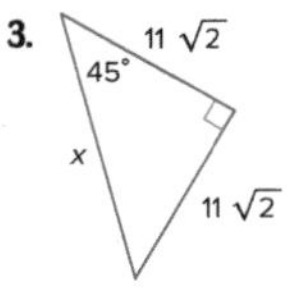

22

Example 3 G.SRT.6 **Find x and y.**

4.

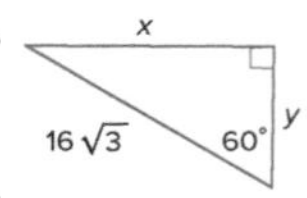

5.

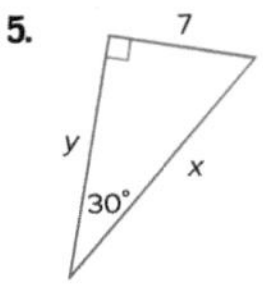

6.

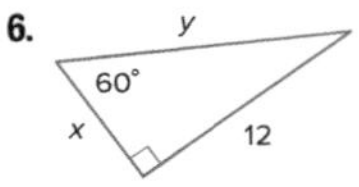

4. $x = 24$; $y = 8\sqrt{3}$
5. $x = 14$; $y = 7\sqrt{3}$
6. $x = 4\sqrt{3}$; $y = 8\sqrt{3}$

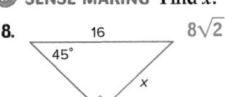

Example 4 G.SRT.6

7. ART Paulo is mailing an engraved plaque that is $3\frac{1}{4}$ inches high to the winner of a chess tournament. He has a mailer that is a triangular prism with 4-inch equilateral triangle bases as shown in the diagram. Will the plaque fit through the opening of the mailer? Explain. See margin.

Practice and Problem Solving

Extra Practice is on page R8.

Examples 1-2 G.SRT.6 **MP SENSE-MAKING Find x.**

8.

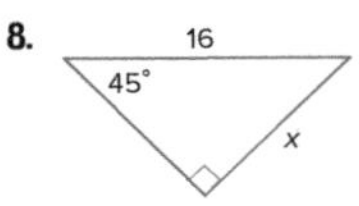

$8\sqrt{2}$

9.

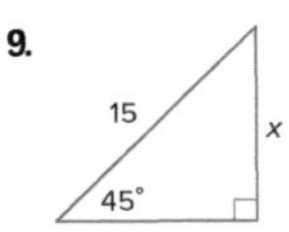

$\frac{15\sqrt{2}}{2}$ or $7.5\sqrt{2}$

10.

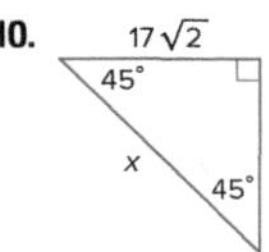

34

11.

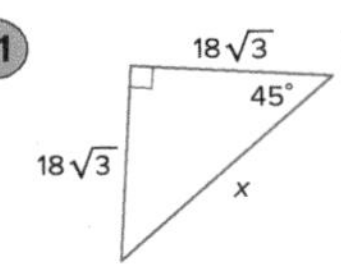

$18\sqrt{6}$

12.

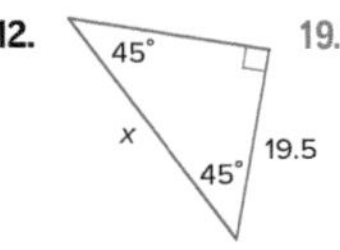

$19.5\sqrt{2}$

13.

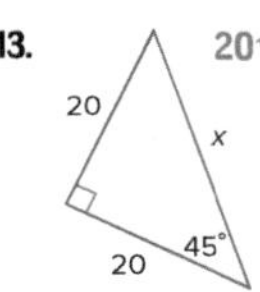

$20\sqrt{2}$

14. If a 45°-45°-90° triangle has a hypotenuse length of 9, find the leg length. $\frac{9\sqrt{2}}{2}$

15. Determine the length of the leg of a 45°-45°-90° triangle with a hypotenuse length of 11. $\frac{11\sqrt{2}}{2}$

16. What is the length of the hypotenuse of a 45°-45°-90° triangle if the leg length is 6 centimeters? $6\sqrt{2}$ or 8.5 cm

17. Find the length of the hypotenuse of a 45°-45°-90° triangle with a leg length of 8 centimeters. $8\sqrt{2}$ or 11.3 cm

Differentiated Homework Options

Levels	AL Basic	OL Core	BL Advanced
Exercises	8–27, 46, 47, 49–59	9–33 odd, 34–37, 39–43 odd, 44–47, 49–59	40–50, (optional: 51–59)
2-Day Option	9–27 odd, 51–59	8–27	
	8–26 even, 46, 47, 49, 50	28–47, 49–59	

You can use ALEKS to provide additional remediation support with personalized instruction and practice.

Go Online! eBook

Interactive Student Guide

Use the *Interactive Student Guide* to deepen conceptual understanding.

- Special Right Triangles

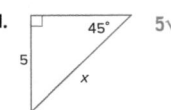

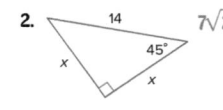

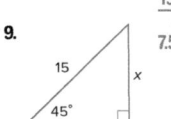

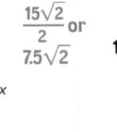

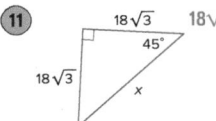

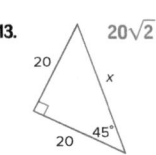

Example 3
G.SRT.6

Find x and y.

18.

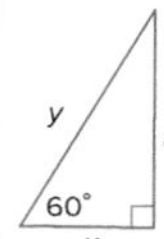

19.

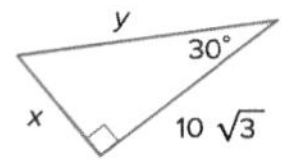

20.

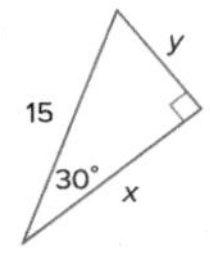

21.

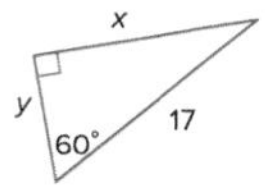

22.

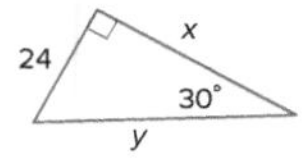

23.

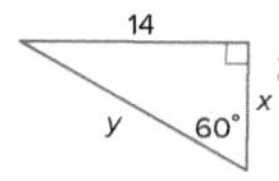

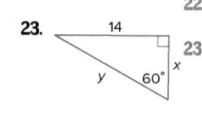

18. $x = 8$; $y = 16$
19. $x = 10$; $y = 20$
20. $x = \frac{15\sqrt{3}}{2}$; $y = \frac{15}{2}$
21. $x = \frac{17\sqrt{3}}{2}$; $y = \frac{17}{2}$
22. $x = 24\sqrt{3}$; $y = 48$
23. $x = \frac{14\sqrt{3}}{3}$; $y = \frac{28\sqrt{3}}{3}$

24. An equilateral triangle has an altitude length of 18 feet. Determine the length of a side of the triangle. $12\sqrt{3}$ or 20.8 ft

25. Find the length of the side of an equilateral triangle that has an altitude length of 24 feet. $16\sqrt{3}$ or 27.7 ft

Example 4
G.SRT.6

26. MP **MODELING** Refer to the beginning of the lesson. Each highlighter is an equilateral triangle with 9-centimeter sides. Will the highlighter fit in a 10-centimeter by 7-centimeter rectangular box? Explain.
No; Sample answer: The height of the box is only 7 cm. and the height of the highlighter is about 7.8 cm, so it will not fit.

27. **EVENT PLANNING** Grace is having a party, and she wants to decorate the gable of the house as shown. The gable is an isosceles right triangle and she knows that the height of the gable is 8 feet. What length of lights will she need to cover the gable below the roof line? 22.6 ft

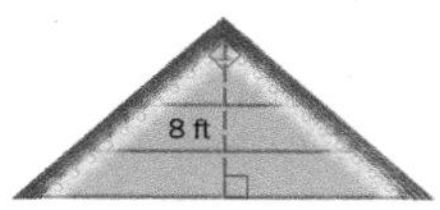

B **Find x and y.**

28.

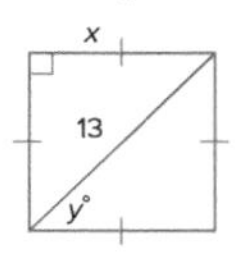

29.

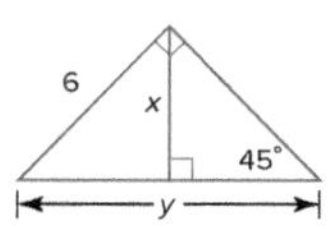

30.

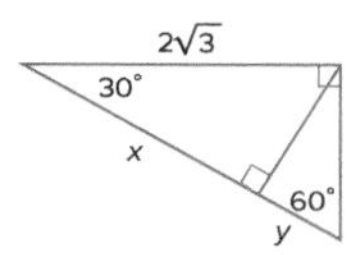

31.

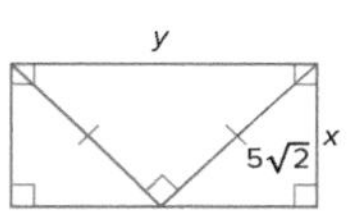

32.

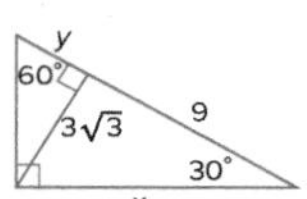

33.

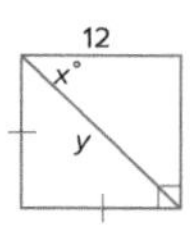

28. $x = \frac{13\sqrt{2}}{2}$; $y = 45$
29. $x = 3\sqrt{2}$; $y = 6\sqrt{2}$
30. $x = 3$; $y = 1$
31. $x = 5$; $y = 10$
32. $x = 6\sqrt{3}$; $y = 3$
33. $x = 45$; $y = 12\sqrt{2}$

34. **QUILTS** The quilt block shown is made up of a square and four isosceles right triangles. What is the value of x? What is the side length of the entire quilt block? 6 in.; 12 in.

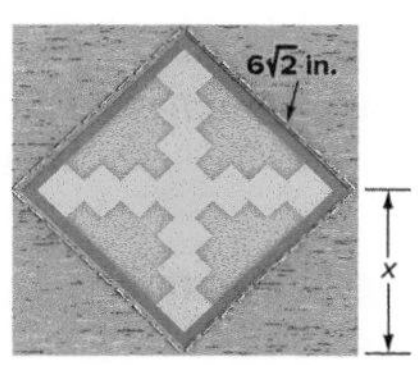

MP Teaching the Mathematical Practices

Modeling Mathematically proficient students can apply the mathematics they know to solve problems arising in everyday life. In Exercise 26, encourage students to make models of the highlighter and packing box.

Levels of Complexity Chart

The levels of the exercises progress from 1 to 3, with Level 1 indicating the lowest level of complexity.

Exercises	8–27	28–39, 51–59	40–50
C Level 3			●
B Level 2		●	
Level 1	●		

Go Online!

The most up-to-date resources available for your program can be found at connectED.mcgraw-hill.com.

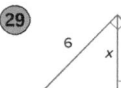

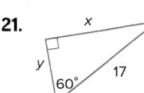

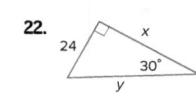

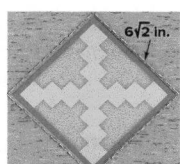

MP Teaching the Mathematical Practices

Modeling Mathematically proficient students can apply the mathematics they know to solve problems arising in everyday life. In Exercise 39, encourage students to make a model of the dump truck that shows how the height changes as the angle increases.

Additional Answers

45a.

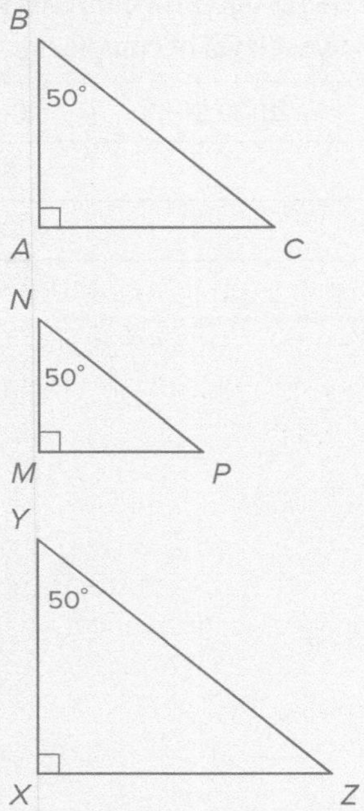

45c. The ratios will always be the same.

35. **ZIP LINE** Suppose a zip line is anchored in one corner of a course shaped like a rectangular prism. The other end is anchored in the opposite corner as shown. If the zip line makes a 60° angle with post $\overline{AF}$, find the zip line's length, AD. **50 ft**

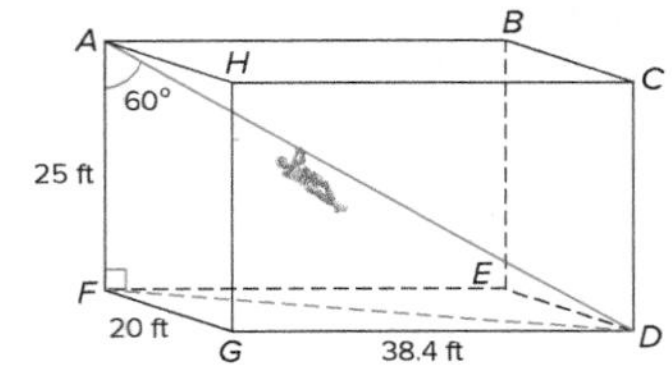

36. **GAMES** Kei is building a bean bag toss for the school carnival. He is using a 2-foot back support that is perpendicular to the ground 2 feet from the front of the board. He also wants to use a support that is perpendicular to the board as shown in the diagram. How long should he make the support? **1.4 ft**

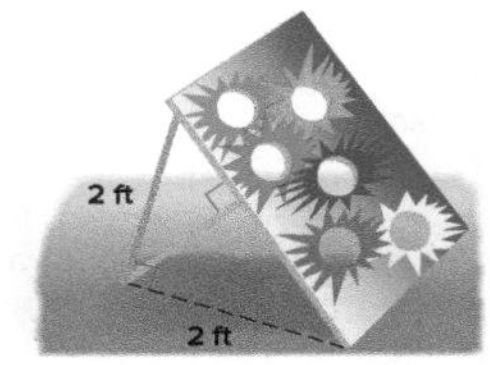

37. Find x, y, and z. **$x = 9\sqrt{2}$; $y = 6\sqrt{3}$; $z = 12\sqrt{3}$**

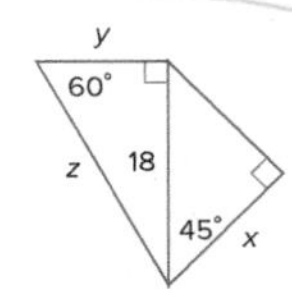

38. Each triangle in the figure is a 45°-45°-90° triangle. Find x. **$\frac{3}{2}$**

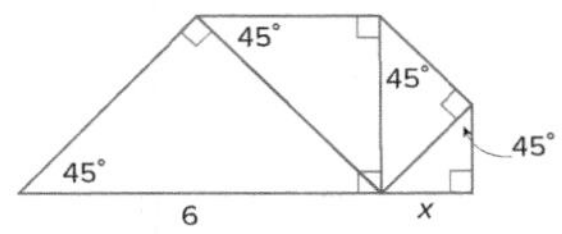

39. MP **MODELING** The dump truck shown has a 15-foot bed length. What is the height of the bed h when angle x is 30°? 45°? 60°?
7.5 ft; 10.6 ft; 13.0 ft

40. Find x, y, and z, and the perimeter of trapezoid $PQRS$. **$x = 6$; $y = 10$; $z = 6\sqrt{3}$; $38 + 6\sqrt{2} + 6\sqrt{3}$ or ≈ 56.9 units**

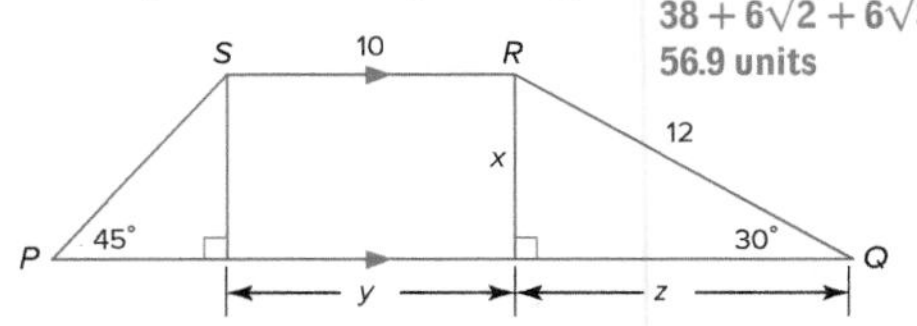

41. **COORDINATE GEOMETRY** $\triangle XYZ$ is a 45°-45°-90° triangle with right angle Z. Find the coordinates of X in Quadrant I for $Y(-1, 2)$ and $Z(6, 2)$. **(6, 9)**

42. **COORDINATE GEOMETRY** $\triangle EFG$ is a 30°-60°-90° triangle with $m\angle F = 90$. Find the coordinates of E in Quadrant III for $F(-3, -4)$ and $G(-3, 2)$. $\overline{FG}$ is the longer leg. **$(-3 - 2\sqrt{3}, -4)$**

43. **COORDINATE GEOMETRY** $\triangle JKL$ is a 45°-45°-90° triangle with right angle K. Find the coordinates of L in Quadrant IV for $J(-3, 5)$ and $K(-3, -2)$. **(4, −2)**

44. Yes; Sample answer: The gazebo is about 127 ft², which will accommodate 16 people. With Eva and her friends, there are a total of 13 at the party, so they will fit.

44. EVENT PLANNING Eva has reserved a gazebo at a local park for a party. She wants to be sure that there will be enough space for her 12 guests to be in the gazebo at the same time. She wants to allow 8 square feet of area for each guest. If the floor of the gazebo is a regular hexagon and each side is 7 feet, will there be enough room for Eva and her friends? Explain. (*Hint:* Use the Polygon Interior Angle Sum Theorem and the properties of special right triangles.)

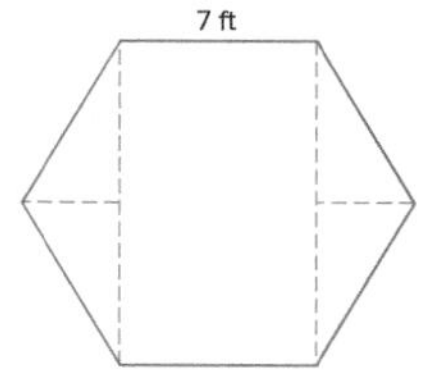

45. MULTIPLE REPRESENTATIONS In this problem, you will investigate ratios in right triangles. Use a protractor and straightedge or dynamic geometry software.

a. Geometric Draw three similar right triangles with a 50° angle. Label one triangle *ABC* where angle *A* is the right angle and *B* is the 50° angle. Label a second triangle *MNP* where *M* is the right angle and *N* is the 50° angle. Label the third triangle *XYZ* where *X* is the right angle and *Y* is the 50° angle. **See margin.**

b. Tabular Copy and complete the table below. **Sample answers given.**

Triangle	Length				Ratio	
ABC	AC	2.4 cm	BC	3.2 cm	$\frac{BC}{AC}$	1.3
MNP	MP	1.7 cm	NP	2.2 cm	$\frac{NP}{MP}$	1.3
XYZ	XZ	3.0 cm	YZ	3.9 cm	$\frac{YZ}{XZ}$	1.3

c. Verbal Make a conjecture about the ratio of the leg opposite the 50° angle to the hypotenuse in any right triangle with an angle measuring 50°. **See margin.**

G.SRT.6

H.O.T. Problems Use Higher-Order Thinking Skills

46. CRITIQUE Carmen and Audrey want to find *x* in the triangle shown. Is either of them correct? Explain. **See margin.**

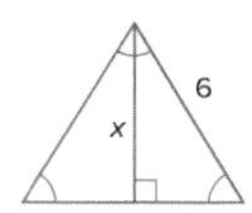

Carmen
$x = \frac{6\sqrt{3}}{2}$
$x = 3\sqrt{3}$

Audrey
$x = \frac{6\sqrt{2}}{2}$
$x = 3\sqrt{2}$

47. OPEN-ENDED Draw a rectangle that has a diagonal twice as long as its width. Then write an equation to find the length of the rectangle. **See margin.**

48. CHALLENGE Find the perimeter of quadrilateral *ABCD*. **59.8**

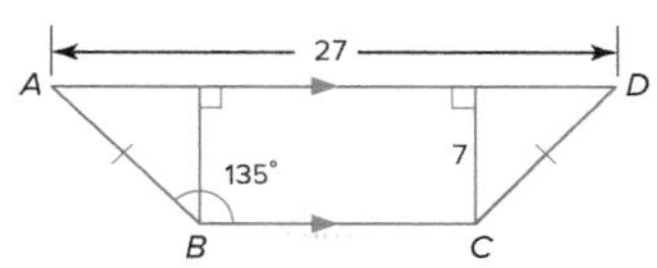

49. REASONING The ratio of the measure of the angles of a triangle is 1:2:3. The length of the shortest side is 8. What is the perimeter of the triangle? **37.9**

50. WRITING IN MATH Why are some right triangles considered *special?* **See margin.**

Standards for Mathematical Practice

Emphasis On	Exercises
1 Make sense of problems and persevere in solving them.	1–6, 8–17
2 Reason abstractly and quantitatively.	28–33, 37, 38, 40
3 Construct viable arguments and critique the reasoning of others.	46
4 Model with mathematics.	7, 27, 34–36, 39, 44, 51
5 Use appropriate tools strategically.	41–43
6 Attend to precision.	47–49
7 Look for and make use of structure.	18–26
8 Look for and express regularity in repeated reasoning.	45, 52–56

Exercise Alert

Protractor and Ruler Exercise 45 requires the use of a protractor and ruler.

Teaching the Mathematical Practices

Critique Mathematically proficient students can distinguish correct logic from flawed reasoning. In Exercise 46, Audrey wrote the expression for the side length incorrectly. Students may confuse the ratios of the lengths of the legs of a 45°-45°-90° triangle with those of a 30°-60°-90° triangle.

Assess

Ticket Out the Door Have students write the side relationships for 45°-45°-90° triangles and 30°-60°-90° triangles. Have students turn in their papers as they exit the class.

Additional Answers

46. Carmen; Sample answer: Because the three angles of the larger triangle are congruent, it is an equilateral triangle and the right triangles formed by the altitude are 30°-60°-90° triangles. The hypotenuse is 6, so the shorter leg is 3 and the longer leg x is $3\sqrt{3}$.

47. Sample answer:

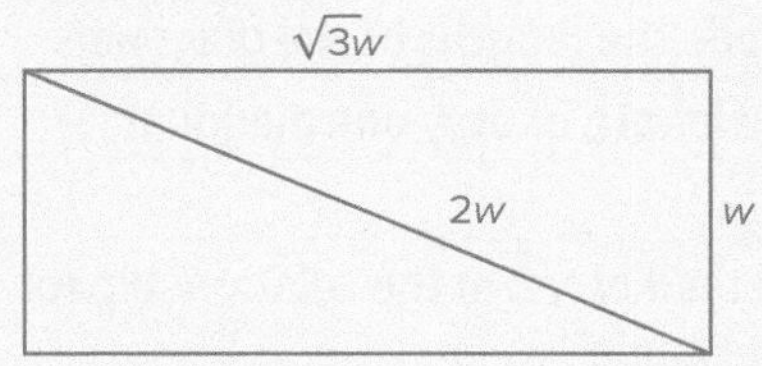

Let ℓ represent the length. $\ell^2 + w^2 = (2w)^2$; $\ell^2 = 3w^2$; $\ell = w\sqrt{3}$.

50. Sample answer: Once you identify that a right triangle is *special* or has a 30°, 60°, or 45° angle measure, you can solve the triangle without the use of a calculator.

Go Online!

eSolutions Manual

Create worksheets, answer keys, and solutions handouts for your assignments.

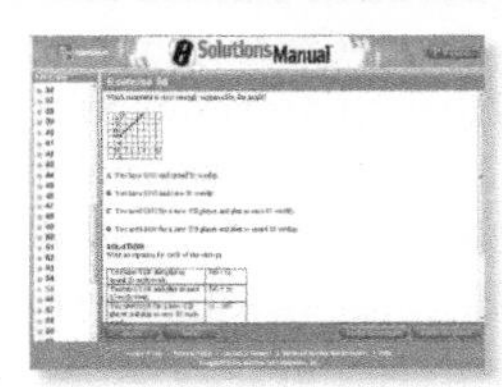

Preparing for Assessment

Exercises 51–59 require students to use the skills they will need on standardized assessments. Exercises are dual-coded with content and standards and mathematical practice standards.

Dual Coding		
Items	Content Standards	MP Mathematical Practices
51	G.SRT.6	4
52–56	G.SRT.6	8
57	G.SRT.6	1, 8
58, 59	G.SRT.6	1

Diagnose Student Errors

Survey student responses for each item. Class trends may indicate common errors and misconceptions.

51.

- A Found the length of short side of right triangle
- B Used $\sqrt{2}$ instead of $\sqrt{3}$ in the relationship for a 30°-60°-90° triangle
- C CORRECT
- D Used incorrect relationship among side lengths in a 30°-60°-90° triangle

54.

- A Did not account for all four sides of the square
- B Did not include the lengths of the diagonals
- C Included the length of only one diagonal
- D CORRECT
- E Used $\sqrt{3}$ instead of $\sqrt{2}$ in the relationship for a 45°-45°-90° triangle

Preparing for Assessment

51. A yield sign approximates an equilateral triangle with sides that are 36 inches long. Which of these is the best estimate of the height of the sign? MP 4 G.SRT.6 C

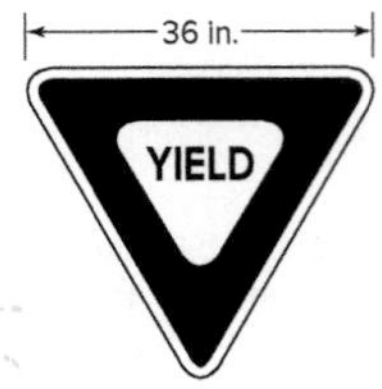

- A 18.0 in.
- B 25.5 in.
- C 31.2 in.
- D 62.4 in.

52. The area of an equilateral triangle is $8\sqrt{3}$ square units. Find the length of one side of the triangle. MP 8 G.SRT.6 $4\sqrt{2}$ units

53. The diagonal of a square measures 10 units. Find the perimeter of the square. MP 8 G.SRT.6 $20\sqrt{2}$ units

54. In a stained-glass window, each colored pane of glass is separated by a metal strip. The window itself is also surrounded by metal strips. Hailey is making a square stained-glass window as shown.

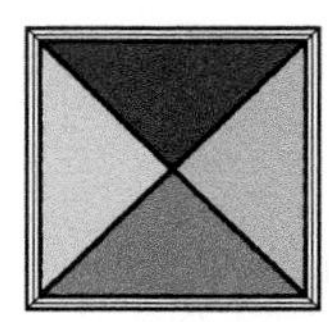

Which of these represents the total length of the metal strips Hailey will need? MP 8 G.SRT.6 D

- A $30 + 60\sqrt{2}$ cm
- B 120 cm
- C $120 + 30\sqrt{2}$ cm
- D $120 + 60\sqrt{2}$ cm
- E $120 + 60\sqrt{3}$ cm

55. What is the value of x? MP 8 G.SRT.6 C

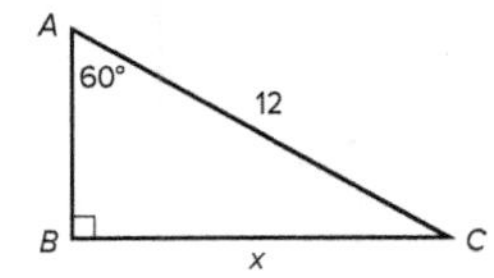

- A 6
- B $4\sqrt{3}$
- C $6\sqrt{3}$
- D $12\sqrt{3}$

56. What is the length of $\overline{KJ}$ in the figure below? MP 8 G.SRT.6 B

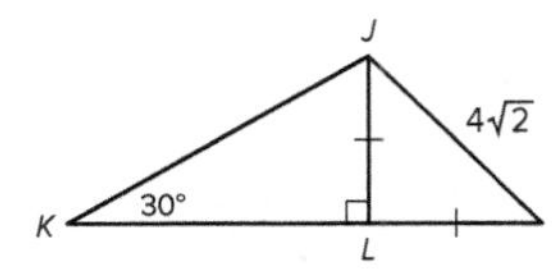

- A $8\sqrt{2}$
- B 8
- C $4\sqrt{3}$
- D 4

57. **MULTI-STEP** A piece of wire measures 24 units. MP 1, 8 G.SRT.6

a. The wire is first bent to form a square. What is the length of a diagonal of the square? $6\sqrt{2}$

b. Then, the wire is bent to form an equilateral triangle. Find the height of the triangle. $4\sqrt{3}$

58. Find the exact value of y. MP 1 G.SRT.6 $6\sqrt{6}$

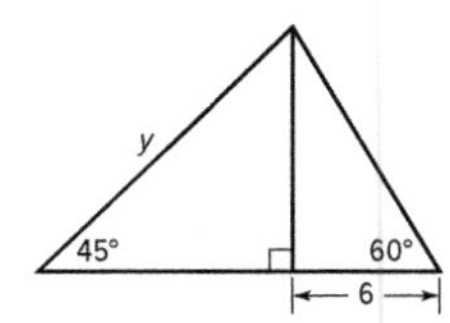

59. $m\angle BCA = 45°$ and $m\angle D = 30°$. If $BC = 6$, find AD. MP 1 G.SRT.6 12

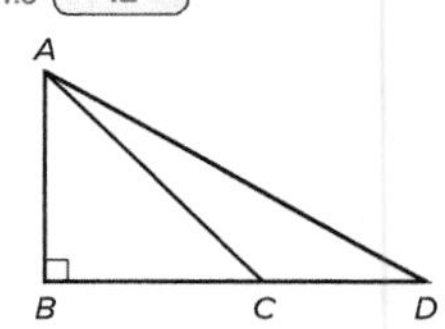

55.

- A Found length of $\overline{AB}$
- B Divided 12 by $\sqrt{3}$ and simplified
- C CORRECT
- D Used incorrect relationship among side lengths in a 30°-60°-90° triangle

56.

- A Used $4\sqrt{2}$ for length of $\overline{JL}$
- B CORRECT
- C Found length of $\overline{KL}$
- D Found length of $\overline{JL}$

Go Online!

Quizzes

Students can use *Self-Check Quizzes* to check their understanding of this lesson and have the results sent to you. You can also give *Quiz 2*, which covers the content in Lessons 8-3 and 8-4.

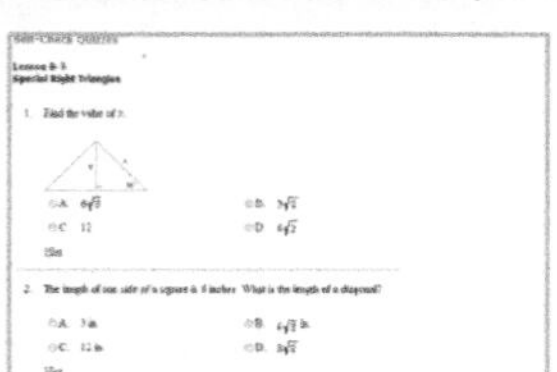

LESSON 8-4

Trigonometry

SUGGESTED PACING (DAYS)

	Explore	Instruction		Extend
90 min.	.25	0.5	.25	
45 min.	0.5	1		0.5

Track Your Progress

Objectives

1 Find trigonometric ratios using right triangles.

2 Use trigonometric ratios to find angle measures in right triangles.

Mathematical Background

A ratio of the lengths of the sides of a right triangle is called a trigonometric ratio. The three most common trigonometric ratios are sine, cosine, and tangent. Trigonometric ratios are used to find missing measures of a right triangle. The inverse of each trigonometric ratio yields the angle measure.

Skills Trace

THEN	NOW	NEXT
G.SRT.6 Understand that by similarity, side ratios in right triangles are properties of the angles in the triangle, leading to definitions of trigonometric ratios for acute angles.	**G.SRT.7** Explain and use the relationship between the sine and cosine of complementary angles.	**G.SRT.8** Use trigonometric ratios and the Pythagorean Theorem to solve right triangles in applied problems.

Go Online! All of these resources and more are available at connectED.mcgraw-hill.com

eLessons utilize the power of your interactive whiteboard in an engaging way. Use **Right Triangle Trigonometry**, Screens 2 and 4–5, to introduce the concepts in this lesson.

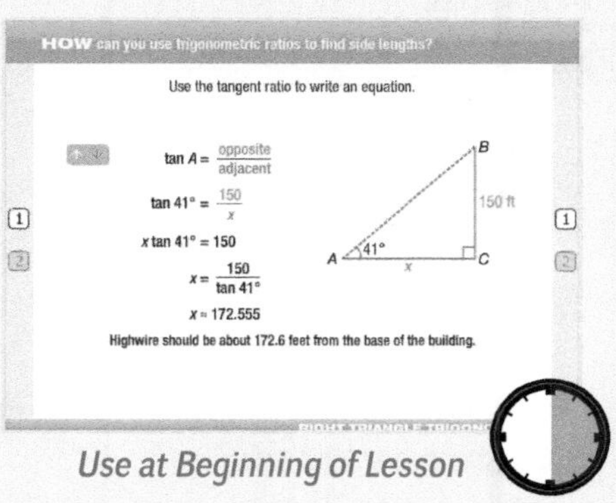

HOW can you use trigonometric ratios to find side lengths?
Use the tangent ratio to write an equation.
tan A = opposite/adjacent
tan 41° = 150/x
x tan 41° = 150
x = 150/tan 41°
x = 172.555
Highwire should be about 172.6 feet from the base of the building.
150 ft
41°

Use at Beginning of Lesson

Personal Tutors (for every example) let students hear real teachers solve problems. Students can pause and repeat as many times as necessary.

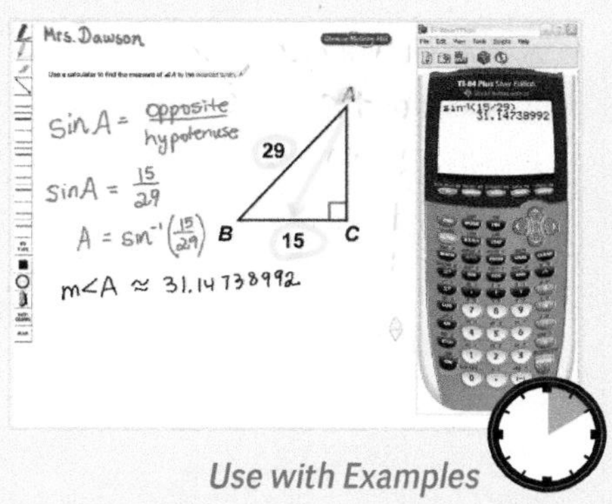

Use with Examples

Use the eGlossary to define *trigonometry, sine, cosine, tangent,* and any other key vocabulary in the lesson.

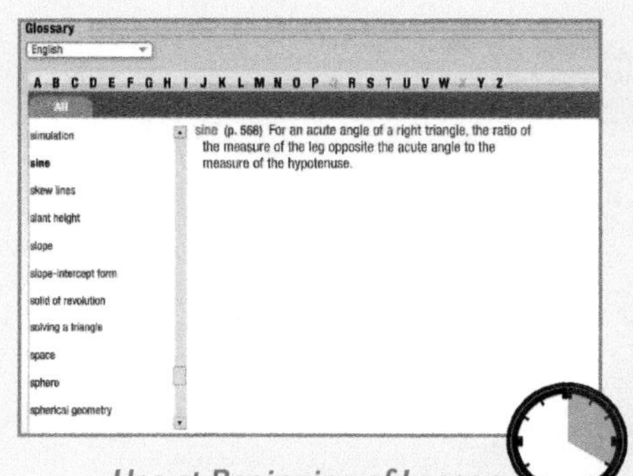

Use at Beginning of Lesson

OER Using Open Educational Resources

Mnemonic Devices Have students work in pairs or threes to write a trigonometric ratios song or a poem, using **Sound Cloud** to record their work. Sound Cloud allows you to create, record, and share audio for free. Have students volunteer to perform, or play the audio, of their mnemonic device in front of the class *Use as homework*

Go Online!
connectED.mcgraw-hill.com
Worksheets

Differentiate Your Resources

Extra Practice Additional practice or homework; Skills Practice is best for approaching-level students and Practice is best for on-level and beyond-level students

Skills Practice

AL OL ELL

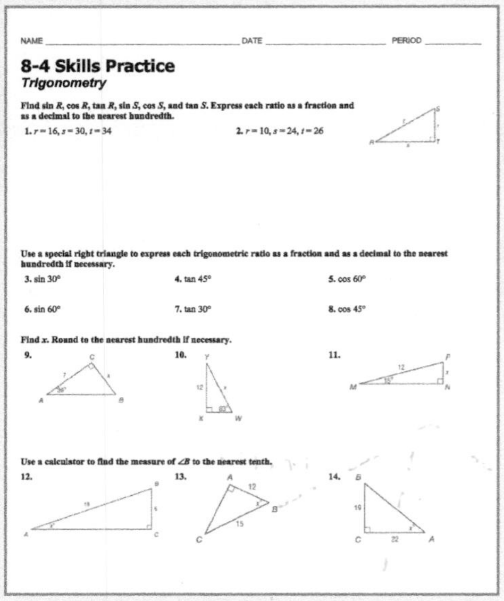
NAME ______ DATE ______ PERIOD ______

8-4 Skills Practice
Trigonometry

Find sin R, cos R, tan R, sin S, cos S, and tan S. Express each ratio as a fraction and as a decimal to the nearest hundredth.

1. r = 16, s = 30, t = 34
2. r = 10, s = 24, t = 26

Use a special right triangle to express each trigonometric ratio as a fraction and as a decimal to the nearest hundredth if necessary.

3. sin 30°
4. tan 45°
5. cos 60°
6. sin 60°
7. tan 30°
8. cos 45°

Find x. Round to the nearest hundredth if necessary.

9.
10.
11.

Use a calculator to find the measure of ∠B to the nearest tenth.

12.
13.
14.

Practice

AL OL BL ELL

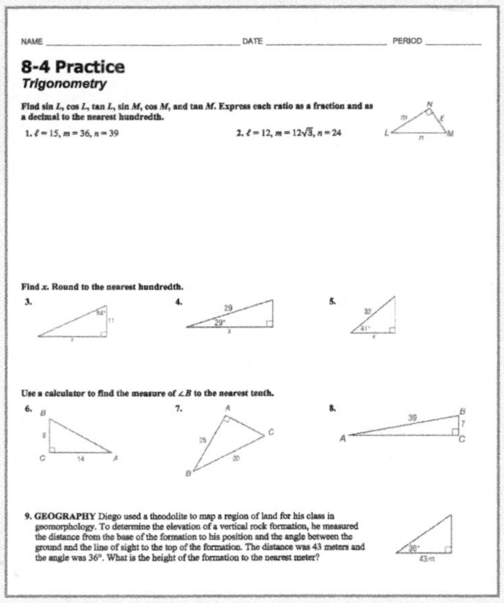
NAME ______ DATE ______ PERIOD ______

8-4 Practice
Trigonometry

Find sin L, cos L, tan L, sin M, cos M, and tan M. Express each ratio as a fraction and as a decimal to the nearest hundredth.

1. ℓ = 15, m = 36, n = 39
2. ℓ = 12, m = 12√3, n = 24

Find x. Round to the nearest hundredth.

3.
4.
5.

Use a calculator to find the measure of ∠B to the nearest tenth.

6.
7.
8.

9. GEOGRAPHY Diego used a theodolite to map a region of land for his class in geomorphology. To determine the elevation of a vertical rock formation, he measured the distance from the base of the formation to his position and the angle between the ground and the line of sight to the top of the formation. The distance was 43 meters and the angle was 36°. What is the height of the formation to the nearest meter?

Word Problem Practice

AL OL BL ELL

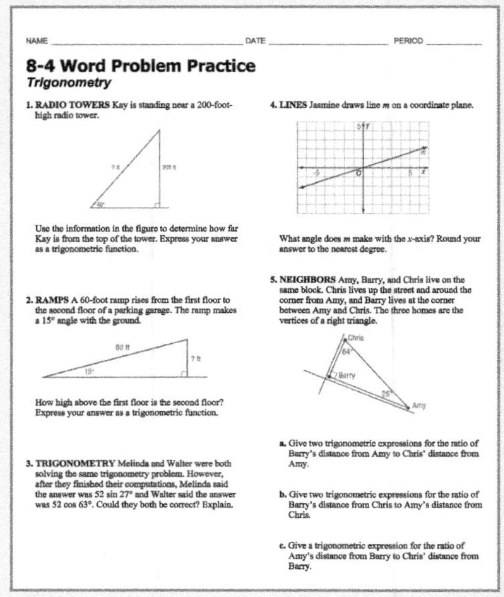
NAME ______ DATE ______ PERIOD ______

8-4 Word Problem Practice
Trigonometry

1. RADIO TOWERS Kay is standing near a 200-foot-high radio tower.

Use the information in the figure to determine how far Kay is from the top of the tower. Express your answer as a trigonometric function.

2. RAMPS A 60-foot ramp rises from the first floor to the second floor of a parking garage. The ramp makes a 15° angle with the ground.

How high above the first floor is the second floor? Express your answer as a trigonometric function.

3. TRIGONOMETRY Melinda and Walter were both solving the same trigonometry problem. However, after they finished their computations, Melinda said the answer was 52 sin 27° and Walter said the answer was 52 cos 63°. Could they both be correct? Explain.

4. LINES Jasmine draws line m on a coordinate plane.

What angle does m make with the x-axis? Round your answer to the nearest degree.

5. NEIGHBORS Amy, Barry, and Chris live on the same block. Chris lives up the street and around the corner from Amy, and Barry lives at the corner between Amy and Chris. The three homes are the vertices of a right triangle.

a. Give two trigonometric expressions for the ratio of Barry's distance from Amy to Chris' distance from Amy.

b. Give two trigonometric expressions for the ratio of Barry's distance from Chris to Amy's distance from Chris.

c. Give a trigonometric expression for the ratio of Amy's distance from Barry to Chris' distance from Barry.

Intervention Reteaching and vocabulary activities that can be used with struggling or absent students and as ELL support

Study Guide and Intervention

AL OL ELL

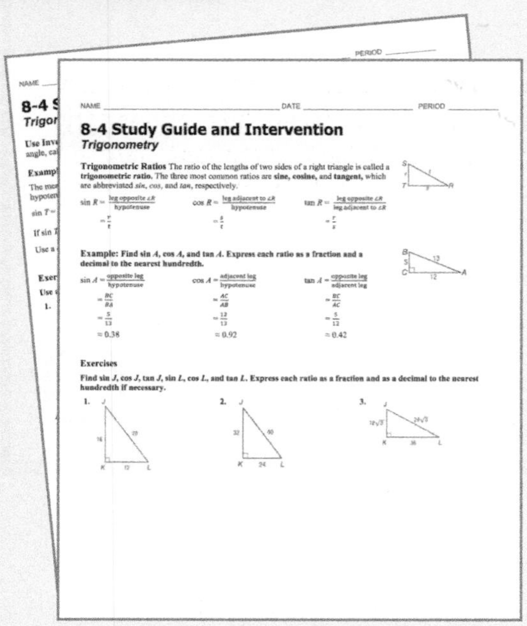
NAME ______ DATE ______ PERIOD ______

8-4 Study Guide and Intervention
Trigonometry

Trigonometric Ratios The ratio of the lengths of two sides of a right triangle is called a trigonometric ratio. The three most common ratios are sine, cosine, and tangent, which are abbreviated sin, cos, and tan, respectively.

Example: Find sin A, cos A, and tan A. Express each ratio as a fraction and a decimal to the nearest hundredth.

Exercises

Find sin J, cos J, tan J, sin L, cos L, and tan L. Express each ratio as a fraction and as a decimal to the nearest hundredth if necessary.

Study Notebook

AL OL BL ELL

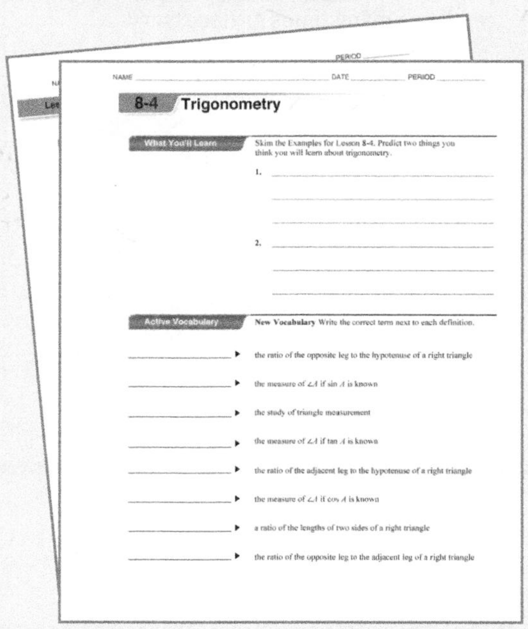
NAME ______ DATE ______ PERIOD ______

8-4 Trigonometry

What You'll Learn — Skim the Examples for Lesson 8-4. Predict two things you think you will learn about trigonometry.

1.
2.

Active Vocabulary — New Vocabulary Write the correct term next to each definition.

the ratio of the opposite leg to the hypotenuse of a right triangle
the measure of ∠A if sin A is known
the study of triangle measurement
the measure of ∠A if tan A is known
the ratio of the adjacent leg to the hypotenuse of a right triangle
the measure of ∠A if cos A is known
a ratio of the lengths of two sides of a right triangle
the ratio of the opposite leg to the adjacent leg of a right triangle

Extension Activities that can be used to extend lesson concepts

Enrichment

OL BL ELL

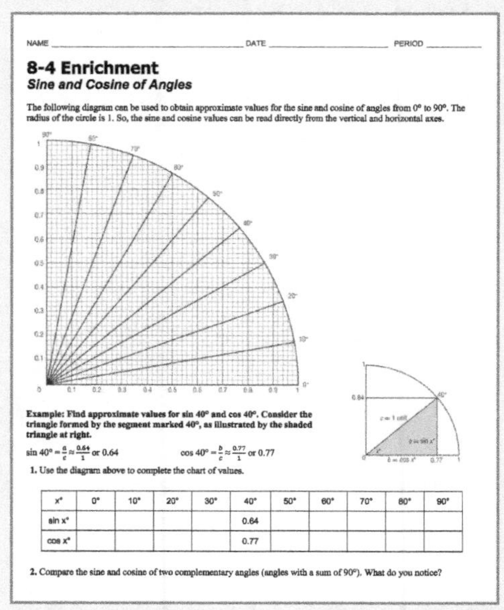
NAME ______ DATE ______ PERIOD ______

8-4 Enrichment
Sine and Cosine of Angles

The following diagram can be used to obtain approximate values for the sine and cosine of angles from 0° to 90°. The radius of the circle is 1. So, the sine and cosine values can be read directly from the vertical and horizontal axes.

Example: Find approximate values for sin 40° and cos 40°. Consider the triangle formed by the segment marked 40°, as illustrated by the shaded triangle at right.

1. Use the diagram above to complete the chart of values.

2. Compare the sine and cosine of two complementary angles (angles with a sum of 90°). What do you notice?

EXPLORE 8-4

Graphing Technology Lab

Trigonometry

You have investigated patterns in the measures of special right triangles. *Trigonometry* is the study of the patterns in all right triangles. You can use the Cabri Jr. application on a graphing calculator to investigate these patterns.

Mathematical Practices

MP 5 Use appropriate tools strategically.

Content Standards

G.SRT.6 Understand that by similarity, side ratios in right triangles are properties of the angles in the triangle, leading to definitions of trigonometric ratios for acute angles.

Activity Investigate Trigonometric Ratios

Work cooperatively.

Step 1 Use the line tool on the **F2** menu to draw a horizontal line. Label the points on the line *A* and *B*.

Step 2 Press **F2** and choose the **Perpendicular** tool to create a perpendicular line through point *B*. Draw and label a point *C* on the perpendicular line.

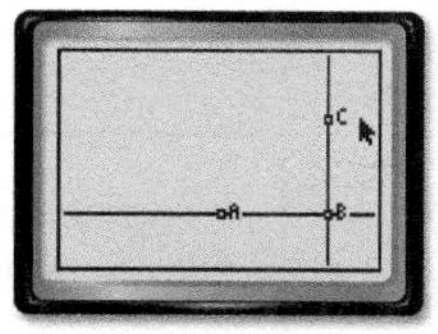

Steps 1 and 2

Step 3 Use the **Segment** tool on the **F2** menu to draw $\overline{AC}$.

Step 4 Find and label the measures of $\overline{BC}$ and $\overline{AC}$ using the **Distance** and **Length** tool under **Measure** on the **F5** menu. Use the **Angle** tool to find the measure of $\angle A$.

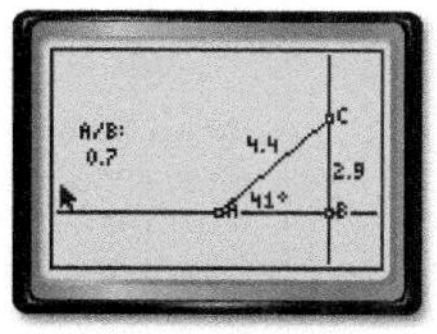

Steps 3 through 5

Step 5 Calculate and display the ratio $\frac{BC}{AC}$ using the **Calculate** tool on the **F5** menu. Label the ratio as *A/B*.

Step 6 Press CLEAR. Then use the arrow keys to move the cursor close to point *B*. When the arrow is clear, press and hold the ALPHA key. Drag *B* and observe the ratio.

Analyze the Results

Work cooperatively.

1. Discuss the effect on $\frac{BC}{AC}$ by dragging point *B* on $\overline{BC}$, $\overline{AC}$, and $\angle A$. **1–3. See margin.**
2. Use the calculate tool to find the ratios $\frac{AB}{AC}$ and $\frac{BC}{AB}$. Then drag *B* and observe the ratios.
3. **MAKE A CONJECTURE** The *sine*, *cosine*, and *tangent* functions are trigonometric functions based on angle measures. Make a note of $m\angle A$. Exit Cabri Jr. and use SIN, COS, and TAN on the calculator to find *sine*, *cosine* and *tangent* for $m\angle A$. Compare the results to the ratios you found in the activity. Make a conjecture about the definitions of sine, cosine, and tangent.

Launch

Objective Use Cabri Jr. to explore trigonometry, the study of the patterns in right triangles.

Materials

- TI-83/84 Plus graphing calculator

Teach ELL

Working in Pairs Arrange students in pairs, mixing abilities. Tell students to go through the steps of the activity.

Ask:

- What do you predict will happen to the ratio as *B* is moved?

Practice Have students complete Exercises 1–3.

Assess

Formative Assessment

Use Exercises 1–3 to assess whether students understand the concept of special right triangles.

From Concrete to Abstract

Tell students to fold a paper diagonally to form a right triangle. Ask them to measure the length of the side opposite the right angle and one leg. What is the ratio of the length of the hypotenuse to the length of the leg? How does this compare to the ratio *A/B* in the activity? The ratio should be the same.

Extending the Concept

Ask:

- How can you use what you have learned about the relationships between the trigonometric functions *sine*, *cosine*, and *tangent*, and the ratios between the side lengths in a right triangle? Find missing measures in a right triangle.

Additional Answers

1. *BC* and *AC* change, but $m\angle A$ and $\frac{BC}{AC}$ are unchanged.
2. $\frac{AB}{AC}$ and $\frac{BC}{AB}$ are unchanged as *B* moves.
3. Sample answer: sine $A = \frac{BC}{AC}$, cosine $A = \frac{AB}{AC}$; and tangent $A = \frac{BC}{AB}$

Go Online!

eLesson

You can use the eLesson on Right Triangle Trigonometry to demonstrate trigonometric ratios. Screens 4–5 may be particularly helpful as you teach this lab.

Launch

Have students read the Why? section of the lesson.

Ask:

- What does percent of grade measure? the steepness of an incline
- What ratio determines the percent of grade? the vertical distance over the horizontal distance
- What is the percent of grade of a trail that falls 8.5 feet over a horizontal distance of 100 feet? 8.5%

Teach

Ask the scaffolded questions for each example to build conceptual understanding for students at all levels.

1 Trigonometric Ratios

Example 1 Find Sine, Cosine, and Tangent Ratios

AL Why isn't it appropriate to find the trigonometric ratios for $\angle R$? Trigonometric ratios only apply to the acute angles in a right triangle.

OL How are sin P and cos Q related? Do you think this will always be true for the acute angles of a right triangle? Explain. They are the same. Yes; sample answer: for the acute angles of a right triangle, the side adjacent to one angle will always be the side opposite the other angle, so the sine of one angle will always be the same as the cosine of the other angle.

LESSON 4

Trigonometry

Then

- You used the Pythagorean Theorem to find missing lengths in right triangles.

Now

1. Find trigonometric ratios using right triangles.
2. Use trigonometric ratios to find angle measures in right triangles.

Why?

- The steepness of a hiking trail is often expressed as a percent of grade. The steepest part of Bright Angel Trail in the Grand Canyon National Park has about a 15.7% grade. This means that the trail rises or falls 15.7 feet over a horizontal distance of 100 feet. You can use trigonometric ratios to determine that this steepness is equivalent to an angle of about 9°.

New Vocabulary

trigonometry
trigonometric ratio
sine
cosine
tangent
inverse sine
inverse cosine
inverse tangent

Mathematical Practices

1 Make sense of problems and persevere in solving them.
2 Reason abstractly and quantitatively.
5 Use appropriate tools strategically.
8 Look for and express regularity in repeated reasoning.

Content Standards

G.SRT.6 Understand that by similarity, side ratios in right triangles are properties of the angles in the triangle, leading to definitions of trigonometric ratios for acute angles.
G.SRT.7 Explain and use the relationship between the sine and cosine of complementary angles.

1 Trigonometric Ratios The word **trigonometry** comes from two Greek terms, *trigon*, meaning triangle, and *metron*, meaning measure. The study of trigonometry involves triangle measurement. A **trigonometric ratio** is a ratio of the lengths of two sides of a right triangle. One trigonometric ratio of $\triangle ABC$ is $\frac{AC}{AB}$.

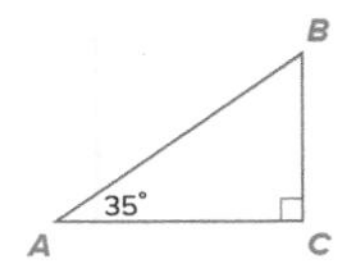

By AA Similarity, a right triangle with a given acute angle measure is similar to every other right triangle with the same acute angle measure. So, trigonometric ratios are constant for a given angle measure.

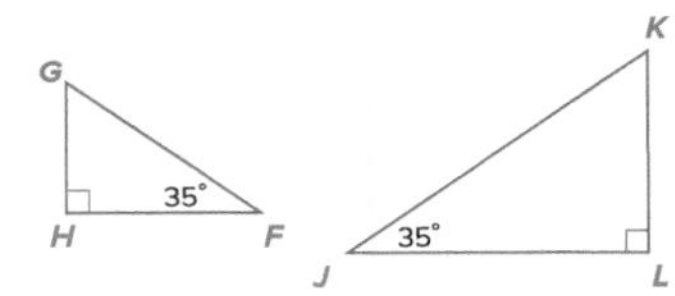

$\triangle ABC \sim \triangle FGH \sim \triangle JKL$, so $\frac{AC}{AB} = \frac{FH}{FG} = \frac{JL}{JK}$

The names of the three most common trigonometric ratios are given below.

Key Concept Trigonometric Ratios

Words	Symbols
If $\triangle ABC$ is a right triangle with acute $\angle A$, then the **sine** of $\angle A$ (written sin A) is the ratio of the length of the leg opposite $\angle A$ (opp) to the length of the hypotenuse (hyp).	$\sin A = \frac{\text{opp}}{\text{hyp}}$ or $\frac{a}{c}$ $\sin B = \frac{\text{opp}}{\text{hyp}}$ or $\frac{b}{c}$
If $\triangle ABC$ is a right triangle with acute $\angle A$, then the **cosine** of $\angle A$ (written cos A) is the ratio of the length of the leg adjacent $\angle A$ (adj) to the length of the hypotenuse (hyp).	$\cos A = \frac{\text{adj}}{\text{hyp}}$ or $\frac{b}{c}$ $\cos B = \frac{\text{adj}}{\text{hyp}}$ or $\frac{a}{c}$
If $\triangle ABC$ is a right triangle with acute $\angle A$, then the **tangent** of $\angle A$ (written tan A) is the ratio of the length of the leg opposite $\angle A$ (opp) to the length of the leg adjacent $\angle A$ (adj).	$\tan A = \frac{\text{opp}}{\text{adj}}$ or $\frac{a}{b}$ $\tan B = \frac{\text{opp}}{\text{adj}}$ or $\frac{b}{a}$

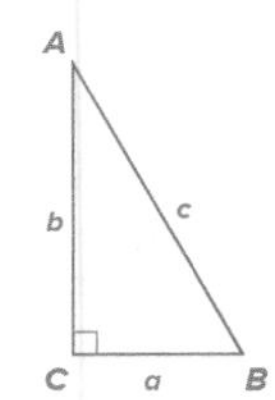

Mathematical Practices Strategies

Make sense of problems and persevere in solving them.

Help students express the relationships between the sine and cosine of complementary angles and help them appropriate trigonometric ratios to solve right triangles. For example, ask:

- What is the relationship between the sine of an angle and the cosine of its complement? They are equal.
- How do you find the measure of an angle in a right triangle? You find a ratio using lengths of given sides and then you compute the inverse of this ratio to find the angle.
- How do you solve a right triangle? You can use the Pythagorean Theorem to find missing side lengths, and you can use trigonometric ratios to find missing angle measures or missing side lengths.

Go Online!

Interactive Whiteboard

Use the *eLesson*, *Lesson Presentation*, or *Interactive Classroom* to present this lesson.

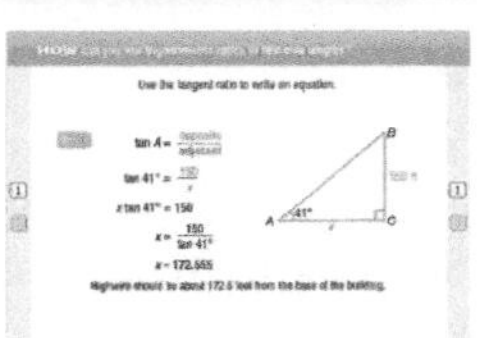

Study Tip

Memorizing Trigonometric Ratios SOH-CAH-TOA is a mnemonic device for learning the ratios for sine, cosine, and tangent using the first letter of each word in the ratios.

$\sin A = \frac{\text{opp}}{\text{hyp}}$

$\cos A = \frac{\text{adj}}{\text{hyp}}$

$\tan A = \frac{\text{opp}}{\text{adj}}$

G.SRT.6

Example 1 Find Sine, Cosine, and Tangent Ratios

Express each ratio as a fraction and as a decimal to the nearest hundredth.

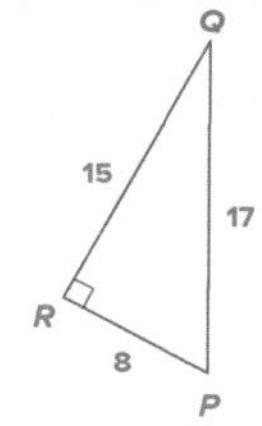

a. sin *P*

$\sin P = \frac{\text{opp}}{\text{hyp}}$

$= \frac{15}{17}$ or about 0.88

b. cos *P*

$\cos P = \frac{\text{adj}}{\text{hyp}}$

$= \frac{8}{17}$ or about 0.47

c. tan *P*

$\tan P = \frac{\text{opp}}{\text{adj}}$

$= \frac{15}{8}$ or about 1.88

d. sin *Q*

$\sin Q = \frac{\text{opp}}{\text{hyp}}$

$= \frac{8}{17}$ or about 0.47

e. cos *Q*

$\cos Q = \frac{\text{adj}}{\text{hyp}}$

$= \frac{15}{17}$ or about 0.88

f. tan *Q*

$\tan Q = \frac{\text{opp}}{\text{adj}}$

$= \frac{8}{15}$ or about 0.53

Guided Practice

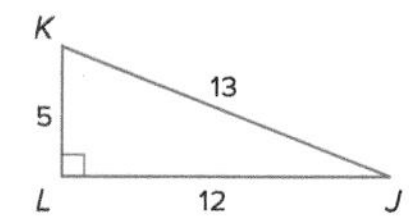

1. Find sin *J*, cos *J*, tan *J*, sin *K*, cos *K*, and tan *K*. Express each ratio as a fraction and as a decimal to the nearest hundredth.

1. $\sin J = \frac{5}{13} \approx 0.38$, $\cos J = \frac{12}{13} \approx 0.92$, $\tan J = \frac{5}{12} \approx 0.42$, $\sin K = \frac{12}{13} \approx 0.92$, $\cos K = \frac{5}{13} \approx 0.38$, $\tan K = \frac{12}{5} \approx 2.4$

Special right triangles can be used to find the sine, cosine, and tangent of 30°, 60°, and 45° angles.

G.SRT.7

Example 2 Use Special Right Triangles to Find Trigonometric Ratios

Use a special right triangle to express the tangent of 30° as a fraction and as a decimal to the nearest hundredth.

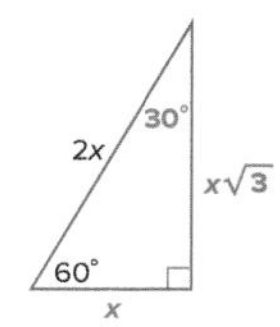

Draw and label the side lengths of a 30°-60°-90° right triangle, with x as the length of the shorter leg.

The side opposite the 30° angle has a measure of x.

The side adjacent to the 30° angle has a measure of $x\sqrt{3}$.

$\tan 30° = \frac{\text{opp}}{\text{adj}}$ — Definition of tangent ratio

$= \frac{x}{x\sqrt{3}}$ — Substitution

$= \frac{1}{\sqrt{3}} \cdot \frac{\sqrt{3}}{\sqrt{3}}$ — Simplify and rationalize the denominator.

$= \frac{\sqrt{3}}{3}$ or about 0.58 — Simplify and use a calculator.

Guided Practice

2. Use a special right triangle to express the cosine of 45° as a fraction and as a decimal to the nearest hundredth. $\frac{\sqrt{2}}{2} \approx 0.71$

BL **How are the tangents of $\angle Q$ and $\angle P$ related? Do you think this will always be true for the acute angles of a right triangle? Explain.** They are inverses. Yes; sample answer: the side adjacent to and opposite one angle will always be the reverse of the other acute angle in the triangle, so the tangents of the two acute angles will always be inverses.

Example 2 Use Special Right Triangles to Find Trigonometric Ratios

AL **Is $\frac{\sqrt{3}}{3}$ the tangent of the 30° angle for all 30°-60°-90° triangles? Explain.** Yes; since we used the relationships between the sides and not specific lengths, the tangent for the 30° angle of all 30°-60°-90° triangles will be the same.

OL **What is the sine of the 30° angle for all 30°-60°-90° triangles?** $\frac{1}{2}$

BL **What is the sine of the 60° angle for all 30°-60°-90° triangles?** $\frac{\sqrt{3}}{2}$ or about 0.87

Need Another Example?

Use a special right triangle to express the cosine of 60° as a fraction and as a decimal to the nearest hundredth. $\frac{1}{2}$, 0.5

Need Another Example?

Express each ratio as a fraction and as a decimal to the nearest hundredth.

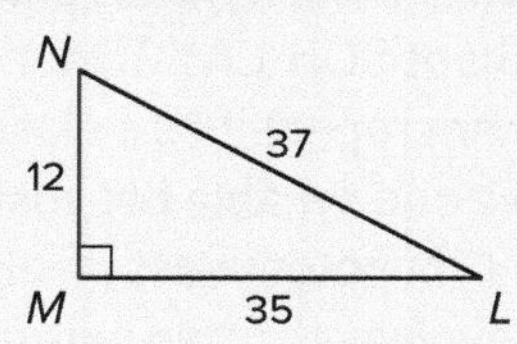

a. sin *L* $\frac{12}{37}$ or 0.32

d. sin *N* $\frac{35}{37}$ or 0.95

b. cos *L* $\frac{35}{37}$ or 0.95

e. cos *N* $\frac{12}{37}$ or 0.32

c. tan *L* $\frac{12}{35}$ or 0.34

f. tan *N* $\frac{35}{12}$ or 2.92

Teaching Tip

Trigonometry The trigonometric ratios are only defined for nonnegative values. These definitions can be extended to give the familiar trigonometric functions defined on all real numbers.

Example 3 Estimate Measures Using Trigonometry

AL When would you need to use trigonometry to estimate a measurement? Sample answer: when you can't easily measure a distance, length, or angle, but you have enough information to use trigonometry

OL If the hiker walked a horizontal distance of 150 feet, what would his change in vertical position be? about 13.1 feet

BL How is the distance along the path affected if the slope of the path increases and the horizontal distance remains the same? The distance along the path also increases.

Need Another Example?

Exercise A fitness trainer sets the incline on a treadmill to 7°. The walking surface is 5 feet long. Approximately how many inches did the trainer raise the end of the treadmill from the floor?

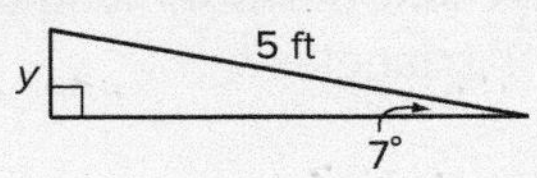

≈ 7.3 in.

Real-World Link

The grade of a trail often changes many times. Average grade is the average of several consecutive running grades of a trail. Maximum grade is the smaller section of a trail that exceeds the trail's typical running grade. Trails often have maximum grades that are much steeper than the average running grade.

Source: Federal Highway Administration

G.SRT.7

Real-World Example 3 Estimate Measures Using Trigonometry

HIKING A certain part of a hiking trail slopes upward at about a 5° angle. After traveling a horizontal distance of 100 feet along this part of the trail, what would be the change in a hiker's vertical position? What distance has the hiker traveled along the path?

Let $m\angle A = 5$. The vertical change in the hiker's position is x, the measure of the leg opposite $\angle A$. The horizontal distance traveled is 100 feet, the measure of the leg adjacent to $\angle A$. Since the length of the leg opposite and the leg adjacent to a given angle are involved, write an equation using a tangent ratio.

$\tan A = \frac{\text{opp}}{\text{adj}}$ Definition of tangent ratio

$\tan 5° = \frac{x}{100}$ Substitution

$100 \cdot \tan 5° = x$ Multiply each side by 100.

Use a calculator to find x.

100 [TAN] 5 [ENTER] 8.748866353

The hiker is about 8.75 feet higher than when he started walking.

The distance y traveled along the path is the length of the hypotenuse, so you can use a cosine ratio to find this distance.

$\cos A = \frac{\text{adj}}{\text{hyp}}$ Definition of cosine ratio

$\cos 5° = \frac{100}{y}$ Substitution

$y \cdot \cos 5° = 100$ Multiply each side by y.

$y = \frac{100}{\cos 5°}$ Divide each side by cos 5°.

Study Tip

Graphing Calculator Be sure your graphing calculator is in degree mode rather than radian mode.

Use a calculator to find y.

100 [÷] [COS] 5 [ENTER] 100.3819838

The hiker has traveled a distance of about 100.38 feet along the path.

Guided Practice

Find x to the nearest hundredth.

3A. 8.39

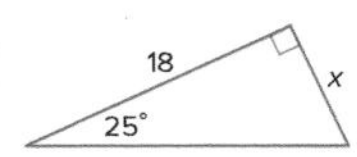

3B. 43.86

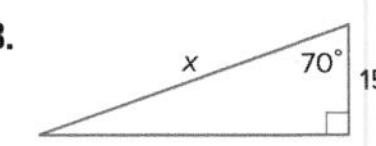

3C. ARCHITECTURE The front of the vacation cottage shown is an isosceles triangle. What is the height x of the cottage above its foundation? What is the length y of the roof? Explain your reasoning.
$x \approx 56$ ft because $x = 32.5 \tan 60°$; since all the angles of the cottage are 60° this is an equilateral triangle, so $y = 65$ ft.

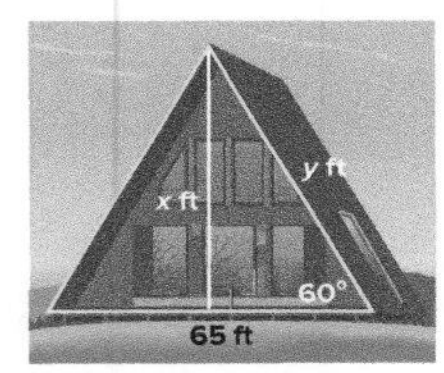

Westend61/Getty Images

Differentiated Instruction AL OL

Auditory/Musical Learners The easiest way for auditory learners to remember the ratios for sine, cosine, and tangent is for them to chant SOH-CAH-TOA. When introducing this mnemonic device to students, have them repeat it as a class a few times in rhythm. Point out that SOH and CAH each have one syllable because the "H" is silent, so students can remember that one "silent" hypotenuse is involved for the sine and cosine ratios. TOA has two syllables and involves the two legs for the tangent ratio.

2 Use Inverse Trigonometric Ratios

Use Inverse Trigonometric Ratios In Example 2, you found that $\tan 30° \approx 0.58$. It follows that if the tangent of an acute angle is 0.58, then the angle measures approximately 30.

If you know the sine, cosine, or tangent of an acute angle, you can use a calculator to find the measure of the angle, which is the inverse of the trigonometric ratio.

> **Reading Math**
> **Inverse Trigonometric Ratios** The expression $\sin^{-1} x$ is read *the inverse sine of x* and is interpreted as the angle with sine *x*. Be careful not to confuse this notation with the notation for negative exponents—$\sin^{-1} x \neq \frac{1}{\sin x}$. Instead, this notation is similar to the notation for an inverse function, $f^{-1}(x)$.

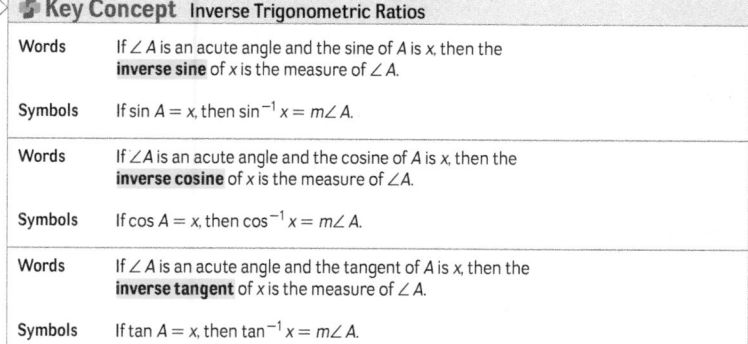

Key Concept Inverse Trigonometric Ratios

Words	If $\angle A$ is an acute angle and the sine of *A* is *x*, then the **inverse sine** of *x* is the measure of $\angle A$.
Symbols	If $\sin A = x$, then $\sin^{-1} x = m\angle A$.
Words	If $\angle A$ is an acute angle and the cosine of *A* is *x*, then the **inverse cosine** of *x* is the measure of $\angle A$.
Symbols	If $\cos A = x$, then $\cos^{-1} x = m\angle A$.
Words	If $\angle A$ is an acute angle and the tangent of *A* is *x*, then the **inverse tangent** of *x* is the measure of $\angle A$.
Symbols	If $\tan A = x$, then $\tan^{-1} x = m\angle A$.

So if $\tan 30° \approx 0.58$, then $\tan^{-1} 0.58 \approx 30°$.

G.SRT.7

Example 4 Find Angle Measures Using Inverse Trigonometric Ratios

Use a calculator to find the measure of $\angle A$ to the nearest tenth.

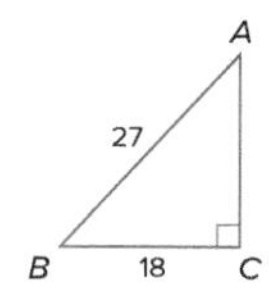

The measures given are those of the leg opposite $\angle A$ and the hypotenuse, so write an equation using the sine ratio.

$\sin A = \frac{18}{27}$ or $\frac{2}{3}$ $\quad \sin A = \frac{\text{opp}}{\text{hyp}}$

If $\sin A = \frac{2}{3}$, then $\sin^{-1} \frac{2}{3} = m\angle A$. Use a calculator.

KEYSTROKES: [2nd] [SIN⁻¹] [(] 2 [÷] 3 [)] [ENTER] 41.8103149

So, $m\angle A \approx 41.8°$.

> **Study Tip**
> **Tools** Use a graphing calculator. The second functions of the [SIN], [COS], and [TAN] keys are usually the inverses.

Guided Practice

Use a calculator to find the measure of $\angle A$ to the nearest tenth.

4A. 16.7°

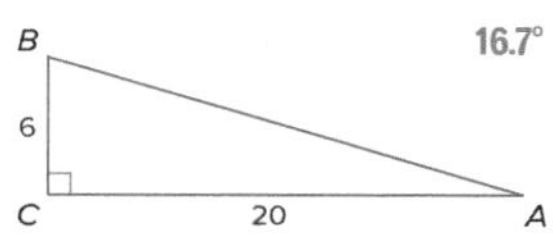

4B. 78.5°

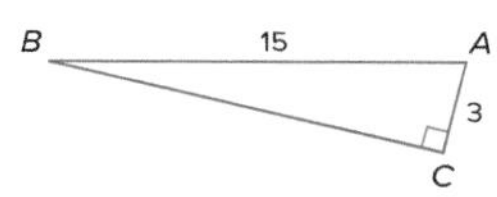

2 Use Inverse Trigonometric Ratios

Example 4 Find Angle Measures Using Inverse Trigonometric Ratios

AL **What does it mean to be the *inverse* of something? Explain.** Sample answer: the inverse of something is the opposite. For example, the inverse of multiplication is division.

OL **Could we use another method to find the measure of angle *A*? Explain.** Yes; sample answer: find the inverse cosine of $\frac{18}{27}$ or $\cos^{-1}\frac{18}{27}$ which is $m\angle B$. Then subtract from 90°.

BL **Can you find the angle measure of any angle of a right triangle given any two sides of the triangle? Explain.** Yes; Sample answer: if you are given any two sides of the triangle, you can use them to find one of the three trigonometric ratios for any angle.

Need Another Example?

Use a calculator to find the measure of $\angle P$ to the nearest tenth.

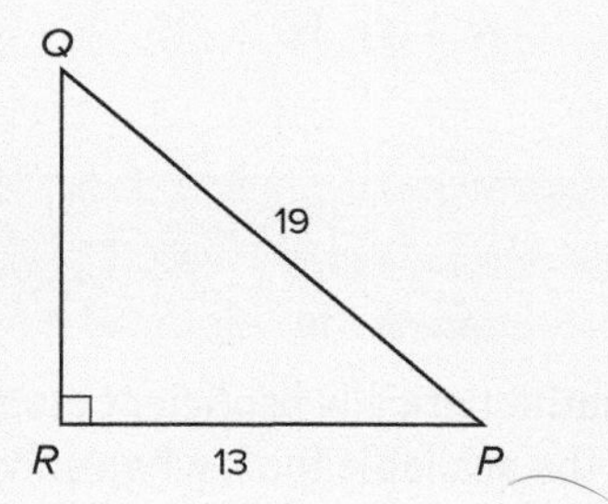

46.8

Watch Out!

Rounding When finding missing measures of a triangle, the angles may not add to 180° because of rounding errors.

Teaching the Mathematical Practices

Tools Mathematically proficient students consider the available tools when solving a mathematical problem. Encourage students to use their graphing calculators to explore trigonometric concepts.

Example 5 Solve a Right Triangle

AL **What does it mean to solve a right triangle?** Determine all of the angle measures and side lengths that are not given.

OL **Could you use only trigonometry to solve this triangle? If yes, how?** Yes; you could also use the tangent ratio to find $m\angle Y$. Then you could use any of the trigonometric ratios to find XY.

BL **If a right triangle has one angle that measures 35° and the length of the hypotenuse is 11, what are the other angle measures and lengths?** The other angle measures 55°. The length of the shorter leg is about 6.3. The length of the longer leg is about 9.

Need Another Example?

Solve the right triangle. Round side measures to the nearest hundredth and angle measures to the nearest degree.

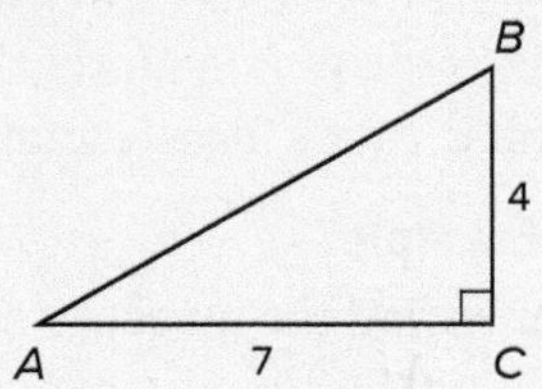

$m\angle A \approx 30$; $m\angle B \approx 60$; $AB \approx 8.06$

MP Teaching the Mathematical Practices

Tools Mathematically proficient students consider the available tools when solving a mathematical problem. In Exercises 12–14, encourage students to use a graphing calculator to find the measure.

Additional Answers (Guided Practice)

5A. $m\angle F \approx 23$; $m\angle G \approx 67$; $FH = 12$

5B. $m\angle C = 28$; $AB \approx 4.7$; $BC \approx 8.8$

5C. $m\angle P = 57$; $QR \approx 24.6$; $PR \approx 29.4$

When you use given measures to find the unknown angle and side measures of a right triangle, this is known as *solving a right triangle*. To solve a right triangle, you need to know

- two side lengths or
- one side length and the measure of one acute angle.

G.SRT.7

Example 5 Solve a Right Triangle

Solve the right triangle. Round side measures to the nearest tenth and angle measures to the nearest degree.

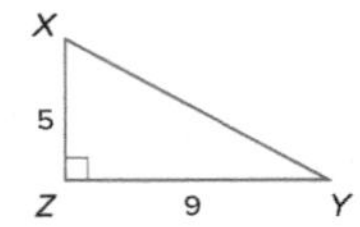

Step 1 Find $m\angle X$ by using a tangent ratio.

$\tan X = \frac{9}{5}$ — $\tan X = \frac{\text{opp}}{\text{adj}}$

$\tan^{-1}\frac{9}{5} = m\angle X$ — Definition of inverse tangent

$60.9453959 \approx m\angle X$ — Use a calculator.

So, $m\angle X \approx 61$.

Step 2 Find $m\angle Y$ using Corollary 4.1, which states that the acute angles of a right triangle are complementary.

$m\angle X + m\angle Y = 90$ — Corollary 4.1

$61 + m\angle Y \approx 90$ — $m\angle X \approx 61$

$m\angle Y \approx 29$ — Subtract 61 from each side.

So, $m\angle Y \approx 29$.

Step 3 Find XY by using the Pythagorean Theorem.

$(XZ)^2 + (ZY)^2 = (XY)^2$ — Pythagorean Theorem

$5^2 + 9^2 = (XY)^2$ — Substitution

$106 = (XY)^2$ — Simplify.

$\sqrt{106} = XY$ — Take the positive square root of each side.

$10.3 \approx XY$ — Use a calculator.

So $XY \approx 10.3$.

Study Tip

Alternative Methods Right triangles can often be solved using different methods. In Example 5, $m\angle Y$ could have been found using a tangent ratio, and $m\angle X$ and a sine ratio could have been used to find XY.

WatchOut!

Approximation If using calculated measures to find other measures in a right triangle, be careful not to round values until the last step. So in the following equation, use $\tan^{-1}\frac{9}{5}$ instead of its approximate value, 61°.

$XY = \frac{9}{\sin X}$

$= \frac{9}{\sin\left(\tan^{-1}\frac{9}{5}\right)}$

≈ 10.3

Guided Practice

Solve each right triangle. Round side measures to the nearest tenth and angle measures to the nearest degree. 5A–5C. See margin.

5A.

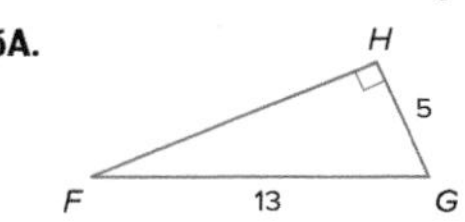

5B.

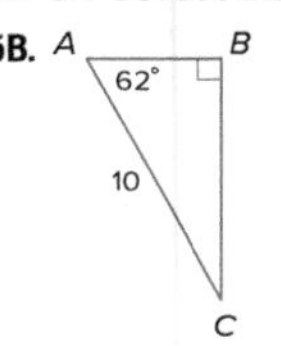

5C.

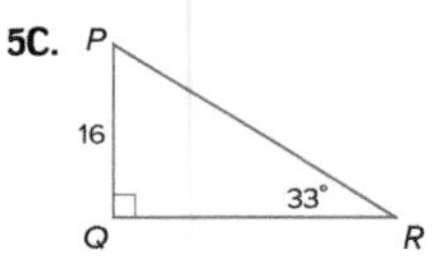

Differentiated Instruction OL BL

Extension Give students the length of one side of a right triangle and the measure of one of its acute angles. Ask students which trigonometric ratio to use if you want to find the length of the hypotenuse. If the side you give them is adjacent to the angle you give them, then use the cosine ratio. If the side you give them is opposite the angle you give them, then use the sine ratio.

Check Your Understanding

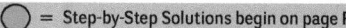

◯ = Step-by-Step Solutions begin on page R13.

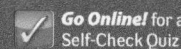

Go Online! for a Self-Check Quiz

Example 1 G.SRT.7

Express each ratio as a fraction and as a decimal to the nearest hundredth.

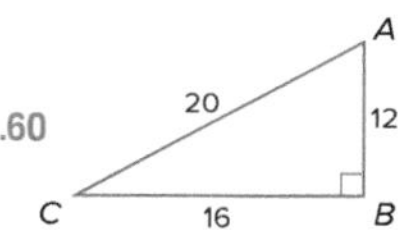

1. sin A $\frac{16}{20} = 0.80$
2. tan C $\frac{12}{16} = 0.75$
3. cos A $\frac{12}{20} = 0.60$
4. tan A
5. cos C
6. sin C

4. $\frac{16}{12} \approx 1.33$
5. $\frac{16}{20} = 0.80$
6. $\frac{12}{20} = 0.60$

Example 2 G.SRT.7

7. Use a special right triangle to express sin 60° as a fraction and as a decimal to the nearest hundredth. See margin.

Example 3 G.SRT.7

Find x. Round to the nearest hundredth.

8. 16.64

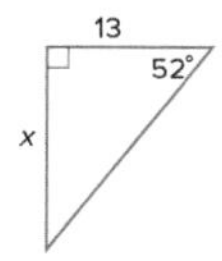

9. 27.44

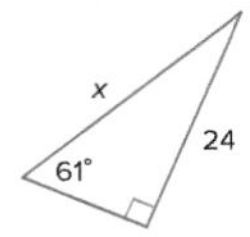

10. 16.93

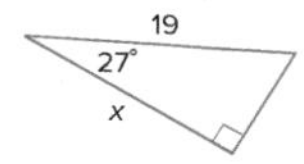

11. **SPORTS** David is building a bike ramp. He wants the angle that the ramp makes with the ground to be 20°. If the board he wants to use for his ramp is $3\frac{1}{2}$ feet long, about how tall will the ramp need to be at the highest point? about 1.2 ft

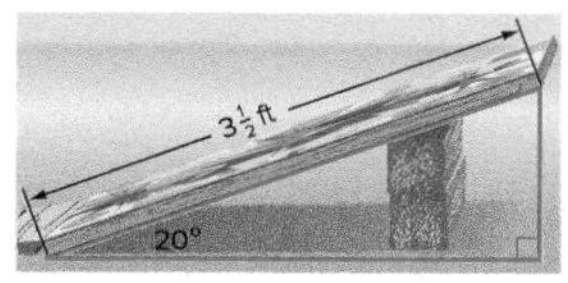

Example 4 G.SRT.7

TOOLS Use a calculator to find the measure of ∠Z to the nearest tenth.

12. 33.7

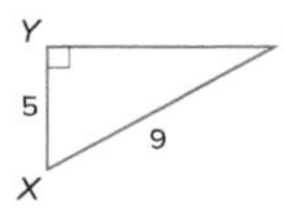

13. 44.4

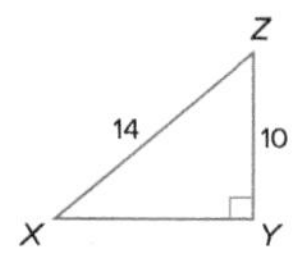

14. 36.9

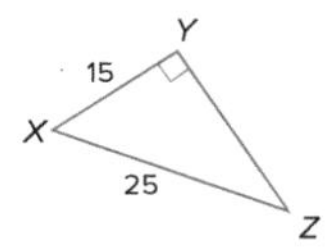

Example 5 G.SRT.7

15. Solve the right triangle. Round side measures to the nearest tenth and angle measures to the nearest degree. See margin.

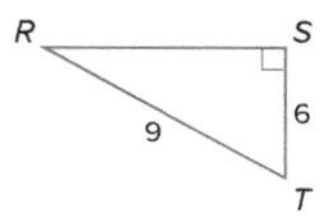

Practice and Problem Solving

Extra Practice is on page R8.

Example 1 G.SRT.7

Find sin J, cos J, tan J, sin L, cos L, and tan L. Express each ratio as a fraction and as a decimal to the nearest hundredth. 16–21. See margin.

16.

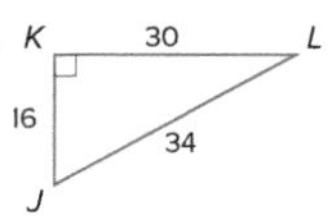

17.

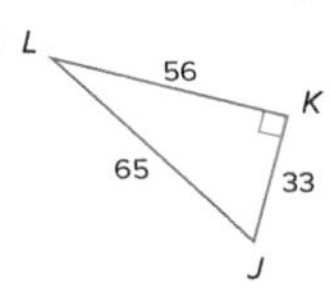

18.

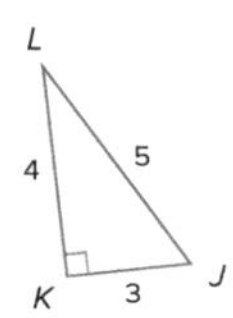

19.

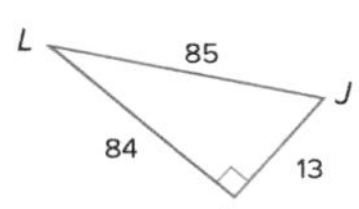

20.

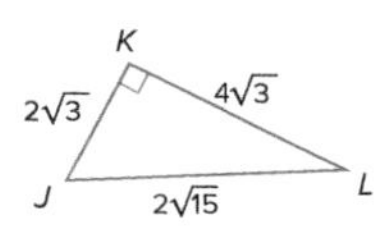

21.

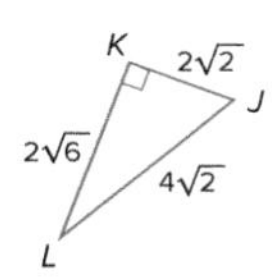

Differentiated Homework Options

Levels	AL Basic	OL Core	BL Advanced
Exercises	16–46, 63–73	17–45 odd, 46, 47, 49, 50, 51–55 odd, 56, 57, 59, 60, 61, 63–73	57–65, (optional: 66–73)
2-Day Option	17–45 odd, 66–73	16–46	
	16–46 even, 63–65	47–61, 63–73	

You can use ALEKS to provide additional remediation support with personalized instruction and practice.

20. $\frac{2\sqrt{5}}{5} \approx 0.89$; $\frac{\sqrt{5}}{5} \approx 0.45$; $\frac{4\sqrt{3}}{2\sqrt{3}} = 2$; $\frac{\sqrt{5}}{5} \approx 0.45$; $\frac{2\sqrt{5}}{5} \approx 0.89$; $\frac{2\sqrt{3}}{4\sqrt{3}} = 0.50$

21. $\frac{\sqrt{3}}{2} \approx 0.87$; $\frac{2\sqrt{2}}{4\sqrt{2}} = 0.50$; $\frac{2\sqrt{6}}{2\sqrt{2}} = \sqrt{3} \approx 1.73$; $\frac{2\sqrt{2}}{4\sqrt{2}} = 0.50$; $\frac{\sqrt{3}}{2} \approx 0.87$; $\frac{\sqrt{3}}{3} \approx 0.58$

Practice

Formative Assessment Use Exercises 1–15 to assess students' understanding of the concepts in this lesson.

The Practice and Problem Solving exercises assess the content taught in the lesson. The Preparing for Assessment page is meant to be used as preparation for end-of-course assessments.

Extra Practice

See page R8 for extra exercises for students who are approaching level or for on-level students who need additional reinforcement.

Levels of Complexity Chart

The levels of the exercises progress from 1 to 3, with Level 1 indicating the lowest level of complexity.

Exercises	16–46	47–56, 66–73	57–65
Level 3			●
Level 2		●	
Level 1	●		

Additional Answers

7. $\frac{\sqrt{3}}{2} \approx 0.87$

15. $RS \approx 6.7$; $m\angle R \approx 42$; $m\angle T \approx 48$

16. $\frac{30}{34} \approx 0.88$; $\frac{16}{34} \approx 0.47$; $\frac{30}{16} \approx 1.88$; $\frac{16}{34} \approx 0.47$; $\frac{30}{34} \approx 0.88$; $\frac{16}{30} \approx 0.53$

17. $\frac{56}{65} \approx 0.86$; $\frac{33}{65} \approx 0.51$; $\frac{56}{33} \approx 1.70$; $\frac{33}{65} \approx 0.51$; $\frac{56}{65} \approx 0.86$; $\frac{33}{56} \approx 0.59$

18. $\frac{4}{5} = 0.80$; $\frac{3}{5} = 0.60$; $\frac{4}{3} \approx 1.33$; $\frac{3}{5} = 0.60$; $\frac{4}{5} = 0.80$; $\frac{3}{4} = 0.75$

19. $\frac{84}{85} \approx 0.99$; $\frac{13}{85} \approx 0.15$; $\frac{84}{13} \approx 6.46$; $\frac{13}{85} \approx 0.15$; $\frac{84}{85} \approx 0.99$; $\frac{13}{84} \approx 0.15$

Go Online! eBook

Interactive Student Guide

Use the *Interactive Student Guide* to deepen conceptual understanding.

· Trigonometry

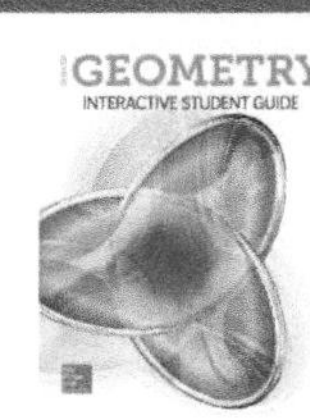

Teaching the Mathematical Practices

Tools Mathematically proficient students consider the available tools when solving a mathematical problem. In Exercises 36–41, encourage students to use a graphing calculator to find the measure.

Example 2 G.SRT.7

Use a special right triangle to express each trigonometric ratio as a fraction and as a decimal to the nearest hundredth.

22. tan 60° $\sqrt{3} \approx 1.73$ **23.** cos 30° $\frac{\sqrt{3}}{2} \approx 0.87$ **24.** sin 45° $\frac{\sqrt{2}}{2} \approx 0.71$

25. sin 30° $\frac{1}{2}$ or 0.5 **26.** tan 45° 1 **27.** cos 60° $\frac{1}{2}$ or 0.5

Example 3 G.SRT.7

Find x. Round to the nearest tenth.

28. 30.7

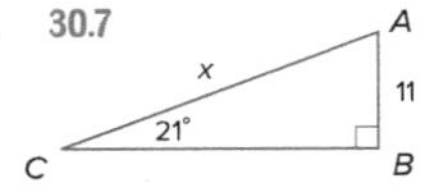

29. 28.7

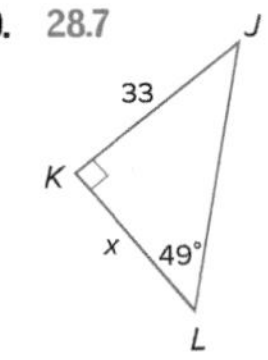

30. 23.2

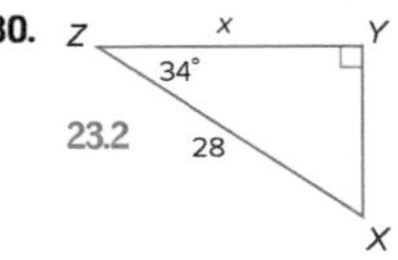

31. 57.2

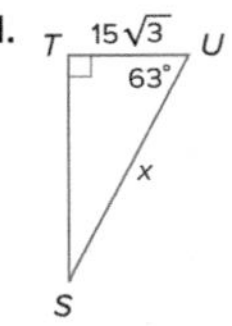

32. 17.7

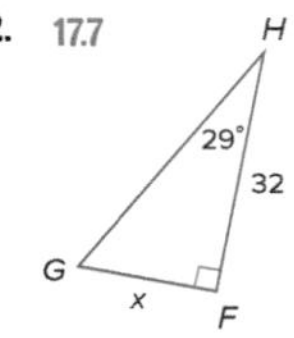

33. 17.4

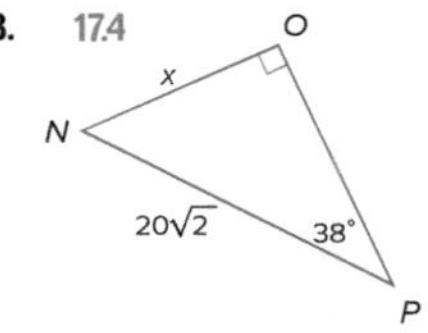

34. GYMNASTICS The springboard that Eric uses in his gymnastics class has 6-inch coils and forms an angle of 14.5° with the base. About how long is the springboard? about 24 in.

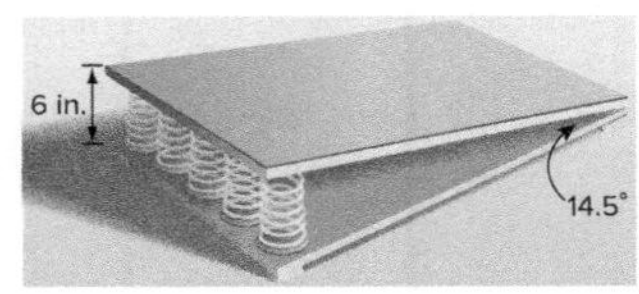

35 ROLLER COASTERS The angle of ascent of the first hill of a roller coaster is 55°. If the length of the track from the beginning of the ascent to the highest point is 98 feet, what is the height of the roller coaster when it reaches the top of the first hill? 80 ft

Example 4 G.SRT.7

MP TOOLS Use a calculator to find the measure of $\angle T$ to the nearest tenth.

36. 33.7

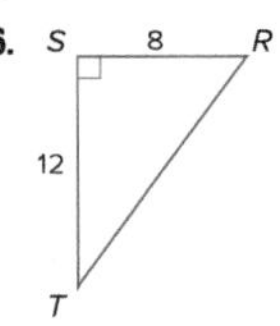

37. 61.4

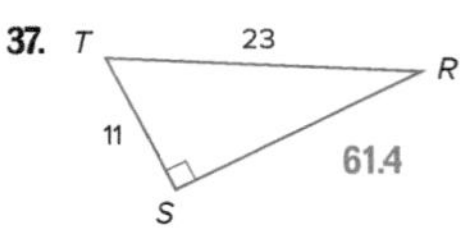

38. 56.4

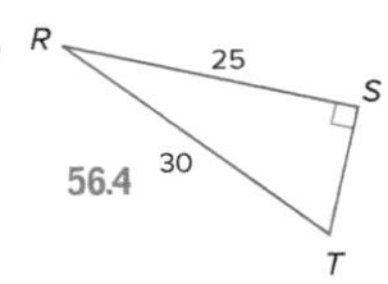

39. 28.5

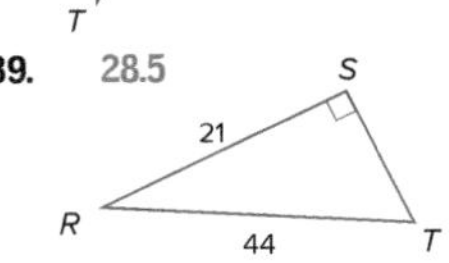

40. 64.6

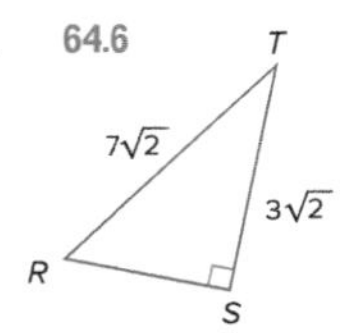

41. 21.8

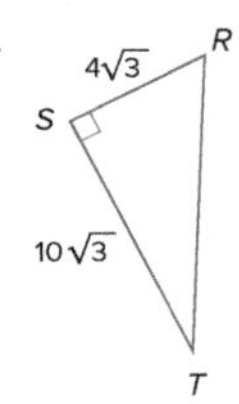

Example 5
G.SRT.7

Solve each right triangle. Round side measures to the nearest tenth and angle measures to the nearest degree.

42. 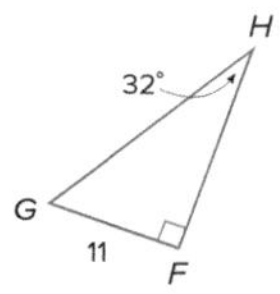

43. 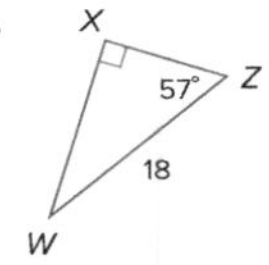

44. 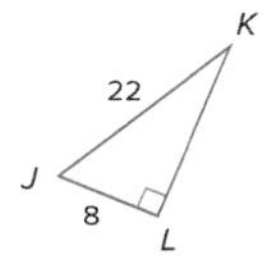

45. 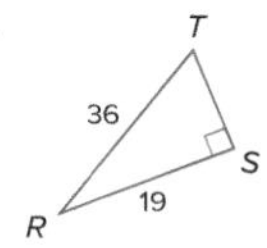

42. $HF = 17.6$; $GH = 20.8$; $m\angle G = 58$
43. $WX = 15.1$; $XZ = 9.8$; $m\angle W = 33$
44. $LK = 20.5$; $m\angle J = 69$; $m\angle K = 21$
45. $ST = 30.6$; $m\angle R = 58$; $m\angle T = 32$

46. **BACKPACKS** Ramón has a rolling backpack that is $3\frac{3}{4}$ feet tall when the handle is extended. When he is pulling the backpack, Ramon's hand is 3 feet from the ground. What angle does his backpack make with the floor? Round to the nearest degree. 53°

B **COORDINATE GEOMETRY** **Find the measure of each angle to the nearest tenth of a degree using the Distance Formula and an inverse trigonometric ratio.**

47. $\angle K$ in right triangle JKL with vertices $J(-2, -3)$, $K(-7, -3)$, and $L(-2, 4)$ 54.5

48. $\angle Y$ in right triangle XYZ with vertices $X(4, 1)$, $Y(-6, 3)$, and $Z(-2, 7)$ 56.3

49. $\angle A$ in right triangle ABC with vertices $A(3, 1)$, $B(3, -3)$, and $C(8, -3)$ 51.3

50. **SCHOOL SPIRIT** Hana is making a pennant for each of the 18 girls on her basketball team. She will use $\frac{1}{2}$-inch seam binding to finish the edges of the pennants.
   a. What is the total length of seam binding needed to finish all of the pennants? about 494 in.
   b. If seam binding is sold in 3-yard packages at a cost of \$1.79, how much will it cost? \$8.95

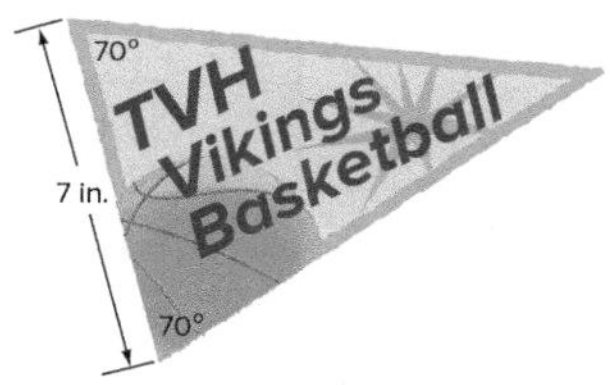

MP **SENSE-MAKING** **Find the perimeter and area of each triangle. Round to the nearest hundredth.**

51. 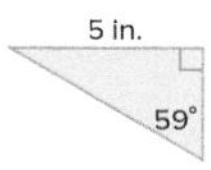

13.83 in.; 7.51 in^2

52. 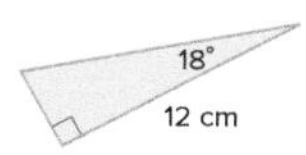

28.52 cm; 23.39 cm^2

53. 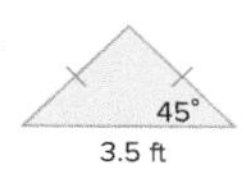

8.45 ft; 3.06 ft^2

54. Find the tangent of the greater acute angle in a triangle with side lengths of 3, 4, and 5 centimeters. 1.33

55. Find the cosine of the smaller acute angle in a triangle with side lengths of 10, 24, and 26 inches. 0.92

56. **ESTIMATION** Ethan and Tariq want to estimate the area of the field that their team will use for soccer practice. They know that the field is rectangular, and they have paced off the width of the field as shown. They used the fence posts at the corners of the field to estimate that the angle between the length of the field and the diagonal is about 40°. If they assume that each of their steps is about 18 inches, what is the area of the practice field in square feet? Round to the nearest square foot. 210, 227 ft^2

Follow-Up

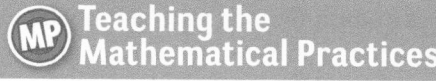

Students have explored trigonometry.

Ask: Why is trigonometry useful? Sample answer: It allows us to solve problems modeled by triangles that cannot be solved using the Pythagorean Theorem.

Teaching the Mathematical Practices

Sense-Making Mathematically proficient students start by explaining the meaning of a problem to themselves and looking for entry points to its solution. They plan a solution pathway rather than simply jumping into a solution attempt. In Exercises 51–53, encourage students to use the Pythagorean Theorem to find the measures of missing sides.

Exercise Alert

Ruler Exercise 61 requires the use of a ruler.

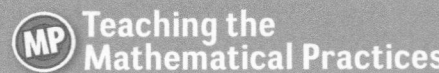

MP Teaching the Mathematical Practices

Reasoning Mathematically proficient students make sense of quantities and their relationships in problem situations. In Exercise 64, encourage students to analyze the relationship between sine and cosine.

Assess

Yesterday's News Have students write how the properties of special right triangles helped in learning trigonometry.

Additional Answer

60. Sample answer:

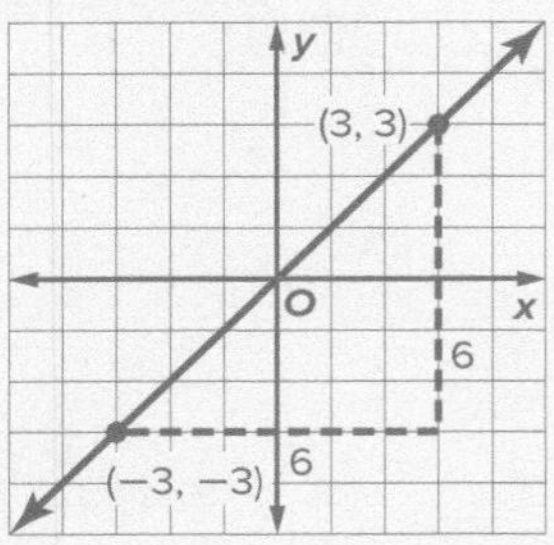

$$\text{Slope} = \frac{-3-3}{-3-3} = \frac{6}{6} = 1$$

Because the slope is 1 and slope is rise over run, which is tan 45° or tan 225°; from a calculator, both equal 1.

C Find x and y. Round to the nearest tenth. 58. $x = 37.2$; $y = 33.4$

57.

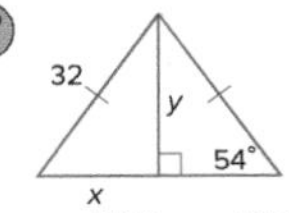

$x = 18.8$; $y = 25.9$

58.

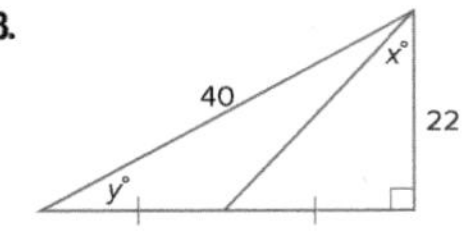

59.

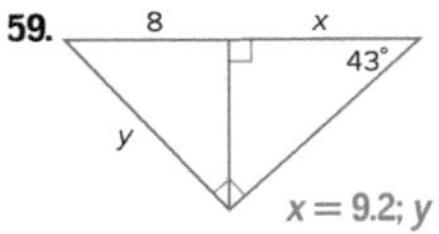

$x = 9.2$; $y = 11.7$

60. **COORDINATE GEOMETRY** Show that the slope of a line at 225° from the x-axis is equal to the tangent of 225°. See margin.

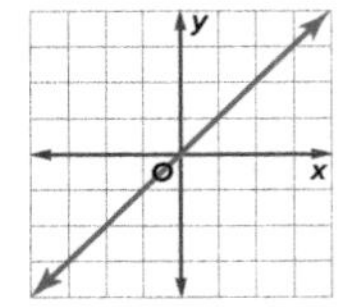

62. $m\angle A = 53$, $m\angle B = 90$, $m\angle C = 37$, $AB = 12$, $BC = 16$, $AC = 20$

63. Sample answer: Yes; since the values of sine and cosine are both calculated by dividing one of the legs of a right triangle by the hypotenuse, and the hypotenuse is always the longest side of a right triangle, the values will always be less than 1. You will always be dividing the smaller number by the larger number.

61. **MULTIPLE REPRESENTATIONS** In this problem, you will investigate an algebraic relationship between the sine and cosine ratios.

a. **Geometric** Draw three right triangles that are not similar to each other. Label the triangles ABC, MNP, and XYZ, with the right angles located at vertices B, N, and Y, respectively. Measure and label each side of the three triangles. See Ch. 8 Answer Appendix.

b. **Tabular** Copy and complete the table below. Sample answers given.

Triangle	Trigonometric Ratios				Sum of Ratios Squared	
ABC	cos A	0.677	sin A	0.742	$(\cos A)^2 + (\sin A)^2 =$	1
	cos C	0.742	sin C	0.677	$(\cos C)^2 + (\sin C)^2 =$	1
MNP	cos M	0.406	sin M	0.906	$(\cos M)^2 + (\sin M)^2 =$	1
	cos P	0.906	sin P	0.406	$(\cos P)^2 + (\sin P)^2 =$	1
XYZ	cos X	0.667	sin X	0.75	$(\cos X)^2 + (\sin X)^2 =$	1
	cos Z	0.75	sin Z	0.667	$(\cos Z)^2 + (\sin Z)^2 =$	1

c. **Verbal** Make a conjecture about the sum of the squares of the cosine and sine of an acute angle of a right triangle. See Ch. 8 Answer Appendix.

d. **Algebraic** Express your conjecture algebraically for an angle X. $(\sin X)2 + (\cos X)2 = 1$

e. **Analytical** Show that your conjecture is valid for angle A in the figure at the right using the trigonometric functions and the Pythagorean Theorem. See Ch. 8 Answer Appendix.

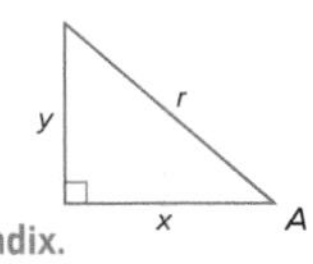

G.SRT.6, G.SRT.7

H.O.T. Problems Use Higher-Order Thinking Skills

62. **CHALLENGE** Solve $\triangle ABC$. Round to the nearest whole number.

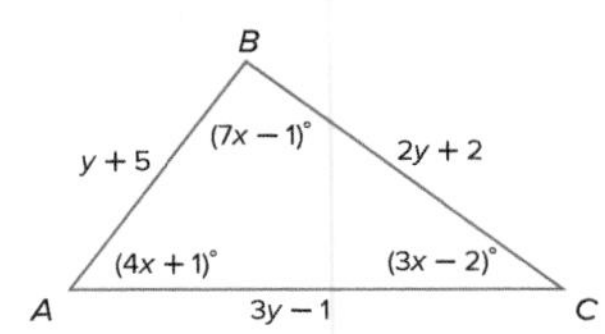

63. **MP REASONING** Are the values of sine and cosine for an acute angle of a right triangle always less than 1? Explain.

64. **MP REASONING** What is the relationship between the sine and cosine of complementary angles? Explain your reasoning and use the relationship to find cos 50 if sin 40 ≈ 0.64. See margin.

65. **WRITING IN MATH** Explain how you can use ratios of the side lengths to find the angle measures of the acute angles in a right triangle. See margin.

MP Standards for Mathematical Practice

Emphasis On	Exercises
1 Make sense of problems and persevere in solving them.	1–10, 51–53, 67, 68, 70–73
2 Reason abstractly and quantitatively.	63, 64
4 Model with mathematics.	11, 34, 35, 46, 50, 56, 66, 69
5 Use appropriate tools strategically.	12–14, 36–41, 47–49, 57–61
6 Attend to precision.	22–33
8 Look for and express regularity in repeated reasoning.	16–21, 42–45

Go Online!

eSolutions Manual

Create worksheets, answer keys, and solutions handouts for your assignments.

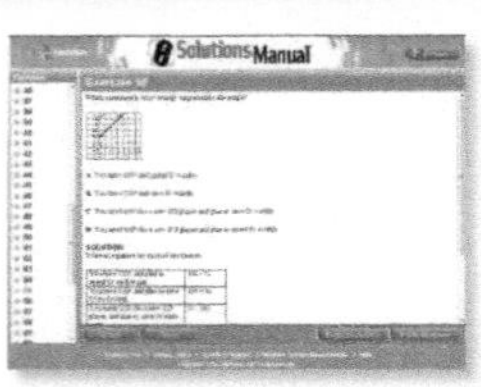

Preparing for Assessment

66. A vertical pole is supported by a guy wire, as shown in the figure. What is the height of the pole, in feet, to the nearest tenth of a foot? MP 4 G.SRT.8 [ ] 20.8 feet

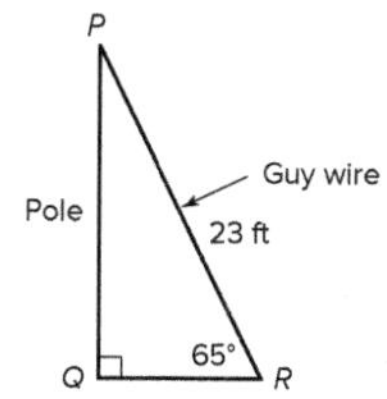

67. The legs of a right triangle are 5 and 6 units long. Find the measure of the second largest angle of the triangle. Round your answer to the nearest tenth. MP 1 G.SRT.8 (50.2°)

68. In right triangle *ABC*, $\sin A = \frac{2}{5}$. Find $\sin(90° - A)$. MP 1 G.SRT.7 [ ] $\frac{\sqrt{21}}{5}$

69. A bookshelf that hangs on a wall is supported by a bracket, as shown in the figure.

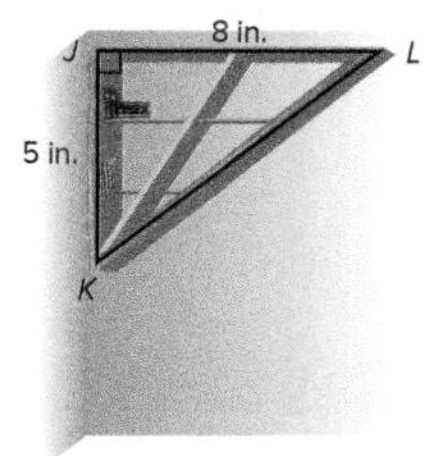

Which of the following is the best estimate of the measure of $\angle L$? MP 4 G.SRT.8 A

- ○ A 32
- ○ B 39
- ○ C 51
- ○ D 58

70. In $\triangle ABC$, $\angle B$ is a right angle and $m\angle A = 40$. Given that $AC = 15$, what is *AB* to the nearest tenth? MP 1 G.SRT.8 (11.5)

71. Erin wants to find the length of $\overline{PN}$ in $\triangle MNP$.

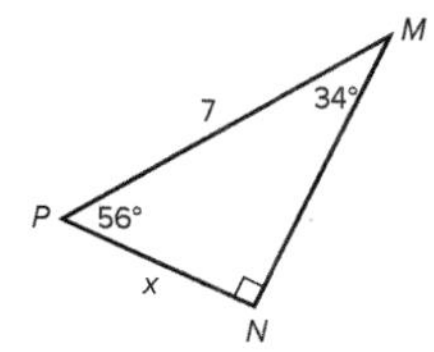

Which of the following equations can Erin use to find the length of $\overline{PN}$? MP 1 G.SRT.8 C

I. $\sin 34° = \frac{x}{7}$

II. $\cos 56° = \frac{x}{7}$

III. $\tan 56° = \frac{7}{x}$

- ○ A I only
- ○ B II only
- ○ C I and II only
- ○ D I and III only
- ○ E I, II, and III

72. A five-meter-long ladder leans against a wall, with the top of the ladder being four meters above the ground. What is the approximate angle that the ladder makes with the ground? Round to the nearest degree. MP 1 G.SRT.8 (53)

73. MULTI-STEP Given an acute angle *A* where $\tan A = \frac{2}{5}$, find: MP 1 G.SRT.7

a. $\cos A$ [ ] $\frac{5\sqrt{29}}{29}$

b. $\sin A$ [ ] $\frac{2\sqrt{29}}{29}$

c. $\cos(90° - A)$ [ ] $\frac{2\sqrt{29}}{29}$

d. $\sin(90° - A)$ [ ] $\frac{5\sqrt{29}}{29}$

e. $\sin^2 A + \cos^2 A$ [ ] 1

Preparing for Assessment

Exercises 66–73 require students to use the skills they will need on standardized assessments. Exercises are dual-coded with content standards and mathematical practice standards.

Dual Coding		
Items	Content Standards	MP Mathematical Practices
66	G.SRT.8	4
68, 73	G.SRT.7	1
69	G.SRT.8	4
67, 70–72	G.SRT.8	1

Diagnose Student Errors

Survey student responses for each item. Class trends may indicate common errors and misconceptions.

69.

A	CORRECT
B	Used $\sin^{-1}\left(\frac{5}{8}\right)$
C	Used $\cos^{-1}\left(\frac{5}{8}\right)$
D	Found $m\angle K$

71.

A	Did not recognize an appropriate equation using the cosine ratio
B	Did not recognize an appropriate equation using the sine ratio
C	CORRECT
D	Chose an equation using an incorrect tangent ratio
E	Chose an equation using an incorrect tangent ratio

Additional Answers

64. In the diagram, $\sin A = x$ and $\cos B = x$; therefore $\sin A = \cos B$.

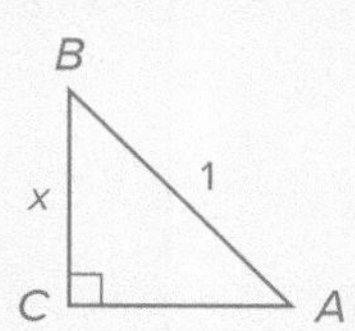

Because the acute angles of a right triangle are complementary, $m\angle B = 90 - m\angle A$. By substitution, $\sin A = \cos(90 - A)$. Because $\sin A = x$, $\cos(90 - A) = x$ by substitution. Applying this relationship, if $\sin 40 \approx 0.64$, then $\cos(90 - 40) \approx 0.64$. Because $90 - 40 = 50$, $\cos 50 \approx 0.64$.

65. Sample answer: to find the measure of an acute angle of a right triangle, you can find the ratio of the leg opposite the angle to the hypotenuse and use a calculator to find the inverse sine of the ratio, you can find the ratio of the leg adjacent to the angle to the hypotenuse and use a calculator to find the inverse cosine of the ratio, or you can find the ratio of the leg opposite the angle to the leg adjacent to the angle and use a calculator to find the inverse tangent of the ratio.

Go Online!

Quizzes

Students can use *Self-Check Quizzes* to check their understanding of this lesson and have the results sent to you. You can also give *Quiz 2*, which covers the content in Lessons 8-3 and 8-4.

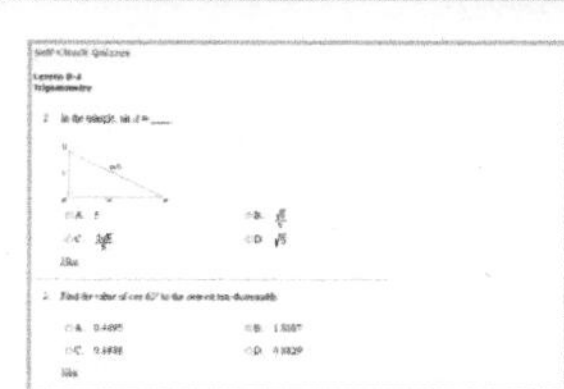

Launch

Objective Explore the trigonometric functions secant, cosecant, and cotangent.

Materials for Each Group

- TI-83/84 Plus or other graphing calculator
- ruler

Teaching Tips

As a variation, have students complete the activity with a 30°-60°-90° triangle and find all of the trigonometric values algebraically, instead of using a calculator.

Teach ELL

Working in Cooperative Groups Have students of mixed abilities work in groups of three. Have students rotate finding each trigonometric function in Step 2 and Step 3.

Show students the equivalence of the two new definitions in symbols of each function by using complex fractions.

Practice Have students complete Exercises 1 and 2.

Assess

Formative Assessment

Use Exercise 3 to assess whether students understand the concepts of secant, cosecant, and cotangent.

From Concrete to Abstract

Give students a table such as that in Step 4 with half of the values filled in, and have them use reciprocals to find the missing values.

Extending the Concept

Have students determine under what conditions sine, cosine, and tangent could be equal to their reciprocals.

EXTEND 8-4

Graphing Technology Lab

Secant, Cosecant, and Cotangent

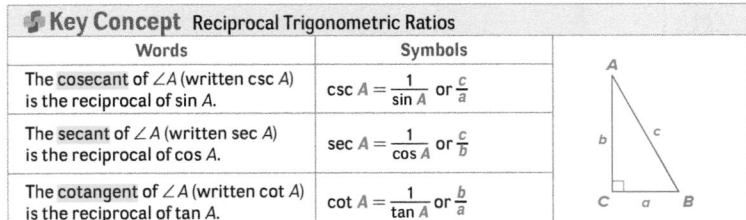

In the previous lesson, you used the trigonometric functions sine, cosine, and tangent to find angle relationships in right angles. In this activity, you will use the reciprocals of those functions, cosecant, secant, and cotangent, to explore angle and side relationships in right triangles.

Mathematical Practices
MP 5 Use appropriate tools strategically.

Content Standards
G.SRT.6 Understand that by similarity, side ratios in right triangles are properties of the angles in the triangle, leading to definitions of trigonometric ratios for acute angles.

Key Concept Reciprocal Trigonometric Ratios

Words	Symbols
The **cosecant** of ∠A (written csc A) is the reciprocal of sin A.	$\csc A = \frac{1}{\sin A}$ or $\frac{c}{a}$
The **secant** of ∠A (written sec A) is the reciprocal of cos A.	$\sec A = \frac{1}{\cos A}$ or $\frac{c}{b}$
The **cotangent** of ∠A (written cot A) is the reciprocal of tan A.	$\cot A = \frac{1}{\tan A}$ or $\frac{b}{a}$

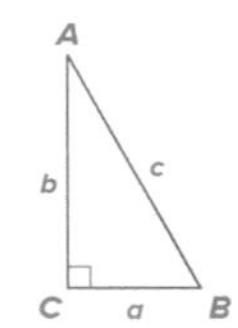

Activity Find Trigonometric Values

Work cooperatively.

Step 1 Draw and label a right triangle with the dimensions shown at the right.

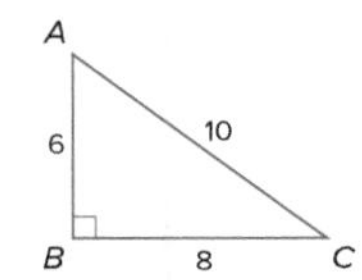

Step 2 Use your graphing calculator to find the values for sin A, cos A, and tan A.

Step 3 Next, find the value for csc A by dividing 1 by [SIN] A. Repeat step 3 to find sec A and cot A.

Step 4 Copy the table below and record your results. Next, find the value of each trigonometric function for angle C.

Angle	sin	cos	tan	csc	sec	cot
A						
C						

Exercises

Work cooperatively.

1. Find the values of the six trigonometric functions for a 45° angle in a 45° –45° –90° triangle with legs that are 4 cm. **1–3. See margin.**
2. In △FGH, $\tan F = \frac{5}{12}$. Find cot F and sin F if ∠G is a right angle.
3. Find the values of the six trigonometric functions for angle T in △RST if $m\angle R = 36°$. Round to the nearest hundredth.

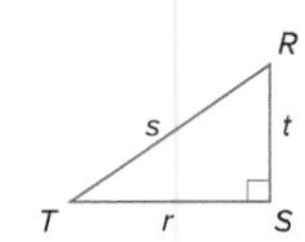

Additional Answers

1. $\sin 45° = \frac{1}{\sqrt{2}} = \frac{\sqrt{2}}{2}$; $\cos 45° = \frac{1}{\sqrt{2}} = \frac{\sqrt{2}}{2}$; $\tan 45° = 1$; $\csc 45° = \sqrt{2}$; $\sec 45° = \sqrt{2}$; $\cot 45° = 1$
2. $\cot F = \frac{12}{5}$ or 2.4; $\sin F = \frac{5}{13}$
3. $\sin T = 0.81$; $\cos T = 0.59$; $\tan T = 1.38$; $\csc T = 1.24$; $\sec T = 1.70$; $\cot T = 0.73$

Go Online!

Graphing Calculators

Students can use the Graphing Calculator Personal Tutors to review the use of the graphing calculator to represent functions. They can also use the Other Calculator Keystrokes, which cover lab content for students with calculators other than the TI-84 Plus.

CHAPTER 8
Mid-Chapter Quiz
Lessons 8-1 through 8-4

Find the geometric mean between each pair of numbers. (Lesson 8-1)

1. 12 and 3 6
2. 63 and 7 21
3. 45 and 20 30
4. 50 and 10 $10\sqrt{5}$

Write a similarity statement identifying the three similar triangles in each figure. (Lesson 8-1)

5. 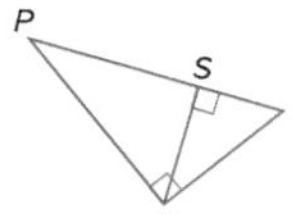

$\triangle PRQ \sim \triangle QRS \sim \triangle PQS$

6. 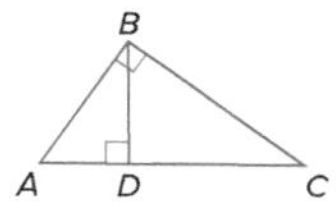

$\triangle ABD \sim \triangle BCD \sim \triangle ACB$

7. Find x, y, and z. (Lesson 8-1) $x = 12, y = 15, z = 20$

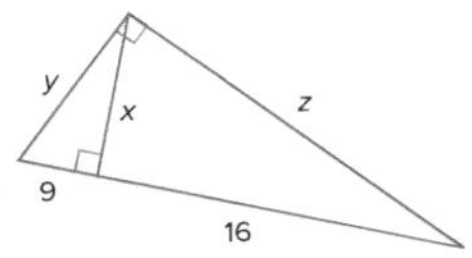

8. **PARKS** There is a small park in a corner made by two perpendicular streets. The park is 100 feet by 150 feet, with a diagonal path, as shown below. What is the length of path $\overline{AC}$? (Lesson 8-2) 180.3 ft

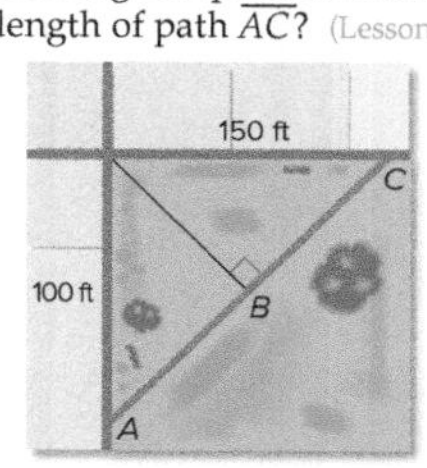

Find x. Round to the nearest hundredth. (Lesson 8-2)

9. 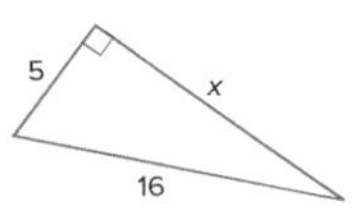

$\sqrt{231} \approx 15.20$

10. 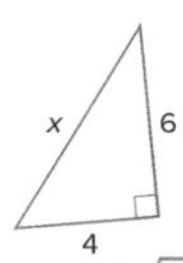

$2\sqrt{13} \approx 7.21$

11. **MULTIPLE CHOICE** Which of the following sets of numbers is not a Pythagorean triple? (Lesson 8-2) D

A 9, 12, 15
B 21, 72, 75
C 15, 36, 39
D 8, 13, 15

Find x. (Lesson 8-3)

12. 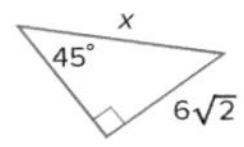

12

13. 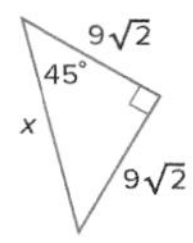

18

14. **DESIGN** Jamie designed a pinwheel to put in her garden. In the pinwheel, the blue triangles are congruent equilateral triangles, each with an altitude of 4 inches. The red triangles are congruent isosceles right triangles. The hypotenuse of a red triangle is congruent to a side of the blue triangle. (Lesson 8-3)

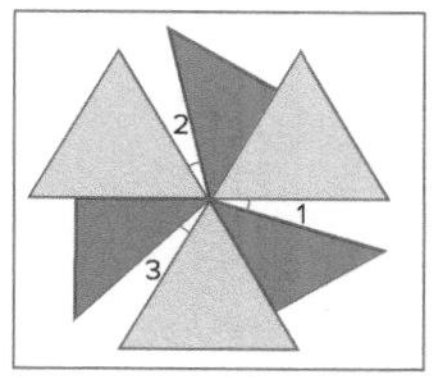

a. If angles 1, 2, and 3 are congruent, find the measure of each angle. 15
b. Find the perimeter of the pinwheel. 55 in.
c. MP What mathematical practice did you use to solve this problem? See students' work.

Find x and y. (Lesson 8-3)

15. 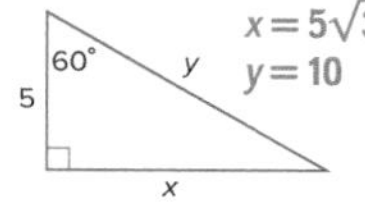

$x = 5\sqrt{3}$; $y = 10$

16. 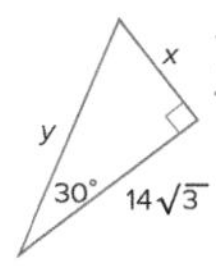

$x = 14$; $y = 28$

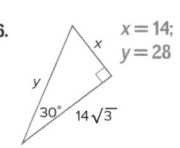

Express each ratio as a fraction and as a decimal to the nearest hundredth. (Lesson 8-4) 17. $\frac{15}{36} = 0.42$

17. tan M
18. cos M
19. cos N $\frac{15}{39} = 0.38$
20. sin N $\frac{36}{39} = 0.92$

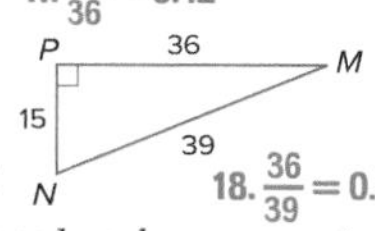

18. $\frac{36}{39} = 0.92$

21. Solve the right triangle. Round angle measures to the nearest degree and side measures to the nearest tenth. (Lesson 8-4) $JG = 41.7$; $m\angle G = 30$; $m\angle J = 60$

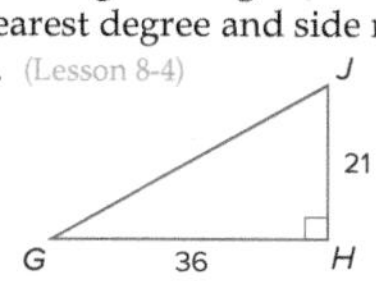

RtI Response to Intervention

Use the Intervention Planner to help you determine your Response to Intervention.

Intervention Planner

TIER 1 On Level OL

IF students miss 25% of the exercises or less,

THEN choose a resource:

SE Lessons 8-1 through 8-4

Go Online!
- Skills Practice
- Chapter Project
- Self-Check Quizzes

TIER 2 Strategic Intervention AL
Approaching grade level

IF students miss 50% of the exercises,

THEN choose a resource:

Quick Review Math Handbook

Go Online!
- Study Guide and Intervention
- Extra Examples
- Personal Tutors
- Homework Help

TIER 3 Intensive Intervention
2 or more grades below level

IF students miss 75% of the exercises,

THEN choose a resource:

Use *Math Triumphs, Geometry*

Go Online!
- Extra Examples
- Personal Tutors
- Homework Help
- Review Vocabulary

Foldables Study Organizer

Dinah Zike's FOLDABLES®

Before students complete the Mid-Chapter Quiz, encourage them to review the information for Lessons 8-1 through 8-4 in their Foldables. Allow students to compare their Foldable with a partner. Encourage them to share what has been helpful to them as they study.

ALEKS can be used as a formative assessment tool to target learning gaps for those who are struggling, while providing enhanced learning for those who have mastered the concepts.

Go Online!

eAssessment

You can use the premade Mid-Chapter Test to assess students' progress in the first half of the chapter. Customize and create multiple versions of your Mid-Chapter Quiz and answer keys that align to your standards. Tests can be delivered on paper or online.

LESSON 8-5

Angles of Elevation and Depression

SUGGESTED PACING (DAYS)

	Instruction
90 min.	0.5
45 min.	1.0

Track Your Progress

Objectives

1 Solve problems involving angles of elevation and depression.

2 Use angles of elevation and depression to find the distance between two objects.

Mathematical Background

An angle of elevation is the angle between the line of sight and the horizontal when an observer looks upward. An angle of depression is the angle between the line of sight and the horizontal when an observer looks downward. Trigonometric ratios can be used to solve problems involving these angles.

Skills Trace

THEN	NOW	NEXT
G.SRT.6 Understand that by similarity, side ratios in right triangles are properties of the angles in the triangle, leading to definitions of trigonometric ratios for acute angles.	**G.SRT.8** Use trigonometric ratios and the Pythagorean Theorem to solve right triangles in applied problems.	**G.SRT.10** Prove the Laws of Sines and Cosines and use them to solve problems.

Go Online! All of these resources and more are available at connectED.mcgraw-hill.com

Use a Self-Check Quiz to assess students' understanding of angles of elevation and angles of depression.

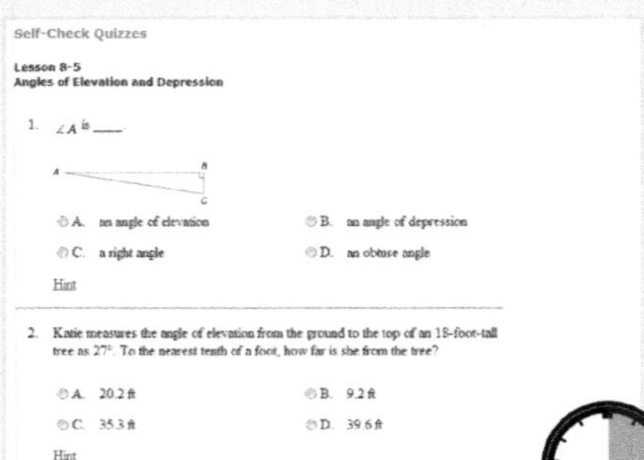

Use at End of Lesson

Personal Tutors (for every example) let students hear real teachers solve problems. Students can pause and repeat as many times as necessary.

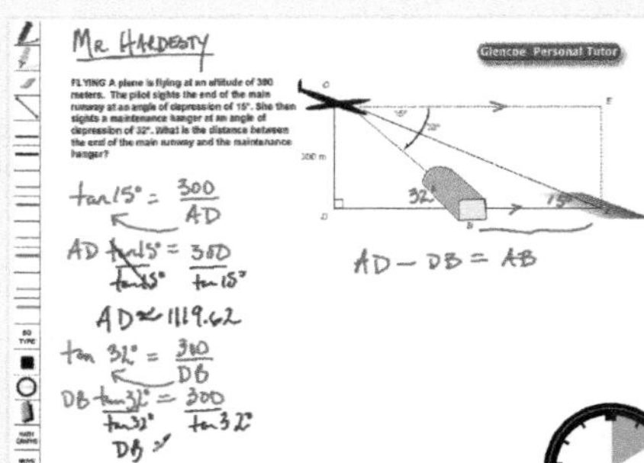

Use with Examples

Use the eGlossary to define *angle of elevation* and *angle of depression*.

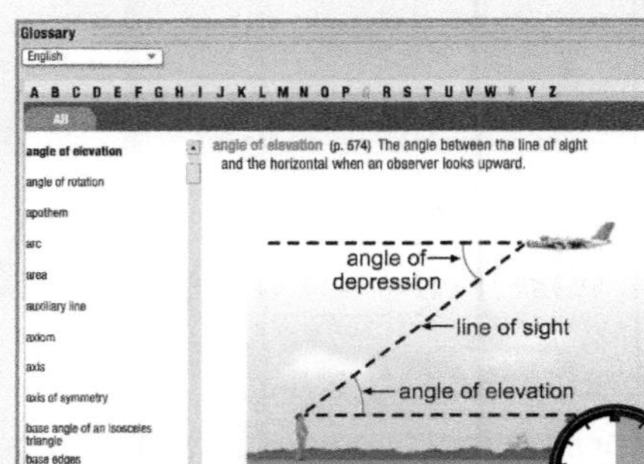

Use at Beginning of Lesson

Using Open Educational Resources

Lesson Sharing Students and teachers can access **Edmodo** to read, collaborate, and watch videos on Angles of Elevation and Depression. This is a free site, but you do have to sign up. *Use as professional development*

Go Online!
connectED.mcgraw-hill.com

Worksheets

Differentiate Your Resources

Extra Practice Additional practice or homework; Skills Practice is best for approaching-level students and Practice is best for on-level and beyond-level students

Skills Practice

AL OL ELL

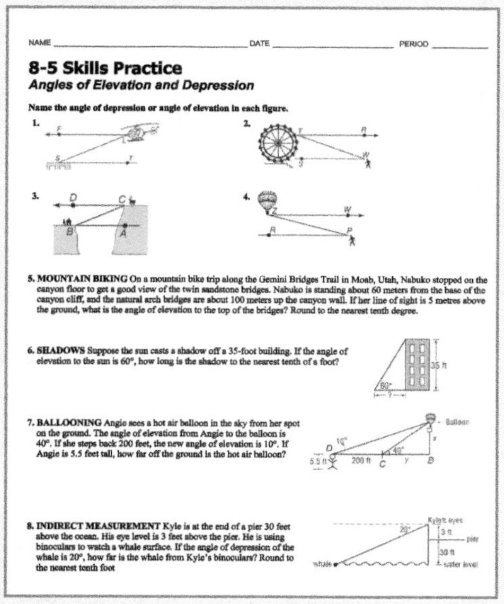
8-5 Skills Practice
Angles of Elevation and Depression

Practice

AL OL BL ELL

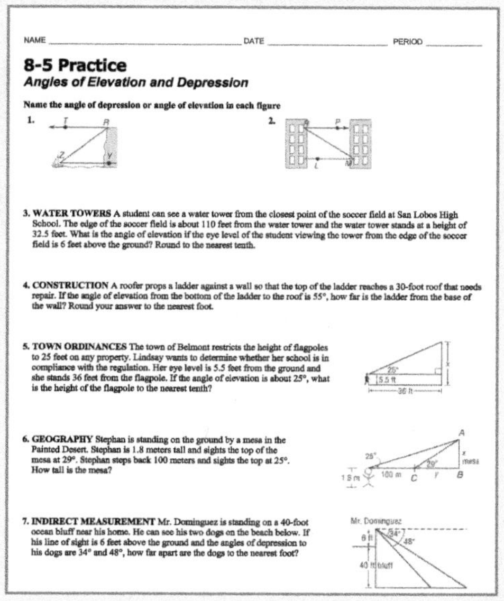
8-5 Practice
Angles of Elevation and Depression

Word Problem Practice

AL OL BL ELL

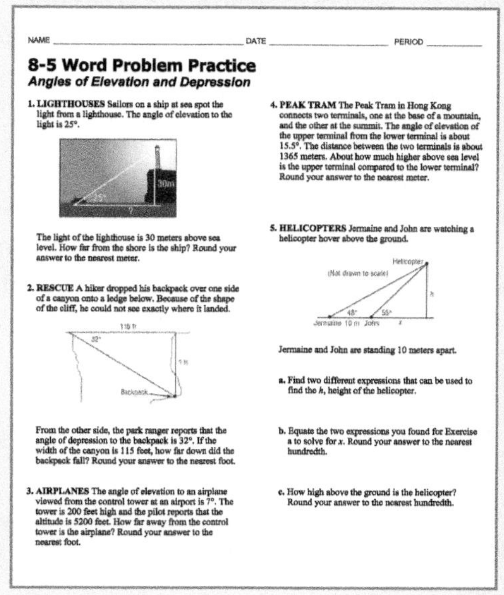
8-5 Word Problem Practice
Angles of Elevation and Depression

Intervention Reteaching and vocabulary activities that can be used with struggling or absent students and as ELL support

Study Guide and Intervention

AL OL ELL

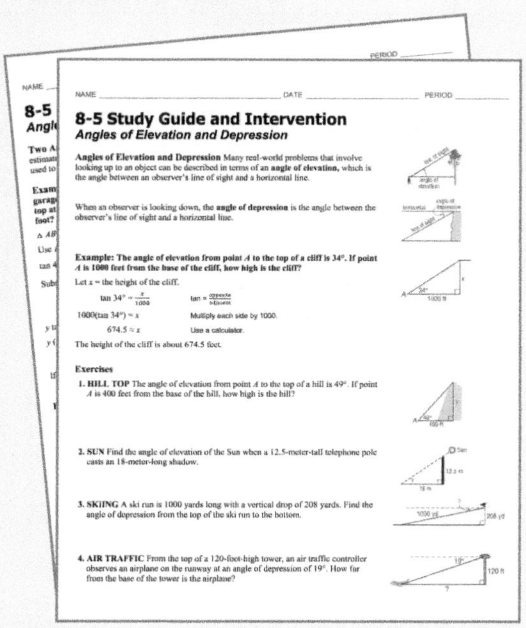
8-5 Study Guide and Intervention
Angles of Elevation and Depression

Study Notebook

AL OL BL ELL

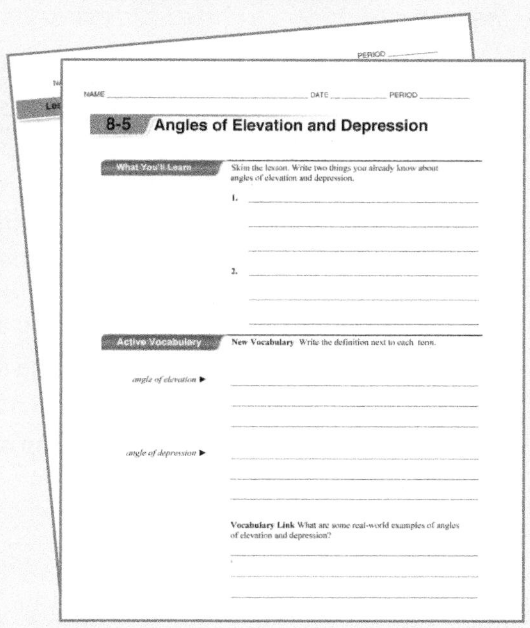
8-5 Angles of Elevation and Depression

Extension Activities that can be used to extend lesson concepts

Enrichment

OL BL ELL

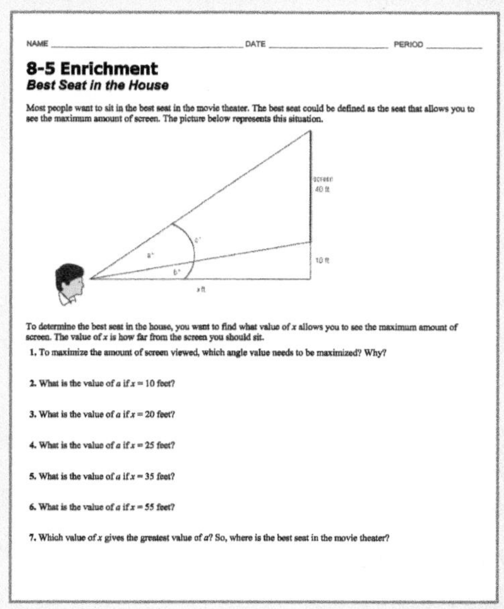
8-5 Enrichment
Best Seat in the House

Launch

Have students read the Why? section of the lesson. Ask:

- What two rays form the angle of elevation? One ray is from the ball to the base of the goal post, and the other is from the ball to the horizontal bar.
- What values could you reasonably expect the angle of elevation to be? Sample answer: 30° to 60°
- Would the angle of elevation be greater if the ball were placed closer to or farther away from the goalpost? closer

Teach

Ask the scaffolded questions for each example to build conceptual understanding for students at all levels.

1 Angles of Elevation and Depression

Example 1 Angle of Elevation

AL What determines whether an angle is an angle of elevation or an angle of depression? the vantage point of the person sighting the angle

OL If a person were looking at Leah from the top of the castle, what would the angle of depression be? 38°

BL If Leah sights a second castle at an angle of elevation of 19° at a distance of 300 feet from the base of the castle, how tall is it? about 98 feet

Go Online!

Interactive Whiteboard

Use the *eLesson*, *Lesson Presentation*, or *Interactive Classroom* to present this lesson.

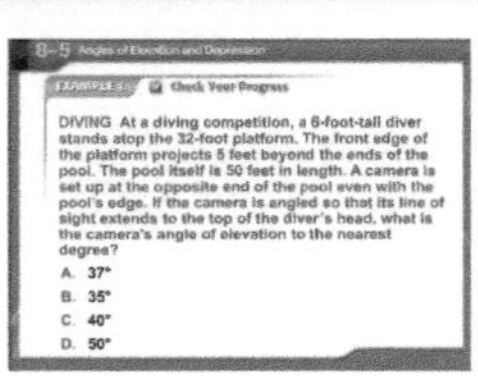

LESSON 5

Angles of Elevation and Depression

Then	Now	Why?
You used similar triangles to measure distances indirectly.	1 Solve problems involving angles of elevation and depression. 2 Use angles of elevation and depression to find the distance between two objects.	To make a field goal, a kicker must kick the ball with enough force and at an appropriate angle of elevation to ensure that the ball will reach the goalpost at a level high enough to make it over the horizontal bar. This angle must change depending on the initial placement of the ball away from the base of the goalpost.

New Vocabulary
angle of elevation
angle of depression

Mathematical Practices
4 Model with mathematics.
1 Make sense of problems and persevere in solving them.

Content Standards
G.SRT.8 Use trigonometric ratios and the Pythagorean Theorem to solve right triangles in applied problems.

1 Angles of Elevation and Depression An **angle of elevation** is the angle formed by a horizontal line and an observer's line of sight to an object above the horizontal line. An **angle of depression** is the angle formed by a horizontal line and an observer's line of sight to an object below the horizontal line.

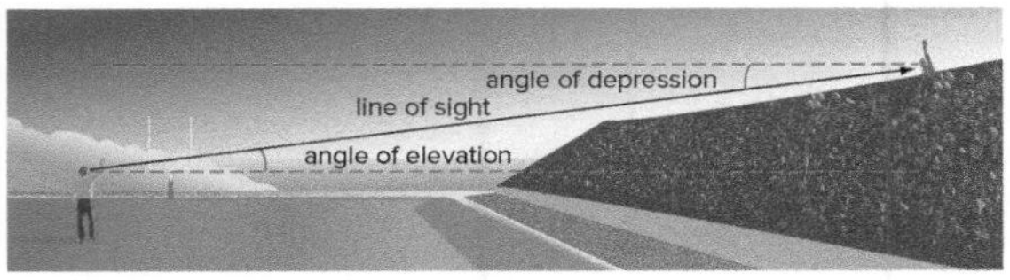

Horizontal lines are parallel, so the angle of elevation and the angle of depression in the diagram are congruent by the Alternate Interior Angles Theorem.

G.SRT.8

Example 1 Angle of Elevation

VACATION **Leah wants to see a castle in an amusement park. She sights the top of the castle at an angle of elevation of 38°. She knows that the castle is 190 feet tall. If Leah is 5.5 feet tall, how far is she from the castle to the nearest foot?**

Make a sketch to represent the situation.

Because Leah is 5.5 feet tall, $BC = 190 - 5.5$ or 184.5 feet. Let x represent the distance from Leah to the castle, AC.

$\tan A = \frac{BC}{AC}$ — $\tan = \frac{\text{opposite}}{\text{adjacent}}$

$\tan 38° = \frac{184.5}{x}$ — $m\angle A = 38$, $BC = 184.5$, $AC = x$

$x = \frac{184.5}{\tan 38°}$ — Solve for x.

$x \approx 236.1$ — Use a calculator.

Leah is about 236 feet from the castle.

Juice Images/Alamy

MP Mathematical Practices Strategies

Attend to precision.
Help students distinguish between an angle of elevation and an angle of depression and use a graphing calculator to find these angles. For example, ask:

- How do you know when you are using an angle of elevation? You are looking up.
- How do you know when you are using an angle of depression? You are looking down.
- How do you find an angle of elevation or depression? You calculate the inverse of the trigonometric ratio formed from two given side lengths.

Guided Practice

1. **FOOTBALL** The cross bar of a goalpost is 10 feet high. If a field goal attempt is made 25 yards from the base of the goalpost that clears the goal by 1 foot, what is the smallest angle of elevation at which the ball could have been kicked to the nearest degree? 8°

G.SRT.8

Example 2 Angle of Depression

EMERGENCY A search and rescue team is airlifting people from the scene of a boating accident when they observe another person in need of help. If the angle of depression to this other person is 42° and the helicopter is 18 feet above the water, what is the horizontal distance from the rescuers to this person to the nearest foot?

Make a sketch of the situation.

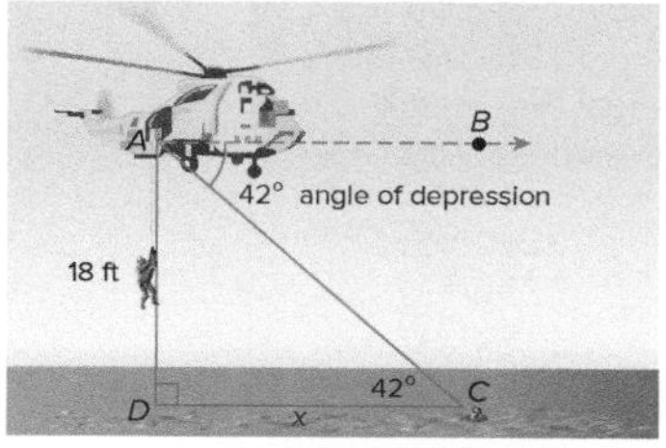

Note: Art not drawn to scale.

Because $\overrightarrow{AB}$ and $\overline{DC}$ are parallel, $m\angle BAC = m\angle ACD$ by the Alternate Interior Angles Theorem.

Let x represent the horizontal distance from the rescuers to the person DC.

$\tan C = \frac{AD}{DC}$	$\tan = \frac{\text{opposite}}{\text{adjacent}}$
$\tan 42° = \frac{18}{x}$	$C = 42$, $AD = 18$, and $DC = x$
$x \tan 42° = 18$	Multiply each side by x.
$x = \frac{18}{\tan 42°}$	Divide each side by tan 42°.
$x \approx 20.0$	Use a calculator.

The horizontal distance from the rescuers to the person is 20.0 feet.

Guided Practice

2. **LIFEGUARDING** A lifeguard is watching a beach from a line of sight 6 feet above the ground. She sees a swimmer at an angle of depression of 8°. How far away from the tower is the swimmer? **about 43 ft**

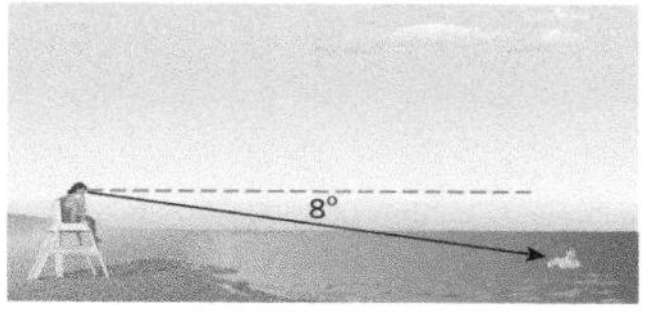

2 Two Angles of Elevation or Depression Angles of elevation or depression to two different objects can be used to estimate the distance between those objects. Similarly, the angles from two different positions of observation to the same object can be used to estimate the object's height.

WatchOut!

Angles of Elevation and Depression To avoid mislabeling, remember that angles of elevation and depression are always formed with a horizontal line and never with a vertical line.

Math HistoryLink

Eratosthenes (276–194 B.C.) Eratosthenes was a mathematician who was born in Cyrene, which is now Libya. He used the angle of elevation of the Sun at noon in the cities of Alexandria and Syene (now Egypt) to measure the circumference of Earth.

Source: *Encyclopaedia Britannica*

Need Another Example?

Circus Acts At the circus, a person in the audience at ground level watches the high-wire routine. A 5-foot-6-inch tall acrobat is standing on a platform that is 25 feet off the ground. How far is the audience member from the base of the platform, if the angle of elevation from the audience member's line of sight to the top of the acrobat's head is 27°? about 60 ft

Example 2 Angle of Depression

AL How do we know this is an angle of depression? The rescuers are looking down.

OL If the rescuer is tethered to the helicopter, at least how long must his tether be in order to be able to swim to the person in need of help? about 27 ft

BL If the helicopter moves 8 feet closer to the water before the rescuer jumps out, what is the new angle of depression? about 27°

Need Another Example?

Distance Maria is at the top of a cliff and sees a seal in the water. If the cliff is 40 feet above the water and the angle of depression is 52°, what is the horizontal distance from the seal to the cliff, to the nearest foot? 31 ft

Differentiated Instruction OL BL

Extension A 14-foot ladder is used to scale a 13-foot wall. At what angle of elevation must the ladder be situated in order to reach the top of the wall? The ladder must be situated with about a 68.2° angle of elevation in order to reach the top of the wall.

2 Two Angles of Elevation or Depression

Example 3 Use Two Angles of Elevation or Depression

AL **Why do we need to use two angles of elevation in this case?** Sample answer: Because she doesn't know how far she is from the tree when she sights the top the first time, Mrs. Long doesn't have enough information to determine the height of the tree. So, she has to sight again to get more information.

OL **For what types of situations does this type of estimation make sense?** Sample answer: in a situation where you don't know how far you are from an object or how tall it is, but you can estimate the angle you use to sight it from two different points that you can measure the distance between

BL **If Mrs. Long sights from the same two locations, but the tree is only 6 meters tall, what will the two angles of elevation be?** about 63° and about 19°

Need Another Example?
Distance Vernon is on the top deck of a cruise ship and observes two dolphins following each other directly away from the ship in a straight line. Vernon's position is 154 meters above sea level, and the angles of depression to the two dolphins are 35° and 36°. Find the distance between the two dolphins to the nearest meter. about 8 m

Real-World Link
In the United States, lumber volume is measured in board-feet, which is defined as a piece of wood containing 144 cubic inches. Woodland owners often estimate the lumber volume of trees they own to determine how many to cut and sell.

Source: The Ohio State University School of Natural Resources

G.SRT.8

Example 3 Use Two Angles of Elevation or Depression

TREE REMOVAL To estimate the height of a tree she wants removed, Mrs. Long sights the tree's top at a 70° angle of elevation. She then steps back 10 meters and sights the top at a 26° angle. If Mrs. Long's line of sight is 1.7 meters above the ground, how tall is the tree to the nearest meter?

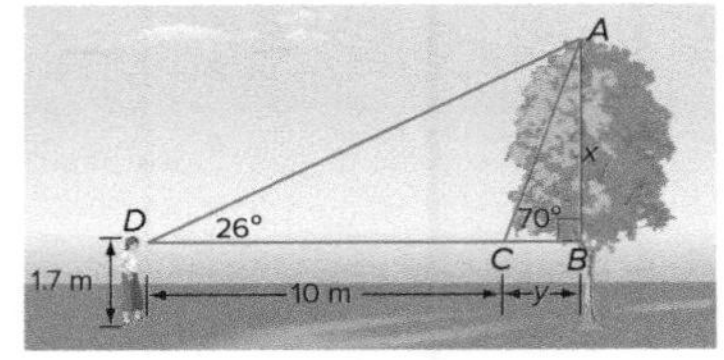

Understand $\triangle ABC$ and $\triangle ABD$ are right triangles. The height of the tree is the sum of Mrs. Long's height and AB.

Plan Since her initial distance from the tree is not given, write and solve a system of equations using both triangles. Let $AB = x$ and $CB = y$. So $DB = y + 10$ and the height of the tree is $x + 1.7$.

Solve Use $\triangle ABC$.

$\tan 70° = \frac{x}{y}$ — $\tan = \frac{\text{opposite}}{\text{adjacent}}$; $m\angle ACB = 70$

$y \tan 70° = x$ — Multiply each side by y.

Use $\triangle ABD$.

$\tan 26° = \frac{x}{y + 10}$ — $\tan = \frac{\text{opposite}}{\text{adjacent}}$; $m\angle D = 26$

$(y + 10) \tan 26° = x$ — Multiply each side by $y + 10$.

Substitute the value for x from $\triangle ABD$ in the equation for $\triangle ABC$ and solve for y.

$$y \tan 70° = x$$
$$y \tan 70° = (y + 10) \tan 26°$$
$$y \tan 70° = y \tan 26° + 10 \tan 26°$$
$$y \tan 70° - y \tan 26° = 10 \tan 26°$$
$$y(\tan 70° - \tan 26°) = 10 \tan 26°$$
$$y = \frac{10 \tan 26°}{\tan 70° - \tan 26°}$$

Use a calculator to find that $y \approx 2.16$. Using the equation from $\triangle ABC$, $x = 2.16 \tan 70°$ or about 5.9. The height of the tree is $5.9 + 1.7$ or 7.6, which is about 8 meters.

Check Substitute the value for y in the equation from $\triangle ABD$.

$x = (2.16 + 10) \tan 26°$ or about 5.9.

When using the angles of depression to two different objects to calculate the distance between them, it is important to remember that the two objects must lie in the same horizontal plane. Eight meters is reasonable for the tree height.

Guided Practice

3. **SKYSCRAPERS** Two buildings are sited from atop a 200-meter skyscraper. Building A is sited at a 35° angle of depression, while Building B is sighted at a 36° angle of depression. How far apart are the two buildings to the nearest meter? 10 m

Differentiated Instruction AL OL BL

Kinesthetic Learners Using a meterstick and a calculator, groups of students can find angles of elevation and depression for different objects in the classroom. Groups can measure one person's eye level from the floor, and the topmost height of a wall clock from the floor. The person stands 5 feet away from the clock, and the group calculates the angle of elevation from the person's line of sight to the top of the object. Repeat for items placed on the floor, and include variations like having the person stand on a platform, or placing two objects on the floor a certain distance from each other.

Check Your Understanding

○ = Step-by-Step Solutions begin on page R13.

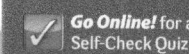

Go Online! for a Self-Check Quiz

Example 1 G.SRT.8

1. **BIKING** Lenora wants to build the bike ramp shown. Find the length of the base of the ramp. 27.5 ft

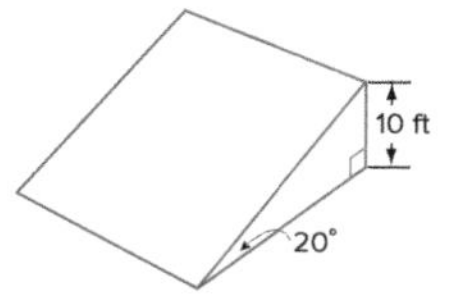

Example 2 G.SRT.8

2. **BASEBALL** A fan is seated in the upper deck of a stadium 200 feet away from home plate. If the angle of depression to the field is 62°, at what height is the fan sitting? 176.6 ft

Example 3 G.SRT.8

3. MP **MODELING** Annabelle and Rich are setting up decorations for their school dance. Rich is standing 5 feet directly in front of Annabelle under a disco ball. If the angle of elevation from Annabelle to the ball is 40° and from Rich to the ball is 50°, how high is the disco ball? 14.2 ft

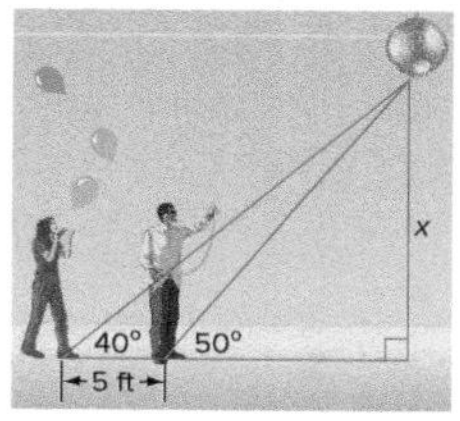

Practice and Problem Solving

Extra Practice is found on page R8.

Example 1 G.SRT.8

4. **HOCKEY** A hockey player takes a shot 20 feet away from a 5-foot goal. If the puck travels at a 15° angle of elevation toward the center of the goal, will the player score? no; 5.4 > 5

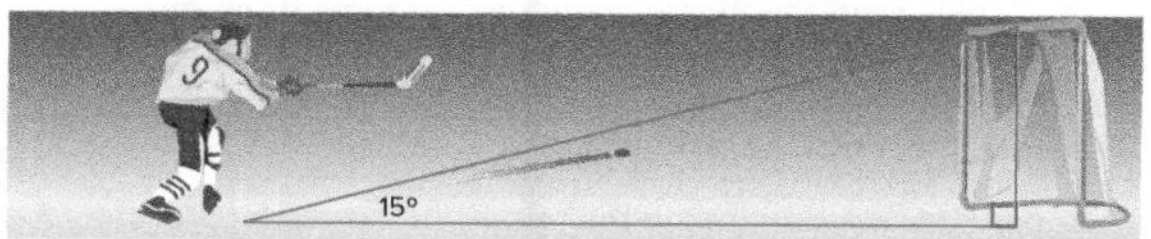

5. **MOUNTAINS** Find the angle of elevation to the peak of a mountain for an observer who is 155 meters from the mountain if the observer's eye is 1.5 meters above the ground and the mountain is 350 meters tall. ≈66°

Example 2 G.SRT.8

6. **WATERPARK** Two water slides are 50 meters apart on level ground. From the top of the taller slide, you can see the top of the shorter slide at an angle of depression of 15°. If you know that the top of the other slide is approximately 15 meters above the ground, about how far above the ground are you? Round to the nearest tenth of a meter. 28.4 m

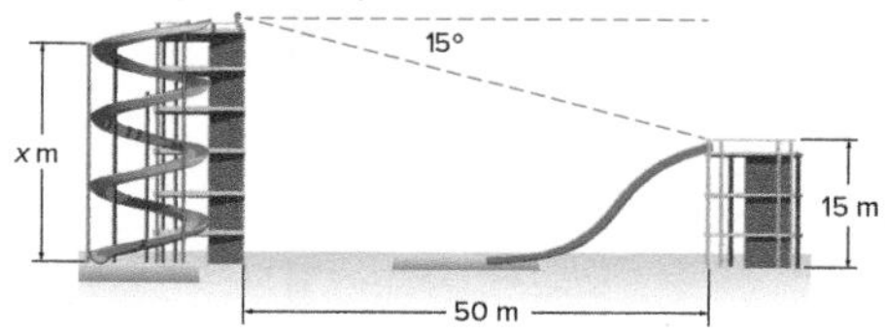

7. **AVIATION** Due to a storm, a pilot flying at an altitude of 528 feet has to land. If he has a horizontal distance of 2000 feet to land, at what angle of depression should he land? 14.8°

Example 3 G.SRT.8

8. **PYRAMIDS** Miko and Tyler are visiting the Great Pyramid in Egypt. From where Miko is standing, the angle of elevation to the top of the pyramid is 48.6°. From Tyler's position, the angle of elevation is 50°. If they are standing 20 feet apart and they are each 5 feet 6 inches tall, how tall is the pyramid? about 475.5 ft

Differentiated Homework Options			
Levels	AL Basic	OL Core	BL Advanced
Exercises	4–11, 23, 25–36	5–11 odd, 12–23, 25–36	20–27, (optional: 28–36)
2-Day Option	5–11 odd, 28–36	4–11	
	4–10 even, 23, 25–27	12–23, 25–36	

You can use ALEKS to provide additional remediation support with personalized instruction and practice.

Practice

Formative Assessment Use Exercises 1–3 to assess students' understanding of the concepts in this lesson.

The Practice and Problem Solving exercises assess the content taught in the lesson. The Preparing for Assessment page is meant to be used as preparation for end-of-course assessments.

MP Teaching the Mathematical Practices

Modeling Mathematically proficient students can apply the mathematics they know to solve problems arising in everyday life. In Exercise 3, encourage students to analyze the figure given to see which trigonometric functions can be used.

Extra Practice

See page R8 for extra exercises for students who are approaching level or for on-level students who need additional reinforcement.

Levels of Complexity Chart

The levels of the exercises progress from 1 to 3, with Level 1 indicating the lowest level of complexity.

Exercises	4–11	12–19, 28–36	20–27
Level 3			●
Level 2		●	
Level 1	●		

Go Online! eBook

Interactive Student Guide

Use the *Interactive Student Guide* to deepen conceptual understanding.

· Angles of Elevation and Depression

Teaching the Mathematical Practices

Modeling Mathematically proficient students can apply the mathematics they know to solve problems arising in everyday life. In Exercises 12 and 18, encourage students to analyze the figure given to see which trigonometric functions can be used.

Additional Answer

15b. Sample answer: the overhang is used to keep sunlight out of the windows in the summer, but allow the sunlight in during the winter. He would want the overhang to be long enough to block all of the sunlight on the longest day when the Sun is at the greatest elevation. For El Paso, this angle is 81.2°. The overhang begins 2 feet above the windows, so it will need to cover 14 feet. The length of the overhang is $L = \frac{14}{\tan 81.2}$ or about 2.17 feet. If the overhang is any longer, then less sunlight will get into the house in the winter.

9. DIVING Austin is standing on the high dive at the local pool. Austin's line of sight is 3 feet above the diving board. Two of his friends are in the water as shown. If the angle of depression to one of his friends is 40°, and 30° to his other friend who is 5 feet beyond the first, how tall is the platform? **6.3 ft**

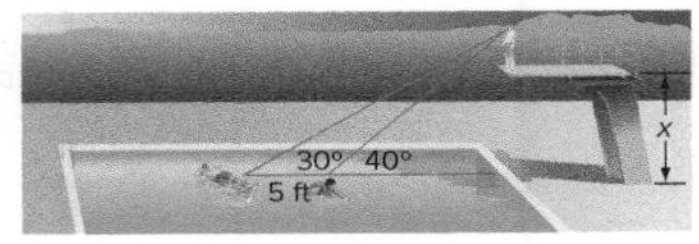

10. BASKETBALL Claire and Marisa are waiting to get a rebound during a basketball game. If the height of the basketball hoop is 10 feet, the angle of elevation between Claire and the goal is 35°, and the angle of elevation between Marisa and the goal is 25°, how far apart are they standing? **7.2 ft**

11. RIVERS Hugo is standing in the top of St. Louis' Gateway Arch, looking down on the Mississippi River. The angle of depression to the closer bank is 45° and the angle of depression to the farther bank is 18°. The arch is 630 feet tall. Estimate the width of the river at that point. **about 1309 ft**

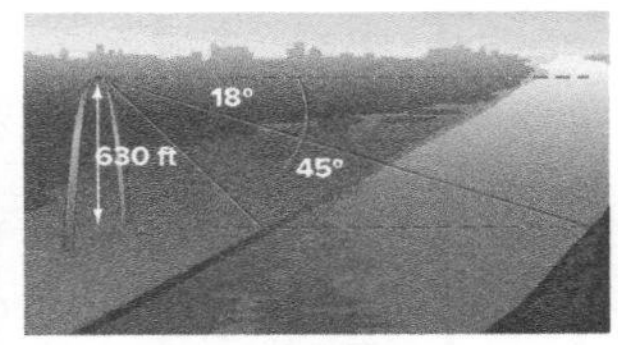

B **12. MODELING** The Unzen Volcano in Japan has a magma reservoir located 15 kilometers beneath the Chijiwa Bay, located east of the volcano. A magma channel, which connects the reservoir to the volcano, rises at a 40° angle of elevation toward the volcano. What length of magma channel is below sea level? **23.3 km**

13. BRIDGES Suppose you are standing in the middle of the platform of the Akashi Kaikyo Bridge. If the height from the top of the platform holding the suspension cables is 297 meters and the length from the platform to the center of the bridge is 995 meters, what is the angle of depression from the center of the bridge to the platform? **16.6°**

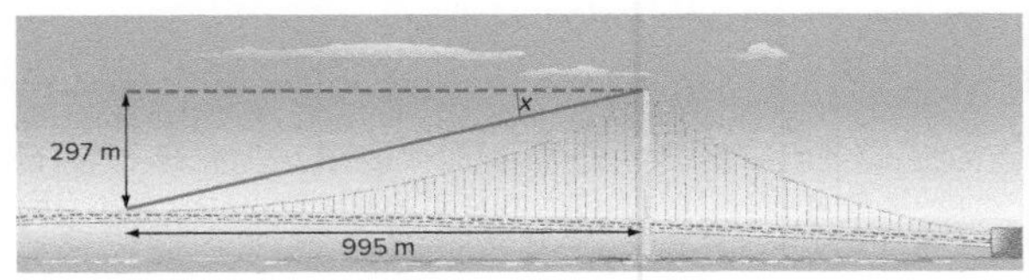

14. Little Gull Island Lighthouse has a span of 866 ft, and Plum Island Lighthouse has a span of 974 ft. So, the light from Plum Island Lighthouse would reach the boat.

14. LIGHTHOUSES Little Gull Island Lighthouse shines a light from a height of 91 feet with a 6° angle of depression. Plum Island Lighthouse, 1800 feet away, shines a light from a height of 34 feet with a 2° angle of depression. Which light will reach a boat that sits exactly between Little Gull Island Lighthouse and Plum Island Lighthouse?

15. MULTI-STEP Tom is designing a passive solar home in El Paso, along the 31.8° latitude. His design will include an overhang to shield the windows from the Sun.

Day of the Year	Angle of Elevation of the Sun
Longest Day	90° + 23° – the latitude
Shortest Day	90° – 23° – the latitude

a. If the windows will be 12 feet high with the overhang beginning 2 feet above the windows, what length should he make the overhang? **about 2.17 ft**

b. Explain your solution process. **See margin.**

Go Online!

The most up-to-date resources available for your program can be found at connectED.mcgraw-hill.com.

16. **MAINTENANCE** Two telephone repair workers arrive at a location to restore electricity after a power outage. One of the workers climbs up the telephone pole while the other worker stands 10 feet to the left of the pole. If the terminal box is located 30 feet above ground on the pole and the angle of elevation from the truck to the repair worker is 70°, how far is the worker on the ground standing from the truck? **20.9 ft**

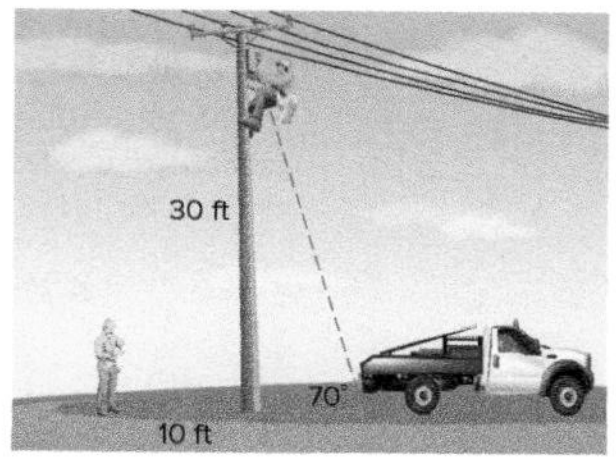

17 **PHOTOGRAPHY** A digital camera with a panoramic lens is described as having a view with an angle of elevation of 38°. If the camera is on a 3-foot tripod aimed directly at a 124-foot-tall monument, how far from the monument should you place the tripod to see the entire monument in your photograph? **≈154.9 ft**

18. MP **MODELING** As a part of their weather unit, Anoki's science class took a hot-air balloon ride. As they passed over a fenced field, the angle of depression of the closer side of the fence was 32°, and the angle of depression of the farther side of the fence was 27°. If the height of the balloon was 800 feet, estimate the width of the field. **289.8 ft**

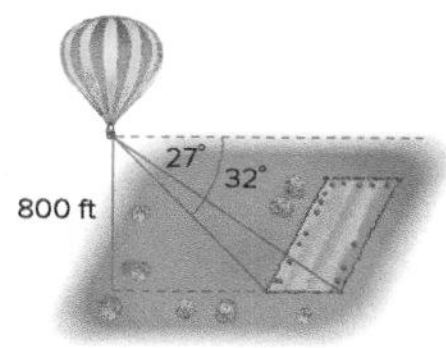

19. **MARATHONS** The Badwater Ultramarathon is a race that begins at the lowest point in California's Death Valley and ends at the highest point of the state, Mount Whitney. The race starts at a depth of 86 meters below sea level and ends 2530 meters above sea level.

a. Determine the angle of elevation to Mount Whitney if the horizontal distance from the base to the peak is 1200 meters. **≈65.4°**

b. If the angle of depression to Death Valley is 38°, what is the horizontal distance from sea level? **≈110.1 m**

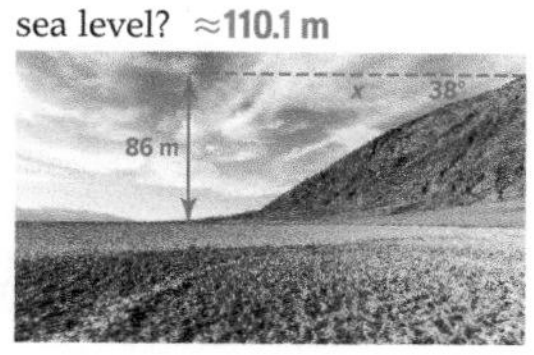

C **20.** **AMUSEMENT PARKS** India, Enrique, and Trina went to an amusement park while visiting Japan. They went on a Ferris wheel that was 100 meters in diameter and on an 80-meter cliff-dropping slide.

a. When Enrique and Trina are at the topmost point on the Ferris wheel shown below, how far are they from India? **119.2 m**

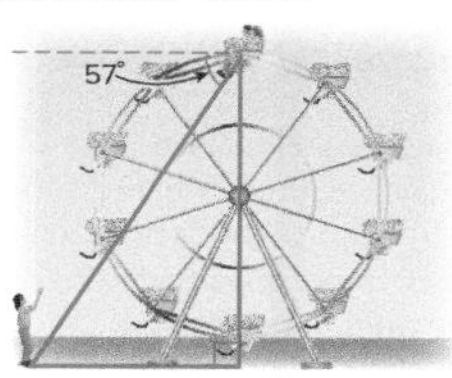

b. If the cliff-dropping ride has an angle of depression of 46°, how long is the slide? **111.2 m**

Differentiated Instruction ELL

Intermediate Instruct a small group of students to write a paragraph describing what is happening in the figure illustrating the angles of depression and elevation. Their paragraphs should describe each part of the diagram in their own words. Ask for volunteers to read their paragraphs. Have students ask for clarification as needed.

Exercise Alert

Ruler and Protractor Exercise 22 requires the use of a ruler and a protractor.

Watch Out!

Error Analysis In Exercise 23, Terrence does not explain the angle of depression correctly. Students should remember that the angle of elevation and the angle of depression are congruent.

MP Teaching the Mathematical Practices

Reasoning Mathematically proficient students make sense of quantities and their relationships in problem situations. In Exercise 25, encourage students to analyze the relationship between the angle of elevation and the sight line of a person watching an object.

Assess

Ticket Out the Door Have students create questions about either angles of elevation or depression that involve real-world situations. Each student will then pick another student's question to solve step-by-step to turn in.

Additional Answer

23. Rodrigo; sample answer: Because your horizontal line of sight is parallel to the other person's horizontal line of sight, the angles of elevation and depression are congruent according to the Alternate Interior Angles Theorem.

Go Online!

eSolutions Manual
Create worksheets, answer keys, and solutions handouts for your assignments.

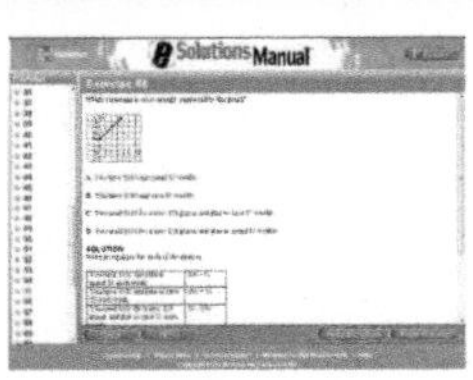

21. **DARTS** Kelsey and José are throwing darts from a distance of 8.5 feet. The center of the bull's-eye on the dartboard is 5.7 feet from the floor. José throws from a height of 6 feet, and Kelsey throws from a height of 5 feet. What are the angles of elevation or depression from which each must throw to get a bull's-eye? Ignore other factors such as air resistance, velocity, and gravity.

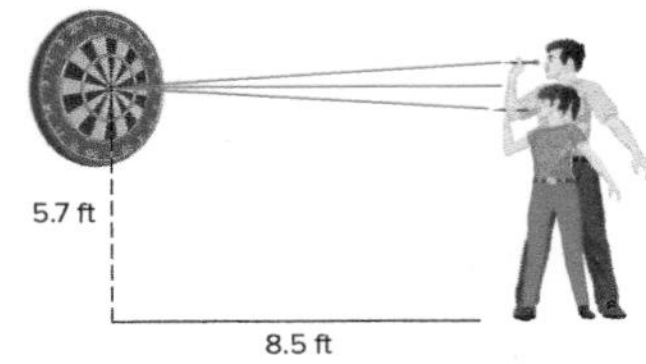

José throws at an angle of depression of 2.02°. Kelsey throws at an angle of elevation of 4.71°.

22. **MULTIPLE REPRESENTATIONS** In this problem, you will investigate relationships between the sides and angles of triangles.
    a. **Geometric** Draw three triangles. Make one acute, one obtuse, and one right. Label one triangle *ABC*, a second *MNP*, and the third *XYZ*. Label the side lengths and angle measures of each triangle. See Ch. 8 Answer Appendix.
    b. **Tabular** Copy and complete the table below. Sample answers given.

Triangle	Ratios		
ABC	$\frac{\sin A}{BC} = 0.3$	$\frac{\sin B}{CA} = 0.3$	$\frac{\sin C}{AB} = 0.3$
MNP	$\frac{\sin M}{NP} = 0.2$	$\frac{\sin N}{PM} = 0.2$	$\frac{\sin P}{MN} = 0.2$
XYZ	$\frac{\sin X}{YZ} = 0.3$	$\frac{\sin Y}{ZX} = 0.3$	$\frac{\sin Z}{XY} = 0.3$

    c. **Verbal** Make a conjecture about the ratio of the sine of an angle to the length of the leg opposite that angle for a given triangle. See Ch. 8 Answer Appendix.

G.SRT.8

H.O.T. Problems Use Higher-Order Thinking Skills

23. **ERROR ANALYSIS** Terrence and Rodrigo are trying to determine the relationship between angles of elevation and depression. Terrence says that if you are looking up at someone with an angle of elevation of 35°, then they are looking down at you with an angle of depression of 55°, which is the complement of 35°. Rodrigo disagrees and says that the other person would be looking down at you with an angle of depression equal to your angle of elevation, or 35°. Is either of them correct? Explain. See margin.

24. **CHALLENGE** Find the value of x. Round to the nearest tenth. 7.9

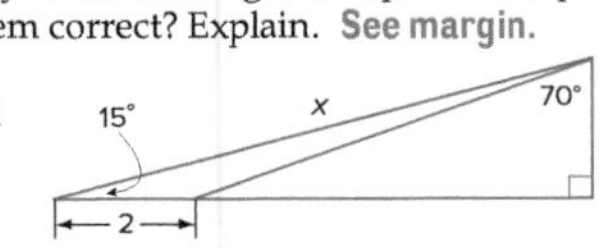

25. **MP REASONING** Classify the statement below as *true* or *false*. Explain. See margin.

As a person moves closer to an object he or she is sighting, the angle of elevation increases.

26. **OPEN-ENDED** A classmate finds the angle of elevation of an object, but she is trying to find the angle of depression. Write a question to help her solve the problem.

26. Sample answer: What is the relationship between the angle of elevation and angle of depression?

27. **WRITING IN MATH** Describe a way that you can estimate the height of an object without using trigonometry by choosing your angle of elevation. Explain your reasoning. See margin.

MP Standards for Mathematical Practice

Emphasis On	Exercises
3 Construct viable arguments and critique the reasoning of others.	23
4 Model with mathematics.	1–21, 28–36
8 Look for and express regularity in repeated reasoning.	22, 24–27

Preparing for Assessment

28. Leon wants to estimate the height of a building. Leon's eyes are 5.5 feet above ground. He stands 20 feet from the building and sights the top of the building, as shown in the figure. What is the building's height to the nearest tenth of a foot? MP 4 G.SRT.8 D

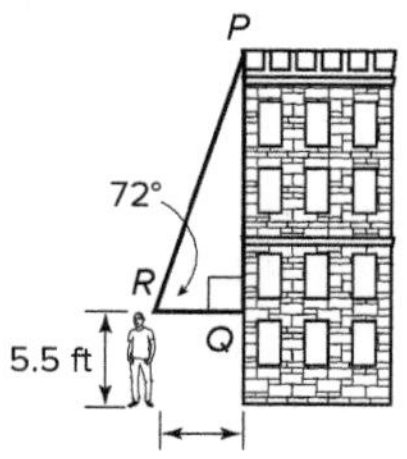

- ○ A 11.8 ft
- ○ B 24.5 ft
- ○ C 61.6 ft
- ○ D 67.1 ft

29. A tree is 70 feet tall. The angle of elevation of the Sun is 60°. Find the exact length of the tree's shadow. MP 4 G.SRT.8 $\frac{70\sqrt{3}}{3}$ ft

30. The pilot of an airplane finds the angle of depression of an airport to be 16°. If the horizontal distance to the airport is 60,000 feet, find the altitude of the plane. MP 4 G.SRT.8 ≈ 17,205 ft

31. A passenger in a hot-air balloon spots a small fire on the ground. The angle of depression to the fire is 30°, and the height of the hot-air balloon is 150 feet. To the nearest foot, what is the horizontal distance from the hot-air balloon to the fire? MP 4 G.SRT.8 D

- ○ A 75 ft
- ○ B 87 ft
- ○ C 130 ft
- ○ D 260 ft
- ○ E 300 ft

32. A searchlight is 6500 feet from a weather station. If the angle of elevation to the spot of light on the clouds above the station is 45°, how high is the cloud ceiling in feet? MP 4 G.SRT.8 6500

33. The angle of depression from the top of a skyscraper to a fountain on the ground is 81°. The skyscraper is 421 meters tall. What is the distance from the base of the skyscraper to the fountain, in meters, rounded to the nearest tenth? MP 4 G.SRT.8 66.7

34. Ariela is standing at the top of a tower that is 50 feet tall. She spots a helicopter in the distance. The angle of elevation from Ariela to the helicopter is 21°, as shown. MP 4 G.SRT.8 D

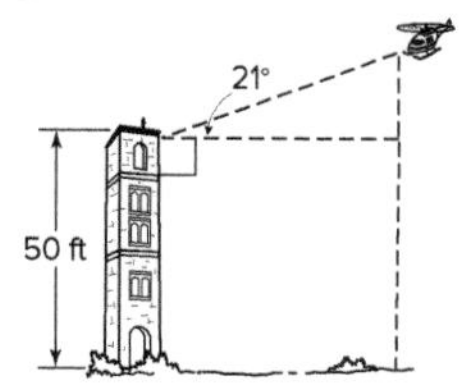

Which of the following best describes what Ariela should do to find the height of the helicopter?

- ○ A Solve $\tan 21° = \frac{x}{50}$.
- ○ B Solve $\tan 21° = \frac{50}{x}$.
- ○ C Solve $\cos 21° = \frac{x}{50}$.
- ○ D There is not enough information to find the height of the helicopter.

35. A ladder rests against a vertical wall. The base of the ladder is 28 ft from the wall. If the angle between the top of the ladder and the wall is 30°, find the length of the ladder. MP 4 G.SRT.8 56 ft

36. **MULTI-STEP** A lamp post is anchored to the ground by a 400-ft wire. The angle the wire makes with the ground is θ, and the end of the wire is 200 ft from the base of the post. MP 4 G.SRT.8

a. Find θ. 60 degrees

The angle the wire makes with the ground is θ, and the end of the wire is x ft from the base of the post.

b. Express x in terms of a trigonometric function of θ. $x = 400 \cos\theta$

25. True; sample answer: As a person moves closer to an object, the horizontal distance decreases, but the height of the object is constant. The tangent ratio will increase, and therefore the measure of the angle also increases.

27. Sample answer: If you sight something with a 45° angle of elevation, you don't have to use trigonometry to determine the height of the object. Because the legs of a 45°-45°-90° are congruent, the height of the object will be the same as your horizontal distance from the object.

Preparing for Assessment

Exercises 28–36 require students to use the skills they will need on standardized assessments. Exercises are dual-coded with content standards and mathematical practice standards.

Dual Coding		
Items	Content Standards	MP Mathematical Practices
28–36	G.SRT.8	4

Diagnose Student Errors

Survey student responses for each item. Class trends may indicate common errors and misconceptions.

28.

A	Solved equation incorrectly
B	Solved equation incorrectly
C	Did not add height of Leon's eyes above ground to distance from eye-level to top of building
D	CORRECT

31.

A	Solved $\cos 60° = \frac{x}{150}$
B	Solved $\tan 30° = \frac{x}{150}$
C	Solved $\sin 60° = \frac{x}{150}$
D	CORRECT
E	Found the straight-line distance from the hot-air balloon to the fire

34.

A	Identified an incorrect equation
B	Identified an incorrect equation
C	Identified an incorrect equation
D	CORRECT

Go Online!

Quizzes

Students can use *Self-Check Quizzes* to check their understanding of this lesson and have the results sent to you. You can also give *Quiz 3*, which covers the content in Lessons 8-5 and 8-6.

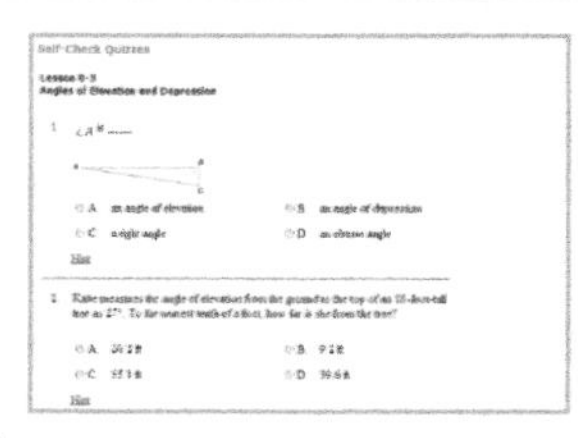

LESSON 8-6

The Law of Sines

SUGGESTED PACING (DAYS)

	Instruction
90 min.	0.75
45 min.	1.5

Track Your Progress

Objectives

1. Find the area of a triangle using two sides and an included angle.
2. Use the Law of Sines to solve triangles.

Mathematical Background

In one case for which the Law of Sines may be used, more than one solution of the triangle is possible. For this ambiguous case, the process of solving the triangle must be performed twice. However, there may still be only one solution for the triangle.

Skills Trace

THEN	NOW	NEXT
G.SRT.8. Use trigonometric ratios and the Pythagorean Theorem to solve right triangles in applied problems	**G.SRT.10** Prove the Laws of Sines and Cosines and use them to solve problems. **G.SRT.11** Understand and apply the Law of Sines and the Law of Cosines to find unknown measurements in right and non-right triangles (e.g. surveying problems, resultant forces).	**G.SRT.10** Prove the Laws of Sines and Cosines and use them to solve problems. **G.SRT.11** Understand and apply the Law of Sines and the Law of Cosines to find unknown measurements in right and non-right triangles (e.g. surveying problems, resultant forces).

Go Online! All of these resources and more are available at connectED.mcgraw-hill.com

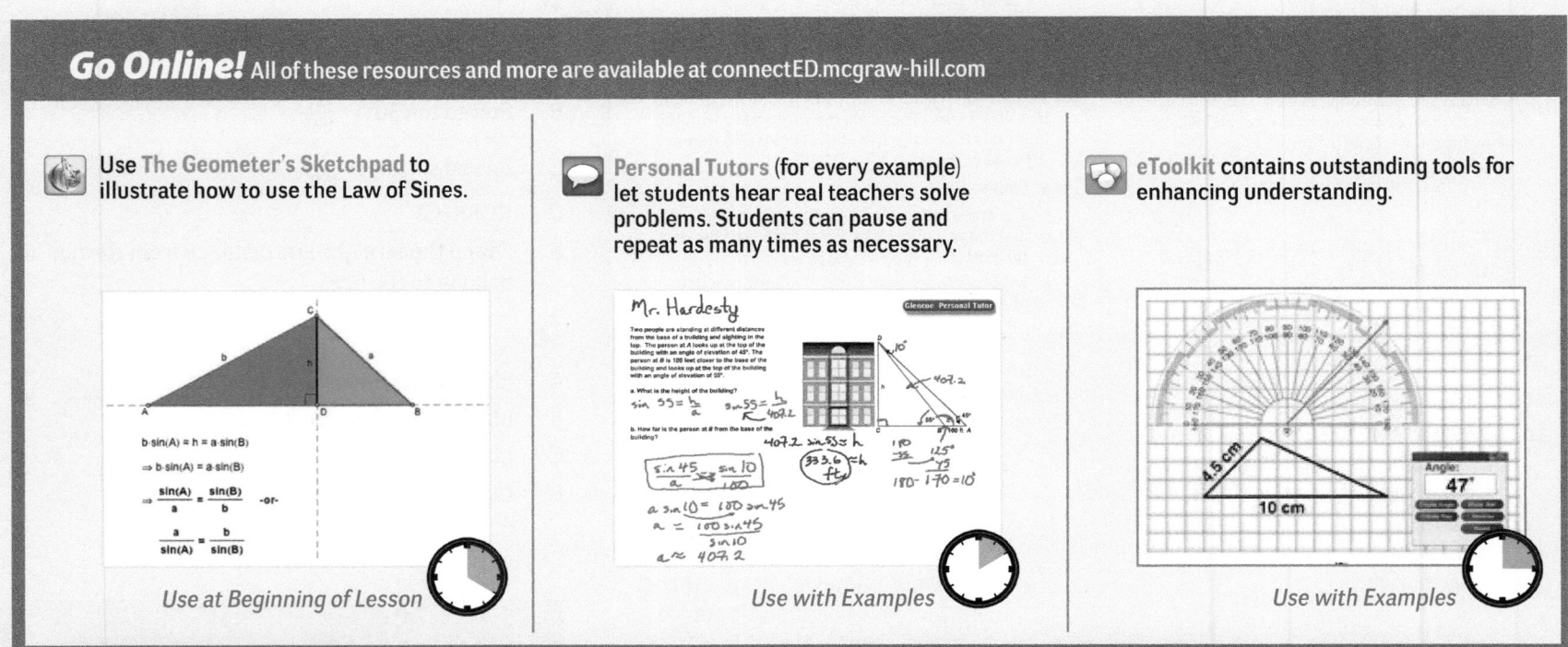

Use **The Geometer's Sketchpad** to illustrate how to use the Law of Sines.

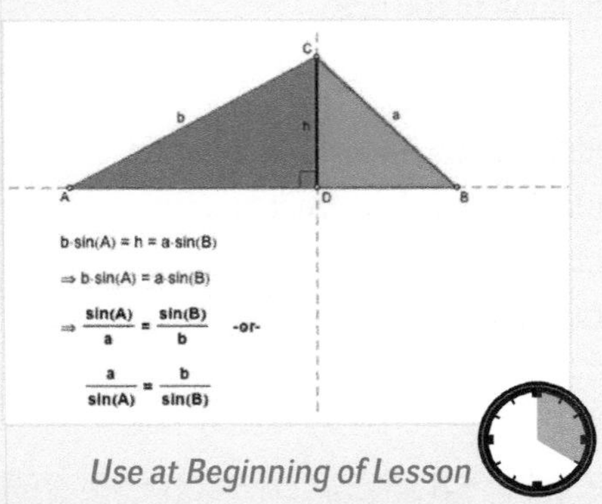

Use at Beginning of Lesson

Personal Tutors (for every example) let students hear real teachers solve problems. Students can pause and repeat as many times as necessary.

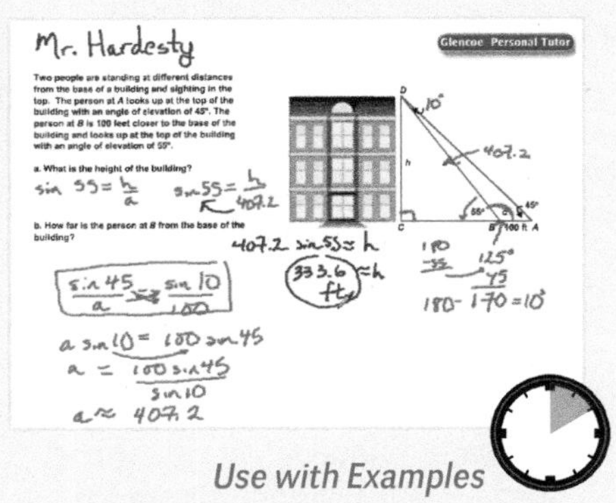

Use with Examples

eToolkit contains outstanding tools for enhancing understanding.

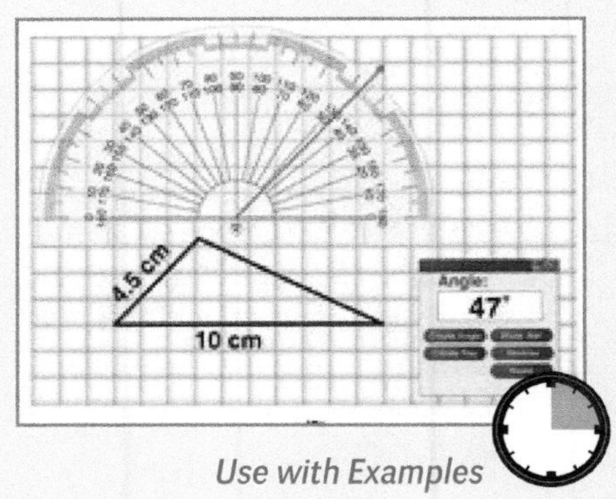

Use with Examples

OER Using Open Educational Resources

Tutorials Have students review the Law of Sines lesson on **illuminations.nctm.org** before beginning the lesson or to reinforce the key concepts. The lesson uses right triangle trigonometry to develop the Law of Sines. *Use as homework*

Go Online!
connectED.mcgraw-hill.com

Worksheets

Differentiate Your Resources

Extra Practice Additional practice or homework; Skills Practice is best for approaching-level students and Practice is best for on-level and beyond-level students

Skills Practice

AL OL ELL

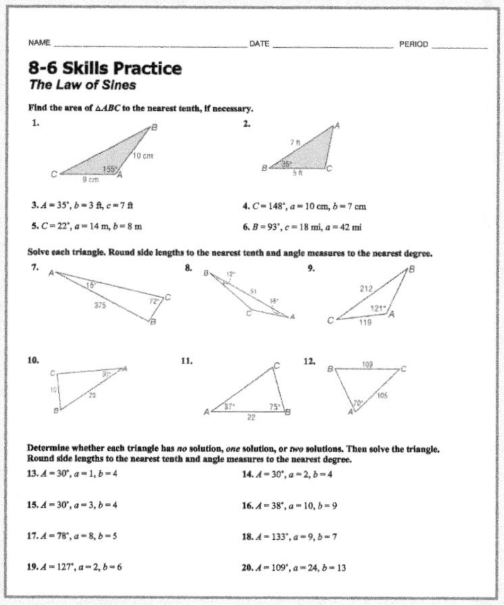
8-6 Skills Practice
The Law of Sines

Practice

AL OL BL ELL

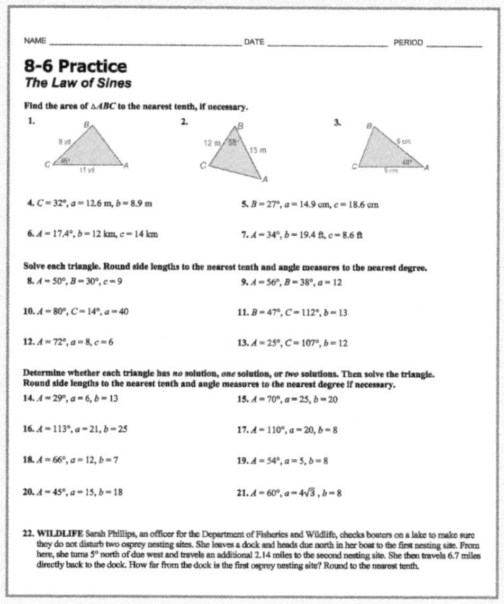
8-6 Practice
The Law of Sines

Word Problem Practice

AL OL BL ELL

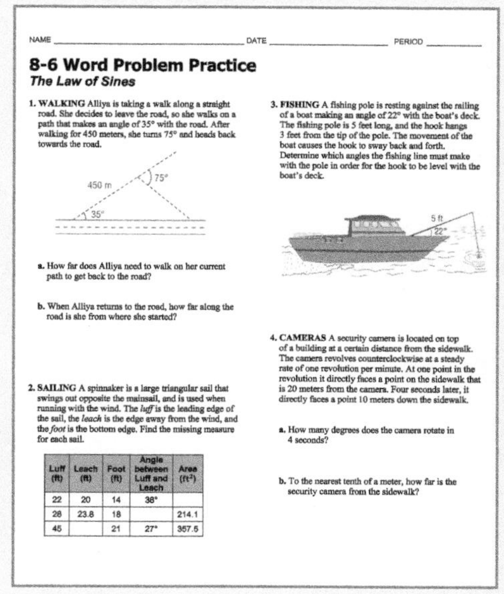
8-6 Word Problem Practice
The Law of Sines

Intervention Reteaching and vocabulary activities that can be used with struggling or absent students and as ELL support

Study Guide and Intervention

AL OL ELL

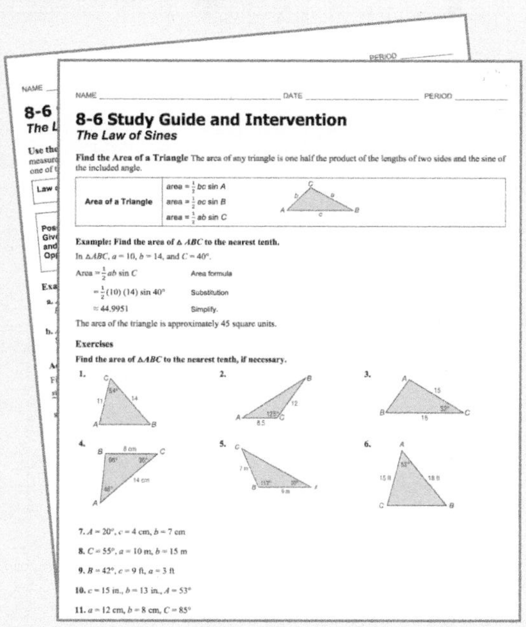
8-6 Study Guide and Intervention
The Law of Sines

Study Notebook

AL OL BL ELL

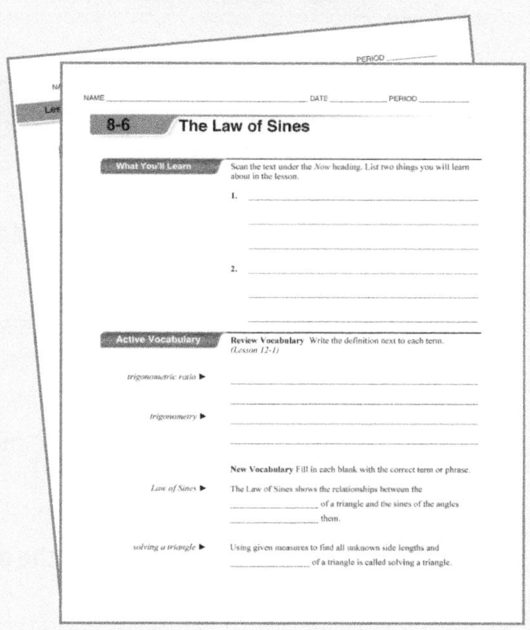
8-6 The Law of Sines

Extension Activities that can be used to extend lesson concepts

Enrichment

OL BL ELL

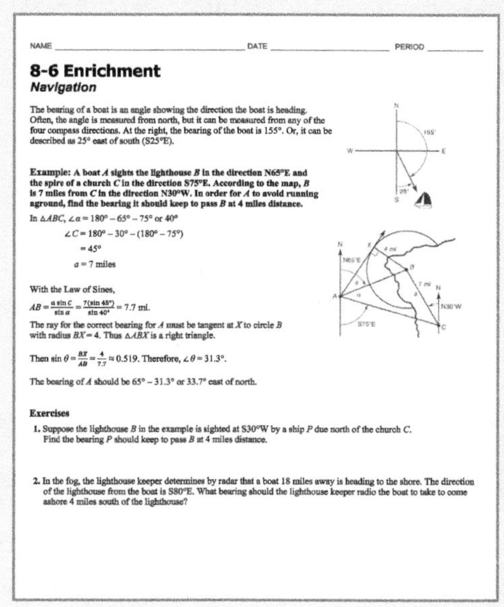
8-6 Enrichment
Navigation

Launch

Have students read the Why? section of the lesson. Ask:

- What is the size of the angle opposite the side connecting Wahoo and Naukan? Wahoo and Wabash? 102°; 23°
- What is the measure of the angle opposite the side connecting Wabash and Naukan? 55°
- What is the distance between Wahoo and Wabash? 1.2 km
- Which crater is at the vertex of the angle across from the longest side? Wabash

Teach

Ask the scaffolded questions for each example to build conceptual understanding for students at all levels.

1 Find the Area of a Triangle

Example 1 Find the Area of a Triangle

AL Is the triangle in Example 1 *acute*, *right*, or *obtuse*? obtuse

OL Why is the answer expressed in square centimeters? The side lengths of the triangle are expressed in centimeters, so the area must be expressed in square centimeters

BL To use this formula for the area of a triangle, what information must you have? the length of two sides of the triangle, and the measure of the included angle

Go Online!

Interactive Whiteboard

Use the *eLesson*, *Lesson Presentation*, or *Interactive Classroom* to present this lesson.

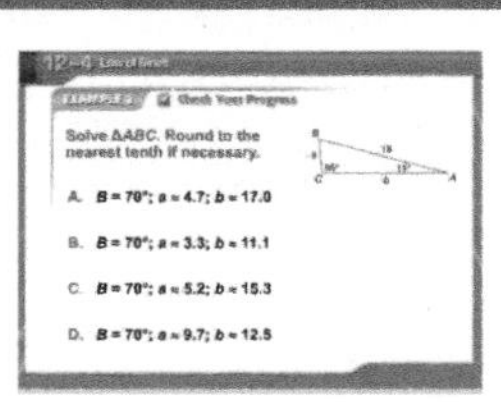

LESSON 6

The Law of Sines

Then

- You found side lengths and angle measures of right triangles.

Now

1. Find the area of a triangle using two sides and an included angle.
2. Use the Law of Sines to solve triangles.

Why?

- Mars has hundreds of thousands of craters. These craters are named after famous scientists, science fiction authors, and towns on Earth. The craters named Wahoo, Wabash, and Naukan are shown in the figure. You can use trigonometry to find the distance between Wahoo and Naukan.

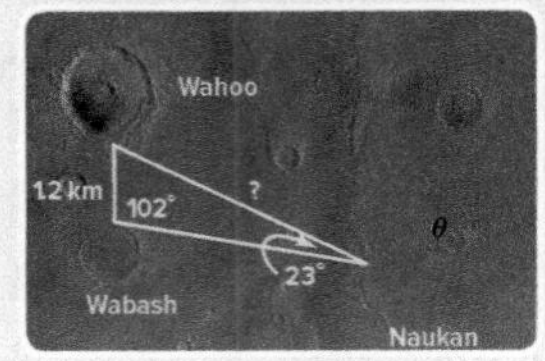

New Vocabulary

Law of Sines
solving a triangle
ambiguous case

Mathematical Practices

1 Make sense of problems and persevere in solving them.
4 Model with mathematics.
5 Use appropriate tools strategically.

Content Standards

G.SRT.10 Prove the Laws of Sines and Cosines and use them to solve problems.
G.SRT.11 Understand and apply the Law of Sines and the Law of Cosines to find unknown measurements in right and non-right triangles (e.g. surveying problems, resultant forces).

1 Find the Area of a Triangle In the triangle at the right, $\sin A = \frac{h}{c}$, or $h = c \sin A$.

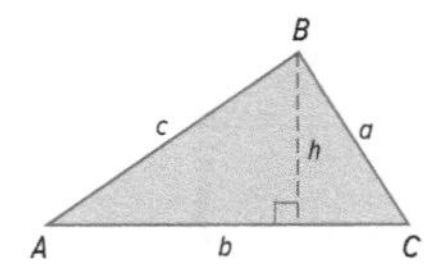

$\text{Area} = \frac{1}{2}bh$ Formula for area of a triangle

$\text{Area} = \frac{1}{2}b(c \sin A)$ Replace h with $c \sin A$.

$\text{Area} = \frac{1}{2}bc \sin A$ Simplify.

You can use this formula or two other formulas to find the area of a triangle if you know the lengths of two sides and the measure of the included angle.

Key Concept Area of a Triangle

Words The area of a triangle is one half the product of the lengths of two sides and the sine of their included angle.

Symbols $\text{Area} = \frac{1}{2}bc \sin A = \frac{1}{2}ac \sin B = \frac{1}{2}ab \sin C$

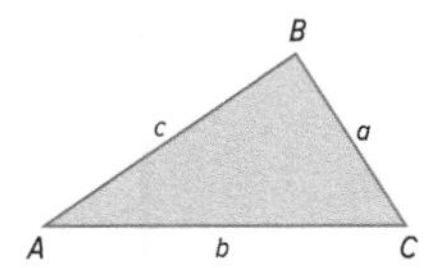

G.SRT.11

Example 1 Find the Area of a Triangle

Find the area of $\triangle ABC$ to the nearest tenth.

In $\triangle ABC$, $a = 8$, $b = 9$, and $C = 104°$.

$\text{Area} = \frac{1}{2}ab \sin C$ Based on the known measures, use the third area formula.

$= \frac{1}{2}(8)(9) \sin 104°$ Substitution

$\approx 34.9 \text{ cm}^2$ Simplify.

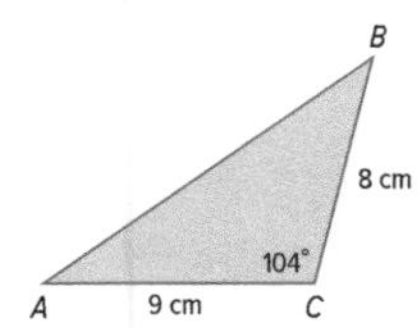

MENTAL CHECK Round the sin 104° to sin 90° because the sin of 90° is 1.

$\frac{1}{2}(8)(9)\sin 90° = \frac{1}{2}(8)(9)(1) = 36$

This is close to the answer of 34.9 square centimeters.

Guided Practice

1. Find the area of $\triangle ABC$ to the nearest tenth if $A = 31°$, $b = 18$ meters, and $c = 22$ meters. 102.0 m^2

NASA/JPL/USGS

Teaching the Mathematical Practices

Use appropriate tools strategically.
Help students identify the tools needed to solve problems using the Law of Sines. For example, ask:

- What is the ambiguous case of the Law of Sines? The ambiguous case occurs when solving triangles given the measures of two sides and the angle opposite one of the angles.
- When is there no solution for the ambiguous case of the Law of Sines if the given angle is acute? when the height of the triangle is greater than the length of the side opposite the given angle
- When are there two solutions for the ambiguous case of the Law of Sines? when the given angle is acute, and the length of the side opposite the given angle is greater than the height of the triangle and less than the length of the other given side

Go Online!

You have used the trigonometric ratios to find missing parts of right triangles. Explore how to find missing parts of oblique triangles using The Geometer's Sketchpad® activity in ConnectED. ELL

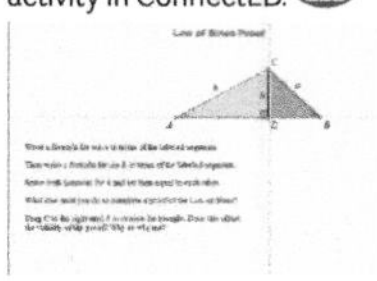

2 Use the Law of Sines to Solve Triangles

You can use the area formulas to derive the **Law of Sines**, which shows the relationships between side lengths of a triangle and the sines of the angles opposite them.

$\frac{1}{2}bc \sin A = \frac{1}{2}ac \sin B = \frac{1}{2}ab \sin C$	Set the area formulas equal to each other.
$bc \sin A = ac \sin B = ab \sin C$	Multiply each expression by 2.
$\frac{bc \sin A}{abc} = \frac{ac \sin B}{abc} = \frac{ab \sin C}{abc}$	Divide each expression by abc.
$\frac{\sin A}{a} = \frac{\sin B}{b} = \frac{\sin C}{c}$	Simplify.

Key Concept Law of Sines

In $\triangle ABC$, if sides with lengths a, b, and c have opposite angles with measures A, B, and C, respectively, then the following is true.

$$\frac{\sin A}{a} = \frac{\sin B}{b} = \frac{\sin C}{c}$$

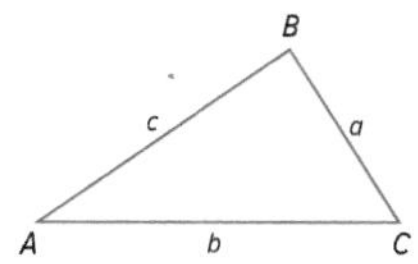

You can use the Law of Sines to solve a triangle if you know either of the following.

- the measures of two angles and any side (AAS or ASA)

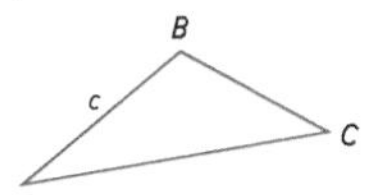

- the measures of two sides and the angle opposite one of the sides (SSA)

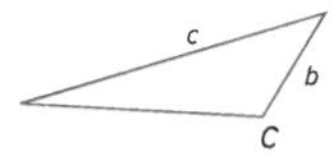

Using given measures to find all unknown side lengths and angle measures of a triangle is called **solving a triangle**.

Study Tip

The Law of Sines may also be written as $\frac{a}{\sin A} = \frac{b}{\sin B} = \frac{c}{\sin C}$. So, the expressions below could also be used to solve the triangle in Example 2.

- $\frac{a}{\sin 55°} = \frac{3}{\sin 80°}$
- $\frac{b}{\sin 45°} = \frac{3}{\sin 80°}$

G.SRT.11

Example 2 Solve a Triangle Given Two Angles and a Side

Solve $\triangle ABC$. Round to the nearest tenth if necessary.

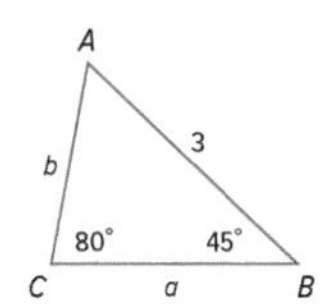

Step 1 Find the measure of the third angle.

$m\angle A = 180 - (80 + 45)$ or $55°$

Step 2 Use the Law of Sines to find side lengths a and b. Write an equation to find each variable.

$\frac{\sin A}{a} = \frac{\sin C}{c}$	Law of Sines	$\frac{\sin B}{b} = \frac{\sin C}{c}$
$\frac{\sin 55°}{a} = \frac{\sin 80°}{3}$	Substitution	$\frac{\sin 45°}{b} = \frac{\sin 80°}{3}$
$a = \frac{3 \sin 55°}{\sin 80°}$	Solve for each variable.	$b = \frac{3 \sin 45°}{\sin 80°}$
$a \approx 2.5$	Use a calculator.	$b \approx 2.2$

So, $A = 55°$, $a \approx 2.5$, and $b \approx 2.2$.

Guided Practice

2. Solve $\triangle NPQ$ if $P = 42°$, $Q = 65°$, and $n = 5$. $N = 73°$, $p \approx 3.5$, $q \approx 4.7$

Need Another Example?

Find the area of $\triangle ABC$ to the nearest tenth.
3.8 cm²

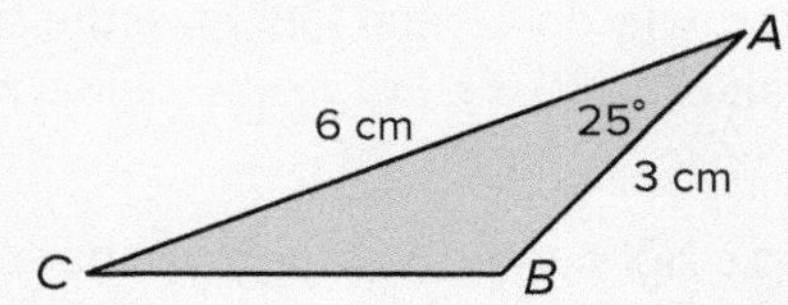

2 Use the Law of Sines to Solve Triangles

Example 2 Solve a Triangle Given Two Angles and a Side

AL How many total values are there when a triangle has been solved? 6

OL Explain how you can find the measure of the third angle if you know the measures of the other two angles in a triangle. You can use the Triangle Angle-Sum Theorem to find the measure of the third angle.

BL What type of expression are you solving when using the Law of Sines? a proportion

Need Another Example?

Solve $\triangle ABC$. Round to the nearest tenth if necessary.

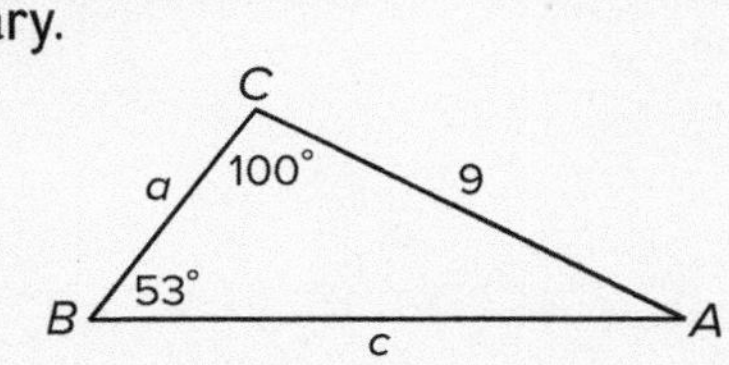

$A = 27°$, $a \approx 5.1$, $c \approx 11.1$

Watch Out!

Unlocking Misconceptions
Students may think that the Law of Sines only works for right trangles. Clarify that this formula works for any triangle, as does the Law of Cosines explored in Lesson 8-7.

MP Teaching the Mathematical Practices

Mathematically proficient students make sense of quantities and their relationships in problem situations. Remind students that ratios and proportions can be written in many forms.

Go Online!

The most up-to-date resources available for your program can be found at connectED.mcgraw-hill.com.

Example 3 Solve a Triangle Given Two Sides and an Angle

AL **In part c, why do 42° and 138° have the same sine values?** 42° and 138° are the same angle reflected in the *y*-axis.

OL **If ∠*A* is a right angle and there is one solution to the triangle, how can you find the measure of the third side?** Use the Pythagorean Theorem.

BL **Explain why if ∠*A* is obtuse and $a \leq b$ there is no solution.** The longest side must always be opposite the largest angle of a triangle. If ∠*A* is obtuse, then ∠*A* is the largest angle of the triangle, so *a* must be the longest side, but we are told that side *b* is longer, so this triangle cannot exist.

Need Another Example?

Determine whether each triangle has *no* solution, *one* solution, or *two* solutions. Then solve the triangle. Round side lengths to the nearest tenth and angle measures to the nearest degree.

a. In △*NPQ*, $Q = 110°$, $q = 11$, and $n = 8$. one; $P = 27°$, $N = 43°$, $p = 5.3$

b. In △*DEF*, $E = 52°$, $e = 5$, and $f = 9$. no solution

c. In △*XYZ*, $X = 28°$, $z = 15$, and $x = 9$. two; $Z = 51°$, $Y = 101°$, $y = 18.8$; $Z = 129°$, $Y = 23°$, $y = 7.6$

Study Tip

Two Solutions A situation in which two solutions for a triangle exist is called the *ambiguous case*.

If you are given the measures of two angles and a side, exactly one triangle is possible. However, if you are given the measures of two sides and the angle opposite one of them, zero, one, or two triangles may be possible. This is known as the **ambiguous case**. So, when solving a triangle using the SSA case, zero, one, or two solutions are possible.

Study Tip ELL

A is Acute In the figures at the right, the altitude *h* is compared to *a* because *h* is the minimum distance from *C* to $\overline{AB}$ when *A* is acute.

$\sin A = \frac{\text{opp}}{\text{hyp}}$

$\sin A = \frac{h}{b}$

Key Concept Possible Triangles in SSA Case

Consider a triangle in which *a*, *b*, and *m*∠*A* are given.

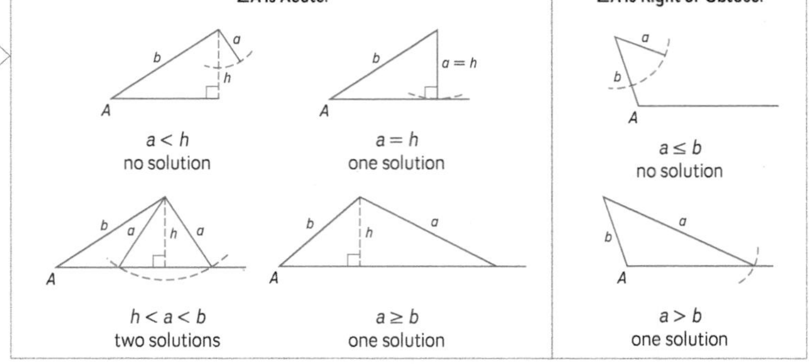

Because $\sin A = \frac{h}{b}$, you can use $h = b \sin A$ to find *h* in acute triangles.

G.SRT.11

Example 3 Solve a Triangle Given Two Sides and an Angle

Determine whether each triangle has *no* solution, *one* solution, or *two* solutions. Then solve the triangle. Round side lengths to the nearest tenth and angle measures to the nearest degree.

a. In △*RST*, $R = 105°$, $r = 9$, and $s = 6$.

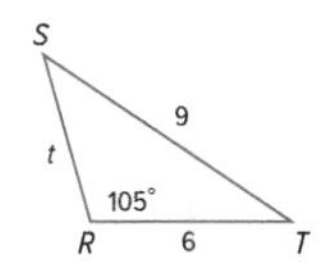

Because ∠*R* is obtuse and $9 > 6$, you know that one solution exists.

Step 1 Use the Law of Sines to find *m*∠*S*.

$\frac{\sin S}{6} = \frac{\sin 105°}{9}$ Law of Sines

$\sin S = \frac{6 \sin 105°}{9}$ Multiply each side by 6.

$\sin S \approx 0.6440$ Use a calculator.

$S \approx 40°$ Use the $\sin^{-1}$ function.

Step 2 Find *m*∠*T*.

$m\angle T \approx 180 - (105 + 40)$ or $35°$

Step 3 Use the Law of Sines to find *t*.

$\frac{\sin 35°}{t} \approx \frac{\sin 105°}{9}$ Law of Sines

$t \approx \frac{9 \sin 35°}{\sin 105°}$ Solve for *t*.

$t \approx 5.3$ Use a calculator.

So, $S \approx 40°$, $T \approx 35°$, and $t \approx 5.3$.

Differentiated Instruction AL OL BL ELL

Intrapersonal Learners Have students write a journal entry about which example they found the most challenging and why. Ask them to include any questions they still have about the lesson.

b. In $\triangle ABC$, $A = 54°$, $a = 6$, and $b = 8$.

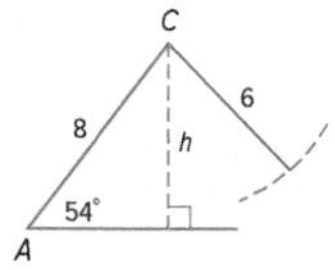

Because $\angle A$ is acute and $6 < 8$, find h and compare it to a.

$b \sin A = 8 \sin 54°$ — $b = 8$ and $A = 54°$

≈ 6.5 — Use a calculator.

Because $6 < 6.5$ or $a < h$, there is no solution.

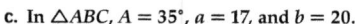

c. In $\triangle ABC$, $A = 35°$, $a = 17$, and $b = 20$.

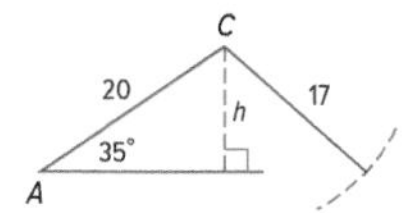

Because $\angle A$ is acute and $17 < 20$, find h and compare it to a.

$b \sin A = 20 \sin 35°$ — $b = 20$ and $A = 35°$

≈ 11.5 — Use a calculator.

Because $11.5 < 17 < 20$ or $h < a < b$, there are two solutions. So, there are two triangles to be solved

Case 1 $\angle B$ **is acute.**

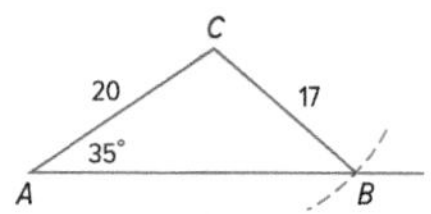

Step 1 Find $m\angle B$.

$\frac{\sin B}{20} = \frac{\sin 35°}{17}$ — Law of Sines

$\sin B = \frac{20 \sin 35°}{17}$ — Solve for sin B.

$\sin B \approx 0.6748$ — Use a calculator.

$B \approx 42°$ — Find $\sin^{-1} 0.6748$.

Step 2 Find $m\angle C$.

$m\angle C \approx 180 - (35 + 42)$ or $103°$

Step 3 Find c.

$\frac{\sin 103°}{c} = \frac{\sin 35°}{17}$ — Law of Sines

$c = \frac{17 \sin 103°}{\sin 35°}$ — Solve for c.

$c \approx 28.9$ — Simplify.

Case 2 $\angle B$ **is obtuse.**

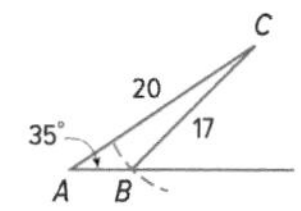

Step 1 Find $m\angle B$.

The sine function also has a positive value in Quadrant II. So, find an obtuse angle B for which $\sin B \approx 0.6748$.

$m\angle B \approx 180° - 42°$ or $138°$

Step 2 Find $m\angle C$.

$m\angle C \approx 180 - (35 + 138)$ or $7°$

Step 3 Find c.

$\frac{\sin 7°}{c} \approx \frac{\sin 35°}{17}$ — Law of Sines

$c \approx \frac{17 \sin 7°}{\sin 35°}$ — Solve for c.

$c \approx 3.6$ — Simplify.

So, one solution is $B \approx 42°$, $C \approx 103°$, and $c \approx 28.9$, and another solution is $B \approx 138°$, $C \approx 7°$, and $c \approx 3.6$.

Study Tip

Reference Angle In the triangle in Case 2, you are using the reference angle 42° to find the other value of B.

Guided Practice

Determine whether each triangle has *no* solution, *one* solution, or *two* solutions. Then solve the triangle. Round side lengths to the nearest tenth and angle measures to the nearest degree.

3A. In $\triangle RST$, $R = 95°$, $r = 10$, and $s = 12$. **no solution**

3B. In $\triangle MNP$, $N = 32°$, $n = 7$, and $p = 4$. **one; $P \approx 18°$, $M \approx 130°$, $m \approx 10.1$**

3C. In $\triangle ABC$, $A = 47°$, $a = 15$, and $b = 18$.

3C. two; $B \approx 61°$, $C \approx 72°$, $c \approx 19.5$; $B \approx 119°$, $C \approx 14°$, $c \approx 5.0$

Example 4 Use the Law of Sines to Solve a Problem

AL **Are you trying to find the length of a side or the measure of an angle in this problem?** side

OL **What information do you have about the triangle?** the measure of two angles and the length of the included side

BL **Explain how you could find the distance between point *B* and third base.** Find the measure of angle *B* using the Triangle Angle-Sum Theorem: 72°. Then, use the Law of Sines to set up and solve the proportion $\frac{\sin 65°}{x} = \frac{\sin 72°}{90}$.

Need Another Example?

Baseball In Example 4, suppose the angles at second base and third base are 58° and 41°, respectively. How far away from second base was the ball caught? about 59.8 ft

Real-World Link

High school and college baseball fields share the same infield dimensions as professional baseball fields. The outfield dimensions vary greatly.

Source: *Baseball Digest Magazine*

G.SRT.11

Real-World Example 4 Use the Law of Sines to Solve a Problem

BASEBALL **A baseball is hit between the second and third bases and is caught at point *B*, as shown in the figure. How far away from second base was the ball caught?**

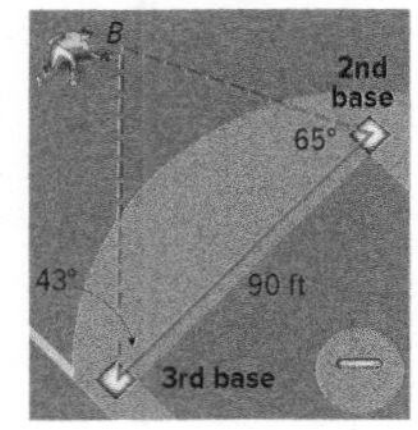

$\frac{\sin 72°}{90} = \frac{\sin 43°}{x}$ Law of Sines

$x \sin 72° = 90 \sin 43°$ Cross products

$x = \frac{90 \sin 43°}{\sin 72°}$ Solve for *x*.

$x \approx 64.5$ Use a calculator.

So, the distance is about 64.5 feet.

Guided Practice

4. How far away from third base was the ball caught? 85.8 ft

Check Your Understanding

(3) = Step-by-Step Solutions begin on page R13.

Go Online! for a Self-Check Quiz

Example 1 G.SRT.11

Find the area of △*ABC* to the nearest tenth, if necessary.

1. 27.9 mm²

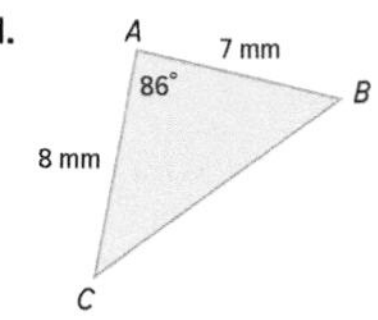

2. 3 yd²

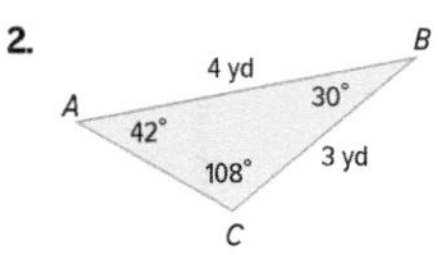

(3) $A = 40°$, $b = 11$ cm, $c = 6$ cm 21.2 cm²

4. $B = 103°$, $a = 20$ in., $c = 18$ in. 175.4 in²

Example 2 G.SRT.11

Solve each triangle. Round side lengths to the nearest tenth and angle measures to the nearest degree.

5.

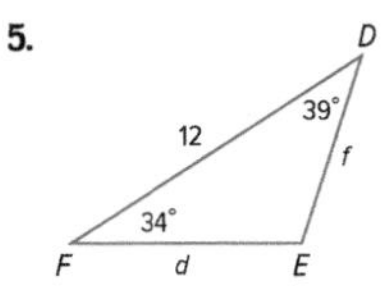

6.

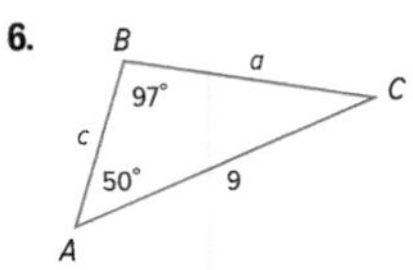

5. $E = 107°$, $d \approx 7.9$, $f \approx 7.0$
6. $C = 33°$, $a \approx 6.9$, $c \approx 4.9$

7. Solve △*FGH* if $G = 80°$, $H = 40°$, and $g = 14$. $F = 60°$, $f \approx 12.3$, $h \approx 9.1$

Example 3 G.SRT.11

MP PERSEVERANCE **Determine whether each △*ABC* has *no* solution, *one* solution, or *two* solutions. Then solve the triangle. Round side lengths to the nearest tenth and angle measures to the nearest degree.** 8. one; $B \approx 39°$, $C \approx 46°$, $c \approx 13.7$

8. $A = 95°$, $a = 19$, $b = 12$
9. $A = 60°$, $a = 15$, $b = 24$ no solution
10. $A = 34°$, $a = 8$, $b = 13$
11. $A = 30°$, $a = 3$, $b = 6$

10. two; $B \approx 65°$, $C \approx 81°$, $c \approx 14.1$; $B \approx 115°$, $C \approx 31°$, $c \approx 7.4$
11. one; $B = 90°$, $C = 60°$, $c \approx 5.2$

Example 4 G.SRT.11

12. **SPACE** Refer to the beginning of the lesson. Find the distance between the Wahoo Crater and the Naukan Crater on Mars. 3 kilometers

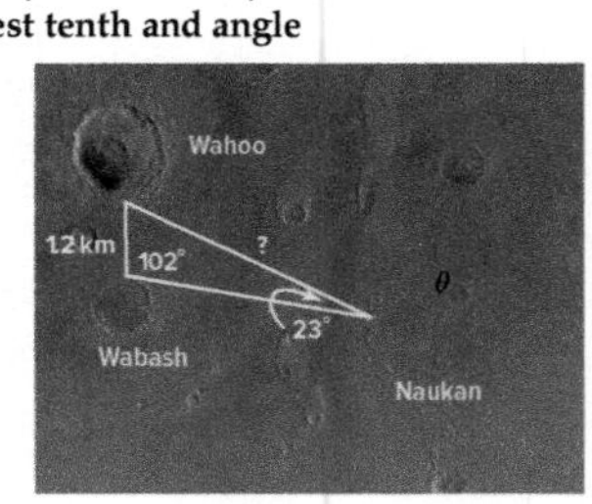

Go Online! eBook

Interactive Student Guide

Use the *Interactive Student Guide* to deepen conceptual understanding.

· The Law of Sines and Law of Cosines

Practice and Problem Solving

Extra Practice is on page R8.

Example 1
G.SRT.11

Find the area of △*ABC* to the nearest tenth.

13. 10.6 km²

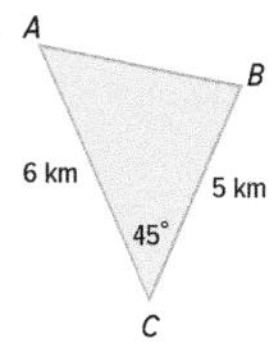

14. 126.1 ft²

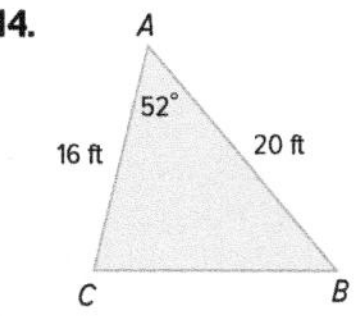

15. 36.8 m²

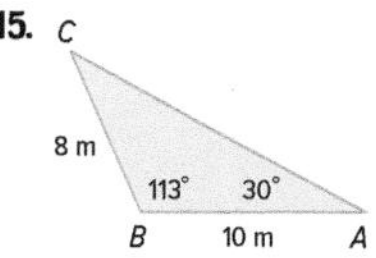

16. 74.1 cm²

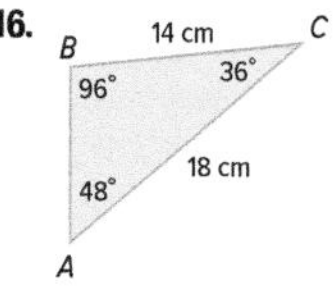

17. $C = 25°$, $a = 4$ ft, $b = 7$ ft 5.9 ft²

18. $A = 138°$, $b = 10$ in., $c = 20$ in. 66.9 in²

19. $B = 92°$, $a = 14.5$ m, $c = 9$ m 65.2 m²

20. $C = 116°$, $a = 2.7$ cm, $b = 4.6$ cm 5.6 cm²

Example 2
G.SRT.11

MP REASONING **Solve each triangle. Round side lengths to the nearest tenth and angle measures to the nearest degree.**

21.

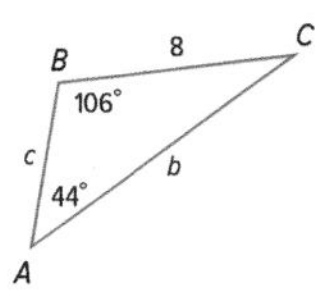

22.

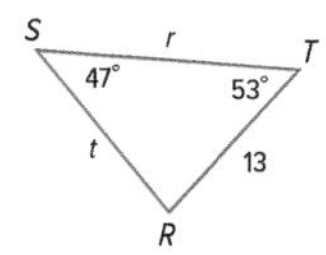

23.

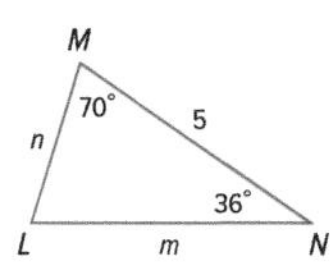

24.

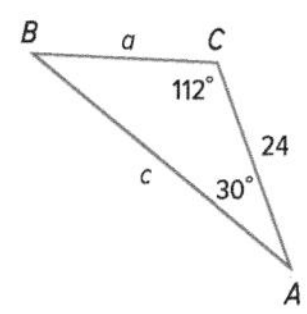

21. $C = 30°$, $b \approx 11.1$, $c \approx 5.8$
22. $R = 80°$, $r \approx 17.5$, $t \approx 14.2$
23. $L = 74°$, $m \approx 4.9$, $n \approx 3.1$
24. $B = 38°$, $a \approx 19.5$, $c \approx 36.1$

25. Solve △*HJK* if $H = 53°$, $J = 20°$, and $h = 31$. $K = 107°$, $j \approx 13.3$, $k \approx 37.1$

26. Solve △*NPQ* if $P = 109°$, $Q = 57°$, and $n = 22$. $N = 14°$, $p \approx 86.0$, $q \approx 76.3$

27. Solve △*ABC* if $A = 50°$, $a = 2.5$, and $C = 67°$. $B = 63°$, $b \approx 2.9$, $c \approx 3.0$

28. Solve △*ABC* if $B = 18°$, $C = 142°$, and $b = 20$. $A = 20°$, $a \approx 22.1$, $c \approx 39.8$

Example 3
G.SRT.11

Determine whether each △*ABC* has *no* solution, *one* solution, or *two* solutions. Then solve the triangle. Round side lengths to the nearest tenth and angle measures to the nearest degree.

29. $A = 100°$, $a = 7$, $b = 3$

30. $A = 75°$, $a = 14$, $b = 11$

31. $A = 38°$, $a = 21$, $b = 18$

32. $A = 52°$, $a = 9$, $b = 20$ no solution

33. $A = 42°$, $a = 5$, $b = 6$

34. $A = 44°$, $a = 14$, $b = 19$

35. $A = 131°$, $a = 15$, $b = 32$ no solution

36. $A = 30°$, $a = 17$, $b = 34$

29. one; $B \approx 25°$, $C \approx 55°$, $c \approx 5.8$
30. one; $B \approx 49°$, $C \approx 56°$, $c \approx 12.0$
31. one; $B \approx 32°$, $C \approx 110°$, $c \approx 32.1$
33. two; $B \approx 53°$, $C \approx 85°$, $c \approx 7.4$; $B \approx 127°$, $C \approx 11°$, $c \approx 1.4$
34. two; $B \approx 71°$, $C \approx 65°$, $c \approx 18.3$; $B \approx 109°$, $C \approx 27°$, $c \approx 9.1$
36. one; $B = 90°$, $C = 60°$, $c \approx 29.4$

Differentiated Homework Options

Levels	AL Basic	OL Core	BL Advanced
Exercises	13–38, 43, 44, 46–54	13–35 odd, 37–44, 46–54	43–48, (optional: 49–54)
2-Day Option	13–37 odd, 49–54	13–38	
	14–38 even, 43, 44, 46–48	39–44, 46–54	

You can use ALEKS to provide additional remediation support with personalized instruction and practice.

Practice

Formative Assessment Use Exercises 1–12 to assess students' understanding of the concepts in this lesson.

The Practice and Problem Solving exercises assess the content taught in the lesson. The Preparing for Assessment page is meant to be used as preparation for end-of-course assessments.

Extra Practice

See page R8 for extra exercises for students who are approaching level or for on-level students who need additional reinforcement.

Levels of Complexity Chart

The levels of the exercises progress from 1–3, with Level 1 indicating the lowest level of complexity.

Exercises	13–38	39–42, 49–54	43–48
Level 3			●
Level 2		●	
Level 1	●		

Go Online!

eSolutions Manual

Create worksheets, answer keys, and solutions handouts for your assignments.

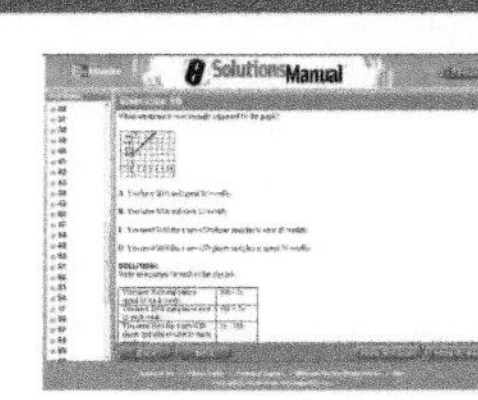

> **Watch Out!**
> **Error Analysis** For Exercise 43, students should see that Gabriela is incorrect because this is not a "no solution" situation. Explain to students that the "no solution" situation is when the side opposite the given angle θ is less than $\sin\theta$ times the length of the side adjacent to θ.

Assess

Name the Math Ask students to state the steps that are necessary for solving a triangle when one side and two angle measures are given.

Additional Answers

41a. Sample answer:

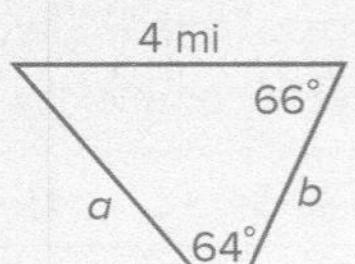

45. Sample answer:

$\sin A = \frac{\text{opposite}}{\text{hypotenuse}}$ Definition of sine

$\sin A = \frac{h}{c}$ h = opposite side, c = hypotenuse

$c \sin A = h$ Multiply both sides by c.

$\text{Area} = \frac{1}{2} \cdot \text{base} \cdot \text{height}$ Area of a triangle

$\text{Area} = \frac{1}{2}bh$ b = base, h = height

$\text{Area} = \frac{1}{2}bc \sin A$ Substitution

47. Sample answer: In the triangle, $B = 115°$. Using the Law of Sines, $\frac{\sin 50°}{a} = \frac{\sin 115°}{b}$. This equation cannot be solved because there are two unknowns. To solve a triangle using the Law of Sines, two sides and an angle must be given or two angles and a side opposite one of the angles must be given.

48. Sample answer: $e = 30$; for no triangle to exist, the length of the side opposite angle E must be less than 33.6 to satisfy the Law of Sines.

Example 4 G.SRT.11

GEOGRAPHY In Hawaii, the distance from Hilo to Kailua is 57 miles, and the distance from Hilo to Captain Cook is 55 miles.

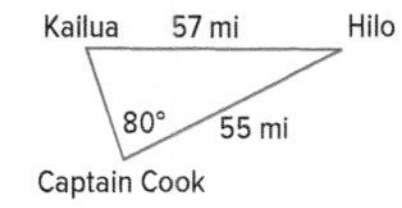

37. What is the measure of the angle formed at Hilo? **about 28°**

38. What is the distance between Kailua and Captain Cook? **about 27.2 mi**

B **39.** **TORNADOES** Tornado sirens A, B, and C form a triangular region in one area of a city. Sirens A and B are 8 miles apart. The angle formed at siren A is 112°, and the angle formed at siren B is 40°. How far apart are sirens B and C? **about 15.8 mi**

40. **MYSTERIES** The Bermuda Triangle is a region of the Atlantic Ocean between Bermuda, Miami, Florida, and San Juan, Puerto Rico. It is an area where ships and airplanes have been rumored to mysteriously disappear.

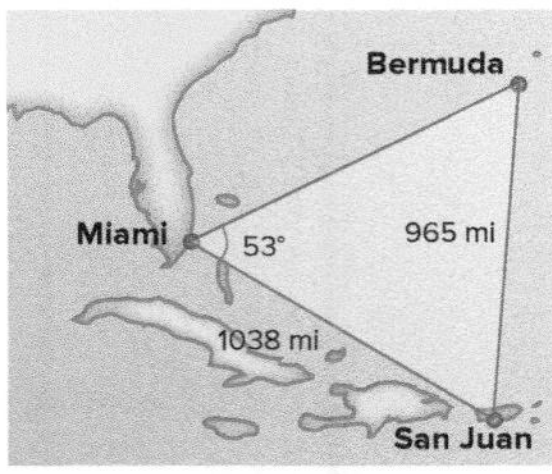

a. What is the distance between Miami and Bermuda? **about 1120.3 mi**

b. What is the approximate area of the Bermuda Triangle? **about 464,366.1 mi²**

41. **BICYCLING** One side of a triangular cycling path is 4 miles long. The angle opposite this side is 64°. Another angle formed by the triangular path measures 66°.

a. Sketch a drawing of the situation. Label the missing sides a and b. **See margin.**

b. Write equations that could be used to find the lengths of the missing sides.

c. What is the perimeter of the path? **about 11.5 mi**

41b. Sample answer: $\frac{\sin 66°}{a} = \frac{\sin 64°}{4}$; $\frac{\sin 50°}{b} = \frac{\sin 64°}{4}$

42. **ROCK CLIMBING** Savannah S and Leon L are standing 8 feet apart in front of a rock climbing wall, as shown at the right. What is the height of the wall? Round to the nearest tenth. **18.9 ft**

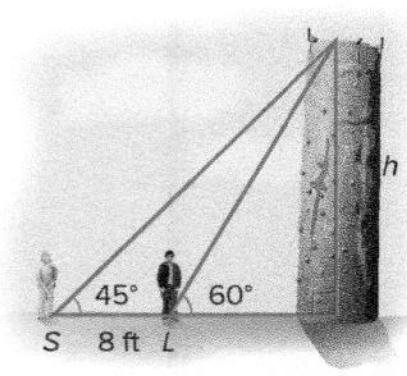

G.SRT.10, G.SRT.11

H.O.T. Problems Use **H**igher-**O**rder **T**hinking Skills

C **43.** **ERROR ANALYSIS** In $\triangle RST$, $R = 56°$, $r = 24$, and $t = 12$. Cameron and Gabriela are using the Law of Sines to find T. Is either of them correct? Explain your reasoning. **Cameron; R is acute and $r > t$, so there is one solution.**

Cameron	Gabriela
$\frac{\sin T}{12} = \frac{\sin 56°}{24}$ $\sin T \approx 0.4145$ $T \approx 24.5°$	Since $r > t$, there is no solution.

44. **OPEN ENDED** Create an application problem involving right triangles and the Law of Sines. Then solve your problem, drawing diagrams if necessary. **See students' work.**

45. **CHALLENGE** Using the figure at the right, derive the formula $\text{Area} = \frac{1}{2}bc \sin A$. **See margin.**

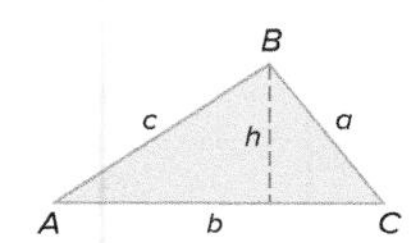

46. MP **REASONING** Find the side lengths of two different triangles ABC that can be formed if $A = 55°$ and $C = 20°$.

46. Sample answer: $a = 12$, $b \approx 14.2$, $c \approx 5.0$; $a = 6$, $b \approx 7.1$, $c \approx 2.5$

47. **WRITING IN MATH** Use the Law of Sines to explain why a and b do not have unique values in the figure shown. **See margin.**

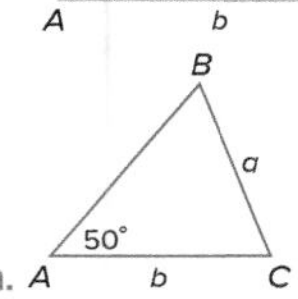

48. **OPEN ENDED** Given that $E = 62°$ and $d = 38$, find a value for e such that no triangle DEF can exist. Explain your reasoning. **See margin.**

MP Standards for Mathematical Practice

Emphasis On	Exercises
1 Make sense of problems and persevere in solving them.	1–11, 13–20, 44, 47–51, 54
2 Reason abstractly and quantitatively.	21–28, 46
3 Construct viable arguments and critique the reasoning of others.	43
4 Model with mathematics.	12, 37–42, 52, 53

Preparing for Assessment

49. In $\triangle XYZ$, $XZ = 2$ centimeters, $XY = 6$ centimeters, and $\angle X = 70°$. What is the area of $\triangle XYZ$ to the nearest square centimeter? MP 1 G.SRT.11

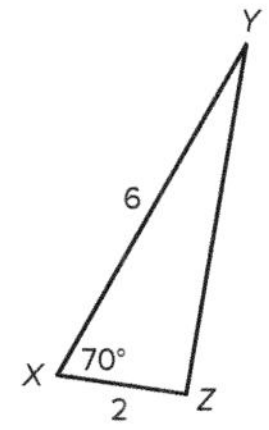

6 cm^2

50. In scalene triangle $\triangle QRS$, angles Q, R, and S measure $x°$, $2x°$, and $3x°$, respectively. What is the ratio of side length s to side length r? MP 1 G.SRT.11 **B**

- ○ A $\frac{\sin 60°}{\sin 90°}$
- ○ B $\frac{\sin 90°}{\sin 60°}$
- ○ C $\frac{\sin 90°}{\sin 30°}$
- ○ D $\frac{\sin 30°}{\sin 60°}$

51. In $\triangle ABC$, $m\angle B = 70°$, $m\angle C = 42°$, and $c = 22$. Which expressions represent the distances a and b? Select all that apply. MP 1 G.SRT.11 **C, F**

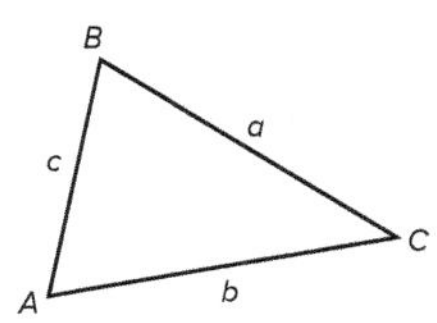

- ☐ A $\frac{22 \sin 42°}{\sin 70°}$
- ☐ B $\frac{22 \sin 70°}{\sin 68°}$
- ☐ C $\frac{22 \sin 68°}{\sin 42°}$
- ☐ D $\frac{22 \sin 68°}{\sin 70°}$
- ☐ E $\frac{22 \sin 42°}{\sin 68°}$
- ☐ F $\frac{22 \sin 70°}{\sin 42°}$

52. The diagram below shows the distance of two boats from shore. MP 1, 4 G.SRT.11 **B, A**

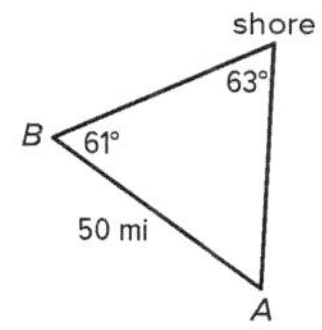

a. How far is boat A from the shore to the nearest tenth of a mile?

- ○ A 46.5 mi
- ○ B 49.1 mi
- ○ C 50.9 mi
- ○ D 53.7 mi

b. How far is boat B from the shore to the nearest tenth of a mile?

- ○ A 46.5 mi
- ○ B 49.1 mi
- ○ C 50.9 mi
- ○ D 53.7 mi

53. MULTI-STEP Juan looks up at the top of a building at an angle of 49°. George, who is 100 feet behind Juan, looks up at the top of a building at an angle of 37°. MP 1, 4 G.SRT.10, G.SRT.11

a. Draw a diagram of the scenario. See margin.

b. How far is George from the building to the nearest tenth of a foot?

289.9 ft

c. How tall is the building to the nearest tenth of a foot?

218.5 ft

54. The area of an acute triangle ABC is $20\sqrt{3}$. The length of $\overline{AB}$ is 8 and the length of $\overline{BC}$ is 10. MP 1 G.SRT.11

a. Which angle is determined by this information?

$\angle B$

b. What is the measure of this angle? 60 degrees

Differentiated Instruction OL BL

Extension Have students compute the area of a 3-4-5 right triangle using the area formula presented in this lesson. Have them use the formula for all three angles of the triangle. 6; 6; 6

52b.

A	CORRECT
B	Found the distance from boat A
C	Reversed the angles in the calculation for boat A
D	Reversed the angles in the calculation

53a.

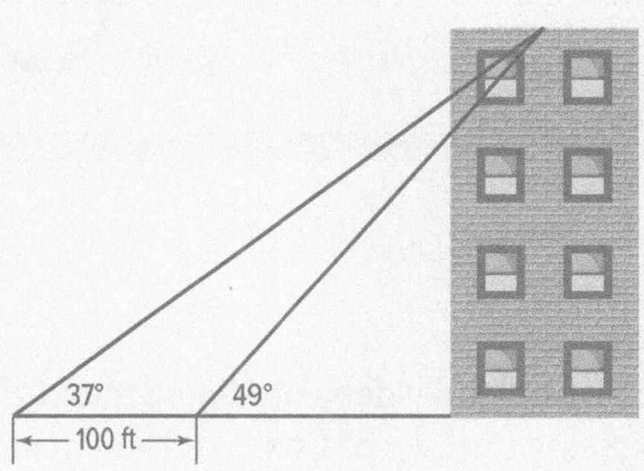

Preparing for Assessment

Exercises 49–54 require students to use the skills they will need on standardized assessments. Each exercise is dual-coded with content and mathematical practice standards.

Dual Coding		
Items	Content Standards	MP Mathematical Practices
49–51, 54	G.SRT.11	1
52	G.SRT.11	1, 4
53	G.SRT.10, G.SRT.11	1, 4

Diagnose Student Errors

Survey student responses for each item. Class trends may indicate common errors and misconceptions.

50.

A	Found the ratio of r to s
B	CORRECT
C	Found the ratio of s to q
D	Found the ratio of q to r

51.

A	Reversed the angles for the ratio
B	Used wrong angles for the ratio
C	CORRECT
D	Used wrong angles for the ratio
E	Reversed the angles for the ratio
F	CORRECT

52a.

A	Found the distance from boat B
B	CORRECT
C	Reversed the angles in the calculation
D	Reversed the angles in the calculation for boat B

Go Online!

Quizzes

Students can use *Self-Check Quizzes* to check their understanding of this lesson and have the results sent to you. You can also give *Quiz 3*, which covers the content in Lesson 8-6.

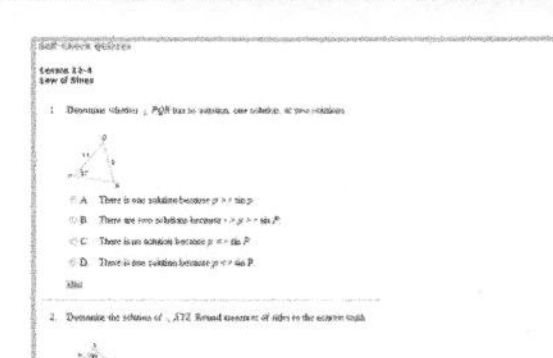

LESSON 8-7

The Law of Cosines

SUGGESTED PACING (DAYS)

	Instruction
90 min.	0.5
45 min.	1.0

Track Your Progress

Objectives

1. Use the Law of Cosines to solve triangles.
2. Choose methods to solve triangles.

Mathematical Background

The Law of Cosines can be used to solve a triangle if all three sides of the triangle are given or if two sides and the included angle are given. Unlike the Law of Sines cases, if a solution exists for cases in which the Law of Cosines can be used, the solution is unique.

Skills Trace

THEN	NOW	NEXT
G.SRT.10 Prove the Laws of Sines and Cosines and use them to solve problems. **G.SRT.11** Understand and apply the Law of Sines and the Law of Cosines to find unknown measurements in right and non-right triangles (e.g. surveying problems, resultant forces).	**G.SRT.10** Prove the Laws of Sines and Cosines and use them to solve problems. **G.SRT.11** Understand and apply the Law of Sines and the Law of Cosines to find unknown measurements in right and non-right triangles (e.g. surveying problems, resultant forces).	**G.CO.1** Know precise definitions of angle, circle, perpendicular line, parallel line, and line segment, based on the undefined notions of point, line, distance along a line, and distance around a circular arc. **G.C.1** Prove that all circles are similar.

Go Online! All of these resources and more are available at connectED.mcgraw-hill.com

Use **The Geometer's Sketchpad** to illustrate how to use the Law of Cosines.

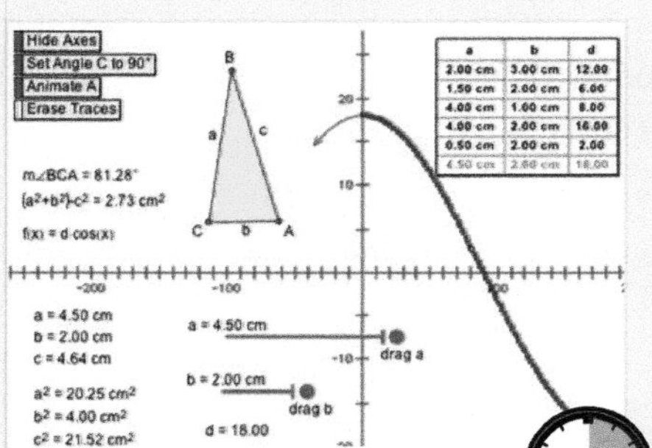

Use at Beginning of Lesson

Personal Tutors (for every example) let students hear real teachers solve problems. Students can pause and repeat as many times as necessary.

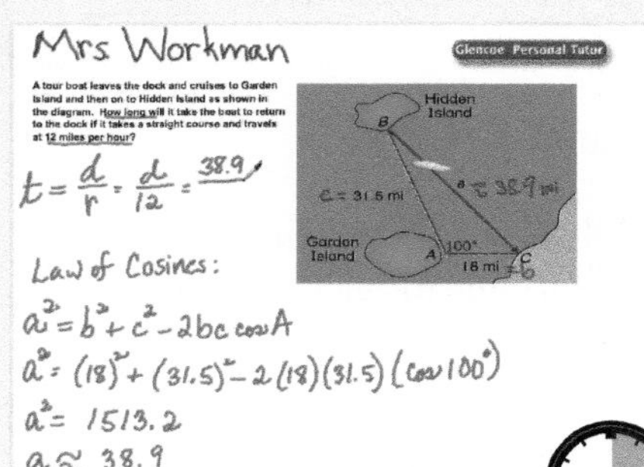

Use with Examples

Chapter Project allows students to create and customize a project as a nontraditional method of assessment.

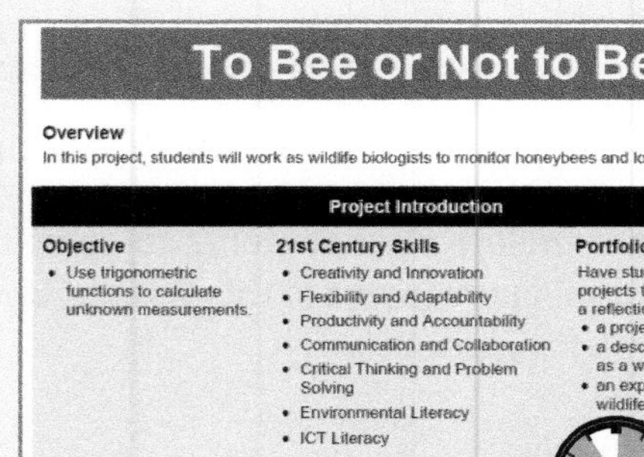

Use at End of Lesson

Using Open Educational Resources

Video Sharing Have students work in groups to record and upload videos on **Vimeo** about this lesson. Have one class explain the Law of Sines while another class explains the Law of Cosines. Then have each class watch and critique the other class' videos. If you are unable to access Vimeo, try **YouTube**, **KidsTube**, **MathATube**, **SchoolTube**, or **TeacherTube**. *Use as homework or classwork*

Go Online!

connectED.mcgraw-hill.com

Worksheets

Differentiate Your Resources

Extra Practice Additional practice or homework; Skills Practice is best for approaching-level students and Practice is best for on-level and beyond-level students

Skills Practice

AL OL ELL

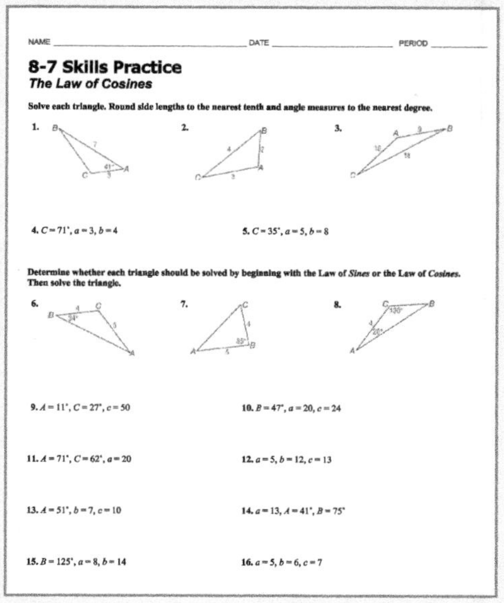
NAME ______ DATE ______ PERIOD ______

8-7 Skills Practice
The Law of Cosines

Solve each triangle. Round side lengths to the nearest tenth and angle measures to the nearest degree.

1. 2. 3.

4. $C = 71°, a = 3, b = 4$
5. $C = 35°, a = 5, b = 8$

Determine whether each triangle should be solved by beginning with the Law of *Sines* or the Law of *Cosines*. Then solve the triangle.

6. 7. 8.

9. $A = 11°, C = 27°, c = 50$
10. $B = 47°, a = 20, c = 24$
11. $A = 71°, C = 62°, a = 20$
12. $a = 5, b = 12, c = 13$
13. $A = 51°, b = 7, c = 10$
14. $a = 13, A = 41°, B = 75°$
15. $B = 125°, a = 8, b = 14$
16. $a = 5, b = 6, c = 7$

Practice

AL OL BL ELL

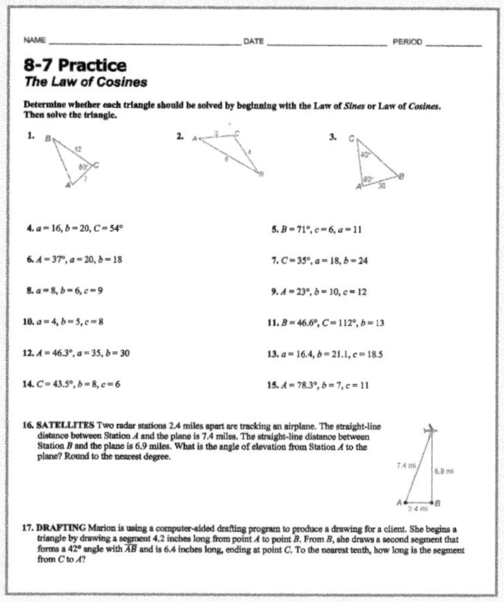
NAME ______ DATE ______ PERIOD ______

8-7 Practice
The Law of Cosines

Determine whether each triangle should be solved by beginning with the Law of *Sines* or Law of *Cosines*. Then solve the triangle.

1. 2. 3.

4. $a = 16, b = 20, C = 54°$
5. $B = 71°, c = 6, a = 11$
6. $A = 37°, a = 20, b = 18$
7. $C = 35°, a = 18, b = 24$
8. $a = 8, b = 6, c = 9$
9. $A = 23°, b = 10, c = 12$
10. $a = 4, b = 5, c = 8$
11. $B = 46.6°, C = 112°, b = 13$
12. $A = 46.3°, a = 35, b = 30$
13. $a = 16.4, b = 21.1, c = 18.5$
14. $C = 43.5°, b = 8, c = 6$
15. $A = 78.3°, b = 7, c = 11$

16. **SATELLITES** Two radar stations 2.4 miles apart are tracking an airplane. The straight-line distance between Station *A* and the plane is 7.4 miles. The straight-line distance between Station *B* and the plane is 6.9 miles. What is the angle of elevation from Station *A* to the plane? Round to the nearest degree.

17. **DRAFTING** Marion is using a computer-aided drafting program to produce a drawing for a client. She begins a triangle by drawing a segment 4.2 inches long from point *A* to point *B*. From *B*, she draws a second segment that forms a 42° angle with $\overline{AB}$ and is 6.4 inches long, ending at point *C*. To the nearest tenth, how long is the segment from *C* to *A*?

Word Problem Practice

AL OL BL ELL

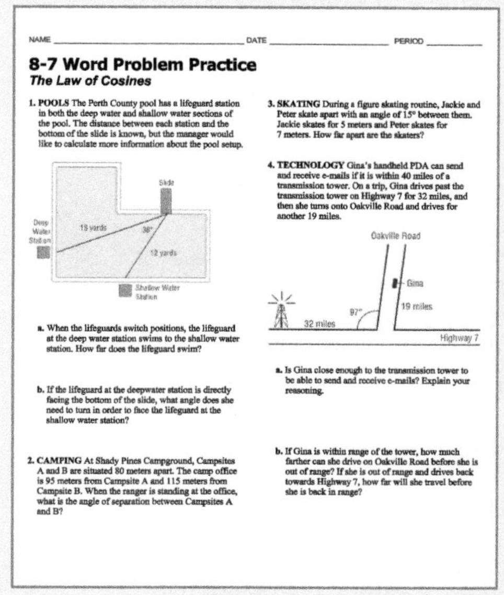
NAME ______ DATE ______ PERIOD ______

8-7 Word Problem Practice
The Law of Cosines

1. **POOLS** The Perth County pool has a lifeguard station in both the deep water and shallow water sections of the pool. The distance between each station and the bottom of the slide is known, but the manager would like to calculate more information about the pool setup.

a. When the lifeguards switch positions, the lifeguard at the deep water station swims to the shallow water station. How far does the lifeguard swim?

b. If the lifeguard at the deepwater station is directly facing the bottom of the slide, what angle does she need to turn in order to face the lifeguard at the shallow water station?

2. **CAMPING** At Shady Pines Campground, Campsites A and B are situated 80 meters apart. The camp office is 93 meters from Campsite A and 115 meters from Campsite B. When the ranger is standing at the office, what is the angle of separation between Campsites A and B?

3. **SKATING** During a figure skating routine, Jackie and Peter skate apart with an angle of 15° between them. Jackie skates for 5 meters and Peter skates for 7 meters. How far apart are the skaters?

4. **TECHNOLOGY** Gina's handheld PDA can send and receive e-mails if it is within 40 miles of a transmission tower. On a trip, Gina drives past the transmission tower on Highway 7 for 32 miles, and then she turns onto Oakville Road and drives for another 19 miles.

a. Is Gina close enough to the transmission tower to be able to send and receive e-mails? Explain your reasoning.

b. If Gina is within range of the tower, how much farther can she drive on Oakville Road before she is out of range? If she is out of range and drives back towards Highway 7, how far will she travel before she is back in range?

Intervention Reteaching and vocabulary activities that can be used with struggling or absent students and as ELL support

Study Guide and Intervention

AL OL ELL

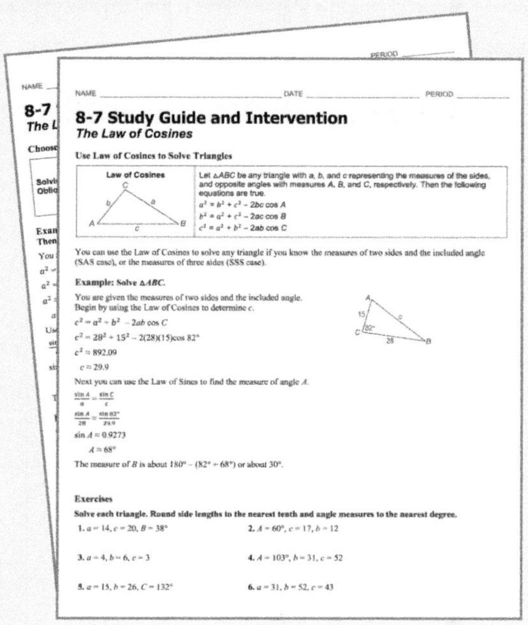
NAME ______ DATE ______ PERIOD ______

8-7 Study Guide and Intervention
The Law of Cosines

Use Law of Cosines to Solve Triangles

Law of Cosines	Let $\triangle ABC$ be any triangle with *a*, *b*, and *c* representing the measures of the sides, and opposite angles with measures *A*, *B*, and *C*, respectively. Then the following equations are true. $a^2 = b^2 + c^2 - 2bc \cos A$; $b^2 = a^2 + c^2 - 2ac \cos B$; $c^2 = a^2 + b^2 - 2ab \cos C$

You can use the Law of Cosines to solve any triangle if you know the measures of two sides and the included angle (SAS case), or the measures of three sides (SSS case).

Example: Solve $\triangle ABC$.

You are given the measures of two sides and the included angle. Begin by using the Law of Cosines to determine *c*.

$c^2 = a^2 + b^2 - 2ab \cos C$
$c^2 = 28^2 + 15^2 - 2(28)(15)\cos 82°$
$c^2 \approx 892.09$
$c \approx 29.9$

Next you can use the Law of Sines to find the measure of angle *A*.

$\frac{\sin A}{a} = \frac{\sin C}{c}$
$\frac{\sin A}{28} = \frac{\sin 82°}{29.9}$
$\sin A \approx 0.9273$
$A \approx 68°$

The measure of *B* is about $180° - (82° + 68°)$ or about 30°.

Exercises

Solve each triangle. Round side lengths to the nearest tenth and angle measures to the nearest degree.

1. $a = 14, c = 20, B = 38°$
2. $A = 60°, c = 17, b = 12$
3. $a = 4, b = 6, c = 3$
4. $A = 103°, b = 31, c = 52$
5. $a = 15, b = 26, C = 132°$
6. $a = 31, b = 52, c = 43$

Study Notebook

AL OL BL ELL

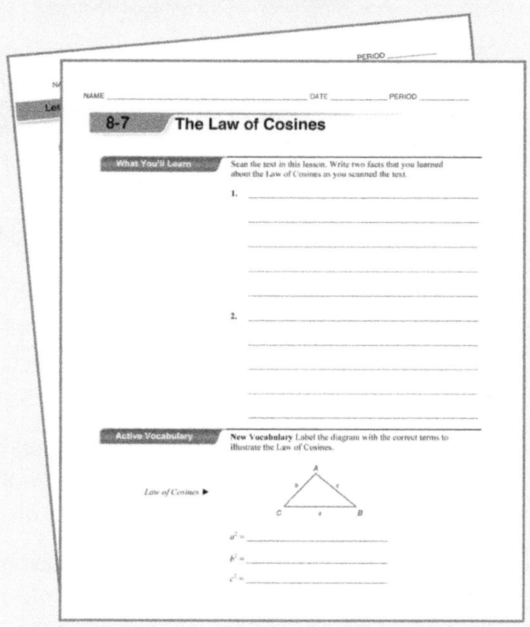
NAME ______ DATE ______ PERIOD ______

8-7 The Law of Cosines

What You'll Learn Scan the text in this lesson. Write two facts that you learned about the Law of Cosines as you scanned the text.

1.
2.

Active Vocabulary New Vocabulary Label the diagram with the correct terms to illustrate the Law of Cosines.

Law of Cosines ►

$a^2 =$
$b^2 =$
$c^2 =$

Extension Activities that can be used to extend lesson concepts

Enrichment

OL BL ELL

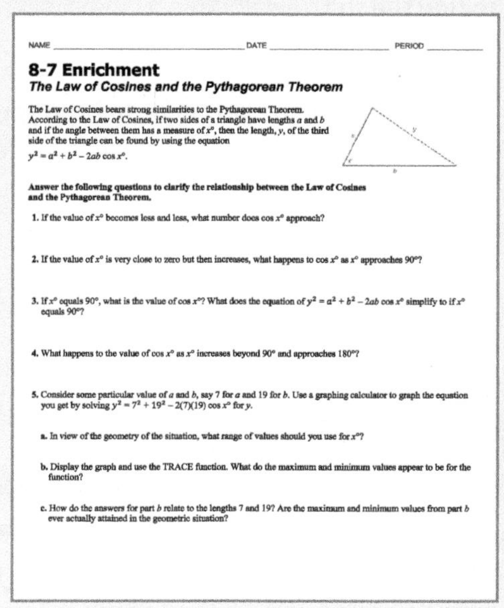
NAME ______ DATE ______ PERIOD ______

8-7 Enrichment
The Law of Cosines and the Pythagorean Theorem

The Law of Cosines bears strong similarities to the Pythagorean Theorem. According to the Law of Cosines, if two sides of a triangle have lengths *a* and *b* and if the angle between them has a measure of *x*°, then the length, *y*, of the third side of the triangle can be found by using the equation $y^2 = a^2 + b^2 - 2ab \cos x°$.

Answer the following questions to clarify the relationship between the Law of Cosines and the Pythagorean Theorem.

1. If the value of *x*° becomes less and less, what number does cos *x*° approach?
2. If the value of *x*° is very close to zero but then increases, what happens to cos *x*° as *x*° approaches 90°?
3. If *x*° equals 90°, what is the value of cos *x*°? What does the equation of $y^2 = a^2 + b^2 - 2ab \cos x°$ simplify to if *x*° equals 90°?
4. What happens to the value of cos *x*° as *x*° increases beyond 90° and approaches 180°?
5. Consider some particular value of *a* and *b*, say 7 for *a* and 19 for *b*. Use a graphing calculator to graph the equation you get by solving $y^2 = 7^2 + 19^2 - 2(7)(19) \cos x°$ for *y*.

a. In view of the geometry of the situation, what range of values should you use for *x*°?

b. Display the graph and use the TRACE function. What do the maximum and minimum values appear to be for the function?

c. How do the answers for part *b* relate to the lengths 7 and 19? Are the maximum and minimum values from part *b* ever actually attained in the geometric situation?

Launch

Have students read the Why? section of the lesson. Ask:

- Is the triangle in the diagram *acute*, *right*, or *obtuse*? acute
- Explain why the angle with vertex at the shipwreck has greater measure than the angle with vertex at the ship. The side opposite the angle with vertex at the shipwreck is longer.
- Explain why the distance between the ship and the shipwreck must be less than 858 meters. The Triangle Inequality Theorem states that the third side of the triangle must be less than the sum of the other two sides of the triangle, so $520 + 338 = 858$ meters.

Teach

Ask the scaffolded questions for each example to build conceptual understanding for students at all levels.

1 Use Law of Cosines to Solve Triangles

Example 1 Solve a Triangle Given Two Sides and the Included Angle

AL What information do you have about the triangle? the length of two sides, and the measure of the included angle

OL Why can't you use the Pythagorean Theorem to find the third side? This triangle is not a right triangle.

BL When finding a second angle, how do you know which one will be the smaller angle? The smaller angle will be opposite the smaller side.

(continued on the next page)

Go Online!

Interactive Whiteboard

Use the *eLesson*, *Lesson Presentation*, or *Interactive Classroom* to present this lesson.

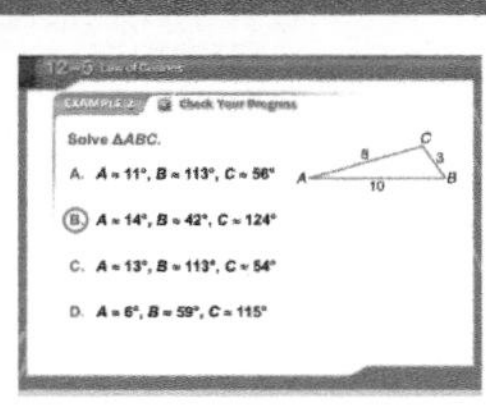

LESSON 7

The Law of Cosines

:·Then

- You solved triangles by using the Law of Sines.

:·Now

1. Use the Law of Cosines to solve triangles.
2. Choose methods to solve triangles.

:·Why?

- You can use trigonometry to find the distance from a ship used to lower a submersible into the ocean and a shipwreck spotted by the submersible on the ocean floor.

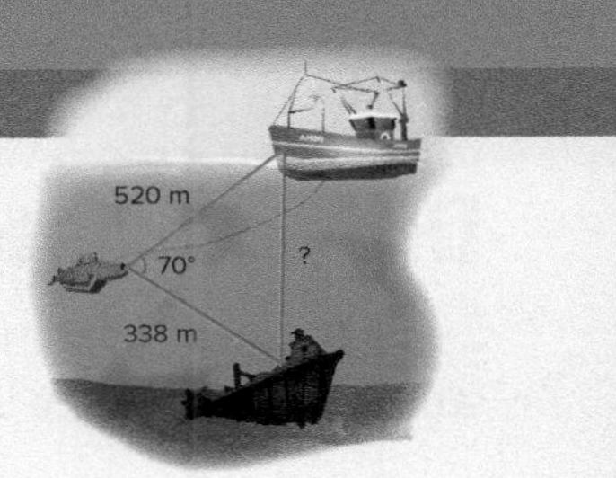

New Vocabulary
Law of Cosines

Mathematical Practices
1 Make sense of problems and persevere in solving them.
4 Model with mathematics.
5 Use appropriate tools strategically.
6 Attend to precision.

Content Standards
G.SRT.10 Prove the Laws of Sines and Cosines and use them to solve problems.
G.SRT.11 Understand and apply the Law of Sines and the Law of Cosines to find unknown measurements in right and non-right triangles (e.g. surveying problems, resultant forces).

1 Use the Law of Cosines to Solve Triangles You cannot use the Law of Sines to solve a triangle like the one shown above. You can use the **Law of Cosines** if:

- the measures of two sides and the included angle are known (SAS).
- the measures of three sides are known (SSS).

Key Concept Law of Cosines

In $\triangle ABC$, if sides with lengths a, b, and c are opposite angles with measures A, B, and C, respectively, then the following are true.

$a^2 = b^2 + c^2 - 2bc \cos A$
$b^2 = a^2 + c^2 - 2ac \cos B$
$c^2 = a^2 + b^2 - 2ab \cos C$

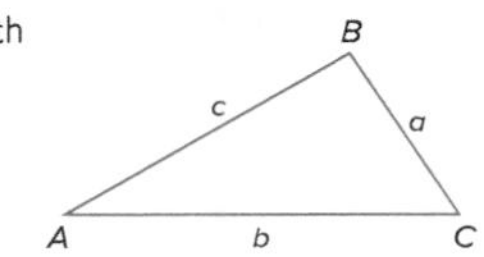

G.SRT.11

Example 1 Solve a Triangle Given Two Sides and the Included Angle

Solve $\triangle ABC$.

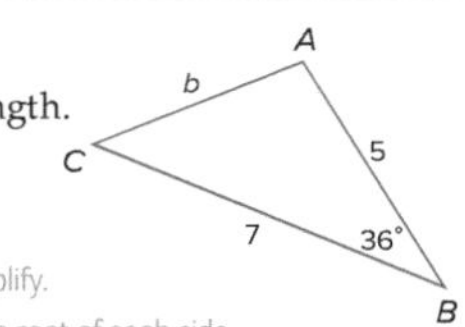

Step 1 Use the Law of Cosines to find the missing side length.

$b^2 = a^2 + c^2 - 2ac \cos B$ Law of Cosines
$b^2 = 7^2 + 5^2 - 2(7)(5) \cos 36°$ $a = 7, c = 5, B = 36°$
$b^2 \approx 17.4$ Use a calculator to simplify.
$b \approx 4.2$ Take the positive square root of each side.

Step 2 Use the Law of Sines to find a missing angle measure. Finding the smaller angle first can help avoid an error if the larger angle might be obtuse.

$\frac{\sin C}{5} \approx \frac{\sin 36°}{4.2}$ $\frac{\sin C}{c} = \frac{\sin B}{b}$
$\sin C \approx \frac{5 \sin 36°}{4.2}$ Multiply each side by 5.
$C \approx 44°$ Use the $\sin^{-1}$ function.

Step 3 Find the measure of the other angle. $m\angle A \approx 180° - (36° + 44°)$ or $100°$
So, $b \approx 4.2$, $A \approx 100°$, and $C \approx 44°$.

Guided Practice

1. Solve $\triangle FGH$ if $G = 82°$, $f = 6$, and $h = 4$. $H \approx 36°$, $F = 62°$, $g = 6.7$

MP Teaching the Mathematical Practices

Use appropriate tools strategically.

Help students identify the tools needed to solve problems using the Law of Cosines. For example, ask:

- When should you use the Law of Cosines? Use the Law of Cosines when you know the measures of two sides and the included angle of a triangle, or when you know the measure of all three sides of a triangle.
- When should you use the Law of Sines? Use the Law of Sines when you know the measures of two angles and any side of a triangle, or when you know the measure of two sides and the angle opposite one of the sides.
- When is there no solution for the Law of Cosines? When you have the required information to use the Law of Cosines, there is not a case when there is no solution.

Go Online!

Watch the **Personal Tutor** describe how to solve trigonometry problems with a partner. Then try describing how to solve a problem for them. Have them ask questions to help your understanding. ELL

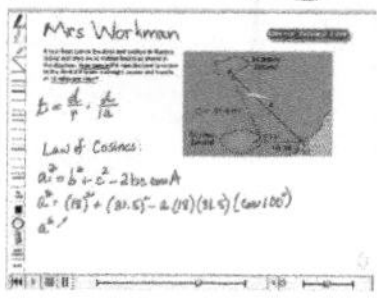

When you are only given the three side lengths of a triangle, you can solve it by using the Law of Cosines. The first step is to find the measure of the largest angle. This is done to ensure the other two angles are acute when using the Law of Sines.

G.SRT.11

Example 2 Solve a Triangle Given Three Sides

Solve $\triangle ABC$.

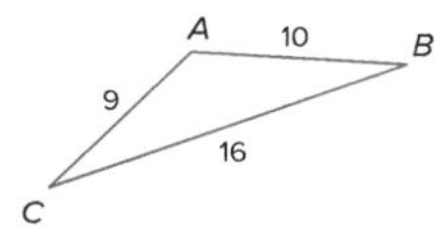

Step 1 Use the Law of Cosines to find the measure of the largest angle, $\angle A$.

$a^2 = b^2 + c^2 - 2bc \cos A$	Law of Cosines
$16^2 = 9^2 + 10^2 - 2(9)(10) \cos A$	$a = 16$, $b = 9$, and $c = 10$
$16^2 - 9^2 - 10^2 = -2(9)(10) \cos A$	Subtract 9^2 and 10^2 from each side.
$\frac{16^2 - 9^2 - 10^2}{-2(9)(10)} = \cos A$	Divide each side by $-2(9)(10)$.
$-0.4167 \approx \cos A$	Use a calculator to simplify.
$115° \approx A$	Use the $\cos^{-1}$ function.

Step 2 Use the Law of Sines to find the measure of $\angle B$.

$\frac{\sin B}{9} \approx \frac{\sin 115°}{16}$	$\frac{\sin B}{b} = \frac{\sin A}{a}$
$\sin B \approx \frac{9 \sin 115°}{16}$	Multiply each side by 9.
$\sin B \approx 0.5098$	Use a calculator.
$B \approx 31°$	Use the $\sin^{-1}$ function.

Step 3 Find the measure of $\angle C$.

$m\angle C \approx 180° - (115° + 31°)$ or about $34°$

So, $A \approx 115°$, $B \approx 31°$, and $C \approx 34°$.

Guided Practice

2. Solve $\triangle ABC$ if $a = 5$, $b = 11$, and $c = 8$. $A \approx 24.6°$, $B \approx 113.6°$, $C \approx 41.8°$

Review Vocabulary

oblique a triangle that has no right angle

2 Choose a Method to Solve Triangles You can use the Law of Sines and the Law of Cosines to solve problems involving oblique triangles. You need to know the measure of at least one side and any two other parts. If the triangle has a solution, you must decide whether to use the Law of Sines or the Law of Cosines to begin solving it.

Concept Summary Solving Oblique Triangles

Given	Begin by Using
two angles and any sides	Law of Sines
two sides and an angle opposite one of them	Law of Sines
two sides and their included angle	Law of Cosines
three sides	Law of Cosines

Need Another Example?
Solve $\triangle ABC$.

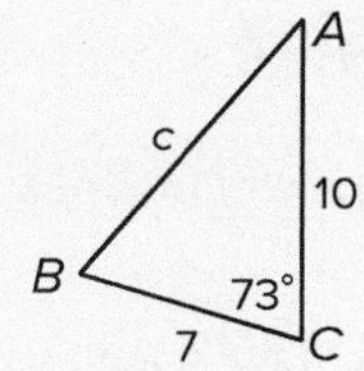

$A \approx 40°$; $B \approx 67°$; $c \approx 10.4$

Example 2 Solve a Triangle Given Three Sides

AL **What information do you have about the triangle?** the length of all three sides of the triangle

OL **Why is $\angle A$ the largest angle?** It is opposite the largest side.

BL **Why will cos A be negative if A is an obtuse angle?** If A is an obtuse angle, then A is in the second quadrant, and cosine is negative in the second quadrant.

Need Another Example?
Solve $\triangle ABC$.

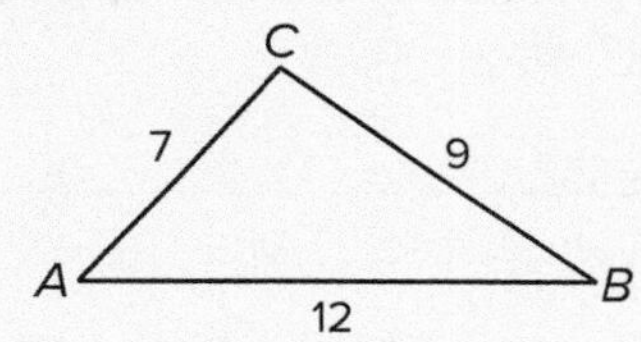

$A \approx 48.2°$; $B \approx 35.4°$; $C \approx 96.4°$

Differentiated Instruction AL OL ELL

IF students struggle with any of the methods shown to solve a triangle,

THEN have students discuss in small groups how to choose which method to use when solving a triangle. Have them compare their approaches and develop a brief explanation to help others decide. Then have each group share their conclusions with the class.

2 Choose a Method to Solve Triangles

Example 3 Use the Law of Cosines

AL Why is the $m\angle A = 60°$? Angle A is the sum of a 40° angle and a 20° angle.

OL What is the measure of the angle formed at the turtle? 73.9°

BL Explain why you can always use the Law of Sines when solving a triangle. When you are given the measure of two angles and the length of any side or the lengths of two side and the measure of an angle opposite either side, then you begin by using the Law of Sines. If you use the Law of Cosines to solve for a missing measure, you can then use the Law of Sines.

Need Another Example?

Airport Two pilots in a stationary airplane look 38° to the left of their runway and see a bus 75 feet away. They look 28° to the right of their runway and see a truck 110 feet away. How far apart are the bus and the truck? about 105 ft

Watch Out!

Preventing Errors When students must decide which method to use to solve, watch for students who think the angle is included. Review the definition of included angles with them.

Practice

Formative Assessment Use Exercises 1–8 to assess students' understanding of the concepts in this lesson.

The Practice and Problem Solving exercises assess the content taught in the lesson. The Preparing for Assessment page is meant to be used as preparation for end-of-course assessments.

Go Online! eBook

Interactive Student Guide

Use the *Interactive Student Guide* to deepen conceptual understanding.

· The Law of Sines and Law of Cosines

G.SRT.11

Real-World Link

The record for the deepest seawater scuba dive was 1090 feet, made by a scuba diver in the Red Sea.

Source: *Guinness Book of World Records*

Real-World Example 3 Use the Law of Cosines

SCUBA DIVING A scuba diver looks up 20° and sees a turtle 9 feet away. She looks down 40° and sees a blue parrotfish 12 feet away. How far apart are the turtle and the blue parrotfish?

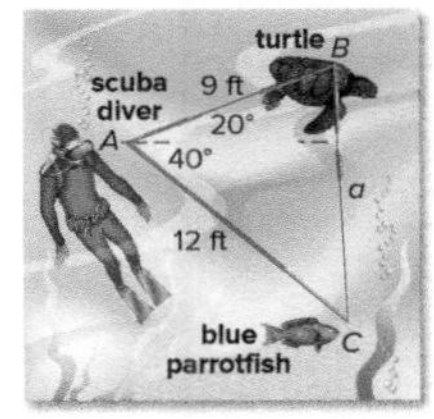

Understand You know the angles formed by the scuba diver's line of sight and her distance from the sea creatures.

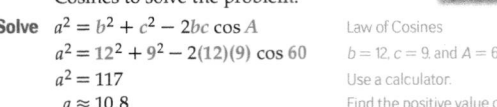

Plan Use the information to draw and label a diagram. Because two sides and the included angle of a triangle are given, you can use the Law of Cosines to solve the problem.

Solve

$a^2 = b^2 + c^2 - 2bc \cos A$ — Law of Cosines

$a^2 = 12^2 + 9^2 - 2(12)(9) \cos 60$ — $b = 12$, $c = 9$, and $A = 60$

$a^2 = 117$ — Use a calculator.

$a \approx 10.8$ — Find the positive value of a.

So, the turtle and the blue parrotfish are about 10.8 feet apart.

Check Using the Law of Sines, you can find that $B \approx 74°$ and $C \approx 46°$. Because $C < A < B$ and $c < a < b$, the solution is reasonable.

You can use the two small triangles to find the two parts of the total distance individually and then confirm that their sum is about 10.8.

Guided Practice

3. **MARATHONS** Amelia ran 6 miles in one direction. She then turned 79° and ran 7 miles. At the end of the run, how far was Amelia from her starting point? about 8.3 mi

Check Your Understanding

◯ = Step-by-Step Solutions begin on page R13.

Go Online! for a Self-Check Quiz

Examples 1–2 G.SRT.11 **Solve each triangle. Round side lengths to the nearest tenth and angle measures to the nearest degree.**

1.

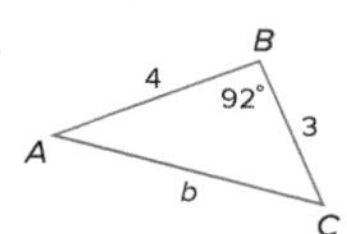

2.

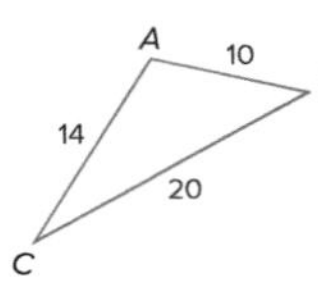

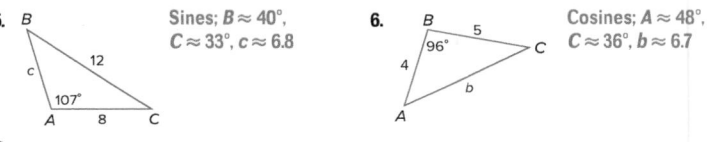

1. $A \approx 36°$, $C \approx 52°$, $b \approx 5.1$
2. $A \approx 112°$, $B \approx 40°$, $C \approx 28°$
3. $A \approx 18°$, $B \approx 29°$, $C \approx 133°$
4. $A \approx 48°$, $C \approx 22°$, $b \approx 7.6$

3. $a = 5, b = 8, c = 12$

4. $B = 110°, a = 6, c = 3$

Example 3 G.SRT.10 **PRECISION Determine whether each triangle should be solved by beginning with the Law of *Sines* or the Law of *Cosines*. Then solve the triangle.**

5.

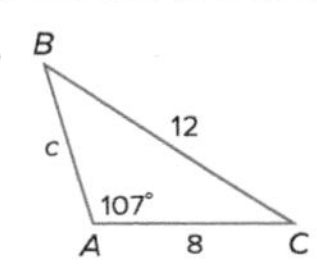

Sines; $B \approx 40°$, $C \approx 33°$, $c \approx 6.8$

6.

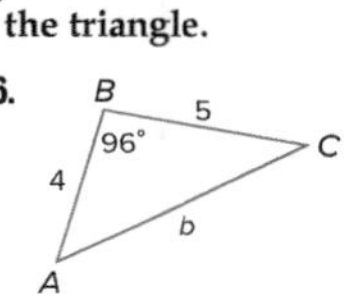

Cosines; $A \approx 48°$, $C \approx 36°$, $b \approx 6.7$

7. In $\triangle RST$, $R = 35°$, $s = 16$, and $t = 9$. Cosines; $S \approx 114°$, $T \approx 31°$, $r \approx 10.1$

8. **FOOTBALL** In a football game, the quarterback is 20 yards from Receiver A. He turns 40° to see Receiver B, who is 16 yards away. How far apart are the two receivers? about 12.9 yd

MP Teaching the Mathematical Practices

Precision Mathematically proficient students try to use clear definitions in their reasoning, calculate accurately and efficiently, and make explicit use of definitions. In Exercises 5 and 6, encourage students to refer to the definitions of the Laws of Sines and Cosines as they determine which should be used first when solving each triangle.

Practice and Problem Solving

Extra Practice is on page R8.

Examples 1–2 G.SRT.11 **Solve each triangle. Round side lengths to the nearest tenth and angle measures to the nearest degree.**

9.
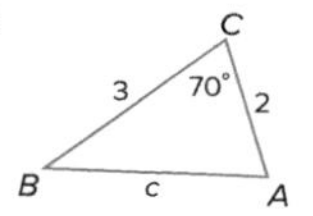

10.
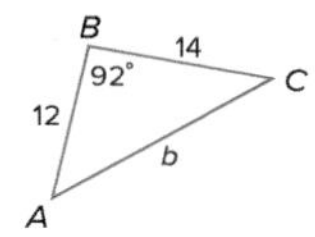

11.
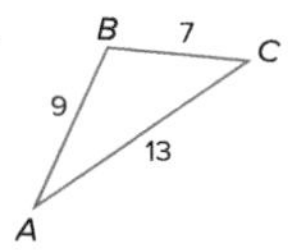

12.
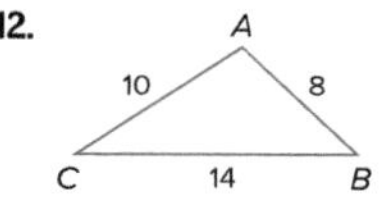

13. $A = 116°, b = 5, c = 3$

14. $C = 80°, a = 9, b = 2$

15. $f = 10, g = 11, h = 4$

16. $w = 20, x = 13, y = 12$

9. $A \approx 70°$, $B \approx 40°$, $c \approx 3.0$
10. $A \approx 48°$, $C \approx 40°$, $b \approx 18.8$
11. $A \approx 31°$, $B \approx 108°$, $C \approx 41°$
12. $A \approx 102°$, $B \approx 44°$, $C \approx 34°$
13. $a \approx 6.9$, $B \approx 41°$, $C \approx 23°$
14. $c \approx 8.9$, $A \approx 87°$, $B \approx 13°$
15. $F \approx 65°$, $G \approx 94°$, $H \approx 21°$

Example 3 G.SRT.11 **Determine whether each triangle should be solved by beginning with the Law of *Sines* or the Law of *Cosines*. Then solve the triangle.**

17.
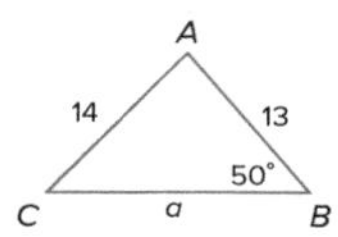

18.
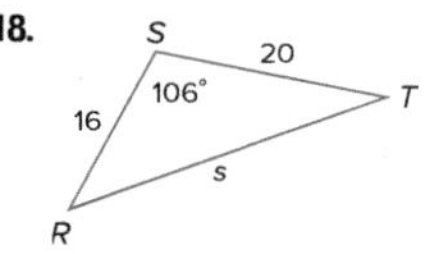

19.
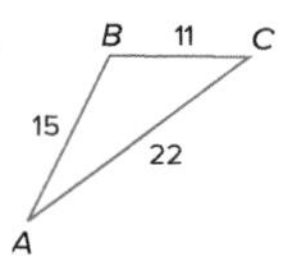

20.
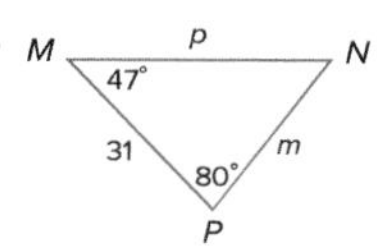

16. $W \approx 106°$, $X \approx 39°$, $Y \approx 35°$
17. Sines; $C \approx 45°$, $A \approx 85°$, $a \approx 18.2$
18. Cosines; $s \approx 28.9$, $R \approx 42°$, $T \approx 32°$
19. Cosines; $A \approx 27°$, $B \approx 115°$, $C \approx 38°$
20. Sines; $N \approx 53°$, $p \approx 38.2$, $m \approx 28.4$

21. Sines; $A \approx 17°$, $B \approx 79°$, $b \approx 6.9$
22. Cosines; $H \approx 48°$, $J = 25°$, $K = 107°$

21. In $\triangle ABC$, $C = 84°$, $c = 7$, and $a = 2$.

22. In $\triangle HJK$, $h = 18$, $j = 10$, and $k = 23$.

23. **EXPLORATION** Find the distance between the ship and the shipwreck shown in the diagram. Round to the nearest tenth. 514.2 m

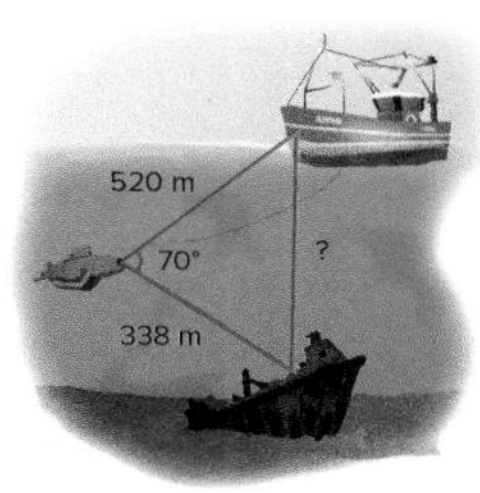

24. **GEOMETRY** A parallelogram has side lengths 8 centimeters and 12 centimeters. One angle between them measures 42°. To the nearest tenth, what is the length of the shorter diagonal? 8.1 cm

B **25.** **RACING** A triangular cross-country course has side lengths 1.8 kilometers, 2 kilometers, and 1.2 kilometers. What are the angles formed between each pair of sides? 81°, 36°, 63°

26. MP **MODELING** A triangular plot of farmland measures 0.9 by 0.5 by 1.25 miles.

a. If the plot of land is fenced on the border, what will be the angles at which the fences of the three sides meet? Round to the nearest degree. 19°, 37°, 124°

b. What is the area of the plot of land? about 0.19 mi^2

27. **LAND** Some land is in the shape of a triangle. The distances between each vertex of the triangle are 140 yards, 210 yards, and 300 yards, respectively. Use the Law of Cosines to find the area of the land to the nearest square yard. about 13,148 yd^2

Differentiated Homework Options

Levels	AL Basic	OL Core	BL Advanced
Exercises	9–24, 35–45	9–23 odd, 24–31, 33, 35–45	29–37, (optional: 38–45)
2-Day Option	9–23 odd, 38–45	9–24	
	10–24 even, 35–37	25–33, 35–45	

You can use ALEKS to provide additional remediation support with personalized instruction and practice.

Extra Practice

See page R8 for extra exercises for students who are approaching level or for on-level students who need additional reinforcement.

Levels of Complexity Chart

The levels of the exercises progress from 1 to 3, with Level 1 indicating the lowest level of complexity.

Exercises	9–24	25–28, 38–45	29–37
C Level 3			●
B Level 2		●	
Level 1	●		

Teaching Tip

For Exercise 28, remind students that sometimes rounding can lead to ambiguous answers, such as a triangle appearing to be 181 degrees.

Go Online!

eSolutions Manual

Create worksheets, answer keys, and solutions handouts for your assignments.

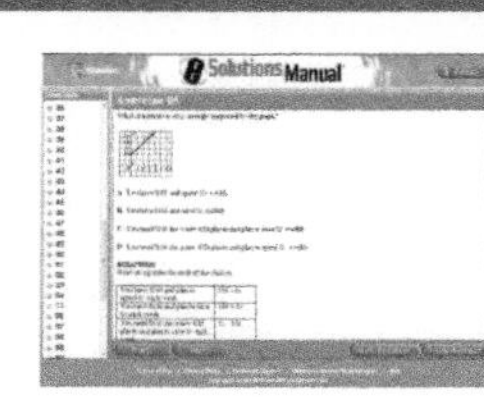

Assess

Name the Math Ask students to state the values that need to be known in order to use the Law of Cosines to solve a triangle.

Additional Answers

29a. Sample answer:

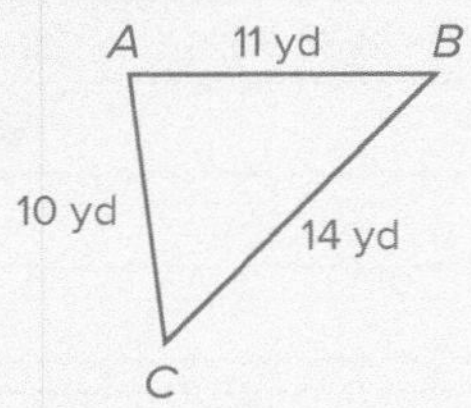

34. $a^2 = (b - x)^2 + h^2$ (Use the Pythagorean Theorem for $\triangle DBC$.)

$a^2 = b^2 - 2bx + x^2 + h^2$
(Expand $(b - x)^2$.)

$a^2 = b^2 - 2bx + c^2$
(In $\triangle ADB$, $c^2 = x^2 + h^2$.)

$a^2 = b^2 - 2b(c \cos A) + c^2$
$\left(\cos A = \frac{x}{c}, \text{ so } x = c \cos A.\right)$

$a^2 = b^2 + c^2 - 2bc \cos A$
(Commutative Property)

37. Sample answer: When two angles and a side are given or when two sides and an angle opposite one of the sides are given, you can use the Law of Sines. When two sides and an included angle or three sides are given, you can use the Law of Cosines.

28. RIDES Two bumper cars at an amusement park ride collide as shown below.

29b. Sample answer: Use the Law of Cosines to find the measure of $\angle A$. Then use the formula Area $= \frac{1}{2}bc \sin A$.

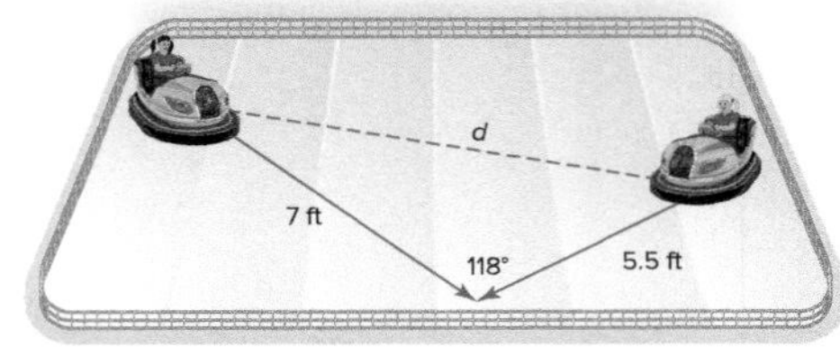

a. How far apart *d* were the two cars before they collided? **about 10.7 ft**

b. Before the collision, a third car was 10 feet from the blue car and 13 feet from the orange car. Describe the angles formed by the three cars before the collision. **78°, 49°, 53°**

29. PICNICS A triangular picnic area is 11 yards by 14 yards by 10 yards.

a. Sketch and label a drawing to represent the picnic area. **See margin.**

b. Describe how you could find the area of the picnic area.

c. What is the area? Round to the nearest tenth. **54.6 yd²**

30. WATERSPORTS A person on a personal watercraft makes a trip from point *A* to point *B* to point *C* traveling 28 miles per hour. She then returns from point *C* back to her starting point traveling 35 miles per hour. How many minutes did the entire trip take? Round to the nearest tenth. **1.5 min**

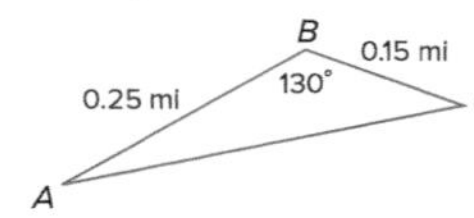

31. $B \approx 39°$, $C \approx 37°$, $c \approx 7.7$
32. $R \approx 107°$, $S \approx 48°$, $q \approx 16.0$
33. $F \approx 42°$, $G \approx 72°$, $H \approx 66°$

Solve each triangle. Round side lengths to the nearest tenth and angle measures to the nearest degree.

31.

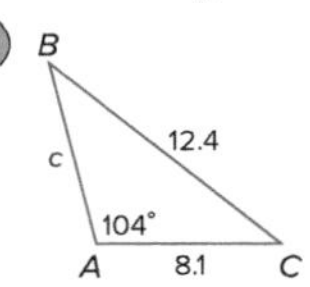

32.

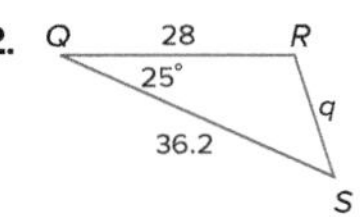

33.

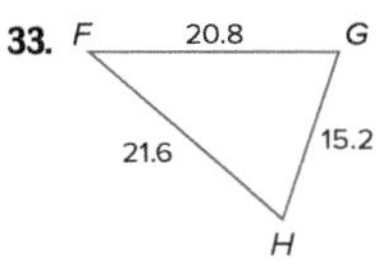

G.SRT.10, G.SRT.11

H.O.T. Problems Use Higher-Order Thinking Skills

35. The longest side is 14.5 centimeters. Use the Law of Cosines to find the measure of the angle opposite the longest side; 102°.

34. CHALLENGE Use the figure and the Pythagorean Theorem to derive the Law of Cosines. Use the hints below. **See margin.**

- First, use the Pythagorean Theorem for $\triangle DBC$.
- In $\triangle ADB$, $c^2 = x^2 + h^2$.
- $\cos A = \frac{x}{c}$

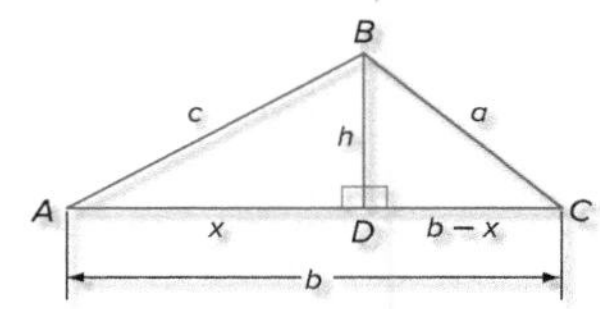

35. MP **CONSTRUCT ARGUMENTS** Three sides of a triangle measure 10.6 centimeters, 8 centimeters, and 14.5 centimeters. Explain how to find the measure of the largest angle. Then find the measure of the angle to the nearest degree.

36. OPEN-ENDED Create an application problem involving right triangles and the Law of Cosines. Then solve your problem, drawing diagrams if necessary. **See students' work.**

37. WRITING IN MATH How do you know which method to use when solving a triangle? **See margin.**

Differentiated Instruction OL BL

Extension Have students use the Law of Cosines to attempt to solve a "triangle" with sides 5, 12, and 18 (such a triangle does not exist). Have them explain what they discover and what it means. Students will get an error when attempting to find the inverse cosine because the value is not between −1 and 1. This means that no such triangle exists.

Preparing for Assessment

38. A manufacturing company produces triangular-shaped support brackets. The side lengths of the brackets measure 6 feet, 8 feet, and 5 feet. What trigonometric relationship represents the measure of the largest interior angle, angle A, formed by the support brackets? MP 4 G.SRT.11 **A**

- ○ A $\cos A = -\frac{1}{20}$
- ○ B $\sin A = -\frac{1}{20}$
- ○ C $\sin A = -\frac{1}{2}$
- ○ D $\cos A = \frac{1}{20}$

39. In $\triangle ABC$, the given dimensions are in the diagram.

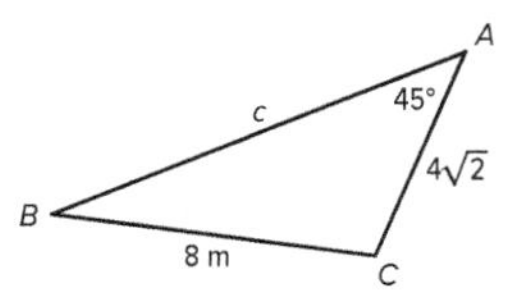

Which of the following trigonometric ratios in $\triangle ABC$ is equal to $\frac{1}{2}$? MP 1, 4 G.SRT.11 **A**

- ○ A $\sin B$
- ○ B $\cos B$
- ○ C $\sin C$
- ○ D $\cos C$

40. Select all of the correct expressions used in finding the missing lengths. MP 4, 5 G.SRT.11 **B, D, E**

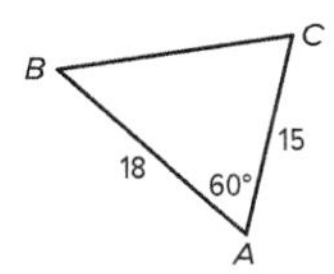

- ☐ A $a^2 = 15^2 + 15^2 - 2\,(15)\,(15)\cos 60°$
- ☐ B $a^2 = 15^2 + 18^2 - 2\,(15)\,(18)\cos 60°$
- ☐ C $C = \sin^{-1}\left(\frac{18 \sin 17°}{60}\right)$
- ☐ D $C = \sin^{-1}\left(\frac{18 \sin 60°}{17}\right)$
- ☐ E $B = \sin^{-1}\left(\frac{15 \sin 60°}{17}\right)$

41. A garden has sides of 8 meters, 11 meters, and 15 meters. What is the area of the garden to the nearest square meter? MP 1, 4 G.SRT.11

[43]

42. MULTI-STEP Carlotta paddled a kayak from a dock and traveled 4 miles east. She then steered the kayak 80° north of east and traveled another 2 miles before she anchored. MP 1, 4, 5 G.SRT.10, G.SRT.11

a. Draw a diagram of the scenario. **See margin.**

b. To the nearest tenth of a mile, find the distance from Carlotta's starting point to the point where she anchored the kayak.

[4.8 feet]

c. What law did you use to find the distance? Explain your reasoning. **See margin.**

d. Find the measure of the two other angles of the triangle to the nearest degree.

[24°, 56°]

43. MULTI-STEP In $\triangle ABC$, $m\angle A = 50°$, $m\angle B = 35°$, and $a = 12$. MP 1 G.SRT.11

a. Find the measure of $\angle C$.

[95 degrees]

b. Find b to the nearest tenth.

[9.0]

c. Find c to the nearest tenth.

[15.6]

d. Find the perimeter of $\triangle ABC$

[36.6]

44. In an isosceles triangle, the vertex angle is 30° and the base is 12 cm long. Find the perimeter of the triangle to the nearest integer. MP 5 G.SRT.11

[58 cm]

45. In a triangle, $\sin A$ is twice the value of $\sin B$. Given that $a = 4$, find the value of b. MP 5 G.SRT.11

[2]

MP Standards for Mathematical Practice

Emphasis On	Exercises
1 Make sense of problems and persevere in solving them.	1–7, 9–22, 31–33, 36–37
3 Construct viable arguments and critique the reasoning of others.	35
4 Model with mathematics.	8, 23–30, 38–42

Additional Answers

42a.

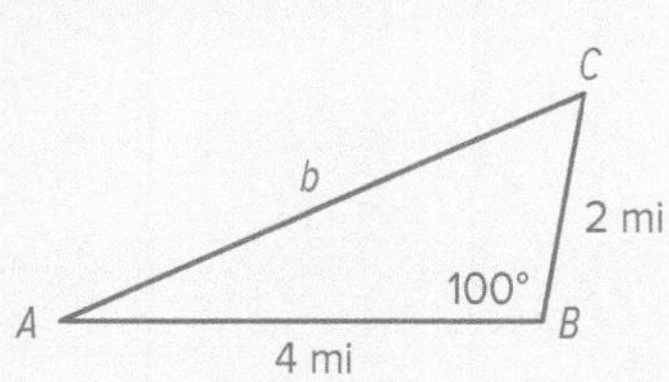

42c. The Law of Cosines had to be used because two sides and the included angle are used.

40.

A	Did not use the other side of 18
B	CORRECT
C	Reversed the side and angle measure
D	CORRECT
E	CORRECT
F	Reversed the side and angle measure

Preparing for Assessment

Exercises 38–45 require students to use the skills they will need on standardized assessments. Each exercise is dual-coded with content and mathematical practice standards.

Dual Coding		
Items	**Content Standards**	**MP Mathematical Practices**
38	G.SRT.11	4
39, 41	G.SRT.11	1, 4
40	G.SRT.11	4, 5
42	G.SRT.10, G.SRT.11	1, 4, 5
43	G.SRT.11	1
44, 45	G.SRT.11	5

Diagnose Student Errors

Survey student responses for each item. Class trends may indicate common errors and misconceptions.

38.

A	CORRECT
B	Replicated cosine with sine in Law of Cosines formula
C	Simplified the ratio incorrectly
D	Did not square the side in the Law of Cosines formula

39.

A	CORRECT
B	Replicated sine with cosine in Law of Sines formula
C	Found wrong angle measure
D	Used the wrong formula and substituted incorrectly

Go Online!

Quizzes

Students can use *Self-Check Quizzes* to check their understanding of this lesson and have the results sent to you.

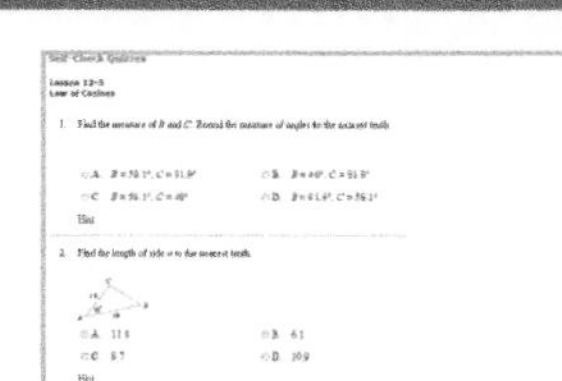

FOLDABLES® Study Organizer

A completed Foldable for this chapter should include the Key Concepts related to right triangles and trigonometry.

Key Vocabulary ELL

The page reference after each word denotes where that term was first introduced. If students have difficulty answering questions 1–6, remind them that they can use these page references to refresh their memories about the vocabulary terms.

Have students work with a partner to complete the Vocabulary Check. Encourage them to reference and compare their notes from Chapter 8.

You can use the detailed reports in ALEKS to automatically monitor students' progress and pinpoint remediation needs prior to the chapter test.

CHAPTER 8

Study Guide and Review

Go Online! for Vocabulary Review Games and key vocabulary in 13 languages

Study Guide

Key Concepts

Geometric Mean (Lesson 8-1)

- For two positive numbers a and b, the geometric mean is the positive number x where $a : x = x : b$ is true.

Pythagorean Theorem (Lesson 8-2)

- Let $\triangle ABC$ be a right triangle with right angle C. Then $a^2 + b^2 = c^2$.

Special Right Triangles (Lesson 8-3)

- The measures of the sides of a 45°-45°-90° triangle are x, x, and $x\sqrt{2}$.
- The measures of the sides of a 30°-60°-90° triangle are x, $2x$, and $x\sqrt{3}$.

Trigonometry (Lesson 8-4)

- $\sin A = \frac{\text{opposite leg}}{\text{hypotenuse}}$
- $\cos A = \frac{\text{adjacent leg}}{\text{hypotenuse}}$
- $\tan A = \frac{\text{opposite leg}}{\text{adjacent leg}}$

Angles of Elevation and Depression (Lesson 8-5)

- An angle of elevation is the angle formed by a horizontal line and the line of sight to an object above.
- An angle of depression is the angle formed by a horizontal line and the line of sight to an object below.

Laws of Sines and Cosines (Lessons 8-6 and 8-7)

Let $\triangle ABC$ be any triangle.

- Law of Sines: $\frac{\sin A}{a} = \frac{\sin B}{b} = \frac{\sin C}{c}$
- Law of Cosines: $a^2 = b^2 + c^2 - 2bc \cos A$
  $b^2 = a^2 + c^2 - 2ac \cos B$
  $c^2 = a^2 + b^2 - 2ab \cos C$
- Area $= \frac{1}{2}bc \sin A = \frac{1}{2}ac \sin B = \frac{1}{2}ab \sin C$

FOLDABLES® Study Organizer

Use your Foldable to review the chapter. Working with a partner can be helpful. Ask for clarification of concepts as needed.

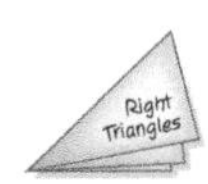

Key Vocabulary

ambiguous case (p. 608)	Law of Cosines (p. 624)
angle of depression (p. 608)	Law of Sines (p. 616)
angle of elevation (p. 608)	Pythagorean triple (p. 576)
cosine (p. 596)	sine (p. 596)
geometric mean (p. 565)	solving a triangle (p. 624)
inverse cosine (p. 599)	tangent (p. 596)
inverse sine (p. 599)	trigonometric ratio (p. 596)
inverse tangent (p. 599)	trigonometry (p. 596)

Vocabulary Check

State whether each sentence is *true* or *false*. If *false*, replace the underlined word or phrase to make a true sentence.

1. The arithmetic mean of two numbers is the positive square root of the product of the numbers. **false, geometric**
2. A Pythagorean triple is a set of three nonzero whole numbers a, b, and c such that $a^2 + b^2 = c^2$. **true**
3. To find the length of the hypotenuse of a right triangle, take the square root of the difference of the squares of the legs. **false, sum**
4. An angle of elevation is the angle formed by a horizontal line and an observer's line of sight to an object below the horizon. **false, depression**
5. The Law of Sines can be used to find an angle measure when given three side lengths. **false, Law of Cosines**
6. A trigonometric ratio is a ratio of the lengths of two sides of a right triangle. **true**

8. It is more useful to solve a triangle by beginning with the Law of Cosines when given three sides of the triangle or when given two sides and their included angle.

Concept Check

7. Explain the relationship between the angle of elevation and angle of depression between two objects. **The angle of elevation is equal to the angle of depression.**
8. Explain when it would be more useful to solve a triangle by beginning with the Law of Cosines than with the Law of Sines.

Answering the Essential Question

Before answering the Essential Question, have students review their answers to the *Building on the Essential Question* exercises found throughout the chapter.

- Why do we use the geometric mean to solve real-world problems? (p. 596)

Go Online!

Vocabulary Review

Students can use the *Vocabulary Review Games* to check their understanding of the vocabulary terms in this chapter. Students should refer to the *Student-Built Glossary* they have created as they went through the chapter to review important terms. You can also give a *Vocabulary Test* over the content of this chapter.

Lesson-by-Lesson Review

8-1 Geometric Mean
G.SRT.4, G.SRT.5

Find the geometric mean between each pair of numbers.

9. 9 and 4 6

10. $\sqrt{20}$ and $\sqrt{80}$ $\sqrt{40}$

11. $\frac{8\sqrt{2}}{3}$ and $\frac{4\sqrt{2}}{3}$ $\frac{8}{3}$

12. Find *x*, *y*, and *z*.
$x = 2\sqrt{13}$,
$y = 3\sqrt{13}$, $z = 6$

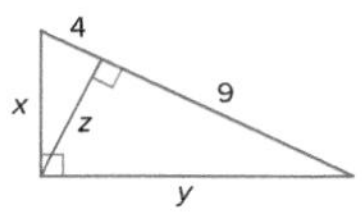

13. **DANCES** Mike is hanging a string of lights on his barn for a square dance. Using a book to sight the top and bottom of the barn, he can see he is 15 feet from the barn. If his eye level is 5 feet from the ground, how tall is the barn? 50 ft

Example 1

Find the geometric mean between 10 and 15.

$x = \sqrt{ab}$ Definition of geometric mean
$= \sqrt{10 \cdot 15}$ $a = 10$ and $b = 15$
$= \sqrt{(5 \cdot 2) \cdot (3 \cdot 5)}$ Factor.
$= \sqrt{25 \cdot 6}$ Associative Property
$= 5\sqrt{6}$ Simplify.

16. yes; right
$25^2 \stackrel{?}{=} 7^2 + 24^2$
$625 = 49 + 576$

17. yes; acute
$16^2 \stackrel{?}{=} 13^2 + 15^2$
$256 < 169 + 225$

18. yes; acute
$88^2 \stackrel{?}{=} 65^2 + 72^2$
$7744 < 4225 + 5184$

8-2 The Pythagorean Theorem and Its Converse
G.SRT.8, G.MG.3

Find *x*.

14. $2\sqrt{221} \approx 29.7$

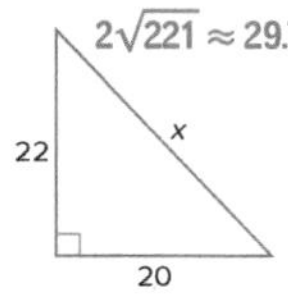

15.

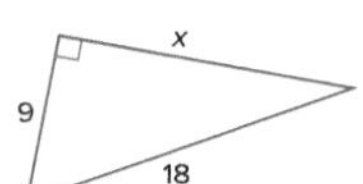

$9\sqrt{3} \approx 15.6$

Determine whether each set of numbers can be the measures of the sides of a triangle. If so, classify the triangle as *acute*, *obtuse*, or *right*. Justify your answer.

16. 7, 24, 25

17. 13, 15, 16

18. 65, 72, 88

19. **SWIMMING** Alexi walks 27 meters south and 38 meters east to get around a lake. Her sister swims directly across the lake. How many meters to the nearest tenth did Alexi's sister save by swimming? 18.4 m

Example 2

Find *x*.

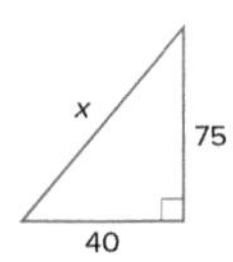

The side opposite the right angle is the hypotenuse, so $c = x$.

$a^2 + b^2 = c^2$ Pythagorean Theorem
$40^2 + 75^2 = x^2$ $a = 40$ and $b = 75$
$7225 = x^2$ Simplify.
$\sqrt{7225} = x$ Take the positive square root of each side.
$85 = x$ Simplify.

Lesson-by-Lesson Review

Intervention If the given examples are not sufficient to review the topics covered by the questions, remind students that the lesson references tell them where to review that topic in their textbook.

Two-Day Option Have students complete the Lesson-by-Lesson Review. Then you can use McGraw-Hill eAssessment to customize another review worksheet that practices all the objectives of this chapter or only the objectives on which your students need more help.

Additional Answer

22. 10 ft; Sample answer: because the ground and the side of the play structure make a 90° angle, this is a 30°-60°-90° triangle. The short side is 5 feet. The climbing wall will be the hypotenuse, so it is 10 feet.

CHAPTER 8

Study Guide and Review *Continued*

8-3 Special Right Triangles

G.SRT.6

Find *x* and *y*.

20.

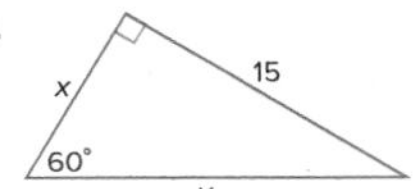

$x = 5\sqrt{3}, y = 10\sqrt{3}$

21.

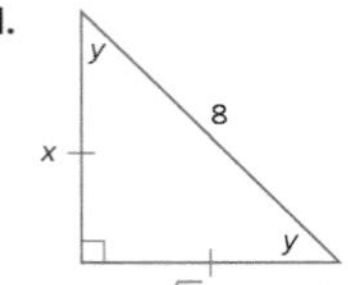

$x = 4\sqrt{2}, y = 45°$

22. **CLIMBING** Jason is adding a climbing wall to his younger brother's swing-set. If he starts building 5 feet away from the existing structure and wants it to have a 60° angle, how long should the wall be? **See margin.**

Example 3

Find *x* and *y*.

The measure of the third angle in this triangle is 90 − 60 or 30. This is a 30°-60°-90° triangle.

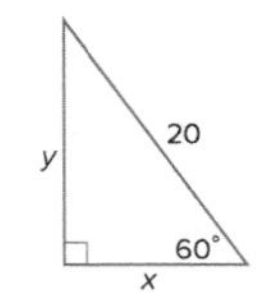

$h = 2s$	30°-60°-90° Triangle Theorem
$20 = 2x$	Substitute.
$10 = x$	Divide.

Now find *y*, the length of the longer leg.

$\ell = s\sqrt{3}$	30°-60°-90° Triangle Theorem
$y = 10\sqrt{3}$	Substitute.

8-4 Trigonometry

G.SRT.6, G.SRT.7

Express each ratio as a fraction and as a decimal to the nearest hundredth.

23. sin *A* **24.** tan *B*

25. sin *B* **26.** cos *A*

27. tan *A* **28.** cos *B*

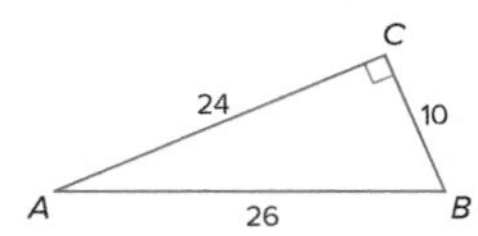

Find *x*.

29.

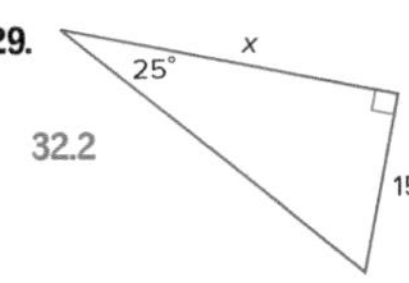

32.2

30.

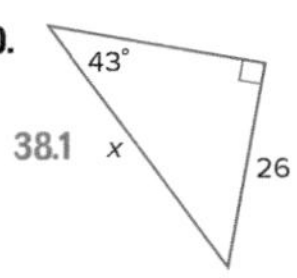

38.1

31. **GARDENING** Sofia wants to put a flower bed in the corner of her yard by laying a stone border that starts 3 feet from the corner of one fence and ends 6 feet from the corner of the other fence. Find the angles, *x* and *y*, the fence makes with the border. **63.4° and 26.6°**

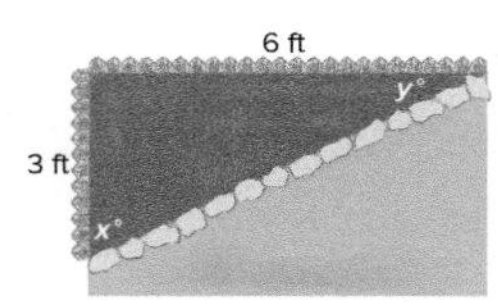

Example 4

Express each ratio as a fraction and as a decimal to the nearest hundredth.

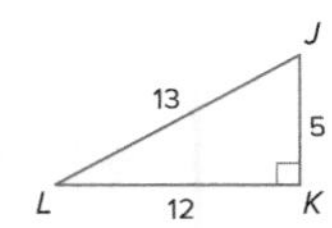

a. sin *L*

$\sin L = \frac{5}{13}$ or about 0.38 $\quad \sin L = \frac{\text{opp}}{\text{hyp}}$

b. cos *L*

$\cos L = \frac{12}{13}$ or about 0.92 $\quad \cos L = \frac{\text{adj}}{\text{hyp}}$

c. tan *L*

$\tan L = \frac{5}{12}$ or 0.42 $\quad \tan L = \frac{\text{opp}}{\text{adj}}$

23. $\frac{5}{13}$, 0.38

24. $\frac{12}{5}$, 2.40

25. $\frac{12}{13}$, 0.92

26. $\frac{12}{13}$, 0.92

27. $\frac{5}{12}$, 0.42

28. $\frac{5}{13}$, 0.38

Additional Answers

34. one solution; $A \approx 21°$, $B \approx 41°$, $b \approx 7.4$

35. two solutions; first solution; $C = 30°$, $B = 125°$, $b = 29.1$; second solution; $C = 150°$, $B = 5°$, $b = 3.1$

8-5 Angles of Elevation and Depression

G.SRT.8

32. **JOBS** Tom delivers papers on a rural route from his car. If he throws a paper from a height of 4 feet, and it lands 15 feet from the car, at what angle of depression did he throw the paper to the nearest degree? 15°

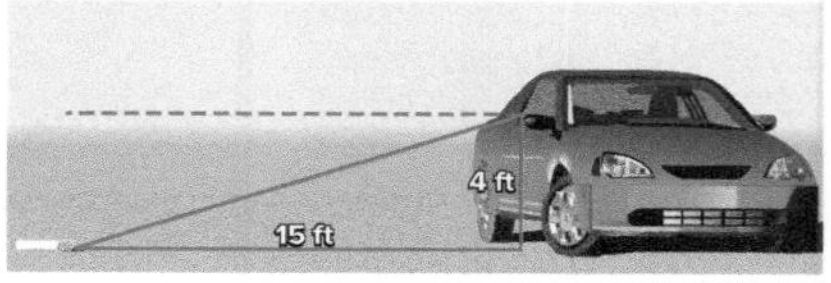

33. **TOWER** There is a cell phone tower in the field across from Jen's house. If Jen walks 50 feet from the tower and finds the angle of elevation from her position to the top of the tower to be 60°, how tall is the tower? 86.6 ft

Example 5

Sarah's cat climbed up a tree. If she sights her cat at an angle of elevation of 40°, and her eyes are 5 feet off the ground, how high up from the ground is her cat?

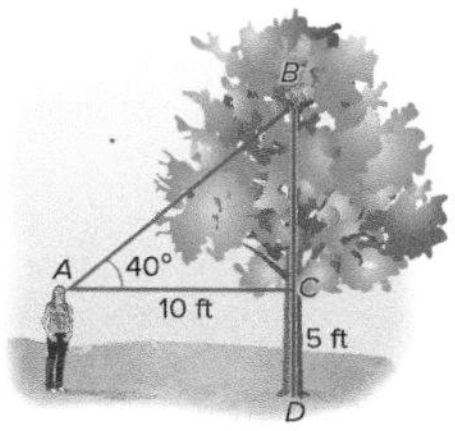

To find how far up the tree the cat is, find *CB*.

$\tan 40 = \frac{CB}{10}$ $\tan = \frac{\text{opposite}}{\text{adjacent}}$

$10(\tan 40) = CB$ Multiply each side by 10.

$8.4 = CB$ Simplify.

Since Sarah's eyes are 5 feet from the ground, add 5 to 8.4. Sarah's cat is 13.4 feet up.

8-6 Law of Sines

G.SRT.10, G.SRT.11

Determine whether each triangle has *no* solution, *one* solution, or *two* solutions. Then solve each triangle. Round measures of sides to the nearest tenth and measures of angles to the nearest degree.

34. $C = 118°$, $c = 10$, $a = 4$ See margin.

35. $A = 25°$, $a = 15$, $c = 18$ See margin.

36. $A = 70°$, $a = 5$, $c = 16$ no solution

37. **BOAT** Kira and Mallory are standing on opposite sides of a river. How far is Kira from the boat? Round to the nearest tenth if necessary. 98.9 ft

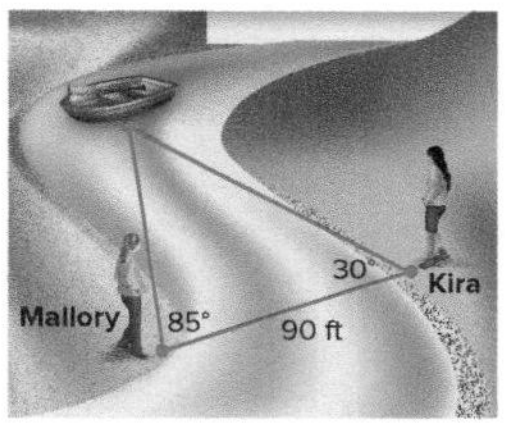

Example 6

Solve $\triangle ABC$.

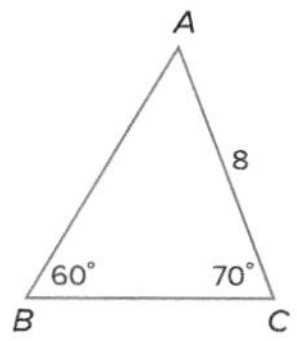

First, find the measure of the third angle.

$60° + 70° + a = 180°$

$A = 50°$

Now use the Law of Sines to find *a* and *c*. Write two equations, each with one variable.

$$\frac{\sin B}{b} = \frac{\sin C}{c} \qquad \frac{\sin B}{b} = \frac{\sin A}{a}$$

$$\frac{\sin 60°}{8} = \frac{\sin 70°}{c} \qquad \frac{\sin 60°}{8} = \frac{\sin 50°}{a}$$

$$c = \frac{8 \sin 70°}{\sin 60°} \qquad a = \frac{8 \sin 50°}{\sin 60°}$$

$$c \approx 8.7 \qquad a \approx 7.1$$

Therefore, $A = 50°$, $c \approx 8.7$, and $a \approx 7.1$.

Go Online!

Anticipation Guide

Students should complete the Chapter 8 Anticipation Guide, and discuss how their responses have changed now that they have completed Chapter 8.

Before the Test

Have students complete the Study Notebook Tie it Together activity to review topics and skills presented in the chapter.

Additional Answers

38. Cosines; $A \approx 46°$, $B \approx 85°$, $C \approx 49°$
39. Sines; $B \approx 52°$, $C \approx 48°$, $c \approx 11.3$
40. Cosines; $A \approx 40°$, $B \approx 65°$, $C \approx 7.5$
41. Sines; $B \approx 75°$, $C \approx 63°$, $c \approx 12.0$ or $B \approx 105°$, $C \approx 33°$, $c \approx 7.3$
42. Cosines; $a \approx 9.9$, $B \approx 28°$, $C \approx 117°$

CHAPTER 8

Study Guide and Review *Continued*

8-7 Law of Cosines

G.SRT.10, G.SRT.11

Determine whether each triangle should be solved by beginning with the Law of *Sines* or Law of *Cosines*. Then solve each triangle. Round measures of sides to the nearest tenth and measures of angles to the nearest degree.

38–42. See margin.

38.

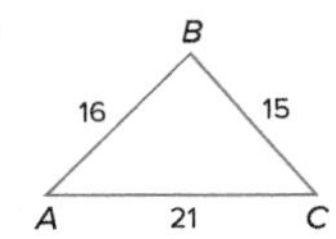

39.

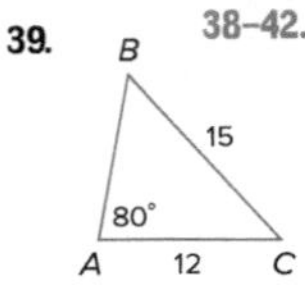

40. $C = 75°$, $a = 5$, $b = 7$
41. $A = 42°$, $a = 9$, $b = 13$
42. $b = 8.2$, $c = 15.4$, $A = 35°$
43. **FARMING** A farmer wants to fence a piece of his land. Two sides of the triangular field have lengths of 120 feet and 325 feet. The measure of the angle between those sides is 70°. How much fencing will the farmer need? about 750.5 ft
44. In a rhombus whose side length is 22 and the smaller angle is 55°, find the length of the shorter diagonal to the nearest tenth. 20.3
45. A triangular walking course has 2 sides of 240 feet and 360 feet, and the angle between these sides measures 38°. Find the length of the third side of the course to the nearest foot. 226 ft
46. Three sides of a triangle measure 20 meters, 30 meters, and 40 meters. Find the largest angle of the triangle to the nearest degree. 104 degrees

Example 7

Solve $\triangle ABC$ for $C = 55°$, $b = 11$, and $a = 18$.

You are given the measure of two sides and the included angle. Begin by drawing a diagram and using the Law of Cosines to determine c.

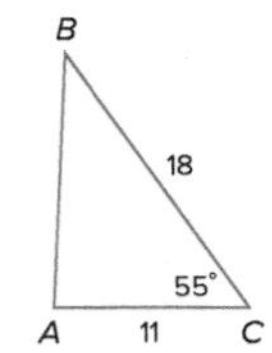

$c^2 = a^2 + b^2 - 2ab \cos C$

$c^2 = 182 + 112 - 2(18)(11) \cos 55°$

$c^2 \approx 217.9$

$c \approx 14.8$

Next, you can use the Law of Sines to find the measure of angle A.

$\frac{\sin A}{18} \approx \frac{\sin 55°}{14.8}$

$\sin A \approx \frac{18 \sin 55°}{14.8}$ or A is about 85.0°

The measure of the angle B is approximately $180 - (85.0 + 55)$ or 40.0°.

Therefore, $c \approx 14.8$, $A \approx 85.0°$, and $B \approx 40.0°$

Go Online!

eAssessment

Customize and create multiple versions of chapter tests and answer keys that align to your standards. Tests can be delivered on paper or online.

CHAPTER 8
Practice Test

Go Online! for another Chapter Test

Find the geometric mean between each pair of numbers.

1. 7 and 11 $\sqrt{77} \approx 8.8$
2. 12 and 9 $6\sqrt{3} \approx 10.4$
3. 14 and 21 $7\sqrt{6} \approx 17.1$
4. $4\sqrt{3}$ and $10\sqrt{3}$ $2\sqrt{30} \approx 11.0$
5. Find *x*, *y*, and *z*. $x = 6, y = 2\sqrt{13}, z = 3\sqrt{13}$

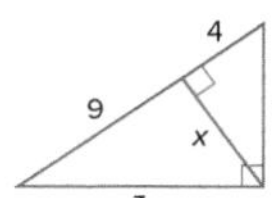

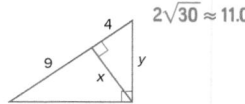

6. **FAIRS** Blake is setting up his tent at a Renaissance fair. If the tent is 8 feet tall and the tether can be staked no more than two feet from the tent, how long should the tether be? 8.2 ft

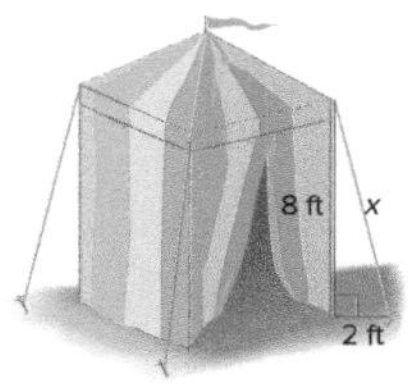

Use a calculator to find the measure of ∠R to the nearest tenth.

7. 70.9

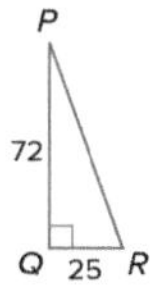

8. 39.6

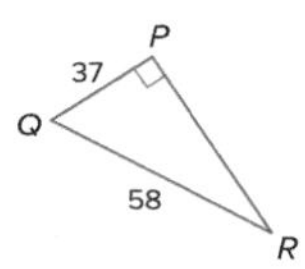

9. Find *x* and *y*. $x = 4\sqrt{2}, y = 4\sqrt{6}$

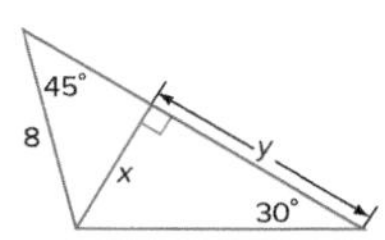

Express each ratio as a fraction and as a decimal to the nearest hundredth.

10. cos *X* 10–13. See margin.
11. tan *X*
12. tan *V*
13. sin *V*

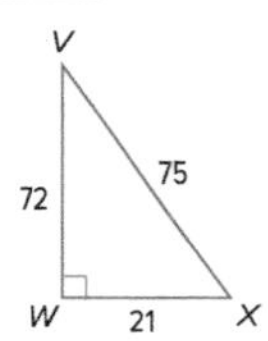

Find the area of △ABC to the nearest tenth.

14. $A = 48°, b = 7$ in., $c = 12$ in. $31.2\ in^2$
15. $C = 128°, a = 1.25$ m, $b = 16$ m $7.9\ m^2$

16. **SPACE** Anna is watching a space shuttle launch 6 miles from Cape Canaveral in Florida. When the angle of elevation from her viewing point to the shuttle is 80°, how high is the shuttle, if it is going straight up? 34 mi

Determine whether each △ABC has *no* solution, *one* solution, or *two* solutions. Then solve the triangle. Round side lengths to the nearest tenth and angle measures to the nearest degree.

17. $A = 23°, a = 14, b = 11$ one; $B \approx 18°, C \approx 139°, c \approx 23.4$
18. $A = 112°, a = 5, b = 9$ no solution
19. **MULTIPLE CHOICE** Which of the following is the length of the leg of a 45°-45°-90° triangle with a hypotenuse of 20? B

    A 10 C 20
    B $10\sqrt{2}$ D $20\sqrt{2}$

Find *x*.

20. 26

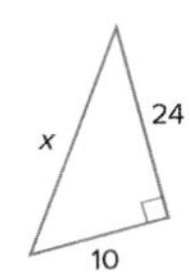

21. $\sqrt{320} \approx 17.9$

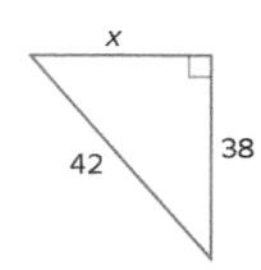

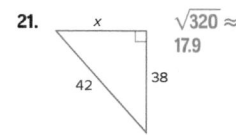

22. **WHALE WATCHING** Isaac is looking through binoculars on a whale watching trip when he notices a sea otter in the distance. If he is 20 feet above sea level in the boat, and the angle of depression is 30°, how far away from the boat is the otter to the nearest foot? 35 ft

Determine whether each triangle should be solved by beginning with the Law of Sines or Law of Cosines. Then solve each triangle. Round side lengths to the nearest tenth and angle measures to the nearest degree.

23. Sines; $B \approx 65°, a \approx 7.4, b \approx 11.1$

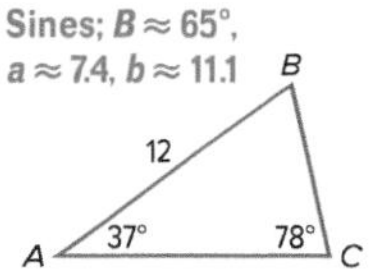

24. Cosines; $A \approx 50°, B \approx 28°, c \approx 10.3$

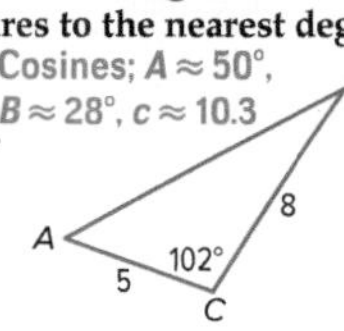

25. Solve △FGH. Round to the nearest degree. $m\angle H = 58, m\angle G = 55, m\angle F = 67$

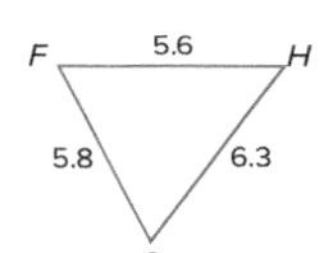

Go Online!

Chapter Tests

You can use premade leveled *Chapter Tests* to differentiate assessment for your students. Students can also take self-checking *Chapter Tests* to plan and prepare for chapter assessments.

Form	Type	Level
1	MC	AL
2A	MC	OL
2B	FR	OL
2C	FR	OL
3	FR	BL
Vocabulary Test		
Extended-Response Test		

MC = multiple-choice questions
FR = free-response questions

RtI Response to Intervention

Use the Intervention Planner to help you determine your Response to Intervention.

Intervention Planner

TIER 1 On Level OL

IF students miss 25% of the exercises or less,

THEN choose a resource:

SE Lessons 8-1 through 8-7

Go Online!
- Skills Practice
- Chapter Project
- Self-Check Quizzes

TIER 2 Strategic Intervention AL
Approaching grade level

IF students miss 50% of the exercises,

THEN choose a resource:

Quick Review Math Handbook

Go Online!
- Study Guide and Intervention
- Extra Examples
- Personal Tutors
- Homework Help

TIER 3 Intensive Intervention
2 or more grades below level

IF students miss 75% of the exercises,

THEN choose a resource:

Use *Math Triumphs, Geometry*

Go Online!
- Extra Examples
- Personal Tutors
- Homework Help
- Review Vocabulary

Additional Answers

10. $\frac{21}{75} = 0.28$
11. $\frac{72}{21} \approx 3.43$
12. $\frac{21}{72} \approx 0.29$
13. $\frac{21}{75} = 0.28$

Launch

Objective Apply concepts and skills from this chapter in a real-world setting.

Teach

Ask:

- Part A: How is the information used? Sample answer: Realize the right triangle and the use of the Pythagorean Theorem.
- Part B: How is an equation formed? Many such equations are possible. Sample answer: Go back to SOH-CAH-TOA and compare with the lengths of sides in the right triangle.
- Part C: What law is used here? Sample answer: The Law of Cosines is used since two sides and the included angle are given and the question asks for the length of the third side.
- Part D: How is the bearing calculated? Sample answer: The Law of Sines is used to calculate the relevant angle, i.e. the angle with the vertex on the island. Then, to find the bearing, add 180°.

The Performance Task focuses on the following content standards and standards for mathematical practice.

Dual Coding

Items	Content Standards	MP Mathematical Practices
1	G.SRT.8	1
2	G.SRT.8	1, 2
3	G.SRT.8	2, 6
4	G.SRT.11	1
5	G.SRT.11	2

CHAPTER 8

Preparing for Assessment

Performance Task

Provide a clear solution to each part of the task. Be sure to show all of your work. Include all relevant drawings and justify your answers.

NAVIGATION Jessika and her family are on vacation at the coast. They take a boat from a small island along a 10 mile path that is perpendicular to the horizontal shoreline of the mainland. A supply store is located 5 miles from the docks on the mainland shoreline.

Part A

1. What is the distance from the supply store to their boat on the island? $5\sqrt{5}$ miles

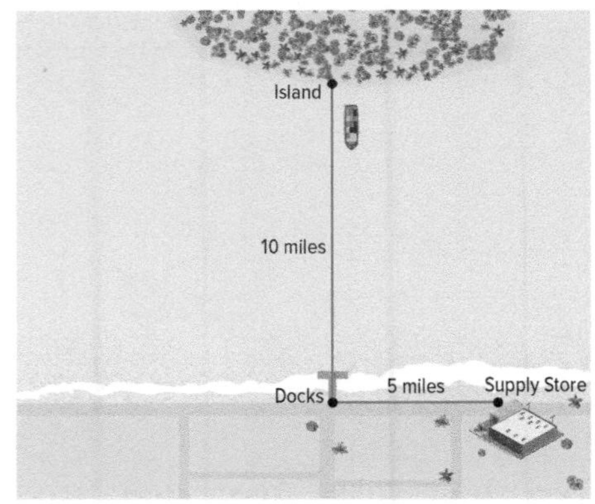

Part B

Jessika wants to find the angle formed by the shoreline and the segment from the supply store to her family's boat on the island.

2. **Reasoning** Write a trigonometric equation to find this angle. Sample answer: $\tan\theta = \frac{10}{5}$
3. Use a calculator to find this angle to the nearest tenth of a degree. 63.4°

Part C

The docks are relocated to a location on the shoreline that is 8 miles farther away from the supply store.

4. How far does the boat have to travel now to get from the island to the new docks? $2\sqrt{41}$ miles

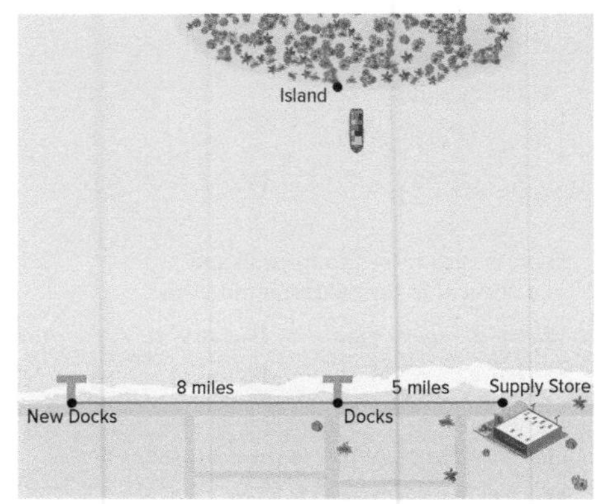

Part D

A bearing is an angle formed clockwise from due north. The island is north of the mainland.

5. **Reasoning** At what bearing does the boat need to travel from the island to reach the new docks? 218.7°

Levels of Complexity Chart

The levels of the exercises progress from 1 to 3, with Level 1 indicating the lowest level of complexity.

Parts	Level 1	Level 2	Level 3
A	●		
B		●	
C		●	
D			●

Go Online! eBook

Interactive Student Guide

Refer to *Interactive Student Guide* for an additional Performance Task.

Test-Taking Strategy

Example

Read the problem. Identify what you need to know. Then use the information in the problem to solve.

The ratio of the width to the height of a high-definition television is 16 : 9. This is also called the *aspect ratio* of the television. The size of a television is given in terms of the diagonal distance across the screen. If an HD television is 25.5 inches tall, what is its screen size?

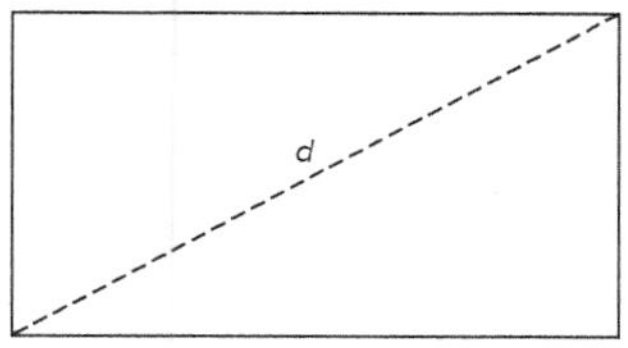

A 48 inches C 51 inches
B 50 inches D 52 inches

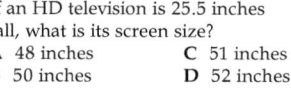

Test-Taking Tip

Use a Formula Sometimes it is necessary to use a formula to solve problems on standardized tests. In some cases, you may even be given a formula sheet for reference.

Step 1 **What are you asked to find?**
The length of the diagonal of the television.

Step 2 **What formula can you use?**
The diagonal, height, and width form a right triangle, so use the Pythagorean Theorem to find the diagonal.

Step 3 **What is the correct answer?**

Find the width of the screen. Set up and solve a proportion using the aspect ratio 16 : 9.

$\frac{16}{9} = \frac{w}{25.5}$ ← width of the screen ← height of the screen

$9w = 408$ Cross Products Property

$w = 45\frac{1}{3}$ Divide each side by 9.

So, the width of the screen is $45\frac{1}{3}$ inches. Use the Pythagorean Theorem to solve for the diagonal distance. Let c = diagonal, a = height, and b = width.

$c^2 = a^2 + b^2$ Pythagorean Theorem

$c^2 = (25.5)^2 + \left(45\frac{1}{3}\right)^2$ Substitute for a and b.

$c \approx 52.01$ Simplify. Take the positive square root of both sides to solve for c.

The diagonal distance of the screen is about 52 inches. So, the answer is D.

Apply the Strategy

Read the problem. Identify what you need to know. Then use the information in the problem to solve.

Christine is flying a kite on the end of a taut string. The kite is 175 feet above the ground and is a horizontal distance of 130 feet from where Christine is standing. How much kite string has Christine let out? Round to the nearest foot. B

A 204 ft C 225 ft
B 218 ft D 236

Answer the questions below.

a. What are you asked to find? **the length of string used to fly the kite**

b. What formula can you use? **Pythagorean Theorem**

c. What is the correct answer? **B**

Test-Taking Strategy

Step 1 What are you asked to find?

Step 2 What formula can you use?

Step 3 What is the correct answer?

Need Another Example?

The ratio of the width and height of a standard-definition television is 4 : 3. This is also called the aspect ratio of the television. The size of the television is given in terms of the diagonal across the screen. If a television is 21.6 inches wide, what is the screen size? B

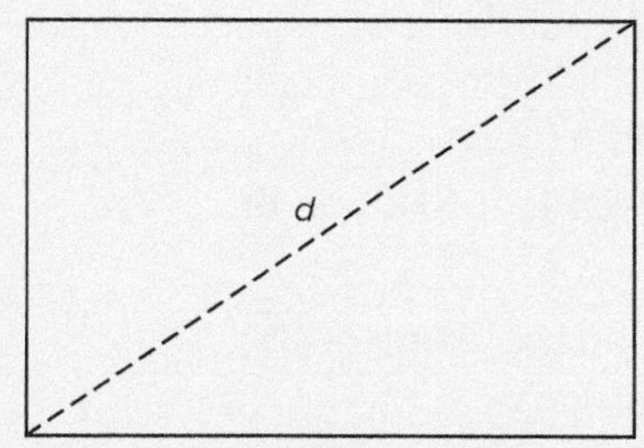

21.6 in.

A 16.2 in.
B 27 in.
C 37.8 in.
D 42 in.

a. What are you asked to find?
The screen size of the television

b. What formula can you use?
The Pythagorean Theorem

c. What is the correct answer? B

Go Online!

Standardized Test Practice

The most up-to-date resources available for your program can be found at connectED.mcgraw-hill.com.

Diagnose Student Errors

Survey student responses for each item. Class trends may indicate common errors and misconceptions.

1.	A	Used $\tan^{-1}\left(\frac{8}{30}\right)$
	B	Found the angle the skateboard makes with the wall
	C	CORRECT
	D	Used $\tan^{-1}\left(\frac{30}{8}\right)$

2. Student may find the width, but fail to find the perimeter. Student may subtract the length from the diagonal to find the width.

3.	A	Found $m\angle D$
	B	Found $m\angle C$
	C	CORRECT
	D	Solved $3x - 10 = x + 10$

4.	A	Found the length of $\overline{QS}$
	B	CORRECT
	C	Subtracted 16 cm from SU to find the length of $\overline{QS}$
	D	Solved $\frac{36}{20} = \frac{x}{44}$

5.	A	Omitted factor of $\frac{1}{2}$ in area formula
	B	Used arithmetic mean rather than geometric mean to find height
	C	CORRECT
	D	Used 16 m as length of base of triangle

6a. Student may find the distance between Tower Y and the fire. Student may solve using a right angle at the fire (500 cos 20°).

7. Student may incorrectly identify the new triangle as a 45°-45°-90° triangle. Student may reverse the roles of the height and base in the new triangle.

8.	A	Incorrectly identified corresponding angles
	B	Assumed lines *m* and *n* are parallel and incorrectly identified corresponding angles
	C	Assumed lines *m* and *n* are parallel
	D	CORRECT

Go Online!

Standardized Test Practice

Students can take self-checking tests in standardized format to plan and prepare for standardized assessments.

CHAPTER 8

Preparing for Assessment

Cumulative Review

Read each question. Then fill in the correct answer on the answer document provided by your teacher or on a sheet of paper.

1. Jeffrey leans his skateboard against a wall. The skateboard is 30 inches long, and the base of the skateboard is 8 inches from the wall.

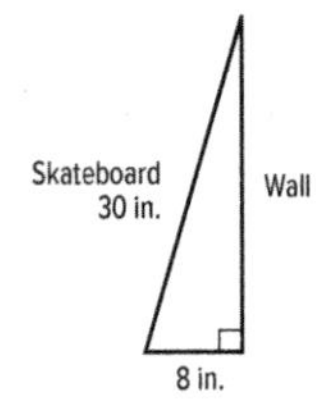

Which of the following is the best estimate of the measure of the angle the skateboard makes with the ground? G.SRT.6 C

○ A 14.9	○ C 74.5
○ B 15.5	○ D 75.1

2. Marisol's new tablet is 9 inches long and has a diagonal of 11 inches. What is the perimeter of the tablet, in inches, to the nearest tenth of an inch? G.SRT.8

[30.6]

Test-Taking Tip

Question 2 This problem requires two steps. First use the Pythagorean Theorem to find the width of the tablet. Then find the perimeter.

3. What should be the value of x in order for quadrilateral $ABCD$ to be a parallelogram? G.CO.11 C

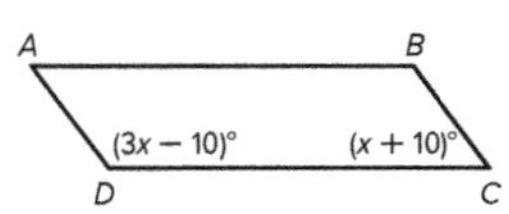

○ A 125	○ C 45
○ B 55	○ D 10

4. Sunny is designing a small bookcase with parallel shelves and slanted sides, as shown in the figure.

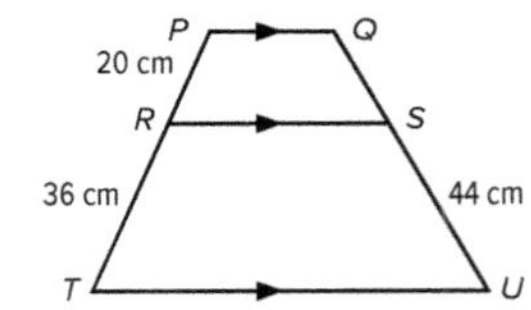

Which of the following is the best estimate of the length of $\overline{QU}$? G.SRT.5 B

○ A 24.4 cm	○ C 28.0 cm
○ B 68.4 cm	○ D 79.2 cm

5. What is the area of $\triangle PQR$? G.SRT.5 C

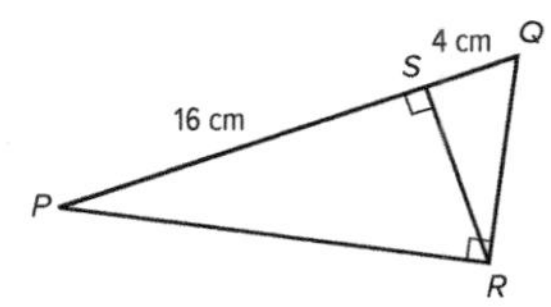

○ A 160 m^2	○ C 80 m^2
○ B 100 m^2	○ D 64 m^2

6. Forest rangers in two observation towers spot a fire in the distance. The towers are 500 feet apart. The rangers each measure the angle to the fire as shown in the figure. G.SRT.11

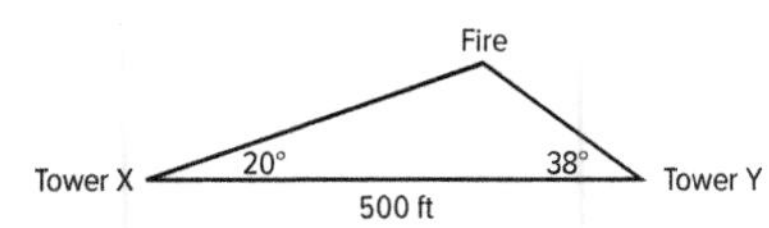

a. What is the distance from Tower X to the fire to the nearest foot?

[363] ft

b. MP What mathematical practice did you use to solve this problem? See students' work.

9.	A	Found distance from Addie to the motorcycle
	B	CORRECT
	C	Calculated 65 sin 52°
	D	Calculated 65 tan 38°

10. Student may find the value of *x*, but fail to find the value of *PQ*. Student may find the value of *PR*.

11.	A	Did not use the fact that the quadrilateral is a parallelogram
	B	Incorrectly determined that an interior angle of the quadrilateral is a right angle
	C	CORRECT
	D	Incorrectly determined that an interior angle of the quadrilateral is a right angle

12.	A	Incorrectly applied the Pythagorean Inequality Theorem
	B	CORRECT
	C	Did not recognize a Pythagorean Triple
	D	Did not apply the Triangle Inequality Theorem

13.	A	CORRECT
	B	Reversed the roles of $\overline{PS}$ and $\overline{PR}$ in the 45°-45°-90° triangle
	C	CORRECT
	D	Incorrectly identified $\triangle STR$ as a 30°-60°-90° triangle
	E	Incorrectly identified $\triangle PSR$ as a 30°-60°-90° triangle and reversed the roles of $\overline{PS}$ and $\overline{PR}$

Go Online! for Standardized Test Practice

7. Kendrick draws and cuts out an equilateral triangle with sides 5 inches long. He folds the triangle in half, as shown. What is the value of x to the nearest tenth of an inch? G.SRT.6

4.3

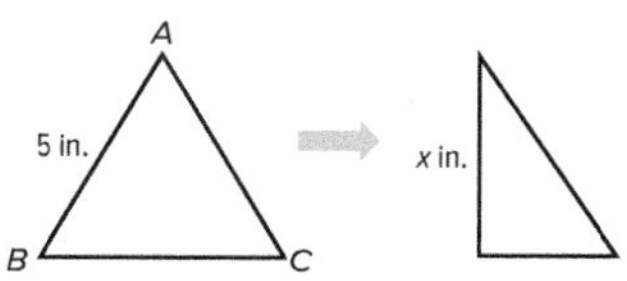

8. Line p is parallel to line q.

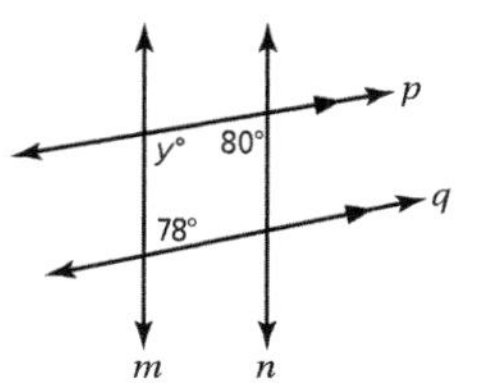

What is the value of y? G.CO.9 D

- A 78
- B 80
- C 100
- D 102

9. From the top of a 65-foot-tall building, Addie spots a motorcycle at street level. The angle of depression from Addie to the motorcycle is 38°. What is the horizontal distance from the base of the building to the motorcycle? G.SRT.8 B

- A 105.6 ft
- B 83.2 ft
- C 51.2 ft
- D 50.8 ft

10. Find the measure of $\overline{PQ}$ if Q is the midpoint of PR, $PQ = 9x - 18$, and $QR = 3x + 36$. G.CO.1

63

11. Quadrilateral $JKLM$ is a parallelogram.

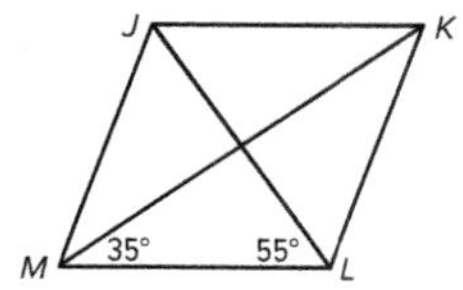

Which of the following is the best name for quadrilateral $JKLM$? G.CO.11 C

- A kite
- B rectangle
- C rhombus
- D square

12. Claire wants to cut three straws and place them together to form an obtuse triangle. Which of the following could be the lengths of the straws that Claire uses? G.SRT.8 B

- A 6 in., 7 in., 8 in.
- B 6 in., 7 in., 10 in.
- C 6 in., 8 in., 10 in.
- D 6 in., 8 in., 14 in.

13. A park is a square with straight paths along the diagonals, as shown.

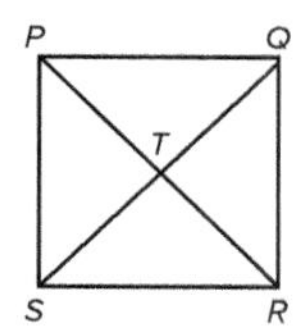

Select all statements about the path that must be true. G.SRT.6 A, C

- ☐ A The length of $\overline{SR}$ is $\sqrt{2}$ times the length of $\overline{TR}$.
- ☐ B The length of $\overline{PS}$ is $\sqrt{2}$ times the length of $\overline{PR}$.
- ☐ C The length of $\overline{QS}$ is $\sqrt{2}$ times the length of $\overline{QR}$.
- ☐ D The length of $\overline{SR}$ is $\sqrt{3}$ times the length of $\overline{TR}$.
- ☐ E The length of $\overline{PS}$ is $\sqrt{3}$ times the length of $\overline{PR}$.

Need Extra Help?

If you missed Question...	1	2	3	4	5	6	7	8	9	10	11	12	13
Go to Lesson...	8-4	8-2	6-3	7-5	8-1	8-6	8-3	2-7	8-5	1-3	6-5	8-2	8-3

Formative Assessment

You can use these pages to benchmark student progress.

Standardized Test Practice

Test Item Formats

In the Cumulative Review, students will encounter different formats for assessment questions to prepare them for standardized tests.

Question Type	Exercises
Multiple Choice	1, 3–5, 8–9, 11–12
Multiple Correct Answers	13
Short Response	2, 6, 7, 10
Extended Response	6

Answer Sheet Practice

Have students simulate taking a standardized test by recording their answers on a practice recording sheet.

Homework Option

Get Ready for Chapter 9 Assign students the exercises on p. 642 as homework to assess whether they possess the prerequisite skills needed for the next chapter.

LEARNSMART®

Use LearnSmart as part of your test-preparation plan to measure student topic retention. You can create a student assignment in LearnSmart for additional practice on these topics.

- Define Trigonometric Ratios and Solve Problems Involving Right Triangles
- Apply Trigonometry to General Triangles

Go Online!

eAssessment

Customize and create multiple versions of chapter tests and answer keys that align to your standards. Tests can be delivered on paper or online.

Lesson 8-1

53. Sample answer: Both the arithmetic and the geometric mean calculate a value between two given numbers. The arithmetic mean of two numbers a and b is $\frac{a+b}{2}$, and the geometric mean of two numbers a and b is $\sqrt{ab}$. The two means will be equal when $a = b$.

Justification:

$$\frac{a+b}{2} = \sqrt{ab}$$
$$\left(\frac{a+b}{2}\right)^2 = ab$$
$$\frac{(a+b)^2}{4} = ab$$
$$(a+b)^2 = 4ab$$
$$a^2 + 2ab + b^2 = 4ab$$
$$a^2 - 2ab + b^2 = 0$$
$$(a-b)^2 = 0$$
$$a - b = 0$$
$$a = b$$

Lesson 8-2

37. Given: In $\triangle ABC$, $c^2 > a^2 + b^2$, where c is the length of the longest side.
Prove: $\triangle ABC$ is an obtuse triangle.

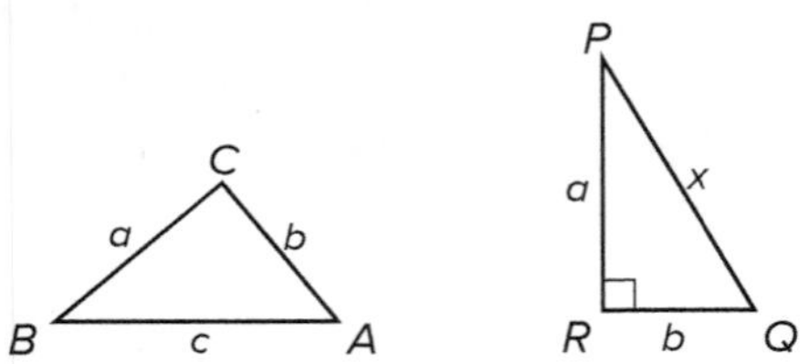

Proof:

Statements (Reasons)

1. In $\triangle ABC$, $c^2 > a^2 + b^2$, where c is the length of the longest side. In $\triangle PQR$, $\angle R$ is a right angle. (Given)
2. $a^2 + b^2 = x^2$ (Pythagorean Theorem)
3. $c^2 > x^2$ (Substitution Property)
4. $c > x$ (A property of square roots)
5. $m\angle R = 90$ (Definition of a right angle)
6. $m\angle C > m\angle R$ (Converse of the Hinge Theorem)
7. $m\angle C > 90$ (Substitution Property of Equality)
8. $\angle C$ is an obtuse angle. (Definition of an obtuse angle)
9. $\triangle ABC$ is an obtuse triangle. (Definition of an obtuse triangle)

Lesson 8-4

61a. Sample answer:

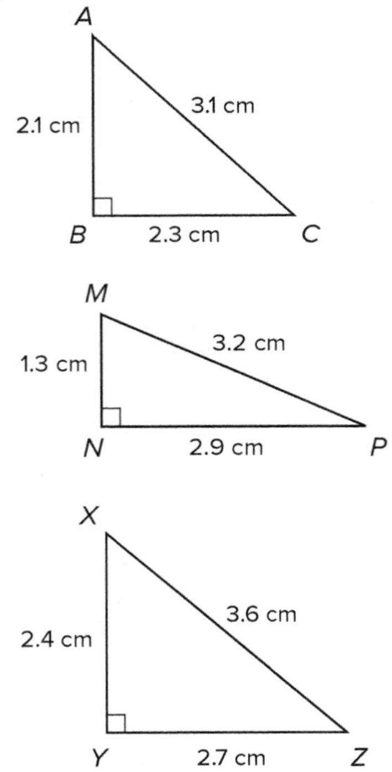

61c. Sample answer: The sum of the cosine squared and the sine squared of an acute angle of a right triangle is 1.

61e. Sample answer:

$(\sin A)^2 + (\cos A)^2 \stackrel{?}{=} 1$ (Conjecture)

$\left(\frac{y}{r}\right)^2 + \left(\frac{x}{r}\right)^2 \stackrel{?}{=} 1$ $\left(\sin A = \frac{y}{r}, \cos A = \frac{x}{r}\right)$

$\frac{y^2}{r^2} + \frac{x^2}{r^2} \stackrel{?}{=} 1$ (Simplify.)

$\frac{y^2 + x^2}{r^2} \stackrel{?}{=} 1$ (Combine fractions with like denominators.)

$\frac{r^2}{r^2} \stackrel{?}{=} 1$ (Pythagorean Theorem)

$1 = 1$ (Simplify.)

Lesson 8-5

22a. Sample answer:

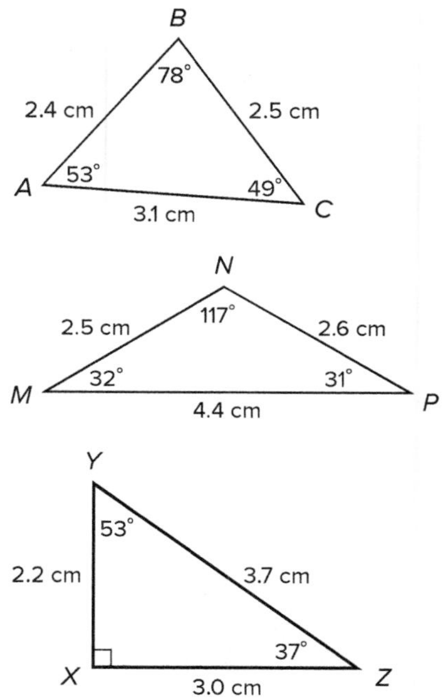

22c. Sample answer: The ratio of the sine of an angle to the length of the leg opposite that angle is approximately equal for all three angles of a triangle.

CHAPTER 9

Circles

SUGGESTED PACING (DAYS)

	Instruction	Review & Assess
90 min.	5	1
45 min.	9	2

Track Your Progress

This chapter focuses on content from the Expressing Geometric Properties with Equations and Congruence domains

THEN

G.SRT.6 Understand that by similarity, side ratios in right triangles are properties of the angles in the triangle, leading to definitions of trigonometric ratios for acute angles.

G.SRT.8 Use trigonometric ratios and the Pythagorean Theorem to solve right triangles in applied problems.

G.SRT.10 Prove the Laws of Sines and Cosines and use them to solve problems.

G.SRT.11 Understand and apply the Law of Sines and the Law of Cosines to find unknown measurements in right and non-right triangles.

NOW

G.C.2 Identify and describe relationships among inscribed angles, radii, and chords.

G.C.3 Construct the inscribed and circumscribed circles of a triangle, and prove properties of angles for a quadrilateral inscribed in a circle.

G.GPE.1 Derive the equation of a circle of given center and radius using the Pythagorean Theorem; complete the square to find the center and radius of a circle given by an equation.

G.GPE.2 Derive the equation of a parabola given a focus and directrix.

NEXT

G.GMD.1 Give an informal argument for the formulas for the circumference of a circle, area of a circle, volume of a cylinder, pyramid, and cone.

G.GPE.7 Use coordinates to prove simple geometric theorems algebraically. Use coordinates to compute perimeters of polygons and areas of triangles and rectangles.

G.MG.1 Use geometric shapes, their measures, and their properties to describe objects.

Standards for Mathematical Practice

All of the Standards for Mathematical Practice will be covered in this chapter. The MP icon notes specific areas of coverage.

MP Teaching the Mathematical Practices

Help students develop the mathematical practices by asking questions like these.

Questioning Strategies

As students approach problems in this chapter, help them develop mathematical practices by asking:

Sense-Making
- What real-world problems can you solve using the circumference of a circle?
- For what can the properties of tangents be used?

Reasoning
- What is the relationship between arcs and chords?
- How can the relationships between arcs, chords, and diameters be used?

Modeling
- How do you use the properties of tangents to solve problems involving circumscribed polygons?
- Knowing the equation of a circle, how do you graph a circle on the coordinate plane?

Precision
- How do you find the measures of angles of inscribed polygons?
- How do you find the measures of angles formed by lines intersecting inside or outside a circle?

Go Online!

StudySync:
SMP Modeling Videos

These demonstrate how to apply the Standards for Mathematical Practice to collaborate, discuss, and solve real-world math problems.

Go Online!

connectED.mcgraw-hill.com

LearnSmart | The Geometer's Sketchpad | Vocabulary | Tutor | Tools | Calculator Resources | Check | Watch

Customize Your Chapter

Use the *Plan & Present*, *Assignment Tracker*, and *Assessment* tools in ConnectED to introduce lesson concepts, assign personalized practice, and diagnose areas of student need.

Differentiated Instruction

Throughout the program, look for the icons to find specialized content designed for your students.

- AL Approaching Level
- OL On Level
- BL Beyond Level
- ELL English Language Learners

Personalize

Differentiated Resources

FOR EVERY CHAPTER	AL	OL	BL	ELL
Chapter Readiness Quizzes	●	●	◐	●
Chapter Tests	●	●	●	●
Standardized Test Practice	●	●	●	●
Vocabulary Review Games	●	●	◐	●
Anticipation Guide (English/Spanish)	●	●	◐	●
Student-Built Glossary	●	●	◐	●
Chapter Project	◐	●	●	●
FOR EVERY LESSON	**AL**	**OL**	**BL**	**ELL**
Personal Tutors (English/Spanish)	●	●	◐	●
Graphing Calculator Personal Tutors	●	●	●	●
Step-by-Step Solutions	●	●	◐	●
Self-Check Quizzes	●	●	●	●
5-Minute Check	●	●	●	●
Study Notebook	●	●	●	●
Study Guide and Intervention	●	●		●
Skills Practice (English/Spanish)	●	◐		●
Practice (English/Spanish)	◐	●	●	●
Word Problem Practice	◐	●	●	◐
Enrichment		●	●	●
Extra Examples	●	◐		◐
Interactive Classroom	●	●	●	●

◐ Aligned to this group ● Designed for this group

Engage

Featured IWB Resources

The Geometer's Sketchpad provides students with a tangible, visual way to learn. *Use with Lessons 9-1 through 9-5 and 9-7.*

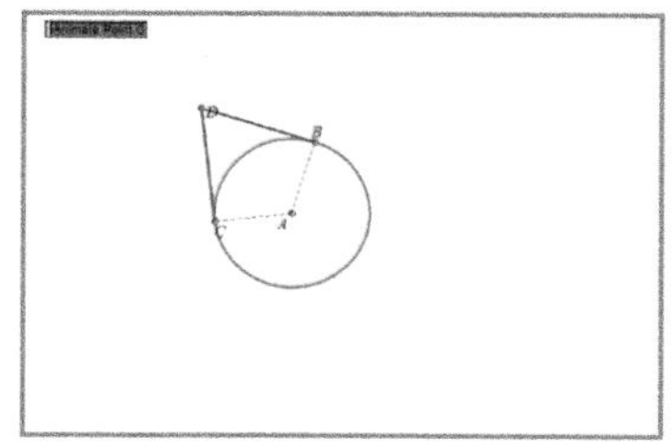

eLessons engage students and help build conceptual understanding of big ideas. *Use with Lessons 9-1 through 9-5 and 9-7.*

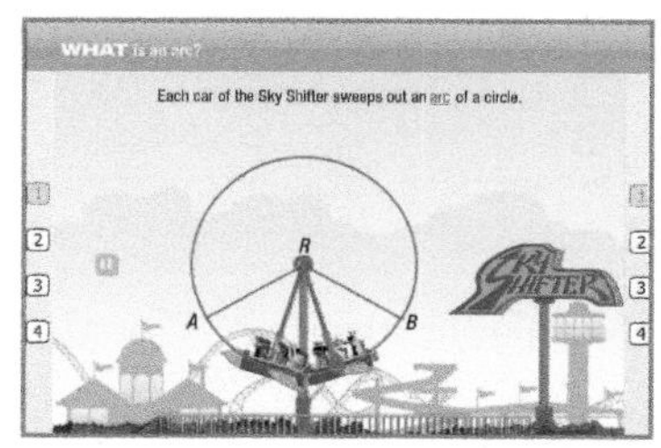

Animations help students make important connections through motion. *Use with Lessons 9-2 and Extend 9-5.*

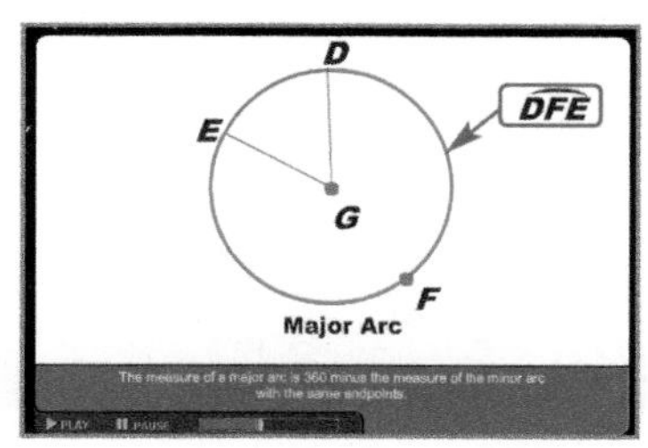

Time Management How long will it take to use these resources? Look for the clock in each lesson interleaf.

Introduce the Chapter

Mathematical Background

A circle is the locus of all points equidistant from a given point. Chords, diameters, and radii are all segments associated with circles. Proportional reasoning is used to find the areas of sectors and arc lengths of circles.

Essential Questions

At the end of this chapter, students should be able to answer the Essential Question.

How can circles be used? Sample answer: Circles can be used to model a circular object or to model an equal distance around a certain point.

Apply Math to the Real World

SCIENCE In this activity, students will use what they know about circles to explore the science of rainbows and why we generally only see an arc of a rainbow. Have students complete this activity individually or in small groups. MP 1

CHAPTER 9

Circles

THEN

You learned about special segments and angle relationships in triangles.

NOW

In this chapter, you will:

- Learn the relationships between central angles, arcs, and inscribed angles in a circle.
- Define and use secants and tangents.
- Use an equation to identify or describe a circle.

MP WHY

SCIENCE The actual shape of a rainbow is a complete circle. The portion of the circle that can be seen above the horizon is a special segment of a circle called an arc.

Use the Mathematical Practices to complete the activity.

1. Use Tools Use the Internet to learn more about the way in which a rainbow is created and why it is actually a full circle.

2. Reasoning If a rainbow is a full circle, why do you think you only see a portion of it? Can you think of a way that could be represented on a coordinate plane?

3. Modeling Use the Explore Circle tool to create a circle representative of a rainbow. Place the circle so that the *x*-axis represents the horizon as we see it and model the arc of the rainbow that we typically see.

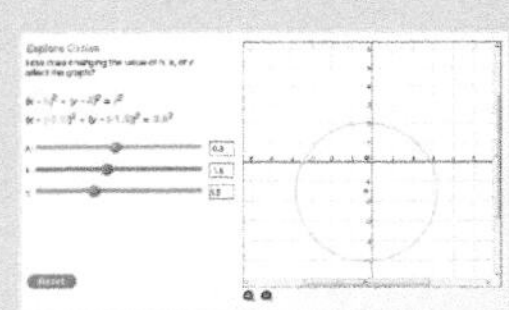

MacMag83/Alamy

ALEKS®

Your Student Success Tool ALEKS is an adaptive, personalized learning environment that identifies precisely what each student knows and is ready to learn—ensuring student success at all levels.

- **Formative Assessment:** Dynamic, detailed reports monitor students' progress toward standards mastery.
- **Automatic Differentiation:** Strengthen prerequisite skills and target individual learning gaps.
- **Personalized Instruction:** Supplement in-class instruction with personalized assessment and learning opportunities.

Go Online!

Chapter Project

Olympic Games Students use what they have learned about circles to complete a project. This chapter project addresses global awareness, as well as several specific skills identified as being essential to student success by the Framework for 21st Century Learning. MP 1, 3, 4, 8

Go Online to Guide Your Learning

Explore & Explain

Triangle Special Segments

Use the **Triangle Special Segments** tool to construct inscribed and circumscribed circles discussed in Lesson 9-1.

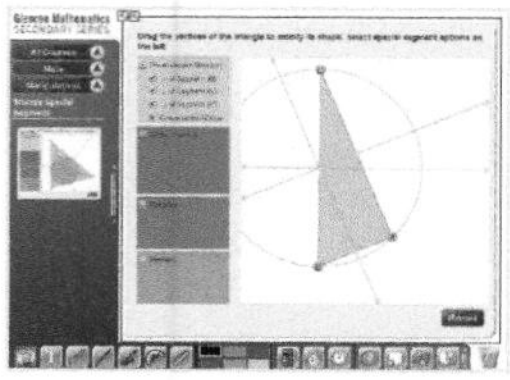

The Geometer's Sketchpad

Use the **The Geometer's Sketchpad** to explore the relationship between a circle's circumference and its diameter, the relationships in a circle between angles and the arcs they intercept, the properties of chords in a circle, and to construct two tangent segments to a circle and investigate their properties.

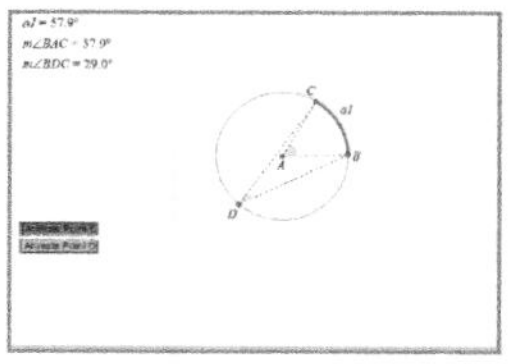

eBook

Interactive Student Guide

Before starting the chapter, answer the **Chapter Focus** preview questions. Check your answers as you complete each lesson. At the end of the chapter, try the **Performance Task**.

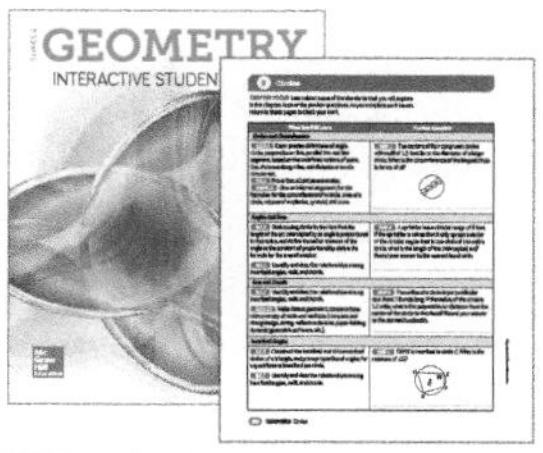

Organize

Foldables

Get organized! Before beginning this chapter, create this Foldable to help you organize your notes on circles.

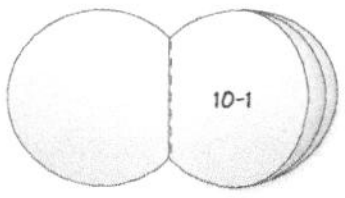

FOLDABLES

Collaborate

Chapter Project

In the **Olympic Games** project, you will use what you have learned about circles to complete a project that addresses global awareness.

Focus

LEARNSMART

Need help studying? Complete the **Connecting Algebra and Geometry Through Coordinates** domain in LearnSmart to review for the chapter test.

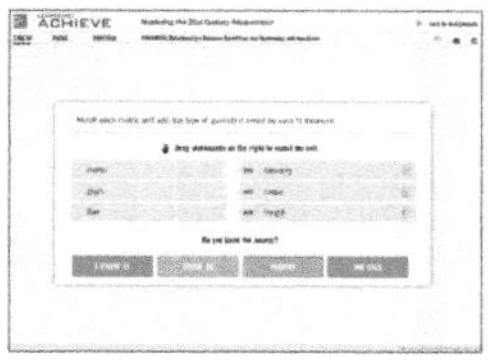

ALEKS

You can use the **Polygons and Circles** topic in ALEKS to explore what you know about circles and what you are ready to learn.*

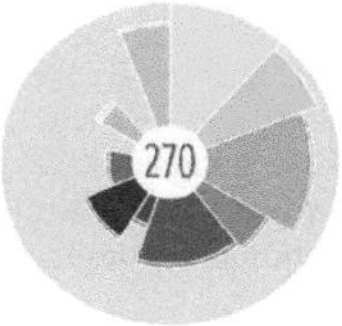

* Ask your teacher if this is part of your program.

Dinah Zike's FOLDABLES®

Focus Students write about circles and angles and the lines that are related to them.

Teach After students make their Foldable, have them label the flaps to correspond with the eight lessons in this chapter. Have students take notes about circles and about angles, arcs, chords, tangents, secants, and segments of circles. Encourage students to apply these concepts by drawing examples and applying the mathematical concepts associated with them.

When to Use It Instruct students to take notes while reading each lesson and listening to instruction. They should include definitions of terms and key concepts, as well as diagrams to illustrate each term.

Go Online!

Creating Vocabulary Flashcards

Not all flashcards are created equal! In this video, Dinah Zike discusses strategies and best practices when creating vocabulary flashcards. MP 5

Get Ready for the Chapter

RtI Response to Intervention

Use the Concept Check results and the Intervention Planner chart to help you determine your Response to Intervention.

Intervention Planner

TIER 1 On Level OL

IF students miss 25% of the exercises or less,

THEN choose a resource:

Go Online!
- Skills Practice, Chapter 8
- Chapter Project
- Self-Check Quizzes

TIER 2 Approaching Level AL

IF students miss 50% of the exercises,

THEN choose a resource:

Go Online!
- Study Guide and Intervention, Ch. 8
- Extra Examples
- Personal Tutors
- Homework Help

Quick Review Math Handbook

TIER 3 Intensive Intervention

IF students miss 75% of the exercises,

THEN Use *Math Triumphs, Geometry*

Go Online!
- Extra Examples
- Personal Tutors
- Homework Help
- Review Vocabulary

Go Online! for Vocabulary Review Games and key vocabulary in 13 languages.

Get Ready for the Chapter

Connecting Concepts

Concept Check

Review the concepts used in this chapter by answering the questions below.

1. If you are asked to find 26% of a number, what is the first step you need to take? **Change 26% to a decimal.**
2. You are asked to find 15% of 35. You convert 15% to 0.15. What is your next step? **Multiply 0.15 by 35.**
3. Classify the triangle shown. **isosceles right triangle**
4. What fact about special right triangles can you use to solve for x?

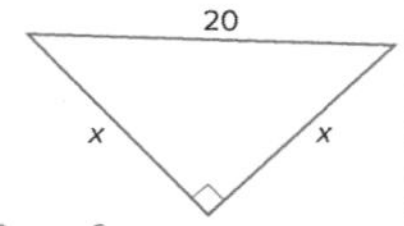

5. What is another way you can solve for x? **Pythagorean Theorem; $x^2 + x^2 = 20^2$**
6. What formula would you use to solve $x^2 + 4x - 40 = 0$? **Quadratic Formula**
7. What process is used to derive the Quadratic Formula? **completing the square**
8. Given a rectangle that is 3 feet wide and 8 feet long, what equation would allow you to determine length of a diagonal that would cut the triangle into two right triangles? $d^2 = 3^2 + 8^2$

4. **The triangle is a 45°-45°-90° right triangle, so the length of a leg is $\frac{\sqrt{2}}{2}$ times the length of the hypotenuse.**

Performance Task Preview

You can use the concepts and skills in the chapter to design a circular badge that circumscribes a circle around different polygons. Understanding circles will help you finish the Performance Task at the end of the chapter.

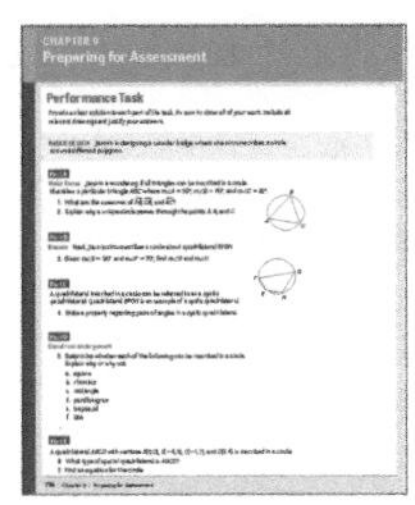

In this Performance Task you will:
- make sense of problems
- reason abstractly and quantitatively
- construct an argument

New Vocabulary

English		Español
circle	p. 643	círculo
center	p. 643	centro
radius	p. 643	radio
chord	p. 643	cuerda
diameter	p. 643	diámetro
circumference	p. 645	circunferencia
pi (π)	p. 645	pi (π)
inscribed	p. 646	inscrito
circumscribed	p. 646	circunscrito
central angle	p. 652	ángulo central
arc	p. 652	arco
inscribed angle	p. 669	ángulo inscrito
intercepted arc	p. 669	arco intersecado
tangent	p. 678	tangente
secant	p. 687	secante
focus	p. 703	foco
directrix	p. 703	directriz

Review Vocabulary

coplanar coplanar points that lie in the same plane

degree grado $\frac{1}{360}$ of the circular rotation about a point

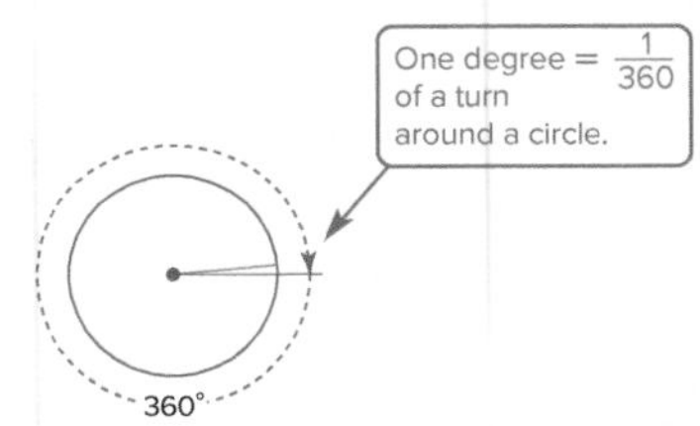

Key Vocabulary ELL

Introduce the key vocabulary in the chapter using the routine below.

Define Concentric circles are coplanar circles that share the same center.

Example

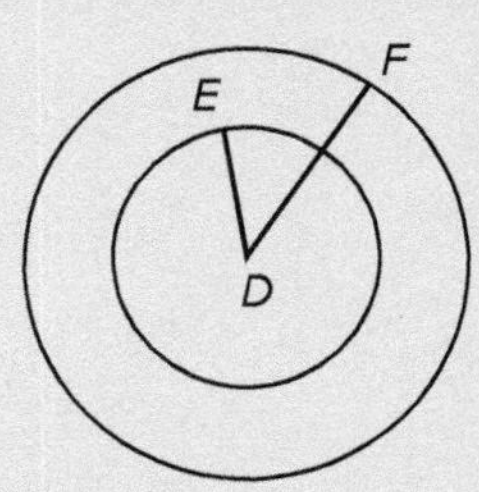

Ask **Are coplanar circles similar or congruent? Explain.** The circles are similar because they have the same shape. The circles are not congruent because they have different radii.

LESSON 9-1

Circles and Circumference

SUGGESTED PACING (DAYS)

90 min.	0.5
45 min.	1.0
	Instruction

Track Your Progress

Objectives

1 Identify and use parts of circles.

2 Solve problems involving the circumference of a circle.

Mathematical Background

A circle is the locus of all points in a plane equidistant from a given point. Any segment with endpoints on the circle is a chord. A chord that contains the center of the circle is a diameter. Any segment with endpoints that are the center and a point on the circle is a radius. For a circumference C and a diameter d or a radius r, $C = \pi d$ or $C = 2\pi r$.

THEN

G.SRT.8 Use trigonometric ratios and the Pythagorean Theorem to solve right triangles in applied problems.

NOW

G.CO.1 Know precise definitions of angle, circle, perpendicular line, parallel line, and line segment, based on the undefined notions of point, line, distance along a line, and distance around a circular arc.

G.C.1 Identify and describe relationships among inscribed angles, radii, and chords. Include the relationship between central, inscribed, and circumscribed angles; inscribed angles on a diameter are right angles; the radius of a circle is perpendicular to the tangent where the radius intersects the circle.

NEXT

G.GMD.1 Give an informal argument for the formulas for the circumference of a circle, area of a circle, volume of a cylinder, pyramid, and cone.

Go Online! All of these resources and more are available at connectED.mcgraw-hill.com

eLessons utilize the power of your interactive whiteboard in an engaging way. Use **Chords, Arcs, and Angles**, Screens 1–2, to introduce the concepts in this lesson.

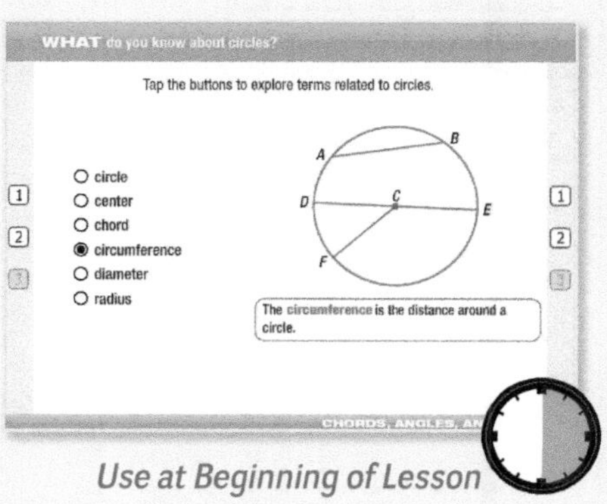

Use at Beginning of Lesson

eToolkit allows students to explore and enhance their understanding of math concepts. Use the Triangle Special Segments tool to construct circumcircles.

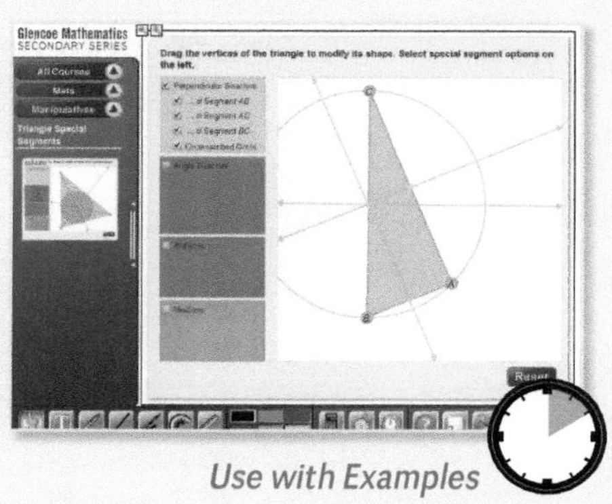

Use with Examples

Use The Geometer's Sketchpad to explore the relationship between a circle's circumference and its diameter.

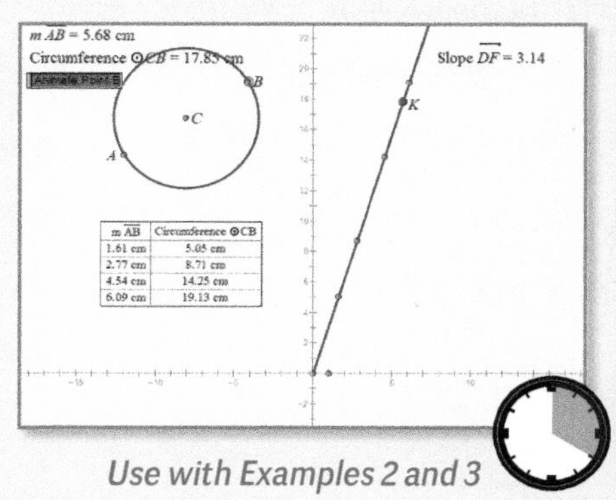

Use with Examples 2 and 3

OER Using Open Educational Resources

Animations Have students explore the relationship between circumference and radius using the *Circle Tool* on the **NCTM** Illumination website. *Use as in-class activity*

Go Online!

connectED.mcgraw-hill.com

Worksheets

Differentiate Your Resources

Extra Practice Additional practice or homework; Skills Practice is best for approaching-level students and Practice is best for on-level and beyond-level students

Skills Practice

AL OL ELL

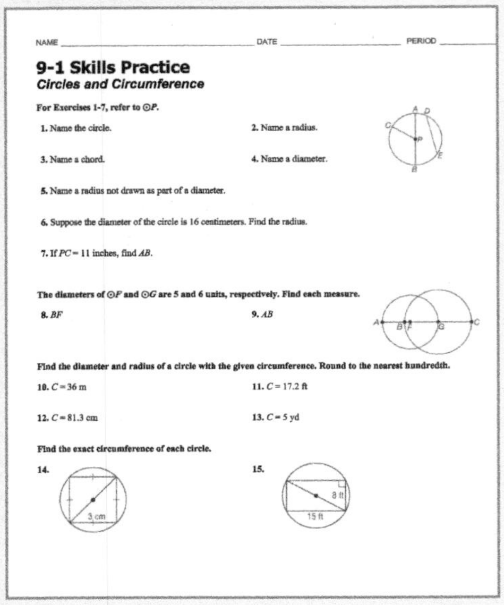

NAME ________ DATE ________ PERIOD ________

9-1 Skills Practice
Circles and Circumference

For Exercises 1–7, refer to ⊙P.

1. Name the circle.
2. Name a radius.
3. Name a chord.
4. Name a diameter.
5. Name a radius not drawn as part of a diameter.
6. Suppose the diameter of the circle is 16 centimeters. Find the radius.
7. If $PC = 11$ inches, find AB.

The diameters of ⊙F and ⊙G are 5 and 6 units, respectively. Find each measure.

8. BF
9. AB

Find the diameter and radius of a circle with the given circumference. Round to the nearest hundredth.

10. $C = 36$ m
11. $C = 17.2$ ft
12. $C = 81.3$ cm
13. $C = 5$ yd

Find the exact circumference of each circle.

14.
15.

Practice

AL OL BL ELL

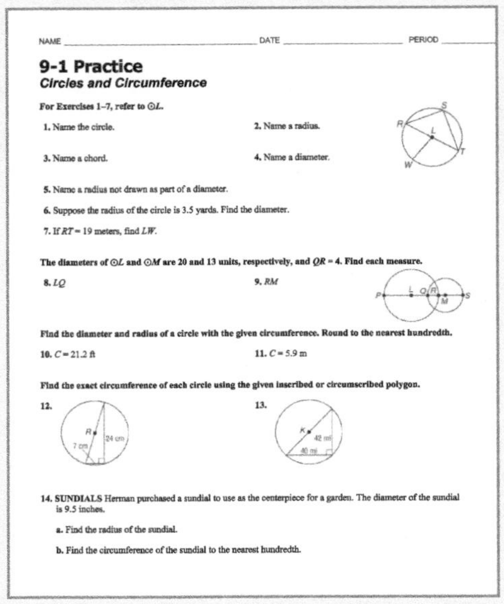

NAME ________ DATE ________ PERIOD ________

9-1 Practice
Circles and Circumference

For Exercises 1–7, refer to ⊙L.

1. Name the circle.
2. Name a radius.
3. Name a chord.
4. Name a diameter.
5. Name a radius not drawn as part of a diameter.
6. Suppose the radius of the circle is 3.5 yards. Find the diameter.
7. If $RT = 19$ meters, find LW.

The diameters of ⊙L and ⊙M are 20 and 13 units, respectively, and $QR = 4$. Find each measure.

8. LQ
9. RM

Find the diameter and radius of a circle with the given circumference. Round to the nearest hundredth.

10. $C = 21.2$ ft
11. $C = 5.9$ m

Find the exact circumference of each circle using the given inscribed or circumscribed polygon.

12.
13.

14. **SUNDIALS** Herman purchased a sundial to use as the centerpiece for a garden. The diameter of the sundial is 9.5 inches.
   a. Find the radius of the sundial.
   b. Find the circumference of the sundial to the nearest hundredth.

Word Problem Practice

AL OL BL ELL

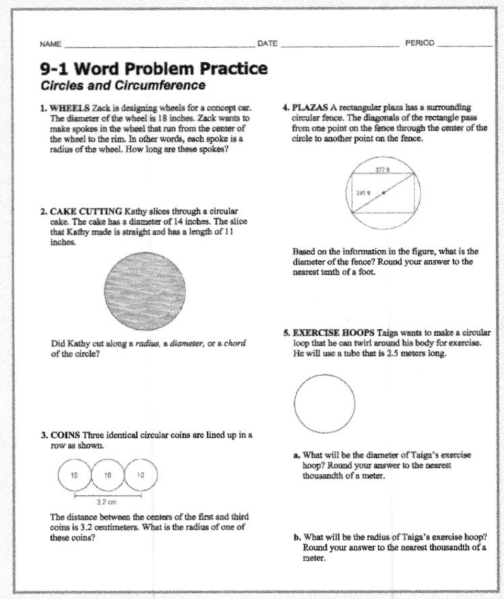

NAME ________ DATE ________ PERIOD ________

9-1 Word Problem Practice
Circles and Circumference

1. **WHEELS** Zack is designing wheels for a concept car. The diameter of the wheel is 18 inches. Zack wants to make spokes in the wheel that run from the center of the wheel to the rim. In other words, each spoke is a radius of the wheel. How long are these spokes?

2. **CAKE CUTTING** Kathy slices through a circular cake. The cake has a diameter of 14 inches. The slice that Kathy made is straight and has a length of 11 inches.

   Did Kathy cut along a *radius*, a *diameter*, or a *chord* of the circle?

3. **COINS** Three identical circular coins are lined up in a row as shown.

   The distance between the centers of the first and third coins is 3.2 centimeters. What is the radius of one of these coins?

4. **PLAZAS** A rectangular plaza has a surrounding circular fence. The diagonals of the rectangle pass from one point on the fence through the center of the circle to another point on the fence.

   Based on the information in the figure, what is the diameter of the fence? Round your answer to the nearest tenth of a foot.

5. **EXERCISE HOOPS** Taiga wants to make a circular loop that he can twirl around his body for exercise. He will use a tube that is 2.5 meters long.
   a. What will be the diameter of Taiga's exercise hoop? Round your answer to the nearest thousandth of a meter.
   b. What will be the radius of Taiga's exercise hoop? Round your answer to the nearest thousandth of a meter.

Intervention Reteaching and vocabulary activities that can be used with struggling or absent students and as ELL support

Study Guide and Intervention

AL OL ELL

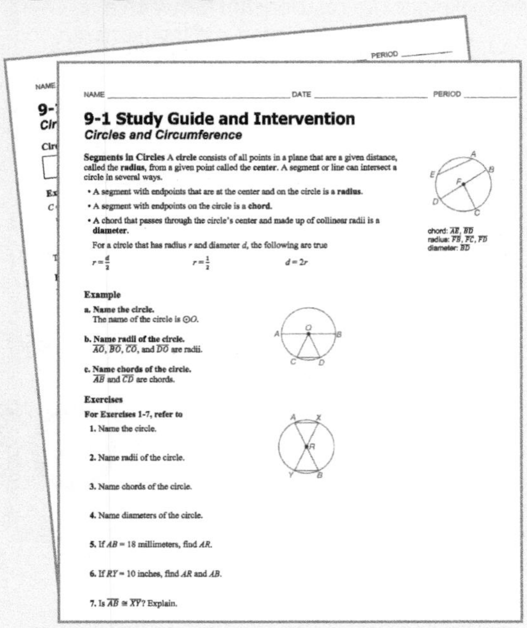

NAME ________ DATE ________ PERIOD ________

9-1 Study Guide and Intervention
Circles and Circumference

Segments in Circles A **circle** consists of all points in a plane that are a given distance, called the **radius**, from a given point called the **center**. A segment or line can intersect a circle in several ways.

- A segment with endpoints that are at the center and on the circle is a **radius**.
- A segment with endpoints on the circle is a **chord**.
- A chord that passes through the circle's center and made up of collinear radii is a **diameter**.

For a circle that has radius r and diameter d, the following are true

$r = \frac{d}{2}$ $r = \frac{1}{2}$ $d = 2r$

chord: $\overline{AE}$, $\overline{BD}$
radius: $\overline{FB}$, $\overline{FC}$, $\overline{FD}$
diameter: $\overline{BD}$

Example

a. Name the circle.
The name of the circle is ⊙O.

b. Name radii of the circle.
$\overline{AO}$, $\overline{BO}$, $\overline{CO}$, and $\overline{DO}$ are radii.

c. Name chords of the circle.
$\overline{AB}$ and $\overline{CD}$ are chords.

Exercises

For Exercises 1–7, refer to

1. Name the circle.
2. Name radii of the circle.
3. Name chords of the circle.
4. Name diameters of the circle.
5. If $AB = 18$ millimeters, find AR.
6. If $RY = 10$ inches, find AR and AB.
7. Is $\overline{AB} \cong \overline{XY}$? Explain.

Study Notebook

AL OL BL ELL

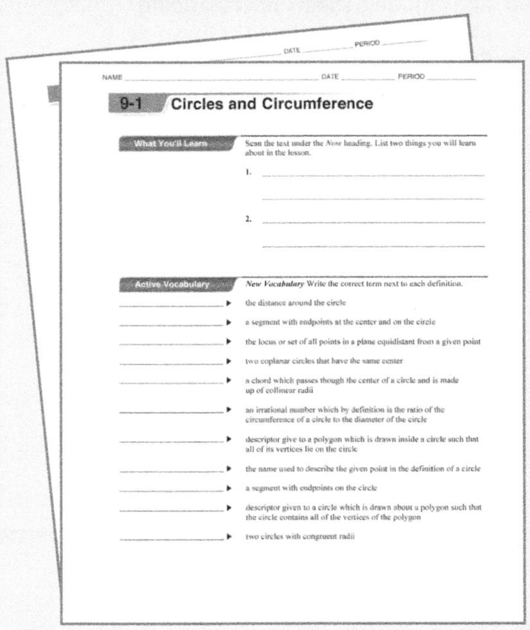

NAME ________ DATE ________ PERIOD ________

9-1 Circles and Circumference

What You'll Learn Scan the text under the *Now* heading. List two things you will learn about in the lesson.

1.
2.

Active Vocabulary *New Vocabulary* Write the correct term next to each definition.

- the distance around the circle
- a segment with endpoints at the center and on the circle
- the locus or set of all points in a plane equidistant from a given point
- two coplanar circles that have the same center
- a chord which passes though the center of a circle and is made up of collinear radii
- an irrational number which by definition is the ratio of the circumference of a circle to the diameter of the circle
- descriptor give to a polygon which is drawn inside a circle such that all of its vertices lie on the circle
- the name used to describe the given point in the definition of a circle
- a segment with endpoints on the circle
- descriptor given to a circle which is drawn about a polygon such that the circle contains all of the vertices of the polygon
- two circles with congruent radii

Extension Activities that can be used to extend lesson concepts

Enrichment

OL BL ELL

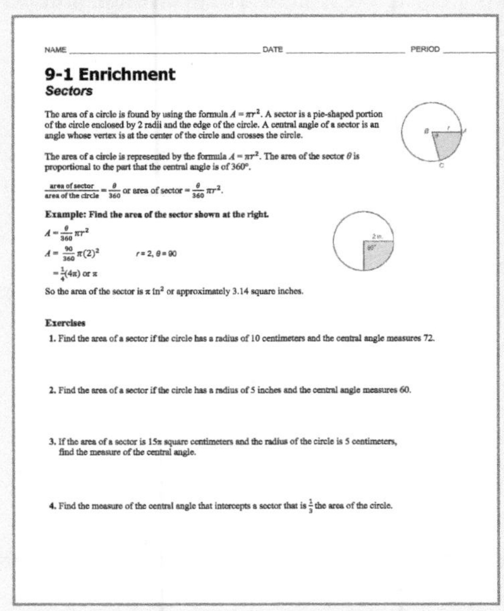

NAME ________ DATE ________ PERIOD ________

9-1 Enrichment
Sectors

The area of a circle is found by using the formula $A = \pi r^2$. A sector is a pie-shaped portion of the circle enclosed by 2 radii and the edge of the circle. A central angle of a sector is an angle whose vertex is at the center of the circle and crosses the circle.

The area of a circle is represented by the formula $A = \pi r^2$. The area of the sector θ is proportional to the part that the central angle is of 360°.

$\frac{\text{area of sector}}{\text{area of the circle}} = \frac{\theta}{360}$ or area of sector $= \frac{\theta}{360}\pi r^2$.

Example: Find the area of the sector shown at the right.

$A = \frac{\theta}{360}\pi r^2$

$A = \frac{90}{360}\pi(2)^2$ $r = 2, \theta = 90$

$= \frac{1}{4}(4\pi)$ or π

So the area of the sector is π in^2 or approximately 3.14 square inches.

Exercises

1. Find the area of a sector if the circle has a radius of 10 centimeters and the central angle measures 72.
2. Find the area of a sector if the circle has a radius of 5 inches and the central angle measures 60.
3. If the area of a sector is 15π square centimeters and the radius of the circle is 5 centimeters, find the measure of the central angle.
4. Find the measure of the central angle that intercepts a sector that is $\frac{1}{3}$ the area of the circle.

LESSON 1

Circles and Circumference

Then

- You identified and used parts of parallelograms.

Now

1. Identify and use parts of circles.
2. Solve problems involving the circumference of a circle.

Why?

- The maxAir ride shown speeds back and forth and rotates counterclockwise. At times, the riders are upside down 140 feet above the ground experiencing "airtime"—a feeling of weightlessness. The ride's width—or *diameter*—is 44 feet. You can find the distance that a rider travels in one rotation by using this measure.

New Vocabulary
circle
center
radius
chord
diameter
concentric circles
circumference
pi (π)
inscribed
circumscribed

Mathematical Practices
4 Model with mathematics.
1 Make sense of problems and persevere in solving them.

Content Standards
G.CO.1 Know precise definitions of angle, circle, perpendicular line, parallel line, and line segment, based on the undefined notions of point, line, distance along a line, and distance around a circular arc.
G.C.1 Prove that all circles are similar.
G.GMD.1 Give an informal argument for the formulas for the circumference of a circle, area of a circle, volume of a cylinder, pyramid, and cone. *Use dissection arguments, Cavalieri's principle, and informal limit arguments.*

1 Segments in Circles

A **circle** is the locus or set of all points in a plane equidistant from a given point called the **center** of the circle.

Segments that intersect a circle have special names.

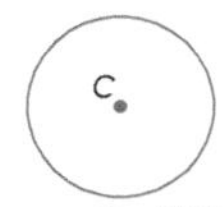

Circle C or ⊙C

Key Concept Special Segments in a Circle

A **radius** (plural radii) is a segment with endpoints at the center and on the circle.
Examples $\overline{CD}$, $\overline{CE}$, and $\overline{CF}$ are radii of ⊙C.

A **chord** is a segment with endpoints on the circle.
Examples $\overline{AB}$ and $\overline{DE}$ are chords of ⊙C.

A **diameter** of a circle is a chord that passes through the center and is made up of collinear radii.
Example $\overline{DE}$ is a diameter of ⊙C. Diameter $\overline{DE}$ is made up of collinear radii $\overline{CD}$ and $\overline{CE}$.

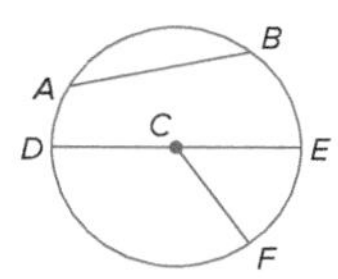

G.CO.1

Example 1 Identify Segments in a Circle

a. Name the circle and identify a radius.

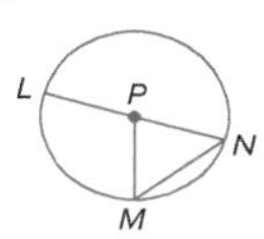

The circle has a center at *P*, so it is named circle *P*, or ⊙*P*. Three radii are shown: $\overline{PL}$, $\overline{PN}$, and $\overline{PM}$.

b. Identify a chord and a diameter of the circle.

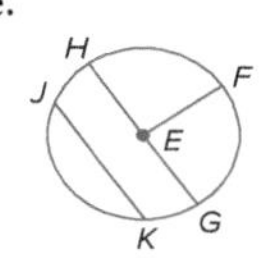

Two chords are shown: $\overline{JK}$ and $\overline{HG}$. $\overline{HG}$ goes through the center, so $\overline{HG}$ is a diameter.

Guided Practice

1. Name the circle, a radius, a chord, and a diameter of the circle.
circle *X*; radius $\overline{XV}$, $\overline{XT}$, $\overline{XU}$, or $\overline{XZ}$; chord $\overline{RS}$, $\overline{TZ}$; diameter $\overline{TZ}$

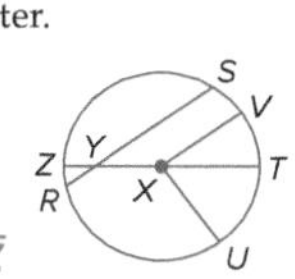

MP Mathematical Practice Strategies

Attend to precision.
Encourage students to use clear definitions in class discussions. For example, in Guided Practice 1, ask the following questions:

- What is the center of the circle? *X*, so the circle is named circle *X*.
- Which line segments have their endpoints at the center and on the circle? radii $\overline{XV}$, $\overline{XT}$, $\overline{XU}$, or $\overline{XZ}$
- Which line segments go from on the circle to on the circle but not through the center? chords $\overline{RS}$, $\overline{TZ}$
- Which line segments go from the circle to the circle but through the center? diameter $\overline{ZT}$

Launch

Have students read the Why? section of the lesson. Ask:

- What does the distance a rider travels in one rotation represent? the circumference of the circular ride
- How could a wheel be used to measure distance? Find the circumference of the wheel and multiply by the number of rotations made in the distance to be measured.
- How is the concept of measuring distance with a wheel applied in real life? Sample answer: Odometers use wheel rotation to record mileage, surveyors use a wheel to measure distance, and so on.
- Why might measuring with a wheel be better than measuring with a meterstick or a tape measure? Sample answer: A wheel measurement is continuous, but a meterstick or tape measure has to be picked up and moved. Also, a wheel can measure around curves, but a meter stick or tape measure is not as accurate around curves.

Teach

Ask the scaffolded questions for each example to build conceptual understanding for students at all levels.

1 Segments in Circles

Example 1 Identify Segments in a Circle

AL In part **a**, how do we know if a segment is a radius? It has an endpoint at the center of the circle and an endpoint on the circle.

OL In part **a**, what is a diameter of circle *P*? $\overline{LN}$

BL In part **b**, what is a radius that is also part of a diameter? Sample answer: $\overline{EH}$

(continued on the next page)

Go Online!

Interactive Whiteboard
Use the *eLesson*, *Lesson Presentation*, or *Interactive Classroom* to present this lesson.

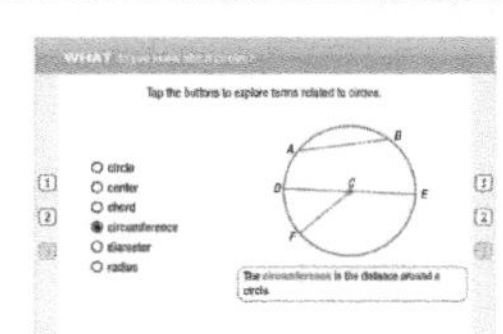

Need Another Example?

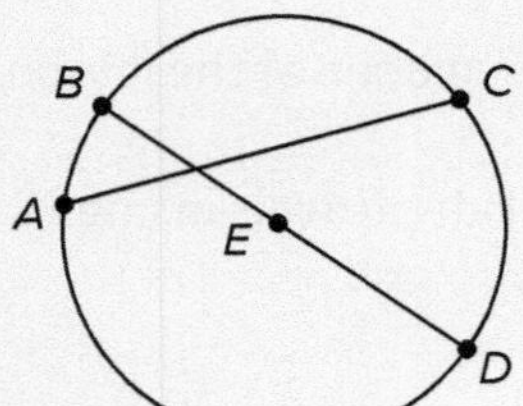

a. Name the circle and identify a radius.
Name: circle E or $\odot E$
Two radii shown: $\overline{EB}$ and $\overline{ED}$

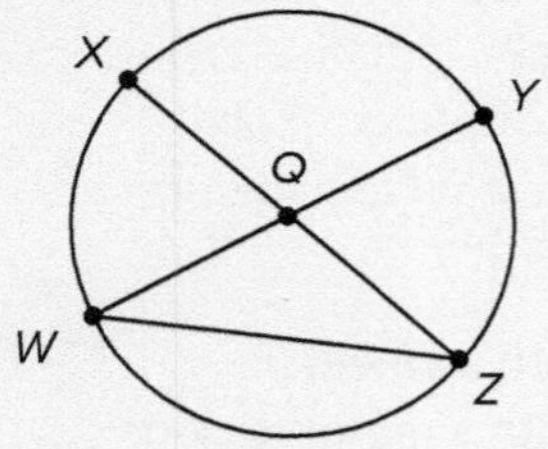

b. Identify a chord and a diameter of the circle.
Three chords: $\overline{WY}$, $\overline{XZ}$, and $\overline{WZ}$
Two diameters: $\overline{WY}$ and $\overline{XZ}$

MP Teaching the Mathematical Practices

Precision Mathematically proficient students use clear definitions in discussion with others and in their own reasoning. Encourage students to use mathematical vocabulary properly, both spoken in class and in writing assignments.

Example 2 Find Radius and Diameter

AL If the radius of a circle is 5 centimeters, what is the diameter? 10 cm

OL If the diameter of a circle is 15 inches, what is the radius of the circle? 7.5 in.

BL If the radius of a circle is $x + 3$ and the diameter is $3x + 1$, what is x? 5

Need Another Example?

If $RT = 21$ cm, what is the length of $\overline{QV}$?

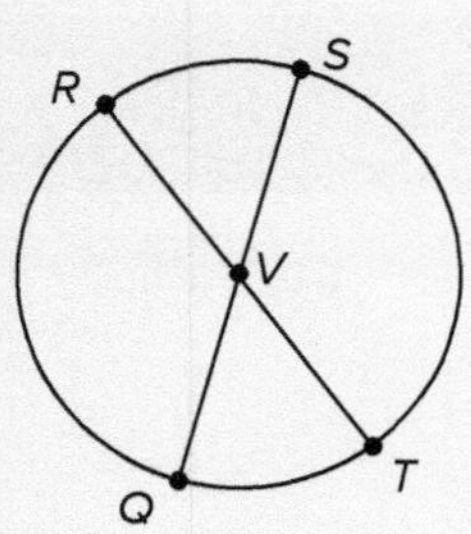

10.5 cm

Reading Math

MP Precision The words *radius* and *diameter* are used to describe lengths as well as segments. Because a circle has many different radii and diameters, the phrases *the radius* and *the diameter* refer to lengths rather than segments.

By definition, the distance from the center of a circle to any point on the circle is always the same. Therefore, all radii r of a circle are congruent. Because a diameter d is composed of two radii, all diameters of a circle are also congruent.

Key Concept Radius and Diameter Relationships

If a circle has radius r and diameter d, the following relationships are true.

Radius Formula $r = \frac{d}{2}$ or $r = \frac{1}{2}d$ **Diameter Formula** $d = 2r$

G.CO.1

Example 2 Find Radius and Diameter

If $QV = 8$ inches, what is the diameter of $\odot Q$?

$d = 2r$ Diameter Formula

$= 2(8)$ or 16 Substitute and simplify.

The diameter of $\odot Q$ is 16 inches.

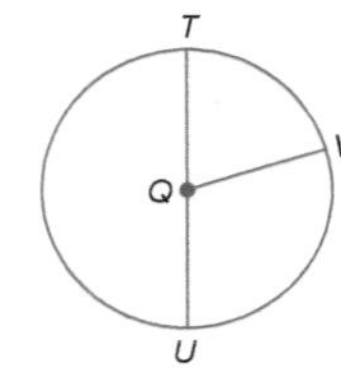

Guided Practice

2A. If $TU = 14$ feet, what is the radius of $\odot Q$? 7 ft

2B. If $QT = 11$ meters, what is QU? 11 m

As with other figures, pairs of circles can be congruent, similar, or share other special relationships.

Review Vocabulary ELL

coplanar points that lie in the same plane

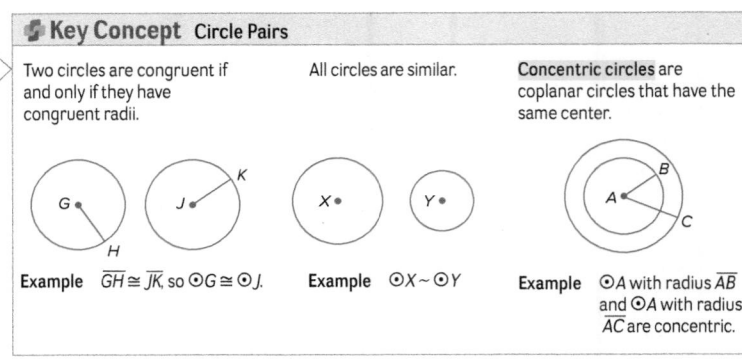

Key Concept Circle Pairs

Two circles are congruent if and only if they have congruent radii.

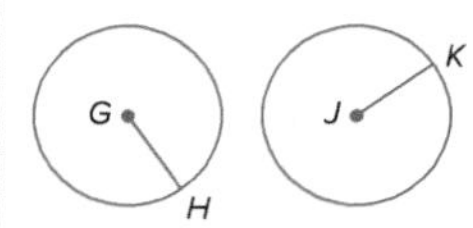

Example $\overline{GH} \cong \overline{JK}$, so $\odot G \cong \odot J$.

All circles are similar.

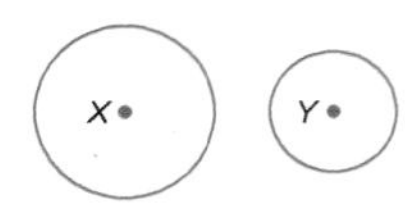

Example $\odot X \sim \odot Y$

Concentric circles are coplanar circles that have the same center.

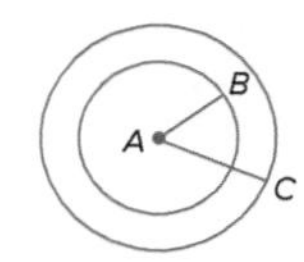

Example $\odot A$ with radius $\overline{AB}$ and $\odot A$ with radius $\overline{AC}$ are concentric.

You will prove that all circles are similar in Exercise 52.

Two circles can intersect in two different ways.

2 Points of Intersection	1 Point of Intersection	No Points of Intersection
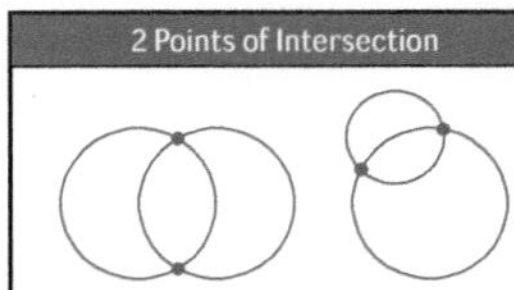	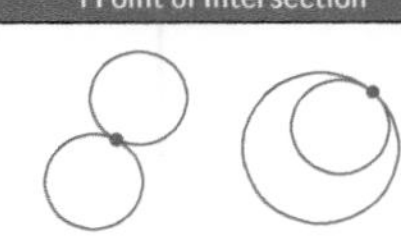	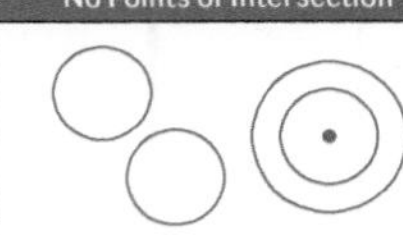

Differentiated Instruction ELL

English Language Learners Have students write about parts of a circle and its circumference in their own words. They can write a paragraph that explains each vocabulary term and the relationship of the terms to each other, or they can list the terms and write a brief explanation and provide an example for each. Students can then be arranged in pairs to quiz each other by giving a definition and asking for the word and an example, or giving the word, and asking for the definition and example.

Go Online!

Circles and circumference are widely used in problems arising in everyday life, society, and the workplace. If you need extra practice, look for **Worksheets** in ConnectED.

The segment connecting the centers of the two intersecting circles contains the radii of the two circles.

G.CO.1

Example 3 Find Measures in Intersecting Circles

The diameter of ⊙S is 30 units, the diameter of ⊙R is 20 units, and $DS = 9$ units. Find CD.

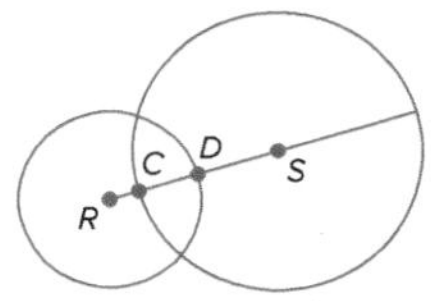

Because the diameter of ⊙S is 30, $CS = 15$. $\overline{CD}$ is part of radius $\overline{CS}$.

$CD + DS = CS$	Segment Addition Postulate
$CD + 9 = 15$	Substitution
$CD = 6$	Subtract 9 from each side.

Guided Practice

3. Use the diagram above to find RC. 4 units

2 Circumference

The **circumference** of a circle is the distance around the circle. By definition, the ratio $\frac{C}{d}$ is an irrational number called **pi (π)**. Two formulas for circumference can be derived by using this definition.

$\frac{C}{d} = \pi$	Definition of pi
$C = \pi d$	Multiply each side by d.
$C = \pi(2r)$	$d = 2r$
$C = 2\pi r$	Simplify.

Key Concept Circumference

Words	If a circle has diameter d or radius r, the circumference C equals the diameter times pi or twice the radius times pi.
Symbols	$C = \pi d$ or $C = 2\pi r$

Real-World Link

The world's highest tennis court doubles as the helipad of the Burj Al Arab hotel in the United Arab Emirates. The helipad has a diameter of 79 feet and is nearly 700 feet high.

Source: Burj Al Arab, Emporis Buildings

ErikdeGraaf/iStock/Getty Images

G.CO.1

Real-World Example 4 Find Circumference

TENNIS Find the circumference of the helipad described at the left.

$C = \pi d$	Circumference Formula
$= \pi(79)$	Substitution
$= 79\pi$	Simplify.
≈ 248.19	Use a calculator.

The circumference of the helipad is 79π feet or about 248.19 feet.

Guided Practice

Find the circumference of each circle described. Round to the nearest hundredth.

4A. radius = 2.5 centimeters 15.71 cm **4B.** diameter = 16 feet 50.27 ft

Example 3 Find Measures in Intersecting Circles

AL What is RS? 19 units

OL What is RC? 4 units

BL What is the width of the figure formed by the circles through the centers of both circles? 44 units

Need Another Example?

The diameter of ⊙X is 22 units, the diameter of ⊙Y is 16 units, and $WZ = 5$ units. Find XY. 14 units

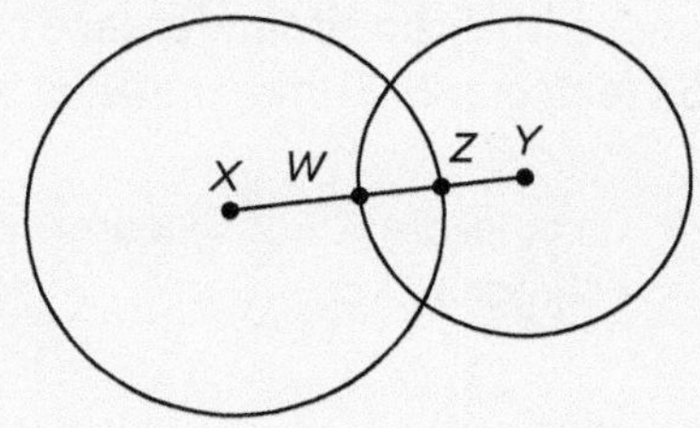

2 Circumference

Example 4 Find Circumference

AL To what measure in polygons does circumference correspond? perimeter

OL If the radius of a circle is 9 feet, what is the circumference of the circle? about 56.5 ft

BL The circumference of a circle is 33 centimeters. What is the diameter of the circle to the nearest tenth? 10.5 cm

Need Another Example?

Crop Circles A series of crop circles was discovered in Alberta, Canada, on September 4, 1999. The largest of the three circles had a radius of 30 feet. Find its circumference. ≈188.50 ft

Watch Out!

Radius or Diameter In problems involving circles, be careful to check if information is given about the radius or the diameter.

Differentiated Instruction OL BL

Extension Have students answer the following question. An asteroid hit Earth and created a huge round crater. Scientists measured the distance around the crater as 78.5 miles. What was the diameter of the crater? ≈25 miles

Example 5 Find Diameter and Radius

AL If the circumference is 345 millimeters, what is the radius? about 54.9 mm

OL What is the formula for the circumference in terms of radius r? $C = 2\pi r$

BL If the circumference of a circle is $2\pi x + 6\pi$, what is the radius? $x + 3$

Need Another Example?
Find the diameter and radius of a circle to the nearest hundredth if the circumference of the circle is 65.4 feet. $d \approx 20.82$ ft; $r \approx 10.41$ ft

Example 6 Circumference of Circumscribed Polygons

AL Because the square is *inscribed* in the circle, what is the relationship in terms of the circle? The circle is circumscribed about the square.

OL Can you find the circumference of a circle using any inscribed polygon? No; Only for cases where we can use lengths on the polygon to find the diameter or radius of the circle.

BL What other method besides the Pythagorean Theorem could we use to solve this problem? Because we know the triangle is an isosceles right triangle (because the inscribed figure is a square), we can use the relationship between the hypotenuse and a side of a 45°-45°-90° triangle to find the length of the diameter; then find the circumference.

Need Another Example?
Find the exact circumference of $\odot K$. 6π units

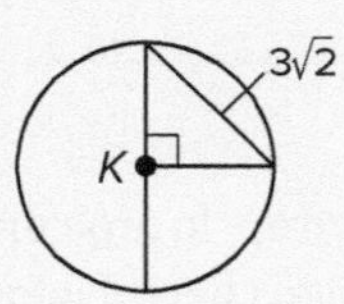

These circumference formulas can also be used to determine the diameter and radius of a circle when the circumference is given.

G.CO.1

Example 5 Find Diameter and Radius

Find the diameter and radius of a circle to the nearest hundredth if the circumference of the circle is 106.4 millimeters.

$C = \pi d$	Circumference Formula	$r = \frac{1}{2}d$	Radius Formula
$106.4 = \pi d$	Substitution	$\approx \frac{1}{2}(33.87)$	$d \approx 33.87$
$\frac{106.4}{\pi} = d$	Divide each side by π.	≈ 16.94 mm	Use a calculator.
$33.87 \text{ mm} \approx d$	Use a calculator.		

Study Tip
Levels of Accuracy Because π is irrational, its value cannot be given as a terminating decimal. Using a value of 3 for π provides a quick estimate in calculations. Using a value of 3.14 or $\frac{22}{7}$ provides a closer approximation. For the most accurate approximation, use the π key on a calculator. Unless stated otherwise, assume that in this text, a calculator with a π key was used to generate answers.

Guided Practice

5. Find the diameter and radius of a circle to the nearest hundredth if the circumference of the circle is 77.8 centimeters. 24.76 cm; 12.38 cm

A polygon is **inscribed** in a circle if all of its vertices lie on the circle. A circle is **circumscribed** about a polygon if it contains all the vertices of the polygon.

- Quadrilateral *LMNP* is *inscribed in* $\odot K$.
- Circle *K* is *circumscribed about* quadrilateral *LMNP*.

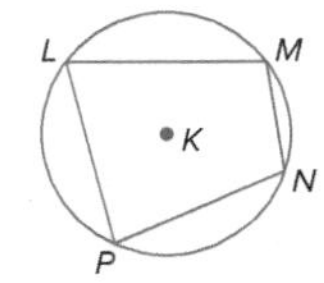

G.CO.1

Example 6 Circumference of Circumscribed Polygons

A square with side length of 9 inches is inscribed in $\odot J$. Find the exact circumference of $\odot J$.

Study Tip
Circumcircle A *circumcircle* is a circle that passes through all of the vertices of a polygon.

You need to find the diameter of the circle and use it to calculate the circumference.

First, draw a diagram. The diagonal of the square is the diameter of the circle and the hypotenuse of a right triangle.

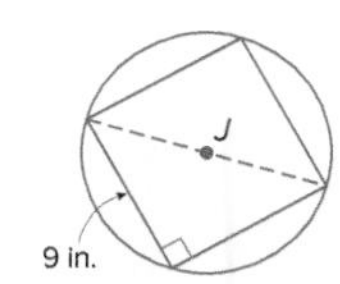

$a^2 + b^2 = c^2$	Pythagorean Theorem
$9^2 + 9^2 = c^2$	Substitution
$162 = c^2$	Simplify.
$9\sqrt{2} = c$	Take the positive square root of each side.

The diameter of the circle is $9\sqrt{2}$ inches.

Find the circumference in terms of π by substituting $9\sqrt{2}$ for d in $C = \pi d$. The exact circumference is $9\pi\sqrt{2}$ inches.

Guided Practice

Find the exact circumference of each circle by using the given polygon.

6A. inscribed right triangle with legs 7 meters and 3 meters long $\pi\sqrt{58}$ m

6B. circumscribed square with side 10 feet long $10\pi\sqrt{2}$ ft

Differentiated Instruction AL OL

Visual/Spatial Learners Instruct students to use a piece of string to estimate the circumference of discs or cylinders. Then have students measure the diameter of the object. Review the formulas for finding circumference by using the diameter and the radius. Have students find the circumference mathematically, using the diameter and then the radius. Have students compare their calculations with the estimate they found by using the string.

Go Online!

The most up-to-date resources available for your program can be found at connectED.mcgraw-hill.com.

Check Your Understanding

○ = Step-by-Step Solutions begin on page R14.

Go Online! for a Self-Check Quiz

Examples 1–2 G.CO.1

For Exercises 1–4, refer to ⊙N.

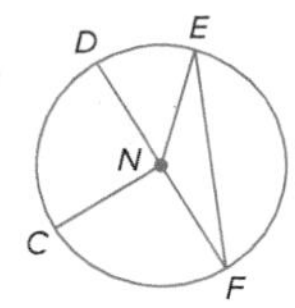

1. Name the circle. ⊙N
2. Identify each.
   a. a chord $\overline{EF}, \overline{DF}$
   b. a diameter $\overline{DF}$
   c. a radius $\overline{NC}, \overline{ND}, \overline{NE}$, or $\overline{NF}$
3. If $CN = 8$ centimeters, find DN. 8 cm
4. If $EN = 13$ feet, what is the diameter of the circle? 26 ft

Example 3 G.CO.1

The diameters of ⊙A, ⊙B, and ⊙C are 8 inches, 18 inches, and 11 inches, respectively. Find each measure.

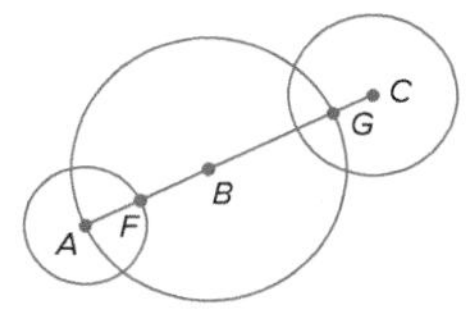

5. FG 14 in.
6. FB 5 in.

Example 4 G.CO.1

7. **RIDES** A circular ride similar to the one described at the beginning of the lesson has a diameter of 44 feet. What are the radius and circumference of the ride? Round to the nearest hundredth, if necessary. 22 ft; 138.23 ft

Example 5 G.CO.1

8. MP **MODELING** The circumference of the circular swimming pool shown is about 56.5 feet. What are the diameter and radius of the pool? Round to the nearest hundredth. 17.98 ft; 8.99 ft

Example 6 G.CO.1

9. The right triangle shown is inscribed in ⊙D. Find the exact circumference of ⊙D. $4\pi\sqrt{13}$ cm

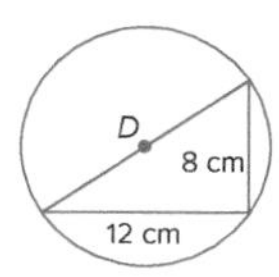

Practice and Problem Solving

Extra Practice is on page R9.

Examples 1–2 G.CO.1

For Exercises 10–13, refer to ⊙R.

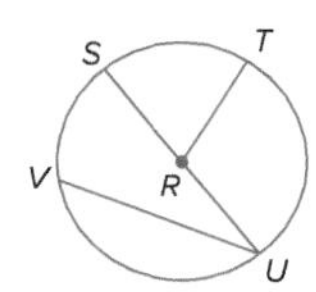

10. Name the center of the circle. R
11. Identify a chord that is also a diameter. $\overline{SU}$
12. Is $\overline{VU}$ a radius? Explain. No; it is a chord.
13. If $SU = 16.2$ centimeters, what is RT? 8.1 cm

For Exercises 14–17, refer to ⊙F.

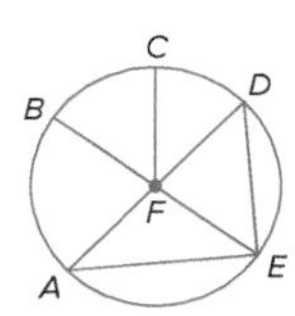

14. Identify a chord that is not a diameter. $\overline{DE}$ or $\overline{AE}$
15. If $CF = 14$ inches, what is the diameter of the circle? 28 in.
16. Is $\overline{AF} \cong \overline{EF}$? Explain. Yes; they are both radii of ⊙F.
17. If $DA = 7.4$ centimeters, what is EF? 3.7 cm

Differentiated Homework Options

Levels	AL Basic	OL Core	BL Advanced
Exercises	10–35, 48, 49, 51, 52, 55–60	11–41 odd, 43–49, 51, 52, 54, 55–60	36–60
2-Day Option	11–35 odd	10–35	
	10–34 even, 48, 49, 51, 52, 54, 55–60	36–49, 51, 52, 54, 55–60	

You can use ALEKS to provide additional remediation support with personalized instruction and practice.

Practice

Formative Assessment Use Exercises 1–9 to assess students' understanding of the concepts in this lesson.

Practice and Problem Solving exercises assess the content taught in the lesson. The Preparing for Assessment page is meant to be used as preparation for end-of-course assessments.

MP Teaching the Mathematical Practices

Modeling Mathematically proficient students can apply the mathematics they know to solve problems arising in everyday life. In Exercise 8, point out to students that they are calculating the radius and diameter of the surface of the water in the pool.

Extra Practice

See page R9 for extra exercises for students who are approaching level or for on-level students who need additional reinforcement.

Go Online! eBook

Interactive Student Guide
Use the *Interactive Student Guide* to deepen conceptual understanding.
· Circles and Circumferences

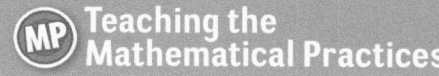

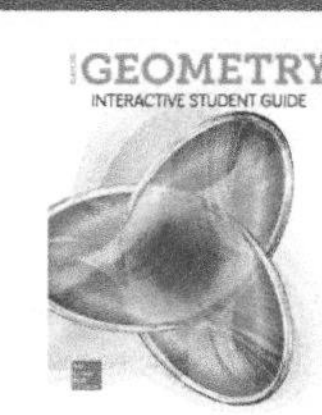

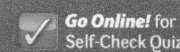

Levels of Complexity Chart

The levels of the exercises progress from 1 to 3, with Level 1 indicating the lowest level of complexity.

Exercises	10–35	36–44, 55–60	45–54
C Level 3			●
B Level 2		●	
Level 1	●		

MP Teaching the Mathematical Practices

Sense-Making Mathematically proficient students create and use representations to organize, record, and communicate mathematical ideas. In Exercises 28–33, encourage students to apply their knowledge of triangles and rectangles to find the radius of each circle.

Example 3 G.CO.1

Circle J has a radius of 10 units, $\odot K$ has a radius of 8 units, and $BC = 5.4$ units. Find each measure.

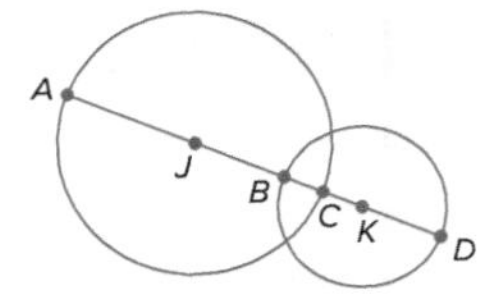

18. CK 2.6
19. AB 14.6
20. JK 12.6
21. AD 30.6

Example 4 G.CO.1

22. **PIZZA** Find the radius and circumference of the pizza shown. Round to the nearest hundredth, if necessary. 8 in.; 50.27 in.

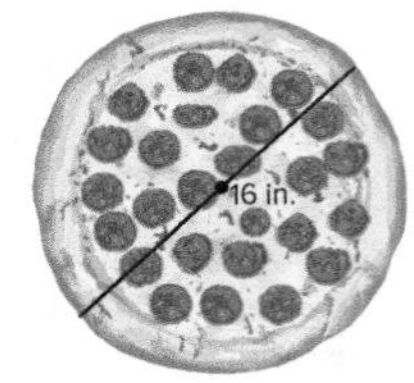

23. **BICYCLES** A bicycle has tires with a diameter of 26 inches. Find the radius and circumference of a tire. Round to the nearest hundredth, if necessary. 13 in.; 81.68 in.

Example 5 G.CO.1

Find the diameter and radius of a circle with the given circumference. Round to the nearest hundredth.

24. $C = 18$ in. 5.73 in.; 2.86 in.
25. $C = 124$ ft 39.47 ft; 19.74 ft
26. $C = 375.3$ cm 119.46 cm; 59.73 cm
27. $C = 2608.25$ m 830.23 m; 415.12 m

Example 6 G.CO.1

MP **SENSE-MAKING** Find the exact circumference of each circle by using the given inscribed or circumscribed polygon.

28.
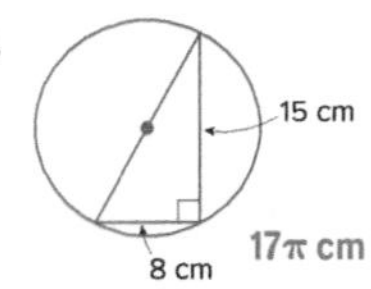

17π cm

29.
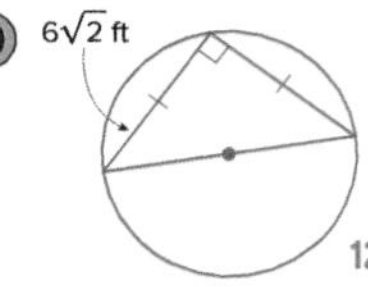

12π ft

30.
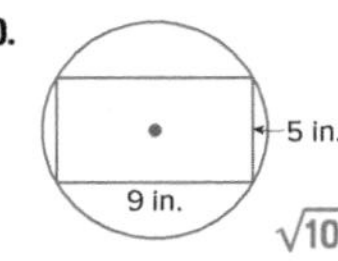

$\sqrt{106}\pi$ in.

31.
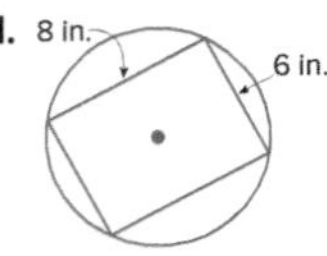

10π in.

32.
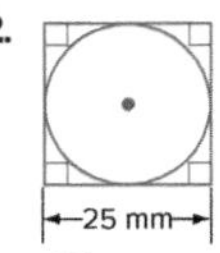

25π mm

33.
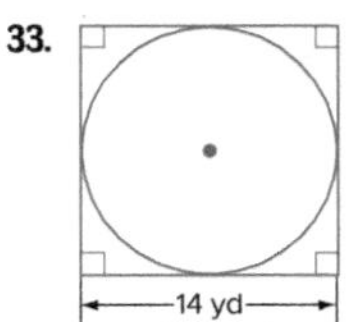

14π yd

34. **DISC GOLF** Disc golf is similar to regular golf, except that a flying disc is used instead of a ball and clubs. For professional competitions, the maximum weight of a disc in grams is 8.3 times the diameter in centimeters. What is the maximum allowable weight for a disc with circumference 66.92 centimeters? Round to the nearest tenth. 176.8 g

35. **PATIOS** Mr. Martinez is going to build the patio shown.
  a. What is the patio's approximate circumference? 31.42 ft
  b. If Mr. Martinez changes the plans so that the inner circle has a circumference of approximately 25 feet, what should the radius of the circle be to the nearest foot? 4 ft

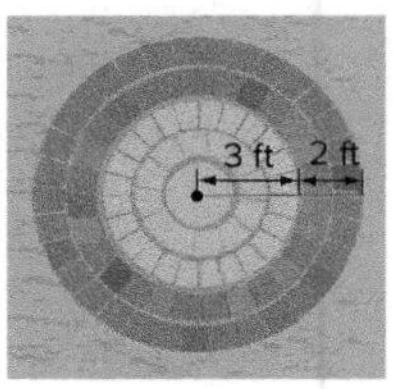

36. 4.25 in.; 26.70 in.
37. 22.80 ft; 71.63 ft
38. $11.14x$ cm; $5.57x$ cm
39. $0.25x$; $0.79x$

B **The radius, diameter, or circumference of a circle is given. Find each missing measure to the nearest hundredth.**

36. $d = 8\frac{1}{2}$ in., $r =$ __?__, $C =$ __?__
37. $r = 11\frac{2}{5}$ ft, $d =$ __?__, $C =$ __?__
38. $C = 35x$ cm, $d =$ __?__, $r =$ __?__
39. $r = \frac{x}{8}$, $d =$ ____, $C =$ __?__

Differentiated Instruction AL OL BL ELL

Kinesthetic/Logical Learners Provide students with the opportunity to use compasses to create circles and to understand the definition of circle through such uses. Ask students to be creative and think of other materials that can be used to create perfect circles in the absence of compasses. Have students use these techniques before continuing with the chapter and create their own definition for the term *circle*.

Determine whether the circles in the figures below appear to be *congruent*, *concentric*, or *neither*.

40.

concentric

41.

neither

42.

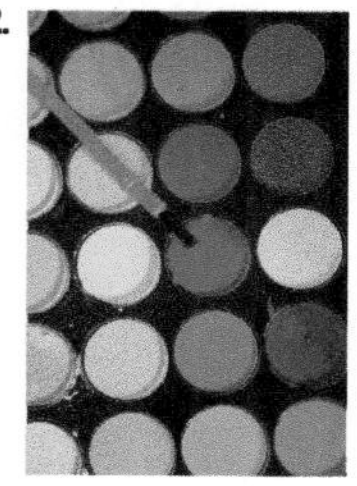

congruent

43 **HISTORY** The *Indian Shell Ring* on Hilton Head Island approximates a circle. If each unit on the coordinate grid represents 25 feet, how far would someone have to walk to go completely around the ring? Round to the nearest tenth. 471.2 ft

44. MP **MODELING** A brick path is being installed around a circular pond. The pond has a circumference of 68 feet. The outer edge of the path is going to be 4 feet from the pond all the way around. What is the approximate circumference of the path? Round to the nearest hundredth. 93.13 ft

C **45. MULTIPLE REPRESENTATIONS** In this problem, you will explore changing dimensions in circles.

a. **Geometric** Use a compass to draw three circles in which the scale factor from each circle to the next larger circle is 1 : 2. See margin.

b. **Tabular** Calculate the radius (to the nearest tenth) and circumference (to the nearest hundredth) of each circle. Record your results in a table. See margin.

c. **Verbal** Explain why these three circles are geometrically similar. They all have the same shape—circular.

d. **Verbal** Make a conjecture about the ratio between the circumferences of two circles when the ratio between their radii is 2. The ratio of their circumferences is also 2.

e. **Analytical** The scale factor from ⊙A to ⊙B is $\frac{b}{a}$. Write an equation relating the circumference (C_A) of ⊙A to the circumference (C_B) of ⊙B. $(C_B) = \frac{b}{a}(C_A)$

f. **Numerical** If the scale factor from ⊙A to ⊙B is $\frac{1}{3}$, and the circumference of ⊙A is 12 inches, what is the circumference of ⊙B? 4 in.

46. BUFFON'S NEEDLE Measure the length ℓ of a needle (or toothpick) in centimeters. Next, draw a set of horizontal lines that are ℓ centimeters apart on a sheet of plain white paper.

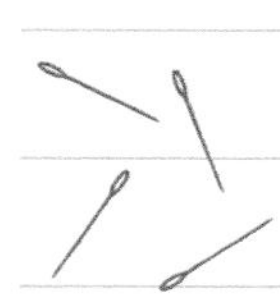

a. Drop the needle onto the paper. When the needle lands, record whether it touches one of the lines as a hit. Record the number of hits after 25, 50, and 100 drops. a–b. See students' work.

b. Calculate the ratio of two times the total number of drops to the number of hits after 25, 50, and 100 drops.

c. How are the values you found in part **b** related to π? Sample answer: The values are approaching 3.14, which is approximately equal to π.

MP Teaching the Mathematical Practices

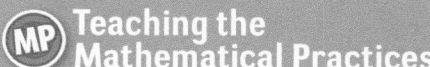

Modeling Mathematically proficient students can apply the mathematics they know to solve problems arising in everyday life. In Exercise 44, encourage students to draw a diagram of the situation that shows the pond and brick path.

Exercise Alerts

Compass **Exercise 45 requires the use of a compass.**

Centimeter Ruler and Toothpicks **Exercise 46 requires the use of a centimeter ruler and toothpicks.**

Additional Answers

45a. Sample answer:

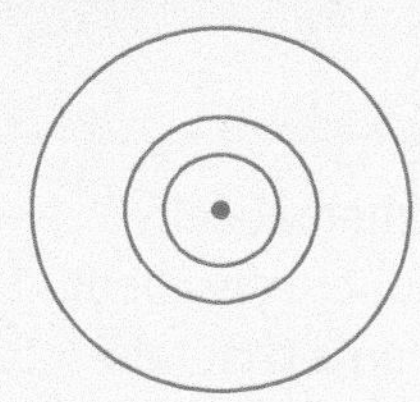

45b. Sample answer:

Circle Radius (cm)	Circumference (cm)
0.5	3.14
1	6.28
2	12.57

Assess

Name the Math Students can practice vocabulary terms in this lesson by describing selected circles and defining terms aloud.

Follow-Up

- How are circles and polygons similar? different? Sample answer: Circles and polygons are similar in that they are shapes that can be used to model real-world objects, and you can find the distance around each figure or the area that the figure takes up. They are different in that polygons are closed figures composed of straight line segments, whereas a circle is made up of a locus of points equidistant from one point. Also, all circles are similar, but all polygons are not similar.

Teaching the Mathematical Practices

Construct Arguments Mathematically proficient students reason inductively about data, making plausible arguments that take into account context from which the data arose. In Exercise 52, encourage students to review the tests for similarity.

Additional Answers

48. Sample answer: A line segment with endpoints on a circle can be described as a chord. If the chord passes through the center of the circle, it can be described as a diameter. A line segment with endpoints at the center and on the circle can be described as a radius.

49a. $8r$ and $6r$; Twice the radius of the circle, $2r$ is the side length of the square, so the perimeter of the square is $4(2r)$ or $8r$. The regular hexagon is made up of six equilateral triangles with side length r, so the perimeter of the hexagon is $6(r)$ or $6r$.

Go Online!

eSolutions Manual

Create worksheets, answer keys, and solutions handouts for your assignments.

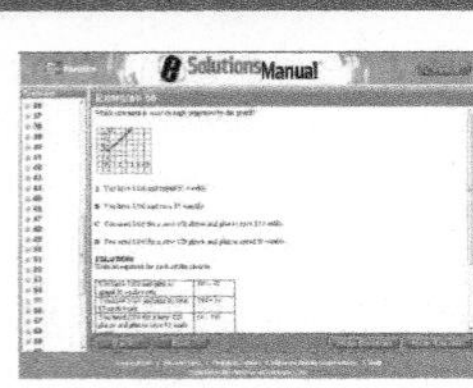

47 **MAPS** The concentric circles on the map below show the areas that are 5, 10, 15, 20, 25, and 30 miles from downtown Phoenix.

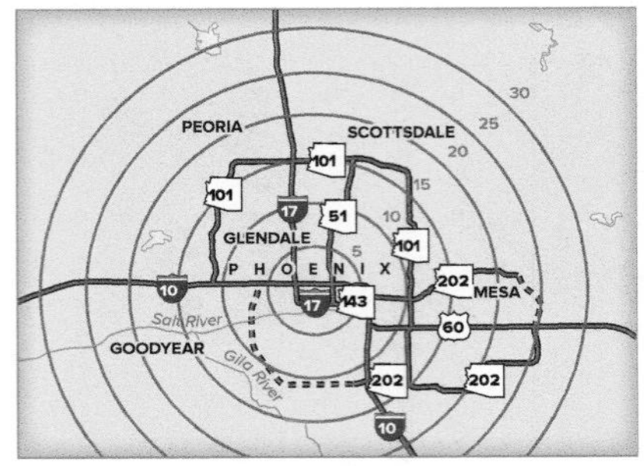

a. How much greater is the circumference of the outermost circle than the circumference of the center circle? 157.1 mi

b. As the radii of the circles increase by 5 miles, by how much does the circumference increase? ≈ 31.4 mi

51. Always; a radius is a segment drawn between the center of the circle and a point on the circle. A segment drawn from the center to a point inside the circle will always have a length less than the radius of the circle.

G.CO.1, G.C.1, G.GMD.1

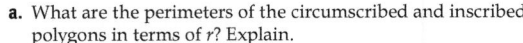

H.O.T. Problems Use Higher-Order Thinking Skills

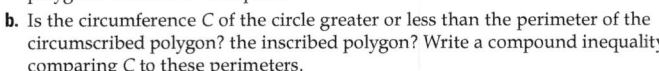

48. **WRITING IN MATH** How can we describe the relationships that exist between circles and lines? See margin.

49. **REASONING** In the figure, a circle with radius r is inscribed in a regular polygon and circumscribed about another. a–d. See margin.

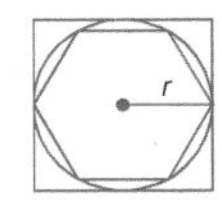

a. What are the perimeters of the circumscribed and inscribed polygons in terms of r? Explain.

b. Is the circumference C of the circle greater or less than the perimeter of the circumscribed polygon? the inscribed polygon? Write a compound inequality comparing C to these perimeters.

c. Rewrite the inequality from part **b** in terms of the diameter d of the circle and interpret its meaning.

d. As the number of sides of both the circumscribed and inscribed polygons increase, what will happen to the upper and lower limits of the inequality from part **c**, and what does this imply?

50. **CHALLENGE** The sum of the circumferences of circles H, J, and K shown at the right is 56π units. Find KJ. 24 units

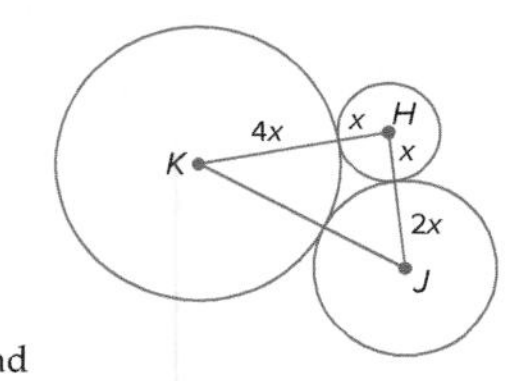

51. **REASONING** Is the distance from the center of a circle to a point in the interior of a circle *sometimes, always,* or *never* less than the radius of the circle? Explain.

52. **CONSTRUCT ARGUMENTS** Use the locus definition of a circle and dilations to prove that all circles are similar. See margin.

53. **CHALLENGE** In the figure, $\odot P$ is inscribed in equilateral triangle LMN. What is the circumference of $\odot P$? $\frac{8\pi}{\sqrt{3}}$ or $\frac{8\pi\sqrt{3}}{3}$ in.

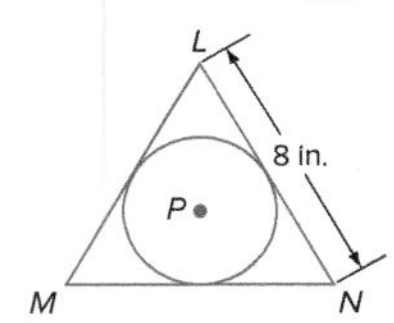

54. **WRITING IN MATH** Research and write about the history of pi and its importance to the study of geometry. See students' work.

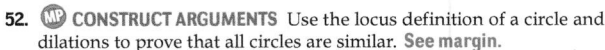

Standards for Mathematical Practice

Emphasis On	Exercises
1 Make sense of problems and persevere in solving them.	28–33, 50, 55–60
2 Reason abstractly and quantitatively.	51
3 Construct viable arguments and critique the reasoning of others.	49, 52
4 Model with mathematics.	8, 22, 23, 34, 35, 43–48, 54
6 Attend to precision.	7, 53, 55–60

Preparing for Assessment

55. What is the circumference of ⊙C to the nearest hundredth? MP 1, 6 G.GMD.1 **25.13**

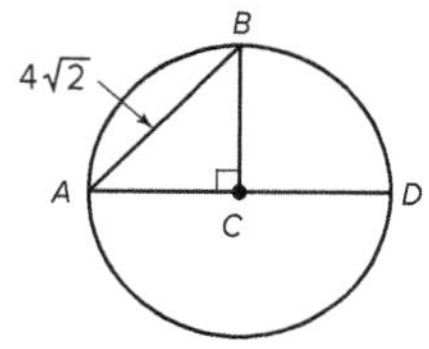

56. $MNPQ$ is a square. The radius of ⊙R is 3.

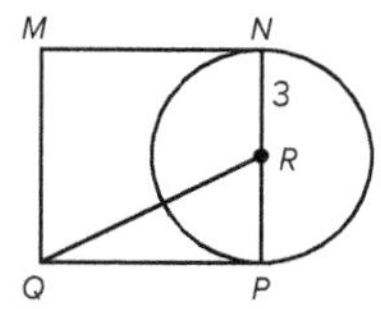

Which of the following is the length of $\overline{QR}$? MP 1, 6 G.C.1, G.SRT.8 **D**

- ○ A 3
- ○ B $3\sqrt{2}$
- ○ C 6
- ○ D $3\sqrt{5}$

57. In the figure, C is the midpoint of $\overline{AE}$, B is the midpoint of $\overline{AC}$, D is the midpoint of $\overline{CE}$, and $AE = 32$.

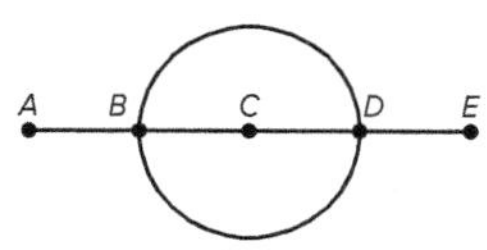

What is the circumference of ⊙C to the nearest hundredth? MP 1, 6 G.CO.1

50.27

58. The right triangle $\triangle JKL$ is inscribed in ⊙M, as shown.

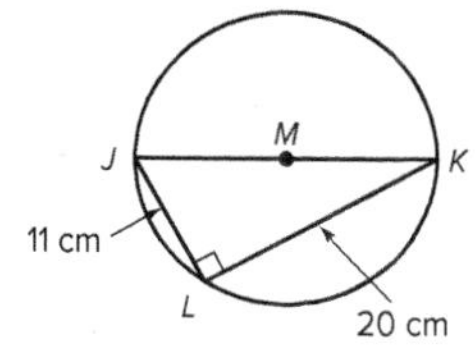

Which of the following is the best estimate of the circumference of ⊙M? MP 1, 6 G.SRT.8, G.GMD.1 **C**

- ○ A 35.9 cm
- ○ B 62.8 cm
- ○ C 71.7 cm
- ○ D 143.4 cm
- ○ E 409.2 cm

59. **MULTI-STEP** Square $JKLM$ has an area of 9 square meters. A circle with center M passes through J and L. MP 1, 6 G.GMD.1

a. Name the circle. **Circle M**

b. Name a line segment that is a radius of the circle. **$\overline{MJ}$ or $\overline{ML}$**

c. What is the circumference of the circle? **6π m**

60a. **$DE = 2$ because it is a side of equilateral triangle DEF. $DF = 2$, so $DG = 1$. Using the Pythagorean Theorem, $1^2 + d^2 = 2^2$ $d = \sqrt{3}$**

60. Triangle DEF is an equilateral triangle with side lengths of 2 inches. MP 1, 6 G.GMD.1

a. Explain how to find the diameter of circle C.

b. What is the circumference of circle C? **$\sqrt{3}\pi$**

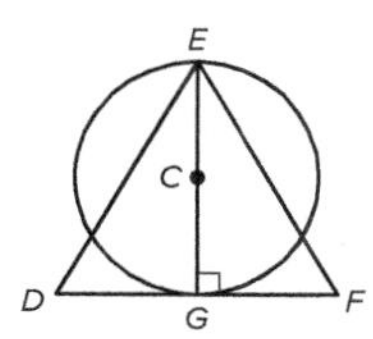

Preparing for Assessment

Exercises 55–60 require students to use the skills they will need on standardized assessments. Exercises are dual-coded with content standards and mathematical practice standards.

Dual Coding		
Items	Content Standards	MP Mathematical Practices
55	G.GMD.1	1, 6
56	G.C.1, G.SRT.8	1, 6
57	G.CO.1	1, 6
58	G.SRT.8, G.GMD.1	1, 6
59	G.GMD.1	1, 6
60	G.GMD.1	1, 6

Diagnose Student Errors

Survey student responses for each item. Class trends may indicate common errors and misconceptions.

56.

A	Found the length of $\overline{PR}$
B	Assumed $QP = PR = 3$
C	Assumed $\triangle QPR$ is a 30°-60°-90° triangle
D	CORRECT

58.

A	Calculated circumference as πr
B	Used 20 cm as diameter of circle
C	CORRECT
D	Calculated circumference as $2\pi d$
E	Calculated area of circle

Additional Answers

49b. less; greater; $6r < C < 8r$

49c. $3d < C < 4d$; The circumference of the circle is between 3 and 4 times its diameter.

49d. These limits will approach a value of πd, implying that $C = \pi d$.

52. A circle is a locus of points in a plane equidistant from a given point. For any two circles ⊙A and ⊙B, there exists a translation that maps center A onto center B, moving ⊙A so that it is concentric with ⊙B. There also exists a dilation with scale factor k such that each point that makes up ⊙A is moved to be the same distance from center A as the points that make up ⊙B are from center B. Therefore, ⊙A is mapped onto ⊙B. Since there exists a rigid motion followed by a scaling that maps ⊙A onto ⊙B, the circles are similar. Thus, all circles are similar.

Go Online!

Quizzes

Students can use *Self-Check Quizzes* to check their understanding of this lesson and have the results sent to you. You can also give *Quiz 1*, which covers the content in Lessons 9-1 and 9-2.

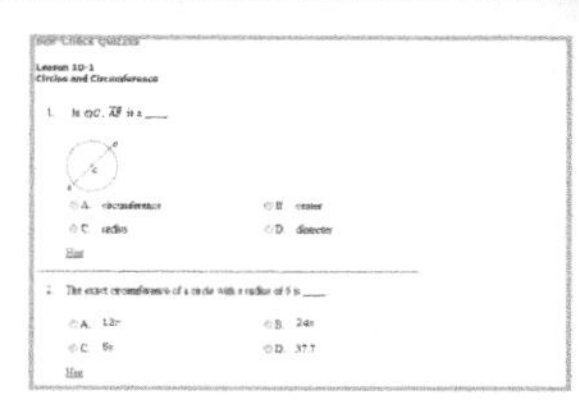

LESSON 9-2

Measuring Angles and Arcs

SUGGESTED PACING (DAYS)

	Instruction
90 min.	0.5
45 min.	1.0

Track Your Progress

Objectives

1 Identify central angles, major arcs, minor arcs, and semicircles, and find their measures.

2 Find arc lengths.

Mathematical Background

A central angle of a circle has the center of the circle as its vertex, and its sides are two radii of the circle. A central angle separates the circle into two arcs. A minor arc degree measure equals the measure of the central angle. The ratio of the arc degree measure to 360 is equal to the ratio of the arc length to the circumference.

THEN

G.CO.1 Know precise definitions of angle, circle, perpendicular line, parallel line, and line segment, based on the undefined notions of point, line, distance along a line, and distance around a circular arc.

G.C.1 Identify and describe relationships among inscribed angles, radii, and chords. Include the relationship between central, inscribed, and circumscribed angles; inscribed angles on a diameter are right angles; the radius of a circle is perpendicular to the tangent where the radius intersects the circle.

NOW

G.C.2 Identify and describe relationships among inscribed angles, radii, and chords. *Include the relationship between central, inscribed, and circumscribed angles; inscribed angles on a diameter are right angles; the radius of a circle is perpendicular to the tangent where the radius intersects the circle.*

G.C.5 Derive using similarity the fact that the length of the arc intercepted by an angle is proportional to the radius, and define the radian measure of the angle as the constant of proportionality; derive the formula for the area of a sector.

NEXT

G.CO.12 Make formal geometric constructions with a variety of tools and methods. *Copying a segment; copying an angle; bisecting a segment; bisecting an angle; constructing perpendicular lines, including the perpendicular bisector of a line segment; and constructing a line parallel to a given line through a point not on the line.*

G.MG.3 Apply geometric methods to solve design problems.

Go Online! All of these resources and more are available at connectED.mcgraw-hill.com

eLessons utilize the power of your interactive whiteboard in an engaging way. Use **Chords, Arcs, and Angles**, Screens 5–9, to introduce the concepts in this lesson.

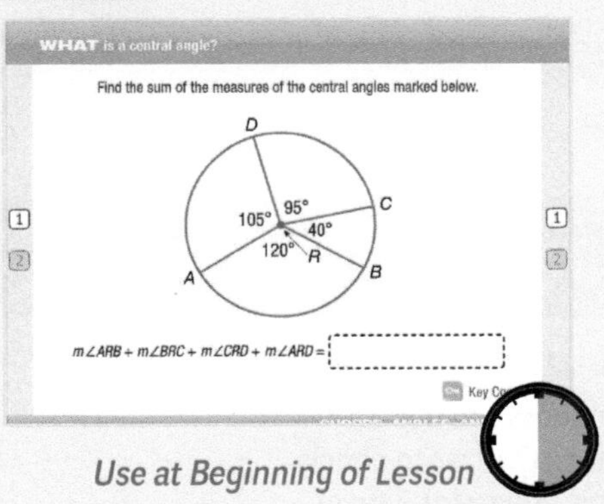

Use at Beginning of Lesson

Use Animations to define minor arcs, major arcs, and semicircles, and to find the measures of minor arcs and major arcs.

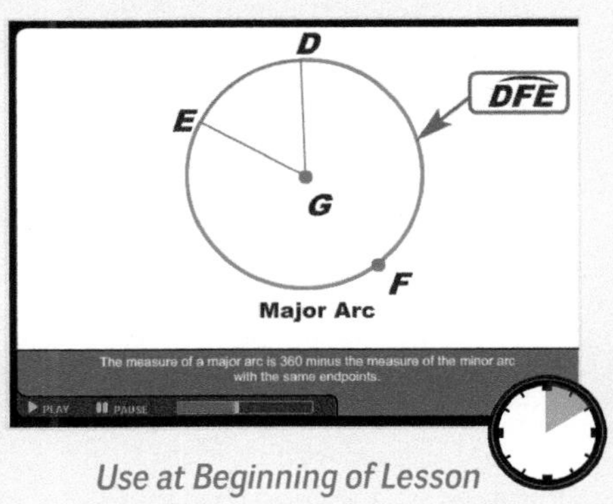

Use at Beginning of Lesson

Use The Geometer's Sketchpad to explore the relationships in a circle between angles and the arcs they intercept.

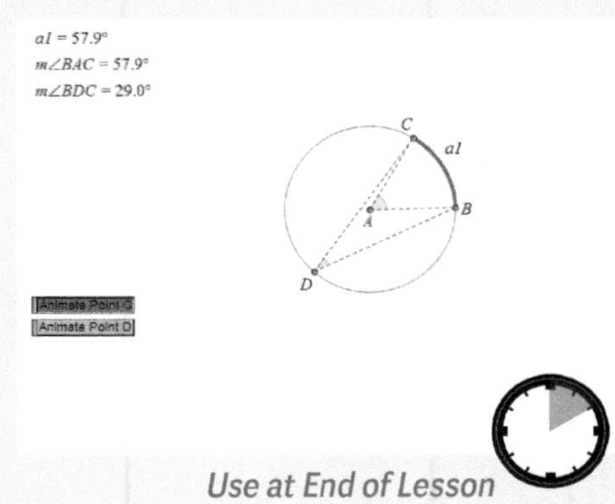

Use at End of Lesson

OER Using Open Educational Resources

Lesson Creation You can create an activity on measuring angles and arcs using templates on **ClassTools.net.** This resource is free and will save your work for an entire school year. *Use as a planning resource*

Go Online!
connectED.mcgraw-hill.com

Worksheets

Differentiate Your Resources

Extra Practice Additional practice or homework; Skills Practice is best for approaching-level students and Practice is best for on-level and beyond-level students

Skills Practice

AL OL ELL

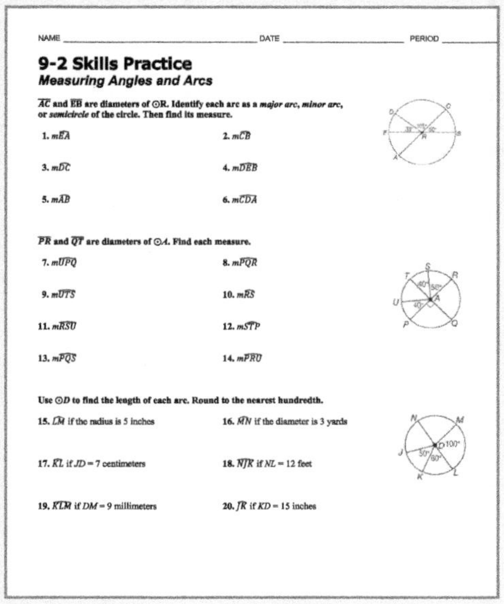

9-2 Skills Practice
Measuring Angles and Arcs

Practice

AL OL BL ELL

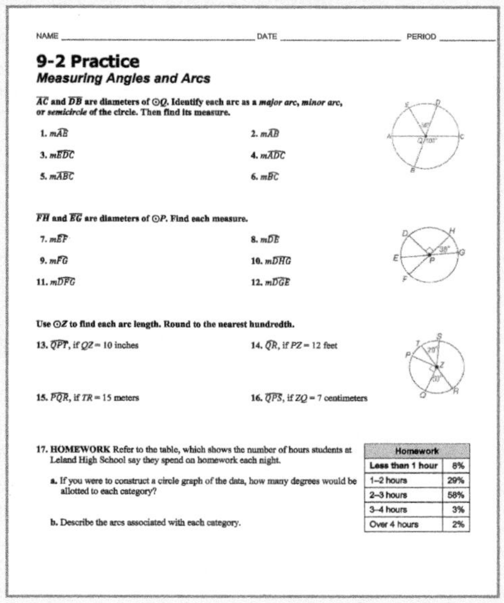

9-2 Practice
Measuring Angles and Arcs

Word Problem Practice

AL OL BL ELL

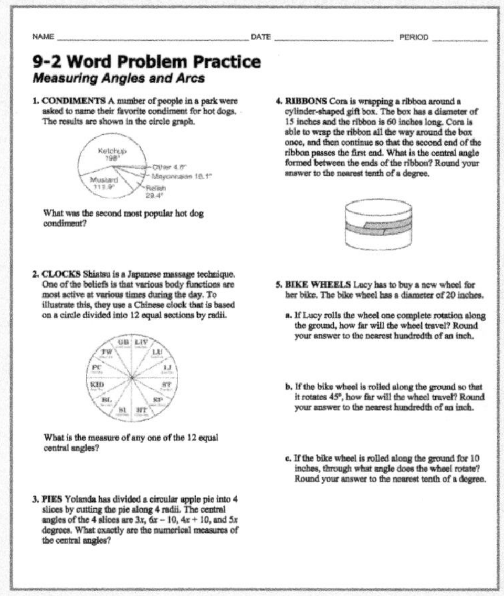

9-2 Word Problem Practice
Measuring Angles and Arcs

Intervention Reteaching and vocabulary activities that can be used with struggling or absent students and as ELL support

Study Guide and Intervention

AL OL ELL

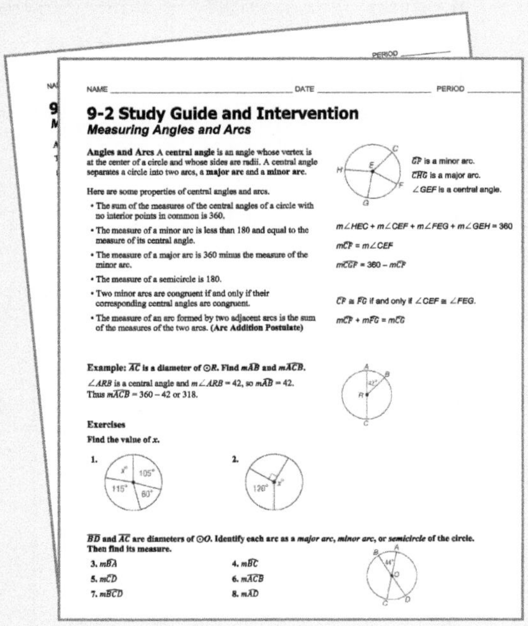

9-2 Study Guide and Intervention
Measuring Angles and Arcs

Study Notebook

AL OL BL ELL

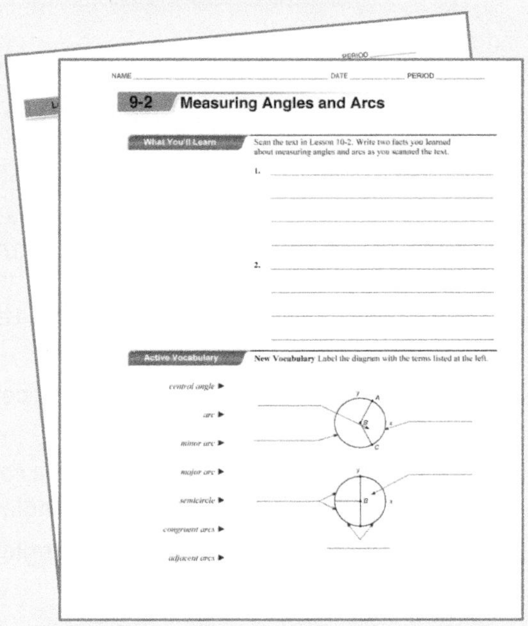

9-2 Measuring Angles and Arcs

Extension Activities that can be used to extend lesson concepts

Enrichment

OL BL ELL

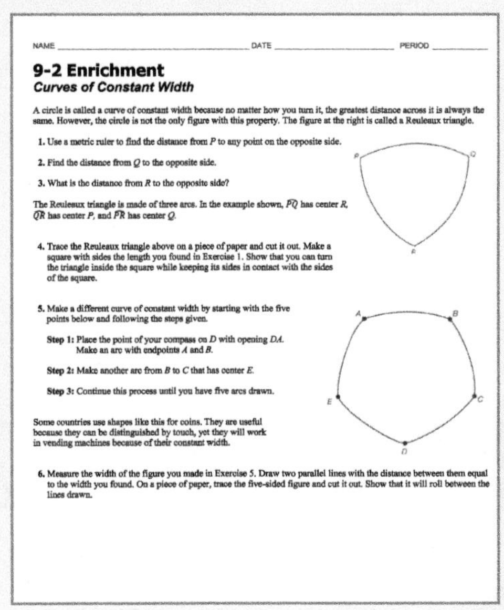

9-2 Enrichment
Curves of Constant Width

Launch

Have students read the Why? section of the lesson. Ask:

- The 13 stars of the Betsy Ross flag are equidistant from what point? The stars are equidistant from the center of the circle.
- Assume that the circumference of the circle of stars is 44 inches. Approximately how far is each star from the center of the circle? about 7 in.
- Make a conjecture about why the central angle in the circle of stars remains constant regardless of the size of the circle. The distance between any two stars and the center of the circle changes proportionally when the circle of stars increases or decreases in circumference.

Teach

Ask the scaffolded questions for each example to build conceptual understanding for students at all levels.

1 Angles and Arcs

Example 1 Find Measures of Central Angles

AL How do we know that $m\angle HFJ$ is 90°? The diagram includes a right angle mark for $\angle HFJ$.

OL How can we check the reasonableness of our solution? Sample answer: Compare $\angle GFJ$ to $\angle GFH$.

BL What would the measure of the central angle created by a diameter of the circle be? 180

LESSON 2

Measuring Angles and Arcs

::Then	::Now	::Why?
You measured angles and identified congruent angles.	1 Identify central angles, major arcs, minor arcs, and semicircles, and find their measures. 2 Find arc lengths.	The thirteen stars of the Betsy Ross flag are arranged equidistant from each other and from a fixed point. The distance between consecutive stars varies depending on the size of the flag, but the measure of the central angle formed by the center of the circle and any two consecutive stars is always the same.

New Vocabulary
central angle
arc
minor arc
major arc
semicircle
congruent arcs
adjacent arcs
arc length
radian measure

Mathematical Practices
6 Attend to precision.
4 Model with mathematics.

Content Standards
G.C.2 Identify and describe relationships among inscribed angles, radii, and chords.
G.C.5 Derive using similarity the fact that the length of the arc intercepted by an angle is proportional to the radius, and define the radian measure of the angle as the constant of proportionality; derive the formula for the area of a sector.

1 Angles and Arcs A **central angle** of a circle is an angle with a vertex in the center of the circle. Its sides contain two radii of the circle. $\angle ABC$ is a central angle of $\odot B$.

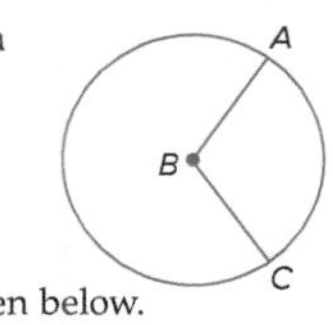

Recall from Lesson 1-4 that a *degree* is $\frac{1}{360}$ of the circular rotation about a point. This leads to the following relationship. The names of the three most common trigonometric ratios are given below.

Key Concept Sum of Central Angles

Words	The sum of the measures of the central angles of a circle with no interior points in common is 360.
Example	$m\angle 1 + m\angle 2 + m\angle 3 = 360$

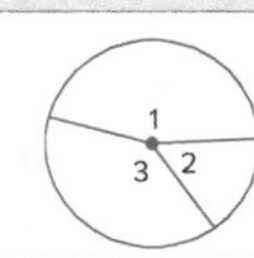

G.C.2

Example 1 Find Measures of Central Angles

Find the value of *x*.

$m\angle GFH + m\angle HFJ + m\angle GFJ = 360$	Sum of Central Angles
$130 + 90 + m\angle GFJ = 360$	Substitution
$220 + m\angle GFJ = 360$	Simplify.
$m\angle GFJ = 140$	Subtract 220 from each side.

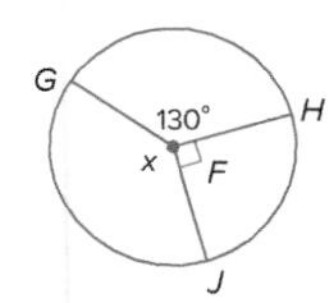

Guided Practice

1A.

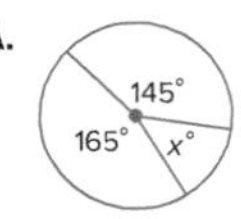

50

1B.

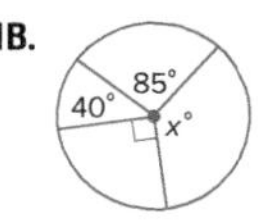

145

An **arc** is a portion of a circle defined by two endpoints. A central angle separates the circle into two arcs with measures related to the measure of the central angle.

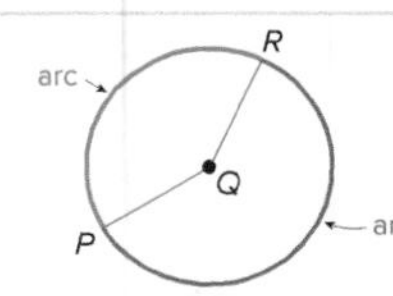

Mathematical Practices Strategies

Reason Abstractly and Quantitatively
Help students to reason quantitatively and find the missing central angle in the circle. For example, in Guided Practice 1A, ask the following questions:

- How would you classify the angles with measures 145°, 165°, and x°? These are central angles.
- What do you know about the sum of central angles? The sum of central angles in a circle is 360°.
- What equation can you write for the central angles given, the missing central angle, and the sum of the central angles? $145 + 165 + m\angle x = 360$
- How do you solve for the missing angle? Simplify by adding 145 and 165 together (which equals 310) and then isolate $m\angle x$ by subtracting 310 from both sides of the equation. So $m\angle x$ is $360 - 310 = 50°$.

Go Online!

Interactive Whiteboard
Use the *eLesson*, *Lesson Presentation*, or *Interactive Classroom* to present this lesson.

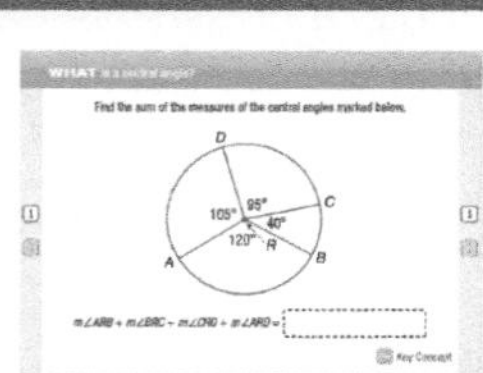

Study Tip ELL
Naming Arcs Minor arcs are named by their endpoints. Major arcs and semicircles are named by their endpoints and another point on the arc that lies between these endpoints.

Key Concept Arcs and Arc Measure

Arc	Measure	
A **minor arc** is the shortest arc connecting two endpoints on a circle.	The measure of a minor arc is less than 180 and equal to the measure of its related central angle. $m\widehat{AB} = m\angle ACB = x$	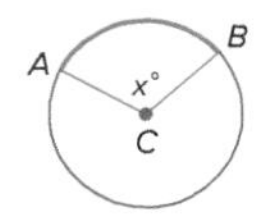
A **major arc** is the longest arc connecting two endpoints on a circle.	The measure of a major arc is greater than 180, and equal to 360 minus the measure of the minor arc with the same endpoints. $m\widehat{ADB} = 360 - m\widehat{AB} = 360 - x$	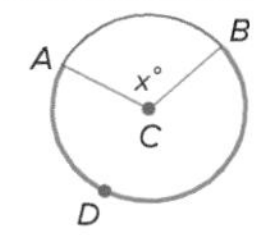
A **semicircle** is an arc with endpoints that lie on a diameter.	The measure of a semicircle is 180. $m\widehat{ADB} = 180$	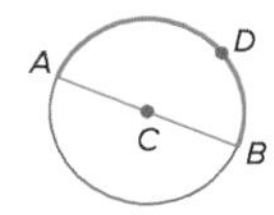

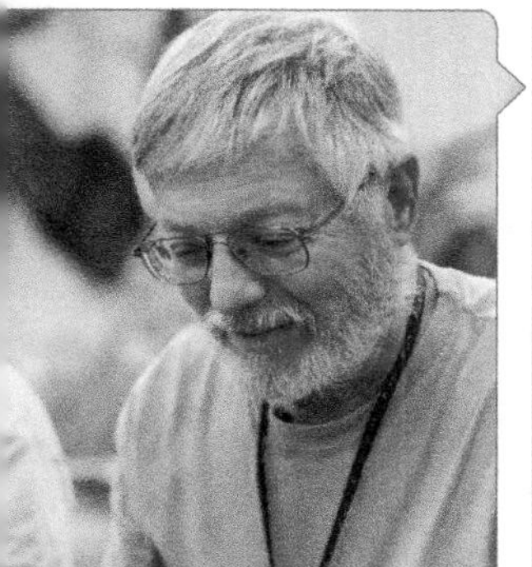

Real-World Career
Historical Researcher Research in museums includes authentication, verification, and description of artifacts. Employment as a historical researcher requires a minimum of a bachelor's degree in history.

G.C.2

Example 2 Classify Arcs and Find Arc Measures

$\overline{GJ}$ is a diameter of $\odot K$. Identify each arc as a *major arc, minor arc,* or *semicircle*. Then find its measure.

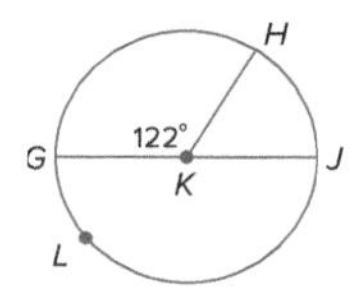

a. $\widehat{GH}$

$\widehat{GH}$ is a minor arc, so $m\widehat{GH} = m\angle GKH$ or 122.

b. $\widehat{GLH}$

$\widehat{GLH}$ is a major arc that shares the same endpoints as minor arc $\widehat{GH}$.

$m\widehat{GHL} = 360 - m\widehat{GH}$

$= 360 - 122$ or 238

c. $\widehat{GLJ}$

$\widehat{GLJ}$ is a semicircle, so $m\widehat{GLJ} = 180$.

Guided Practice

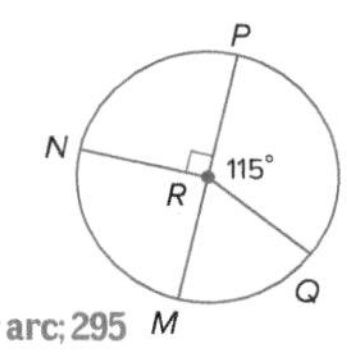

$\overline{PM}$ is a diameter of $\odot R$. Identify each arc as a *major arc, minor arc,* or *semicircle*. Then find its measure.

2A. $\widehat{MQ}$ minor arc; 65 **2B.** $\widehat{MNP}$ semicircle; 180 **2C.** $\widehat{MNQ}$ major arc; 295

Congruent arcs are arcs in the same or congruent circles that have the same measure.

Theorem 9.1

Words In the same circle or in congruent circles, two minor arcs are congruent if and only if their central angles are congruent.

Example If $\angle 1 \cong \angle 2$, then $\widehat{FG} \cong \widehat{HJ}$.
If $\widehat{FG} \cong \widehat{HJ}$, then $\angle 1 \cong \angle 2$.

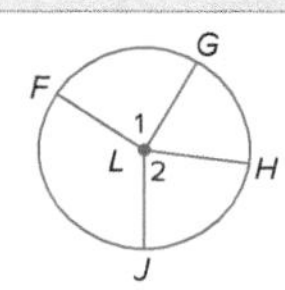

You will prove Theorem 9.1 in Exercise 54.

Differentiated Instruction ELL

Intermediate Before reading the lesson, have students take a close look at the visual support. Have them use the diagrams in the Key Concepts as they work in pairs to form questions about arcs and measuring arcs. After reading, have partners discuss how their ideas changed or stayed the same. Move around the room to monitor progress.

Advanced Have student pairs take turns reading the text to one another. Move around the room, correcting pronunciation as necessary. Ask students what they learn from the title and how the title makes them approach the text. What do they know about angles or arcs of circles, and what do they expect to learn? Have them share with the class. Record their contributions on the board.

Advanced High Have students write a paragraph explaining and evaluating the diagrams in the Key Concepts and Theorems in relation to the content of the lesson. What was its purpose? How effective was it? Have volunteers share their evaluations with the group.

Need Another Example?
Find the value of x. 7

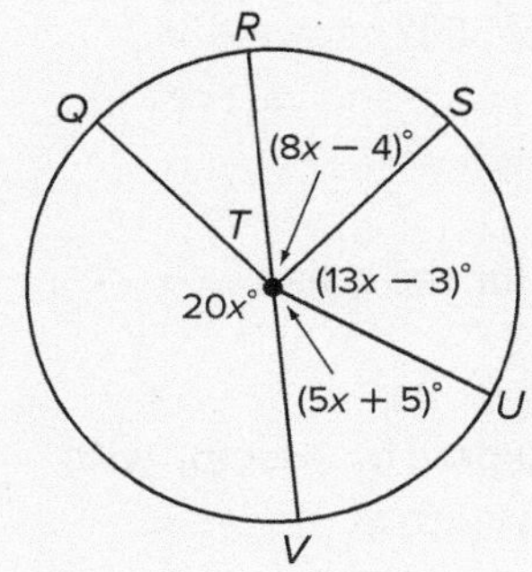

Example 2 Classify Arcs and Find Arc Measures

AL Describe the difference between a major arc, a minor arc, and a semicircle. A major arc has a measure greater than 180 and less than 360. A minor arc measures less than 180. A semicircle measures exactly 180.

OL What is $m\widehat{HJ}$? 58

BL Can a circle contain both a major arc and a semicircle? Explain. Yes; The major arc and semicircle must overlap, but a circle can contain each.

Need Another Example?
$\overline{WC}$ is a radius of $\odot C$. Identify each arc as a *major arc, minor arc,* or *semicircle*. Then find its measure.

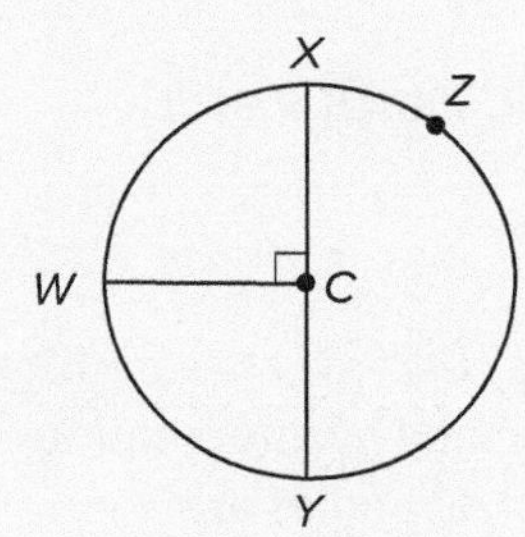

a. $\widehat{XZY}$
semicircle; $m\widehat{XZY} = 180$

b. $\widehat{WZX}$
major arc; $m\widehat{WZX} = 270$

c. $\widehat{XW}$
minor arc; $m\widehat{XW} = 90$

Example 3 Find Arc Measures in Circle Graphs

AL Why did we find 18% of 360? because 360 represents the whole circle and we are looking for 18% of the whole

OL Find the arc measure for the area representing *softball.* 57.6

BL Which sport is represented by a sector with an arc length of 72? basketball

Need Another Example?

Bicycles Refer to the circle graph.

Bicycles Bought (by type)

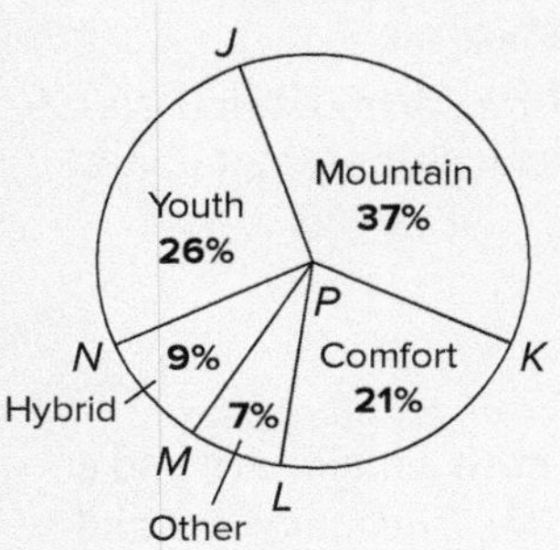

a. Find $m\widehat{KL}$. 75.6
b. Find $m\widehat{NJL}$. 302.4

Example 4 Use Arc Addition to Find Measures of Arcs

AL How would you find $m\widehat{ABC}$? $m\widehat{AB} + m\widehat{BC}$

OL What is $m\widehat{ADB}$? 243

BL What do you think $m\widehat{BC}$ is? Sample answer: 63; Because $\widehat{AE}$ and $\widehat{BC}$ are formed by intersecting diameters, I think the central angles are vertical angles that have the same measure. Therefore, the arc angles are also congruent.

Need Another Example?

Find each measure in $\odot M$.

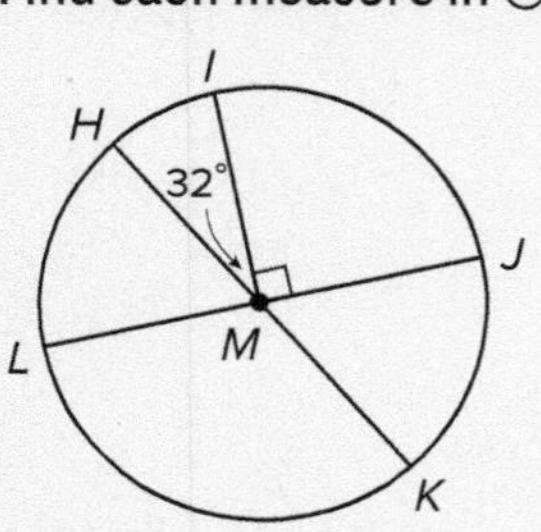

a. $m\widehat{LHI}$ 90
b. $m\widehat{IJK}$ 148

G.C.5

Real-World Example 3 Find Arc Measures in Circle Graphs

SPORTS Refer to the circle graph. Find $m\widehat{CD}$.

$\widehat{CD}$ is a minor arc. $m\widehat{CD} = m\angle CSD$

$\angle CSD$ represents 18% of the whole, or 18% of the circle.

$m\angle CSD = 0.18(360)$ Find 18% of 360.

$= 64.8$ Simplify.

Female Participation in Sports

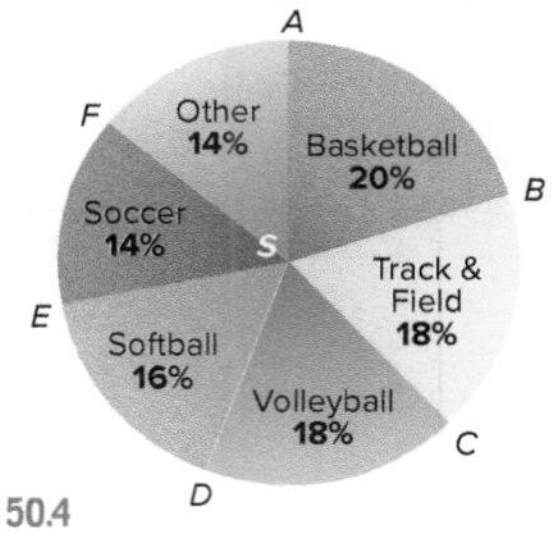

Guided Practice

3A. $m\widehat{EF}$ 50.4 **3B.** $m\widehat{FA}$ 50.4

Adjacent arcs are arcs in a circle that have exactly one point in common. In $\odot M$, $\widehat{HJ}$ and $\widehat{JK}$ are adjacent arcs. As with adjacent angles, you can add the measures of adjacent arcs.

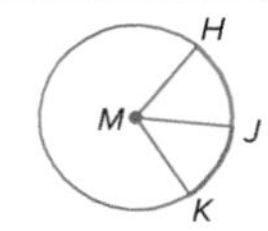

Math History Link

Euclid (c. 325–265 B.C.) The 13 books of Euclid's *Elements* are influential works of science. In them, geometry and other branches of mathematics are logically developed. Book 3 of *Elements* is devoted to circles, arcs, and angles.

Postulate 9.1 Arc Addition Postulate

Words The measure of an arc formed by two adjacent arcs is the sum of the measures of the two arcs.

Example $m\widehat{XYZ} = m\widehat{XY} + m\widehat{YZ}$

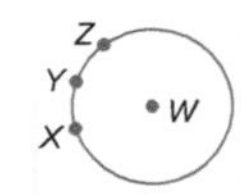

G.C.2

Example 4 Use Arc Addition to Find Measures of Arcs

Find $m\widehat{AED}$ in $\odot F$.

$m\widehat{AED} = m\widehat{AE} + m\widehat{ED}$ Arc Addition Postulate

$= m\angle AFE + m\angle EFD$ $m\widehat{AE} = m\angle AFE$, $m\widehat{ED} = m\angle EFD$

$= 63 + 90$ or 153 Substitution

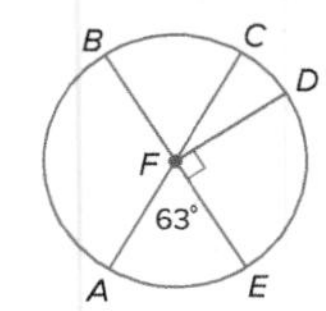

Guided Practice

4A. $m\widehat{CE}$ 117 **4B.** $m\widehat{ABD}$ 207

Watch Out! ELL

Arc Length The length of an arc is given in linear units, such as centimeters. The measure of an arc is given in degrees.

2 Arc Length **Arc length** is the distance between the endpoints along an arc measured in linear units. Because an arc is a portion of a circle, its length is a fraction of the circumference.

Key Concept Arc Length

Words The ratio of the length of an arc ℓ to the circumference of the circle is equal to the ratio of the degree measure of the arc to 360.

Proportion $\frac{\ell}{2\pi r} = \frac{x}{360}$ or

Equation $\ell = \frac{x}{360} \cdot 2\pi r$

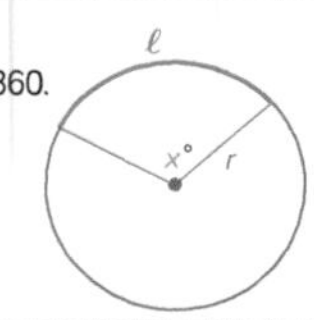

Differentiated Instruction OL BL

Interpersonal Learners Draw a circle segmented with different sizes of central angles. Shade each portion of the circle with a different color. Repeat for two other circles the same size, but with different central angles. Laminate the paper, cut out the circles, and separate each portion. Provide the cutouts to groups of students who can fit the pieces together to form the three circles, find the central angle measures, arc measures, circumferences and arc lengths. Groups can compare to check results and/or determine which group is the most efficient at finding all the correct information.

G.C.5

Example 5 Find Arc Length

Find the length of $\widehat{ZY}$. Round to the nearest hundredth.

a.

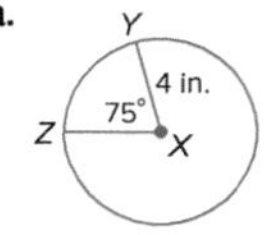

$\ell = \frac{x}{360} \cdot 2\pi r$ Arc Length Equation

$= \frac{75}{360} \cdot 2\pi(4)$ Substitution

≈ 5.24 in. Use a calculator.

b.

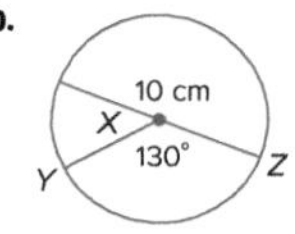

$\ell = \frac{x}{360} \cdot 2\pi r$ Arc Length Equation

$= \frac{130}{360} \cdot 2\pi(5)$ Substitution

≈ 11.34 cm Use a calculator.

Study Tip

Sense-Making The arc lengths in Examples 5a and 5b could also have been calculated using the arc length proportion $\frac{\ell}{2\pi r} = \frac{x}{360}$.

Guided Practice

Find the length of $\widehat{AB}$. Round to the nearest hundredth.

5A.

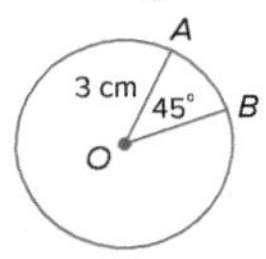

2.36 cm

5B.

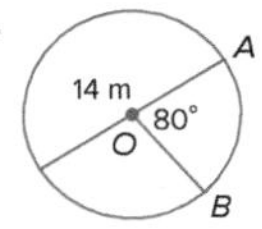

9.77 m

5C.

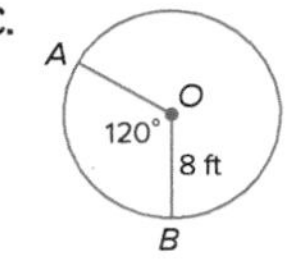

16.76 ft

Angles can also be measured in units that are based on arc length. The **radian measure**, θ, of a central angle is the ratio of the arc length to the radius of the circle: $\theta = \frac{\ell}{r}$ radians.

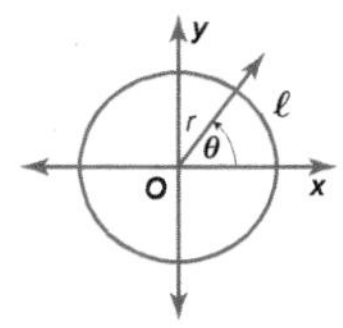

$\theta = \frac{\ell}{r}$ radians

Study Tip

Radian Measure The circumference of a circle is $2\pi r$. So, one complete revolution around a circle equals 2π radians.

$\theta = \frac{2\pi r}{r}$

$= 2\pi$ radians $= 360°$

G.C.5

Example 6 Find Arc Length Using Radian Measure

Find the length of $\widehat{ZY}$. Round to the nearest hundredth.

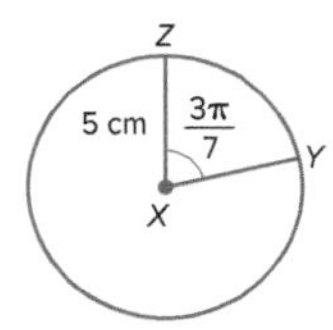

$\theta = \frac{\ell}{r}$ Arc Length Equation

$\frac{3}{7}\pi = \frac{\ell}{5}$ $\theta = \frac{3}{7}\pi, r = 5$

$5\left(\frac{3}{7}\pi\right) = \ell$ Multiply each side by 5.

$\frac{15}{7}\pi = \ell$ Simplify.

$6.73 \approx \ell$ Use a calculator.

Guided Practice

6A.

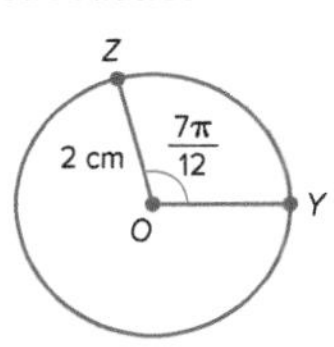

3.67 cm

6B.

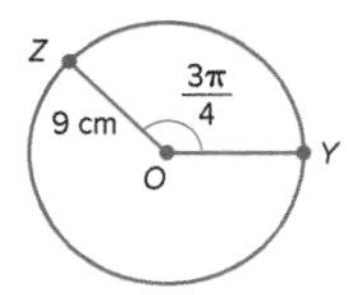

21.21 cm

Need Another Example?

Find the length of $\widehat{AB}$. Round to the nearest hundredth. 15.71

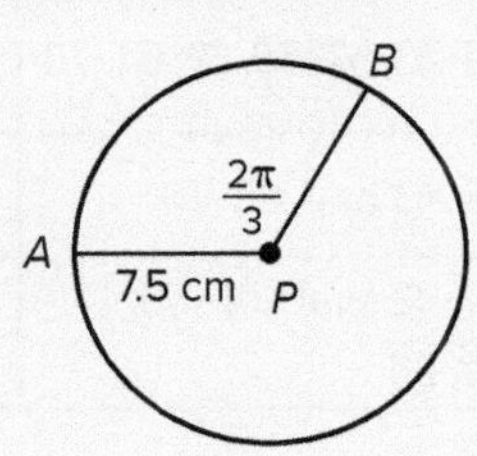

2 Arc Length

Teaching Tip

Sense-Making Advise students that two arcs can have equivalent measures, but different arc lengths. Explain using the formula for the length of an arc and show students that the length of the arc depends on the radius of the circle.

Example 5 Find Arc Length

AL In part **b**, why did we use 5 instead of 10 for *r*? 10 is the diameter, so *r*, the radius, is 5.

OL If the radius in part **a** is 6 inches, what is $\widehat{ZY}$ to the nearest hundredth? 7.85 in.

BL In part **a**, what is the length of the major arch formed by the radii with endpoints *Z* and *Y*? 19.9 in.

Need Another Example?

Find the length of $\widehat{DA}$. Round to the nearest hundredth.

a.

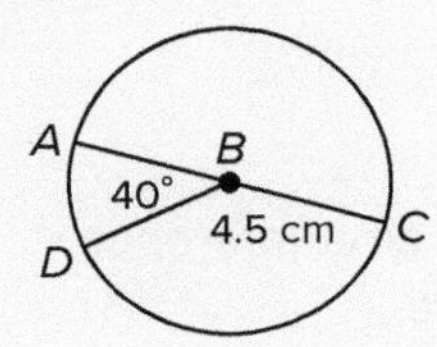

π or about 3.14 cm

b.

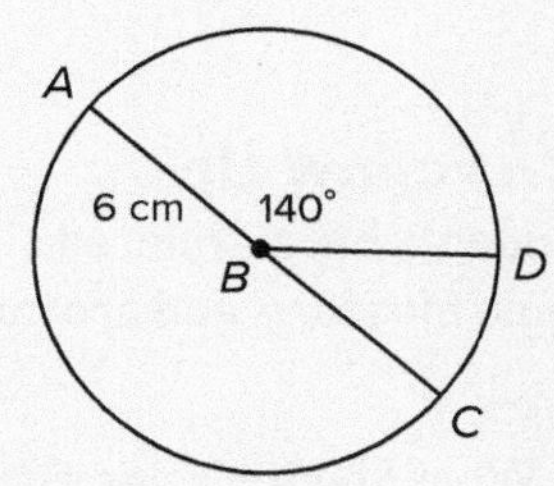

14.66 cm

Example 6 Find Arc Length Using Radian Measure

AL How are radians similar to degrees? different? Sample answer: Both radians and degrees are used to measure central angles of a circle. Degrees are not based on arc length and radius of the circle, but radians are.

OL What is the arc length of $\widehat{ZY}$ if the radius is 10 centimeters? 13.46 cm

BL Do you think you can compare radians and degrees? Explain. Sample answer: Yes; Because the measure in radians is a ratio between the arc length and the radius, I think the measure would correspond to a specific degree measure.

Practice

Formative Assessment Use Exercises 1–13 to assess students' understanding of the concepts in this lesson.

The Practice and Problem Solving exercises assess the content taught in the lesson. The Preparing for Assessment page is meant to be used as preparation for end-of-course assessments.

Extra Practice

See page R9 for extra exercises for students who are approaching level or for on-level students who need additional reinforcement.

> **MP Teaching the Mathematical Practices**
>
> **Precision** Mathematically proficient students use clear definitions in discussion with others and in their own reasoning. In Exercises 3–5, encourage students to choose the best term for each arc.

Follow-Up

Students have explored circles, circumference, angle measure, and arc measure.

Ask:

- What about circles makes them useful? Sample answers: They have a well-known shape; all circles are similar; they can be used to create graphical displays.

Go Online! eBook

Interactive Student Guide

Use the *Interactive Student Guide* to deepen conceptual understanding.

· Angles and Arcs

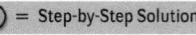

Check Your Understanding ◯ = Step-by-Step Solutions begin on page R14.

Go Online! for a Self-Check Quiz

Example 1 G.C.2

Find the value of x.

1. 170

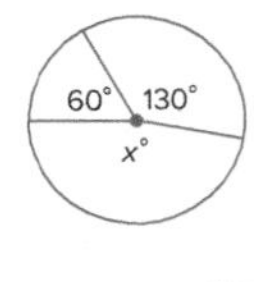

2. 150

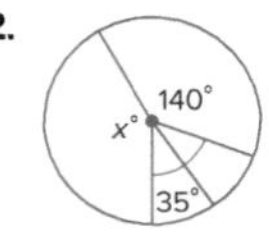

Example 2 G.C.2

MP PRECISION $\overline{HK}$ and $\overline{IG}$ are diameters of ⊙L. Identify each arc as a *major arc, minor arc,* or *semicircle*. Then find its measure.

3. $\widehat{IHJ}$ major arc; 270

4. $\widehat{HI}$ minor arc; 59

5. $\widehat{HGK}$ semicircle; 180

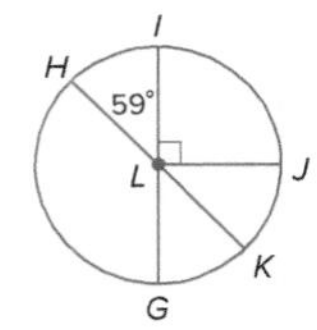

Example 3 G.C.5

6. **FITNESS** The graph shows the results of a survey taken by high school students regarding what activities they participate in after school.

a. Find $m\widehat{AB}$. 32.4

b. Find $m\widehat{BC}$. 43.2

c. Describe the type of arc that the category Sports represents. major arc

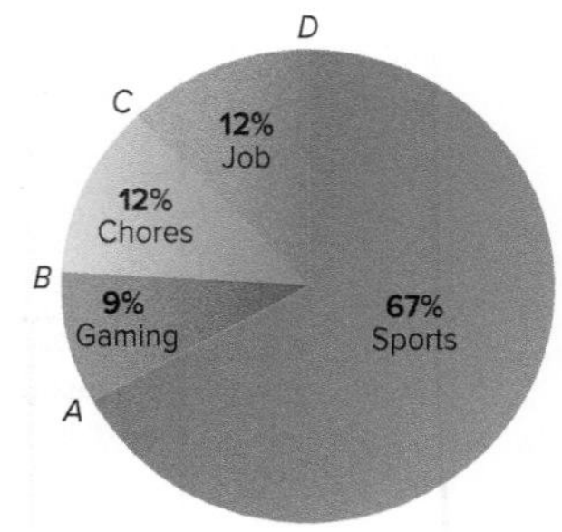

Example 4 G.C.2

$\overline{QS}$ is a diameter of ⊙V. Find each measure.

7. $m\widehat{STP}$ 147

8. $m\widehat{QRT}$ 255

9. $m\widehat{PQR}$ 123

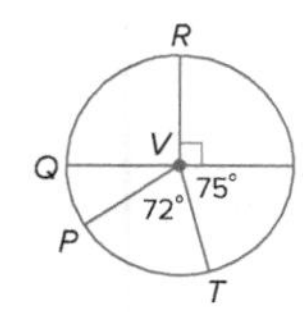

Examples 5-6 G.C.5

Find the length of $\widehat{JK}$. Round to the nearest hundredth.

10. 1.05 ft

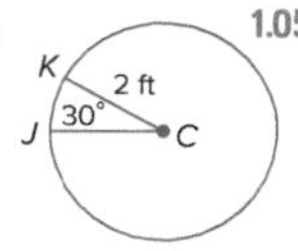

11. 13.74 cm

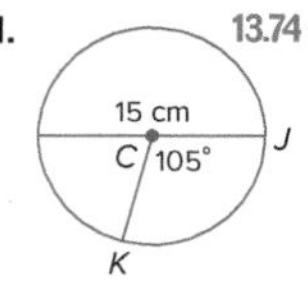

12. 43.5 m

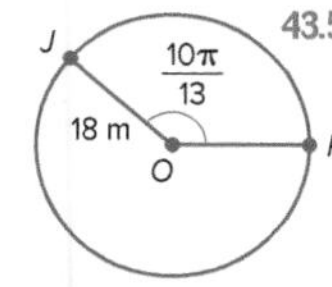

13. 3.14 cm

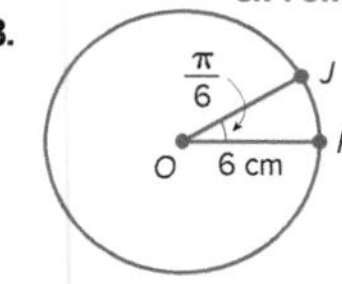

Practice and Problem Solving Extra Practice is on page R9.

Example 1 G.C.2

Find the value of x.

14. 80

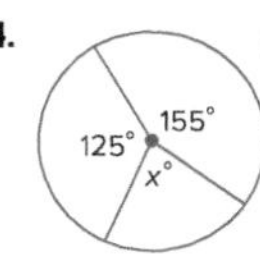

15 225

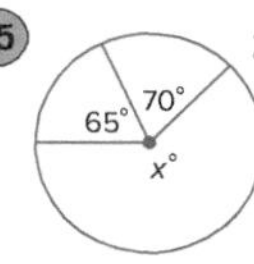

16. 35

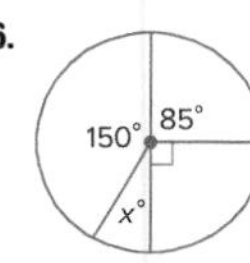

17. 40

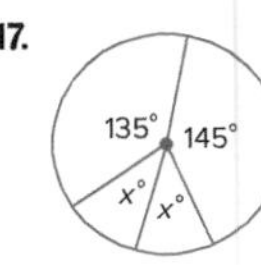

Differentiated Homework Options

Levels	AL Basic	OL Core	BL Advanced
Exercises	14–43, 57–60, 62, 64–70	15–51 odd, 53–60, 62–64, 65–70	54–64, (optional: 65–70)
2-Day Option	15–43 odd, 65–70	14–43	
	14–42 even, 57–60, 62, 64	47–52, 53, 57–60, 62, 64–70	

You can use ALEKS to provide additional remediation support with personalized instruction and practice.

Example 2
G.C.2

$\overline{AD}$ and $\overline{CG}$ are diameters of $\odot B$. Identify each arc as a *major arc, minor arc,* or *semicircle.* Then find its measure.

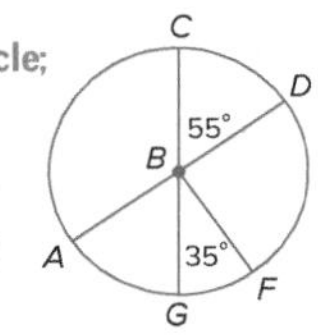

18. $m\widehat{CD}$ minor arc; 55
19. $m\widehat{AC}$ minor arc; 125
20. $m\widehat{CFG}$ 20. semicircle; 180
21. $m\widehat{CGD}$ major arc; 305
22. $m\widehat{GCF}$ major arc; 325
23. $m\widehat{ACD}$ semicircle; 180
24. $m\widehat{AG}$ minor arc; 55
25. $m\widehat{ACF}$ major arc; 270

Example 3
G.C.5

26. **SHOPPING** The graph shows the results of a survey in which teens were asked where the best place was to shop for clothes.

Best Places to Clothes Shop

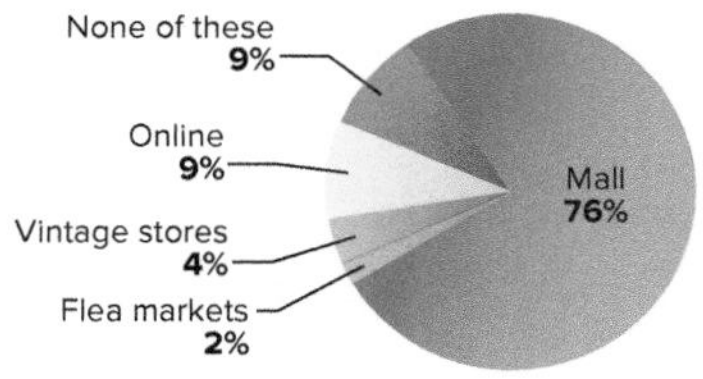

a. What would be the arc measures associated with the mall and vintage stores categories? 273.6, 14.4

b. Describe the kinds of arcs associated with the category "Mall" and the category "None of these." major arc; minor arc

c. Are there any congruent arcs in this graph? Explain. See margin.

27. MP **MODELING** The table shows the distribution of endangered animals by species in a south central part of the United States.

Endangered Animals in South Central U.S.	
mammals	25%
fish	28%
reptiles	21%
amphibians	11%
invertebrates	15%

Source: All About Wildlife

a. If you were to construct a circle graph of this information, what would be the arc measures associated with the first two categories? 90; 100.8

b. Describe the kind of arcs associated with the first and last category. minor; minor

c. Are there any congruent arcs in this graph? Explain. No; no categories share the same percentage of the circle.

Example 2,4
G.C.2

ENTERTAINMENT Use the Ferris wheel shown to find each measure.

28. $m\widehat{FG}$ 40
29. $m\widehat{JH}$ 60
30. $m\widehat{JKF}$ 180
31. $m\widehat{JFH}$ 300
32. $m\widehat{GHF}$ 320
33. $m\widehat{GHK}$ 180
34. $m\widehat{HK}$ 100
35. $m\widehat{JKG}$ 220
36. $m\widehat{KFH}$ 260
37. $m\widehat{HGF}$ 120

Examples 5-6
G.C.5

Use $\odot P$ to find the length of each arc. Round to the nearest hundredth.

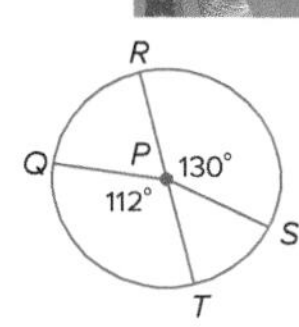

38. $\widehat{RS}$, if the radius is 2 inches 4.54 in.
39. $\widehat{QT}$, if the diameter is 9 centimeters 8.80 cm
40. $\widehat{QR}$, if $PS = 4$ millimeters 4.75 mm
41. $\widehat{RS}$, if $RT = 15$ inches 17.02 in.
42. $\widehat{QRS}$, if $RT = 11$ feet 19.01 ft
43. $\widehat{RTS}$, if $PQ = 3$ meters 12.04 m

Levels of Complexity Chart

The levels of the exercises progress from 1 to 3, with Level 1 indicating the lowest level of complexity.

Exercises	14–43	44–53, 65–70	54–64
C Level 3			●
B Level 2		●	
Level 1	●		

Additional Answer

26c. Yes; the arcs associated with the online; none of these categories have the same arc measure because each category accounts for the same percentage of the circle, 9%.

MP Teaching the Mathematical Practices

Modeling Mathematically proficient students can apply the mathematics they know to solve problems arising in everyday life. They identify important quantities in a practical situation and map their relationships using graphs. In Exercise 27, encourage students to use the information given to construct a circle graph.

Differentiated Instruction OL BL

Extension Have students find the arc length of a circle by using the University of Texas clock tower as a model of a circle. The University of Texas clock face is 14 feet 8 inches in diameter. Find the measure of the central angle of the hands of the clock tower at 5 o'clock. Find the arc length of the hands of the clock tower at 5 o'clock. The measure of the central angle is 150. The measure of the arc length is ≈230 inches or 19 feet 2 inches.

Teaching the Mathematical Practices

Reasoning Mathematically proficient students make sense of quantities and their relationships in problem situations. In Exercises 47–49, encourage students to use the relationship between arc length and radius.

Additional Answers

44. $360 \div 13$ stars ≈ 27.7 between each star

45. The length of the arc would double.

56a. $m\widehat{\ell_1} = m\widehat{\ell_2}$; $\ell_1 < \ell_2$; these comparisons suggest that arc measure is not affected by the size of the circle but that arc length is affected.

56b. Because all circles are similar, the larger circle is a dilation of the smaller by some factor k, so $r_2 = kr_1$ or $k = \frac{r_2}{r_1}$. Likewise, the arc intercepted on the larger circle is a dilation of the arc intercepted on the smaller circle, so $\ell_2 = k\ell_1$ or $k = \frac{\ell_2}{\ell_1}$. Thus $\frac{r_2}{r_1} = \frac{\ell_2}{\ell_1}$ or $\frac{\ell_1}{r_1} = \frac{\ell_2}{r_2}$.

56c. $\ell_1 = \frac{\pi r_1 x}{180}$ and $\ell_2 = \frac{\pi r_2 x}{180}$; $k = \frac{\pi x}{180}$

62. Sample answer:

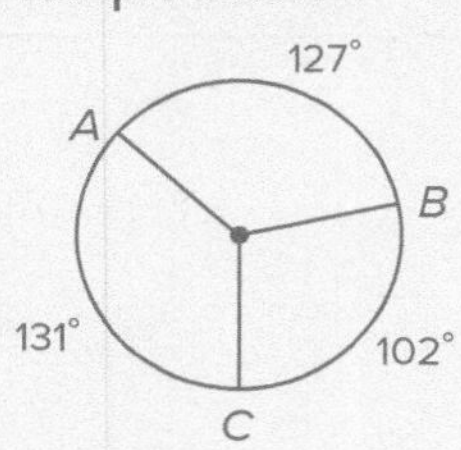

64. Sample answer: minor arc, major arc, semicircle; the measure of a minor arc equals the measure of the corresponding central angle. The measure of a major arc equals 360 minus the measure of the minor arc with the same endpoints. The measure of a semicircle is 180.

B **HISTORY** The figure shows the stars in the Betsy Ross flag referenced at the beginning of the lesson.

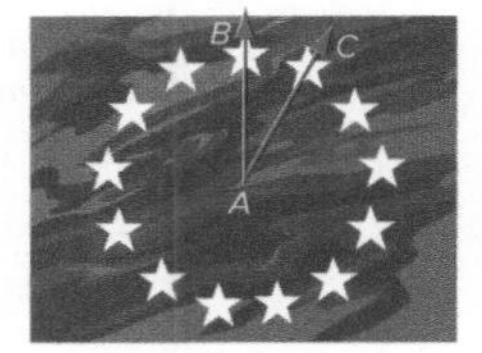

44. What is the measure of central angle A? Explain how you determined your answer. See margin.

45. If the diameter of the circle were doubled, what would be the effect on the arc length from the center of one star B to the next star C? See margin.

46. **FARMS** The *Pizza Farm* in Madera, California, is a circle divided into eight equal slices, as shown at the right. Each "slice" is used for growing or grazing pizza ingredients.

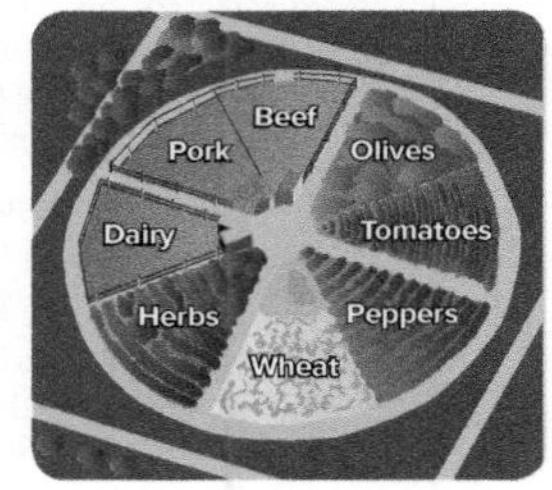

a. What is the total arc measure of the slices containing olives, tomatoes, and peppers? 135

b. The circle is 125 feet in diameter. What is the arc length of one slice? Round to the nearest hundredth. 49.09 ft

REASONING **Find each measure. Round each linear measure to the nearest hundredth and each arc measure to the nearest degree.**

47. circumference of $\odot S$ 40.83 in.

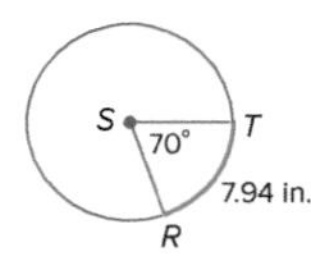

48. $m\widehat{CD}$ 150°

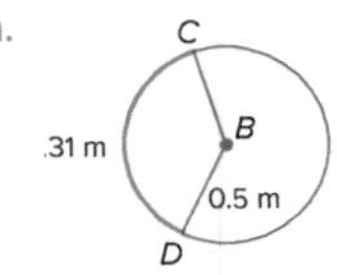

49. radius of $\odot K$ 9.50 ft

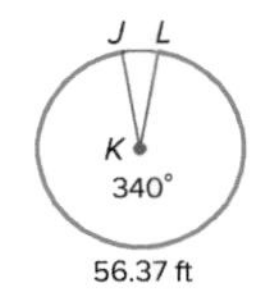

ALGEBRA In $\odot C$, $m\angle HCG = 2x$ and $m\angle HCD = 6x + 28$. Find each measure.

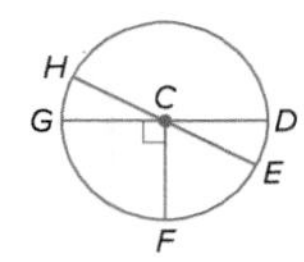

50. $m\widehat{EF}$ 52 **51.** $m\widehat{HD}$ 142 **52.** $m\widehat{HGF}$ 128

53 **RIDES** A pirate ship ride follows a semicircular path, as shown in the diagram.

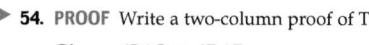

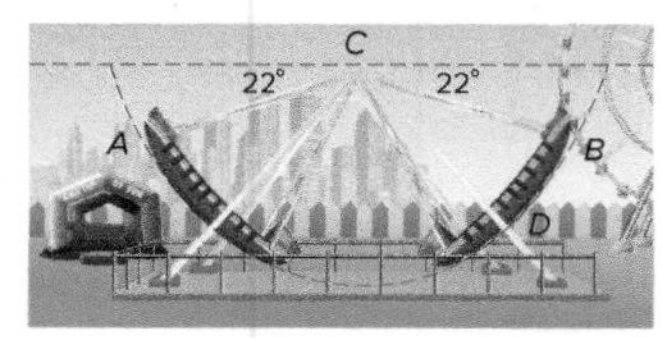

a. What is $m\widehat{AB}$? 136

b. If $CD = 62$ feet, what is the length of $\widehat{AB}$? Round to the nearest hundredth. 147.17 ft

54. Proof:

Statements (Reasons)

1. $\angle BAC \cong \angle DAE$ (Given)
2. $m\angle BAC = m\angle DAE$ (Definition of $\cong$ ∠s)
3. $m\angle BAC = m\widehat{BC}$, $m\angle DAE = m\widehat{DE}$ (Definition of arc measure)
4. $m\widehat{BC} = m\widehat{DE}$ (Substitution)
5. $\widehat{BC} \cong \widehat{DE}$ (Definition of $\cong$ arcs)

C **54.** **PROOF** Write a two-column proof of Theorem 9.1.

Given: $\angle BAC \cong \angle DAE$

Prove: $\widehat{BC} \cong \widehat{DE}$

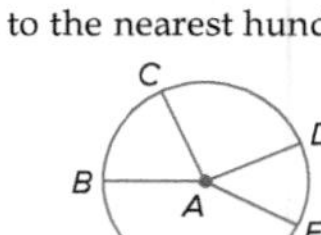

Differentiated Instruction AL OL BL

Extension Circle graphs are a very simple yet effective way of displaying data. Allow students the opportunity to develop and answer a research question related to an area of interest. Ask students to display the results using a circle graph with accurate arc measurements to represent their data.

55. **COORDINATE GEOMETRY** In the graph, point M is located at the origin. Find each measure in $\odot M$. Round each linear measure to the nearest hundredth and each arc measure to the nearest tenth degree.

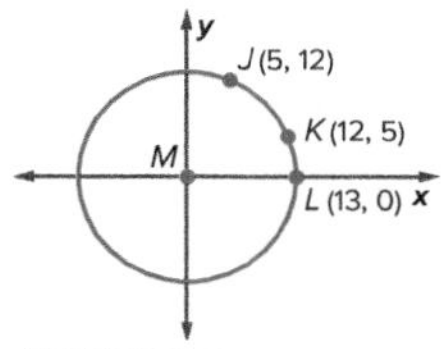

a. $m\widehat{JL}$ 67.4 b. $m\widehat{KL}$ 22.6 c. $m\widehat{JK}$ 44.8

d. length of $\widehat{JL}$ 15.29 units e. length of $\widehat{JK}$ 10.16 units

G.C.5 56. **ARC LENGTH AND RADIAN MEASURE** In this problem, you will use concentric circles to show that the length of the arc intercepted by a central angle of a circle is dependent on the circle's radius.

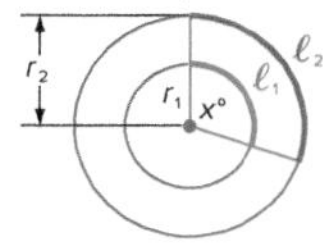

a. Compare the measures of arc ℓ_1 and arc ℓ_2. Then compare the lengths of arc ℓ_1 and arc ℓ_2. What do these two comparisons suggest? a–c. See margin.

b. Use similarity transformations (dilations) to explain why the length of an arc ℓ intercepted by a central angle of a circle is proportional to the circle's radius r. That is, explain why we can say that for this diagram, $\frac{\ell_1}{r_1} = \frac{\ell_2}{r_2}$.

c. Write expressions for the lengths of arcs ℓ_1 and ℓ_2. Use these expressions to identify the constant of proportionality k in $\ell = kr$.

d. The expression that you wrote for k in part **c** converts the degree measure of an angle to the *radian measure* of an angle. Use it to find the radian measure of an angle measuring 90°. $\frac{\pi}{2}$

G.C.2, G.C.5

H.O.T. Problems Use **H**igher-**O**rder **T**hinking Skills

57. **ERROR ANALYSIS** Brody says that $\widehat{WX}$ and $\widehat{YZ}$ are congruent since their central angles have the same measure. Selena says they are not congruent. Is either of them correct? Explain your reasoning.

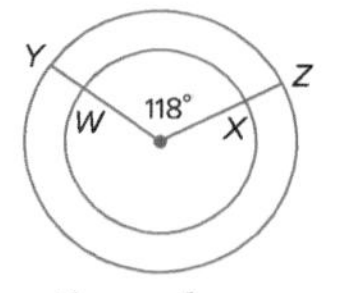

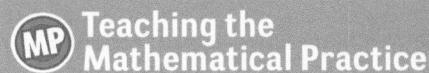

Selena; the circles are not congruent because they do not have congruent radii. So, the arcs are not congruent.

CONSTRUCT ARGUMENTS Determine whether each statement is *sometimes, always,* or *never* true. Explain your reasoning.

58. The measure of a minor arc is less than 180.

58. Always; by definition, an arc that measures less than 180 is a minor arc.

59. If a central angle is obtuse, its corresponding arc is a major arc.

59. Never; obtuse angles intersect arcs that measure between 90° and 180°.

60. The sum of the measures of adjacent arcs of a circle depends on the measure of the radius.

60. Never; the sum of the measures of adjacent arcs depends on the measures of the arcs.

61. **CHALLENGE** The measures of $\widehat{LM}$, $\widehat{MN}$, and $\widehat{NL}$ are in the ratio 5 : 3 : 4. Find the measure of each arc.
$m\widehat{LM} = 150$, $m\widehat{MN} = 90$, $m\widehat{NL} = 120$

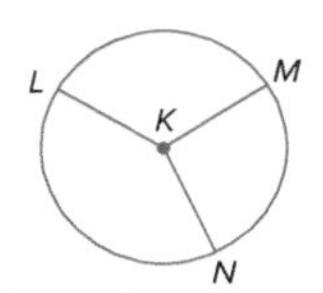

62. **OPEN-ENDED** Draw a circle and locate three points on the circle. Estimate the measures of the three nonoverlapping arcs that are formed. Then use a protractor to find the measure of each arc. Label your circle with the arc measures. See margin.

63. **CHALLENGE** The time shown on an analog clock is 8:10. What is the measure of the angle formed by the hands of the clock? 175

64. **WRITING IN MATH** Describe the three different types of arcs in a circle and the method for finding the measure of each one. See margin.

Standards for Mathematical Practice

Emphasis On	Exercises
1 Make sense of problems and persevere in solving them.	50–52, 67, 70
2 Reason abstractly and quantitatively.	6, 44–45, 47–49
3 Construct viable arguments and critique the reasoning of others.	26, 56–64
4 Model with mathematics.	27, 46
6 Attend to precision.	3–5, 53, 55, 65–66, 68–69
8 Look for and express regularity in repeated reasoning.	28–37

Assess

Ticket Out the Door Ask students to sketch a circle with a central angle. Have them identify the length of the radius and then draw and label the degrees of a central angle. Instruct students to find the arc length for either the major or the minor arc. Have students turn in their work before they leave the classroom.

Exercise Alert

Compass, Straightedge, and Protractor
Exercises 56 and 62 require the use of a compass, a straightedge, and a protractor.

Watch Out!

Error Analysis In Exercise 57, students should realize that concentric circles that share a central angle will always have the same arc measure. However, the larger the circle is, the greater the distance between the angle endpoints will be. Therefore, the arc length increases in direct proportion to the diameter of the circle. Selena is correct.

Challenge For Exercise 61, remind students that the order of the factors matters in proportions. For example, if the ratio of A to B to C is 1 to 2 to 3, $A : B : C = 1 : 2 : 3$.

Teaching the Mathematical Practices

Construct Arguments Mathematically proficient students understand and use stated assumptions and definitions in constructing arguments. They make conjectures and build a logical progression of statements to explore the truth of their conjectures. In Exercises 58–60, encourage students to draw a diagram of the situation described.

Go Online!

eSolutions Manual
Create worksheets, answer keys, and solutions handouts for your assignments.

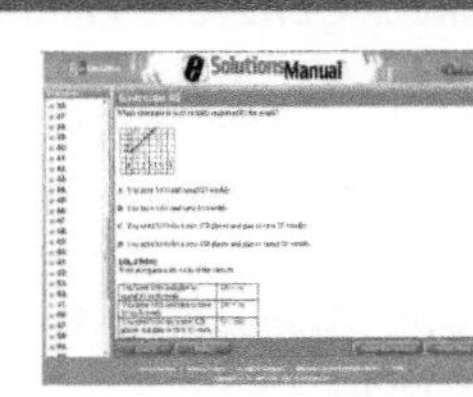

Preparing for Assessment

Exercises 65–70 require students to use the skills they will need on standardized assessments. Exercises are dual-coded with content standards and mathematical practice standards.

Dual Coding

Items	Content Standards	MP Mathematical Practices
65	G.C.5	6
66	G.C.5	6
67	G.C.2	6
68	G.C.2, G.C.5	6
69	G.C.5	6
70	G.C.2, G.C.5	2

Diagnose Student Errors

Survey student responses for each item. Class trends may indicate common errors and misconceptions.

65.

A	Calculated circumference only
B	Used 4 as the radius
C	CORRECT
D	Used 2 as the diameter

66.

A	Incorrectly calculated measure of central angle
B	Incorrectly calculated measure of central angle and used 12 as radius
C	Used 12 as radius
D	CORRECT
E	Omitted factor of 2 in arc length formula

Go Online!

Quizzes

Students can use *Self-Check Quizzes* to check their understanding of this lesson and have the results sent to you. You can also give *Quiz 1*, which covers the content in Lessons 9-1 and 9-2.

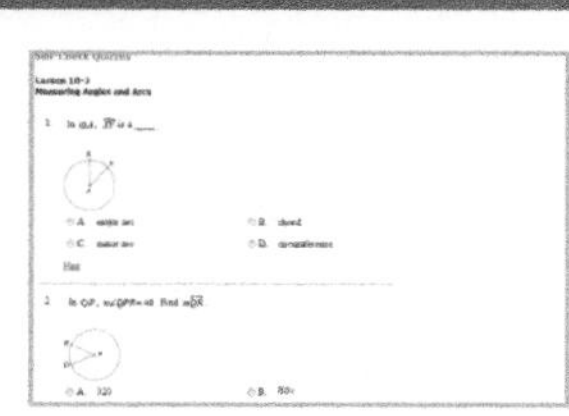

Preparing for Assessment

65. A model train runs on a circular track with a diameter of 4 meters, as shown. Which of the following is the best estimate of the distance the train travels as it moves from the station to the grain silo? MP 6 G.C.5 **C**

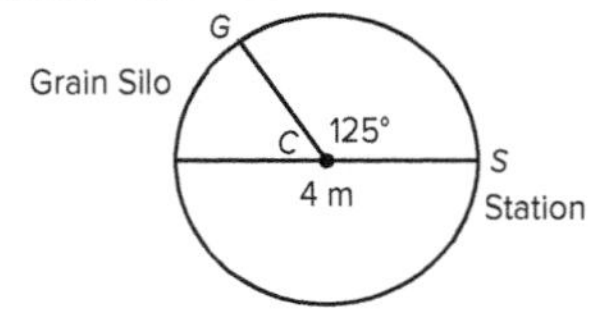

○ A 12.6 m
○ B 8.7 m
○ C 4.4 m
○ D 2.2 m

66. In ⊙J, $\angle KJL \cong \angle LJM \cong \angle MJN$. Sofia wants to calculate the length of $\widehat{LN}$.

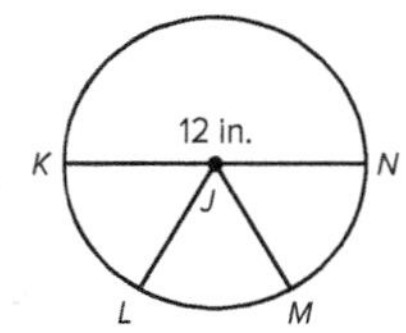

Which expression can Sofia use to find the required length? MP 6 G.C.5 **D**

○ A $\frac{60}{360} \cdot 12\pi$
○ B $\frac{60}{360} \cdot 24\pi$
○ C $\frac{120}{360} \cdot 24\pi$
○ D $\frac{120}{360} \cdot 12\pi$
○ E $\frac{120}{360} \cdot 6\pi$

67. In ⊙B, $m\angle LBM = 3x$ and $m\angle LBQ = 4x + 61$.

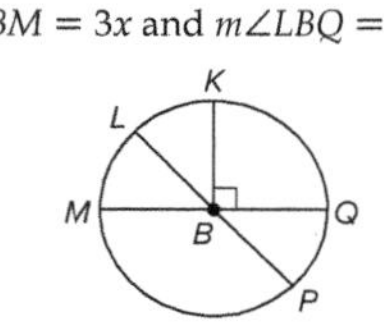

What is the measure of $\angle PBQ$? MP 6 G.C.2

51

68. MULTI-STEP The table shows the polling numbers for an upcoming election. MP 6 G.C.2, G.C.5

Distribution of Voters	
Candidate A	32%
Candidate B	30%
Candidate C	28%
Candidate D	5%
Candidate E	5%

a. If you were to construct a circle graph of this information, what would be the arc measures for candidates B and D? **108; 18**

b. Suppose candidates A and B are combined on the circle graph. What would be the arc measure? And what type of arc would this be? **223.2, major arc**

c. Suppose candidates C, D, and E are combined on the circle graph. What would be the arc measure? And what type of arc would this be? **136.8; minor arc**

d. Are there any congruent arcs in this graph? Explain. **Yes, the arcs for D and E are congruent since candidates D and E each account for the same percentage.**

69. The minute hand of a clock is 3 inches long. Which of the following is the best estimate of the distance the tip of the hand moves as the time changes from 12:30 to 12:45? MP 6 G.C.5 **C**

○ A 0.8 in.
○ B 2.4 in.
○ C 4.7 in.
○ D 9.4 in.

70. In ⊙Q, the length of $\widehat{ST}$ is 3π centimeters.

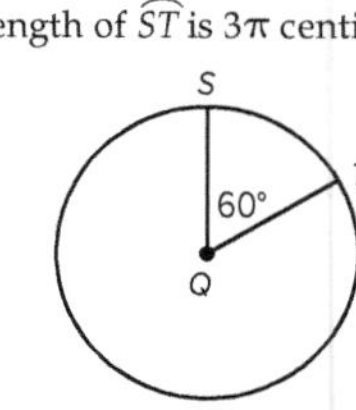

What is the radius of the circle? MP 2 G.C.2, G.C.5 **C**

○ A 0.11 cm
○ B 1.5 cm
○ C 9 cm
○ D 18 cm

69.

A	Used 15 as measure of central angle
B	Used 1.5 as radius
C	CORRECT
D	Used 6 as radius

70.

A	Incorrectly solved $3\pi = \frac{1}{3}\pi r$ by multiplying both sides by $\frac{1}{3}$
B	Omitted factor of $\frac{60}{360}$
C	CORRECT
D	Found diameter

LESSON 9-3

Arcs and Chords

SUGGESTED PACING (DAYS)

	Instruction
90 min.	0.5
45 min.	1.0

Track Your Progress

Objectives

1. Recognize and use relationships between arcs and chords.
2. Recognize and use relationships between arcs, chords, and diameters.

Mathematical Background

The endpoints of a chord are also endpoints of an arc. Two minor arcs are congruent if and only if their corresponding chords are congruent. Two chords are congruent if and only if they are equidistant from the center of the circle.

THEN

G.C.2 Identify and describe relationships among inscribed angles, radii, and chords.

G.C.5 Derive using similarity the fact that the length of the arc intercepted by an angle is proportional to the radius, and define the radian measure of the angle as the constant of proportionality; derive the formula for the area of a sector.

NOW

G.CO.12 Make formal geometric constructions with a variety of tools and methods (compass and straightedge, string, reflective devices, paper folding, dynamic geometric software, etc.).

G.C.2 Identify and describe relationships among inscribed angles, radii, and chords.

G. MG.3 Apply geometric methods to solve design problems (e.g., designing an object or structure to satisfy physical constraints or minimize cost; working with typographic grid systems based on ratios).

NEXT

G.C.3 Construct the inscribed and circumscribed circles of a triangle, and prove properties of angles for a quadrilateral inscribed in a circle.

Go Online! All of these resources and more are available at connectED.mcgraw-hill.com

eLessons **utilize the power of your interactive whiteboard in an engaging way. Use Chords, Arcs, and Angles, Screens 10–12, to introduce the concepts in this lesson.**

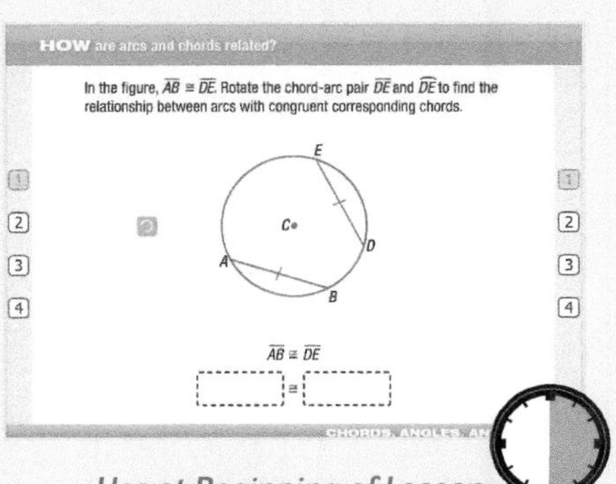

Use at Beginning of Lesson

Personal Tutors (for every example) let students hear real teachers solve problems. Students can pause and repeat as many times as necessary.

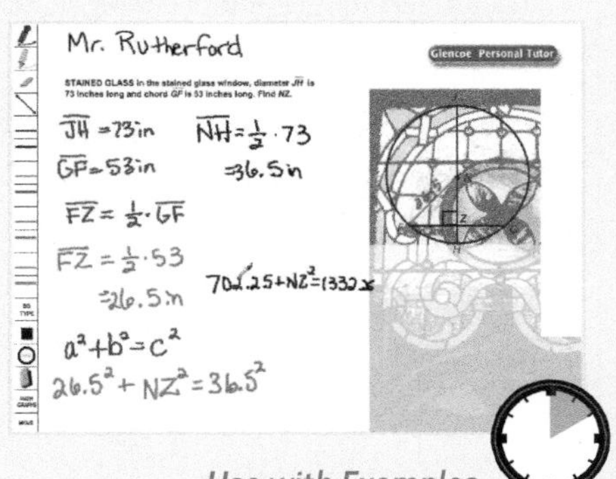

Use with Examples

Use The Geometer's Sketchpad to explore the properties of chords in a circle.

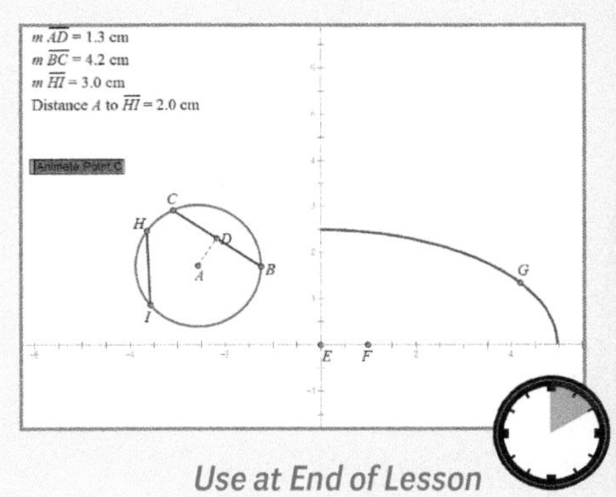

Use at End of Lesson

OER Using Open Educational Resources

Interactive Activity Have students use the gizmo *Chords and Arcs* by **Explorelearning** to explore the relationships between chords and arcs in circles. You can register for a free 30-day trial. *Use as in-class activity*

Go Online!

connectED.mcgraw-hill.com

Worksheets

Differentiate Your Resources

Extra Practice Additional practice or homework; Skills Practice is best for approaching-level students and Practice is best for on-level and beyond-level students

Skills Practice

AL OL ELL

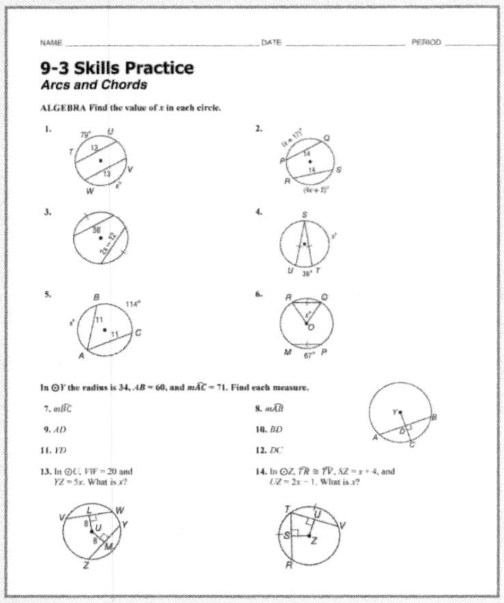
9-3 Skills Practice
Arcs and Chords
ALGEBRA Find the value of x in each circle.

Practice

AL OL BL ELL

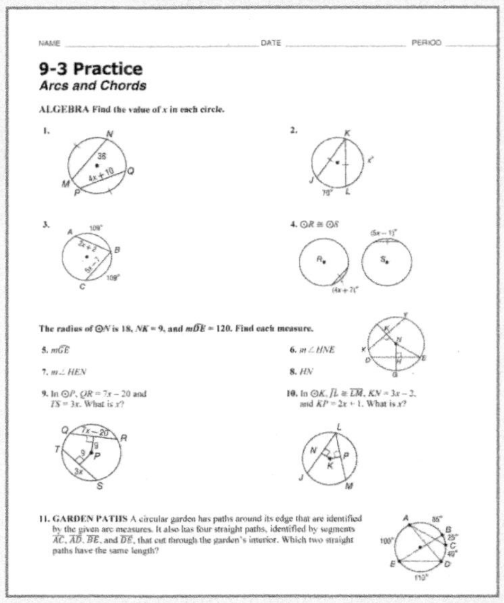
9-3 Practice
Arcs and Chords
ALGEBRA Find the value of x in each circle.

Word Problem Practice

AL OL BL ELL

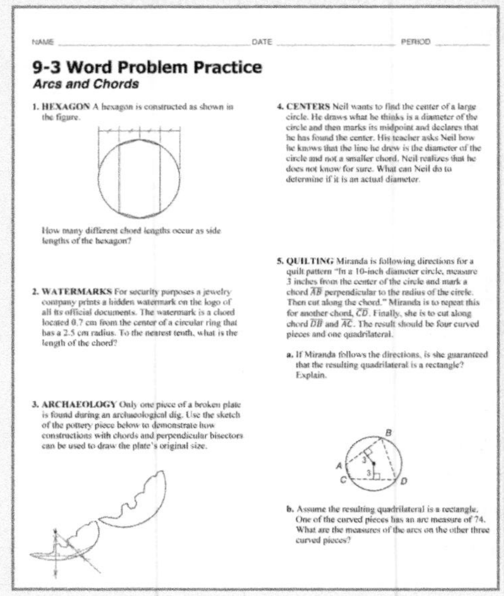
9-3 Word Problem Practice
Arcs and Chords

Intervention Reteaching and vocabulary activities that can be used with struggling or absent students and as ELL support

Study Guide and Intervention

AL OL ELL

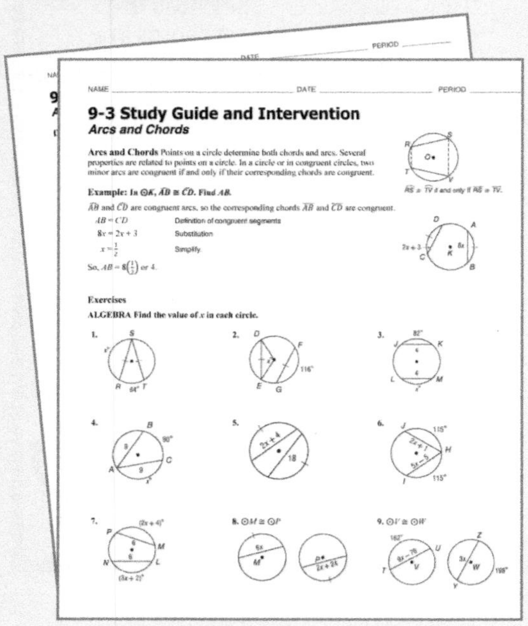
9-3 Study Guide and Intervention
Arcs and Chords
Exercises
ALGEBRA Find the value of x in each circle.

Study Notebook

AL OL BL ELL

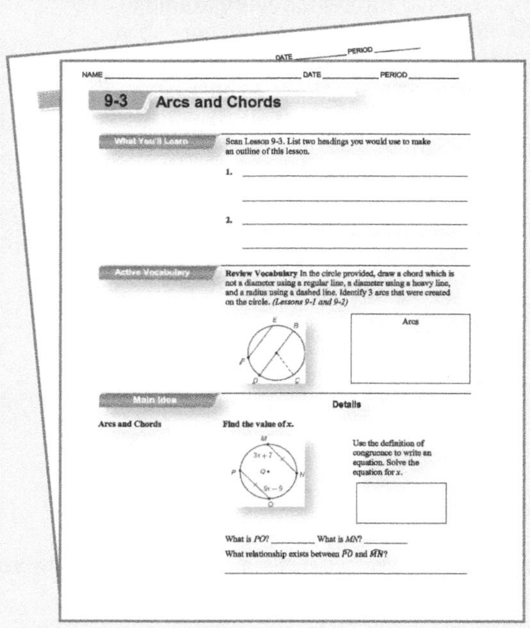
9-3 Arcs and Chords

Extension Activities that can be used to extend lesson concepts

Enrichment

OL BL ELL

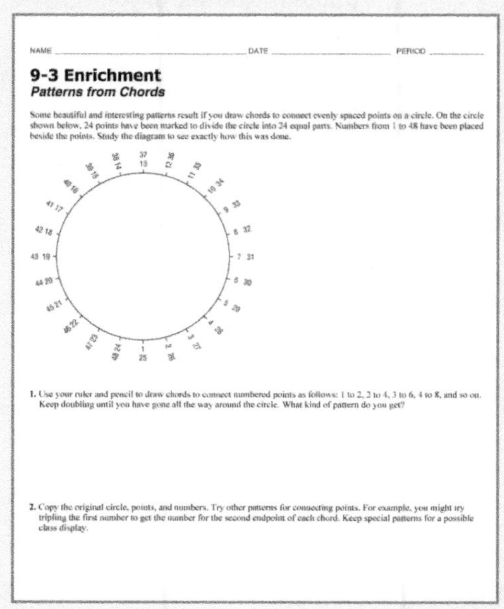
9-3 Enrichment
Patterns from Chords

LESSON 3

Arcs and Chords

Then	Now	Why?
• You used the relationships between arcs and angles to find measures.	• **1** Recognize and use relationships between arcs and chords. **2** Recognize and use relationships between arcs, chords, and diameters.	• Embroidery hoops are used in sewing, quilting, and cross-stitching, as well as for embroidering. The endpoints of the snowflake shown are both the endpoints of a chord and the endpoints of an arc.

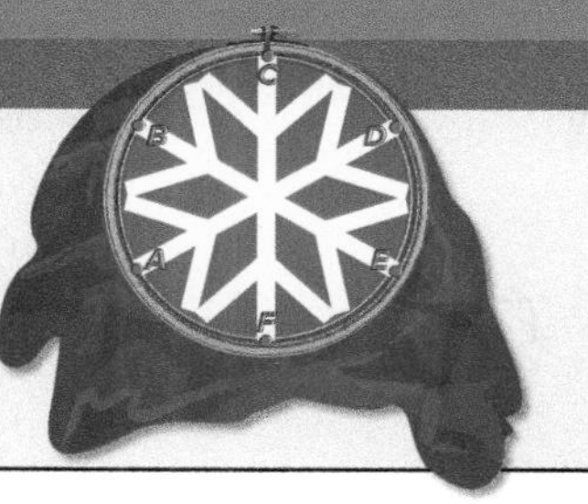

MP Mathematical Practices

4 Model with mathematics.

3 Construct viable arguments and critique the reasoning of others.

Content Standards

G.C.2 Identify and describe relationships among inscribed angles, radii, and chords.

G.MG.3 Apply geometric methods to solve problems (e.g., designing an object or structure to satisfy physical constraints or minimize cost; working with typographic grid systems based on ratios).

G.CO.12 Make formal geometric constructions with a variety of tools and methods (compass and straightedge, string, reflective devices, paper folding, dynamic geometric software, etc.).

1 Arcs and Chords A *chord* is a segment with endpoints on a circle. If a chord is not a diameter, then its endpoints divide the circle into a major and a minor arc.

Theorem 9.2

Words In the same circle or in congruent circles, two minor arcs are congruent if and only if their corresponding chords are congruent.

Example $\widehat{FG} \cong \widehat{HJ}$ if and only if $\overline{FG} \cong \overline{HJ}$.

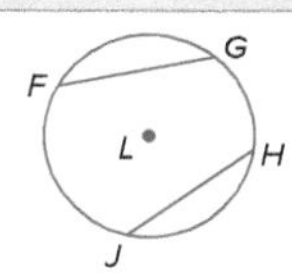

Proof Theorem 9.2 (part 1)

Given: $\odot P$; $\widehat{QR} \cong \widehat{ST}$

Prove: $\overline{QR} \cong \overline{ST}$

Proof:

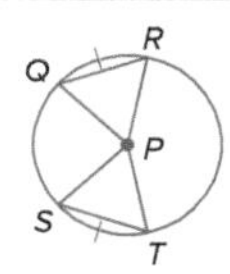

Statements	Reasons
1. $\odot P$, $\widehat{QR} \cong \widehat{ST}$	1. Given
2. $\angle QPR \cong \angle SPT$	2. If arcs are ≅, their corresponding central ∠s are ≅.
3. $\overline{QP} \cong \overline{PR} \cong \overline{SP} \cong \overline{PT}$	3. All radii of a circle are ≅.
4. $\triangle PQR \cong \triangle PST$	4. SAS
5. $\overline{QR} \cong \overline{ST}$	5. CPCTC

You will prove part 2 of Theorem 9.2 in Exercise 25.

G.C.2

Real-World Example 1 Use Congruent Chords to Find Arc Measure

CRAFTS In the embroidery hoop, $\overline{AB} \cong \overline{CD}$ and $m\widehat{AB} = 60$. Find $m\widehat{CD}$.

$\overline{AB}$ and $\overline{CD}$ are congruent chords, so the corresponding arcs $\widehat{AB}$ and $\widehat{CD}$ are congruent. $m\widehat{AB} = m\widehat{CD} = 60$

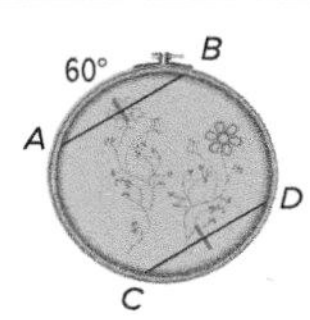

Guided Practice

1. If $m\widehat{AB} = 78$ in the embroidery hoop, find $m\widehat{CD}$. 78

MP Mathematical Practices Strategies

Construct viable arguments and critique the reasoning of others.
Help students to construct viable arguments using the theorem: two minor arcs are congruent if and only their corresponding chords are congruent. For example in Guided Practice 1, ask the following questions:

- What are $\overline{AB}$ and $\overline{CD}$? chords
- What are $\widehat{AB}$ and $\widehat{CD}$? arcs
- How do you mark the figure to show two chords are congruent? one line through each chord
- How do you know that $m\widehat{AB} = m\widehat{CD}$? Because of the theorem; if chord $\overline{AB} = \overline{CD}$ then $m\widehat{AB} = m\widehat{CD}$.

Launch

Have students read the Why? section of the lesson. Ask:

- **What is the measure of one central angle of the embroidered snowflake?** 60
- **Assume that the embroidery hoop is 12 inches in diameter. What is the arc length of one central angle? Round to the nearest hundredth.** 6.28 in.
- **Assume that the size of the embroidery hoop is increased by 125%. Make a conjecture about the new length of a chord and an arc.** Both lengths will also increase by 125%.

Teach

Ask the scaffolded questions for each example to build conceptual understanding for students at all levels.

1 Arcs and Chords

Example 1 Use Congruent Chords to Find Arc Measure

AL If $m\widehat{CD} = 55$, what is $m\widehat{AB}$? 55

OL What is $m\widehat{AC} + m\widehat{BD}$? 240

BL Can we determine if the chords are parallel? Explain. No; sample answer: the chords could be anywhere on the circle and still be congruent, so we can't determine if they are parallel with the information given.

(continued on the next page)

Go Online!

Interactive Whiteboard

Use the *eLesson*, *Lesson Presentation*, or *Interactive Classroom* to present this lesson.

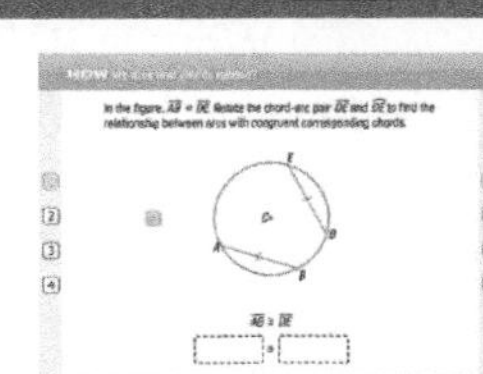

Need Another Example?

Jewelry A circular piece of jade is hung from a chain by two wires wrapped around the stone. $\overline{JM} \cong \overline{KL}$ and $m\widehat{KL} = 90$. Find $m\widehat{JM}$.

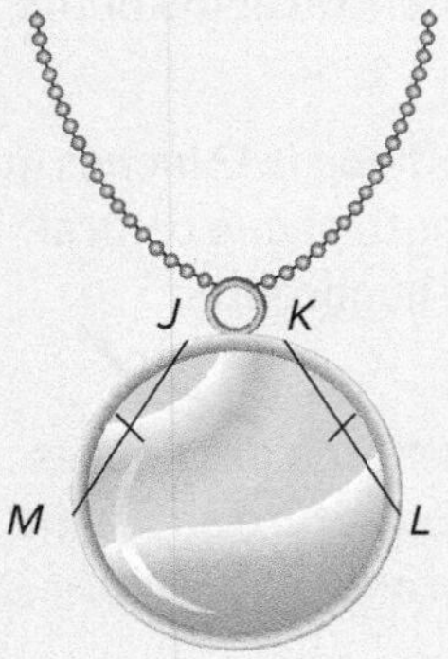

$m\widehat{KL} = m\widehat{JM} = 90$

Example 2 Use Congruent Arcs to Find Chord Lengths

AL If MN is 5, what is PQ? 5

OL If $MN = 2y + 7$ and $PQ = 5y - 2$, what is y? 3

BL If an arc on one circle has the same measure as an arc on a second circle, are the two circles necessarily congruent? Explain. No; sample answer: a pair of arcs with the same measure is not enough to guarantee that two circles are congruent. The arcs could correspond to different central angles and chord lengths.

Need Another Example?

Algebra In the figure, $\odot A \cong \odot B$ and $\widehat{WX} \cong \widehat{YZ}$. Find WX.

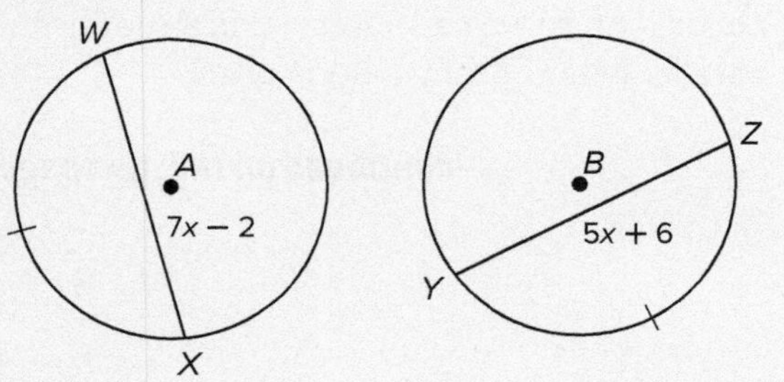

$WX = 26$

2 Bisecting Arcs and Chords

Example 3 Use a Radius Perpendicular to a Chord

AL What is PT? 6

OL If $m\widehat{QR} = 65$, what is $m\widehat{PQR}$? 130

BL If $m\widehat{PQ} = m\widehat{QR}$, and $TR = 8$, what is PR? 16

G.C.2

Example 2 Use Congruent Arcs to Find Chord Lengths

ALGEBRA In the figures, $\odot J \cong \odot K$ and $\widehat{MN} \cong \widehat{PQ}$. Find PQ.

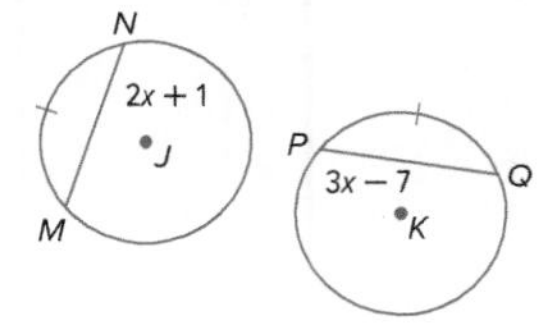

$\widehat{MN}$ and $\widehat{PQ}$ are congruent arcs in congruent circles, so the corresponding chords $\overline{MN}$ and $\overline{PQ}$ are congruent.

$MN = PQ$	Definition of congruent segments
$2x + 1 = 3x - 7$	Substitution
$8 = x$	Simplify.

So, $PQ = 3(8) - 7$ or 17.

Guided Practice

2. In $\odot W$, $\widehat{RS} \cong \widehat{TV}$. Find RS. 11

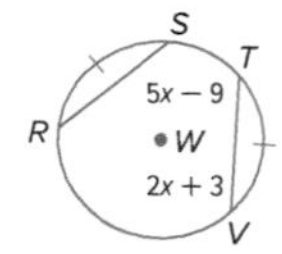

Study Tip ELL

Arc Bisectors In the figure below, $\overline{FH}$ is an arc bisector of $\widehat{JG}$.

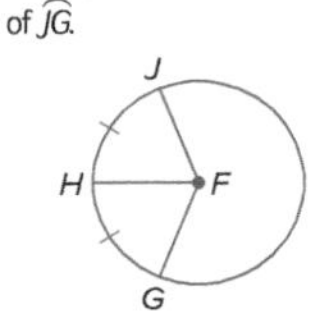

2 Bisecting Arcs and Chords If a line, segment, or ray divides an arc into two congruent arcs, then it *bisects* the arc.

Theorems

9.3 If a diameter (or radius) of a circle is perpendicular to a chord, then it bisects the chord and its arc.

Example If diameter $\overline{AB}$ is perpendicular to chord $\overline{XY}$, then $\overline{XZ} \cong \overline{ZY}$ and $\widehat{XB} \cong \widehat{BY}$.

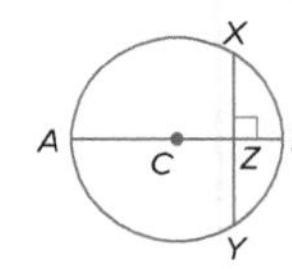

9.4 The perpendicular bisector of a chord is a diameter (or radius) of the circle.

Example If $\overline{AB}$ is a perpendicular bisector of chord $\overline{XY}$, then $\overline{AB}$ is a diameter of $\odot C$.

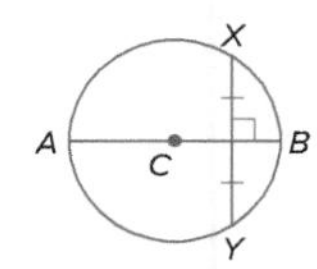

You will prove Theorems 9.3 and 9.4 in Exercises 26 and 28, respectively.

G.C.2

Example 3 Use a Radius Perpendicular to a Chord

In $\odot S$, $m\widehat{PQR} = 98$. Find $m\widehat{PQ}$.

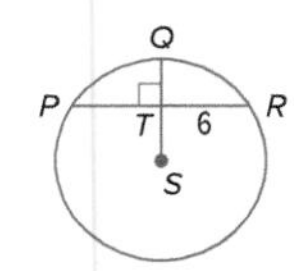

Radius $\overline{SQ}$ is perpendicular to chord $\overline{PR}$. So by Theorem 9.3, $\overline{SQ}$ bisects $\widehat{PQR}$. Therefore, $m\widehat{PQ} = m\widehat{QR}$. By substitution, $m\widehat{PQ} = \frac{98}{2}$ or 49.

Guided Practice

3. In $\odot S$, find PR. 12 units

Need Another Example?

In $\odot G$, $m\widehat{DEF} = 150$. Find $m\widehat{DE}$.

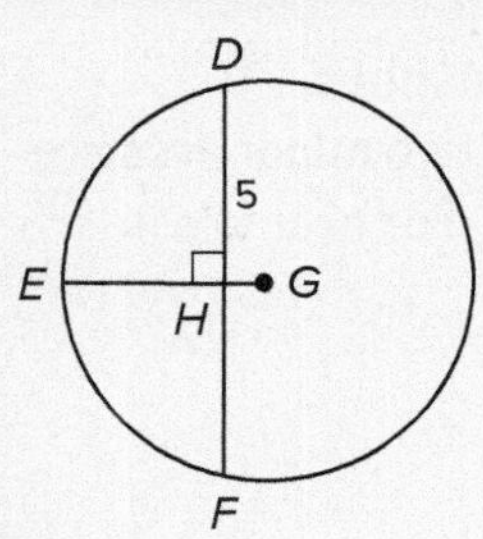

$m\widehat{DE} = 75$

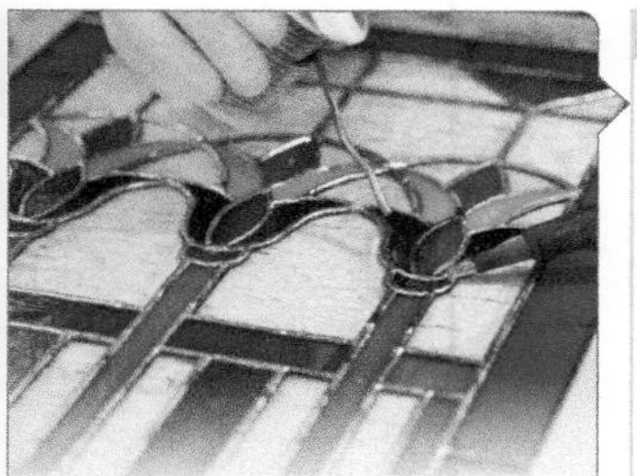

Real-World Link

To make stained glass windows, glass is heated to a temperature of 2000 degrees, until it is the consistency of taffy. The colors are caused by the addition of metallic oxides.

Source: *Artistic Stained Glass by Regg*

G.C.2

Real-World Example 4 Use a Diameter Perpendicular to a Chord

STAINED GLASS **In the stained glass window, diameter $\overline{GH}$ is 30 inches long and chord $\overline{KM}$ is 22 inches long. Find JL.**

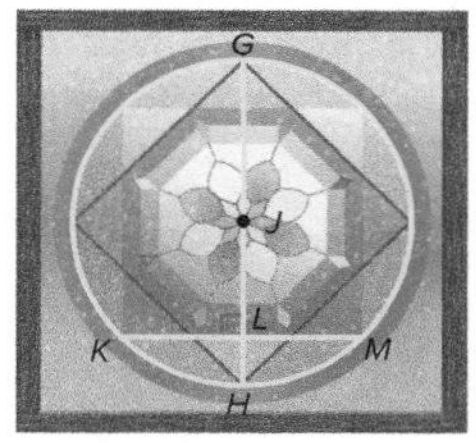

Step 1 Draw radius $\overline{JK}$.

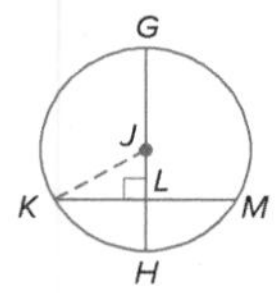

This forms right $\triangle JKL$.

Step 2 Find JK and KL.

Because $GH = 30$ inches, $JH = 15$ inches. All radii of a circle are congruent, so $JK = 15$ inches.

Because diameter $\overline{GH}$ is perpendicular to $\overline{KM}$, $\overline{GH}$ bisects chord $\overline{KM}$ by Theorem 9.3. So, $KL = \frac{1}{2}(22)$ or 11 inches.

Step 3 Use the Pythagorean Theorem to find JL.

$KL^2 + JL^2 = JK^2$	Pythagorean Theorem
$11^2 + JL^2 = 15^2$	$KL = 11$ and $JK = 15$
$121 + JL^2 = 225$	Simplify.
$JL^2 = 104$	Subtract 121 from each side.
$JL = \sqrt{104}$	Take the positive square root of each side.

So, JL is $\sqrt{104}$ or about 10.20 inches long.

Guided Practice

4. In $\odot R$, find TV. Round to the nearest hundredth. 18.44 units

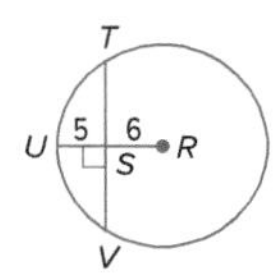

Go Online!

You can add any known information to a figure to help you solve a problem. In Example 4 radius $\overline{JK}$ was drawn. Work with a partner to complete the Self-Check Quiz. Take turns describing how to solve each problem and any information added to each figure. Ask for clarification as you need it. ELL

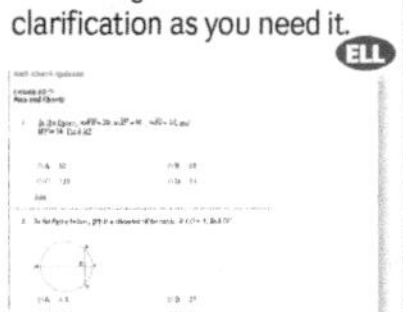

In addition to Theorem 9.2, you can use the following theorem to determine whether two chords in a circle are congruent.

Theorem 9.5

Words In the same circle or in congruent circles, two chords are congruent if and only if they are equidistant from the center.

Example $\overline{FG} \cong \overline{JH}$ if and only if $LX = LY$.

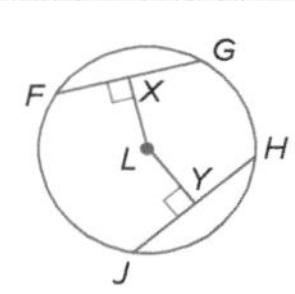

You will prove Theorem 9.5 in Exercises 29 and 30.

Teaching Tip

Mark What Is Known Any known information can be added to a figure to help solve problems. Angles, segment lengths, arcs, radii, and diameters all exist even if they are not drawn. Remind students to be careful to follow geometric conditions and definitions when they add elements to a figure.

Example 4 Use a Diameter Perpendicular to a Chord

AL What is LH? about 4.8 in.

OL If the diameter of the window is increased by 25%, what is KL? 13.75 in.

BL If the diameter of the window is increased by 25%, what is JL? about 12.75 in.

Need Another Example?

Ceramic Tile In the ceramic stepping stone below, diameter $\overline{AB}$ is 18 inches long, and chord $\overline{EF}$ is 8 inches long. Find CD.

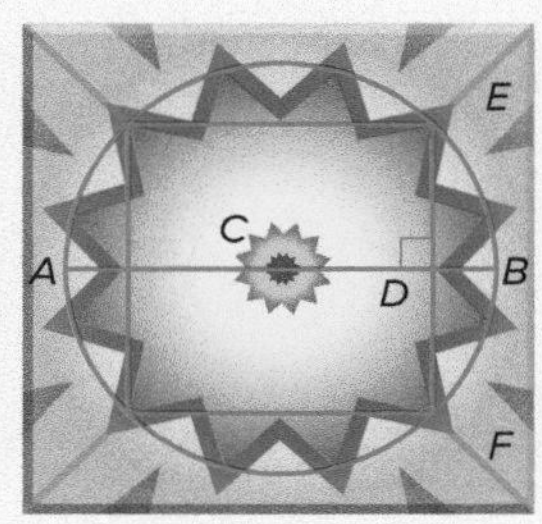

$CD = \sqrt{65} \approx 8.06$

Differentiated Instruction AL OL ELL

Verbal/Linguistic Learners Have students construct a circle with two congruent chords and the perpendicular bisectors. Then have them write a proof supporting the congruency of their construction.

Go Online!

The most up-to-date resources available for your program can be found at connectED.mcgraw-hill.com.

Example 5 Chords Equidistant from Center

AL If $BA = 3$, what is AC? 3

OL If $AB = AC$, $WX = 2z + 1$, and $XY = 3z - 7$, what is z? 8

BL Can we prove that $XC = CY$? Explain. Yes; If we draw $\overline{AY}$, we know that $AX = AY$ because they are both radii. They share leg AC. Therefore, by HL, the triangles formed are congruent and $XC = CY$.

Need Another Example?

Algebra In ⊙P, $EF = GH = 24$. Find PQ.

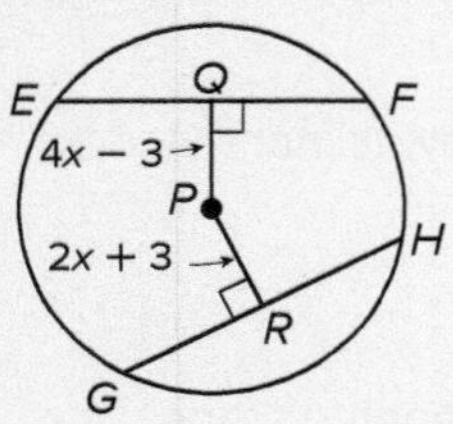

$PQ = 9$

G.C.2

Example 5 Chords Equidistant from Center

ALGEBRA In ⊙A, $WX = XY = 22$. Find AB.

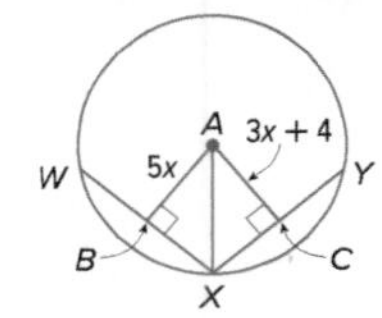

Because chords $\overline{WX}$ and $\overline{XY}$ are congruent, they are equidistant from A. So, $AB = AC$.

$AB = AC$

$5x = 3x + 4$ Substitution

$x = 2$ Simplify.

So, $AB = 5(2)$ or 10.

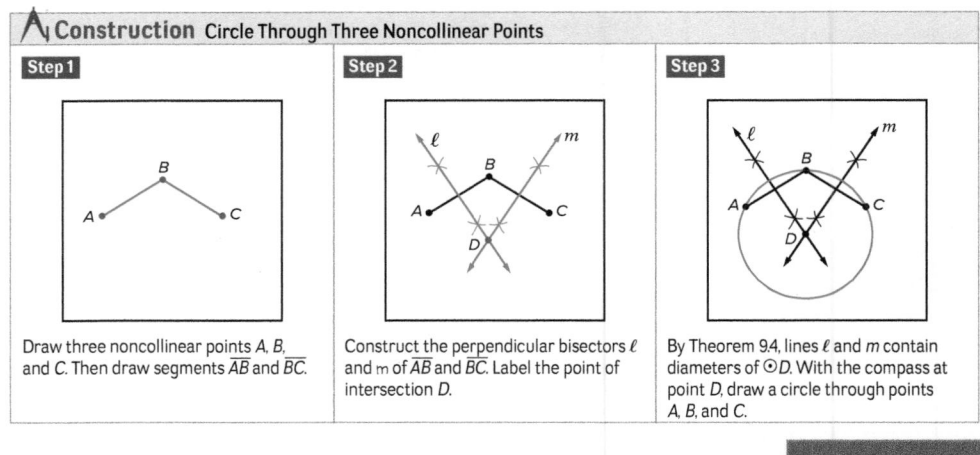

Guided Practice

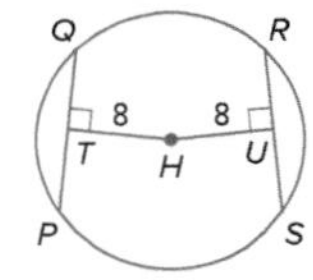

5. In ⊙H, $PQ = 3x - 4$ and $RS = 14$. Find x. 6

You can use Theorem 9.5 to find the point equidistant from three noncollinear points.

Construction Circle Through Three Noncollinear Points

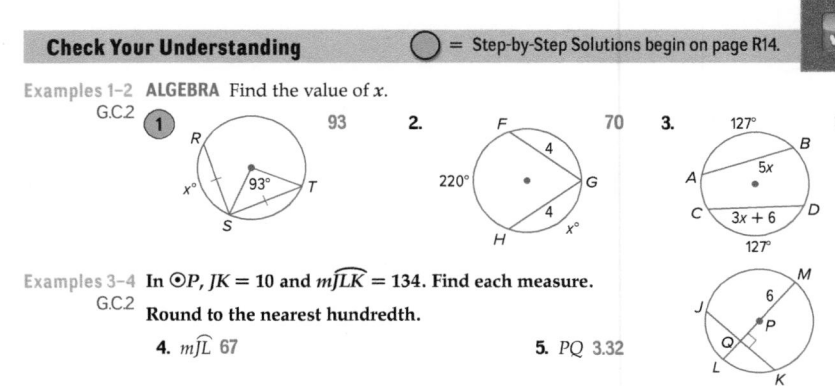

Step 1

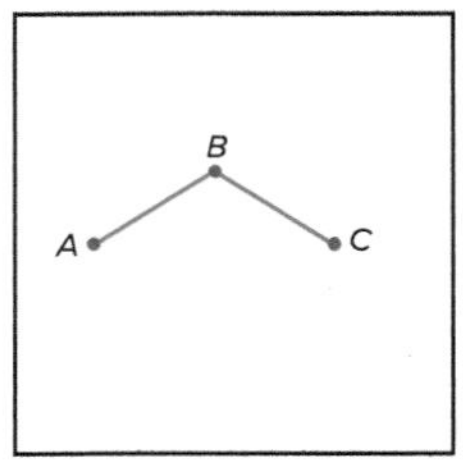

Draw three noncollinear points A, B, and C. Then draw segments $\overline{AB}$ and $\overline{BC}$.

Step 2

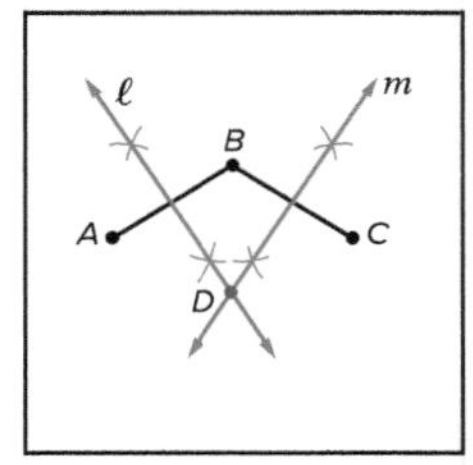

Construct the perpendicular bisectors ℓ and m of $\overline{AB}$ and $\overline{BC}$. Label the point of intersection D.

Step 3

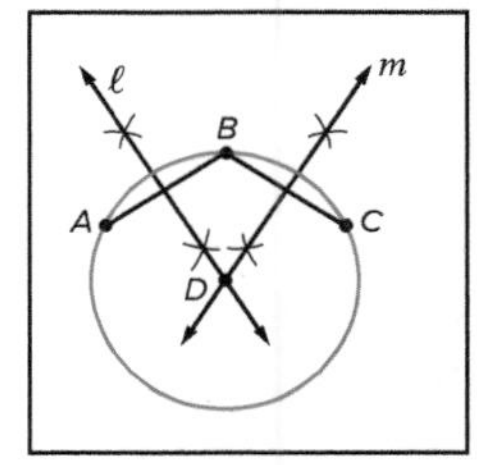

By Theorem 9.4, lines ℓ and m contain diameters of ⊙D. With the compass at point D, draw a circle through points A, B, and C.

Go Online! for a Self-Check Quiz

Check Your Understanding ○ = Step-by-Step Solutions begin on page R14.

Examples 1–2 G.C.2 **ALGEBRA** Find the value of x.

1. 93

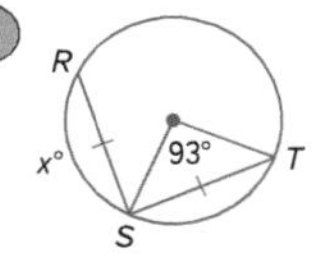

2. 70

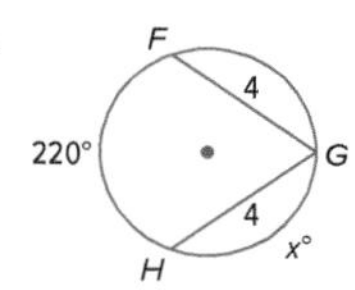

3. 3

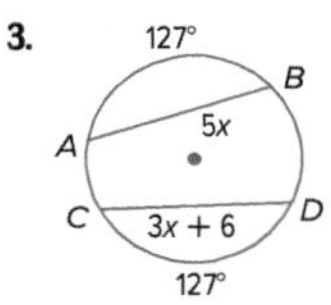

Examples 3–4 G.C.2 **In ⊙P, $JK = 10$ and $m\widehat{JLK} = 134$. Find each measure. Round to the nearest hundredth.**

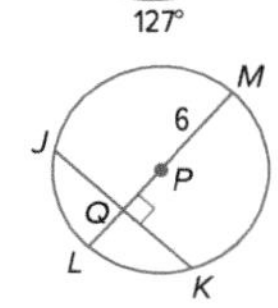

4. $m\widehat{JL}$ 67

5. PQ 3.32

Differentiated Instruction OL BL

Extension Have students draw two circles on a sheet of paper. Tell students to draw a chord anywhere on the first circle, and then construct and label a perpendicular bisector for this chord. For the second circle, have students draw two radii that do not form a diameter of the circle. Construct two congruent chords that are perpendicular to the two radii. See students' work.

Go Online! eBook

Interactive Student Guide

Use the *Interactive Student Guide* to deepen conceptual understanding.

· Arcs and Chords

Example 5
G.C.2

6. In $\odot J$, $GH = 9$, $KL = 4x + 1$. Find x. 2

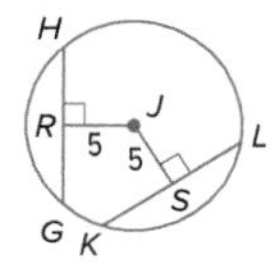

Practice and Problem Solving

Extra Practice is on page R9.

Examples 1–2 G.C.2 **ALGEBRA** Find the value of x.

7. 21

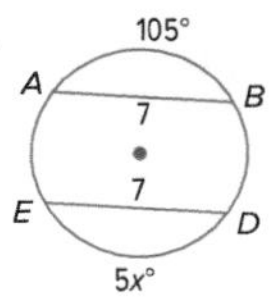

8. 70

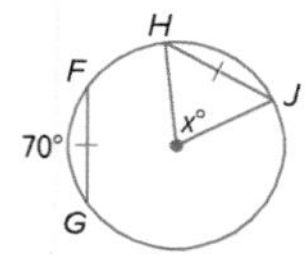

9. 127

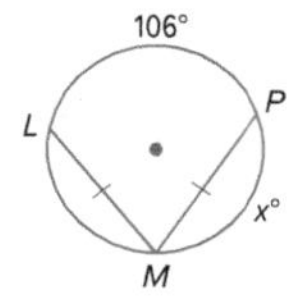

10. 72

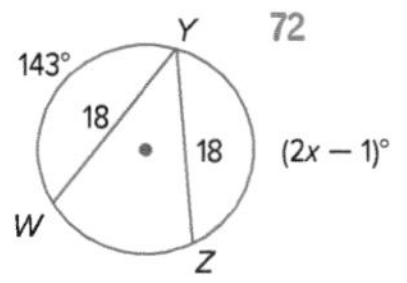

11. 7

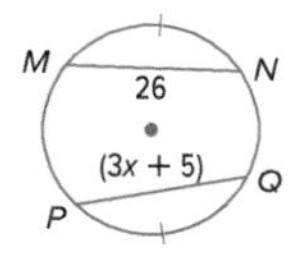

12. 4

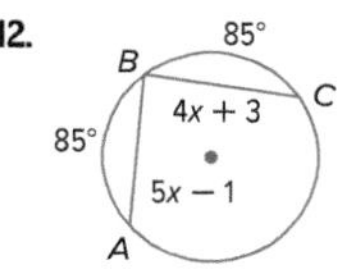

13 $\odot C \cong \odot D$ 27

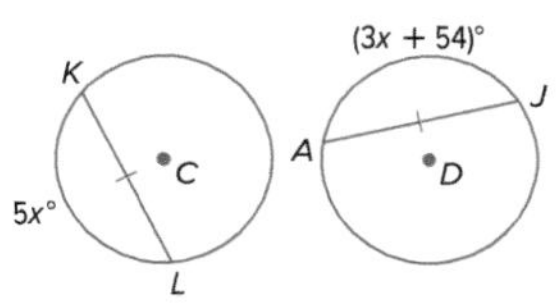

14. $\odot P \cong \odot Q$ 11

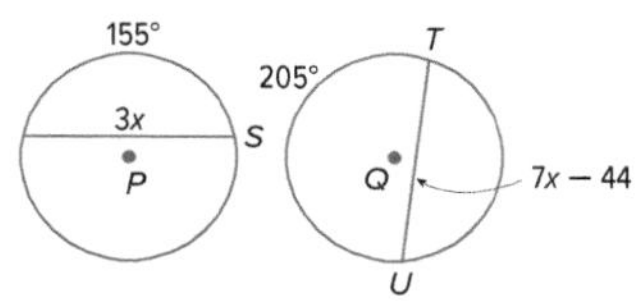

15. **MODELING** Angie is in a jewelry-making class at her local arts center. She wants to make a pair of triangular earrings from a metal circle. She knows that $\widehat{AC}$ is 115°. If she wants to cut two equal parts off so that $\widehat{AB} = \widehat{BC}$, what is x? 122.5°

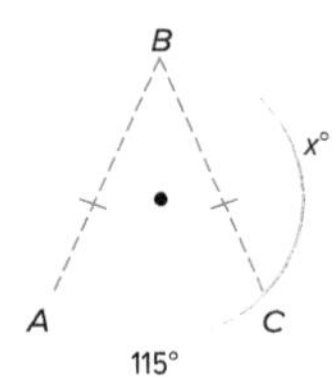

Examples 3–4 G.C.2 **In $\odot A$, the radius is 14 and $CD = 22$. Find each measure. Round to the nearest hundredth, if necessary.**

16. CE 11

17. EB 5.34

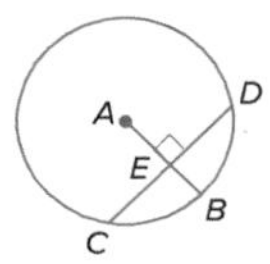

In $\odot H$, the diameter is 18, $LM = 12$, and $m\widehat{LM} = 84$. Find each measure. Round to the nearest hundredth, if necessary.

18. $m\widehat{LK}$ 42

19. HP 6.71

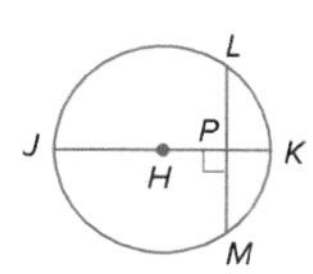

Differentiated Homework Options			
Levels	AL Basic	OL Core	BL Advanced
Exercises	7–23, 32, 38–45	7–23 odd, 24–34, 38–45	24–45
2-Day Option	7–23 odd	7–23	
	8–22 even, 36, 38–39, 40–45	24–34, 36, 38–39, 40–45	

You can use ALEKS to provide additional remediation support with personalized instruction and practice.

Practice

Formative Assessment Use Exercises 1–6 to assess students' understanding of the concepts in this lesson.

The Practice and Problem Solving exercises assess the content taught in the lesson. The Preparing for Assessment page is meant to be used as preparation for end-of-course assessments.

Exercise Alert

See page R9 for extra exercises for students who are approaching level or for on-level students who need additional reinforcement.

MP Teaching the Mathematical Practices

Modeling Mathematically proficient students can apply the mathematics they know to solve problems arising in everyday life. In Exercise 15, point out to students that $m\widehat{AB} + m\widehat{BC} + m\widehat{AC} = 360$.

Levels of Complexity Chart

The levels of the exercises progress from 1 to 3, with Level 1 indicating the lowest level of complexity.

Exercises	7–23	24–30, 40–45	31–39
C Level 3			●
B Level 2		●	
Level 1	●		

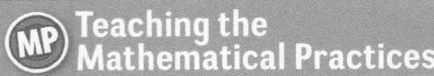

MP Teaching the Mathematical Practices

Construct Arguments Mathematically proficient students understand and use stated assumptions and definitions in constructing arguments. They make conjectures and build a logical progression of statements to explore the truth of their conjectures. In Exercises 28, 29, and 30, encourage students to use the examples of each theorem in the text to begin each proof.

Additional Answers

24. Given: $\odot P$, $\overline{KM} \perp \overline{JP}$
Prove: $\overline{JP}$ bisects $\overline{KM}$ and $\widehat{KM}$.

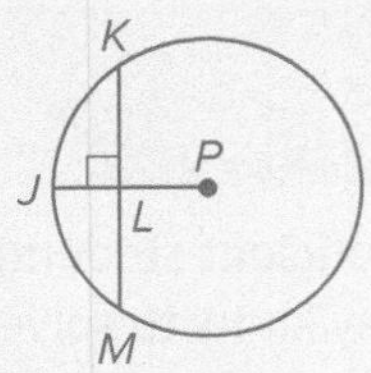

Proof:
Statements (Reasons)
1. $\overline{KM} \perp \overline{JP}$ (Given)
2. Draw radii $\overline{PK}$ and $\overline{PM}$. (2 points determine a line.)
3. $\overline{PK} \cong \overline{PM}$ (All radii of a ⊙ are ≅.)
4. $\overline{PL} \cong \overline{PL}$ (Reflex. Prop. of ≅)
5. $\angle PLM$ and $\angle PLK$ are right ∡. (Def. of ⊥)
6. $\angle PLM \cong \angle PLK$ (All right ∡ are ≅.)
7. $\triangle PLM \cong \triangle PLK$ (SAS)
8. $\overline{ML} \cong \overline{KL}$ (CPCTC)
9. $\overline{PJ}$ bisects $\overline{KM}$. (Def. of bisect)
10. $\angle MPJ \cong \angle KPJ$ (CPCTC)
11. $\widehat{MJ} \cong \widehat{KJ}$ (In the same circle, two arcs are congruent if their corresponding central angles are congruent.)
12. $\overline{JP}$ bisects $\widehat{KM}$. (Def. of bisect)

25. Proof:
Because all radii are congruent, $\overline{QP} \cong \overline{PR} \cong \overline{SP} \cong \overline{PT}$. You are given that $\overline{QR} \cong \overline{ST}$, so $\triangle PQR \cong \triangle PST$ by SSS. Thus, $\angle QPR \cong \angle SPT$ by CPCTC. Because the central angles have the same measure, their intercepted arcs have the same measure and are therefore congruent. Thus, $\widehat{QR} \cong \widehat{ST}$.

26. Proof:
Statements (Reasons)
1. $\odot C$, $\overline{AB} \perp \overline{XY}$ (Given)
2. $\overline{CX} \cong \overline{CY}$ (All radii of a ⊙ are ≅.)
3. $\overline{CZ} \cong \overline{CZ}$ (Reflexive Prop.)
4. $\angle XZC$ and $\angle YZC$ are rt. ∡ (Definition of ⊥ lines)
5. $\triangle XZC \cong \triangle YZC$ (HL)
6. $\overline{XZ} \cong \overline{YZ}$, $\angle XCZ \cong \angle YCZ$ (CPCTC)
7. $\widehat{XB} \cong \widehat{YB}$ (If central ∡ are ≅, intercepted arcs are ≅.)

20. SNOWBOARDING The snowboarding rail shown is an arc of a circle in which $\overline{BD}$ is part of the diameter. If $\widehat{ABC}$ is about 32% of a complete circle, what is $m\widehat{AB}$? **57.6**

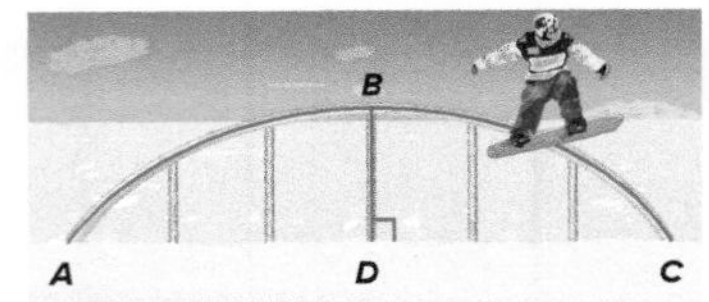

21. ROADS The curved road at the right is part of $\odot C$, which has a radius of 88 feet. What is AB? Round to the nearest tenth. **98.3 ft**

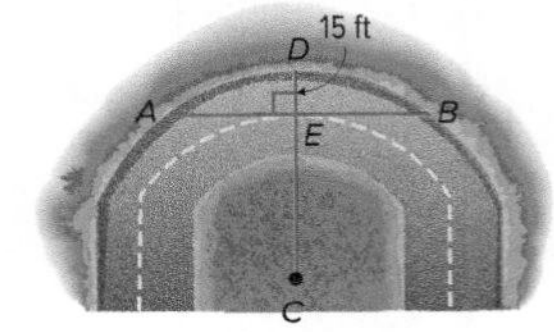

Example 5
G.C.2

22. ALGEBRA In $\odot F$, $\overline{AB} \cong \overline{BC}$, $DF = 3x - 7$, and $FE = x + 9$. What is x? **8**

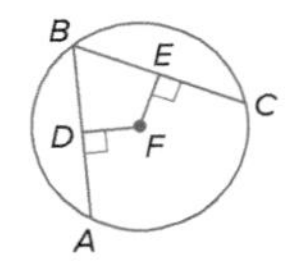

23. ALGEBRA In $\odot S$, $LM = 16$ and $PN = 4x$. What is x? **4**

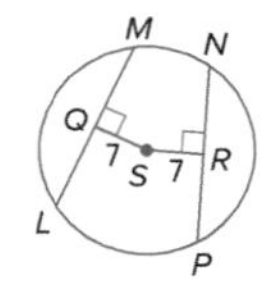

B **PROOF** Write a two-column proof.

24. Given: $\odot P$, $\overline{KM} \perp \overline{JP}$
Prove: $\overline{JP}$ bisects $\overline{KM}$ and $\widehat{KM}$. **See margin.**

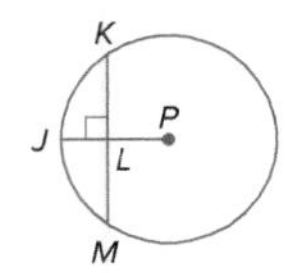

PROOF Write the specified type of proof. **25, 26. See margin.**

25. paragraph proof of Theorem 9.2, part 2
Given: $\odot P$, $\overline{QR} \cong \overline{ST}$
Prove: $\widehat{QR} \cong \widehat{ST}$

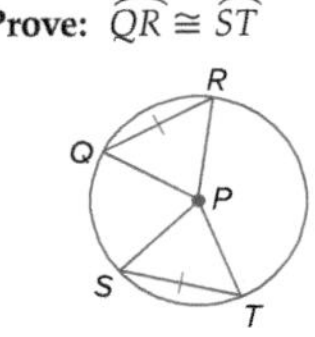

26. two-column proof of Theorem 9.3
Given: $\odot C$, $\overline{AB} \perp \overline{XY}$
Prove: $\overline{XZ} \cong \overline{YZ}$, $\widehat{XB} \cong \widehat{YB}$

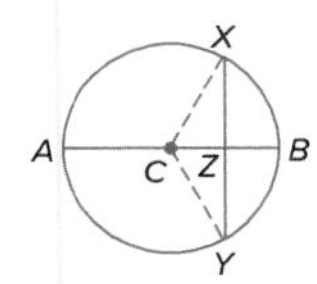

27. DESIGN Roberto is designing a logo for a friend's coffee shop according to the design at the right, where each chord is equal in length. What is the measure of each arc and the length of each chord?
Each arc is 90° and each chord is 2.12 ft.

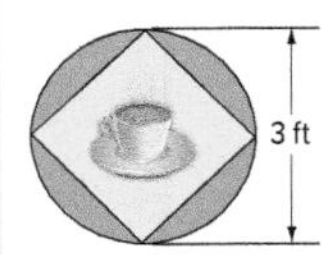

28. MP **CONSTRUCT ARGUMENTS** Write a two-column proof of Theorem 9.4. **See margin.**

28. Given: $\odot A$, $\overline{ED}$ is the ⊥ bisector of $\overline{BC}$.
Prove: $\overline{ED}$ is a diameter of $\odot A$.
Proof:
Statements (Reasons):
1. $\overline{ED}$ is the ⊥ bisector of $\overline{BC}$. (Given)
2. A is equidistant from B and C. (All radii of a ⊙ are ≅.)
3. A lies on the ⊥ bisector of $\overline{BC}$. (Conv. of the ⊥ Bisector Thm.)
4. $\overline{ED}$ is a diameter of $\odot A$. (Def. of diameter)

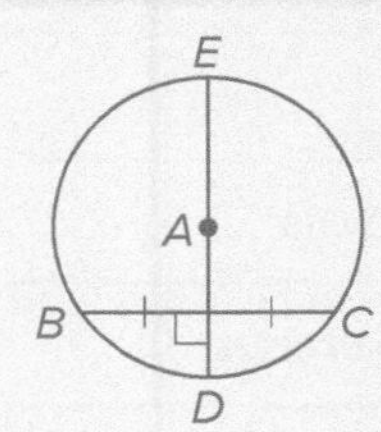

MP **CONSTRUCT ARGUMENTS** Write a two-column proof of the indicated part of Theorem 9.5.

29. In a circle, if two chords are equidistant from the center, then they are congruent.

30. In a circle, if two chords are congruent, then they are equidistant from the center.

29, 30. See margin.

C **ALGEBRA** Find the value of x.

31. $\overline{AB} \cong \overline{DF}$ **2**

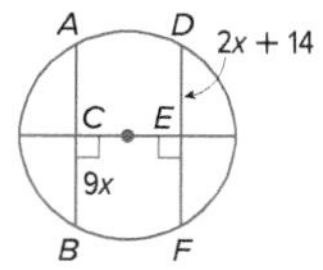

32. $\overline{GH} \cong \overline{KJ}$ **55**

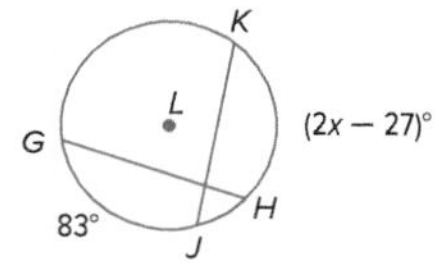

33. $\widehat{WTY} \cong \widehat{TWY}$ **5**

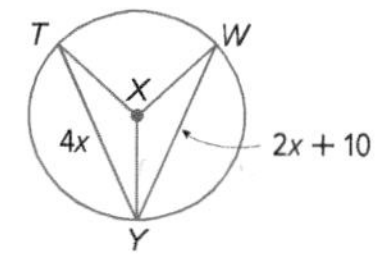

34. **MULTI-STEP** A retail store manager wants to set up a display of a new fashion line. There are three entrances into the store.

a. Where should the display be placed to get maximum exposure? **It should be equidistant from each entrance.**

b. Describe your solution process including any assumptions made. Include a diagram with your response. **See Ch. 9 Answer Appendix.**

G.C.2, G.GMG.3, G.CO.12

H.O.T. Problems — Use Higher-Order Thinking Skills

35. **CHALLENGE** The common chord $\overline{AB}$ between $\odot P$ and $\odot Q$ is perpendicular to the segment connecting the centers of the circles. If $AB = 10$, what is the length of $\overline{PQ}$? Explain your reasoning. **See Ch. 9 Answer Appendix.**

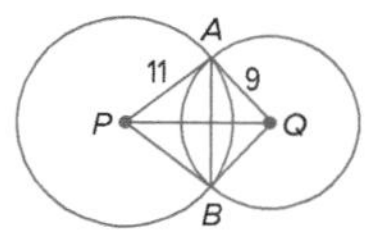

36. MP **REASONING** In a circle, $\overline{AB}$ is a diameter and $\overline{HG}$ is a chord that intersects $\overline{AB}$ at point X. Is it *sometimes*, *always*, or *never* true that $HX = GX$? Explain.

36. Sometimes; if the diameter is perpendicular to the chord, then it bisects the chord.

37. **CHALLENGE** Use a compass to draw a circle with chord $\overline{AB}$. Refer to this construction for the following problem. **See Ch. 9 Answer Appendix.**

Step 1 Construct $\overline{CD}$, the perpendicular bisector of $\overline{AB}$.

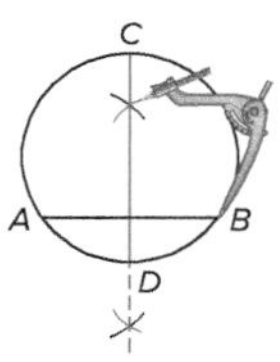

Step 2 Construct $\overline{FG}$, the perpendicular bisector of $\overline{CD}$. Label the point of intersection O.

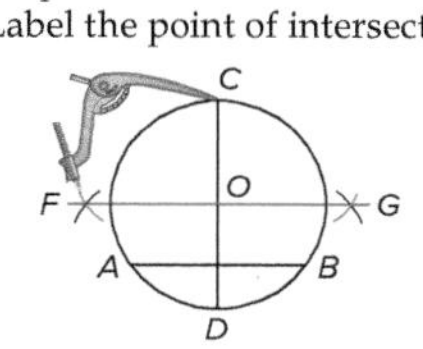

a. Use an indirect proof to show that $\overline{CD}$ passes through the center of the circle by assuming that the center of the circle is *not* on $\overline{CD}$.

b. Prove that O is the center of the circle.

38. **OPEN-ENDED** Construct a circle and draw a chord. Measure the chord and the distance that the chord is from the center. Find the length of the radius. **See Ch. 9 Answer Appendix.**

39. **WRITING IN MATH** If the measure of an arc in a circle is tripled, will the chord of the new arc be three times as long as the chord of the original arc? Explain your reasoning. **See Ch. 9 Answer Appendix.**

MP Standards for Mathematical Practice

Emphasis On	Exercises
1 Make sense of problems and persevere in solving them.	27, 34–35, 43
2 Reason abstractly and quantitatively.	1–3, 7–14, 22–23, 31–33, 44
3 Construct viable arguments and critique the reasoning of others.	24–26, 28–30, 36, 39, 41
4 Model with mathematics.	15
5 Use tools strategically.	37–38
6 Attend to precision.	20–21, 40, 42, 45

Exercise Alert

Compass and Straightedge Exercises 37–38 require the use of a compass and a straightedge.

Additional Answers

29. Given: $\odot L$, $\overline{LX} \perp \overline{FG}$, $\overline{LY} \perp \overline{JH}$, $\overline{LX} \cong \overline{LY}$

Prove: $\overline{FG} \cong \overline{JH}$

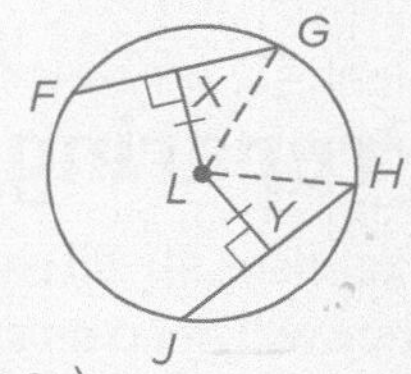

Proof:

Statements (Reasons):

1. $\overline{LG} \cong \overline{LH}$ (All radii of a ⊙ are ≅.)
2. $\overline{LX} \perp \overline{FG}$, $\overline{LY} \perp \overline{JH}$, $\overline{LX} \cong \overline{LY}$ (Given)
3. $\angle LXG$ and $\angle LYH$ are right ∠s. (Definition of ⊥ lines)
4. $\triangle XGL \cong \triangle YHL$ (HL)
5. $\overline{XG} \cong \overline{YH}$ (CPCTC)
6. $XG = YH$ (Definition of ≅ segments)
7. $2(XG) = 2(YH)$ (Multiplication Property)
8. $\overline{LX}$ bisects $\overline{FG}$; $\overline{LY}$ bisects $\overline{JH}$. (A radius ⊥ to a chord bisects the chord.)
9. $FG = 2(XG)$, $JH = 2(YH)$ (Definition of segment bisector)
10. $FG = JH$ (Substitution)
11. $\overline{FG} \cong \overline{JH}$ (Definition of ≅ segments)

30. Given: $\odot L$, $\overline{FG} \cong \overline{JH}$, $\overline{LG}$ and $\overline{LH}$ are radii. $\overline{LX} \perp \overline{FG}$; $\overline{LY} \perp \overline{JH}$

Prove: $\overline{LX} \cong \overline{LY}$

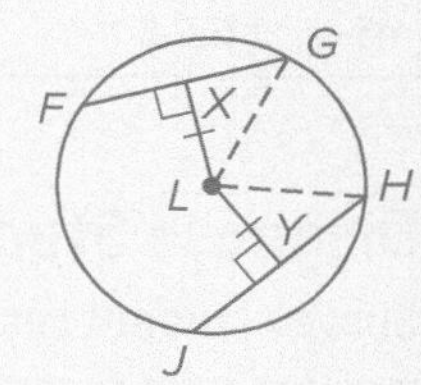

Proof:

Statements (Reasons):

1. $\odot L$, $\overline{FG} \cong \overline{JH}$ and $\overline{LG}$ and $\overline{LH}$ are radii. $\overline{LX} \perp \overline{FG}$; $\overline{LY} \perp \overline{JH}$ (Given)
2. $\overline{LX}$ bisects $\overline{FG}$; $\overline{LY}$ bisects $\overline{JH}$. ($\overline{LX}$ and $\overline{LY}$ are contained in radii. A radius ⊥ to a chord bisects the chord.)
3. $XG = \frac{1}{2}FG$, $YH = \frac{1}{2}JH$ (Definition of bisector)
4. $FG = JH$ (Definition of ≅ segments)
5. $\frac{1}{2}FG = \frac{1}{2}JH$ (Multiplication Property)
6. $XG = YH$ (Substitution)
7. $\overline{XG} \cong \overline{YH}$ (Definition of ≅ segments)
8. $\overline{LG} \cong \overline{LH}$ (All radii of a circle are ≅.)
9. $\angle GXL$ and $\angle HYL$ are right ∠s. (Def. of ⊥ lines)
10. $\triangle XLG \cong \triangle YLH$ (HL)
11. $\overline{LX} \cong \overline{LY}$ (CPCTC)

Go Online!

eSolutions Manual

Create worksheets, answer keys, and solutions handouts for your assignments.

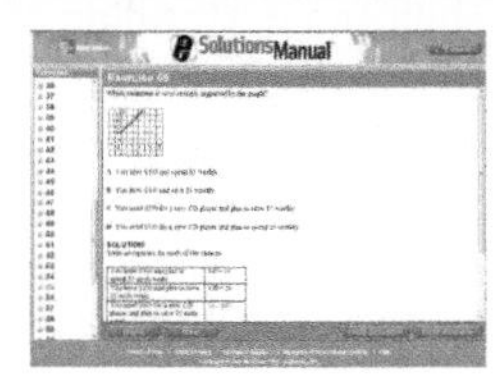

Assess

Yesterday's News Have students write a paragraph that explains how the lesson about angles and arcs helped them in the lesson about arcs and chords.

Preparing for Assessment

Exercises 40–45 require students to use the skills they will need on standardized assessments. Exercises are dual-coded with content standards and mathematical practice standards.

Dual Coding		
Items	Content Standards	MP Mathematical Practices
40	G.C.2	6
41	G.C.2	2
42	G.C.2	6
43	G.C.2	2, 6
44	G.C.2	2
45	G.C.2	6

Preparing for Assessment

40. In the figure, $\odot G \cong \odot H$ and $\widehat{EF} \cong \widehat{KL}$. What is the length of $\overline{KL}$? MP 6 G.C.2 **B**

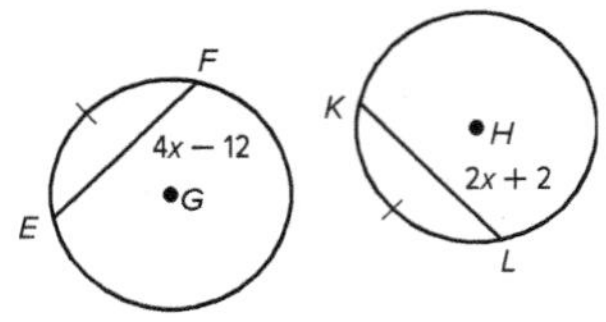

- ○ A 32
- ○ B 16
- ○ C 12
- ○ D 7

41. Which of the following is a valid conclusion that Matthew can make based on the figure? MP 2 G.C.2 **D**

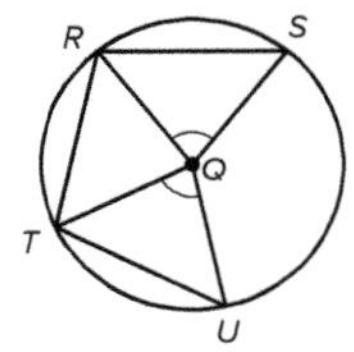

I. $\overline{RS} \cong \overline{TU}$
II. $\widehat{RT} \cong \widehat{TU}$
III. $\widehat{RS} \cong \widehat{TU}$

- ○ A I only
- ○ B III only
- ○ C I and II only
- ○ D I and III only
- ○ E I, II, and III

42. If $CW = WF$ and $ED = 30$, what is DF? MP 6 G.C.2 **D**

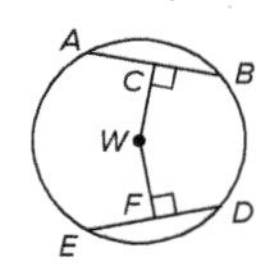

- ○ A 60
- ○ B 45
- ○ C 30
- ○ D 15

43. **MULTI-STEP** A chord $\overline{KM}$ is 24 feet and the diameter $\overline{GH}$ is 36 feet. Find the length of $\overline{JL}$. MP 2, 6 G.C.2

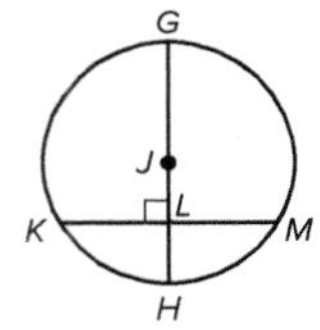

43b. $\overline{LM}$ is $\frac{1}{2}$ of 24 feet or 12 feet; the chord is bisected because it is perpendicular to the diameter. $\overline{JM}$ is the radius which is $\frac{1}{2}$ the diameter of 36 feet or 18 feet.

a. Name a triangle that includes $\overline{JL}$ as its side. **△JLM or △JLK**

b. Find the lengths of the two sides of your triangle (other than $\overline{JL}$). Explain.

c. Use the Pythagorean Theorem to write an equation that includes JL as the variable. **$JL^2 + 12^2 = 18^2$**

d. Solve the equation and find JL. **$6\sqrt{5}$ ft**

44. In $\odot P$, $PS = PT = 12$, $HJ = 2x + 10$, and $KL = 4x - 8$.

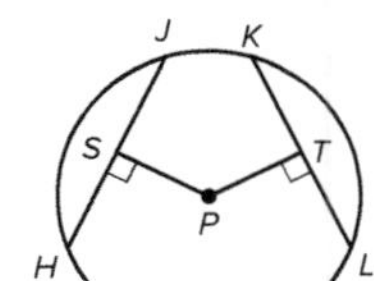

What is the length of $\overline{HS}$? MP 2 G.C.2 **C**

- ○ A 6
- ○ B 9
- ○ C 14
- ○ D 28

45. In $\odot C$, the diameter is 22 centimeters and $MN = 18$ centimeters.

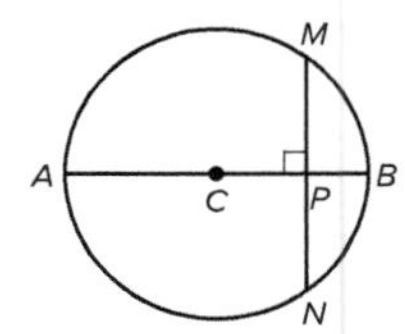

Which is the best estimate of the length of $\overline{CP}$? MP 6 G.C.2 **B**

- ○ A 2.0 cm
- ○ B 6.3 cm
- ○ C 4.0 cm
- ○ D 14.2 cm

Diagnose Student Errors

Survey student responses for each item. Class trends may indicate common errors and misconceptions.

40.

A	Found the sum of *EF* and *KL*
B	CORRECT
C	Incorrectly combined 12 and 2 to get 10
D	Found the value of *x* but not $\overline{KL}$

41.

A	Did not recognize that congruent chords determine congruent arcs
B	Did not recognize that congruent arcs determine congruent chords
C	Assumed that $\angle RQT \cong \angle TQU$
D	CORRECT
E	Assumed that $\angle RQT \cong \angle TQU$

42.

A	Multiplied 30 by 2
B	Divided 30 by 2 and then added the result to 30
C	Assumed $DF = ED$
D	CORRECT

45.

A	Subtracted, 11 cm − 9 cm
B	CORRECT
C	Subtracted, 22 cm − 18 cm
D	Used Pythagorean Theorem incorrectly and calculated $\sqrt{11^2 + 9^2}$

Go Online!

Quizzes

Students can use *Self-Check Quizzes* to check their understanding of this lesson and have the results sent to you. You can also give *Quiz 2*, which covers the content in Lessons 9-3 and 9-4.

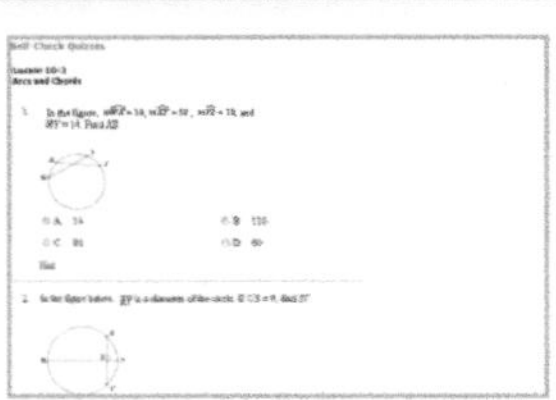

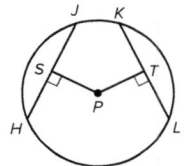

LESSON 9-4
Inscribed Angles

SUGGESTED PACING (DAYS)

	Instruction
90 min.	0.5
45 min.	1.0

Track Your Progress

Objectives

1. Find measures of inscribed angles.
2. Find measures of angles of inscribed polygons.

Mathematical Background

An inscribed angle is an angle that has its vertex on the circle and its sides contained in chords of the circle. If an angle is inscribed in a circle, then the measure of the angle equals one-half of the measure of its intercepted arc. If two inscribed angles intercept congruent arcs or the same arc, then the angles are congruent.

THEN

G.C.2 Identify and describe relationships among inscribed angles, radii, and chords.

NOW

G.C.2 Identify and describe relationships among inscribed angles, radii, and chords.

G.C.3 Construct inscribed and circumscribed circles of a triangle. Prove the properties of angles for a quadrilateral inscribed inside a circle.

NEXT

G.C.4 Construct a tangent line from a point outside a given circle to the circle.

Go Online! All of these resources and more are available at connectED.mcgraw-hill.com

eLessons utilize the power of your interactive whiteboard in an engaging way. Use **Chords, Arcs, and Angles**, Screens 11–12, to introduce the concepts in this lesson.

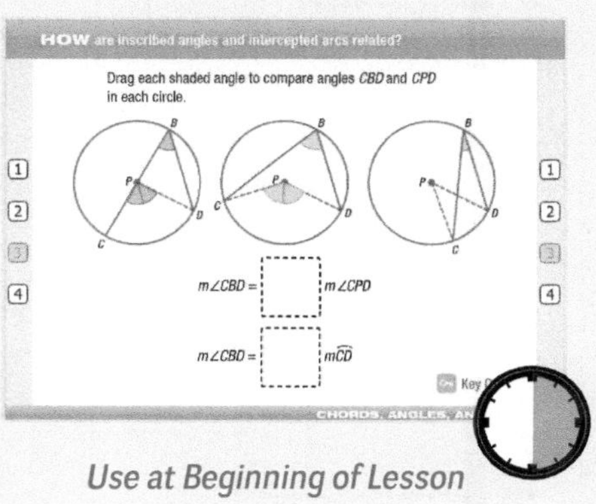

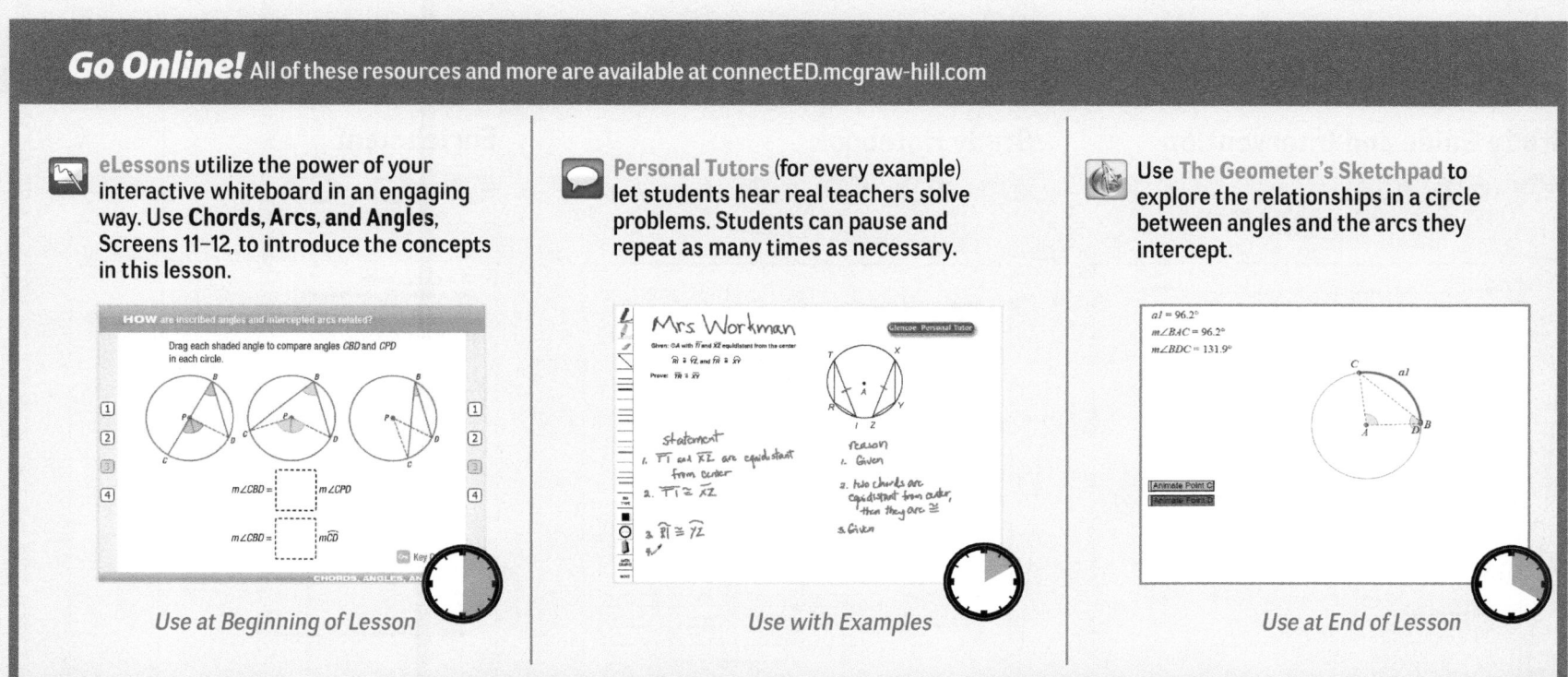

Use at Beginning of Lesson

Personal Tutors (for every example) let students hear real teachers solve problems. Students can pause and repeat as many times as necessary.

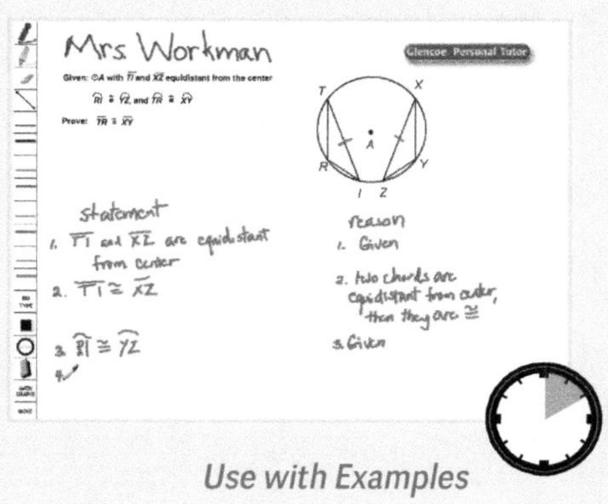

Use with Examples

Use **The Geometer's Sketchpad** to explore the relationships in a circle between angles and the arcs they intercept.

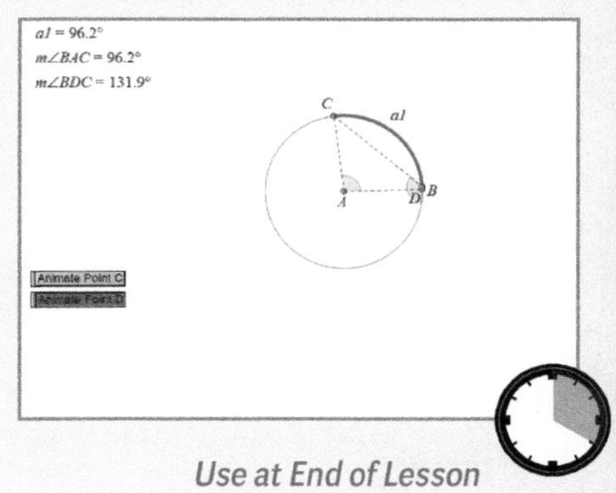

Use at End of Lesson

OER Using Open Educational Resources

Lesson Sharing Look on **TeacherTube** for new ways to teach inscribed angles. Struggling students may also want to watch these videos. If you are unable to access TeacherTube, try **KidsTube**, **MathATube**, **SchoolTube**, or **YouTube**. *Use as lesson preparation*

Go Online!

connectED.mcgraw-hill.com

Worksheets

Differentiate Your Resources

Extra Practice Additional practice or homework; Skills Practice is best for approaching-level students and Practice is best for on-level and beyond-level students

Skills Practice

AL OL ELL

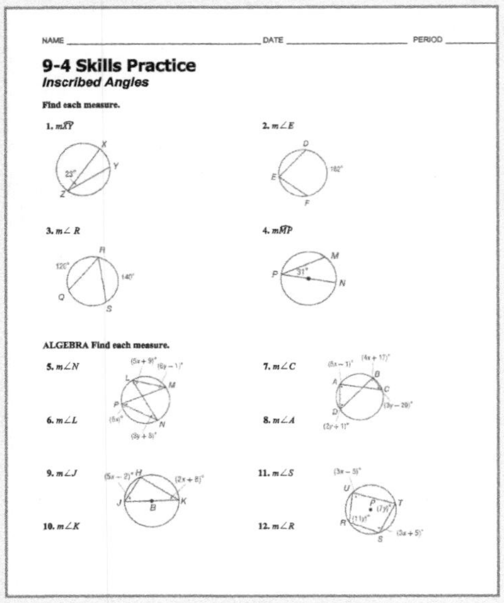

NAME ______ DATE ______ PERIOD ______

9-4 Skills Practice

Inscribed Angles

Practice

AL OL BL ELL

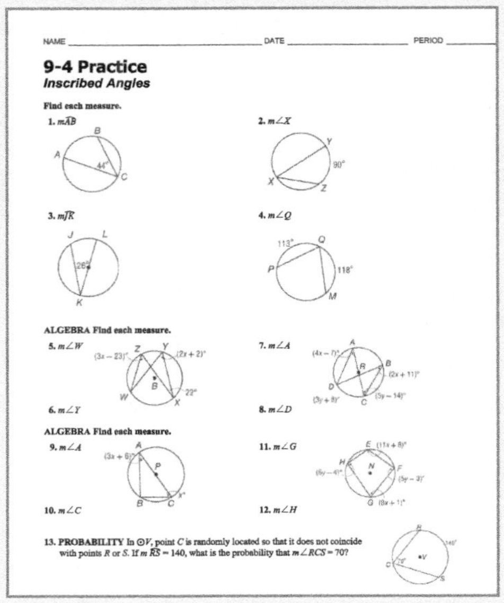

NAME ______ DATE ______ PERIOD ______

9-4 Practice

Inscribed Angles

Word Problem Practice

AL OL BL ELL

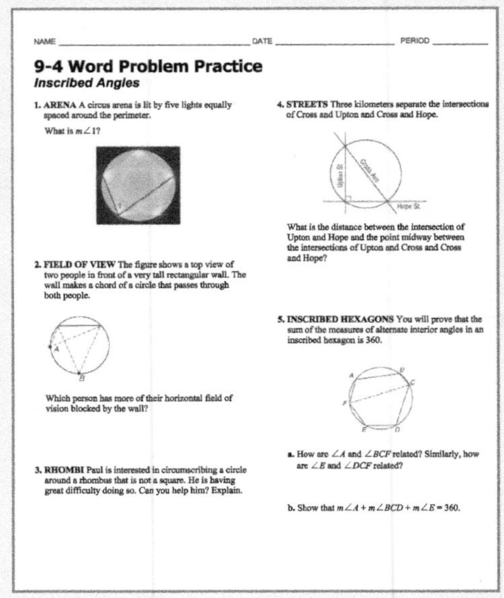

NAME ______ DATE ______ PERIOD ______

9-4 Word Problem Practice

Inscribed Angles

Intervention Reteaching and vocabulary activities that can be used with struggling or absent students and as ELL support

Study Guide and Intervention

AL OL ELL

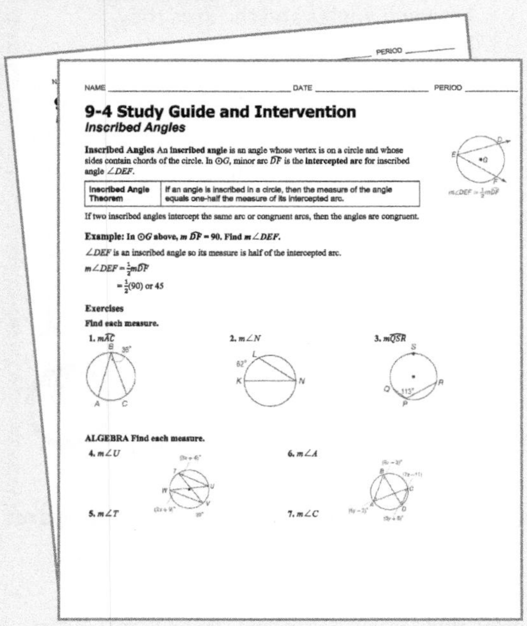

NAME ______ DATE ______ PERIOD ______

9-4 Study Guide and Intervention

Inscribed Angles

Study Notebook

AL OL BL ELL

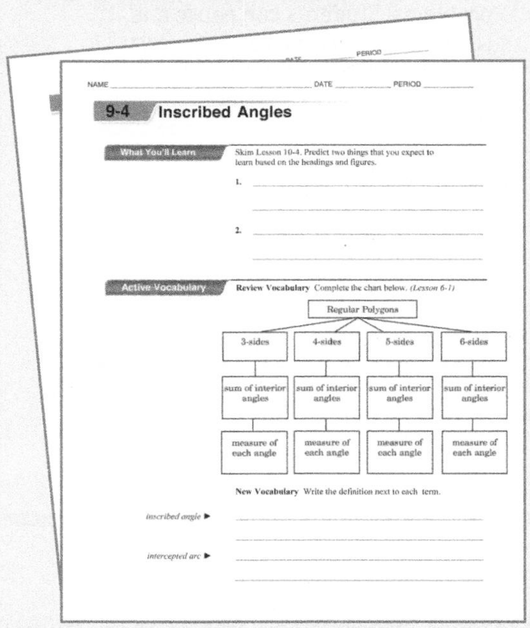

NAME ______ DATE ______ PERIOD ______

9-4 Inscribed Angles

Extension Activities that can be used to extend lesson concepts

Enrichment

OL BL ELL

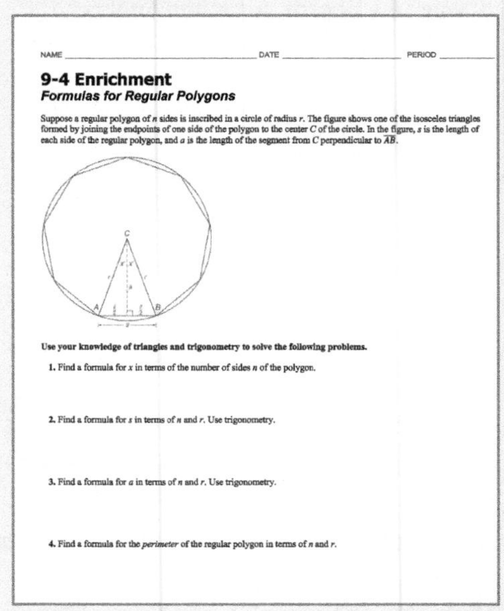

NAME ______ DATE ______ PERIOD ______

9-4 Enrichment

Formulas for Regular Polygons

LESSON 4

Inscribed Angles

Then

- You found measures of interior angles of polygons.

Now

1. Find measures of inscribed angles.
2. Find measures of angles of inscribed polygons.

Why?

- The entrance to a school prom has a semicircular arch. Streamers are attached with one end at point *A* and the other end at point *B*. The middle of each streamer can then be attached to a different point *P* along the arch.

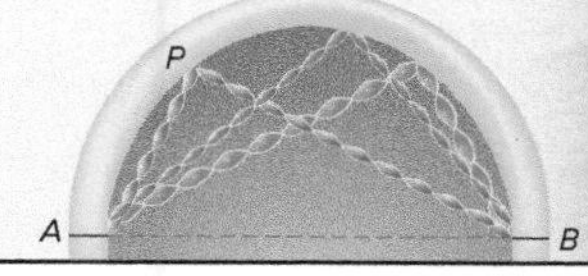

New Vocabulary
inscribed angle
intercepted arc

Mathematical Practices
3 Construct viable arguments and critique the reasoning of others.
7 Look for and make use of structure.
8 Look for and express regularity in repeated reasoning.

Content Standards
G.C.2 Identify and describe relationships among inscribed angles, radii, and chords.
G.C.3 Construct the inscribed and circumscribed circles of a triangle, and prove properties of angles for a quadrilateral inscribed in a circle.

1 Inscribed Angles

Notice that the angle formed by each streamer appears to be congruent, no matter where point *P* is placed along the arch. An **inscribed angle** has a vertex on a circle and sides that contain chords of the circle. In ⊙*C*, ∠*QRS* is an inscribed angle.

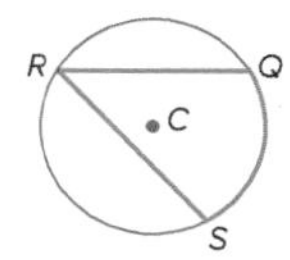

An **intercepted arc** has endpoints on the sides of an inscribed angle and lies in the interior of the inscribed angle. In ⊙*C*, minor arc $\overset{\frown}{QS}$ is intercepted by ∠*QRS*.

There are three ways that an angle can be inscribed in a circle.

Case 1	Case 2	Case 3
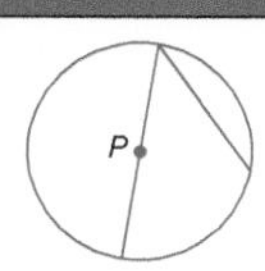 Center *P* is on a side of the inscribed angle.	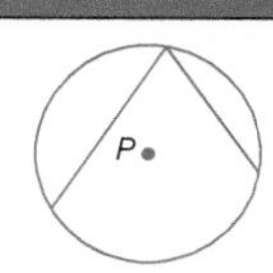 Center *P* is inside the inscribed angle.	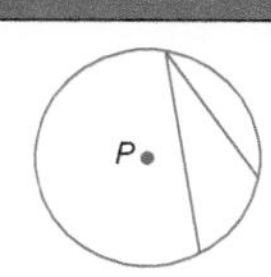 The center *P* is in the exterior of the inscribed angle.

In Case 1, one side of the angle is a diameter of the circle.

For each of these cases, the following theorem holds true.

Theorem 9.6 Inscribed Angle Theorem

Words If an angle is inscribed in a circle, then the measure of the angle equals one half the measure of its intercepted arc.

Example $m\angle 1 = \frac{1}{2}m\overset{\frown}{AB}$ and $m\overset{\frown}{AB} = 2m\angle 1$

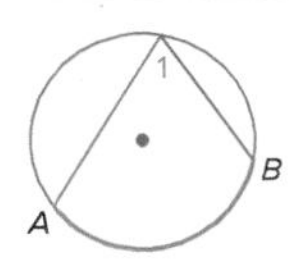

You will prove Cases 2 and 3 of the Inscribed Angle Theorem in Exercises 37 and 38.

Launch

Have students read the Why? section of the lesson. Ask:

- What kind of arc would the top of the doorway and a horizontal streamer form? semicircle
- Assume that the measure of the arc from point *B* to the point where the streamer attaches to the arch is 60°. What would be the measure of the arc from point *A* to the point where the streamer is attached to the arch? 120
- Assume that the doorway is three feet wide. How could you find the arc length of the doorway? The radius is half the width of the doorway, or 18 inches. Because the arch is a semicircle, the measure of the arc is 180°. Substitute the radius and the measure of the arc in the formula for arc length $\ell = \frac{180}{360}2\pi(18)$.

MP Mathematical Practices Strategies

Make sense of problems and persevere in solving them.
Have students discuss how they solve geometric problems. Guide the class in a discussion about what strategies they already understand and use well. For example, ask:

- How does a diagram help you to make sense of a geometric problem?
- When you are solving a problem with circles, what parts of the circles and/or lines do you always draw?
- What kind of problems do you find the most easy to solve? Why is that?
- What kind of problems do you find the most difficult to solve? What strategies could help you with those kinds of problems? Discuss with other students to learn some suggestions. Write some of these strategies down to try in the future.

Go Online!

Interactive Whiteboard
Use the *eLesson*, *Lesson Presentation*, or *Interactive Classroom* to present this lesson.

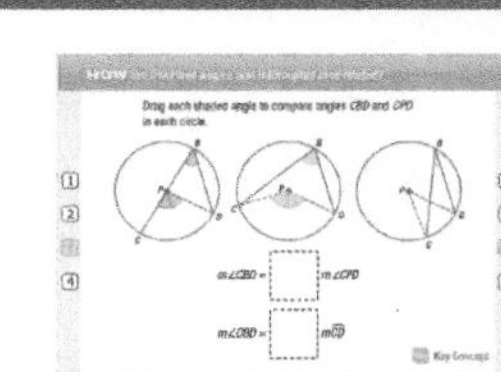

Teach

Ask the scaffolded questions for each example to build conceptual understanding for students at all levels.

1 Inscribed Angles

Example 1 Use Inscribed Angles to Find Measures

AL **What are the two inscribed angles in this example? the intercepted arcs?** $\angle P$ and $\angle N$; $\widehat{MN}$ and $\widehat{PO}$

OL **If $m\widehat{PO} = 148$, what is $m\angle N$?** 74

BL **If an inscribed angle has endpoints on the diameter of a circle, what do you think the measure of the angle is? Explain.** 90°; Sample answer: Because the measure of a semicircle is 180°, an inscribed angle that intercepts the arc would be half of that, or 90°.

Need Another Example?
Find each measure.

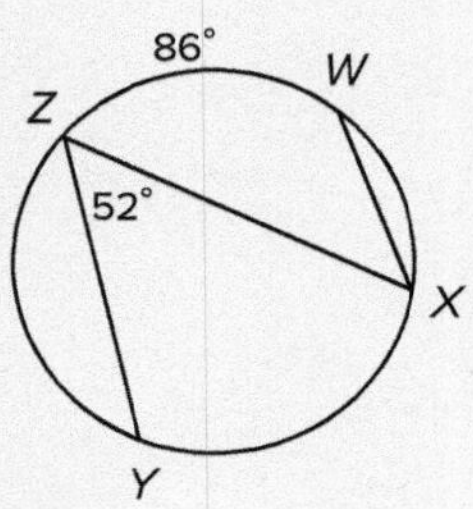

a. $m\angle X$ 43
b. $m\widehat{YX}$ 104

Vocabulary Link ELL
Inscribed
Everyday Use: written on or in a surface, such as inscribing the inside of a ring with an inscription
Math Use: touching only the sides (or interior) of another figure

Proof Inscribed Angle Theorem (Case 1)

Given: $\angle B$ is inscribed in $\odot P$.
Prove: $m\angle B = \frac{1}{2}m\widehat{AC}$

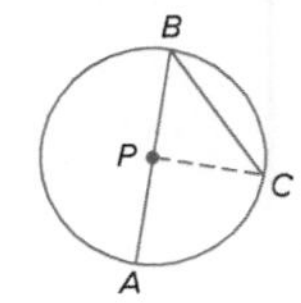

Proof:

Statements	Reasons
1. Draw an auxiliary radius $\overline{PC}$.	1. Two points determine a line.
2. $\overline{PB} \cong \overline{PC}$	2. All radii of a circle are ≅.
3. $\triangle PBC$ is isosceles.	3. Definition of isosceles triangle
4. $m\angle B = m\angle C$	4. Isosceles Triangle Theorem
5. $m\angle APC = m\angle B + m\angle C$	5. Exterior Angle Theorem
6. $m\angle APC = 2m\angle B$	6. Substitution (Steps 4, 5)
7. $m\widehat{AC} = m\angle APC$	7. Definition of arc measure
8. $m\widehat{AC} = 2m\angle B$	8. Substitution (Steps 6, 7)
9. $2m\angle B = m\widehat{AC}$	9. Symmetric Property of Equality
10. $m\angle B = \frac{1}{2}m\widehat{AC}$	10. Division Property of Equality

G.C.2

Example 1 Use Inscribed Angles to Find Measures

Find each measure.

a. $m\angle P$

$m\angle P = \frac{1}{2}m\widehat{MN}$
$= \frac{1}{2}(70)$ or 35

b. $m\widehat{PO}$

$m\widehat{PO} = 2m\angle N$
$= 2(56)$ or 112

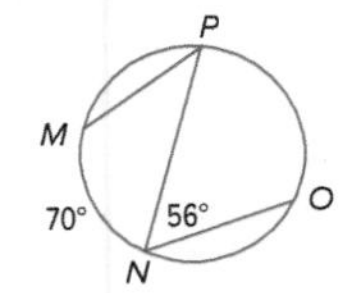

Guided Practice

1A. $m\widehat{CF}$ 80

1B. $m\angle C$ 49

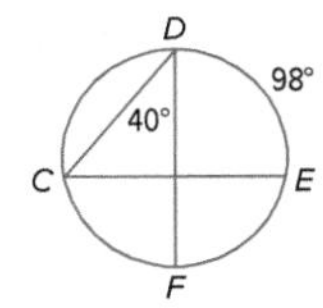

Two inscribed angles that intercept the same arc of a circle are related.

Theorem 9.7

Words If two inscribed angles of a circle intercept the same arc or congruent arcs, then the angles are congruent.

Example $\angle B$ and $\angle C$ both intercept $\widehat{AD}$. So, $\angle B \cong \angle C$.

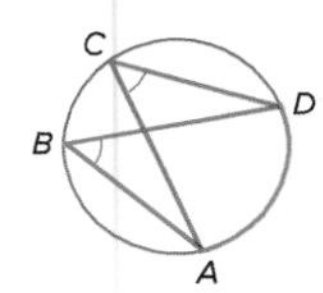

You will prove Theorem 9.7 in Exercise 39.

Differentiated Instruction OL BL

Logical Learners Lesson 9-4 includes a proof using multiple cases. Locate some other examples using a college geometry text or the Internet that involve this type of proof to allow mathematically talented students to develop an understanding of why certain proofs require the consideration of multiple cases.

Study Tip
Inscribed Polygons Remember that for a polygon to be an inscribed polygon, *all* of its vertices must lie on the circle.

G.C.2

Example 2 Use Inscribed Angles to Find Measures

ALGEBRA Find $m\angle T$.

$\angle T \cong \angle U$	$\angle T$ and $\angle U$ both intercept $\widehat{SV}$.
$m\angle T = m\angle U$	Definition of congruent angles
$3x - 5 = 2x + 15$	Substitution
$x = 20$	Simplify.

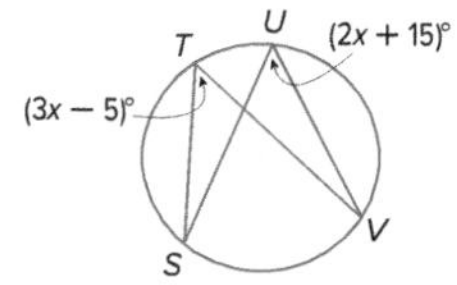

So, $m\angle T = 3(20) - 5$ or 55.

Guided Practice

2. If $m\angle S = 3x$ and $m\angle V = (x + 16)$, find $m\angle S$. 24

G.C.2

Example 3 Use Inscribed Angles in Proofs

Write a two-column proof.

Given: $\widehat{JM} \cong \widehat{KL}$

Prove: $\triangle JMN \cong \triangle KLN$

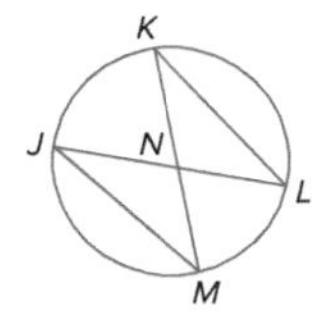

Proof:

Statements	Reasons
1. $\widehat{JM} \cong \widehat{KL}$	1. Given
2. $\overline{JM} \cong \overline{KL}$	2. If minor arcs are ≅, their corresponding chords are ≅.
3. $\angle M$ intercepts $\widehat{JK}$. $\angle L$ intercepts $\widehat{JK}$.	3. Definition of intercepted arc
4. $\angle M \cong \angle L$	4. Inscribed ∠s of same arc are ≅.
5. $\angle JNM \cong \angle KNL$	5. Vertical ∠s are ≅.
6. $\triangle JMN \cong \triangle KLN$	6. AAS

Guided Practice

3. **Given:** $\widehat{QR} \cong \widehat{ST}$, $\widehat{PQ} \cong \widehat{PT}$ See margin.
Prove: $\triangle PQR \cong \triangle PTS$

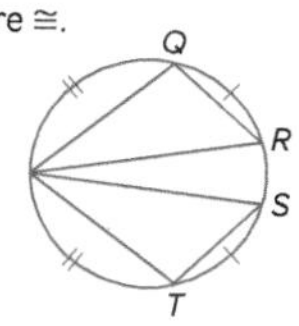

2 Angles of Inscribed Polygons

Triangles and quadrilaterals that are inscribed in circles have special properties.

Go Online!

Tap into the power of your graphing calculator with Graphing Calculator Easy Files™. Practice vocabulary in English or Spanish with Lesson Vocabulary Review Files. Or review with a 5-Minute Check. Ask your teacher to assign them to you in ConnectED.

Theorem 9.8

Words An inscribed angle of a triangle intercepts a diameter or semicircle if and only if the angle is a right angle.

Example If $\widehat{FJH}$ is a semicircle, then $m\angle G = 90$. If $m\angle G = 90$, then $\widehat{FJH}$ is a semicircle and $\overline{FH}$ is a diameter.

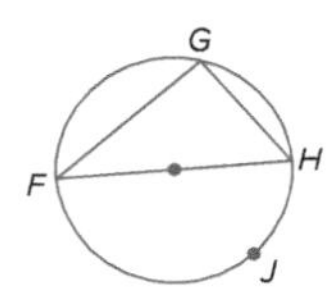

You will prove Theorem 9.8 in Exercise 40.

Additional Answer (Guided Practice)

3. **Proof:**
Statements (Reasons)
1. $\widehat{QR} \cong \widehat{ST}$, $\widehat{PQ} \cong \widehat{PT}$ (Given)
2. $m\widehat{QR} = m\widehat{ST}$, $m\widehat{PQ} = m\widehat{PT}$ (Def. of ≅ arcs)
3. $\frac{1}{2}m\widehat{QR} = \frac{1}{2}m\widehat{ST}$, $\frac{1}{2}m\widehat{PQ} = \frac{1}{2}m\widehat{PT}$ (Mult. Prop.)
4. $m\angle QPR = \frac{1}{2}m\widehat{QR}$, $m\angle TPS = \frac{1}{2}m\widehat{ST}$, $m\angle QRP = \frac{1}{2}m\widehat{PQ}$, $m\angle TSP = \frac{1}{2}m\widehat{PT}$ (Inscribed ∠ Theorem)
5. $m\angle QPR = m\angle TPS$, $m\angle QRP = m\angle TSP$ (Substitution)
6. $\angle QPR \cong \angle TPS$, $\angle QRP \cong \angle TSP$ (Definition of ≅ ∠s)
7. $\overline{QR} \cong \overline{ST}$ (≅ arcs have ≅ chords.)
8. $\triangle PQR \cong \triangle PTS$ (AAS)

Example 2 Use Inscribed Angles to Find Measures

AL **How do we know that $\angle T$ is congruent to $\angle U$?** They are both inscribed angles that intercept the same arc, so they are congruent.

OL **If $m\widehat{SV} = 130$, what is $m\angle T$?** 65

BL **If $m\widehat{SV} = 14x - 4$ and $m\angle T = 3x + 6$, what is x?** 2

Need Another Example?
Algebra Find $m\angle R$.

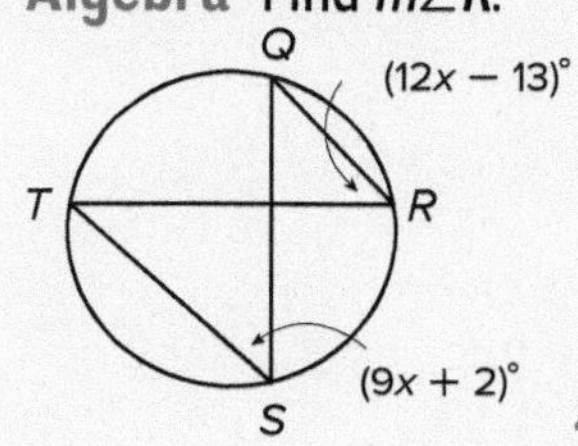

47

Example 3 Use Inscribed Angles in Proofs

AL **Why didn't we need to show that $\angle J$ is congruent to $\angle K$?** We only needed to use two angles with AAS.

OL **Can we prove that N is the midpoint of $\overline{JL}$ and $\overline{KM}$? Explain.** Yes. We can use corresponding parts to show that $\overline{KN} \cong \overline{MN}$ and $\overline{JN} \cong \overline{LN}$.

BL **Do you think that we prove that N is the center of circle N? Explain.** Sample answer: No; We can prove that it is the midpoint of $\overline{JL}$ and $\overline{KM}$, but not that the segments are diameters.

Need Another Example?
Write a two-column proof.
Given: $\widehat{LO} \cong \widehat{MN}$
Prove: $\triangle MNP \cong \triangle LOP$

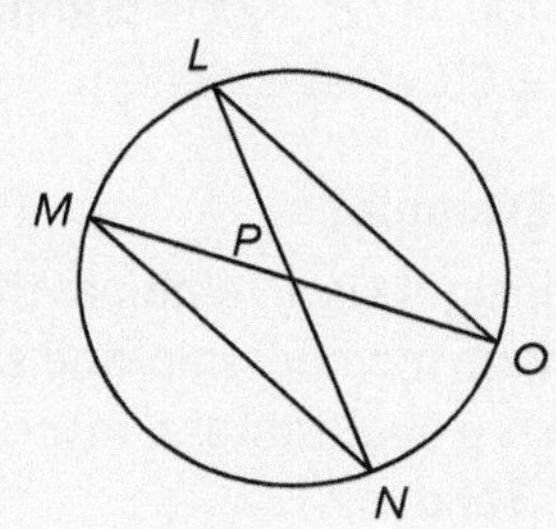

Statements (Reasons)
1. $\widehat{LO} \cong \widehat{MN}$ (Given)
2. $\overline{LO} \cong \overline{MN}$ (If minor arcs are ≅, then corr. chords are ≅.)
3. $\angle M$ intercepts $\widehat{NO}$ and $\angle L$ intercepts $\widehat{NO}$. (Def. of intercepted arc)
4. $\angle M \cong \angle L$ (Inscribed angles of same arc are ≅.)
5. $\angle MPN \cong \angle OPL$ (Vertical angles are congruent.)
6. $\triangle MNP \cong \triangle LOP$ (AAS)

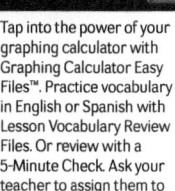

2 Angles of Inscribed Polygons

Example 4 Find Angle Measures in Inscribed Triangles

AL What is $m\angle H$? 60

OL What is $m\widehat{FG}$? 120

BL If $m\widehat{FG} = 116$, what is $m\angle F$? 32

Need Another Example?

Algebra Find $m\angle B$.

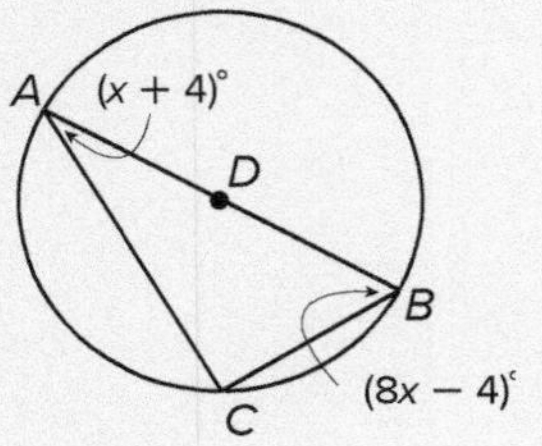

$m\angle B = 76$

MP Teaching the Mathematical Practices

Construct Arguments Mathematically proficient students understand and use stated assumptions and definitions in constructing arguments. They make conjectures and build a logical progression of statements to explore the truth of their conjectures. Encourage students to take notes on each theorem to reference while writing proofs.

Example 5 Find Angle Measures

AL What is $m\angle D$? 70

OL What is $m\widehat{ADC}$? 220

BL If $m\angle A = 100$, $m\angle B = 2x + 5$, and $m\angle D = x + 25$, what is x? 50

Need Another Example?

Insignias An insignia is an emblem that signifies rank, achievement, membership, and so on. The insignia shown is a quadrilateral inscribed in a circle. Find $m\angle S$ and $m\angle T$.

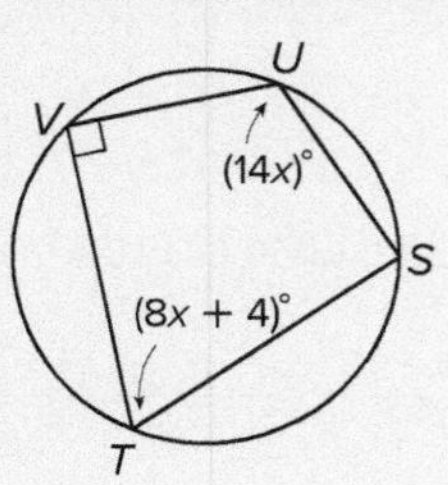

$m\angle S = 90$
$m\angle T = 68$

G.C.2

Example 4 Find Angle Measures in Inscribed Triangles

ALGEBRA Find $m\angle F$.

$\triangle FGH$ is a right triangle because $\angle G$ inscribes a semicircle.

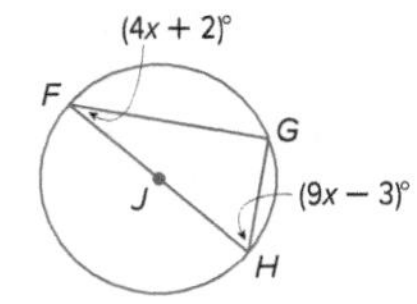

$m\angle F + m\angle G + m\angle H = 180$	$\triangle$ Angle-Sum Theorem
$(4x + 2) + 90 + (9x - 3) = 180$	Substitution
$13x + 89 = 180$	Simplify.
$13x = 91$	Subtract 89 from each side.
$x = 7$	Divide each side by 13.

So, $m\angle F = 4(7) + 2$ or 30.

Guided Practice

4. If $m\angle F = 7x + 2$ and $m\angle H = 17x - 8$, find x. 4

While many different types of triangles, including right triangles, can be inscribed in a circle, only certain quadrilaterals can be inscribed in a circle.

Study Tip ELL
Construct Arguments Theorem 9.9 can be verified by considering that the arcs intercepted by opposite angles of an inscribed quadrilateral form a circle.

Theorem 9.9

Words If a quadrilateral is inscribed in a circle, then its opposite angles are supplementary.

Example If quadrilateral $KLMN$ is inscribed in $\odot A$, then $\angle L$ and $\angle N$ are supplementary and $\angle K$ and $\angle M$ are supplementary.

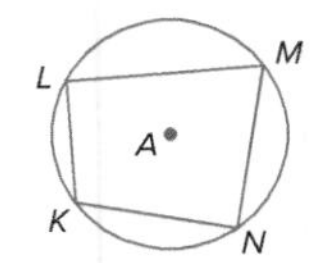

You will prove Theorem 9.9 in Exercise 31.

G.C.2

Real-World Example 5 Find Angle Measures

JEWELRY The necklace charm shown uses a quadrilateral inscribed in a circle. Find $m\angle A$ and $m\angle B$.

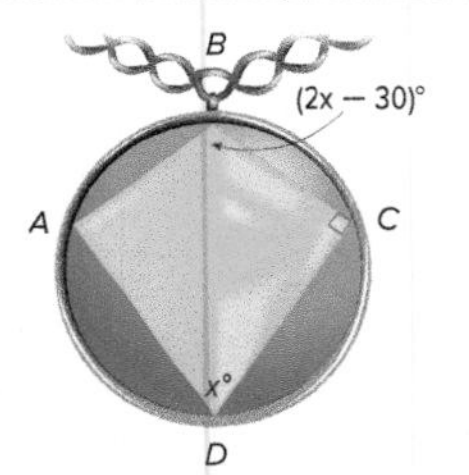

Because $ABCD$ is inscribed in a circle, opposite angles are supplementary.

$m\angle A + m\angle C = 180$	$m\angle B + m\angle D = 180$
$m\angle A + 90 = 180$	$(2x - 30) + x = 180$
$m\angle A = 90$	$3x - 30 = 180$
	$3x = 210$
	$x = 70$

So, $m\angle A = 90$ and $m\angle B = 2(70) - 30$ or 110.

Real-World Link
Charms for jewelry first became popular during the age of the Egyptian Pharaohs. They were repopularized by Queen Victoria in the early twentieth century and by Louis Vuitton in 2001.
Source: *My Mother's Charms*

Guided Practice

5. Quadrilateral $WXYZ$ is inscribed in $\odot V$. Find $m\angle X$ and $m\angle Y$. 120; 85

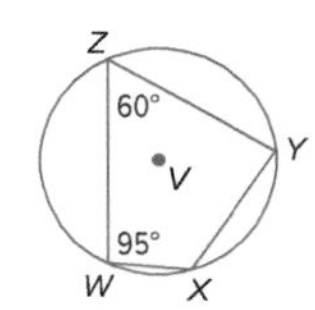

Differentiated Instruction AL OL

Intrapersonal Learners Select or provide examples that cover each concept in the lesson so that students can sit quietly and work at their desks. Ask students to make a note if a particular type of problem gives them difficulty. Encourage students to reread and use the examples and theorems to work and understand the problems.

Levels of Complexity Chart

The levels of the exercises progress from 1 - 3, with Level 1 indicating the lowest level of complexity.

Exercises	11–30	31–38, 51–54	39–50
Level 3			●
Level 2		●	
Level 1	●		

Check Your Understanding

◯ = Step-by-Step Solutions begin on page R13.

Go Online! for a Self-Check Quiz

Example 1 G.C.2 **Find each measure.**

1. $m\angle B$ 30

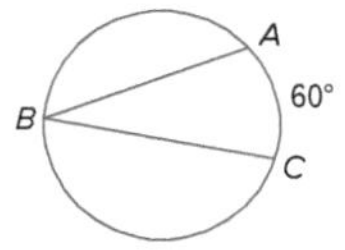

2. $m\widehat{RT}$ 126

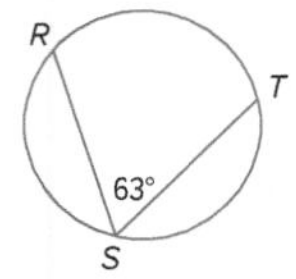

3. $m\widehat{WX}$ 66

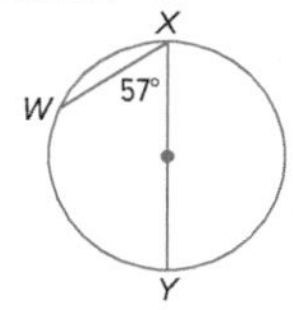

4. SCIENCE The diagram shows how light bends in a raindrop to make the colors of the rainbow. If $m\widehat{ST} = 144$, what is $m\angle R$? 72

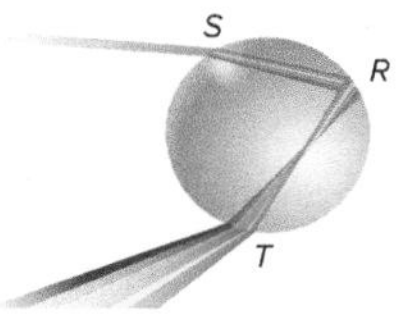

Example 2 G.C.2 **ALGEBRA Find each measure.**

5. $m\angle H$ 54

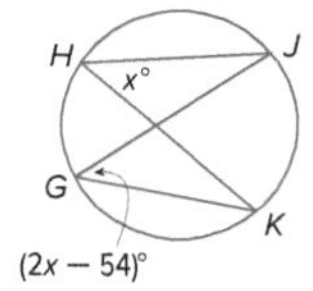

6. $m\angle B$ 36

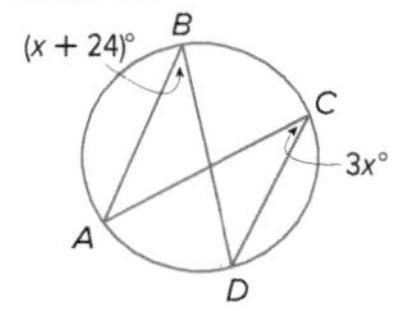

Example 3 G.C.2 **7. PROOF Write a two-column proof.** See margin.

Given: $\widehat{RT} \cong \widehat{UT}$

Prove: $\triangle RVS \cong \triangle UVT$

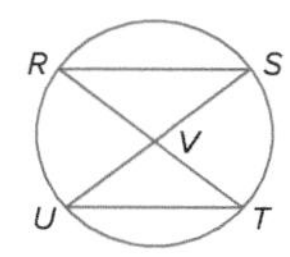

Examples 4–5 G.C.2 **STRUCTURE Find each value.**

8. $m\angle R$ 62

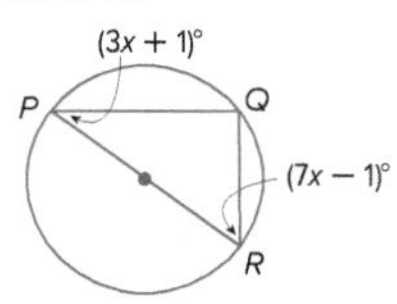

9. x 25

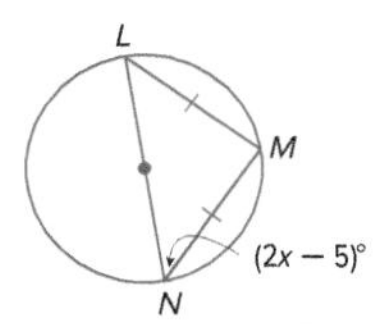

10. $m\angle C$ and $m\angle D$ 122; 80

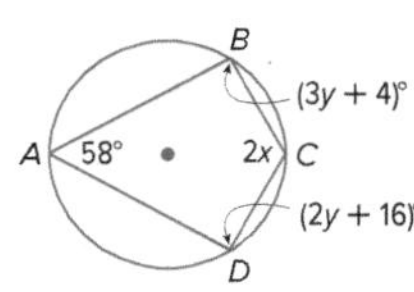

Practice and Problem Solving

Extra Practice is on page R9.

Example 1 G.C.2 **Find each measure.**

11. $m\widehat{DH}$ 162

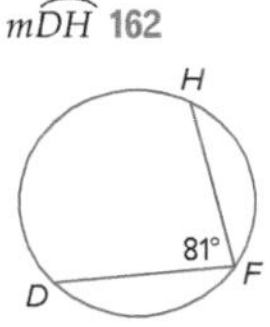

12. $m\angle K$ 46

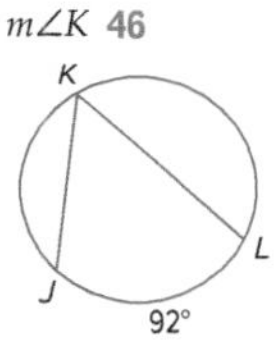

13. $m\angle P$ 70

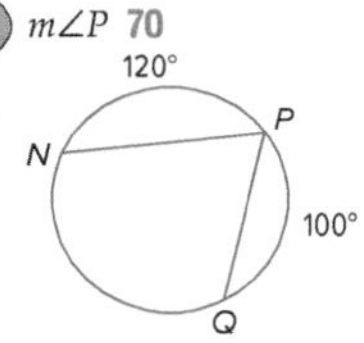

Differentiated Homework Options

Levels	AL Basic	OL Core	BL Advanced
Exercises	11–30, 42–46, 48–54	11–39 odd, 41–46, 48–54	39–50, (optional: 51–54)
2-Day Option	11–29 odd, 51–54	11–30	
	12–30 even, 42–46, 48–50	31–46, 48–54	

You can use ALEKS to provide additional remediation support with personalized instruction and practice.

Practice

Formative Assessment Use Exercises 1–10 to assess students' understanding of the concepts in this lesson.

The Practice and Problem Solving exercises assess the content taught in the lesson. The Preparing for Assessment page is meant to be used as preparation for end-of-course assessments.

Extra Practice

See page R9 for extra exercises for students who are approaching level or for on-level students who need additional reinforcement.

Teaching the Mathematical Practices

Structure Mathematically proficient students look closely to discern a pattern or structure. They also can step back for an overview and shift perspective. In Exercises 8–10, encourage students to analyze each figure for right triangles.

Additional Answer

7. **Given:** $\widehat{RS} \cong \widehat{UT}$
Prove: $\triangle RVS \cong \triangle UVT$

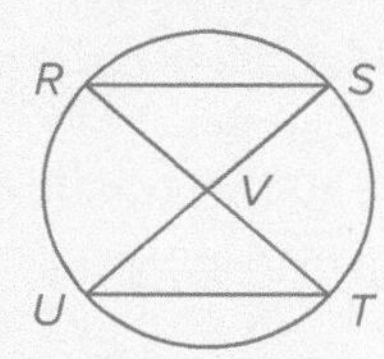

Proof:

Statements (Reasons)

1. $\widehat{RS} \cong \widehat{UT}$ (Given)
2. $\overline{RS} \cong \overline{UT}$ (If minor arcs are ≅, their corresponding chords are ≅.)
3. $\angle S$ intercepts $\widehat{RU}$. $\angle T$ intercepts $\widehat{RU}$. $\angle R$ intercepts $\widehat{ST}$. $\angle U$ intercepts $\widehat{ST}$. (Def. of intercepted arc)
4. $\angle S \cong \angle T$, $\angle R \cong \angle U$ (Inscribed ∠s of same arc are ≅.)
5. $\triangle RVS \cong \triangle UVT$ (ASA)

Go Online! eBook

Interactive Student Guide

Use the *Interactive Student Guide* to deepen conceptual understanding.

· Inscribed Angles

Teaching the Mathematical Practices

Structure Mathematically proficient students look closely to discern a pattern or structure. They also can step back for an overview and shift perspective. In Exercises 27–30, encourage students to analyze each figure for angles that are supplementary.

Additional Answers

21. Proof: Given $m\angle T = \frac{1}{2}m\angle S$ means that $m\angle S = 2m\angle T$. Because $m\angle S = \frac{1}{2}m\widehat{TUR}$ and $m\angle T = \frac{1}{2} m\widehat{URS}$, the equation becomes $\frac{1}{2}m\widehat{TUR} = 2\left(\frac{1}{2}m\widehat{URS}\right)$. Multiplying each side of the equation by 2 results in $m\widehat{TUR} = 2m\widehat{URS}$.

22. Statements (Reasons):
1. $\odot C$ (Given)
2. $\angle H \cong \angle L$ (Inscribed ∠s intercepting same arc are ≅.)
3. $\angle KML \cong \angle JMH$ (Vertical ∠s are ≅.)
4. $\triangle KML \sim \triangle JMH$ (AA Similarity)

31. Given: Quadrilateral $ABCD$ is inscribed in $\odot O$.
Prove: $\angle A$ and $\angle C$ are supplementary. $\angle B$ and $\angle D$ are supplementary.

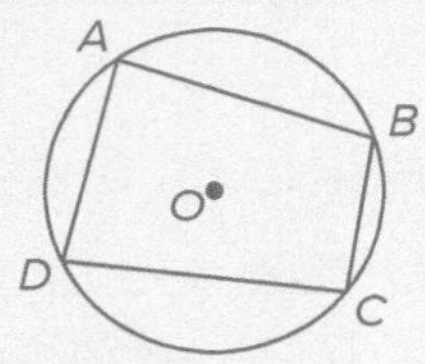

Proof: By arc addition and the definitions of arc measure and the sum of central angles, $m\widehat{DCB} + m\widehat{DAB} = 360$. Because by Theorem 10.6, $m\angle C = \frac{1}{2}m\widehat{DAB}$ and $m\angle A = \frac{1}{2}m\widehat{DCB}$, $m\angle C + m\angle A = \frac{1}{2}(m\widehat{DCB} + m\widehat{DAB})$, but $m\widehat{DCB} + m\widehat{DAB} = 360$, so $m\angle C + m\angle A = \frac{1}{2}(360)$ or 180. This makes $\angle C$ and $\angle A$ supplmentary. Because the sum of the measures of the interior angles of a quadrilateral is 360, $m\angle A + m\angle C + m\angle B + m\angle D = 360$. But $m\angle A + m\angle C = 180$, so $m\angle B + m\angle D = 180$, making them supplementary also.

37. Proof:
Statements (Reasons)
1. $m\angle ABC = m\angle ABD + m\angle DBC$ (∠ Addition Postulate)
2. $m\angle ABD = \frac{1}{2}m\widehat{AD}$ $\quad m\angle DBC = \frac{1}{2}m\widehat{DC}$ (The measure of an inscribed ∠ whose side is a diameter is half the measure of the intercepted arc (Case 1).)
3. $m\angle ABC = \frac{1}{2}m\widehat{AD} + \frac{1}{2}m\widehat{DC}$ (Substitution)
4. $m\angle ABC = \frac{1}{2}(m\widehat{AD} + m\widehat{DC})$ (Factor)
5. $m\widehat{AD} + m\widehat{DC} = m\widehat{AC}$ (Arc Addition Postulate)
6. $m\angle ABC = \frac{1}{2}m\widehat{AC}$ (Substitution)

14. $m\widehat{AC}$ 48

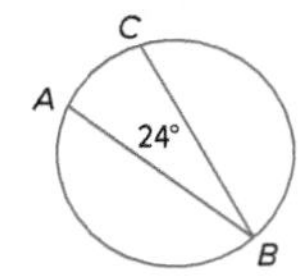

15. $m\widehat{GH}$ 144

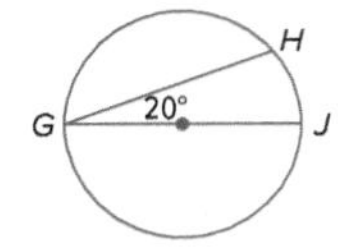

16. $m\angle S$ 66

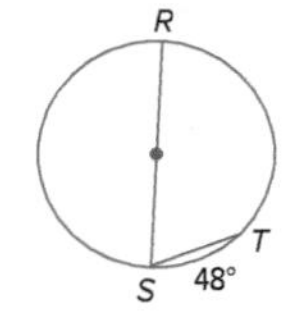

Example 2 G.C.2 **ALGEBRA Find each measure.**

17. $m\angle R$ 32
18. $m\angle S$ 34

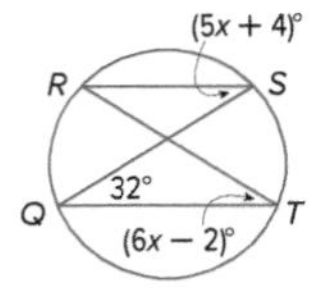

19. $m\angle A$ 20
20. $m\angle C$ 47

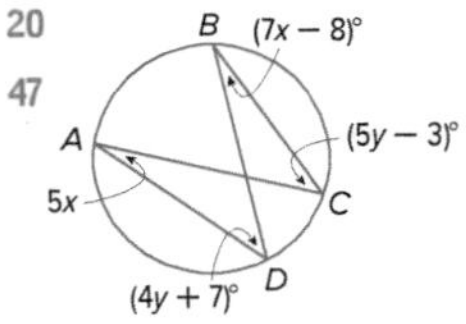

Example 3 G.C.2 **PROOF Write the specified type of proof.** 21, 22. See margin.

21. paragraph proof
Given: $m\angle T = \frac{1}{2}m\angle S$
Prove: $m\widehat{TUR} = 2m\widehat{URS}$

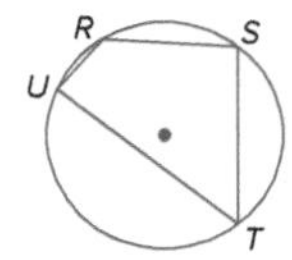

22. two-column proof
Given: $\odot C$
Prove: $\triangle KML \sim \triangle JMH$

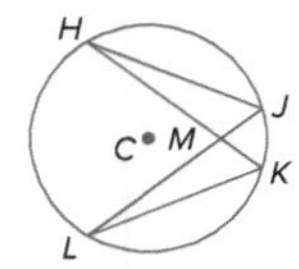

Example 4 G.C.2 **ALGEBRA Find each value.**

23. x 30
24. $m\angle T$ 60

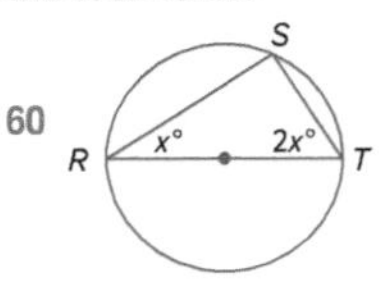

25. x 12.75
26. $m\angle C$ 51.75

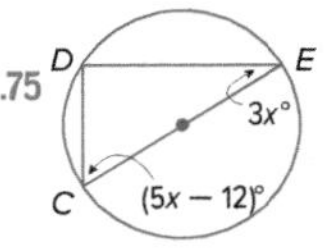

Example 5 G.C.2 **STRUCTURE Find each measure.**

27. $m\angle T$ 135
28. $m\angle Z$ 80

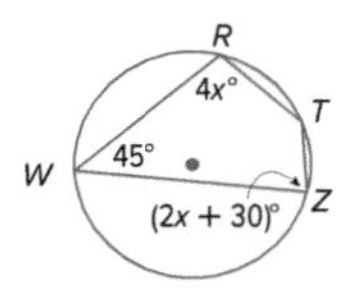

29. $m\angle H$ 106
30. $m\angle G$ 93

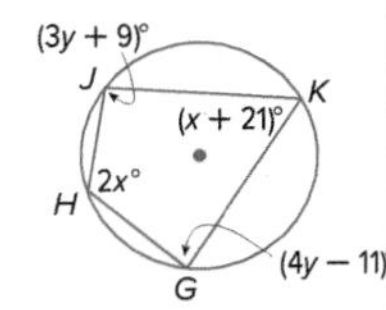

31. PROOF Write a paragraph proof for Theorem 9.9. See margin.

SIGNS A stop sign in the shape of a regular octagon is inscribed in a circle. Find each measure.

32. $m\widehat{NQ}$ 135
33. $m\angle RLQ$ 22.5
34. $m\angle LRQ$ 112.5
35. $m\angle LSR$ 135

38. Proof:
Statements (Reasons)
1. $m\angle ABC = m\angle DBC - m\angle DBA$ (∠ Addition Postulate, Subtraction Property of Equality)
2. $m\angle DBC = \frac{1}{2}m\widehat{DC}$
$m\angle DBA = \frac{1}{2}m\widehat{DA}$
(The measure of an inscribed ∠ whose side is a diameter is half the measure of the intercepted arc (Case 1).)
3. $m\angle ABC = \frac{1}{2}m\widehat{DC} - \frac{1}{2}m\widehat{DA}$ (Substitution)
4. $m\angle ABC = \frac{1}{2}(m\widehat{DC} - m\widehat{DA})$ (Factor).
5. $m\widehat{DA} + m\widehat{AC} = m\widehat{DC}$ (Arc Addition Postulate)
6. $m\widehat{AC} = m\widehat{DC} - m\widehat{DA}$ (Subtraction Property of Equality)
7. $m\angle ABC = \frac{1}{2}m\widehat{AC}$ (Substitution)

36. ART Four different string art star patterns are shown. If all of the inscribed angles of each star shown are congruent, find the measure of each inscribed angle.

a. 36
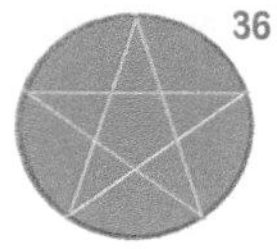

b. 60
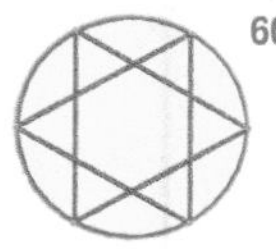

c.

d. 45
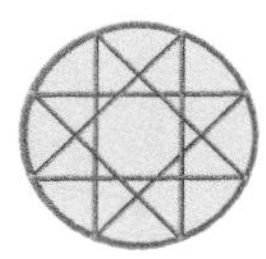

PROOF **Write a two-column proof for each case of Theorem 9.6.** 36c. $\frac{180}{7}$ or about 25.7

37. Case 2 See margin.

Given: *P* lies inside $\angle ABC$.
$\overline{BD}$ is a diameter.
Prove: $m\angle ABC = \frac{1}{2}m\widehat{AC}$

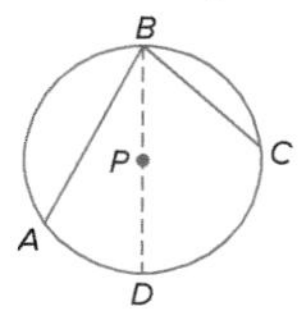

38. Case 3 See margin.

Given: *P* lies outside $\angle ABC$.
$\overline{BD}$ is a diameter.
Prove: $m\angle ABC = \frac{1}{2}m\widehat{AC}$

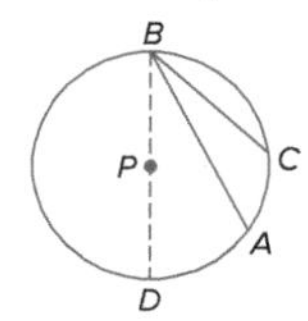

PROOF **Write the specified proof for each theorem.** 39. See margin. 40. See Ch. 9 Answer Appendix.

39. Theorem 9.7, two-column proof

40. Theorem 9.8, paragraph proof

41. MULTIPLE REPRESENTATIONS In this problem, you will investigate the relationship between the arcs of a circle that are cut by two parallel chords.

a. Geometric Use a compass to draw a circle with parallel chords $\overline{AB}$ and $\overline{CD}$. Connect points *A* and *D* by drawing segment $\overline{AD}$. See Ch. 9 Answer Appendix.

b. Numerical Use a protractor to find $m\angle A$ and $m\angle D$. Then determine $m\widehat{AC}$ and $m\widehat{BD}$. What is true about these arcs? Explain. See Ch. 9 Answer Appendix.

c. Verbal Draw another circle and repeat parts **a** and **b**. Make a conjecture about arcs of a circle that are cut by two parallel chords.

41c. Sample answer: In a circle, two parallel chords cut congruent arcs. See students' work.

d. Analytical Use your conjecture to find $m\widehat{PR}$ and $m\widehat{QS}$ in the figure at the right. Verify by using inscribed angles to find the measures of the arcs. 70; 70

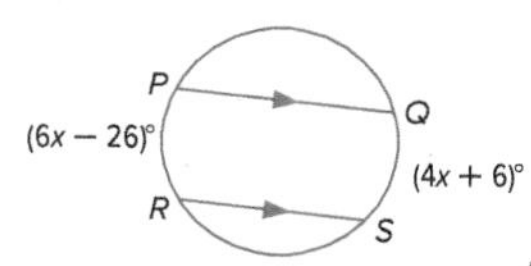

G.C.2, G.C.3

H.O.T. Problems Use Higher-Order Thinking Skills

MP CONSTRUCT ARGUMENTS **Determine whether the quadrilateral can *always*, *sometimes*, or *never* be inscribed in a circle. Explain your reasoning.** 42–46. See Ch. 9 Answer Appendix.

42. square **43.** rectangle **44.** parallelogram **45.** rhombus **46.** kite

47. MP CHALLENGE A square is inscribed in a circle. What is the ratio of the area of the circle to the area of the square? $\frac{\pi}{2}$

48. WRITING IN MATH A 45°-45°-90° right triangle is inscribed in a circle. If the radius of the circle is given, explain how to find the lengths of the right triangle's legs. See Ch. 9 Answer Appendix.

49. OPEN-ENDED Find and sketch a real-world logo with an inscribed polygon. See students' work.

50. WRITING IN MATH Compare and contrast inscribed angles and central angles of a circle. If they intercept the same arc, how are they related? See Ch. 9 Answer Appendix.

MP Standards for Mathematical Practice

Emphasis On	Exercises
1 Make sense of problems and persevere in solving them.	32–36
2 Reason abstractly and quantitatively.	21, 22, 31, 37, 38, 41–50
6 Attend to precision.	14–20, 23–30

Exercise Alert

Compass, Protractor, and Straightedge
Exercise 41 requires the use of a compass, a protractor, and a straightedge.

MP Teaching the Mathematical Practices

Construct Arguments Mathematically proficient students understand and use stated assumptions and definitions in constructing arguments. They are able to analyze situations by breaking them into cases, and can recognize and use counterexamples. In Exercises 42–46, dynamic geometry software can help students visualize each situation.

Assess

Crystal Ball Have students write how Lesson 9-4, Inscribed Angles, will help them understand tangents that occur outside the circle.

Additional Answer

39. Given: $\angle FAE$ and $\angle CBD$ are inscribed; $\widehat{EF} \cong \widehat{DC}$
Prove: $\angle FAE \cong \angle CBD$
Proof:

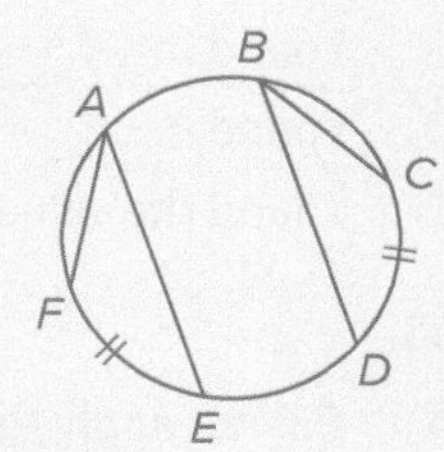

Statements (Reasons)
1. $\angle FAE$ and $\angle CBD$ are inscribed; $\widehat{EF} \cong \widehat{DC}$ (Given)
2. $m\angle FAE = \frac{1}{2}m\widehat{EF}$; $m\angle CBD = \frac{1}{2}m\widehat{DC}$ (Measure of an inscribed ∠ = half measure of intercepted arc.)
3. $m\widehat{EF} = m\widehat{DC}$ (Def. of ≅ arcs)
4. $\frac{1}{2}m\widehat{EF} = \frac{1}{2}m\widehat{DC}$ (Mult. Prop.)
5. $m\angle FAE = m\angle CBD$ (Substitution)
6. $\angle FAE \cong \angle CBD$ (Def. of ≅ ∡)

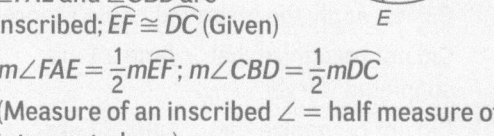

Go Online!

eSolutions Manual
Create worksheets, answer keys, and solutions handouts for your assignments.

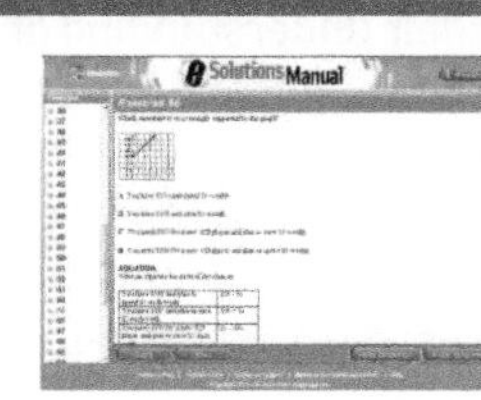

Preparing for Assessment

Exercises 51–54 require students to use the skills they will need on standardized assessments. Exercises are dual-coded with content standards and mathematical practice standards.

Dual Coding		
Exercises	Content Standards	MP Mathematical Practices
51	G.C.2	6
52	G.C.3	6
53	G.C.3	2
54	G.C.2	2, 3

Diagnose Student Errors

Survey student responses for each item. Class trends may indicate common errors and misconceptions.

52.

A	Found $m\widehat{PS}$
B	CORRECT
C	Found $m\angle R$
D	Found $m\angle P$
E	Found the value of x

53.

A	Did not apply the Inscribed Angle Theorem to $\angle J$
B	Did not recognize that $\angle J$ and $\angle L$ are supplementary
C	Did not recognize that $\angle J$ and $\angle L$ are supplementary and incorrectly identified $\angle L$ and $\angle M$ as opposite angles
D	CORRECT

Go Online!

Quizzes

Students can use *Self-Check Quizzes* to check their understanding of this lesson and have the results sent to you. You can also give *Quiz 2*, which covers the content in Lessons 9-3 and 9-4.

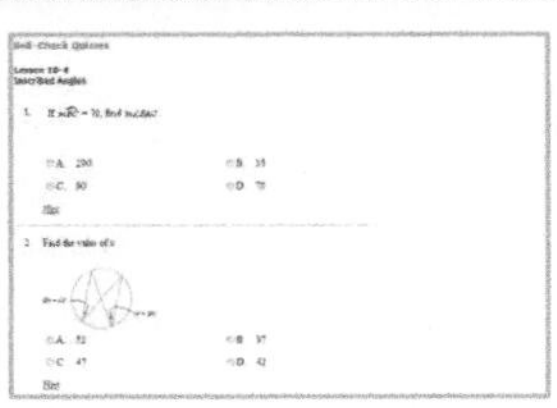

Preparing for Assessment

51. Quadrilateral *ABCD* is inscribed in ⊙*K*. What is the measure of $\angle A$ in degrees? MP 6 G.C.2 **108**

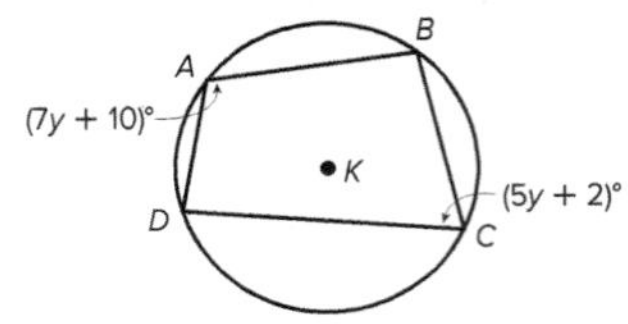

52. What is $m\widehat{SR}$? MP 6 G.C.3 **B**

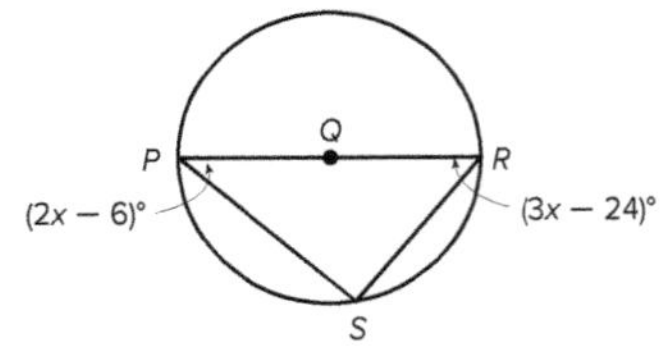

- ○ **A** 96
- ○ **B** 84
- ○ **C** 48
- ○ **D** 42
- ○ **E** 24

53. Quadrilateral *JKLM* is inscribed in ⊙*C*, as shown.

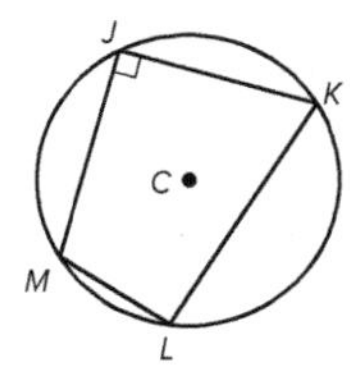

Which of the following statements must be true? MP 2 G.C.3 **D**

I. Quadrilateral *JKLM* contains at least two right angles.

II. $\widehat{MLK}$ is a semicircle.

III. $\angle L$ and $\angle M$ are supplementary.

- ○ **A** I only
- ○ **B** II only
- ○ **C** II and III only
- ○ **D** I and II only

54. MULTI-STEP Look at the figure. MP 2, 3 G.C.2

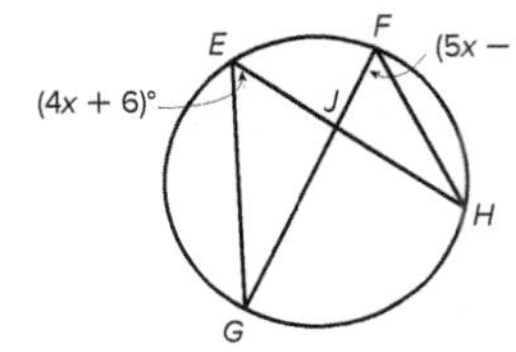

a. Which statements are true? Check all that apply. **C, F, H**

- ☐ **A** $m\angle GFH = 2m\angle FEH$
- ☐ **B** $m\angle GEH = 2m\angle GFH$
- ☐ **C** $m\angle GEH = m\angle GFH$
- ☐ **D** $m\angle GEH = 11.2$
- ☐ **E** The measure of an inscribed angle is twice the measure of its intercepted arc.
- ☐ **F** The measure of an inscribed angle is half the measure of its intercepted arc.
- ☐ **G** The measure of an inscribed angle is equal to the measure of its intercepted arc.
- ☐ **H** All angles inscribed by the same arc have the same measure.

b. The solution for x below contains an error. Choose the step where the error occurs. **C**

- ○ **A** $m\angle GEH = m\angle GFH$
- ○ **B** $4x + 6 = 5x - 6$
- ○ **C** $9x = 12$
- ○ **D** $x = 1.33$

c. What is the measure of $\angle GFH$? **C**

- ○ **A** 22°
- ○ **B** 27°
- ○ **C** 54°
- ○ **D** 108°

d. Can you prove $\triangle EJG \cong \triangle FJH$? Explain. **See margin.**

e. Complete the following proof that shows $\triangle EJG \sim \triangle FJH$.

Statements	Reasons
1. $\angle GEH \cong \angle HFG$	**1.** Inscribed ∡ of same arc are ≅.
2. **$\angle EGF \cong \angle FHE$**	**2.** Inscribed ∡ of same arc are ≅.
3. $\triangle EJG \sim \triangle FJH$	**3.** AA Similarity

Differentiated Instruction OL BL

Extension Have students describe the difference between a central angle and an inscribed angle, and how their measures are related if they intercept the same arc. The vertex of the central angle is the center of the circle, and its sides are radii of the circle. An inscribed angle has a vertex that is a point on the circle, and its sides are chords of the circle. The measure of an inscribed angle is half the measure of a central angle that intercepts the same arc.

CHAPTER 9
Mid-Chapter Quiz
Lessons 9-1 through 9-4

For Exercises 1–3, refer to ⊙A. (Lesson 9-1)

1. Name the circle. ⊙A
2. Name a diameter. $\overline{EC}$
3. Name a chord that is not a diameter. $\overline{ED}$

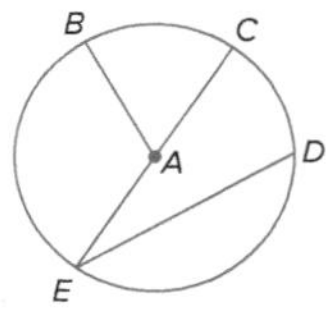

4. **BICYCLES** A bicycle has tires that are 24 inches in diameter. (Lesson 9-1)
   a. Find the circumference of one tire. **75.4 in.**
   b. How many inches does the tire travel after 100 rotations? **7540 in.**
   c. MP What mathematical practice did you use to solve this problem? **See students' work.**

Find the radius and diameter of a circle with the given circumference. Round to the nearest hundredth. (Lesson 9-1)

5. $C = 23$ cm **3.66 cm; 7.32 cm**
6. $C = 78$ ft **12.41 ft; 24.83 ft**
7. **MULTIPLE CHOICE** What is the length of $\widehat{BC}$? (Lesson 9-2) **B**
   - A 18°
   - B 2.20 cm
   - C 168°
   - D 30.79 cm

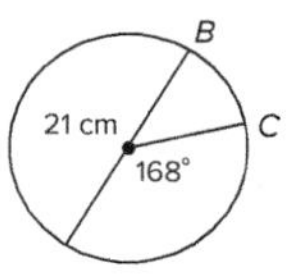

8. **GARDENS** The garden hose caddy shown has a diameter of 14.5 inches. (Lesson 9-2)

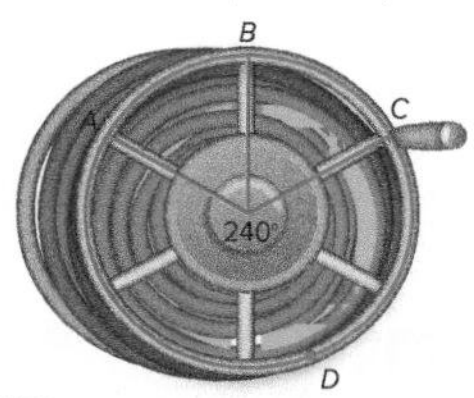

   a. Find $m\widehat{ADC}$. **240**
   b. Find the length of $\widehat{ADC}$. **30.4 in.**

9. Find the value of x. (Lesson 9-3) **70**

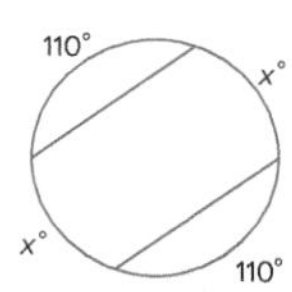

10. In ⊙B, $CE = 13.5$. Find BD. Round to the nearest hundredth. (Lesson 9-3) **4.29**

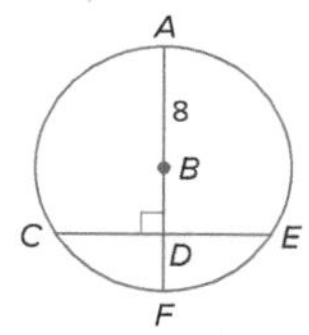

11. The two circles shown are congruent. Find x and the length of the chord. (Lesson 9-3) **$x = 16$; 41**

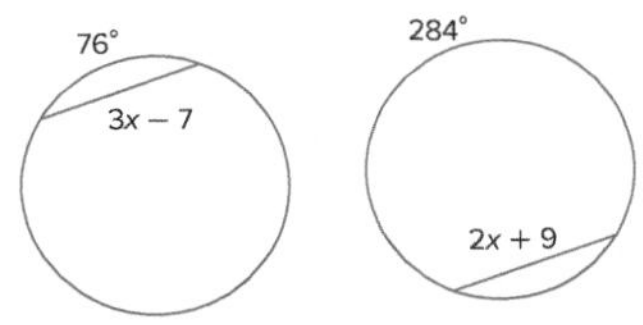

Find each measure. (Lesson 9-4)

12. $m\widehat{TU}$ **46**

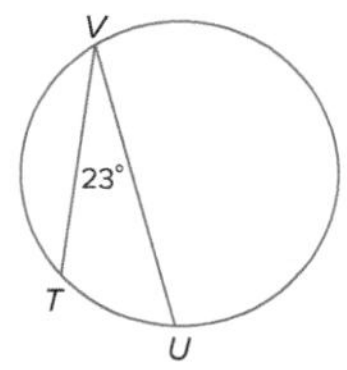

13. $m\angle A$ **85**

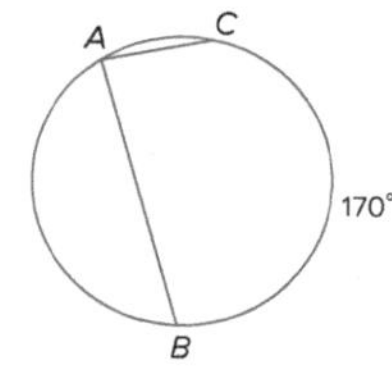

14. **MULTIPLE CHOICE** Find x. (Lesson 9-4) **B**

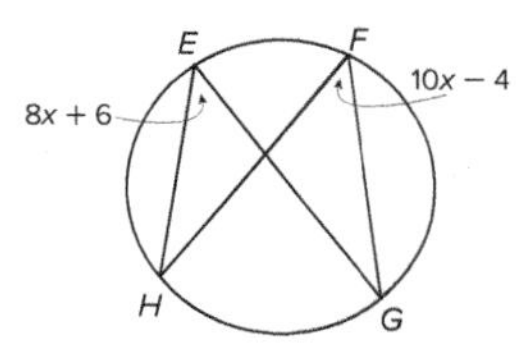

   - A 1.8
   - B 5
   - C 46
   - D 90

15. If a square with sides of 14 inches is inscribed in a circle, what is the diameter of the circle? (Lesson 9-4) **$14\sqrt{2}$ in.**

RtI Response to Intervention

Use the Intervention Planner to help you determine your Response to Intervention.

Intervention Planner

TIER 1 On Level OL

IF students miss 25% of the exercises or less,

THEN choose a resource:

SE Lessons 9-1, 9-2, 9-3, and 9-4

Go Online!
- Skills Practice
- Chapter Project
- Self-Check Quizzes

TIER 2 Strategic Intervention AL
Approaching grade level

IF students miss 50% of the exercises,

THEN choose a resource:

Quick Review Math Handbook

Go Online!
- Study Guide and Intervention
- Extra Examples
- Personal Tutors
- Homework Help

TIER 3 Intensive Intervention
2 or more grades below level

IF students miss 75% of the exercises,

THEN choose a resource:

Use *Math Triumphs, Geometry*

Go Online!
- Extra Examples
- Personal Tutors
- Homework Help
- Review Vocabulary

Foldables Study Organizer

Dinah Zike's FOLDABLES®

Before students complete the Mid-Chapter Quiz, encourage them to review the information for Lessons 9-1 through 9-4 in their Foldables. Ask students to share the items they have added to their Foldables that have been helpful as they study Chapter 9.

ALEKS can be used as a formative assessment tool to target learning gaps for those who are struggling, while providing enhanced learning for those who have mastered the concepts.

Go Online!

eAssessment

You can use the premade Mid-Chapter Test to assess students' progress in the first half of the chapter. Customize and create multiple versions of your Mid-Chapter Quiz and answer keys that align to your standards. Tests can be delivered on paper or online.

LESSON 9-5

Tangents

SUGGESTED PACING (DAYS)

90 min.	0.5
45 min.	1.0
	Instruction

Track Your Progress

Objectives

1 Use properties of tangents.

2 Solve problems involving circumscribed polygons.

Mathematical Background

A tangent intersects a circle in exactly one point. This point is called the point of tangency. More than one line can be tangent to the same circle. Circles can be inscribed in polygons, just as polygons can be inscribed in circles. If a circle is inscribed in a polygon, then every side of the polygon is tangent to the circle.

THEN	NOW	NEXT
G.C.3 Construct inscribed and circumscribed circles of a triangle. Prove the properties of angles for a quadrilateral inscribed inside a circle.	**G.C.2** Identify and describe relationships among inscribed angles, radii, and chords. **G.C.4** Construct a tangent line from a point outside a given circle to the circle.	**G.CO.13** Construct an equilateral triangle, a square, and a regular hexagon inscribed in a circle.

Go Online! All of these resources and more are available at connectED.mcgraw-hill.com

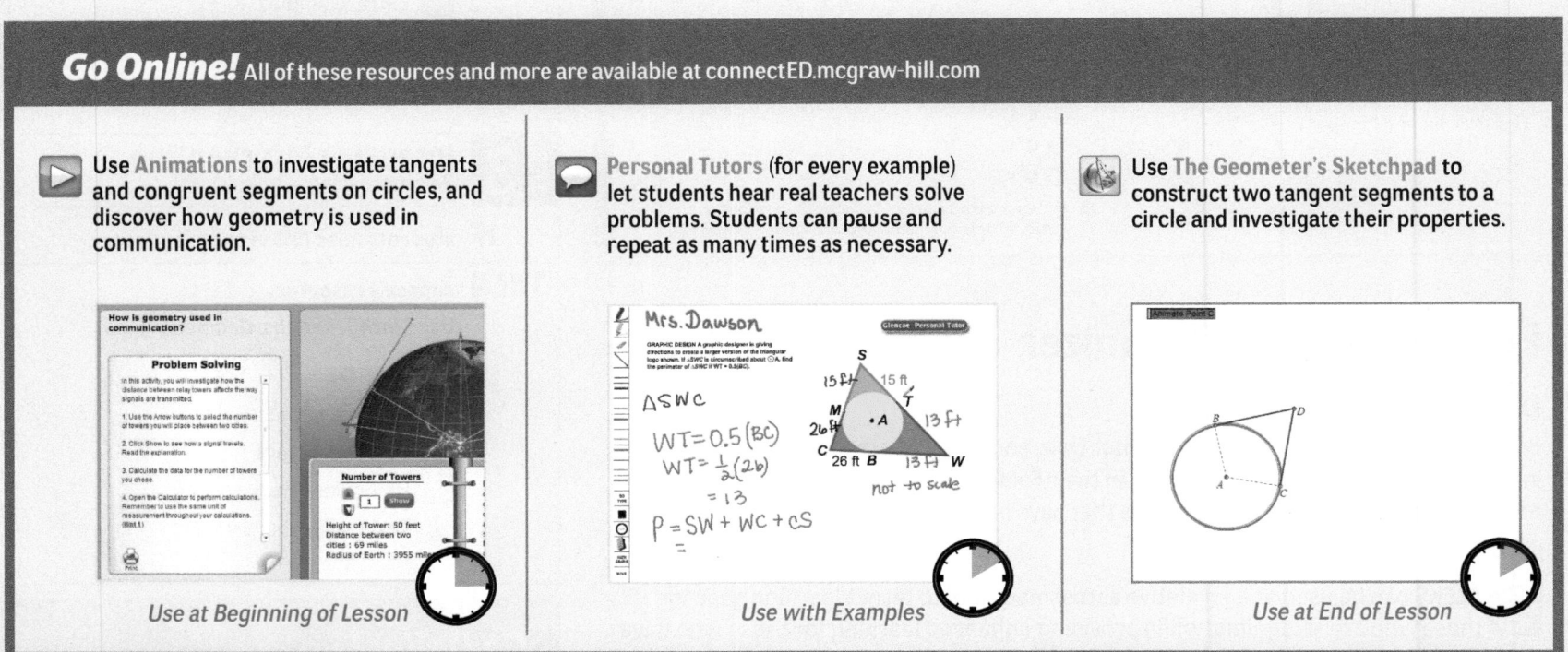

Use **Animations** to investigate tangents and congruent segments on circles, and discover how geometry is used in communication.

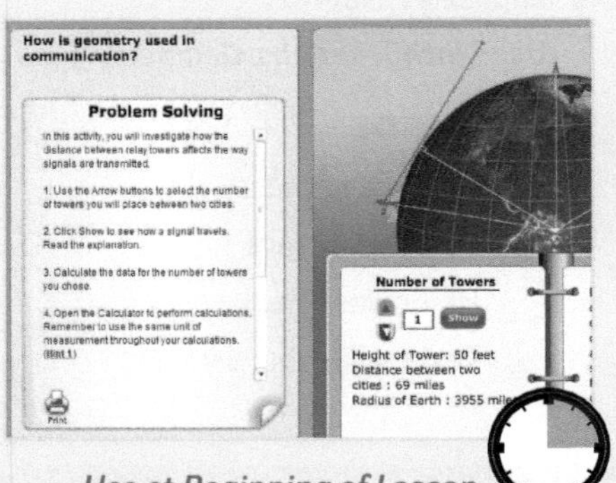

Use at Beginning of Lesson

Personal Tutors (for every example) let students hear real teachers solve problems. Students can pause and repeat as many times as necessary.

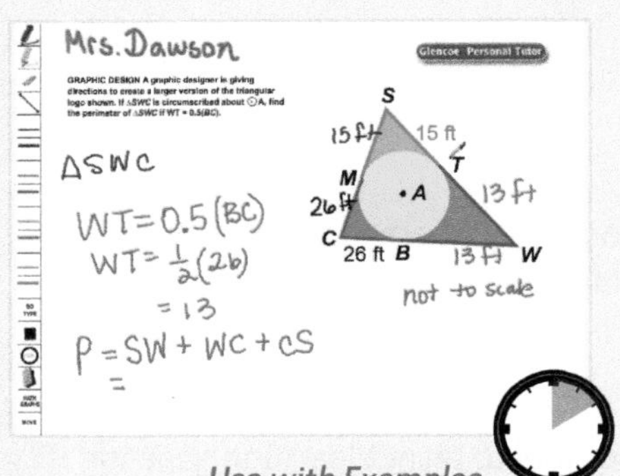

Use with Examples

Use **The Geometer's Sketchpad** to construct two tangent segments to a circle and investigate their properties.

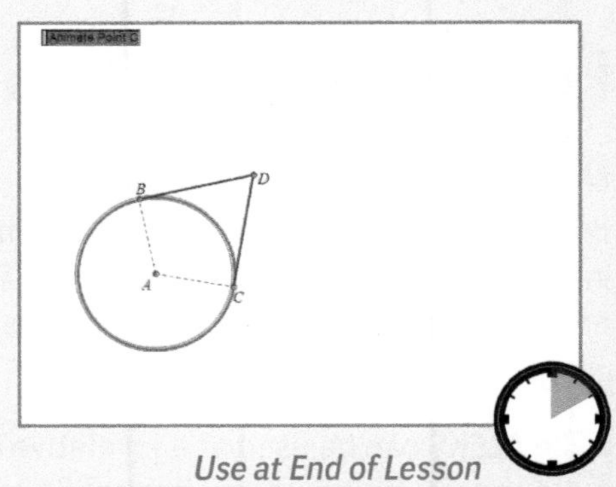

Use at End of Lesson

OER Using Open Educational Resources

Publishing Have students make an interactive poster or manual explaining how to solve problems using tangents on **glogster**. Glogster allows students to insert text, images, photos, audio, videos, and special effects. Students can trade with each other and critique the manual or poster on understandability and creativity. Ask for volunteers to share with the class. *Use as homework or classwork*

Go Online!
connectED.mcgraw-hill.com

Worksheets

Differentiate Your Resources

Extra Practice Additional practice or homework; Skills Practice is best for approaching-level students and Practice is best for on-level and beyond-level students

Skills Practice

AL OL ELL

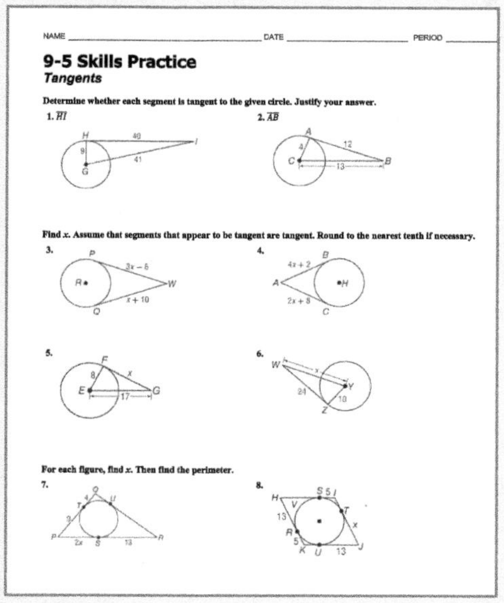
NAME ______ DATE ______ PERIOD ______

9-5 Skills Practice
Tangents

Determine whether each segment is tangent to the given circle. Justify your answer.

1. $\overline{HI}$ 2. $\overline{AB}$

Find *x*. Assume that segments that appear to be tangent are tangent. Round to the nearest tenth if necessary.

3. 4. 5. 6.

For each figure, find *x*. Then find the perimeter.

7. 8.

Practice

AL OL BL ELL

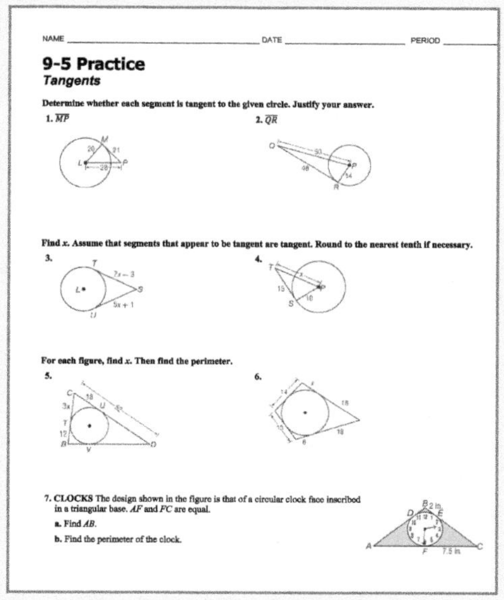
NAME ______ DATE ______ PERIOD ______

9-5 Practice
Tangents

Determine whether each segment is tangent to the given circle. Justify your answer.

1. $\overline{MP}$ 2. $\overline{QR}$

Find *x*. Assume that segments that appear to be tangent are tangent. Round to the nearest tenth if necessary.

3. 4.

For each figure, find *x*. Then find the perimeter.

5. 6.

7. **CLOCKS** The design shown in the figure is that of a circular clock face inscribed in a triangular base. *AF* and *FC* are equal.

a. Find *AB*.

b. Find the perimeter of the clock.

Word Problem Practice

AL OL BL ELL

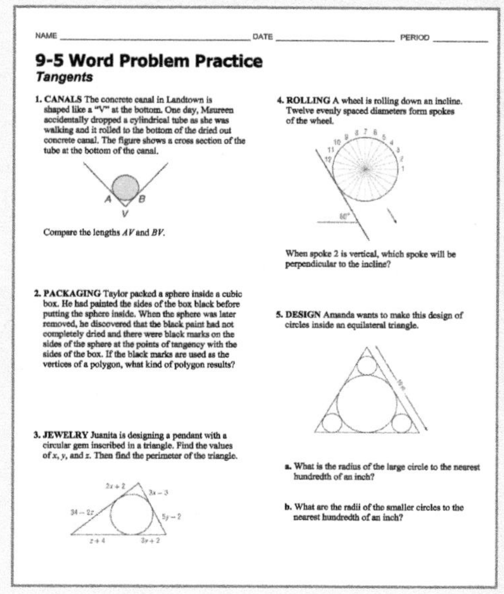
NAME ______ DATE ______ PERIOD ______

9-5 Word Problem Practice
Tangents

1. **CANALS** The concrete canal in Landtown is shaped like a "V" at the bottom. One day, Maureen accidentally dropped a cylindrical tube as she was walking and it rolled to the bottom of the dried out concrete canal. The figure shows a cross section of the tube at the bottom of the canal.

Compare the lengths *AV* and *BV*.

2. **PACKAGING** Taylor packed a sphere inside a cubic box. He had painted the sides of the box black before putting the sphere inside. When the sphere was later removed, he discovered that the black paint had not completely dried and there were black marks on the sides of the sphere at the points of tangency with the sides of the box. If the black marks are used as the vertices of a polygon, what kind of polygon results?

3. **JEWELRY** Juanita is designing a pendant with a circular gem inscribed in a triangle. Find the values of *x*, *y*, and *z*. Then find the perimeter of the triangle.

4. **ROLLING** A wheel is rolling down an incline. Twelve evenly spaced diameters form spokes of the wheel.

When spoke 2 is vertical, which spoke will be perpendicular to the incline?

5. **DESIGN** Amanda wants to make this design of circles inside an equilateral triangle.

a. What is the radius of the large circle to the nearest hundredth of an inch?

b. What are the radii of the smaller circles to the nearest hundredth of an inch?

Intervention Reteaching and vocabulary activities that can be used with struggling or absent students and as ELL support

Study Guide and Intervention

AL OL ELL

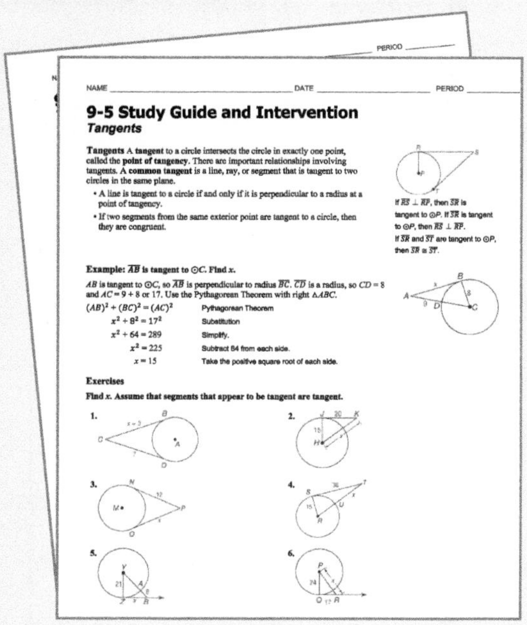
NAME ______ DATE ______ PERIOD ______

9-5 Study Guide and Intervention
Tangents

Tangents A **tangent** to a circle intersects the circle in exactly one point, called the **point of tangency**. There are important relationships involving tangents. A **common tangent** is a line, ray, or segment that is tangent to two circles in the same plane.

- A line is tangent to a circle if and only if it is perpendicular to a radius at a point of tangency.
- If two segments from the same exterior point are tangent to a circle, then they are congruent.

Example: $\overline{AB}$ **is tangent to** $\odot C$. **Find *x*.**

$\overline{AB}$ is tangent to $\odot C$, so $\overline{AB}$ is perpendicular to radius $\overline{BC}$. $\overline{CD}$ is a radius, so $CD = 8$ and $AC = 9 + 8$ or 17. Use the Pythagorean Theorem with right $\triangle ABC$.

$(AB)^2 + (BC)^2 = (AC)^2$ Pythagorean Theorem

$x^2 + 8^2 = 17^2$ Substitution

$x^2 + 64 = 289$ Simplify.

$x^2 = 225$ Subtract 64 from each side.

$x = 15$ Take the positive square root of each side.

Exercises

Find *x*. Assume that segments that appear to be tangent are tangent.

1. 2. 3. 4. 5. 6.

Study Notebook

AL OL BL ELL

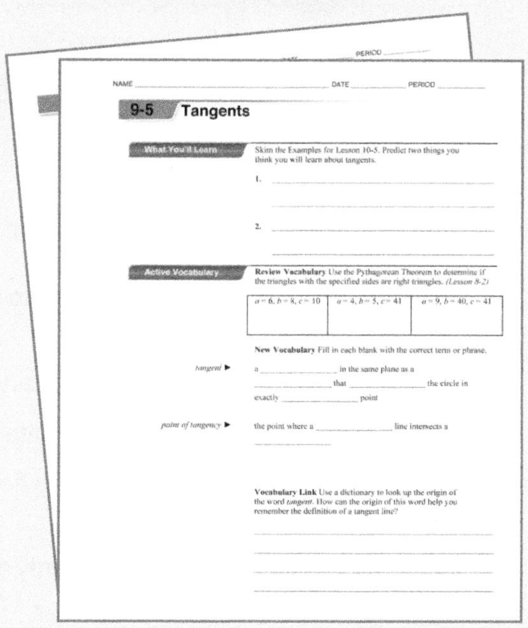
NAME ______ DATE ______ PERIOD ______

9-5 Tangents

What You'll Learn Skim the Examples for Lesson 10-5. Predict two things you think you will learn about tangents.

1. ______

2. ______

Active Vocabulary **Review Vocabulary** Use the Pythagorean Theorem to determine if the triangles with the specified sides are right triangles. (Lesson 8-2)

$a = 6, b = 8, c = 10$	$a = 4, b = 5, c = 41$	$a = 9, b = 40, c = 41$

New Vocabulary Fill in each blank with the correct term or phrase.

tangent ▸ a ______ in the same plane as a ______ that ______ the circle in exactly ______ point

point of tangency ▸ the point where a ______ line intersects a ______

Vocabulary Link Use a dictionary to look up the origin of the word *tangent*. How can the origin of this word help you remember the definition of a tangent line?

Extension Activities that can be used to extend lesson concepts

Enrichment

OL BL ELL

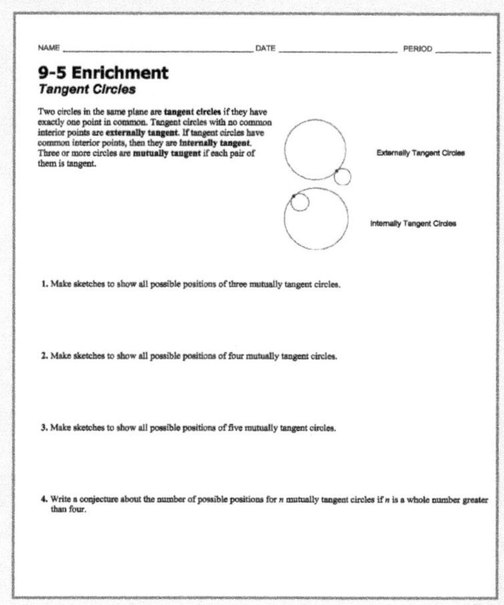
NAME ______ DATE ______ PERIOD ______

9-5 Enrichment
Tangent Circles

Two circles in the same plane are **tangent circles** if they have exactly one point in common. Tangent circles with no common interior points are **externally tangent**. If tangent circles have common interior points, then they are **internally tangent**. Three or more circles are **mutually tangent** if each pair of them is tangent.

Externally Tangent Circles

Internally Tangent Circles

1. Make sketches to show all possible positions of three mutually tangent circles.

2. Make sketches to show all possible positions of four mutually tangent circles.

3. Make sketches to show all possible positions of five mutually tangent circles.

4. Write a conjecture about the number of possible positions for *n* mutually tangent circles if *n* is a whole number greater than four.

Launch

Have students read the Why? section of the lesson. Ask:

- **What geometric figure does each gear represent?** a circle
- **How is the bike chain like a tangent?** It connects the circles with a straight line.
- **How is the bike chain not like a tangent?** The chain touches the gear at more than one point. Tangents are straight lines that intersect a circle at exactly one point.

Teach

Ask the scaffolded questions for each example to build conceptual understanding for students at all levels.

1 Tangents

Example 1 Identify Common Tangents

AL **Do circles necessarily need to be touching in order to have common tangents?** No; Circles can have common tangents whether or not they are touching.

OL **If two circles share a common center, but are not the same size, do they have a common tangent or tangents? Explain.** No; If there were a tangent to the smaller circle, the point of tangency would be inside the larger circle, so they cannot share a common tangent.

BL **Do you think three circles can share a common tangent? Explain.** Sample answer: Yes; If three congruent circles are placed so that all three centers lie on a line, then there will be tangents to the top and the bottom of all three circles.

Go Online!

Interactive Whiteboard

Use the *eLesson*, *Lesson Presentation*, or *Interactive Classroom* to present this lesson.

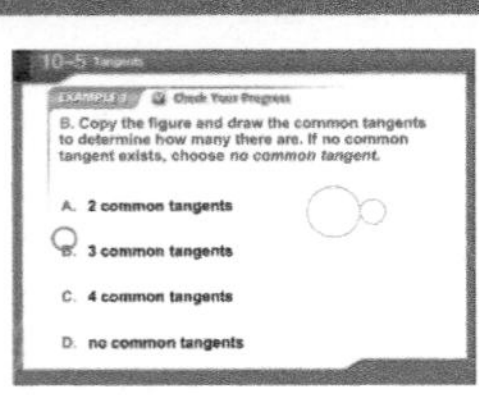

LESSON 5

Tangents

Then

- You used the Pythagorean Theorem to find side lengths of right triangles.

Now

1. Use properties of tangents.
2. Solve problems involving circumscribed polygons.

Why?

- The first bicycles were moved by pushing your feet on the ground. Modern bicycles use pedals, a chain, and gears. The chain loops around circular gears. The length of the chain between these gears is measured from the points of tangency.

New Vocabulary
tangent
point of tangency
common tangent

Mathematical Practices
1 Make sense of problems and persevere in solving them.
2 Reason abstractly and quantitatively.

Content Standards
G.C.2 Identify and describe relationships among inscribed angles, radii, and chords.
G.C.4 Construct a tangent line from a point outside a given circle to the circle.

1 Tangents A **tangent** is a line in the same plane as a circle that intersects the circle in exactly one point, called the **point of tangency**. $\overleftrightarrow{AB}$ is tangent to ⊙C at point A. $\overline{AB}$ and $\overrightarrow{AB}$ are also called tangents.

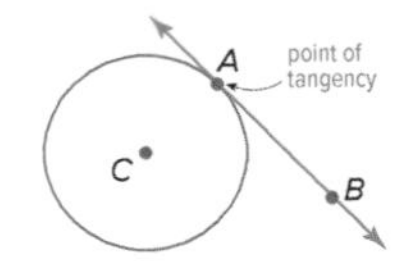

A **common tangent** is a line, ray, or segment that is tangent to two circles in the same plane. In each figure below, line ℓ is a common tangent of circles F and G.

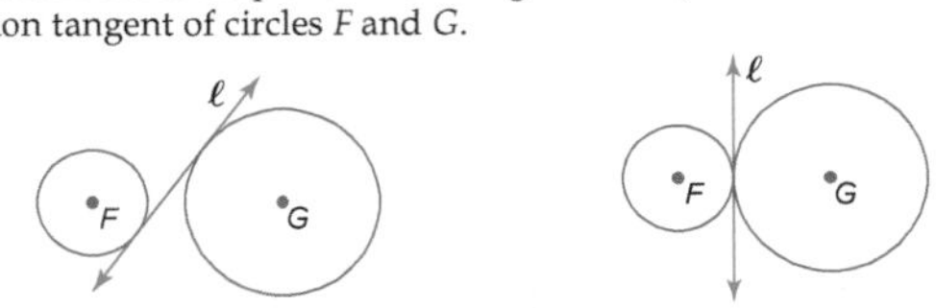

G.C.4

Example 1 Identify Common Tangents

Copy each figure and draw the common tangents. If no common tangent exists, state *no common tangent*.

a.

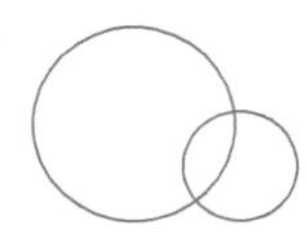

These circles have two common tangents.

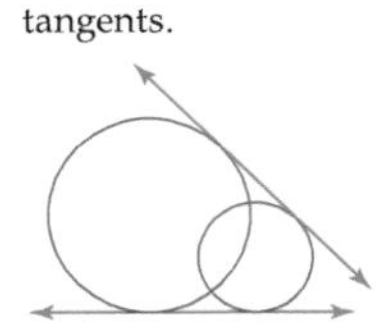

b.

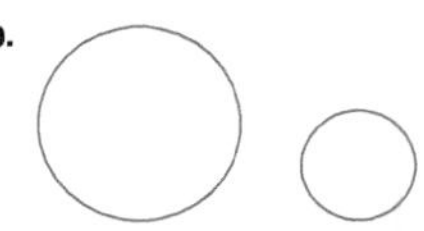

These circles have four common tangents.

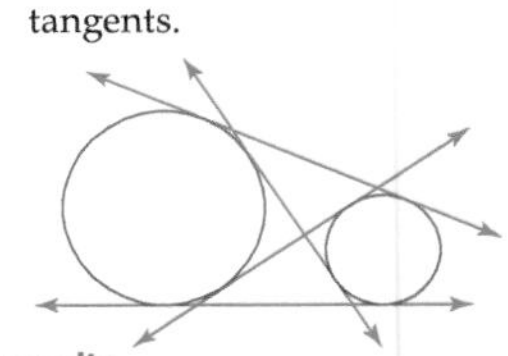

Guided Practice 1A, 1B. See Ch. 9 Answer Appendix.

1A.

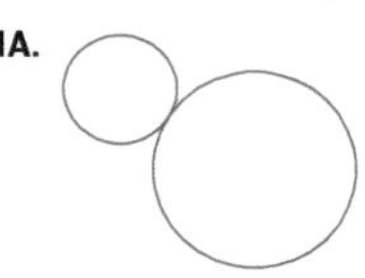

1B.

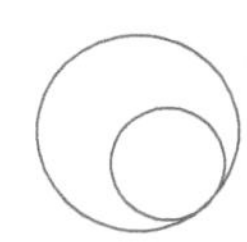

MP Mathematical Practices Strategies

Attend to precision.
Help students understand the definition of a tangent. For example, ask:

- **How do you know if a line is tangent to a circle?** A segment perpendicular to the line passes through the center of the circle.
- **Could there be a circle that had no tangents?** no
- **Could there be a circle with an infinite number of tangents?** Yes; they all do.
- **Could there be a pair of circles with no common tangent? Explain.** Yes, if one is inside the other.
- **When does a pair of circles have only one common tangent?** when they touch at one point

The shortest distance from a tangent to the center of a circle is the radius drawn to the point of tangency.

Theorem 9.10

Words	In a plane, a line is tangent to a circle if and only if it is perpendicular to a radius drawn to the point of tangency.
Example	Line ℓ is tangent to $\odot S$ if and only if $\ell \perp \overline{ST}$.

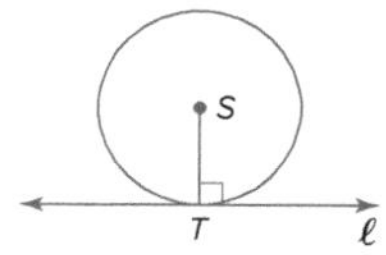

You will prove both parts of Theorem 9.10 in Exercises 32 and 33.

G.C.2

Example 2 Identify a Tangent

$\overline{JL}$ is a radius of $\odot J$. Determine whether $\overline{KL}$ is tangent to $\odot J$. Justify your answer.

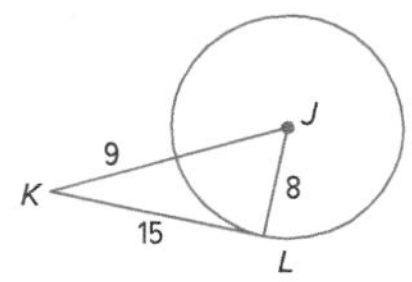

Test to see if $\triangle JKL$ is a right triangle.

$8^2 + 15^2 \stackrel{?}{=} (8 + 9)^2$ Pythagorean Theorem

$289 = 289$ ✓ Simplify.

$\triangle JKL$ is a right triangle with right angle JLK.
So $\overline{KL}$ is perpendicular to radius $\overline{JL}$ at point L.
Therefore, by Theorem 9.10, $\overline{KL}$ is tangent to $\odot J$.

Guided Practice

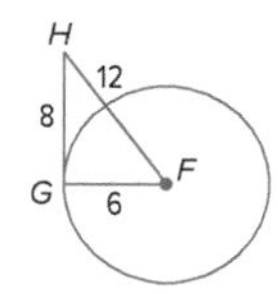

2. Determine whether $\overline{GH}$ is tangent to $\odot F$. Justify your answer. **no; $100 \neq 324$**

You can also use Theorem 9.10 to identify missing values.

G.C.2

Example 3 Use a Tangent to Find Missing Values

$\overline{JH}$ is tangent to $\odot G$ at J. Find the value of x.

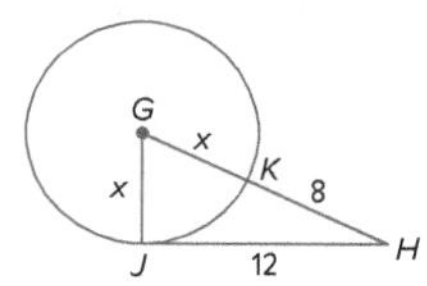

By Theorem 9.10, $\overline{JH} \perp \overline{GJ}$. So, $\triangle GHJ$ is a right triangle.

$GJ^2 + JH^2 = GH^2$ Pythagorean Theorem

$x^2 + 12^2 = (x + 8)^2$ $GJ = x$, $JH = 12$, and $GH = x + 8$

$x^2 + 144 = x^2 + 16x + 64$ Multiply.

$80 = 16x$ Simplify.

$5 = x$ Divide each side by 16.

Problem-Solving Tip ELL

Solve a Simpler Problem
You can use the *solve a simpler problem* strategy by sketching and labeling the right triangles without the circles. A drawing of the triangle in Example 3 is shown below.

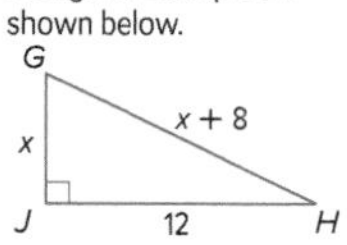

Guided Practice

Find the value of x. Assume that segments that appear to be tangent are tangent.

3A. $\sqrt{93} \approx 9.64$

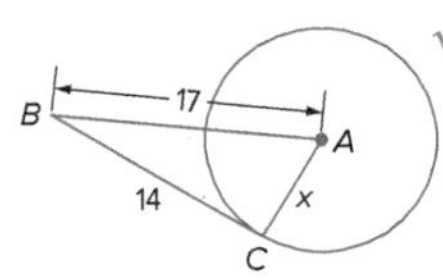

3B. 3

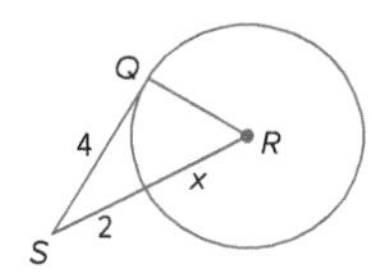

Need Another Example?

Copy each figure and draw the common tangents. If no common tangent exists, state *no common tangent*.

a. no common tangents

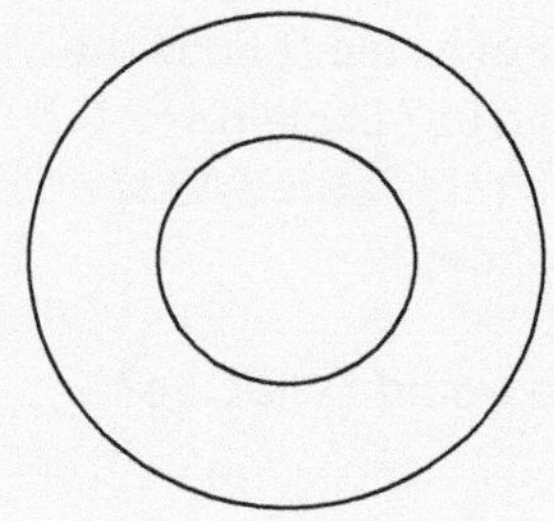

b. two common tangents

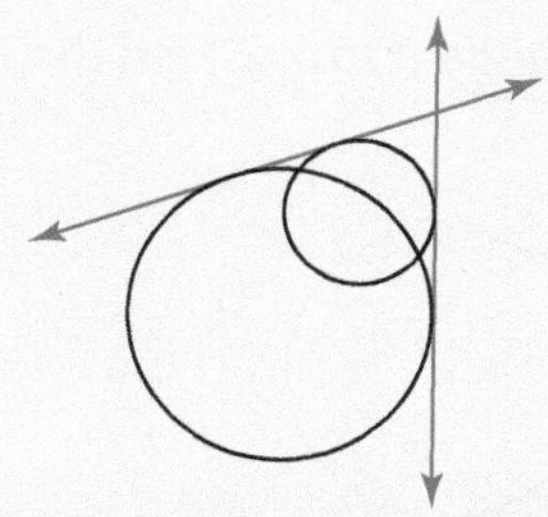

Example 2 Identify a Tangent

AL What is the point of tangency? L

OL If $JL = 7$, is L on the interior or exterior of the circle? interior

BL If you drew a second triangle with vertices J, L, and M, where M lies on $\overline{KL}$, would $\triangle JKM$ necessarily be a right triangle? Explain. Yes; Because we know that $\overline{KL}$ is tangent to circle J, the radius drawn through L must be perpendicular, so the triangle would be right.

Need Another Example?

$\overline{KL}$ is a radius of $\odot K$. Determine whether $\overline{LM}$ is tangent to $\odot K$. Justify your answer.

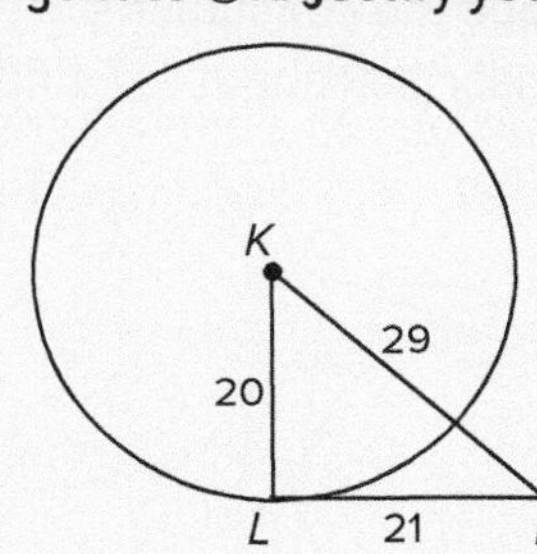

$\overline{LM}$ is tangent to $\odot K$ by the converse of the Pythagorean Theorem.

Example 3 Use a Tangent to Find Missing Values

AL How do we know that $\triangle GHJ$ is a right triangle? Because J is a point of tangency, the radius from the center of the circle to J must be perpendicular to the tangent, so it is a right triangle.

OL If we know that $m\angle H = 45$, and $JH = 7$, what is the radius of the circle? 7

BL If we know that $m\angle H = 30$, and $JH = 7$, what is KH? $\frac{7\sqrt{3}}{3}$

Need Another Example?

In the figure, $\overline{WE}$ is tangent to $\odot D$ at W. Find the value of x. 10

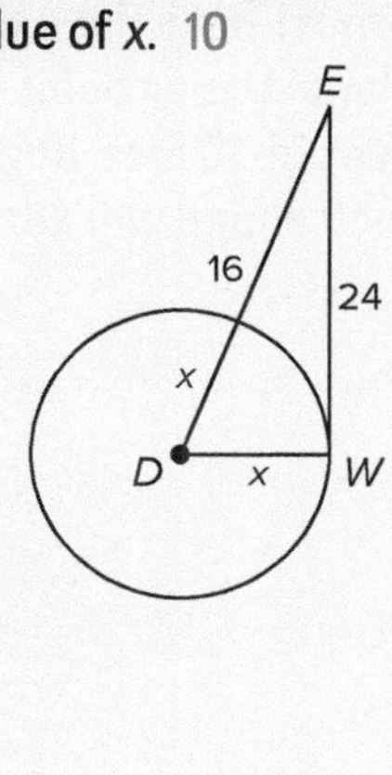

Example 4 Use Congruent Tangents to Find Measures

AL If $AB = 9$, what is CB? 9

OL If B lies in the interior of circle D, does the relationship still hold true? Explain. No; If B lies in the interior of circle D, then $\overline{AB}$ and $\overline{CB}$ would no longer be tangents.

BL What type of triangle would $\triangle ABC$ be? isosceles

Need Another Example?

Algebra $\overline{AC}$ and $\overline{BC}$ are tangent to $\odot Z$. Find the value of x. 5

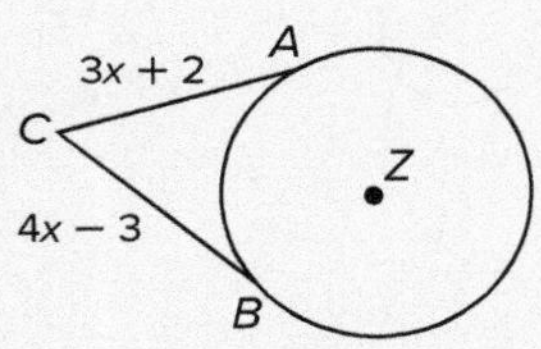

2 Circumscribed Polygons

Example 5 Find Measures in Circumscribed Polygons

AL What are the points of tangency? D, E, and F

OL What is the largest angle of the logo? Explain. The largest is $\angle C$, because it is opposite the longest side of the triangle.

BL What type of triangle is $\triangle ABC$? Explain. obtuse, because $AB^2 > AC^2 + CB^2$

Need Another Example?

Packaging The round cookies are marketed in a triangular package to pique the consumer's interest. If $\triangle QRS$ is circumscribed about $\odot T$, find the perimeter of $\triangle QRS$.

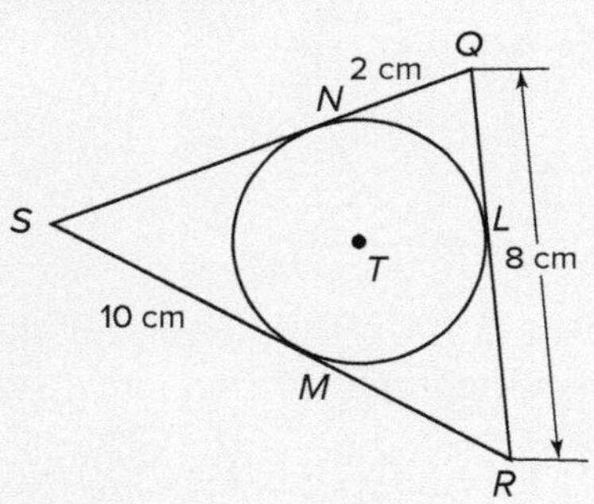

36 cm

You can use Theorems 9.8 and 9.10 to construct a line tangent to a circle.

Construction Line Tangent to a Circle Through an External Point

Step 1 Use a compass to draw circle C and a point A outside circle C. Then draw $\overline{CA}$.

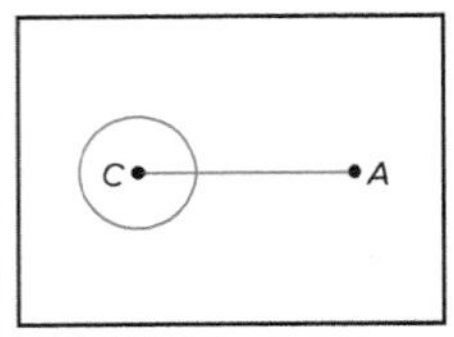

Step 2 Construct line ℓ, the perpendicular bisector of $\overline{CA}$. Label the point of intersection X.

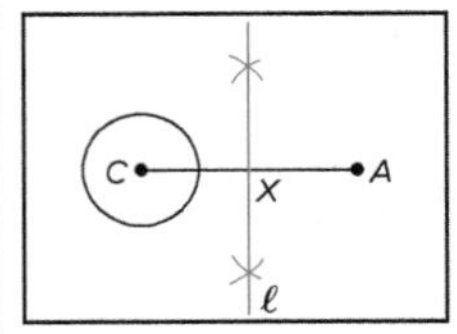

Step 3 Construct circle X with radius $\overline{XC}$. Label the points of intersection of the two circles D and E.

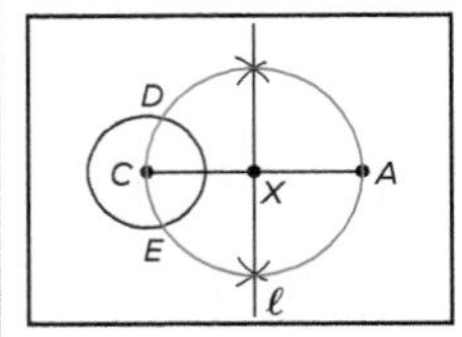

Step 4 Draw $\overleftrightarrow{AD}$ and $\overline{DC}$. $\triangle ADC$ is inscribed in a semicircle. So, $\angle ADC$ is a right angle and $\overleftrightarrow{AD}$ is tangent to $\odot C$.

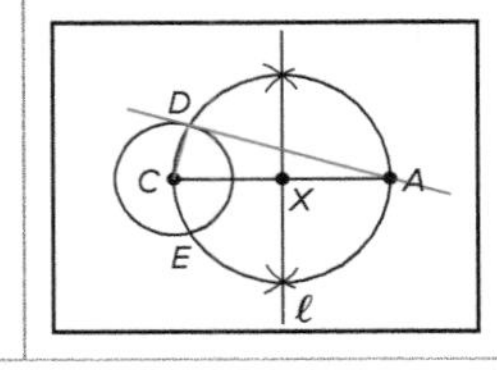

You will justify this construction in Exercise 36 and construct a line tangent to a circle through a point on the circle in Exercise 34.

More than one line can be tangent to the same circle.

Theorem 9.11

Words If two segments from the same exterior point are tangent to a circle, then they are congruent.

Example If $\overline{AB}$ and $\overline{CB}$ are tangent to $\odot D$, then $\overline{AB} \cong \overline{CB}$.

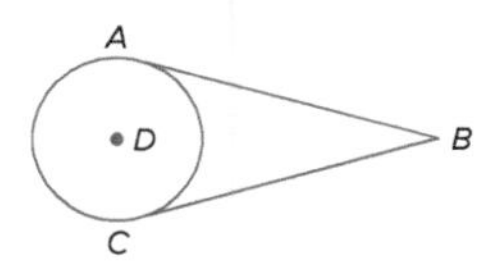

You will prove Theorem 9.11 in Exercise 28.

G.C.2

Example 4 Use Congruent Tangents to Find Measures

ALGEBRA $\overline{AB}$ and $\overline{CB}$ are tangent to $\odot D$. Find the value of x.

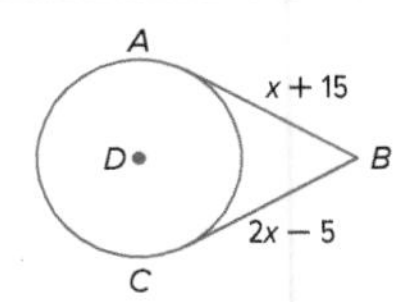

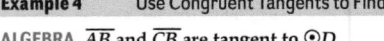

$AB = CB$	Tangents from the same exterior point are congruent.
$x + 15 = 2x - 5$	Substitution
$15 = x - 5$	Subtract x from each side.
$20 = x$	Add 5 to each side.

Go Online!

Construct tangents and compare the lengths of two tangent segments from the common intersection point to the points of tangency with a Geometer's Sketchpad® sketch in ConnectED.

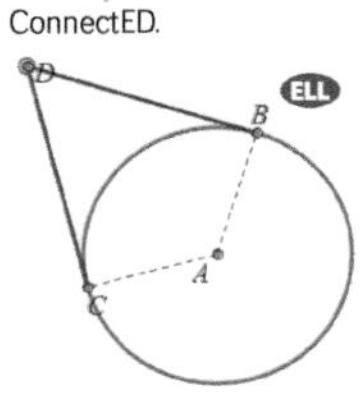

ELL

Guided Practice

ALGEBRA Find the value of x. Assume that segments that appear to be tangent are tangent.

4A. 6

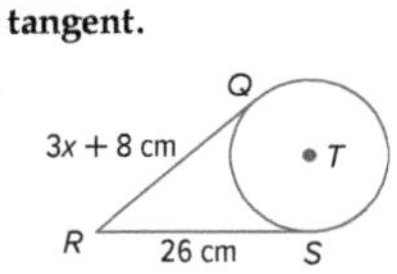

4B. 3

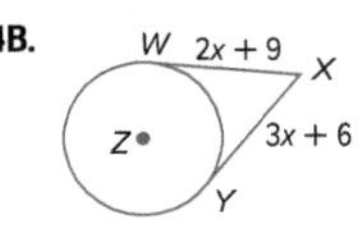

Differentiated Instruction AL OL

Social/Interpersonal Learners Organize students in small groups. Explain that a company wants to market a new toy with a diameter of 5 inches. Their task is to design a container for the toy that takes up the least amount of shelf space. The container must have flat sides, and therefore cannot be circular. Have students draw and label the circular toy and the container surrounding it. If the display shelf is 3 feet by 10 feet, how many toy containers will fit in a single layer on the shelf? Which shape will allow the maximum number of toys to be displayed on the shelf?

Watch Out ELL

Identifying Circumscribed Polygons If a circle is tangent to one or more of the sides of a polygon, it does not mean that the polygon is circumscribed about the circle, as shown in the set of figures on the right.

2 Circumscribed Polygons

A polygon is circumscribed about a circle if every side of the polygon is tangent to the circle.

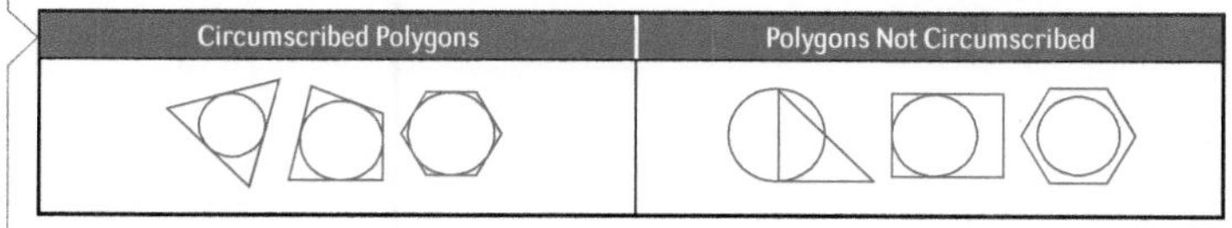

You can use Theorem 9.11 to find missing measures in circumscribed polygons.

G.C.2

Real-World Example 5 Find Measures in Circumscribed Polygons

GRAPHIC DESIGN A graphic designer is giving directions to create a larger version of the triangular logo shown. If $\triangle ABC$ is circumscribed about $\odot G$, find the perimeter of $\triangle ABC$.

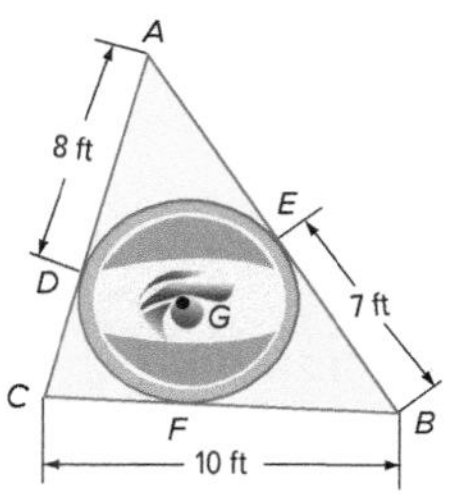

Step 1 Find the missing measures.

Because $\triangle ABC$ is circumscribed about $\odot G$, $\overline{AE}$ and $\overline{AD}$ are tangent to $\odot G$, as are $\overline{BE}$, $\overline{BF}$, $\overline{CF}$, and $\overline{CD}$. Therefore, $\overline{AE} \cong \overline{AD}$, $\overline{BF} \cong \overline{BE}$, and $\overline{CF} \cong \overline{CD}$.

So, $AE = AD = 8$ feet, $BF = BE = 7$ feet.

By Segment Addition, $CF + FB = CB$, so $CF = CB - FB = 10 - 7$ or 3 feet. So, $CD = CF = 3$ feet.

Step 2 Find the perimeter of $\triangle ABC$.

$$\text{perimeter} = AE + EB + BC + CD + DA$$
$$= 8 + 7 + 10 + 3 + 8 \text{ or } 36$$

So, the perimeter of $\triangle ABC$ is 36 feet.

Guided Practice

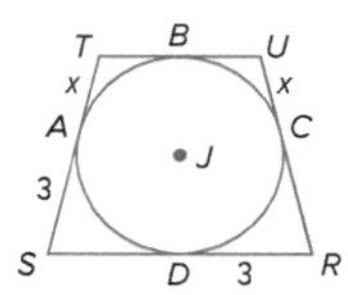

5. Quadrilateral *RSTU* is circumscribed about $\odot J$. If the perimeter is 18 units, find x. 1.5 units

Check Your Understanding ◯ = Step-by-Step Solutions begin on page R13.

Go Online! for a Self-Check Quiz

Example 1 G.C.4

1. Copy the figure shown, and draw the common tangents. If no common tangent exists, state *no common tangent*. no common tangent

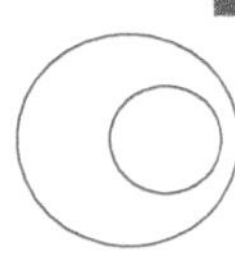

Example 2 G.C.2

Determine whether $\overline{FG}$ is tangent to $\odot E$. Justify your answer.

2.

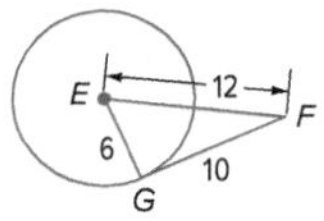

3.

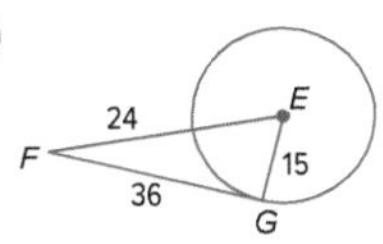

2. no; $136 \neq 144$
3. yes; $1521 = 1521$

Differentiated Homework Options

Levels	AL Basic	OL Core	BL Advanced
Exercises	9–25, 36–44	9–29 odd, 30–34, 36–44	31–39, (optional: 40–44)
2-Day Option	9–25 odd, 40-44	9–25	
	9–25 even, 36–39	26–34, 36–44	

You can use ALEKS to provide additional remediation support with personalized instruction and practice.

Practice

Formative Assessment Use Exercises 1–8 to assess students' understanding of the concepts in this lesson.

The Practice and Problem Solving exercises assess the content taught in the lesson. The Preparing for Assessment page is meant to be used as preparation for end-of-course assessments.

Extra Practice

See page R9 for extra exercises for students who are approaching level or for on-level students who need additional reinforcement.

Levels of Complexity Chart

The levels of the exercises progress from 1 to 3, with Level 1 indicating the lowest level of complexity.

Exercises	9–25	26–30, 40–44	31–39
Level 3			●
Level 2		●	
Level 1	●		

Go Online! eBook

Interactive Student Guide

Use the *Interactive Student Guide* to deepen conceptual understanding.
· Tangents

MP Teaching the Mathematical Practices

Sense-Making Mathematically proficient students start by explaining the meaning of a problem to themselves and looking for entry points to its solution. In Exercises 8 and 24–25, encourage students to identify the segments tangent to the circle first.

Additional Answers

9.

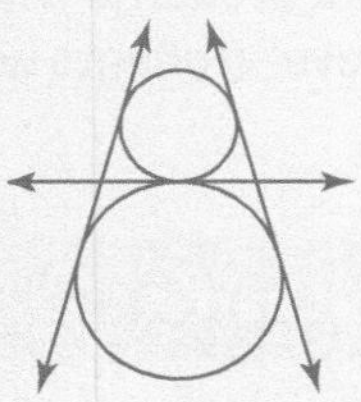

11.

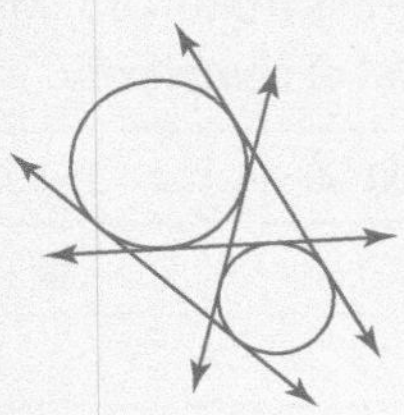

12.

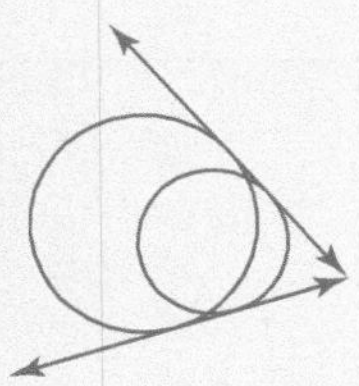

Examples 3–4 G.C.2 **Find x. Assume that segments that appear to be tangent are tangent.**

4. 20

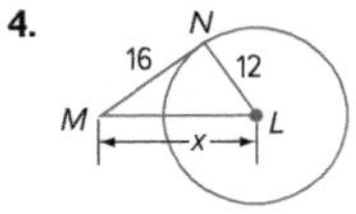

5. 16

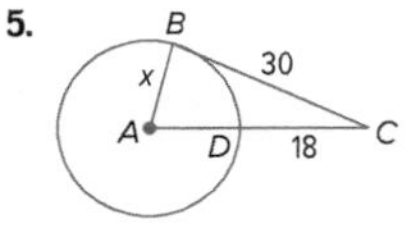

6. 4

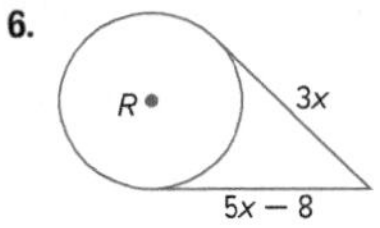

7. CITY PLANNING A landscape architect is designing a public park with two adjacent circular fountains. The walking paths are tangent to the fountains as shown. The lengths are given in feet. Find x and y. $x = 4$; $y = 15$

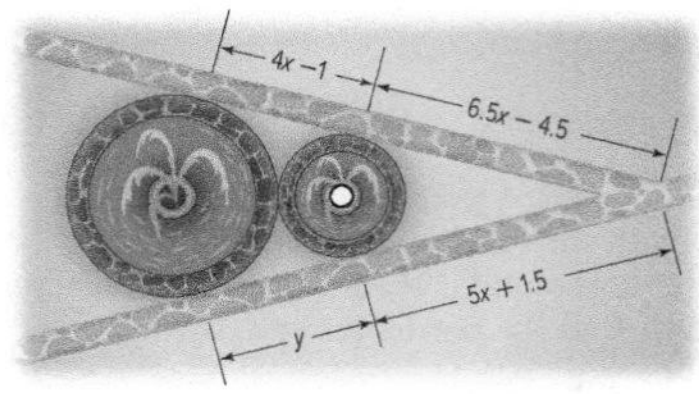

Example 5 G.C.2

8. MP **SENSE-MAKING** Triangle JKL is circumscribed about $\odot R$.

a. Find x. 4

b. Find the perimeter of $\triangle JKL$. 52 units

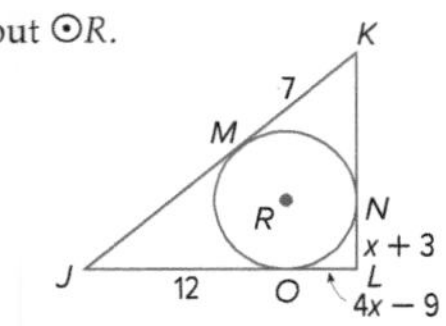

Practice and Problem Solving

Extra Practice is on page R9.

Example 1 G.C.4 **Copy each figure and draw the common tangents. If no common tangent exists, state *no common tangent*.** 9, 11, 12. See margin.

9.

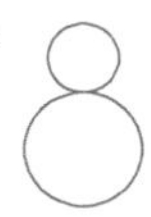

10.

no common tangent

11.

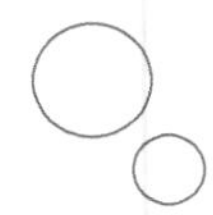

12.

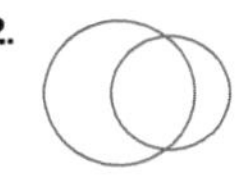

Example 2 G.C.2 **Determine whether each $\overline{XY}$ is tangent to the given circle. Justify your answer.**

13.

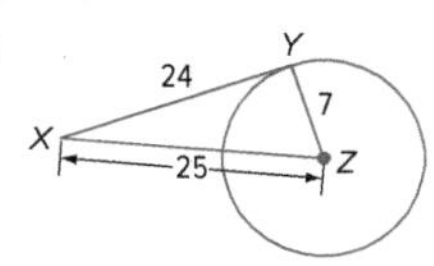

14.

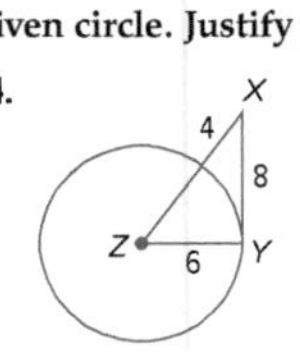

13. yes; $625 = 625$
14. yes; $100 = 100$
15. no; $89 \neq 64$
16. yes; $80 = 80$

15

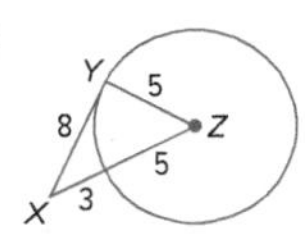

16.

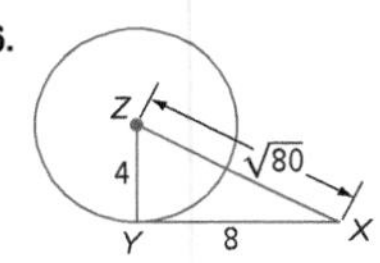

Go Online!

The most up-to-date resources available for your program can be found at connectED.mcgraw-hill.com.

Examples 3–4 G.C.2 **Find x. Assume that segments that appear to be tangent are tangent. Round to the nearest tenth if necessary.**

17. 26

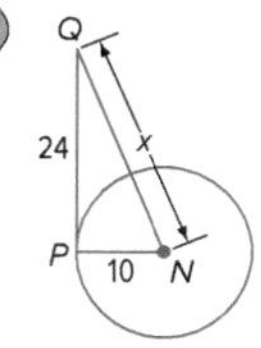

18. 8.5

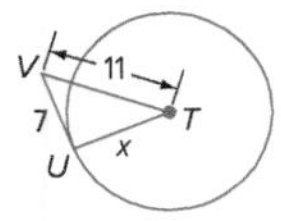

19. 9

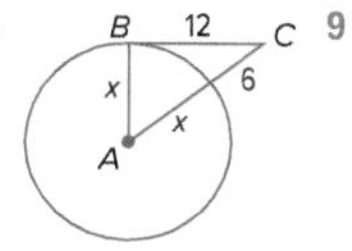

20. 10.7

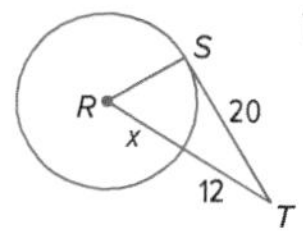

21. 4

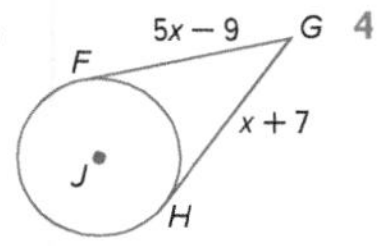

22. 1

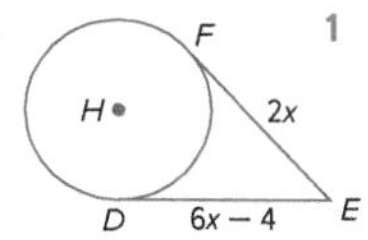

23. ARBORS In the arbor shown, $\overline{AC}$ and $\overline{BC}$ are tangents to ⊙D. The radius of the circle is 26 inches and $EC = 20$ inches. Find each measure to the nearest hundredth.

a. AC 37.95 in. **b.** BC 37.95 in.

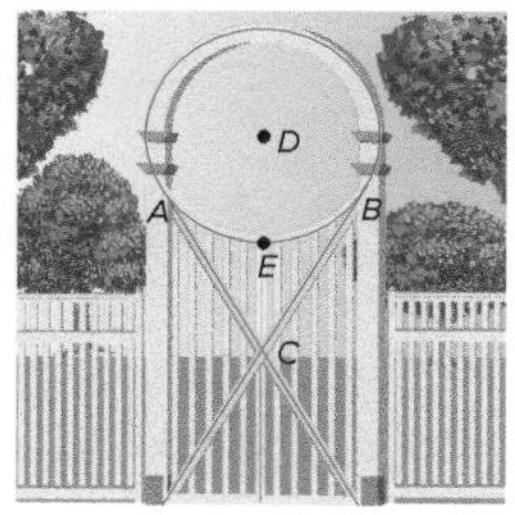

Example 5 G.C.2 **SENSE-MAKING Find the value of x. Then find the perimeter.**

24. 7; 82 in.

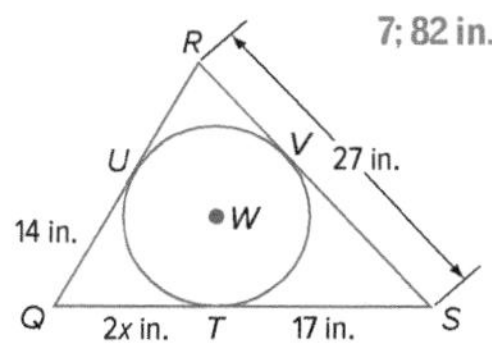

25. 8; 52 cm

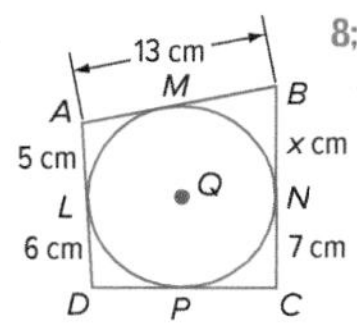

B **Find x to the nearest hundredth. Assume that segments that appear to be tangent are tangent.**

26. 9

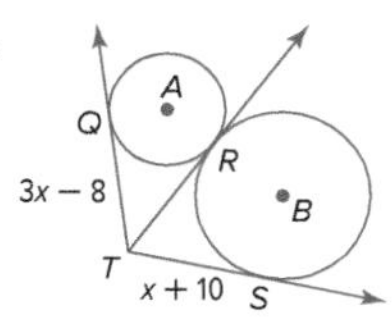

27. 8.06

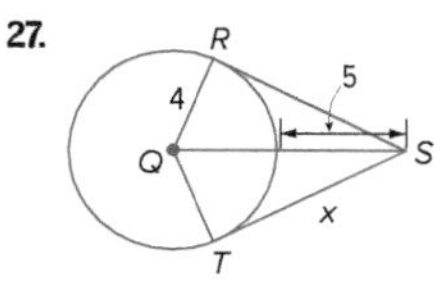

Write the specified type of proof. 28, 29. See margin.

28. Two-column proof of Theorem 9.11

Given: $\overline{AC}$ is tangent to ⊙H at C. $\overline{AB}$ is tangent to ⊙H at B.

Prove: $\overline{AC} \cong \overline{AB}$

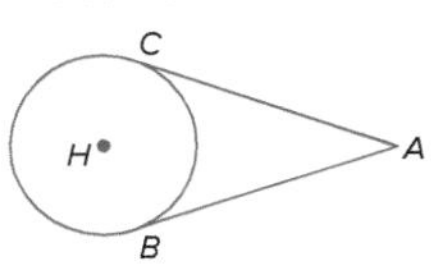

29. Two-column proof

Given: Quadrilateral $ABCD$ is circumscribed about ⊙P.

Prove: $AB + CD = AD + BC$

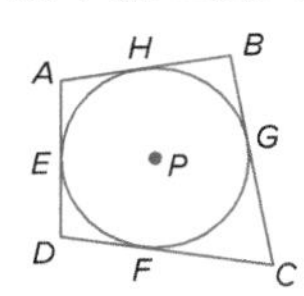

Watch Out!

Identifying Tangents Remind students that they should not assume that a segment that appears to be tangent to a circle is tangent, unless you are told so. The figure must either have a right angle symbol or include the measurements that confirm a right angle.

Additional Answers

28. Proof:

Statements (Reasons)

1. $\overline{AC}$ is tangent to ⊙H at C; $\overline{AB}$ is tangent to ⊙H at B. (Given)
2. Draw $\overline{AH}$, $\overline{BH}$, and $\overline{CH}$. (Through any two points, there is one line.)
3. $\overline{AC} \perp \overline{CH}$, $\overline{AB} \perp \overline{BH}$ (Line tangent to a circle is ⊥ to the radius at the pt. of tangency.)
4. $\angle ACH$ and $\angle ABH$ are right angles. (Def. of ⊥ lines)
5. $\overline{CH} \cong \overline{BH}$ (All radii of a circle are ≅.)
6. $\overline{AH} \cong \overline{AH}$ (Reflexive Prop.)
7. $\triangle ACH \cong \triangle ABH$ (HL)
8. $\overline{AC} \cong \overline{AB}$ (CPCTC)

29. Statements (Reasons)

1. Quadrilateral $ABCD$ is circumscribed about ⊙P. (Given)
2. Sides $\overline{AB}$, $\overline{BC}$, $\overline{CD}$, and $\overline{DA}$ are tangent to ⊙P at points H, G, F, and E, respectively. (Def. of circumscribed)
3. $\overline{EA} \cong \overline{AH}$; $\overline{HB} \cong \overline{BG}$; $\overline{GC} \cong \overline{CF}$; $\overline{FD} \cong \overline{DE}$ (Two segments tangent to a circle from the same exterior point are ≅.)
4. $AB = AH + HB$, $BC = BG + GC$, $CD = CF + FD$, $DA = DE + EA$ (Segment Addition)
5. $AB + CD = AH + HB + CF + FD$; $DA + BC = DE + EA + BG + GC$ (Substitution)
6. $AB + CD = AH + BG + GC + FD$; $DA + BC = FD + AH + BG + GC$ (Substitution)
7. $AB + CD = FD + AH + BG + GC$ (Comm. Prop. of Add.)
8. $AB + CD = DA + BC$ (Substitution)

Exercise Alert

Compass and Straightedge Exercise 34 requires the use of a compass and a straightedge.

MP Teaching the Mathematical Practices

Tools Mathematically proficient students consider the available tools when solving a mathematical problem. In Exercise 34, students can use either a compass and straightedge or dynamic geometry software.

Assess

Ticket Out the Door Provide an example on the board with a triangle formed by a tangent, a radius, and the line from the center of the circle to a point on the tangent. Assign lengths to the figure and ask students to write the equation necessary to solve the problem. Have them state the answer as they leave the classroom.

Additional Answers

31. 1916 mi;

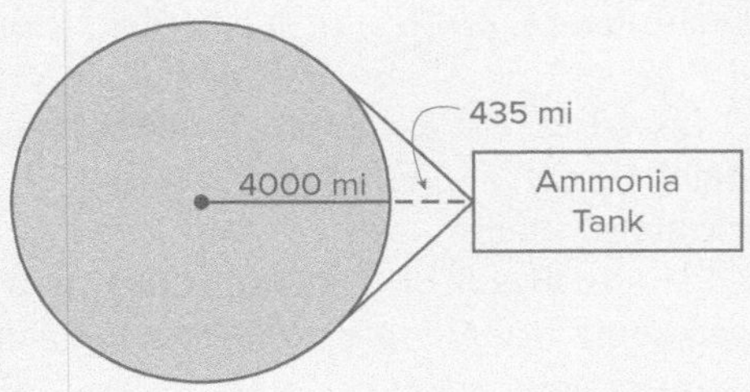

32. **Proof:** Assume that ℓ is not $\perp$ to $\overline{ST}$. If ℓ is not $\perp$ to $\overline{ST}$, some other segment $\overline{SQ}$ must be $\perp$ to ℓ. Also, there is a point R on $\overleftrightarrow{TR}$ as shown in the diagram such that $\overline{QT} \cong \overline{QR}$. $\angle SQT$ and $\angle SQR$ are right angles by the definition of perpendicular. $\angle SQT \cong \angle SQR$ and $\overline{SQ} \cong \overline{SQ}$. $\triangle SQT \cong \triangle SQR$ by SAS, so $\overline{ST} \cong \overline{SR}$ by CPCTC. Thus, both T and R are on $\odot S$. For two points of ℓ to also be on $\odot S$ contradicts the given fact that ℓ is tangent to $\odot S$ at T. Therefore, $\ell \perp \overline{ST}$ must be true.

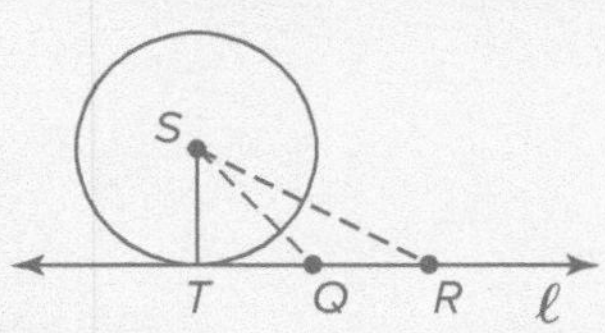

Go Online!

eSolutions Manual

Create worksheets, answer keys, and solutions handouts for your assignments.

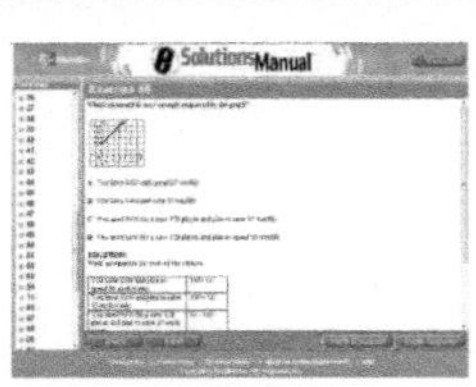

---

30. **SATELLITES** A satellite is 720 kilometers above Earth, which has a radius of 6360 kilometers. The region of Earth that is visible from the satellite is between the tangent lines $\overline{BA}$ and $\overline{BC}$. What is BA? Round to the nearest hundredth. 3110.76 km

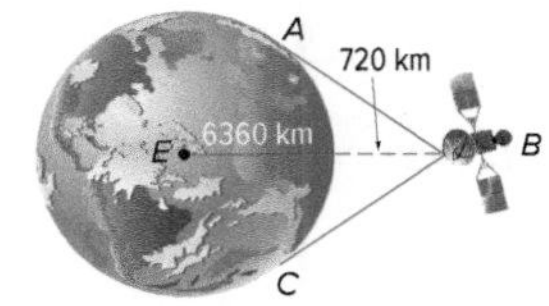

31. **SPACE TRASH** *Orbital debris* refers to materials from space missions that still orbit Earth. In 2007, a 1400-pound ammonia tank was discarded from a space mission. Suppose the tank has an altitude of 435 miles. What is the distance from the tank to the farthest point on Earth's surface from which the tank is visible? Assume that the radius of Earth is 4000 miles. Round to the nearest mile, and include a diagram of this situation with your answer. See margin.

32. **PROOF** Write an indirect proof to show that if a line is tangent to a circle, then it is perpendicular to a radius of the circle. (Part 1 of Theorem 9.10)

Given: ℓ is tangent to $\odot S$ at T; $\overline{ST}$ is a radius of $\odot S$.

Prove: $\ell \perp \overline{ST}$

(*Hint:* Assume ℓ is *not* $\perp$ to $\overline{ST}$.) See margin.

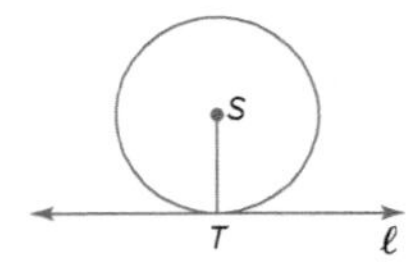

33. **PROOF** Write an indirect proof to show that if a line is perpendicular to the radius of a circle at its endpoint, then the line is a tangent of the circle. (Part 2 of Theorem 9.10)

Given: $\ell \perp \overline{ST}$; $\overline{ST}$ is a radius of $\odot S$.

Prove: ℓ is tangent to $\odot S$.

(*Hint:* Assume ℓ is *not* tangent to $\odot S$.)

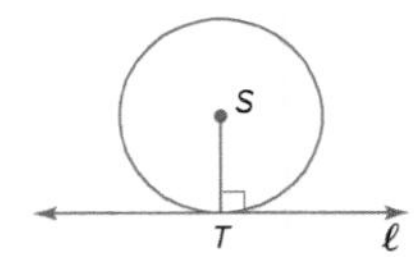

33. Proof: Assume that ℓ is not tangent to $\odot S$. Since ℓ intersects $\odot S$ at T, it must intersect the circle in another place. Call this point Q. Then $ST = SQ$. $\triangle STQ$ is isosceles, so $\angle T \cong \angle Q$. Since $\overline{ST} \perp \ell$, $\angle T$ and $\angle Q$ are right angles. This contradicts that a triangle can only have one right angle. Therefore, ℓ is tangent to $\odot S$.

34. **MP TOOLS** Construct a line tangent to a circle through a point on the circle. Use a compass to draw $\odot A$. Choose a point P on the circle and draw $\overleftrightarrow{AP}$. Then construct a segment through point P perpendicular to $\overleftrightarrow{AP}$. Label the tangent line t. Explain and justify each step. See Ch. 9 Answer Appendix.

G.C.2, G.C.4

H.O.T. Problems Use Higher-Order Thinking Skills

35. **CHALLENGE** $\overline{PQ}$ is tangent to circles R and S in the diagram to the right. Find PQ. Explain your reasoning. See Ch. 9 Answer Appendix.

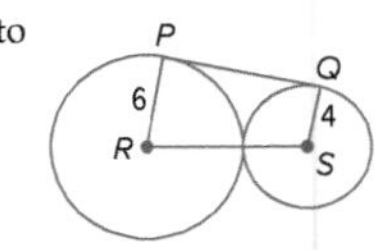

36. **WRITING IN MATH** Explain each step in the construction in page 680. Provide a justification for each step of the construction. See Ch. 9 Answer Appendix.

37. **OPEN-ENDED** Draw a circumscribed triangle and an inscribed triangle. See Ch. 9 Answer Appendix.

38. **REASONING** In the figure, $\overline{XY}$ and $\overline{XZ}$ are tangent to $\odot A$. $\overline{XZ}$ and $\overline{XW}$ are tangent to $\odot B$. Explain how segments $\overline{XY}$, $\overline{XZ}$, and $\overline{XW}$ can all be congruent if the circles have different radii.

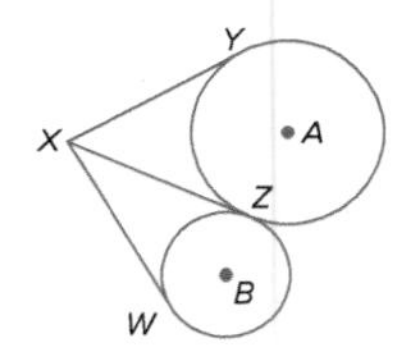

38. By Theorem 9.11, if two segments from the same exterior point are tangent to a circle, then they are congruent. So, $\overline{XY} \cong \overline{XZ}$ and $\overline{XZ} \cong \overline{XW}$. Thus, $\overline{XY} \cong \overline{XZ} \cong \overline{XW}$.

39. **WRITING IN MATH** Is it possible to draw a tangent from a point that is located anywhere outside, on, or inside a circle? Explain. See Ch. 9 Answer Appendix.

MP Standards for Mathematical Practice

Emphasis On	Exercises
1 Make sense of problems and persevere in solving them.	23, 30, 31
2 Construct viable arguments and critique the reasoning of others.	28, 29, 32–39
6 Attend to precision.	17–22, 24–27

Preparing for Assessment

40. $\overline{MN}$ and $\overline{MP}$ are tangent to ⊙G, as shown, with $MN = 2y - 2$, $MP = 4y - 32$, and $NP = y + 8$.

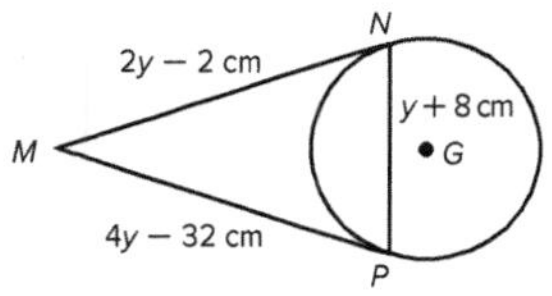

What is the perimeter of $\triangle MNP$? MP 1, 6 G.C.2, G.C.4 **E**

- A 15 cm
- B 28 cm
- C 44 cm
- D 56 cm
- E 79 cm

41. A square is inscribed in a circle with a radius of 6 inches. Find the length of each side of the square to the nearest tenth of an inch. MP 1, 6 G.C.2, G.C.4 **8.5 in.**

42. Circle C has a radius of 10. $\overline{KJ}$ is tangent to ⊙C at point K, and $LJ = 12$.

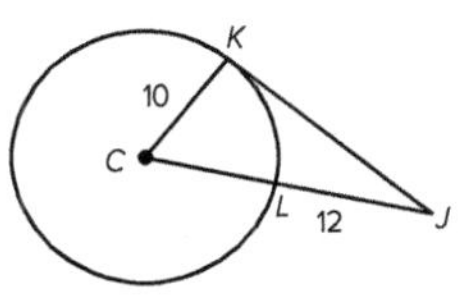

Which of the following is the best estimate of the length of $\overline{KJ}$? MP 2, 6 G.C.2, G.C.4 **B**

- A 22.0
- B 19.6
- C 12.0
- D 6.6

43. $\overline{PQ}$ is tangent to ⊙S at point Q, $m\angle PQS = (4y + 30)$, and $m\angle SPQ = (y + 51)$. What is $m\angle SPQ$? MP 2, 6 G.C.2, G.C.4 **C**

- A 15
- B 58
- C 66
- D 90

44. MULTI-STEP Look at the figure. $\overline{RS}$ is tangent to the circle at point R. MP 1, 2 G.C.2, G.C.4

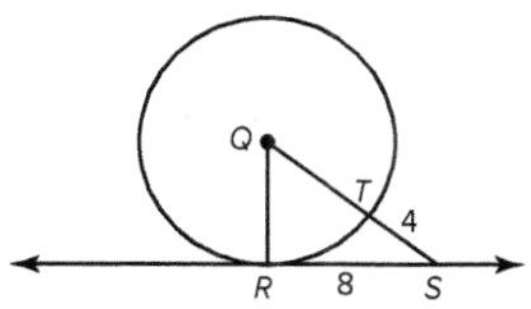

a. Which statements are true? Check all that apply. **A, D, F**

- ☐ A $\overline{QR} \cong \overline{QT}$
- ☐ B $\overline{QR} \cong \overline{QS}$
- ☐ C $\overline{QT} \cong \overline{RS}$
- ☐ D $QR^2 + RS^2 = QS^2$
- ☐ E $QS^2 + QR^2 = RS^2$
- ☐ F $\overline{QT} + \overline{TS} = \overline{QS}$

b. Which fact is true only because $\overline{QR}$ is tangent to $\overline{RS}$? **C**

- A $\overline{QR} \cong \overline{QT}$
- B $\overline{QR} \cong \overline{QS}$
- C $QR^2 + RS^2 = QS^2$
- D $QS^2 + QR^2 = RS^2$

c. What are the lengths of $\overline{QT}$ and $\overline{QS}$, respectively? **D**

- A 4, 6
- B 8, 12
- C 4, 8
- D 6, 10

Preparing for Assessment

Exercises 40–44 require students to use the skills they will need on standardized assessments. Exercises are dual-coded with content standards and mathematical practice standards.

Dual Coding

Exercises	Content Standards	MP Mathematical Practices
40	G.C.2, G.C.4	1, 6
41	G.C.2, G.C.4	1, 6
42	G.C.2, G.C.4	2, 6
43	G.C.2, G.C.4	2, 6
44	G.C.2, G.C.4	1, 2

Diagnose Student Errors

Survey student responses for each item. Class trends may indicate common errors and misconceptions.

40.

A	Found the value of y
B	Found the length of $\overline{MN}$
C	Solved $2y - 2 = y + 8$
D	Did not include the length of $\overline{NP}$ in perimeter
E	CORRECT

42.

A	Assumed $\overline{KJ} \cong \overline{CJ}$
B	CORRECT
C	Assumed $\overline{KJ} \cong \overline{LJ}$
D	Calculated $\sqrt{12^2 - 10^2}$

43.

A	Found the value of y
B	Solved $4y + 30 = y + 51$
C	CORRECT
D	Found $m\angle PQS$

Differentiated Instruction OL BL

Extension A circle is circumscribed about a square. The radius of the circle is r. Have the students write an expression for the perimeter of the square in terms of r. $4r\sqrt{2} \approx 5.66r$

Go Online!

Quizzes

Students can use *Self-Check Quizzes* to check their understanding of this lesson and have the results sent to you. You can also give *Quiz 3*, which covers the content in Lessons 9-5 and 9-6.

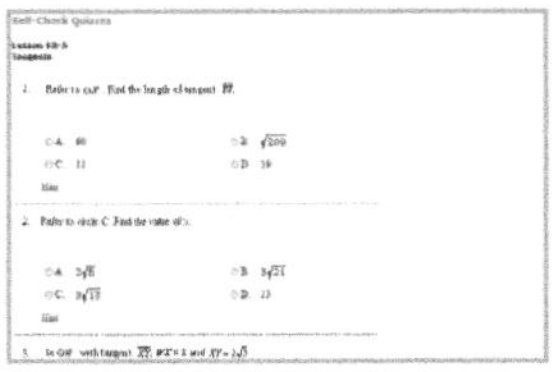

Focus

Objective Construct inscribed circles and circumscribed triangles.

Materials for Each Group

- straightedge
- compass

Teaching Tips

Explain that students will use the incenter of a triangle to construct a circle so that the triangle is circumscribed about the circle, and they will use the circumcenter of a triangle to construct a circle in which the triangle is circumscribed. They will also learn how to construct an equilateral triangle circumscribed about a circle.

Teach ELL

Working in Cooperative Groups Arrange students in groups of three or four, mixing abilities. Then have groups complete Activities 1–2 and Exercises 1–2.

Practice Have students individually complete Exercises 3–4.

Assess

Formative Assessment

Use Exercises 3–4 to analyze the students' constructions and conjectures about the term *incenter*.

From Concrete to Abstract

Have students make conjectures about why the formula for circumference is $C = 2\pi r$ and not $6r$ when the radius is used to divide the circle into six congruent arcs.

Extending the Concept

Challenge students to repeat the activities for different types of polygons and practice the constructions.

EXTEND 9-5

Geometry Lab

Inscribed and Circumscribed Circles

In this lab, you will perform constructions that involve inscribing or circumscribing a circle.

MP 5 Use appropriate tools strategically.

Content Standards

G.CO.13 Construct an equilateral triangle, a square, and a regular hexagon inscribed in a circle.

G.C.3 Construct the inscribed and circumscribed circles of a triangle, and prove properties of angles for a quadrilateral inscribed in a circle.

Activity 1 Construct a Circle Inscribed in a Triangle

Step 1

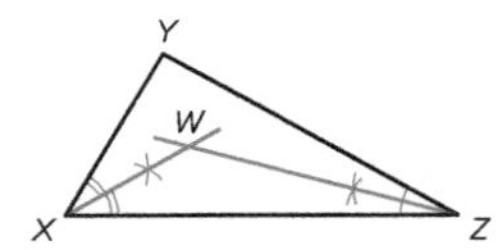

Draw a triangle *XYZ* and construct two angle bisectors of the triangle to locate the incenter *W*.

Step 2

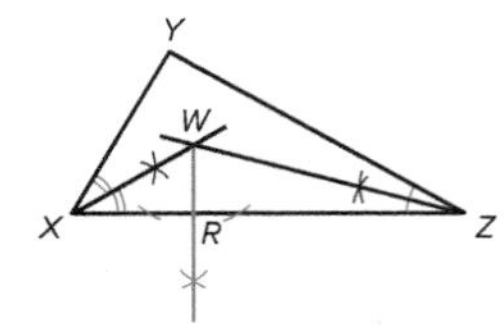

Construct a segment perpendicular to a side through the incenter. Label the intersection *R*.

Step 3

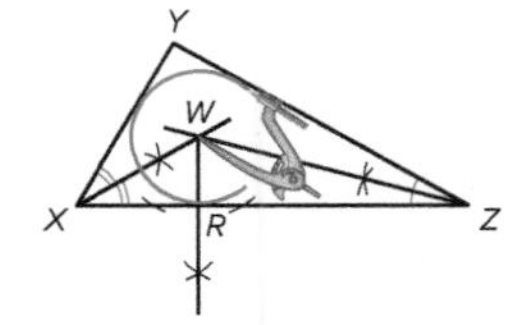

Set a compass of the length of $\overline{WR}$. Put the point of the compass on *W* and draw a circle with that radius.

Activity 2 Construct a Triangle Circumscribed About a Circle

Step 1

Construct a circle and draw a point. Use the same compass setting you used to construct the circle to construct an arc on the circle from the point. Continue as shown.

Step 2

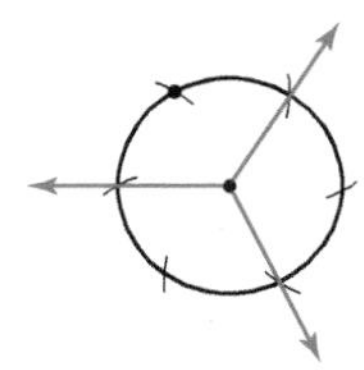

Draw rays from the center through every other arc.

Step 3

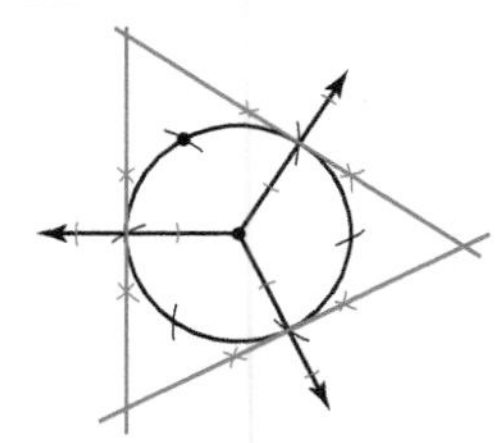

Construct a line perpendicular to each of the rays.

Model 2–4. See Ch. 9 Answer Appendix.

1. Draw a right triangle and inscribe a circle in it. See margin.
2. Inscribe a regular hexagon in a circle. Then inscribe an equilateral triangle in a circle. (*Hint:* The first step of each construction is identical to Step 1 in Activity 2.)
3. Inscribe a square in a circle. Then circumscribe a square about a circle.
4. **CHALLENGE** Circumscribe a regular hexagon about a circle.

Additional Answer

1. Sample answer:

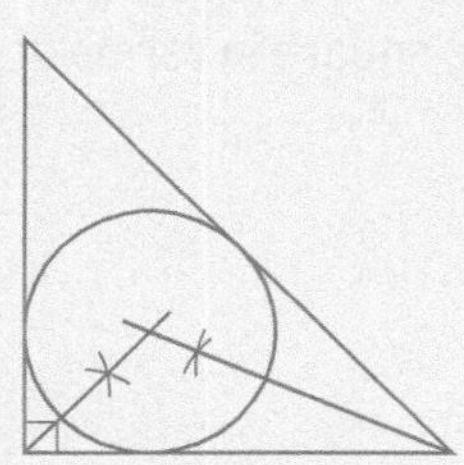

LESSON 9-6
Secants, Tangents, and Angle Measures

SUGGESTED PACING (DAYS)

	Explore Lab	Instruction
90 min.	0.5	0.5
45 min.	1	1

Track Your Progress

Objectives

1. Find measures of angles formed by lines intersecting on or inside a circle.
2. Find measures of angles formed by lines intersecting outside the circle.

Mathematical Background

A line that intersects a circle in exactly two points is called a *secant*. When two secants intersect inside a circle, the angles formed are related to the arcs they intercept.

THEN

G.C.4 Construct a tangent line from a point outside a given circle to the circle.

NOW

G.C.2 Identify and describe relationships among inscribed angles, radii, and chords.

NEXT

G.GPE.1 Derive the equation of a circle of given center and radius by using the Pythagorean Theorem; complete the square to find the center and radius of a circle given by an equation.

G.GPE.4 Use coordinates to prove simple geometric theorems algebraically.

Go Online! All of these resources and more are available at connectED.mcgraw-hill.com

Chapter Projects allow students to apply their learning to a real-world project about hosting the Olympics.

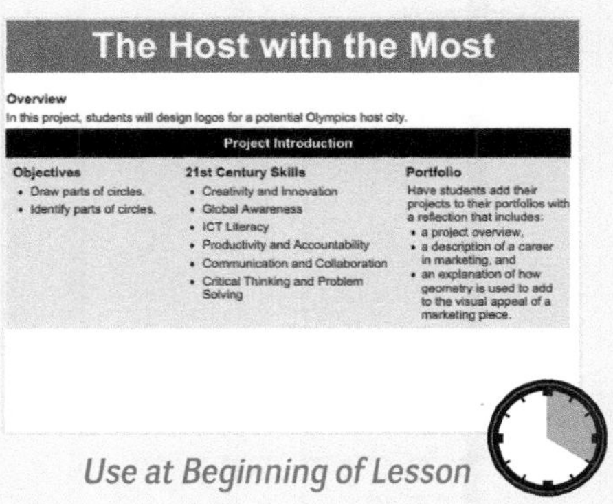

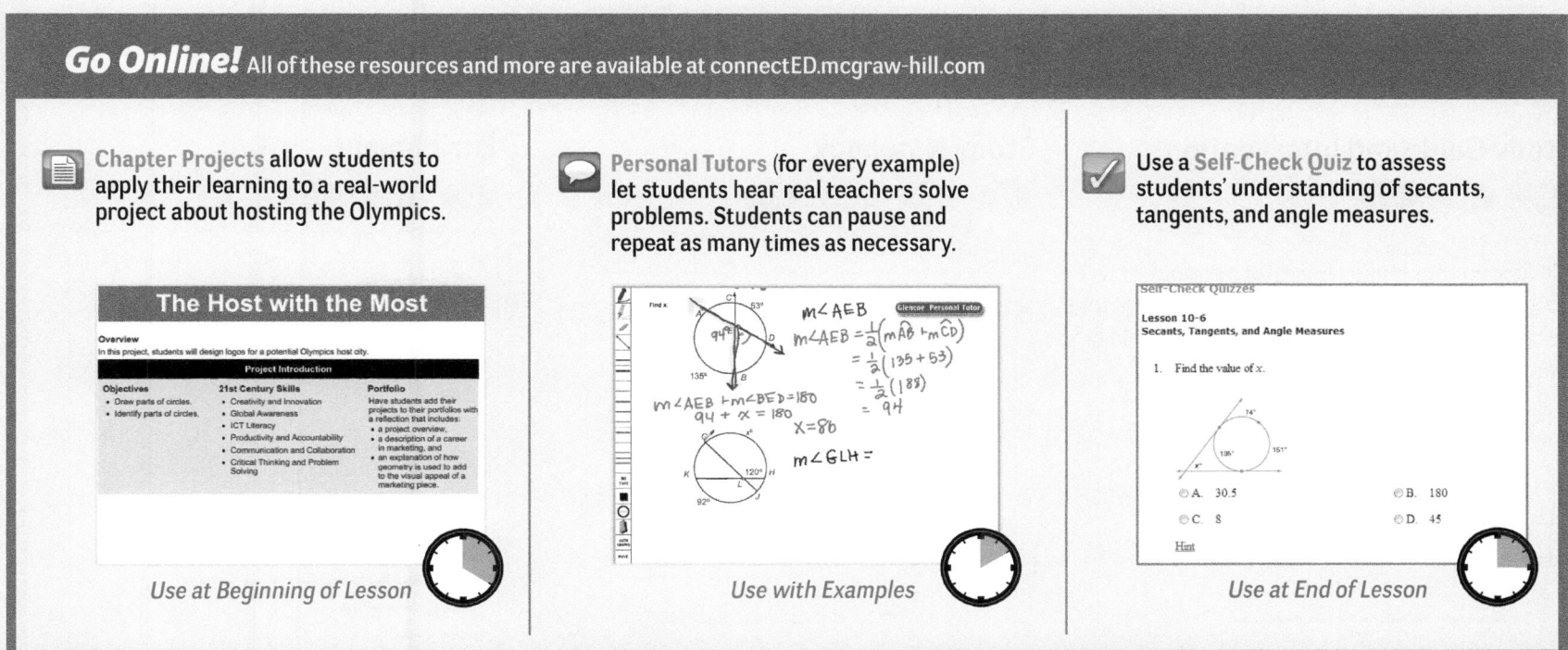

Use at Beginning of Lesson

Personal Tutors (for every example) let students hear real teachers solve problems. Students can pause and repeat as many times as necessary.

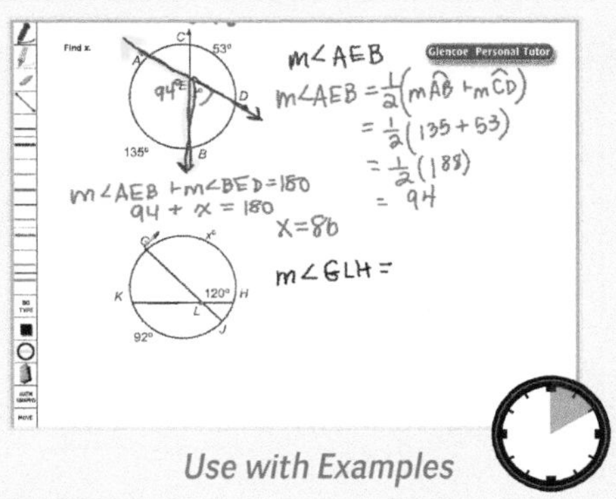

Use with Examples

Use a **Self-Check Quiz** to assess students' understanding of secants, tangents, and angle measures.

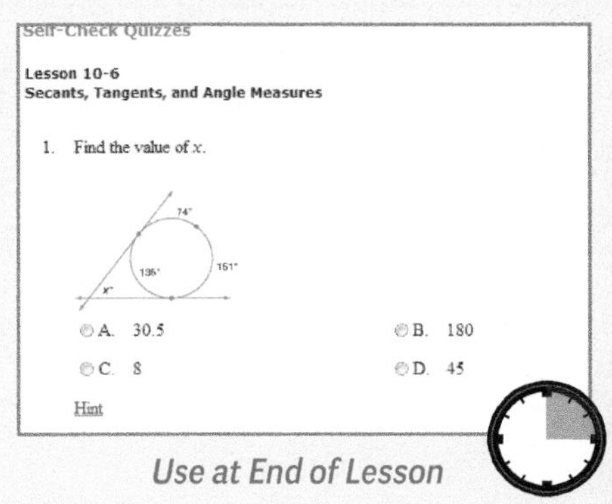

Use at End of Lesson

OER Using Open Educational Resources

Publishing Have students compete in a question and answer game with other students on **Skype** to demonstrate their knowledge of secants, tangents, and angle measure. Skype in the classroom allows your students to compete with other students in the district or in other states. *Use as review*

Go Online!
connectED.mcgraw-hill.com
Worksheets

Differentiate Your Resources

Extra Practice Additional practice or homework; Skills Practice is best for approaching-level students and Practice is best for on-level and beyond-level students

Skills Practice

AL OL ELL

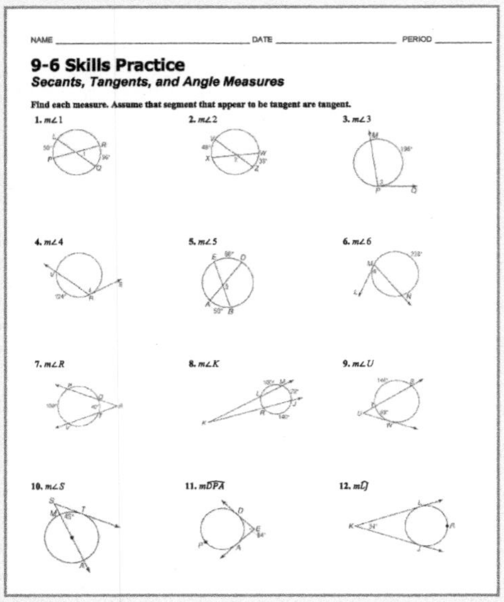

9-6 Skills Practice
Secants, Tangents, and Angle Measures
Find each measure. Assume that segment that appear to be tangent are tangent.

Practice

AL OL BL ELL

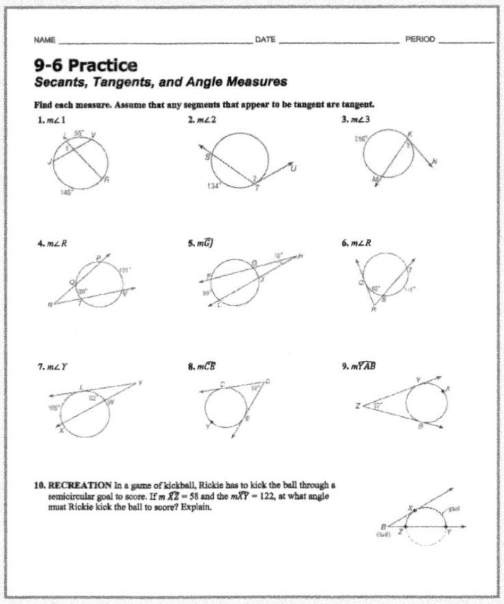

9-6 Practice
Secants, Tangents, and Angle Measures
Find each measure. Assume that any segments that appear to be tangent are tangent.

Word Problem Practice

AL OL BL ELL

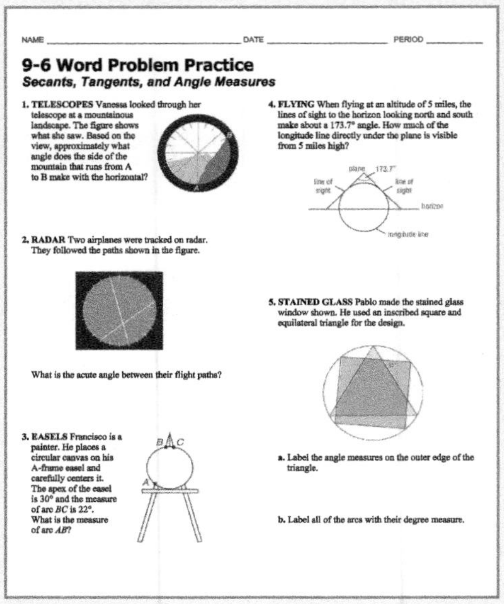

9-6 Word Problem Practice
Secants, Tangents, and Angle Measures

Intervention Reteaching and vocabulary activities that can be used with struggling or absent students and as ELL support

Study Guide and Intervention

AL OL ELL

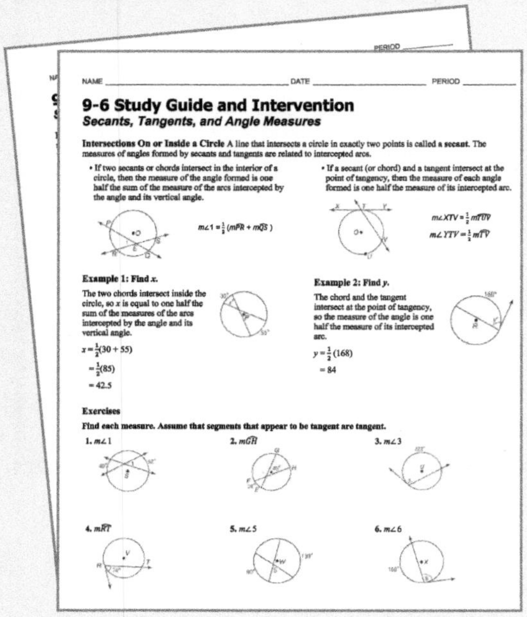

9-6 Study Guide and Intervention
Secants, Tangents, and Angle Measures
Example 1: Find x.
Example 2: Find y.
Exercises

Study Notebook

AL OL BL ELL

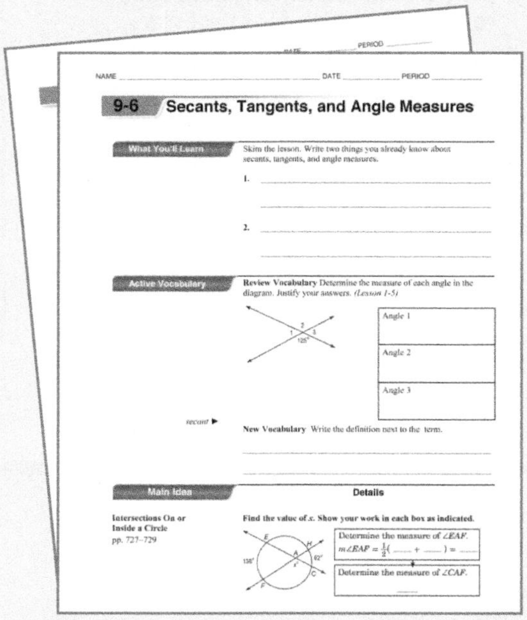

9-6 Secants, Tangents, and Angle Measures
What You'll Learn
Active Vocabulary
Main Idea
Details

Extension Activities that can be used to extend lesson concepts

Enrichment

OL BL ELL

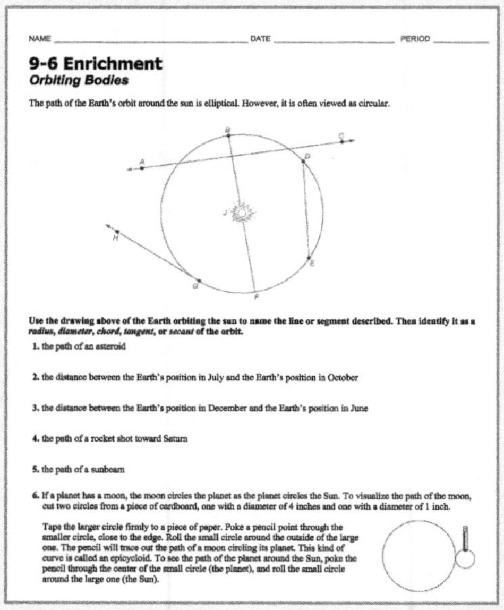

9-6 Enrichment
Orbiting Bodies
The path of the Earth's orbit around the sun is elliptical. However, it is often viewed as circular.

LESSON 6

Secants, Tangents, and Angle Measures

Then

- You found measures of segments formed by tangents to a circle.

Now

1. Find measures of angles formed by lines intersecting on or inside a circle.
2. Find measures of angles formed by lines intersecting outside the circle.

Why?

- An average person's field of vision is about 180°. Most cameras, including smartphone cameras, have a much narrower viewing angle of between 20° and 60°. Using specialized software, some smartphones can capture panoramic images that show a field of vision similar to or greater than that of the human eye. The viewing angle determines how much of a subject a camera can capture.

New Vocabulary
secant

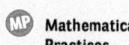

Mathematical Practices
2 Reason abstractly and quantitatively.
3 Construct viable arguments and critique the reasoning of others.

Content Standards
G.C.2 Identify and describe relationships among inscribed angles, radii, and chords.

1 Intersections On or Inside a Circle

A **secant** is a line that intersects a circle in exactly two points. Lines j and k are secants of $\odot C$.

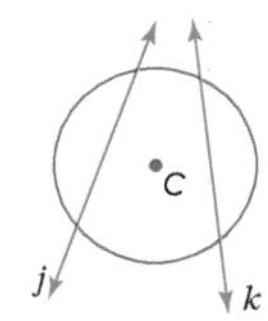

When two secants intersect inside a circle, the angles formed are related to the arcs they intercept.

Theorem 9.12

Words If two secants or chords intersect in the interior of a circle, then the measure of an angle formed is one half the *sum* of the measure of the arcs intercepted by the angle and its vertical angle.

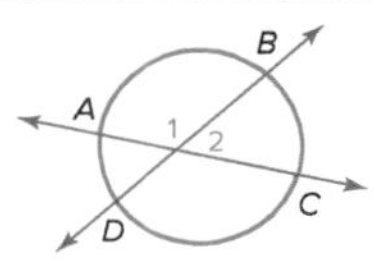

Example $m\angle 1 = \frac{1}{2}(m\widehat{AB} + m\widehat{CD})$ and $m\angle 2 = \frac{1}{2}(m\widehat{DA} + m\widehat{BC})$

Proof

Given: $\overleftrightarrow{HK}$ and $\overleftrightarrow{JL}$ intersect at M.

Prove: $m\angle 1 = \frac{1}{2}(m\widehat{JH} + m\widehat{LK})$

Proof:

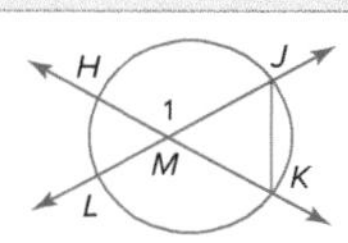

Statements	Reasons
1. $\overleftrightarrow{HK}$ and $\overleftrightarrow{JL}$ intersect at M.	1. Given
2. $m\angle 1 = m\angle MJK + m\angle MKJ$	2. Exterior Angle Theorem
3. $m\angle MJK = \frac{1}{2}m\widehat{LK}$, $m\angle MKJ = \frac{1}{2}m\widehat{JH}$	3. The measure of an inscribed $\angle$ equals half the measure of the intercepted arc.
4. $m\angle 1 = \frac{1}{2}m\widehat{LK} + \frac{1}{2}m\widehat{JH}$	4. Substitution
5. $m\angle 1 = \frac{1}{2}(m\widehat{JH} + m\widehat{LK})$	5. Distributive Property

Launch

Have students read the Why? section of the lesson. Ask:

- What percentage of the measure of a circle is 180°? 50%
- If a camera has a viewing angle of 50°, how much less of a viewing angle does the camera have compared to the average person's field of vision? 130°

Mathematical Practices Strategies

Construct viable arguments and critique the reasoning of others.
Help students solidify their strategies for working with theorems to write proofs. For example, ask:

- What strategies do you have for remembering the possible theorems that you can use in proofs involving circles? Sample answer: keep an ongoing list of theorems and postulates to refer to when writing proofs
- How do you know which theorem to use when you approach a proof? Sample answer: look for theorems that are relevant to the given information and/or the proof statement
- How do you know when you might have chosen the wrong theorem? Sample answer: the logical progression of the proof does not lead to the prove statement

Go Online!

Interactive Whiteboard

Use the *eLesson*, *Lesson Presentation*, or *Interactive Classroom* to present this lesson.

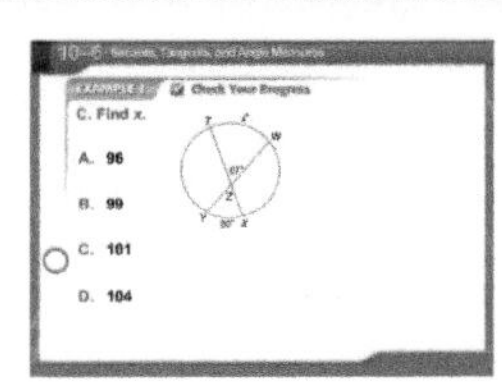

Teach

Ask the scaffolded questions for each example to build conceptual understanding for students at all levels.

1 Intersections On or Inside a Circle

Example 1 Use Intersecting Chords or Secants

AL In part **a**, what is $m\angle RVS$? 107

OL In part **a**, what is $m\angle SVU$? 73

BL In part **c**, what is $m\widehat{GK} + m\widehat{JH}$? 140

Need Another Example?

Find x.

a.

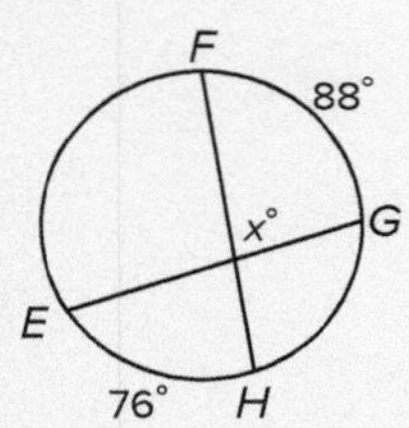

82

b.

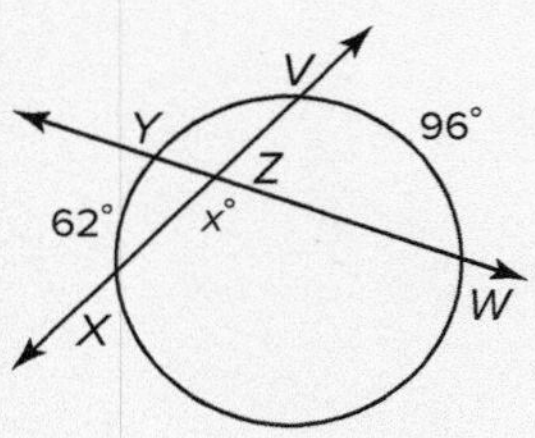

101

c.

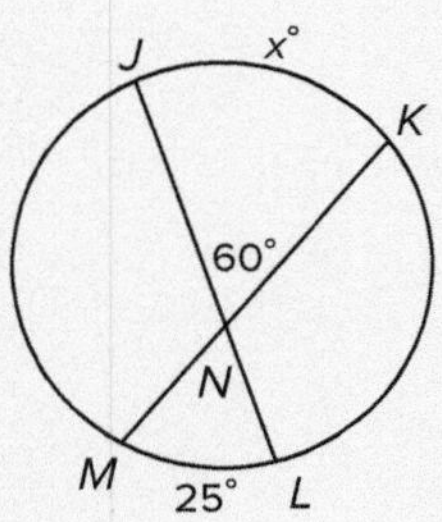

95

G.C.2

Example 1 Use Intersecting Chords or Secants

Find x.

a.

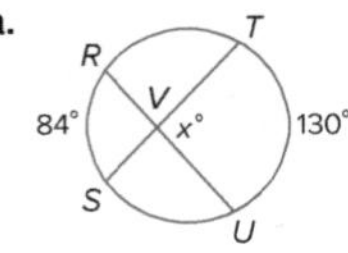

$m\angle TVU = \frac{1}{2}(m\widehat{RS} + m\widehat{TU})$ Theorem 9.12

$x = \frac{1}{2}(84 + 130)$ Substitution

$= \frac{1}{2}(214)$ or 107 Simplify.

Study Tip ELL

Alternative Method In Example 1b, $m\angle DEB$ can also be found by first finding the sum of the measures of $\widehat{AC}$ and $\widehat{BD}$.

$m\widehat{AC} + m\widehat{BD}$

$= 360 - (m\widehat{AC} + m\widehat{CD})$

$= 360 - (143 + 75) = 142$

$m\angle DEB$

$= \frac{1}{2}(m\widehat{AC} + m\widehat{BD})$

$= \frac{1}{2}(142) = 71$

b.

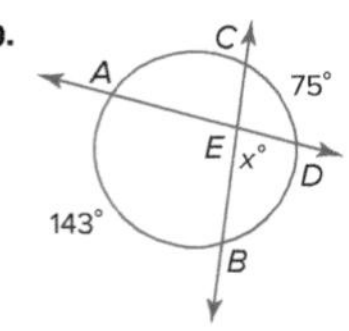

Step 1 Find $m\angle AEB$.

$m\angle AEB = \frac{1}{2}(m\widehat{AB} + m\widehat{CD})$ Theorem 9.12

$= \frac{1}{2}(143 + 75)$ Substitution

$= \frac{1}{2}(218)$ or 109 Simplify.

Step 2 Find x, the measure of $\angle DEB$.

$\angle AEB$ and $\angle DEB$ are supplementary angles.

So, $x = 180 - 109$ or 71.

c.

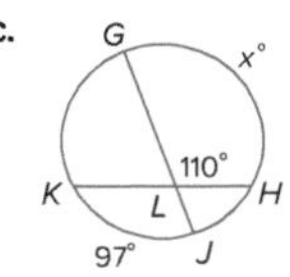

$m\angle GLH = \frac{1}{2}(m\widehat{GH} + m\widehat{KJ})$ Theorem 9.12

$110 = \frac{1}{2}(x + 97)$ Substitution

$220 = x + 97$ Multiply each side by 2.

$123 = x$ Subtract 97 from each side.

Guided Practice

Find the value for x in each diagram.

1A.

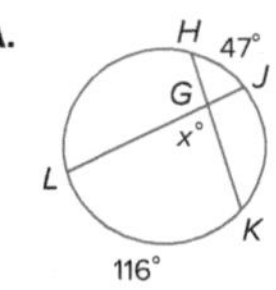

1B.

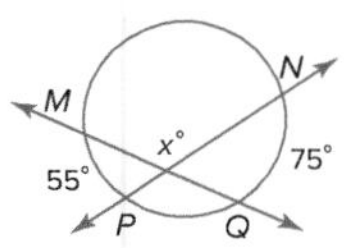

1C.

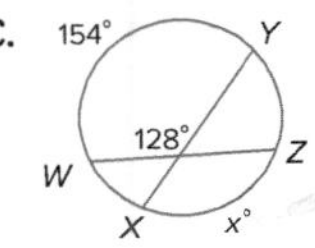

1A. 81.5
1B. 115
1C. 102

Recall that Theorem 9.6 states that the measure of an inscribed angle is half the measure of its intercepted arc. If one of the sides of this angle is tangent to the circle, this relationship still holds true.

Theorem 9.13

Words If a secant and a tangent intersect at the point of tangency, then the measure of each angle formed is one half the measure of its intercepted arc.

Example $m\angle 1 = \frac{1}{2}m\widehat{AB}$ and $m\angle 2 = \frac{1}{2}m\widehat{ACB}$

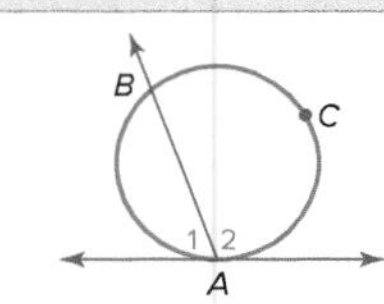

You will prove Theorem 9.13 in Exercise 33.

Differentiated Instruction AL OL BL ELL

Naturalist Learners Explain that the relationships presented in this chapter are naturally occurring relationships that have been mathematically defined and explained. Tell students that scientists from all fields can use these relationships to examine everything from raindrops and soap bubbles to cells and microorganisms.

Go Online!

Follow along as you watch a **Personal Tutor** solve a problem involving secants and tangents.

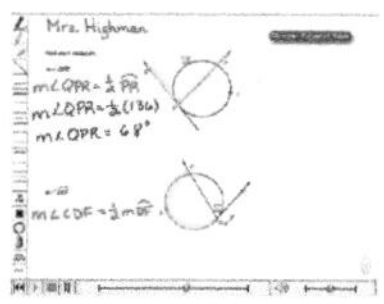

Example 2 Use Intersecting Secants and Tangents

Find each measure.

a. $m\angle QPR$

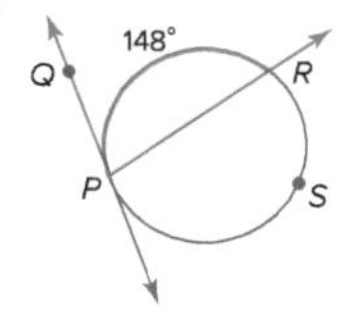

$m\angle QPR = \frac{1}{2}m\widehat{PR}$ Theorem 9.13

$= \frac{1}{2}(148)$ or 74 Substitute and simplify.

b. $m\widehat{DEF}$

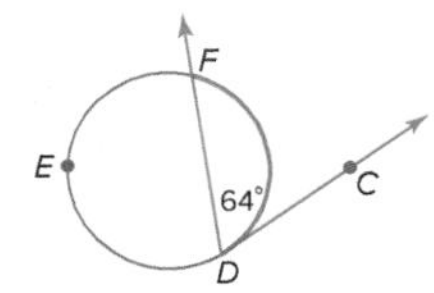

$m\angle CDF = \frac{1}{2}m\widehat{FD}$ Theorem 9.13

$64 = \frac{1}{2}m\widehat{FD}$ Substitution

$128 = m\widehat{FD}$ Multiply each side by 2.

$m\widehat{DEF} = 360 - m\widehat{FD} = 360 - 128$ or 232

Guided Practice

2A. Find $m\widehat{JLK}$. 232

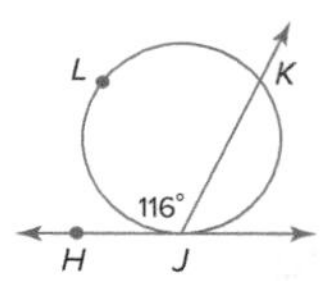

2B. Find $m\angle RQS$ if $m\widehat{QTS} = 238$. 61

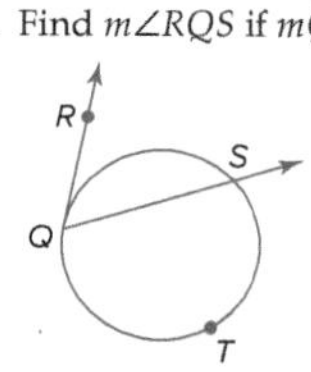

2 Intersections Outside a Circle

Secants and tangents can also meet outside a circle. The measure of the angle formed also involves half of the measures of the arcs they intercept.

Theorem 9.14

Words If two secants, a secant and a tangent, or two tangents intersect in the exterior of a circle, then the measure of the angle formed is one half the *difference* of the measures of the intercepted arcs.

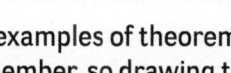

Examples

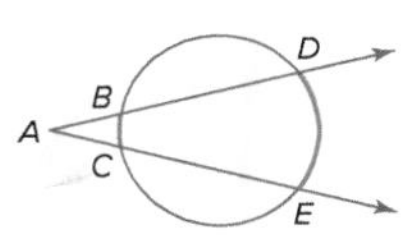

Two Secants

$m\angle A = \frac{1}{2}(m\widehat{DE} - m\widehat{BC})$

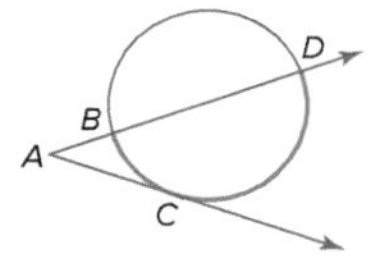

Secant-Tangent

$m\angle A = \frac{1}{2}(m\widehat{DC} - m\widehat{BC})$

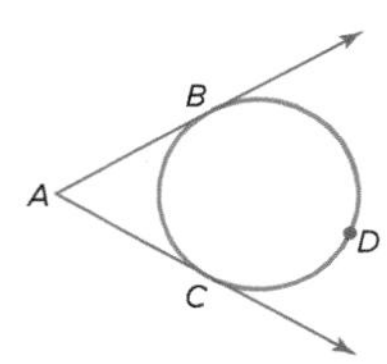

Two Tangents

$m\angle A = \frac{1}{2}(m\widehat{BDC} - m\widehat{BC})$

You will prove Theorem 9.14 in Exercises 30–32.

Study Tip ELL

MP **Sense-Making** The measure of each $\angle A$ is half the absolute value of the difference of the arc measure. In this way, the order of the arc measures does not affect the outcome of the calculation.

Differentiated Instruction AL OL BL ELL

Kinesthetic Learners Allow students time to create examples of theorems like 9.14 for themselves. These theorems are difficult to remember, so drawing their own examples may help students to recall or derive the relationships later.

Example 2 Use Intersecting Secants and Tangents

AL In part **a**, what is $m\widehat{RSP}$? 212

OL In part **b**, if you extended $\overline{CD}$ to the left to include point X, what would $m\angle FDX$ be? 116

BL How is the angle formed by a secant and a tangent like an inscribed angle? Sample answer: Both have measures equal to half of the arc they intercept.

Need Another Example?

Find each measure.

a. $m\angle QPS$ 125

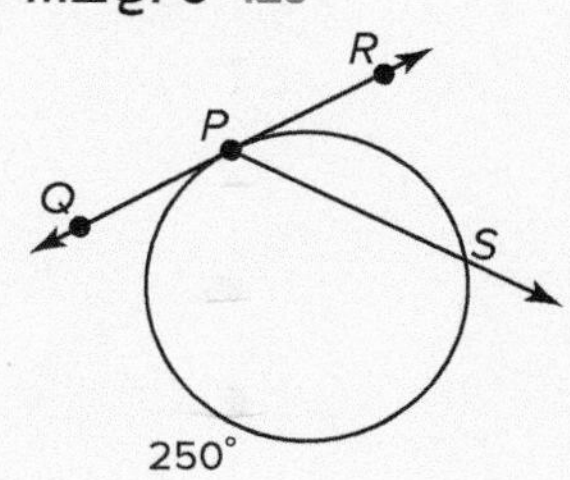

b. $m\widehat{BCD}$ 144

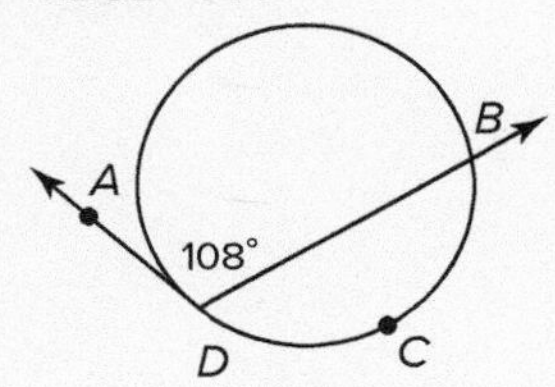

2 Intersections Outside a Circle

Example 3 Use Tangents and Secants That Intersect Outside a Circle

AL In part **a**, what is $m\widehat{HJK}$? 258

OL In part **b**, what is $m\widehat{BD}$? 58

BL In part **b**, would the relationship still apply if $\overrightarrow{AC}$ passed through the interior of the circle? Yes; it applies to two secants, a secant and a tangent, or two tangents.

Need Another Example?
Find each measure.

a. $m\widehat{BC}$ 17

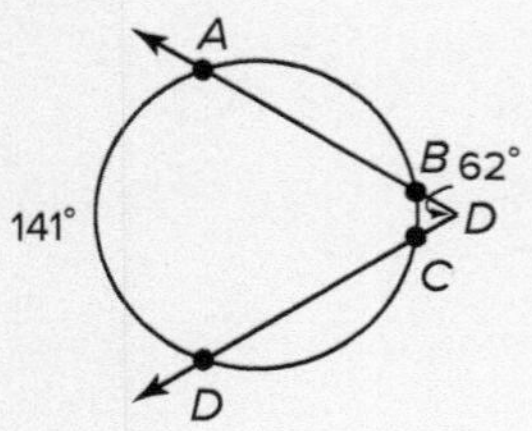

b. $m\widehat{XYZ}$ 220

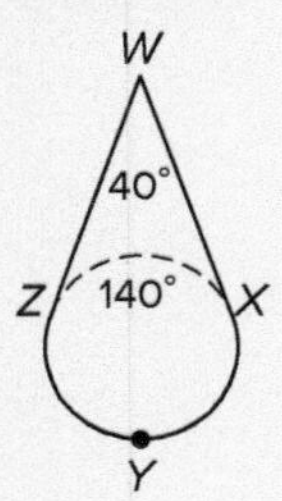

G.C.2

Example 3 Use Tangents and Secants that Intersect Outside a Circle

Find each measure.

a. $m\angle L$

$m\angle L = \frac{1}{2}(m\widehat{HJK} - m\widehat{HK})$ Theorem 9.14

$= \frac{1}{2}(360 - 102) - 102$ Substitution

$= \frac{1}{2}(258 - 102)$ or 78 Simplify.

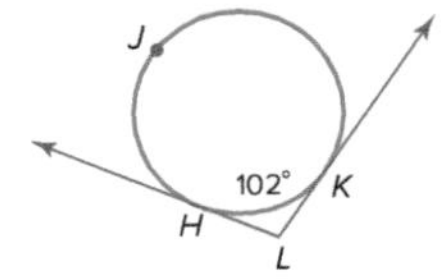

b. $m\widehat{CD}$

$m\angle A = \frac{1}{2}(m\widehat{CD} - m\widehat{BC})$ Theorem 9.14

$56 = \frac{1}{2}(m\widehat{CD} - 95)$ Substitution

$112 = m\widehat{CD} - 95$ Multiply each side by 2.

$207 = m\widehat{CD}$ Add 95 to each side.

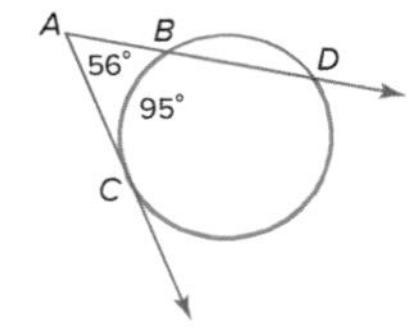

Guided Practice

3A. $m\angle S$ 54

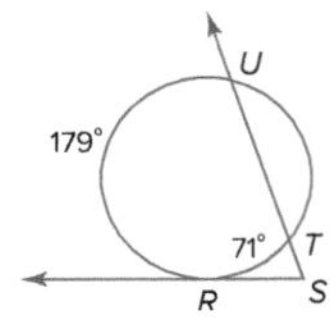

3B. $m\widehat{XZ}$ 88

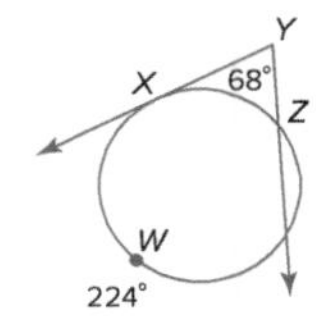

Real-World Link

There is a difference in the *index of refraction* between the two mediums such as air and glass. The index of refraction N is given by the equation $N = \frac{c}{V}$ where c is the speed of light and V is the velocity of light in that material.

Source: Microscopy Resource Center

You can apply the properties of intersecting secants to solve real-world problems.

G.C.2

Real-World Example 4 Apply Properties of Intersecting Secants

SCIENCE The diagram shows the path of a light ray as it hits a drop of water. The ray is bent, or *refracted*, at points A, B, and C. If $m\widehat{AC} = 128$ and $m\widehat{XBY} = 84$, what is $m\angle D$?

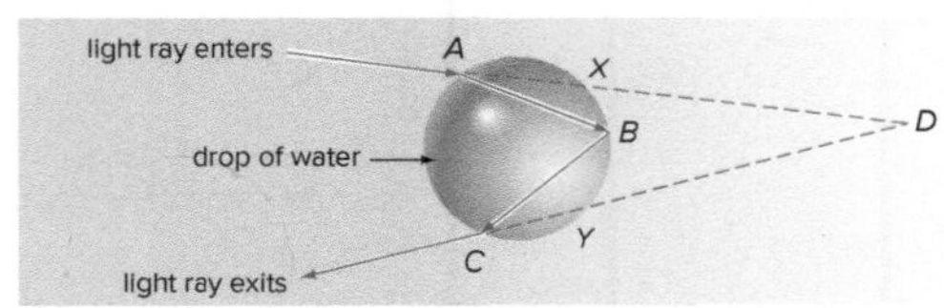

$m\angle D = \frac{1}{2}(m\widehat{AC} - m\widehat{XBY})$ Theorem 9.14

$= \frac{1}{2}(128 - 84)$ Substitution

$= \frac{1}{2}(44)$ or 22 Simplify.

Guided Practice

4. Find the value of x. 60

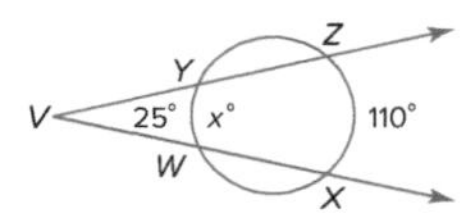

Example 4 Apply Properties of Intersecting Secants

AL What are $\overrightarrow{DA}$ and $\overrightarrow{DC}$ in relationship to the circle? secants

OL What is $m\widehat{ABC}$? 232

BL What is $m\angle ABC$? 64

Need Another Example?

Physics The diagram shows the path of a light ray as it hits a cut diamond. The ray is bent, or refracted, at points A, B, and C. If $m\widehat{AC} = 96$ and $m\angle S = 35$, what is $m\widehat{RBT}$? 26

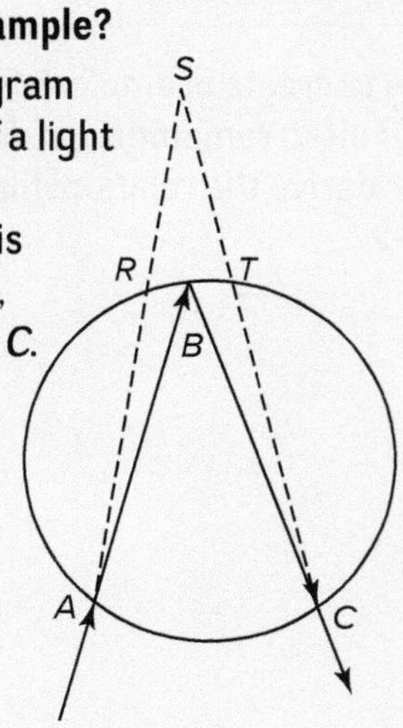

Follow-Up

Students have explored special segments and angles in circles.

Ask:

- Why might studying the relationships between the measures of segments and angles drawn in and around circles be useful in the real world? Sample answer: Many mechanical objects, such as tires and pulleys, are circular. Understanding these circle relationships could help solve problems involving these objects.

Key Concept Circle and Angle Relationships

Vertex of Angle	Model(s)	Angle Measure
on the circle	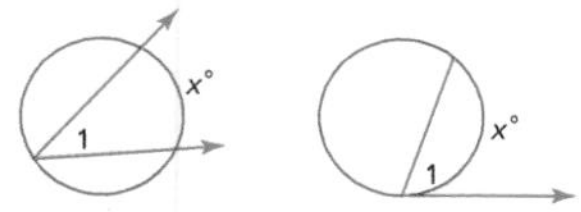	one half the measure of the intercepted arc $m\angle 1 = \frac{1}{2}x$
inside the circle	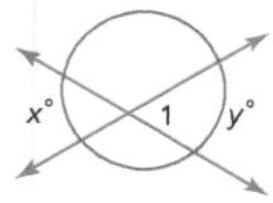	one half the measure of the sum of the intercepted arc $m\angle 1 = \frac{1}{2}(x + y)$
outside the circle	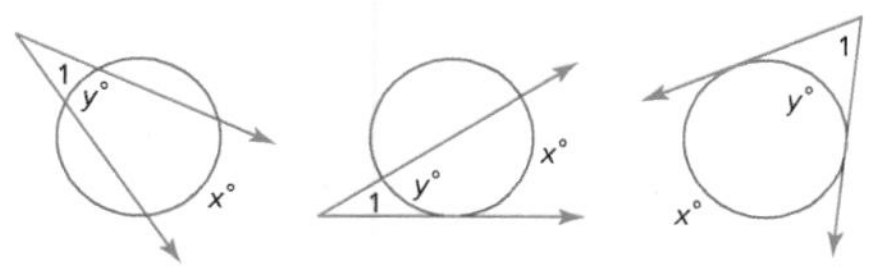	one half the measure of the difference of the intercepted arcs $m\angle 1 = \frac{1}{2}(x - y)$

Check Your Understanding

◯ = Step-by-Step Solutions begin on page R14.

Go Online! for a Self-Check Quiz

Examples 1–2 G.C.2 **Find each measure. Assume that segments that appear to be tangent are tangent.**

1. $m\angle 1$ 110

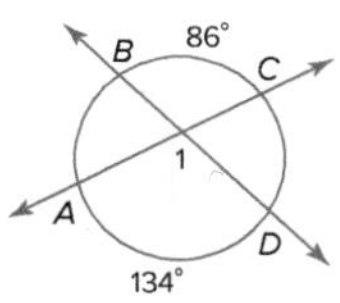

2. $m\widehat{TS}$ 144

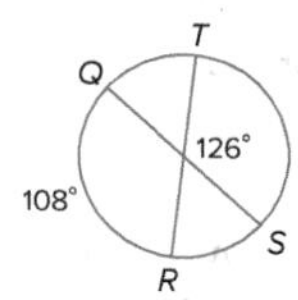

3. $m\angle 2$ 73

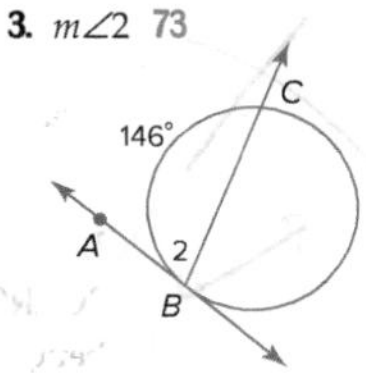

Examples 3–4 G.C.2

4. $m\angle H$ 31

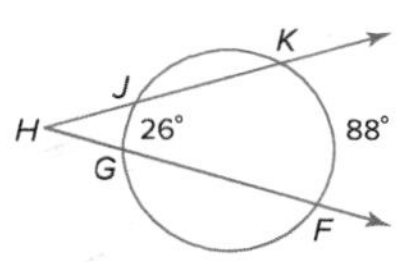

5. $m\widehat{QTS}$ 248

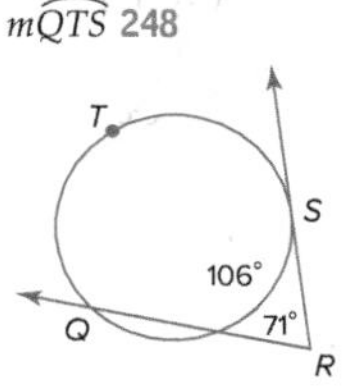

6. $m\widehat{LP}$ 150

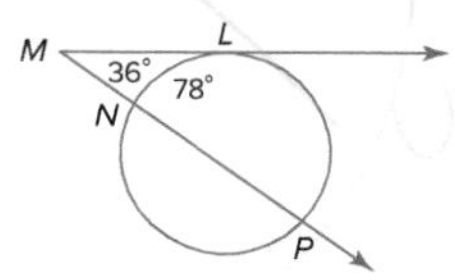

7 **STUNTS** A ramp is attached to the first of several barrels that have been strapped together for a circus motorcycle stunt as shown. What is the measure of the angle the ramp makes with the ground? 15

Practice

Formative Assessment Use Exercises 1–7 to assess students' understanding of the concepts in this lesson.

The Practice and Problem Solving exercises assess the content taught in the lesson. The Preparing for Assessment page is meant to be used as preparation for end-of-course assessments..

Exercise Alert

See page R9 for extra exercises for students who are approaching level or for on-level students who need additional reinforcement.

Levels of Complexity Chart

The levels of the exercises progress from 1 to 3, with Level 1 indicating the lowest level of complexity.

Exercises	8–25	26–34, 42–46	35–41
C Level 3			●
B Level 2		●	
Level 1	●		

Differentiated Homework Options

Levels	AL Basic	OL Core	BL Advanced
Exercises	8–25, 36, 38–46	9–29 odd, 30–36, 38–46	35–41, (optional: 42–46)
2-Day Option	9–25 odd , 42–46	8–25	
	8–24 even, 36, 38–41	26–36, 38–46	

You can use ALEKS to provide additional remediation support with personalized instruction and practice.

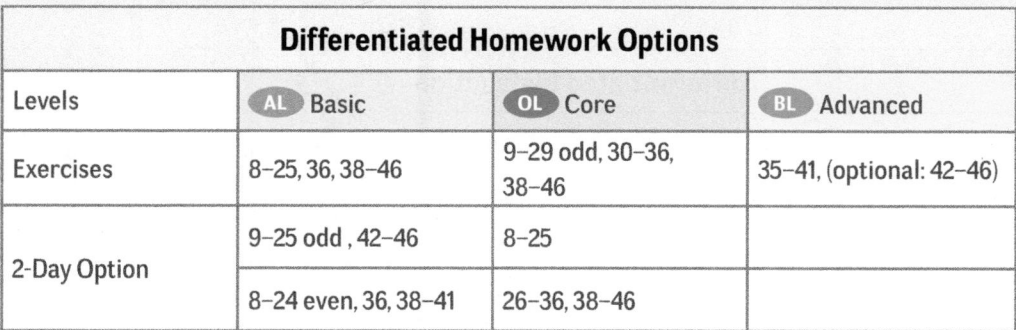

MP Teaching the Mathematical Practices

Structure Mathematically proficient students look closely to discern a pattern or structure. They also can step back for an overview and shift perspective. In Exercises 18–23, encourage students to identify the tangents and secants and use Theorem 9.14.

Additional Answer

30. <u>Statements (Reasons)</u>

1. AD and AE are secants to the circle. (Given)
2. $m\angle DCE = \frac{1}{2}m\widehat{DE}$, $m\angle ADC = \frac{1}{2}m\widehat{BC}$ (The measure of an inscribed $\angle = \frac{1}{2}$ the measure of its intercepted arc.)
3. $m\angle DCE = m\angle ADC + m\angle A$ (Exterior ∆ Theorem)
4. $\frac{1}{2}m\widehat{DE} = \frac{1}{2}m\widehat{BC} + m\angle A$ (Substitution)
5. $\frac{1}{2}m\widehat{DE} - \frac{1}{2}m\widehat{BC} = m\angle A$ (Subtraction Prop.)
6. $\frac{1}{2}(m\widehat{DE} - m\widehat{BC}) = m\angle A$ (Distributive Prop.)

Practice and Problem Solving

Extra Practice is on page R9.

Examples 1–2 G.C.2 **Find each measure. Assume that segments that appear to be tangent are tangent.**

8. $m\angle 3$ 82

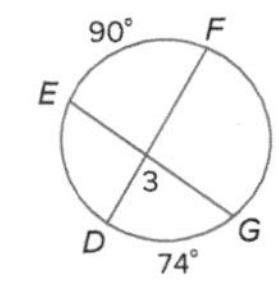

9. $m\angle 4$ 71.5

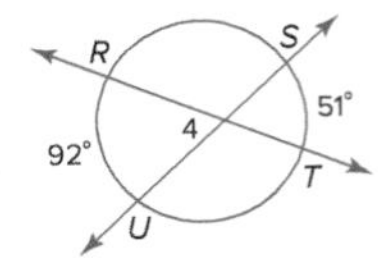

10. $m\angle JMK$ 102

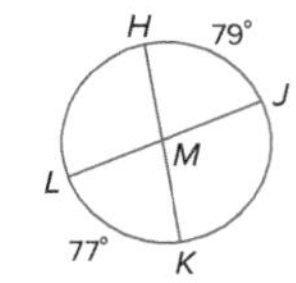

11. $m\widehat{RQ}$ 28

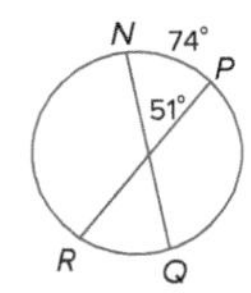

12. $m\angle K$ 97

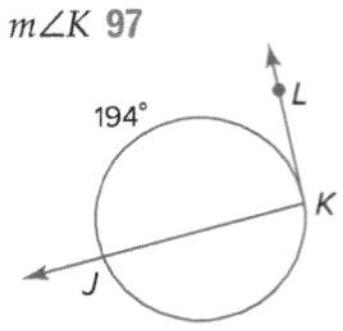

13. $m\widehat{PM}$ 144

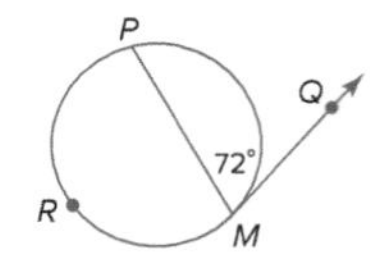

14. $m\angle ABD$ 103

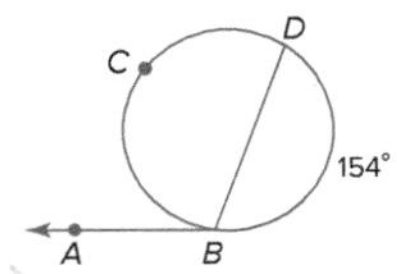

15. $m\angle DAB$ 125

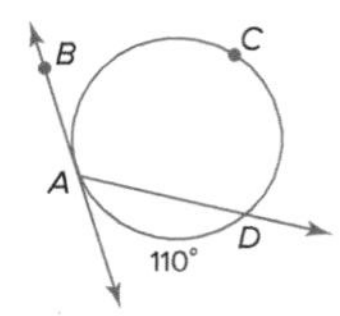

16. $m\widehat{GJF}$ 196

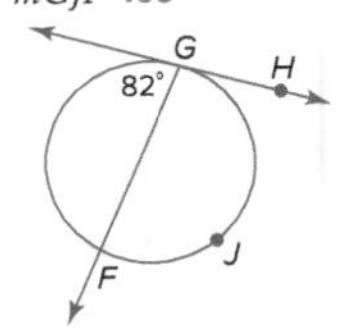

17. SPORTS The multi-sport field shown includes a softball field and a soccer field. If $m\widehat{ABC} = 200$, find each measure.

a. $m\angle ACE$ 100

b. $m\angle ADC$ 20

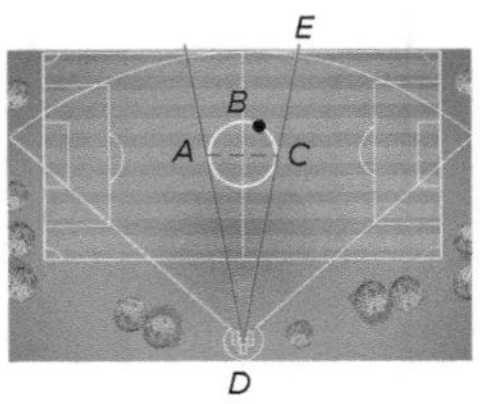

Examples 3–4 G.C.2 **MP STRUCTURE** **Find each measure.**

18. $m\angle A$ 81

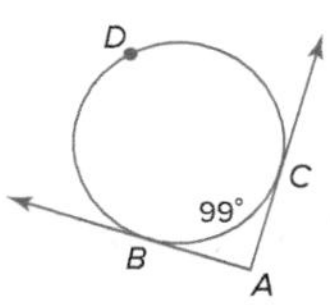

19. $m\angle W$ 74

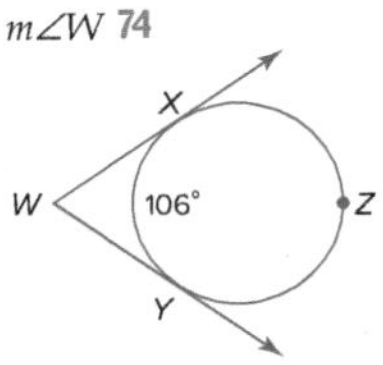

20. $m\widehat{JM}$ 205

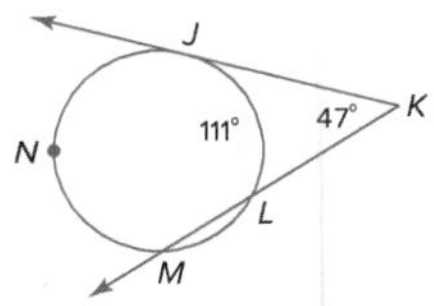

21. $m\widehat{XY}$ 185

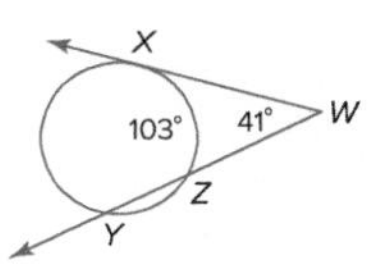

22. $m\angle R$ 30

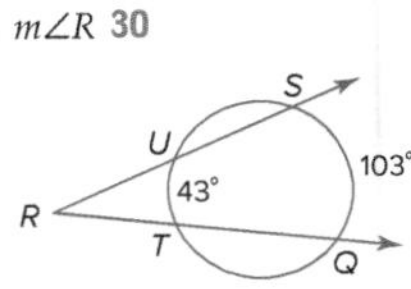

23. $m\widehat{SU}$ 22

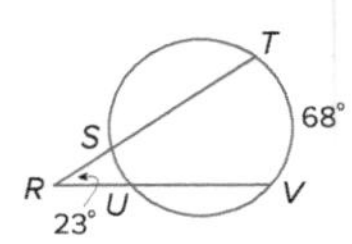

Differentiated Instruction OL BL

Extension If two chords in the same circle cut two arcs of 75 degrees, what do you know about the chords? If the arcs have an endpoint on each chord, then the chords are parallel. If the arcs have both endpoints on the same chord, then the chords are congruent.

24. **JEWELRY** In the circular necklace shown, A and B are tangent points. If $x = 260$, what is y? **80**

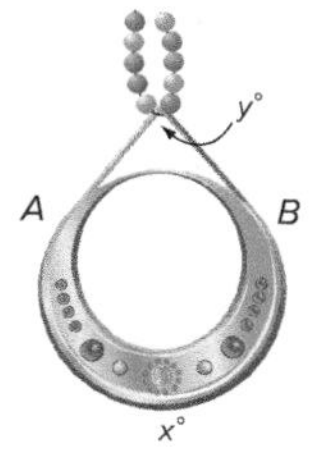

25. **SPACE** A satellite orbits above Earth's equator. Find x, the measure of the planet's arc, that is visible to the satellite. **168**

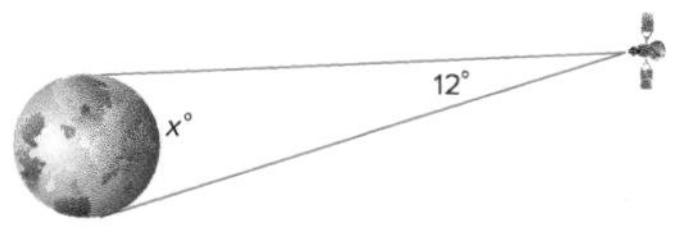

B **ALGEBRA** **Find the value of x.**

26.

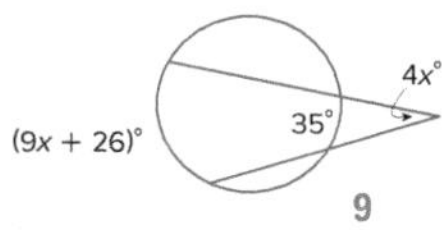

9

27.

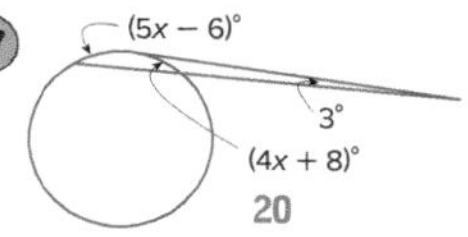

20

28.

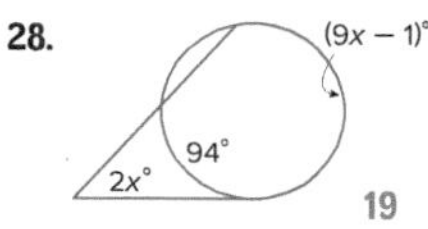

19

29. **PHOTOGRAPHY** A photographer frames a carousel in his camera shot as shown so that the lines of sight form tangents to the carousel.

a. If the camera's viewing angle is 35°, what is the arc measure of the carousel that appears in the shot? **145**

b. If you want to capture an arc measure of 150° in the photograph, what viewing angle should be used? **30**

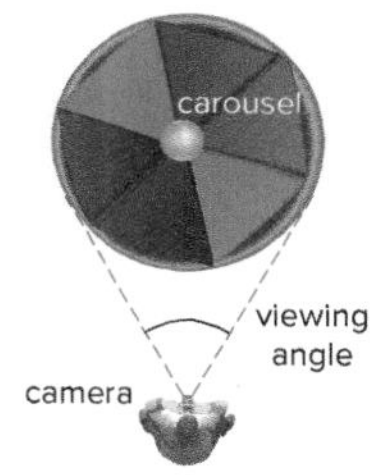

MP CONSTRUCT ARGUMENTS **For each case of Theorem 9.14, write a two-column proof.** **30–32. See margin.**

30. **Case 1**

Given: secants $\overrightarrow{AD}$ and $\overrightarrow{AE}$

Prove: $m\angle A = \frac{1}{2}(m\widehat{DE} - m\widehat{BC})$

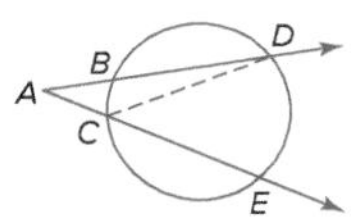

31. **Case 2**

Given: tangent $\overrightarrow{FM}$ and secant $\overrightarrow{FL}$

Prove: $m\angle F = \frac{1}{2}(m\widehat{LH} - m\widehat{GH})$

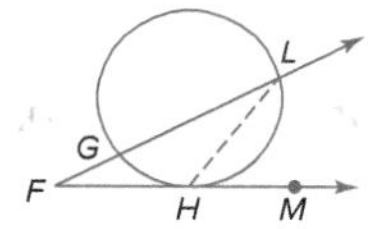

32. **Case 3**

Given: tangents $\overrightarrow{RS}$ and $\overrightarrow{RV}$

Prove: $m\angle R = \frac{1}{2}(m\widehat{SWT} - m\widehat{ST})$

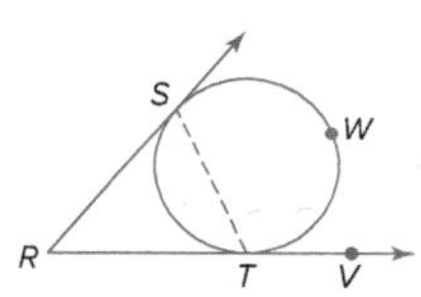

33. **PROOF** Write a paragraph proof of Theorem 9.13.

a. **Given:** $\overleftrightarrow{AB}$ is a tangent of $\odot O$. $\overrightarrow{AC}$ is a secant of $\odot O$. $\angle CAE$ is acute.

Prove: $m\angle CAE = \frac{1}{2}m\widehat{CA}$ **See margin.**

b. Prove that if $\angle CAB$ is obtuse, $m\angle CAB = \frac{1}{2}m\widehat{CDA}$. **See margin.**

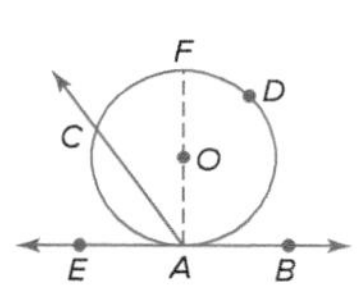

33a. Proof: By Theorem 9.10, $\overline{OA} \perp \overline{AB}$. So, $\angle FAE$ is a right $\angle$ with measure 90, and $\widehat{FCA}$ is a semicircle with measure of 180. Because $\angle CAE$ is acute, C is in the interior of $\angle FAE$. By the Angle and Arc Addition Postulates, $m\angle FAE = m\angle FAC + m\angle CAE$ and $m\widehat{FCA} = m\widehat{FC} + m\widehat{CA}$. By substitution, $90 = m\angle FAC + m\angle CAE$ and $180 = m\widehat{FC} + m\widehat{CA}$. So, $90 = \frac{1}{2}m\widehat{FC} + \frac{1}{2}m\widehat{CA}$ by Division Prop., and $m\angle FAC + m\angle CAE = \frac{1}{2}m\widehat{FC} + \frac{1}{2}m\widehat{CA}$ by substitution. $m\angle FAC = \frac{1}{2}m\widehat{FC}$ since $\angle FAC$ is inscribed, so substitution yields $\frac{1}{2}m\widehat{FC} + m\angle CAE = \frac{1}{2}m\widehat{FC} + \frac{1}{2}m\widehat{CA}$. By Subt. Prop., $m\angle CAE = \frac{1}{2}m\widehat{CA}$.

33b. Given: $\angle CAB$ is obtuse.
Prove: $m\angle CAB = \frac{1}{2}m\widehat{CDA}$
Proof: Using the Angle and Arc Addition Postulates, $m\angle CAB = m\angle CAF + m\angle FAB$ and $m\widehat{CDA} = m\widehat{CF} + m\widehat{FDA}$. Since $\overline{OA} \perp \overline{AB}$ and $\overline{FA}$ is a diameter, $\angle FAB$ is a right angle with a measure of 90 and arc FDA is a semicircle with a measure of 180. By substitution, $m\angle CAB = m\angle CAF + 90$ and $m\widehat{CDA} = m\widehat{CF} + 180$. Because $\angle CAF$ is inscribed, $m\angle CAF = \frac{1}{2}m\widehat{CF}$ and by substitution, $m\angle CAB = \frac{1}{2}m\widehat{CF} + 90$. Using the Division and Subtraction Properties on the Arc Addition equation yields $\frac{1}{2}m\widehat{CDA} - \frac{1}{2}m\widehat{CF} = 90$. By substituting for 90, $m\angle CAB = \frac{1}{2}m\widehat{CF} + \frac{1}{2}m\widehat{CDA} - \frac{1}{2}m\widehat{CF}$. By subtraction, $m\angle CAB = \frac{1}{2}m\widehat{CDA}$.

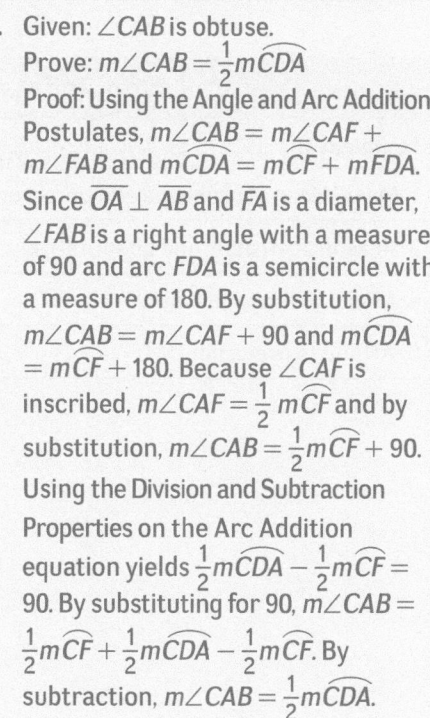

MP Teaching the Mathematical Practices

Construct Arguments Mathematically proficient students understand and use stated assumptions and definitions in constructing arguments. They make conjectures and build a logical progression of statements to explore the truth of their conjectures. In Exercises 30–32, encourage students to use the Exterior Angles Theorem in their proofs.

Additional Answers

31. Statements (Reasons)
 1. $\overrightarrow{FM}$ is a tangent to the circle and $\overrightarrow{FL}$ is a secant to the circle. (Given)
 2. $m\angle FLH = \frac{1}{2}m\widehat{HG}$, $m\angle LHM = \frac{1}{2}m\widehat{LH}$ (The meas. of an inscribed $\angle = \frac{1}{2}$ the measure of its intercepted arc.)
 3. $m\angle LHM = m\angle FLH + m\angle F$ (Exterior $\triangle$ Theorem)
 4. $\frac{1}{2}m\widehat{LH} = \frac{1}{2}m\widehat{HG} + m\angle F$ (Substitution)
 5. $\frac{1}{2}m\widehat{LH} - \frac{1}{2}m\widehat{HG} = m\angle F$ (Subtraction Prop.)
 6. $\frac{1}{2}(m\widehat{LH} - m\widehat{HG}) = m\angle F$ (Distributive Prop.)

32. Statements (Reasons)
 1. $\overrightarrow{RS}$ and $\overrightarrow{RV}$ are tangents to the circle. (Given)
 2. $m\angle STV = \frac{1}{2}m\widehat{SWT}$, $m\angle RST = \frac{1}{2}m\widehat{ST}$ (The meas. of a secant-tangent $\angle = \frac{1}{2}$ the measure of its intercepted arc.)
 3. $m\angle STV = m\angle RST + m\angle R$ (Exterior $\triangle$ Theorem)
 4. $\frac{1}{2}m\widehat{SWT} = \frac{1}{2}m\widehat{ST} + m\angle R$ (Substitution)
 5. $\frac{1}{2}m\widehat{SWT} - \frac{1}{2}m\widehat{ST} = m\angle R$ (Subtraction Prop.)
 6. $\frac{1}{2}(m\widehat{SWT} - m\widehat{ST}) = m\angle R$ (Distributive Prop.)

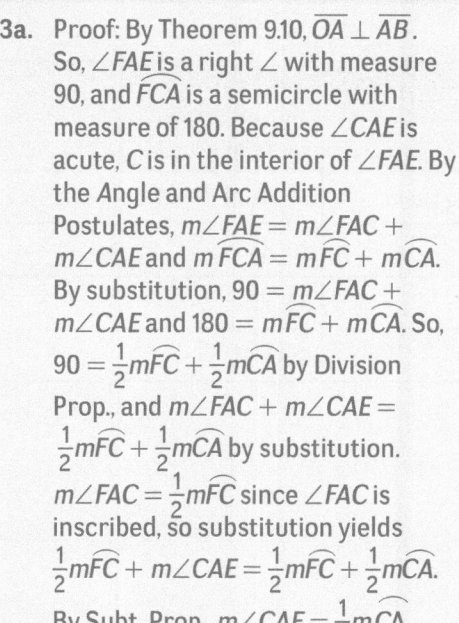

Exercise Alert

Compass, Straightedge, and Protractor
Exercise 40 requires the use of a compass, a straightedge, and a protractor.

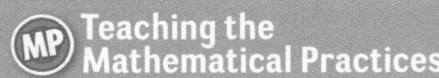

MP Teaching the Mathematical Practices

Construct Arguments Mathematically proficient students understand and use stated assumptions, definitions, and previously established results in constructing arguments. In Exercise 39, encourage students to recognize the relationship between a diameter and its intercepted arc.

Assess

Name the Math Select examples and ask students to call out the names of the segments in the figure as they leave the classroom.

Additional Answers

35a.

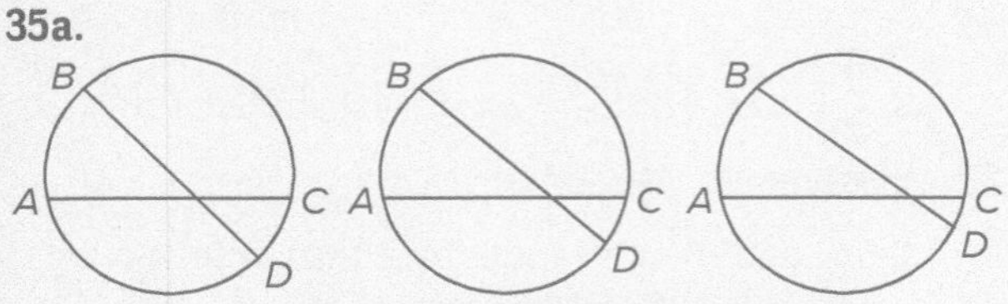

35b.

	Circle 1	Circle 2	Circle 3
$m\widehat{CD}$	25	15	5
$m\widehat{AB}$	50	50	50
x	37.5	32.5	27.5

38. Sample answer: $m\widehat{AB} = m\widehat{BC}$; $m\angle BAC = m\angle BCA$ because the triangle is isosceles. Because $\angle BAC$ and $\angle BCA$ are inscribed angles, by Theorem 9.6, $m\widehat{AB} = 2m\angle BCA$ and $m\widehat{BC} = 2m\angle BAC$. So, $m\widehat{AB} = m\widehat{BC}$.

39b. $m\widehat{KH} = 56$; $m\widehat{HJ} = 124$; Because a diameter is involved, the intercepted arcs measure $(180 - x)$ and x degrees. Hence solving $\frac{180 - x - x}{2} = 34$ leads to the answer.

Go Online!

eSolutions Manual
Create worksheets, answer keys, and solutions handouts for your assignments.

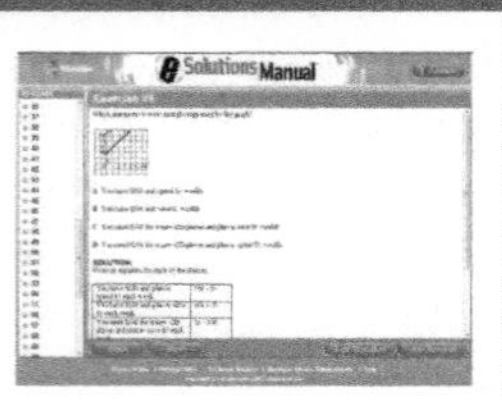

---

34. **WALLPAPER** In the wallpaper design shown, $\overline{BC}$ is a diameter of $\odot Q$. If $m\angle A = 26$ and $m\widehat{CE} = 67$, what is $m\widehat{DE}$? 98

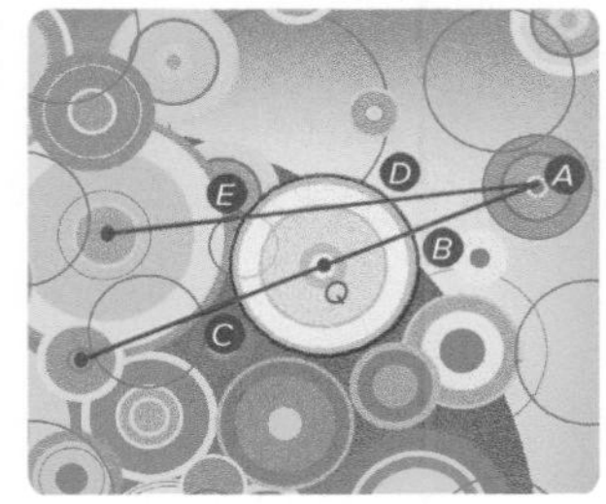

G.C.2

35. **MULTIPLE REPRESENTATIONS** In this problem, you will explore the relationship between Theorems 9.12 and 9.6.

a. **Geometric** Copy the figure shown. Then draw three successive figures in which the position of point D moves closer to point C, but points A, B, and C remain fixed. See margin.

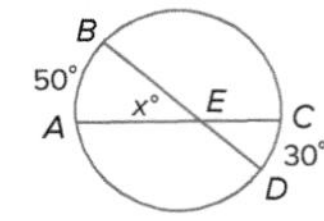

b. **Tabular** Estimate the measure of $\widehat{CD}$ for each successive circle, recording the measures of $\widehat{AB}$ and $\widehat{CD}$ in a table. Then calculate and record the value of x for each circle. See margin.

c. **Verbal** Describe the relationship between $m\widehat{AB}$ and the value of x as $m\widehat{CD}$ approaches zero. What type of angle does $\angle AEB$ become when $m\widehat{CD} = 0$?

d. **Analytical** Write an algebraic proof to show the relationship between Theorems 9.12 and 9.6 described in part **c**.
$x = \frac{1}{2}(m\widehat{AB} + m\widehat{CD})$; $x = \frac{1}{2}(m\widehat{AB} + 0)$; $x = \frac{1}{2}m\widehat{AB}$

35c. As the measure of $\widehat{CD}$ gets closer to 0, the measure of x approaches half of $m\widehat{AB}$; $\angle AEB$ becomes an inscribed angle.

G.C.2

H.O.T. Problems Use Higher-Order Thinking Skills

36. **WRITING IN MATH** Explain how to find the measure of an angle formed by a secant and a tangent that intersect outside a circle.
Find the difference of the two intercepted arcs and divide by 2.

37. **CHALLENGE** The circles below are concentric. What is x? 15

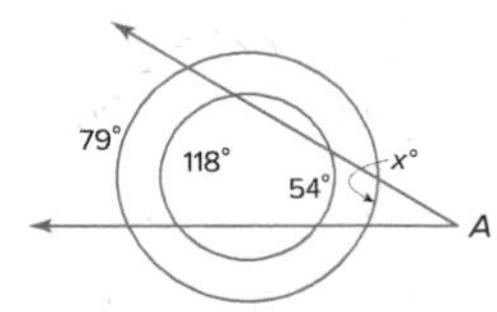

38. **MP REASONING** Isosceles $\triangle ABC$ is inscribed in $\odot D$. What can you conclude about $m\widehat{AB}$ and $m\widehat{BC}$? Explain. See margin.

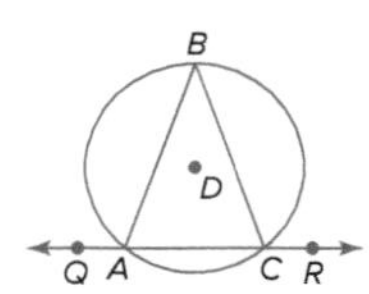

39a. $m\angle G \leq 90$; $m\angle G < 90$ for all values except when $\overrightarrow{JG} \perp \overrightarrow{GH}$ at G, then $m\angle G = 90$.

39. **MP CONSTRUCT ARGUMENTS** In the figure, $\overline{JK}$ is a diameter and $\overleftrightarrow{GH}$ is a tangent.

a. Describe the range of possible values for $m\angle G$. Explain your reasoning

b. If $m\angle G = 34$, find the measures of minor arcs $\widehat{HJ}$ and $\widehat{KH}$. Explain your reasoning. See margin.

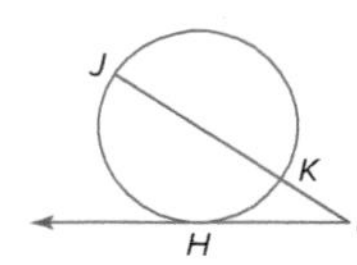

40. **OPEN-ENDED** Draw a circle and two tangents that intersect outside the circle. Use a protractor to measure the angle that is formed. Find the measures of the minor and major arcs formed. Explain your reasoning. See margin.

41. **WRITING IN MATH** A circle is inscribed within $\triangle PQR$. If $m\angle P = 50$ and $m\angle Q = 60$, describe how to find the measures of the three minor arcs formed by the points of tangency.

41. Sample answer: Using Theorem 9.14, $60° = \frac{1}{2}[(360 - x) - x] = 120°$; repeat for 50° to get 130°. The third arc can be found by adding 50° and 60° and subtracting from 360 to get 110°.

MP Standards for Mathematical Practice

Emphasis On	Exercises
1 Make sense of problems and persevere in solving them.	17, 24–29, 37–39
2 Reason abstractly and quantitatively.	30–33
4 Model with mathematics.	34, 35
6 Attend to precision.	8–16, 41

Preparing for Assessment

42. In the figure, $\overrightarrow{TW}$ bisects $\angle VTU$ and $m\widehat{TV} = 104$.

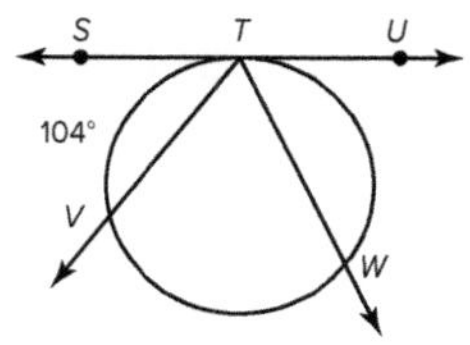

What is the measure of $\angle UTW$? MP 6 G.C.2 **C**

- ○ A 38
- ○ B 52
- ○ C 64
- ○ D 76
- ○ E 128

43. If $m\angle AED = 95$ and $m\widehat{AD} = 120$, what is $m\angle BAC$? MP 6 G.C.2 **35**

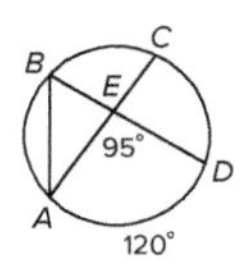

44. $\overline{MN}$ is tangent to ⊙C at point N.

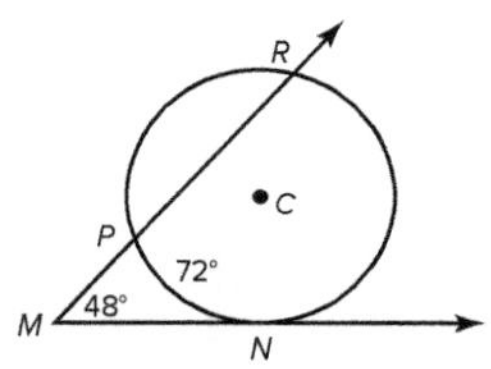

What is the measure of $\widehat{NR}$? MP 6 G.C.2 **D**

- ○ A 24
- ○ B 96
- ○ C 120
- ○ D 168

45. $\overline{GH}$ and $\overline{JK}$ are chords of a circle that intersect at point L. Given that $m\widehat{GJ} = 122$ and $m\widehat{HK} = 80$, what is $m\angle HLK$? MP 6 G.C.2 **A**

- ○ A 101
- ○ B 61
- ○ C 40
- ○ D 21

46. **MULTI-STEP** Look at the figure. MP 2, 3 G.C.2

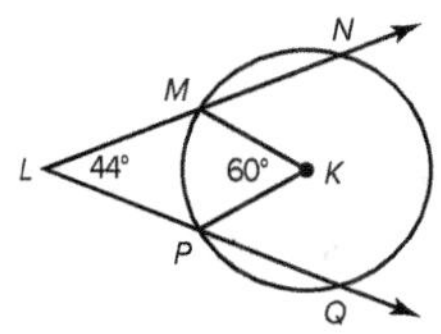

a. In the diagram, what is the arc measure of $\widehat{MP}$? **C**

- ○ A 30°
- ○ B 45°
- ○ C 60°
- ○ D 120°

b. Which statements are true? Check all that apply. **A, B**

- ☐ A $m\angle L = \frac{1}{2}(m\widehat{NQ} - m\widehat{MP})$
- ☐ B $44 = \frac{1}{2}(m\widehat{NQ} - 60)$
- ☐ C $88 = m\widehat{NQ} + 60$
- ☐ D $28 = m\widehat{NQ}$
- ☐ E The interior measure is equal to the arc measure.
- ☐ F An interior angle measure is always half the arc measure.

c. In the diagram, what is the arc measure of $\widehat{NQ}$? **D**

- ○ A 28°
- ○ B 52°
- ○ C 104°
- ○ D 148°

40. Sample answer:

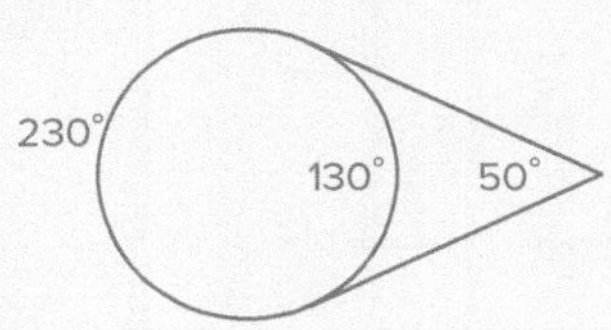

By Theorem 9.13, $m\angle 1 = \frac{1}{2}(x - y)$. So, $50 = \frac{1}{2}[(360 - x) - x]$. Therefore, x (minor arc) = 130, and y (major arc) = 360 − 130 or 230.

Preparing for Assessment

Exercises 42–46 require students to use the skills they will need on standardized assessments. Exercises are dual-coded with content standards and mathematical practice standards.

Dual Coding		
Exercises	Content Standards	MP Mathematical Practices
42	G.C.2	6
43	G.C.2	6
44	G.C.2	6
45	G.C.2	6
46	G.C.2	2, 3

Diagnose Student Errors

Survey student responses for each item. Class trends may indicate common errors and misconceptions.

42.

A	Calculated $\frac{1}{2}(180 - 104)$
B	Found $m\angle STV$
C	CORRECT
D	Calculated 180 − 104
E	Found $m\angle UTV$

44.

A	Solved $48 = \frac{1}{2}(x + 72)$
B	Assumed $m\widehat{NR}$ is $2m\angle RMN$
C	Added, 48 + 72
D	CORRECT

45.

A	CORRECT
B	Assumed $m\angle HLK$ is $\frac{1}{2}m\widehat{GJ}$
C	Assumed $m\angle HLK$ is $\frac{1}{2}m\widehat{HK}$
D	Calculated $\frac{1}{2}(122 - 80)$

Go Online!

Quizzes

Students can use *Self-Check Quizzes* to check their understanding of this lesson and have the results sent to you. You can also give *Quiz 3*, which covers the content in Lessons 9-5 and 9-6.

LESSON 9-7

Equations of Circles

SUGGESTED PACING (DAYS)

	Instruction		Extend Lab
90 min.	0.5	0.5	
45 min.	1.0		1.0

Track Your Progress

Objectives

1 Write the equation of a circle.

2 Graph a circle on the coordinate plane.

Mathematical Background

An equation for a circle with center at (h, k) and radius of r units is $(x - h)^2 + (y - k)^2 = r^2$. The equation of a circle can be used to graph the circle on a coordinate plane. A circle can be graphed from three known points, and its equation can be found.

THEN

G.C.2 Identify and describe relationships among inscribed angles, radii, and chords.

G.MG.3 Apply geometric methods to solve design problems.

NOW

G.GPE.1 Derive the equation of a circle with given center and radius, using the Pythagorean Theorem; complete the square to find the center and radius of a circle given by an equation.

G.GPE.4 Use coordinates to prove simple geometric theorems algebraically.

NEXT

G.GPE.2 Derive the equation of a parabola given a focus and directrix.

Go Online! All of these resources and more are available at connectED.mcgraw-hill.com

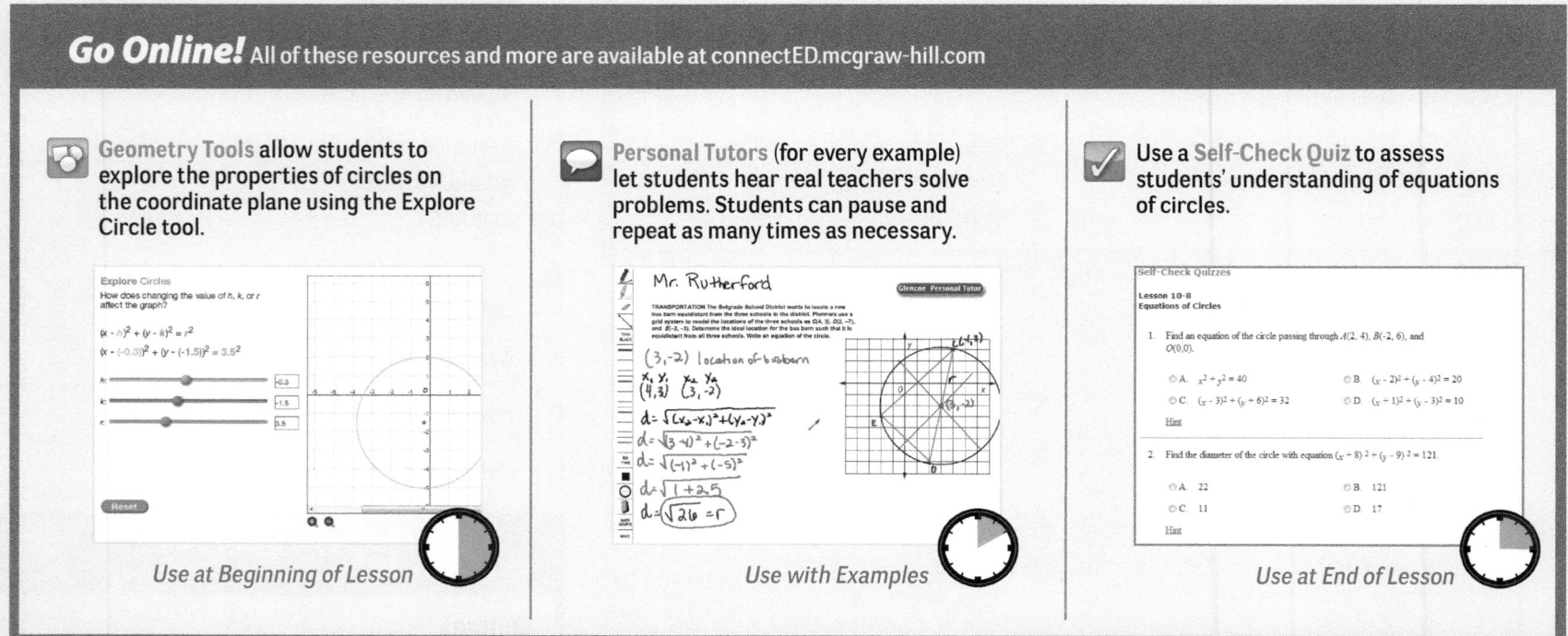

Geometry Tools allow students to explore the properties of circles on the coordinate plane using the Explore Circle tool.

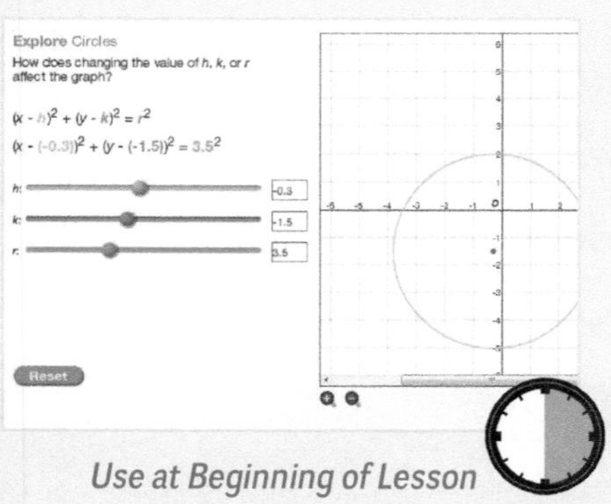

Use at Beginning of Lesson

Personal Tutors (for every example) let students hear real teachers solve problems. Students can pause and repeat as many times as necessary.

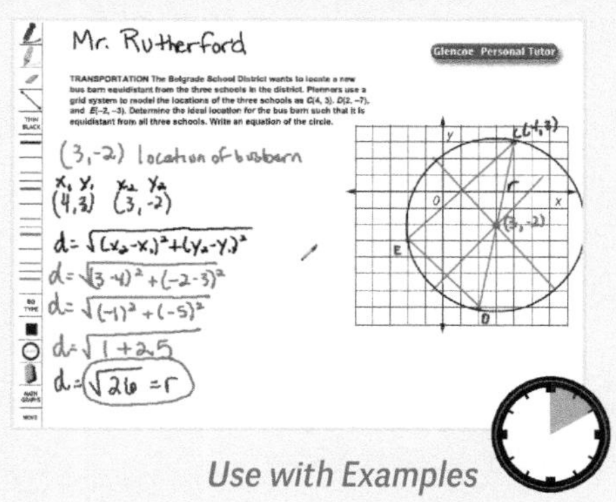

Use with Examples

Use a **Self-Check Quiz** to assess students' understanding of equations of circles.

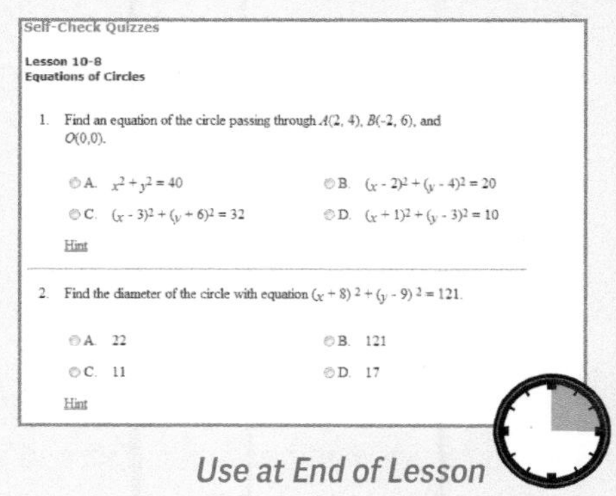

Use at End of Lesson

OER Using Open Educational Resources

Practice Have students review their work on **webmath.com** at **Discovery Education**. They can graph circles given their equations. If they make a mistake on a quiz or test they can use this site to see where they went wrong. *Use as homework*

Differentiate Your Resources

Extra Practice Additional practice or homework; Skills Practice is best for approaching-level students and Practice is best for on-level and beyond-level students

Skills Practice

AL OL ELL

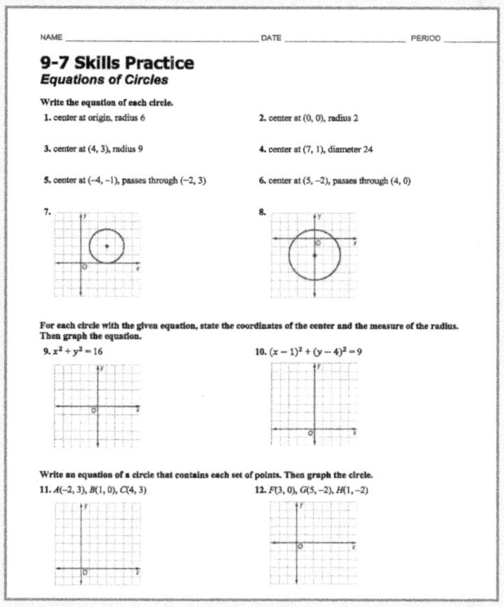
NAME ______ DATE ______ PERIOD ______

9-7 Skills Practice
Equations of Circles

Write the equation of each circle.
1. center at origin, radius 6
2. center at (0, 0), radius 2
3. center at (4, 3), radius 9
4. center at (7, 1), diameter 24
5. center at (−4, −1), passes through (−2, 3)
6. center at (5, −2), passes through (4, 0)
7.
8.

For each circle with the given equation, state the coordinates of the center and the measure of the radius. Then graph the equation.
9. $x^2 + y^2 = 16$
10. $(x - 1)^2 + (y - 4)^2 = 9$

Write an equation of a circle that contains each set of points. Then graph the circle.
11. $A(-2, 3)$, $B(1, 0)$, $C(4, 3)$
12. $F(3, 0)$, $G(5, -2)$, $H(1, -2)$

Practice

AL OL BL ELL

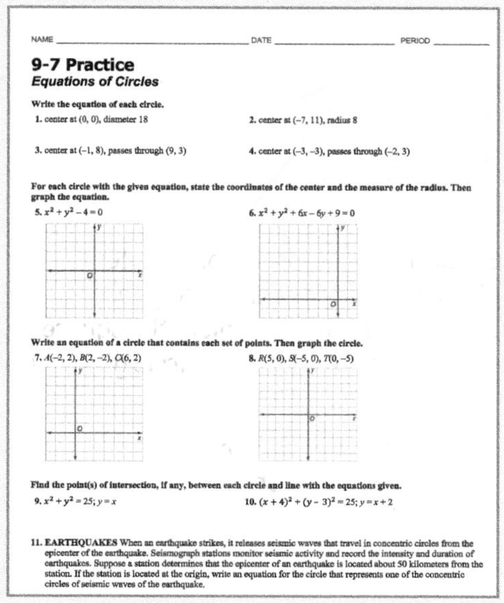
NAME ______ DATE ______ PERIOD ______

9-7 Practice
Equations of Circles

Write the equation of each circle.
1. center at (0, 0), diameter 18
2. center at (−7, 11), radius 8
3. center at (−1, 8), passes through (9, 3)
4. center at (−3, −3), passes through (−2, 3)

For each circle with the given equation, state the coordinates of the center and the measure of the radius. Then graph the equation.
5. $x^2 + y^2 - 4 = 0$
6. $x^2 + y^2 + 6x - 6y + 9 = 0$

Write an equation of a circle that contains each set of points. Then graph the circle.
7. $A(-2, 2)$, $B(2, -2)$, $C(6, 2)$
8. $R(5, 0)$, $S(-5, 0)$, $T(0, -5)$

Find the point(s) of intersection, if any, between each circle and line with the equations given.
9. $x^2 + y^2 = 25$; $y = x$
10. $(x + 4)^2 + (y - 3)^2 = 25$; $y = x + 2$

11. **EARTHQUAKES** When an earthquake strikes, it releases seismic waves that travel in concentric circles from the epicenter of the earthquake. Seismograph stations monitor seismic activity and record the intensity and duration of earthquakes. Suppose a station determines that the epicenter of an earthquake is located about 50 kilometers from the station. If the station is located at the origin, write an equation for the circle that represents one of the concentric circles of seismic waves of the earthquake.

Word Problem Practice

AL OL BL ELL

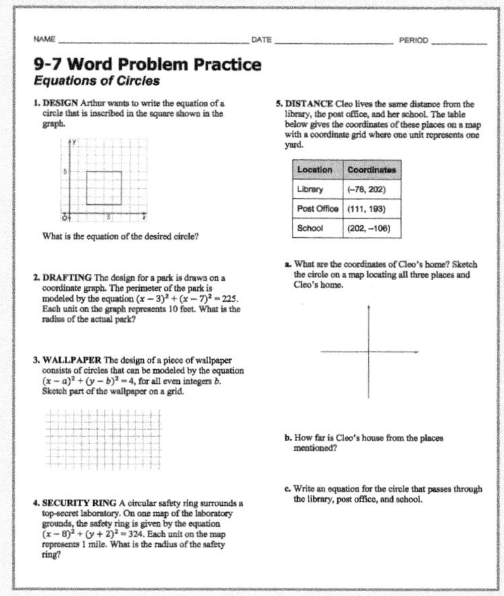
NAME ______ DATE ______ PERIOD ______

9-7 Word Problem Practice
Equations of Circles

1. **DESIGN** Arthur wants to write the equation of a circle that is inscribed in the square shown in the graph.

What is the equation of the desired circle?

2. **DRAFTING** The design for a park is drawn on a coordinate graph. The perimeter of the park is modeled by the equation $(x - 3)^2 + (x - 7)^2 = 225$. Each unit on the graph represents 10 feet. What is the radius of the actual park?

3. **WALLPAPER** The design of a piece of wallpaper consists of circles that can be modeled by the equation $(x - a)^2 + (y - b)^2 = 4$, for all even integers b. Sketch part of the wallpaper on a grid.

4. **SECURITY RING** A circular safety ring surrounds a top-secret laboratory. On one map of the laboratory grounds, the safety ring is given by the equation $(x - 8)^2 + (y + 2)^2 = 324$. Each unit on the map represents 1 mile. What is the radius of the safety ring?

5. **DISTANCE** Cleo lives the same distance from the library, the post office, and her school. The table below gives the coordinates of these places on a map with a coordinate grid where one unit represents one yard.

Location	Coordinates
Library	(−78, 202)
Post Office	(111, 193)
School	(202, −106)

a. What are the coordinates of Cleo's home? Sketch the circle on a map locating all three places and Cleo's home.

b. How far is Cleo's house from the places mentioned?

c. Write an equation for the circle that passes through the library, post office, and school.

Intervention Reteaching and vocabulary activities that can be used with struggling or absent students and as ELL support

Study Guide and Intervention

AL OL ELL

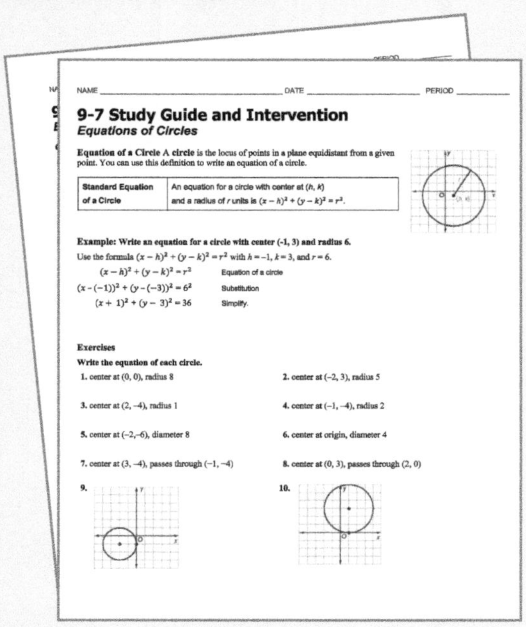
NAME ______ DATE ______ PERIOD ______

9-7 Study Guide and Intervention
Equations of Circles

Equation of a Circle A circle is the locus of points in a plane equidistant from a given point. You can use this definition to write an equation of a circle.

Standard Equation of a Circle	An equation for a circle with center at (h, k) and a radius of r units is $(x - h)^2 + (y - k)^2 = r^2$.

Example: Write an equation for a circle with center (−1, 3) and radius 6.
Use the formula $(x - h)^2 + (y - k)^2 = r^2$ with $h = -1$, $k = 3$, and $r = 6$.
$(x - h)^2 + (y - k)^2 = r^2$ Equation of a circle
$(x - (-1))^2 + (y - (-3))^2 = 6^2$ Substitution
$(x + 1)^2 + (y - 3)^2 = 36$ Simplify.

Exercises
Write the equation of each circle.
1. center at (0, 0), radius 8
2. center at (−2, 3), radius 5
3. center at (2, −4), radius 1
4. center at (−1, −4), radius 2
5. center at (−2, −6), diameter 8
6. center at origin, diameter 4
7. center at (3, −4), passes through (−1, −4)
8. center at (0, 3), passes through (2, 0)
9.
10.

Study Notebook

AL OL BL ELL

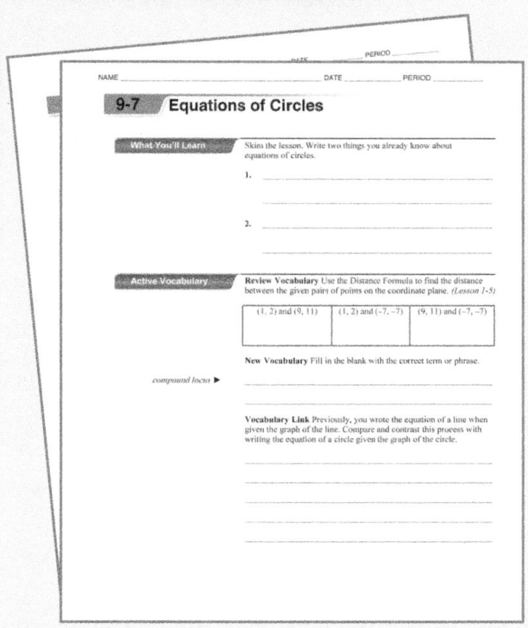
NAME ______ DATE ______ PERIOD ______

9-7 Equations of Circles

What You'll Learn Skim the lesson. Write two things you already know about equations of circles.
1.
2.

Active Vocabulary **Review Vocabulary** Use the Distance Formula to find the distance between the given pairs of points on the coordinate plane. *(Lesson 1-5)*

(1, 2) and (9, 11)	(1, 2) and (−7, −7)	(9, 11) and (−7, −7)

New Vocabulary Fill in the blank with the correct term or phrase.
compound locus ►

Vocabulary Link Previously, you wrote the equation of a line when given the graph of the line. Compare and contrast this process with writing the equation of a circle given the graph of the circle.

Extension Activities that can be used to extend lesson concepts

Enrichment

OL BL ELL

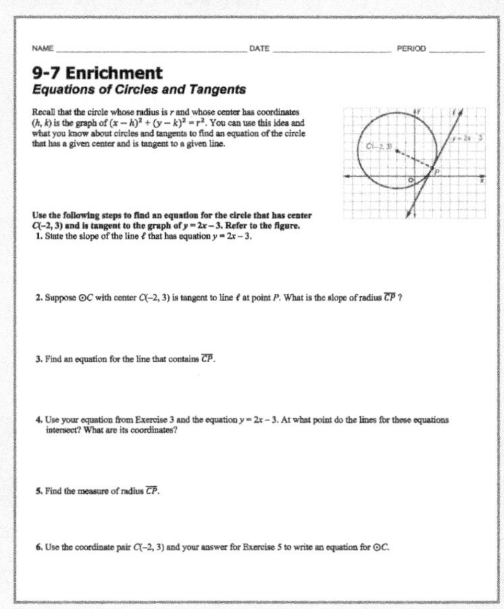
NAME ______ DATE ______ PERIOD ______

9-7 Enrichment
Equations of Circles and Tangents

Recall that the circle whose radius is r and whose center has coordinates (h, k) is the graph of $(x - h)^2 + (y - k)^2 = r^2$. You can use this idea and what you know about circles and tangents to find an equation of the circle that has a given center and is tangent to a given line.

Use the following steps to find an equation for the circle that has center $C(-2, 3)$ and is tangent to the graph of $y = 2x - 3$. Refer to the figure.
1. State the slope of the line ℓ that has equation $y = 2x - 3$.
2. Suppose ⊙C with center $C(-2, 3)$ is tangent to line ℓ at point P. What is the slope of radius $\overline{CP}$?
3. Find an equation for the line that contains $\overline{CP}$.
4. Use your equation from Exercise 3 and the equation $y = 2x - 3$. At what point do the lines for these equations intersect? What are its coordinates?
5. Find the measure of radius $\overline{CP}$.
6. Use the coordinate pair $C(-2, 3)$ and your answer for Exercise 5 to write an equation for ⊙C.

Launch

Have students read the Why? section of the lesson. Ask:

- Where is the tower located in relationship to the area it covers? the center
- What does the distance from the tower to the farthest point of the service area represent? the radius
- A certain cellular tower sends out a signal with a 15-mile radius. To increase the service area by 50%, how many more miles does the signal from the tower have to reach? ≈3.37 miles

Teach

Ask the scaffolded questions for each example to build conceptual understanding for students at all levels.

1 Equations of a Circle

Example 1 Write an Equation Using the Center and Radius

AL In part **b**, how do we know that the radius is 3? Sample answer: Count on the coordinate plane from the center to the edge of the circle.

OL If a circle has center $(-4, -11)$ and radius $\sqrt{6}$, what is the equation for the circle? $(x + 4)^2 + (y + 11)^2 = 6$

BL What are the center and radius of the circle $(x + 3)^2 + (y - 7)^2 = 25$? center: $(-3, 7)$ and radius: 5

(continued on the next page)

LESSON 7

Equations of Circles

Then

- You wrote equations of lines using information about their graphs.

Now

1. Write the equation of a circle.
2. Graph a circle on the coordinate plane.

Why?

- Telecommunications towers emit radio signals that are used to transmit cellular calls. Each tower covers a circular area, and towers are arranged so that a signal is available at any location in the coverage area.

New Vocabulary
compound locus

MP Mathematical Practices
2 Reason abstractly and quantitatively.
7 Look for and make use of structure.

Content Standards
G.GPE.1 Derive the equation of a circle of given center and radius using the Pythagorean Theorem; complete the square to find the center and radius of a circle given by an equation.
G.GPE.4 Use coordinates to prove simple geometric theorems algebraically.

1 Equation of a Circle Because all points on a circle are equidistant from the center, you can find an equation of a circle by using the Distance Formula.

Let (x, y) represent a point on a circle centered at the origin. Using the Pythagorean Theorem, $x^2 + y^2 = r^2$.

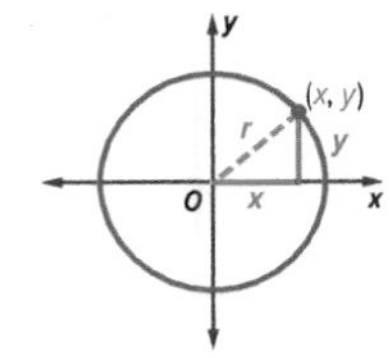

Now suppose that the center is not at the origin, but at the point (h, k). You can use the Distance Formula to develop an equation for the circle.

$d = \sqrt{(x_2 - x_1)^2 + (y_2 - y_1)^2}$ Distance Formula

$r = \sqrt{(x - h)^2 + (y - k)^2}$ $d = r, (x_1, y_1) = (h, k), (x_2, y_2) = (x, y)$

$r^2 = (x - h)^2 + (y - k)^2$ Square each side.

Key Concept Equation of a Circle in Standard Form

The standard form of the equation of a circle with center at (h, k) and radius r is $(x - h)^2 + (y - k)^2 = r^2$.

The standard form of the equation of a circle is also called the *center-radius* form.

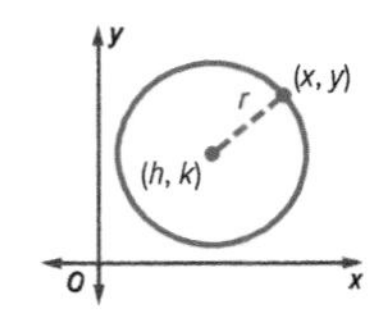

G.GPE.1

Example 1 Write an Equation Using the Center and Radius

Write the equation of each circle.

a. center at (1, −8), radius 7

$(x - h)^2 + (y - k)^2 = r^2$ Equation of a circle

$(x - 1)^2 + [y - (-8)]^2 = 7^2$ $(h, k) = (1, -8), r = 7$

$(x - 1)^2 + (y + 8)^2 = 49$ Simplify.

b. the circle graphed at the right

The center is at (0, 4) and the radius is 3.

$(x - h)^2 + (y - k)^2 = r^2$ Equation of a circle

$(x - 0)^2 + (y - 4)^2 = 3^2$ $(h, k) = (0, 4), r = 3$

$x^2 + (y - 4)^2 = 9$ Simplify.

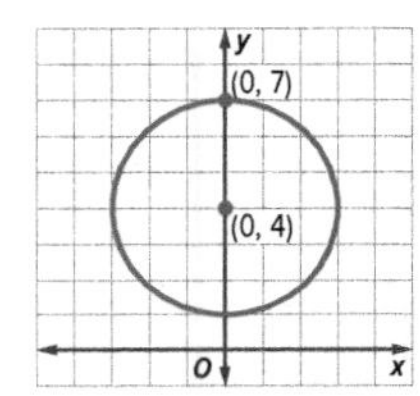

Guided Practice **1A.** $x^2 + y^2 = 10$ **1B.** $(x - 4)^2 + (y + 1)^2 = 16$

1A. center at origin, radius $\sqrt{10}$

1B. center at (4, −1), diameter 8

MP Mathematical Practices Strategies

Model with mathematics.
Help students connect the mathematics of circles to real-world problems. For example, ask:

- What information do you need to write an equation of a circle? radius and center
- What are some real-world situations where graphing a circle on a coordinate plane could be useful? Sample answer: the radius of a delivery service, the radius of an emergency siren, radius of a wi-fi signal

Go Online!

Interactive Whiteboard
Use the *eLesson*, *Lesson Presentation*, or *Interactive Classroom* to present this lesson.

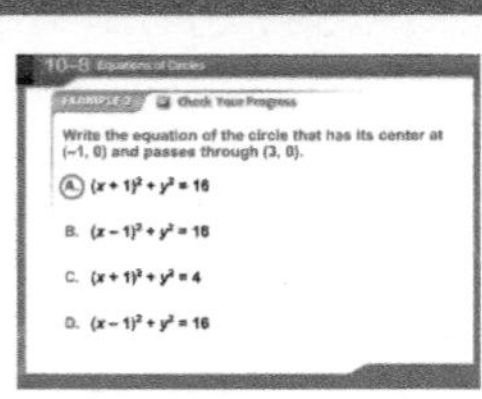

G.GPE.1, G.GPE.4

Example 2 Write an Equation Using the Center and a Point

Write the equation of the circle with center at (−2, 4), that passes through (−6, 7).

Step 1 Find the distance between the points to determine the radius.

$r = \sqrt{(x_2 - x_1)^2 + (y_2 - y_1)^2}$ Distance Formula

$= \sqrt{[-6 - (-2)]^2 + (7 - 4)^2}$ $(x_1, y_1) = (-2, 4)$ and $(x_2, y_2) = (-6, 7)$

$= \sqrt{25}$ or 5 Simplify.

Step 2 Write the equation using $h = -2$, $k = 4$, and $r = 5$.

$(x - h)^2 + (y - k)^2 = r^2$ Equation of a circle

$[x - (-2)]^2 + (y - 4)^2 = 5^2$ $h = -2$, $k = 4$, and $r = 5$

$(x + 2)^2 + (y - 4)^2 = 25$ Simplify.

Guided Practice $(x + 3)^2 + (y + 5)^2 = 34$

2. Write the equation of the circle with center at (−3, −5) that passes through (0, 0).

3A. (0, 0); 2

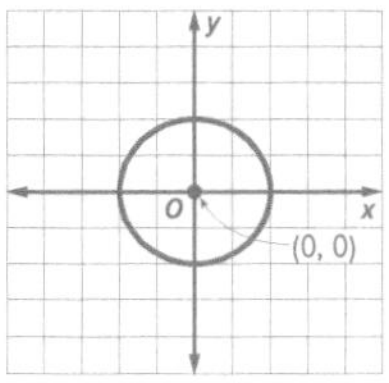

3B. (−4, 7); 5

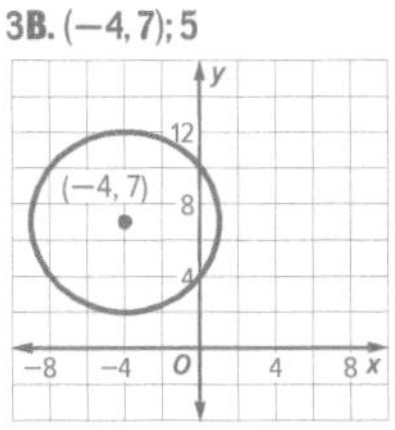

2 Graph Circles

You can use the equation of a circle to graph it on a coordinate plane. To do so, you may need to write the equation in standard form first.

G.GPE.1

Example 3 Graph a Circle

The equation of a circle is $x^2 + y^2 - 8x + 2y = -8$. State the coordinates of the center and the measure of the radius. Then graph the equation.

Write the equation in standard form by completing the square.

$x^2 + y^2 - 8x + 2y = -8$ Original equation

$x^2 - 8x + y^2 + 2y = -8$ Isolate and group like terms.

$x^2 - 8x + 16 + y^2 + 2y + 1 = -8 + 16 + 1$ Complete the squares.

$(x - 4)^2 + (y + 1)^2 = 9$ Factor and simplify.

$(x - 4)^2 + [y - (-1)]^2 = 3^2$ Write +1 as − (−1) and 9 as 3^2.

With the equation now in standard form, you can identify h, k, and r.

$(x - 4)^2 + [y - (-1)]^2 = 3^2$

↑ ↑ ↑

$(x - h)^2 + (y - k)^2 = r^2$

So, $h = 4$, $k = -1$, and $r = 3$. The center is at (4, −1), and the radius is 3. Plot the center and four points that are 3 units from this point. Sketch the circle through these four points.

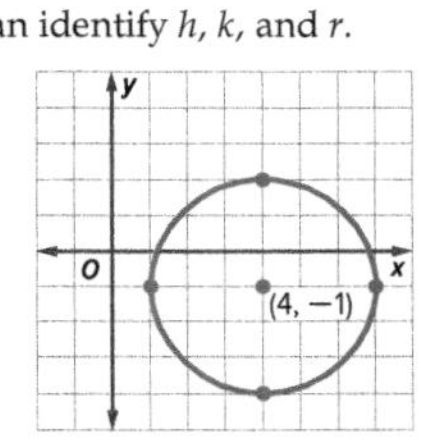

Go Online!

To complete the square for any quadratic expression of the form $x^2 + bx$, follow these steps.

Step 1 Find one half of b.

Step 2 Square the result in Step 1.

Step 3 Add the result of Step 2 to $x^2 + bx$.

Ask your teacher any questions you have about completing the square by sending a message in ConnectED.

Guided Practice

For each circle with the given equation, state the coordinates of the center and the measure of the radius. Then graph the equation.

3A. $x^2 + y^2 - 4 = 0$

3B. $x^2 + y^2 + 8x - 14y + 40 = 0$

Watch Out!

Distance Formula When using the distance formula, remind students to be careful to keep the x- and y-coordinates in the correct order and to keep track of their signs.

Need Another Example?

The equation of a circle is $x^2 - 4x + y^2 + 6y = -9$. State the coordinates of the center and the measure of the radius. Then graph the equation.
(2, −3); 2

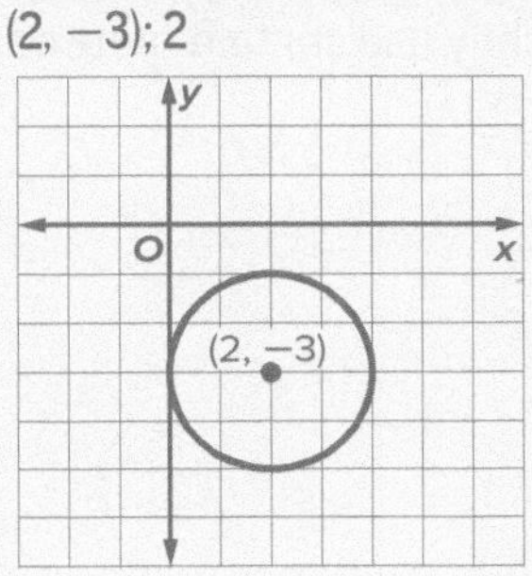

Need Another Example?

Write the equation of each circle.

a. center at (3, −3), radius 6 $(x - 3)^2 + (y + 3)^2 = 36$

b. the circle graphed below

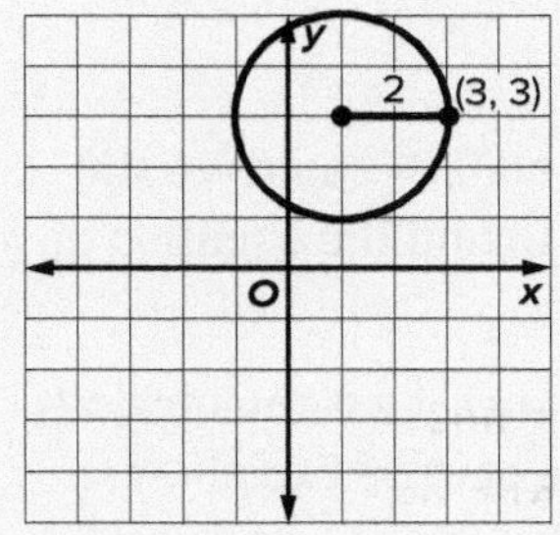

$(x - 1)^2 + (y - 3)^2 = 4$

Example 2 Write an Equation Using the Center and a Point

AL How can we check the reasonableness of this solution? Sample answer: Graph the circle and estimate.

OL If the circle has center (−2, 4) and passes through (−2, 7), what is the equation for the circle? $(x + 2)^2 + (y - 4)^2 = 9$

BL If you can't remember the distance formula, is there another way to determine the radius of the circle? Explain. Yes; Sample answer: Graph the circle on the coordinate plane and use the Pythagorean Theorem to find the radius.

Need Another Example?

Write the equation of the circle with center at (−3, −2), that passes through (1, −2).
$(x + 3)^2 + (y + 2)^2 = 16$

2 Graph Circles

Example 3 Graph a Circle

AL After you find the center and radius, why is it good to find other points on the circle before you sketch it? Sample answer: Finding points on each side of the center makes the graph more accurate.

OL Is it possible to draw a perfect circle using just 4 points? No; it is a sketch of the circle.

BL If you needed to know an exact point on a circle and it was not located at whole number coordinates, what is one way to find the coordinates? Sample answer: Use a graphing calculator or other graphing program.

Example 4 Use Three Points to Write an Equation

AL **How did we determine that the radius is 4?** Sample answer: Since $\overline{BC}$ is a diameter of the circle, we know that the radius is half of its length, or 4.

OL **If point *C* was located at (0, 3), could we still use the same method to find the equation of the circle?** yes

BL **Will this method still work if a diameter does not connect two of the points? Explain.** Yes; Sample answer: If two of the points given don't lie on a diameter, you can just use the perpendicular bisectors to find the center and determine the radius of the circle.

Need Another Example?

Electricity Strategically located substations are extremely important in the transmission and distribution of a power company's electric supply. Suppose three substations are modeled by the points $D(3, 6)$, $E(-1, 2)$, and $F(3, -4)$. Determine the location of a town equidistant from all three substations, and write an equation for the circle. $(4, 1)$; $(x-4)^2+(y-1)^2=26$

Example 5 Intersections with Circles

AL **How many times can a line intersect a circle? Explain.** 1 or 2; once if it is tangent to the circle and twice if it passes into the interior of the circle.

OL **What are the point(s) of intersection between $x^2+y^2=4$ and $y=2$?** $(0, 2)$

BL **A circle intersects the line $y=-x$ at $(-3, 3)$ and $(3, -3)$. What is the equation of the circle centered at the origin?** $x^2+y^2=18$

Need Another Example?

Find the point(s) of intersection between $x^2+y^2=32$ and $y=x+8$. $(-4, 4)$

Additional Answer

7. $(3, -2)$; 4

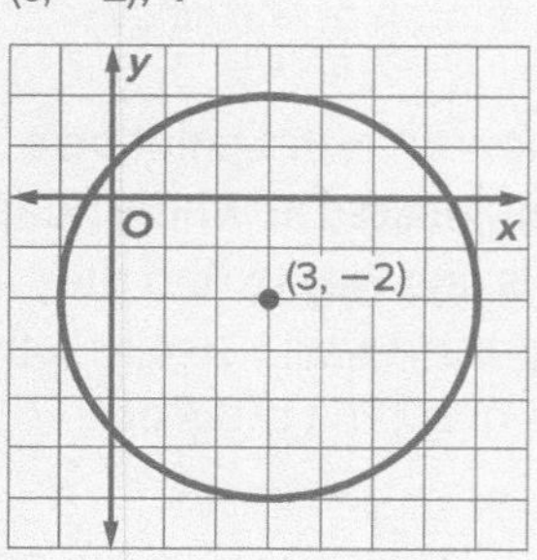

Real-World Link

About 1000 tornadoes are reported across the United States each year. The most violent tornadoes have wind speeds of 250 mph or more. Damage paths can be a mile wide and 50 miles long.

Source: National Oceanic & Atmospheric Administration

G.GPE.1

Real-World Example 4 Use Three Points to Write an Equation

TORNADOES Three tornado sirens are placed strategically on a circle around a town so they can be heard by all. Write the equation of the circle on which they are placed if the coordinates of the sirens are $A(-8, 3)$, $B(-4, 7)$, and $C(-4, -1)$.

Understand You are given three points that lie on a circle.

Plan Graph $\triangle ABC$. Construct the perpendicular bisectors of two sides to locate the center of the circle. Then find the radius.

Use the center and radius to write an equation.

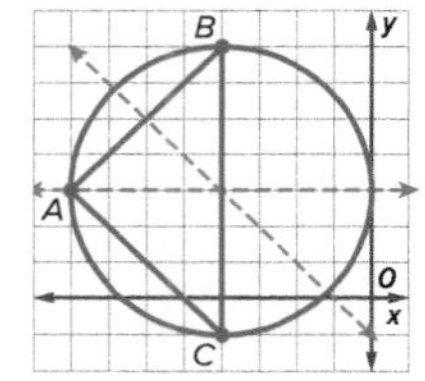

Solve The center appears to be at $(-4, 3)$. The radius is 4. Write an equation.

$$(x-h)^2+(y-k)^2=r^2$$
$$[x-(-4)]^2+(y-3)^2=4^2$$
$$(x+4)^2+(y-3)^2=16$$

Check Verify the center by finding the equations of the two bisectors and solving the system of equations. Verify the radius by finding the distance between the center and another point on the circle. ✓

Analyze the graph to find the relationship between the radius and center of the circle and the given information.

Guided Practice $(x+2)^2+(y-1)^2=10$

4. Write an equation of a circle that contains $R(1, 2)$, $S(-3, 4)$, and $T(-5, 0)$.

A line can intersect a circle in at most two points.

G.GPE.4

Example 5 Intersections with Circles

Find the point(s) of intersection between $x^2+y^2=4$ and $y=x$.

Graph these equations on the same coordinate plane. The points of intersection are solutions of both equations. You can estimate these points on the graph to be at about $(-1.4, -1.4)$ and $(1.4, 1.4)$. Use substitution to find the coordinates of these points algebraically.

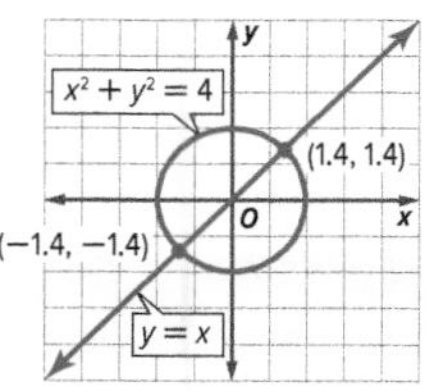

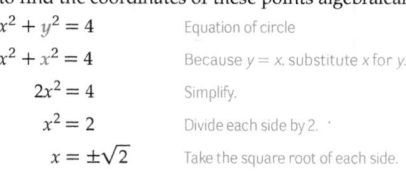

$x^2+y^2=4$	Equation of circle
$x^2+x^2=4$	Because $y=x$, substitute x for y.
$2x^2=4$	Simplify.
$x^2=2$	Divide each side by 2.
$x=\pm\sqrt{2}$	Take the square root of each side.

Study Tip

MP Sense-Making In addition to taking square roots, other quadratic techniques that you may need to apply in order to solve equations of the form $ax^2+bx+c=0$ include completing the square, factoring, and the Quadratic Formula, $x=\frac{-b\pm\sqrt{b^2-4ac}}{2a}$.

So $x=\sqrt{2}$ or $x=-\sqrt{2}$. Use the equation $y=x$ to find the corresponding y values.

$y=x$	Equation of line	$y=x$
$y=\sqrt{2}$	$x=\sqrt{2}$ or $x=-\sqrt{2}$	$y=-\sqrt{2}$

The points of intersection are located at $(\sqrt{2}, \sqrt{2})$ and $(-\sqrt{2}, -\sqrt{2})$ or at about $(-1.4, -1.4)$ and $(1.4, 1.4)$. Check these solutions in both of the original equations.

Guided Practice $(-2, 2)$ and $(2, -2)$

5. Find the point(s) of intersection between $x^2+y^2=8$ and $y=-x$.

Differentiated Instruction OL BL

Logical Learners Explain that students will rely heavily on their geometric knowledge and reasoning skills to solve the problems in this lesson. Allow students to explain how to explore and collaborate as they work through examples and exercises. Students need to recall definitions, concepts, and theorems to help explain why they use certain methods to solve problems.

Check Your Understanding

◯ = Step-by-Step Solutions begin on page R14.

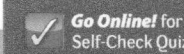

Go Online! for a Self-Check Quiz

Examples 1–2 G.GPE.1 **Write the equation of each circle.**

1. center at (9, 0), radius 5
2. center at (3, 1), diameter 14
3. center at origin, passes through (2, 2)
4. center at (−5, 3), passes through (1, −4)

5. 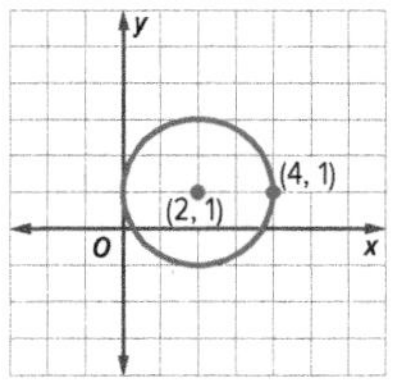

6. 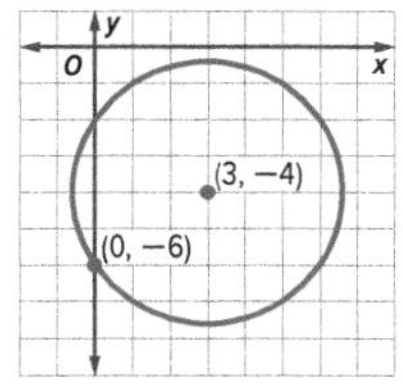

1. $(x-9)^2+y^2=25$
2. $(x-3)^2+(y-1)^2=49$
3. $x^2+y^2=8$
4. $(x+5)^2+(y-3)^2=85$
5. $(x-2)^2+(y-1)^2=4$
6. $(x-3)^2+(y+4)^2=13$

Example 3 G.GPE.1 **For each circle with the given equation, state the coordinates of the center and the measure of the radius. Then graph the equation.** 7, 8. See margin.

7. $x^2-6x+y^2+4y=3$
8. $x^2+(y+1)^2=4$

Example 4 G.GPE.1

9. RADIOS Three radio towers are modeled by the points $R(4, 5)$, $S(8, 1)$, and $T(-4, 1)$. Determine the location of another tower equidistant from all three towers, and write an equation for the circle. (2, −1); $(x-2)^2+(y+1)^2=40$

10. COMMUNICATION Three cell phone towers can be modeled by the points $X(6, 0)$, $Y(8, 4)$, and $Z(3, 9)$. Determine the location of another cell phone tower equidistant from the other three, and write an equation for the circle. (3, 4); $(x-3)^2+(y-4)^2=25$

Example 5 G.GPE.4 **Find the point(s) of intersection, if any, between each circle and line with the equations given.**

11. $(x-1)^2+y^2=4$ (1, 2), (−1, 0)
$y=x+1$

12. $(x-2)^2+(y+3)^2=18$ $(-1, 0), \left(2\frac{3}{5}, -7\frac{1}{5}\right)$
$y=-2x-2$

Practice and Problem Solving

Extra Practice is on page R9.

Examples 1–2 G.GPE.1 MP STRUCTURE **Write the equation of each circle.**

13. center at origin, radius 4
14. center at (6, 1), radius 7
15. center at (−2, 0), diameter 16
16. center at (8, −9), radius $\sqrt{11}$
17. center at (−3, 6), passes through (0, 6)
18. center at (1, −2), passes through (3, −4)

19. 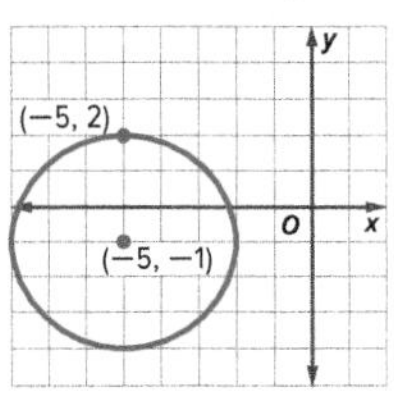

20. 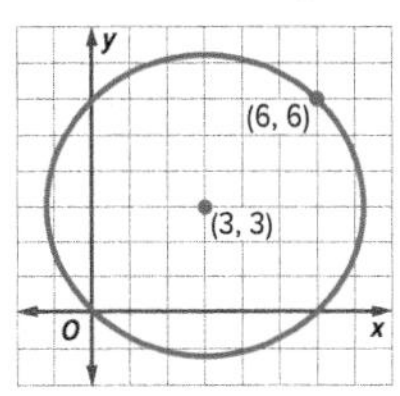

13. $x^2+y^2=16$
14. $(x-6)^2+(y-1)^2=49$
15. $(x+2)^2+y^2=64$
16. $(x-8)^2+(y+9)^2=11$
17. $(x+3)^2+(y-6)^2=9$
18. $(x-1)^2+(y+2)^2=8$
19. $(x+5)^2+(y+1)^2=9$
20. $(x-3)^2+(y-3)^2=18$

21. WEATHER A Doppler radar screen shows concentric rings around a storm. If the center of the radar screen is the origin and each ring is 15 miles farther from the center, what is the equation of the third ring? $x^2+y^2=2025$

22. GARDENING A sprinkler waters a circular area that has a diameter of 10 feet. The sprinkler is located 20 feet north of the house. If the house is located at the origin, what is the equation for the circle of area that is watered? $x^2+(y-20)^2=25$

Differentiated Homework Options

Levels	AL Basic	OL Core	BL Advanced
Exercises	13–34, 47–49, 52–56	13–37 odd, 38–43, 45, 47–49, 52–56	40–52, (optional: 53–56)
2-Day Option	13–33 odd, 53–56	13–34	
	14–34 even, 47–49, 52	35–45, 47–49, 52–56	

You can use ALEKS to provide additional remediation support with personalized instruction and practice.

Practice

Formative Assessment Use Exercises 1–12 to assess students' understanding of the concepts in this lesson.

The Practice and Problem Solving exercises assess the content taught in the lesson. The Preparing for Assessment page is meant to be used as preparation for end-of-course assessments.

Extra Practice

See page R9 for extra exercises for students who are approaching level or for on-level students who need additional reinforcement.

MP Teaching the Mathematical Practices

Structure Mathematically proficient students look closely to discern a pattern or structure. They also can step back for an overview and shift perspective. In Exercises 13–20, encourage students to identify *h*, *k*, and *r*.

Levels of Complexity Chart

The levels of the exercises progress from 1 to 3, with Level 1 indicating the lowest level of complexity.

Exercises	13–34	35–39, 53–56	40–52
Level 3			●
Level 2		●	
Level 1	●		

Additional Answer

8. (0, −1); 2

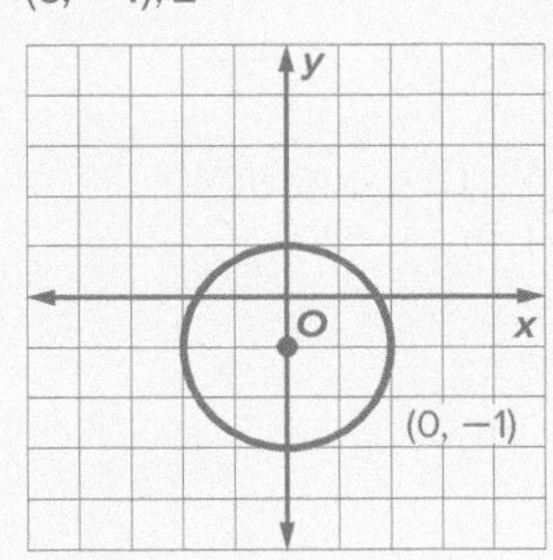

Go Online! eBook

Interactive Student Guide

Use the *Interactive Student Guide* to deepen conceptual understanding.

· Equations of Circles

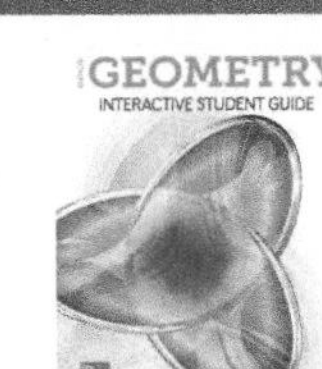

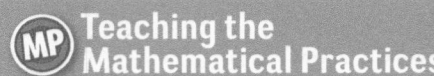

Teaching the Mathematical Practices

Modeling Mathematically proficient students can apply the mathematics they know to solve problems arising in everyday life. In Exercise 37, encourage students to interpret their results in the context of the situation.

Exercise Alert

Graph Paper Exercises 23–28, 39, 40, 42, and 48 require the use of graph paper.

Additional Answers

23. (0, 0); 6

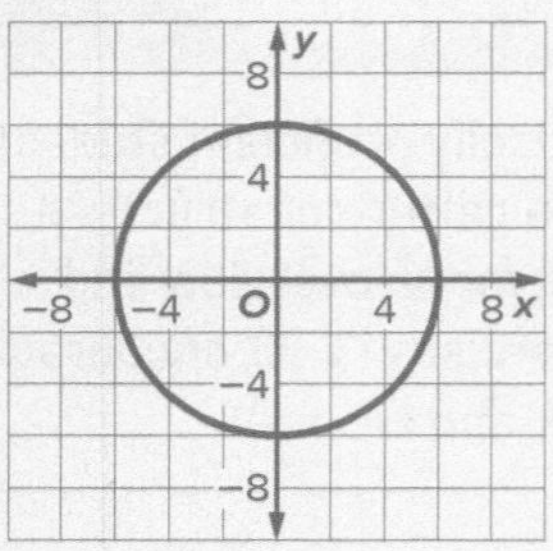

24. (2, 1); 2

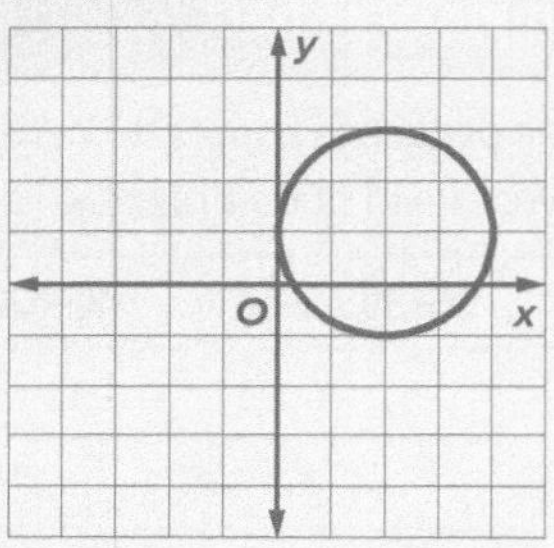

25. (−4, 2); 4

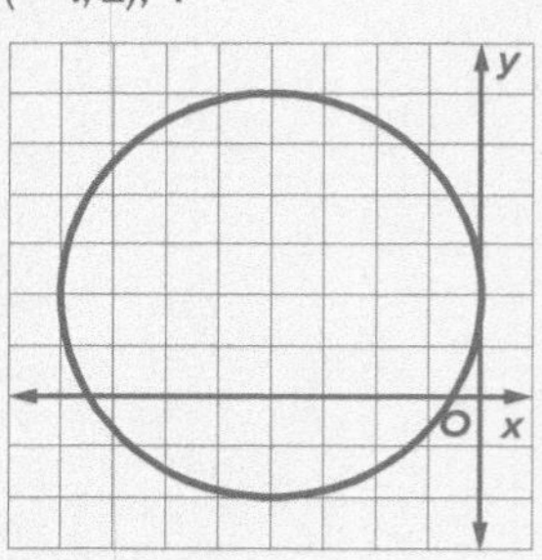

26. (8, 0); 8

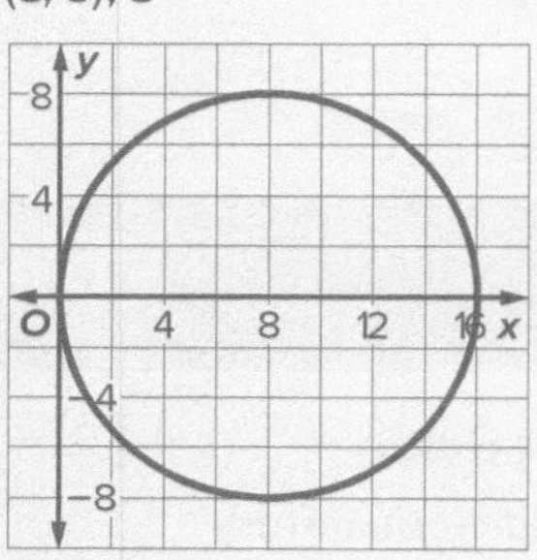

32. $\left(-1\frac{3}{5}, 4\frac{4}{5}\right)$, (1, −3)

33. $\left(\frac{\sqrt{2}}{2}, \frac{3\sqrt{2}}{2}\right), \left(-\frac{\sqrt{2}}{2}, -\frac{3\sqrt{2}}{2}\right)$

Example 3 G.GPE.1 **For each circle with the given equation, state the coordinates of the center and the measure of the radius. Then graph the equation.** 23–26. See margin.

23. $x^2 + y^2 = 36$

24. $x^2 + y^2 - 4x - 2y = -1$

25. $x^2 + y^2 + 8x - 4y = -4$

26. $x^2 + y^2 - 16x = 0$

Example 4 G.GPE.1 **Write an equation of a circle that contains each set of points. Then graph the circle.**

27. $A(1, 6)$, $B(5, 6)$, $C(5, 0)$ See margin.

28. $F(3, -3)$, $G(3, 1)$, $H(7, 1)$ See margin.

Example 5 G.GPE.4 **Find the point(s) of intersection, if any, between each circle and line with the equations given.**

29. $x^2 + y^2 = 5$, $y = \frac{1}{2}x$ (−2, −1), (2, 1)

30. $x^2 + y^2 = 2$, $y = -x + 2$ (1, 1)

31. $x^2 + (y + 2)^2 = 8$, $y = x - 2$ (−2, −4), (2, 0)

32. $(x + 3)^2 + y^2 = 25$, $y = -3x$ See margin.

33. $x^2 + y^2 = 5$, $y = 3x$ See margin.

34. $(x - 1)^2 + (y - 3)^2 = 4$, $y = -x$ no points of intersection

B **Write the equation of each circle.** 36. $(x + 13)^2 + (y - 6)^2 = 121$

35. a circle with a diameter having endpoints at (0, 4) and (6, −4) $(x - 3)^2 + y^2 = 25$

36. a circle with $d = 22$ and a center translated 13 units left and 6 units up from the origin

37. MP **MODELING** The higher a model rocket travels after it is launched, the larger the circle of possible landing sites becomes. Under normal wind conditions, the landing radius is three times the altitude of the rocket.

a. Write the equation of the landing circle for a rocket that travels 300 feet in the air. Assume the center of the circle is at the origin. $x^2 + y^2 = 810{,}000$

b. What would be the radius of the landing circle for a rocket that travels 1000 feet in the air? Assume the center of the circle is at the origin. 3000 ft

38. **SKYDIVING** Three of the skydivers in the circular formation shown have approximate coordinates of $G(13, -2)$, $H(-1, -2)$, and $J(6, -9)$.

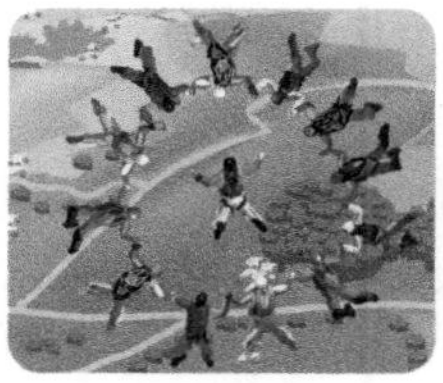

a. What are the approximate coordinates of the center skydiver? (6, −2)

b. If each unit represents 1 foot, what is the diameter of the skydiving formation? 14 ft

39. **MULTI-STEP** Consuela's favorite pizza place offers free delivery within a certain radius of the restaurant. The pizza place is 4 miles west and 5 miles north of Consuela's house. Her house is at the edge of their free-delivery radius.

a. Consuela rode her bike 1 mile south and 1 mile west to her friend's house. If they order pizza, will they get free delivery?

b. Describe your solution process. See Ch. 9 Answer Appendix.

39a. No, her friend's house is outside the free delivery area.

C **40.** **INTERSECTIONS OF CIRCLES** Graph $x^2 + y^2 = 4$ and $(x - 2)^2 + y^2 = 4$ on the same coordinate plane. e. $(1, \sqrt{3})$, $(1, -\sqrt{3})$; The coordinates are approximately the same.

a. Estimate the point(s) of intersection between the two circles. ≈(1, 1.7) and (1, −1.7)

b. Solve $x^2 + y^2 = 4$ for y. $y = \pm\sqrt{4 - x^2}$

c. Substitute the value you found in part **b** into $(x - 2)^2 + y^2 = 4$ and solve for x. $x = 1$

d. Substitute the value you found in part **c** into $x^2 + y^2 = 4$ and solve for y. $y = \pm\sqrt{3}$

e. Use your answers to parts **c** and **d** to write the coordinates of the points of intersection. Compare these coordinates to your estimate from part **a**.

f. Verify that the point(s) you found in part **d** lie on both circles. See margin.

27. $(x - 3)^2 + (y - 3)^2 = 13$

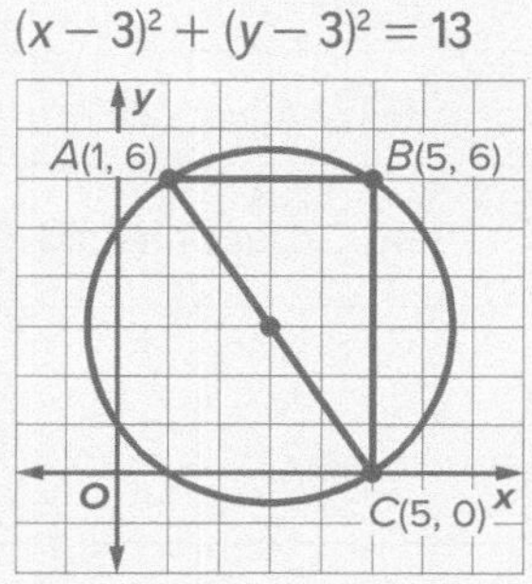

28. $(x - 5)^2 + (y + 1)^2 = 8$

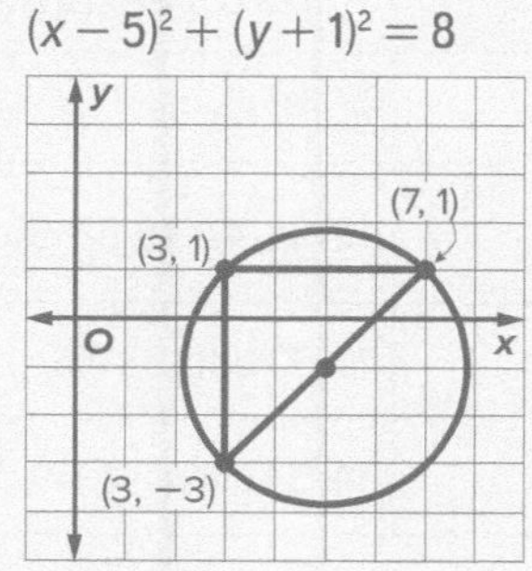

40f. Verify $(1, \sqrt{3})$.

$1^2 + (\sqrt{3})^2 = 4$

$1 + 3 = 4$ ✓

$(1 - 2)^2 + (\sqrt{3})^2 = 4$

$(-1)^2 + 3 = 4$

$1 + 3 = 4$ ✓

Verify $(1, -\sqrt{3})$.

$1^2 + (-\sqrt{3})^2 = 4$

$1 + 3 = 4$ ✓

$(1 - 2)^2 + (-\sqrt{3})^2 = 4$

$(-1)^2 + 3 = 4$

$1 + 3 = 4$ ✓

41 Prove or disprove that the point $(1, 2\sqrt{2})$ lies on a circle centered at the origin and containing the point $(0, -3)$. See margin.

42. MULTIPLE REPRESENTATIONS A **compound locus** satisfies more than one distinct set of conditions. Consider the points *A* and *B* in the coordinate plane. a,b. See margin.

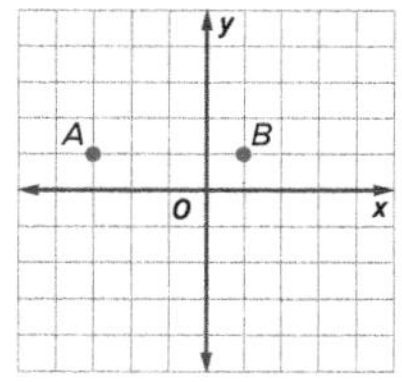

a. Determine and graph the locus of points equidistant from *A* and *B*.

b. Determine and graph the locus of all points in a plane that are a distance *AB* from *B*.

c. Describe the locus of all points in a plane equidistant from a single point. Then describe the locus of all points that are both equidistant from *A* and *B* and are a distance of *AB* from *B*. Describe the graph of the compound locus. See Ch. 9 Answer Appendix.

Write an equation for each graph described. Then determine whether each point lies *on*, *inside*, or *outside* the circle.

43. a circle with center at the origin and radius 4 units $x^2 + y^2 = 16$

a. (4, 4) outside **b.** $(3, \sqrt{7})$ on **c.** $(2, \sqrt{5})$ inside **d.** $(2\sqrt{3}, -2)$ on

44. a circle with center at (2, 4) and radius 3 units $(x - 2)^2 + (y - 4)^2 = 9$

a. (2, 1) on **b.** (0, 4) inside **c.** (2, 7) on **d.** (3, 1) outside

45. A circle with a diameter of 12 has its center in the second quadrant. The lines $y = -4$ and $x = 1$ are tangent to the circle. Write an equation of the circle. $(x + 5)^2 + (y - 2)^2 = 36$

G.GPE.1, G.GPE.4

H.O.T. Problems Use Higher-Order Thinking Skills

46. CHALLENGE Write a coordinate proof to show that if an inscribed angle intercepts the diameter of a circle, as shown, the angle is a right angle. See Ch. 9 Answer Appendix.

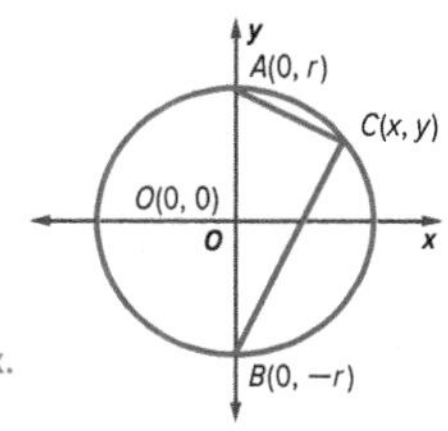

47. MP REASONING A circle has the equation $(x - 5)^2 + (y + 7)^2 = 16$. If the center of the circle is shifted 3 units right and 9 units up, what would be the equation of the new circle? Explain your reasoning. See Ch. 9 Answer Appendix.

48. OPEN-ENDED Graph three noncollinear points and connect them to form a triangle. Then construct the circle that circumscribes it. See Ch. 9 Answer Appendix.

49. WRITING IN MATH Seven new radio stations must be assigned broadcast frequencies. The stations are located at *A*(9, 2), *B*(8, 4), *C*(8, 1), *D*(6, 3), *E*(4, 0), *F*(3, 6), and *G*(4, 5), where 1 unit = 50 miles.

a. If stations that are more than 200 miles apart can share the same frequency, what is the least number of frequencies that can be assigned to these stations?

b. Describe two different beginning approaches to solving this problem.

c. Choose an approach, solve the problem, and explain your reasoning.

49. a–c. See Ch. 9 Answer Appendix.

CHALLENGE **Find the coordinates of point *P* on $\overrightarrow{AB}$ that partitions the segment into the given ratio *AP* to *PB*.**

50. *A*(0, 0), *B*(3, 4), 2 to 3 (1.2, 1.6)

51. *A*(0, 0), *B*(−8, 6), 4 to 1 (−6.4, 4.8)

52. WRITING IN MATH Describe the relationship between the Distance Formula, the equation of a circle centered at the origin, and the equation of a circle centered at a point not on the origin. See Ch. 9 Answer Appendix.

MP Standards for Mathematical Practice

Emphasis On	Exercises
1 Make sense of problems and persevere in solving them.	9–11, 21, 22, 37–40
3 Construct viable arguments and critique the reasoning of others.	41, 42, 46–52
4 Model with mathematics.	1–8, 13–20, 43–45

MP Teaching the Mathematical Practices

Reasoning Mathematically proficient students make sense of quantities and their relationships in problem situations. They abstract a situation and represent it symbolically. In Exercise 47, point out to students that the circle is translated so the radius is not changing.

Exercise Alert

Compass and Ruler Exercise 42 requires the use of a compass and a ruler.

Assess

Name the Math Let students take turns saying an equation of a circle. Then they should name the centers of the circles, and state the lengths of the radii.

Additional Answers

41. The equation of a circle centered at the origin and containing the point (0, −3) is $x^2 + y^2 = 9$. The point $(1, 2\sqrt{2})$ lies on the circle, since evaluating $x^2 + y^2 = 9$ for $x = 1$ and $y = 2\sqrt{2}$ results in a true equation.

$1^2 + (2\sqrt{2})^2 = 9$

$1 + 8 = 9$

$9 = 9$ ✓

42a.

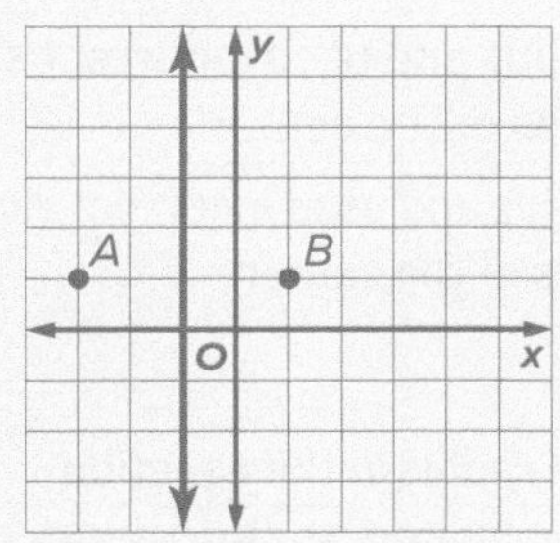

42b.

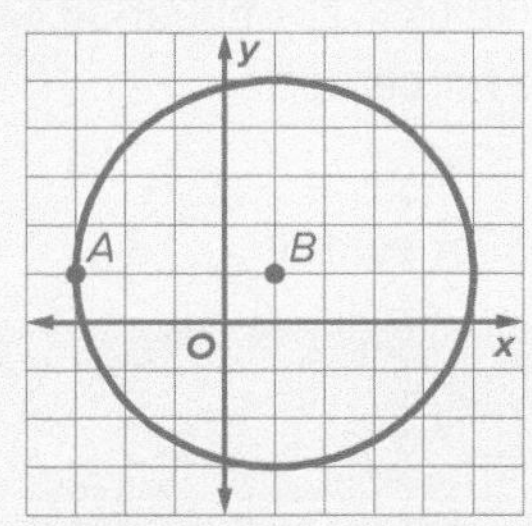

Go Online!

eSolutions Manual

Create worksheets, answer keys, and solutions handouts for your assignments.

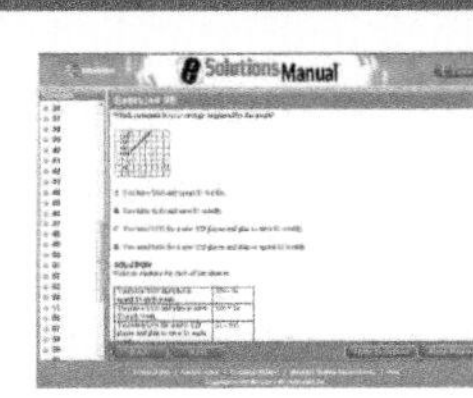

Preparing for Assessment

Exercises 53–56 require students to use the skills they will need on standardized assessments. Exercises are dual-coded with content standards and mathematical practice standards.

Dual Coding		
Exercises	Content Standards	MP Mathematical Practices
53	G.GPE.1, G.GPE.4	3
54	G.GPE.1, G.GPE.4	7
55	G.GPE.1, G.GPE.4	4
56	G.GPE.1, G.GPE.4	1, 4, 7

Diagnose Student Errors

Survey student responses for each item. Class trends may indicate common errors and misconceptions.

53.

A	CORRECT
B	Forgot that the radius is squared in the equation
C	Used incorrect signs for the center
D	Forgot that the radius is squared in the equation and used incorrect signs for the center

54.

A	Used r^2 as the radius
B	Used incorrect signs for the coordinates of the center
C	CORRECT
D	Used r^2 as the radius and used incorrect signs for the coordinates of the center
E	Used r^2 as the radius and used incorrect signs for the coordinates of the center

55.

A	Did not square the radius in the equation
B	Did not square the radius in the equation and used incorrect signs for center
C	CORRECT
D	Used incorrect signs for center

Go Online!

Quizzes
Students can use *Self-Check Quizzes* to check their understanding of this lesson and have the results sent to you. You can also give *Quiz 4*, which covers the content in Lessons 9-7 and 9-8.

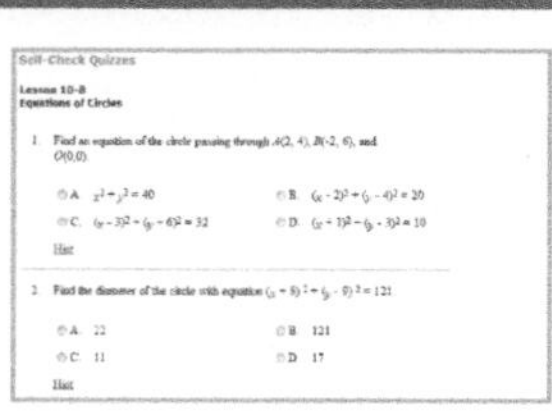

Preparing for Assessment

53. Ethan wrote the equation $(x + 1)^2 + (y + 2)^2 = 4$ for the circle shown in the figure.
MP 3 G.GPE.1, G.GPE.4 **A**

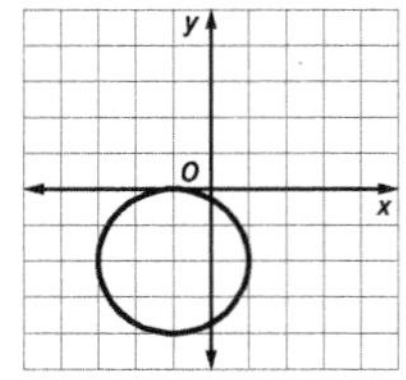

Which of the following is the best description of the equation Ethan wrote?

- ○ **A** His equation is correct.
- ○ **B** His equation shows an incorrect radius.
- ○ **C** His equation shows an incorrect center.
- ○ **D** His equation shows an incorrect radius and center.

54. The equation of a circle is $x^2 + y^2 + 4x - 8y = -16$. Which of the following is a true statement about the circle? MP 7 G.GPE.1, G.GPE.4 **C**

I. The radius of the circle is 4.
II. The center of the circle is (2, −4).
III. The circle passes through (0, 4).

- ○ **A** I only
- ○ **B** II only
- ○ **C** III only
- ○ **D** I and II only
- ○ **E** I, II, and III

55. What is the equation of the circle that passes through (0, −2), (8, −2), and (4, −6)?
MP 4 G.GPE.1, G.GPE.4 **C**

- ○ **A** $(x - 4)^2 + (y + 2)^2 = 4$
- ○ **B** $(x + 4)^2 + (y - 2)^2 = 4$
- ○ **C** $(x - 4)^2 + (y + 2)^2 = 16$
- ○ **D** $(x + 4)^2 + (y - 2)^2 = 16$

56. **MULTI-STEP** Samantha is using a coordinate plane to design a video game. In the game, a character travels in a circle to pick up coins. Samantha places coins at $P(1, 2)$, $Q(4, -1)$, and $R(1, -4)$. Now she needs to determine the equation of a circle through those three points. MP 1, 4, 7 G.GPE.1, G.GPE.4

a. What two pieces of information does Samantha need in order to write the equation of a circle? **C, D**

- ☐ **A** two points on the circle
- ☐ **B** the tangent equation
- ☐ **C** the center
- ☐ **D** the radius
- ☐ **E** a point in the interior of the circle
- ☐ **F** a point exterior to the circle

b. Describe a set of steps Samantha can take to find the equation of a circle through the points. Use a graph to support your description. **See margin**

c. What are the coordinates of the center of the circle? **B**

- ○ **A** (0, 1)
- ○ **B** (1, −1)
- ○ **C** (−1, 0)
- ○ **D** (−1, −1)

d. What is the radius of the circle? **C**

- ○ **A** −1
- ○ **B** 1
- ○ **C** 3
- ○ **D** 9

e. What is the equation of the circle? **D**

- ○ **A** $(x - 1)^2 - (y + 1)^2 = 9$
- ○ **B** $(x - 1)^2 - (y)^2 = 9$
- ○ **C** $(x - 1)^2 + (y)^2 = 9$
- ○ **D** $(x - 1)^2 + (y + 1)^2 = 9$

Differentiated Instruction OL BL

Extension What is the relationship between concentric circles with the same radius? Explain. They are the same circle. A center and a radius are all it takes to define a circle. Two circles that share a center and have the same radius are identical.

56 b.

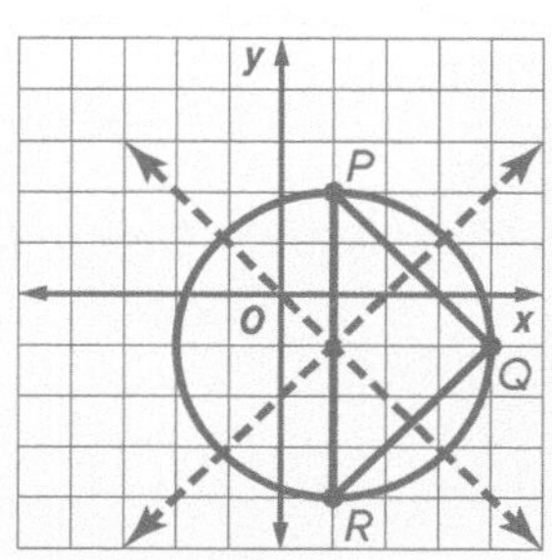

Draw △*PQR* and construct the perpendicular bisectors of *PQ* and *QR*. The perpendicular bisectors intersect at (1, −1), so this is the center of the circle. The distance from each coin to the circle is 3 units, so the radius of the circle is 3 units.

LESSON 9-8

Equations of Parabolas

SUGGESTED PACING (DAYS)

	Instruction
90 min.	0.5
45 min.	1.0

Track Your Progress

Objectives

1 Write the equation of a parabola.

2 Graph parabolas on the coordinate plane.

Mathematical Background

Geometrically, a parabola is the locus of points that are equidistant from a fixed point called the *focus* and a fixed line called the *directrix*. You can use this definition and the Distance Formula to derive the equation of a parabola in the coordinate plane. The equation is the result of setting the distance from a point to the focus equal to the distance from the point to the directrix.

THEN

G.GPE.1 Write the equation of a circle. Prove that all circles are similar.

G.GPE.4 Use coordinates to prove simple geometric theorems algebraically.

NOW

G.GPE.2 Derive the equation of a parabola given a focus and directrix.

NEXT

G.C.5 Find arc lengths and areas of sectors of circles. Derive using similarity the fact that the length of the arc intercepted by an angle is proportional to the radius, and define the radian measure of the angle as the constant of proportionality; derive the formula for the area of a sector.

G.GMD.1 Explain volume formulas and use them to solve problems. Give an informal argument for the formulas for circumference of a circle, area of a circle, volume of a cylinder, and cone.

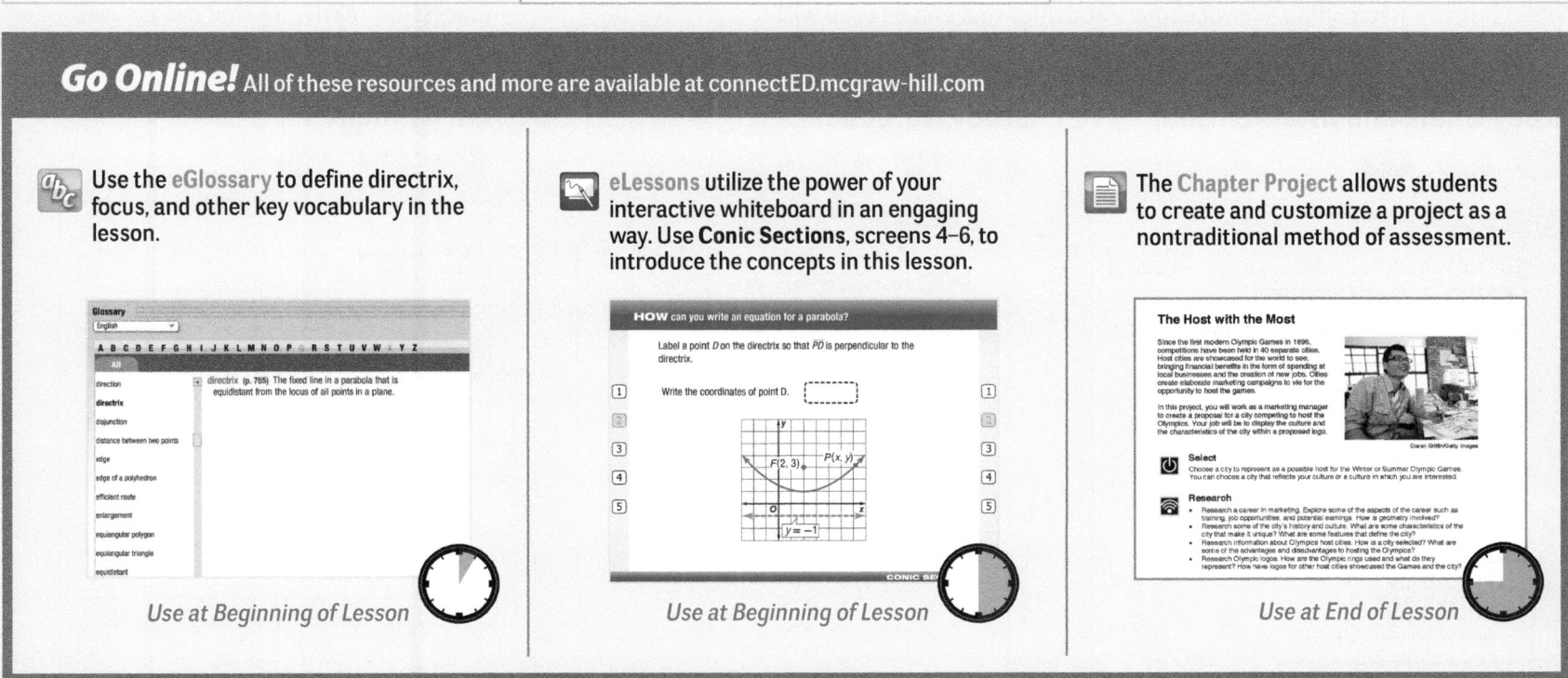

Go Online! All of these resources and more are available at connectED.mcgraw-hill.com

Use the eGlossary to define directrix, focus, and other key vocabulary in the lesson.

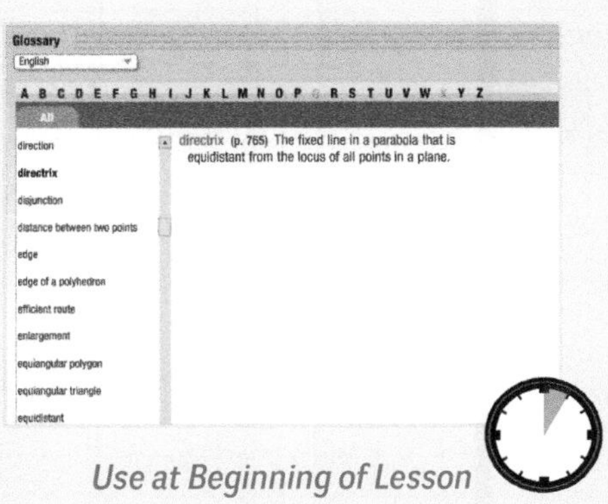

Use at Beginning of Lesson

eLessons utilize the power of your interactive whiteboard in an engaging way. Use **Conic Sections**, screens 4–6, to introduce the concepts in this lesson.

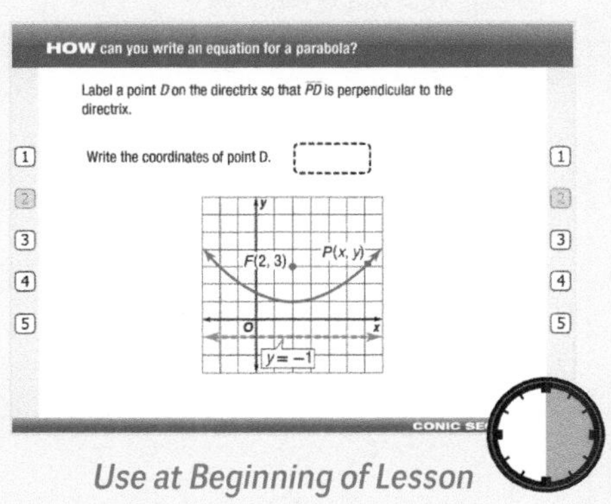

Use at Beginning of Lesson

The Chapter Project allows students to create and customize a project as a nontraditional method of assessment.

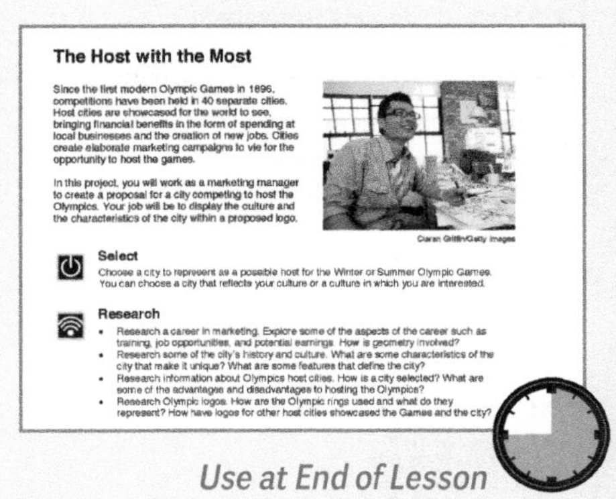

Use at End of Lesson

OER Using Open Educational Resources

Practice Have students review their work on **webmath.com** at **Discovery Education**. They can graph parabolas given their equations. If they make a mistake on a quiz or test they can use this site to see where they went wrong. *Use as homework*

Go Online!
connectED.mcgraw-hill.com

Worksheets

Differentiate Your Resources

Extra Practice Additional practice or homework; Skills Practice is best for approaching-level students and Practice is best for on-level and beyond-level students

Skills Practice

AL OL ELL

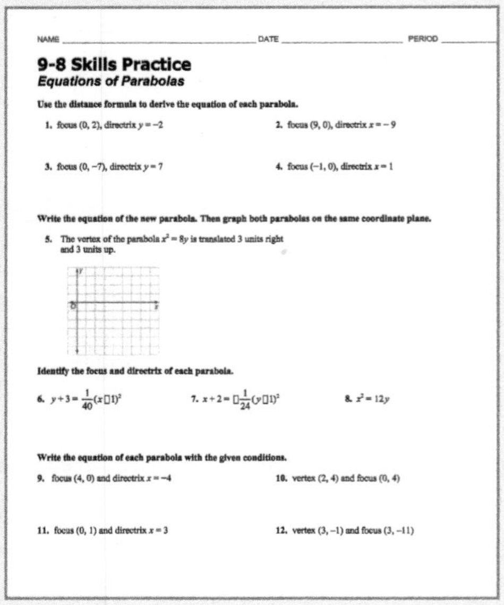
NAME ______ DATE ______ PERIOD ______

9-8 Skills Practice
Equations of Parabolas

Use the distance formula to derive the equation of each parabola.

1. focus (0, 2), directrix $y = -2$
2. focus (9, 0), directrix $x = -9$
3. focus (0, −7), directrix $y = 7$
4. focus (−1, 0), directrix $x = 1$

Write the equation of the new parabola. Then graph both parabolas on the same coordinate plane.

5. The vertex of the parabola $x^2 = 8y$ is translated 3 units right and 3 units up.

Identify the focus and directrix of each parabola.

8. $x^2 = 12y$

Write the equation of each parabola with the given conditions.

9. focus (4, 0) and directrix $x = -4$
10. vertex (2, 4) and focus (0, 4)
11. focus (0, 1) and directrix $x = 3$
12. vertex (3, −1) and focus (3, −11)

Practice

AL OL BL ELL

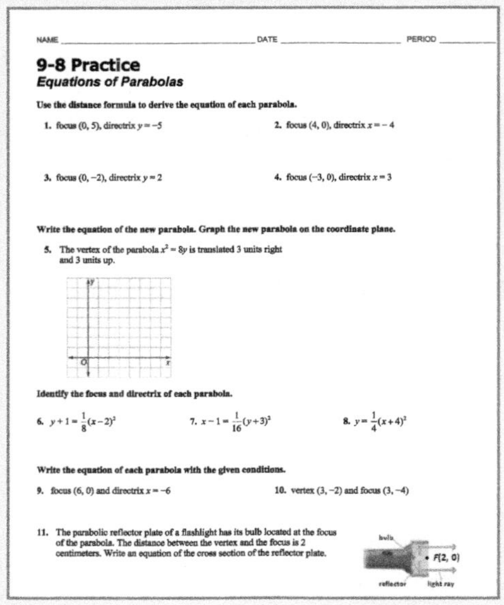
NAME ______ DATE ______ PERIOD ______

9-8 Practice
Equations of Parabolas

Use the distance formula to derive the equation of each parabola.

1. focus (0, 5), directrix $y = -5$
2. focus (4, 0), directrix $x = -4$
3. focus (0, −2), directrix $y = 2$
4. focus (−3, 0), directrix $x = 3$

Write the equation of the new parabola. Graph the new parabola on the coordinate plane.

5. The vertex of the parabola $x^2 = 8y$ is translated 3 units right and 3 units up.

Identify the focus and directrix of each parabola.

6. $y + 1 = \frac{1}{8}(x - 2)^2$
7. $x - 1 = \frac{1}{16}(y + 3)^2$
8. $y = \frac{1}{4}(x + 4)^2$

Write the equation of each parabola with the given conditions.

9. focus (6, 0) and directrix $x = -6$
10. vertex (3, −2) and focus (3, −4)
11. The parabolic reflector plate of a flashlight has its bulb located at the focus of the parabola. The distance between the vertex and the focus is 2 centimeters. Write an equation of the cross section of the reflector plate.

Word Problem Practice

AL OL BL ELL

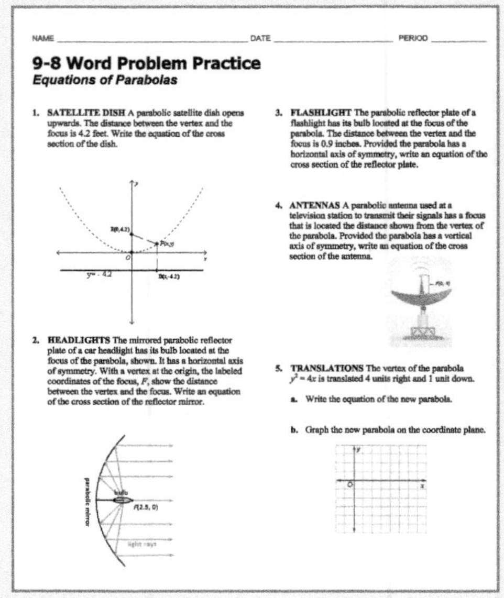
NAME ______ DATE ______ PERIOD ______

9-8 Word Problem Practice
Equations of Parabolas

1. **SATELLITE DISH** A parabolic satellite dish opens upwards. The distance between the vertex and the focus is 4.2 feet. Write the equation of the cross section of the dish.
2. **HEADLIGHTS** The mirrored parabolic reflector plate of a car headlight has its bulb located at the focus of the parabola, shown. It has a horizontal axis of symmetry. With a vertex at the origin, the labeled coordinates of the focus, F, show the distance between the vertex and the focus. Write an equation of the cross section of the reflector mirror.
3. **FLASHLIGHT** The parabolic reflector plate of a flashlight has its bulb located at the focus of the parabola. The distance between the vertex and the focus is 0.9 inches. Provided the parabola has a horizontal axis of symmetry, write an equation of the cross section of the reflector plate.
4. **ANTENNAS** A parabolic antenna used at a television station to transmit their signals has a focus that is located the distance shown from the vertex of the parabola. Provided the parabola has a vertical axis of symmetry, write an equation of the cross section of the antenna.
5. **TRANSLATIONS** The vertex of the parabola $y^2 = 4x$ is translated 4 units right and 1 unit down.
   a. Write the equation of the new parabola.
   b. Graph the new parabola on the coordinate plane.

Intervention Reteaching and vocabulary activities that can be used with struggling or absent students and as ELL support

Study Guide and Intervention

AL OL ELL

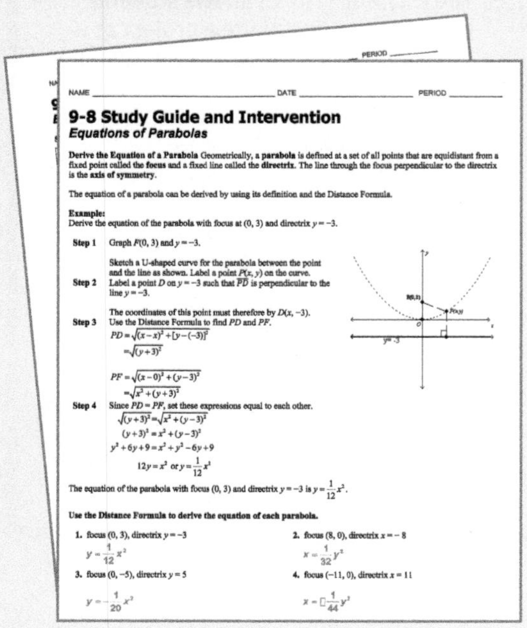
NAME ______ DATE ______ PERIOD ______

9-8 Study Guide and Intervention
Equations of Parabolas

Derive the Equation of a Parabola Geometrically, a **parabola** is defined as a set of all points that are equidistant from a fixed point called the **focus** and a fixed line called the **directrix**. The line through the focus perpendicular to the directrix is the **axis of symmetry**.

The equation of a parabola can be derived by using its definition and the Distance Formula.

Example:
Derive the equation of the parabola with focus at (0, 3) and directrix $y = -3$.

Step 1 Graph $F(0, 3)$ and $y = -3$.

Sketch a U-shaped curve for the parabola between the point and the line as shown. Label a point $P(x, y)$ on the curve.

Step 2 Label a point D on $y = -3$ such that $\overline{PD}$ is perpendicular to the line $y = -3$.

The coordinates of this point must therefore by $D(x, -3)$.

Step 3 Use the Distance Formula to find PD and PF.

$PD = \sqrt{(x-x)^2 + [y-(-3)]^2} = \sqrt{(y+3)^2}$

$PF = \sqrt{(x-0)^2 + (y-3)^2} = \sqrt{x^2 + (y-3)^2}$

Step 4 Since $PD = PF$, set these expressions equal to each other.

$\sqrt{(y+3)^2} = \sqrt{x^2 + (y-3)^2}$

$(y+3)^2 = x^2 + (y-3)^2$

$y^2 + 6y + 9 = x^2 + y^2 - 6y + 9$

$12y = x^2$ or $y = \frac{1}{12}x^2$

The equation of the parabola with focus (0, 3) and directrix $y = -3$ is $y = \frac{1}{12}x^2$.

Use the Distance Formula to derive the equation of each parabola.

1. focus (0, 3), directrix $y = -3$
2. focus (8, 0), directrix $x = -8$
3. focus (0, −5), directrix $y = 5$
4. focus (−11, 0), directrix $x = 11$

Study Notebook

AL OL BL ELL

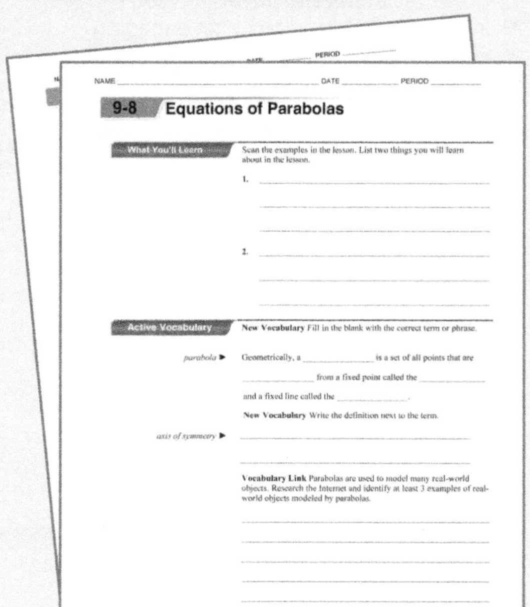
NAME ______ DATE ______ PERIOD ______

9-8 Equations of Parabolas

What You'll Learn Scan the examples in the lesson. List two things you will learn about in the lesson.

1.

2.

Active Vocabulary **New Vocabulary** Fill in the blank with the correct term or phrase.

parabola ► Geometrically, a ______ is a set of all points that are ______ from a fixed point called the ______ and a fixed line called the ______.

New Vocabulary Write the definition next to the term.

axis of symmetry ►

Vocabulary Link Parabolas are used to model many real-world objects. Research the Internet and identify at least 3 examples of real-world objects modeled by parabolas.

Extension Activities that can be used to extend lesson concepts

Enrichment

OL BL ELL

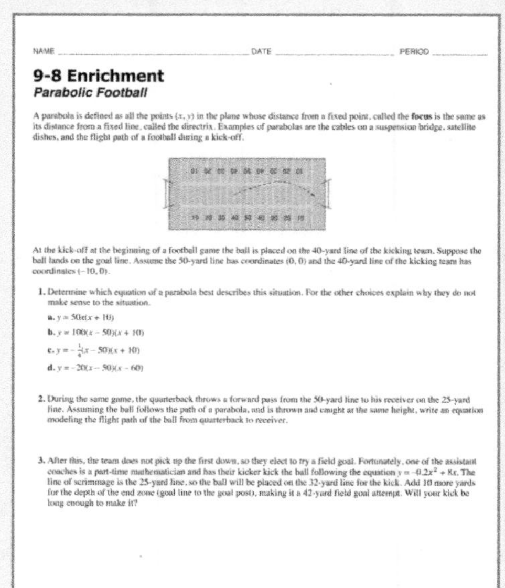
NAME ______ DATE ______ PERIOD ______

9-8 Enrichment
Parabolic Football

A parabola is defined as all the points (x, y) in the plane whose distance from a fixed point, called the **focus** is the same as its distance from a fixed line, called the directrix. Examples of parabolas are the cables on a suspension bridge, satellite dishes, and the flight path of a football during a kick-off.

At the kick-off at the beginning of a football game the ball is placed on the 40-yard line of the kicking team. Suppose the ball lands on the goal line. Assume the 50-yard line has coordinates (0, 0) and the 40-yard line of the kicking team has coordinates (−10, 0).

1. Determine which equation of a parabola best describes this situation. For the other choices explain why they do not make sense to the situation.
2. During the same game, the quarterback throws a forward pass from the 50-yard line to his receiver on the 25-yard line. Assuming the ball follows the path of a parabola, and is thrown and caught at the same height, write an equation modeling the flight path of the ball from quarterback to receiver.
3. After this, the team does not pick up the first down, so they elect to try a field goal. Fortunately, one of the assistant coaches is a part-time mathematician and has their kicker kick the ball following the equation $y = -0.2x^2 + 8x$. The line of scrimmage is the 25-yard line, so the ball will be placed on the 32-yard line for the kick. Add 10 more yards for the depth of the end zone (goal line to the goal post), making it a 42-yard field goal attempt. Will your kick be long enough to make it?

LESSON 8

Equations of Parabolas

:: Then	:: Now	:: Why?
• You found the equation of a circle by using the Distance Formula.	• **1** Write the equation of a parabola. **2** Graph parabolas on the coordinate plane.	• Parabolas are used to describe and model satellite dishes and parabolic telescopes. Incoming signals are concentrated at an antenna at the parabola's focus and then transmitted from there.

New Vocabulary
parabola
focus
directrix
axis of symmetry
vertex

Mathematical Practices
1 Make sense of problems and persevere in solving them.
2 Reason abstractly and quantitatively.
4 Model with mathematics.
7 Look for and make use of structure.

Content Standards
G.GPE.2 Derive the equation of a parabola given a focus and directrix.

1 Write Equations of Parabolas Geometrically, a **parabola** is a set of all points that are equidistant from a fixed point called the **focus** and a fixed line called the **directrix**. The line through the focus perpendicular to the directrix is the **axis of symmetry**. The point where the axis of symmetry intersects the parabola is the **vertex**.

Consider a parabola with focus $F(0, p)$ and directrix $y = -p$. The axis of symmetry is $x = 0$ and the vertex is (0, 0).

Let $P(x, y)$ be any point on the parabola. Recall that the distance between a point and a line is the length of the segment perpendicular to the line through the point. So the distance from (x, y) to the directrix is PD for $D(x, -p)$. By the definition of a parabola, the distance from P to the focus, PF, and the distance from P to the directrix, PD, are equal.

$$PF = PD$$
$$\sqrt{(x-0^2) + (y-p)^2} = \sqrt{(x-x)^2 + (y-(-p))^2}$$
$$\sqrt{x^2 + (y-p)^2} = \sqrt{(y+p)^2}$$
$$x^2 + (y-p)^2 = (y+p)^2$$
$$x^2 + y^2 - 2py + p^2 = y^2 + 2py + p^2$$
$$x^2 = 4yp$$

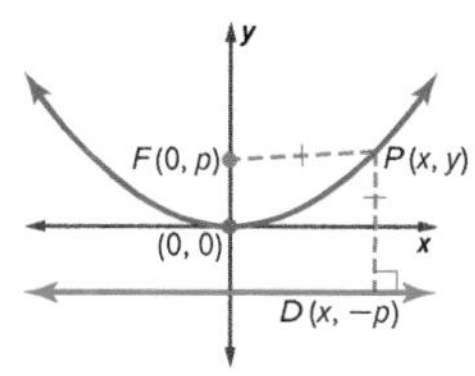

So, the equation of a parabola that has a vertical axis of symmetry is $x^2 = 4py$, or $\frac{1}{y = 4p}x^2$. Notice that when p is positive the parabola opens up. When p is negative, the parabola opens down.

The derivation of the equation of a parabola with a horizontal axis of symmetry is similar. Thus the equation of a parabola with vertex (0, 0) that has a horizontal axis of symmetry is $y^2 = 4px$. When p is positive the parabola opens right. When p is negative, the parabola opens left.

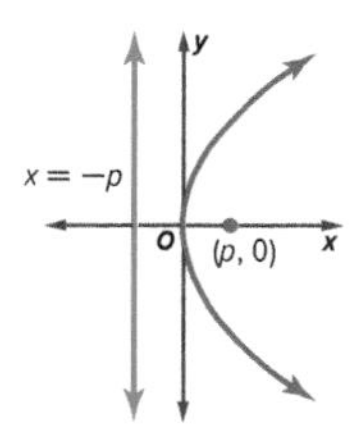

A parabola is translated in the plane in the same way as other geometric figures. Translating a parabola so that the vertex of the new parabola is (h, k) allows for standard forms of an equation of parabola with vertex at (h, k).

MP Mathematical Practices Strategies

Reason abstractly and quantitatively.
Help students understand relationships among the equations for parabolas. For example, ask:

- Which variable term is squared when the graph of a parabola opens up or down? the x-term
- Which variable term is squared when the graph of a parabola opens to the right or to the left? the y-term
- How can drawing a sketch of a parabola that includes key features like the vertex, focus, and directrix help you find the equation of the parabola? Sample answer: A sketch helps you visualize whether the parabola has a vertical or horizontal axis of symmetry, which in turn helps you focus on choosing the correct standard form of the equation.

Launch

Have students read the Why? section of the lesson. Ask:

- Where is the antenna of the satellite dish located in relationship to the parabola? It is located at the focus of the parabola.
- What does the length of the antenna represent? The length of the antenna is the distance from the vertex of the parabola (the base) to the tip of the antenna.
- Why might a wider satellite dish give a better signal? It can focus more rays of the signal.

Teach

Ask the scaffolded questions for each example to build conceptual understanding for students at all levels.

1 Write Equations of Parabolas

Example 1 Write the Equation of a Parabola

AL Will the graph of a parabola ever intersect its directrix? no

OL How are the directrix and axis of symmetry for a parabola related? the vertex and the axis of symmetry? The directrix is perpendicular to the axis of symmetry. The vertex is on the axis of symmetry.

BL How can the Distance Formula used to find the equation of a parabola? Because a parabola is defined as the set of points that are equidistant from a fixed point (the focus), and a fixed line (the directrix), the Distance Formula can be used to write an equation expressing the equal distances.

Go Online!

Interactive Whiteboard
Use the *eLesson*, *Lesson Presentation*, or *Interactive Classroom* to present this lesson.

Need Another Example?

Write an equation of each parabola.

a. focus (0, −4) and directrix $y = 4$ $x^2 = -16y$ or $y = -\frac{1}{16}x^2$

b. vertex (−2, 6), focus (−2, −2) $(x + 2)^2 = -32(y - 6)$

Example 2 Write an Equation of a Parabola

AL How do you know that the axis of symmetry is vertical? If the parabola opens upward or downward, the axis of symmetry is vertical.

OL Why choose (0, 0) as the vertex? This makes for the simplest equation.

BL If the satellite dish is rotated so that it opens to the right, how does this change the equation of the cross section? The x and y variables are exchanged.

Need Another Example?

A parabolic telescope mirror opening upward has a diameter of 1.5 meters. The distance between the vertex and the focus is 0.8 meter. Write the equation of a cross section of the mirror. $x^2 = 3.2y$

Teaching Tip

Have groups of students use paper folding to construct shapes to simulate satellite dishes with antennae as foci. Then have them find the equations for their shapes.

Essential Question

How do you find the equation of a parabola given the focus F and directrix? Choose a general point $P(x, y)$ on the parabola and locate a point D on the directrix such that the distance from D to P is equal to the distance from F to P. Then use the Distance Formula to solve the equation created by setting the two distances equal to each other.

Teaching Tip

Double-Napped Cone In later courses, students will learn that conic sections are figures formed when a plane intersects a double-napped cone. Using this definition, students will explore another conic section called the *hyperbola*, which is formed by the intersection of a double-napped cone and a plane that is parallel to the axis of the cone.

Key Concept Standard Form of Equations of Parabolas

Equation: $(x - h)^2 = 4p(y - k)$ — Axis of Symmetry: vertical, $x = h$

Focus: $(h, k + p)$ — Vertex: (h, k)

Directrix: $y = k - p$ — Opens: up if $p > 0$, down if $p < 0$

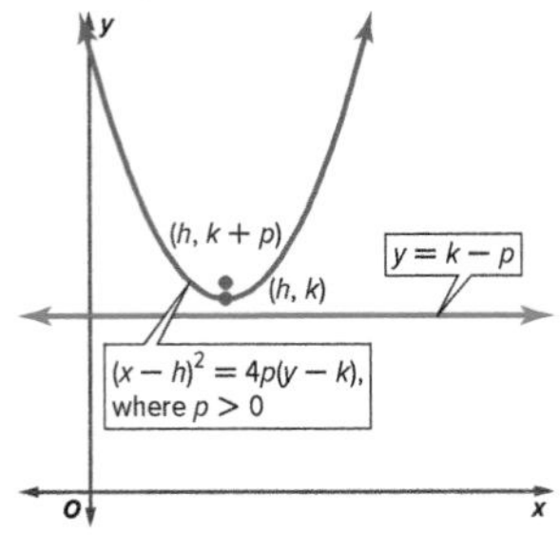

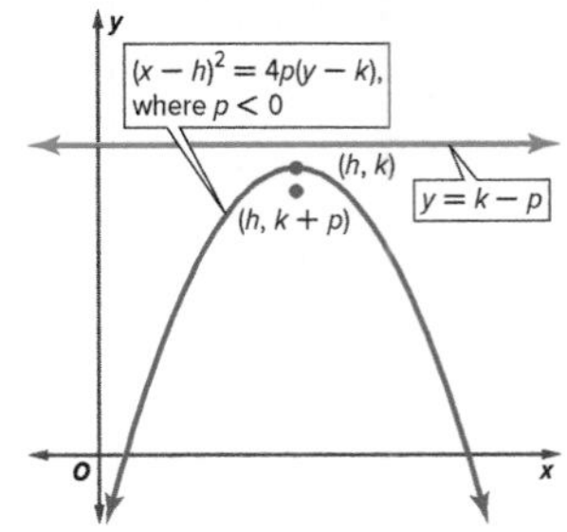

Equation: $(y - k)^2 = 4p(x - h)$ — Axis of Symmetry: horizontal, $y = k$

Focus: $(h + p, k)$ — Vertex: (h, k)

Directrix: $x = h - p$ — Opens: right if $p > 0$, left if $p < 0$

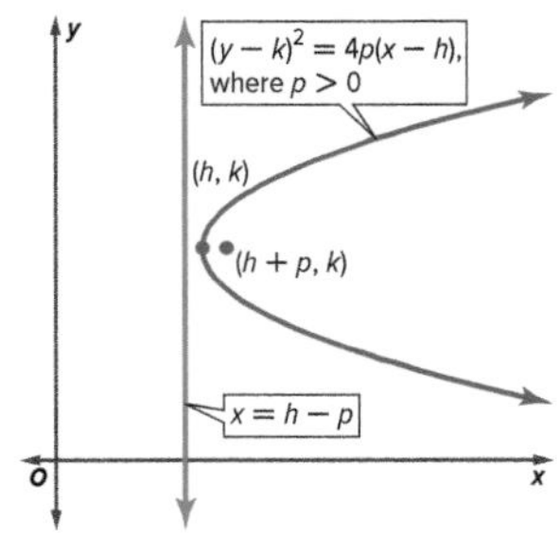

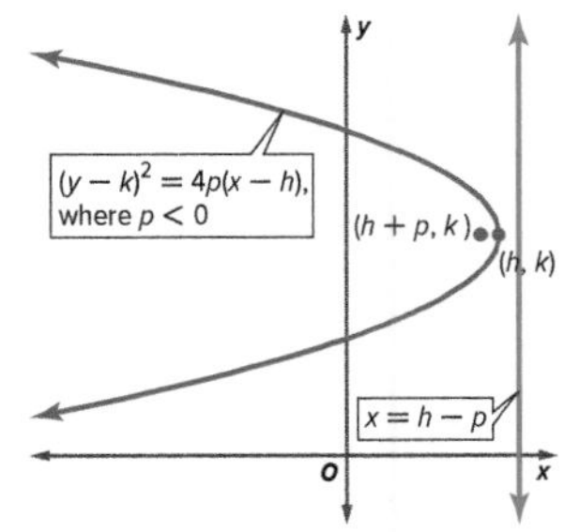

G.GPE.2

Example 1 Write the Equation of a Parabola

Write an equation for each parabola.

a. focus at (0, 1) and directrix $y = -1$

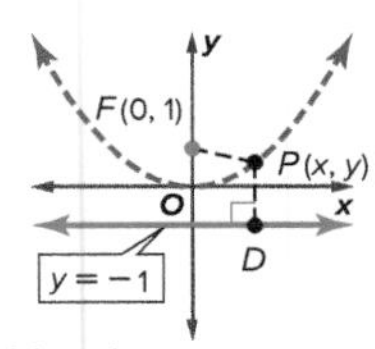

The directrix is horizontal, so the axis of symmetry is vertical. The equation is of the form $(x - h)^2 = 4p(y - k)$.

Use the focus and directrix to find the values of h, k, and p.

The focus is $(h, k + p) = (0, 1)$, so $h = 0$ and $k + p = 1$.

The directrix is $y = k - p$, so $k - p = -1$. Solve the system to find k and p.

$$\begin{aligned} k + p &= 1 \\ k - p &= -1 \\ \hline 2k &= 0 \\ k &= 0 \end{aligned} \qquad \begin{aligned} k + p &= 1 \\ 0 + p &= 1 \\ p &= 1 \end{aligned}$$

Study Tip

Structure The sign of p helps you determine which way the graph of the parabola opens. If $p < 0$, the graph will open down or to the left. If $p > 0$, the graph will open up or to the right.

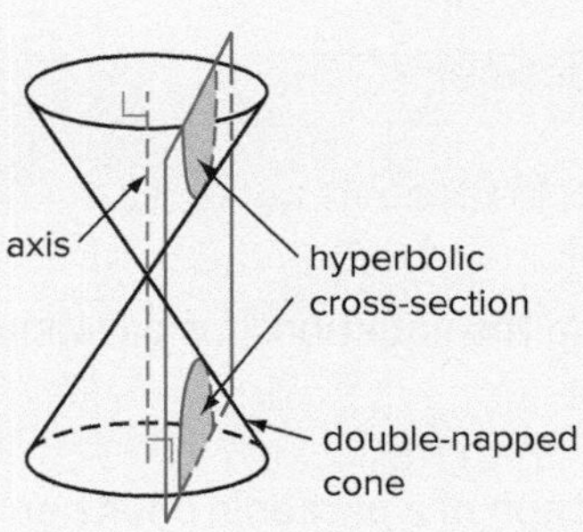

Substitute to find the equation.

$(x - h)^2 = 4p(y - k)$

$(x - 0)^2 = 4(1)(y - 0)$

$x^2 = 4y$

The equation is $x^2 = 4y$ or $y = \frac{1}{4}x^2$.

b. vertex (−1, 4) and focus (−3, 4)

The vertex is (−1, 4), so $h = -1$ and $k = 4$.

The vertex and the focus lie on the axis of symmetry, so the equation of the axis of symmetry is $y = 4$. Thus, the axis of symmetry is horizontal and the equation is of the form $(y - k)^2 = 4p(x - h)$.

The focus is $(h + p, k)$. Use the x-coordinate to find the value of p.

$h + p = -3$

$-1 + p = -3$

$p = -2$

Write the equation.

$(y - k)^2 = 4p(x - h)$

$(y - 4)^2 = 4(-2)(x - (-1))$

$(y - 4)^2 = -8(x + 1)$

The equation of the parabola is $(y - 4)^2 = -8(x + 1)$.

Guided Practice

1A. focus at (0, −2) and directrix at $y = 2$ $y = -\frac{1}{8}x^2$

1B. vertex (−2, −1), focus (−4, −1) $(y + 1)^2 = -8(x + 2)$

Parabolic reflectors are often used in the real world to collect or send waves.

Real-World Example 2 Write an Equation of a Parabola

SATELLITES A parabolic satellite dish opens upward. The dish reflects the collected signals to the focus of the parabola. The distance between the vertex and the focus is 9.6 meters. Write an equation to represent a cross section of the dish.

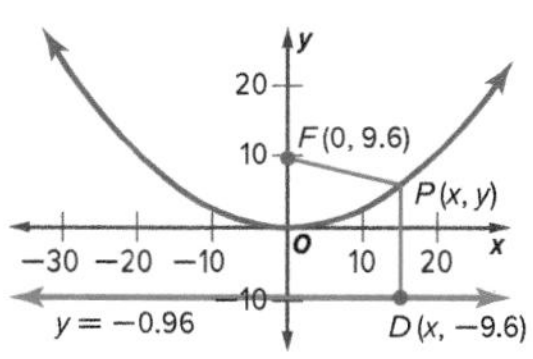

The parabola opens upward, so the axis of symmetry is vertical. The equation is of the form $(x - h)^2 = 4p(y - k)$.

Use (0, 0) as the vertex, so $h = 0$ and $k = 0$. The focus is 9.6 meters from the vertex, so $p = 9.6$ and the focus is (0, 9.6).

Teaching the Mathematical Practices

Construct Arguments Mathematically proficient students use previously established results in constructing arguments. Point out to students that the derivation of the standard equation of a parabola is a proof that started with the definition of a parabola. It used the Distance Formula, which is a previously established result, to show that the equation represents a parabola. Now that the standard equation is proven, it can be used without further development using the Distance Formula.

Follow-Up

Students have explored how to derive the equation of a parabola. Ask: How do you find the equation of a parabola given the vertex, focus, and directrix? Sample answer: Make a sample U-shaped curve of the given information to determine which way the graph opens and the value of p as the distance between the focus and vertex. Then choose the corresponding standard form of the parabola and substitute the known values into the form.

Differentiated Instruction BL

Extension How can an equation of a real-world parabola be found experimentally? Sample answer: Assuming the parabola opens upward, analyze a cross section of the parabolic shape and estimate the coordinates of several important points, including the vertex and points of the parabola. Use a graphing calculator to do a quadratic regression on at least 3 points. This will give an equation of the parabola that can be converted to standard form, if needed.

2 Graph Parabolas

Example 3 Analyze and Graph a Parabola

AL **How do you know that you can write the equation in part a in the form $(y-k)^2 = 4p(x-h)$?** The y is squared.

OL **If a parabola has a horizontal directrix, what can you conclude about its axis of symmetry? Why?** The axis of symmetry is vertical, because the directrix and the axis of symmetry are always perpendicular.

BL **How can you use what you know about reflections in the coordinate plane to help determine the direction of the opening of a parabola?** Taking the opposite of the x-coordinates reflects a figure in the y-axis and a negative value of p reflects a parabola that would open to the right so that it opens to the left. Similarly, taking the opposite of the y-coordinates reflects a figure in the x-axis and a negative value of p reflects a parabola that would open up so that it opens down.

Need Another Example?
Graph each equation.

a. $y = 2(x-1)^2 - 5$

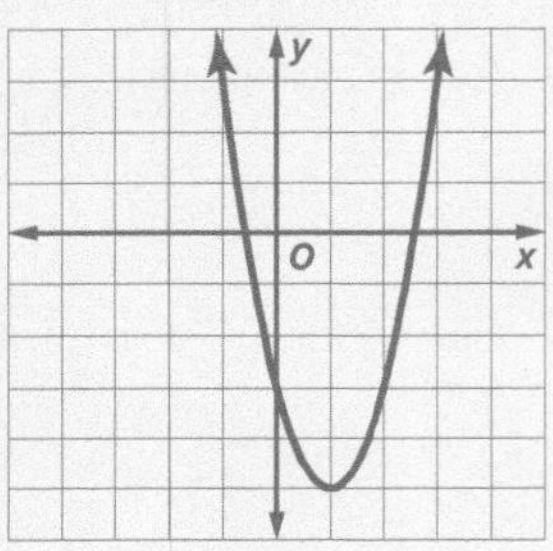

b. $-(x-3) = (y-2)^2$

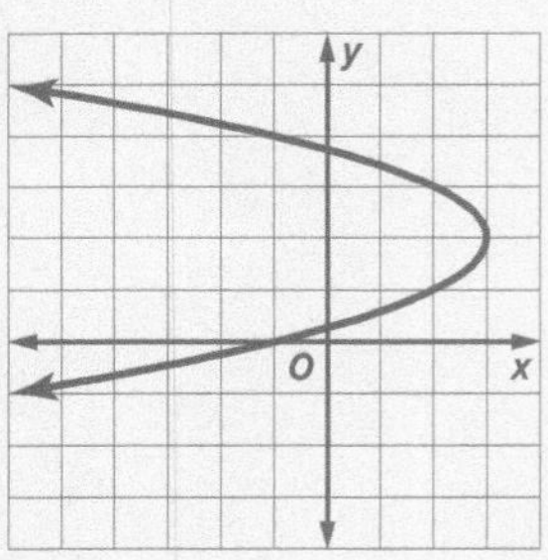

Substitute to find the equation.

$(x-h)^2 = 4p(y-k)$

$(x-0)^2 = 4(9.6)(y-0)$

$x^2 = 38.4y$

The equation is $x^2 = 38.4y$ or about $y = 0.026x^2$.

Guided Practice

2. **SEARCHLIGHTS** A searchlight uses parabolic reflectors to concentrate and project a beam of light. Suppose a reflector opens to the right and the distance between the vertex and the focus is 2.2 feet. Write an equation of the cross section of the reflector.

2. Sample answer: $y^2 = 8.8x$

2 Graph Parabolas You can analyze the equation of a parabola to find the key features of the parabola and to draw its graph.

Example 3 Analyze and Graph a Parabola

Graph each equation.

a. $x - 3 = -\frac{1}{16}(y+1)^2$

Step 1 Write the equation in the standard form to identify h, k, and p.

$x - 3 = -\frac{1}{16}(y+1)^2$ Original equation

$-16(x-3) = (y+1)^2$ Multiply each side by -16.

$(y+1)^2 = -16(x-3)$ Symmetric Property

$(y-(-1))^2 = 4(-4)(x-3)$ $1 = -(-1)$ and $-16 = 4(-4)$

Thus $h = 3$, $k = -1$, and $p = -4$.

Step 2 Identify some key features of the graph. Then draw.

focus, $(h+p, k)$: $(3 + (-4), -1)$ or $(-1, -1)$

vertex, (h, k): $(3, -1)$

axis of symmetry, $y = k$: $y = -1$

directrix, $x = h - p$: $x = 3 - (-4)$ or $x = 7$

direction of opening: left since $p < 0$

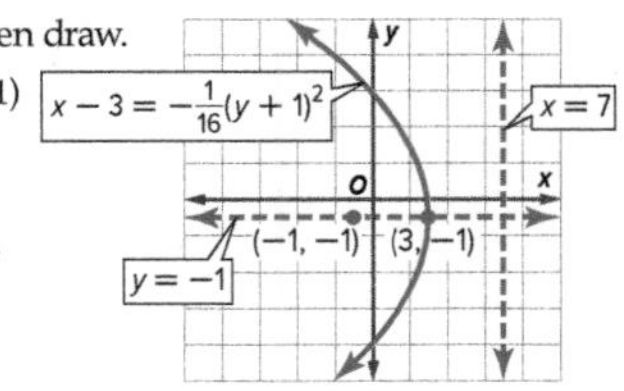

b. $y = -2(x+4)^2 - 1$

Step 1

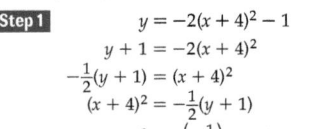

$y = -2(x+4)^2 - 1$ Original equation

$y + 1 = -2(x+4)^2$ Add 1 to each side.

$-\frac{1}{2}(y+1) = (x+4)^2$ Multiply each side by $-\frac{1}{2}$.

$(x+4)^2 = -\frac{1}{2}(y+1)$ Symmetric Property

$(x-(-4))^2 = 4\left(-\frac{1}{8}\right)(y-(-1))$ $-\frac{1}{2} = 4\left(-\frac{1}{8}\right)$, $1 = -(-1)$, $4 = -(-4)$

Thus $h = -4$, $k = -1$, and $p = -\frac{1}{8}$.

Step 2 **focus:** $\left(-4, -1+\left(-\frac{1}{8}\right)\right)$ or $\left(-4, -\frac{9}{8}\right)$

vertex: $(-4, -1)$

axis of symmetry: $x = -4$

directrix: $y = -\frac{7}{8}$

direction of opening: down

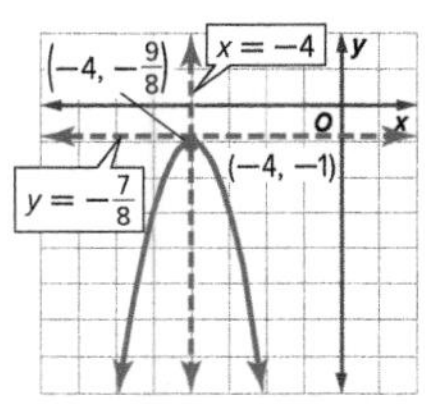

Guided Practice

3A. $x = \frac{1}{3}(y+2)^2 + 7$ **3B.** $y = (x+3)^2 - 13$ See margin.

Standards for Mathematical Practice

Emphasis On	Exercises
1 Make sense of problems.	1–6, 12–27, 45–55, 63, 71, 75, 77, 78, 80, 82
2 Reason abstractly.	8–11, 29–43, 56–61, 67–70, 72–74, 79
3 Construct viable arguments.	62, 76
4 Model with mathematics.	7, 28, 44, 65, 66, 81
5 Use appropriate tools strategically.	64
6 Attend to precision.	77

Check Your Understanding

◯ = Step-by-Step Solutions begin on page R13.

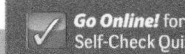

Go Online! for a Self-Check Quiz

Example 1 G.GPE.2

Write an equation for each parabola.

1. focus (0, 6), directrix $y = -6$ $x^2 = 24y$
2. focus (0, −8), directrix $y = 8$ $x^2 = -32y$
3. focus (−2, 0), directrix $x = 2$ $y^2 = -8x$
4. focus (3, 0), directrix $x = -3$ $y^2 = 12x$
5. vertex $\left(-\frac{9}{16}, 1\right)$, focus $\left(-\frac{9}{16}, 3\right)$ $\left(x + \frac{9}{16}\right)^2 = 8(y - 1)$
6. vertex $\left(\frac{3}{8}, -2\right)$, directrix $x = -\frac{3}{8}$ $(y+2)^2 = 3\left(x - \frac{3}{8}\right)$

Example 2

7. **MP MODELING** The parabolic reflector plate of a flashlight has its bulb located at the focus of the parabola. The distance between the vertex and the focus is 1.8 centimeters. Write an equation to represent the cross section of the reflector plate. Sample answer: $x^2 = 7.2y$

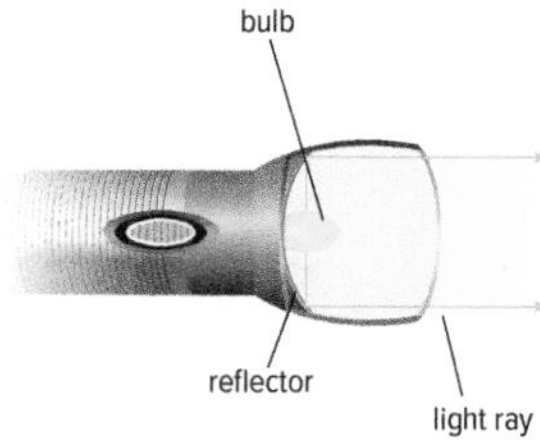

Example 3

Graph each equation. 8–11. See Ch. 9 Answer Appendix.

8. $y = (x - 4)^2 - 6$
9. $y = 4(x + 5)^2 + 3$
10. $y = \frac{1}{8}x^2 + 2$
11. $x = -\frac{1}{4}(y - 4)^2 - 2$

16. $(x-1)^2 = 16y$ 18. $(y-2)^2 = 12(x-2)$ 22. $(x-4)^2 = 4(y-4)$ 24. $(y-1)^2 = 20(x-5)$

Practice and Problem Solving

Extra Practice is on page R9.

Example 1 G.GPE.2

Write an equation for each parabola.

12. focus $\left(\frac{5}{2}, 0\right)$, directrix $x = -\frac{5}{2}$ $y^2 = 10x$
13. focus $\left(0, -\frac{7}{4}\right)$, directrix $y = \frac{7}{4}$ $x^2 = -7y$
14. focus (0, 8), directrix, $y = -8$ $x^2 = 32y$
15. focus (0, −10), directrix, $y = 10$ $x^2 = -40y$
16. focus (1, 4), directrix, $y = -4$
17. focus (2, −1), directrix, $y = 3$ $(x-2)^2 = -8(y-1)$
18. focus (5, 2), directrix, $x = -1$
19. focus (4, −1), directrix, $x = 8$ $(y+1)^2 = -8(x-6)$
20. vertex (0, 0), directrix, $y = -2$ $x^2 = 8y$
21. vertex (0, 0), directrix, $x = 3$ $y^2 = -12x$
22. vertex (4, 4), directrix, $y = 3$
23. vertex (1, −1), directrix, $y = 1$ $(x-1)^2 = -8(y+1)$
24. vertex (5, 1), directrix, $x = 0$
25. vertex (−3, 1), directrix, $x = -4$ $(y-1)^2 = 4(x+3)$
26. vertex (0, 6), directrix, $x = 2$ $(y-6)^2 = -8x$
27. vertex (−7, 0), directrix, $x = -2$ $y^2 = -20(x+7)$

Example 2 G.GPE.2

28. **CARS** The parabolic reflector plate of a car headlight has its bulb located at the focus of the parabola. The distance between the vertex and the focus is 6.5 centimeters.
    a. Write an equation of the cross section of the reflector plate.
    b. Graph the parabola. 28a, b. See Ch. 9 Answer Appendix.

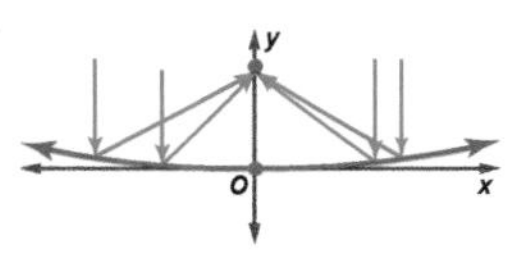

Example 3

Graph each equation. 29–40. See Ch. 9 Answer Appendix.

29. $y = 2x^2$
30. $y = \frac{1}{3}x^2$
31. $y = -2x^2$
32. $x = \frac{1}{2}y^2$
33. $y = 2(x - 1)^2 - 4$
34. $x = -\frac{1}{32}y^2 - 6$
35. $y = \frac{1}{12}x^2 + 1$
36. $y = -2(x - 2)^2 + 3$
37. $x = -\frac{1}{16}(y + 5)^2 - 1$
38. $y = -\frac{1}{12}(x - 3)^2 + 5$
39. $x = \frac{1}{8}(y + 4)^2 - 4$
40. $x = -\frac{1}{16}(y - 4)^2 + 6$

Practice

Formative Assessment Use Exercises 1–11 to assess students' understanding of the concepts in the lesson.

The Practice and Problem Solving exercises assess the content taught in the lesson. The Preparing for Assessment page is meant to be used as preparation for end-of-course assessments.

Extra Practice

See page R9 for extra exercises for students who are approaching level or for on-level students who need additional reinforcement.

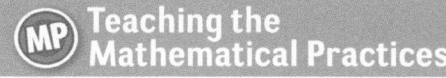

MP Teaching the Mathematical Practices

Sense-Making Mathematically proficient students can explain how to write the equation of a parabola in Exercises 14–17 from the given conditions. The conditions connect the parts of the geometric graph of the parabola with the algebraic equation of the parabola.

Levels of Complexity Chart

The levels of the exercises progress from 1 to 3, with Level 1 indicating the lowest level of complexity.

Exercises	12–40	41–62, 76–82	63–75
C Level 3			●
B Level 2		●	
Level 1	●		

Differentiated Homework Options

Use this chart to customize assignments for your students.

Levels	AL Basic	OL Core	BL Advanced
Exercises	12–40, 67–70, 72–74, 76–82	13–61 odd, 63–70, 72–74, 76–82	63–75, (optional: 76–82)
2-Day Option	13–39 odd, 76–82	12–40	
	12–40 even, 67–70, 72–74	41–70, 72–74, 76–82	

You can use ALEKS to provide additional remediation support with personalized instruction and practice.

Watch Out!

Students may have difficulty finding the coordinates of the vertex and focus in Exercises 56–61. Suggest that they convert the equation to one of the two standard forms before proceeding. This will help ensure that the value of p is calculated correctly.

Teaching Tip

Error Analysis Encourage students to work with a partner to describe the errors in the parabola graphs in Exercise 62. Have them use graphing software to justify their comments.

Additional Answers

51. Conjecture: The equation of the new parabola is $(y - 2)^2 = 16(x - 3)$. The graph, shown below, verifies that $(y - 2)^2 = 16(x - 3)$ is a translation of $y^2 - 16x = 0$ by 3 units to the right and 2 units up.

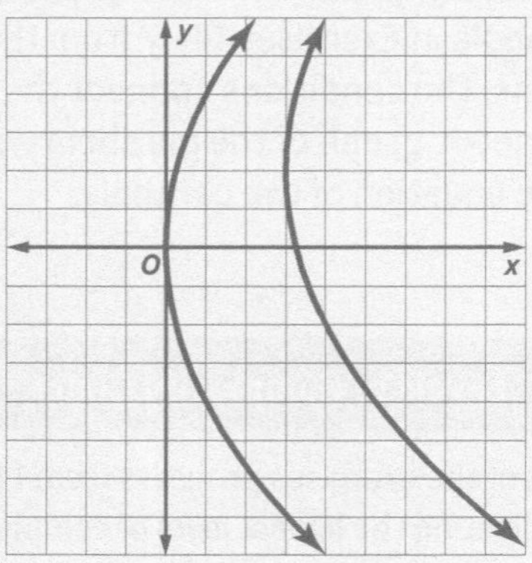

59. vertex: $(4, -6)$, focus: $\left(4\frac{1}{4}, -6\right)$; directrix: $x = 3\frac{3}{4}$

60. vertex: $(-1, 1)$, focus: $\left(-\frac{15}{16}, 1\right)$; directrix: $x = -\frac{17}{16}$

61. vertex: $(0, 4)$, focus: $\left(0, 4\frac{1}{4}\right)$; directrix: $y = 3\frac{3}{4}$

62a. The graph should be open down. This is the graph of $x^2 - 4y = 0$.

62b. The directrix should be the line $x = -\frac{1}{2}$.

63a. Sample answer: (0, 4), (2, 0)

63b. $x = 0$ or $x = 2$

63c. $y = 4$ or $y = 0$

63d. (0, 4) and (2, 0); They are the same intersection points.

63e. Check the solution (0, 4): For $y = -x^2 + 4$,: $4 = -02 + 4$, so (0, 4) is a solution; For $(x - 2)^2 = (0 - 2)^2 = 4$, so (0, 4) is a solution. Check the solution (2, 0): For $y = -x^2 + 4$, $0 = -2^2 + 4$, so (2, 0) is a solution; For $(x - 2)^2 = (2 - 2)^2 = 0$, so (2, 0) is a solution. So, the points lie on both parabolas.

B **Identify the focus and directrix of each parabola.**

41. $\frac{1}{8}(x + 2)^2 - (y - 3) = 0$ $F(-2, 5)$, $y = 1$

42. $x - 4 = -\frac{1}{4}y^2$ $F(3, 0)$, $x = 5$

43. $(y - 1)^2 - 24(x + 3) = 0$ $F(3, 1)$, $x = -9$

44. **SOLAR ENERGY** Solar energy can be concentrated using parabolic reflecting plates. The collected energy is used to heat homes and produce electricity. Write an equation to represent the cross section of the parabolic plate shown. $x^2 = 34y$

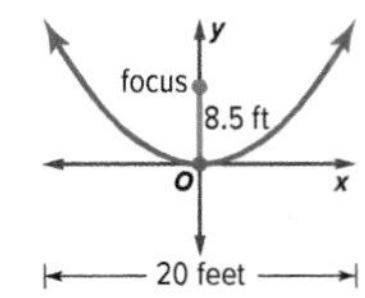

Write the equation of the parabola with the given directrix and with vertex at (0, 0).

45. $x = -\frac{3}{2}$ $y^2 = 6x$

46. $y = \frac{1}{12}$ $x^2 = -\frac{1}{3}y$

47. $y = -\frac{11}{6}$ $x^2 = \frac{22}{3}y$

48. $y = \frac{5}{12}$ $x^2 = -\frac{5}{3}y$

49. $x = -4$ $y^2 = 16x$

50. $x = \frac{1}{8}$ $y^2 = -\frac{1}{2}x$

51. A parabola with vertex (0, 0) has equation $y^2 - 16x = 0$ and is shifted 3 units to the right and 2 units up. Write the equation of the new parabola. Then graph both parabolas on the same coordinate plane. **See margin.**

Write an equation of each parabola.

52. focus (0, −3), directrix $y = 3$ $x^2 = -12y$

53. focus (0, 7), directrix $y = -7$ $x^2 = 28y$

54. vertex $\left(-\frac{9}{5}, 1\right)$, focus $\left(-\frac{9}{5}, 3\right)$ $\left(x + \frac{9}{5}\right)^2 = 8(y - 1)$

55. vertex $\left(\frac{3}{4}, -2\right)$, directrix $x = -\frac{3}{4}$ $6\left(x - \frac{3}{4}\right) = (y + 2)^2$

Identify the coordinates of the vertex and focus, and the equation of the directrix of each parabola. 56. vertex: (1, −2), focus: (1, −1); directrix: $y = -3$

56. $y + 2 = \frac{1}{4}(x - 1)^2$

57. $x - 4 = 12(y + 2)^2$

58. $y = 8(x - 2)^2$

59. $x - 4 = (y + 6)^2$

60. $x + 1 = 4(y - 1)^2$

61. $y - 4 = x^2$

59–61. See margin.

57. vertex: (4, −2), focus: $\left(4\frac{1}{48}, -2\right)$; directrix: $x = 3\frac{47}{48}$

58. vertex: (2, 0), focus: $\left(2, \frac{1}{32}\right)$; directrix: $y = -\frac{1}{32}$

62. **CRITIQUE ARGUMENTS** Describe the error in the graph of each parabola. 62, 63. See margin.

a. $x^2 + 4y = 0$

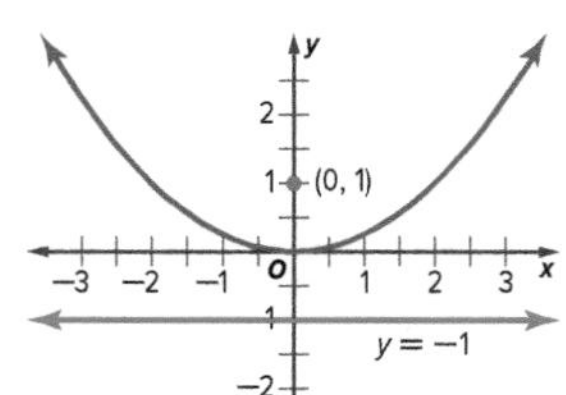

b. $\frac{1}{2}y^2 - x = 0$

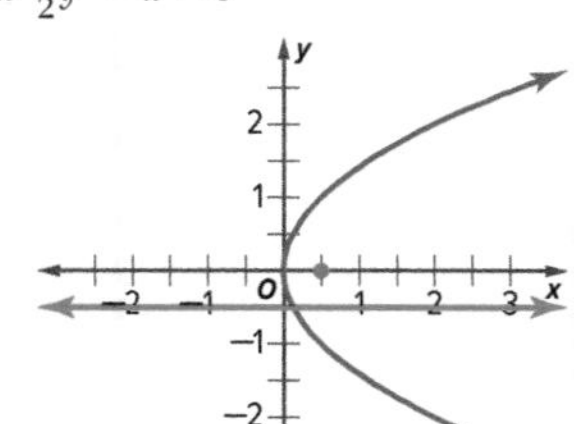

C 63. Graph $y = -x^2 + 4$ and $(x - 2)^2 = y$ on the same coordinate plane.

a. Estimate the point(s) of intersection of the two parabolas.

b. Substitute the expression $(x - 2)^2$ for y into $y = -x^2 + 4$ and solve for x.

c. Substitute the value(s) you found in part **b** into $y = -x^2 + 4$ and solve for y.

d. Use your answers to parts **b** and **c** to write the coordinates of the point(s) of intersection of the two graphs. Compare this to your estimates in part **a**.

e. Verify that the point(s) you found in part **d** lie on both parabolas.

65a.

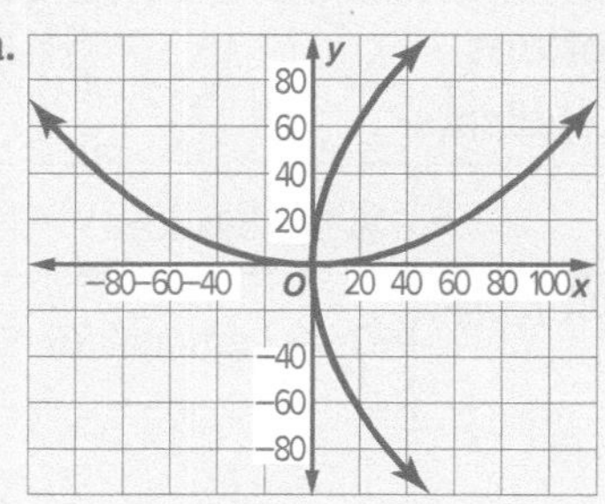

65b. $y^2 = 200x$; $x^2 = 200y$

65c. No. The depth of the antenna is the same for both sketches. It is equal to the distance between the focus and the vertex, 50 inches.

64. Graph $y = \sqrt{x + 2} - 1$ on a graphing calculator.
   a. This graph is reflected in the line $y = -1$. Write the equation of the image. $y = -\sqrt{x+2} - 1$
   b. Write an equation that represents the parabola formed by the original graph and its image. $(y+1)^2 = x + 2$

65. **TELEVISION** A television station uses parabolic antennas to transmit their signals. An antenna used to transmit the signal has a focus 50 inches from the vertex. See margin.
   a. Make two sketches of the antenna: one opening upwards and one opening to the right.
   b. Use your sketches to write an equation for each sketch. Use the forms $x^2 = 4py$ and $y^2 = 4px$.
   c. Does the equation you found in part **b** affect the depth of the antenna? Explain.

66. **ASTRONOMY** In astronomy, a radio telescope dish is shaped like a parabola and has special antennas to detect signals from space, known as the "radio universe." A radio telescope can be over 100 meters in diameter, but it can vary greatly in design, size, and configuration.
   a. In a typical antenna, the distance between the focus and the vertex is 25 meters. What is an equation of the parabola? Assume that vertex is (0, 0). Sample answer: $x^2 = 100y$
   b. Explain how a single dish antenna may work in a parabola-shaped telescope dish. See margin.

H.O.T. Problems Use Higher-Order Thinking Skills

67. **WRITING IN MATH** Explain how to find the distance from the focus to the directrix for the parabola $x = 4y^2$. See margin.

68. **WRITING IN MATH** The parabolic reflector plate of a bicycle head lamp has its bulb located at the focus of the parabola. Explain the possible advantages to using this design. See margin.

69. **REASONING** Explain how to find the equation of a parabola which has a vertex at (3, −2) and a focus at (6, −2). See Ch. 9 Answer Appendix.

70. **WRITING IN MATH** As the value of p increases, how does the width of the graph of $y = \frac{1}{4p}x^2$ change? Justify your reasoning. See margin.

71. **CHALLENGE**
   a. What part of a parabola can be modeled by the equation $y = \sqrt{x}$?
   b. What is the domain and range of the function in part **a**?
   c. Explain how the equation $y = \sqrt{x}$ is related to a parabola of the form $y^2 = 4px$.
   d. State a rule that you could use to help you use a graphing calculator to show the graph of $y^2 = 4px$. See margin.

72. **REASONING** How are a and p related in the same parabola expressed both as $y = ax^2$ and $x^2 = 4py$? $a = \frac{1}{4p}$

73. **REASONING** Predict how a change in the value of p in the equation $y^2 = 4px$ will affect the focus, directrix, and graph of $y^2 = 4px$. Then verify your prediction by graphing both in same coordinate plane. 73, 74. See Ch. 9 Answer Appendix.

74. **WRITING IN MATH** Explain the relationship between the Distance Formula, the equation of a parabola with vertex (0, 0), and the equation of a congruent parabola with a vertex not at the origin.

75. **CHALLENGE** Prove or disprove that the point (−8, −4) lies on a parabola with vertex (0, 0) and containing the point $\left(-2\sqrt{2}, -\frac{\sqrt{2}}{8}\right)$. See margin.

66b. Sample answer: As the signals come in, they are essentially parallel and are therefore reflected from the parabolic surface to the focus. The signals become magnified because they are added together before they are transmitted to a receiver.

67. Sample answer: If you rewrite the equation of the parabola as $y^2 = \frac{1}{4}x$, it is of the form $y^2 = 4px$.

Therefore, $4p = \frac{1}{4}$, and $p = \frac{1}{16}$. The value of p represents the distance from the focus to the vertex and from the vertex to the directrix. So, the distance from the focus to the directrix must be $2p$, or $\frac{1}{8}$ in this case.

68. Sample answer: If the bulb is located at the focus, then the light rays will all be deflected to the focus, which will concentrate the light beams to make the output brighter.

70. Sample answer: As the value of p increases, the width of the graph increases because $\frac{1}{4p}$ becomes smaller and smaller. This is because if the coefficient of the x^2-term is less than 1, then the graph of the parabola becomes wider.

Assess

Formative Assessment Use Exercises 52 and 55 to assess whether students understand how to find the equation of a parabola from given conditions.

Ticket Out the Door

Make several copies of each of the exercises on writing the equation of a parabola. As the students leave the room, ask them to describe how to find the equations.

Additional Answers

71a. Top half of a parabola that has vertex (0, 0) and is open to the right

71b. Domain: $x \geq 0$; Range: $x \geq 0$

71c. Sample answer: If you square both sides of $y = \sqrt{x}$, you get $y^2 = x$. This is related to $y^2 = 4px$ because the coefficient of x in $y^2 = 4px$ is $4p$. So they are part of the same family of parabolas $y^2 = x$. If $p = \frac{1}{4}$, then the equations are identical.

71d. Sample answer: Make a list of values for p, including values less than 1, and then use the calculator to graph the family of functions of the form $y = \sqrt{4px}$ and $y = -\sqrt{4px}$ to see the complete parabolas.

75. Sample answer: Graph the three points to see that they are located on a parabola with vertex (0, 0) that is opening downward. Because the vertex is (0, 0), substitute the coordinates into $x^2 = 4py$, and solve for p. If p is the same for both points, then the points are solutions to the same parabola.

(−8, 4):	$\left(-2\sqrt{2}, -\frac{\sqrt{2}}{8}\right)$:
$x^2 = 4py$	$x^2 = 4py$
$(-8)^2 = 4p(-4)$	$(-2\sqrt{2})^2 = 4p\left(-\frac{\sqrt{2}}{8}\right)$
$64 = -16p$	$8 = 4p\left(-\frac{\sqrt{2}}{8}\right)$
$-4 = p$	$\frac{-16}{\sqrt{2}} = p$

Because the value of p is different for each point, the points are not on the same parabola.

Go Online! eBook

Interactive Student Guide
Use the *Interactive Student Guide* to deepen conceptual understanding.
· Equations of Parabolas

Preparing for Assessment

Exercises 76–82 require students to use the skills they will need on standardized assessments. Each exercise is dual-coded with content standards and mathematical practice standards.

Dual Coding

Items	Content Standards	MP Mathematical Practices
76	G.GPE.2	3
77	G.GPE.2	1, 6
78	G.GPE.2	1
79		2
80		1
81	G.GPE.2	4
82	G.GPE.2	1

Diagnose Student Errors

77b.

A	CORRECT
B–D	Remind students to sketch the parabola first to determine the direction of opening.

77d.

A	CORRECT
B	Subtracted incorrectly
C	Thought the directrix was $x = p$
D	Thought the directrix was vertical

78.

A	Student reversed the signs of *h* and *k*.
B	Remind students that if the directrix is a vertical line, the parabola opens to the right or left. It has a y^2-term.
C	CORRECT
D	Because the value of *p* is negative, the coefficient of the *x*- term must be negative.

80.

A	Used wrong a value.
B	Used wrong *h* and *k* value
C	Used wrong *k* value
D	CORRECT

Go Online!

Quizzes

Students can use *Self-Check Quizzes* to check their understanding of this lesson and have the results sent to you. You can also give *Quiz 4*, which covers the content in Lessons 9-7 and 9-8.

Preparing for Assessment

76. Use the Distance Formula to derive the equation of a parabola with focus (0, 4) and directrix $y = -4$. MP 3 G.GPE.2

$x^2 = 16y$

77. **MULTI-STEP** Consider the parabola with vertex (−4, 2) and focus (−4, 5).

a. Write the equation of the parabola. MP 1 G.GPE.2

$(x + 4)^2 = 12(y - 2)$

b. Which of the following statements is true about the graph of the parabola? MP 1 A

- ○ A The graph opens upward.
- ○ B The graph opens downward.
- ○ C The graph opens to the right.
- ○ D The graph opens to the left.

c. Which of the following points are on the graph of the parabola? Select all that apply. MP 6 A, D, E

- ☐ A (2, 5)
- ☐ B $\left(-3, \frac{3}{4}\right)$
- ☐ C (0, 0)
- ☐ D (8, 14)
- ☐ E (−4, 2)
- ☐ F (6, 3)

d. Which of the following is the equation of the directrix of the parabola? MP 1 A

- ○ A $y = -1$
- ○ B $y = 1$
- ○ C $x = 3$
- ○ D $x = -1$

e. Describe how the vertex of the graph is translated from (0, 0). MP 1

The vertex is translated 4 units left and 2 units up.

78. Which of the following is the equation of a parabola with vertex (3, −5) and directrix $x = 7$? MP 1 G.GPE.2 C

- ○ A $(y - 5)^2 = -16(x + 3)$
- ○ B $(x - 3)^2 = -16(y + 5)$
- ○ C $(y + 5)^2 = -16(x - 3)$
- ○ D $(y + 5)^2 = 16(x - 3)$

79. Consider the parabola $(y - 1)^2 = -8(x + 5)$. MP 2

a. Identify the vertex.

(−5, 1)

b. Identify the focus.

(−7, 1)

c. Identify the directrix.

$x = -3$

80. The graph of $x^2 = -2y$ is translated 1 unit down and 4 units left. Which of the following is the equation of the new parabola? MP 1 D

- ○ A $(x + 1)^2 = 2(y - 4)$
- ○ B $(x - 4)^2 = -2(y - 1)$
- ○ C $(x + 4)^2 = -2(y - 1)$
- ○ D $(x + 4)^2 = -2(y + 1)$

81. The parabolic reflector of a theatrical stage light has a bulb located at the focus of the reflector. If the focus of the parabola is 8.5 inches from the vertex, what are two possible equations of the parabola? MP 4 G.GPE.2

Sample answer: $x^2 = 34y$ or $y^2 = 34x$

82. Write an equation of the parabola with focus (−4, −1) and directrix $y = 13$. MP 1 G.GPE.2

$(x + 4)^2 = -28(y - 6)$

CHAPTER 9

Study Guide and Review

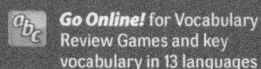

Go Online! for Vocabulary Review Games and key vocabulary in 13 languages

Study Guide

Key Concepts

Circles and Circumference (Lesson 9-1)

- The circumference of a circle is equal to πd or $2\pi r$.

Angles, Arcs, Chords, and Inscribed Angles
(Lessons 9-2 to 9-4)

- The sum of the measures of the central angles of a circle is 360°.
- The length of an arc is proportional to the length of the circumference.
- Diameters perpendicular to chords bisect chords and intercepted arcs.
- The measure of an inscribed angle is half the measure of its intercepted arc.

Tangents, Secants, and Angle Measures
(Lessons 9-5 and 9-6)

- A line that is tangent to a circle intersects the circle in exactly one point and is perpendicular to a radius.
- Two segments tangent to a circle from the same exterior point are congruent.
- The measure of an angle formed by two secant lines is half the positive difference of its intercepted arcs.
- The measure of an angle formed by a secant and tangent line is half its intercepted arc.

Equations of Circles and Parabolas
(Lessons 9-7 and 9-8)

- The equation of a circle with center (h, k) and radius r is $(x - h)^2 - (y - k)^2 = r^2$.
- A parabola is the locus of all points in a plane equidistant from a fixed point, called the focus, and a fixed line, called the directrix. The equation of a parabola can be found using the locus definition and the Distance Formula.

9. A tangent line intersects the circle at exactly one point, while a secant line intersects the circle at exactly two points.

FOLDABLES Study Organizer

Use your Foldable to review the chapter. Working with a partner can be helpful. Ask for clarification of concepts as needed.

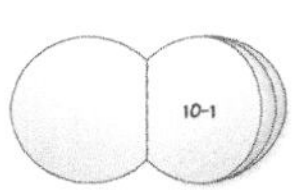

Key Vocabulary

adjacent arcs (p. 654)	directrix (p. 703)
arc (p. 652)	focus (p. 703)
arc length (p. 654)	inscribed (p. 646)
axis of symmetry (p. 703)	inscribed angle (p. 669)
center (p. 643)	intercepted arc (p. 669)
central angle (p. 652)	major arc (p. 653)
chord (p. 643)	minor arc (p. 653)
circle (p. 643)	parabola (p. 703)
circumference (p. 645)	pi (π) (p. 645)
circumscribed (p. 646)	point of tangency (p. 678)
common tangent (p. 678)	radian measure (p. 655)
concentric circles (p. 644)	radius (p. 643)
congruent arcs (p. 653)	secant (p. 687)
diameter (p. 643)	semicircle (p. 653)
	tangent (p. 678)

Vocabulary Check

State whether each sentence is *true* or *false*. If *false*, replace the underlined word or phrase to make a true sentence.

1. Any segment with both endpoints on the circle is a radius of the circle. false; chord
2. A chord passing through the center of a circle is a diameter. true
3. A central angle has the center as its vertex and its sides contain two radii of the circle. true
4. An arc with a measure of less than 180° is a major arc. false; minor arc
5. An intercepted arc is an arc that has its endpoints on the sides of an inscribed angle and lies in the interior of the inscribed angle. true
6. A common tangent is the point at which a line in the same plane as a circle intersects the circle. false; point of tangency
7. Two circles are concentric circles if and only if they have congruent radii. false; congruent

Concept Check

8. Explain the relationship between an inscribed angle and its intercepted arc. The degree measure of an inscribed angle is half the measure of its intercepted arc.
9. Explain the difference between tangent and secant lines to a circle.

FOLDABLES Study Organizer

A completed Foldable for this chapter should include the Key Concepts related to circles.

Key Vocabulary ELL

The page reference after each word denotes where that term was first introduced. If students have difficulty answering questions 1–7, remind them that they can use these page references to refresh their memories about the vocabulary terms.

Have students work together to match the correct terms to each sentence in the Vocabulary Check. Have students take turns saying each sentence aloud while the other student listens carefully.

You can use the detailed reports in ALEKS to automatically monitor students' progress and pinpoint remediation needs prior to the chapter test.

Answering the Essential Question

Before answering the Essential Question, have students review their answers to the *Building on the Essential Question* exercises found throughout the chapter.

- How are circles and polygons similar? different? (p. 650)
- What about circles makes them useful? (p. 656)
- Why might studying the relationships between the measures of segments and angles drawn in and around circles be useful in the real world? (p. 690)

Go Online!

Vocabulary Review

Students can use the *Vocabulary Review Games* to check their understanding of the vocabulary terms in this chapter. Students should refer to the *Student-Built Glossary* they have created as they went through the chapter to review important terms. You can also give a *Vocabulary Test* over the content of this chapter.

Lesson-by-Lesson Review

Intervention If the given examples are not sufficient to review the topics covered by the questions, remind students that the lesson references tell them where to review that topic in their textbook.

Two-Day Option Have students complete the Lesson-by-Lesson Review. Then you can use McGraw-Hill eAssessment to customize another review worksheet that practices all the objectives of this chapter or only the objectives on which your students need more help.

Additional Answers

13. 13.69 cm; 6.84 cm
14. 8.50 yd; 4.25 yd
15. 34.54 ft; 17.27 ft
16. 71.91 mm; 35.95 mm

CHAPTER 9

Study Guide and Review *Continued*

Lesson-by-Lesson Review

9-1 Circles and Circumference

G.CO.1, G.C.1, G.GMD.1

For Exercises 10–12, refer to ⊙*D*.

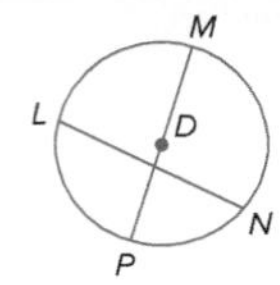

10. Name the circle. **⊙*D***
11. Name a radius. **$\overline{DM}$ or $\overline{DP}$**
12. Name a chord that is not a diameter. **$\overline{LN}$**

Find the diameter and radius of a circle with the given circumference. Round to the nearest hundredth.

13. $C = 43$ cm
14. $C = 26.7$ yd
15. $C = 108.5$ ft
16. $C = 225.9$ mm

13–16. See margin.

Example 1

Find the circumference of ⊙*A*.

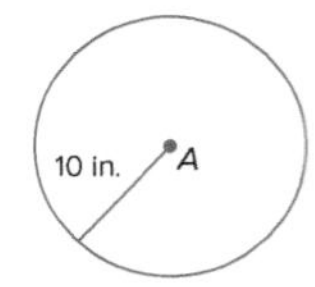

$C = 2\pi r$	Circumference formula
$= 2\pi(10)$	Substitution
≈ 62.83	Use a calculator.

The circumference of ⊙*A* is about 62.83 inches.

9-2 Measuring Angles and Arcs

G.C.2, G.C.5

Find the value of *x*.

17.

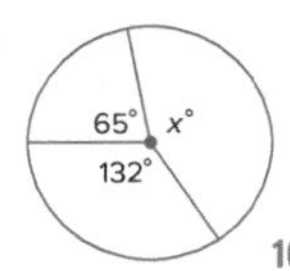

163

18.

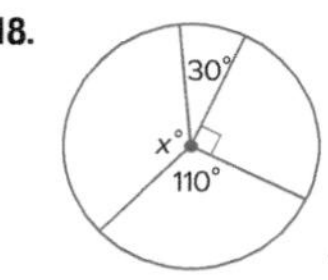

130

19. **MOVIES** The pie chart below represents the results of a survey taken by Mrs. Jameson regarding her students' favorite types of movies. Find each measure.

Mrs. Jameson's Students' Favorite Types of Movies

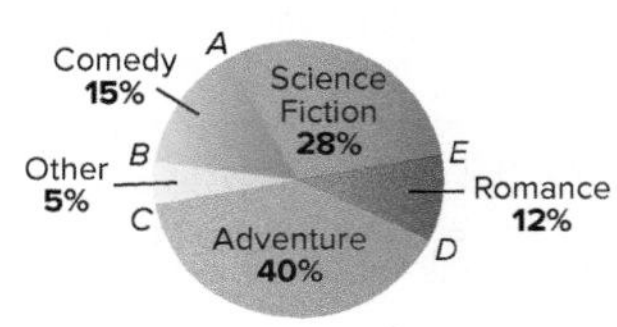

a. $m\widehat{AE}$ **100.8**

b. $m\widehat{BC}$ **18**

c. Describe the type of arc that the category Adventure represents. **minor arc**

Example 2

Find the value of *x*.

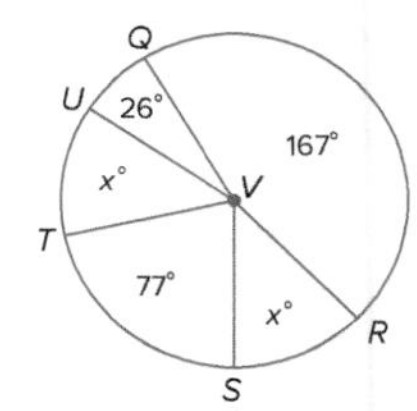

$m\angle QVR + m\angle RVS + m\angle SVT + m\angle TVU + m\angle UVQ = 360$	Sum of Central Angles
$167 + x + 77 + x + 26 = 360$	Substitution
$270 + 2x = 360$	Simplify.
$2x = 90$	Subtract.
$x = 45$	Divide.

9-3 Arcs and Chords

G.C.2, G.CO.12, G.MG.3

20. Find the value of x. 8

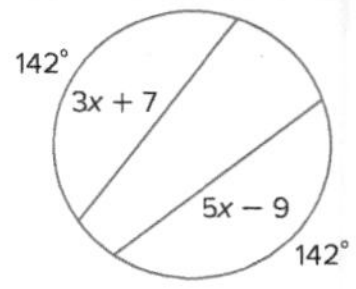

In ⊙K, $MN = 16$ and $m\widehat{MN} = 98$. Find each measure. Round to the nearest hundredth.

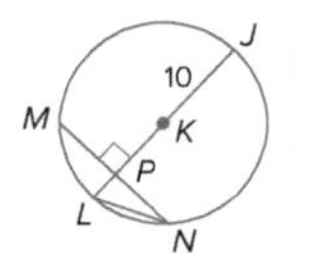

21. $m\widehat{NJ}$ 131 **22.** LN 8.94

23. GARDENING The top of the trellis shown is an arc of a circle in which $\overline{CD}$ is part of the diameter and $\overline{CD} \perp \overline{AB}$. If $\widehat{ACB}$ is about 28% of a complete circle, what is $m\widehat{CB}$? 50.4

Example 3

ALGEBRA In ⊙E, $EG = EF$. Find AB.

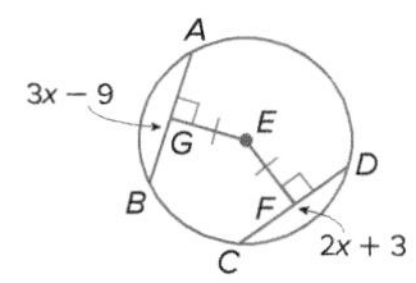

Because $\overline{EG}$ and $\overline{EF}$ are congruent, they are equidistant from E. So, $AB = CD$.

$AB = CD$	Theorem 10.5
$3x - 9 = 2x + 3$	Substitution
$3x = 2x + 12$	Add.
$x = 12$	Simplify.

So, $AB = 3(12) - 9$ or 27.

9-4 Inscribed Angles

G.C.2, G.C.3

Find each measure.

24. $m\angle 1$ 109

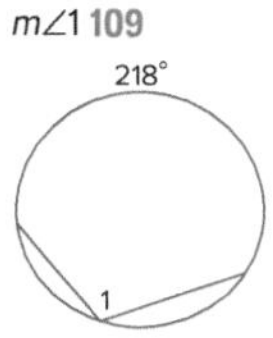

25. $m\widehat{GH}$ 56

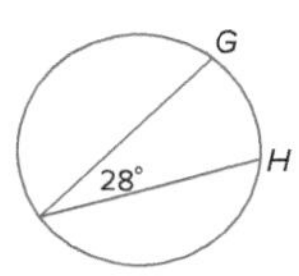

26. MARKETING In the logo at the right, $m\angle 1 = 42$. Find $m\angle 5$. 42

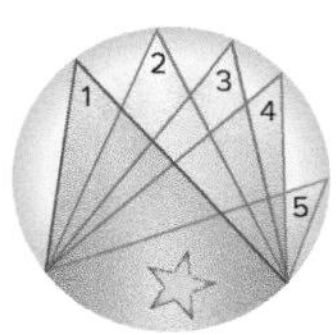

Example 4

Find $m\angle D$ and $m\angle B$.

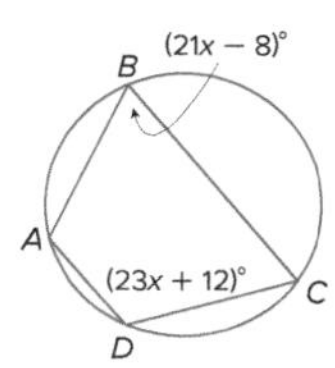

Because $ABCD$ is inscribed in a circle, opposite angles are supplementary.

$m\angle D + m\angle B = 180$	Definition of supplementary
$23x + 12 + 21x - 8 = 180$	Substitution
$44x + 4 = 180$	Simplify.
$44x = 176$	Subtract.
$x = 4$	Divide.

So, $m\angle D = 23(4) + 12$ or 104 and $m\angle B = 21(4) - 8$ or 76.

Go Online!

The most up-to-date resources available for your program can be found at connectED.mcgraw-hill.com.

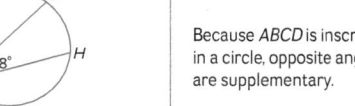

Additional Answer

27.

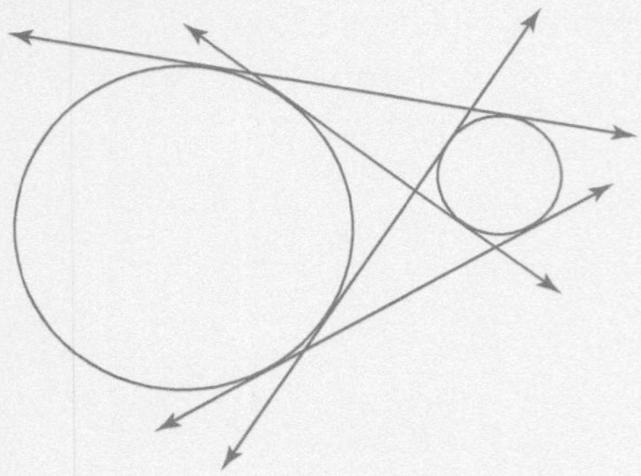

CHAPTER 9

Study Guide and Review *Continued*

9-5 Tangents

G.C.2, G.C.4

27. **SCIENCE FICTION** In a story Todd is writing, instantaneous travel between a two-dimensional planet and its moon is possible when the time-traveler follows a tangent. Copy the figures below and draw all possible travel paths. **See margin.**

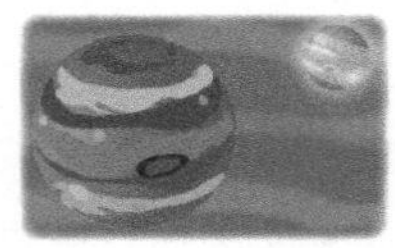

28. Find x and y. Assume that segments that appear to be tangent are tangent. Round to the nearest tenth if necessary. **$x = 10$, $y = 12.6$**

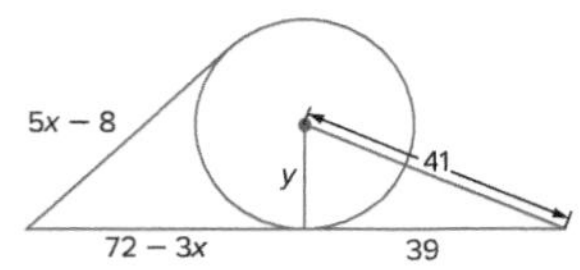

Example 5

In the figure, $\overline{KL}$ is tangent to ⊙M at K. Find the value of x.

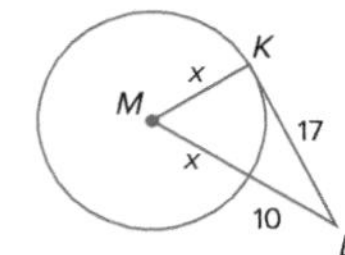

By Theorem 10.10, $\overline{MK} \perp \overline{KL}$. So, $\triangle MKL$ is a right triangle.

$KM^2 + KL^2 = ML^2$	Pythagorean Theorem
$x^2 + 17^2 = (x + 10)^2$	Substitution
$x^2 + 289 = x^2 + 20x + 100$	Multiply.
$289 = 20x + 100$	Simplify.
$189 = 20x$	Subtract.
$9.45 = x$	Divide.

9-6 Secants, Tangents, and Angle Measures

G.C.2

Find each measure. Assume that segments that appear to be tangent are tangent.

29. $m\angle 1$ **97**

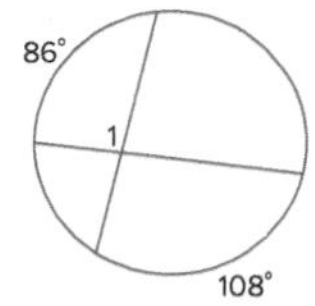

30. $m\widehat{AC}$ **56**

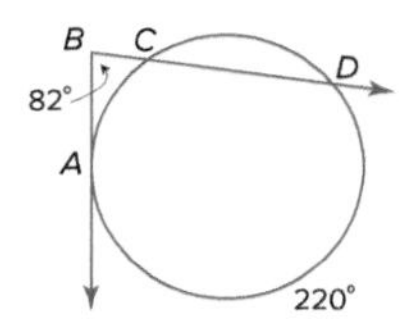

31. **PHOTOGRAPHY** Ahmed needs to take a close-up shot of an orange for his art class. He frames a shot of an orange as shown below, so that the lines of sight form tangents to the orange. If the measure of the camera's viewing angle is 34°, what is $m\widehat{ACB}$? **214**

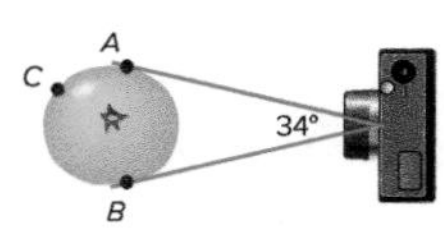

Example 6

Find the value of x.

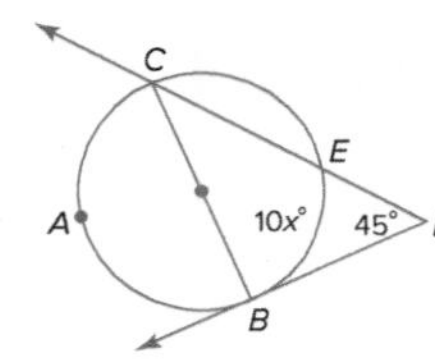

$\widehat{CAB}$ is a semicircle because $\overline{CB}$ is a diameter.

So, $m\widehat{CAB} = 180$.

$m\angle D = \frac{1}{2}(m\widehat{CAB} - m\widehat{EB})$	Theorem 10.14
$45 = \frac{1}{2}(180 - 10x)$	Substitution
$90 = 180 - 10x$	Multiply.
$-90 = -10x$	Subtract.
$9 = x$	Divide.

Go Online!

Anticipation Guide

Students should complete the *Chapter 9 Anticipation Guide*, and discuss how their responses have changed now that they have completed Chapter 9.

9-7 Equations of Circles

G.GPE.1, G.GPE.4

Write the equation of each circle.

32. center at (–2, 4), radius 5 $(x+2)^2+(y-4)^2=25$

33. center at (1, 2), diameter 14 $(x-1)^2+(y-2)^2=49$

Give the coordinates of the center and the measure of the radius of each circle.

34. $x^2+y^2=16$ (0, 0); $r=4$

35. $(x-1)^2+(y+5)^2-4=0$ (1, –5); $r=2$

36. $y^2+(y+4)^2=9$ (0, –4); $r=3$

37. $(x-3)^2+(y-1)^2+7=16$ (3, 1); $r=3$

38. $(x-5)^2+(y+1)^2=36$ (5, –1); $r=6$

39. $(y+2)^2=49-(x+8)^2$ (–8, –2); $r=7$

Find the point(s) of intersection between the circle and line.

40. $(x-1)^2+y^2=25$; $y=5$ (1, 5)

41. $(x-3)^2+(y+2)^2=25$; $y=x$ (3, 3), (–2, –2)

42. $(x+3)^2+(y-4)^2=9$; $y=-x+4$ (–3, 7), (0, 4)

43. **FIREWOOD** In an outdoor training course, Kat learns a wood-chopping safety check that involves making a circle with her arm extended, to ensure she will not hit anything overhead as she chops. If her reach is 19 inches, the hatchet handle is 15 inches, and her shoulder is located at the origin, what is the equation of Kat's safety circle? $x^2+y^2=1156$

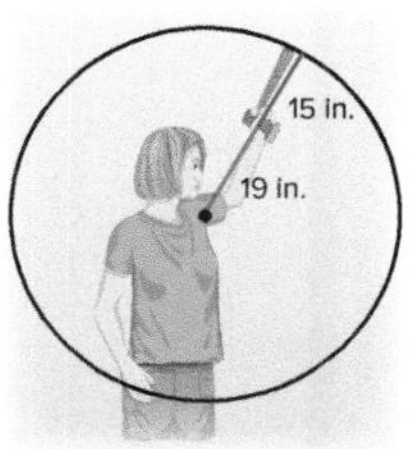

Example 7

Write the equation of the circle graphed below.

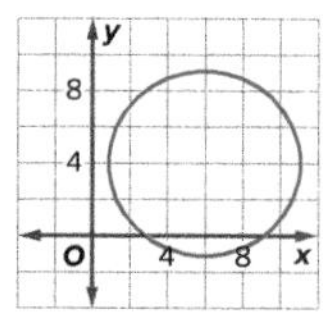

The center is at (6, 4) and the radius is 5.

$(x-h)^2+(y-k)^2=r^2$ Equation of a circle

$(x-6)^2+(y-4)^2=5^2$ $(h, k)=(6, 4)$ and $r=5$

$(x-6)^2+(y-4)^2=25$ Simplify.

Before the Test

Have students complete the Study Notebook Tie it Together activity to review topics and skills presented in the chapter.

Go Online!

eAssessment

Customize and create multiple versions of chapter tests and answer keys that align to your standards. Tests can be delivered on paper or online.

CHAPTER 9
Study Guide and Review *Continued*

9-8 Equations of Parabolas

G.GPE.2

Write an equation of each parabola.

44. focus (0, 2), directrix $y = -2$ $x^2 = 8y$

45. focus (4, 0), directrix $x = -4$ $y^2 = 16x$

46. focus (0, −5), directrix $y = 5$ $x^2 = -20y$

47. focus (4, −3), vertex (1, −3) $(y + 3)^2 = 12(x - 1)$

48. focus $\left(-2, -\frac{1}{2}\right)$, directrix $y = \frac{5}{2}$ $(x + 2)^2 = -6(y - 1)$

Example 8

Write an equation of the parabola with focus at (0, 3) and directrix $y = -3$.

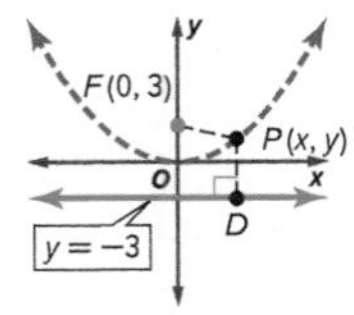

Step 1 Graph $F(0, 3)$ and $y = -3$.

Step 2 Label a point $D(x, -3)$ on $y = -3$ such that $\overline{PD}$ is perpendicular to the line $y = -3$.

Step 3 Use the Distance Formula to find PD and PF.

$$PD = \sqrt{(x - x)^2 + [y - (-3)]^2} = \sqrt{(y + 3)^2}$$
$$PF = \sqrt{(x - 0)^2 + (y - 3)^2} = \sqrt{x^2 + (y - 3)^2}$$

Step 4 Because $PD = PF$, set these expressions equal to each other.

$$\sqrt{(y + 3)^2} = \sqrt{x^2 + (y - 3)^2} \quad PD = PF$$
$$(y + 3)^2 = x^2 + (y - 3)^2 \quad \text{Square each side.}$$
$$y^2 + 6y + 9 = x^2 + y^2 - 6y + 9 \quad \text{Square binomials.}$$
$$12y = x^2 \text{ or } y = \frac{1}{12}x^2 \quad \text{Subtract.}$$

CHAPTER 9

Practice Test

Go Online! for another Chapter Test

1. **POOLS** Amanda's family has a swimming pool that is 4 feet deep in their backyard. If the diameter of the pool is 25 feet, what is the circumference of the pool to the nearest foot? **79 ft**

2. Find the exact circumference of the circle below. **32π**

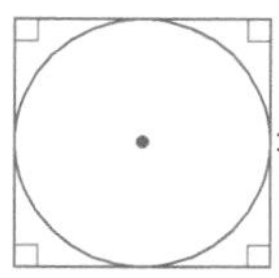

Find the value of x.

3. **23**

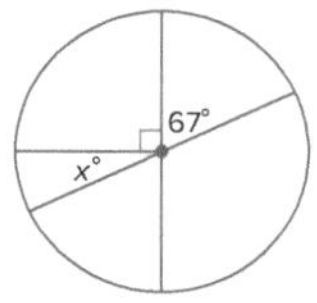

4. **95**

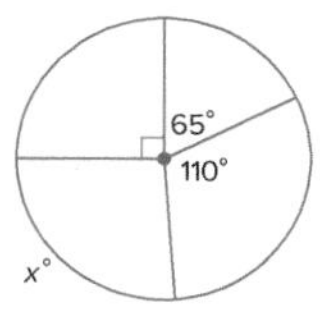

5. **4.1 in.**

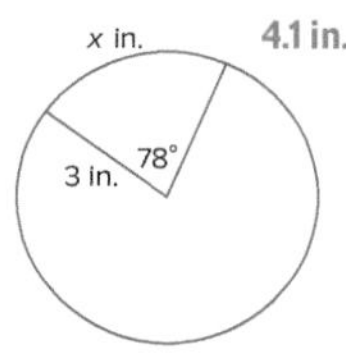

6. **3**

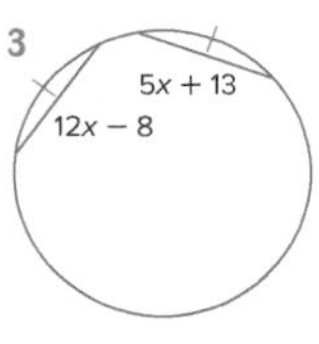

7. **MULTIPLE CHOICE** What is CD? **D**

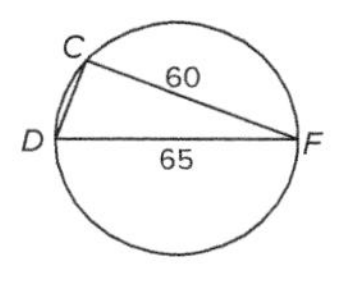

A 15

B 25

C 88.5

D Not enough information is given.

8. Find x if $\odot M \cong \odot N$. **9**

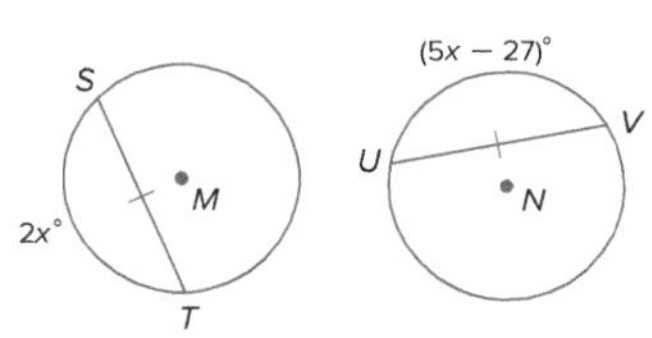

9. **MULTIPLE CHOICE** If $\overline{HK}$ is tangent to circle O, what is the radius of the circle? **A**

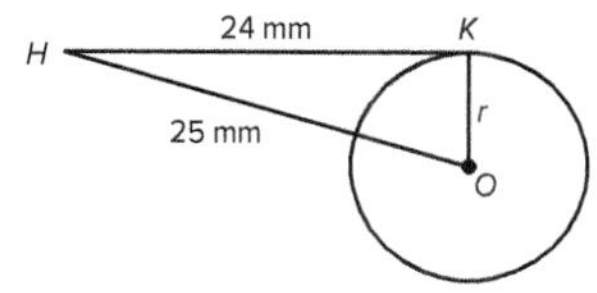

A 7 mm

B 8 mm

C 9 mm

D 10 mm

10. Determine whether $\overline{FG}$ is tangent to $\odot E$. Justify your answer. **See margin.**

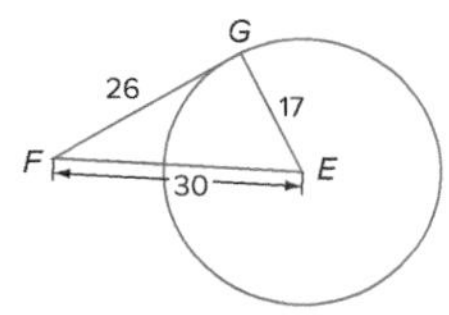

11. Find the perimeter of the triangle at the right. Assume that segments that appear to be tangent are tangent. **58**

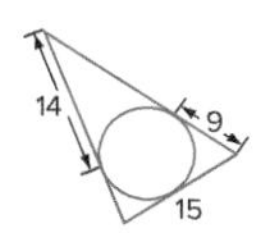

Find each measure.

12. $m\angle T$ **77**

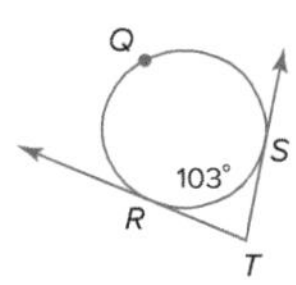

13. $m\angle AEB$ **115**

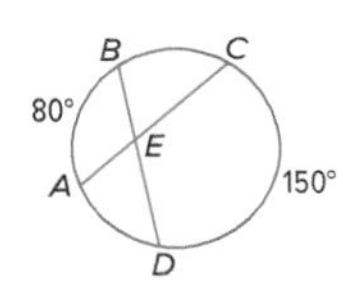

Write the equation of each circle.

14. center at $(-2, 5)$, radius 4 **$(x + 2)^2 + (y - 5)^2 = 16$**

15. center at $(1, 0)$, diameter 12 **$(x - 1)^2 + y^2 = 36$**

Find an equation of the parabola with the focus and directrix given.

16. $(0, 6)$, $y = -6$ **$y = \frac{1}{24}x^2$**

17. $\left(-\frac{3}{4}, 0\right)$, $x = \frac{3}{4}$ **$x = -\frac{1}{3}y^2$**

Go Online!

Chapter Tests

You can use premade leveled *Chapter Tests* to differentiate assessment for your students. Students can also take self-checking *Chapter Tests* to plan and prepare for chapter assessments.

MC = multiple-choice questions

FR = free-response questions

Form	Type	Level
1	MC	AL
2A	MC	OL
2B	FR	OL
2C	FR	OL
3	FR	BL
Vocabulary Test		
Extended-Response Test		

RtI Response to Intervention

Use the Intervention Planner to help you determine your Response to Intervention.

Intervention Planner

TIER 1 On Level OL

IF students miss 25% of the exercises or less,

THEN choose a resource:

SE Lessons 9-1 through 9-8

Go Online!

- Skills Practice
- Chapter Project
- Self-Check Quizzes

TIER 2 Strategic Intervention AL

Approaching grade level

IF students miss 50% of the exercises,

THEN choose a resource:

Quick Review Math Handbook

Go Online!

- Study Guide and Intervention
- Extra Examples
- Personal Tutors
- Homework Help

TIER 3 Intensive Intervention

2 or more grades below level

IF students miss 75% of the exercises,

THEN choose a resource:

Use *Math Triumphs, Geometry*

Go Online!

- Extra Examples
- Personal Tutors
- Homework Help
- Review Vocabulary

Additional Answer

10. No; $\triangle EFG$ is not a right triangle, so $\angle G$ is not a right angle and $\overline{FG}$ cannot be tangent.

Launch

Objective Apply concepts and skills from this chapter in a real-world setting.

Teach

Ask:

- Part A: How do we use the information? Sample answer: Use the property that inscribed angles measure half the intercepted arc.
- Part B: How do we find the measures of the angles? Sample answer: We find the measures of the arcs intercepted by the given angles and then subtract from 360° to find the measures of the remaining arcs.
- Part C: How do we find the property? Sample answer: We use the inscribed angle measure property and the fact that the sum of the measures of the arcs of a circle is 360°.
- Part D: How do we determine which types are cyclic quadrilaterals? Sample answer: We visualize the angle properties of each type of quadrilateral and apply the property we found in part C.
- Part E: How do we find the equation of the circle? Sample answer: We use the properties of the quadrilateral to find the center and the radius of the circle.

The Performance Task focuses on the following content standards and standards for mathematical practice.

Dual Coding		
Items	Content Standards	MP Mathematical Practices
1	G.C.2	1
2	G.C.2	2
3	G.C.3	5
4	G.C.3	5
5	G.CO.11, G.C.3	5
6	G.CO.11	2
7	G.GPE.1	1

Go Online! eBook

Interactive Student Guide

Refer to *Interactive Student Guide* for an additional Performance Task.

CHAPTER 9
Preparing for Assessment

Performance Task

Provide a clear solution to each part of the task. Be sure to show all of your work. Include all relevant drawings and justify your answers.

BADGE DESIGN Jasmin is designing a circular badge where she circumscribes a circle around different polygons.

Part A

Sense-Making Jasmin is wondering if all triangles can be inscribed in a circle. She takes a particular triangle ABC where $m\angle A = 58°$; $m\angle B = 60°$, and $m\angle C = 62°$.

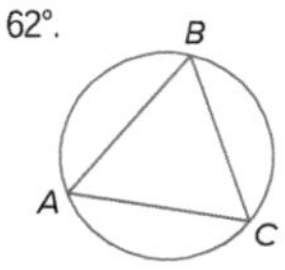

1. What are the measures of $\widehat{AB}$, $\widehat{CB}$, and $\widehat{AC}$? 1. $m\widehat{AB} = 124°$; $m\widehat{CB} = 116°$; $m\widehat{AC} = 120°$
2. Explain why a unique circle passes through the points A, B, and C. By the Circumcenter Theorem, the perpendicular bisectors of the sides of $\triangle ABC$ intersect at a point P that is equidistant from A, B, and C. The required circle has its center at point P and has radius AP, and there is only one such circle.

Part B

Reasoning Next, Jasmin circumscribes a circle about quadrilateral $EFGH$.

3. Given $m\angle E = 130°$ and $m\angle F = 70°$, find $m\angle G$ and $m\angle H$. $m\angle H = 110°$; $m\angle G = 50°$

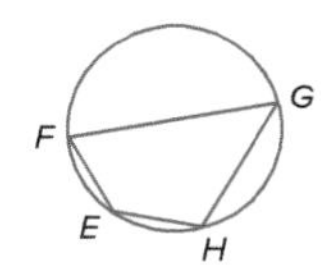

Part C

A quadrilateral inscribed in a circle can be referred to as a ***cyclic quadrilateral.*** Quadrilateral $EFGH$ is an example of a cyclic quadrilateral.

4. State a property regarding pairs of angles in a cyclic quadrilateral. Opposite angles are supplementary.

Part D

Construct an Argument

5. Determine whether each of the following can be inscribed in a circle. Explain why or why not.
   a. square Yes; opposite angles of a square are always supplementary.
   b. rhombus Yes; if the rhombus is a square.
   c. rectangle Yes; opposite angles of a rectangle are always supplementary.
   d. parallelogram Yes; if the parallelogram is a rectangle.
   e. trapezoid Yes; if the trapezoid is isosceles and has opposite angles that are supplememtary.
   f. kite Yes; if one pair of opposite angles are right angles.

Part E 7. $\left(x+\frac{1}{2}\right)^2+\left(y-\frac{7}{2}\right)^2=\frac{25}{2}$

A quadrilateral $ABCD$ with vertices $A(0, 0)$, $B(-4, 3)$, $C(-1, 7)$, and $D(3, 4)$ is inscribed in a circle.

6. What type of special quadrilateral is $ABCD$? square
7. Find an equation for the circle.

Levels of Complexity Chart

The levels of the exercises progress from 1 to 3, with Level 1 indicating the lowest level of complexity.

Parts	Level 1	Level 2	Level 3
A	●		
B		●	
C		●	
D			●
E			●

Differentiated Instruction

Extension Given the vertices of a rectangle, find an equation of the circumscribed circle.

Test-Taking Strategy

Example

Read the problem. Identify what you need to know. Then use the given information to solve the problem.

Solve for x in the figure.

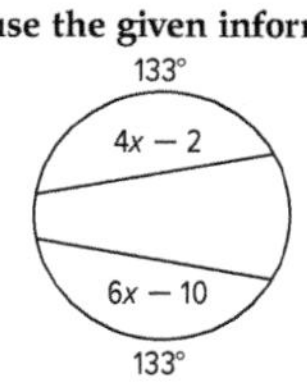

A 2
B 3
C 4
D 6

Step 1 **What parts of a circle are given in the diagram?**
two chords and two arc lengths

Step 2 **What properties can you use?**
Two chords are congruent if and only if their corresponding minor arcs are congruent.

Step 3 **How can you solve the problem?**
The minor arcs are congruent, so the chords are congruent. Write and solve an equation.

$4x - 2 = 6x - 10$ Definition of Congruent Segments

$-2x = -8$

$x = 4$ Simplify.

Step 4 **What is the answer?** C

Test-Taking Tip

Properties of Circles
When solving problems involving circles, start by identifying special properties and relationships among angles, arcs, and segments that intersect the circle. Then use those relationships to solve for unknown measures.

Apply the Strategy

Read each problem. Identify what you need to know. Then use the given information to solve the problem.

In the figure shown, what is $m\angle S$?

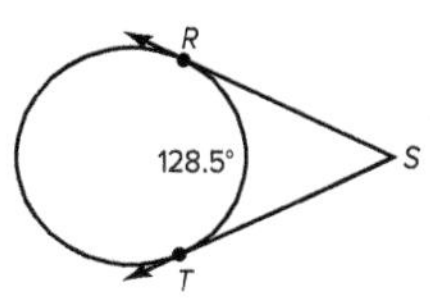

A 51.5
B 77
C 128.5
D 257

a. What parts of a circle are given in the diagram? two tangents

b. What properties can you use? an angle and intercepted arcs on a circle

c. How can you solve the problem? The measure of the angle is one half the difference of the measures of the intercepted arcs. $m\angle S = \frac{1}{2}(231.5° - 128.5°) = 51.5°$

d. What is the answer? A

Test-Taking Strategy

Step 1 Review the parts of a circle and their relationships. Key parts include radius, diameter, arc, chord, tangent, secant.

Step 2 Determine what you are being asked to find and determine what theorems or properties apply to the problem situation.

Step 3 Apply the theorems or properties to solve the problem

Step 4 Find the answer and check it to make sure it makes sense.

Need Another Example?

Solve for x in the figure.

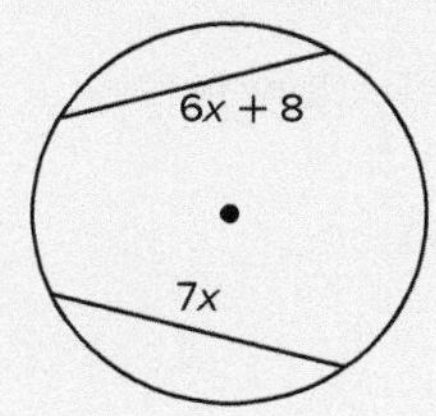

A 1
B 8
C 13
D not enough information given

Ask:

a. What parts of a circle are given in the diagram? two chords

b. What properties can you use? none; There is not enough information given.

c. How can you solve the problem? If the minor arcs were congruent, the chords would be congruent.

d. What is the answer? D

Go Online!

The most up-to-date resources available for your program can be found at connectED.mcgraw-hill.com.

Diagnose Student Errors

Survey student responses for each item. Class trends may indicate common errors and misconceptions.

1.	A	Calculated $\sqrt{23^2 + 9^2}$ for the length of $\overline{RS}$
	B	CORRECT
	C	Found $RQ + SQ$
	D	Found RS

2.	A	CORRECT
	B	Used incorrect signs for the coordinates of the center
	C	Took r^2 to be the radius
	D	Used incorrect signs for the coordinates of the center and took r^2 to be the radius

3.	A	Did not realize that two reflections is the same as a translation
	B	Did not realize that two reflections is the same as a translation
	C	CORRECT
	D	Did not realize that a translation is needed to map the image to the preimage

5a.	A	Found distance from R to S
	B	CORRECT
	C	Found distance along major arc
	D	Set up arc length equation as $\ell = \frac{360}{58} \cdot 2\pi r$

6.	A	Assumed that $\angle KLM \cong \angle JKL$
	B	CORRECT
	C	Found the value of y
	D	Solved $2y + 36 = 50$

8.	A	Did not recognize that an isosceles triangle must have line symmetry
	B	Did not recognize that a parallelogram must have rotational symmetry
	C	Did not recognize that a regular pentagon must have line and rotational symmetry
	D	CORRECT
	E	CORRECT

Go Online!

Standardized Test Practice

Students can take self-checking tests in standardized format to plan and prepare for standardized assessments.

CHAPTER 9

Preparing for Assessment

Cumulative Review

Read each question. Then fill in the correct answer on the answer document provided by your teacher or on a sheet of paper.

1. $\overline{RS}$ is tangent to circle Q at point R.

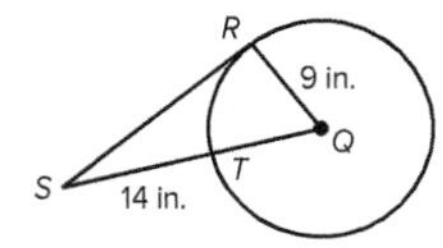

Which of the following is the best estimate of the perimeter of $\triangle QRS$? G.C.2 **B**

- ○ A 56.7 in.
- ○ B 53.2 in.
- ○ C 32.0 in.
- ○ D 21.2 in.

2. Which of the following is the best description of the circle with equation $x^2 + y^2 - 6x + 4y + 9 = 0$? G.GPE.1 **A**

- ○ A The center is (3, −2) and the radius is 2.
- ○ B The center is (−3, 2) and the radius is 2.
- ○ C The center is (3, −2) and the radius is 4.
- ○ D The center is (−3, 2) and the radius is 4.

3. Trapezoid $ABCD$ is shown below. G.CO.5 **C**

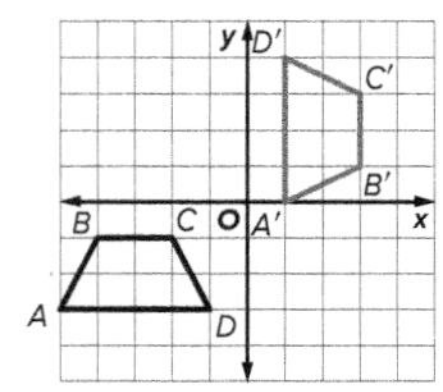

$ABCD$ is transformed to create a congruent image. What sequence of transformations created $A'B'C'D'$?

- ○ A Two reflections and a translation
- ○ B Two reflections and a rotation
- ○ C Rotation, reflection, and translation
- ○ D Rotation and reflection

4. Sean draws a triangle with vertices A, B, and C so that $AB = 11.6$ centimeters and $BC = 14.7$ centimeters. What is the greatest possible whole-number length of $\overline{AC}$, in centimeters? G.CO.10 **26**

5. A pendulum sweeps out an arc of a circle as shown. G.C.5

a. Which of the following is the best estimate of the distance the tip of the pendulum travels as it moves from point R to point S and back to point R? **B**

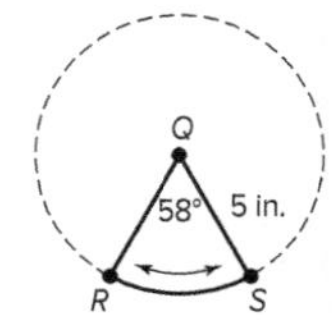

- ○ A 5.1 in.
- ○ B 10.1 in.
- ○ C 52.7 in.
- ○ D 390.0 in.

b. MP What mathematical practice did you use to solve this problem? **See students' work.**

6. What is $m\angle KLM$? G.C.2 **B**

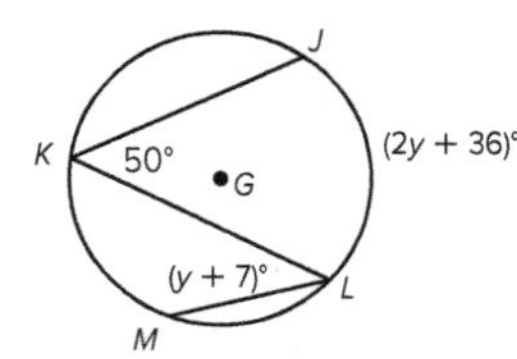

- ○ A 50
- ○ B 39
- ○ C 32
- ○ D 14

Test-Taking Tip

Question 6 There are two steps to solving this problem. First work with $\angle JKL$ and $\overset{\frown}{JL}$, then work with $\angle KLM$ once you know the value of y.

9.	A	Subtracted $22 - 18$
	B	CORRECT
	C	Calculated $\sqrt{11^2 + 9^2}$
	D	Calculated $\sqrt{22^2 - 9^2}$

10.	A	CORRECT
	B	Took slope of given line to be 2
	C	Found equation of line parallel to given line
	D	Took slope of given line to be 2 and found equation of line parallel to given line

11.	A	Found the value of x
	B	Found $m\angle LKM$
	C	Assumed $\overset{\frown}{LM} \cong \overset{\frown}{LK}$
	D	CORRECT

12.	A	Doubled the value of y
	B	CORRECT
	C	Found the value of y
	D	Found length of $\overline{NL}$

13.	A	Reflected image of point P in x-axis rather than y-axis
	B	CORRECT
	C	Found distance from P to image of P under first transformation
	D	Took first transformation to be a reflection in x-axis

Go Online! for Standardized Test Practice

7. Square $ABCD$ is inscribed in $\odot Q$, as shown. What is the circumference of $\odot Q$, in meters? Round to the nearest tenth. G.GMD.1 31.1

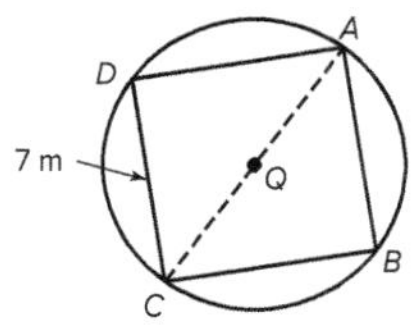

8. Melinda drew a figure with no line symmetry and no rotational symmetry. Select all terms that could describe the figure Melinda drew. G.CO.3 D, E

- ☐ A Isosceles triangle
- ☐ B Parallelogram
- ☐ C Regular pentagon
- ☐ D Scalene triangle
- ☐ E Trapezoid

9. The diameter of $\odot K$ is 22 centimeters and $\overline{PQ}$ is 18 centimeters long.

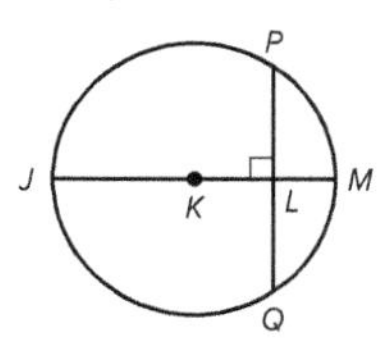

Which of the following is closest to the length of $\overline{KL}$? G.C.2 B

- ○ A 4.0 cm
- ○ C 14.2 cm
- ○ B 6.3 cm
- ○ D 20.1 cm

10. What is the equation of the line through (2, 2) that is perpendicular to the line $2x + y = 1$? G.GPE.5 A

- ○ A $y = \frac{1}{2}x + 1$
- ○ C $y = -2x + 6$
- ○ B $y = -\frac{1}{2}x + 3$
- ○ D $y = 2x - 2$

11. In the figure, $m\angle JKL = (2x + 2)$.

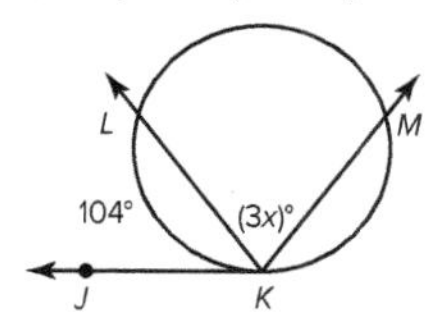

What is $m\widehat{LM}$? G.C.2 D

- ○ A 25
- ○ C 104
- ○ B 75
- ○ D 150

12. Quadrilateral $JKLM$ is a rectangle.

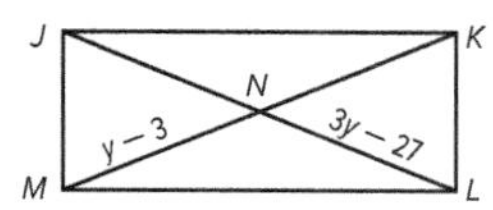

What is the length of the diagonal $\overline{JL}$? G.CO.11 B

- ○ A 24
- ○ C 12
- ○ B 18
- ○ D 9

13. Dinesh plotted the point $P(-1, 3)$. Then he applied the transformation $(x, y) \rightarrow (-y, x)$ followed by the transformation $(x, y) \rightarrow (-x, y)$. What is the distance between point P and its final image? G.CO.5 B

- ○ A $2\sqrt{2}$
- ○ C $2\sqrt{5}$
- ○ B $4\sqrt{2}$
- ○ D $2\sqrt{10}$

Need Extra Help?

If you missed Question...	1	2	3	4	5	6	7	8	9	10	11	12	13
Go to Lesson...	9-5	9-7	3-4	5-5	9-2	9-4	9-1	3-5	9-3	2-8	9-6	6-4	3-4

LEARNSMART®

Use LearnSmart as part of your test-preparation plan to measure student topic retention. You can create a student assignment in LearnSmart for additional practice on these topics.

- Understand Circles on the Coordinate Plane
- Understand Parabolas on the Coordinate Plane

Formative Assessment

You can use these pages to benchmark student progress.

Standardized Test Practice

Test Item Formats

In the Cumulative Review, students will encounter different formats for assessment questions to prepare them for standardized tests.

Question Type	Exercises
Multiple-Choice	1–3, 5–6, 9–13
Multiple Correct Answers	8
Short Response	4, 7
Extended Response	5

Answer Sheet Practice

Have students simulate taking a standardized test by recording their answers on a practice recording sheet.

Homework Option

Get Ready for Chapter 10 Assign students the exercises on p. 724 as homework to assess whether they possess the prerequisite skills needed for the next chapter.

Go Online!

eAssessment

Customize and create multiple versions of chapter tests and answer keys that align to your standards. Tests can be delivered on paper or online.

Lesson 9-3

34b. Sample answer: I assumed that there was only one entrance per wall of the store. If there were 2 entrances on one wall or all three entrances on the same wall, the display could not be equidistant from each entrance. The display should be at the center of the circle that intersects each entrance. By Th. 9.4, the perpendicular bisector of a chord is a diameter or radius of the circle. I constructed the perpendicular bisectors of pathways between each entrance. The intersection of the perpendicular bisectors is the center of the circle.

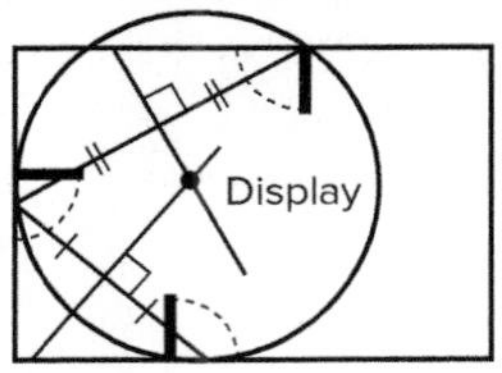

35. About 17.3; P and Q are equidistant from the endpoints of $\overline{AB}$ so they both lie on the perpendicular bisector of $\overline{AB}$, so $\overline{PQ}$ is the perpendicular bisector of $\overline{AB}$. Hence, both segments of $\overline{AB}$ are 5. Because $\overline{PS}$ is perpendicular to chord $\overline{AB}$, $\angle PSA$ is a right angle. So, $\triangle PSA$ is a right triangle. By the Pythagorean Theorem, $PS = \sqrt{(PA)^2 - (AS)^2}$. By substitution, $PS = \sqrt{11^2 - 5^2}$ or $\sqrt{96}$. Similarly, $\triangle ASQ$ is a right triangle with $SQ = \sqrt{(AQ)^2 - (AS)^2} = \sqrt{9^2 - 5^2}$ or $\sqrt{56}$. Because $PQ = PS + SQ$, $PQ = \sqrt{96} + \sqrt{56}$ or about 17.3.

37a. Given: $\overline{CD}$ is the perpendicular bisector of chord $\overline{AB}$ in $\odot X$.

Prove: $\overline{CD}$ contains point X.

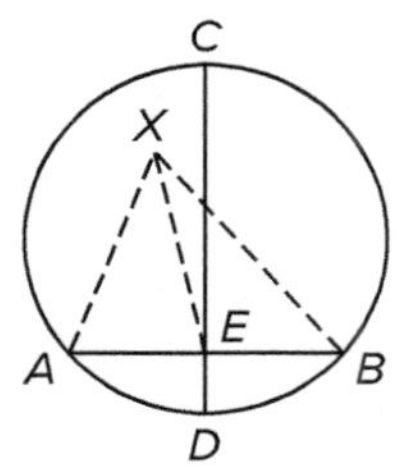

Proof:

Suppose X is not on $\overline{CD}$. Draw $\overline{XE}$ and radii $\overline{XA}$ and $\overline{XB}$. Because $\overline{CD}$ is the perpendicular bisector of $\overline{AB}$, E is the midpoint of $\overline{AB}$ and $\overline{AE} \cong \overline{EB}$. Also, $\overline{XA} \cong \overline{XB}$, since all radii of a $\odot$ are $\cong$. $\overline{XE} \cong \overline{XE}$ by the Reflexive Property. So, $\triangle AXE \cong \triangle BXE$ *by SSS*. By CPCTC, $\angle XEA \cong \angle XEB$. Because they also form a linear pair, $\angle XEA$ and $\angle XEB$ are right angles. So $\overline{XE} \perp \overline{AB}$. By definition $\overline{XE}$ is the perpendicular bisector of $\overline{AB}$. But $\overline{CD}$ is also the perpendicular bisector of $\overline{AB}$. This contradicts the uniqueness of a perpendicular bisector of a segment. Thus, the assumption is false, and center X must be on $\overline{CD}$.

37b. Given: In $\odot X$, X is on $\overline{CD}$ and $\overline{FG}$ bisects $\overline{CD}$ at O.

Prove: Point O is point X.

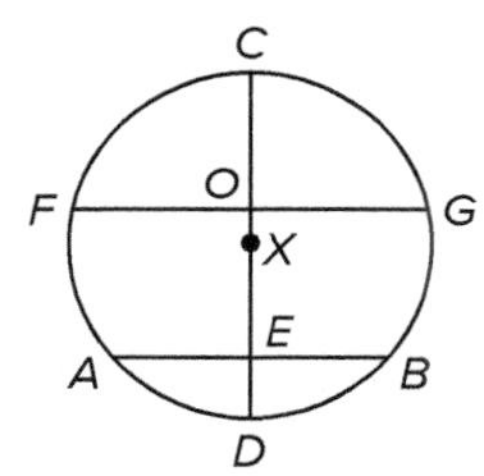

Proof:

Because point X is on $\overline{CD}$ and C and D are on $\odot X$, $\overline{CD}$ is a diameter of $\odot X$. Because $\overline{FG}$ bisects $\overline{CD}$ at O, O is the midpoint of $\overline{CD}$. Because the midpoint of a diameter is the center of a circle, O is the center of the circle. Therefore, point O is point X.

38. Sample answer:

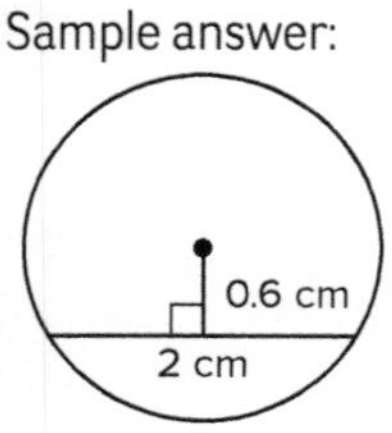

radius $\approx$ 1.2 cm

39. No; sample answer: In a circle with a radius of 12, an arc with a measure of 60 determines a chord of length 12. The triangle related to a central angle of 60 is equilateral. If the measure of the arc is tripled to 180, then the chord determined by the arc is a diameter and has a length of 2(12) or 24, which is not three times as long as the original chord.

Lesson 9-4

40. Part I: **Given:** $\widehat{ADC}$ is a semicircle.

Prove: $\angle ABC$ is a right angle.

Proof: Because $\widehat{ADC}$ is a semicircle, then $m\widehat{ADC} = 180$. Because $\angle ABC$ is an inscribed angle, then $m\angle ABC = \frac{1}{2}m\widehat{ADC}$ or 90. So by definition $\angle ABC$ is a right angle.

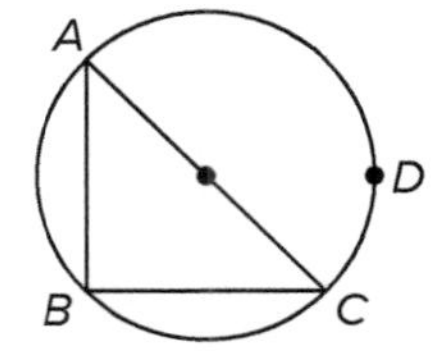

Part II: **Given:** $\angle ABC$ a right angle.

Prove: $\widehat{ADC}$ is a semicircle.

Proof: Because $\angle ABC$ is an inscribed angle, then $m\angle ABC = \frac{1}{2}m\widehat{ADC}$ and by the Multiplication Property of Equality, $m\widehat{ADC} = 2m\angle ABC$. Because $\angle ABC$ is a right angle, $m\angle ABC = 90$. Then $m\widehat{ADC} = 2(90)$ or 180. So by definition, $\widehat{ADC}$ is a semicircle.

41a.

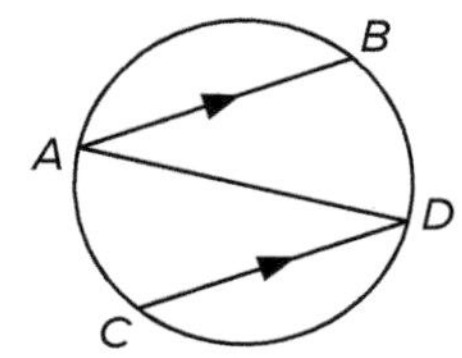

41b. Sample answer: $m\angle A = 30$, $m\angle D = 30$; $m\widehat{AC} = 60$, $m\widehat{BD} = 60$; The arcs are congruent because they have equal measures.

42. Always; squares have right angles at each vertex, therefore each pair of opposite angles will be supplementary and inscribed in a circle.

43. Always; rectangles have right angles at each vertex, therefore each pair of opposite angles will be supplementary and inscribed in a circle.

44. Sometimes; a parallelogram can be inscribed in a circle as long as it is a rectangle.

45. Sometimes; a rhombus can be inscribed in a cirlce as long as it is a square. Because the opposite angles of rhombi that are not squares are not supplementary, they cannot be inscribed in a circle.

46. Sometimes; as long as the angles that compose the congruent pair of opposite angles are right angles.

48. Sample answer: According to Theorem 9.8, an inscribed angle of a triangle intercepts a diameter if the angle is a right angle. Therefore, the hypotenuse is a diameter and has a length of $2r$. Using trigonometry, each leg $= \sin 45° \cdot 2r$ or $\sqrt{2}r$.

50. An inscribed angle has its vertex on the circle. A central angle has its vertex at the center of the circle. If an inscribed angle and a central angle intercept the same arc, then the measure of the inscribed angle is one-half the measure of the central angle.

Lesson 9-5 (Guided Practice)

1A.

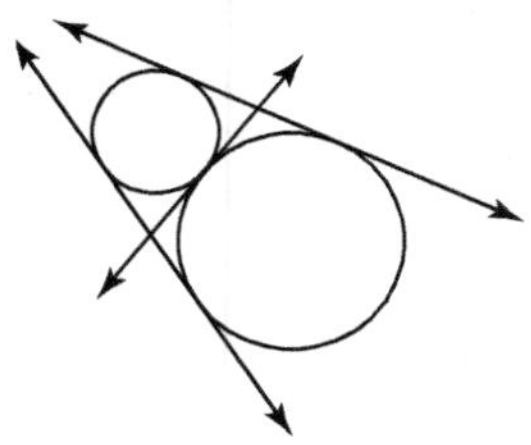

1B.

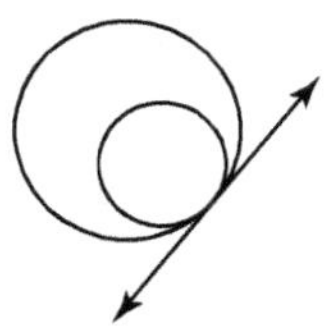

Lesson 9-5

34. Sample answer:

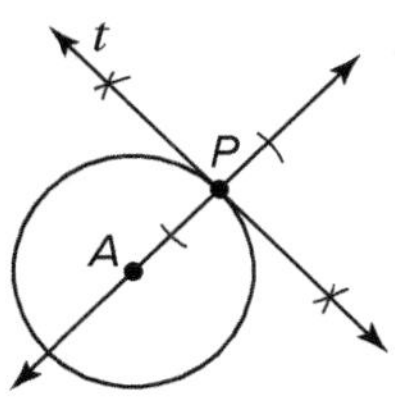

a. Draw $\overleftrightarrow{AP}$. (Two points determine a line.)

b. Construct a perpendicular at P. (The tangent is perpendicular to the radius at its endpoint.)

35. Sample answer:

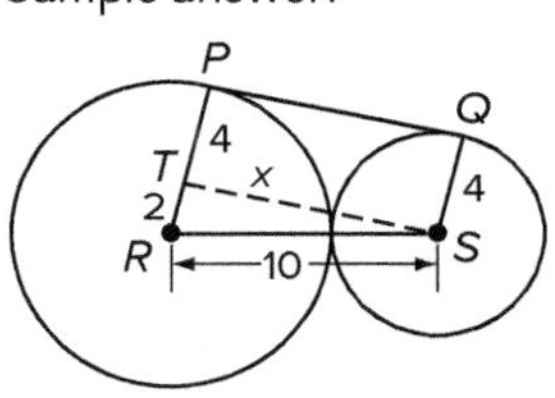

Using the Pythagorean Theorem, $2^2 + x^2 = 10^2$, so $x \approx 9.8$. Since $PQST$ is a rectangle, $PQ = x = 9.8$.

36. First, a compass is used to draw circle C and a point A outside circle C. Segment $\overline{CA}$ is drawn. There is exactly one line through points A and C. Next, a line ℓ is constructed bisecting $\overline{CA}$. According to the definition of a perpendicular bisector, point X is the midpoint of $\overline{AC}$. A second circle, X, is then drawn with a radius $\overline{XC}$ which intersects circle C at points D and E. Two circles can intersect at a maximum of two points. $\overleftrightarrow{AD}$ and $\overline{DC}$ are then drawn, and $\triangle ADC$ is inscribed in a semicircle. $\angle ADC$ is a right angle and $\overleftrightarrow{AD}$ is tangent to $\odot C$. $\overleftrightarrow{AD}$ is tangent to $\odot C$ at point D because it intersects the circle in exactly one point.

37. Sample answer:

circumscribed

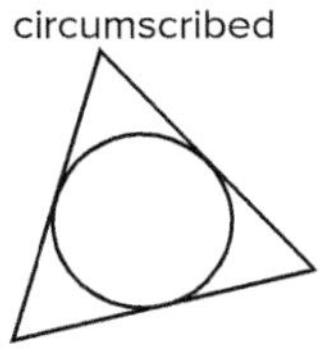

inscribed

39. No; sample answer: from a point outside the circle, two tangents can be drawn. From a point on the circle, one tangent can be drawn. From a point inside the circle, no tangents can be drawn because a line would intersect the circle in two points.

Extend 9-5

2. Sample answers:

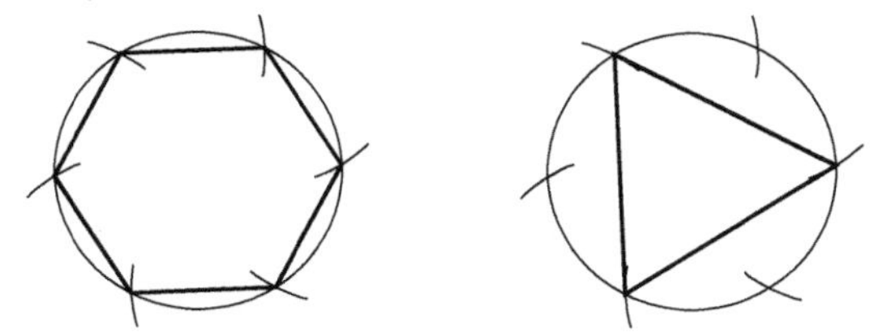

3. Sample answers:

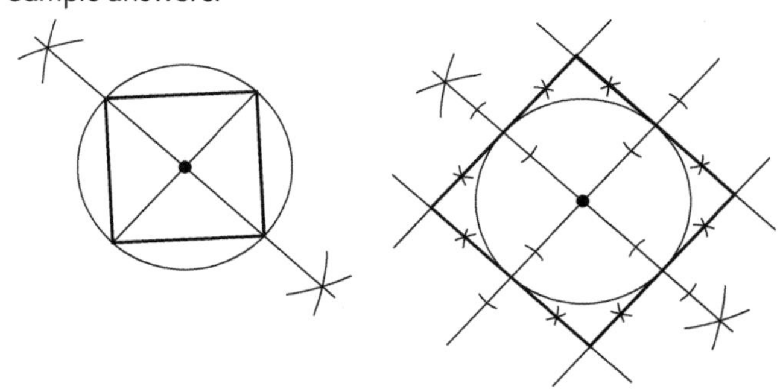

4. Sample answer:

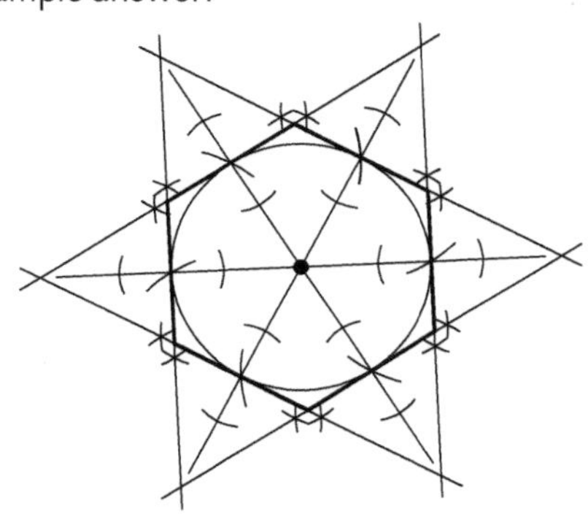

Lesson 9-7

39b. I used a coordinate grid with Consuela's house at (0, 0), and the pizza restaurant at (−4, 5). By the Pythagorean Theorem, Consuela's house is $\sqrt{41}$ or approximately 6.4 miles away from the pizza place. The equation of the circle for free delivery is $(x + 4)^2 + (y - 5)^2 = 41$. Consuela's friend's house is at (−1, −1). Substitute this ordered pair into the equation of the circle for free delivery.

$(x + 4)^2 + (y - 5)^2 = 41$	Equation of circle for free delivery
$(-1 + 4)^2 + (-1 - 5)^2 \stackrel{?}{=} 41$	Substitute (−1, −1) for (x, y).
$3^2 + (-6)^2 \stackrel{?}{=} 41$	Simplify.
$9 + 36 \stackrel{?}{=} 41$	Square each term.
$45 > 41$	Compare.

This means that Consuela's friend's house is farther away from the pizza place than Consuela's house. Because Consuela's house is at the edge of the free delivery area, her friend's house is outside of the free delivery area.

42c. The locus of all points in a plane equidistant from a point is a circle. The locus of points that are both equidistant from *A* and *B* and are a distance of *AB* from *B* is the intersection of the locus of points equidistant from *A* and *B* and the locus of points that are a distance of *AB* from *B*. Graphically, the compound locus is represented as two points.

46. Given: $\overline{AB}$ is a diameter of $\odot O$, and *C* is a point on $\odot O$.

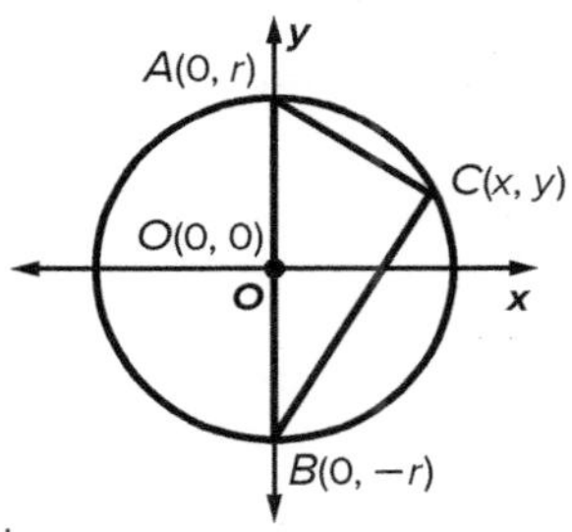

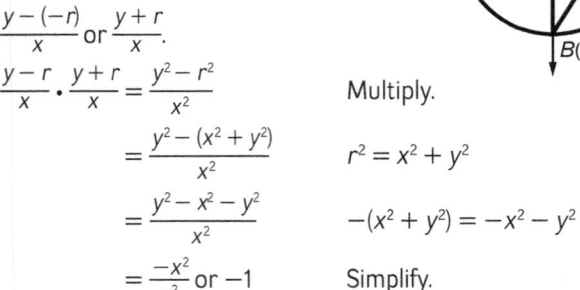

Prove: $\angle ACB$ is a right angle.

Proof:

$\overline{AC}$ has slope $\frac{y-r}{x}$, and $\overline{CB}$ has slope $\frac{y-(-r)}{x}$ or $\frac{y+r}{x}$.

$\frac{y-r}{x} \cdot \frac{y+r}{x} = \frac{y^2-r^2}{x^2}$ Multiply.

$= \frac{y^2-(x^2+y^2)}{x^2}$ $r^2 = x^2 + y^2$

$= \frac{y^2-x^2-y^2}{x^2}$ $-(x^2+y^2) = -x^2 - y^2$

$= \frac{-x^2}{x^2}$ or -1 Simplify.

Because the product of the slopes of $\overline{AC}$ and $\overline{CB}$ is -1, $\overline{AC} \perp \overline{CB}$ and $\angle ACB$ is a right angle.

47. $(x-8)^2 + (y-2)^2 = 16$; the first circle has its center at (5, −7). If the circle is shifted 3 units right and 9 units up, the new center is at (8, 2), so the new equation becomes $(x-8)^2 + (y-2)^2 = 16$.

48. Sample answer:

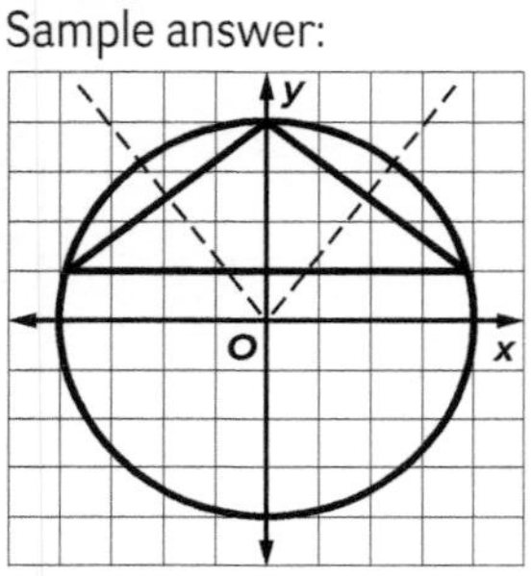

49a. 4

49b–c. Method 1: Draw a circle of radius 200 miles centered on each station. Method 2: Use the Pythagorean Theorem to identify stations that are more than 200 miles apart. Using Method 2, plot the points representing the stations on a graph. Stations that are more than 4 units apart on the graph will be more than 200 miles apart and will thus be able to use the same frequency. Assign station A to the first frequency. Station B is within 4 units of station A, so it must be assigned the second frequency. Station C is within 4 units of both stations A and B, so it must be assigned a third frequency. Station D is also within 4 units of stations A, B, and C, so it must be assigned a fourth frequency, Station E is $\sqrt{29}$ or about 5.4 units away from station A, so it can share the first frequency. Station F is $\sqrt{29}$ or about 5.4 units away from station B, so it can share the second frequency. Station G is $\sqrt{32}$ or about 5.7 units away from station C, so it can share the third frequency. Therefore, the least number of frequencies that can be assigned is 4.

52. The equation of a circle centered at the origin is the square of the Distance Formula, where $(x_1, y_1) = (0, 0)$ and the distance from the origin to the point on the circle is the radius *r*. The equation of a circle centered at a point not on the origin is the square of the distance formula, where (x_1, y_1) are the coordinates of the circle's center and the distance from $(x_1, y_1) = r$.

Lesson 9-8

8.

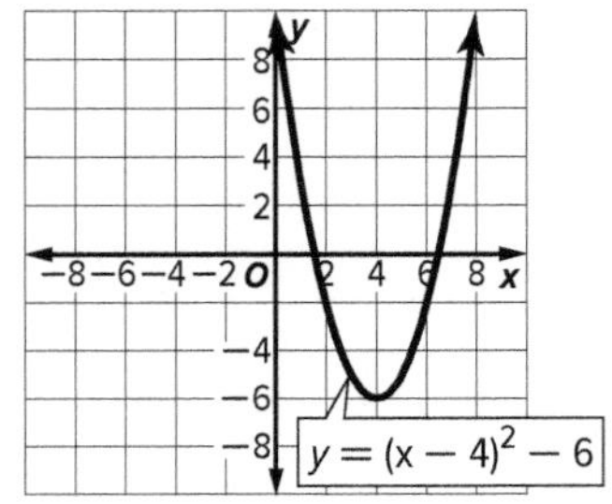

9.

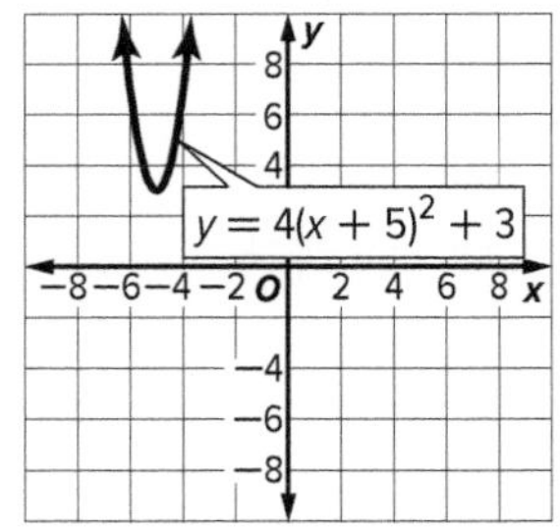

10.

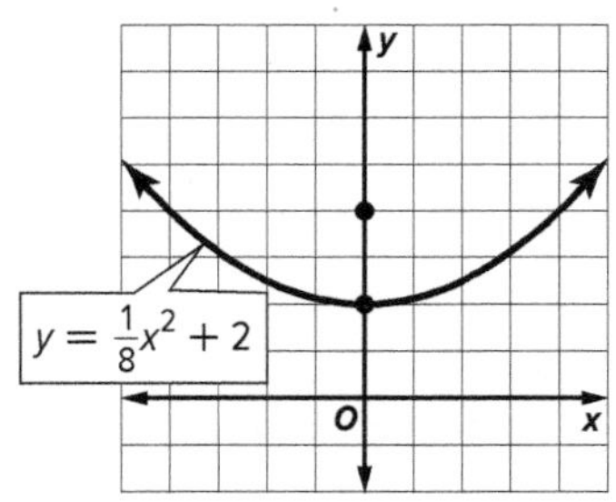

11.

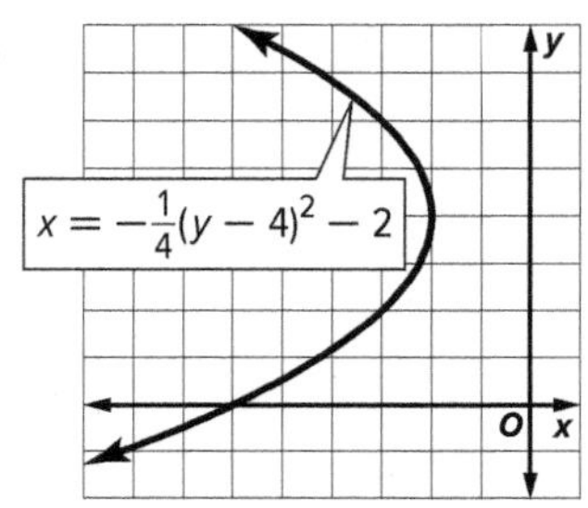

29.

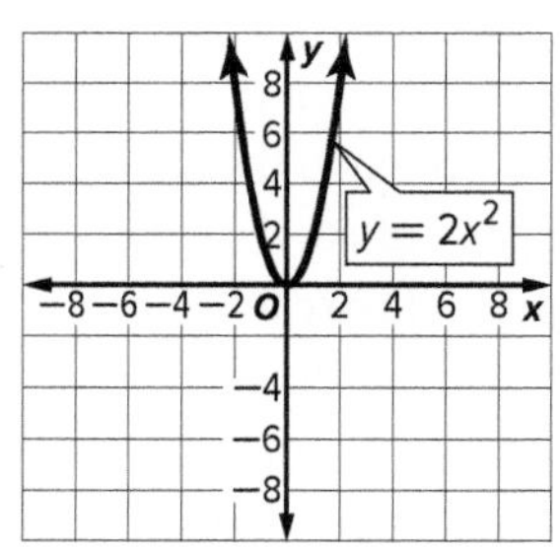

30.

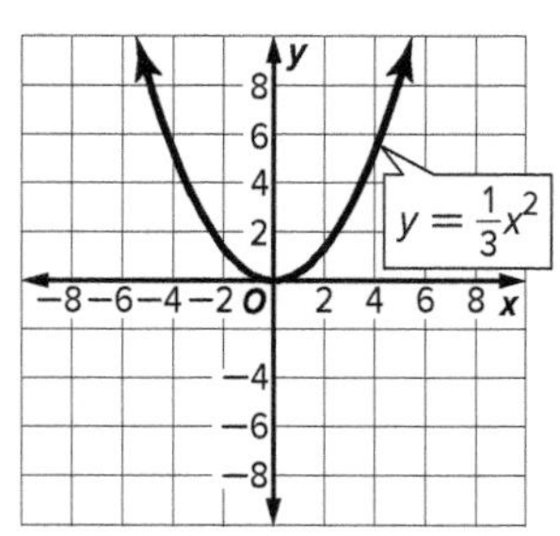

31.
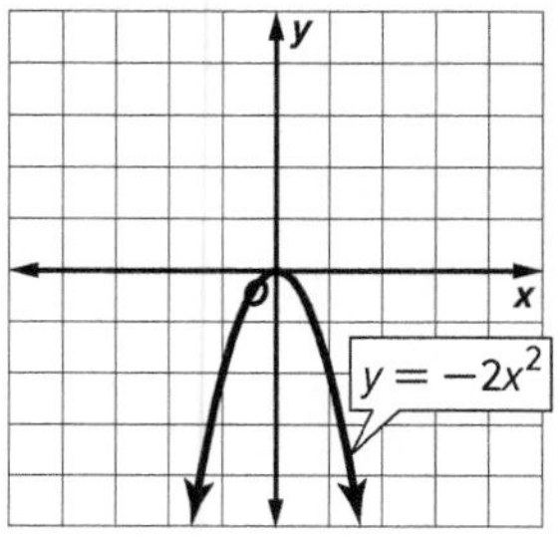

32.
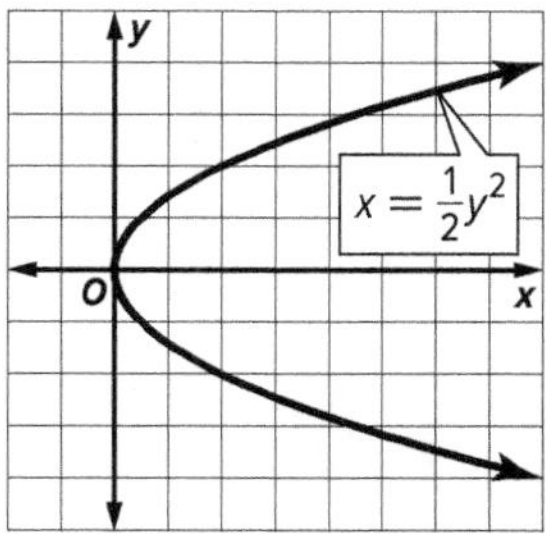

33.
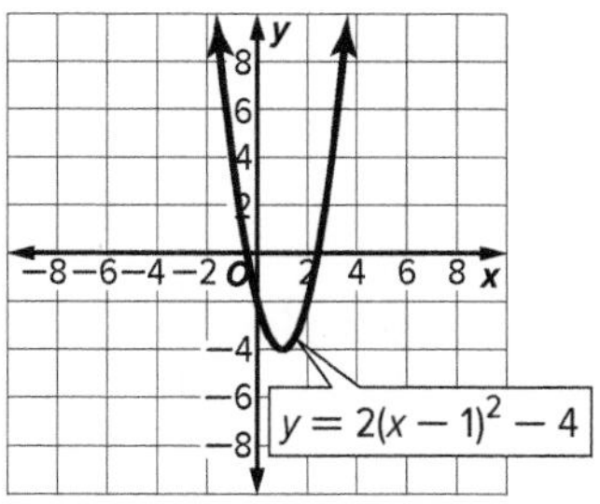

34.
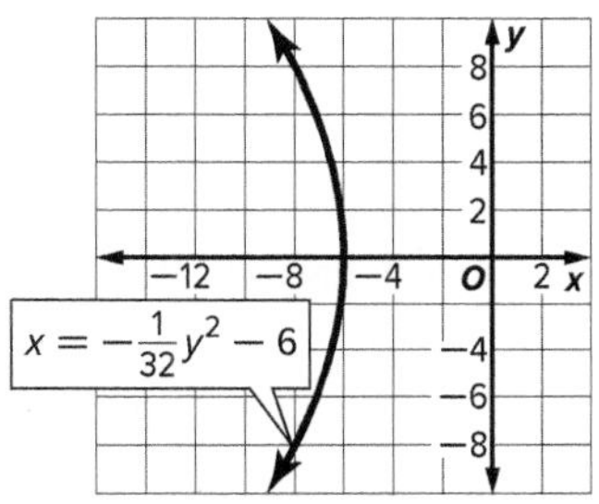

35.
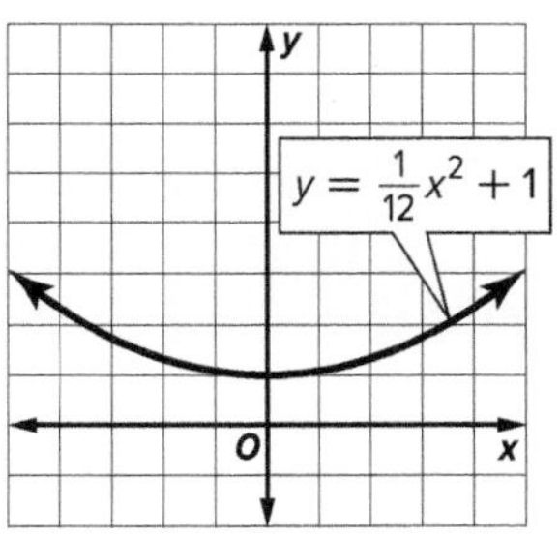

36.
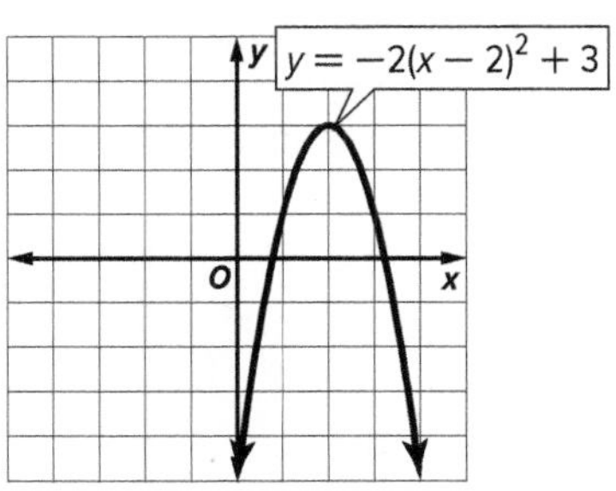

37.
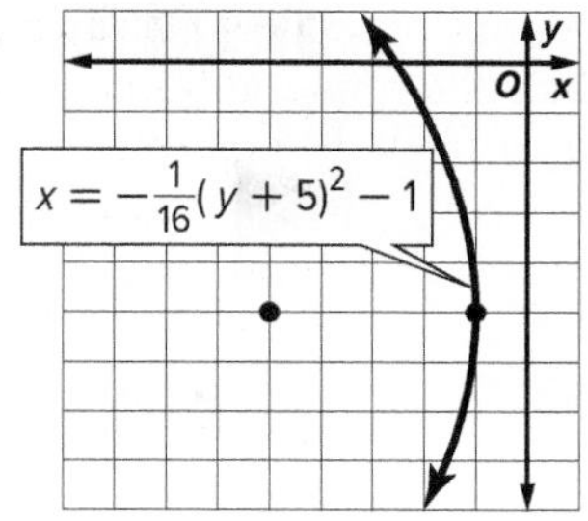

38.
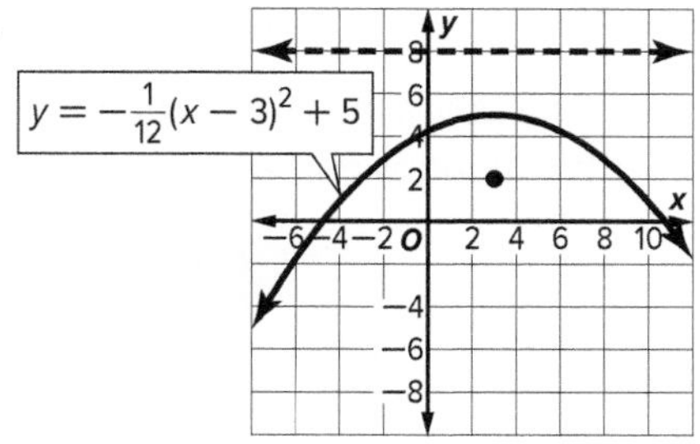

39.
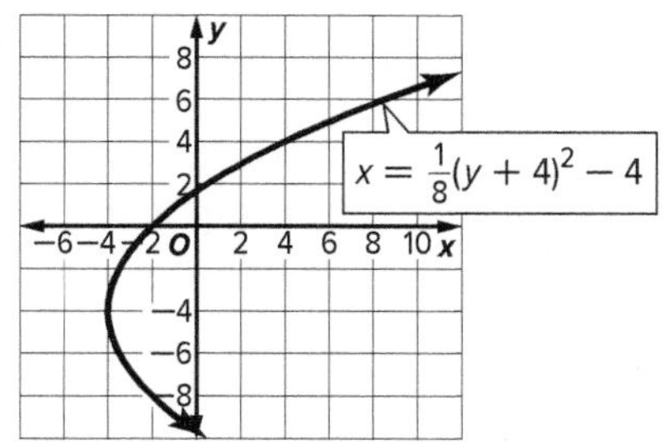

40.
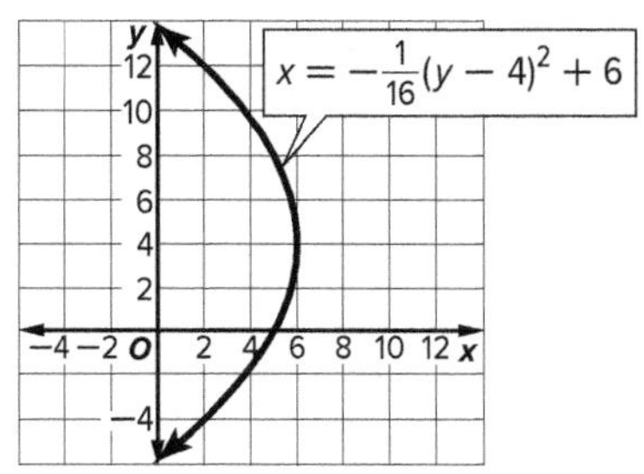

69. Sample answer: Make a sketch of the parabola by graphing the vertex and focus. Since they are on the same horizontal line and the focus is to the right of the vertex, the parabola opens to the right and will be of the form $(y - k)^2 = 4p(x - h)$ with vertex (h, k). So, $h = 3$ and $k = -2$. The distance between the focus and the vertex is the value of p, or 3. Substitute the values into $(y - k)^2 = 4p(x - h)$ to get the equation, $(y + 2)^2 = 4(3)(x - 3)$, or $(y + 2)^2 = 12(x - 3)$.

73. Sample answer: As p increases, the focus gets further away from the vertex of the graph of $y^2 = 4px$, and the distance between the focus and directrix increases. As p decreases, the focus gets closer to the vertex of the graph of $y^2 = 4px$, and the distance between the focus and directrix decreases. This is verified by graphing.

74. Sample answer: This Distance Formula can be used to find the equations of both parabolas with vertex (0, 0), and parabolas that are translated. The Distance Formula verifies that the distance from the focus to a point on the parabola is equal to the distance from the point to the directrix. This does not change if the parabola is translated.

CHAPTER 10

Extending Area

SUGGESTED PACING (DAYS)

	Instruction	Review & Assess
90 min.	6	1
45 min.	10	2

Track Your Progress

This chapter focuses on content from the Modeling with Geometry, Geometric Measurement and Dimension, and Expressing Geometric Properties with Equations domains.

THEN

G.C.2 Identify and describe relationships among inscribed angles, radii, and chords.

G.C.3 Construct the inscribed and circumscribed circles of a triangle, and prove properties of angles for a quadrilateral inscribed in a circle.

G.GPE.1 Derive the equation of a circle of given center and radius using the Pythagorean Theorem; complete the square to find the center and radius of a circle given by an equation.

G.GPE.2 Derive the equation of a parabola given a focus and directrix.

NOW

G.GPE.7 Use coordinates to prove simple geometric theorems algebraically. Use coordinates to compute perimeters of polygons and areas of triangles and rectangles.

G.MG.1 Use geometric shapes, their measures, and their properties to describe objects.

G.MG.3 Apply geometric methods to solve design problems.

NEXT

G.GMD.1 Give an informal argument for the formulas for the circumference of a circle, area of a circle, volume of a cylinder, pyramid, and cone.

G.GMD.3 Use volume formulas for cylinders, pyramids, cones, and spheres to solve problems.

G.GMD.4 Identify the shapes of two-dimensional cross-sections of three-dimensional objects, and identify three-dimensional objects generated by rotations of two-dimensional objects.

G.MG.2 Apply concepts of density based on area and volume in modeling situations.

Standards for Mathematical Practice

All of the Standards for Mathematical Practice will be covered in this chapter. The MP icon notes specific areas of coverage.

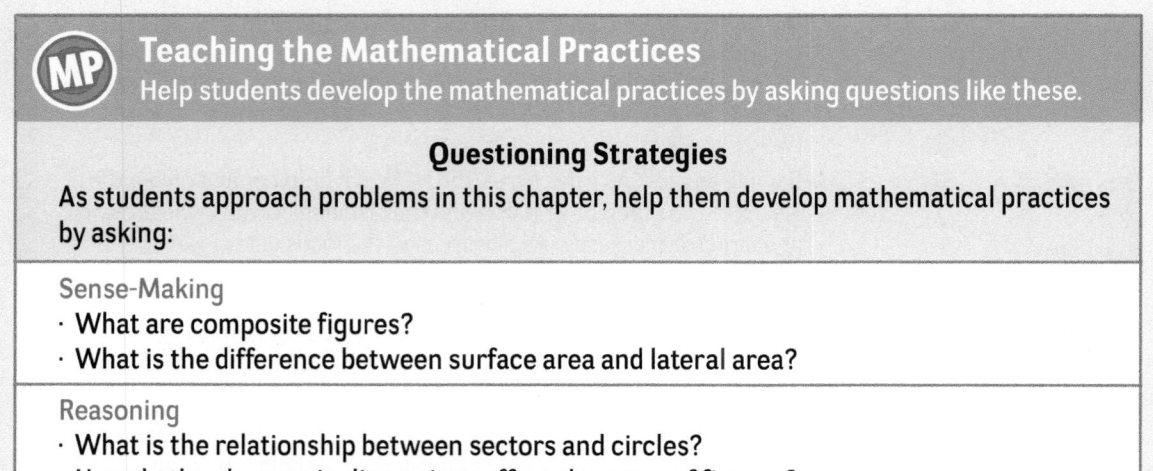

MP Teaching the Mathematical Practices

Help students develop the mathematical practices by asking questions like these.

Questioning Strategies

As students approach problems in this chapter, help them develop mathematical practices by asking:

Sense-Making
- What are composite figures?
- What is the difference between surface area and lateral area?

Reasoning
- What is the relationship between sectors and circles?
- How do the changes in dimensions affect the areas of figures?

Construct Arguments
- How do you find the perimeters and areas of parallelograms and triangles?
- How do you find the areas of trapezoids, rhombi, kites, circles, and regular polygons?
- How do you find the lateral areas and surface areas of prisms and cylinders?
- How do you find the lateral areas and surface areas of pyramids and cones?

Modeling
- When given similar figures, how can you use scale factors to find areas?

Go Online!

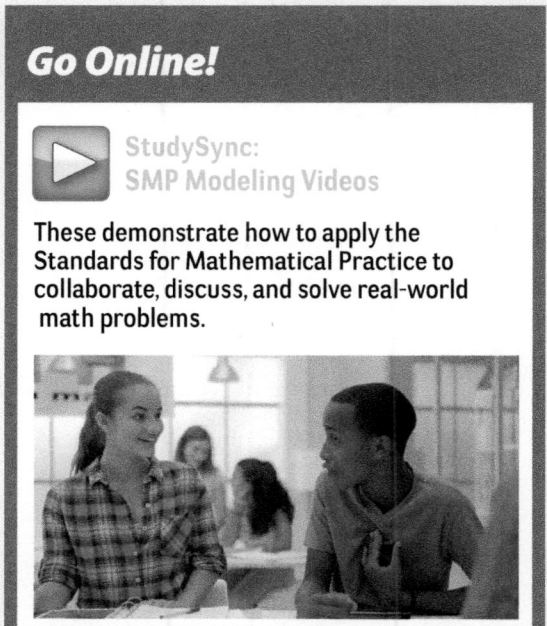

StudySync:
SMP Modeling Videos

These demonstrate how to apply the Standards for Mathematical Practice to collaborate, discuss, and solve real-world math problems.

Go Online!

connectED.mcgraw-hill.com

LearnSmart | The Geometer's Sketchpad | Vocabulary | Tutor | Tools | Calculator Resources | Check | Watch

Customize Your Chapter

Use the *Plan & Present*, *Assignment Tracker*, and *Assessment* tools in ConnectED to introduce lesson concepts, assign personalized practice, and diagnose areas of student need.

Differentiated Instruction

Throughout the program, look for the icons to find specialized content designed for your students.

- AL Approaching Level
- OL On Level
- BL Beyond Level
- ELL English Language Learners

Personalize

Differentiated Resources

FOR EVERY CHAPTER	AL	OL	BL	ELL
Chapter Readiness Quizzes	●	●	◐	●
Chapter Tests	●	●	●	●
Standardized Test Practice	●	●	●	●
Vocabulary Review Games	●	●	◐	●
Anticipation Guide (English/Spanish)	●	●	◐	●
Student-Built Glossary	●	●	◐	●
Chapter Project	◐	●	●	●
FOR EVERY LESSON	**AL**	**OL**	**BL**	**ELL**
Personal Tutors (English/Spanish)	●	●	◐	●
Graphing Calculator Personal Tutors	●	●	●	●
Step-by-Step Solutions	●	●	◐	●
Self-Check Quizzes	●	●	●	●
5-Minute Check	●	●	●	●
Study Notebook	●	●	●	●
Study Guide and Intervention	●	●		●
Skills Practice (English/Spanish)	●	◐		●
Practice (English/Spanish)	◐	●	●	●
Word Problem Practice	◐	●	●	◐
Enrichment		●	●	●
Extra Examples	●	◐		◐
Interactive Classroom	●	●	●	●

◐ Aligned to this group ● Designed for this group

Engage

Featured IWB Resources

The Geometer's Sketchpad provides students with a tangible, visual way to learn. *Use with Lessons 10-1, 10-2, 10-4, and 10-5.*

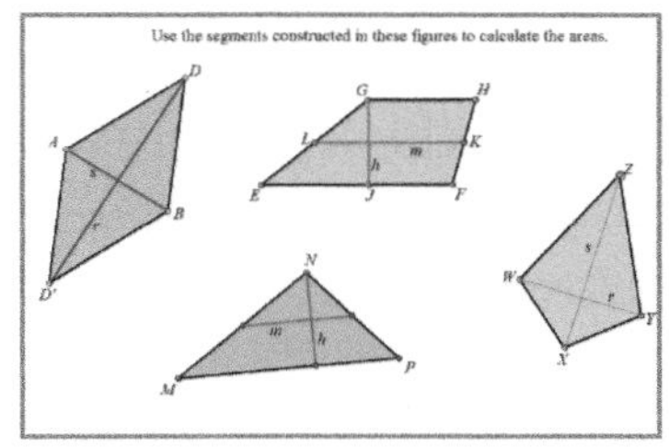

eLessons engage students and help build conceptual understanding of big ideas. *Use with Lessons 10-1, 10-2, and 10-4.*

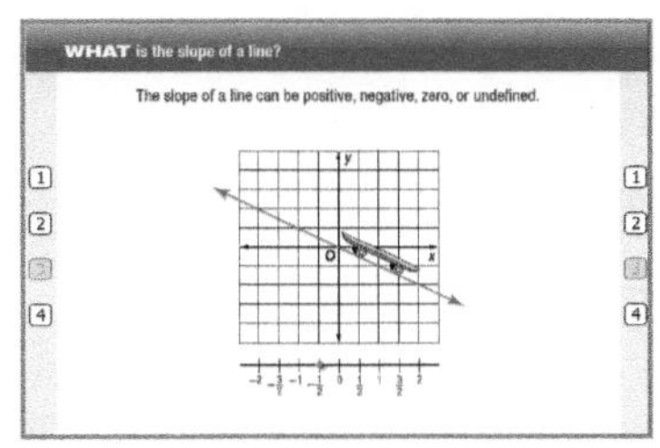

Animations help students make important connections through motion. *Use with Explore 10-4 and Lessons 10-4.*

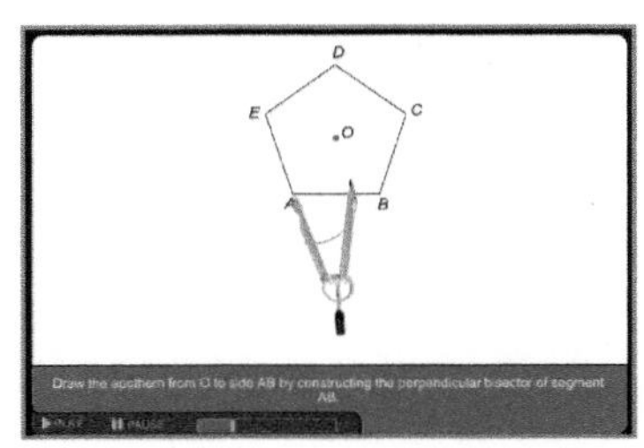

Time Management How long will it take to use these resources? Look for the clock in each lesson interleaf.

Introduce the Chapter

Mathematical Background

The formulas for the areas of parallelograms, triangles, trapezoids, rhombi, and kites are developed from the definitions and properties of the polygons. The properties of circles and regular polygons are used to find the areas of inscribed and circumscribed polygons.

Essential Question

At the end of this chapter, students should be able to answer the Essential Question.

How can decomposing and recomposing shapes help us build our understanding of mathematics? Sample answers: By doing so, you can visualize how different formulas are developed; you can solve problems involving composite figures.

Apply Math to the Real World

AGRICULTURE In this activity, students will use what they already know about finding the area of circles in an agricultural irrigation application. Have students complete this activity individually or in small groups. MP 1

Go Online!

Chapter Project

Real Estate Students use what they have learned about areas of polygons and circles to complete a project. This chapter project addresses business literacy, as well as several specific skills identified as being essential to student success by the Framework for 21st Century Learning. MP 1, 3, 4, 8

CHAPTER 10

Extending Area

THEN

You learned about circles and angles within circles.

NOW

In this chapter, you will:

- Find areas of polygons.
- Solve problems involving areas and sectors of circles.
- Find scale factors using similar figures.

MP WHY

AGRICULTURE Center-pivot irrigation systems are credited with the formation of crop circles.

Use the Mathematical Practices to complete the activity.

1. **Sense Making** How might farmers use areas to determine the placement of irrigation systems?
2. **Use Tools** Use the Internet to learn more about center-pivot irrigation. What is a typical radius for one of these systems?
3. **Reasoning** If you know the radius of the center-pivot irrigation system, what else can you determine about the field it will irrigate?
4. **Modeling** Use the 2-D Figures tool to find the area irrigated by a typical center-pivot irrigation system.

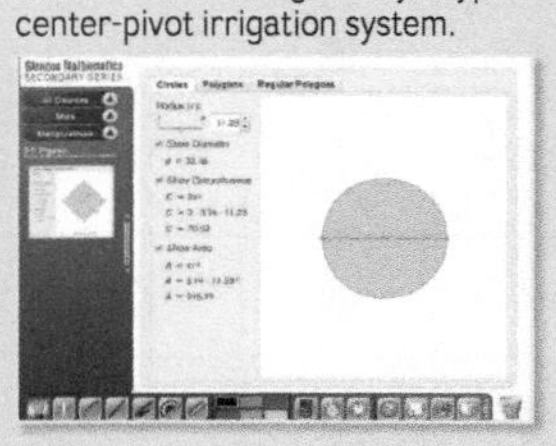

5. **Discuss** In what other ways would information about the area irrigated by the center-pivot system be useful?

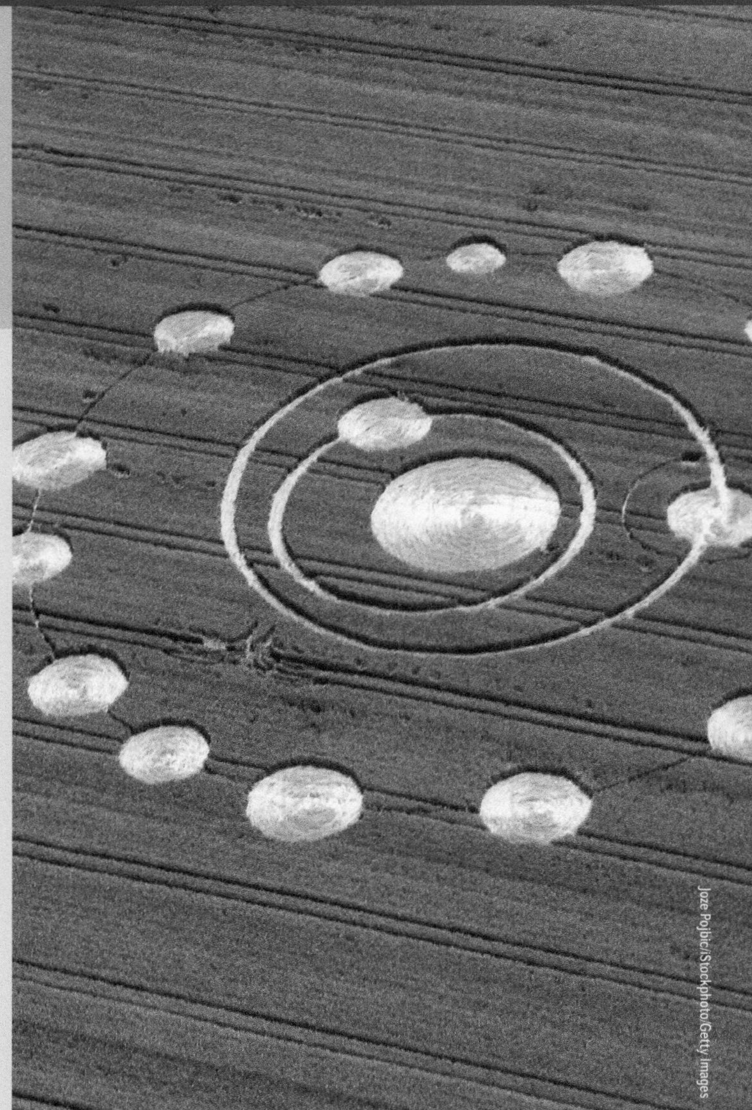

Jaze Pojbic/Stockphoto/Getty Images

ALEKS®

Your Student Success Tool ALEKS is an adaptive, personalized learning environment that identifies precisely what each student knows and is ready to learn—ensuring student success at all levels.

- **Formative Assessment:** Dynamic, detailed reports monitor students' progress toward standards mastery.
- **Automatic Differentiation:** Strengthen prerequisite skills and target individual learning gaps.
- **Personalized Instruction:** Supplement in-class instruction with personalized assessment and learning opportunities.

Go Online to Guide Your Learning

Explore & Explain

3-D Figures
Use the **3-D Figures** tool find the surface areas of pyramids and cones, discussed in Lesson 10-6.

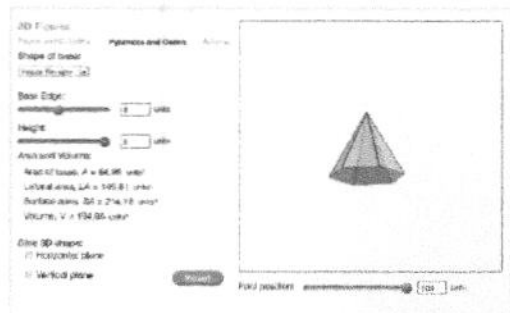

The Geometer's Sketchpad
Use **The Geometer's Sketchpad** to illustrate how to construct a square within a square and explore the relationship between them. You can also use The Geometer's Sketchpad to explore the relationships between the area of parallelograms and triangles and between the areas of similar figures.

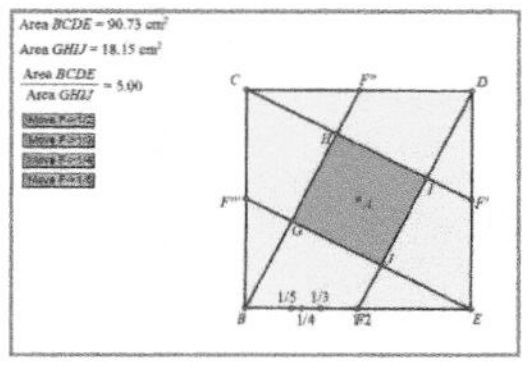

eBook
Interactive Student Guide
Before starting the chapter, answer the **Chapter Focus** preview questions. Check your answers as you complete each lesson. At the end of the chapter, try the **Performance Task**.

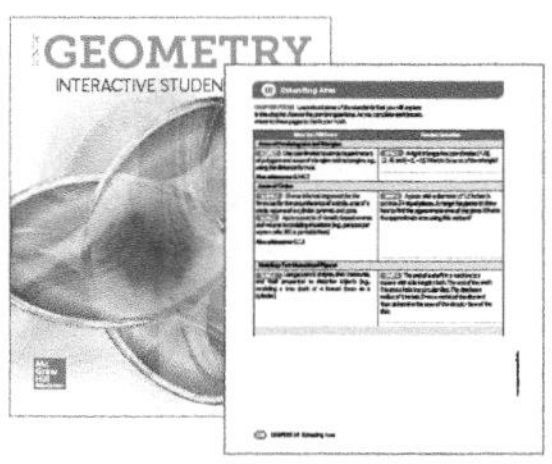

Organize

Foldables
Get organized! Before you begin this chapter, create this Foldable to help you organize your notes about areas of polygons and circles.

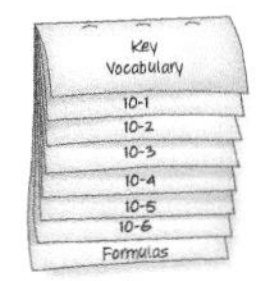

Collaborate

Chapter Project
In the **Real Estate** project, you will use what you have learned about areas of polygons and circles to complete a project that addresses business literacy.

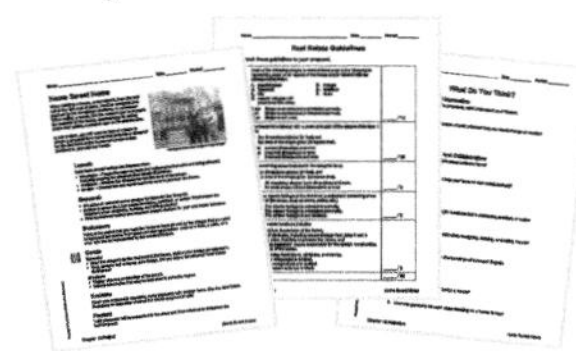

Focus

LEARNSMART
Need help studying? Complete the **Circles** domain in LearnSmart to review for the chapter test.

ALEKS
You can use the **Polygons and Circles** and **Coordinate Geometry** topics in ALEKS to explore what you know about extending area and what you are ready to learn.*

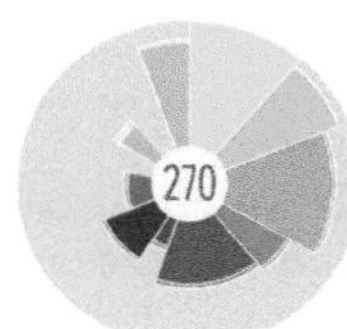

* Ask your teacher if this is part of your program.

Dinah Zike's FOLDABLES®

Focus Students write about polygons and circles.

Teach After students make their Foldables, have them label the tabs to correspond with the six lessons in this chapter. Instruct students to take notes while reading each lesson and listening to instruction. They should include definitions of terms and key concepts, as well as diagrams and examples related to each lesson.

When to Use It Use the appropriate tabs as students cover each lesson in this chapter. Students can add to the vocabulary tab during each lesson.

For a more durable Foldable, have students add a folded sheet of construction paper as a cover before stapling the paper.

Go Online!

Vocabulary Flashcard Pocketbooks
Help your students take their vocabulary flashcards to the next level! Watch this video to learn how to quickly create a pocketbook that can be used to store vocabulary flashcards. MP 6

Get Ready for the Chapter

RtI Response to Intervention

Use the Concept Check results and the Intervention Planner chart to help you determine your Response to Intervention.

Intervention Planner

TIER 1 On Level OL

IF students miss 25% of the exercises or less,

THEN choose a resource:

Go Online!

- Skills Practice, Chapter 1 and Chapter 8
- Chapter Project
- Self-Check Quizzes

TIER 2 Approaching Level AL

IF students miss 50% of the exercises,

THEN choose a resource:

Go Online!

- Study Guide and Intervention, Ch. 1 and Ch. 8
- Extra Examples
- Personal Tutors
- Homework Help

Quick Review Math Handbook

TIER 3 Intensive Intervention

IF students miss 75% of the exercises,

THEN Use *Math Triumphs, Geometry*

Go Online!

- Extra Examples
- Personal Tutors
- Homework Help
- Review Vocabulary

Get Ready for the Chapter

Go Online! for Vocabulary Review Games and key vocabulary in 13 languages.

Connecting Concepts

Concept Check

Review the concepts used in this chapter by answering the questions below.

1. What is the equation to determine the area of a rectangle? $A = \ell \times w$
2. If you know the area of a rectangle and the length of one side of the rectangle, how could determine its width? **Divide the area by the length.**
3. Given $a = 9$, $b = 10$, $c = 12$, and $d = 13$, what would be your first step in evaluating $\frac{1}{2}(ab + cd)$? **substitution**
4. Given $A = 2(8 + 36)$, what would be the first step to solving the equation? **adding numbers in parentheses**
5. In the figure shown, what is the term for the side with length h? **hypotenuse**

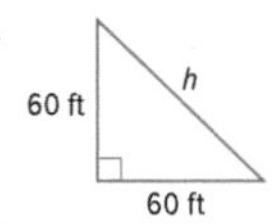

6. What type of triangle is this? **45°–45°–90° triangle**
7. For this type of triangle, what is the value of the hypotenuse in terms of the length of the leg? $h = (\sqrt{2})\ell$
8. Find the value of h to the nearest hundredth. **84.85 ft**

Performance Task Review

You can use the concepts and skills in the chapter to solve problems in a real-world setting. Knowing how to determine the area of a polygon will help you finish the Performance Task at the end of the chapter in which you use your knowledge to determine the costs of projects in and around a home.

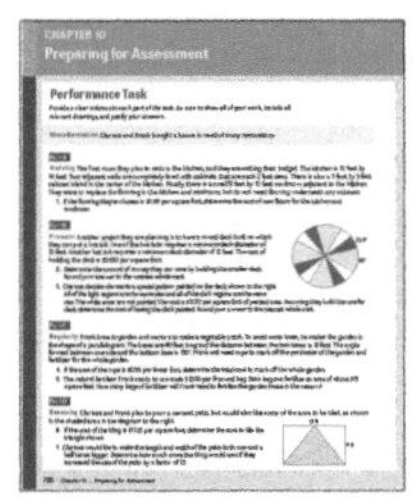

In this Performance Task you will:

- reason abstractly and quantitatively
- model with mathematics
- attend to precision
- look for and express regularity in repeated reasoning

New Vocabulary

English		Español
base of a parallelogram	p. 725	base de un paralelogramo
base of a triangle	p. 727	base de un triángulo
height of a triangle	p. 727	altura de un triángulo
height of a trapezoid	p. 735	altura de un trapecio
sector of a circle	p. 744	sector de un círculo
segment of a circle	p. 748	segmento de un círculo
radius of a regular polygon	p. 752	radio de un polígono regular
central angle of a regular polygon	p. 752	ángulo central de un polígono regular
apothem	p. 752	apotema
composite figure	p. 754	figura compuesta
lateral face	p. 770	cara lateral
lateral edge	p. 770	arista lateral
altitude	p. 770	altura
lateral area	p. 770	área lateral
axis	p. 771	eje
regular pyramid	p. 773	pirámide regular
slant height	p. 773	altura oblicua
right cone	p. 775	cono recto
oblique cone	p. 775	cono oblicuo

Review Vocabulary

arc arco a part of a circle that is defined by two endpoints

central angle ángulo central an angle that intersects a circle in two points and has its vertex at the center of the circle

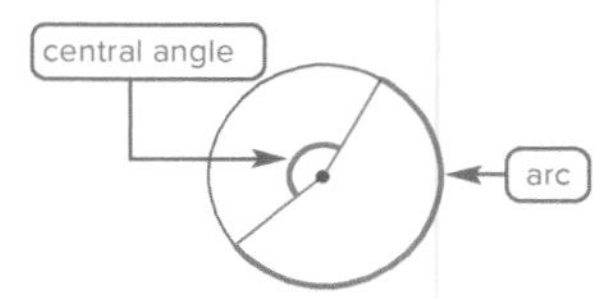

diagonal diagonal a segment that connects nonconsecutive vertices of a polygon

Key Vocabulary ELL

Introduce the key vocabulary in the chapter using the routine below.

Define The apothem is a segment drawn perpendicular to a side of a regular polygon from the center point.

Example apothem = $\overline{PX}$

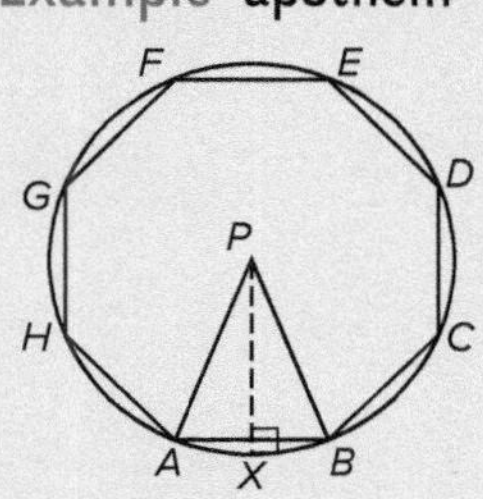

Ask

- How does the apothem relate to the central angle of a regular polygon? The apothem bisects the central angle of a regular polygon.
- How does the radius of a circle circumscribed about a regular polygon relate to the apothem? The radius of a circle circumscribed about a regular polygon forms the hypotenuse of a right triangle with the apothem and half the length of the side of the polygon that is being bisected by the apothem.

LESSON 10-1

Areas of Parallelograms and Triangles

SUGGESTED PACING (DAYS)

90 min.	0.5
45 min.	1.0
	Instruction

Track Your Progress

Objectives

1 Find perimeters and areas of parallelograms.

2 Find perimeters and areas of triangles.

Mathematical Background

Any side of a parallelogram can be called a base, and for each base, there is a corresponding altitude that is perpendicular to the base. The altitude corresponds to the height of the parallelogram. If a parallelogram has an area A, a base b, and a height h, then $A = bh$.

Skills Trace

THEN	NOW	NEXT
G.SRT.4 Prove theorems about triangles. **G.SRT.5** Use congruence and similarity criteria for triangles to solve problems and to prove relationships in geometric figures.	**G.GPE.7** Use coordinates to compute perimeters of polygons and areas of triangles and rectangles, e.g. using the distance formula.	**G.MG.3** Apply geometric methods to solve design problems.

Go Online! All of these resources and more are available at connectED.mcgraw-hill.com

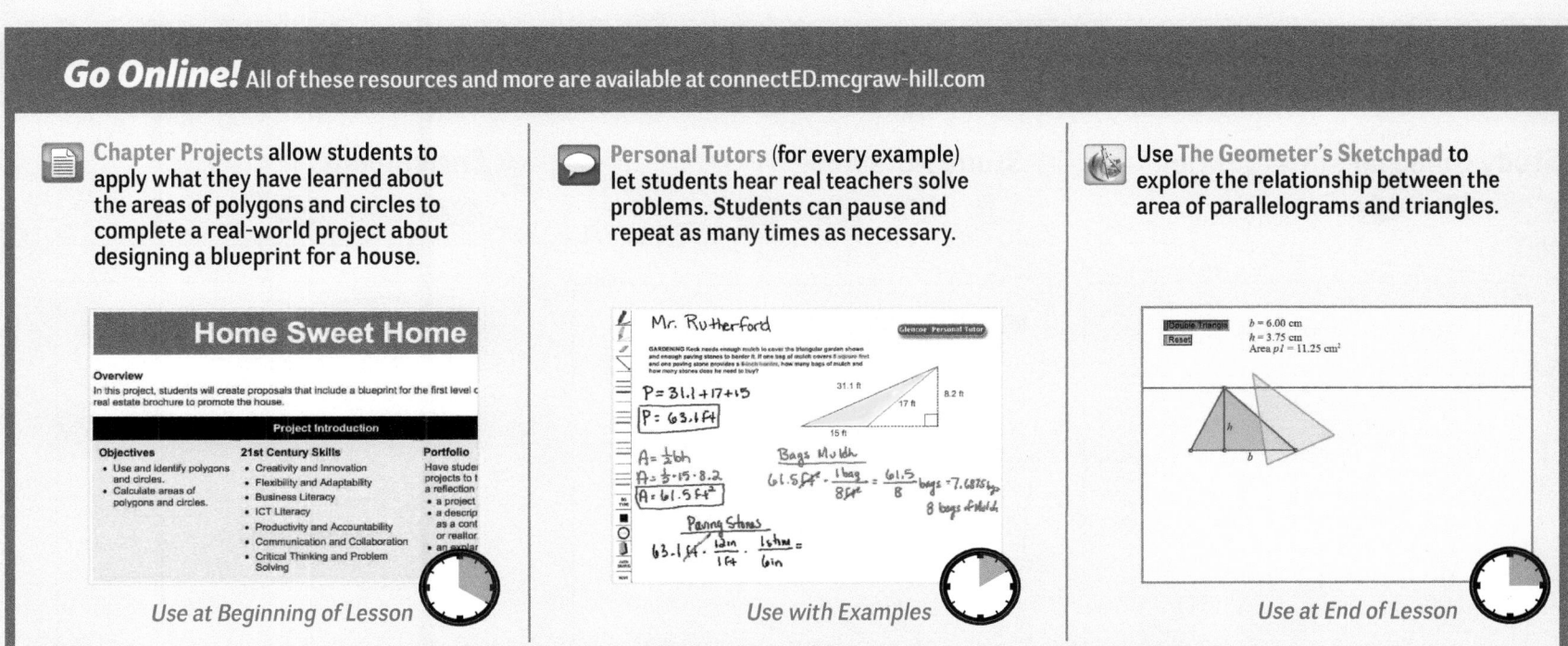

Chapter Projects allow students to apply what they have learned about the areas of polygons and circles to complete a real-world project about designing a blueprint for a house.

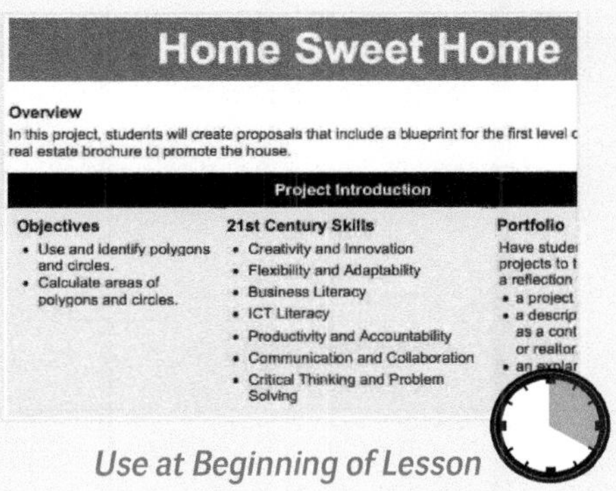

Use at Beginning of Lesson

Personal Tutors (for every example) let students hear real teachers solve problems. Students can pause and repeat as many times as necessary.

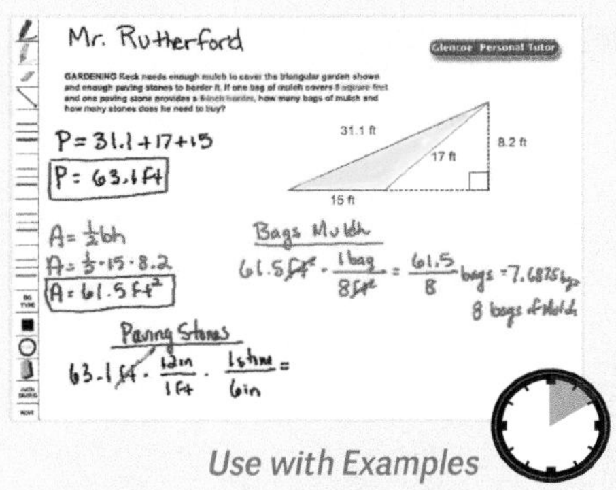

Use with Examples

Use The Geometer's Sketchpad to explore the relationship between the area of parallelograms and triangles.

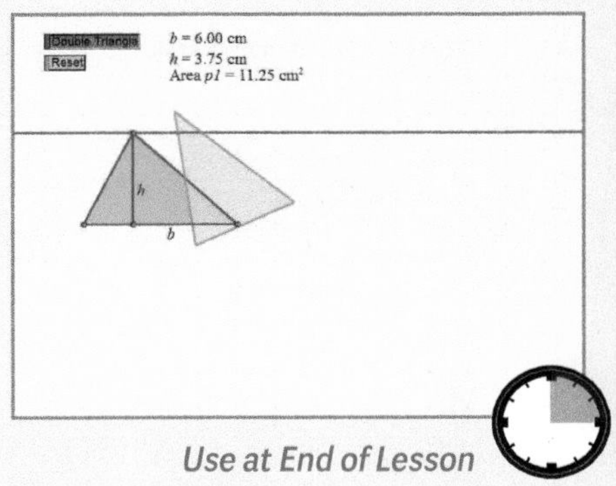

Use at End of Lesson

Using Open Educational Resources

Games Have students play the *Finding Areas of Parallelograms* and *Finding Perimeters of Parallelograms* games on **XP Math**. *Use as homework or classwork*

Go Online!
connectED.mcgraw-hill.com

Worksheets

Differentiate Your Resources

Extra Practice Additional practice or homework; Skills Practice is best for approaching-level students and Practice is best for on-level and beyond-level students

Skills Practice

AL OL ELL

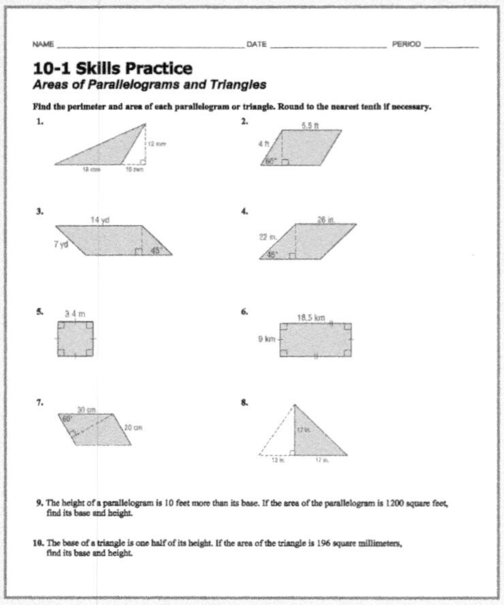
NAME ______ DATE ______ PERIOD ______

10-1 Skills Practice
Areas of Parallelograms and Triangles

Find the perimeter and area of each parallelogram or triangle. Round to the nearest tenth if necessary.

9. The height of a parallelogram is 10 feet more than its base. If the area of the parallelogram is 1200 square feet, find its base and height.

10. The base of a triangle is one half of its height. If the area of the triangle is 196 square millimeters, find its base and height.

Practice

AL OL BL ELL

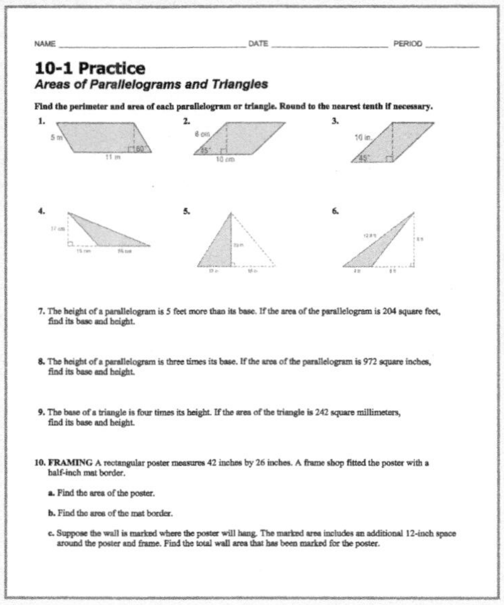
NAME ______ DATE ______ PERIOD ______

10-1 Practice
Areas of Parallelograms and Triangles

Find the perimeter and area of each parallelogram or triangle. Round to the nearest tenth if necessary.

7. The height of a parallelogram is 5 feet more than its base. If the area of the parallelogram is 204 square feet, find its base and height.

8. The height of a parallelogram is three times its base. If the area of the parallelogram is 972 square inches, find its base and height.

9. The base of a triangle is four times its height. If the area of the triangle is 242 square millimeters, find its base and height.

10. FRAMING A rectangular poster measures 42 inches by 26 inches. A frame shop fitted the poster with a half-inch mat border.

a. Find the area of the poster.

b. Find the area of the mat border.

c. Suppose the wall is marked where the poster will hang. The marked area includes an additional 12-inch space around the poster and frame. Find the total wall area that has been marked for the poster.

Word Problem Practice

AL OL BL ELL

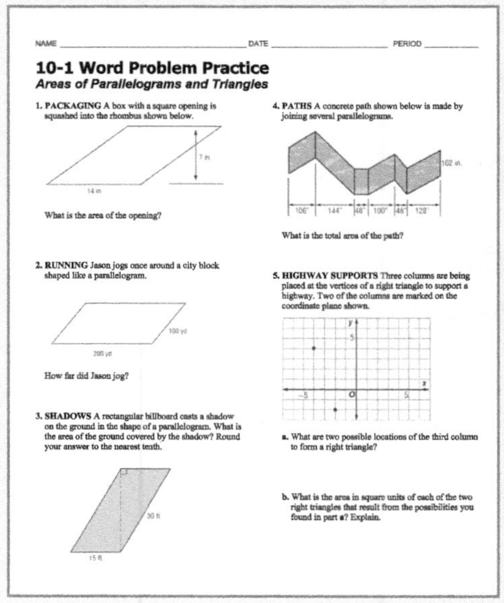
NAME ______ DATE ______ PERIOD ______

10-1 Word Problem Practice
Areas of Parallelograms and Triangles

1. PACKAGING A box with a square opening is squashed into the rhombus shown below.

What is the area of the opening?

2. RUNNING Jason jogs once around a city block shaped like a parallelogram.

How far did Jason jog?

3. SHADOWS A rectangular billboard casts a shadow on the ground in the shape of a parallelogram. What is the area of the ground covered by the shadow? Round your answer to the nearest tenth.

4. PATHS A concrete path shown below is made by joining several parallelograms.

What is the total area of the path?

5. HIGHWAY SUPPORTS Three columns are being placed at the vertices of a right triangle to support a highway. Two of the columns are marked on the coordinate plane shown.

a. What are two possible locations of the third column to form a right triangle?

b. What is the area in square units of each of the two right triangles that result from the possibilities you found in part a? Explain.

Intervention Reteaching and vocabulary activities that can be used with struggling or absent students and as ELL support

Study Guide and Intervention

AL OL ELL

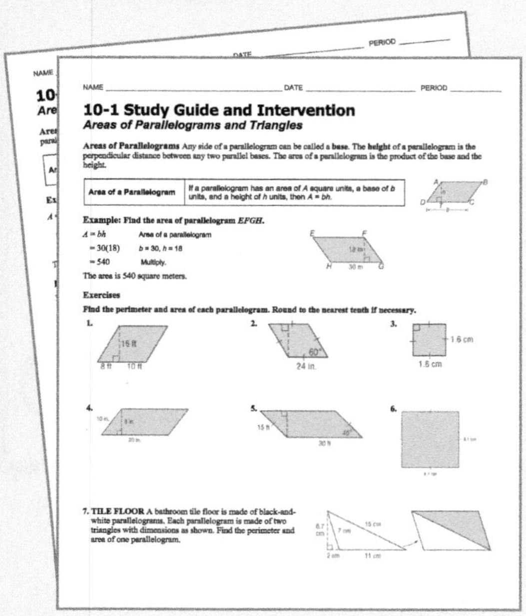
NAME ______ DATE ______ PERIOD ______

10-1 Study Guide and Intervention
Areas of Parallelograms and Triangles

Areas of Parallelograms Any side of a parallelogram can be called a **base**. The **height** of a parallelogram is the perpendicular distance between any two parallel bases. The area of a parallelogram is the product of the base and the height.

Area of a Parallelogram	If a parallelogram has an area of A square units, a base of b units, and a height of h units, then A = bh.

Example: Find the area of parallelogram EFGH.

$A = bh$ Area of a parallelogram
$= 30(18)$ $b = 30, h = 18$
$= 540$ Multiply.

The area is 540 square meters.

Exercises

Find the perimeter and area of each parallelogram. Round to the nearest tenth if necessary.

7. TILE FLOOR A bathroom tile floor is made of black-and-white parallelograms. Each parallelogram is made of two triangles with dimensions as shown. Find the perimeter and area of one parallelogram.

Study Notebook

AL OL BL ELL

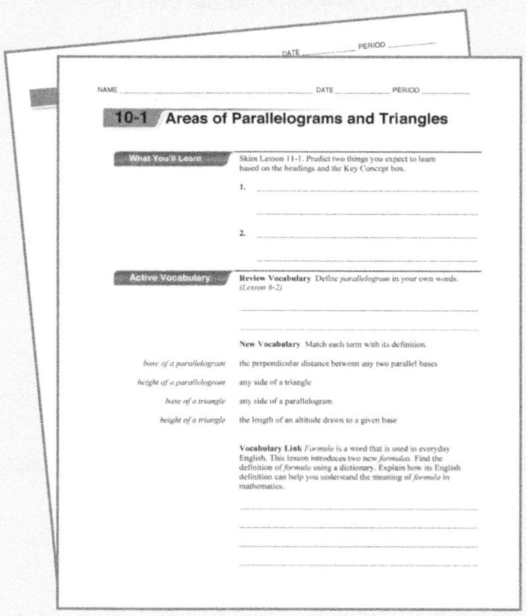
NAME ______ DATE ______ PERIOD ______

10-1 Areas of Parallelograms and Triangles

What You'll Learn — Skim Lesson 11-1. Predict two things you expect to learn based on the headings and the Key Concept box.

1.

2.

Active Vocabulary — Review Vocabulary Define *parallelogram* in your own words. (Lesson 6-2)

New Vocabulary Match each term with its definition.

base of a parallelogram — the perpendicular distance between any two parallel bases
height of a parallelogram — any side of a triangle
base of a triangle — any side of a parallelogram
height of a triangle — the length of an altitude drawn to a given base

Vocabulary Link *Formula* is a word that is used in everyday English. This lesson introduces two new *formulas*. Find the definition of *formula* using a dictionary. Explain how its English definition can help you understand the meaning of *formula* in mathematics.

Extension Activities that can be used to extend lesson concepts

Enrichment

OL BL ELL

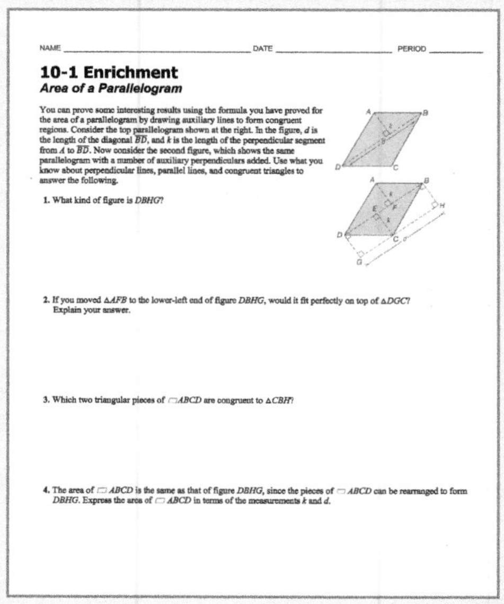
NAME ______ DATE ______ PERIOD ______

10-1 Enrichment
Area of a Parallelogram

You can prove some interesting results using the formula you have proved for the area of a parallelogram by drawing auxiliary lines to form congruent regions. Consider the top parallelogram shown at the right. In the figure, d is the length of the diagonal $\overline{BD}$, and k is the length of the perpendicular segment from A to $\overline{BD}$. Now consider the second figure, which shows the same parallelogram with a number of auxiliary perpendicular lines added. Use what you know about perpendicular lines, parallel lines, and congruent triangles to answer the following.

1. What kind of figure is DBHG?

2. If you moved △AFB to the lower-left end of figure DBHG, would it fit perfectly on top of △DGC? Explain your answer.

3. Which two triangular pieces of ▱ABCD are congruent to △CBH?

4. The area of ▱ABCD is the same as that of figure DBHG, since the pieces of ▱ABCD can be rearranged to form DBHG. Express the area of ▱ABCD in terms of the measurements k and d.

LESSON 1

Areas of Parallelograms and Triangles

Then

- You found areas of rectangles and squares.

Now

1. Find perimeters and areas of parallelograms.
2. Find perimeters and areas of triangles.

Why?

- A tangram is an ancient Chinese puzzle that can be rearranged to form different images, such as the animals shown. The area of the puzzle, before and after being rearranged, remains the same. It is the sum of all the areas of its pieces.

New Vocabulary
base of a parallelogram
height of a parallelogram
base of a triangle
height of a triangle

Mathematical Practices
1 Make sense of problems and persevere in solving them.
7 Look for and make use of structure.

Content Standards
G.GPE.7 Use coordinates to compute perimeters of polygons and areas of triangles and rectangles, e.g., using the distance formula.
G.MG.1 Use geometric shapes, their measures, and their properties to describe objects.

1 Areas of Parallelograms

In Lesson 6-2, you learned that a *parallelogram* is a quadrilateral with both pairs of opposite sides parallel. Any side of a parallelogram can be called the **base of a parallelogram**. The **height of a parallelogram** is the perpendicular distance between any two parallel bases.

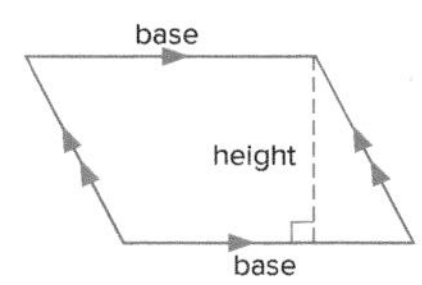

You can use the following postulate to develop the formula for the area of a parallelogram.

Postulate 10.1 Area Addition Postulate

The area of a region is the sum of the areas of its nonoverlapping parts.

In the figures below, a right triangle is cut off from one side of a parallelogram and translated to the other side as shown to form a rectangle with the same base and height.

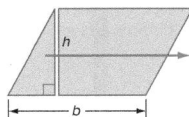

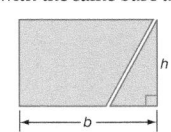

Recall from Lesson 1-6 that the area of a rectangle is the product of its base and height. By the Area Addition Postulate, a parallelogram with base b and height h has the same area as a rectangle with base b and height h.

Key Concept Area of a Parallelogram

Words	The area A of a parallelogram is the product of a base b and its corresponding height h.
Symbols	$A = bh$

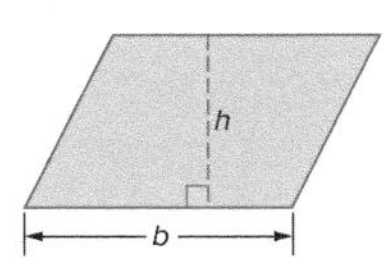

Launch

Have students read the Why? section of the lesson. Ask:

- **Can each of the figures shown be created from the square tangram puzzle?** yes
- **Explain why the areas of the second and fourth figure are identical.** The area of the pieces that make up each figure are the same.
- **What is an easy way to find the area of one of the figures?** Sample statement: Find the area of the square.

MP Mathematical Practices Strategies

Make sense of problems and persevere in solving them.
Help students maintain oversight of the process of deriving and applying the formulas for the area of parallelograms and triangles. For example, ask:

- **Compare the base and height of the resulting shape to that of the parallelogram when the triangle was cut off and moved.** The base and height are unchanged.
- **How can you find the height of a parallelogram that has a 30 degree angle?** Use the special ratios for a 30-60-90 right triangle.
- **When a parallelogram is cut in half along a diagonal, how can you be sure that the triangles are congruent?** Each triangle will have two adjacent sides of the parallelogram as sides, and the third side will represent the common cut, so the triangles are congruent by SSS.

Go Online!

Interactive Whiteboard
Use the *eLesson*, *Lesson Presentation*, or *Interactive Classroom* to present this lesson.

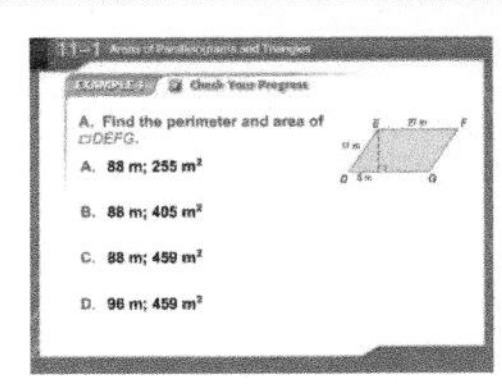

Teach

Ask the scaffolded questions for each example to build conceptual understanding for students at all levels.

1 Areas of Parallelograms

Example 1 Perimeter and Area of a Parallelogram

AL How are units of perimeter different from units of area? Units of perimeter are units of length. Units of area are square units.

OL If the height is 3 inches, what is the area? 30 in^2

BL If the height changes, will the perimeter necessarily change? Explain. No; The height affects the area. The area could be changed without changing the perimeter.

Need Another Example?

Find the perimeter and area of ▱ *RSTU*.

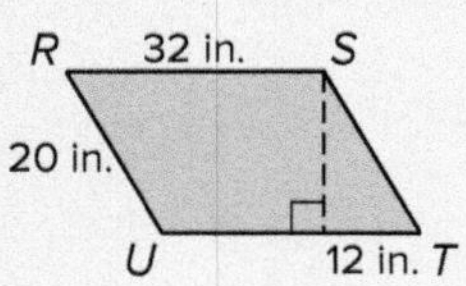

perimeter = 104 in.; area = 512 in^2

Example 2 Area of a Parallelogram

AL What is the perimeter of the parallelogram? 47 mm

OL If $EH = 8\sqrt{2}$, what is the area of the parallelogram? 120 mm^2

BL If $m\angle H = 30$, what is the area of *EFGH*? 63.75 mm^2

Need Another Example?

Find the area of ▱ *PQRS*.

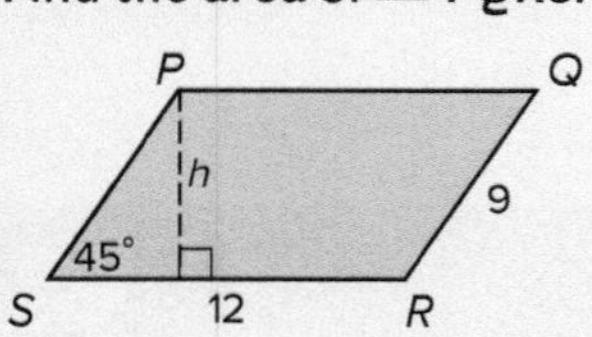

76.4 cm^2

Example 1 Perimeter and Area of a Parallelogram

Find the perimeter and area of ▱*ABCD*.

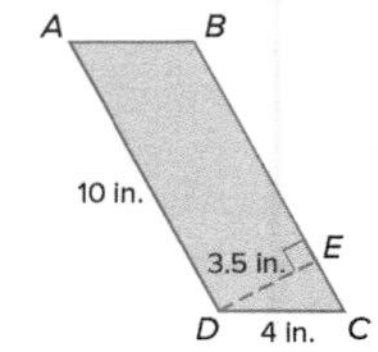

Perimeter

Because opposite sides of a parallelogram are congruent, $\overline{AB} \cong \overline{DC}$ and $\overline{BC} \cong \overline{AD}$. So $AB = 4$ inches and $BC = 10$ inches.

Perimeter of ▱$ABCD = AB + BC + DC + AD$
$= 4 + 10 + 4 + 10$ or 28 in.

Area

The height given, *DE*, is 3.5 inches. $\overline{BC}$ is the base, which measures 10 inches.

$A = bh$ — Area of a parallelogram

$= (10)(3.5)$ or 35 in^2 — $b = 10$ and $h = 3.5$

Study Tip

Heights of Figures The height of a figure can be measured by extending a base. In Example 1, the height of ▱*ABCD* that corresponds to base $\overline{DC}$ can be measured by extending $\overline{DC}$.

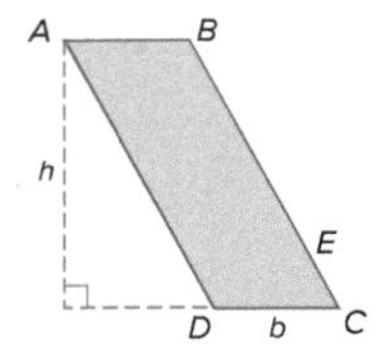

Guided Practice

Find the perimeter and area of each parallelogram.

1A. 76 cm, 315 cm^2

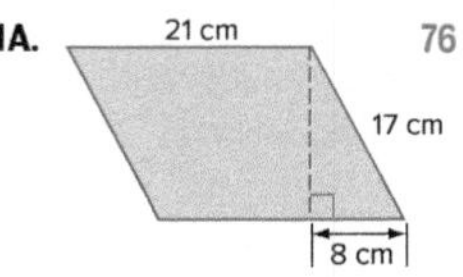

1B. 96 ft, 552 ft^2

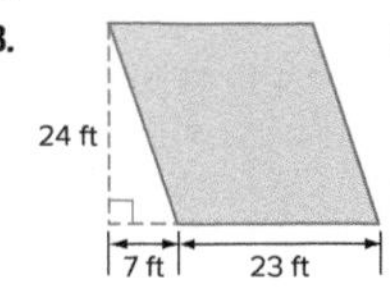

You may need to use trigonometry to find the area of a parallelogram.

Example 2 Area of a Parallelogram

Find the area of ▱*EFGH*.

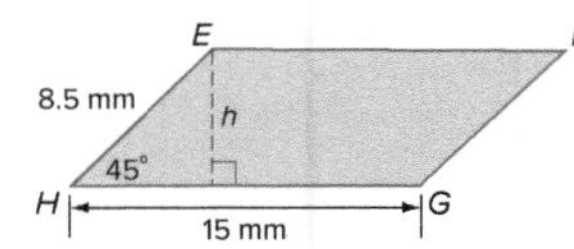

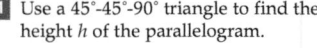

Step 1 Use a 45°-45°-90° triangle to find the height *h* of the parallelogram.

Recall that if the measure of the leg opposite the 45° angle is *h*, then the measure of the hypotenuse is $h\sqrt{2}$.

$h\sqrt{2} = 8.5$ — Substitute 8.5 for the measure of the hypotenuse.

$h = \frac{8.5}{\sqrt{2}}$ or about 6 mm — Divide each side by $\sqrt{2}$.

Step 2 Find the area.

$A = bh$ — Area of a parallelogram

$\approx (15)(6)$ or 90 mm^2 — $b = 15$ and $h \approx 6$

Watch Out

MP Precision Remember that perimeter is measured in linear units such as inches and centimeters. Area is measured in square units such as square feet and square millimeters.

Guided Practice

Find the area of each parallelogram. Round to the nearest tenth if necessary.

2A. 153 yd^2

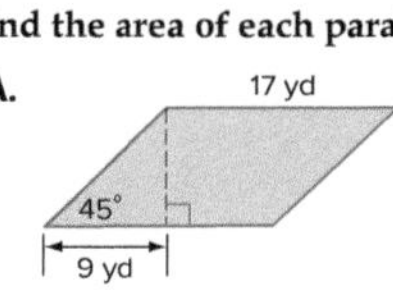

2B. 665.1 m^2

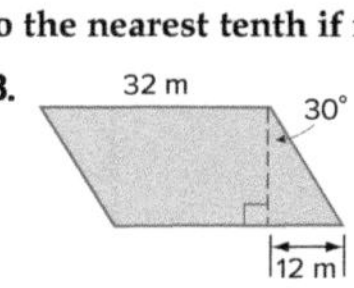

MP Teaching the Mathematical Practices

Precision Mathematically proficient students are careful about specifying units of measure. They calculate accurately and efficiently. Encourage students to read each exercise carefully to determine the units of the result.

Watch Out!

Identifying Height The height of a parallelogram is the perpendicular distance between two parallel sides. Because parallelograms have two pairs of parallel sides, there are two heights. Depending on the orientation of the parallelogram, the given height does not have to be a vertical distance.

Review Vocabulary ELL

altitude of a triangle
a segment from a vertex of a triangle to the line containing the opposite side and perpendicular to the line containing that side

2 Areas of Triangles

Like the base of a parallelogram, the **base of a triangle** can be any side. The **height of a triangle** is the length of an altitude drawn to a given base.

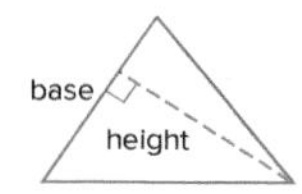

You can use the following postulate to develop the formula for the area of a triangle.

Postulate 10.2 Area Congruence Postulate

If two figures are congruent, then they have the same area.

In the figures below, a parallelogram is cut in half along a diagonal to form two congruent triangles with the same base and height.

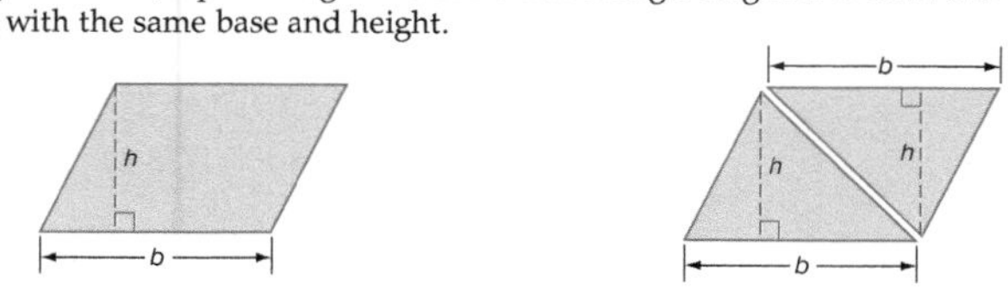

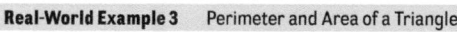

By the Area Congruence Postulate, the two congruent triangles have the same area. So, one triangle with base b and height h has half the area of a parallelogram with base b and height h.

Key Concept Area of a Triangle

Words	The area A of a triangle is one half the product of a base b and its corresponding height h.
Symbols	$A = \frac{1}{2}bh$ or $A = \frac{bh}{2}$

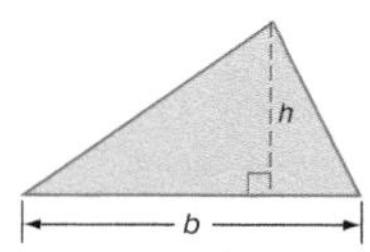

G.MG.1

Real-World Example 3 Perimeter and Area of a Triangle

GARDENING **D'Andre needs enough mulch to cover the triangular garden shown and enough paving stones to border it. If one bag of mulch covers 12 square feet and one paving stone provides a 4-inch border, how many bags of mulch and how many stones does he need to buy?**

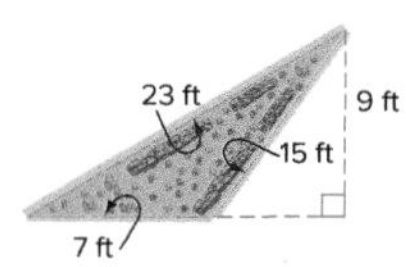

Step 1 Find the perimeter of the garden.

Perimeter of garden = 23 + 15 + 7 or 45 ft

Step 2 Find the area of the garden.

$A = \frac{1}{2}bh$ Area of a triangle

$= \frac{1}{2}(7)(9)$ or 31.5 ft² $b = 7$ and $h = 9$

Step 3 Use unit analysis to determine how many of each item are needed.

Bags of Mulch

$31.5 \text{ ft}^2 \cdot \frac{1 \text{ bag}}{12 \text{ ft}^2} = 2.625 \text{ bags}$

Paving Stones

$45 \text{ ft} \cdot \frac{12 \text{ in.}}{1 \text{ ft}} \cdot \frac{1 \text{ stone}}{4 \text{ in.}} = 135 \text{ stones}$

Round the number of bags up so there is enough mulch. He will need 3 bags of mulch and 135 paving stones.

Real-World Link

Triangular gardens can serve as focal points in landscaping or simply result from intersecting walkways.

Differentiated Instruction AL OL BL ELL

Visual/Spatial Learners Have students cut out two parallelograms of different sizes. First, have students cut a right triangle from the end of one of the parallelograms and rearrange the pieces to form a rectangle. Then, ask students to find the area of the rectangle. Next, have students cut the second parallelogram in half diagonally and determine the area of the resulting triangles.

2 Areas of Triangles

Example 3 Perimeter and Area of a Triangle

AL Why is the height drawn outside of the triangle? Because the height must be perpendicular, the distance from the vertex to the horizontal line containing the base is not inside the triangle.

OL When will the height of a triangle lie inside the triangle? when the triangle is acute

BL When is it possible to calculate the area of a triangle given only the side lengths? when the triangle is a right triangle

Need Another Example?

Sandbox You need to buy enough boards to make the frame of the triangular sandbox shown and enough sand to fill it. If one board is 3 feet long and one bag of sand fills 9 square feet of the sandbox, how many boards and bags do you need to buy?

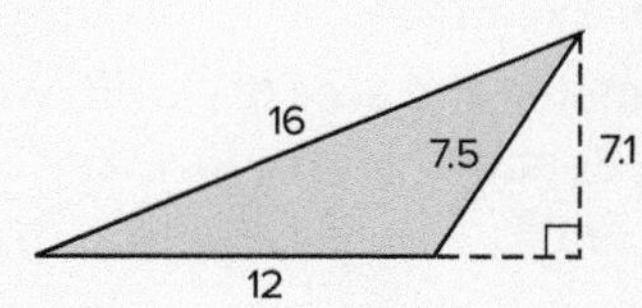

12 boards, 5 bags

Teaching Tip

Sense-Making You can have students create various figures on graph paper to verify the area formulas for parallelograms and triangles.

Example 4 Perimeter and Area on the Coordinate Plane

AL How could we estimate the perimeter and area before we do the calculations? We could count the units and square units using the graph.

OL Why is it most convenient to use $\overline{QR}$ as the base when finding the area of $\triangle PQR$? Because $\overline{QR}$ is horizontal, it is easy to determine the corresponding height from the graph.

BL If none of the sides of the triangle were horizontal or vertical, how could we find the height of the triangle? Find the slope of the line containing a side, then find the slope of a perpendicular. Write an equation for the line perpendicular to the side and passing through the opposite vertex. Find the intersection of the line and the line containing the side. Find the distance from the vertex to that point.

Need Another Example?

Find the perimeter and area of $\triangle ABC$ with vertices $A(4, -2)$, $B(12, 6)$, and $C(-4, 6)$. $16 + 16\sqrt{2}$ or about 38.6 units; 64 units^2

Teaching Tip

Modeling Help students understand the relationship between the area of a triangle and the area of a parallelogram or rectangle by showing them a model. Cut a piece of 8.5-inch × 11-inch paper in half along the diagonal to demonstrate that the area of a triangle is half the area of the rectangle that has the same base and height. Then cut a right triangle from an end of another sheet of 8.5-inch × 11-inch paper so that it has the same height as the original paper. Form a parallelogram from the sheet by sliding it to the other side of the sheet. Then cut it in half along the diagonal. The area of a triangle is half the area of this corresponding parallelogram.

Guided Practice

Find the perimeter and area of each triangle.

3A. 100.4 in., 285 in^2

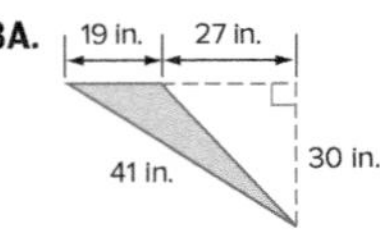

3B. 71.7 cm, 167.2 cm^2

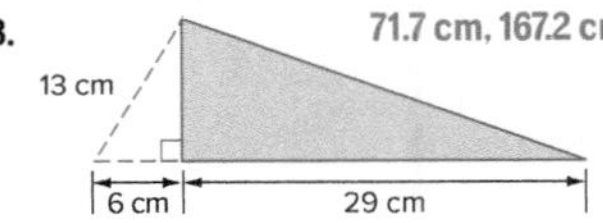

You can use the Distance Formula to find the perimeter of a polygon graphed on a coordinate plane.

G.GPE.7

Example 4 Perimeter and Area on the Coordinate Plane

Find the perimeter and area of $\triangle PQR$ with $P(-1, 3)$, $Q(-3, -1)$, and $R(4, -1)$.

Step 1 Find the perimeter of $\triangle PQR$.

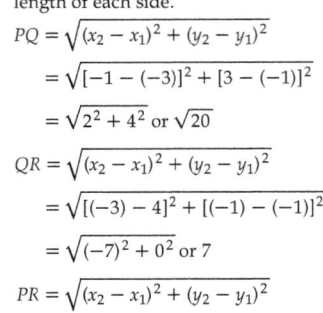

Use the Distance Formula to find the length of each side.

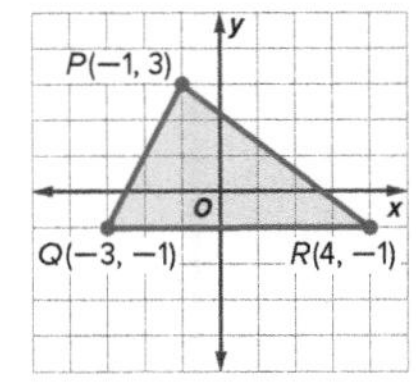

$PQ = \sqrt{(x_2 - x_1)^2 + (y_2 - y_1)^2}$

$= \sqrt{[-1 - (-3)]^2 + [3 - (-1)]^2}$

$= \sqrt{2^2 + 4^2}$ or $\sqrt{20}$

$QR = \sqrt{(x_2 - x_1)^2 + (y_2 - y_1)^2}$

$= \sqrt{[(-3) - 4]^2 + [(-1) - (-1)]^2}$

$= \sqrt{(-7)^2 + 0^2}$ or 7

$PR = \sqrt{(x_2 - x_1)^2 + (y_2 - y_1)^2}$

$= \sqrt{(-1 - 4)^2 + [3 - (-1)]^2}$

$= \sqrt{(-5)^2 + 4^2}$ or $\sqrt{41}$

The perimeter of $\triangle PQR$ is $\sqrt{20} + 7 + \sqrt{41}$ or about 17.9 units.

Step 2 Find the area of $\triangle PQR$.

Using $\overline{QR}$ as the base, the height is the perpendicular distance from P to $\overline{QR}$. From the graph, the height is 4 units.

$A = \frac{1}{2}bh$ Area of a triangle

$= \frac{1}{2}(7)(4)$ or 14 Substitute and simplify.

The area of $\triangle PQR$ is 14 square units.

Guided Practice

4. Find the perimeter and area of $\triangle ABC$ with $A(6, -1)$, $B(1, -1)$, and $C(1, 6)$.
$12 + \sqrt{74}$ or about 20.6 units; 17.5 units^2

Check Your Understanding

◯ = Step-by-Step Solutions begin on page R13.

Go Online! for a Self-Check Quiz

Examples 1–3 **Find the perimeter and area of each parallelogram or triangle. Round to the nearest tenth if necessary.**

1.
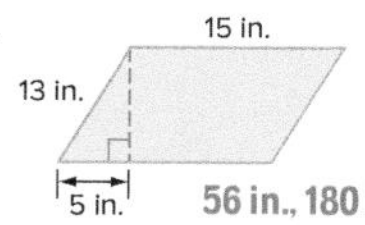

56 in., 180 in^2

2.
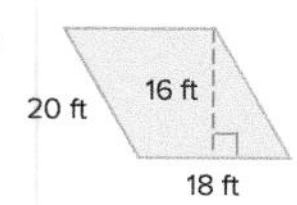

76 ft, 288 ft^2

3.
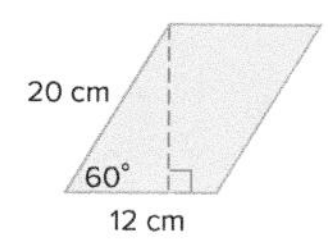

64 cm, 207.8 cm^2

4.
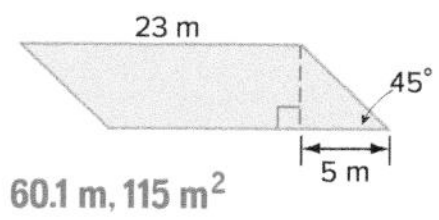

60.1 m, 115 m^2

5.
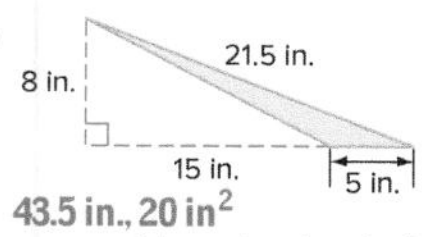

43.5 in., 20 in^2

6.
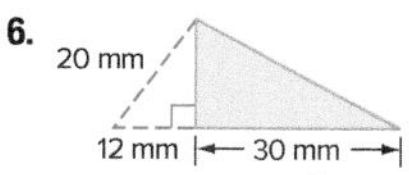

80 mm, 240 mm^2

G.MG.1 **7. CRAFTS** Marquez and Victoria are making pinwheels. Each pinwheel is composed of 4 triangles with the dimensions shown. Find the perimeter and area of one triangle. 32.5 in., 33.8 in^2

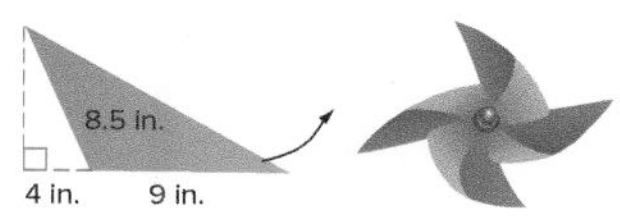

Example 4 G.GPE.7 **Find the perimeter and area of each triangle.**

8. $\triangle JKL$ with $J(5, 6)$, $K(-3, -1)$, and $L(-2, 6)$ $7 + 5\sqrt{2} + \sqrt{113}$ or about 24.7 units; 24.5 units^2

9. $\triangle WXY$ with $W(7, 4)$, $X(-1, 5)$, and $Y(7, -1)$ $15 + \sqrt{65}$ or about 23.1 units; 20 units^2

Practice and Problem Solving

Extra Practice is on page R10.

Examples 1–3 **MP STRUCTURE** **Find the perimeter and area of each parallelogram or triangle. Round to the nearest tenth if necessary.**

10.
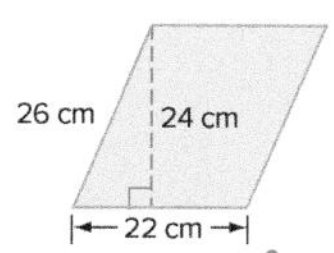

96 cm, 528 cm^2

(11)
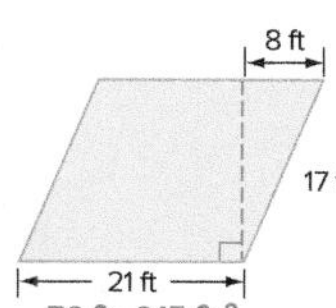

76 ft, 315 ft^2

12.
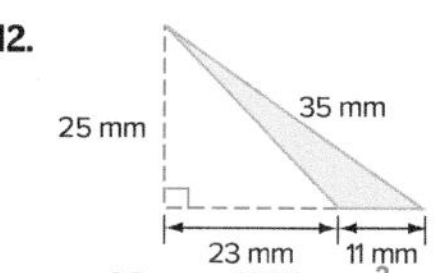

80 mm, 137.5 mm^2

13.
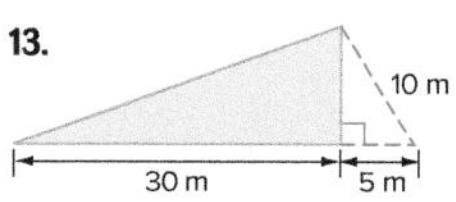

69.9 m, 129.9 m^2

14.
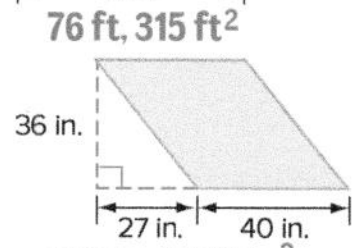

170 in., 1440 in^2

15.
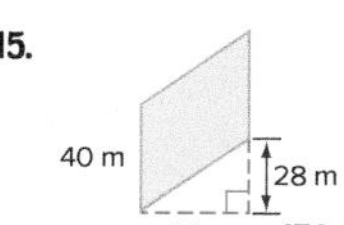

174.4 m, 1520 m^2

G.MG.1 **16. TANGRAMS** The tangram shown is a 4-inch square.

a. Find the perimeter and area of the purple triangle. Round to the nearest tenth. 9.7 in.; 4 in^2

b. Find the perimeter and area of the blue parallelogram. Round to the nearest tenth. 6.8 in.; 2 in^2

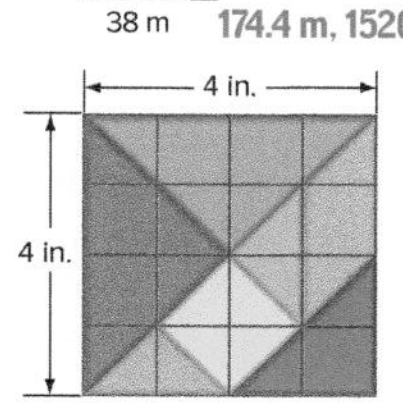

Practice

Formative Assessment Use Exercises 1–9 to assess students' understanding of the concepts in this lesson.

The Practice and Problem Solving exercises assess the content taught in the lesson. The Preparing for Assessment page is meant to be used as preparation for end-of-course assessments.

MP Teaching the Mathematical Practices

Structure Mathematically proficient students look closely to discern a pattern or structure. They also can step back for an overview and shift perspective. In Exercises 10–15, encourage students to make a plan for solving these problems.

Levels of Complexity Chart

The levels of the exercises progress from 1 to 3, with Level 1 indicating the lowest level of complexity.

Exercises	10–27	28–35, 42–49	36–41
Level 3			●
Level 2		●	
Level 1	●		

Extra Practice

See page R10 for extra exercises for students who are approaching level or for on-level students who need additional reinforcement.

Differentiated Homework Options

Levels	AL Basic	OL Core	BL Advanced
Exercises	10–27, 38–49	11–27 odd, 28, 29–35 odd, 36, 38–49	36–41, (optional: 42–49)
2-Day Option	11–27 odd, 42–49	10–27	
	10–26 even, 38–41	28–36, 38–49	

You can use ALEKS to provide additional remediation support with personalized instruction and practice.

Go Online! eBook

Interactive Student Guide

Use the *Interactive Student Guide* to deepen conceptual understanding.

· Areas of Parallelograms and Triangles

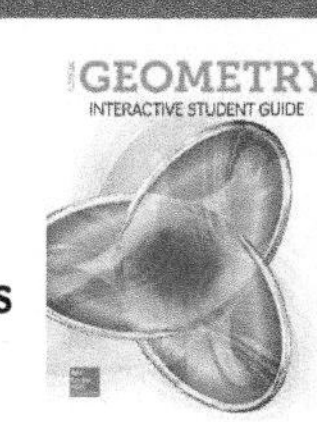

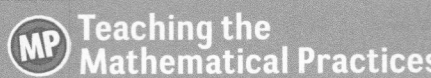

MP Teaching the Mathematical Practices

Structure Mathematically proficient students look closely to discern a pattern or structure. They also can step back for an overview and shift perspective. In Exercises 17–22, encourage students to analyze each figure for special right triangles.

Additional Answers

29b. Sample answer: I created two tables to organize the information provided and my calculations. The first table shows the relationship between each size paint container and the amount of area each will cover.

Size	8 oz	1 qt (32 oz in a qt)	1 gal (4 qt in a gal)
Cost ($)	3.75	14	30
Area covered (ft^2)	21.875	87.5	350

The second table shows the relationship between the paint color, the area to be covered, and the possible purchase options and cost.

Color	Area (ft^2)	Area to Paint (ft^2)	Possible Purchase	Cost ($)
Red	$A_R = \frac{1}{2}(5)(6) = 15$	$(15)(3) = 45$	• three 8-oz bottles	• 11.25
Purple	$A_P = (1)(4) = 4$	$(4)(3) = 12$	• one 8-oz bottle	• 3.75
Blue	$A_B = (12)(5) - 4 = 56$	$(56)(3) = 168$	• 1 qt + four 8-oz bottles • 2 quarts	• 29 • 28
Yellow	$A_Y = (12)(20) - (56 + 4 + 15) = 165$	$(165)(3) = 495$	• 2 gal • 1 gal + 2 qt • 1 gal + 1 qt + three 8-oz bottles	• 60 • 58 • 55.25

Madison should buy three 8-oz bottles of red paint, one 8-oz bottle of purple paint, 2 qts of blue paint, and 1 gal, 1 qt, and three 8-oz bottles of yellow paint.

35a. 10.9 units^2

35b. $\sqrt{s(s-a)(s-b)(s-c)} \stackrel{?}{=} \frac{1}{2}bh$

$\sqrt{15(15-5)(15-12)(15-13)} \stackrel{?}{=} \frac{1}{2}(5)(12)$

$\sqrt{15(10)(3)(2)} \stackrel{?}{=} 30$

$\sqrt{900} \stackrel{?}{=} 30$

$30 = 30$

Go Online!

The most up-to-date resources available for your program can be found at connectED.mcgraw-hill.com.

Example 2 G.MG.3

MP **STRUCTURE** Find the area of each parallelogram. Round to the nearest tenth if necessary.

17. 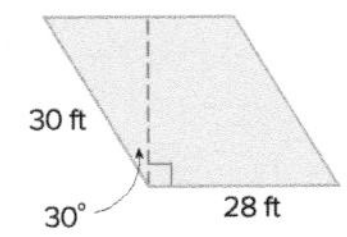

727.5 ft^2

18. 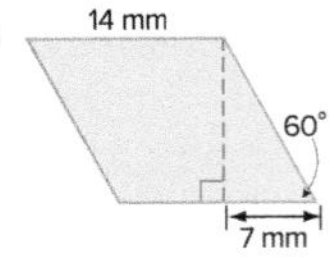

169.7 mm^2

19. 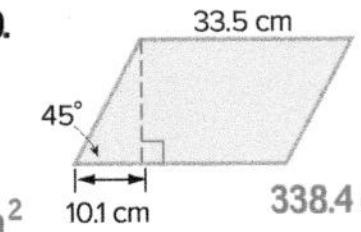

338.4 cm^2

20. 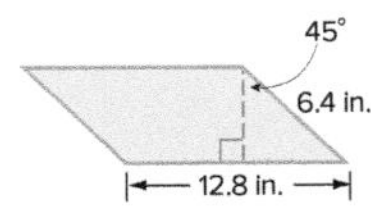

57.9 in^2

21. 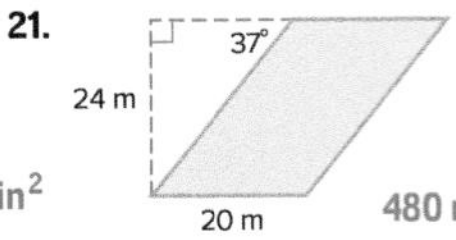

480 m^2

22. 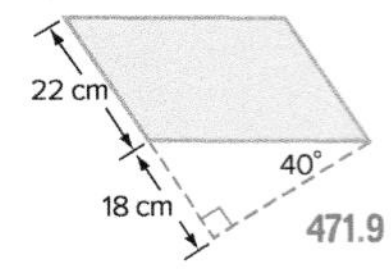

471.9 cm^2

G.MG.1

23. **WEATHER** Tornado watch areas are often shown on weather maps using parallelograms. What is the area of the region affected by the tornado watch shown? Round to the nearest square mile. 55,948 mi^2

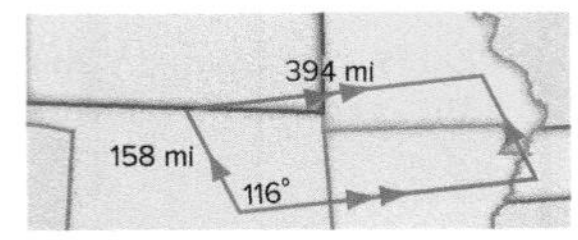

Example 4 G.MG.3

Find the perimeter and area of each figure.

24. $\triangle DEF$ with $D(4, -4)$, $E(-5, 1)$, and $F(11, -4)$ $7 + \sqrt{281} + \sqrt{106}$ or about 34.1 units; 17.5 units^2

25. $\triangle RST$ with $R(-8, -2)$, $S(-2, -2)$, and $T(-3, -7)$ $6 + 5\sqrt{2} + \sqrt{26}$ or about 18.2 units; 15 units^2

26. $\triangle MNP$ with $M(0, 6)$, $N(-2, 8)$, and $P(-2, -1)$ $9 + 2\sqrt{2} + \sqrt{53}$ or about 19.1 units; 9 units^2

27. $\square ABCD$ with $A(4, 7)$, $B(2, 1)$, $C(8, 1)$, and $D(10, 7)$ $12 + 4\sqrt{10}$ or about 24.6 units; 36 units^2

B **28.** **FLAGS** Omar wants to make a replica of Guyana's national flag.

a. What is the area of the piece of fabric he will need for the red region? for the yellow region? 1 ft^2; 1 ft^2

b. If the fabric costs $3.99 per square yard for each color and he buys exactly the amount of fabric he needs, how much will it cost to make the flag? $1.77

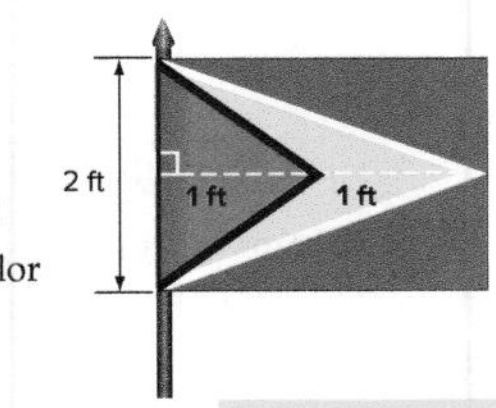

29. **MULTI-STEP** Madison is in charge of the set design for *Romeo and Juliet*. The backdrop shown is 12 feet wide and 20 feet tall and needs 3 coats of paint. The window is 4 feet wide and 1 foot high. The paint store has the following available. One quart of paint covers 87.5 square feet.

Size	8 oz	1 qt	1 gal
Cost ($)	3.75	14	30

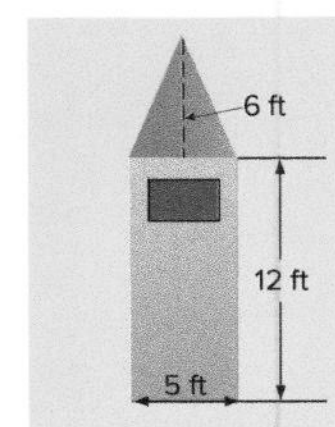

a. What should she buy to minimize cost?

b. Explain your solution process. See margin.

29a. yellow: 1 gal, 1 qt, and 3 8-oz bottles; blue: 2 qt; red: 3 8-oz bottles; purple: 1 8-oz bottle

Find the perimeter and area of each figure. Round to the nearest hundredth, if necessary.

30. 8 m; 4 m^2 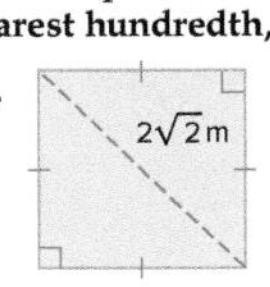

31. 9.19 in.; 4.79 in^2 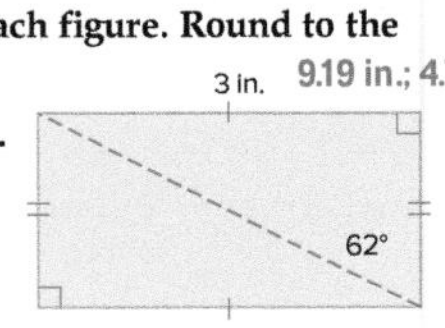

32. 37.95 yd; 68.55 yd^2 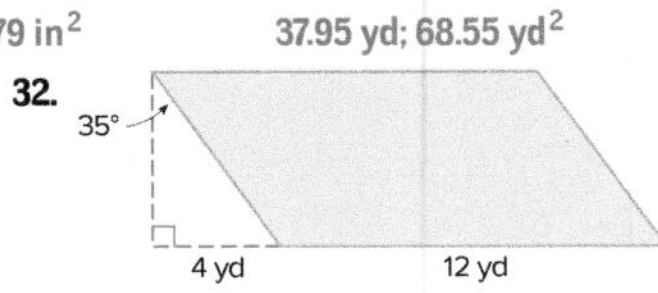

36a. $P = 2x + 2y$; $A = xy$

36b.

Length, x	Width, y	Area
1	5	5
2	4	8
3	3	9
4	2	8
5	1	5

36c. 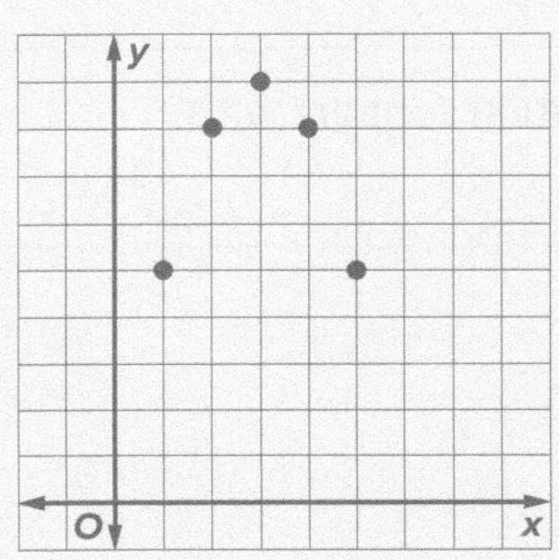

36d. Sample answer: The area increases as the length increases from 1 to 3, is highest at 3, then decreases as the length increases to 5.

36e. Sample answer: The graph reaches its highest point when $x = 3$, so the area of the rectangle will be greatest when the length is 3. The graph reaches its lowest points when $x = 1$ and 5, so the area of the rectangle will be the smallest when the length is 1 or 5.

Follow-Up

Students have explored the formulas for the areas of parallelograms and triangles.

Ask:

- Why do we have specific formulas that we use to find the areas of certain polygons? Sample answer: The formulas typically represent the most efficient ways to calculate the areas.

33. **ALGEBRA** The base of a triangle is twice its height. If the area of the triangle is 49 square feet, find its base and height. **$b = 14$ ft; $h = 7$ ft**

34. **ALGEBRA** The height of a triangle is 3 meters less than its base. If the area of the triangle is 44 square meters, find its base and height. **$b = 11$ ft; $h = 8$ ft**

35. **HERON'S FORMULA** Heron's Formula relates the lengths of the sides of a triangle to the area of the triangle. The formula is $A = \sqrt{s(s-a)(s-b)(s-c)}$, where s is the *semiperimeter*, or one half the perimeter of the triangle, and a, b, and c are the side lengths. **a–b. See margin.**

a. Use Heron's Formula to find the area of a triangle with side lengths 7, 10, and 4.

b. Show that the areas found for a 5-12-13 right triangle are the same using Heron's Formula and using the triangle area formula you learned earlier in this lesson.

36. **MULTIPLE REPRESENTATIONS** In this problem, you will investigate the relationship between the area and perimeter of a rectangle. **a–e. See margin.**

C

a. Algebraic A rectangle has a perimeter of 12 units. If the length of the rectangle is x and the width of the rectangle is y, write equations for the perimeter and area of the rectangle.

b. Tabular Tabulate all possible whole-number values for the length and width of the rectangle, and find the area for each pair.

c. Graphical Graph the area of the rectangle with respect to its length.

d. Verbal Describe how the area of the rectangle changes as its length changes.

e. Analytical For what whole-number values of length and width will the area be greatest? least? Explain your reasoning.

G.GPE.7

H.O.T. Problems — Use Higher-Order Thinking Skills

37. **CHALLENGE** Find the area of $\triangle ABC$ graphed at the right. Explain your method.

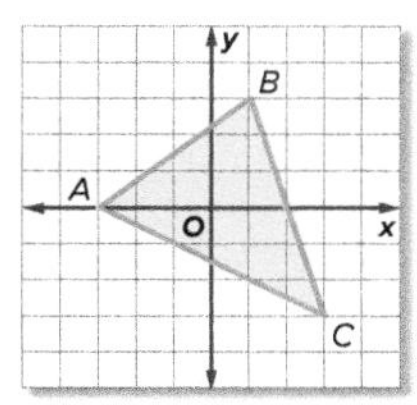

38. **CONSTRUCT ARGUMENTS** Will the perimeter of a nonrectangular parallelogram *always*, *sometimes*, or *never* be greater than the perimeter of a rectangle with the same area and the same height? Explain. **See margin.**

39. **WRITING IN MATH** Points J and L lie on line m. Point K lies on line p. If lines m and p are parallel, describe how the area of $\triangle JKL$ will change as K moves along line p.

39–41. See Ch. 10 Answer Appendix.

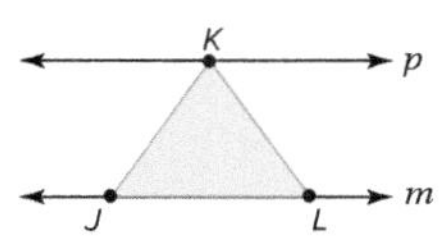

40. **OPEN-ENDED** The area of a polygon is 35 square units. The height is 7 units. Draw three different triangles and three different parallelograms that meet these requirements. Label the base and height on each.

41. **WRITING IN MATH** Describe two different ways you could use measurement to find the area of parallelogram $PQRS$.

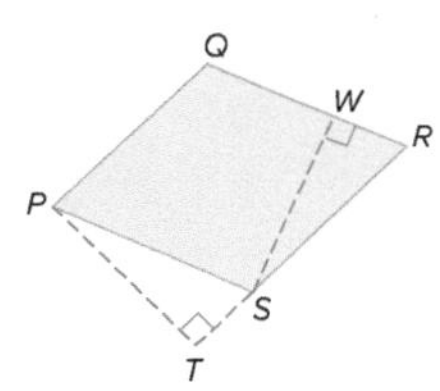

Standards for Mathematical Practice

Emphasis On	Exercises
1 Make sense of problems and persevere in solving them.	29, 33, 34, 36, 37, 40, 42, 43, 46, 47
2 Reason abstractly and quantitatively.	35, 47
3 Construct viable arguments and critique the reasoning of others.	38, 39, 41
4 Model with mathematics.	7, 16, 23, 28
7 Look for and make use of structure.	10–15, 17–22, 42, 44, 45

Teaching the Mathematical Practices

Construct Arguments Mathematically proficient students understand and use stated assumptions and definitions in constructing arguments. They make conjectures and build a logical progression of statements to explore the truth of their conjectures. In Exercise 38, encourage students to draw a diagram of the situation described.

Assess

Name the Math Have students describe how to find the area of a triangle.

Additional Answers

37. 15 units^2; Sample answer: I inscribed the triangle in a 6-by-6 square. I found the area of the square and subtracted the areas of the three right triangles inside the square that were positioned around the given triangle. The area of the given triangle is the difference, or 15 units^2.

38. Always; Sample answer: If the areas are equal, the perimeter of the nonrectangular parallelogram will always be greater because the side that is not perpendicular to the height forms a right triangle with the height. The height is a leg of the triangle and the side of the parallelogram is the hypotenuse of the triangle. Because the hypotenuse is always the longest side of a right triangle, the nonperpendicular side of the parallelogram is always greater than the height. The bases of the quadrilaterals have to be the same because the areas and the heights are the same. Because the bases are the same and the height of the rectangle is also the length of a side, the perimeter of the parallelogram will always be greater.

Go Online!

eSolutions Manual

Create worksheets, answer keys, and solutions handouts for your assignments.

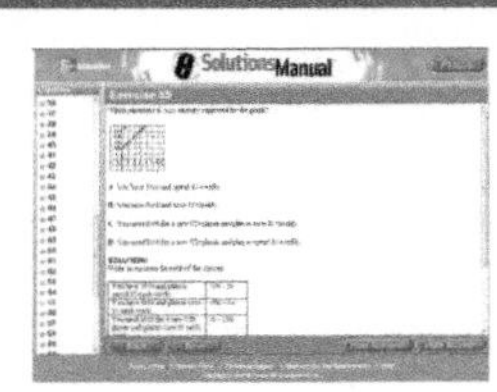

Preparing for Assessment

Exercises 42–49 require students to use the skills they will need on standardized assessments. Exercises are dual-coded with content standards and mathematical practice standards.

Dual Coding		
Items	Content Standards	MP Mathematical Practices
42, 43	G.GPE.7	1, 7
44	G.MG.1	4
45		7
46	G.GPE.7	7
47	G.MG.1	1, 4
48		1, 2

Diagnose Student Errors

Survey student responses for each item. Class trends may indicate common errors and misconceptions.

42.

A	Forgot to add *BD*
B	CORRECT
C	Found square of *BD*
D	Found twice the perimeter

43.

A	CORRECT
B	Used *BD* as the base and *BC* as height
C	Used *CD* as the base and *BD* as height
D	Used *CD* as the base and *BC* as height

Preparing for Assessment

Consider △*BCD*.

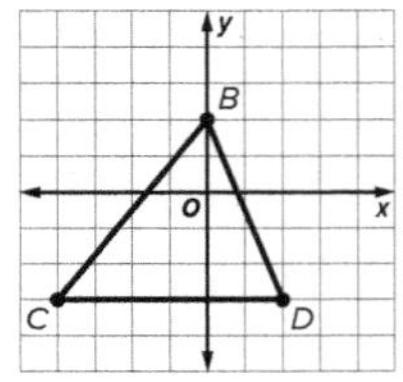

42. Find the perimeter of △*BCD*. If necessary, round to the nearest tenth. MP 1, 7 G.GPE.7 B

- ○ A 12.4 units
- ○ B 17.8 units
- ○ C 29.0 units
- ○ D 35.6 units

43. Find the area of △*BCD*. If necessary, round to the nearest tenth. MP 1, 7 G.GPE.7 A

- ○ A 15 units²
- ○ B 16.2 units²
- ○ C 17.2 units²
- ○ D 19.2 units²

44. Katie makes coasters by cutting pieces of cardboard into equilateral triangles with the dimensions shown.

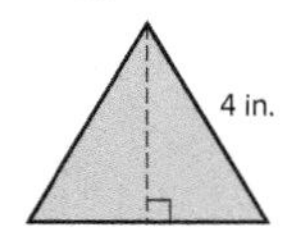

What is the area of each coaster? MP 4 G.MG.1 D

- ○ A $2\sqrt{3}$ in²
- ○ B 4 in²
- ○ C $4\sqrt{2}$ in²
- ○ D $4\sqrt{3}$ in²

45. A parallelogram is in the shape of a rectangle. The parallelogram has a length of 7.5 meters and a width of 6.5 meters. What is the perimeter and area of the parallelogram? MP 1, 7 D

- A 19 meters and 36 square meters
- B 21 meters and 40 square meters
- C 25 meters and 50 square meters
- D 28 meters and 48.75 square meters

46. The area of parallelogram *STUV* is four times the area of parallelogram *MNPQ*.

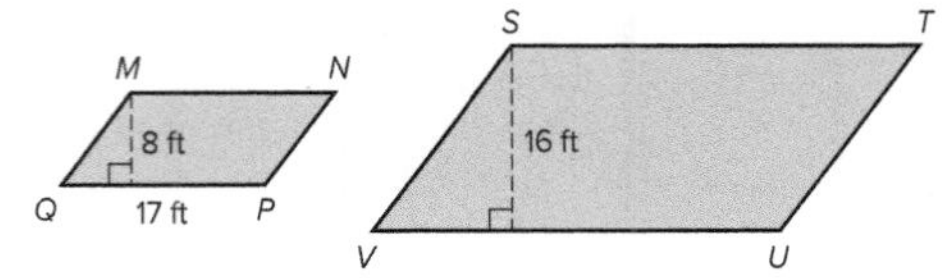

What is the length of $\overline{VU}$? MP 7 B

- ○ A 68
- ○ B 34
- ○ C 32
- ○ D 25

47. Ben uses software to draw a right triangle with a hypotenuse that has endpoints at (6, 0) and (0, 6). What is the area of the triangle in square units? MP 7 G.GPE.7

18

48. A raised garden is shaped like a parallelogram with two sides that meet at a 45° angle. The garden has an area of $84\sqrt{2}$ square feet and a base of 14 feet. What is the perimeter of the garden in feet? MP 1, 4 G.MG.1

52

49. **MULTI-STEP** A parallelogram has a base that is six times the length of the height. MP 1, 2

a. What is an expression for the area of the parallelogram in terms of the height, *h*? $6h^2$

b. A triangle has the same area and height *h* as the parallelogram. What is an expression for the base of the triangle? $12h$

c. Find the area of the parallelogram if the height is 6. 216

d. Find the length of the base of a triangle that has the same area and a height of 6. 72

Differentiated Instruction OL BL

Extension Point out that each parallelogram has two altitudes. Ask each student to write a paragraph demonstrating why you do not use both altitudes to get the area of the parallelogram. See students' work.

Go Online!

Quizzes

Students can use *Self-Check Quizzes* to check their understanding of this lesson and have the results sent to you. You can also give *Quiz 1*, which covers the content in Lessons 10-1 and 10-2.

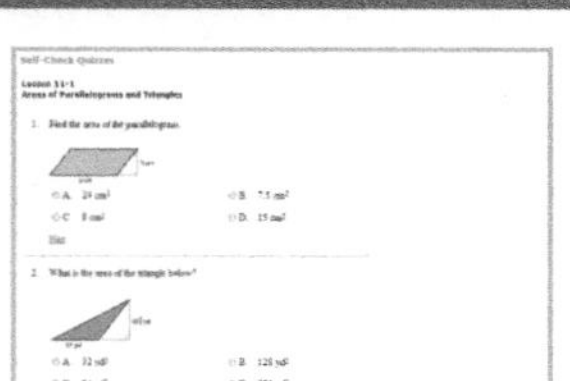

44.

A	Used 2 in. for base
B	Used $2\sqrt{2}$ in. for base and height
C	Took height to be $2\sqrt{2}$ in. rather than $2\sqrt{3}$ in.
D	CORRECT

46.

A	Multiplied 17 ft by 4
B	CORRECT
C	Doubled 16 ft
D	Added 9 to 16 ft

LESSON 10-2

Area of Trapezoids, Rhombi, and Kites

SUGGESTED PACING (DAYS)

	Explore	Instruction	Extend
90 min.	0.5	0.75	.25
45 min.	1	1.5	0.5

Track Your Progress

Objectives

1 Find areas of trapezoids.

2 Find areas of rhombi and kites.

Mathematical Background

If a trapezoid has an area A, bases b_1 and b_2, and a height h, then $A = \frac{1}{2}h(b_1 + b_2)$. If a rhombus or kite has an area A and diagonals d_1 and d_2, then $A = \frac{1}{2}d_1d_2$.

Skills Trace

THEN	NOW	NEXT
G.GPE.7 Use coordinates to compute perimeters of polygons and areas of triangles and rectangles, e.g., using the distance formula.	**G.MG.3** Apply geometric methods to solve design problems.	**G.GMD.1** Give an informal argument for the formulas for the circumference of a circle, area of a circle, volume of a cylinder, pyramid, and cone.

Go Online! All of these resources and more are available at connectED.mcgraw-hill.com

eToolkit allows students to explore and enhance their understanding of math concepts. Use the 2-D Figures tool to provide additional practice in finding areas.

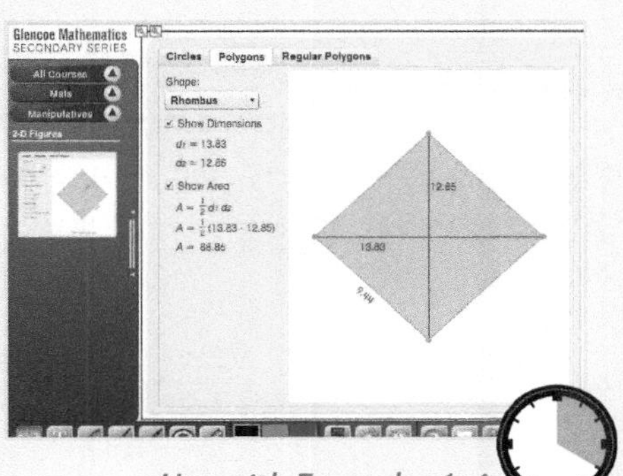

Use with Examples 1–4

Personal Tutors (for every example) let students hear real teachers solve problems. Students can pause and repeat as many times as necessary.

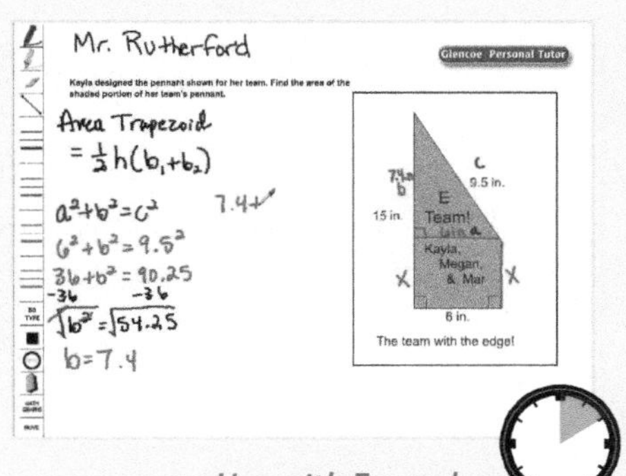

Use with Examples

Use **the Geometer's Sketchpad** to explore possible alternative formulas for the area of a kite, rhombus, and trapezoid.

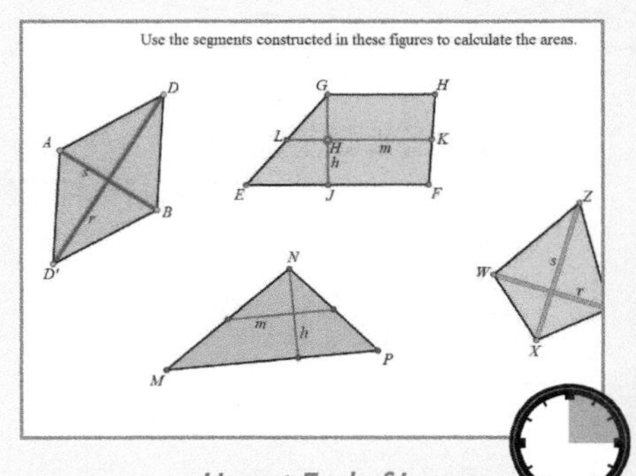

Use the segments constructed in these figures to calculate the areas.

Use at End of Lesson

OER Using Open Educational Resources

Research Have students work in groups to research the areas of trapezoids, rhombi, and kites on **SweetSearch**. Have them cite useful sources. *Use as homework or a class project*

Differentiate Your Resources

Extra Practice Additional practice or homework; Skills Practice is best for approaching-level students and Practice is best for on-level and beyond-level students

Skills Practice

AL OL ELL

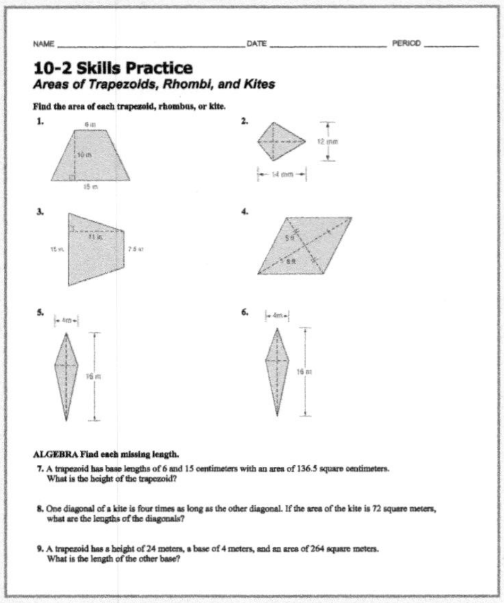

NAME ______ DATE ______ PERIOD ______

10-2 Skills Practice
Areas of Trapezoids, Rhombi, and Kites

Find the area of each trapezoid, rhombus, or kite.

ALGEBRA Find each missing length.

7. A trapezoid has base lengths of 6 and 15 centimeters with an area of 136.5 square centimeters. What is the height of the trapezoid?

8. One diagonal of a kite is four times as long as the other diagonal. If the area of the kite is 72 square meters, what are the lengths of the diagonals?

9. A trapezoid has a height of 24 meters, a base of 4 meters, and an area of 264 square meters. What is the length of the other base?

Practice

AL OL BL ELL

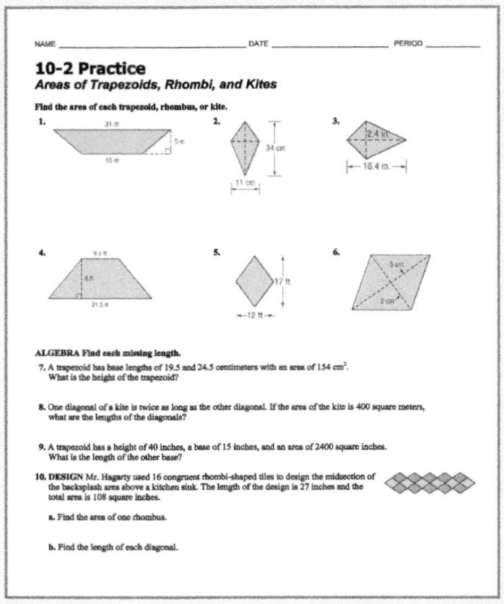

NAME ______ DATE ______ PERIOD ______

10-2 Practice
Areas of Trapezoids, Rhombi, and Kites

Find the area of each trapezoid, rhombus, or kite.

ALGEBRA Find each missing length.

7. A trapezoid has base lengths of 19.5 and 24.5 centimeters with an area of 154 cm^2. What is the height of the trapezoid?

8. One diagonal of a kite is twice as long as the other diagonal. If the area of the kite is 400 square meters, what are the lengths of the diagonals?

9. A trapezoid has a height of 40 inches, a base of 15 inches, and an area of 2400 square inches. What is the length of the other base?

10. DESIGN Mr. Hagarty used 16 congruent rhombi-shaped tiles to design the midsection of the backsplash area above a kitchen sink. The length of the design is 27 inches and the total area is 108 square inches.

a. Find the area of one rhombus.

b. Find the length of each diagonal.

Word Problem Practice

AL OL BL ELL

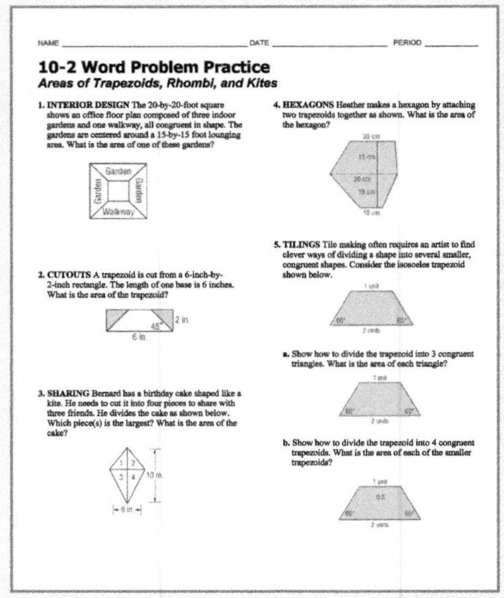

NAME ______ DATE ______ PERIOD ______

10-2 Word Problem Practice
Areas of Trapezoids, Rhombi, and Kites

1. INTERIOR DESIGN The 20-by-20-foot square shows an office floor plan composed of three indoor gardens and one walkway, all congruent in shape. The gardens are centered around a 15-by-15 foot lounging area. What is the area of one of these gardens?

2. CUTOUTS A trapezoid is cut from a 6-inch-by-2-inch rectangle. The length of one base is 6 inches. What is the area of the trapezoid?

3. SHARING Bernard has a birthday cake shaped like a kite. He needs to cut it into four pieces to share with three friends. He divides the cake as shown below. Which piece(s) is the largest? What is the area of the cake?

4. HEXAGONS Heather makes a hexagon by attaching two trapezoids together as shown. What is the area of the hexagon?

5. TILINGS Tile making often requires an artist to find clever ways of dividing a shape into several smaller, congruent shapes. Consider the isosceles trapezoid shown below.

a. Show how to divide the trapezoid into 3 congruent triangles. What is the area of each triangle?

b. Show how to divide the trapezoid into 4 congruent trapezoids. What is the area of each of the smaller trapezoids?

Intervention Reteaching and vocabulary activities that can be used with struggling or absent students and as ELL support

Study Guide and Intervention

AL OL ELL

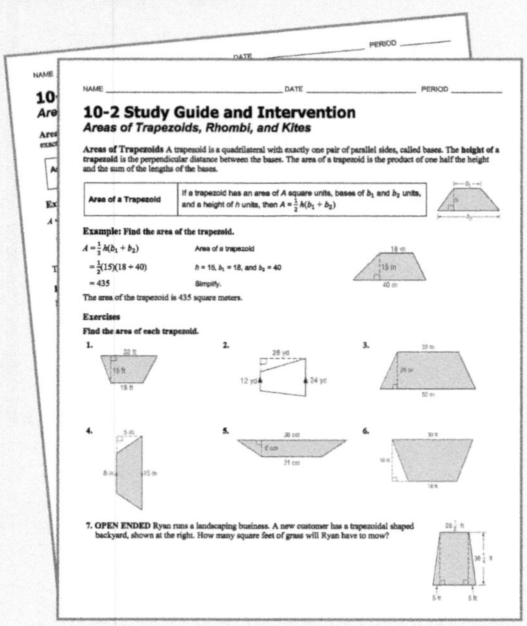

NAME ______ DATE ______ PERIOD ______

10-2 Study Guide and Intervention
Areas of Trapezoids, Rhombi, and Kites

Areas of Trapezoids A trapezoid is a quadrilateral with exactly one pair of parallel sides, called bases. The height of a trapezoid is the perpendicular distance between the bases. The area of a trapezoid is the product of one half the height and the sum of the lengths of the bases.

Area of a Trapezoid	If a trapezoid has an area of A square units, bases of b_1 and b_2 units, and a height of h units, then $A = \frac{1}{2}h(b_1 + b_2)$

Example: Find the area of the trapezoid.

$A = \frac{1}{2}h(b_1 + b_2)$ Area of a trapezoid
$= \frac{1}{2}(15)(18 + 40)$ $h = 15$, $b_1 = 18$, and $b_2 = 40$
$= 435$ Simplify.

The area of the trapezoid is 435 square meters.

Exercises

Find the area of each trapezoid.

7. OPEN ENDED Ryan runs a landscaping business. A new customer has a trapezoidal shaped backyard, shown at the right. How many square feet of grass will Ryan have to mow?

Study Notebook

AL OL BL ELL

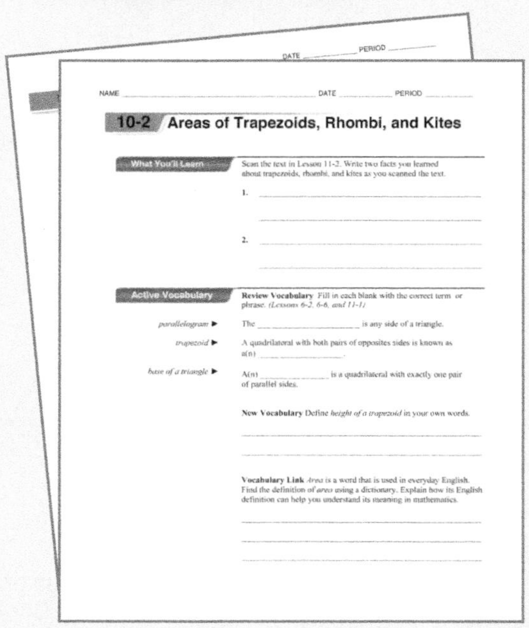

NAME ______ DATE ______ PERIOD ______

10-2 Areas of Trapezoids, Rhombi, and Kites

What You'll Learn

Active Vocabulary

Extension Activities that can be used to extend lesson concepts

Enrichment

OL BL ELL

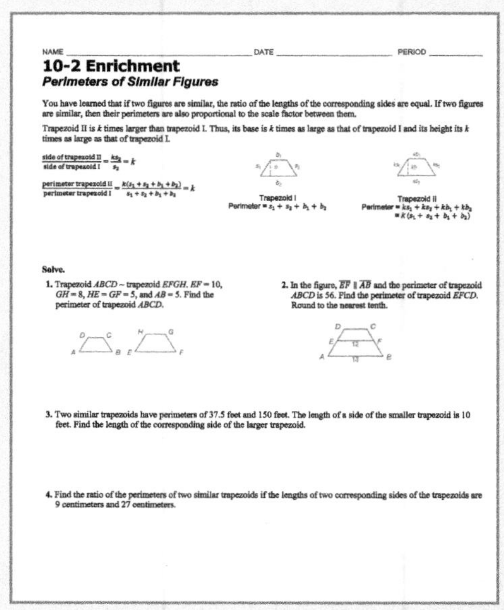

NAME ______ DATE ______ PERIOD ______

10-2 Enrichment
Perimeters of Similar Figures

You have learned that if two figures are similar, the ratio of the lengths of the corresponding sides are equal. If two figures are similar, then their perimeters are also proportional to the scale factor between them.

Solve.

1. Trapezoid $ABCD \sim$ trapezoid $EFGH$. $EF = 10$, $GH = 8$, $HE = GF = 5$, and $AB = 5$. Find the perimeter of trapezoid $ABCD$.

2. In the figure, $\overline{EF} \parallel \overline{AB}$ and the perimeter of trapezoid $ABCD$ is 56. Find the perimeter of trapezoid $EFCD$. Round to the nearest tenth.

3. Two similar trapezoids have perimeters of 37.5 feet and 150 feet. The length of a side of the smaller trapezoid is 10 feet. Find the length of the corresponding side of the larger trapezoid.

4. Find the ratio of the perimeters of two similar trapezoids if the lengths of two corresponding sides of the trapezoids are 9 centimeters and 27 centimeters.

EXPLORE 10-2

Graphing Technology Lab

Areas of Trapezoids, Rhombi, and Kites

You can use the TI-Nspire Technology to explore special quadrilaterals.

Mathematical Practices
MP 5 Use appropriate tools strategically.

Activity 1

Work cooperatively.

Step 1 Open a new **Graphs** page. Select **Show Grid** from the **View** menu so that points can be placed at integer coordinates.

Step 2 Select **Line** from the **Points & Lines** menu, and draw a horizontal line.

Step 3 Select **Parallel** from the **Construction** menu to draw a line parallel to your original line through a point with the same x-coordinate as a point in Step 2.

Step 4 Place an additional point on the parallel line you just constructed using **Point on** from the **Points & Lines** menu. Label the four points as shown.

Step 5 From the **Shapes** menu, select **Polygon**, and draw a polygon using the four points you created. From the **Actions** menu, select **Attributes**, select the polygon, and increase the line thickness of the polygon.

Step 6 Display the area of the polygon using the **Area** tool from the **Measurement** menu. Move each of the points and observe the effect on the area.

Step 1:

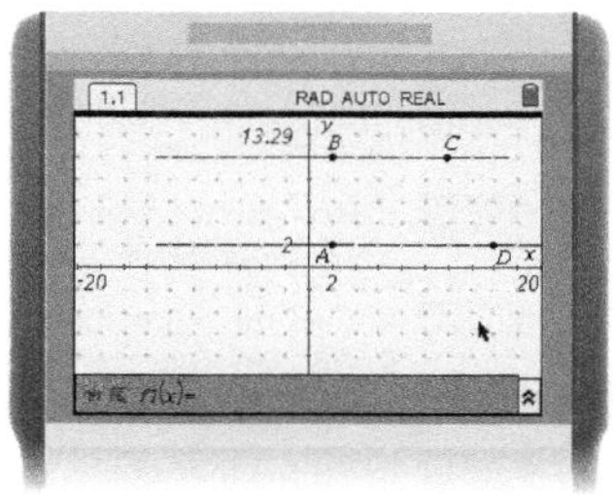

Step 5:

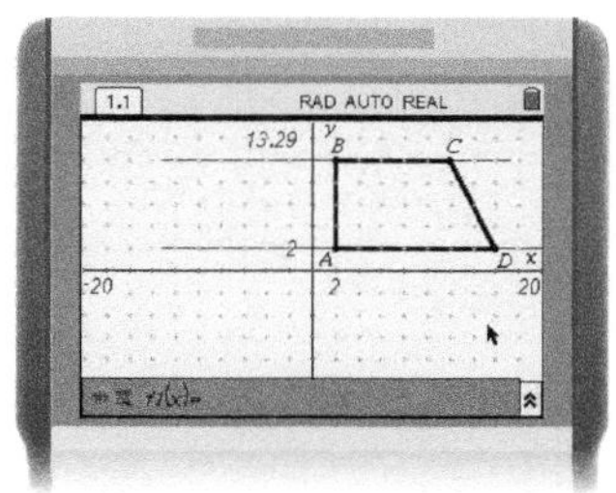

Step 6:

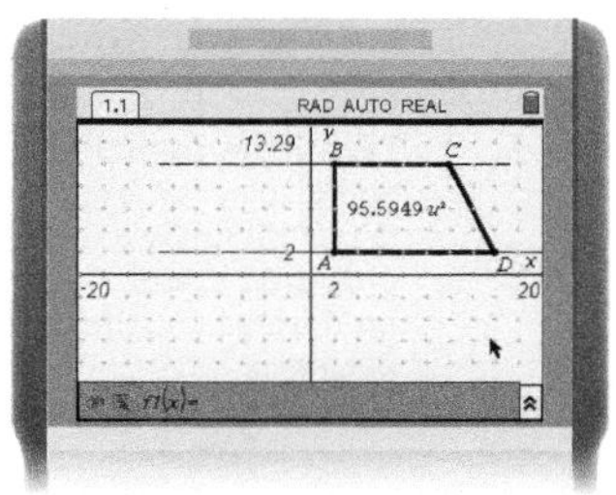

Analyze the Results

Work cooperatively

1. What type of quadrilateral is $ABCD$? Explain your reasoning. **1–2. See margin.**
2. **MAKE A CONJECTURE** Using the formulas you learned in Lesson 10-1, make a conjecture about the formula for the area of this type of quadrilateral if BC is b_1, AD is b_2, and AB is h. Explain.

(continued on the next page)

Additional Answers

1. Sample answer: Because exactly one pair of the sides of the quadrilateral is parallel, it is a trapezoid.
2. Sample answer: Divide the figure into a rectangle and a triangle and use the area formulas for each figure.

$$A = b_1h + \frac{1}{2}(b_2 - b_1)h$$
$$2A = 2b_1h + (b_2 - b_1)h$$
$$2A = 2b_1h + b_2h - b_1h$$
$$2A = h(2b_1 + b_2 - b_1)$$
$$2A = h(b_1 + b_2)$$
$$A = \frac{1}{2}h(b_1 + b_2)$$

Launch

Objective Investigate the areas of polygons using the TI-Nspire Technology.

Materials

- TI-Nspire Technology

Teach ELL

Working in Cooperative Groups Organize students into groups of two or three, mixing abilities. Have them complete Activity 1 and Activity 2.

Activity 1

Ask:

- **Into what two shapes can this quadrilateral shown be divided?** a right triangle and a parallelogram, which can be more precisely classified as a rectangle
- **Move points B and C each the same number of units to the left along line BC. How are the two shapes that make up the figure affected?** The right triangle becomes obtuse and the parallelogram can no longer be classified as a rectangle.
- **What effect does this have on the area of the figure? Explain.** The area remains constant. The base and height of the parallelogram and of the triangle that make up the figure, remain the same. Because these measures are used to calculate the areas of these figures, the total area of the figure will remain unchanged.

Go Online!

Graphing Calculators

Students can use the Graphing Calculator Personal Tutors to review the use of the graphing calculator to represent functions. They can also use the Other Calculator Keystrokes, which cover lab content for students with calculators other than the TI-84 Plus.

Activity 2

Ask:

- In Activity 2, what happens when you drag W along the line? The area increases or decreases.
- Why does the area change? Moving W changes the length of a base. The area is determined by the altitude, which stays the same, and the length of the base, which can change.

Practice Have students complete Exercises 1–5.

Assess

Formative Assessment

Have students write responses to the questions in each activity to assess whether students comprehend what they have been taught about area.

From Concrete to Abstract

Allow students to verify the area formulas for a triangle, trapezoid, and rhombus by cutting the shapes out of paper. Encourage them to show how the formulas can be derived from other polygons.

Ask:

- If a rhombus has an area of 25 units^2 and one diagonal is 5 units long, what is the measure of the other diagonal? 10 units

Additional Answers

3. Sample answer: Because the diagonals are perpendicular, and pairs of adjacent sides are congruent, the quadrilateral is a kite.
4. Sample answer: Divide the figure into two triangles and use the area formula for a triangle. $\overline{WY}$ bisects $\overline{XZ}$.

$$A = \frac{1}{2}d_1\left(\frac{1}{2}d_2\right) + \frac{1}{2}d_1\left(\frac{1}{2}d_2\right)$$

$$A = \frac{1}{4}d_1 d_2 + \frac{1}{4}d_1 d_2$$

$$A = \frac{1}{2}d_1 d_2$$

EXPLORE 10-2

Graphing Technology Lab

Areas of Trapezoids, Rhombi, and Kites *Continued*

Activity 2

Work cooperatively.

Step 1 Open a new **Graphs** page. Select **Show Grid** from the **View** menu so that points can be placed at integer coordinates.

Step 2 Select **Line** from the **Points & Lines** menu, and draw a line.

Step 3 Place a point above the line by selecting **Point** from the **Points & Lines** menu.

Step 4 Reflect the point above the line by choosing **Reflection** from the **Transformation** menu, then select the point and then the line.

Step 5 Label the four points as shown.

Step 6 From the **Shapes** menu, select **Polygon**, and draw a polygon using points W, X, Y, and Z.

Step 7 Display the area of the polygon using the **Area** tool from the **Measurement** menu. Move points W, X, and Y, and observe the effect on the area.

Step 1:

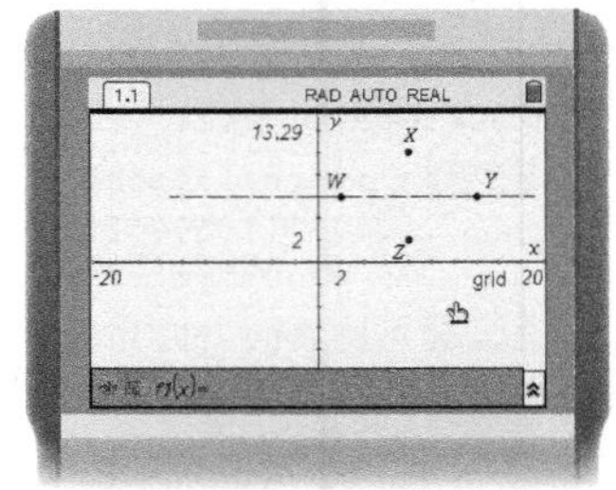

Step 6:

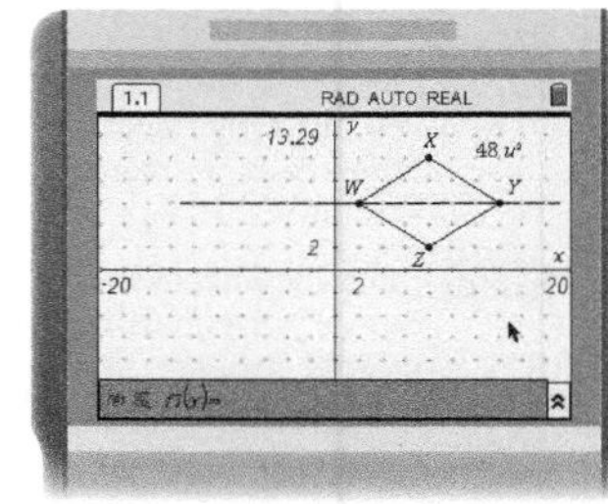

Step 8 Select **Segment** from the **Points & Lines** menu to draw the diagonals of $WXYZ$.

Step 9 Display the lengths of the diagonals using the **Length** tool from the **Measurement** menu, and display the angle between the diagonals using the **Angle** tool. Continue to move points W, X, and Y, and observe the effect on the area and the angle between the diagonals.

Step 8:

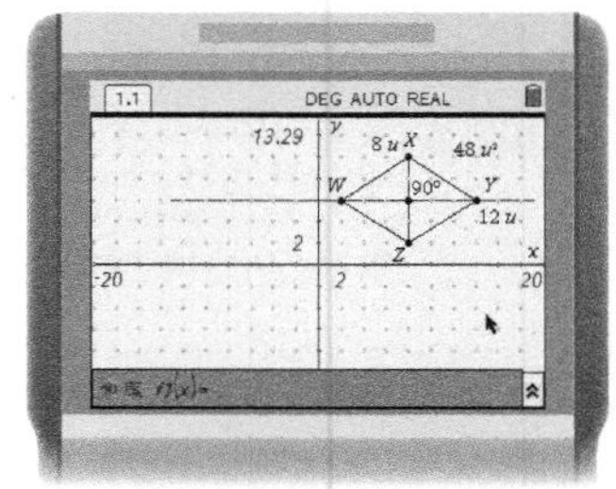

Analyze the Results

Work cooperatively

3. What type of quadrilateral is $WXYZ$? Explain your reasoning. 3–5. See margin.
4. **MAKE A CONJECTURE** Using the formulas you learned in Lesson 10-1, develop a formula for the area of this type of quadrilateral. Let WY be d_1, and let XZ be d_2. Explain your reasoning.
5. **CHALLENGE** Construct a quadrilateral using two perpendicular lines and reflecting a point on each as you did in Step 4 of Activity 2. What type of quadrilateral is formed? Does the formula for the area you developed in Exercise 4 apply?

5. Sample answer:

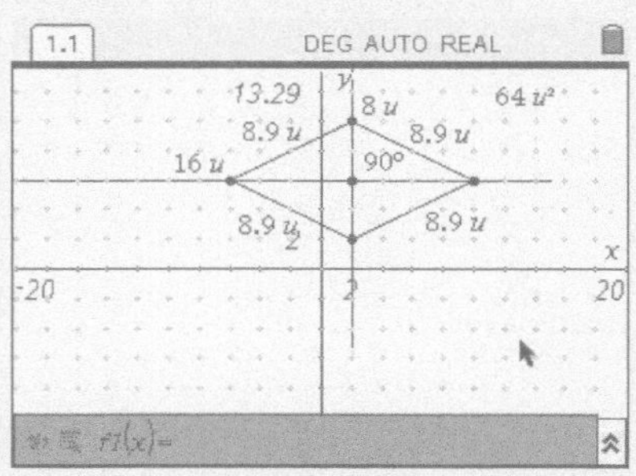

The quadrilateral is a rhombus because all four of the sides are congruent and the diagonals are perpendicular. The formula developed in Exercise 4 does apply, because $\frac{1}{2}d_1d_2 = \frac{1}{2}(9.7996)(5.8505) \approx 28.67$, which is the area of the quadrilateral.

LESSON 2

Areas of Trapezoids, Rhombi, and Kites

Then

- You found areas of triangles and parallelograms.

Now

1. Find areas of trapezoids.
2. Find areas of rhombi and kites.

Why?

- Brianna has turned her hobby of making designer handbags and totes into a small business. Among her designs is a trapezoid-shaped handbag. To estimate the amount of material needed to produce each handbag, she needs to calculate the area of a trapezoid.

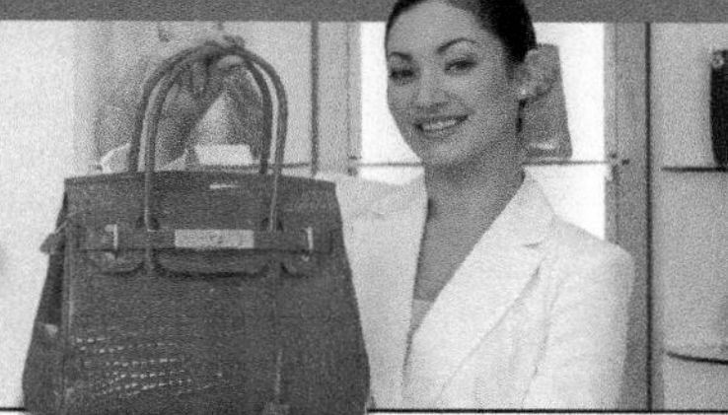

New Vocabulary
height of a trapezoid

Mathematical Practices
1 Make sense of problems and persevere in solving them.
7 Look for and make use of structure.

Content Standards
G.MG.3 Apply geometric methods to solve problems (e.g., designing an object or structure to satisfy physical constraints or minimize cost; working with typographic grid systems based on ratios). ★

1 Areas of Trapezoids In Lesson 6-6, you learned that a *trapezoid* is a quadrilateral with exactly one pair of parallel sides. These parallel sides are called *bases*. The **height of a trapezoid** is the perpendicular distance between its bases.

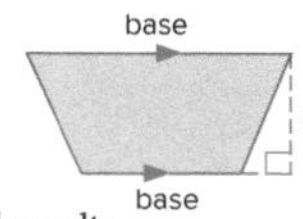

In the figure below, a translation and rotation of the first trapezoid results in two congruent trapezoids that fit together to form a parallelogram.

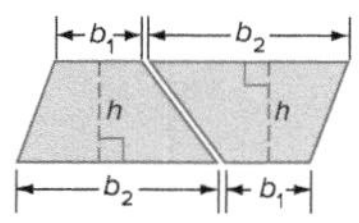

The area of the parallelogram is the product of the height h and the sum of the two bases, b_1 and b_2. The area of one trapezoid is one half the area of the parallelogram.

Key Concept Area of a Trapezoid

Words	The area A of a trapezoid is one half the product of the height h and the sum of its bases, b_1 and b_2.	
Symbols	$A = \frac{1}{2}h(b_1 + b_2)$	

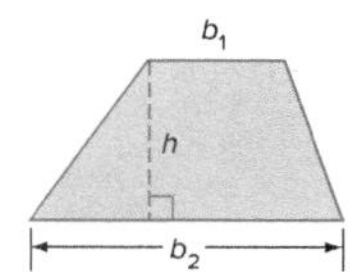

G.MG.3

Real-World Example 1 Area of a Trapezoid

CRAFTS One of Brianna's trapezoid-shaped totes is shown. Find the amount of material used to make the side shown.

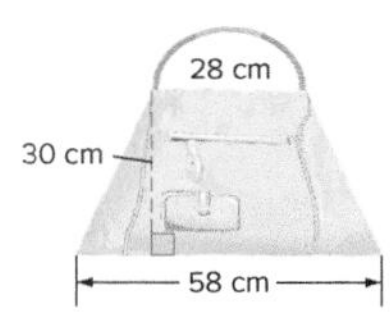

$A = \frac{1}{2}h(b_1 + b_2)$ — Area of a trapezoid

$= \frac{1}{2}(30)(28 + 58)$ — $h = 30, b_1 = 28, b_2 = 58$

$= 1290$ — Simplify.

The tote requires 1290 square centimeters.

Guided Practice

1. **AUTOMOBILES** Find the area of glass used to make the windshield of a van shown at the right. 2983 in^2

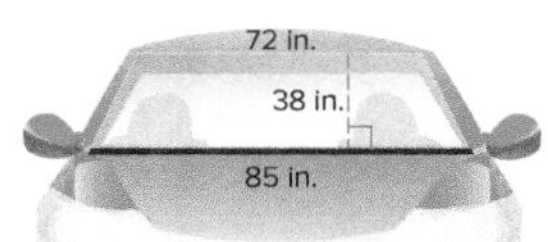

Mathematical Practices Strategies

Look for and make use of structure.
Help students maintain oversight of the process of deriving and applying the formulas for the area of trapezoids, rhombi, and kites. For example, ask:

- What is the formula for the area of a parallelogram? $(b_1 + b_2)h$
- How can you derive the formula for the area of a trapezoid from the formula of a parallelogram? Apply the Commutative Property of Multiplication, then multiply by $\frac{1}{2}$ to find the area of one trapezoid.
- Explain how dividing a trapezoid into triangles can help you find lengths that are missing. We can apply the Pythagorean Theorem or special right triangles.
- How can we derive the formula for a rhombus or a kite? Divide the rhombus or kite on a diagonal that produces two congruent triangles, and then rearrange the two triangles to form a parallelogram. The area will be the same as for the rhombus or kite.

Launch

Have students read the Why? section of the lesson. Ask:

- What other shapes are common for handbags? Sample answers: squares, rectangles
- What could be an advantage of a trapezoid-shaped handbag? Sample statement: It has a wide opening.
- What would be a simple way to make an upper estimate for the area of the trapezoid? Sample statement: Find the area of a rectangle that has the same height and that has a width that is equal to the longer base of the trapezoid.

Teach

Ask the scaffolded questions for each example to build conceptual understanding for students at all levels.

1 Areas of Trapezoids

Example 1 Area of a Trapezoid

AL Define the height of a trapezoid in your own words. The height of a trapezoid is the perpendicular distance between the parallel bases.

OL Can you define different bases and heights for trapezoids in the way that you can define bases and heights of parallelograms and triangles? Explain. No; The bases are the two parallel sides, so the height must be the perpendicular distance between those two sides.

BL If the area of a trapezoid is 549 cm², has a height of 18 cm², and has one base that measures 35 inches, what is the length of the second base? 26 cm

(continued on next page)

Go Online!

Interactive Whiteboard
Use the *eLesson*, *Lesson Presentation*, or *Interactive Classroom* to present this lesson.

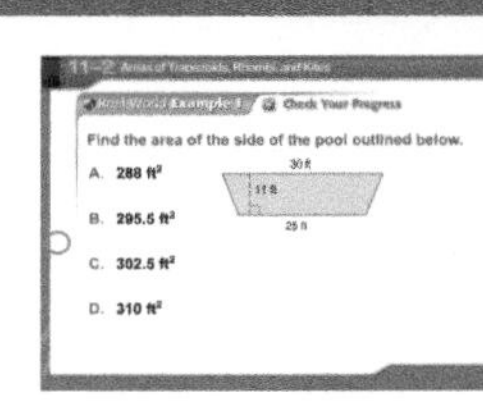

Need Another Example?

Shaving Find the area of steel used to make the razor blade shown below.

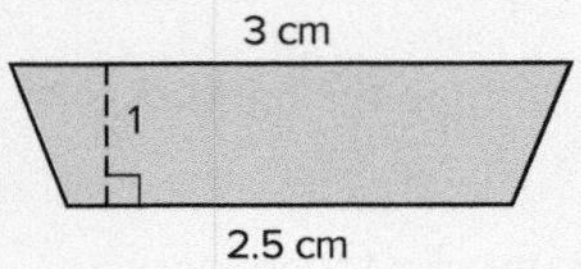

2.75 cm^2

Example 2 Area of a Trapezoid

AL How do we know that the height is 4 inches? Since one of the legs is perpendicular to both bases, its length is the height.

OL If Emilia decided the pennant looked too pointy and changed the length of the longer leg from 8.5 inches to 5 inches, keeping the rest of the pennant the same, what would the new area be? 16 in^2

BL What figures is it possible to break a trapezoid into for the purpose of finding the area using composite figures? triangles, squares, and rectangles

Need Another Example?

Miguel designed a deck shaped like the trapezoid shown below. Find the area of the deck.

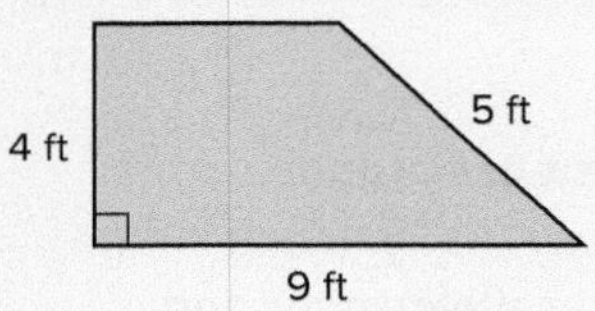

30 ft^2

Watch Out!

Identifying Height The height of a trapezoid is the perpendicular between its bases. Depending on the orientation of the trapezoid, the height may not be a vertical distance.

G.MG.3

Example 2 Area of a Trapezoid

JEWELRY **Emelia designed the pennant shown for her team. Find the area of the shaded portion of her team's pennant.**

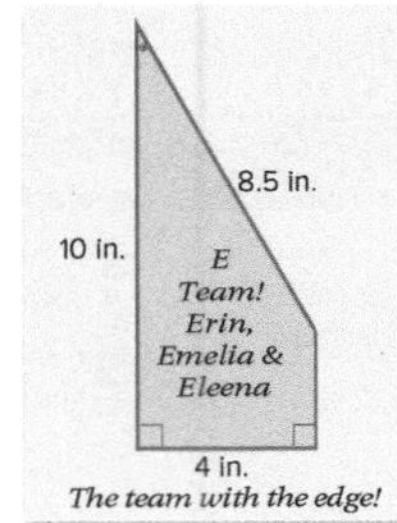

Read the Item

You are given a trapezoid with one base measuring 10 inches, a height of 4 inches, and a third side measuring 8.5 inches. To find the area of the trapezoid, first find the measure of the other base.

Study Tip

MP Modeling To solve some area problems, you need to draw in parallel and/or perpendicular lines to find information not provided.

Solve the Item

Draw the segment shown to form a right triangle and a rectangle. The triangle has a hypotenuse of 8.5 inches and legs of 4 and ℓ inches. The rectangle has a length of 4 inches and a width of x inches.

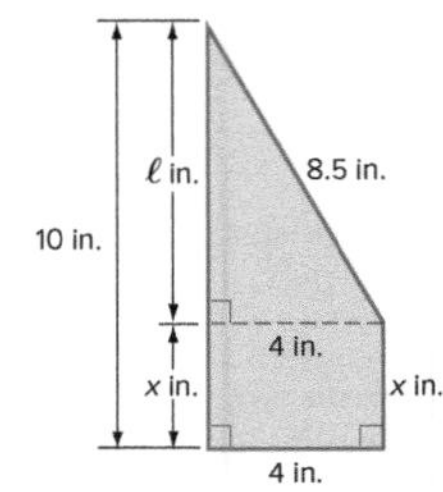

Use the Pythagorean Theorem to find ℓ.

$a^2 + b^2 = c^2$ Pythagorean Theorem

$\ell^2 + 4^2 = 8.5^2$ $a = \ell$, $b = 4$, and $c = 8.5$

$\ell^2 + 16 = 72.25$ Simplify.

$\ell^2 = 56.25$ Subtract 16 from each side.

$\ell = 7.5$ Take the positive square root of each side.

By Segment Addition, $\ell + x = 10$. So, $7.5 + x = 10$ and $x = 2.5$. The width of the rectangle is also the measure of the second base of the trapezoid.

$A = \frac{1}{2}h(b_1 + b_2)$ Area of a trapezoid

$= \frac{1}{2}(4)(10 + 2.5)$ $h = 4$, $b_1 = 10$, and $b_2 = 2.5$

$= 25$ Simplify.

So the pennant has an area of 25 square inches.

Real-World Career

Craft Artist Craft artists create their art by hand to sell or exhibit. They work with a wide variety of materials including textiles, woods, metal, and ceramics. Most artists receive some type of postsecondary training, and about 63% are self-employed. Craft artists make up about 3% of all artists.

CHECK The area of the trapezoid is the sum of the areas of the right triangle and rectangle. The area of the triangle is $\frac{1}{2}(4)(7.5)$ or 15 square inches. The area of the rectangle is (4)(2.5) or 10 square inches. So the area of the trapezoid is 15 + 10 or 25 square inches. ✓

Guided Practice

2. JEWELRY Owen designed the silver earrings shown that are shaped like isosceles trapezoids. What is the area of each earring? 8.5 cm^2

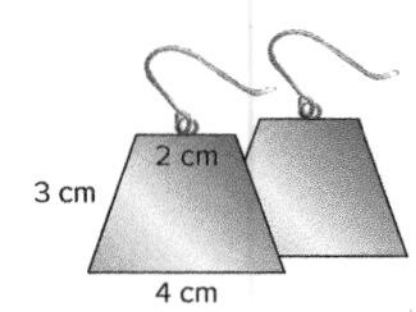

Review Vocabulary ELL

diagonal a segment that connects any two nonconsecutive vertices in a polygoninverses.

2 Areas of Rhombi and Kites

Recall from Lessons 6-5 and 6-6 that a *rhombus* is a parallelogram with all four sides congruent and a *kite* is a quadrilateral with exactly two pairs of consecutive congruent sides.

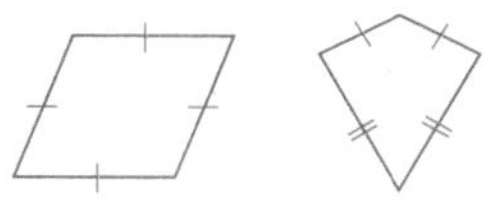

rhombus　　kite

The areas of rhombi and kites are related to the lengths of their diagonals.

Key Concept Area of a Rhombus or Kite

Words The area A of a rhombus or kite is one half the product of the lengths of its diagonals, d_1 and d_2.

Symbols $A = \frac{1}{2}d_1d_2$

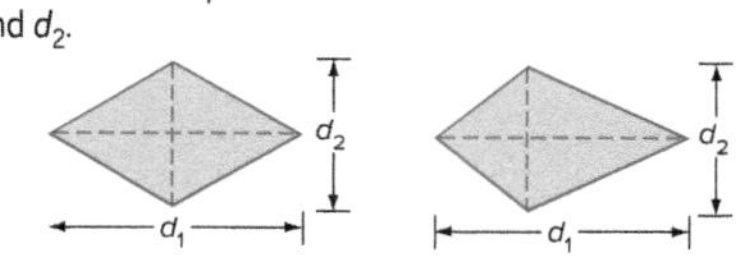

You will derive the formulas for the area of a kite and the area of a rhombus in Exercises 23 and 24.

G.MG.3

Example 3 Area of a Rhombus and a Kite

Find the area of each rhombus or kite.

a.

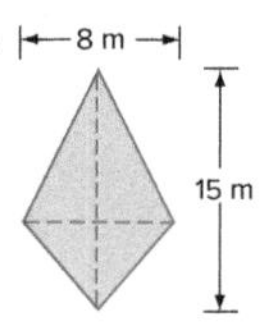

$A = \frac{1}{2}d_1d_2$ Area of a kite

$= \frac{1}{2}(8)(15)$ $d_1 = 8$ and $d_2 = 15$

$= 60 \text{ m}^2$ Simplify.

b.

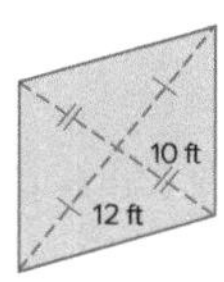

Step 1 Find the length of each diagonal.

Because the diagonals of a rhombus bisect each other, the lengths of the diagonals are 12 + 12 or 24 feet and 10 + 10 or 20 feet.

Step 2 Find the area of the rhombus.

$A = \frac{1}{2}d_1d_2$ Area of a rhombus

$= \frac{1}{2}(24)(20)$ $d_1 = 24$ and $d_2 = 20$

$= 240 \text{ ft}^2$ Simplify.

Guided Practice

Find the area of each rhombus or kite.

3A. 84 mm²

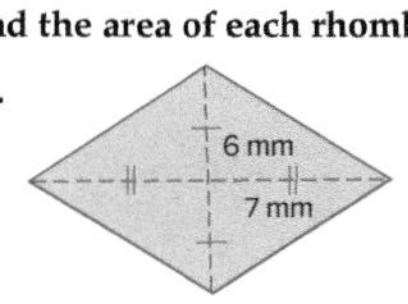

3B. 72 in²

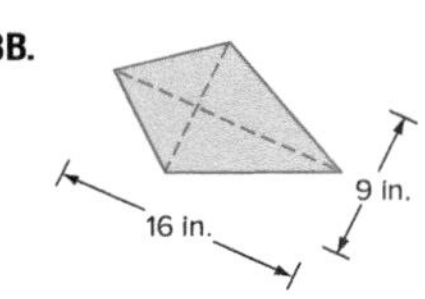

You can use algebra to solve for unknown measures in trapezoids, rhombi, and kites.

Math History Link

Heron of Alexandria (c. 10–70 A.D.) Heron was a mathematician and engineer in Roman Egypt. He developed a formula for finding the area of a triangle if the lengths of the sides are known.

2 Areas of Rhombi and Kites

Example 3 Area of a Rhombus and a Kite

AL **How are rhombi and kites different?** In a rhombus, all four sides are congruent and opposite angles are congruent. In a kite, two pairs of consecutive sides are congruent and only the angles formed by the vertices that form the shorter diagonal are congruent.

OL **The diagonals of a kite are 5 inches and 9 inches. What is the area of the kite?** 22.5 in²

BL **The area of a rhombus is 82.5 square centimeters. If the length of one diagonal is 11 cm, what is the length of the other?** 15 cm

Need Another Example?

Find the area of each rhombus or kite.

a.

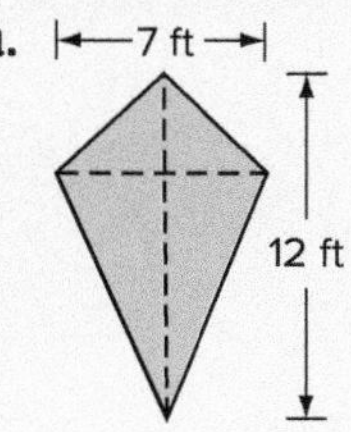

42 ft²

b.

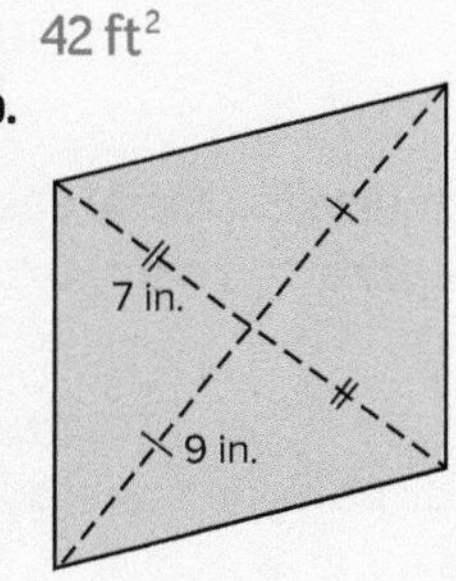

126 in²

Differentiated Instruction AL OL BL ELL

Visual/Spatial Learners Stress that in some triangles, one side seems to be an altitude. This is not true unless the triangle is a right triangle, in which the legs are perpendicular. Students should not assume that angles are right angles unless they are clearly marked.

Example 4 Use Area to Find Missing Measures

AL Could we represent the lengths of the diagonals in another way? Yes; We could also use x and $\frac{1}{2}x$ for the diagonals.

OL One diagonal of a rhombus is 3 units longer than the length of the other diagonal. If the area of the rhombus is 44 square millimeters, what are the lengths of the diagonals? 8 mm; 11 mm

BL The diagonals of a rhombus are congruent. If the area of the rhombus is 50 square inches, what is the measure of each diagonal? 10 in

Need Another Example?

Algebra One diagonal of a rhombus is half as long as the other diagonal. If the area of the rhombus is 64 square inches, what are the lengths of the diagonals? $US = 16$ in.; $RT = 8$

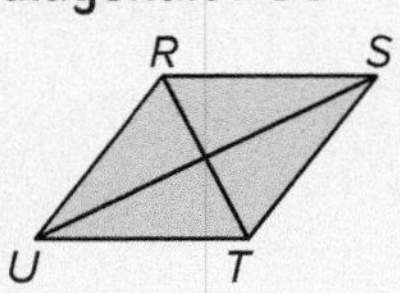

Follow-Up

Students have explored the formulas for the areas of parallelograms, triangles, trapezoids, rhombi, and kites.

Ask:

- How are the area formulas for polygons related? Sample answer: The formula for the area of a parallelogram can be used to derive the formulas for the areas of other polygons.

G.MG.3

Example 4 Use Area to Find Missing Measures

ALGEBRA One diagonal of a rhombus is twice as long as the other diagonal. If the area of the rhombus is 169 square millimeters, what are the lengths of the diagonals?

Step 1 Write an expression to represent each measure.

Let x represent the length of one diagonal. Then the length of the other diagonal is $2x$.

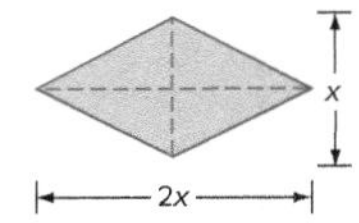

Step 2 Use the formula for the area of a rhombus to find x.

$A = \frac{1}{2}d_1d_2$ — Area of a rhombus

$169 = \frac{1}{2}(x)(2x)$ — $A = 169$, $d_1 = x$, and $d_2 = 2x$

$169 = x^2$ — Simplify.

$13 = x$ — Take the positive square root of each side.

So the lengths of the diagonals are 13 millimeters and 2(13) or 26 millimeters.

Go Online!

The area formulas in this Concept Summary are important to remember. Log into your eStudent Edition to bookmark this page. ELL

Guided Practice

ALGEBRA Find x.

4A. $A = 92$ in^2 8.4 in.

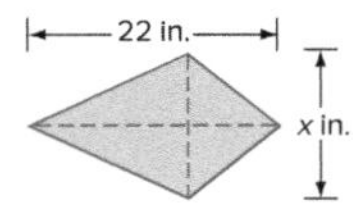

4B. $A = 177$ cm^2 16.2 cm

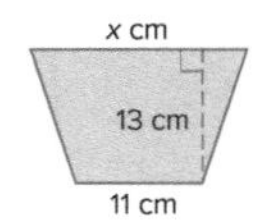

4C. ALGEBRA What is the area of the kite shown? 168 in^2

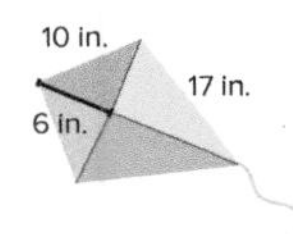

Concept Summary Areas of Polygons

Parallelogram	Triangles	Trapezoids	Rhombi and Kites
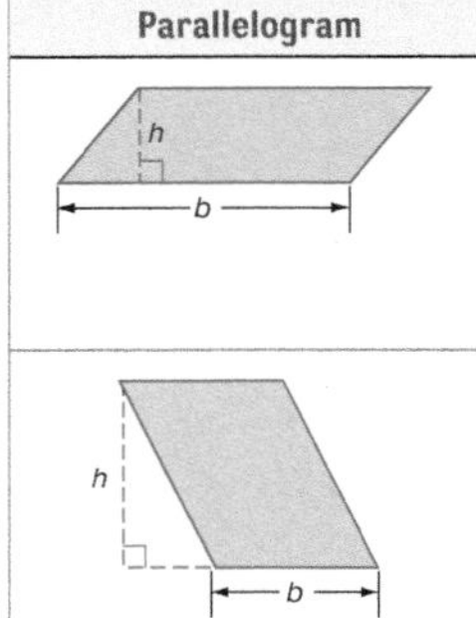	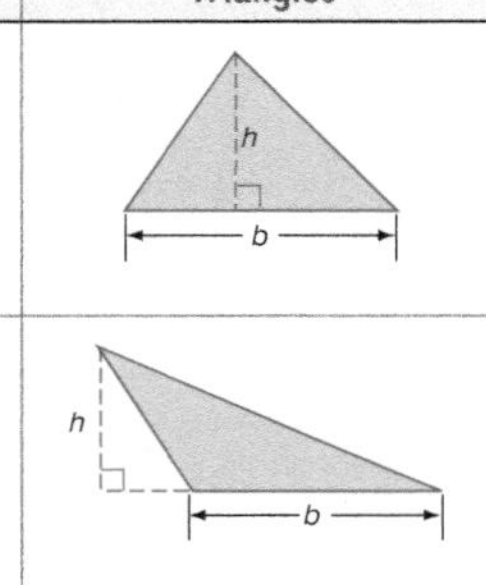	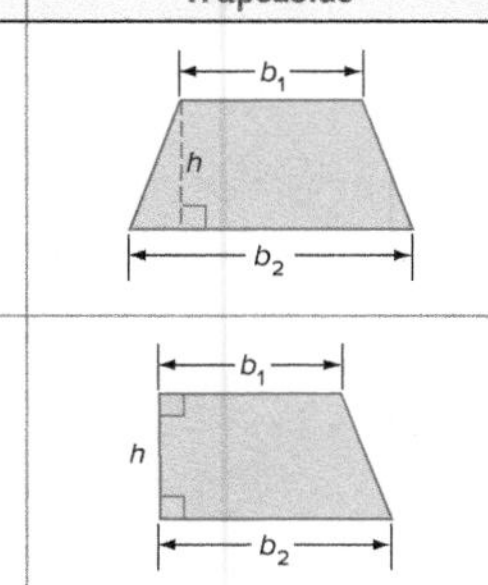	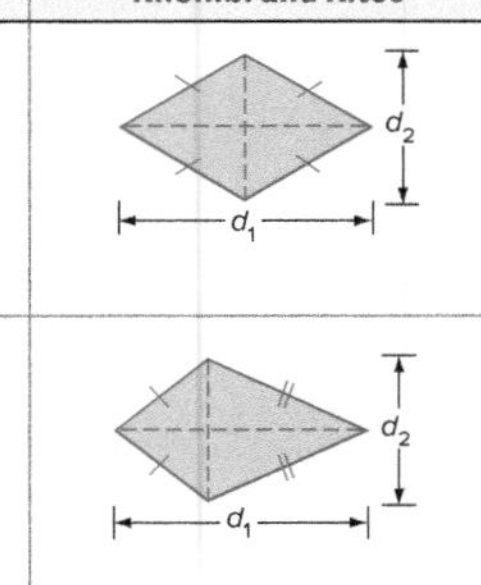
$A = bh$	$A = \frac{1}{2}bh$	$A = \frac{1}{2}h(b_1 + b_2)$	$A = \frac{1}{2}d_1d_2$

Differentiated Instruction OL BL

Extension Draw on students' prior knowledge by having them create a blueprint of their kitchen including the bases of all structures. Ask students to include a scale. Use these drawings to have students estimate the number of tiles that would be needed to cover the floor. Varying the size of the tile is an easy way to differentiate this task for different ability levels. This task enables students to view area as something that is not always neat and formulaic.

Check Your Understanding

◯ = Step-by-Step Solutions begin on page R13.

Go Online! for a Self-Check Quiz

Examples 1–3 G.MG.3 **Find the area of each trapezoid, rhombus, or kite.**

1. $132\ ft^2$

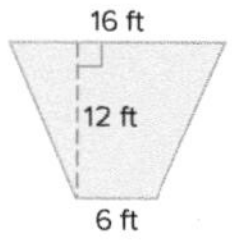

2. $90\ m^2$

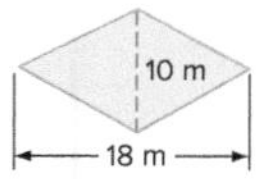

3. $178.5\ m^2$

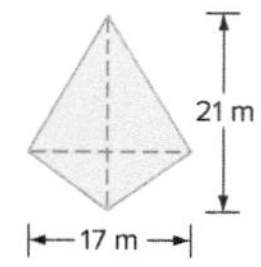

4. PEP RALLY Suki is designing posters for the Homecoming game. Her design is shown at the right. What is the area of the poster in square feet? $4.375\ ft^2$

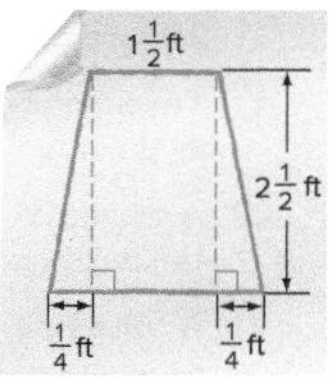

Example 4 G.MG.3 **ALGEBRA Find x.**

5. $A = 78\ cm^2$ 8 cm

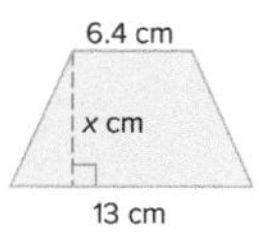

6. $A = 96\ in^2$ 6.6 in.

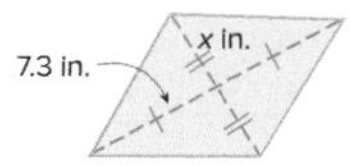

7. $A = 104\ ft^2$ 6.3 ft

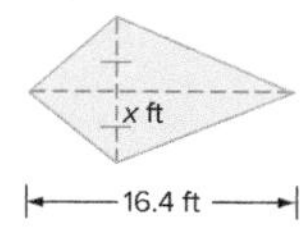

Practice and Problem Solving

Extra Practice is on page R10.

Examples 1–3 G.MG.3 MP **STRUCTURE Find the area of each trapezoid, rhombus, or kite.** 8–13. See margin.

8.

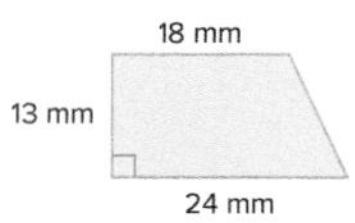

9.

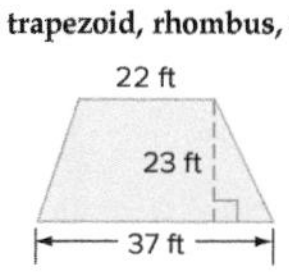

10.

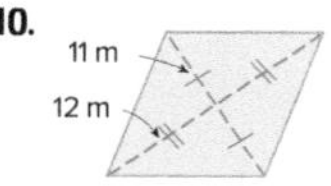

11.

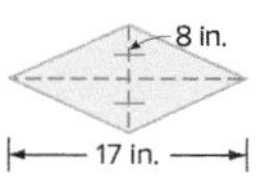

12.

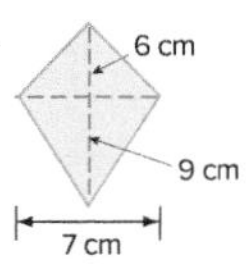

13.

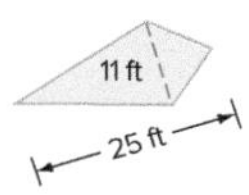

MICROSCOPES Find the area of the identified portion of each magnified image. Assume that the identified portion is either a trapezoid, rhombus, or kite. Measures are provided in microns. 14–16. See margin.

14. human skin

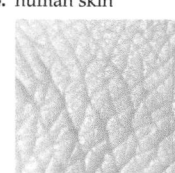

(15) heartleaf plant

16. eye of a fly

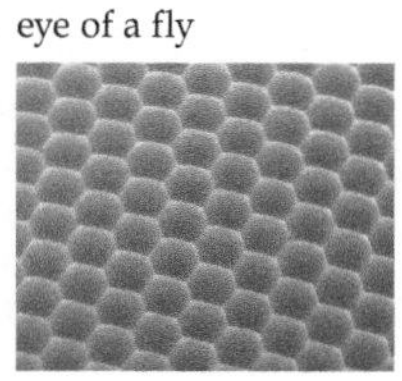

Differentiated Homework Options			
Levels	AL Basic	OL Core	BL Advanced
Exercises	8–22, 34, 36–44	9–27 odd, 28, 29, 31, 33, 34, 36–44	29–38, (optional: 39–44)
2-Day Option	9–21 odd, 39–44	8–22	
	8–22 even, 34, 36–38	23–34, 36–44	

You can use ALEKS to provide additional remediation support with personalized instruction and practice.

Practice

Formative Assessment Use Exercises 1–7 to assess students' understanding of the concepts in this lesson.

The Practice and Problem Solving exercises assess the content taught in the lesson. The Preparing for Assessment page is meant to be used as preparation for end-of-course assessments.

Extra Practice

See page R10 for extra exercises for students who are approaching level or for on-level students who need additional reinforcement.

MP Teaching the Mathematical Practices

Structure Mathematically proficient students look closely to discern a pattern or structure. They also can step back for an overview and shift perspective. In Exercises 8–13, encourage students to classify each figure first.

Levels of Complexity Chart

The levels of the exercises progress from 1 to 3, with Level 1 indicating the lowest level of complexity.

Exercises	8–22	23–28, 39–44	29–38
C Level 3			●
B Level 2		●	
Level 1	●		

Additional Answers

8. $273\ mm^2$
9. $678.5\ ft^2$
10. $264\ m^2$
11. $136\ in^2$
12. $52.5\ cm^2$
13. $137.5\ ft^2$
14. 26 square microns
15. 24.5 square microns
16. 9.9 square microns

Teaching the Mathematical Practices

Sense-Making Mathematically proficient students start by explaining the meaning of a problem to themselves and looking for entry points to its solution. They plan a solution pathway rather than simply jumping into a solution attempt. In Exercises 26–27, encourage students to plot the vertices first and then classify the quadrilateral.

Additional Answers

23. The area of $\triangle HJF = \frac{1}{2}d_1\left(\frac{1}{2}d_2\right)$ and the area of $\triangle HGF = \frac{1}{2}d_1\left(\frac{1}{2}d_2\right)$. Therefore, the area of $\triangle HJF = \frac{1}{4}d_1d_2$, and the area of $\triangle HGF = \frac{1}{4}d_1d_2$. The area of kite $FGHJ$ is equal to the area of $\triangle HJF$ + the area of $\triangle HGF$ or $\frac{1}{4}d_1d_2 + \frac{1}{4}d_1d_2$. After simplification, the area of kite $FGHJ$ is equal to $\frac{1}{2}d_1d_2$.

24. The area of $\triangle ZWX = \frac{1}{2}d_1\left(\frac{1}{2}d_2\right)$ and the area of $\triangle ZYX = \frac{1}{2}d_1\left(\frac{1}{2}d_2\right)$. Therefore, the area of $\triangle ZWX = \frac{1}{4}d_1d_2$, and the area of $\triangle ZYX = \frac{1}{4}d_1d_2$. The area of rhombus $WXYZ$ is equal to the area of $\triangle ZWX$ + the area of $\triangle ZYX$ or $\frac{1}{4}d_1d_2 + \frac{1}{4}d_1d_2$. After simplification, the area of rhombus $WXYZ$ is equal to $\frac{1}{2}d_1d_2$.

17. **JOBS** Jimmy works on his neighbors' yards after school to earn extra money to buy a car. He is going to plant grass seed in Mr. Troyer's yard. What is the area of the yard? $784\ ft^2$

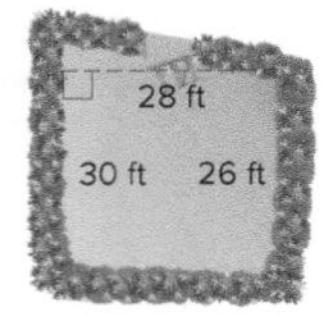

Example 4 G.MG.3

ALGEBRA Find each missing length.

18. One diagonal of a kite is twice as long as the other diagonal. If the area of the kite is 240 square inches, what are the lengths of the diagonals? 15.5 in., 31.0 in.

19. The area of a rhombus is 168 square centimeters. If one diagonal is three times as long as the other, what are the lengths of the diagonals? 10.6 cm, 31.7 cm

20. A trapezoid has base lengths of 12 and 14 feet with an area of 322 square feet. What is the height of the trapezoid? 24.8 ft

21. A trapezoid has a height of 8 meters, a base length of 12 meters, and an area of 64 square meters. What is the length of the other base? 4 m

22. **HONORS** Estella has been asked to join an honor society at school. Before the first meeting, new members are asked to sand and stain the front side of a piece of wood in the shape of an isosceles trapezoid. What is the surface area that Estella will need to sand and stain? $1.2\ in^2$

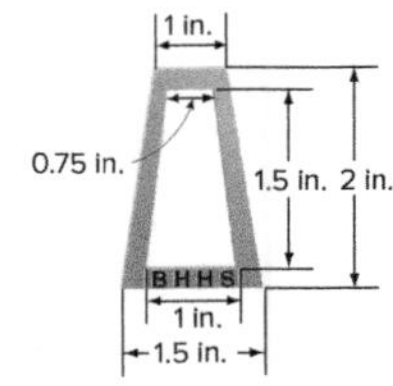

For each figure, provide a justification showing that $A = \frac{1}{2}d_1d_2$.

23.

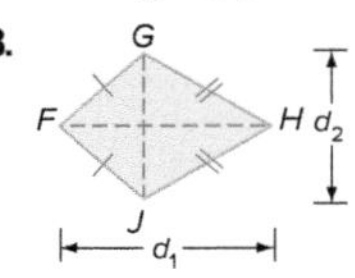

23–24. See margin.

24.

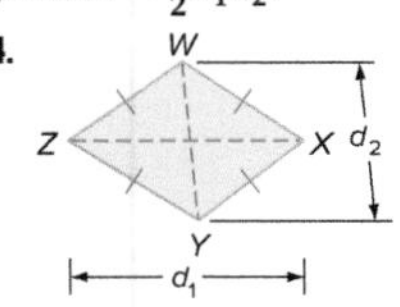

25. **CRAFTS** Ashanti is competing in a kite festival. The yellow, red, orange, green, and blue pieces of her kite design shown are congruent rhombi.

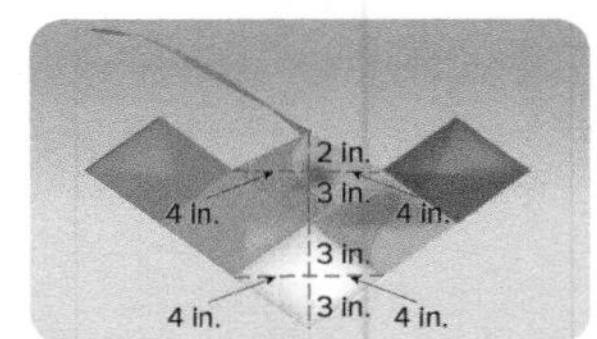

a. How much fabric of each color does she need to buy? 25a. $24\ in^2$ each of yellow, red, orange, green, and blue; $20\ in^2$ of purple

b. Ashanti wants the total area of her kite to be no greater than 200 square inches. Does her kite meet this requirement? Explain. Yes; her kite has an area of $140\ in^2$, which is less than $200\ in^2$.

SENSE-MAKING Find the area of each quadrilateral with the given vertices.

26. $A(-8, 6)$, $B(-5, 8)$, $C(-2, 6)$, and $D(-5, 0)$ 24 units²

27. $W(3, 0)$, $X(0, 3)$, $Y(-3, 0)$, and $Z(0, -3)$ 18 units²

28. **METALS** When magnified in very powerful microscopes, some metals are composed of grains that have various polygonal shapes.

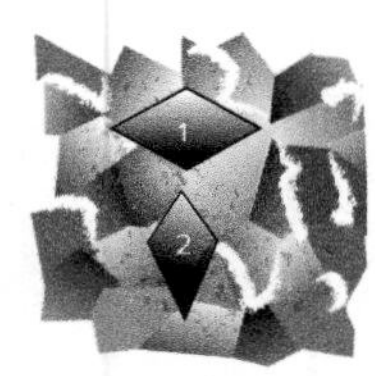

a. What is the area of figure 1 if the grain has a height of 4 microns and bases with lengths of 5 and 6 microns? 22 square microns

b. If figure 2 has perpendicular diagonal lengths of 3.8 microns and 4.9 microns, what is the area of the grain? 9.3 square microns

Differentiated Instruction ELL

Intermediate Instruct a small group of students to write a paragraph describing what is happening in the figure illustrating the verification of the area of a trapezoid. Their paragraphs should describe each part of the diagram in their own words. Ask for volunteers to read their paragraphs. Have students ask for clarification as needed.

C **29. PROOF** The figure at the right is a trapezoid that consists of two congruent right triangles and an isosceles right triangle. In 1876, James A. Garfield, the 20th president of the United States, discovered a proof of the Pythagorean Theorem using this diagram. Prove that $x^2 + y^2 = z^2$. See margin.

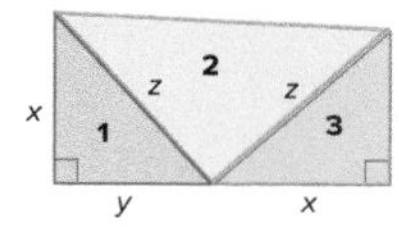

DIMENSIONAL ANALYSIS Find the perimeter and area of each figure in feet. Round to the nearest tenth, if necessary.

30.

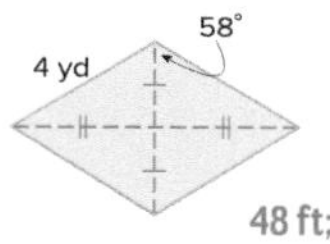

48 ft; 129.4 ft²

31.

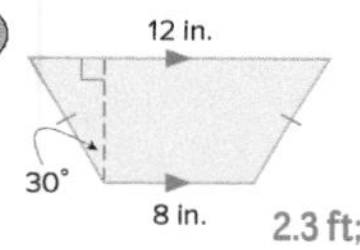

2.3 ft; 0.2 ft²

32.

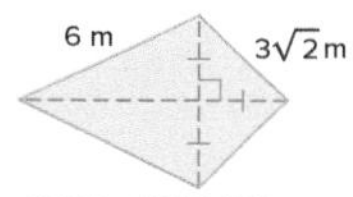

67.6 ft; 267.8 ft²

33. MULTIPLE REPRESENTATIONS In this problem, you will investigate perimeters of kites. a–e. See Ch. 10 Answer Appendix.

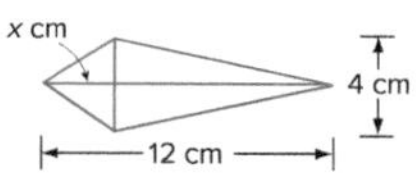

a. **Geometric** Draw a kite like the one shown if $x = 2$.

b. **Geometric** Repeat the process in part **a** for three x-values between 2 and 10 and for an x-value of 10. The overall length of the kite should remain 12 centimeters.

c. **Tabular** Measure and record in a table the perimeter of each kite, along with the x-value.

d. **Graphical** Graph the perimeter versus the x-value using the data from your table.

e. **Analytical** Make a conjecture about the value of x that will minimize the perimeter of the kite. What is the significance of this value?

34. Madeline; sample answer: There is more than one trapezoid with a height of 4 units and an area of 18 square units. The sum of the bases of the trapezoid has to be 9, so one possibility is a trapezoid with bases of 4 and 5 units and a height of 4 units. Another is a trapezoid with bases of 3 and 6 units and a height of 4 units.

G.MG.3

H.O.T. Problems Use Higher-Order Thinking Skills

34. CRITIQUE ARGUMENTS Antonio and Madeline want to draw a trapezoid that has a height of 4 units and an area of 18 square units. Antonio says that only one trapezoid will meet the criteria. Madeline disagrees and thinks that she can draw several different trapezoids with a height of 4 units and an area of 18 square units. Is either of them correct? Explain your reasoning.

35. CHALLENGE Find x in parallelogram $ABCD$. 7.2

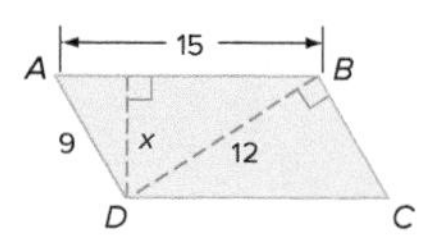

36. OPEN-ENDED Draw a kite and a rhombus with an area of 6 square inches. Label and justify your drawings. See Ch. 10 Answer Appendix.

37. MP REASONING If the areas of two rhombi are equal, are the perimeters *sometimes*, *always*, or *never* equal? Explain. Sometimes; sample answer: If the areas are equal, it means that the products of the diagonals are equal. The only time that the perimeters will be equal is when the diagonals are also equal, or when the two rhombi are congruent.

38. See Ch. 10 Answer Appendix.

38. WRITING IN MATH How can you use trigonometry to find the area of a figure?

MP Standards for Mathematical Practice

Emphasis On	Exercises
1 Make sense of problems and persevere in solving them.	18–21, 26, 27, 39, 40–42
2 Reason abstractly and quantitatively.	5–7
3 Construct viable arguments and critique the reasoning of others.	23, 24, 29, 33, 34, 36–38
4 Model with mathematics.	4, 14–17, 22, 25, 28, 39
7 Look for and make use of structure.	8–13, 30–32, 35, 39, 42

Exercise Alert

Ruler Exercises 33 and 36 require the use of a ruler.

MP Teaching the Mathematical Practices

Critique Arguments Mathematically proficient students can distinguish correct logic from flawed reasoning. In Exercise 34, students should see that the sum of the bases of the trapezoid has to be 9; $\frac{1}{2} \cdot 4 \cdot 9 = 18$. Madeline is correct because there are many different trapezoids that have the sum of their bases equal to 9.

Assess

Ticket Out the Door Ask students to list all the formulas for area they have learned so far in this chapter. Have them include a labeled diagram corresponding to each formula. Have students turn in their statements before they leave the classroom.

Additional Answers

29. The area of a trapezoid is $\frac{1}{2}h(b_1 + b_2)$. So, $A = \frac{1}{2}(x + y)(x + y)$ or $\frac{1}{2}(x^2 + 2xy + y^2)$. The area of $\triangle 1 = \frac{1}{2}(y)(x)$, $\triangle 2 = \frac{1}{2}(z)(z)$, and $\triangle 3 = \frac{1}{2}(x)(y)$. The area of $\triangle 1 + \triangle 2 + \triangle 3 = \frac{1}{2}xy + \frac{1}{2}z^2 + \frac{1}{2}xy$. Set the area of the trapezoid equal to the combined areas of the triangles to get $\frac{1}{2}(x^2 + 2xy + y^2) = \frac{1}{2}xy + \frac{1}{2}z^2 + \frac{1}{2}xy$. Multiply by 2 on each side: $x^2 + 2xy + y^2 = 2xy + z^2$. When simplified, $x^2 + y^2 = z^2$.

Go Online!

eSolutions Manual

Create worksheets, answer keys, and solutions handouts for your assignments.

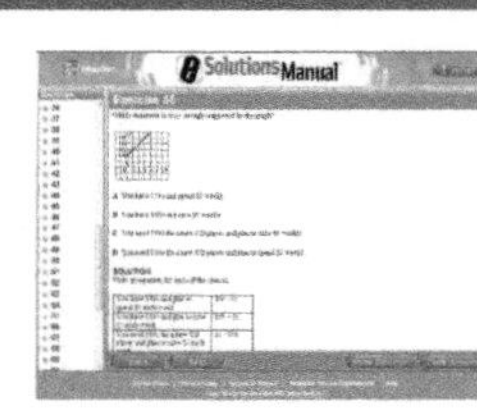

Preparing for Assessment

Exercises 39–44 require students to use the skills they will need on standardized assessments. Exercises are dual-coded with content standards and mathematical practice standards.

Dual Coding		
Items	Content Standards	MP Mathematical Practices
39	G.MG.1	1, 4, 7
40	G.MG.3	1, 4
41		1
42	G.MG.1	1, 4, 7
43	G.MG.1	1, 4, 7
44	G.MG.1	1, 4, 7

Diagnose Student Errors

Survey student responses for each item. Class trends may indicate common errors and misconceptions.

39.

A	assumed the area increases by half the amount of one dimension
B	assumed the area increases by the same amount of one dimension
C	assumed the area increases by twice the amount of one dimension
D	CORRECT

40.

A	CORRECT
B	Doubled the dimensions
C	CORRECT
D	Forgot to multiply the sum of the bases by $\frac{1}{2}$.

Preparing for Assessment

39. The Jays' team logo is a rhombus, as shown.

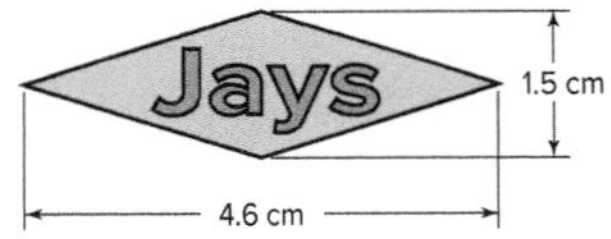

The team's manager makes an enlargement of the logo in which each dimension is 4 times larger than the version shown here. Which of the following best describes how the areas of the logos compare? MP 1, 4, 7 G.MG.1 **D**

- ○ **A** The area of the enlargement is 2 times the area of the original.
- ○ **B** The area of the enlargement is 4 times the area of the original.
- ○ **C** The area of the enlargement is 8 times the area of the original.
- ○ **D** The area of the enlargement is 16 times the area of the original.

40. Li Mei drew the trapezoid shown below as the plan for a new concrete driveway apron. The contractor will charge \$9.50 per square foot to install the concrete. The homeowner will seal the concrete with sealer that costs \$40 for a container that covers 80 square feet.

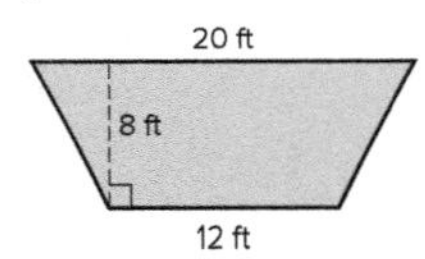

Which of the following statements about the driveway apron are true? Select all that apply. MP 1, 4 G.MG.3 **A, C**

- ☐ **A** It will cost \$1216 for the concrete.
- ☐ **B** The homeowner will need four containers of sealer to seal the concrete.
- ☐ **C** A \$1300 budget for the concrete and sealer is enough for the project.
- ☐ **D** The area of concrete is 288 square feet.

41. One diagonal of a rhombus is four times as long as the other diagonal. If the area of the rhombus is 288 square meters, what are the lengths of the diagonals? MP 1, 7 **12 meters and 48 meters**

42. The figure shows a kite that Alex created using geometry software.

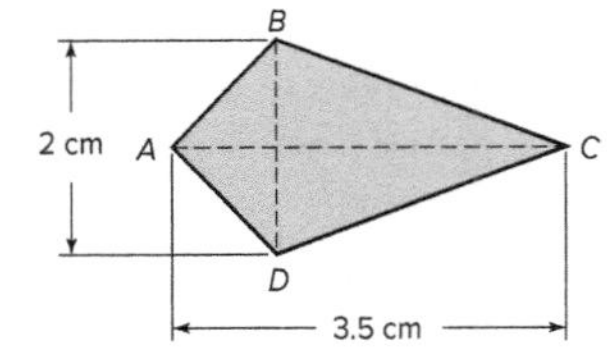

Which of the following will result in a kite with twice the area of *ABCD*? MP 1, 4, 7 G.MG.1 **D**

I. Double the length of each diagonal.

II. Double the length of $\overline{BD}$.

III. Double the length of $\overline{AC}$.

- ○ **A** I only
- ○ **B** II only
- ○ **C** III only
- ○ **D** II and III

43. The sides of a soccer goal are in the form of a trapezoid. The bottom base of the trapezoid is 6.5 feet long, the top base of the trapezoid is 4.25 feet long, and the height of the trapezoid is 8 feet high. Find the area of one side of the soccer goal. MP 1, 4, 7 G.MG.1 **C**

- **A** 38 square feet
- **B** 40 square feet
- **C** 43 square feet
- **D** 50 square feet

44. **MULTI-STEP** The area of a kite is 50 square inches. MP 1, 4, 7 G.MG.1

a. If each diagonal is a whole number, how many distinct diagonal pairs have whole number lengths? **5**

b. Which diagonal length, in inches, will guarantee that the kite is also a rhombus? **10**

c. If the area of the kite is doubled, how many distinct diagonal pairs have whole number lengths? **6**

42.

A	Assumed that doubling all dimensions doubles the area
B	Did not recognize that doubling the length of either diagonal doubles the area
C	Did not recognize that doubling the length of either diagonal doubles the area
D	CORRECT

Go Online!

Quizzes

Students can use *Self-Check Quizzes* to check their understanding of this lesson and have the results sent to you. You can also give *Quiz 1*, which covers the content in Lessons 10-1 and 10-2.

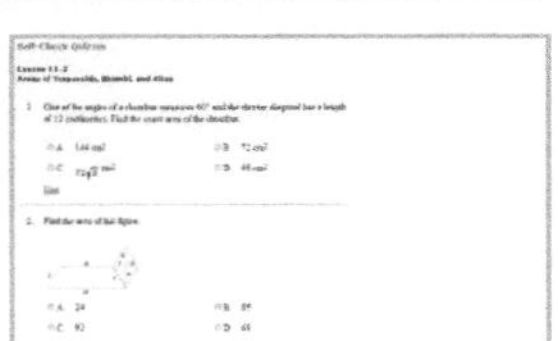

LESSON 10-3

Areas of Circles and Sectors

SUGGESTED PACING (DAYS)	
90 min.	0.5
45 min.	1.0
	Instruction

Track Your Progress

Objectives

1 Find areas of circles.

2 Find areas of sectors of circles.

Mathematical Background

If a circle has an area A and a radius r, then $A = \pi r^2$. A sector of a circle is a region of a circle bounded by a central angle and its intercepted arc. If a sector of a circle has an area A, a central angle measuring $N°$, and a radius r, then $A = \frac{N}{360}\pi r^2$.

Skills Trace

THEN	NOW	NEXT
G.MG.3 Apply geometric methods to solve design problems.	**G.C.5** Derive using similarity the fact that the length of an arc intercepted by an angle is proportional to the radius, and define the radian measure of the angle as the constant of proportionality; derive the formula for the area of a sector. **G.GMD.1** Give an informal argument for the formulas for the circumference of a circle, area of a circle, volume of a cylinder, pyramid, and cone.	**G.GMD.3** Use volume formulas for cylinders, pyramids, cones, and spheres to solve problems.

Go Online! All of these resources and more are available at connectED.mcgraw-hill.com

Use the 2-D Figures tool from eToolkit to find the areas of circles.

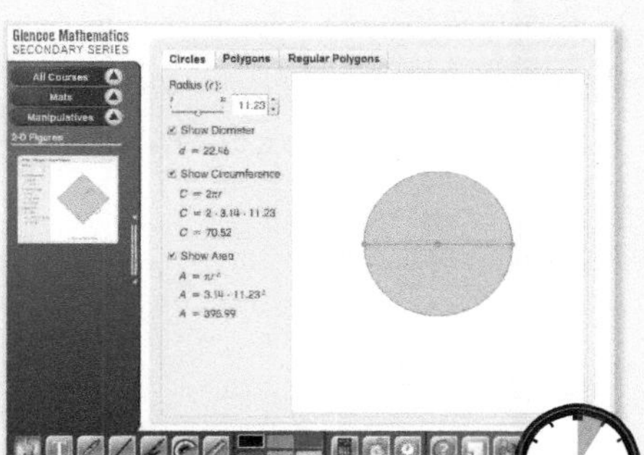

Use at End of Lesson

Personal Tutors (for every example) let students hear real teachers solve problems. Students can pause and repeat as many times as necessary.

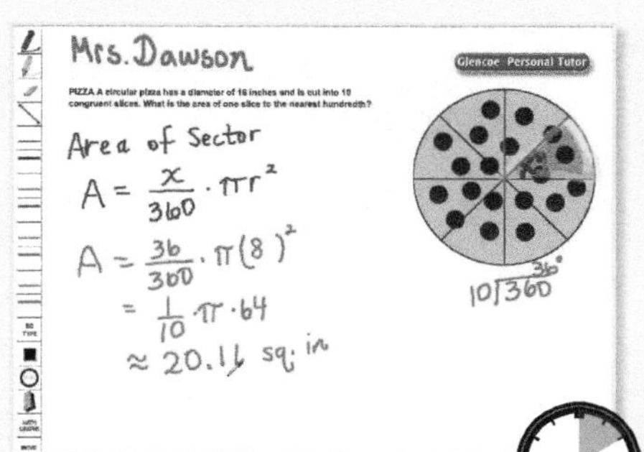

Use with Examples

Use a Self-Check Quiz to assess students' understanding of areas of circles and sectors

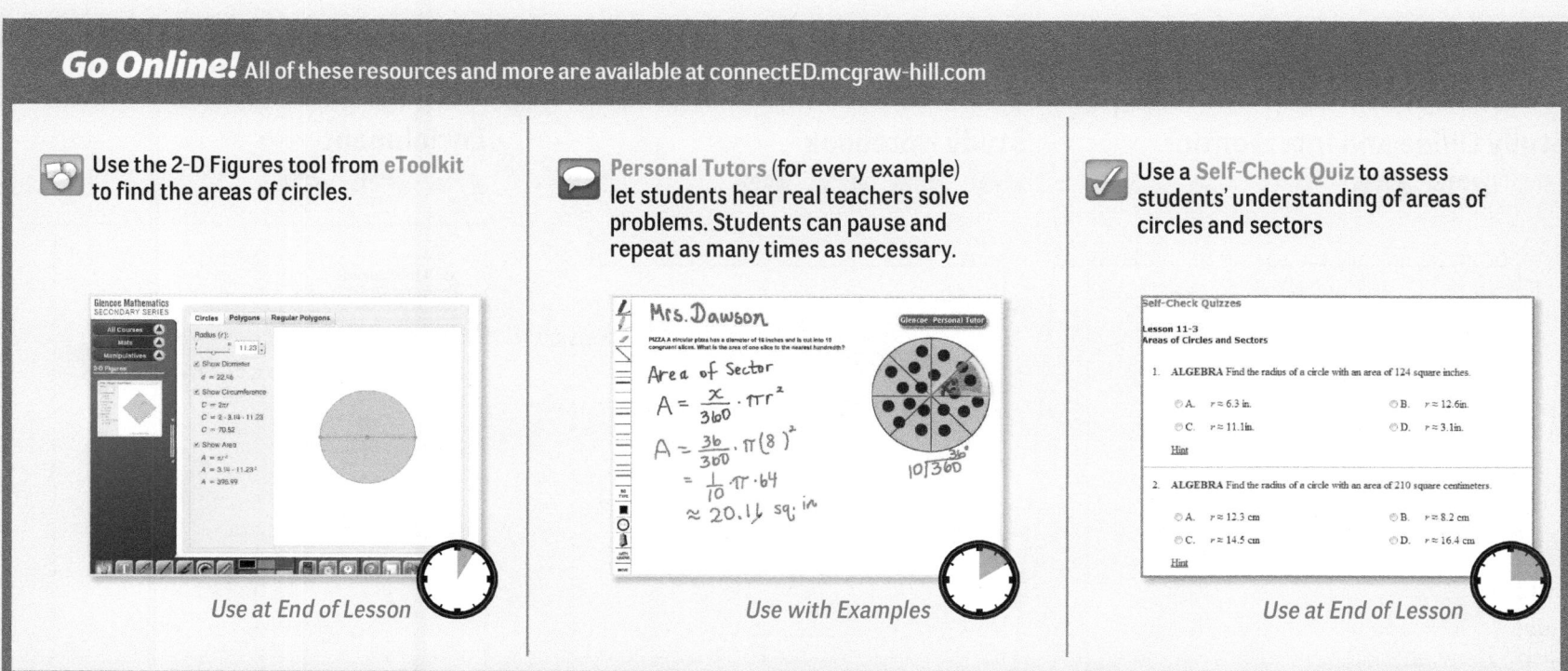

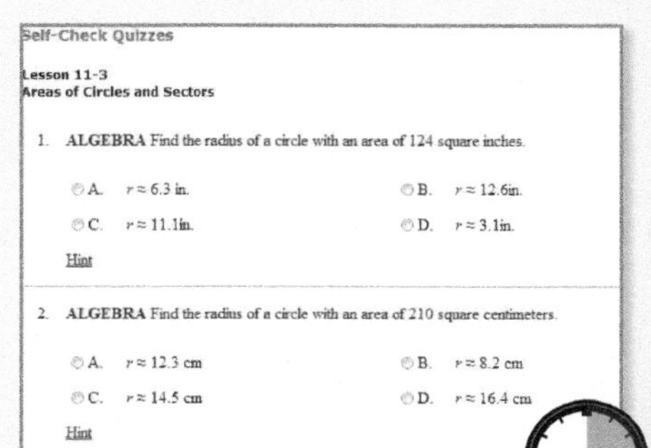

Use at End of Lesson

OER Using Open Educational Resources

Activity Use the explore activity *Piece of Cake* on **teachmathematics.net** to help students develop an intuitive understanding of the formulas for the area of circles and sectors. Students can work in pairs or small groups. Students can also visit this site for review games and virtual manipulatives. *Use as in-class activity*

Go Online!
connectED.mcgraw-hill.com

Worksheets

Differentiate Your Resources

Extra Practice Additional practice or homework; Skills Practice is best for approaching-level students and Practice is best for on-level and beyond-level students

Skills Practice

AL OL ELL

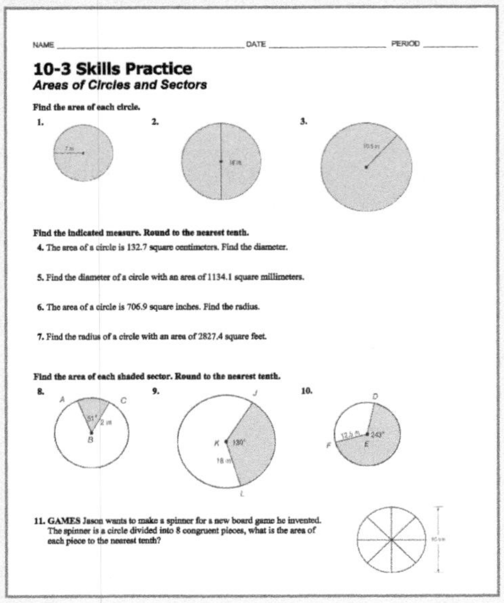

10-3 Skills Practice
Areas of Circles and Sectors

Find the area of each circle.

Find the indicated measure. Round to the nearest tenth.

4. The area of a circle is 132.7 square centimeters. Find the diameter.

5. Find the diameter of a circle with an area of 1134.1 square millimeters.

6. The area of a circle is 706.9 square inches. Find the radius.

7. Find the radius of a circle with an area of 2827.4 square feet.

Find the area of each shaded sector. Round to the nearest tenth.

11. GAMES Jason wants to make a spinner for a new board game he invented. The spinner is a circle divided into 8 congruent pieces, what is the area of each piece to the nearest tenth?

Practice

AL OL BL ELL

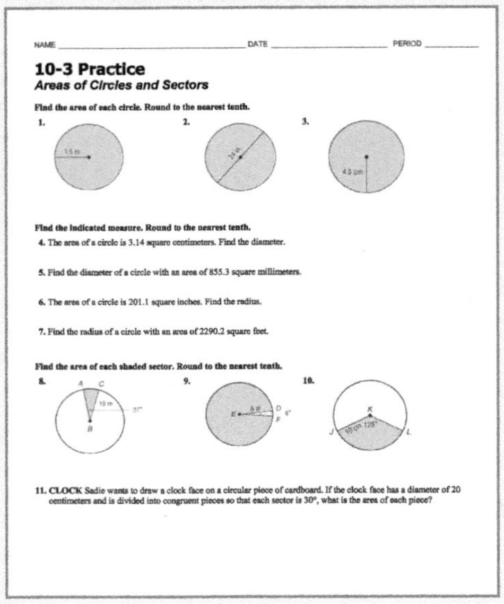

10-3 Practice
Areas of Circles and Sectors

Find the area of each circle. Round to the nearest tenth.

Find the indicated measure. Round to the nearest tenth.

4. The area of a circle is 3.14 square centimeters. Find the diameter.

5. Find the diameter of a circle with an area of 855.3 square millimeters.

6. The area of a circle is 201.1 square inches. Find the radius.

7. Find the radius of a circle with an area of 2290.2 square feet.

Find the area of each shaded sector. Round to the nearest tenth.

11. CLOCK Sadie wants to draw a clock face on a circular piece of cardboard. If the clock face has a diameter of 20 centimeters and is divided into congruent pieces so that each sector is 30°, what is the area of each piece?

Word Problem Practice

AL OL BL ELL

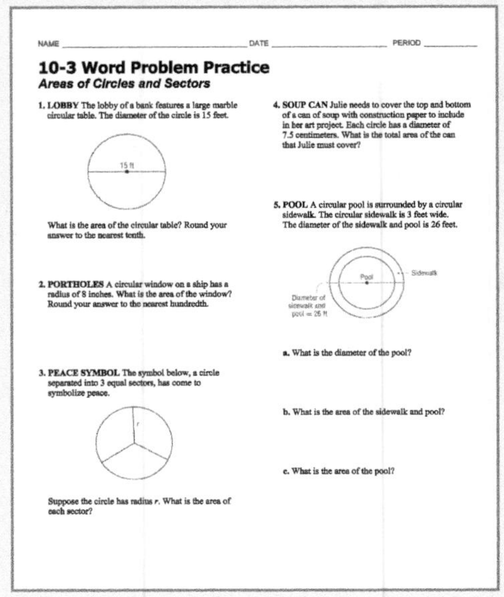

10-3 Word Problem Practice
Areas of Circles and Sectors

1. LOBBY The lobby of a bank features a large marble circular table. The diameter of the circle is 15 feet.

What is the area of the circular table? Round your answer to the nearest tenth.

2. PORTHOLES A circular window on a ship has a radius of 8 inches. What is the area of the window? Round your answer to the nearest hundredth.

3. PEACE SYMBOL The symbol below, a circle separated into 3 equal sectors, has come to symbolize peace.

Suppose the circle has radius *r*. What is the area of each sector?

4. SOUP CAN Julie needs to cover the top and bottom of a can of soup with construction paper to include in her art project. Each circle has a diameter of 7.5 centimeters. What is the total area of the can that Julie must cover?

5. POOL A circular pool is surrounded by a circular sidewalk. The circular sidewalk is 3 feet wide. The diameter of the sidewalk and pool is 26 feet.

a. What is the diameter of the pool?

b. What is the area of the sidewalk and pool?

c. What is the area of the pool?

Intervention Reteaching and vocabulary activities that can be used with struggling or absent students and as ELL support

Study Guide and Intervention

AL OL ELL

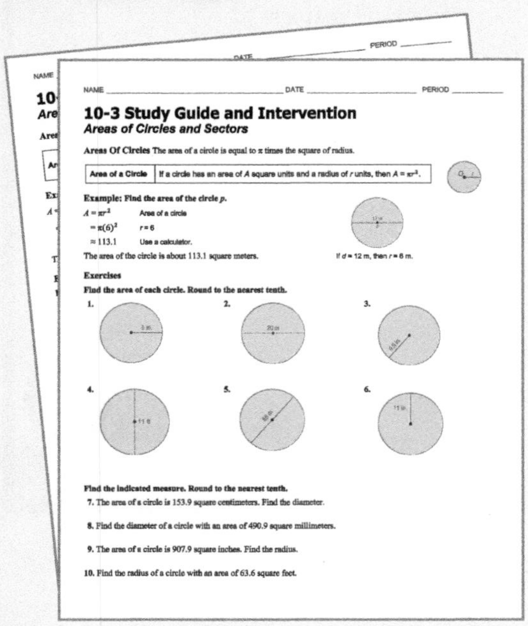

10-3 Study Guide and Intervention
Areas of Circles and Sectors

Find the indicated measure. Round to the nearest tenth.

7. The area of a circle is 153.9 square centimeters. Find the diameter.

8. Find the diameter of a circle with an area of 490.9 square millimeters.

9. The area of a circle is 907.9 square inches. Find the radius.

10. Find the radius of a circle with an area of 63.6 square feet.

Study Notebook

AL OL BL ELL

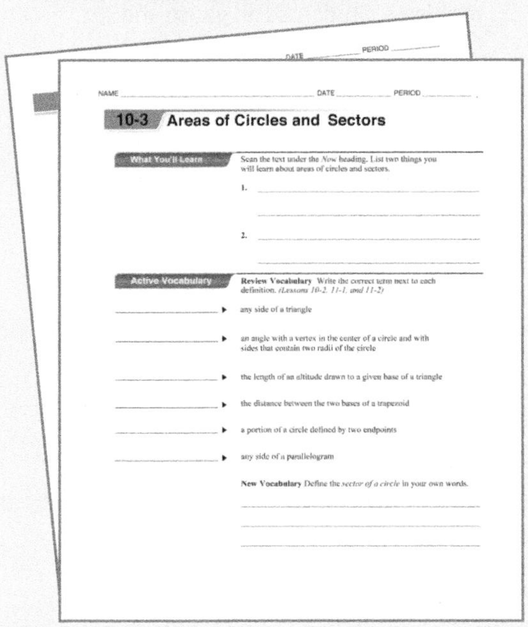

10-3 Areas of Circles and Sectors

What You'll Learn

Active Vocabulary

Extension Activities that can be used to extend lesson concepts

Enrichment

OL BL ELL

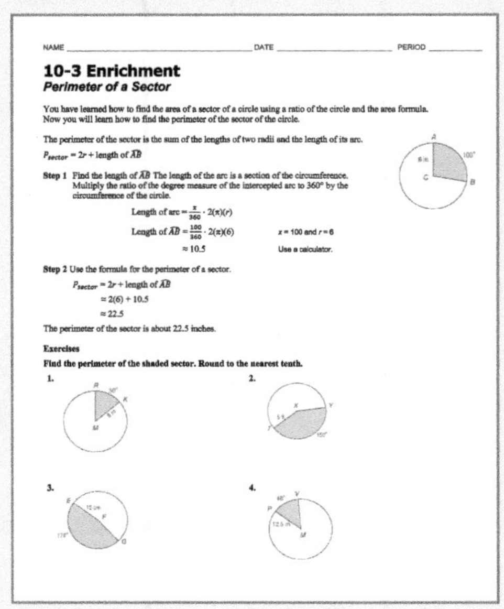

10-3 Enrichment
Perimeter of a Sector

The perimeter of the sector is about 22.5 inches.

Exercises

Find the perimeter of the shaded sector. Round to the nearest tenth.

LESSON 3

Areas of Circles and Sectors

Then	Now	Why?
• You found the circumference of a circle.	• 1 Find areas of circles. 2 Find areas of sectors of circles.	• To determine whether a medium, large, or extra-large pizza is a better value, you can compare the cost per square inch. Divide the cost of each pizza by its area.

New Vocabulary
sector of a circle
segment of a circle

Mathematical Practices
1 Make sense of problems and persevere in solving them.
6 Attend to precision.

Content Standards
G.C.5 Derive using similarity the fact that the length of the arc intercepted by an angle is proportional to the radius, and define the radian measure of the angle as the constant of proportionality; derive the formula for the area of a sector.
G.GMD.1 Give an informal argument for the formulas for the circumference of a circle, area of a circle, volume of a cylinder, pyramid, and cone.

1 Areas of Circles In Lesson 9-1, you learned that the formula for the circumference C of a circle with radius r is given by $C = 2\pi r$. You can use this formula to develop the formula for the area of a circle.

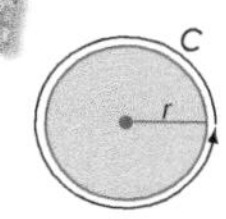

Below, a circle with radius r and circumference C has been divided into congruent pieces and then rearranged to form a figure that resembles a parallelogram.

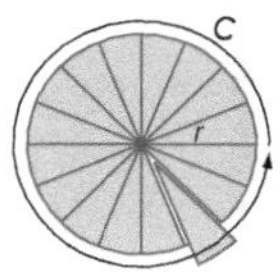

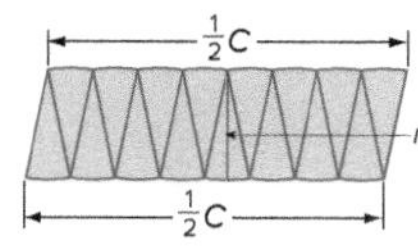

As the number of congruent pieces increases, the rearranged figure more closely approaches a parallelogram. The base of the parallelogram is $\frac{1}{2}C$ and the height is r, so its area is $\frac{1}{2}C \cdot r$. Because $C = 2\pi r$, the area of the parallelogram is also $\frac{1}{2}(2\pi r)r$ or πr^2.

Key Concept Area of a Circle

Words The area A of a circle is equal to π times the square of the radius r.

Symbols $A = \pi r^2$

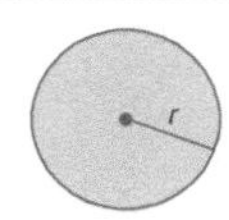

G.GMD.1

Real-World Example 1 Area of a Circle

SPORTS **What is the area of the circular putting green shown to the nearest square foot?**

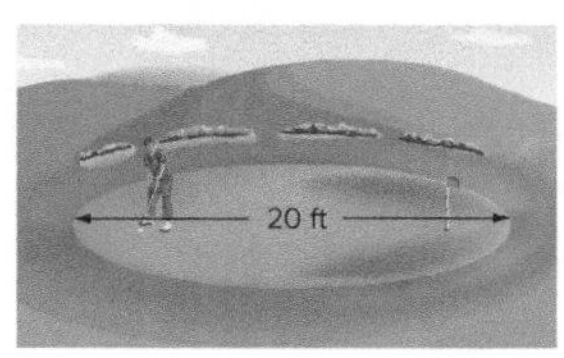

The diameter is 20 feet, so the radius is 10 feet.

$A = \pi r^2$	Area of a circle
$= \pi(10)^2$	$r = 10$
≈ 314	Use a calculator.

So, the area is about 314 square feet.

Guided Practice

1. SPORTS An archery target has a radius of 12 inches. What is the area of the target to the nearest square inch? 452 in^2

Launch

Have students read the Why? section of the lesson. Ask:

- **How many degrees are in a circle?** 360°
- **If a pizza is cut into eight wedge-shaped pieces of equal size, how many degrees is the angle made by one slice?** 45°
- **If the slices are all of equal size, how does the area of one slice compare with the total area of the pizza?** One slice is one eighth the area of the entire pizza.

Teach

Ask the scaffolded questions for each example to build conceptual understanding for students at all levels.

1 Areas of Circles

Example 1 Area of a Circle

AL **If the radius is 12 feet, what is the area of the putting green?** about 452 ft^2

OL **If the diameter is 25 feet, what is the area of the putting green?** about 491 ft^2

BL **If the area of the putting green is 255 square feet, what is the diameter?** about 18 ft

MP Mathematical Practices Strategies

Attend to precision.
Help students calculate accurately and efficiently. Encourage the class to use clear definitions in discussion. For example, ask:

- **If you know the diameter of a circle, how can you find the area?** Find half of the diameter, which is the radius, and then substitute that value into the area formula.
- **Given the area of a circle, how can you find the radius?** Substitute the area into the area formula, and then use algebra to solve for the radius.
- **When considering the ratio of the arc measure to the total degrees of a circle, what does the ratio represent in lowest terms?** It represents a fraction of the whole circle.
- **What is the arc measure for a semicircle? Explain.** It is 180 degrees; a semicircle is half of a full circle.
- **What is the maximum arc measure for a circle? Explain.** It is 360 degrees, which is a complete circle.

Go Online!

Interactive Whiteboard
Use the *eLesson*, *Lesson Presentation*, or *Interactive Classroom* to present this lesson.

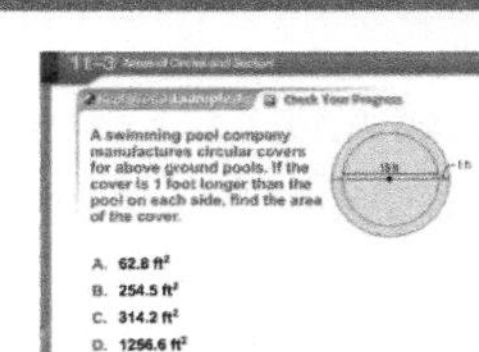

Need Another Example?

Manufacturing An outdoor accessories company manufactures circular covers for outdoor umbrellas. If the cover is 8 inches longer than the umbrella on each side, find the area of the cover in square inches. about 6082 in^2

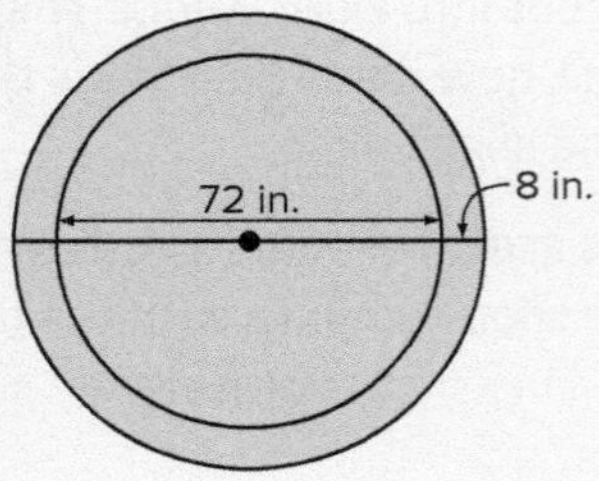

Example 2 Use the Area of a Circle to Find a Missing Measure

AL What is the diameter of the circle? about 11 cm

OL If the area of a circle is 755 square centimeters, what is the diameter of the circle? about 31 cm

BL The area of a circle is 144π square centimeters. If the radius of the circle is $x + 3$, what is the value of x? 9

Need Another Example?

Algebra Find the radius of a circle with an area of 58 square inches. 4.3 in.

2 Areas of Sectors

Example 3 Area of a Sector

AL What is a sector of a circle in your own words? Sample answer: It is an area that is made up of the area of a circle between two radii, like a slice of pie.

OL On a pie graph, a sector represents 20% of the graph. What is the central angle measure of the sector? 72°

BL The area of a sector of a circle with radius 8 inches is 68 square inches. What is the measure of the central angle of the sector? about 122°

Need Another Example?

Pie A pie has a diameter of 9 inches and is cut into 10 congruent slices. What is the area of one slice to the nearest hundredth? 6.36 in^2

G.GMD.1

Example 2 Use the Area of a Circle to Find a Missing Measure

ALGEBRA Find the radius of a circle with an area of 95 square centimeters.

$A = \pi r^2$ Area of a circle

$95 = \pi r^2$ $A = 95$

$\frac{95}{\pi} = r^2$ Divide each side by π.

$5.5 \approx r$ Use a calculator. Take the positive square root of each side.

The radius of the circle is about 5.5 centimeters.

Guided Practice

2. ALGEBRA The area of a circle is 196π square yards. Find the diameter. 28 yd

Review Vocabulary ELL

central angle an angle with a vertex in the center of a circle and with sides that contain two radii of the circle

arc a portion of a circle defined by two endpoints

2 Areas of Sectors A slice of a circular pizza is an example of a sector of a circle. A **sector of a circle** is a region of a circle bounded by a central angle and its intercepted major or minor arc. The formula for the area of a sector is similar to the formula for arc length.

Key Concept Area of a Sector

The ratio of the **area A of a sector** to the **area of the whole circle**, πr^2, is equal to the ratio of the **degree measure of the intercepted arc x** to 360.

Proportion: $\frac{A}{\pi r^2} = \frac{x}{360}$

Equation: $A = \frac{x}{360} \cdot \pi r^2$

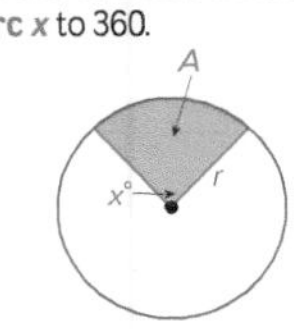

Real-World Link

About 3 billion pizzas are sold each year in the United States. That is equivalent to about 46 slices per person annually.

Source: Statistic Brain

G.C.5

Real-World Example 3 Area of a Sector

PIZZA A circular pizza has a diameter of 12 inches and is cut into 8 congruent slices. What is the area of one slice to the nearest hundredth?

Step 1 Find the arc measure of a pizza slice.

Because the pizza is equally divided into 8 slices, each slice will have an arc measure of 360 ÷ 8 or 45.

Step 2 Find the radius of the pizza. Use this measure to find the area of the sector, or slice.

The diameter is 12 inches, so the radius is 6 inches.

$A = \frac{x}{360} \cdot \pi r^2$ Area of a sector

$= \frac{45}{360} \cdot \pi(6)^2$ $x = 45$ and $r = 6$

≈ 14.14 Use a calculator.

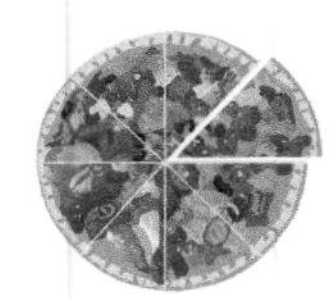

So, the area of one slice of this pizza is about 14.14 square inches.

Differentiated Instruction AL OL BL ELL

Verbal/Linguistic Learners Have students discuss how the area of a sector relates to the area of the entire circle. Have them write how the equation for a sector logically represents a portion of the circle.

Go Online!

Watch Personal Tutor videos to hear descriptions of solving problems involving areas of circles and sectors. Try to describe how to solve a problem for a partner. Have them ask you questions to help your understanding.

ELL

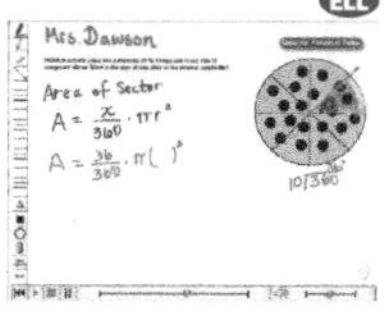

Guided Practice

Find the area of the shaded sector. Round to the nearest tenth.

3A. 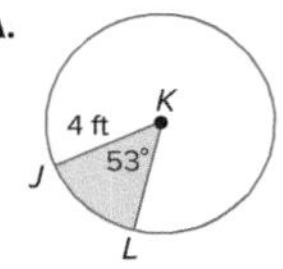

7.4 ft^2

3B. 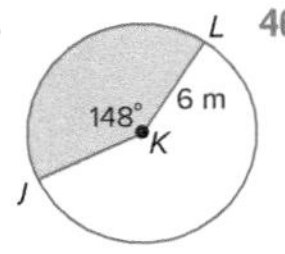

46.5 m^2

3C. 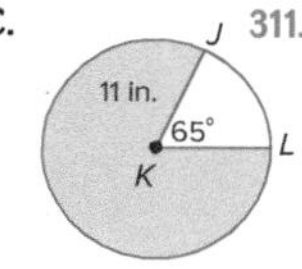

311.5 in^2

3D. CRAFTS The color wheel at the right is a tool that artists use to organize color schemes. If the diameter of the wheel is 10 inches and each of the 12 sections is congruent, find the approximate area covered by green hues. 19.6 in^2

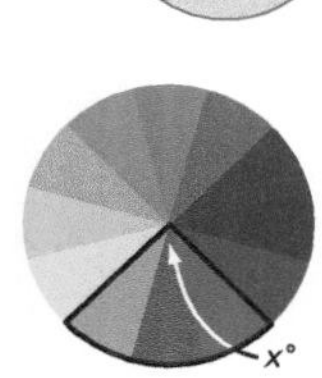

Check Your Understanding

◯ = Step-by-Step Solutions begin on page R13.

Go Online! for a Self-Check Quiz

Example 1 G.GMD.1

CONSTRUCTION Find the area of each circle. Round to the nearest tenth.

1.  1385.4 yd^2

2. 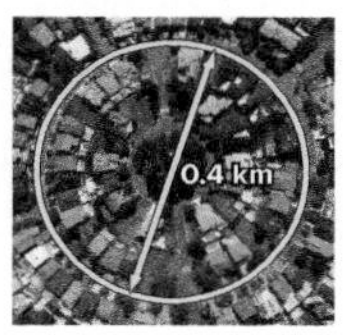

0.1 km^2

Example 2 G.G.5

Find the indicated measure. Round to the nearest tenth.

3. Find the diameter of a circle with an area of 74 square millimeters. 9.7 mm

4. The area of a circle is 88 square inches. Find the radius. 5.3 in.

Example 3 G.C.5

Find the area of each shaded sector. Round to the nearest tenth.

5. 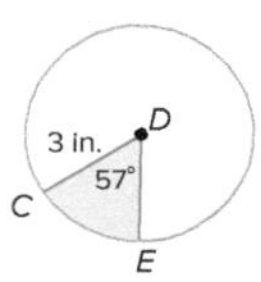

4.5 in^2

6. 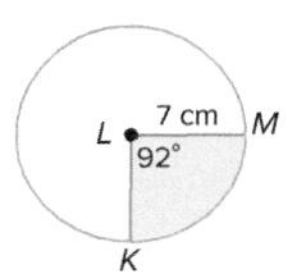

39.3 cm^2

7. BAKING Chelsea is baking pies for a fundraiser at her school. She divides each 9-inch pie into 6 equal slices.

a. What is the area, in square inches, for each slice of pie? 10.6 in^2

b. If each slice costs $0.25 to make and she sells 8 pies at $1.25 for each slice, how much money will she raise? $48

Practice

Formative Assessment Use Exercises 1–7 to assess students' understanding of the concepts in this lesson.

The Practice and Problem Solving exercises assess the content taught in the lesson. The Preparing for Assessment page is meant to be used as preparation for end-of-course assessments.

Extra Practice

See page R10 for extra exercises for students who are approaching level or for on-level students who need additional reinforcement.

Levels of Complexity Chart

The levels of the exercises progress from 1 to 3 with Level 1 indicating the lowest level of complexity.

Exercises	8–25	26–38, 50–57	39–49
C Level 3			●
B Level 2		●	
Level 1	●		

Differentiated Homework Options

Levels	AL Basic	OL Core	BL Advanced
Exercises	8–25, 44, 46–57	9–25 odd, 26, 27, 29–31, 33–43 odd, 44, 46–57	39–49, (optional: 50–57)
2-Day Option	9–25 odd, 50–57	8–25	
	8–24 even, 44, 46–49	26–44, 46–57	

You can use ALEKS to provide additional remediation support with personalized instruction and practice.

Go Online! eBook

Interactive Student Guide

Use the *Interactive Student Guide* to deepen conceptual understanding.

· Areas of Circles

MP Teaching the Mathematical Practices

Modeling Mathematically proficient students can apply the mathematics they know to solve problems arising in everyday life. In Exercises 8–13, encourage students to be careful about specifying the units of measure for each exercise.

Additional Answer

24. rap: 172.8°, 1.51 units^2; rock & roll: 93.6°, 0.82 units^2; alternative: 50.4°, 0.44 units^2; country: 36°, 0.31 units^2; classical: 7.2°, 0.06 units^2

Practice and Problem Solving

Extra Practice is on page R10.

Example 1 G.GMD.1

8. 95.0 ft^2
9. 78.5 yd^2
10. 50.3 ft^2
11. 14.2 in^2
12. 254.5 in^2
13. 78.5 ft^2

MP MODELING Find the area of each circle. Round to the nearest tenth.

8.
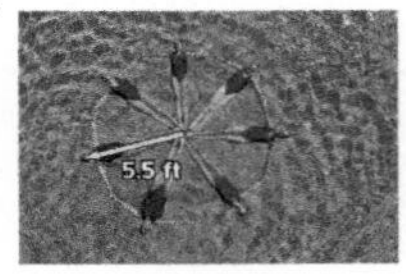

9.
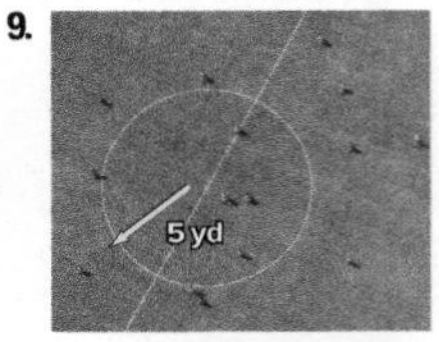

10.
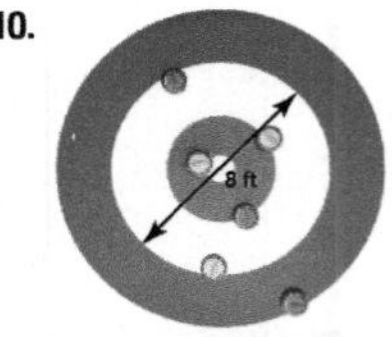

11.
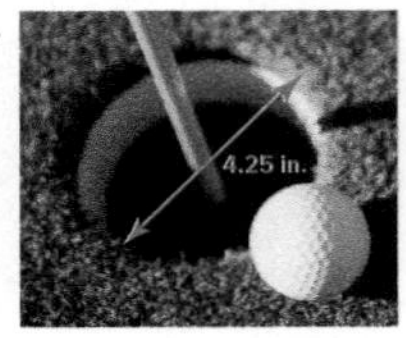

12.
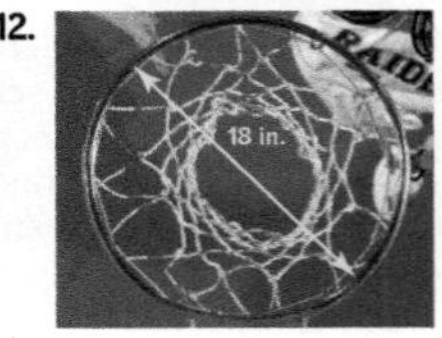

13.
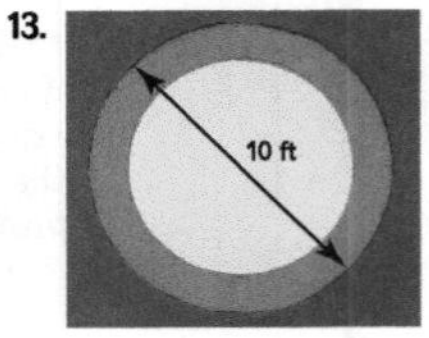

Example 2 G.C.5

Find the indicated measure. Round to the nearest tenth, if necessary.

14. The area of a circle is 68 square centimeters. Find the diameter. 9.3 cm

15. Find the diameter of a circle with an area of 94 square millimeters. 10.9 mm

16. The area of a circle is 112 square inches. Find the radius. 6 in.

17. Find the radius of a circle with an area of 206 square feet. 8.1 ft

Example 3 G.C.5

Find the area of each shaded sector. Round to the nearest tenth, if necessary.

18. 10 in^2
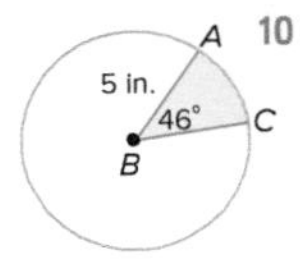

19. 40.2 cm^2
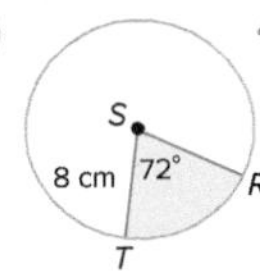

20. 167.1 ft^2
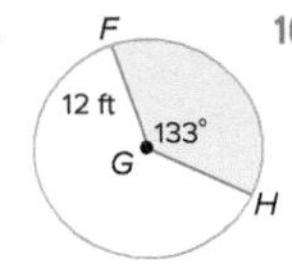

21. 322 m^2
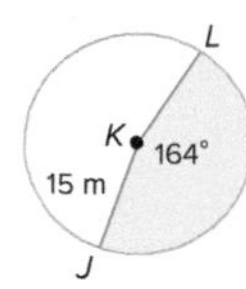

22. 333.9 mm^2
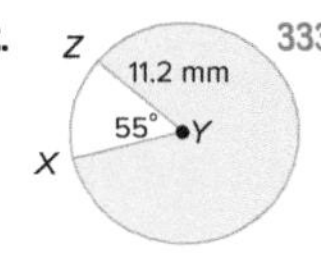

23. 284 in^2
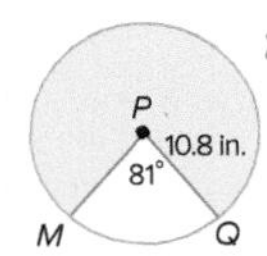

24. MUSIC The music preferences of students at Thomas Jefferson High are shown in the circle graph. Find the area of each sector and the degree measure of each intercepted arc if the radius of the circle is 1 unit. See margin.

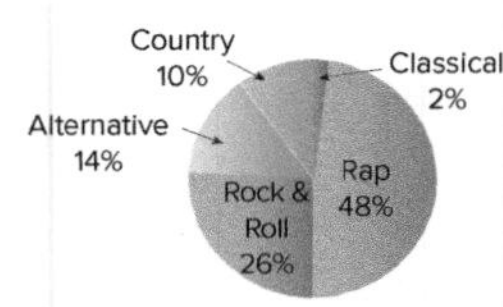

25. JEWELRY A jeweler makes a pair of earrings by cutting two 50° sectors from a silver disk.

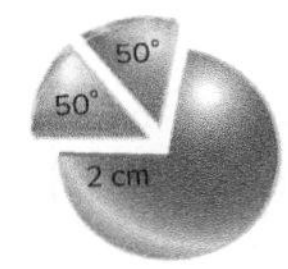

a. Find the area of each sector. 1.7 cm^2

b. If the weight of the silver disk is 2.3 grams, how many milligrams does the silver wedge for each earring weigh? about 319.4 mg

Go Online!

The most up-to-date resources available for your program can be found at connectED.mcgraw-hill.com.

B **26. PROM** Students voted on their favorite prom theme.

a. Create a circle graph with a diameter of 2 inches to represent these data. a–b. See margin.

b. Find the area of each theme's sector in your graph. Round to the nearest hundredth of an inch.

Theme	Percent
An Evening of Stars	11
Mardi Gras	32
Springtime in Paris	8
Night in Times Square	47
Undecided	2

MP **SENSE-MAKING** **The area A of each shaded region is given. Find x.**

27. $A = 66 \text{ cm}^2$ 13

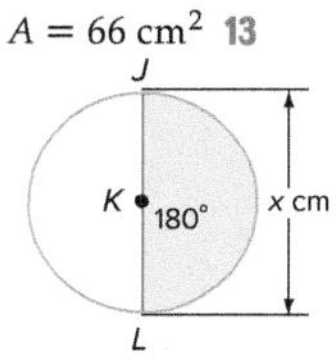

28. $A = 94 \text{ in}^2$ 55

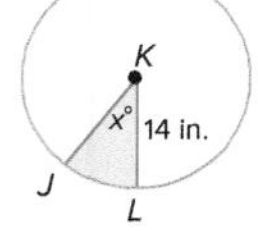

29. $A = 128 \text{ ft}^2$ 9.8

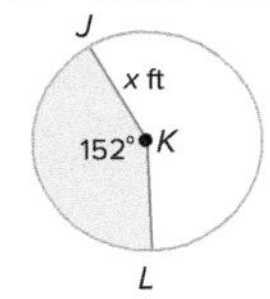

30. MULTI-STEP Luna is organizing a banquet for the Honor Society, and she needs 13 tablecloths for the round tables in the hall. The area of each table is approximately 29.27 square feet. She can rent tablecloths for $16 each or she can make them herself. Her local fabric store carries three different bolts of suitable fabric. The standard bolt is 60 inches wide and 100 yards long and costs $75. The wide bolt is 81 inches wide, 25 yards long, and costs $125. The extra-wide bolt is 90 inches wide, 25 yards long, and costs $150. Each tablecloth should cover the table with 9 inches of overhang.

a. How can Luna minimize the cost of the tablecloths? She should rent 3 tablecloths and make 10 tablecloths from the 90″ wide bolt.

b. Explain your reasoning. See margin.

c. What assumptions did you make? See margin.

31. TREES The age of a living tree can be determined by multiplying the diameter of the tree by its growth factor, or rate of growth.

a. What is the diameter of a live oak tree with a circumference of 36 feet? 11.5 ft

b. If the growth factor of the live oak tree is 130, what is the age of the tree? 1495 yr

Find the area of the shaded region. Round to the nearest tenth.

32. 69.5 ft^2

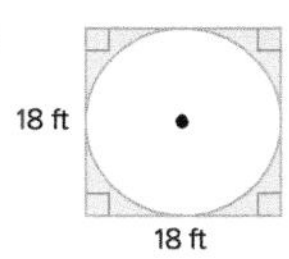

33. 53.5 m^2

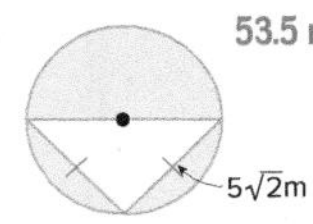

34. 77 mm^2

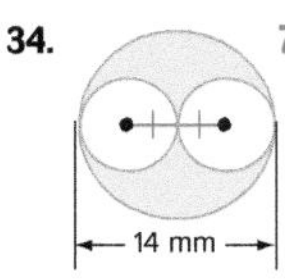

35. 10.7 cm^2

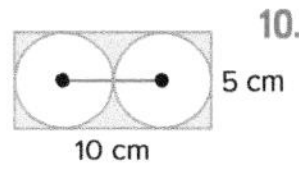

36. 7.9 m^2

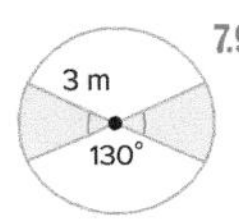

37. 7.9 in^2

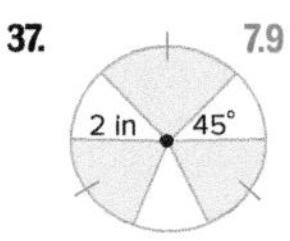

38. COORDINATE GEOMETRY What is the area of sector ABC shown on the graph? 28.3 square units

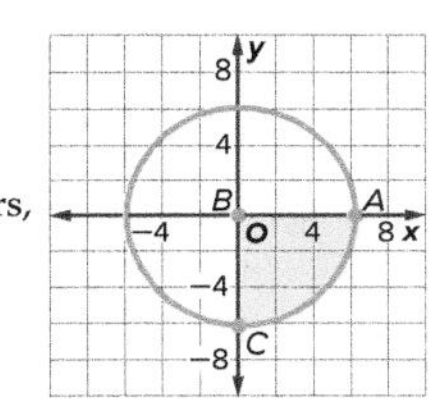

C **39. ALGEBRA** The figure shown below is a sector of a circle. If the perimeter of the figure is 22 millimeters, find its area in square millimeters 30 mm²

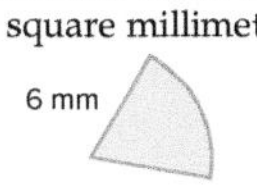

MP Standards for Mathematical Practice

Emphasis On	Exercises
1 Make sense of problems and persevere in solving them.	27–29, 50, 52, 53, 55, 56
2 Reason abstractly and quantitatively.	38, 39
3 Construct viable arguments and critique the reasoning of others.	30, 43, 44, 46, 47
4 Model with mathematics.	1, 2, 7–13, 24–26, 31, 51
6 Attend to precision.	45, 50–56

MP Teaching the Mathematical Practices

Sense-Making Mathematically proficient students start by explaining the meaning of a problem to themselves and looking for entry points to its solution. They plan a solution pathway rather than simply jumping into a solution attempt. In Exercises 27–29, encourage students to make a plan to solve each problem first.

Additional Answers

26a.

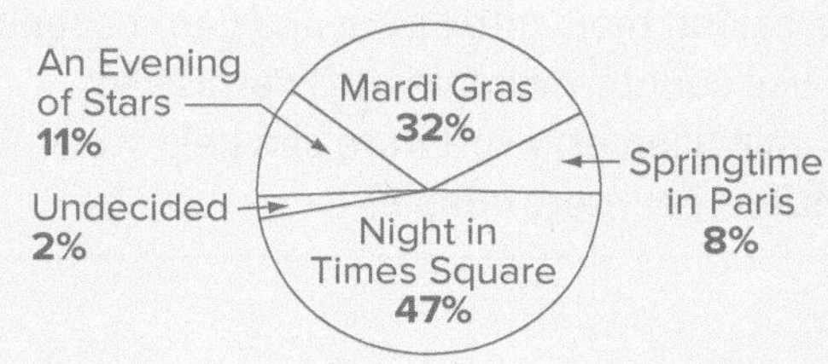

26b. An Evening of Stars: 0.35 in^2; Mardi Gras: 1.01 in^2; Springtime in Paris: 0.25 in^2; Night in Times Square: 1.48 in^2; Undecided: 0.06 in^2

30b. Sample answer: The area of the table is about 29.27 ft^2. Using the formula for the area of a circle, $A = \pi r^2$, we can find the radius and diameter for the tablecloth. The radius is about 3 ft, so the diameter is about 6 ft. She wants the fabric to extend 9 inches over the edge of the table, so add 18 inches to the diameter for a total of 6(12) + 18 or 90 inches. The only bolt of fabric that could be used is the widest bolt. Cut the fabric into 90-in squares and then cut circles. 25(3)(12) ÷ 90 = 10, so Luna can make 10 tablecloths from a bolt at a cost of $150. Each tablecloth would cost $15. However, she would still need to rent 3 tablecloths to cover all of the tables for a total cost of $198.

30c. I assumed that there were no other costs associated with making her own tablecloths; she only had to buy the fabric. I also assumed that it didn't matter that the tablecloths didn't match.

Watch Out!

Error Analysis Students should remember that the formula for the area of a sector requires the radius of the circle. In Exercise 44, Kristen used the diameter instead of the radius.

MP Teaching the Mathematical Practices

Construct Arguments Mathematically proficient students understand and use stated assumptions and definitions in constructing arguments. They are able to analyze situations by breaking them into cases, and can recognize and use counterexamples. In Exercise 46, dynamic geometry software can help students identify a counterexample.

Find the area of each shaded region.

40. 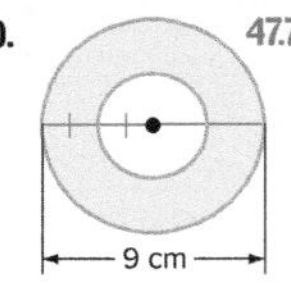

47.7 cm²

41. 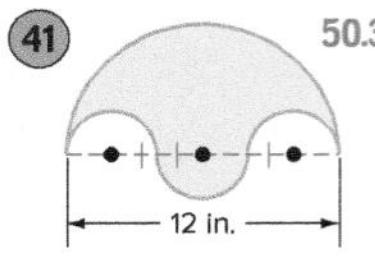

50.3 in²

42. 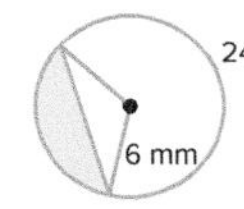

22.1 mm²

43. MULTIPLE REPRESENTATIONS In this problem, you will investigate segments of circles. A **segment of a circle** is the region bounded by an arc and a chord.

a. **Algebraic** Write an equation for the area A of a segment of a circle with a radius r and a central angle of $x°$. (*Hint*: Use trigonometry to find the base and height of the triangle.) **a–d. See margin.**

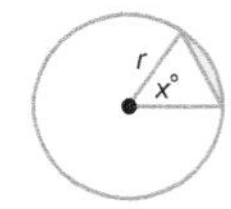

b. **Tabular** Calculate and record in a table ten values of A for x-values ranging from 10 to 90 if r is 12 inches. Round to the nearest tenth.

c. **Graphical** Graph the data from your table with the x-values on the horizontal axis and the A-values on the vertical axis.

d. **Analytical** Use your graph to predict the value of A when x is 63. Then use the formula you generated in part **a** to calculate the value of A when x is 63. How do the values compare?

G.C.5, G.GMD.1

H.O.T. Problems Use Higher-Order Thinking Skills

44. ERROR ANALYSIS Kristen and Chase want to find the area of the shaded region in the circle shown. Is either of them correct? Explain your reasoning.

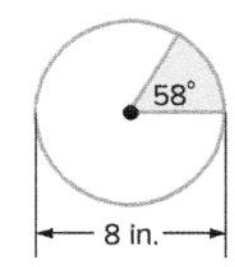

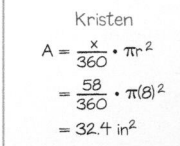

Kristen

$A = \frac{x}{360} \cdot \pi r^2$

$= \frac{58}{360} \cdot \pi(8)^2$

$= 32.4$ in²

Chase

$A = \frac{x}{360} \cdot \pi r^2$

$= \frac{58}{360} \cdot \pi(4)^2$

$= 8.1$ in²

44. Chase; sample answer: Kristen used the diameter in the area formula instead of the radius.

45. CHALLENGE Find the area of the shaded region. Round to the nearest tenth. **449.0 cm²**

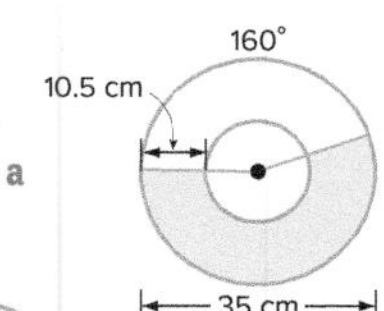

46. MP **CONSTRUCT ARGUMENTS** Refer to Exercise 43. Is the area of a sector of a circle *sometimes*, *always*, or *never* greater than the area of its corresponding segment?

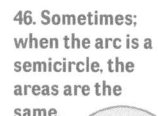

46. Sometimes; when the arc is a semicircle, the areas are the same.

47. WRITING IN MATH Describe two methods you could use to find the area of the shaded region of the circle. Which method do you think is more efficient? Explain your reasoning. **See margin.**

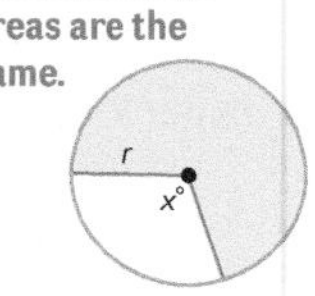

48. CHALLENGE Derive the formula for the area of a sector of a circle using the formula for arc length. **See Ch. 10 Answer Appendix.**

49. WRITING IN MATH If the radius of a circle doubles, will the measure of a sector of that circle double? Will it double if the arc measure of that sector doubles? **See Ch. 10 Answer Appendix.**

Assess

Ticket Out the Door Have students describe how to find the area of a circle, given its circumference.

Additional Answers

43a. $A = \frac{x\pi r^2}{360} - r^2\left[\sin\left(\frac{x}{2}\right)\cos\left(\frac{x}{2}\right)\right]$

43b.

x	A
10	0.1
20	0.5
30	1.7
40	4.0
45	5.6
50	7.7
60	13.0
70	20.3
80	29.6
90	41.1

43c. **Area and Central Angles**

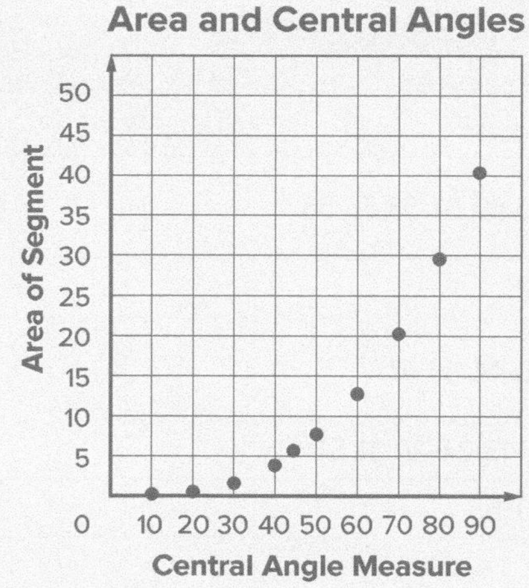

43d. Sample answer: From the graph, it looks like the area would be about 15.5 when x is 63°. Using the formula, the area is 15.0 when x is 63°. The values are very close because I used the formula to create the graph.

47. Sample answer: You can find the shaded area of the circle by subtracting x from 360° and using the resulting measure in the formula for the area of a sector. You could also find the shaded area by finding the area of the entire circle, finding the area of the unshaded sector using the formula for the area of a sector, and subtracting the area of the unshaded sector from the area of the entire circle. The method in which you find the ratio of the area of a sector to the area of the whole circle is more efficient. It requires fewer steps, is faster, and there is a lower probability for error.

Go Online!

eSolutions Manual

Create worksheets, answer keys, and solutions handouts for your assignments.

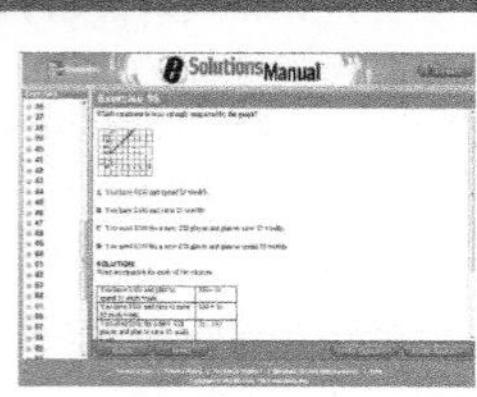

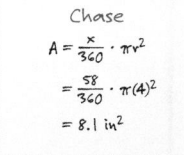

Preparing for Assessment

50. Visitors at a school carnival have a chance to toss a bean onto a circular tabletop that is divided into equal sectors, as shown.

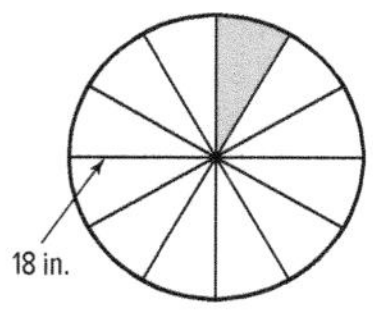

Visitors win a prize if the bean lands in the shaded sector. What is the area of this sector in square inches? Round to the nearest tenth. MP 1, 6 G.MG.1

84.8

51. A lawn sprinkler sprays water 25 feet and moves back and forth through an angle of 150°.

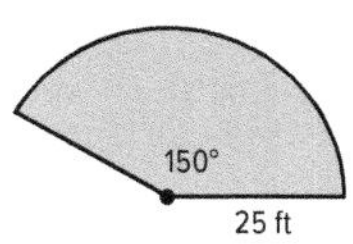

Which of the following is the best estimate of the area of the lawn that gets watered? MP 6 G.MG.1 B

- A 65 ft^2
- B 818 ft^2
- C 1963 ft^2
- D 4712 ft^2

52. A sector of a circle has an intercepted arc that measures 120°. The area of the sector is 155.8 square centimeters. What is the radius of the circle in centimeters? Round to the nearest tenth. MP 1, 6 G.C.5

12.2

53. One pizza with radius 9 inches is cut into 8 congruent sectors. Another pizza with the same radius is cut into 10 congruent sectors. How much more pizza, in square inches, is in a slice from the pizza cut into 8 sectors? MP 1, 6 G.MG.1 A

- A 6.4
- B 25.4
- C 31.8
- D 57.2

54. Which expression represents the area of the shaded sector in square meters? MP 6 G.C.5 C

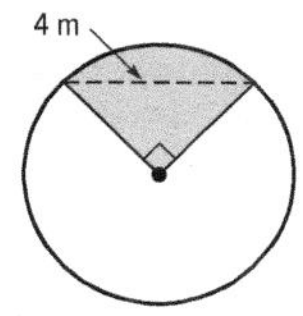

- A $\frac{\sqrt{2}}{2}\pi$
- B $\sqrt{2}\pi$
- C 2π
- D 4π

55. In ⊙C, a sector has an area of 24π square inches. The radius of ⊙C is 12 inches. What is the measure, in degrees, of the arc that is intercepted by the sector? MP 1, 6 G.C.5 C

- A 360
- B 60π
- C 60
- D $\frac{180}{\pi}$

56. A circular pie has a diameter of 8 inches and is cut into 6 congruent slices. What is the area of one slice of pie? MP 1, 6 G.C.5 B

- A 6 square inches
- B 8.4 square inches
- C 21.6 square inches
- D 33.5 square inches

57. MULTI-STEP A regular hexagon, inscribed in a circle, is divided into 6 congruent triangles. The perimeter of the hexagon is 48 inches. MP 1, 6 G.C.5

a. What is the radius of the circle? 8 in.

b. Find the area of each of the 6 sectors of the circle that have sides that coincide with sides of the congruent triangles. Round to the nearest tenth. 33.5 in^2

c. What is the area of one of the triangles? Round to the nearest tenth. 27.7 in^2

d. How much greater is the sector area than that of one of the triangles? Round to the nearest tenth. 5.8 in^2

Preparing for Assessment

Exercises 50–57 require students to use the skills they will need on standardized assessments. Exercises are dual-coded with content standards and mathematical practice standards.

Dual Coding

Items	Content Standards	MP Mathematical Practices
50	G.MG.1	1, 6
51	G.MG.1	6
52	G.C.5	1, 6
53	G.MG.1	1, 6
54	G.C.5	6
55	G.C.5	1, 6
56	G.MG.1	1, 6
57	G.C.5	1, 6

Diagnose Student Errors

Survey student responses for each item. Class trends may indicate common errors and misconceptions.

51.

A	Found length of intercepted arc
B	CORRECT
C	Found area of complete circle
D	Calculated area as $\frac{360}{150} \cdot \pi(25)^2$

53.

A	CORRECT
B	Found the area of a slice of the pizza cut into 8 slices
C	Found the area of a slice of the pizza cut into 10 slices
D	Found the sum of the areas of each slice type

54.

A	Did not square radius in formula for area of sector
B	Found length of intercepted arc
C	CORRECT
D	Used $r = 4$

55.

A	Assumed 24π was length of intercepted arc
B	Omitted π in formula for area of sector
C	CORRECT
D	Solved $12 = \frac{x}{360} \cdot 24\pi$

56.

A	Determined the number of slices
B	CORRECT
C	Found the perimeter of a single slice
D	Used $r = 8$

Go Online!

Quizzes

Students can use *Self-Check Quizzes* to check their understanding of this lesson and have the results sent to you. You can also give *Quiz 2*, which covers the content in Lesson 10-3.

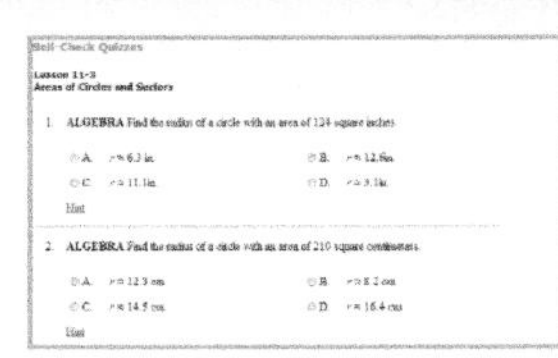

RtI Response to Intervention

Use the Intervention Planner to help you determine your Response to Intervention.

Intervention Planner

TIER 1 On Level OL

IF students miss 25% of the exercises or less,

THEN choose a resource:

SE Lessons 10-1, 10-2, and 10-3

Go Online!

- Skills Practice
- Chapter Project
- Self-Check Quizzes

TIER 2 Strategic Intervention AL
Approaching grade level

IF students miss 50% of the exercises,

THEN choose a resource:

Quick Review Math Handbook

Go Online!

- Study Guide and Intervention
- Extra Examples
- Personal Tutors
- Homework Help

TIER 3 Intensive Intervention
2 or more grades below level

IF students miss 75% of the exercises,

THEN choose a resource:

Use *Math Triumphs, Geometry*

Go Online!

- Extra Examples
- Personal Tutors
- Homework Help
- Review Vocabulary

Go Online!

eAssessment

You can use the premade Mid-Chapter Test to assess students' progress in the first half of the chapter. Customize and create multiple versions of your Mid-Chapter Quiz and answer keys that align to your standards. Tests can be delivered on paper or online.

CHAPTER 10

Mid-Chapter Quiz

Lessons 10-1 through 10-3

Find the perimeter and area of each parallelogram or triangle. Round to the nearest tenth if necessary. (Lesson 10-1)

1.
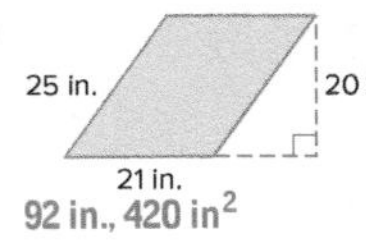

92 in., 420 in^2

2.
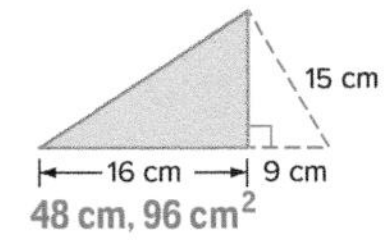

48 cm, 96 cm^2

3.
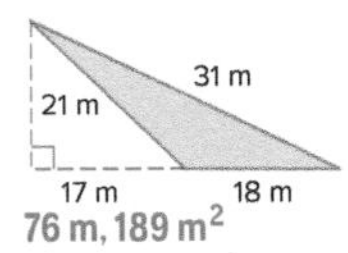

76 m, 189 m^2

4.
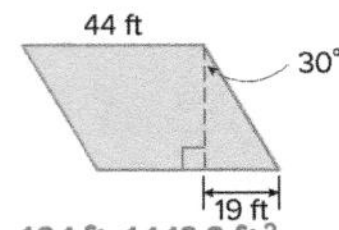

164 ft, 1448.0 ft^2

5. Find the perimeter and area of $\triangle FGH$ with $F(-3, 5)$, $G(-3, 10)$, and $H(0, 6)$. (Lesson 10-1) $10 + \sqrt{10}$ or about 13.2 units; 7.5 units^2

6. **DESIGN** A plaque, as shown below, is made with a rhombus in the middle. (Lesson 10-2)

a. If the diagonals of the rhombus measure 7 inches and 9 inches, how much space is available for engraving text onto the award? 31.5 in^2

b. MP What mathematical practice did you use to solve this problem? See students' work.

7. **MULTIPLE CHOICE** The area of a kite is 4 square feet. If the tail is to be 3 times longer than the kite's long diagonal, and the short diagonal measures 2 feet, how long should the kite's tail be? (Lesson 10-2) D

A 4 feet C 7 feet
B 6 feet D 12 feet

Find the area of each trapezoid, rhombus, or kite. (Lesson 10-2)

8.
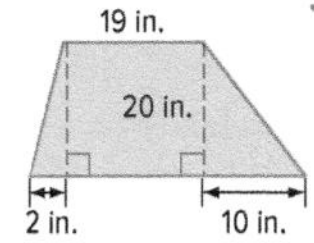

500 in^2

9.
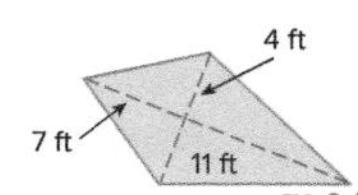

72 ft^2

10.
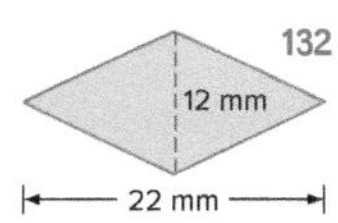

132 mm^2

11.
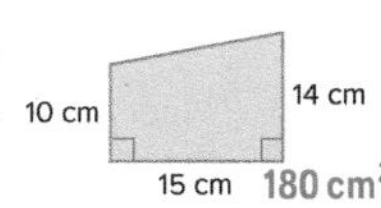

180 cm^2

12. **ARCHAEOLOGY** The most predominant shape in Incan architecture is the trapezoid. The doorway pictured below is 3 feet wide at the top and 4 feet wide at the bottom. A person who is 5 feet 8 inches tall can barely pass through the doorway. How much fabric would be necessary to make a curtain for the doorway? (Lesson 10-2) 19.8 ft^2

13. **ALGEBRA** A sector of a circle has a central angle measure of 30° and radius r. Write an expression for the perimeter of the sector in terms of r. (Lesson 10-3) $\frac{1}{6}\pi r + 2r$

Find the area of each shaded sector. Round to the nearest tenth. (Lesson 10-3)

14.
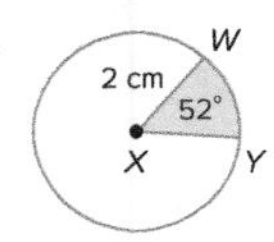

1.8 cm^2

15.
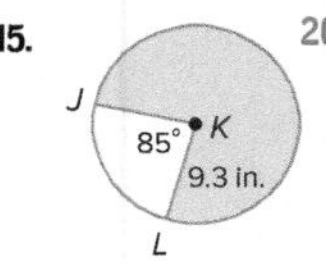

207.6 in^2

16.
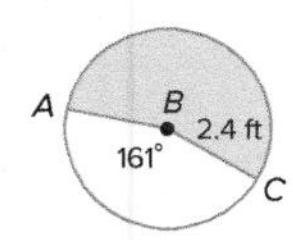

10.0 ft^2

17.
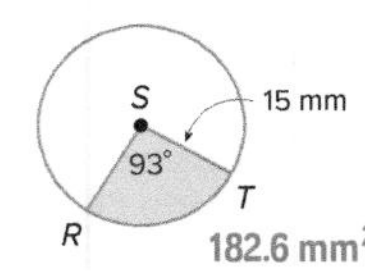

182.6 mm^2

Find the indicated measure. Round to the nearest tenth. (Lesson 10-3)

18. The area of a circle is 52 square inches. Find the diameter. 8.1 in.

19. Find the radius of a circle with an area of 104 square meters. 5.8 m

20. **FRUIT** The diameter of the orange slice shown is 9 centimeters. If each of the orange's 10 sections are congruent, find the approximate area covered by 8 sections. (Lesson 10-3) 50.9 cm^2

Foldables Study Organizer

Dinah Zike's FOLDABLES®

Before students complete the Mid-Chapter Quiz, encourage them to review the information for Lessons 10-1 through 10-3 in their Foldables. Allow students to compare their Foldable with a partner. Encourage them to share what has been helpful to them as they study.

ALEKS can be used as a formative assessment tool to target learning gaps for those who are struggling, while providing enhanced learning for those who have mastered the concepts.

LESSON 10-4

Areas of Regular Polygons and Composite Figures

SUGGESTED PACING (DAYS)

	Explore	Instruction	Extend
90 min.	.25	1.0	0.5
45 min.	0.5	1.5	1

Track Your Progress

Objectives

1. Find areas of regular polygons.
2. Find areas of composite figures.

Mathematical Background

A regular polygon can be divided into congruent isosceles triangles. The area can be determined by adding the areas of the triangles. The area of a *composite figure* is the sum of the areas of its parts.

Skills Trace

THEN	NOW	NEXT
G.GPE.7 Use coordinates to compute perimeters of polygons and areas of triangles and rectangles, e.g., using the distance formula.	**G.MG.3** Apply geometric methods to solve design problems (e.g., designing an object or structure to satisfy physical constraints or minimize cost; working with typographic grid systems based on ratios).	**G.C.5** Derive using similarity the fact that the length of the arc intercepted by an angle is proportional to the radius, and define the radian measure of the angle as the constant of proportionality; derive the formula for the area of a sector. **G.GMD.1** Give an informal argument for the formulas for the circumference of a circle, area of a circle, volume of a cylinder, pyramid, and cone.

Go Online! All of these resources and more are available at connectED.mcgraw-hill.com

eToolkit allows students to explore and enhance their understanding of math concepts. Use the 2-D Figures tool to provide additional practice in finding the area of regular polygons.

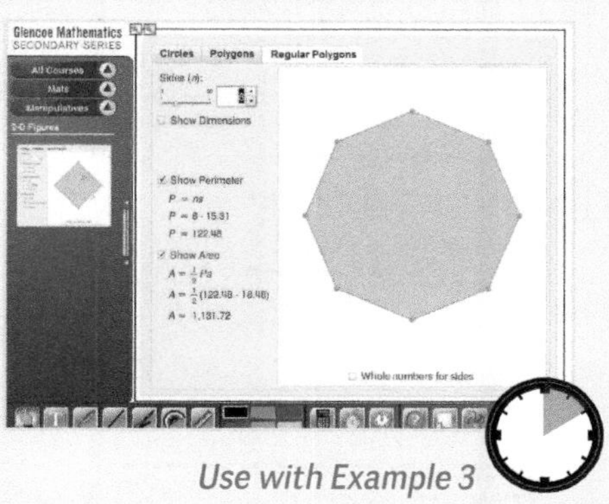

Use with Example 3

Personal Tutors (for every example) let students hear real teachers solve problems. Students can pause and repeat as many times as necessary.

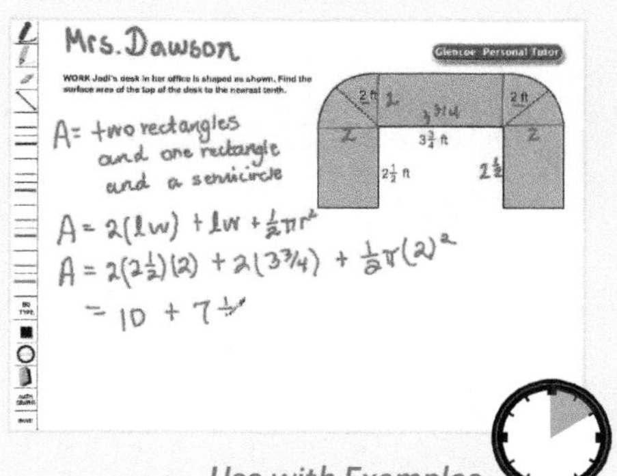

Use with Examples

Use **the Geometer's Sketchpad** to illustrate how to construct a square within a square and explore the relationship between them.

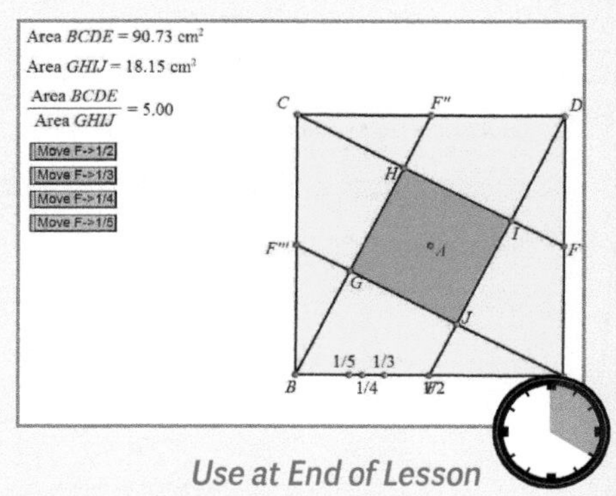

Use at End of Lesson

OER Using Open Educational Resources

Games Have students compete against classmates and other users by playing the *Area and Perimeter of Composite Figures with Circles* game on **ck12.org**. *Use as in-class activity*

Differentiate Your Resources

Extra Practice Additional practice or homework; Skills Practice is best for approaching-level students and Practice is best for on-level and beyond-level students

Skills Practice

AL OL ELL

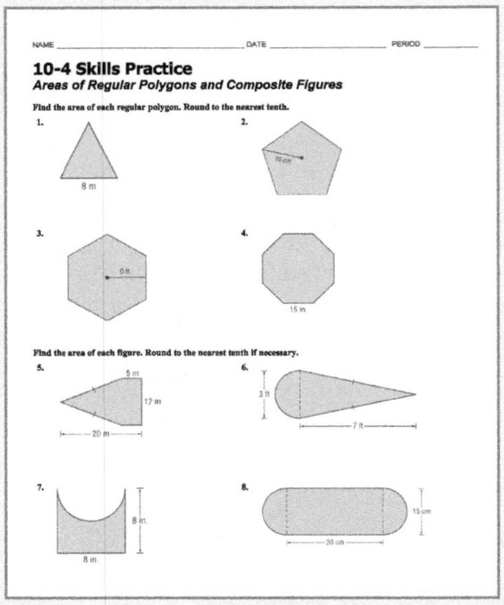

Practice

AL OL BL ELL

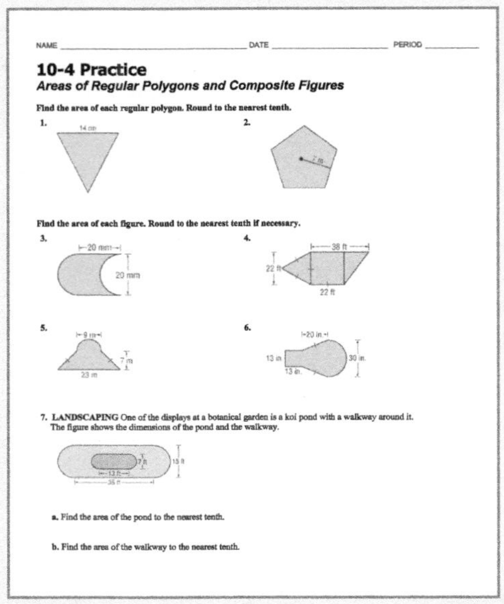

Word Problem Practice

AL OL BL ELL

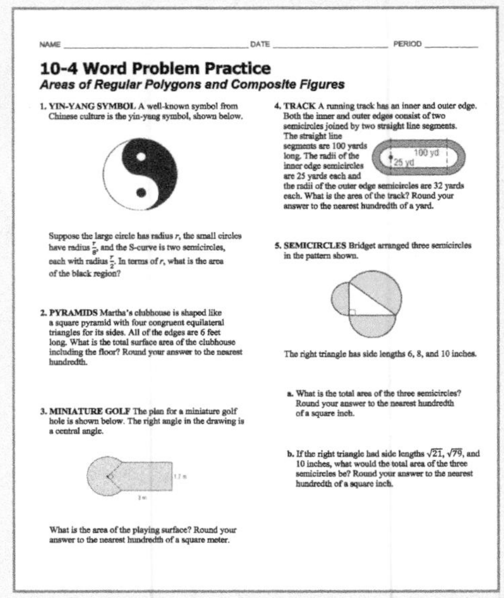

Intervention Reteaching and vocabulary activities that can be used with struggling or absent students and as ELL support

Study Guide and Intervention

AL OL ELL

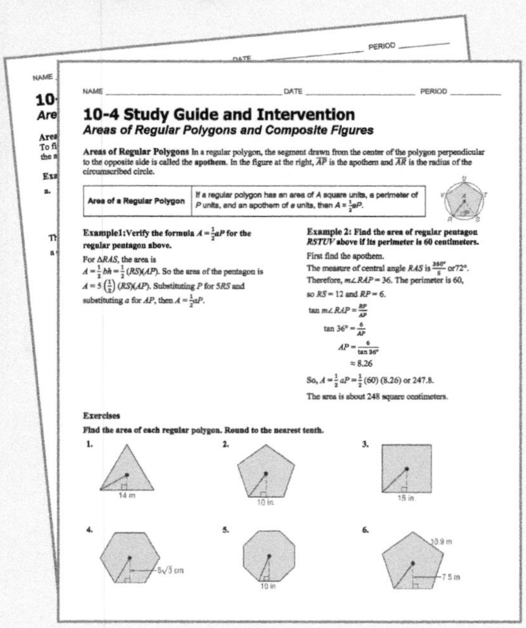

Study Notebook

AL OL BL ELL

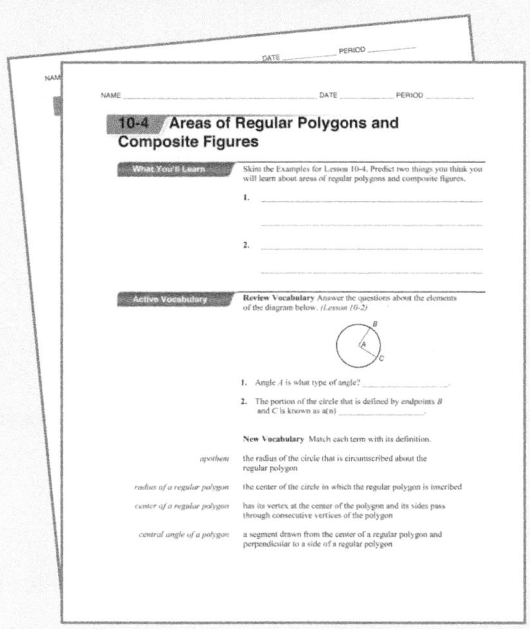

Extension Activities that can be used to extend lesson concepts

Enrichment

OL BL ELL

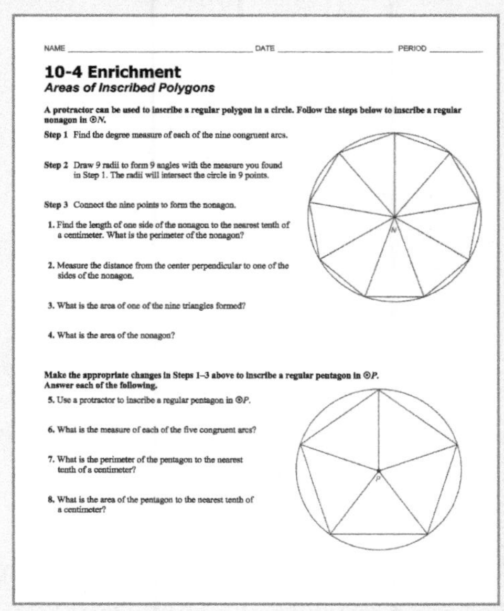

EXPLORE 10-4
Geometry Lab
Investigating Areas of Regular Polygons

The point in the interior of a regular polygon that is equidistant from all of the vertices is the *center* of the polygon. A segment from the center that is perpendicular to a side of the polygon is an **apothem**.

Mathematical Practices

MP 5 Use appropriate tools strategically.

MP 7 Look for and make use of structure.

Activity

Work cooperatively.

Step 1 Copy regular pentagon *ABCDE* and its center *O*.

Step 2 Draw the apothem from *O* to side $\overline{AB}$ by constructing the perpendicular bisector of $\overline{AB}$. Label the apothem measure as *a*. Label the measure of $\overline{AB}$ as *s*.

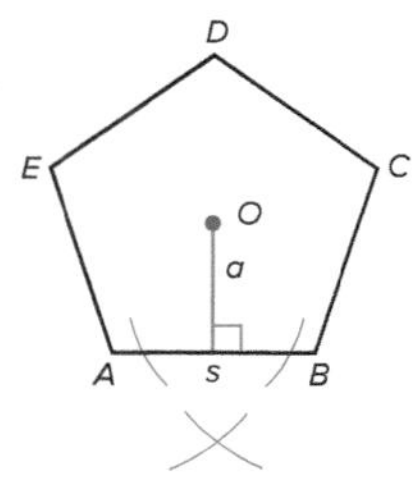

Step 3 Use a straightedge to draw $\overline{OA}$ and $\overline{OB}$.

Step 4 What measure in $\triangle AOB$ represents the base of the triangle? What measure represents the height? *s; a*

Step 5 Find the area of $\triangle AOB$ in terms of *s* and *a*. $\frac{1}{2}sa$

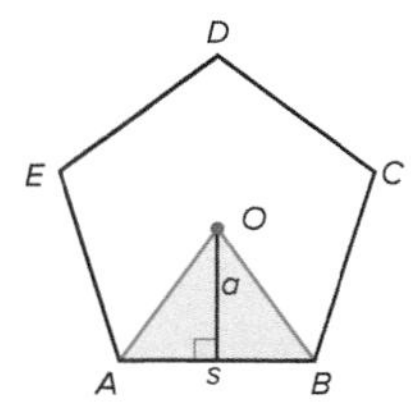

Step 6 Draw $\overline{OC}$, $\overline{OD}$, and $\overline{OE}$. What is true of the five small triangles formed? They are congruent.

Step 7 How do the areas of the five triangles compare? The areas are the same.

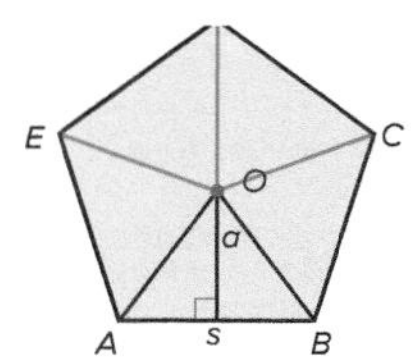

Analyze the Results

Work cooperatively

1. The area of a pentagon *ABCDE* can be found by adding the areas of the given triangles that make up the pentagonal region.

$$A = \frac{1}{2}sa + \frac{1}{2}sa + \frac{1}{2}sa + \frac{1}{2}sa + \frac{1}{2}sa$$

$$A = \frac{1}{2}(sa + sa + sa + sa + sa) \text{ or } \frac{1}{2}(5sa)$$

What does 5*s* represent? The perimeter of the pentagon.

2. Write a formula for the area of a pentagon in terms of perimeter *P*. $A = \frac{1}{2}Pa$

Extending the Concept

Ask:

- Does this strategy for finding the area of a regular polygon apply to irregular polygons? Explain your reasoning. No; not all of the triangular areas would be the same.

From Concrete to Abstract

Ask:

- Could this strategy for finding the area of a regular polygon be used to find the area of an irregular polygon if the irregular polygon were constructed from two or more regular polygons? Explain your reasoning. Yes; the sum of the two areas would equal the area of the irregular polygon.

Launch

Objective Investigate the formula for the area of regular polygons.

Materials

- straightedge
- compass

Teaching Tips

Discuss with students the characteristics of regular polygons. Every regular polygon can be divided into congruent triangles. The sum of the areas of each triangle (or the product of the area of one triangle and the number of sides of the polygon) equals the area of the polygon. The apothem bisects the central angle resulting in two congruent right triangles.

Teach ELL

Working in Cooperative Groups Arrange students in mixed-ability groups of three or four. Direct students to discuss strategies for constructing a regular pentagon and the center point as they work through Steps 1–7 of the activity.

Ask:

- How do you know the five triangles inside the pentagon are congruent? Pentagon *ABCDE* is a regular pentagon, so all of its faces have the same length. The other two sides of each triangle are drawn from the center of the pentagon to each vertex. By definition, the distance is the same for all vertices. Therefore, the triangles are congruent by SSS.

Practice Have students complete Analyze the Results 1 and 2.

Assess

Use Analyze the Results 2 to assess whether students understand the correlation between the area of a triangle and the area of the corresponding regular polygon.

Launch

Have students read the Why? section of the lesson. Ask:

- How many sides does the table have? six
- If the area of one of the triangular sections of the table is 5 square feet, what is the area of the table? 30 ft^2
- How can you find the area of a table that is composed of 10 triangular parts? Find the sum of the areas of the triangular sections.

Teach

Ask the scaffolded questions for each example to build conceptual understanding for students at all levels.

1 Areas of Regular Polygons

Example 1 Identify Segments and Angles in Regular Polygons

AL What is another radius that we could draw? Sample answer: $\overline{KF}$

OL If we drew all possible radii, name another central angle that would be formed. Sample answer: $\angle FKG$

BL If a polygon inscribed in a circle has 8 central angles, what is the polygon? an octagon

(continued on the next page)

LESSON 4

Areas of Regular Polygons and Composite Figures

Then

- You used inscribed and circumscribed figures and found the areas of circles.

Now

1. Find areas of regular polygons.
2. Find areas of composite figures.

Why?

- The top of the table shown is a regular hexagon. Notice that the top is composed of six congruent triangular sections. To find the area of the table top, you can find the sum of the areas of the sections.

New Vocabulary
center of a regular polygon
radius of a regular polygon
apothem
central angle of a regular polygon
composite figure

Mathematical Practices
1 Make sense of problems and persevere in solving them.
6 Attend to precision.

Content Standards
G.MG.3 Apply geometric methods to solve problems (e.g., designing an object or structure to satisfy physical constraints or minimize cost; working with typographic grid systems based on ratios). ★

1 Areas of Regular Polygons In the figure, a regular pentagon is *inscribed* in ⊙P, and ⊙P is *circumscribed* about the pentagon. The **center of a regular polygon** and the **radius of a regular polygon** are also the center and the radius of its circumscribed circle.

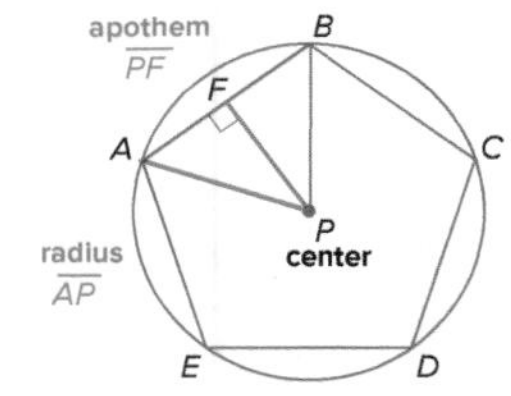

$\angle APB$ is a central angle of regular pentagon $ABCDE$.

A segment drawn from the center of a regular polygon perpendicular to a side of the polygon is called an **apothem**. Its length is the height of an isosceles triangle that has two radii as legs.

A **central angle of a regular polygon** has its vertex at the center of the polygon and its sides pass through consecutive vertices of the polygon. The measure of each central angle of a regular n-gon is $\frac{360}{n}$.

Example 1 Identify Segments and Angles in Regular Polygons

Square $FGHJ$ is inscribed in ⊙K. Identify the center, a radius, an apothem, and a central angle of the polygon. Then find the measure of a central angle.

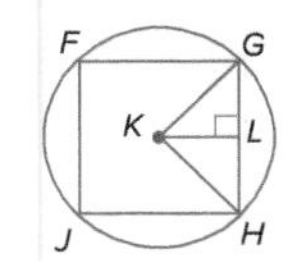

center: point K radius: $\overline{KG}$ or $\overline{KH}$

apothem: $\overline{KL}$ central angle: $\angle GKH$

A square is a regular polygon with 4 sides. Thus, the measure of each central angle of square $FGHJ$ is $\frac{360}{4}$ or 90.

Guided Practice

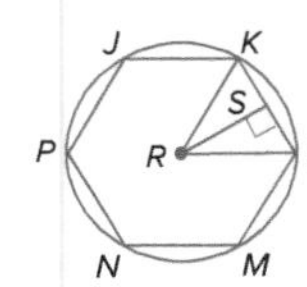

1. In the figure, regular hexagon $JKLMNP$ is inscribed in ⊙R. Identify the center, a radius, an apothem, and a central angle of the polygon. Then find the measure of a central angle. center: point R, radius: $\overline{RK}$, apothem: $\overline{RS}$, central angle: $m\angle KRL$, 60

You can find the area of any regular n-gon by dividing the polygon into congruent isosceles triangles. This strategy is sometimes called *decomposing the polygon into triangles.*

MP Mathematical Practices Strategies

Make sense of problems and persevere in solving them.
Help students understand the strategies for finding the area of regular polygons and composite shapes. For example, ask:

- How can a regular polygon be decomposed into equivalent isosceles triangles? by drawing segments from the center to each vertex
- How can you find the measure of the vertex angle in the isosceles triangle? Divide 360° by the number of sides of the polygon.
- How is the apothem related to the isosceles triangle? It is the height of the triangle.
- What strategy can you use to find the area of the regular polygon once the area of the isosceles triangle is calculated? Multiply the area by the number of sides of the polygon.
- For shapes that are not regular polygons, what strategy could you use to calculate area? Decompose the shape into shapes with formulas for area and sum the areas for the larger shape.

Go Online!

Interactive Whiteboard
Use the *eLesson, Lesson Presentation,* or *Interactive Classroom* to present this lesson.

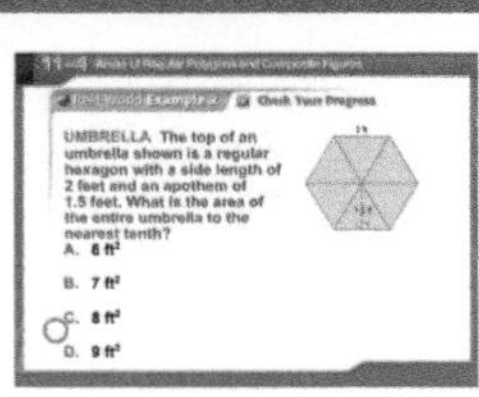

G.MG.3

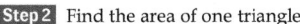

Real-World Example 2 Area of a Regular Polygon

Reading Math ELL
Apothem Like the *radius* of a circle, the *apothem* of a polygon refers to the length of any apothem of the polygon.

ART Kang created the stained glass window shown. The window is a regular octagon with a side length of 15 inches and an apothem of 18.1 inches. What is the area covered by the window?

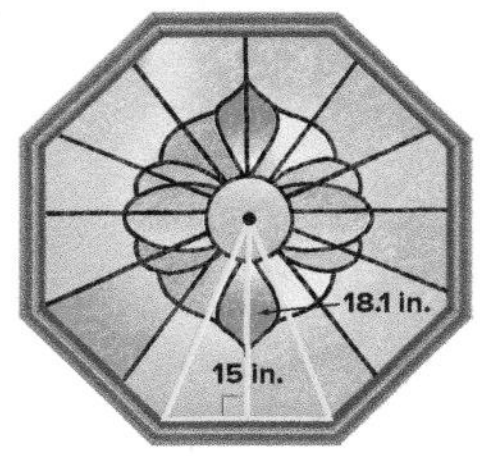

Step 1 Divide the polygon into congruent isosceles triangles.

Because the polygon has 8 sides, the polygon can be divided into 8 congruent isosceles triangles, each with a base of 15 inches and a height of 18.1 inches.

Step 2 Find the area of one triangle.

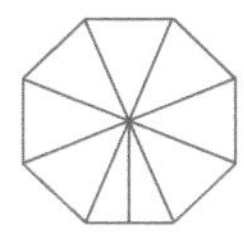

$A = \frac{1}{2}bh$ — Area of a triangle

$= \frac{1}{2}(15)(18.1)$ — $b = 15$ and $h = 18.1$

$= 135.75 \text{ in}^2$ — Simplify.

Step 3 Multiply the area of one triangle by the total number of triangles.

Because there are 8 triangles, the area of the stained glass is 135.75 • 8 or 1086 square inches.

Guided Practice

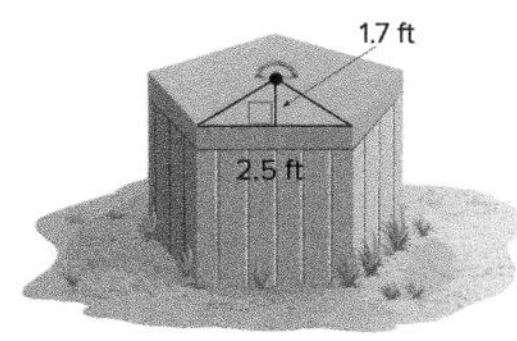

2. HOT TUBS The cover of the hot tub shown is a regular pentagon. If the side length is 2.5 feet and the apothem is 1.7 feet, find the area of the lid to the nearest tenth. 10.6 ft^2

Watch Out!
Area of Regular Polygon this approach can only be applied to *regular* polygons.

From Example 2, we can develop a formula for the area of a regular n-gon with side length s and apothem a.

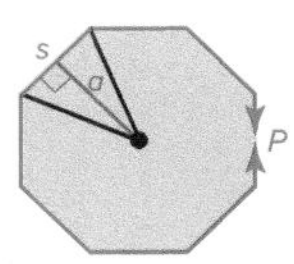

A = area of one triangle • number of triangles

$= \frac{1}{2}$ • base • height • number of triangles

$= \frac{1}{2} \cdot s \cdot a \cdot n$ — Base of triangle is s and height is a. The number of triangles is n.

$= \frac{1}{2} \cdot a \cdot (n \cdot s)$ — Commutative and Associative Properties

$= \frac{1}{2} \cdot a \cdot P$ — The perimeter P of the polygon is $n \cdot s$.

Key Concept Area of a Regular Polygon

Words	The area A of a regular n-gon with side length s is one half the product of the apothem a and perimeter P.
Symbols	$A = \frac{1}{2}a(ns)$ or $A = \frac{1}{2}aP$.

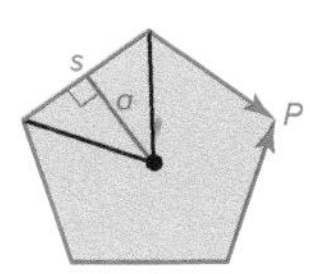

Teaching Tip

Reasoning Remind students that the area of a regular polygon can be found using two different methods. Demonstrate to students that they can find the area of the component triangles or use the formula for the area of a regular polygon. Encourage students to use whichever method they are most comfortable with.

Need Another Example?

In the figure, pentagon $PQRST$ is inscribed in $\odot X$. Identify the center, a radius, an apothem, and a central angle of the polygon. Then find the measure of a central angle.

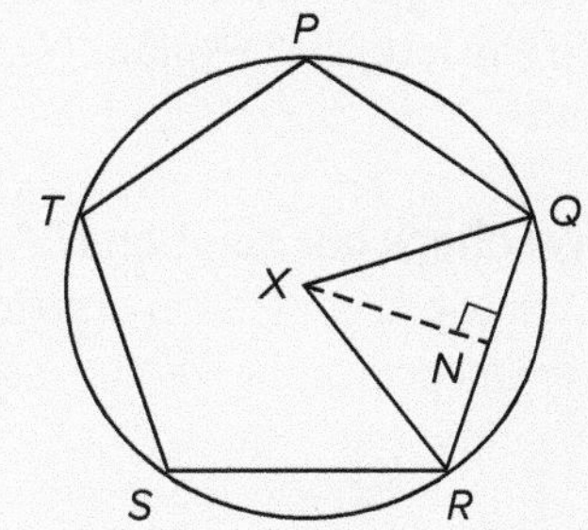

center: point X; radius: $\overline{XR}$ or $\overline{XQ}$; apothem: $\overline{XN}$; central angle: $\angle RXQ$; $m\angle RXQ = 72$

Example 2 Area of a Regular Polygon

AL When you find the area of a polygon, how is the number of triangles formed related to the number of sides of the polygon? They are the same.

OL If the radius of the octagonal window is 15 inches and the side length is 11.5 inches, what is the area of the window? about 637.3 in^2

BL Can you determine the area of a regular polygon given only the radius and number of sides? Explain. Yes; If I calculate the measure of each angle, I can use it to find the apothem and side length. Then I can calculate the area of the polygon using triangles

Need Another Example?

Furniture The top of the table shown is a regular hexagon with a side length of 3 feet and an apothem of 1.7 feet. What is the area of the tabletop to the nearest tenth?

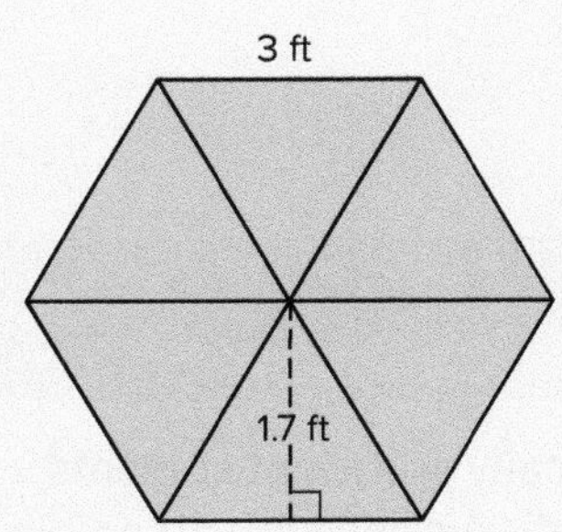

15.3 ft^2

Example 2 Use the Formula for the Area of a Regular Polygon

AL **If you can't remember the rules for a 30°-60°-90° triangle in part a, is there another way to find the lengths? Explain.** Yes; I can use trigonometry.

OL **How can we check our solutions?** Sample answer: Find the area of a triangle formed by two radii of the polygon and multiply by the number of sides.

BL **If a regular hexagon has a side length of 8 meters, what is the area of the hexagon?** about 166.3 m^2

Need Another Example?

Find the area of each regular polygon. Round to the nearest tenth.

a. regular hexagon

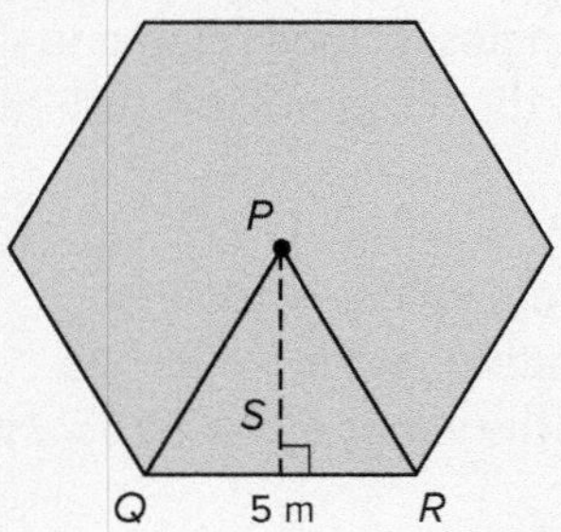

about 65.0 m^2

b. regular pentagon

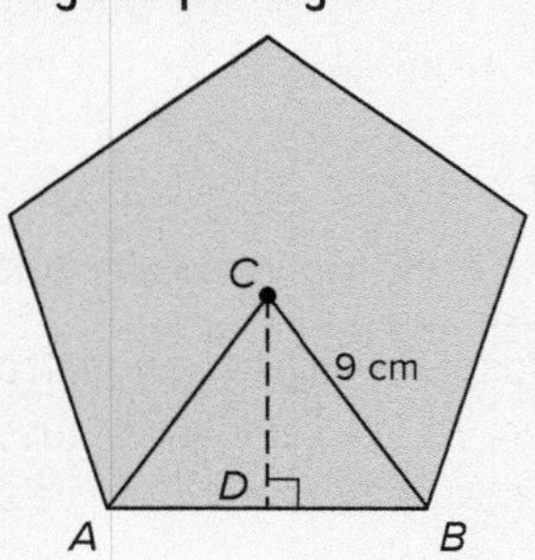

192.6 cm

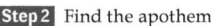

MP Teaching the Mathematical Practices

Precision Mathematically proficient students use clear definitions in discussion with others and in their own reasoning. Encourage students to connect the altitude of a triangle to the altitude of a polygon.

Example 3 Use the Formula for the Area of a Regular Polygon

Find the area of each regular polygon. Round to the nearest tenth.

a. regular hexagon

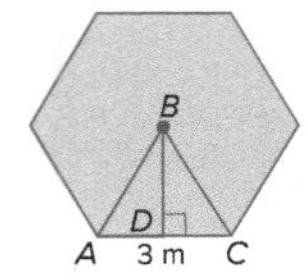

Step 1 Find the measure of a central angle.

A regular hexagon has 6 congruent central angles, so $m\angle ABC = \frac{360}{6}$ or 60.

Step 2 Find the apothem.

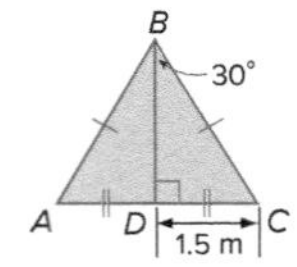

Apothem $\overline{BD}$ is the height of isosceles $\triangle ABC$. It bisects $\angle ABC$, so $m\angle DBC = 30$. It also bisects $\overline{AC}$, so $DC = 1.5$ meters.

$\triangle BDC$ is a $30°-60°-90°$ triangle with a shorter leg that measures 1.5 meters, so $BD = 1.5\sqrt{3}$ meters.

> **Study Tip**
> **MP Precision** The altitude of an isosceles triangle from its vertex to its base is also an angle bisector and median of the triangle.

Step 3 Use the apothem and side length to find the area.

$A = \frac{1}{2}aP$ — Area of a regular polygon

$= \frac{1}{2}(1.5\sqrt{3})(18)$ — $a = 1.5\sqrt{3}$ and $P = 6(3)$ or 18

$\approx 23.4 \text{ m}^2$ — Use a calculator.

b. regular pentagon

Step 1 A regular pentagon has 5 congruent central angles, so $m\angle QPR = \frac{360}{5}$ or 72.

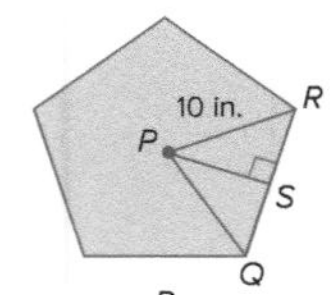

Step 2 Apothem $\overline{PS}$ is the height of isosceles $\triangle RPQ$. It bisects $\angle RPQ$, so $m\angle RPS = 36$. Use trigonometric ratios to find the side length and apothem of the polygon.

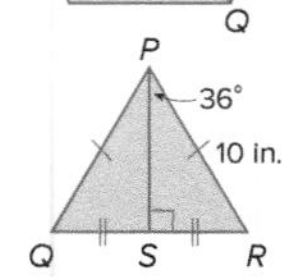

$\sin 36° = \frac{SR}{10}$ $\qquad$ $\cos 36° = \frac{PS}{10}$

$10 \sin 36° = SR$ $\qquad$ $10 \cos 36° = PS$

$QR = 2SR$ or $2(10 \sin 36°)$. So the pentagon's perimeter is $5 \cdot 2(10 \sin 36°)$ or $10(10 \sin 36°)$. The length of the apothem $\overline{PS}$ is $10 \cos 36°$.

Step 3 $A = \frac{1}{2}aP$ — Area of a regular polygon

$= \frac{1}{2}(10 \cos 36°)[10(10 \sin 36°)]$ — $a = 10 \cos 36°$, $P = 10(10 \sin 36°)$

$\approx 237.8 \text{ in}^2$ — Use a calculator.

Guided Practice

3A. 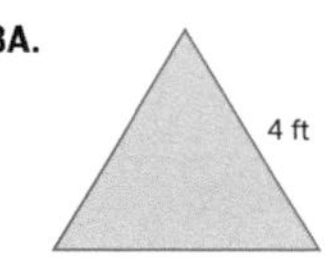

6.9 ft^2

3B. 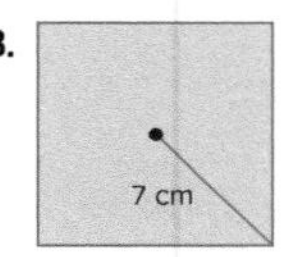

98 cm^2

3C. 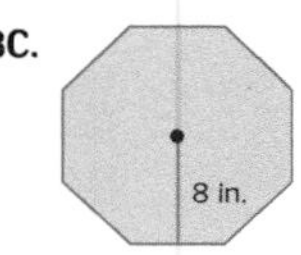

212.1 in^2

2 Areas of Composite Figures

A **composite figure** is a figure that can be separated into regions that are basic figures, such as triangles, rectangles, trapezoids, and circles. To find the area of a composite figure, find the area of each basic figure and then use the Area Addition Postulate.

Differentiated Instruction OL BL

Extension Have students describe how to find the area of an inscribed polygon. First, find the apothem, or the distance from the center of the polygon perpendicular to the midpoint of the opposite side. Then, find half the product of the perimeter and the apothem.

Real-World Link

The first miniature golf course was built in Pinehurst, North Carolina, on a private estate owned by James Barber. There are currently between 5000 and 7500 miniature golf courses in the United States.

Source: Miniature Golf Association of the United States

G.MG.3

Example 4 Find the Area of a Composite Figure by Adding

When viewed from above, the putting green at a miniature golf course is composed of a semicircle, trapezoid, and triangle. Which of the following best represents the area of carpet needed to cover the green?

A 21 B 32 C 35 D 37

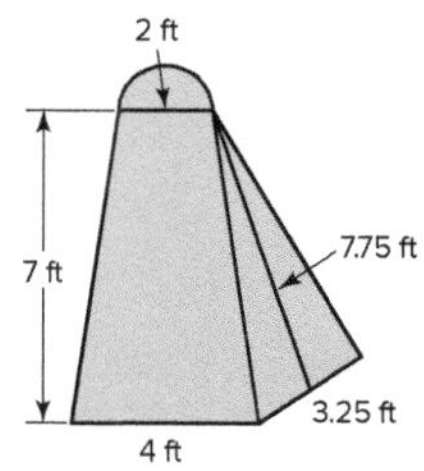

Read the Item

The area to be carpeted can be separated into a trapezoid with a height of 7 feet and bases of 2 feet and 4 feet, a triangle with a base of 3.25 feet and height of 7.75 feet, hypotenuse of 5.7 feet, and a semicircle with a diameter of 2 feet. Find the area of each figure separately and add to get the total area.

Solve the Item

Area of green = area of trapezoid + area of triangle + area of semicircle

$$= \frac{1}{2} \cdot h\,(b_1 + b_2) \quad + \frac{1}{2} \cdot b \cdot h \quad + \frac{1}{2}\pi r^2$$

$$\approx \frac{1}{2} \cdot 7 \cdot (2 + 4) \quad + \frac{1}{2} \cdot 3.25 \cdot 7.75 \quad + \frac{1}{2}\pi(1)^2$$

$$\approx 21 + 12.59 + 1.57 \text{ or about } 35.16 \text{ ft}^2$$

So, about 35 square feet of carpet is needed. The correct answer is C.

Guided Practice

The figure shown is composed of a semicircle, regular hexagon, and trapezoid. What is the area of the figure? D

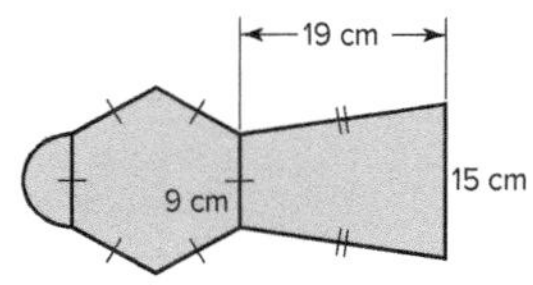

A 427.8 cm^2 C 454.3 cm^2
B 438.4 cm^2 D 470.2 cm^2

The areas of some figures can be found by subtracting the areas of basic figures.

Example 5 Find the Area of a Composite Figure by Subtracting

Find the area of the figure. Round to the nearest tenth if necessary.

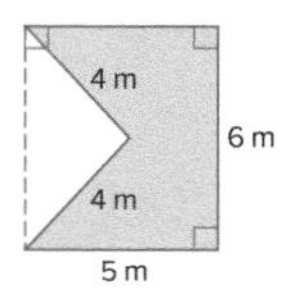

To find the area of the figure, subtract the area of the triangle from the area of the rectangle.

Using the Pythagorean Theorem, the height h of the triangle is $\sqrt{4^2 - 3^2}$ or $\sqrt{7}$ meters.

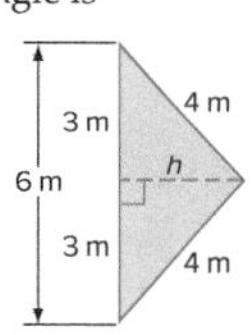

Area of figure = Area of rectangle − Area of triangle

$$= b \cdot h \quad - \quad \frac{1}{2}bh$$

$$= 5 \cdot 6 \quad - \quad \frac{1}{2}(6)(\sqrt{7})$$

$$\approx 30 - 7.9 \text{ or about } 22.1 \text{ m}^2$$

Guided Practice

5A. 63.2 m^2

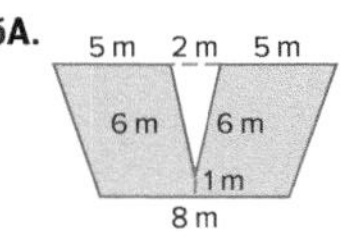

5B. 63 ft^2

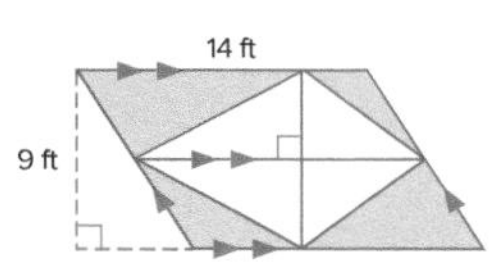

Go Online!

Log into ConnectED to watch an Animation about areas of composite figures.

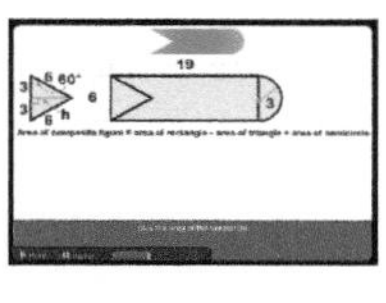

Brand X Pictures/Stockbyte/Getty Images

2 Areas of Composite Figures

Example 4 Find the Area of a Composite Figure by Adding

AL How can we estimate the solution? Sample answer: The solution should be more than the area of a 4 by 7 rectangle, or 28 square feet.

OL If the triangular portion of the putting green is removed, what is the new area to the nearest tenth? about 22.6 ft^2

BL If the base of the trapezoid is increased to 6 feet, what is the new area of the putting green? about 42 ft^2

Need Another Example?

Pool The dimensions of an irregularly shaped pool are shown. What is the area of the surface of the pool? C

A 1556.2 ft^2 C 953.1 ft^2
B 1193.1 ft^2 D 852.5 ft^2

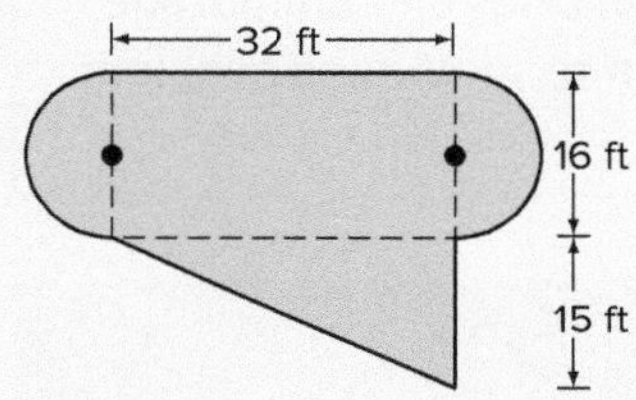

Example 5 Find the Area of a Composite Figure by Subtracting

AL How do we know that the base of the triangle is 6 meters? The base of the triangle is formed by what would be the length of the rectangle, or 6 meters.

OL If we removed an isosceles right triangle from the rectangle shown, where the hypotenuse is the length of the rectangle, what would be the area of the figure formed? 21 m^2

BL If a triangle of the same size were removed from the other side of the rectangle, would a composite figure be formed? Explain. No; Because the height of each triangle is greater than one half the width of the rectangle, two triangles would be formed.

Need Another Example?

Find the area of the shaded figure. 8500 ft^2

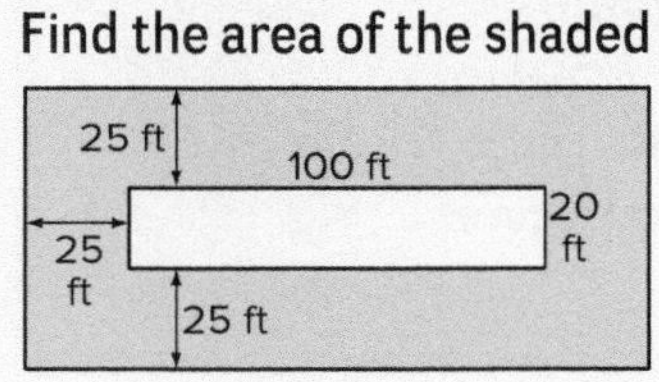

Differentiated Instruction OL BL

Extension Have the students find the area of the white stars on the United States flag. The regular pentagon in the center of each star has an apothem of 0.69 centimeters. The five triangles of each star have bases of 1 centimeter and height of 1.5 centimeters. The area of each star is 5.475 cm^2. So, the area of all the stars is 273.75 cm^2.

Practice

Formative Assessment Use Exercises 1–7 to assess students' understanding of the concepts in this lesson.

The Practice and Problem Solving exercises assess the content taught in the lesson. The Preparing for Assessment page is meant to be used as preparation for end-of-course assessments.

Extra Practice

See page R10 for extra exercises for students who are approaching level or for on-level students who need additional reinforcement.

MP Teaching the Mathematical Practices

Sense-Making Mathematically proficient students start by explaining the meaning of a problem to themselves and looking for entry points to its solution. They plan a solution pathway rather than simply jumping into a solution attempt. In Exercises 8–9, encourage students to make a plan to solve each problem first.

Levels of Complexity Chart

The levels of the exercises progress from 1 to 3, with Level 1 indicating the lowest level of complexity.

Exercises	8–21	22–33, 40–47	34–39
Level 3			●
Level 2		●	
Level 1	●		

Additional Answers

1. center: point P, radius: $\overline{PC}$, apothem: $\overline{PR}$, central angle: $\angle BPC$, ≈ 51.4
8. center: point X, radius: $\overline{XV}$, apothem: $\overline{XY}$, central angle: $\angle VXT$, 72
9. center: point R, radius: $\overline{RO}$, apothem: $\overline{RT}$, central angle: $\angle ORN$, 45

Go Online! eBook

Interactive Student Guide

Use the *Interactive Student Guide* to deepen conceptual understanding.

· Modeling: Two-Dimensional Figures

Go Online! for a Self-Check Quiz

Check Your Understanding

◯ = Step-by-Step Solutions begin on page R13.

Example 1

1. In the figure, regular heptagon $ABCDEFG$ is inscribed in $\odot P$. Identify the center, a radius, an apothem, and a central angle of the polygon. Then find the measure of a central angle. **See margin.**

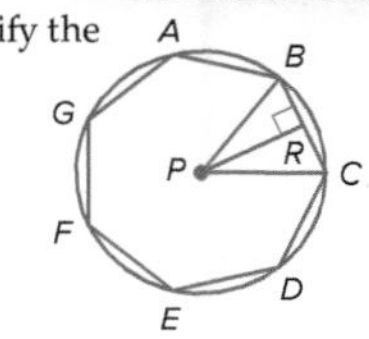

Examples 2–3 **Find the area of each regular polygon. Round to the nearest tenth.**

2. **15.6 m²**

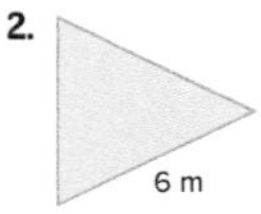

3. **162 in²**

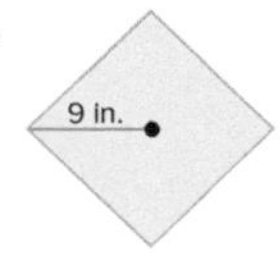

4. **166.3 cm²**

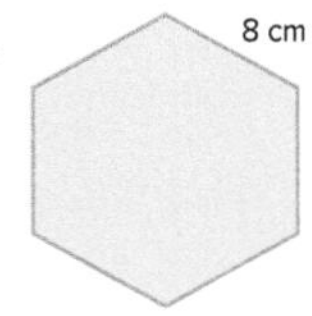

G.MG.3

5. **POOLS** Kenton's job is to cover the community pool during fall and winter. Because the pool is in the shape of an octagon, he needs to find the area in order to have a custom cover made. If the pool has the dimensions shown at the right, what is the area of the pool? **120 ft²**

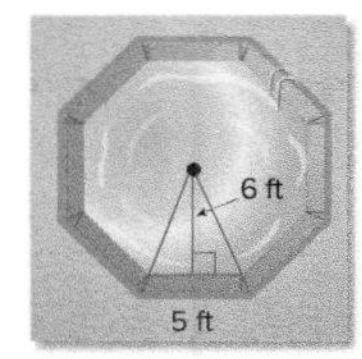

Example 4

6. **MULTIPLE CHOICE** The figure shown is composed of a regular hexagon and equilateral triangles. Which of the following best represents the area? **D**

A 37.5 in^2 C 75 in^2

B $37.5\sqrt{3} \text{ in}^2$ D $75\sqrt{3} \text{ in}^2$

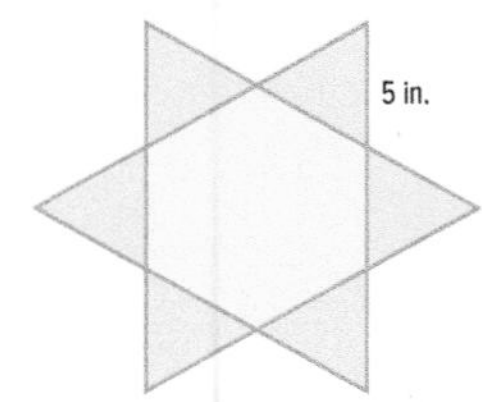

Example 5 G.MG.3

7. **BASKETBALL** The basketball court in Jeff's school is painted as shown.

a. What area of the court is blue? Round to the nearest square foot.

b. What area of the court is red? Round to the nearest square foot.

a. 371 ft² **b. 311 ft²**

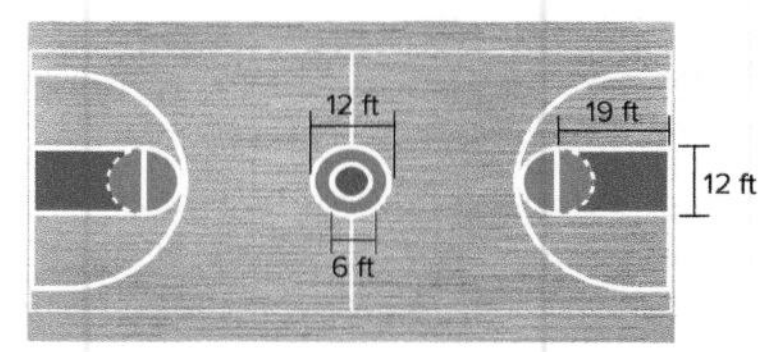

Note: Art not drawn to scale.

Practice and Problem Solving

Extra Practice is on page R10.

Example 1

MP SENSE-MAKING In each figure, a regular polygon is inscribed in a circle. Identify the center, a radius, an apothem, and a central angle of each polygon. Then find the measure of a central angle. **8–9. See margin.**

8.

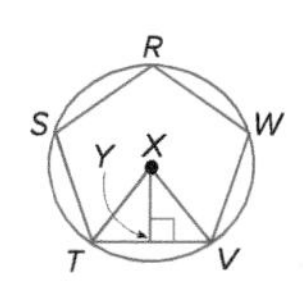

9.

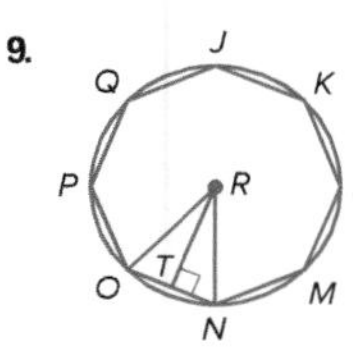

Differentiated Homework Options

Levels	AL Basic	OL Core	BL Advanced
Exercises	8–21, 35–47	9–33 odd, 34–47	34–39, (optional: 40–47)
2-Day Option	9–21 odd, 40–47	8–21	
	8–20 even, 35–39	22–47	

You can use ALEKS to provide additional remediation support with personalized instruction and practice.

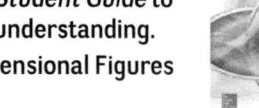

Examples 2–3 **Find the area of each regular polygon. Round to the nearest tenth.**

10.

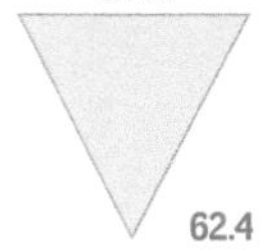

62.4 mm²

11.

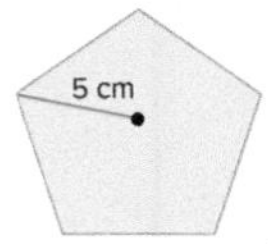

59.4 cm²

12.

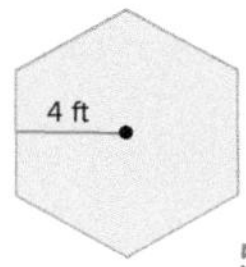

55.4 ft²

13.

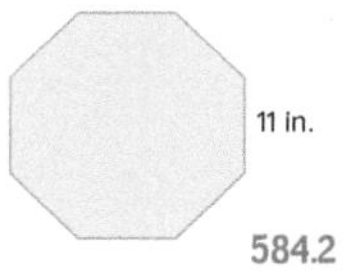

584.2 in²

Example 4 G.MG.3

14. CARPETING Ignacio's family is getting new carpet in their family room, and they want to determine how much the project will cost.

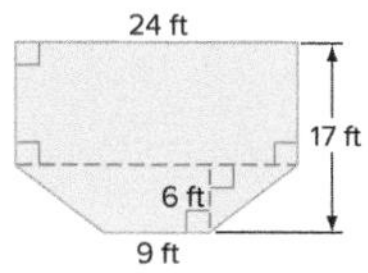

a. Use the floor plan shown to find the area to be carpeted. 363 ft²

b. If the carpet costs \$4.86 per square yard, how much will the project cost? \$196.02

Examples 4–5 **SENSE-MAKING Find the area of each figure. Round to the nearest tenth if necessary.**

15

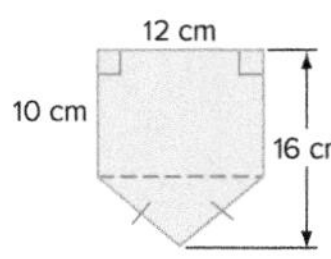

156 cm²

16.

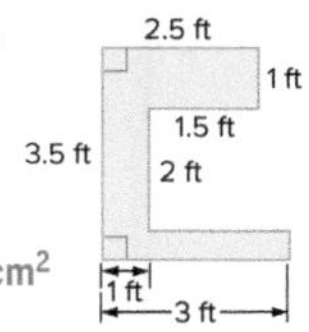

6 ft²

17.

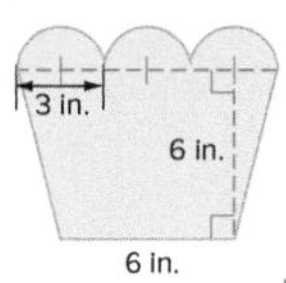

55.6 in²

18.

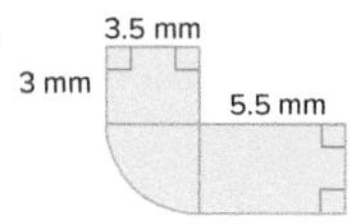

39.4 mm²

19. CRAFTS Latoya's greeting card company is making envelopes for a card from the pattern shown.

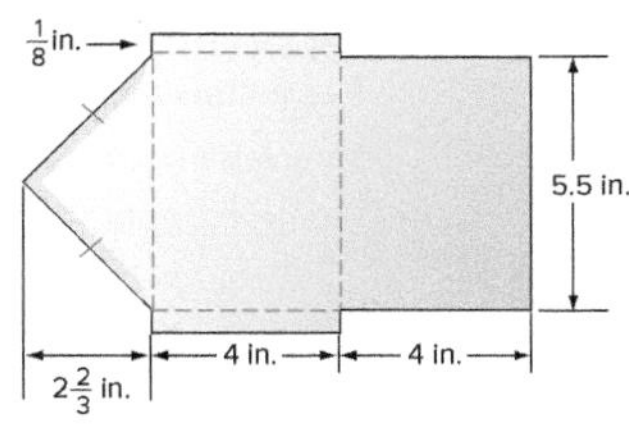

a. Find the perimeter and area of the pattern. Round to the nearest tenth. 29.7 in., 52.3 in²

b. If Latoya orders sheets of paper that are 2 feet by 4 feet, how many envelopes can she make per sheet? 16

20. VOLUNTEERING James is making pinwheels at a summer camp. If they want to paint one side of each pinwheel, what is the approximate total area of 10 pinwheels?

≈1023 in²

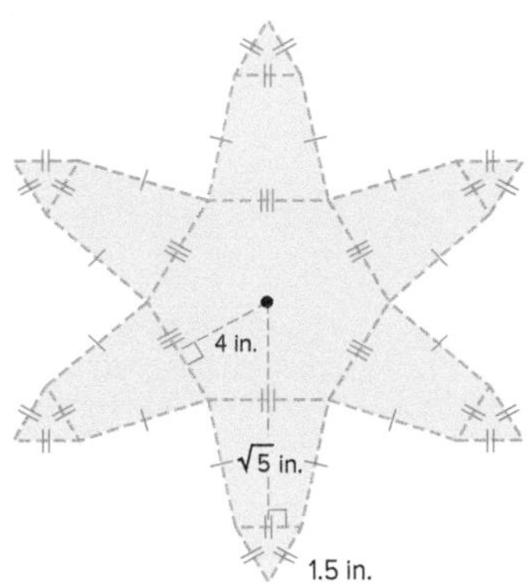

Teaching the Mathematical Practices

Sense-Making Mathematically proficient students check their answers to problems using a different method, and they continually ask themselves, "does this make sense?" In Exercises 15–18, encourage students to check their answers.

Differentiated Instruction AL OL ELL

Interpersonal Learners Have the students discuss how finding the area of a composite figure is similar to finding the area of a parallelogram, triangle, or trapezoid. Students should realize that throughout this chapter, they have separated figures into simpler regions to find area.

MP Teaching the Mathematical Practices

Perseverance Mathematically proficient students check their answers to problems using a different method, and they continually ask themselves, "does this make sense?" In Exercises 29–31, encourage students to check their answers.

Follow-Up

Students have explored the formula for the areas of regular polygons.

Ask:

- Is there more than one formula that can be used to find the area of a given polygon? **Explain.** Yes; Sample answer: Every polygon can be decomposed into two or more figures. For example, a right trapezoid can be decomposed into a rectangle and a triangle. Therefore, another area formula that could be used is $A = r + t$, where r is the area of the rectangle and t is the area of the triangle.

21. **THEATRE** Alison's drama club is planning on painting the amphitheater stage. Find the total area of the stage. ≈354 ft^2

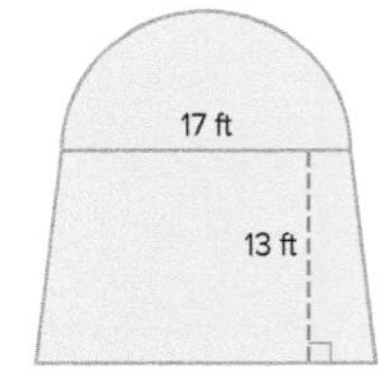

B **Find the area of each shaded region formed by each circle and regular polygon. Round to the nearest tenth.**

22. 76.4 cm^2

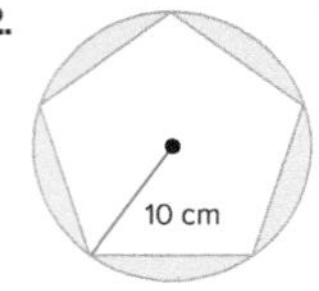

23. 1.9 in^2

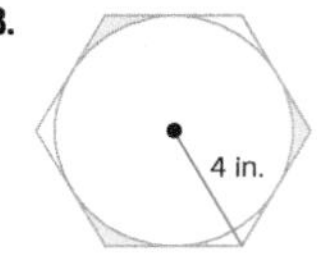

24. 2.5 ft^2

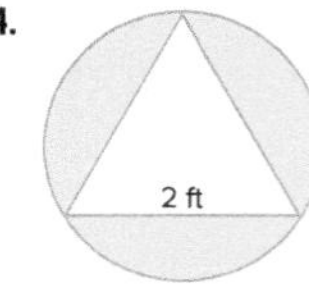

25. **FLOORING** JoAnn wants to lay 12″ × 12″ tile on her bathroom floor.

a. Find the area of the bathroom floor in her apartment floor plan. 50.9 ft^2

b. If the tile comes in boxes of 15 and JoAnn buys no extra tile, how many boxes will she need? 4 boxes

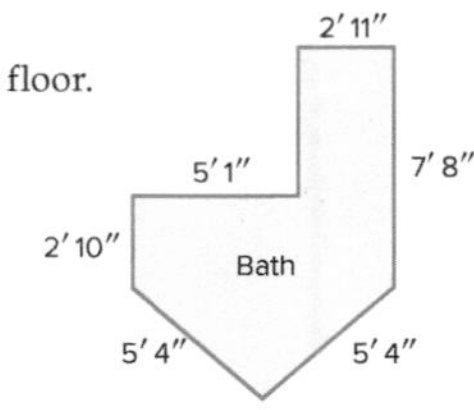

Find the perimeter and area of each figure. Round to the nearest tenth, if necessary.

26. **a regular hexagon with a side length of 12 centimeters** 72 cm; 374.1 cm^2

27. **a regular pentagon circumscribed about a circle with a radius of 8 millimeters** 58.1 mm; 232.4 mm^2

28. **a regular octagon inscribed in a circle with a radius of 5 inches** 30.6 in.; 70.7 in^2

MP PERSEVERANCE **Find the area of each shaded region. Round to the nearest tenth.**

29.

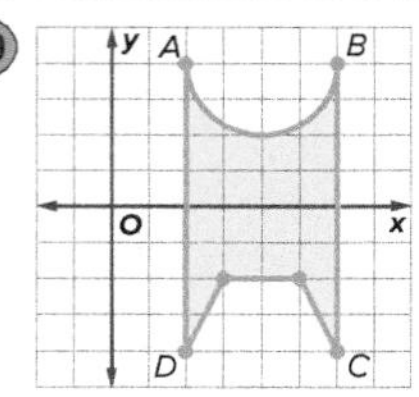

19.7 $units^2$

30.

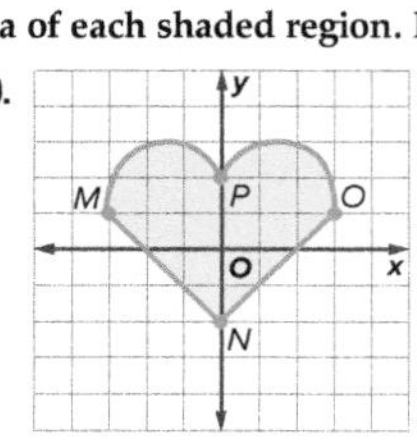

19.9 $units^2$

31.

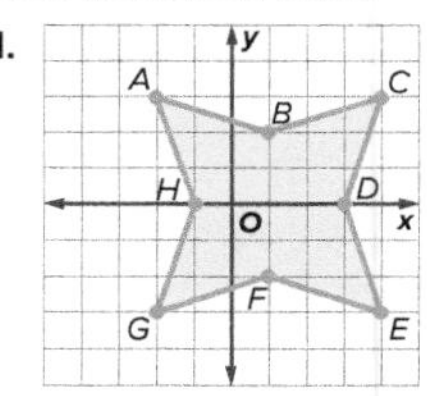

24 $units^2$

32. Find the total area of the shaded regions. Round to the nearest tenth. 52.0 in^2

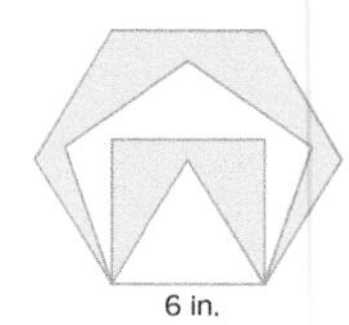

33. 0.43 in^2; 0.56 in^2; 0.62 in^2; 0.65 in^2; Sample answer: When the perimeter of a regular polygon is constant, as the number of sides increases, the area of the polygon increases.

33. **CHANGING DIMENSIONS** Calculate the area of an equilateral triangle with a perimeter of 3 inches. Calculate the areas of a square, a regular pentagon, and a regular hexagon with perimeters of 3 inches. How does the area of a regular polygon with a fixed perimeter change as the number of sides increases?

MP Standards for Mathematical Practice

Emphasis On	Exercises
1 Make sense of problems and persevere in solving them.	8, 9, 15–18, 29–31, 36
4 Model with mathematics.	5, 7, 14, 19–21, 25

34. MULTIPLE REPRESENTATIONS In this problem, you will investigate the areas of regular polygons inscribed in circles.

a. **Geometric** Draw a circle with a radius of 1 unit and inscribe a square. Repeat twice, inscribing a regular pentagon and hexagon. **See margin.**

b. **Algebraic** Use the inscribed regular polygons from part **a** to develop a formula for the area of an inscribed regular polygon in terms of angle measure x and number of sides n. $A = n \cos\left(\frac{x}{2}\right) \sin\left(\frac{x}{2}\right)$

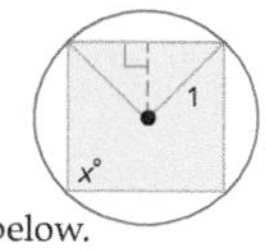

c. **Tabular** Use the formula you developed in part **b** to complete the table below. Round to the nearest hundredth.

Number of Sides, n	4	5	6	8	10	20	50	100
Interior Angle Measure, x	90°	108°	120°	135°	144°	162°	172.8°	176.4°
Area of Inscribed Regular Polygon	2.00	2.38	2.60	2.83	2.94	3.09	3.13	3.14

d. **Verbal** Make a conjecture about the area of an inscribed regular polygon with a radius of 1 unit as the number of sides increases.

34d. Sample answer: As the number of sides of the polygon increases, the area of a regular polygon inscribed in a circle approaches the area of the circle or π.

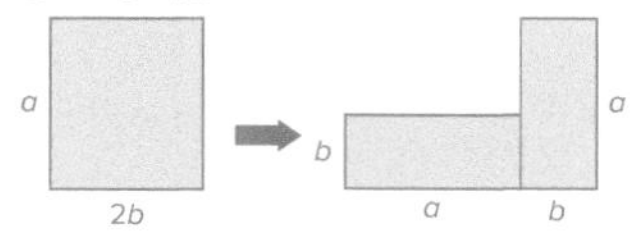

38b. Sample answer: $2ab = ab + ab$

H.O.T. Problems Use Higher-Order Thinking Skills

35. ERROR ANALYSIS Chloe and Flavio want to find the area of the hexagon shown. Is either of them correct? Explain your reasoning. **See margin.**

Chloe

$A = \frac{1}{2}Pa$

$= \frac{1}{2}(66)(9.5)$

$= 313.5 \text{ in}^2$

Flavio

$A = \frac{1}{2}Pa$

$= \frac{1}{2}(33)(9.5)$

$= 156.8 \text{ in}^2$

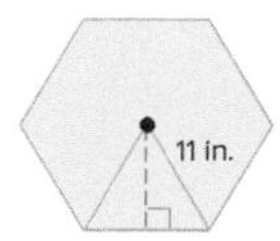

36. MP **SENSE-MAKING** Using the map of Nevada shown, estimate the area of the state. Explain your reasoning. **See margin.**

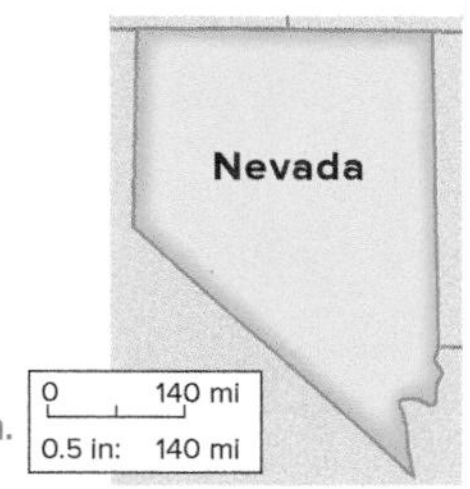

37. OPEN-ENDED Draw a pair of composite figures that have the same area. Make one composite figure out of a rectangle and a trapezoid, and make the other composite figure out of a triangle and a rectangle. Show the area of each basic figure. **See margin.**

38. WRITING IN MATH Consider the sequence of area diagrams shown. **a. See margin**

a. What algebraic theorem do the diagrams prove? Explain your reasoning.

b. Create your own sequence of diagrams to prove a different algebraic theorem.

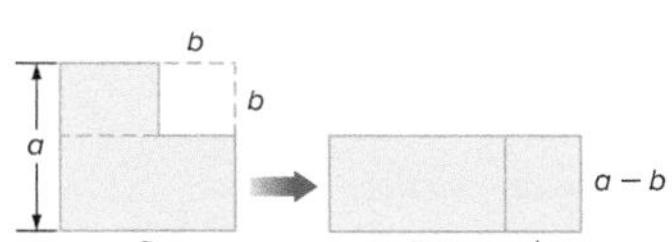

39. **WRITING IN MATH** How can you find the area of any figure? **See Ch. 10 Answer Appendix.**

36. Sample answer: Divide Nevada into a rectangle that is about 315 miles by about 210 miles and a right triangle with a base of about 315 miles and a height of about 280 miles. Finding the areas of the two basic figures and adding to find the area of the composite figure, the area of Nevada is about 110,250 mi².

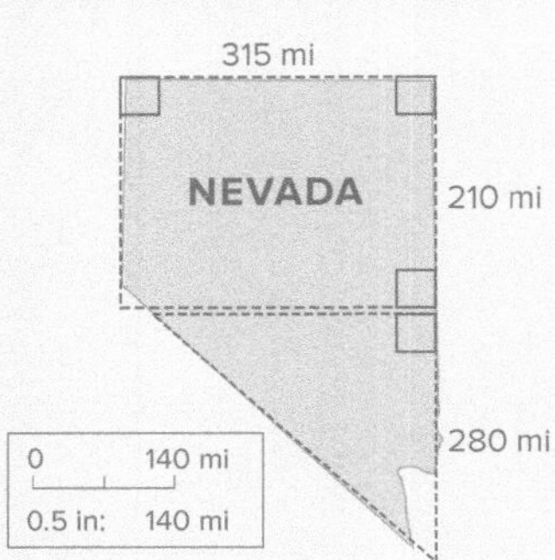

37. Sample answer:

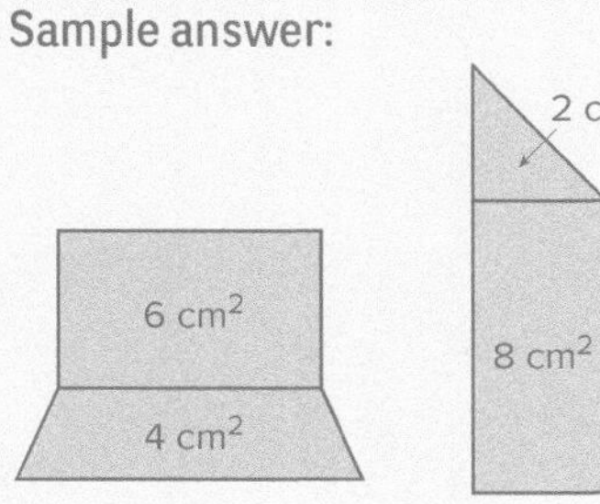

38a. $a^2 - b^2 = (a + b)(a - b)$; Sample answer: The area of the first figure is equal to the area of the larger square a^2 minus the area of the smaller square b^2 or $a^2 - b^2$. The area of the second figure is the area of a rectangle with side lengths $a + b$ and $a - b$ or $(a + b)(a - b)$. Because the figures are composed of congruent shapes, the areas are equal, so $a^2 - b^2 = (a + b)(a - b)$.

Watch Out!

Error Analysis Students should understand that a hexagon is composed of six equilateral triangles. In Exercise 35, the length of one side of the hexagon is 11 inches and its perimeter is 66 inches. Chloe calculated the perimeter correctly.

MP Teaching the Mathematical Practices

Sense-Making Mathematically proficient students consider analogous problems and try simpler forms of the original problem in order to gain insight into its solution. In Exercise 36, encourage students to divide the shape of the state into a triangle and rectangle.

Assess

Name the Math Have students explain how to find the area of a composite figure.

Additional Answers

34a.

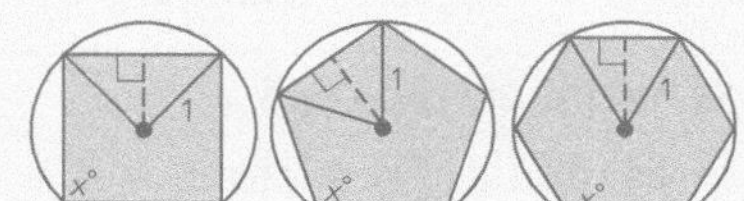

35. Chloe; Sample answer: The measure of each angle of a regular hexagon is 120°, so the segments from the center to each vertex form 60° angles. The triangles formed by the segments from the center to each vertex are equilateral, so each side of the hexagon is 11 in. The perimeter of the hexagon is 66 in. Using trigonometry, the length of the apothem is about 9.5 in. Putting the values into the formula for the area of a regular polygon and simplifying, the area is about 313.5 in².

Go Online!

eSolutions Manual

Create worksheets, answer keys, and solutions handouts for your assignments.

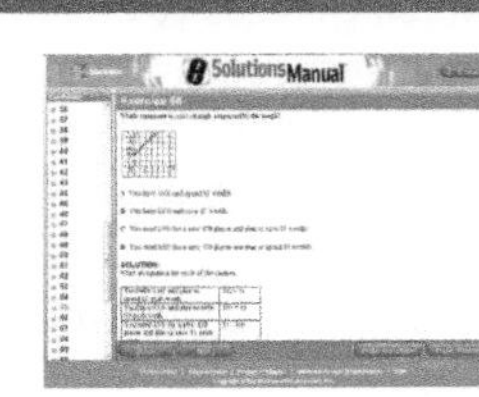

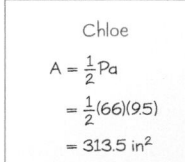

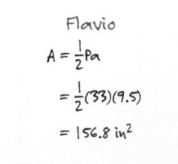

Preparing for Assessment

Exercises 40–47 require students to use the skills they will need on standardized assessments. Exercises are dual-coded with content standards and mathematical practice standards.

Dual Coding		
Items	Content Standards	MP Mathematical Practices
40	G.MG.3	1, 6
41		1, 6
42, 43	G.MG.3	1, 6
44		1, 6
45	G.MG.3	1, 6
46, 47		1, 6

Diagnose Student Errors

Survey student responses for each item. Class trends may indicate common errors and misconceptions.

40.

A	CORRECT
B	Included area of complete circle rather than semicircle
C	Omitted factor of $\frac{1}{2}$ in area of triangle
D	Took 21 in. as height of trapezoid
E	Used 15.65 in. as radius of semicircle

41.

A	CORRECT
B	Took radius of square to be 2 ft
C	Used $\frac{1}{2}aP$, but with $P = 4$
D	Took diagonal of square to be 2 ft

42.

A	Determined apothem to be $\frac{x}{2}\sqrt{2}$ rather than $\frac{x}{2}\sqrt{3}$
B	Omitted factor of 6 in perimeter of hexagon
C	Determined apothem to be $x\sqrt{3}$ rather than $\frac{x}{2}\sqrt{3}$
D	CORRECT

Go Online!

Quizzes

Students can use *Self-Check Quizzes* to check their understanding of this lesson and have the results sent to you. You can also give *Quiz 3*, which covers the content in Lesson 10-4.

Preparing for Assessment

40. Which of the following is the best estimate of the area of the concrete patio shown here? MP 1, 6 G.MG.3 **A**

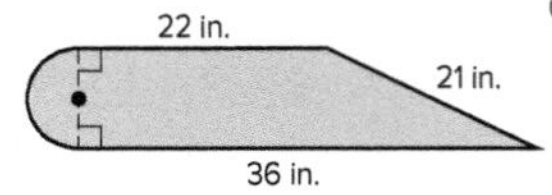

- ○ A 550 in^2
- ○ B 646 in^2
- ○ C 660 in^2
- ○ D 782 in^2
- ○ E 839 in^2

41. What is the area of a square with an apothem of 2 feet? MP 1, 6 **A**

- ○ A 16 ft^2
- ○ B 8 ft^2
- ○ C 4 ft^2
- ○ D 2 ft^2

42. A picnic table shaped like a regular hexagon has sides that are x units long.

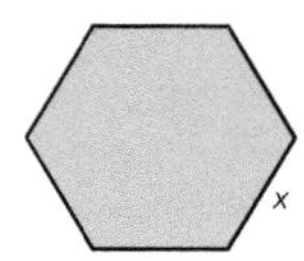

Which of the following expressions represents the area of the table in square units? MP 1, 6 G.MG.3 **D**

- ○ A $\frac{3\sqrt{2}}{2}x^2$
- ○ B $\frac{\sqrt{3}}{4}x^2$
- ○ C $3\sqrt{3}\,x^2$
- ○ D $\frac{3\sqrt{3}}{2}x^2$

43. 84.3 square inches

43. A stained glass panel is shaped like a regular pentagon has a side length of 7 inches. What is the area, to the nearest tenth? MP 1, 6 G.MG.3

44. Find the area of the shaded figure in square inches. Round to the nearest tenth. MP 1, 6 **420**

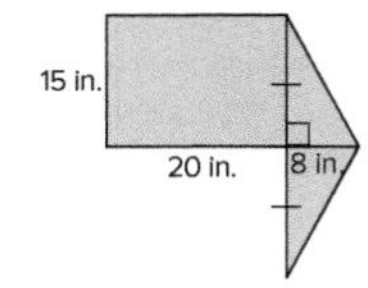

45. **MULTI-STEP** The dimensions of a patio are shown in the diagram. If the surface of the patio is to be painted, about how many square feet will be painted? MP 1, 6 G.MG.3 **B**

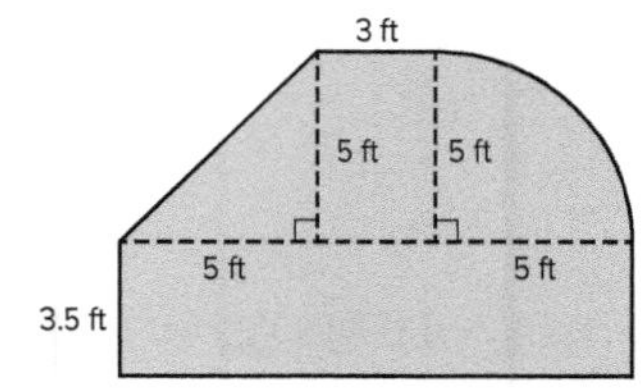

- ○ A 66.8 ft^2
- ○ B 92.6 ft^2
- ○ C 112.3 ft^2
- ○ D 151.5 ft^2

46. Find the area of the figure. Round to the nearest tenth. MP 1, 6 **112.5**

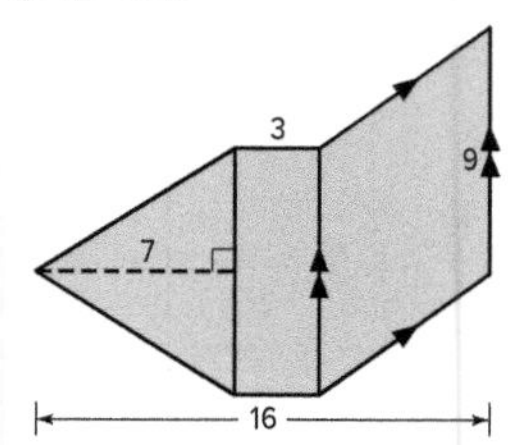

47. A circle is inscribed in a square. The diameter of the circle is 12 inches and is equal to the length of the sides of the square. If the circle is cut out of the square, what is the area of the remaining part of the square? Round your answer to the nearest tenth. MP 1, 6 **30.9 square inches.**

EXTEND 10-4

Geometry Lab

Regular Polygons on the Coordinate Plane

If you know the coordinates of two consecutive vertices of a regular polygon, you can use the Distance Formula to find the length of each side. For example, in the figure shown, the length of $\overline{AB}$ is $\sqrt{(3-1)^2+(1-4)^2}$ or $\sqrt{13}$. Using this measure, you can then find the perimeter and area of the figure using the techniques presented in Lesson 10-4.

You can also use the Distance Formula to find the perimeter and area of a regular polygon inscribed in a circle given the coordinates of the endpoints of a radius.

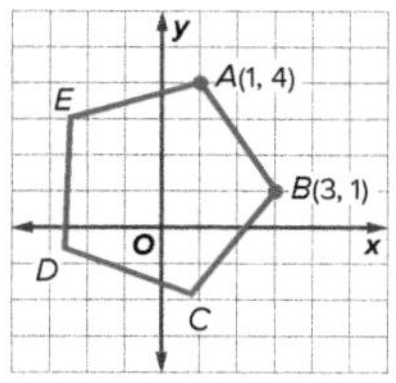

Mathematical Practices

MP 8 Look for and express regularity in repeated reasoning.

Activity 1 Inscribed Polygon

Work cooperatively. Find the perimeter and area of octagon *ABCDEFGH*, which is inscribed in ⊙*O*. Round to the nearest tenth, if necessary.

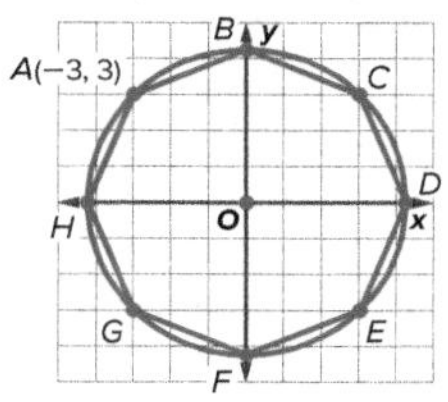

Step 1 Use the Distance Formula to find a radius of ⊙*O*.

$OA = \sqrt{(-3-0)^2+(3-0)^2}$ $x_2 = -3, x_1 = 0, y_2 = 3$, and $y_1 = 0$

$= \sqrt{18}$ or $3\sqrt{2}$ Simplify.

Step 2 Find the perimeter and area.

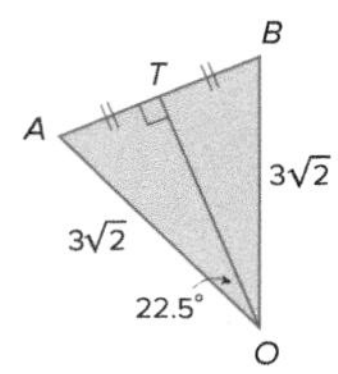

Because the octagon is inscribed in ⊙*O*, $\overline{OA}$ and $\overline{OB}$ are both radii of ⊙*O*. Therefore, $OA = OB = 3\sqrt{2}$. Let $\overline{OT}$ be an apothem of the octagon with length a. Then $\overline{OT}$ is also the height of isosceles $\triangle AOB$. Because the octagon is regular, $m\angle AOB$ is $360 \div 8$ or 45. Because $\overline{OT}$ bisects $\angle AOB$ and side $\overline{AB}$, $m\angle AOT = 45 \div 2$ or 22.5, and $AB = 2(AT)$.

Use trigonometric ratios to find a and AT.

$\cos 22.5° = \frac{a}{3\sqrt{2}}$ $\cos\theta = \frac{\text{adj}}{\text{hyp}}$

$a = 3\sqrt{2}\cos 22.5°$ Solve for a.

$\sin 22.5° = \frac{AT}{3\sqrt{2}}$ $\sin\theta = \frac{\text{opp}}{\text{hyp}}$

$AT = 3\sqrt{2}\sin 22.5°$ Solve for AT.

$AB = 2(AT)$, so $AB = 2(3\sqrt{2}\sin 22.5°)$ and the perimeter P of the octagon is $8(2)3\sqrt{2}\sin 22.5°$ or about 26.0 units. The area of the octagon is $\frac{1}{2}aP$, which is $\frac{1}{2}3\sqrt{2}\cos 22.5° \cdot 8(2)3\sqrt{2}\sin 22.5°$ or about 50.9 units^2.

Launch

Objective Find areas and perimeters of regular polygons, including inscribed and circumscribed polygons, on the coordinate plane.

Materials for Each Group

- grid paper

Easy to Make Manipulatives

Teaching Geometry with Manipulatives

- template for grid paper, p. 1

Teaching Tip

Encourage students to estimate the perimeter and area of each polygon before calculating each measure. One way to estimate the area of each polygon is to count the number of whole and partial squares inside the figure. An estimate of the figure's area is then $A \approx$ (whole squares) + $\frac{1}{2}$(partial squares). If the figure is inscribed in a circle, the area of the polygon is a little less than the area of the circle. If the figure is circumscribed about a circle, the area of the polygon is a little more than the area of the circle. The magnitude of the error will decrease as the number of sides increases.

Teach ELL

Working in Cooperative Groups Organize students into groups of three or four, mixing abilities. Have groups complete Activities 1 and 2.

Practice Have students complete Exercises 1-6.

Assess

Formative Assessment

Use Exercises 1–6 to assess whether students understand how to find the areas and perimeters of regular polygons, including inscribed and circumscribed polygons, on the coordinate plane.

From Concrete to Abstract

In this lab, students are given the coordinates of two consecutive vertices in order to find the perimeter and area of a regular polygon. Have students write about whether or not the coordinates of two nonconsecutive vertices could be used to find the perimeter and area.

EXTEND 10-4

Geometry Lab

Regular Polygons on the Coordinate Plane *Continued*

You can also use the Distance Formula to find the perimeter and area of a regular polygon circumscribed about a circle given the coordinates of the endpoints of a radius.

Activity 2 Circumscribed Polygon

Work cooperatively. Find the perimeter and area of hexagon *ABCDEF*, which is circumscribed about ⊙*Q*. Round to the nearest tenth, if necessary.

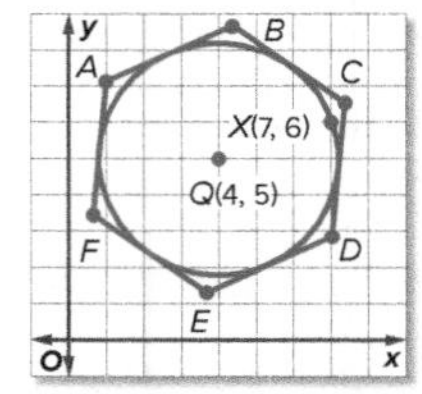

Step 1 Use the Distance Formula to find a radius of ⊙*Q*.

$QX = \sqrt{(7-4)^2 + (6-5)^2}$ or $\sqrt{10}$ $x_2 = 7, x_1 = 4, y_2 = 6$, and $y_1 = 5$

Step 2 Find the perimeter and area of hexagon *ABCDEF*.

Because the hexagon is circumscribed about ⊙*Q*, $\overline{AB}$ is tangent to the circle. Let the point of tangency be *T*. Since all radii of a circle are congruent, radius $\overline{QT}$ also measures $\sqrt{10}$. $\overline{QT}$ is an apothem of the hexagon, so $a = \sqrt{10}$.

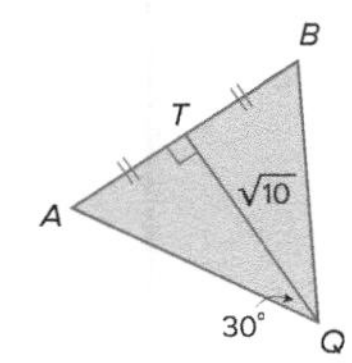

The apothem is also the height of isosceles △*AQB*. Because the hexagon is regular, $m\angle AQB$ is 360 ÷ 6 or 60. Because $\overline{QT}$ bisects ∠*AQB* and side $\overline{AB}$, $m\angle AQT = 60 \div 2$ or 30, and $AB = 2(AT)$. Use trigonometric ratios to find *AT*. Then find *AB*.

$\tan 30° = \frac{AT}{\sqrt{10}}$ $\tan\theta = \frac{\text{opp}}{\text{adj}}$

$AT = \sqrt{10}\tan 30°$ Solve for *AT*.

$AT = \sqrt{10}\left(\frac{\sqrt{3}}{3}\right)$ or $\frac{\sqrt{30}}{3}$ $\tan 30° = \frac{\sqrt{3}}{3}$

$AB = 2(AT)$

$= 2\left(\frac{\sqrt{30}}{3}\right)$

$= \frac{2\sqrt{30}}{3}$

The perimeter *P* of the hexagon is $6 \cdot \frac{2\sqrt{30}}{3}$ or $4\sqrt{30}$, which is about 21.9 units. The area of the hexagon is $\frac{1}{2}aP$, which is $\frac{1}{2}\sqrt{10}(4\sqrt{30})$ or about 34.6 units^2.

Exercises

Work cooperatively. Find the perimeter and area of each regular polygon with the given consecutive vertices. Round to the nearest tenth, if necessary.

1. pentagon *ABCDE*; *A*(1, 4), *B*(3, 1)
   18.0 units, 22.4 units^2
2. hexagon *ABCDEF*; *A*(−4, 2), *B*(0, 5)
   30 units, 65.0 units^2

Find the perimeter and area of each regular polygon inscribed in ⊙*O*, centered at the origin, and containing the given point. Round to the nearest tenth, if necessary.

3. pentagon *ABCDE*; *E*(−4, −1)
   24.2 units, 40.4 units^2
4. hexagon *ABCDEF*; *D*(4, −5)
   38.4 units, 106.5 units^2

Find the perimeter and area of each regular polygon circumscribed about ⊙*Q*, with the given center and point *X* on the circle. Round to the nearest tenth, if necessary.

5. pentagon *ABCDE*; *Q*(−2, 1); *X*(−1, 3) **16.2 units, 18.2 units^2**
6. octagon *ABCDEFGH*; *Q*(3, −1); *X*(1, −3) **18.7 units, 26.5 units^2**

LESSON 10-5
Area and Nonrigid Transformations

SUGGESTED PACING (DAYS)

	Instruction
90 min.	0.5
45 min.	1.0

Track Your Progress

Objectives

1. Find areas of similar figures by using scale factors.
2. Determine how changes in dimensions affect the areas of figures.

Mathematical Background

If two polygons are similar, then the perimeters are proportional to the scale factor between them. The areas of two similar polygons are proportional to the square of the scale factor between them.

THEN

G.SRT.2 Given two figures, use the definition of similarity in terms of similarity transformations to decide if they are similar.

G.SRT.5 Use congruence and similarity criteria for triangles to solve problems and to prove relationships in geometric figures.

NOW

G.GMD.1 Give an informal argument for the formulas for the circumference of a circle, area of a circle, volume of a cylinder, pyramid, and cone.

G.MG.1 Use geometric shapes, their measures, and their properties to describe objects (e.g., modeling a tree trunk or a human torso as a cylinder).

NEXT

G.GMD.3 Use volume formulas for cylinders, pyramids, cones, and spheres to solve problems.

Go Online! All of these resources and more are available at connectED.mcgraw-hill.com

Chapter Projects allow students to apply what they have learned about areas of polygons and circles to complete a real-world project about designing a blueprint for a house.

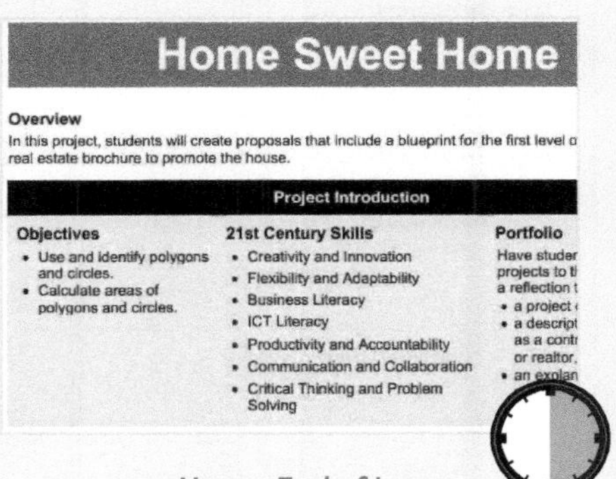

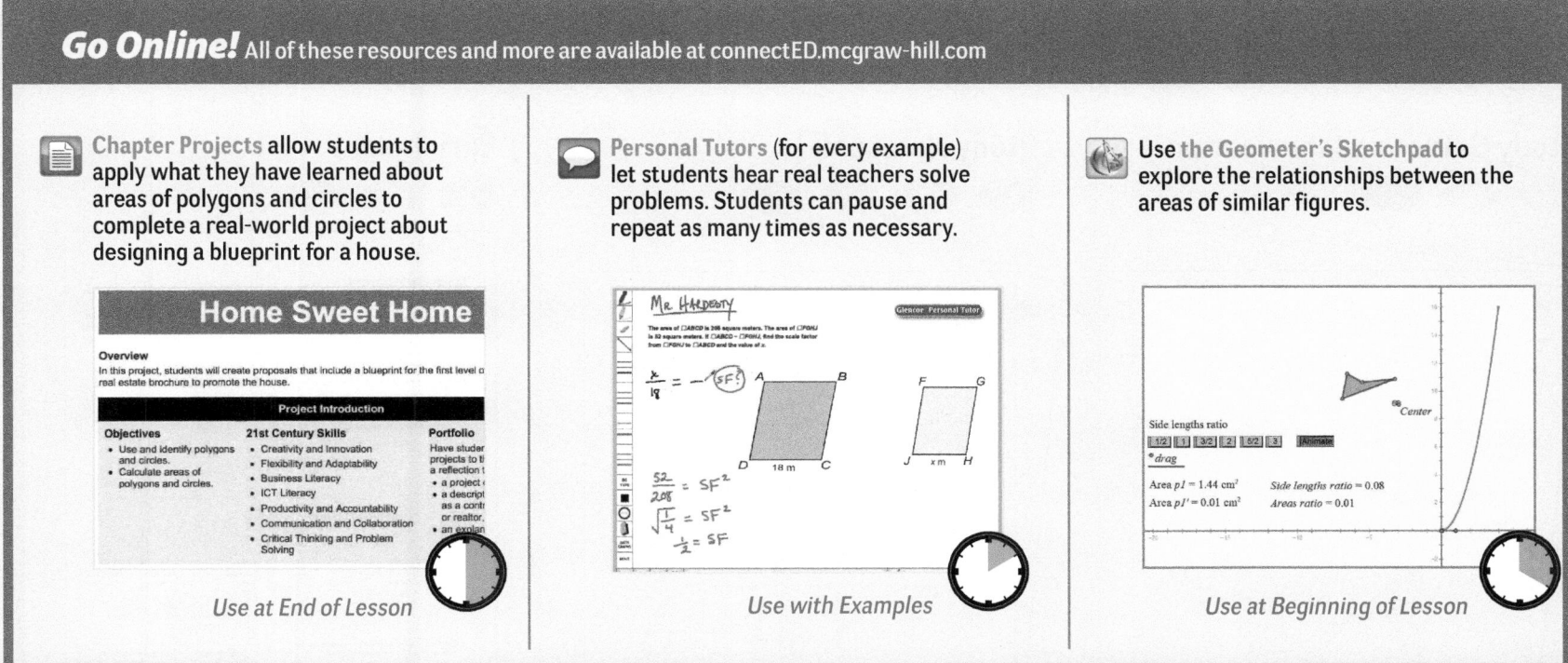

Use at End of Lesson

Personal Tutors (for every example) let students hear real teachers solve problems. Students can pause and repeat as many times as necessary.

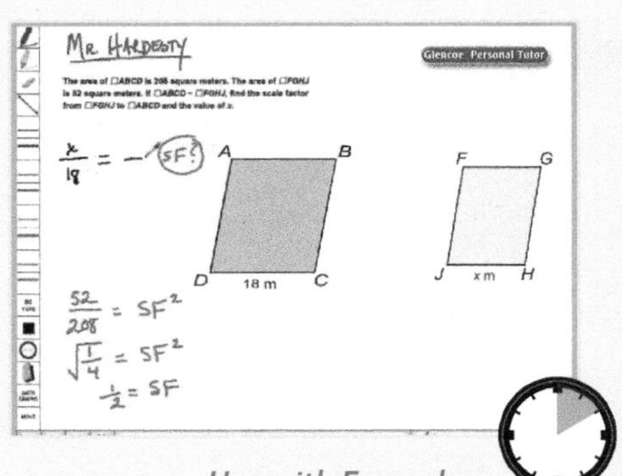

Use with Examples

Use the Geometer's Sketchpad to explore the relationships between the areas of similar figures.

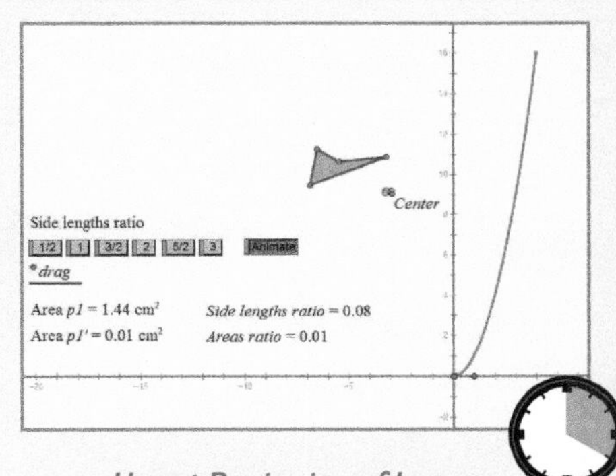

Use at Beginning of Lesson

OER Using Open Educational Resources

Video Conferencing Have absent students view lessons they have missed on **Wetoku. Wetoku** offers a way for students to see your presentation and the class's participation at the same time. It does not require any software installation. All calls are automatically recorded so it can also be used for struggling students who need the lesson repeated. *Use as remediation*

Go Online!
connectED.mcgraw-hill.com

Worksheets

Differentiate Your Resources

Extra Practice Additional practice or homework; Skills Practice is best for approaching-level students and Practice is best for on-level and beyond-level students

Skills Practice

AL OL ELL

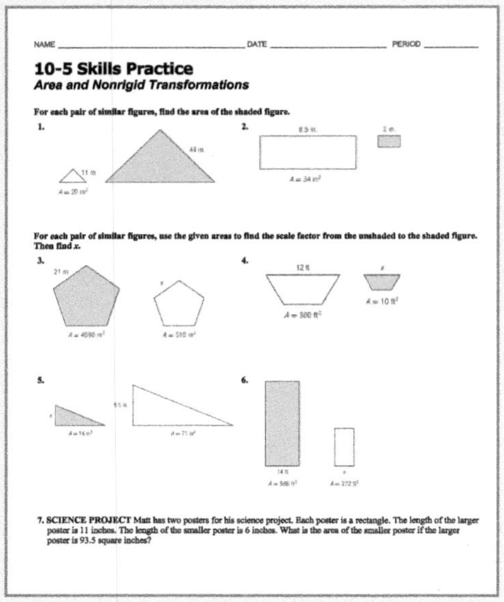
NAME ____ DATE ____ PERIOD ____

10-5 Skills Practice
Area and Nonrigid Transformations

Practice

AL OL BL ELL

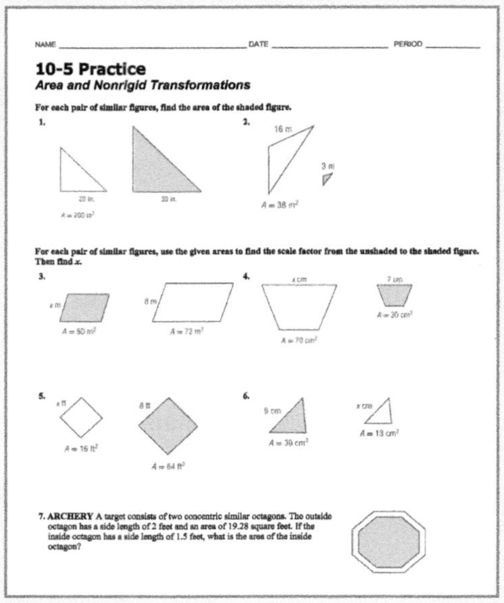
NAME ____ DATE ____ PERIOD ____

10-5 Practice
Area and Nonrigid Transformations

Word Problem Practice

AL OL BL ELL

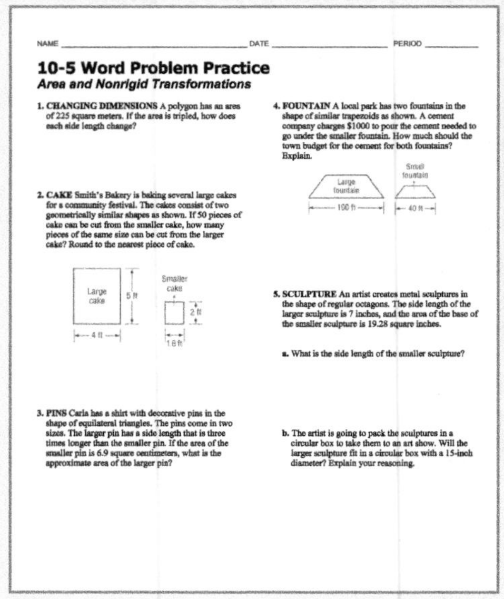
NAME ____ DATE ____ PERIOD ____

10-5 Word Problem Practice
Area and Nonrigid Transformations

Intervention Reteaching and vocabulary activities that can be used with struggling or absent students and as ELL support

Study Guide and Intervention

AL OL ELL

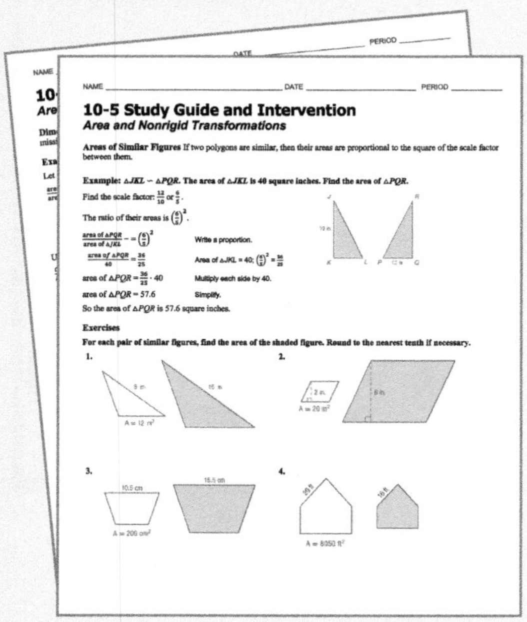
NAME ____ DATE ____ PERIOD ____

10-5 Study Guide and Intervention
Area and Nonrigid Transformations

Study Notebook

AL OL BL ELL

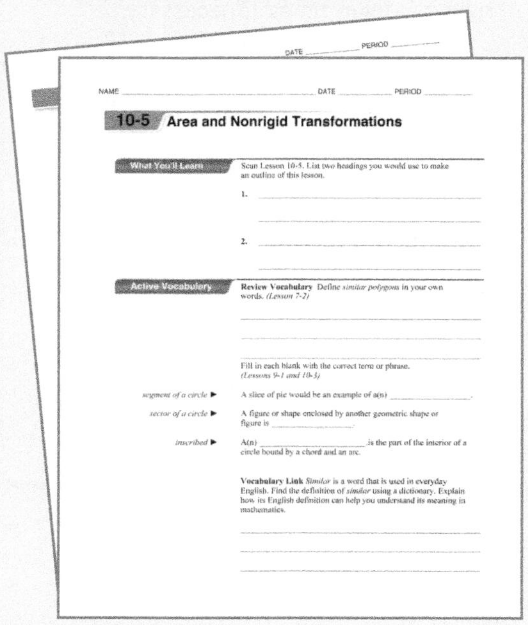
NAME ____ DATE ____ PERIOD ____

10-5 Area and Nonrigid Transformations

What You'll Learn

Active Vocabulary

Extension Activities that can be used to extend lesson concepts

Enrichment

OL BL ELL

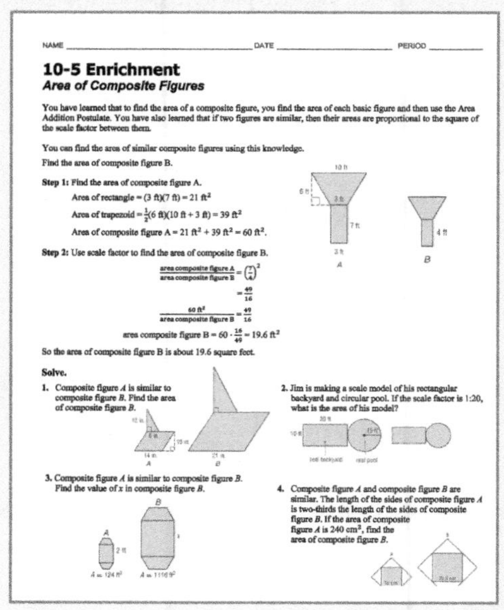
NAME ____ DATE ____ PERIOD ____

10-5 Enrichment
Area of Composite Figures

LESSON 5

Area and Nonrigid Transformations

Then
- You used scale factors and proportions to solve problems involving the perimeters of similar figures.

Now
1. Find areas of similar figures by using scale factors.
2. Determine how changes in dimensions affect the areas of figures.

Why?
- Architecture firms often hire model makers to make scale models of projects that are used to sell their designs. Since the base of a model is geometrically similar to the base of the actual building it represents, their areas are related.

Lane Oatey/Blue Jean Images/Getty Images

MP Mathematical Practices
1 Make sense of problems and persevere in solving them.
3 Construct viable arguments and critique the reasoning of others.
4 Model with mathematics.

Content Standards
G.GMD.1 Give an informal argument for the formulas for the circumference of a circle, area of a circle, volume of a cylinder, pyramid, and cone.
G.MG.1 Use geometric shapes, their measures, and their properties to describe objects (e.g., modeling a tree trunk or a human torso as a cylinder).

1 Areas of Similar Figures In Chapter 7 you learned that a nonrigid transformation changes the size but not the shape of a figure, producing a similar figure. In Lesson 7-2, you learned that if two polygons are similar, then their perimeters are proportional to the scale factor between them. The areas of two similar polygons share a different relationship.

$\frac{\text{perimeter of figure } B}{\text{perimeter of figure } A} = \frac{28k}{28}$ or k

$\frac{\text{area of figure } B}{\text{area of figure } A} = \frac{45k^2}{45}$ or k^2

Theorem 10.1 Areas of Similar Polygons

Words If two polygons are similar, then their areas are proportional to the square of the scale factor between them.

Example If $ABCD \sim FGHJ$, then $\frac{\text{area of } FGHJ}{\text{area of } ABCD} = \left(\frac{FG}{AB}\right)^2$.

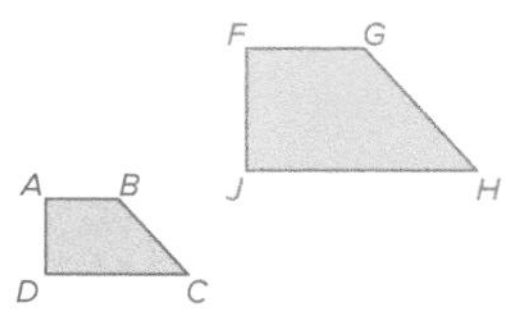

You will prove Theorem 10.1 for triangles in Exercise 22.

Example 1 Find Areas of Similar Polygons G.GMD.1

If $\triangle JKL \sim \triangle PQR$ and the area of $\triangle JKL$ is 30 square inches, find the area of $\triangle PQR$.

The scale factor between $\triangle PQR$ and $\triangle JKL$ is $\frac{15}{12}$ or $\frac{5}{4}$, so the ratio of their areas is $\left(\frac{5}{4}\right)^2$.

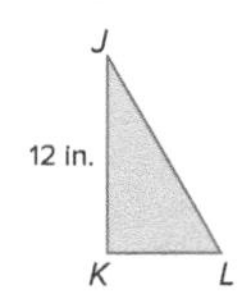

$\frac{\text{area of } \triangle PQR}{\text{area of } \triangle JKL} = \left(\frac{5}{4}\right)^2$ Write a proportion.

$\frac{\text{area of } \triangle PQR}{30} = \frac{25}{16}$ Area of $\triangle JKL = 30$ and $\left(\frac{5}{4}\right)^2 = \frac{25}{16}$

area of $\triangle PQR = \frac{25}{16} \cdot 30$ Multiply each side by 30.

area of $\triangle PQR = 46.875$ Simplify.

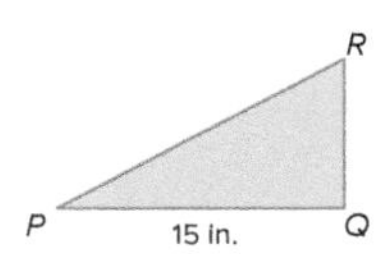

So the area of $\triangle PQR$ is about 46.9 square inches.

MP Mathematical Practices Strategies

Look for and make use of structure.
Help students discern patterns and apply rules to related problems. They can also express patterns and rules algebraically. Ask:

- What categories of two-dimensional figures, like equilateral triangles, contain all similar figures? Explain your answer. Squares, regular pentagons, regular hexagons, etc., and circles; These catagories of figures have the same shape but different sizes.
- When you double the dimensions of a two-dimensional figure, like a rectangle, both dimensions are doubled. How does this doubling affect the area? Show your answer algebraically. Because both length and width are doubled, the original area is multiplied by 2 twice: *Original area* $= l \times w$. *New length* $= 2l$. *New width* $= 2w$. *New area* $= 2l \times 2w = 4(l \times w)$.
- Explain why using any scale factor k causes the area to be multiplied by k^2. If both dimensions of a two-dimensional figure are multiplied by k, then the area is multiplied by k twice, which is the same as k^2.

Launch

Have students read the Why? section of the lesson. Ask:

- How tall is a building if the model is 2.5 feet tall and the scale factor is 12 feet to 1 inch? 360 ft
- If the side lengths of a rectangle are doubled, is the rectangle's area doubled? No, it quadruples.
- Are the proportions of the side lengths of similar figures and the proportions of the areas of similar figures always the same? no

Teach

Ask the scaffolded questions for each example to build conceptual understanding for students at all levels.

1 Areas of Similar Figures

Example 1 Find Areas of Similar Polygons

AL Why do you think we need to square the scale factor when we use it to find areas? Sample answer: The scale factor applies to length, and for area, we multiply a length by a length. So, to find the area using scale factor, we need to multiply a scale factor by a scale factor.

OL The scale factor of two squares is $\frac{3}{4}$ and the area of the larger square is 400 cm^2. What is the area of the smaller square? 225 cm^2

BL What do you think you would do to the scale factor when using it to find similar volumes? cube it

Go Online!

Interactive Whiteboard
Use the *eLesson*, *Lesson Presentation*, or *Interactive Classroom* to present this lesson.

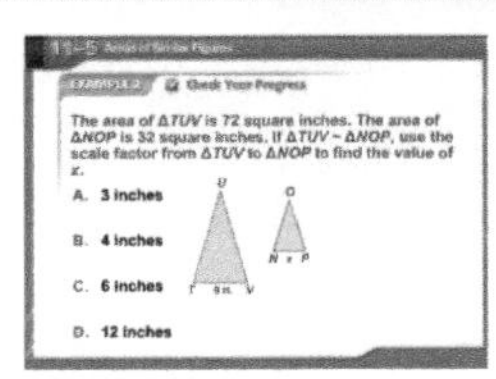

Need Another Example?

If $ABCD \sim PQRS$ and the area of $ABCD$ is 48 square inches, find the area of $PQRS$.

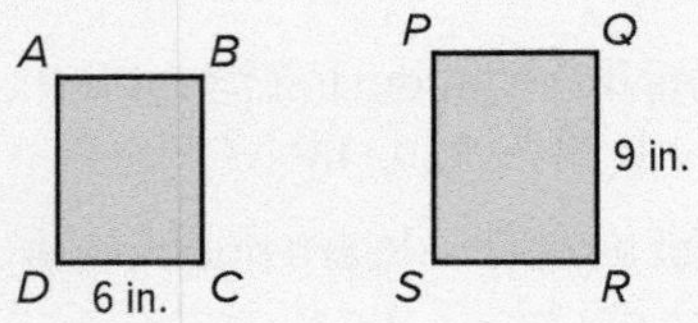

60.75 square inches

Example 2 Use Areas of Similar Figures

AL The ratio of two areas is $\frac{25}{49}$. What is the scale factor of the two figures? $\frac{5}{7}$

OL If the area of Triangle A is 108 cm^2 and the area of Triangle B is 300 cm^2, what is the scale factor of Triangle B to Triangle A? $\frac{5}{3}$

BL The ratio of the area of Figure A to Figure B is $\frac{25}{4}$. What is the ratio of the perimeter of Figure A to Figure B? $\frac{5}{2}$

Need Another Example?

The area of $\triangle ABC$ is 98 square inches. The area of $\triangle RTS$ is 50 square inches. If $\triangle ABC \sim \triangle RTS$, find the scale factor from $\triangle ABC$ to $\triangle RTS$ and the value of x.

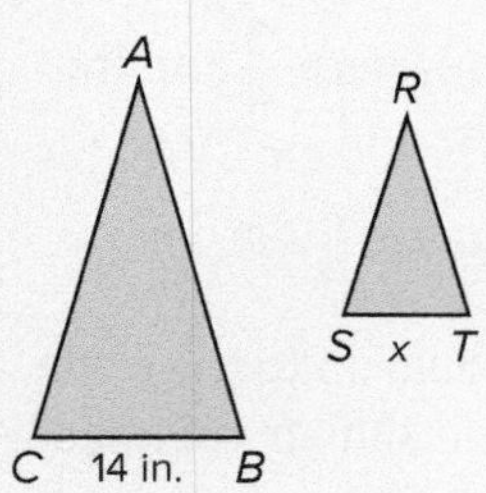

scale factor: $\frac{7}{5}$; 10

Go Online!

Discover a relationship between the areas of similar figures with a Geometer's Sketchpad® sketch in ConnectED.

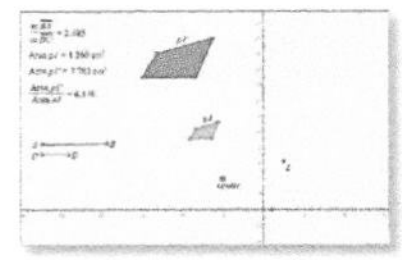

Guided Practice

For each pair of similar figures, find the area of the green figure.

1A. 12.5 cm^2

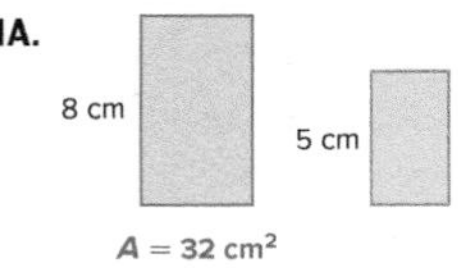

1B. 24 ft^2

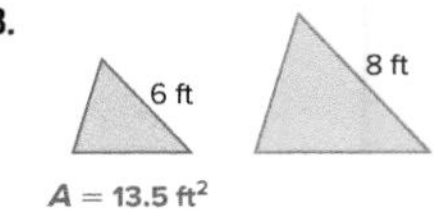

You can use the areas of similar figures to find the scale factor between them or a missing measure.

G.GMD.1

Example 2 Use Areas of Similar Figures

The area of ▱$ABCD$ is 150 square meters. The area of ▱$FGHJ$ is 54 square meters. If ▱$ABCD \sim$ ▱$FGHJ$, find the scale factor of ▱$FGHJ$ to ▱$ABCD$ and the value of x.

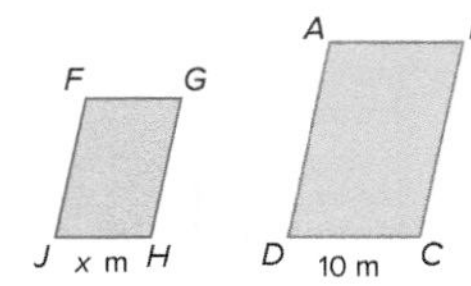

Let k be the scale factor between ▱$FGHJ$ and ▱$ABCD$.

$\frac{\text{area of ▱}FGHJ}{\text{area of ▱}ABCD} = k^2$ Theorem 10.1

$\frac{54}{150} = k^2$ Substitution

$\frac{9}{25} = k^2$ Simplify.

$\frac{3}{5} = k$ Take the positive square root of each side.

So the scale factor of ▱$FGHJ$ to ▱$ABCD$ is $\frac{3}{5}$. Use this scale factor to find the value of x.

$\frac{JH}{DC} = k$ The ratio of corresponding lengths of similar polygons is equal to the scale factor between the polygons.

$\frac{x}{10} = \frac{3}{5}$ Substitution

$x = \frac{3}{5} \cdot 10$ or 6 Multiply each side by 10.

CHECK Confirm that $\frac{JH}{DC}$ is equal to the scale factor.

$\frac{JH}{DC} = \frac{6}{10} = \frac{3}{5}$ ✓

Watch Out!

Writing Ratios When finding the ratio of the area of Figure *A* to the area of Figure *B*, be sure to write your ratio as $\frac{\text{area of figure } A}{\text{area of figure } B}$.

Reading Math

Ratios Ratios can be written in different ways. For example, x to y, $x:y$, and $\frac{x}{y}$ are all representations of the ratio of x and y.

Guided Practice

For each pair of similar figures, use the given areas to find the scale factor of the blue to the green figure. Then find x.

2A. $\frac{5}{6}$; 5

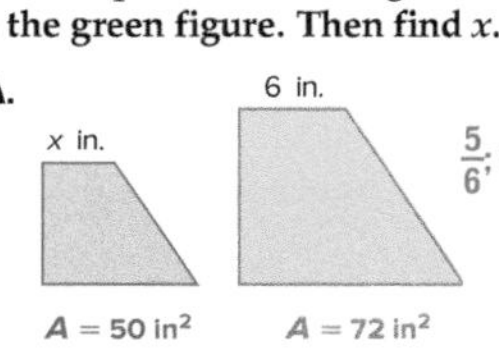

2B. $\frac{5}{2}$ or 2.5; 16

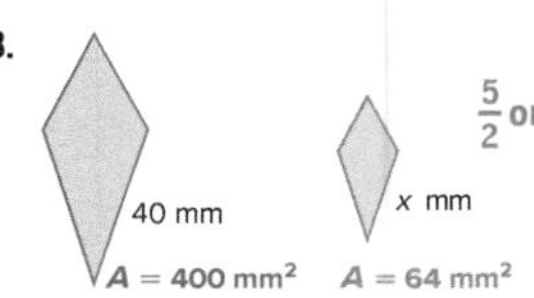

Go Online!

The most up-to-date resources available for your program can be found at connectED.mcgraw-hill.com.

2 Dimensional Changes

When the dimensions of a figure are changed proportionally, the new figure is similar to the original figure. Changing the dimensions nonproportionally does not result in similar figures.

G.GMD.1, G.MG.1

Real-World Example 3 Changing Dimensions

GARDENING Orlando and Mia each have 12-feet by 15-feet rectangular gardens which they plan to expand. Orlando's new garden will measure 18 feet by 22.5 feet while Mia's new garden will measure 18 feet by 18.75 feet. Describe how the changes in dimensions affect the areas of each garden.

Draw a diagram and label the measurements.

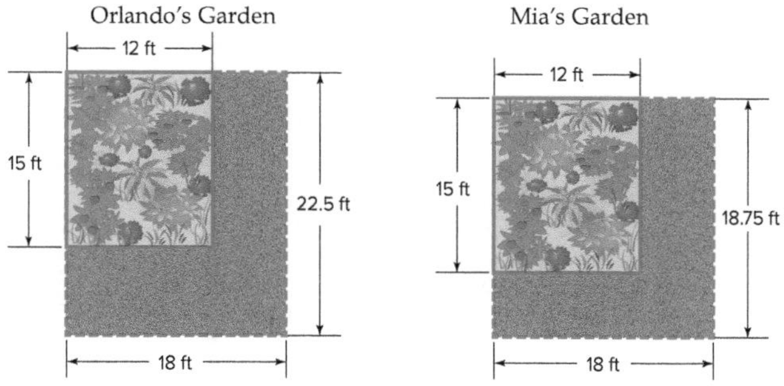

Next, compare the new dimensions to the original dimensions to determine whether the increases are proportional or nonproportional.

Orlando's Garden		Mia's Garden
$\frac{18\text{ ft}}{12\text{ ft}} = \frac{3}{2}$	$\frac{\text{new width}}{\text{original width}}$	$\frac{18\text{ ft}}{12\text{ ft}} = \frac{3}{2}$
$\frac{22.5\text{ ft}}{15\text{ ft}} = \frac{3}{2}$	$\frac{\text{new length}}{\text{original length}}$	$\frac{18.75\text{ ft}}{15\text{ ft}} = \frac{5}{4}$

Because each dimension of Orlando's garden increased by the same scale factor, this is a proportional dimension change. So the original garden and new garden are similar figures. By Theorem 10.1, the ratio of the areas is the square of the scale factor.

$$\frac{\text{new area}}{\text{original area}} = \frac{(18)(22.5)}{(12)(15)} = \frac{405}{180} = \frac{9}{4} = \left(\frac{3}{2}\right)^2$$

Because different scale factors were used for each dimension, Mia's garden is not changing proportionally. Compute the ratio of the new area to the original using the scale factors applied to each dimension.

$$\frac{\text{new area}}{\text{original area}} = \frac{(12 \cdot 1.5)(15 \cdot 1.25)}{(12)(15)} = 1.5 \cdot 1.25 \text{ or } 1.875$$

Notice that the ratio of the new area to the original area is the product of the scale factors used to enlarge the dimensions.

Orlando's garden is increasing proportionally so the ratio of the new area to the original area is the square of the scale factor. Mia's garden is not increasing proportionally. The ratio of the new area to the original area is the product of the scale factors.

Reading Math

Similar Circles Since all circles have the same shape, all circles are similar. Therefore, the areas of two circles are also related by the square of the scale factor between them.

Guided Practice

3. **CRAFTS** Miyoki is crocheting two circles. If the diameter of the smaller circle is about 8 centimeters and the diameter of the larger circle is about 12.6 centimeters, describe how the difference in dimensions affects the areas of the circles.
The area of the larger circle is about 2.5 times larger than the area of the smaller circle.

2 Dimensional Changes

Example 3 Changing Dimensions

AL What does it mean to increase the dimensions of the garden proportionally? Sample answer: the length and width increase by the same scale factor.

OL Suppose Mia decides to double the length of her garden and keep the width the same. How does this change in dimension affect the area of the garden? The area of the new garden would be double the original area.

BL Describe how the changes in dimensions affect the perimeters of each garden. Does the perimeter change at the same scale factor as the area? The area does not change with the same scale factor as the perimeter. Orlando's perimeter scale factor is 1.5, but his area scale factor is 2.25. Mia's ratios are also not the same.

Need Another Example?

Crafts Jonathon has a banner that measures 1.5 feet by 6 feet. He makes two additional banners that measure 3 feet by 12 feet and 3 feet by 10 feet, respectively. Describe how the difference in dimensions affects the areas of the banners. The dimensions of the first banner increase proportionally by a scale factor of 2, so the area of the first banner is 4 times the area of the original banner. On the second banner, the width doubles and the length increases by a factor of about 1.67 so it is a nonproportional change. The area of the second banner increases by the product of the scale factors of each dimension, so the area is 3.34 times greater than the area of the original.

Differentiated Instruction AL OL BL

Logical Learners Have students write a proof of Theorem 10.1 for a rectangle. The area of rectangle $ABCD = AB \cdot BC$ and the area of a similar rectangle $EFGH = EF \cdot FG$. The ratio of the areas is $\frac{\text{area of rectangle } ABCD}{\text{area of rectangle } EFGH} = \frac{AB \cdot BC}{EF \cdot FG} = \left(\frac{AB}{EF}\right) \cdot \left(\frac{BC}{FG}\right)$.

The ratios of corresponding sides are equal so by substitution $\left(\frac{AB}{EF}\right) \cdot \left(\frac{BC}{FG}\right) = \left(\frac{AB}{EF}\right) \cdot \left(\frac{AB}{EF}\right) = \left(\frac{AB}{EF}\right)^2$, which is the square of the ratio of the corresponding sides.

Practice

Formative Assessment Use Exercises 1–5 to assess students' understanding of the concepts in this lesson.

The Practice and Problem Solving exercises assess the content taught in the lesson. The Preparing for Assessment page is meant to be used as preparation for end-of-course assessments.

Extra Practice

See page R10 for extra exercises for students who are approaching level or for on-level students who need additional reinforcement.

MP Teaching the Mathematical Practices

Structure Mathematically proficient students look closely to discern a pattern or structure. They also can step back for an overview and shift perspective. In Exercises 10–13, encourage students to write a proportion relating the areas of the similar figures.

Levels of Complexity Chart

The levels of the exercises progress from 1 to 3, with Level 1 indicating the lowest level of complexity.

Exercises	6–15	16–22, 30–36	23–29
Level 3			●
Level 2		●	
Level 1	●		

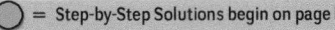

Check Your Understanding

◯ = Step-by-Step Solutions begin on page R14.

Go Online! for a Self-Check Quiz

Example 1 G.GMD.1

For each pair of similar figures, find the area of the green figure.

1. 9 yd²

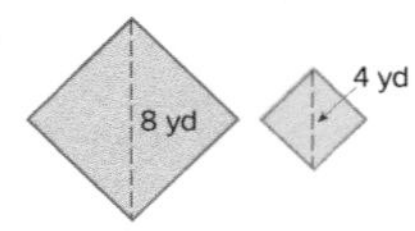

2. 78.4 m²

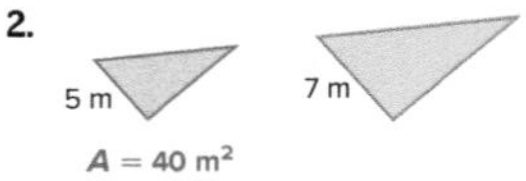

Example 2 G.GMD.1

For each pair of similar figures, use the given areas to find the scale factor from the blue to the green figure. Then find x.

3. $\frac{5}{3}$; 35

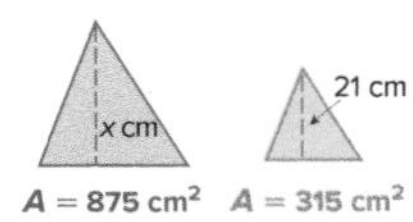

4. $\frac{3}{4}$; 20

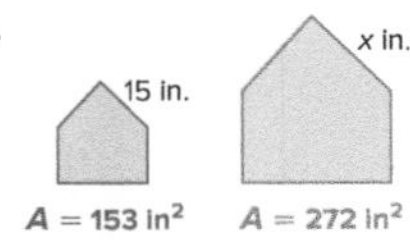

Example 3 G.GMD.1, G.MG.1

5. **MEMORIES** Zola has a picture frame that holds all of her school pictures. Each small opening is similar to the large opening in the center. If the center opening has an area of 33 square inches, what is the area of each small opening? 5.28 in²

Practice and Problem Solving

Extra Practice is on page R10.

Example 1 G.GMD.1

For each pair of similar figures, find the area of the green figure.

6. 81 mm²

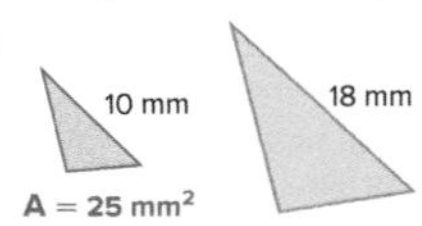

7. 240 ft²

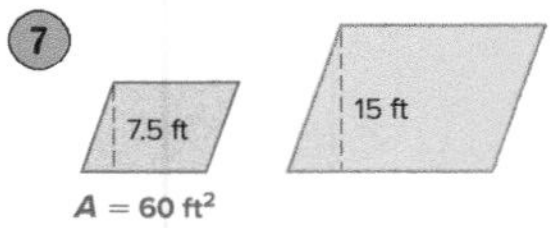

8. 151.25 in²

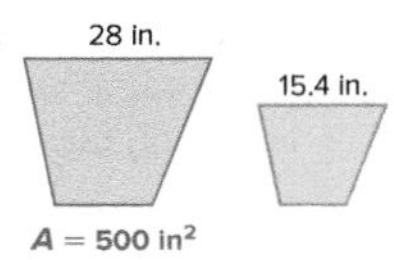

9. 672 cm²

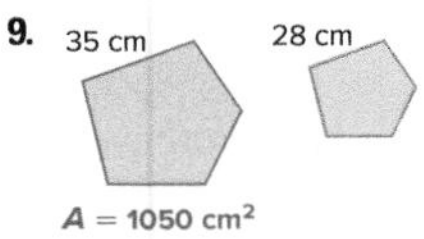

Example 2 G.GMD.1

MP STRUCTURE For each pair of similar figures, use the given areas to find the scale factor of the blue to the green figure. Then find x.

10. $\frac{6}{5}$; 10

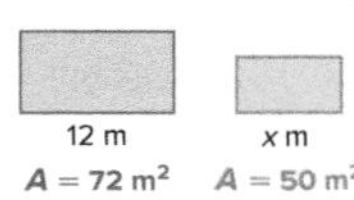

11. $\frac{4}{5}$; 17.5

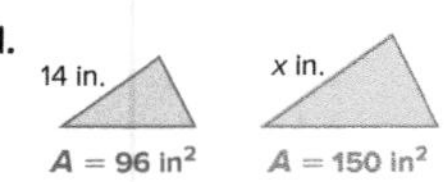

12. $\frac{3}{7}$; 6

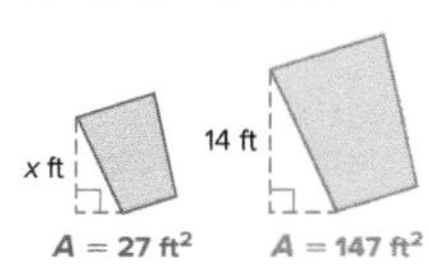

13. $\frac{3}{2}$; 36

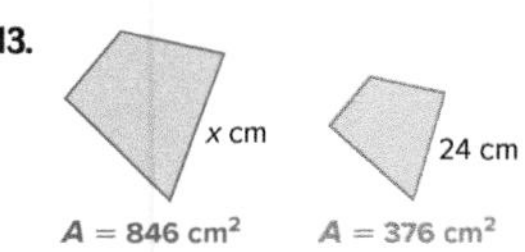

Differentiated Homework Options

Levels	AL Basic	OL Core	BL Advanced
Exercises	6–17, 25, 27–36	7–17 odd, 18, 19–23 odd, 24, 25, 27–36	23–29, (optional: 30–36)
2-Day Option	7–17 odd, 30–36	6–17	
	6–16 even, 25, 27–29	18–25, 27–36	

You can use ALEKS to provide additional remediation support with personalized instruction and practice.

Example 3
G.GMD.1,
G.MG.1

14. CRAFTS Marina crafts unique trivets and other kitchenware. Her basic trivet design is an equilateral triangle with an area of about 3.9 square inches. She plans to make trivet A by increasing each side by $\frac{4}{3}$. To make trivet B, Marina will double the length of one side while keeping the height as measured from the doubled side the same as the basic trivet. What are the approximate areas of trivets A and B? **trivet A: 6.9 in²; trivet B: 7.8 in²**

15. CHANGING DIMENSIONS A circle has a radius of 24 inches. **a–c. See margin.**

a. If the area is doubled, how does the radius change?

b. How does the radius change if the area is tripled?

c. What is the change in the radius if the area is increased by a factor of x?

16. CHANGING DIMENSIONS A polygon has an area of 144 square meters.

a. If the area is doubled, how does each side length change? **a–c. See margin.**

b. How does each side length change if the area is tripled?

c. What is the change in each side length if the area is increased by a factor of x?

17. BAKING Kaitlyn wants to use one of two regular hexagonal cake pans for a recipe she is making. The side length of the larger pan is 4.5 inches, and the area of the base of the smaller pan is 41.6 square inches.

a. What is the side length of the smaller pan? **4 in.**

b. The recipe that Kaitlyn is using calls for a circular cake pan with an 8-inch diameter. Which pan should she choose? Explain your reasoning. **See margin.**

B **18.** MP **MODELING** Federico's family is putting hardwood floors in the two geometrically similar rooms shown. If the cost of flooring is constant and the flooring for the kitchen cost \$2000, what will be the total flooring cost for the two rooms? Round to the nearest hundred dollars. **\$7600**

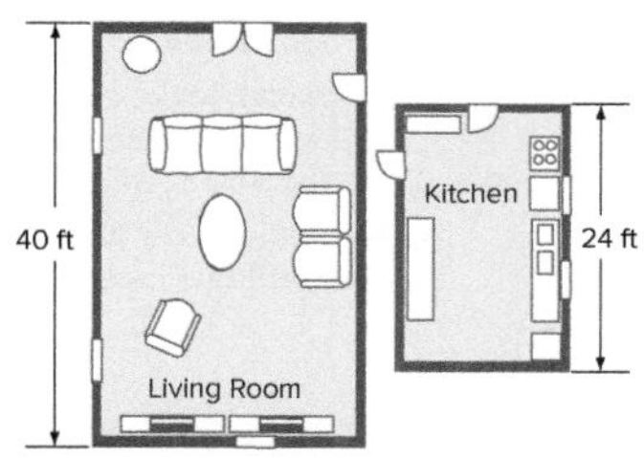

19. area of $\triangle JKL = 15$; area of $\triangle J'K'L' \approx 5.4$
20. area of $WXYZ = 30$; area of $W'X'Y'Z' \approx 53.3$

COORDINATE GEOMETRY Find the area of each figure. Use the segment length given to find the area of a similar polygon. **21.** area of $ABCD = 18$; area of $A'B'C'D' \approx 56.2$

19 $J'L' = 3$

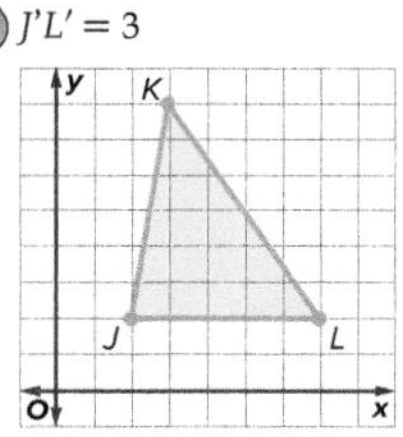

20. $W'X' = 8$

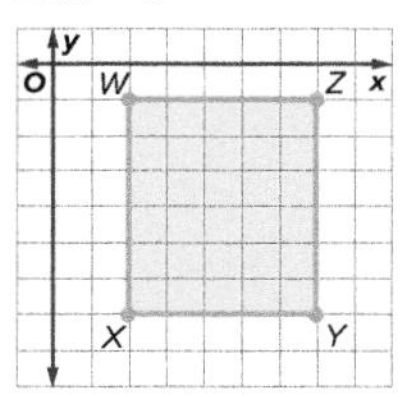

21. $B'C' = 5$

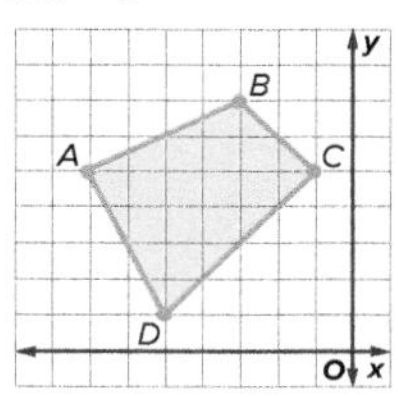

22. PROOF Write a paragraph proof. **See margin.**

Given: $\triangle ABC \sim \triangle XYZ$

Prove: $\frac{\text{area of } \triangle ABC}{\text{area of } \triangle XYZ} = \frac{a^2}{x^2}$

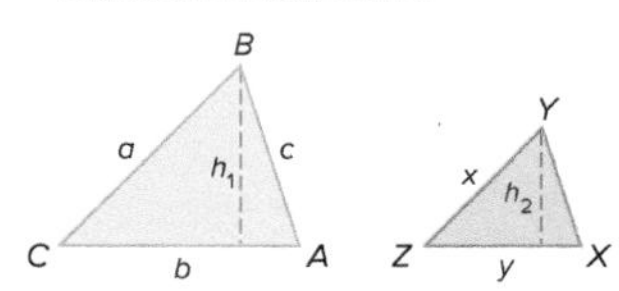

MP Teaching the Mathematical Practices

Modeling Mathematically proficient students can apply the mathematics they know to solve problems arising in everyday life. In Exercise 18, encourage students to use the information given to write a proportion.

Additional Answers

15a. If the area is doubled, the radius changes from 24 in. to 33.9 in.

15b. If the area is tripled, the radius changes from 24 in. to 41.6 in.

15c. If the area changes by a factor of x, then the radius changes from 24 in. to $24\sqrt{x}$ in.

16a. If the area is doubled, each side length will increase by a factor of $\sqrt{2}$.

16b. If the area is tripled, each side length will increase by a factor of $\sqrt{3}$.

16c. If the area changes by a factor of x, then each side length will change by a factor of $\sqrt{x}$.

17b. Larger; Sample answer: The area of a circular pie pan with an 8 in. diameter is about 50 in². The area of the larger pan is 52.6 in², and the area of the smaller pan is 41.6 in². The area of the larger pan is closer to the area of the circle, so Kaitlyn should choose the larger pan to make the recipe.

22. The area of $\triangle ABC = \frac{1}{2}b \cdot h_1$, and the area of $\triangle XYZ = \frac{1}{2}y \cdot h_2$. The ratio of the area of $\frac{\triangle ABC}{\triangle XYZ} = \frac{h_1 b}{h_2 y}$ or $\frac{h_1}{h_2} \cdot \frac{b}{y}$. The ratio of the corresponding measures are $\frac{a}{x} = \frac{b}{y} = \frac{h_1}{h_2}$. Therefore, by substitution, $\frac{\triangle ABC}{\triangle XYZ} = \left(\frac{a}{x}\right)\left(\frac{a}{x}\right)$ or $\frac{a^2}{x^2}$.

MP Standards for Mathematical Practice

Emphasis On	Exercises
1 Make sense of problems and persevere in solving them.	24, 26
2 Reason abstractly and quantitatively.	3, 4, 10–13, 16, 17, 19–21, 23, 27, 30–34
3 Construct viable arguments and critique the reasoning of others.	22
4 Model with mathematics.	5, 14, 15, 18
7 Look for and make use of structure.	1, 2, 6–9, 25, 28, 29, 30–34

Teaching the Mathematical Practices

Critique Arguments Mathematically proficient students can distinguish correct logic from flawed reasoning. In Exercise 25, students should understand that the area formula should include the square of the scale factor *k*. Neither Violeta nor Gavin is correct.

Assess

Crystal Ball Ask students how they think the volumes of similar objects are related.

Additional Answers

23a. Sample answer: The graph is misleading because the tennis balls used to illustrate the number of participants are similar circles. When the diameter of the tennis ball increases, the area of the tennis ball also increases. Because the area of the tennis ball increases at a greater rate than the diameter of the tennis ball, it looks like the number of participants in high school tennis is increasing more than it actually is.

23b. Sample answer: If you use a figure with a constant width to represent the participation in each year and only change the height, the graph would not be misleading.

24b. Sample answer: The ratio increases at a greater rate than the scale factor, so the relationship is not linear.

24c.

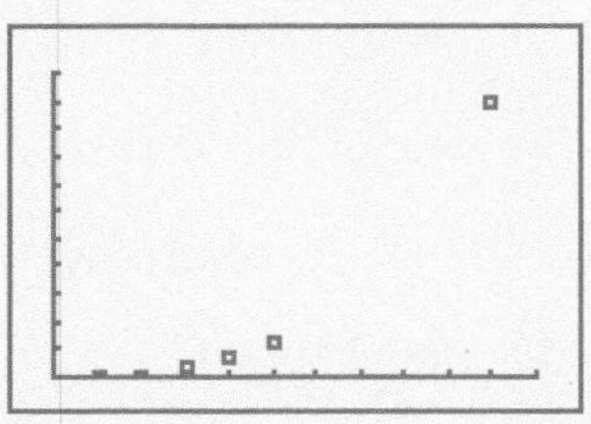

[0, 11] scl: 1 by [0, 1100] scl: 100; $y \approx x^3$

26. $\sqrt{\frac{x}{100}}$ or $\frac{1}{10}\sqrt{x}$

23. **STATISTICS** The graph shows the increase in high school tennis participation from 2000 to 2010.

a. Explain why the graph is misleading.

b. How could the graph be changed to more accurately represent the growth in high school tennis participation? **a–b. See margin.**

24. **MULTIPLE REPRESENTATIONS** In this problem, you will investigate changing dimensions proportionally in three-dimensional figures.

a. **Tabular** Copy and complete the table below for each scale factor of a rectangular prism that is 2 inches by 3 inches by 5 inches.

Scale Factor	Length (in.)	Width (in.)	Height (in.)	Volume (in³)	Ratio of Scaled Volume to Initial Volume
1	3	2	5	30	1
2	6	4	10	240	8
3	9	6	15	810	27
4	12	8	20	1920	64
5	15	10	25	3750	125
10	30	20	50	30,000	1000

b. **Verbal** Make a conjecture about the relationship between the scale factor and the ratio of the scaled volume to the initial volume. **b–c. See margin.**

c. **Graphical** Make a scatter plot of the scale factor and the ratio of the scaled volume to the initial volume using the **STAT PLOT** feature on your graphing calculator. Then use the **STAT CALC** feature to approximate the function represented by the graph.

d. **Algebraic** Write an algebraic expression for the ratio of the scaled volume to the initial volume in terms of scale factor *k*. k^3

G.GMD.1, G.MG.1

H.O.T. Problems Use Higher-Order Thinking Skills

25. **CRITIQUE ARGUMENTS** Violeta and Gavin are trying to come up with a formula that can be used to find the area of a circle with a radius *r* after it has been enlarged by a scale factor *k*. Is either of them correct? Explain your reasoning. **See Ch. 10 Answer Appendix.**

Violeta	Gavin
$A = k\pi r^2$	$A = \pi(r^2)^k$

26. **CHALLENGE** If you want the area of a polygon to be *x*% of its original area, by what scale factor should you multiply each side length? **See margin.**

27. **REASONING** A regular *n*-gon is enlarged, and the ratio of the area of the enlarged figure to the area of the original figure is *R*. Write an equation relating the perimeter of the enlarged figure to the perimeter of the original figure *Q*. $P_{enlarged} = Q\sqrt{R}$

28. **OPEN-ENDED** Draw a pair of similar figures with areas that have a ratio of 4 : 1. Explain. **28–29. See margin.**

29. **WRITING IN MATH** Explain how to find the area of an enlarged polygon if you know the area of the original polygon and the scale factor of the enlargement.

Differentiated Instruction AL OL BL ELL

Extension Have students describe the ratio between the areas of two similar composite figures. See students' work.

28.

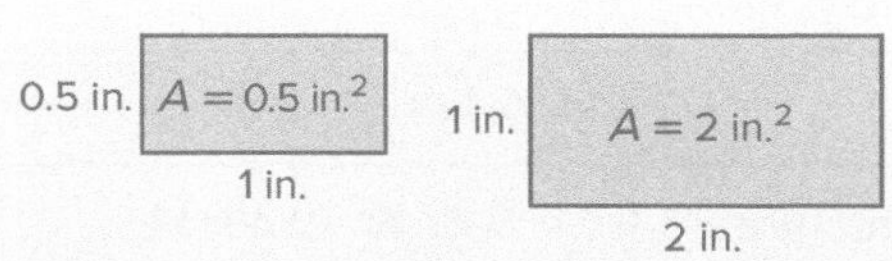

Sample answer: Because the ratio of the areas should be 4:1, the ratio of the lengths of the sides will be $\sqrt{4}:\sqrt{1}$ or 2:1. Thus a 0.5-inch by 1-inch rectangle and a 1-inch by 2-inch rectangle are similar, and the ratio of their areas is 4:1.

29. Sample answer: If you know the area of the original polygon and the scale factor of the enlargement, you can find the area of the enlarged polygon by multiplying the original area by the scale factor squared.

Go Online!

eSolutions Manual

Create worksheets, answer keys, and solutions handouts for your assignments.

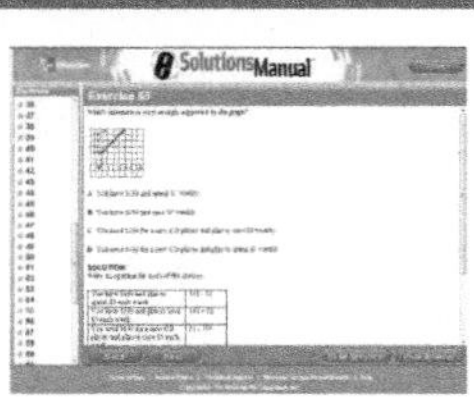

Preparing for Assessment

30. In the figure, $\triangle PQR \sim \triangle STU$. The area of $\triangle PQR$ is 50 square centimeters and the area of $\triangle STU$ is 32 square centimeters.

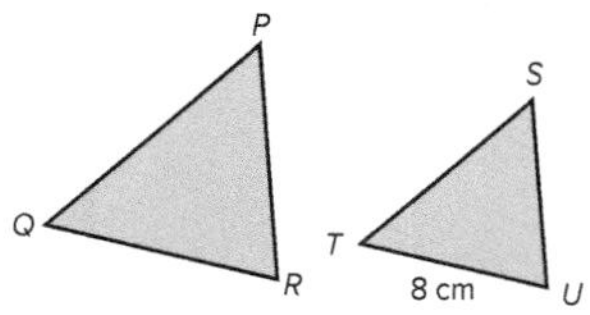

What is the length of $\overline{QR}$? MP 1 C

- A 5.12 cm
- B 6.4 cm
- C 10 cm
- D 12.5 cm
- E 26 cm

31. Connor drew the trapezoids below so that trapezoid $ABCD \sim$ trapezoid $WXYZ$. The area of trapezoid $ABCD$ is 55 square feet. MP 2

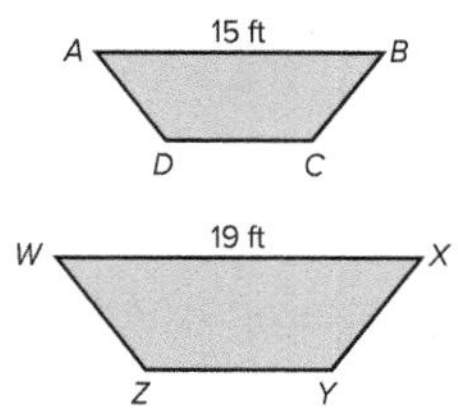

Which of the following is the best estimate of the area of trapezoid $WXYZ$? A

- A 88 ft²
- B 70 ft²
- C 43 ft²
- D 34 ft²

32. If the area of a circle of radius r is 154 cm², what is the area of a circle of radius $4r$? MP 6 2464 cm²

33. Two parallelograms are similar. Parallelogram A has an area of 48 square feet and has a base of 16 feet. Parallelogram B has an area of 27 square feet and has a base of x feet. What is the scale factor from parallelogram A to parallelogram B and was is the value of x? MP 1 Scale factor: $\frac{4}{3}$; $x = 12$

34. One right $\triangle ABC$ has an area of 36 square inches. A similar right $\triangle DEF$ has an area of 4 square inches. One leg of $\triangle ABC$ is 6 inches. Find the length of the corresponding leg of $\triangle DEF$. Explain your work. MP 2

34. The ratio of the areas of the triangles is equal to the square of the scale factor between them:

$\frac{\text{area of } \triangle DEF}{\text{area of } \triangle ABC} = k^2 = \frac{4}{36} = \frac{1}{9} \quad k = \frac{1}{3}$

The ratio of the sides is 1 to 3:

$\frac{x}{6} = \frac{1}{3} \quad x = 2 \text{ in.}$

35. **MULTI-STEP** Alisha uses geometry software to draw ▱$FGHJ$, as shown. According to the software, the area of ▱$FGHJ$ is 200 square millimeters. Alisha also uses the software to create ▱$KLMN$ so that ▱$FGHJ \sim$ ▱$KLMN$. MP 2

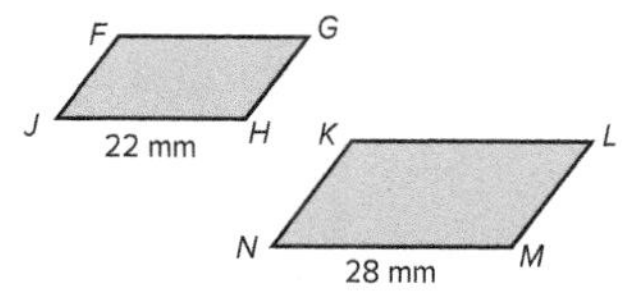

a. Write and simplify a ratio to show the scale factor between ▱$KLMN$ and ▱$FGHJ$. $\frac{14}{11}$

b. Write a proportion to show the ratio of the areas of the two parallelograms. $\frac{\text{area of } KLMN}{\text{area of } FGHJ} = \left(\frac{14}{11}\right)^2$

c. Solve the proportion to find the area of $KLMN$. Give the correct units. $\text{area of } KLMN = \frac{196}{121} \cdot 200 \approx 324$ The area of $KLMN$ is about 324 mm².

36. Triangles ABC and DEF are similar. The area of triangle ABC is 15 square inches. The height of triangle ABC is 5 inches. The height of triangle DEF is 13 inches.

a. What is the scale factor from triangle DEF to triangle ABC? MP 1 2.6

b. What is the area of triangle DEF? MP 1 C

- A 26 square inches
- B 86 square inches
- C 101 square inches
- D 106 square inches
- E 156 square inches

Differentiated Instruction OL BL

Extension In many social studies classes, students learn about distortion on different types of maps. Challenge students to determine which parts of Earth are most distorted on a globe. Ask them to develop a mathematically sound presentation demonstrating how this distortion affects the scale area of a region. What should the scale area be based on the actual area of that region and the globe's scale?

Preparing for Assessment

Exercises 30–36 require students to use the skills they will need on standardized assessments. Each exercise is dual-coded with content standards and mathematical practice standards.

Dual Coding		
Items	Content Standards	MP Mathematical Practices
30		1
31		2
32		6
33		1
34		2, 7
35		2
36		1

Diagnose Student Errors

Survey student responses for each item. Class trends may indicate common errors and misconceptions.

30.

A	Solved $\frac{x}{8} = \frac{16}{25}$
B	Solved $\frac{x}{8} = \frac{4}{5}$
C	CORRECT
D	Solved $\frac{x}{8} = \frac{25}{16}$
E	Added 18 cm to length of $\overline{TU}$

31.

A	CORRECT
B	Solved $\frac{x}{55} = \frac{19}{15}$
C	Solved $\frac{x}{55} = \frac{15}{19}$
D	Solved $\frac{x}{55} = \left(\frac{15}{19}\right)^2$

Go Online!

Quizzes

Students can use *Self-Check Quizzes* to check their understanding of this lesson and have the results sent to you. You can also give *Quiz 4*, which covers the content in Lesson 10-5.

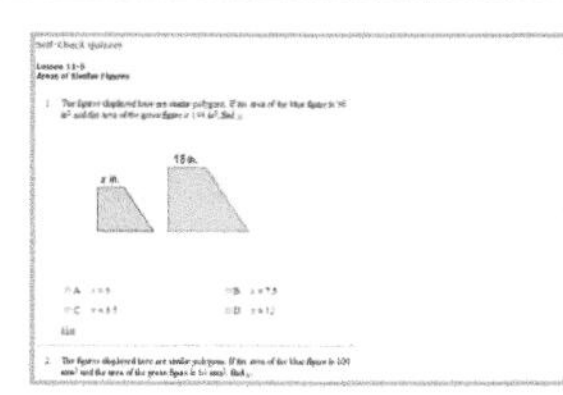

LESSON 10-6
Surface Area

SUGGESTED PACING (DAYS)

90 min.	1
45 min.	2
	Instruction

Track Your Progress

Objectives

1 Find the surface area of prisms and cylinders.

2 Find the surface area of pyramids and cones.

Mathematical Background

The surface area of a three-dimensional object is the sum of the area of all the faces and bases of the object. There are formulas available that provide shortcuts for finding the surface area of prisms, cylinders, pyramids, and cones.

Skills Trace

THEN	NOW	NEXT
G.GMD.1 Give an informal argument for the formulas for the circumference of a circle, area of a circle, volume of a cylinder, pyramid, and cone. **G.MG.1** Use geometric shapes, their measures, and their properties to describe objects (e.g., modeling a tree trunk or a human torso as a cylinder).	**G.MG.1** Use geometric shapes, their measures, and their properties to describe objects (e.g., modeling a tree trunk or a human torso as a cylinder). **G.MG.3** Apply geometric methods to solve problems (e.g., designing and object or structure to satisfy physical constrains or minimize cost; working with typographic grid systems based on ratios).	**G.GMD.4** Identify the shapes of two-dimensional cross-sections of three-dimensional objects, and identify three-dimensional objects generated by rotations of two-dimensional objects.

Go Online! All of these resources and more are available at connectED.mcgraw-hill.com

eLessons utilize the power of your interactive whiteboard in an engaging way. Use Surface Area, Screens 1–8, to introduce the concepts in this lesson.

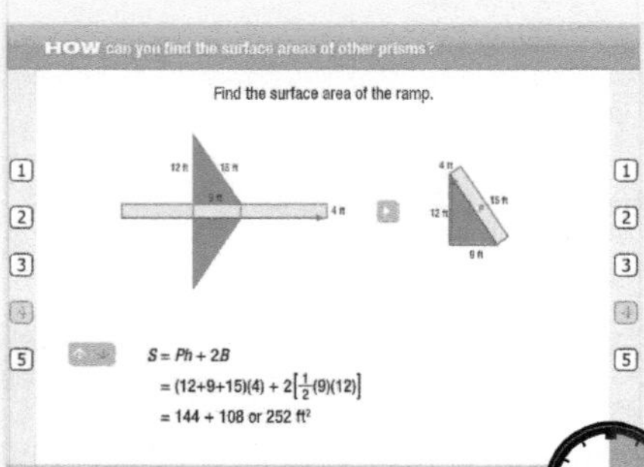

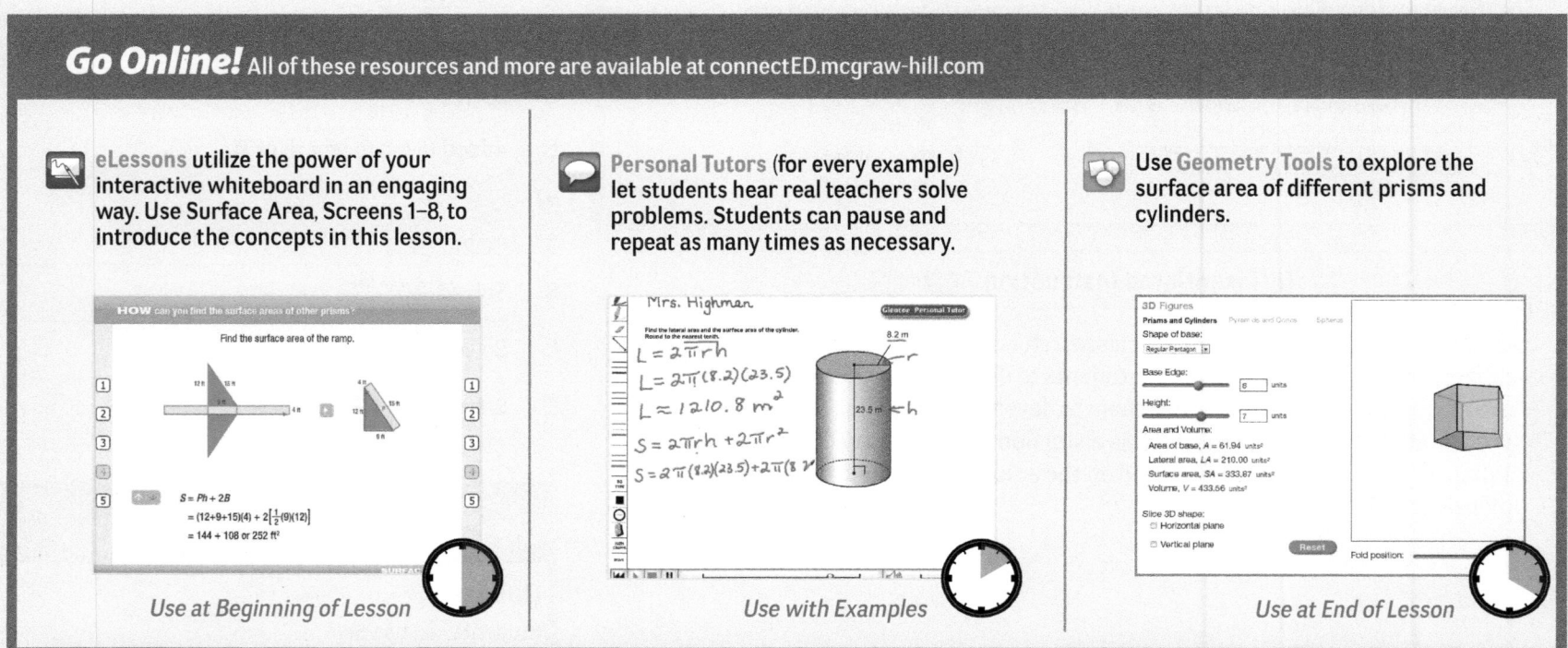

Use at Beginning of Lesson

Personal Tutors (for every example) let students hear real teachers solve problems. Students can pause and repeat as many times as necessary.

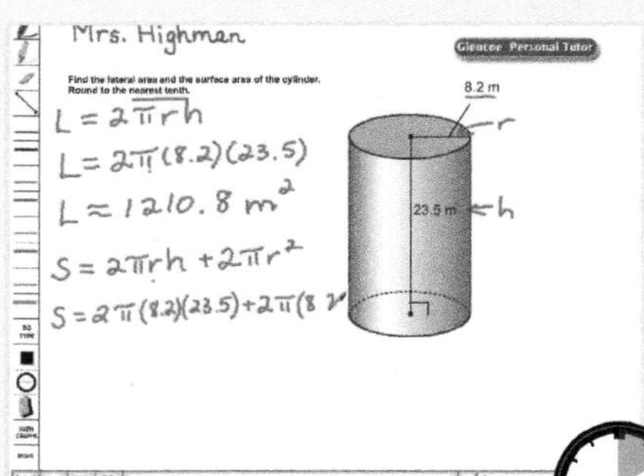

Use with Examples

Use **Geometry Tools** to explore the surface area of different prisms and cylinders.

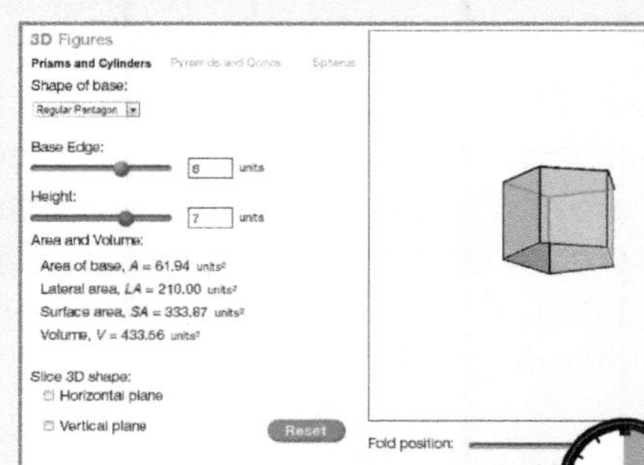

Use at End of Lesson

OER Using Open Educational Resources

Professional Development Use the *Surface Area of Prisms* lesson from **Interactivate** to help create an instructional plan for this topic. **Interactivate** provides a lesson outline with suggestions for discussions, applets, and independent practice. **Interactivate** also provides alternative outlines for schools with limited computer access. *Use as professional development*

Go Online!
connectED.mcgraw-hill.com

Worksheets

Differentiate Your Resources

Extra Practice Additional practice or homework; Skills Practice is best for approaching-level students and Practice is best for on-level and beyond-level students

Skills Practice

AL OL ELL

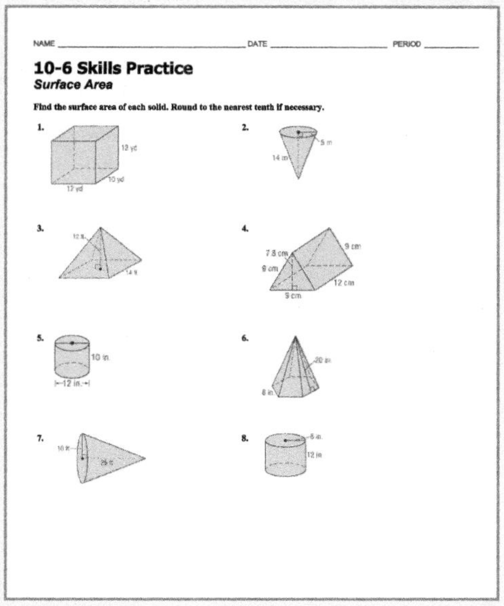

10-6 Skills Practice
Surface Area
Find the surface area of each solid. Round to the nearest tenth if necessary.

Practice

AL OL BL ELL

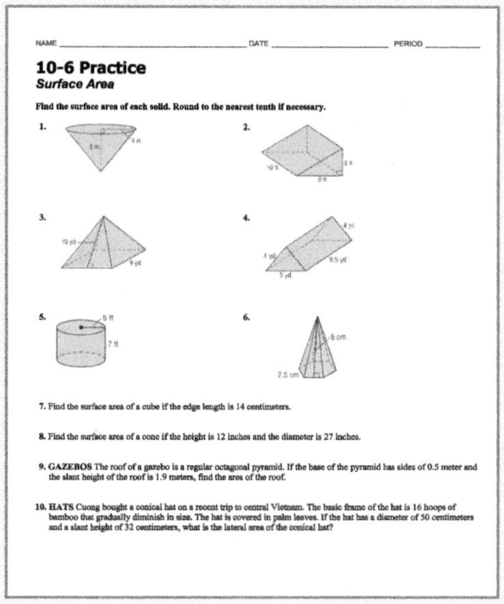

10-6 Practice
Surface Area
Find the surface area of each solid. Round to the nearest tenth if necessary.

Word Problem Practice

AL OL BL ELL

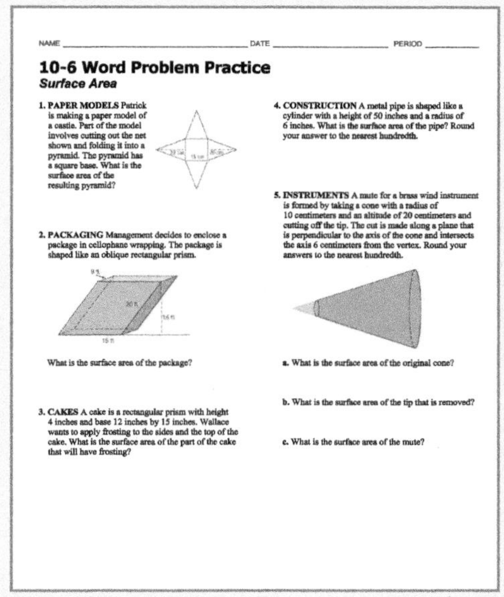

10-6 Word Problem Practice
Surface Area

Intervention Reteaching and vocabulary activities that can be used with struggling or absent students and as ELL support

Study Guide and Intervention

AL OL ELL

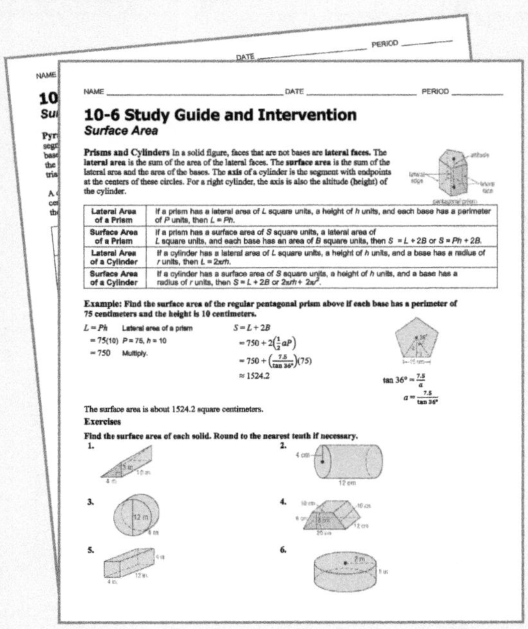

10-6 Study Guide and Intervention
Surface Area

Study Notebook

AL OL BL ELL

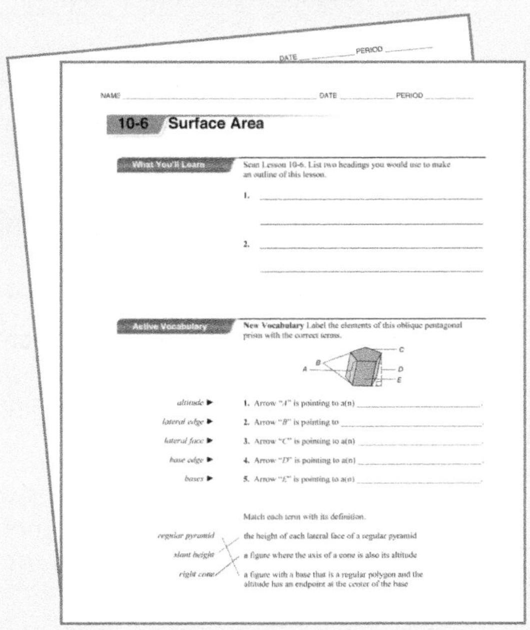

10-6 Surface Area

Extension Activities that can be used to extend lesson concepts

Enrichment

OL BL ELL

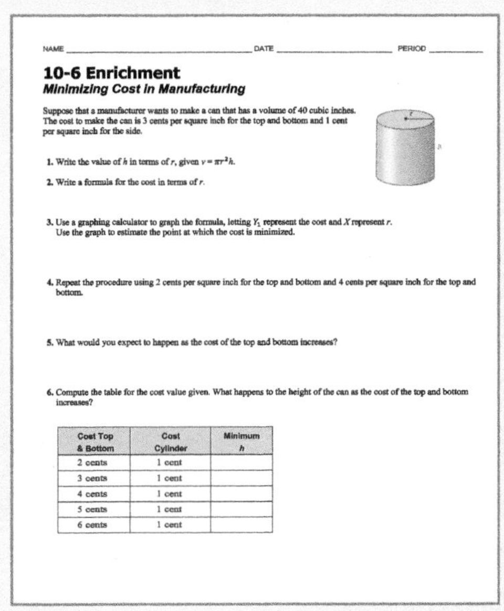

10-6 Enrichment
Minimizing Cost in Manufacturing

Launch

Have students read the Why? section of the lesson. Ask:

- What is the shape of the fish tank shown? cylinder
- How can you determine how much material is needed to make the fish tank? Find the total area of all of the outside surfaces.
- If you are given the area and length of material that covers the circular surface, how can you find the width? Divide the area by the length.

LESSON 6

Surface Area

Then

- Find the perimeters and areas of similar figures by using scale factors.

Now

1. Find surface areas of prisms and cylinders.
2. Find surface areas of pyramids and cones.

Why?

- There are many styles of fish tanks that are cylinders and prisms. The style of tank like the one on the right allows people to walk around the tank to find the best view as they observe the fish.

New Vocabulary

lateral face
lateral edge
base edge
altitude
height
lateral area
axis
regular pyramid
slant height
composite solid

Mathematical Practices

1 Make sense of problems and preserve in solving them.
2 Reason abstractly and quantitatively.
6 Attend to precision.

Content Standards
G.MG.1 Use geometric shapes, their measures, and their properties to describe objects (e.g., modeling a tree trunk or a human torso as a cylinder).
G.MG.3 Apply geometric methods to solve problems (e.g., designing and object or structure to satisfy physical constrains or minimize cost; working with typographic grid systems based on ratios).

1 Prisms and Cylinders

In a solid figure, faces that are not bases are called **lateral faces**. Lateral faces intersect each other at the **lateral edges**, which are parallel and congruent. The lateral faces intersect the base at the **base edges**. The **altitude** is a perpendicular segment that joins the planes of the bases. The **height** is the length of the altitude.

Recall that a prism is a polyhedron with two parallel congruent bases. In a right prism, the lateral edges are altitudes and the lateral faces are rectangles. In an oblique prism, the lateral edges are not perpendicular to the bases. At least one lateral face is not a rectangle.

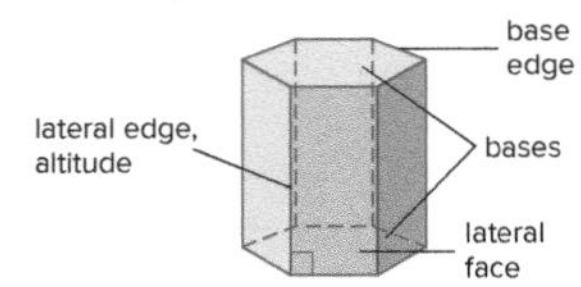

Right Prism

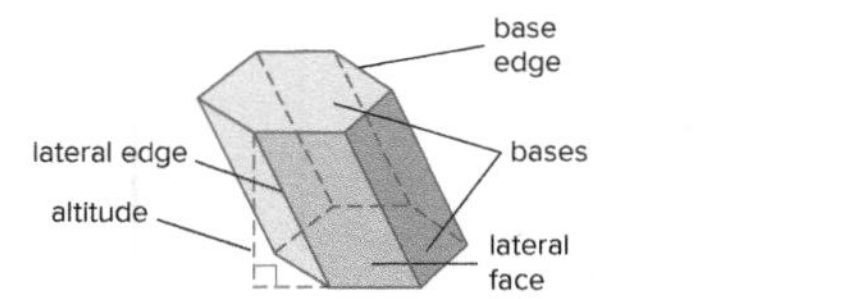

Oblique Prism

The **lateral area** L of a prism is the sum of the areas of the lateral faces. The net at the right shows how to find the lateral area of a prism.

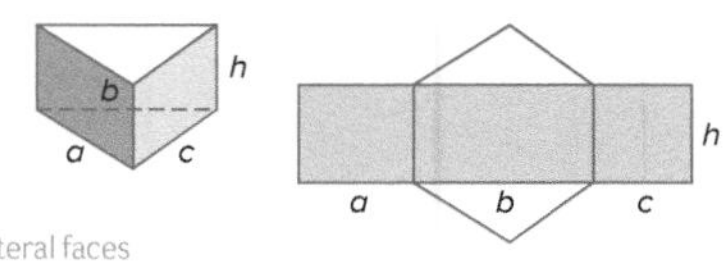

$L = a(h) + b(h) + c(h)$ Sum of the areas of the lateral faces
$= (a + b + c)(h)$ Distributive Property
$= Ph$ $P = a + b + c$

The surface area of a prism is the sum of the lateral area and the areas of the bases.

Key Concepts Lateral and Surface Area of a Prism

Words: The lateral area L of a right prism is the product of the perimeter of the base P and the height of the prism h.	**Words:** The surface area S of a right prism is the sum of the lateral area and twice the area of a base B.
Symbols: $L = Ph$	**Symbols:** $S = L + 2B$ or $S = Ph + 2B$

From this point on, you can assume that solids in the text are right solids. If a solid is oblique, it will be clearly stated.

Vicnt/iStock/Getty Images

Mathematical Practices Strategies

Attend to precision.
Help students attend to precision when finding the surface area. Ask:

- What type of units are used to express surface area? square units or units^2
- Why is the shape of the base important to know when finding the surface area of a prism or cylinder? The shape of the base is needed to find the area(s) of the base(s); the shape of the base also indicates how to find the lateral area of the three-dimensional object.
- Why is it important not to round answers until the end of the problem? Sample answer: This provides the most accurate final result.

Go Online!

Interactive Whiteboard
Use the *eLesson, Lesson Presentation,* or *Interactive Classroom* to present this lesson.

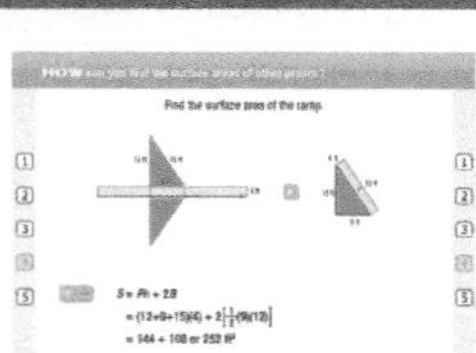

WatchOut!

Right Prisms The bases of a right prism are congruent, but the lateral faces are not always congruent.

Example 1 Surface Area of a Prism

Find the surface area of the prism. Round to the nearest tenth.

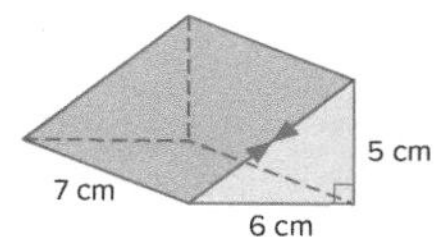

Step 1 Find the missing side length of the base.

$c^2 = 6^2 + 5^2$ Pythagorean Theorem

$c^2 = 61$ Simplify.

$c \approx 7.8$ Take the positive square root of each side.

Step 2 Find the surface area.

$S = Ph + 2B$ Surface area of a prism

$\approx (5 + 6 + 7.8)(7) + 2\left(\frac{1}{2}\right)(5)(6)$ Substitution

≈ 161.6 Simplify.

The surface area of the prism is approximately 161.6 square centimeters.

Guided Practice

Find the surface area of each prism.

1A. A rectangular prism has a base with dimensions of 9 feet by 4 feet and a height of 6 feet. 228 ft^2

1B. A regular hexagonal prism with side length of 5 centimeters for the base and a height of 12 centimeters. $\approx$490 cm^2

Real-World Example 2 Lateral Area of a Prism G.MG.3

PACKAGING **The Marketing Department of a shoe manufacturer is designing what will be printed on the boxes. Each box is a rectangular prism with a base measuring 6 inches by 14 inches and a height of 5 inches. What is the surface area of the shoebox available for printing?**

$L = Ph + 2B$ Surface area of a prism

$= (2(6) + 2(14))(5) + 2(6)(14)$ Substitution

$= 368$ Simplify.

The surface area of the shoebox is 368 square inches.

Guided Practice

2. FOOD A piece of cheese in the shape of a triangular prism is shrink wrapped for sale. The base is a right triangle with legs 3 centimeters and 4 centimeters. The height of the piece is 4 centimeters. **What is the surface area of the shrink wrap? 60 cm^2**

The **axis** of a cylinder is the segment with endpoints that are centers of the circular bases. If the axis is also an altitude, then the cylinder is a right cylinder. If not then the cylinder is oblique.

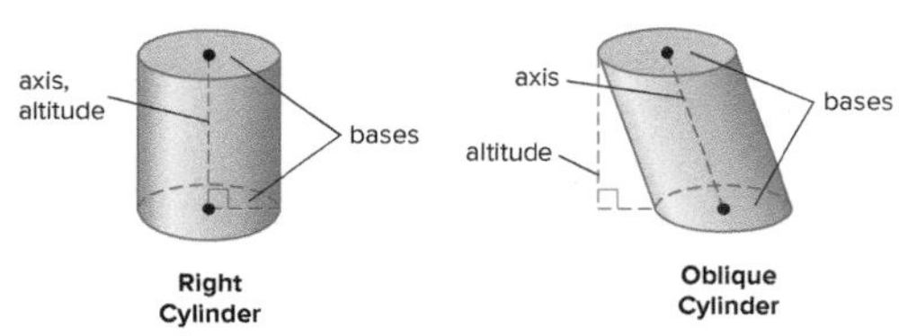

Teaching Tip

Reasoning Ask students if they can derive an alternative formula for the surface area of a right rectangular prism. Have students write their derivations on the board, or show students that an alternative formula is $L = 2\ell w + 2\ell h + 2wh$.

Teach

Ask the scaffolded questions for each example to build conceptual understanding for students at all levels.

1 Prisms and Cylinders

Example 1 Surface Area of a Prism

AL Is there another way to find the surface area if you cannot remember the formulas? Yes; Sample answer: I can find the area of each face and add them together.

OL If the height of the prism is decreased to 5, what is the surface area of the prism? 124 cm^2

BL If each given dimension is increased by 1 centimeter, what is the surface area of the prism? 219.6 cm^2

Need Another Example?

Find the surface area of the rectangular prism. 360 cm^2

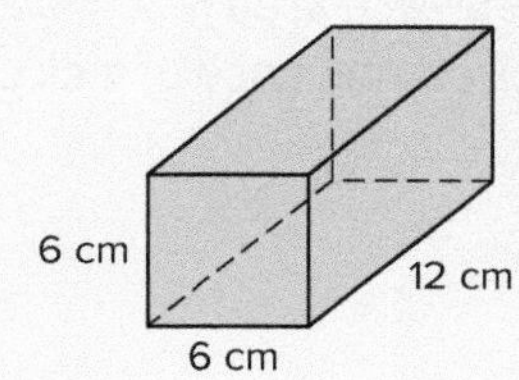

Example 2 Lateral Area of a Prism

AL What is another way to find the surface area of the box? Sample answer: Find the area of each face and add the results.

OL How do you find the perimeter of the base? $2\ell + 2w$ or add all side lengths together. How do you find the area of the base? Multiply the length and width, ℓw.

BL Can different values be used for the base? Explain. Sample answer: Yes, 5 inches and 6 inches can be used for the dimensions of the base and the height of the prism would be 14 inches. The result is still the same surface area.

Need Another Example?

A tube is in the shape of a regular pentagonal prism with side length of 5 millimeters and base area about 43 square millimeters. If the height of the tube is 20 millimeters, what is the surface area of the prism? 586 mm^2

Example 3 Surface Area of a Cylinder

AL What is the shape of the lateral surface of a cylinder? a rectangle

OL If the diameter of the cylinder is 20 millimeters, what is the new surface area? about 1758.4 mm^2

BL If the diameter of the cylinder is changed and the new lateral area is 424 square millimeters, what is the new diameter? about 7.5 mm

Need Another Example?

Find the surface area of the cylinder. Round to the nearest tenth. 2813.4 ft^2

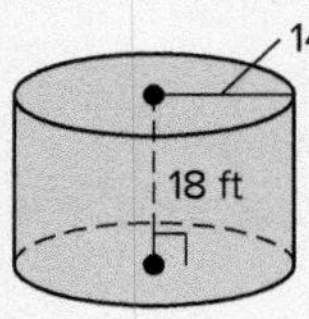

Teaching Tip

Use Multiple Representations An alternative formula for the surface area is $S = \pi dh + 2\pi r^2$ with πd as the circumference of a circle.

The lateral area of a right cylinder is the area of the curved surface. Like a right prism, the lateral area L equals Ph. Because the base is a circle, the perimeter is the circumference of the circle C.

So, the lateral area is $Ch = 2\pi rh$.

The surface area is the sum of the lateral area and the areas of the bases.

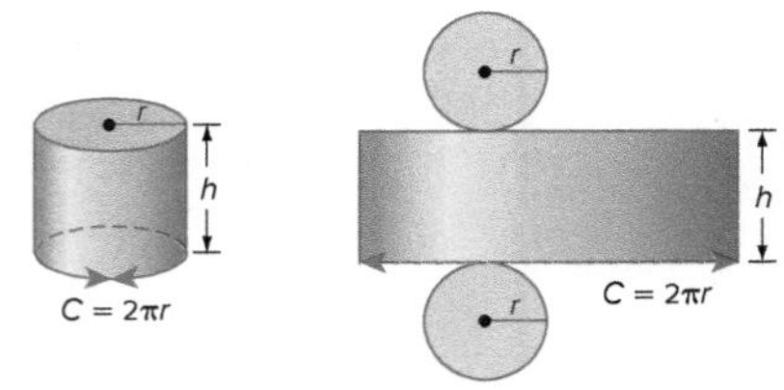

StudyTip
Formulas The formula for the surface area, $S = L + 2B$, is the same for a right prism and a right cylinder.

Key Concepts Lateral and Surface Area of a Cylinder

Words: The lateral area L of a right cylinder with radius r is the product of the circumference of the base C and the height h of the cylinder.	**Words:** The surface area S of a right cylinder is the sum of the lateral area and twice the area of a base B.
Symbols: $L = Ch$ or $L = 2\pi rh$.	**Symbols:** $S = L + 2B$, $S = Ch + 2B$, or $S = 2\pi rh + 2\pi r^2$.

StudyTip
Estimation Before finding the lateral area of a cylinder, use mental math to estimate. To estimate, multiply the diameter by 3 (to approximate π) and then by the height of the cylinder.

Example 3 Surface Area of a Cylinder

Find the surface area of the cylinder. Round to the nearest tenth.

$S = 2\pi rh + 2\pi r^2$ — Surface area of a cylinder

$= 2\pi(7.5)(18) + 2\pi(7.5)^2$ — Replace r with 7.5 and h with 18.

≈ 1201.6 — Simplify.

The surface area of the cylinder is about 1201.7 square millimeters.

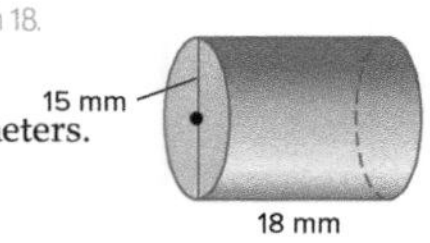

Guided Practice

3A. The radius is 5 inches and the height is 9 inches. ≈ 439.8 $in.^2$

3B. The diameter is 6 centimeters and the height is 4.8 centimeters. ≈ 147.0 cm^2

You can use surface area formulas to solve real-world problems.

G.MG.1

Real World Example 4 Use the Lateral Area of a Cylinder

CRAFTS Sheree used the rectangular piece of felt shown at the right to cover the curved surface of her cylindrical pencil holder. The circumference corresponds to the side measuring 12.6 inches. What is the surface area of the entire pencil holder to the nearest tenth?

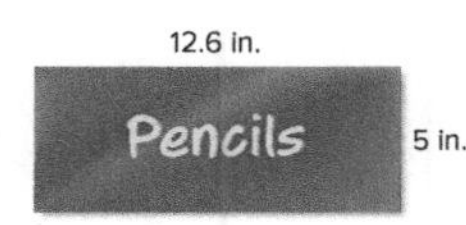

Step 1 Find the radius.

$C = 2\pi r$ — Circumference of a circle

$12.6 = 2\pi r$ — Replace C with 12.6.

$4.013 \approx 2r$ — Divide both sides by π.

$2.0 \approx r$ — Divide both sides by 2.

The radius of the pencil holder is about 2 inches.

Differentiated Instruction OL BL

Logical Learners Show students that the formula for the surface area of a cylinder is the lateral surface area plus the area of each circle at the ends of the cylinder.

Step 2 Find the surface area.

$S = L + 2B$ — Surface area of a cylinder

$\approx 12.6 \cdot 5 + 2\pi(2.0)^2$ — Replace L with $12.6 \cdot 5$ and r with 2.0.

≈ 88.1 — Simplify.

The surface area of the pencil holder is about 88.1 square inches.

Guided Practice

9. **MANUFACTURING** A cylindrical juice can has a rectangular label with a length of 20 centimeters, which corresponds to the circumference, and height of 8 centimeters. What is the surface area of material needed to manufacture the can? 224.3 cm^2

2 Pyramids and Cones

The *lateral faces* of a pyramid intersect at a common point called a *vertex*. Two lateral faces intersect at a *lateral edge*. A lateral face and the base intersect at a *base edge*. The *altitude* is the segment from the vertex perpendicular to the base.

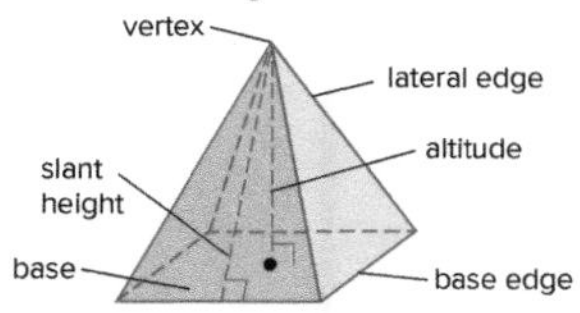

Regular Pyramid

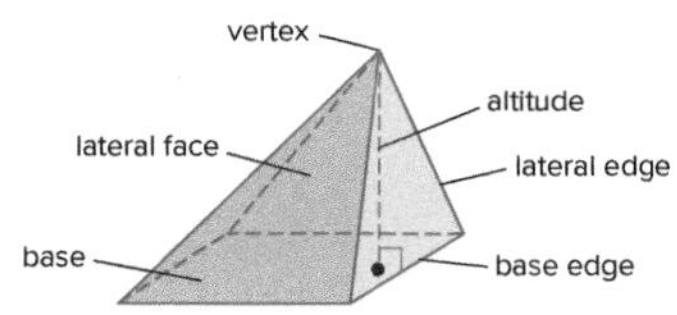

Nonregular Pyramid

A **regular pyramid** has a base that is a regular polygon and the altitude has an endpoint at the center of the base. All the lateral edges are congruent and all the lateral faces are congruent isosceles triangles. The height of each lateral face is called the **slant height** ℓ of the pyramid.

The lateral area L of a regular pentagonal pyramid is the sum of the areas of the lateral faces, all of which are congruent triangles, as shown in the net at the right.

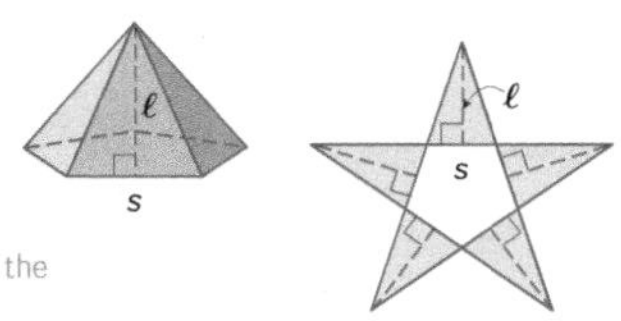

$L = \frac{1}{2}s\ell + \frac{1}{2}s\ell + \frac{1}{2}s\ell + \frac{1}{2}s\ell + \frac{1}{2}s\ell$ — Sum of the areas of the lateral faces

$= \frac{1}{2}\ell(s + s + s + s + s)$ — Distributive Property

$= \frac{1}{2}P\ell$ — $P = s + s + s + s + s$

The surface area of a pyramid is the sum of the lateral area and the area of the base.

StudyTip

Making Connections The surface area of a pyramid equals $L + B$, not $L + 2B$, because a pyramid has only one base.

Key Concepts Lateral and Surface Area Formulas for a Pyramid

Words: The lateral area L of a regular pyramid is the product of one half the perimeter P of the base and the slant height ℓ.	**Words:** The surface area S of a right pyramid is the sum of the lateral area and twice the area of a base B.
Symbols: $L = \frac{1}{2}P\ell$	**Symbols:** $S = L + B$, or $S = \frac{1}{2}P\ell + B$

Example 4 Use the Lateral Area of a Cylinder

AL What is the circumference of the circular base of the pencil holder? 12.6 in.

OL When finding the surface area, why is L replaced by $12.6 \cdot 5$? 12.6 in. corresponds to the circumference of the pencil sharpener and 5 in. is the height. So $12.6 \cdot 5$ is the lateral area.

BL If the lateral area of a cylindrical postal mailer is 302 square inches, and the diameter of the mailer is 4 inches, what is the height? about 24 in.

Need Another Example?

An oatmeal cylindrical canister has a height of 12 inches and a diameter of 8 inches. What is the surface area of the entire canister to the nearest tenth? 402.1 in^2

Watch Out!

Common Misconceptions A common error is to assume that the formulas in this lesson apply to any pyramid. Point out that these formulas apply only to *regular* pyramids. The surface area on a nonregular pyramid would require finding the areas of triangles that are not congruent.

2 Pyramids and Cones

Example 5 Surface Area of a Pyramid

AL If you decide to find the surface area of this pyramid by adding the surface area of all of the faces, how many triangular faces should you include? 6

OL If the slant height of the pyramid is increased to 11 centimeters, what is the surface area? about 229.5 cm^2

BL If the side length is decreased to 3.5 centimeters and the slant height remains unchanged, what is the new surface area? about 115.8 cm^2

Need Another Example?
Find the surface area of a regular hexagonal pyramid with base edge 10.4 centimeters and a slant height of 15 centimeters. Round to the nearest tenth. 749.0 cm^2

Example 6 Use the Surface Area of a Pyramid

AL If you decide to find the surface area of this pyramid by adding the surface area of all of the faces, how many triangular faces should you include? 4 What shape is the other face? a square

OL What is the area to be painted if the base is not painted? 240 in^2

BL If the base edge is increased by 6 inches and the slant height remains unchanged, what is the new surface area? 684 in^2

Need Another Example?
A terrarium shaped like a square pyramid has a height of 10 inches and a base edge of 10 inches. What is the surface area of the glass needed to make the terrarium? Round to the nearest tenth. 323.6 in^2

Example 5 Surface Area of a Regular Pyramid

Find the surface area of the regular pyramid. Round to the nearest tenth.

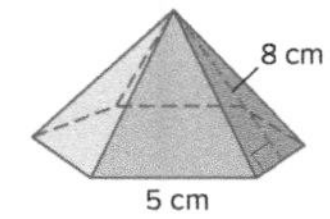

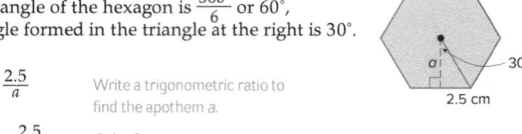

Step 1 Find the perimeter of the base.
$P = 6 \cdot 5$ or 30 centimeters

Step 2 Find the length of the apothem and the area of the base.

A central angle of the hexagon is $\frac{360°}{6}$ or 60°, so the angle formed in the triangle at the right is 30°.

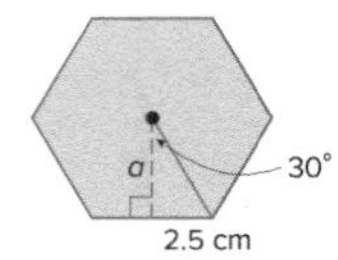

$\tan 30° = \frac{2.5}{a}$ — Write a trigonometric ratio to find the apothem *a*.

$a = \frac{2.5}{\tan 30°}$ — Solve for *a*.

≈ 4.3 — Use a calculator.

$A = \frac{1}{2}Pa$ — Area of a regular polygon

$\approx \frac{1}{2}(30)(4.3)$ — Replace *P* with 30 and *a* with 4.3.

≈ 64.5 — Multiply.

So, the area of the base *B* is about 64.5 square centimeters.

ReviewVocabulary
Trigonometric Ratios
$\sin A = \frac{opp}{hyp}$
$\cos A = \frac{adj}{hyp}$
$\tan A = \frac{opp}{adj}$

Step 3 Find the surface area of the pyramid.

$S = \frac{1}{2}P\ell + B$ — Surface area of a regular pyramid

$= \frac{1}{2}(30)(8) + 64.5$ — Substitute.

≈ 184.5 — Simplify.

The surface area of the pyramid is about 184.5 square centimeters.

Guided Practice 5A. 87.6 ft^2 5B. 554.1 cm^2

Find the surface area of each pyramid. Round to the nearest tenth.

5A. an equilateral triangular pyramid with base edge 6 feet and a slant height of 8 feet

5B. a square pyramid with a base edge of 12 cm and a height of 16 cm

G.MG.1

Real-World Example 6 Use the Surface Area of a Pyramid

MODELS **Alison plans to paint a model of the Great Pyramid. What is the surface area if the model is a square pyramid with slant height of 10 inches and a base edge of 12 inches?**

$S = \frac{1}{2}P\ell + B$ — Surface area of a regular pyramid

$= \frac{1}{2}(48)10 + 144$ — Replace *P* with 48, ℓ with 10, and *B* with 144.

$= 384$ — Simplify.

The surface area of the pyramid is 384 square inches.

Guided Practice

6. The height of another square pyramid model is 7 centimeters, and the base edge is 8 centimeters. What is the surface area of this model? 193 cm^2

Differentiated Instruction AL OL

Logical Learners Ask students to name a similarity and a difference between finding the surface area of a pyramid and a surface area of a prism.
The similarity is that both formulas use the perimeter of the base. The differences are the prism uses the height and the pyramid uses one half of the perimeter and the slant height. Another difference is the prism has the area of 2 bases and the pyramid has the area of 1 base.

Recall that a cone has a circular base and a vertex. The axis of a cone is the segment with endpoints at the vertex and the center of the base. If the axis is also an altitude, then the cone is a *right cone*. If the axis is not the altitude, then the cone is an *oblique cone*.

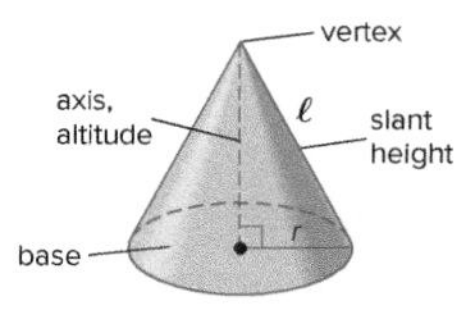

Right Cone

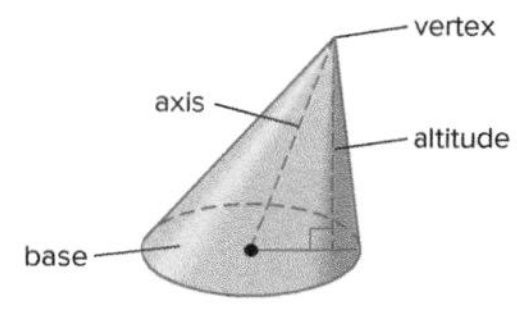

Oblique Cone

The net for a cone is shown at the right. The circle with radius r is the base of the cone. It has a circumference of $2\pi r$ and an area of πr^2. The sector with radius ℓ is the lateral surface of the cone. Its arc measure is $2\pi r$. You can use a proportion to find its area.

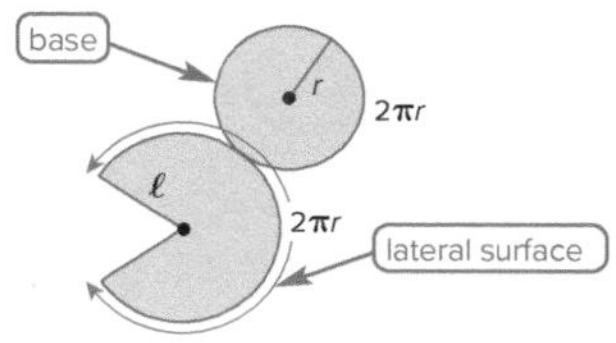

$$\frac{\text{area of sector}}{\text{area of circle}} = \frac{\text{measure of arc}}{\text{circumference of circle}}$$

$$\frac{\text{area of sector}}{\pi\ell^2} = \frac{2\pi r}{2\pi\ell}$$

$$\text{area of sector} = \pi\ell^2\left(\frac{2\pi r}{2\pi\ell}\right) = \pi r\ell$$

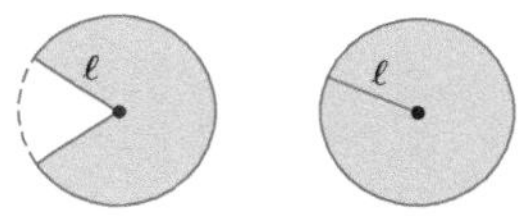

sector **circle that contains the sector**

The surface area of a cone is the sum of the lateral and the area of the base.

Key Concepts Lateral and Surface Area of a Cone

Words: The lateral area L of a right circular cone is the product of π, the radius r, and the slant height ℓ.	**Words:** The surface area S of a right circular cone is the sum of the lateral area and the area of a base.
Symbols: $L = \pi r\ell$.	**Symbols:** $S = L + B$ or $S = \pi r\ell + \pi r^2$.

Study Tip

MP Sense Making Like a pyramid, the lateral area L of a right circular cone equals $\frac{1}{2}P\ell$ where perimeter P is the circumference C of the base.

$L = \frac{1}{2}P\ell$

$= \frac{1}{2}C\ell$

$= \frac{1}{2}(2\pi r)\ell$

$= \pi r\ell$

Example 7 Surface Area of a Cone

Find the surface area of the cone. Round to the nearest tenth.

$S = \pi r\ell + \pi r^2$ Surface area of a cone

$= \pi(7.4)(15) + \pi(7.4)^2$ $r = 7.4$ and $\ell = 15$

≈ 520.8 Use a calculator.

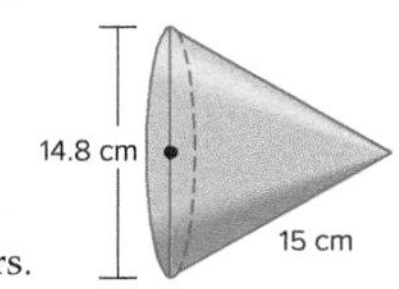

The surface area of the cone is about 520.8 square centimeters.

Guided Practice

Find the surface area of each cone. Round to the nearest tenth.

7A. The radius is 0.8 millimeters with a slant height of 2.2 millimeters. ≈ 7.5 mm^2

7B. The diameter is 12 inches with a slant height of 7 inches. ≈ 245.0 in^2

Teaching Tip

To help students visualize the derivation of the lateral area of a cone, use a cone filter or conical water cup. Have students cut and measure the cone filter or water cup.

Example 7 Surface Area of a Cone

AL What shape is the base of a cone? a circle What part of the cone makes up the lateral surface area? the surface from the circle to the vertex

OL If the diameter of the cone is decreased to 12 centimeters, what is the new surface area? about 395.8 cm^2

BL If the diameter is still 14.8 centimeters and the slant height is changed so that the new lateral area is 831 square centimeters, what is the new surface area? about 1003.0 cm^2

Need Another Example?

Find the surface area of the cone. Round to the nearest tenth. 20.2 cm^2

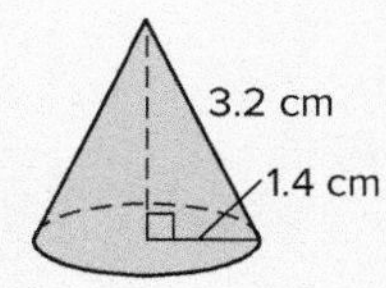

MP Teaching the Mathematical Practices

Sense-Making Mathematically proficient students consider analogous problems and try simpler forms of the original problem in order to gain insight on the solution. Encourage students to make connections between lateral and surface areas of different solids.

Example 8 Find the Lateral Area of a Composite Solid

AL What two figures make up the composite figure? a cone and a cylinder

OL If the radius of the tower is doubled, what is the new lateral area of the tower? about 3682.8 ft^2

BL The slant height of the tower increases, and the new lateral surface area of the structure is 1710 ft^2. What is the new slant height? about 25.4 ft

Need Another Example?

Buildings A cylindrical storage building has a base with a radius of 6 feet. The conical roof is 4 feet tall and the entire building is 12 feet tall. Find the lateral area of the building to the nearest tenth. about 437.5 ft^2

A **composite solid** is a three-dimensional figure that is composed of simpler figures. To find the lateral area or surface area of a composite figure, analyze each of the simpler figures contained in the composite figure.

Real-World Link
The construction of the town wall of Tallinn, Estonia, was begun in 1310. It was added to UNESCO's list of World Heritage Sites in 1997.

G.MG.1,

Real-World Example 8 Find the Lateral Area of a Composite Solid

ARCHITECTURE **A tower similar to the one shown at the left has a height of 16 feet and a radius of 12 feet. The cylindrical base is 10 feet tall. Find the lateral area of the tower.**

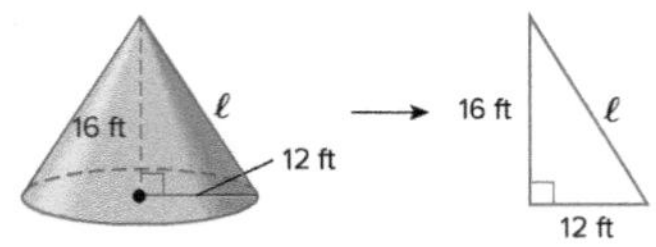

Step 1 Find the lateral area of the cone.

Use the Pythagorean Theorem to find the slant height.

$\ell^2 = 12^2 + 16^2$

$\ell^2 = 400$ Pythagorean Theorem

$\ell = 20$ Take the positive square root of each side.

Find the lateral area.

$L = \pi r \ell$ Lateral area of the cone

$= \pi(12)(20)$

≈ 754 $r = 12$ and $h = 20$

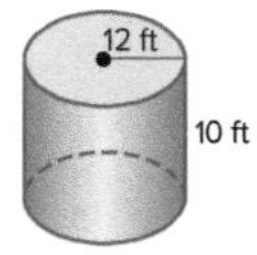

Step 2 Find the lateral area of the cylindrical base.

$L = 2\pi rh$ Lateral area of the cylinder

$= 2\pi(12)(10)$

≈ 754 $r = 12$ and $h = 10$

Step 3 Add the lateral areas.

$L_{cone} + L_{cylinder} = 754 + 754$

$= 1508$

The lateral area of the structure is about 1508 square feet.

Guided Practice

8. **OBELISK** An obelisk is a composite solid made of a square pyramid atop a rectangular prism. If the obelisk has a total height of 50 feet, a side length of 6 feet, and the pyramid is 8 feet tall, find the lateral area of the obelisk to the nearest tenth. 1110.5 ft^2

Check Your Understanding

◯ = Step-by-Step Solutions begin on page R13.

Go Online! for a Self-Check Quiz

Examples 1, 3, 5, 7 **Find the surface area of each solid. Round to the nearest tenth if necessary.**

1. 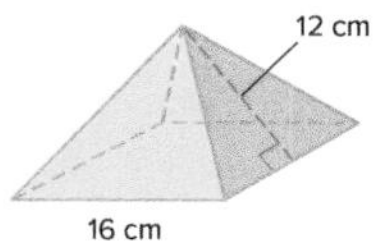

640 cm^2

2. 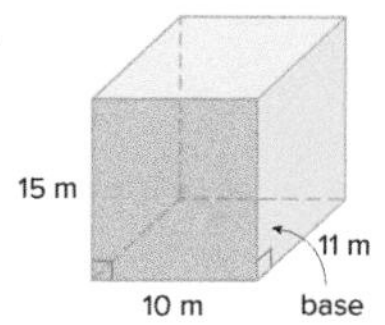

850 m^2

3. 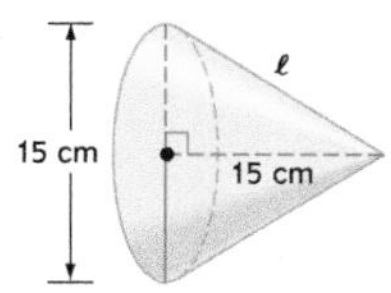

≈571.9 cm^2

4. 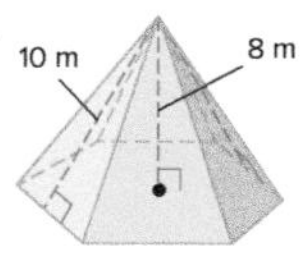

≈332.6 m^2

5. 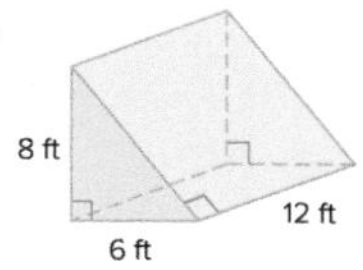

336 ft^2

6. 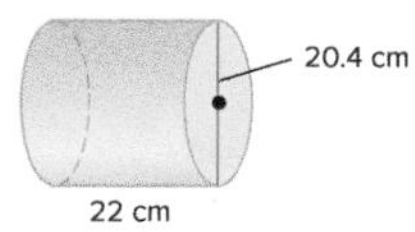

≈2063.6 cm^2

Examples 2, 4, 6, 8 G.GMD.1

7. **CARS** Evan is buying new tire rims that are 14 inches in diameter and 6 inches wide. Determine the surface area of each rim. Round to the nearest tenth. ≈571.8 in^2

8. **PATIO STONES** A patio stone has a rectangular base that is 3 inches by 8 inches and a height of 4 inches. What is the surface area of the stone? ≈136 in.^{2}

9. **ROOFING** A pyramid shaped roof has a square base that is 30 feet wide and a slant height of 14 feet. How much roofing material is needed to cover the roof? 840 ft^2

10. **TANKS** A storage tank is shown at the right. Round to the nearest tenth.
 a. Find the lateral area of the cylinder. 483.8 ft^2
 b. Find the lateral area of the cone. 197.9 ft^2
 c. Find the total lateral area of the tank. 681.7 ft^2

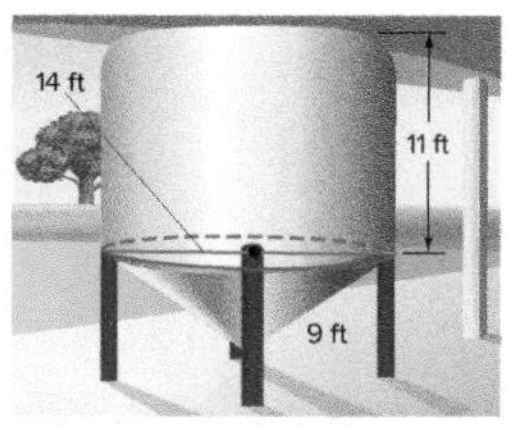

Practice and Problem Solving

Extra Practice is found on page R10.

Examples 1, 3, 5, 7 **Find the surface area of each solid. Round to the nearest tenth if necessary.**

11. 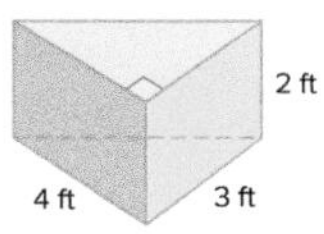

36 ft^2

12. 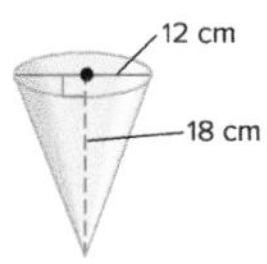

≈470.7 cm^2

Differentiated Homework Options			
Levels	AL Basic	OL Core	BL Advanced
Exercises	11–31, 42–54	11–31 odd, 32–37, 40–54	36–48, (optional: 49–54)
2-Day Option	11–31 odd, 49–54	11–31	
	12–30 even, 42–48	32–54	

You can use ALEKS to provide additional remediation support with personalized instruction and practice.

Practice

Formative Assessment Use Exercises 1–10 to assess students' understanding of the concepts in the lesson.

The Practice and Problem Solving exercises assess the content taught in the lesson. The Preparing for Assessment page is meant to be used as preparation for end-of-course assessments.

MP Teaching the Mathematical Practices

Sense-Making Mathematically proficient students start by explaining the meaning of a problem to themselves and looking for entry points to its solution. They plan a solution pathway rather than simply jumping into a solution attempt. In Exercises 7–10, encourage students to make a plan to solve each problem first.

Differentiated Instruction AL OL

Kinesthetic Learners While working with a partner have students construct a prism by using grid paper, tape, and scissors. Then, have students find the lateral area and the surface area of that prism. They should label each face of their prism as a base or lateral face and have the type of prism labeled as well. Have them repeat this activity with several prisms of various sizes.

Levels of Complexity Chart

The levels of the exercises progress from 1 to 3, with Level 1 indicating the lowest level of complexity.

Exercises	1–24	25–35, 49–54	36–48
C Level 3			●
B Level 2		●	
Level 1	●		

Examples 1, 3, 5, 7 **Find the surface area of each solid. Round to the nearest tenth if necessary.**

13. ≈32.8 cm²

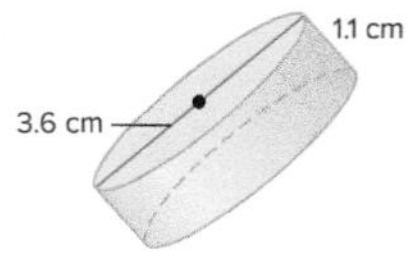

14. 151.9 m²

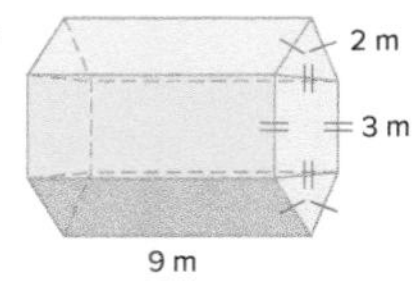

15. ≈236.6 ft²

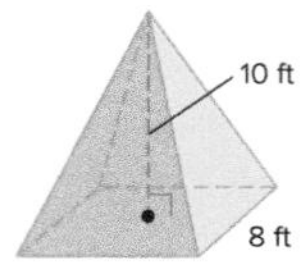

16. ≈302.9 cm²

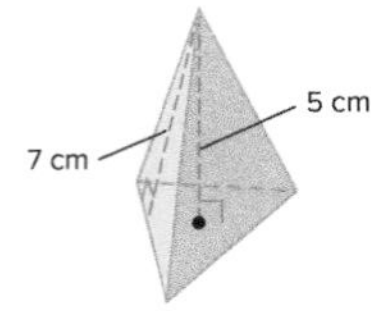

17. A cone has a diameter of 3.4 centimeters and the slant height is 6.5 centimeters. ≈43.8 cm²

18. A rectangular prism has $\ell = 25$ centimeters, $w = 18$ centimeters, and $h = 12$ centimeters. 1932 cm²

19. A regular hexagonal pyramid has a base edge of 6 millimeters and a slant height of 9 millimeters. ≈255 mm²

20. A right triangular prism has $h = 6$ inches and a base with legs 9 inches and 12 inches long. 324 in²

21. A cylinder has a diameter of 8 inches and a height of 6.2 inches. ≈256.4 in²

22. A square pyramid has an altitude of 12 inches and a slant height of 18 inches. ≈1686.0 in²

23. A cylinder has a radius of 3 millimeters and a height of 15 millimeters. ≈339.3 mm²

24. A cone has an altitude of 5 feet and a slant height of 9.5 feet. ≈446.1 ft²

Examples 2, 4, 6, 8 G.MG.1

25. Find the lateral area of the tent to the nearest tenth. ≈311.2 ft²

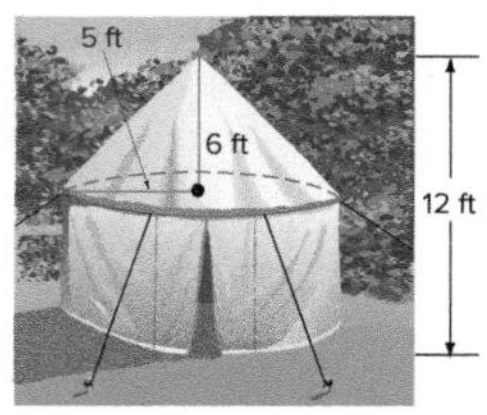

26. Find the lateral area of the dog house with a 12-inch square cut out of one face for the door. ≈6465.1 in²

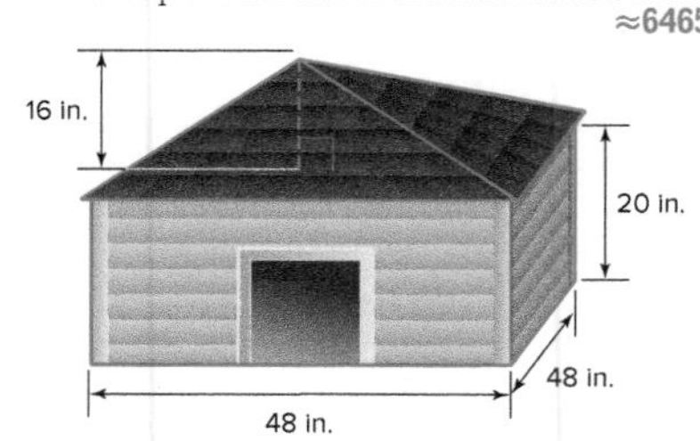

Find the surface area of each composite solid. Round to the nearest tenth if necessary.

27. ≈427.6 in²

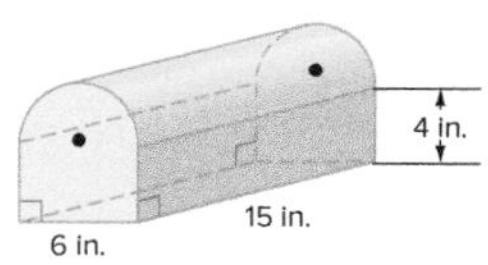

28. ≈1059.1 cm²

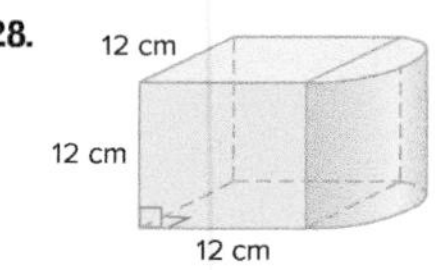

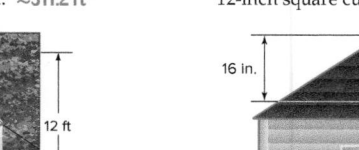

29. MOUNTAINS A conical mountain has a radius of 1.6 kilometers and a height of 0.5 kilometer. What is the lateral area of the mountain? **≈ 8.4 km^2**

30. AQUARIUMS The Tower Aquarium in Henley Beach, Australia, is the world's largest cylindrical aquarium. It reaches a height of over 40 meters and is 36 meters in diameter. Visitors ascend through a column of water as they ride a split-level glass elevator up seven floors through the center of the aquarium. What is the approximate lateral area of the outside of the aquarium? **≈ 4524 m^2**

31. HISTORY Archaeologists recently discovered a 1500-year-old pyramid in Mexico City. The square pyramid measures 165 yards on each base edge and once stood 20 yards tall. What was the original lateral area of the pyramid? **28,013.6 yd^2**

B **32. MONUMENTS** A *monolith* mysteriously appeared overnight at Seattle, Washington's Manguson Park. A hollow rectangular prism, the monolith was 9 feet tall, 4 feet wide, and 1 foot deep.

a. Find the area in square feet of the structure's surfaces that lie above the ground. **≈ 94 ft^2**

b. Use dimensional analysis to find the area in square yards. **10.4 yd^2**

33. TEEPES The dimensions of two canvas tepees are shown in the table below. Including the floors, approximately how much more canvas is used to make Tepee B than Tepee A. **about 380.1 ft^2**

Tepee	Diameter (ft)	Height (ft)
A	14	6
B	20	9

34b. side lengths of triangular bases about 10.39 inches each; height 38 inches; 1278 in^2

34. DESIGN A mailer needs to hold a poster that is almost 38 inches long and has a maximum rolled diameter of 6 inches. **See margin.**

a. Design a mailer that is a triangular prism. Sketch the mailer and its net.

b. Suppose you want to minimize the surface area of the mailer. What would be the dimensions of the mailer and its surface area?

35. MULTI-STEP Hector is designing a glass greenhouse for a city park. He has a 40-foot by 20-foot rectangular plot available. He wants the roof to be a triangular prism in which the center of the roof is 4 feet higher than the edges. The glass costs $25 per square foot, and Hector cannot spend more than $60,000 on glass.

a. What is the maximum height that Hector should make the edge of the roof? **about 12 ft**

b. Describe your solution process. **b–c. See margin.**

c. What assumptions did you make?

C **36. PETS** A *frustum* is the part of a solid that remains after the top portion has been cut by a plane parallel to the base. The ferret tent shown at the right is a frustum of a regular pyramid.

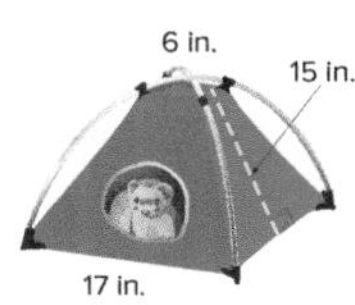

a. Describe the faces of the solid. **4 trapezoids, 2 squares**

36b. 1015 in^2 **b.** Find the surface area of the frustum formed by the tent.

c. Another pet tent is made by cutting the top half of a pyramid with a height of 12 centimeters, slant height of 20 centimeters, and square base with side length of 32 centimeters. Find the surface area of the frustum. **2240 cm^2**

37. The three-dimensional box needs to have a clear coating painted on all six faces. What is the approximate surface area of the box? **2824.8 cm^2**

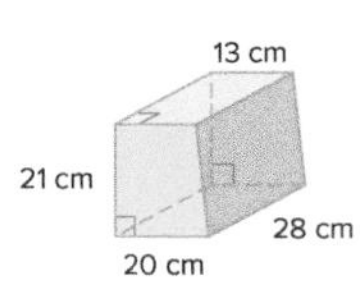

Extra Practice

See page R10 for extra exercises for students who are approaching level or for on-level students who need additional reinforcement.

Additional Answers

34a. Sample answer:

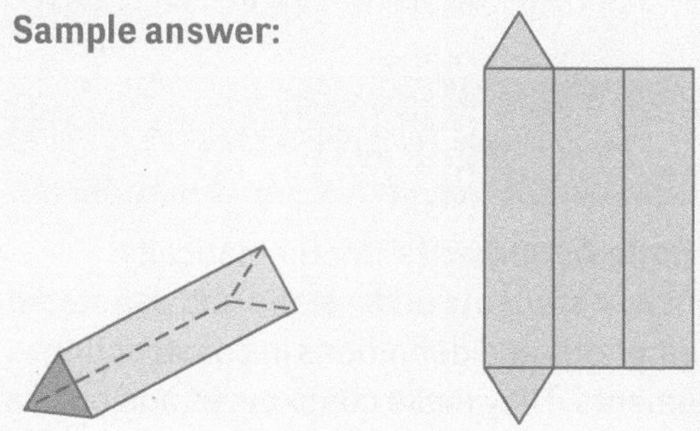

35b. Sample answer: First, find the sum of the surface areas of each individual section. The rectangular section of the front and back is $2 \times 20 \times g$ or $40g$ ft^2. The sides cover $2 \times 40 \times g$ or $80g$ ft^2. The triangular tops of the front and back of the greenhouse cover 2(0.5)(4)(20) or 80 ft^2. The slant of the roof is $\sqrt{116} \approx 10.77$. Thus, the roof covers 2(40)(10.77) or 861 ft^2. The total surface area is $861 + 80 + 120g$ ft^2. Hector can use up to $60{,}000 \div 25$ or 2400 ft^2. Therefore, g is approximately 12.1. Rounding down, we get a height of 12 ft.

35c. Sample answer: Hector used the entire available plot. There was no glass used for the base. The entrance was made of glass. The top of the roof ran along the 40-ft length of the greenhouse.

Follow-Up

What is the difference between the surface area of a prism and a cylinder? a pyramid and a cone? Sample answer: the shape of the base

What is the difference between the surface area of a prism and a pyramid? a cylinder and a cone? Sample answer: the number of bases

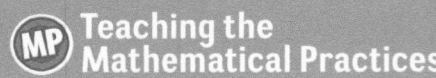

MP Teaching the Mathematical Practices

Critique Arguments Mathematically proficient students understand and use stated assumptions and definitions in constructing arguments. They make conjectures and build a logical progression of statements to explore the truth of their conjectures. For Exercise 44, have students divide into pairs and have each student explain their reasoning to their partner.

Assess

Ticket Out the Door Have students explain how what they learned about surface area of prisms, cylinders, pyramids, and cones will help them predict the volume of prisms, cylinder, pyramids, and cones.

Additional Answers

42. The lateral area of the square prism is greater than that of the triangular prism. The square prism has four faces, while the triangular prism has three.

43. They are not equal. The slant height of the cone is $\frac{2\sqrt{\pi}}{\pi}$ or about 1.13 times greater than the slant height of the square pyramid.

47. $\frac{\sqrt{3}}{2}\ell^2 + 3\ell h$; the area of an equilateral triangle of side ℓ is $\frac{\sqrt{3}}{4}\ell^2$ and the perimeter of the triangle is 3ℓ. So, the total surface area is $\frac{\sqrt{3}}{2}\ell^2 + 3\ell h$.

Go Online!

eSolutions Manual

Create worksheets, answer keys, and solutions handouts for your assignments.

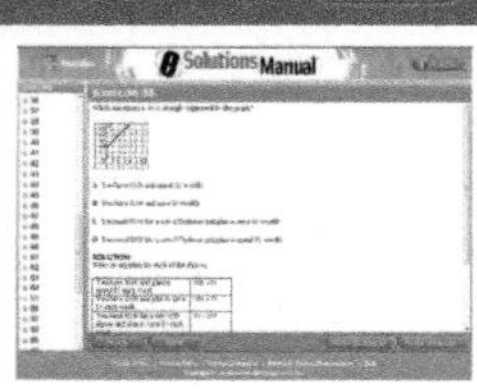

Find the surface area of each solid. Round to the nearest tenth.

38. 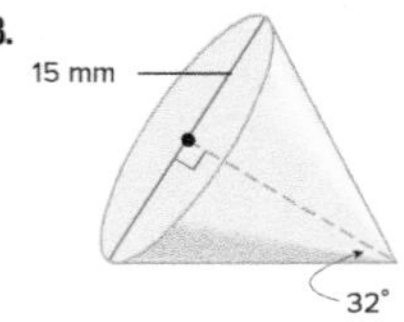

≈510.2 mm²

39. 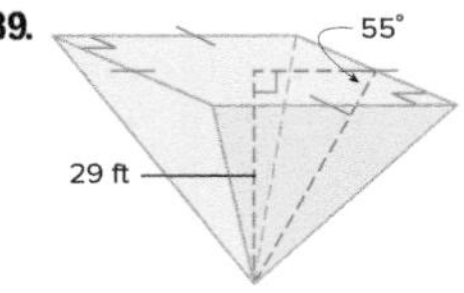

≈4524.8 ft²

40. **CONSTRUCTION** A road roller is a construction vehicle with smooth and heavy rollers used for compacting roads and pavement. One of these rollers has a diameter of 48 inches and is 36 inches in length. What is the area covered by the roller in two full turns? 10,857.4 in²

41. **SUNCATCHERS** Abby makes suncatchers of glass to sell at art shows. One style of suncatcher is a right hexagonal prism with a height of 9 centimeters and each base edge of 4 centimeters. What is the surface area of each suncatcher? (*Hint:* First, find the length of the apothem of the base.) about 299.1 cm²

H.O.T. Problems Use Higher-Order Thinking Skills

42. **WRITING IN MATH** A square-based prism and a triangular prism are the same height. The base of the triangular prism is an equilateral triangle, with an altitude equal in length of the side of the square. Compare the lateral areas of the prisms. See margin.

43. MP **REASONING** A cone and a square pyramid have the same surface area. If the areas of their bases are also equal, do they have the same slant height as well? Explain. See margin.

44. MP **CRITIQUE ARGUMENTS** Montell and Derek are finding the surface area of a cylinder with a height of 5 centimeters and a radius of 6 centimeters. Is either of them correct? Explain your answer.

Montell	Derek
$S = \pi(6)^2 + \pi(6)(5)$	$S = 2\pi(6)^2 + 2\pi(6)(5)$
$= 36\pi + 30\pi$	$= 72\pi + 60\pi$
$= 66\pi$ cm²	$= 132\pi$ cm²

44. Derek; Sample answer: $S = 2\pi r^2 + 2\pi rh$, so the surface area of the cylinder is $2\pi(6)^2 + 2\pi(6)(5)$ or 132π cm².

45. MP **REASONING** Classify the following statement as *sometimes*, *always*, or *never* true. Justify your reasoning.

The surface area of a cone of radius r and height h is less than the surface area of a cylinder of radius r and height h.

45. Always; if the heights and radii are the same, the surface area of the cylinder will be greater since it has two circular bases and additional lateral area.

46. MP **ARGUMENTS** Determine whether the following is *true* or *false*. Explain your reasoning.

A regular polygonal pyramid and a cone both have height h units and base perimeter P units. Therefore, they have the same total surface area.

46. False; the lateral area and the base of the cone are greater than the lateral area and base of the pyramid.

47. MP **REASONING** A right prism has a height of h units and a base that is an equilateral triangle of side ℓ units. Find the general formula for the total surface area of the prism. Explain your reasoning. See margin.

48. **WRITING IN MATH** Describe how to find the surface area of a regular polygonal pyramid with an n-gon base, height h units, and an apothem of a units. See margin.

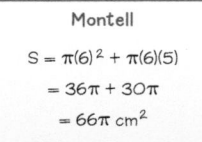

MP Standards for Mathematical Practice

Emphasis On	Exercises
1 Make sense of problems and preserve in solving them.	1–6, 11–24, 38, 39, 49–54
2 Reason abstractly and quantitatively.	43, 44
3 Construct viable arguments and critique the reasoning of others.	42–48
4 Model with mathematics.	7–10, 29–36, 40, 41, 52
6 Attend to precision.	10, 25–28, 37–39, 41, 42, 50, 52–54

48. Use the apothem, the height, and the Pythagorean Theorem to find the slant height ℓ of the pyramid. Then use the central angle of the n-gon and the apothem to find the length of one side of the n-gon. Then find the perimeter. Finally, use $S = \frac{1}{2}P\ell + B$ to find the surface area. The area of the base B is $\frac{1}{2}Pa$.

Preparing for Assessment

49. Olivia makes a cylinder by bending the cardboard rectangle shown below so that the 8-centimeter sides join to form the lateral area of a cylinder. Then, she cuts out two cardboard circles to form the bases and attaches these to the lateral face.

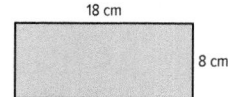

Which of the following is the best estimate of the surface area of the cylinder Olivia makes?
MP 1 G.MG.3 D

- ○ A 26 cm²
- ○ B 52 cm²
- ○ C 144 cm²
- ○ D 196 cm²

54c. The prism has six faces and the pyramid has only five. All of the faces of the prism are rectangles, but the pyramid has four faces that are triangles and only one that is a rectangle.

50. A cylindrical can has a circumference of 16π inches and a height of 20 inches. What is the surface area of the can in square inches? Round to the nearest tenth. MP 1, 6 G.GMD.1

1407.4

51. DeMarco is wrapping presents for a party. Each present is in a box shaped like a rectangular prism with the dimensions shown here. DeMarco plans to wrap 8 of the boxes.

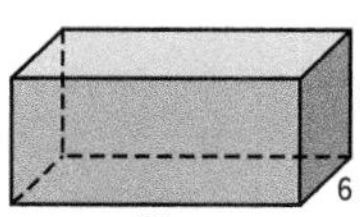

Which of the following is the best estimate for the least amount of wrapping paper DeMarco will need to buy? MP 1 G.GMD.1 C

- ○ A 1728 in²
- ○ B 2016 in²
- ○ C 2304 in²
- ○ D 2592 in²

52. The top of a gazebo in a park is the shape of a regular pentagonal pyramid. Each side of the pentagon is 10 feet long. If the slant height of the roof is about 6.9 feet, what is the lateral area of the roof to the nearest tenth? MP 1, 4, 6 G.GMD.1, G.MG.3

172.5

53. A model of a cone is used to demonstrate a new filter with top. To the nearest square millimeter, what is the surface area of the cone?
MP 1, 6 G.GMD.1 B

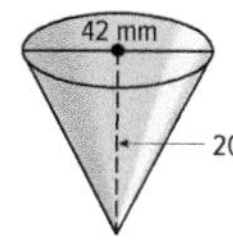

- ○ A 2705 mm²
- ○ B 3299 mm²
- ○ C 8820 mm²
- ○ D 9368 mm²

54. **MULTI-STEP** There are two separate buildings next to each other. The first is in the shape of a square prism. The dimensions of the base are 100 feet by 100 feet and the height of the building is 22 feet. The second building is in the shape of a square pyramid with the same dimensions.
MP 1, 6 G.MG.1, G.MG.3

a. What is the surface area of the first building? B

- ○ A 19,600 ft²
- ○ B 28,800 ft²
- ○ C 31,500 ft²
- ○ D 48,000 ft²

b. What is the surface area of the second building? C

- ○ A 16,420 ft²
- ○ B 18,720 ft²
- ○ C 20,925 ft²
- ○ D 38,000 ft²

c. Why are the surface areas of the buildings different even though the dimensions are the same?

Differentiated Instruction OL BL

Extension Ask students whether the lateral faces of a regular pyramid are congruent. Then have them justify their conjectures. Sample answer: yes, by SSS

Preparing for Assessment

Exercises 49–54 require students to use the skills they will need on standardized assessments. Each exercise is dual-coded with content standards and mathematical practice standards.

Dual Coding		
Items	Content Standards	MP Mathematical Practices
49	G.MG.3	1
50	G.MG.1	1, 6
51	G.MG.1	1
52	G.GMD.1, G.MG.3	1, 4, 6
53	G.MG.1	1, 6
54	G.MG.1, G.MG.3	1, 6

Diagnose Student Errors

Survey student responses for each item. Class trends may indicate common errors and misconceptions.

49.

A	Found area of the base
B	Omitted lateral area in calculating surface area
C	Found lateral area
D	CORRECT

51.

A	Accounted for lateral area only
B	Included only one base area in calculating surface area
C	CORRECT
D	Calculated volume of prism

53.

A	Used height instead of slant height
B	CORRECT
C	Used radius squared times height
D	Used the diameter as a radius

Go Online!

Quizzes

Students can use *Self-Check Quizzes* to check their understanding of this lesson and have the results sent to you. You can also give *Quiz 2*, which covers the content in Lessons 10-3 and 10-4.

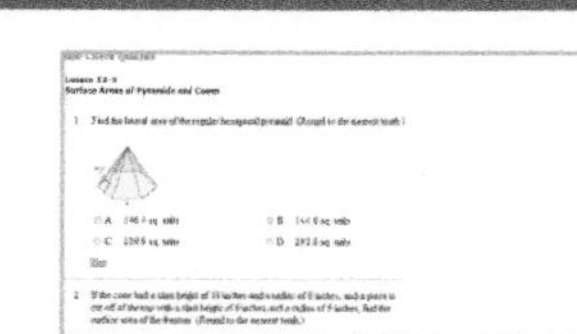

FOLDABLES Study Organizer

A completed Foldable for this chapter should include the Key Concepts related to the area of polygons and circles.

Key Vocabulary ELL

The page reference after each word denotes where that term was first introduced. If students have difficulty answering questions 1–8, remind them that they can use these page references to refresh their memories about the vocabulary terms.

Have students work together to review. Encourage them to summarize their understanding and ask each other questions about the content of Chapter 10.

You can use the detailed reports in ALEKS to automatically monitor students' progress and pinpoint remediation needs prior to the chapter test.

CHAPTER 10

Study Guide and Review

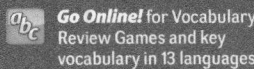

Go Online! for Vocabulary Review Games and key vocabulary in 13 languages

Study Guide

Key Concepts

Areas of Parallelograms and Triangles (Lesson 10-1)

- Area of a parallelogram: $A = bh$
- Area of a triangle: $A = \frac{1}{2}bh$ or $A = \frac{bh}{2}$

Areas of Trapezoids, Rhombi, and Kites (Lesson 10-2)

- Area of a trapezoid: $A = \frac{1}{2}h(b_1 + b_2)$
- Area of a rhombus or kite: $A = \frac{1}{2}d_1d_2$

Areas of Circles and Sectors (Lesson 10-3)

- Area of a circle: $A = \pi r^2$
- The ratio of the area A of a sector to the area of the whole circle, πr^2, is equal to the ratio of the degree measure of the intercepted arc x to 360.

  Proportion: $\frac{A}{\pi r^2} = \frac{x}{360}$ Equation: $A = \frac{x}{360} \cdot \pi r^2$

Areas of Regular Polygons and Composite Figures (Lesson 10-4)

- The area A of a regular n-gon with side length s is one half the product of the apothem a and perimeter P.

  $A = \frac{1}{2}a(ns)$ or $A = \frac{1}{2}aP$

Area and Nonrigid Transformations (Lesson 10-5)

- If two polygons are similar, then their areas are proportional to the square of the scale factor between them.

  If $ABCD \sim FGHJ$, then $\frac{\text{area of } FGHJ}{\text{area of } ABCD} = \left(\frac{FG}{AB}\right)^2$.

Surface Area (Lesson 10-6)

- Lateral surface area of a right prism: $L = Ph$
- Lateral surface area of a right cylinder: $L = 2\pi rh$
- Lateral surface area of a pyramid: $L = \frac{1}{2}p\ell$
- Lateral surface area of a right cone: $L = \pi r\ell$

9. If two polygons are similar, then their areas are proportional to the square of the scale factor between them.

FOLDABLES Study Organizer

Use your Foldable to review the chapter. Working with a partner can be helpful. Ask for clarification of concepts as needed.

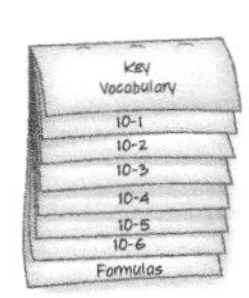

Key Vocabulary

altitude (p. 770)
apothem (p. 752)
axis (p. 771)
base edges (p. 770)
base of a parallelogram (p. 725)
base of a triangle (p. 727)
composite figure (p. 754)
height of a parallelogram (p. 725)
height of a solid (p. 770)
height of a trapezoid (p. 735)
height of a triangle (p. 727)
lateral area (p. 770)
lateral edge (p. 770)
lateral faces (p. 770)
oblique cone (p. 775)
regular pyramid (p. 775)
right cone (p. 775)
sector of a circle (p. 744)
slant height (p. 773)

Vocabulary Check

State whether each sentence is *true* or *false*. If *false*, replace the underlined term to make a true sentence.

1. The center of a trapezoid is the perpendicular distance between the bases. **false; height**
2. A slice of pizza is a sector of a circle. **true**
3. The center of a regular polygon is the distance from the middle to the circle circumscribed around the polygon. **false; radius**
4. The segment from the center of a square to the corner can be called the radius of the square. **true**
5. A segment drawn perpendicular to a side of a regular polygon is called an apothem of the polygon. **true**
6. The measure of each radial angle of a regular n-gon is $\frac{360}{n}$. **false; central**
7. The slant height is the height of each lateral face of a pyramid or cone. **true**
8. The height of a triangle is the length of an altitude drawn to a given base. **true**

10. The center of a regular polygon is the center of its circumscribed circle.

Concept Check

9. Explain how the areas of two similar polygons are related.
10. Explain how to determine the center of a regular polygon.

Answering the Essential Question

Before answering the Essential Question, have students review their answers to the *Building on the Essential Question* exercises found throughout the chapter.

- Why do we have specific formulas that we use to find the areas of certain polygons? (p. 730)
- How are the area formulas for polygons related? (p. 738)
- Is there more than one formula that can be used to find the area of a given polygon? Explain. (p. 758)
- What is the difference between the surface area of a prism and a pyramid? a cylinder and a cone? (p. 780)
- What is the difference between the surface area of a prism and a cylinder? a pyramid and a cone? (p. 780)

Go Online!

Vocabulary Review

Students can use the *Vocabulary Review Games* to check their understanding of the vocabulary terms in this chapter. Students should refer to the *Student-Built Glossary* they have created as they went through the chapter to review important terms. You can also give a *Vocabulary Test* over the content of this chapter.

Lesson-by-Lesson Review

10-1 Areas of Parallelograms and Triangles

G.GPE.7

Find the perimeter and area of each parallelogram or triangle. Round to the nearest tenth if necessary. **11–14. See margin.**

11.

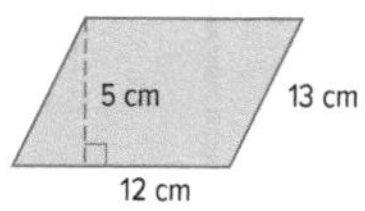

12.

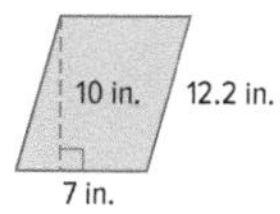

13.

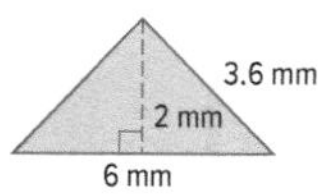

14.

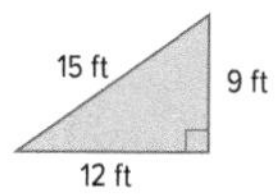

15. **PAINTING** Two of the walls of an attic in an A-frame house are triangular, each with a height of 12 feet and a width of 22 feet. How much paint is needed to paint one end of the attic? **132 ft²**

Example 1

Find the perimeter and area of ▱*JKLM*.

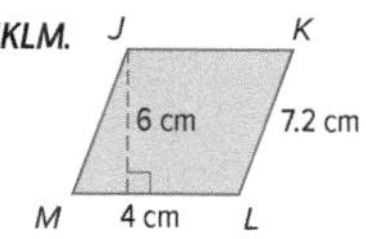

Perimeter

Perimeter of ▱$JKLM = JK + KL + LM + JM$

$= 4 + 7.2 + 4 + 7.2$ or 22.4 cm

Area

$A = bh$ Area of a parallelogram

$= (4)(6)$ or 24 cm^2 $b = 4$ and $h = 6$

10-2 Areas of Trapezoids, Rhombi, and Kites

G.MG.3

Find the area of each trapezoid, rhombus, or kite.

16.

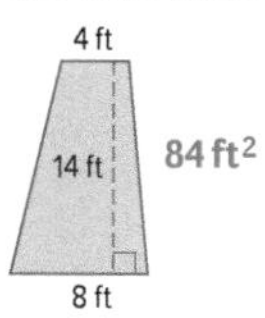

84 ft²

17.

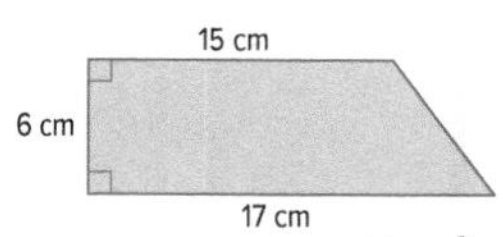

96 cm²

18.

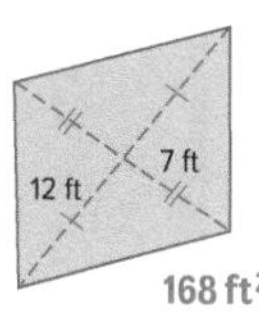

168 ft²

19.

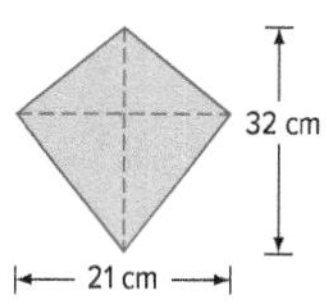

336 cm²

20. **KITES** Team Dragon's kite is 4 feet long and 3 feet across. How much fabric does it take to make their kite? **6 ft²**

Example 2

Find the area of each rhombus or kite.

a.

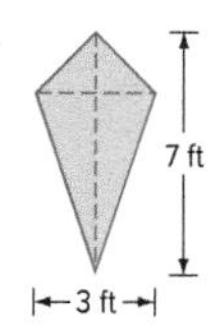

$A = \frac{1}{2}d_1d_2$ Area of a kite

$= \frac{1}{2}(7)(3)$ $d_1 = 7$ and $d_2 = 3$

$= 10.5\text{ ft}^2$ Simplify.

b.

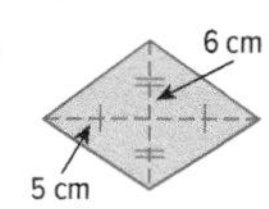

Since the diagonals of a rhombus bisect each other, the lengths of the diagonals are 6 + 6 or 12 centimeters and 5 + 5 or 10 centimeters.

$A = \frac{1}{2}d_1d_2$ Area of a rhombus

$= \frac{1}{2}(10)(12)$ $d_1 = 10$ and $d_2 = 12$

$= 60\text{ cm}^2$ Simplify.

Lesson-by-Lesson Review

Intervention If the given examples are not sufficient to review the topics covered by the questions, remind students that the lesson references tell them where to review that topic in their textbook.

Two-Day Option Have students complete the Lesson-by-Lesson Review. Then you can use McGraw-Hill eAssessment to customize another review worksheet that practices all the objectives of this chapter or only the objectives on which your students need more help.

Additional Answers

11. $P = 50$ cm; $A = 60\text{ cm}^2$
12. $P = 38.4$ in.; $A = 70\text{ in}^2$
13. $P = 13.2$ mm; $A = 6\text{ mm}^2$
14. $P = 36$ ft; $A = 54\text{ ft}^2$

CHAPTER 10
Study Guide and Review *Continued*

10-3 Areas of Circles and Sectors
G.C.5, G.GMD.1

Find the area of each shaded sector. Round to the nearest tenth.

21. 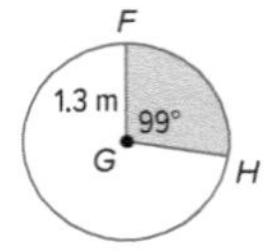

$1.5\ m^2$

22. 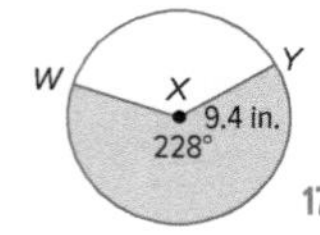

$175.8\ in^2$

23. **BICYCLES** A bicycle tire decoration covers $\frac{1}{9}$ of the circle formed by the tire. If the tire has a diameter of 26 inches, what is the area of the decoration? $59\ in^2$

24. **PIZZA** Charlie and Kris ordered a 16-inch pizza and cut the pizza into 12 slices.
   a. If Charlie ate 3 pieces, what area of the pizza did he eat? $50.27\ in^2$
   b. If Kris ate 2 pieces, what area of the pizza did she eat? $33.51\ in^2$
   c. What is the area of leftover pizza? $117.29\ in^2$

Example 3

Find the area of the shaded sector. Round to the nearest tenth.

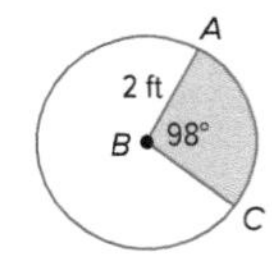

$A = \frac{x}{360} \cdot \pi r^2$ Area of a sector

$= \frac{98}{360} \cdot \pi(2)^2$ Substitution

$\approx 3.4\ ft^2$ Simplify.

10-4 Areas of Regular Polygons and Composite Figures
G.MG.3

Find the area of each regular polygon or composite figure. Round to the nearest tenth.

25. 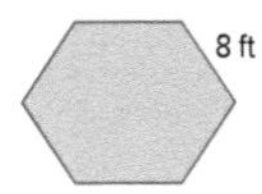

$166.3\ ft^2$

26. 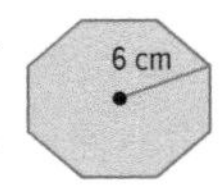

$101.8\ cm^2$

27. 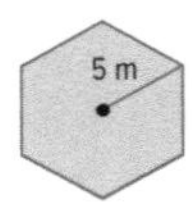

$65.0\ m^2$

28. 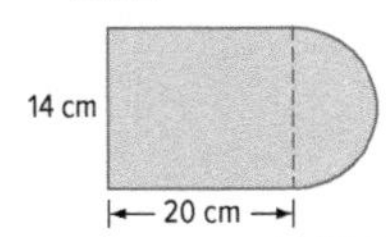

$357.0\ cm^2$

29. **JEWELRY** What is the area of the pendant shown below? Round to the nearest hundredth. $7.66\ cm^2$

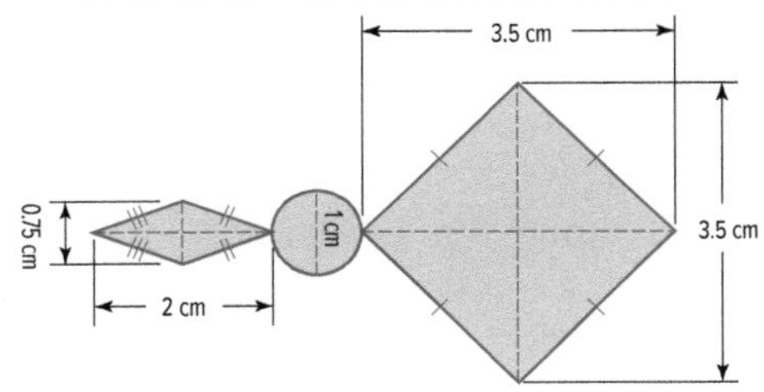

Example 4

Find the area of the figure.

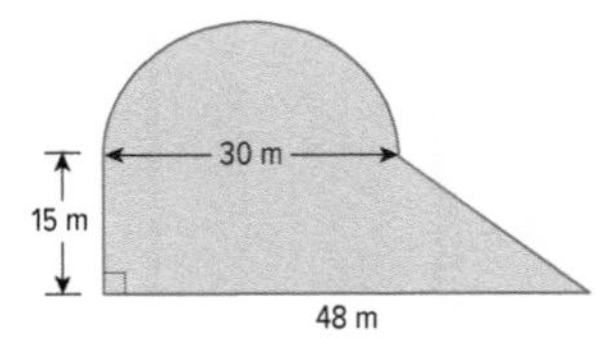

The composite shape is made up of a semicircle and a trapezoid.

Area = Area of semicircle + Area of trapezoid

$= \frac{180}{360} \cdot \pi \cdot r^2 + \frac{1}{2} \cdot h \cdot (b_1 + b_1)$

$\approx \frac{180}{360} \cdot \pi \cdot 15^2 + \frac{1}{2} \cdot 15 \cdot (30 + 48)$

$\approx 112.5\pi + 585$ or about $938.4\ m^2$

Go Online!

Anticipation Guide

Students should complete the *Chapter 10 Anticipation Guide*, and discuss how their responses have changed now that they have completed Chapter 10.

10-5 Area and Nonrigid Transformations

G.GMD.1, G.MG.1

For each pair of similar figures, use the given areas to find the scale factor from the blue to the green figure. Then find x.

30–32. See margin.

30.

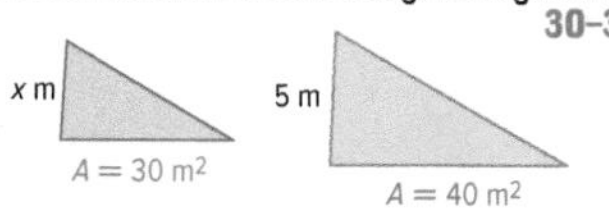

31.

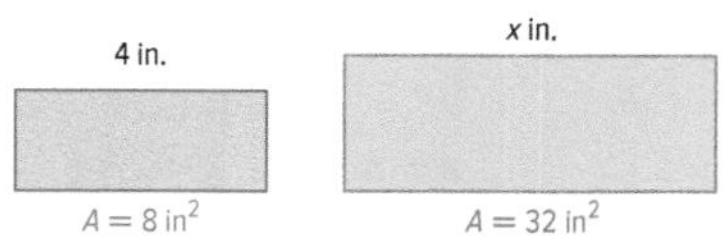

32.

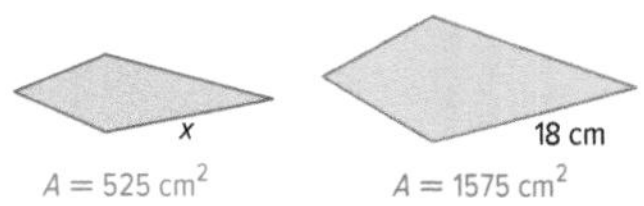

COORDINATE GEOMETRY Find the area of each figure. Use the segment length given to find the area of a similar polygon.

33–34. See margin.

33. $R'S' = 3$

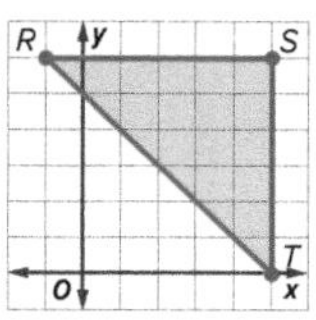

34. $K'L' = 15$

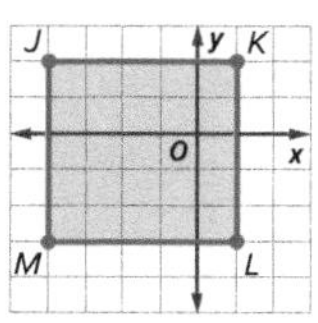

35. **LAND OWNERSHIP** Joshua's land is 600 square miles. He purchases an additional plot that is half the length and one-fourth the width of his original plot. What is the new area of his land? **75 mi²**

Example 5

For the pair of similar figures, use the given areas to find the scale factor from the blue to the green figure. Then find x.

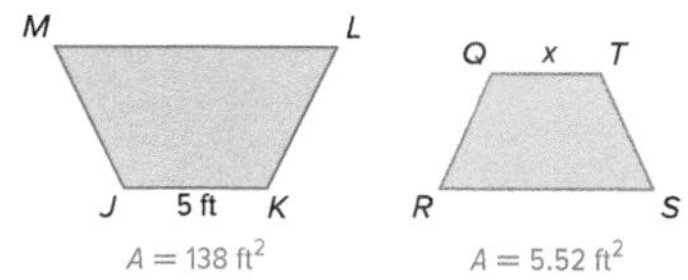

Let k be the scale factor between trapezoid $JKLM$ and trapezoid $QRST$.

$\frac{\text{Area of trapezoid } JKLM}{\text{Area of trapezoid } QRST} = k^2$	Theorem 10.1
$\frac{138}{5.52} = k^2$	Substitution
$5 = k$	Take the positive square root of each side.

So, the scale factor from trapezoid $JKLM$ to trapezoid $QRST$ is 5. Use this scale factor to find the value of x.

$\frac{JK}{QT} = k$	The ratio of corresponding lengths of similar polygons is equal to the scale factor between the polygons.
$\frac{5}{x} = 5$	Substitution
$1 = x$	Simplify.

Before the Test

Have students complete the Study Notebook Tie it Together activity to review topics and skills presented in the chapter.

Additional Answers

30. $\frac{\sqrt{3}}{2}; \frac{5\sqrt{3}}{2}$

31. $\frac{1}{2}; 8$

32. $\frac{\sqrt{3}}{3}; 6\sqrt{3}$

33. area of $\triangle RST = 18$ square units; area of $\triangle R'S'T' = 4.5$ square units

34. area of $\triangle JKL = 25$ square units; area of $\triangle J'K'L' = 225$ square units

Go Online!

eAssessment

Customize and create multiple versions of chapter tests and answer keys that align to your standards. Tests can be delivered on paper or online.

CHAPTER 10
Study Guide and Review *Continued*

10-6 Surface Area

G.GMD.1, G.MG.1, G.MG.3

Find the lateral area and surface area of each prism. Round to the nearest tenth if necessary.

36.

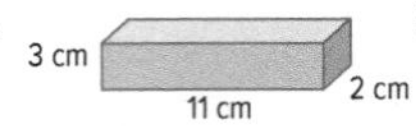

Sample answer: 78 cm^2; 122 cm^2

37.

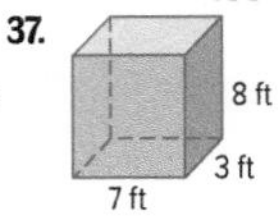

Sample answer: 160 ft^2; 202 ft^2

Find the lateral area and surface area of each cylinder. Round to the nearest tenth. 113.1 cm^2; 169.6 cm^2

38.

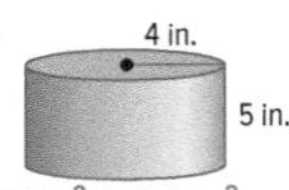

125.7 in^2; 226.2 in^2

39.

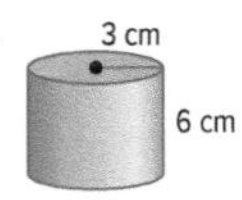

Find the lateral area and the surface area of each figure. Round to the nearest tenth.

40.

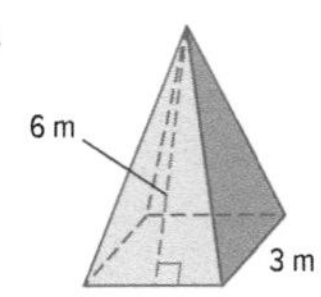

36 m^2; 45 m^2

41.

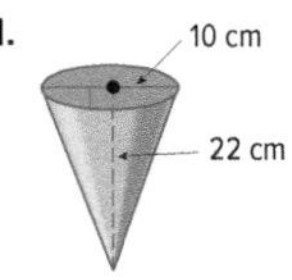

354.4 cm^2; 432.9 cm^2

Example 6

Find the surface area of the rectangular prism.

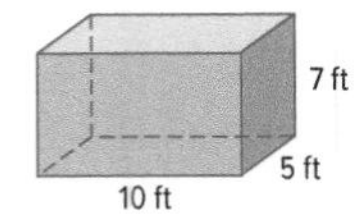

Use the 10-foot by 5-foot rectangle as the base.

$S = Ph + 2B$	Surface area of a prism
$= (2 \cdot 10 + 2 \cdot 5)(7) + 2(10 \cdot 5)$	Substitution
$= 310$	Simplify.

The surface area is 310 square feet.

Example 7

Find the surface area of the square pyramid. Round to the nearest tenth.

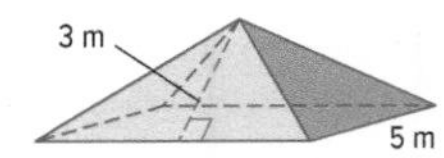

$S = \frac{1}{2}P\ell + B$	Surface area of a regular pyramid
$= \frac{1}{2}(4 \cdot 5)3 + 5 \cdot 5$	$P = 4 \cdot 5$ or 20, $\ell = 3$, $B = 5 \cdot 5$
$= 55$	Simplify.

The surface area is 55 square feet.

CHAPTER 10 Practice Test

Go Online! for another Chapter Test

Find the area and perimeter of each figure. Round to the nearest tenth if necessary. 1–4. See margin.

1. 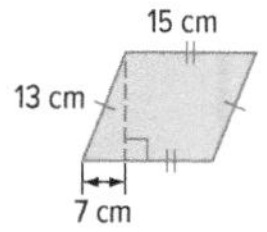

2. 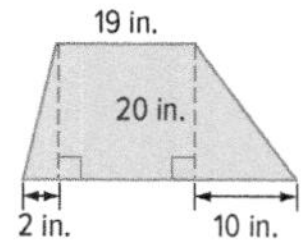

3. 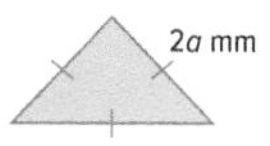

4. 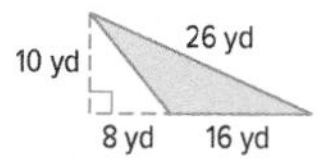

5. **ARCHAELOGY** The tile pattern shown was used in Pompeii for paving. If the diagonals of each rhombus are 2 and 3 inches, what area makes up each "cube" in the pattern? 9 in^2

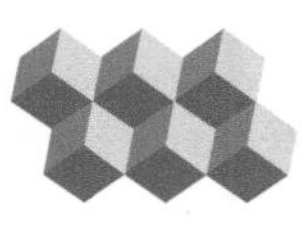

Find the area of each figure. Round to the nearest tenth if necessary.

6. 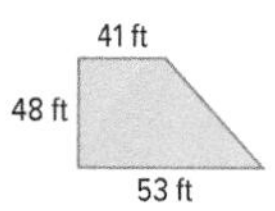

2256 ft^2

7. 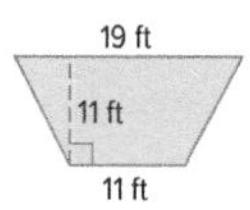

165 ft^2

8. 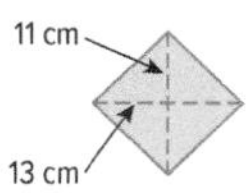

286 cm^2

9. 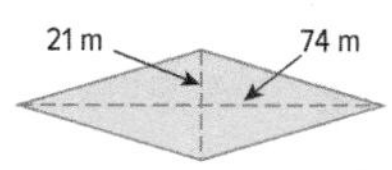

3108 m^2

10. **GEMOLOGY** A gem is cut in a kite shape. It is 6.2 millimeters wide at its widest point and 5 millimeters long. What is the area? 15.5 mm^2

11. **ALGEBRA** The area of a triangle is 16 square units. The base of the triangle is $x + 4$ and the height is x. Find x. 4

12. **ASTRONOMY** A large planetarium in the shape of a dome is being built. When it is complete, the base of the dome will have a circumference of 870 meters. How many square meters of land were required for this planetarium? $60{,}232\text{ m}^2$

Find the area of each circle or sector. Round to the nearest tenth.

13. 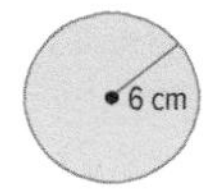

113.1 cm^2

14. 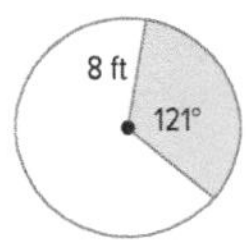

67.6 ft^2

15. **MURALS** An artisan is creating a circular street mural for an art festival. The mural is going to be 50 feet wide. One sector of the mural spans 38°. What is the area of this sector to the nearest square foot? 207 ft^2

Find the perimeter and area of each figure. Round to the nearest tenth if necessary.

16. 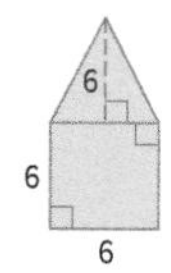

31.4; 54

17. 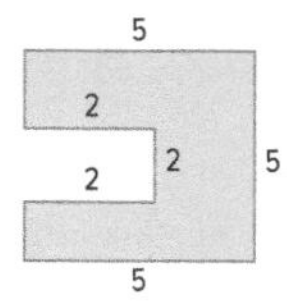

24; 21

18. **FLOORING** Brian's service project is to build a tree house in the city park. Find the shaded area in the tree house. Round to the nearest tenth. 54.9 ft^2

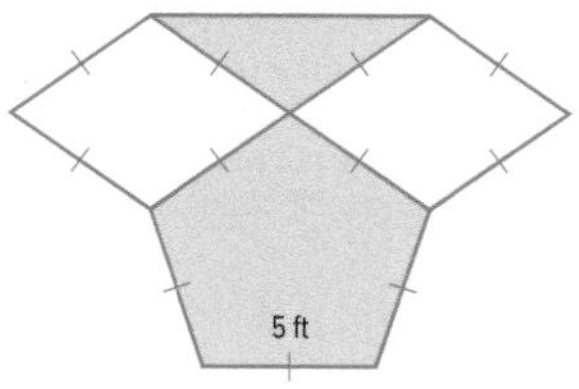

19. Find the lateral area and surface area of the tent model. Round to the nearest tenth if necessary. 634.7 ft^2 746.7 ft^2

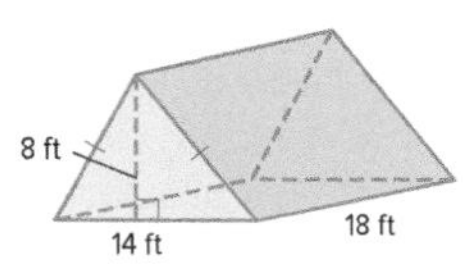

20. **BEEHIVE** Estimate the lateral area and surface area of the Turkish beehive room. Round to the nearest tenth if necessary. 620.1 ft^2, 874.6 ft^2

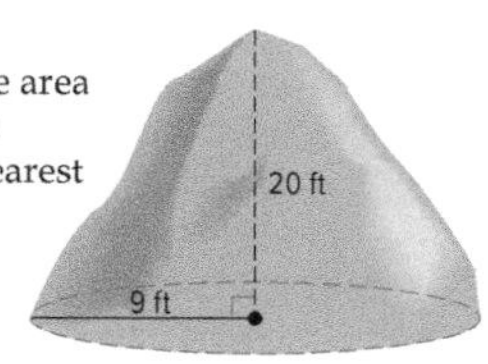

Go Online!

Chapter Tests

You can use premade leveled *Chapter Tests* to differentiate assessment for your students. Students can also take self-checking *Chapter Tests* to plan and prepare for chapter assessments.

Form	Type	Level
1	MC	AL
2A	MC	OL
2B	FR	OL
2C	FR	OL
3	FR	BL
Vocabulary Test		
Extended-Response Test		

MC = multiple-choice questions
FR = free-response questions

RtI Response to Intervention

Use the Intervention Planner to help you determine your Response to Intervention.

Intervention Planner

TIER 1 On Level OL

IF students miss 25% of the exercises or less,

THEN choose a resource:

SE Lessons 10-1 through 10-6

Go Online!
- Skills Practice
- Chapter Project
- Self-Check Quizzes

TIER 2 Strategic Intervention AL
Approaching grade level

IF students miss 50% of the exercises,

THEN choose a resource:

Quick Review Math Handbook

Go Online!
- Study Guide and Intervention
- Extra Examples
- Personal Tutors
- Homework Help

TIER 3 Intensive Intervention
2 or more grades below level

IF students miss 75% of the exercises,

THEN choose a resource:

Use *Math Triumphs, Geometry*

Go Online!
- Extra Examples
- Personal Tutors
- Homework Help
- Review Vocabulary

Additional Answers

1. $P = 56\text{ cm}, A = 164.3\text{ cm}^2$
2. $P = 92.5\text{ in.}, A = 500\text{ in}^2$
3. $P = 6a\text{ mm}, A = a^2\sqrt{3}\text{ mm}^2$
4. $P = 54.8\text{ yd}, A = 80\text{ yd}^2$

Launch

Objective Apply concepts and skills from this chapter in a real-world setting.

Teach

Ask:

- **If two adjacent walls are lined with cabinets 2 feet deep, what does that make the new length and width of the room?** Sample answer: 10 and 12
- **How many square feet greater is the 12.5-foot deck than the 10-foot deck? Do you need to find the cost of both decks?** Sample answer: 11π, or about 34.56, square feet. No, I can multiply the difference in square feet by the cost per square foot.
- **What do the angle measures tell you about the area of each sector?** Sample answer: The angle measures tell me the fraction of the area the sector occupies.
- **What is the distance between the two bases called? How can you find the lengths of the two sides? Why is the angle measure important?** Sample answer: the height; Sketch in a triangle and find the missing side length. The angle measure tells us that the triangle is a 30°-60°-90° triangle.
- **What are the base and height of the triangle? What are the lengths after the patio size is increased?** Sample answer: The base is 12 feet and the height is 8 feet. After the size is increased, the base is 18 and the height is 12.

The Performance Task focuses on the following content standards and standards for mathematical practice.

Dual Coding		
Parts	Content Standards	MP Mathematical Practices
A	G.MG.3	2, 4
B	G.C.5	6
C	G.MG.3	6, 8
D	G.MG.3	2, 8

Go Online! eBook

Interactive Student Guide

Refer to *Interactive Student Guide* for an additional Performance Task.

CHAPTER 10

Preparing for Assessment

Performance Task

Provide a clear solution to each part of the task. Be sure to show all of your work, include all relevant drawings, and justify your answers.

Home Renovation Clarissa and Frank bought a house in need of many renovations.

Part A

Modeling The first room they plan to redo is the kitchen, and they are setting their budget. The kitchen is 12 feet by 14 feet. Two adjacent walls are completely lined with cabinets that are each 2 feet deep. There is also a 5 feet by 3 feet cabinet island in the center of the kitchen. Finally, there is a small 8 feet by 10 feet mudroom adjacent to the kitchen. They want to replace the flooring in the kitchen and mudroom, but do not need flooring underneath any cabinets.

1. If the flooring they've chosen is $2.99 per square foot, determine the cost of new floors for the kitchen and mudroom. $553.15

Part B

Precision Another project they are planning is to have a round deck built on which they can put a hot tub. One of the hot tubs requires a minimum deck diameter of 10 feet. Another hot tub requires a minimum deck diameter of 12 feet. The cost of building the deck is $35.00 per square foot.

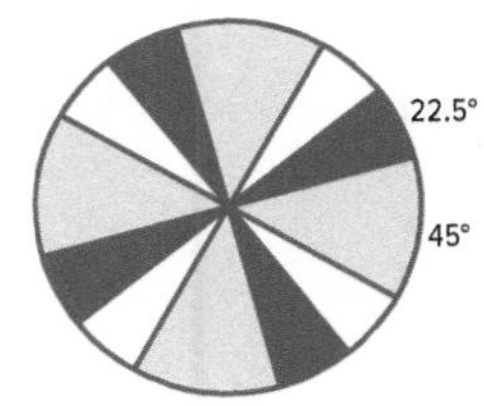

2. Determine the amount of money they can save by building the smaller deck. Round your answer to the nearest whole cent. $1244.60
3. Clarissa decides she wants a special pattern painted on the deck, shown to the right. All of the light regions are the same size and all of the dark regions are the same size. The white areas are not painted. The cost is $12.50 per square foot of painted area. Assuming they build the smaller deck, determine the cost of having the deck painted. Round your answer to the nearest whole cent. $735.00

Part C

Regularity Frank loves to garden and wants a to make a vegetable patch. To avoid some trees, he makes the garden in the shape of a parallelogram. The bases are 40 feet long and the distance between the two bases is 10 feet. The angle formed between one side and the bottom base is 150°. Frank will need rope to mark off the perimeter of the garden and fertilizer for the whole garden.

4. If the cost of the rope is $0.55 per linear foot, determine the total cost to mark off the whole garden. $66.00
5. The natural fertilizer Frank wants to use costs $12.00 per 8-pound bag. Each bag can fertilize an area of about 375 square feet. How many bags of fertilizer will Frank need to fertilize the garden twice in the season? 3

Part D

Reasoning Clarissa and Frank plan to pour a cement patio, but would also like some of the area to be tiled, as shown in the shaded area in the diagram to the right.

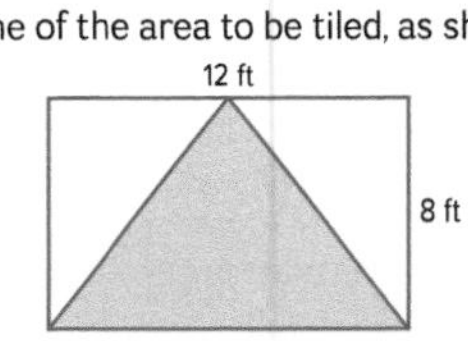

6. If the cost of the tiling is $11.25 per square foot, determine the cost to tile the triangle shown. $540.00
7. Clarissa would like to make the length and width of the patio both one and a half times bigger. Determine how much more the tiling would cost if they increased the size of the patio by a factor of 1.5. $675.00

Levels of Complexity Chart			
Parts	Level 1	Level 2	Level 3
A	●		
B			●
C		●	
D			●

Test-Taking Strategy

Example

Read the problem. Identify what you need to know. Then use the information in the problem to solve.

What is the area of the triangle? Round your answer to the nearest tenth.

A 112.5 m^2 **C** 152.5 m^2

B 172.5 m^2 **D** 195.5 m^2

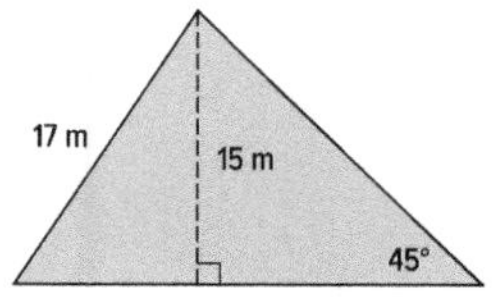

Step 1 **What are you being asked to solve? What information is given?**

I need to find the area of the triangle. The problem gives the height of the triangle, one side length, and one angle measure.

Step 2 **Are there any intermediate steps that need to be completed before you can solve the problem?**
To find the area, I need to find the length of the triangle's base.

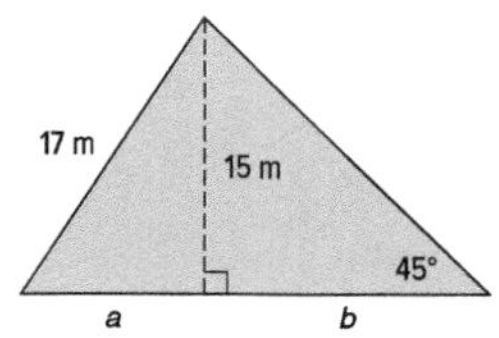

Step 3 **What steps will you take to solve the problem?**
I'll use the Pythagorean Theorem of find a and the special rules of right triangles to find b. Adding these together will give me the length of the base. Then I can use the formula for area of a triangle.

Step 4 **What is the correct answer?** The correct answer is B.

Test-Taking Tip

Multi-Step Problems
When solving multi-step problems, decide what you're being asked to sove, list the information given, and choose a strategy to solve the problem.

Apply the Strategy

Read the problem. Identify what you need to know. Then use the information in the problem to solve.

Which of the following best represents the area of the figure shown?

A 350 in^2 **C** 460 in^2

B 410 in^2 **D** 470 in^2

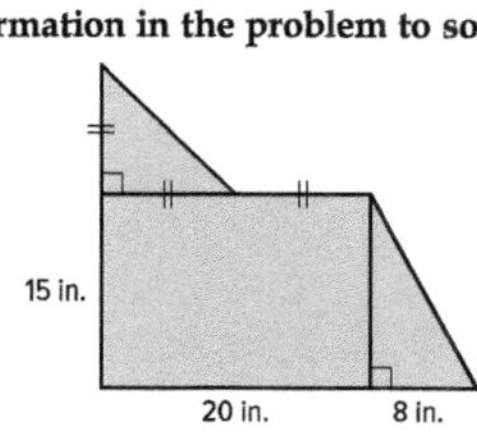

Answer the questions below.

a. What are you being asked to solve? What information is given? the area of a composite figure; The length and width of the rectangle, the base of one of the triangles, and the side lengths of the second triangle are equal to half the length of the rectangle.

b. Are there any intermediate steps that need to be completed before you can solve the problem? I need to find the lengths of the missing base and heights of the triangles.

c. What steps will you take to solve the problem? I'll use the width of the rectangle to find the height of the first triangle. I'll divided the length of the rectangle in half to find both the base and height of the second triangle. Then I'll find the area of each shape using the appropriate formulas and add them all together.

d. What is the correct answer? B

Test-Taking Strategy

Step 1 Read the problem. Identify what you're being asked to solve and what key information is given. Determine whether there are any intermediate steps needed before the problem can be solved.

Step 2 List the steps needed to solve the problem. Make sure you're using the most efficient way to solve.

Step 3 Solve the problem. Check your solution if time permits.

Ask:

a. What are you being asked to solve? What information is given? Are there any intermediate steps that need to be completed before you can solve the problem? the area of the kite; the length of one side and of the longer diagonal; I need to find the length of the shorter diagonal.

b. What steps will you take to solve the problem? If there is more than one way to solve, are you using the most efficient way? I'll use the special rules of right triangles to find the shorter diagonal. Then I'll use the formula for area of a kite.

c. What is the correct answer? A

Need Another Example?

What is the area of the kite? Round your answer to the nearest tenth if necessary. A

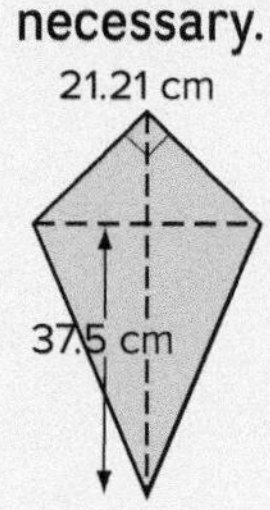

A 787.3 cm^2
B 850.1 cm^2
C 1125 cm^2
D 1245.2 cm^2

Go Online!

The most up-to-date resources available for your program can be found at connectED.mcgraw-hill.com.

Diagnose Student Errors

Survey student responses for each item. Class trends may indicate common errors and misconceptions.

1. A	Solved $\frac{x}{18} = \frac{9}{49}$
B	Solved $\frac{x}{18} = \frac{3}{7}$
C	CORRECT
D	Solved $\frac{x}{18} = \frac{49}{9}$

2. A	CORRECT
B	Took r^2 to be the radius
C	Determined incorrect radius
D	CORRECT
E	CORRECT

3. A	Omitted factor of $\frac{1}{2}$ in area formula
B	CORRECT
C	Used $\frac{4}{\tan 45°}$ for apothem
D	Used 8 for perimeter

6. A	Found area of $\triangle RST$ and multiplied by 4
B	CORRECT
C	Used $\overline{RT}$ as height of triangle
D	Used $\overline{SU}$ as base of triangle

8. A	Included area of whole circle rather than semicircle
B	CORRECT
C	Used 9 cm as one of the bases of the trapezoid
D	Found area of trapezoid only

12. A	Solved $180 = \frac{360}{135} \cdot \pi x^2$
B	Solved $180 = \pi x^2$
C	CORRECT
D	Solved $180 = \frac{135}{360} \cdot 2\pi x$

Go Online!

Standardized Test Practice

Students can take self-checking tests in standardized format to plan and prepare for standardized assessments.

CHAPTER 10

Preparing for Assessment

Cumulative Review

Read each question. Then fill in the correct answer on the answer document provided by your teacher or on a sheet of paper.

1. In the figure, $\triangle JKL \sim \triangle MNP$. The area of $\triangle JKL$ is 324 square meters and the area of $\triangle MNP$ is 1764 square meters.

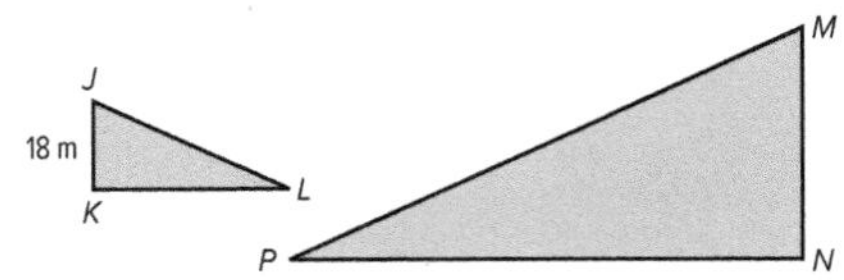

Which of the following is closest to the length of $\overline{MN}$? G.GPE.7 C

- A 3 m
- B 8 m
- C 42 m
- D 98 m

2. Which of the following are true about the circle with equation $x^2 + y^2 - 6x + 6y = -14$? G.GMD.1 A,D,E

- A The circle lies entirely in Quadrant IV.
- B The radius of the circle is 4.
- C The circle intersects both axes.
- D The center of the circle is $(3, -3)$.
- E The area of the circle is 4π.

3. Which of the following is the best estimate of the area of the regular octagon shown below? G.1(C) B

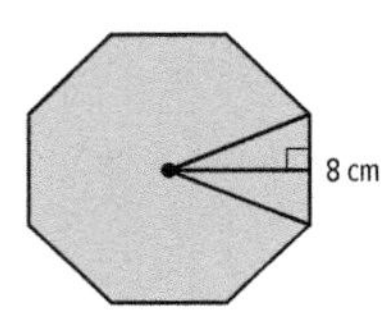

- A 618 cm^2
- B 309 cm^2
- C 128 cm^2
- D 39 cm^2

4. Malia wants to put a fence around the three sides of a right-triangular plot in her garden. She measures one side length and one acute angle, as shown in the figure.

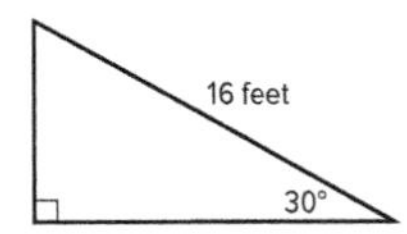

To the nearest foot, how many feet of fence does Malia need? G.GPE.7 38 feet

5. A circular pizza has a diameter of 18 inches. Charles slices the pizza into 12 equal sectors. What is the area of each sector, in square inches? Round to the nearest tenth. G.GMD.1 21.2

> **Test-Taking Tip**
>
> **Question 5** There are two ways to solve this problem. You can determine the measure of the intercepted arc for each sector and then use the formula for the area of a sector, or you can find the area of the whole pizza and divide by 12.

6. Kento enlarges $\triangle RST$ so that each dimension is 4 times the corresponding dimension shown in the figure.

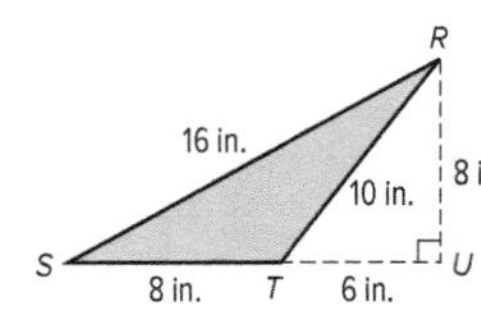

What is the area- of the enlarged triangle? G.MG.1 B

- A 128 in^2
- B 512 in^2
- C 640 in^2
- D 896 in^2

7. In parallelogram $ABCD$, side AB is 20 inches, side BC is 24 inches, and angle DAB is 60°. What are the area and perimeter of the parallelogram $ABCD$? G.GPE.7 C

- A 88 in; 207.9 in^2
- B 44 in; 357.5 in^2
- C 88 in; 415.7 in^2
- D 44 in; 408.6 in^2

Go Online! for Standardized Test Practice

8. Which of the following is the best estimate of the area of the composite figure shown here? G.MG.3 B

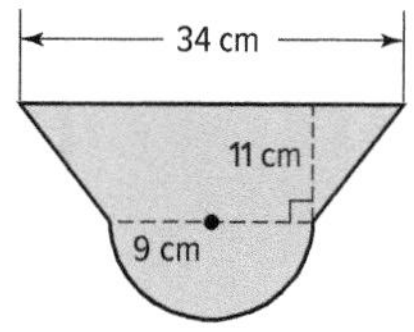

○ A 540 cm² ○ C 364 cm²

○ B 413 cm² ○ D 286 cm²

9. What is the surface area of the pyramid shown? G.MG.1

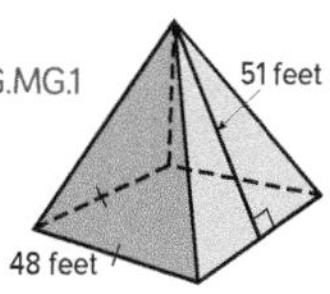

7,200 ft²

10. Dayana drew the trapezoid shown here.

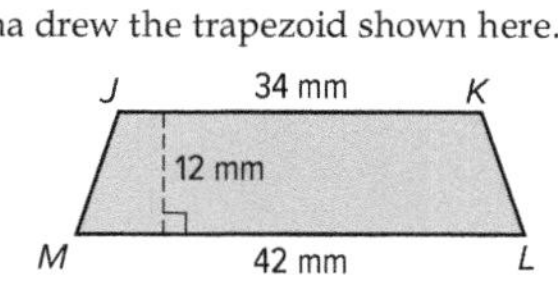

Which of the following will allow Dayana to create a new trapezoid with half the area of trapezoid *JKLM*? Select all that apply. G.MG.1 A, B

☐ A Draw a trapezoid in which each base is half as long as in trapezoid *JKLM*.

☐ B Draw a trapezoid in which the height is half as long as in trapezoid *JKLM*.

☐ C Draw a trapezoid in which only one base is half as long as in trapezoid *JKLM*.

☐ D Draw a trapezoid in which the height and only one base is half as long as in trapezoid *JKLM*.

☐ E Draw a trapezoid in which every dimension is half the corresponding dimension in trapezoid *JKLM*.

11. A rhombus has a longer diagonal of 18 centimeters and a perimeter of 45 centimeters. What is the area of the rhombus? G.MG.3

112.5 cm²

12. Marcello is making a cone-shaped base for a lamp. He goes online to order a piece of metal that is a sector of a circle, as shown. According to the website, the area of the sector is 180 square inches.

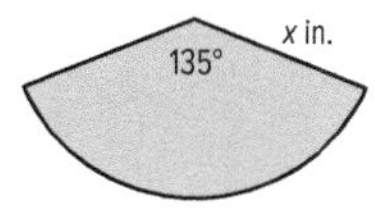

Which of the following is the best estimate of the value of x? G.GMD.1 C

○ A 4.6 ○ C 12.4

○ B 7.6 ○ D 76.4

13. What is the surface area of the figure shown? Round your answer to the nearest whole number. G.GMD.1

829 in²

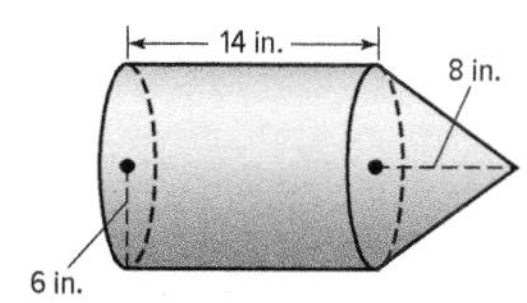

14. A kite has diagonals measuring 29 cm and 23 cm. What is the area of the kite? G.MG.3 B

○ A 52 cm² ○ C 667 cm²

○ B 333.5 cm² ○ D 1334 cm²

Need Extra Help?

If you missed Question...	1	2	3	4	5	6	7	8	9	10	11	12	13	14
Go to Lesson...	10-1	10-3	10-4	10-1	10-3	10-5	10-1	10-4	10-6	10-5	10-2	10-3	10-6	10-2

Formative Assessment

You can use these pages to benchmark student progress.

Standardized Test Practice

Exercise Question Types	
Question Type	Exercises
Multiple Choice	1, 3, 6, 7
Multiple Correct Answers	2, 9, 11
Type Entry: Short Response	4, 5, 8, 10, 12

Answer Sheet Practice

Have students simulate taking a standardized test by recording their answers on a practice recording sheet.

Homework Option

Get Ready for Chapter 11 Assign students the exercises on p. 794 as homework to assess whether they possess the prerequisite skills needed for the next chapter.

LEARNSMART®

Use LearnSmart as part of your test-preparation plan to measure student topic retention. You can create a student assignment in LearnSmart for additional practice on these topics.

- Understand and apply theorems about circles.
- Determine circle measurements.

Go Online!

eAssessment

Customize and create multiple versions of chapter tests and answer keys that align to your standards. Tests can be delivered on paper or online.

Lesson 10-1

39. Sample answer: The area will not change as *K* moves along line *p*. Because lines *m* and *p* are parallel, the perpendicular distance between them is constant. That means that no matter where *K* is on line *p*, the perpendicular distance to line *p*, or the height of the triangle, is always the same. Because point *J* and *L* are not moving, the distance between them, or the length of the base, is constant. Because the height of the triangle and the base of the triangle are both constant, the area will always be the same.

40.

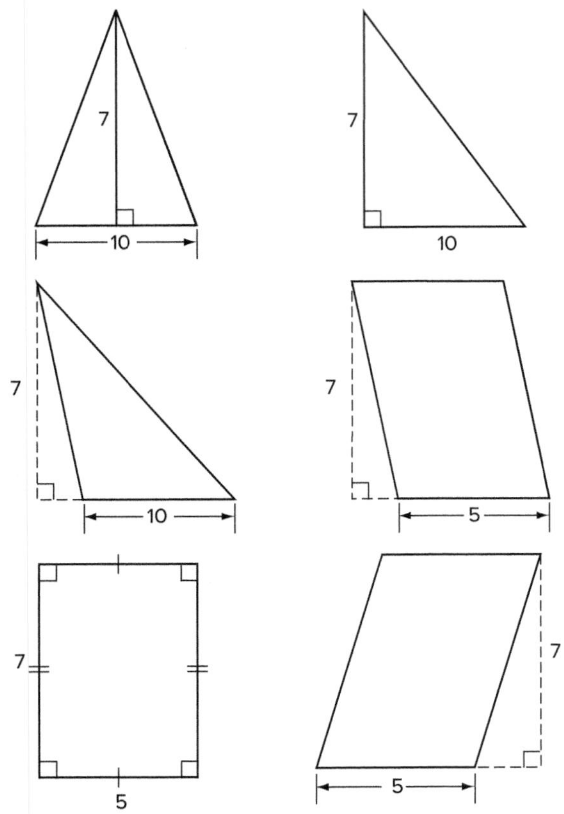

41. Sample answer: To find the area of the parallelogram, you can measure the height $\overline{PT}$ and then measure one of the bases $\overline{PQ}$ or $\overline{SR}$ and multiply the height by the base to get the area. You can also measure the height $\overline{SW}$ and measure one of the bases $\overline{QR}$ or $\overline{PS}$ and then multiply the height by the base to get the area. It doesn't matter which side you choose to use as the base, as long as you use the height that is perpendicular to that base to calculate the area.

Lesson 10-2

33a.

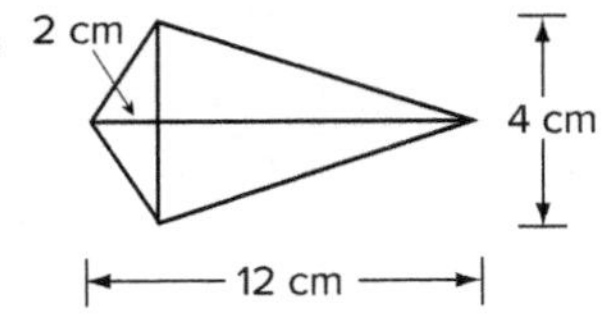

33b.

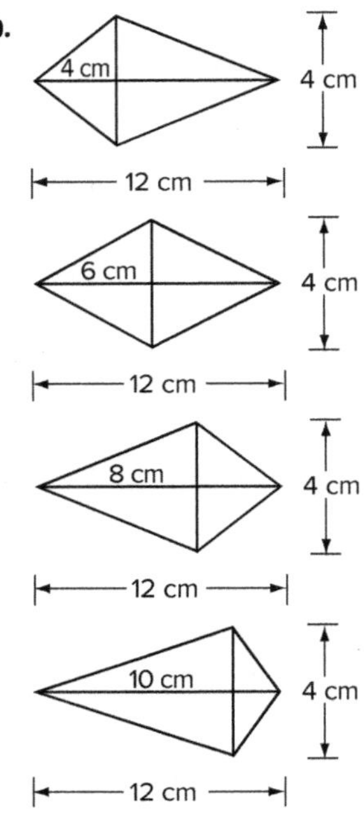

33c.

x	*P*
2 cm	26.1 cm
4 cm	25.4 cm
6 cm	25.3 cm
8 cm	25.4 cm
10 cm	26.1 cm

33d.

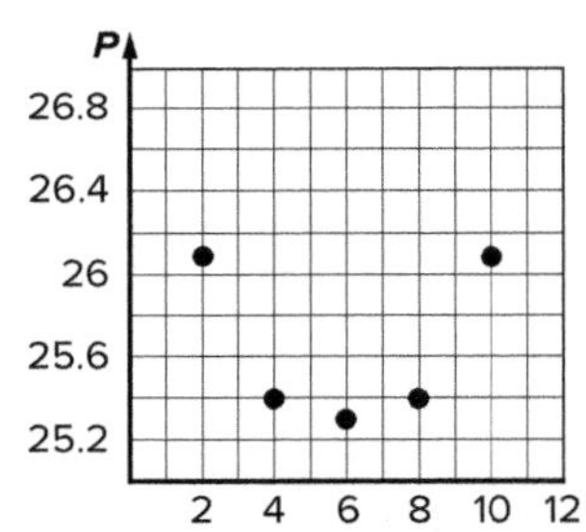

33e. Sample answer: Based on the graph, the perimeter will be minimized when $x = 6$. This value is significant because when $x = 6$, the figure is a rhombus.

36.

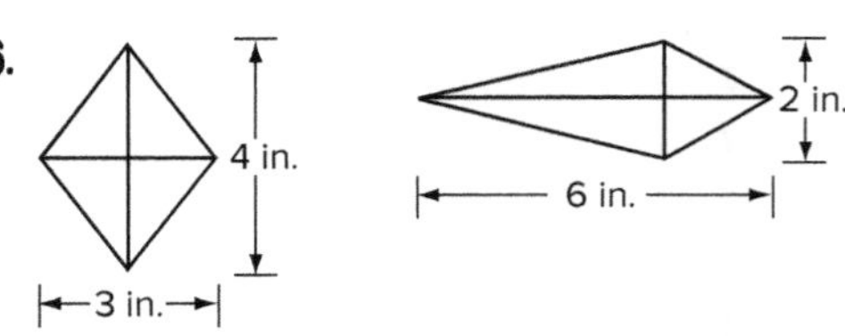

Sample answer: Because the area formula for both a rhombus and a kite is one half the product of the lengths of the two diagonals, if the area is 6 square inches, the product of the two diagonals must be 12. I used 3 and 4 inches for the diagonals of the rhombus and 2 and 6 inches for the diagonals of the kite.

38. Sample answer: You can use trigonometry and known angle and side measures to find unknown triangular measures that are required to calculate the area.

Lesson 10-3

48. The ratio of the area of a sector to the area of a whole circle is equal to the ratio of the corresponding arc length to the circumference of the circle. Let A represent the area of the sector.

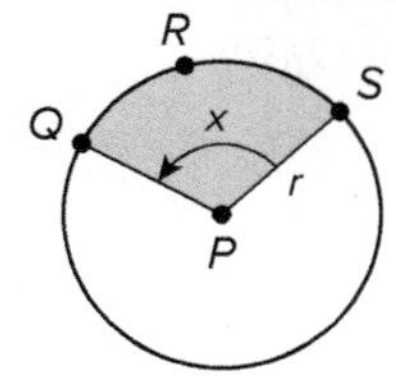

$\frac{A}{\pi r^2} = \frac{\text{length of } \widehat{QRS}}{2\pi r}$ $\quad$ $\frac{\text{area of sector}}{\text{area of circle}} = \frac{\text{arc length}}{\text{circumference of circle}}$

$\frac{A}{\pi r^2} = \frac{\frac{\pi r x}{180}}{2\pi r}$ $\quad$ The length of $\widehat{QRS}$ is $\frac{\pi r x}{180}$.

$A = \frac{\pi r^2 x}{360}$ $\quad$ Solve for A.

49. Sample answer: If the radius of the circle doubles, the area will not double. If the radius of the circle doubles, the area will be four times as great. Because the radius is squared, if you multiply the radius by 2, you multiply the area by 2^2, or 4. If the arc length of a sector is doubled, the area of the sector is doubled. Because the arc length is not raised to a power, if the arc length is doubled, the area would also be twice as large.

Lesson 10-4

39. Sample answer: You can decompose the figure into shapes of which you know the area formulas. Then, you can sum all of the areas to find the total area of the figure.

Lesson 10-5

25. Neither; sample answer: in order to find the area of the enlarged circle, you can multiply the radius by the scale factor and substitute it into the area formula, or you can multiply the area formula by the scale factor squared. The formula for the area of the enlargement is $A = \pi(kr)^2$ or $A = k^2\pi r^2$.

CHAPTER 11

Extending Volume

SUGGESTED PACING (DAYS)

	Instruction	Review & Assess
90 min.	6	1
45 min.	11	2

Track Your Progress

This chapter focuses on content from the **Geometric Measrurement and Dimension** and **Modeling with Geometry** domains.

THEN	NOW	NEXT
G.GMD.1 Give an informal argument for the formulas for the circumference of a circle, area of a circle, volume of a cylinder, pyramid, and cone. **G.GPE.7** Use coordinates to prove simple geometric theorems algebraically. Use coordinates to compute perimeters of polygons and areas of triangles and rectangles. **G.MG.1** Use geometric shapes, their measures, and their properties to describe objects. **G.MG.3** Apply geometric methods to solve problems.	**G.GMD.1** Give an informal argument for the formulas for the circumference of a circle, area of a circle, volume of a cylinder, pyramid, and cone. **G.GMD.3** Use volume formulas for cylinders, pyramids, cones, and spheres to solve problems. **G.GMD.4** Identify the shapes of two-dimensional cross-sections of three-dimensional objects, and identify three-dimensional objects generated by rotations of two-dimensional objects. **G.MG.2** Apply concepts of density based on area and volume in modeling situations.	**S.CP.1** Describe events as subsets of a sample space using characteristics of the outcomes, or as unions, intersections, or complements of other events. **S.CP.2** Understand that two events A and B are independent if the probability of A and B occurring together is the product of their probabilities, and use this characterization to determine if they are independent. **S.CP.9** Use permutations and combinations to compute probabilities of compound events and solve problems. **S.MD.7** Analyze decisions and strategies using probability concepts.

Standards for Mathematical Practice

All of the Standards for Mathematical Practice will be covered in this chapter. The MP icon notes specific areas of coverage.

Teaching the Mathematical Practices

Help students develop the mathematical practices by asking questions like these.

Questioning Strategies As students approach problems in this chapter, help them develop mathematical practices by asking:

Sense-Making
- What are plane and axis symmetries in three-dimensional figures?
- How do you describe sets of points on a sphere?
- What is a congruent solid and how is it different than a similar solid?

Reasoning
- What is the difference between reflectional and rotational symmetry in two-dimensional figures?
- How would you compare and contrast Euclidean and spherical geometries?

Construct Arguments
- How do you find the volume of prisms, cylinders, pyramids, cones, or spheres?
- How do you find the surface area of a sphere?

Modeling
- How would you draw isometric views of three-dimensional figures?
- How would you use scale factors to find areas of similar figures?

Go Online!

StudySync:
SMP Modeling Videos

These demonstrate how to apply the Standards for Mathematical Practice to collaborate, discuss, and solve real-world math problems.

Go Online!

connectED.mcgraw-hill.com

LearnSmart | The Geometer's Sketchpad | Vocabulary | Tutor | Tools | Calculator Resources | Check | Watch

Customize Your Chapter

Use the *Plan & Present*, *Assignment Tracker*, and *Assessment* tools in ConnectED to introduce lesson concepts, assign personalized practice, and diagnose areas of student need.

Differentiated Instruction

Throughout the program, look for the icons to find specialized content designed for your students.

- AL Approaching Level
- OL On Level
- BL Beyond Level
- ELL English Language Learners

Personalize

Differentiated Resources

FOR EVERY CHAPTER	AL	OL	BL	ELL
Chapter Readiness Quizzes	●	●	◐	●
Chapter Tests	●	●	●	●
Standardized Test Practice	●	●	●	●
Vocabulary Review Games	●	●	◐	●
Anticipation Guide (English/Spanish)	●	●	◐	●
Student-Built Glossary	●	●	◐	●
Chapter Project	◐	●	●	●
FOR EVERY LESSON	**AL**	**OL**	**BL**	**ELL**
Personal Tutors (English/Spanish)	●	●	◐	●
Graphing Calculator Personal Tutors	●	●	●	●
Step-by-Step Solutions	●	●	◐	●
Self-Check Quizzes	●	●	●	●
5-Minute Check	●	●	●	●
Study Notebook	●	●	●	●
Study Guide and Intervention	●	●		●
Skills Practice (English/Spanish)	●	◐		●
Practice (English/Spanish)	◐	●	●	●
Word Problem Practice	◐	●	●	◐
Enrichment		●	●	●
Extra Examples	●	◐		◐
Interactive Classroom	●	●	●	●

◐ Aligned to this group ● Designed for this group

Engage

Featured IWB Resources

Personal Tutors let you hear a real teacher discuss each step to solving a problem. *Use with Lessons 11-1 through 11-6.*

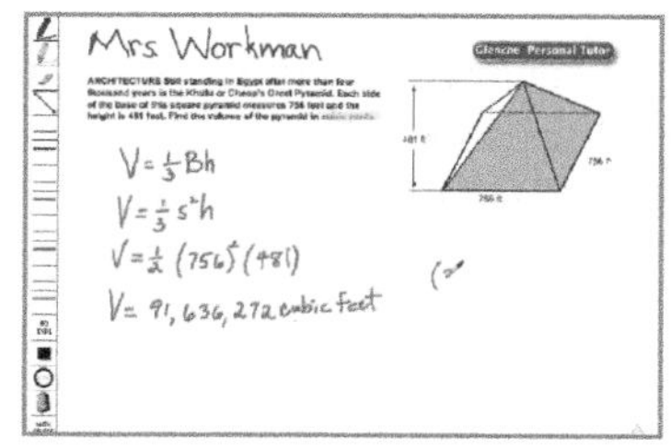

eLessons engage students and help build conceptual understanding of big ideas. *Use with Lessons 11-2 through 11-4.*

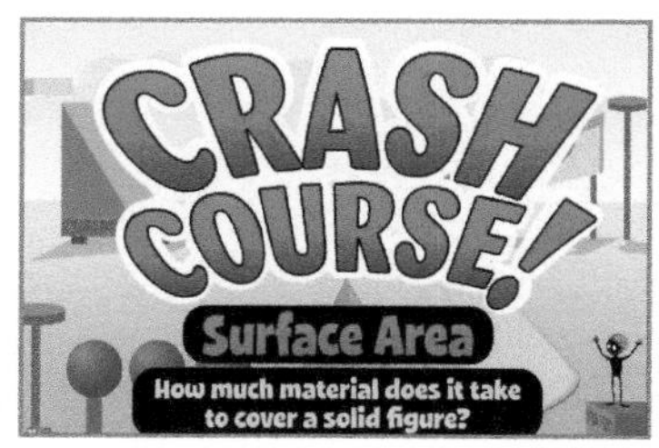

Geometry Tools provide students with tools to explore three-dimensional figures.

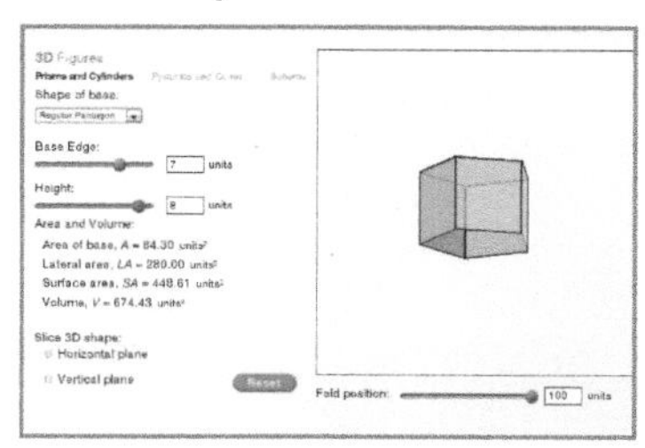

Time Management How long will it take to use these resources? Look for the clock in each lesson interleaf.

Introduce the Chapter

Mathematical Background

The surface area and volume of prisms, pyramids, spheres, cones, cylinders, and composites of these figures are given by formulas which can be used to solve problems. When one or more dimensions of a figure are changed, the corresponding change in volume and area can be calculated using the formulas for each figure.

Essential Question

At the end of this chapter, students should be able to answer the Essential Question.

How are two-dimensional and three-dimensional figures related? Sample answer: The faces and bases of three-dimensional figures are two-dimensional figures. For example, a pyramid has faces that are triangles and a base that is a polygon.

Apply Math to the Real World

ARCHITECTURE In this activity, students use what they already know about calculating area and volume to explore why these are important considerations in the design of buildings—in this case Biosphere 2. Have students complete this activity individually or in small groups. MP 1

CHAPTER 11

Extending Volume

THEN

You identified three-dimensional figures and calculated the surface areas and volumes for some common solids.

NOW

In this chapter, you will:

- Find lateral areas, surface areas, and volumes of various three-dimensional figures.
- Investigate Euclidean and spherical geometries.
- Use properties of similar solids.

MP WHY

ARCHITECTURE Architects use shapes to create designs that are interesting and functional. A striking example of this is Biosphere 2.

Use the Mathematical Practices to complete the activity.

1. **Use Tools** Use the Internet to learn more about the Biosphere 2 project.
2. **Reasoning** Why was it important for architects to know the surface areas of each biome?
3. **Apply Math** Choose one of the sections of Biosphere 2 and estimate its total surface area.
4. **Modeling** Use the 2-D Figures tool to find the area of the shapes that make up the section you selected.

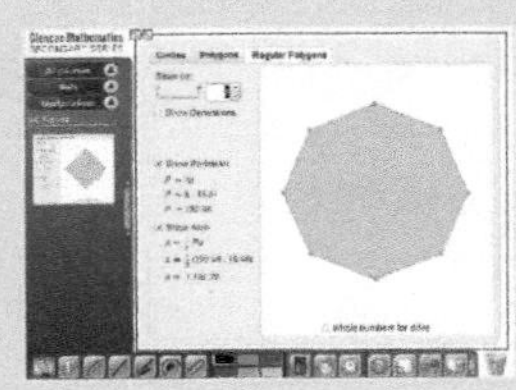

5. **Discuss** Why would knowing the volumes of the sections in Biosphere 2 be important?

ALEKS®

Your Student Success Tool ALEKS is an adaptive, personalized learning environment that identifies precisely what each student knows and is ready to learn—ensuring student success at all levels.

- **Formative Assessment**: Dynamic, detailed reports monitor students' progress toward standards mastery.
- **Automatic Differentiation**: Strengthen prerequisite skills and target individual learning gaps.
- **Personalized Instruction**: Supplement in-class instruction with personalized assessment and learning opportunities.

Go Online!

Chapter Project

Vacation Resorts Students use what they have learned about surface areas and volumes to complete a project. This chapter project addresses business literacy, as well as several specific skills identified as being essential to student success by the Framework for 21st Century Learning. MP 1, 3, 4, 8

Go Online to Guide Your Learning

Explore & Explain

3-D Figures

Use the **3-D Figures** tool to explore the volume of different pyramids and cones, as discussed in Lesson 11-3, or to find the volume and surface area of a sphere, as discussed in Lesson 11-4.

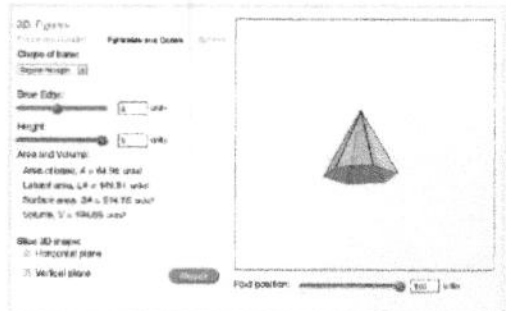

The Geometer's Sketchpad

Use **The Geometer's Sketchpad** to explore symmetries of regular polygons in Lesson 11-1 and the relationships between areas of similar figures in Lesson 11-6.

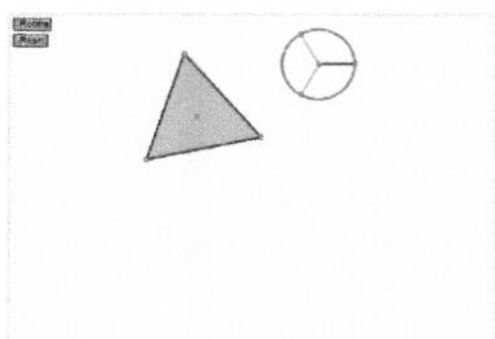

eBook Interactive Student Guide

Before starting the chapter, answer the **Chapter Focus** preview questions. Check your answers as you complete each lesson. At the end of the chapter, try the **Performance Task**.

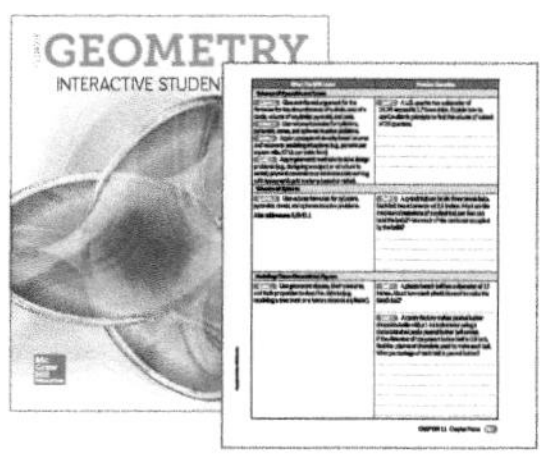

Organize

Foldables

Get organized! Create a **Surface Area and Volume Foldable** before you start the chapter to help you organize your notes about surface area and volume.

Collaborate

Chapter Project

In the **Vacation Resorts** project, you will use what you have learned about surface areas and volumes to complete a project that addresses business literacy.

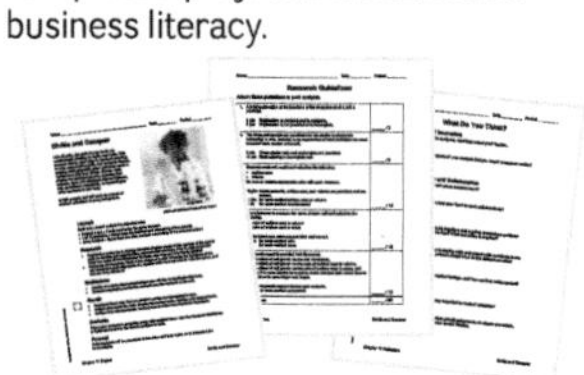

Focus

LEARNSMART

Need help studying? Complete the **Extend to Three Dimensions** domain in LearnSmart to review for the chapter test.

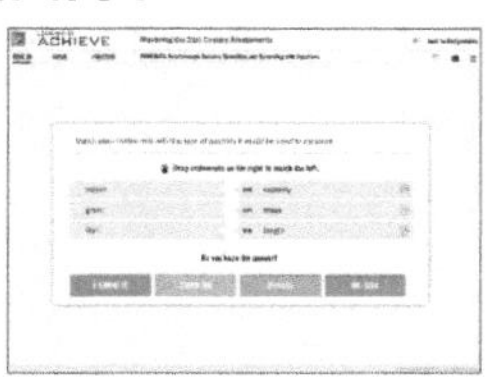

ALEKS

You can use the **Volumes and Surface Areas** topic in ALEKS to explore what you know about extending area and what you are ready to learn.*

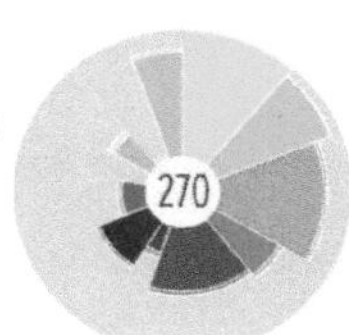

* Ask your teacher if this is part of your program.

Dinah Zike's FOLDABLES

Focus Use this Foldable concept map for students writing about three-dimensional figures.

Teach Begin with the central chapter theme of *Volume* as the title. Have students list the five types of solids introduced in Lesson 1-8 on each half of their Foldables, leaving room between each to list related formulas and definitions. Students can use their Foldables to take notes, define terms, record concepts, and define basic concepts.

When to Use It Use the appropriate tabs as students cover each lesson in this chapter. Students can add to the vocabulary tab during each lesson.

Go Online!

Extending Vocabulary

Looking for more interesting assessments? Learn strategies for teaching and assessing vocabulary with pocketbooks and notebook Foldables.

MP 3, 5

Get Ready for the Chapter

RtI Response to Intervention

Use the Concept Check results and the Intervention Planner chart to help you determine your Response to Intervention.

Intervention Planner

TIER 1 On Level OL

IF students miss 25% of the exercises or less,

THEN choose a resource:

Go Online!

- Skills Practice, Chapter 1, Chapter 10
- Self-Check Quiz

TIER 2 Approaching Level AL

IF students miss 50% of the exercises,

THEN choose a resource:

Go Online!

- Study Guide and Intervention, Ch. 1 and Ch. 10
- Extra Examples
- Personal Tutors
- Homework Help

Quick Review Math Handbook

TIER 3 Intensive Intervention

IF students miss 75% of the exercises,

THEN Use *Math Triumphs, Geometry*

Go Online!

- Extra Examples
- Personal Tutors
- Homework Help
- Review Vocabulary

Get Ready for the Chapter

Go Online! for Vocabulary Review Games and key vocabulary in 13 languages.

Connecting Concepts

Concept Check

Review the concepts used in this chapter by answering the questions below.

1. **CRAFTS** Michelle wants to cover a kite frame with fabric. The length of one diagonal is 16 inches and the other diagonal is 22 inches.
   a. Describe how to find the area of a kite. **Take one-half the product of the lengths of the diagonals**
   b. Find the area of the surface of the kite. **176 in^2**

Find the area of each figure.

2. 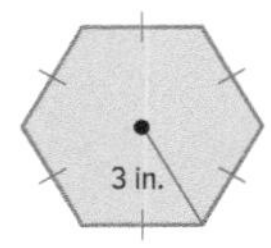

23.4 in^2

3. 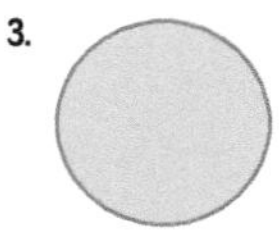
$C = 16\pi$
64 π

4. What is the equation to determine the area of a trapezoid? $A = \frac{1}{2}h(b_1 + b_2)$
5. Given $8^2 + 7^2 = c^2$, what would be the first step to solve the equation? **Evaluate the exponents.**
6. Given $c^2 = 133$, how would you solve the equation for c? **Take the square root of each side.**

Performance Task Review

You can use the concepts and skills in the chapter to solve problems for a candle and soap company. Knowing how to determine surface areas and volumes will help you finish the Performance Task at the end of the chapter.

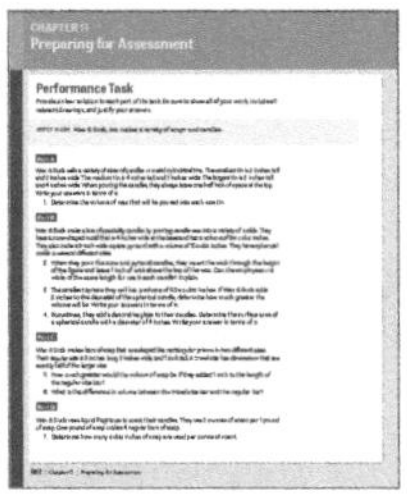

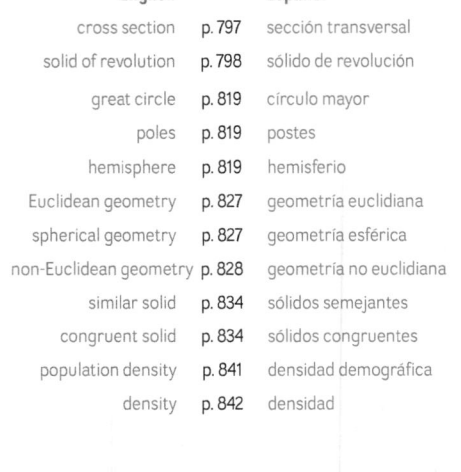

MP In this Performance Task you will:

- make sense of problems and persevere in solving them
- model with mathematics
- attend to precision

New Vocabulary

English		Español
cross section	p. 797	sección transversal
solid of revolution	p. 798	sólido de revolución
great circle	p. 819	círculo mayor
poles	p. 819	postes
hemisphere	p. 819	hemisferio
Euclidean geometry	p. 827	geometría euclidiana
spherical geometry	p. 827	geometría esférica
non-Euclidean geometry	p. 828	geometría no euclidiana
similar solid	p. 834	sólidos semejantes
congruent solid	p. 834	sólidos congruentes
population density	p. 841	densidad demográfica
density	p. 842	densidad

Review Vocabulary

regular polyhedron poliedro regular a polyhedron in which all of the faces are regular congruent polygons

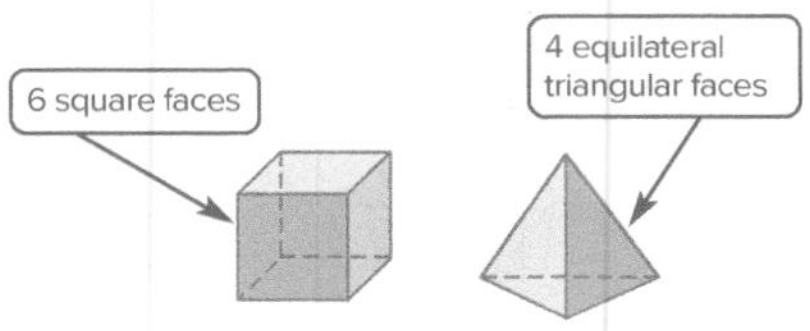

Key Vocabulary ELL

Introduce the key vocabulary in the chapter using the routine below.

Define A cross section is the intersection of a solid and a plane, and it depends on the angle of the plane.

Example The horizontal cross section of a cube is a square.

Ask What is the cross section of a sphere? What are the possible cross sections of a square prism? circle; square or rectangle

LESSON 11-1

Cross Sections and Solids of Revolution

SUGGESTED PACING (DAYS)

	Explore	Instruction
90 min.	0.5	0.5
45 min.	1.0	1.0

Track Your Progress

Objectives

1 Identify cross sections of three-dimensional figures.

2 Identify three-dimensional objects generated by rotations of two-dimensional objects.

Mathematical Background

The intersection of a solid with a plane is called a cross section of the solid. By rotating a two-dimensional shape around a line of rotation, a three-dimensional figure is formed.

THEN

G.CO.4. Develop definitions of rotations, reflections, and translations in terms of angles, circles, perpendicular lines, parallel lines, and line segments.

NOW

G.GMD.4 Identify the shapes of two-dimensional cross-sections of three-dimensional objects, and identify three-dimensional objects generated by rotations of two-dimensional objects.

NEXT

G.GMD.1. Give an informal argument for the formulas for the circumference of a circle, area of a circle, volume of a cylinder, pyramid, and cone.

G.GMD.3. Use volume formulas for cylinders, pyramids, cones, and spheres to solve problems.

Go Online! All of these resources and more are available at connectED.mcgraw-hill.com

Chapter Projects provide students the opportunity to use what they have learned about volumes to complete a real-world project about cell growth.

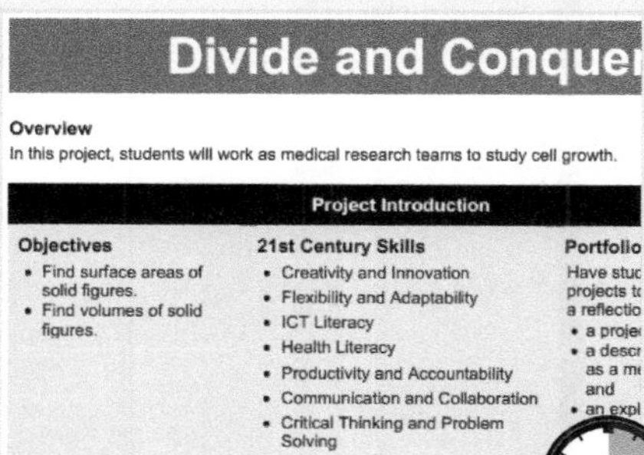

Use at Beginning of Lesson

Use the **eGlossary** to define cross section, solid of revolution, and other key vocabulary in the lesson.

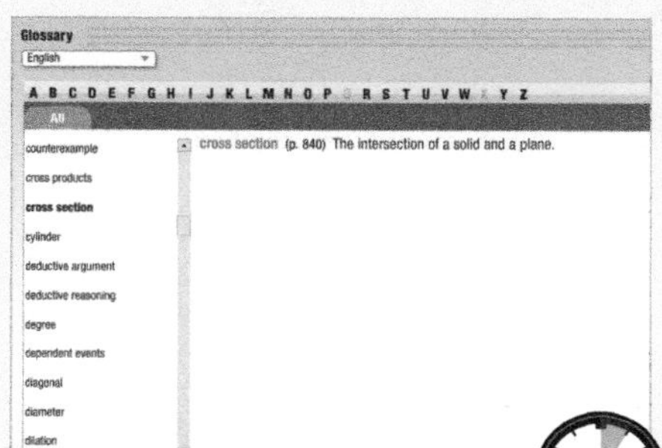

Glossary
English
cross section (p. 840) The intersection of a solid and a plane.

Use at Beginning of Lesson

eToolkit allows students to explore and enhance their understanding of math concepts.

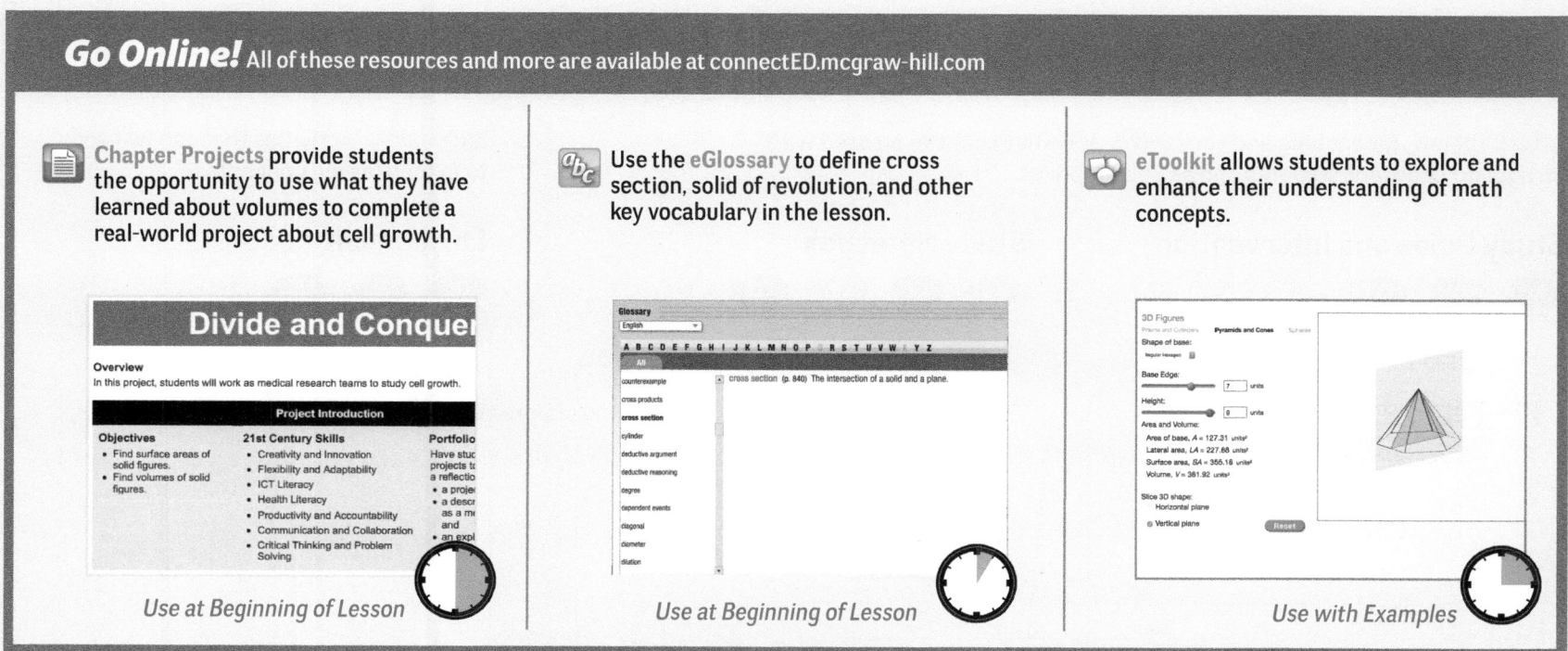

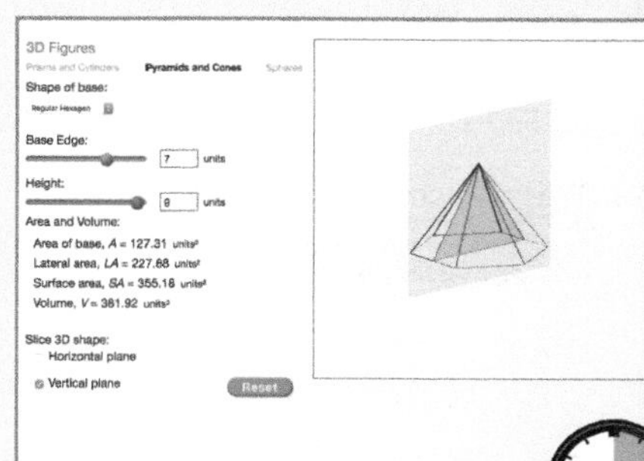

Use with Examples

OER Using Open Educational Resources

SketchUp Have students create and explore three-dimensional figures and their cross sections using **SketchUp**. *Use as in-class activity*

Go Online!
connectED.mcgraw-hill.com

Worksheets

Differentiate Your Resources

Extra Practice Additional practice or homework; Skills Practice is best for approaching-level students and Practice is best for on-level and beyond-level students

Skills Practice

AL OL ELL

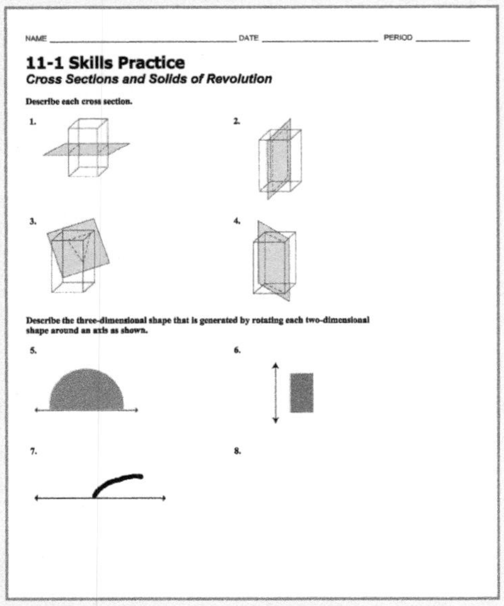

Practice

AL OL BL ELL

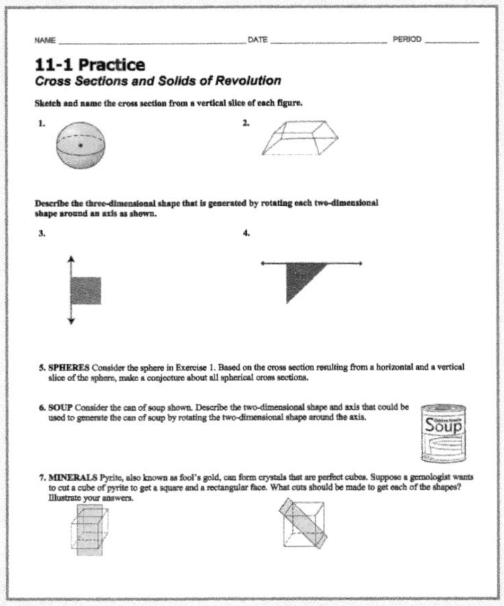

Word Problem Practice

AL OL BL ELL

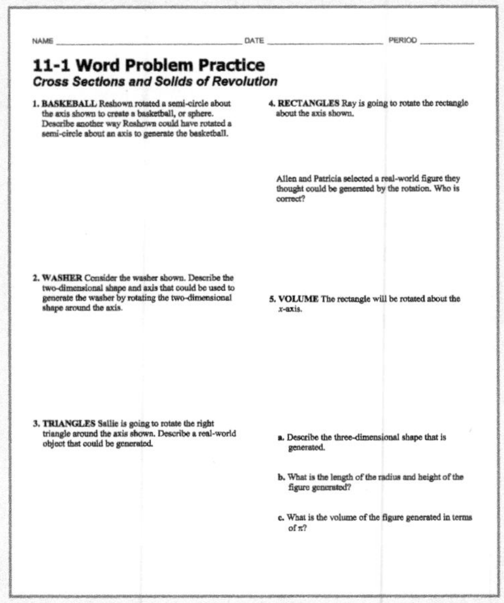

Intervention Reteaching and vocabulary activities that can be used with struggling or absent students and as ELL support

Study Guide and Intervention

AL OL ELL

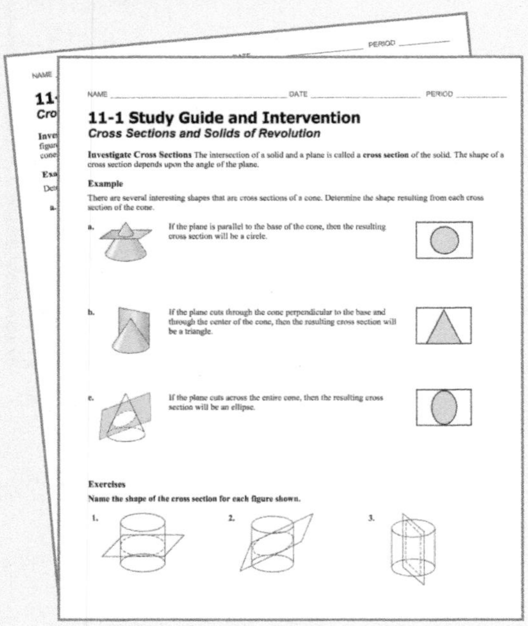

Study Notebook

AL OL BL ELL

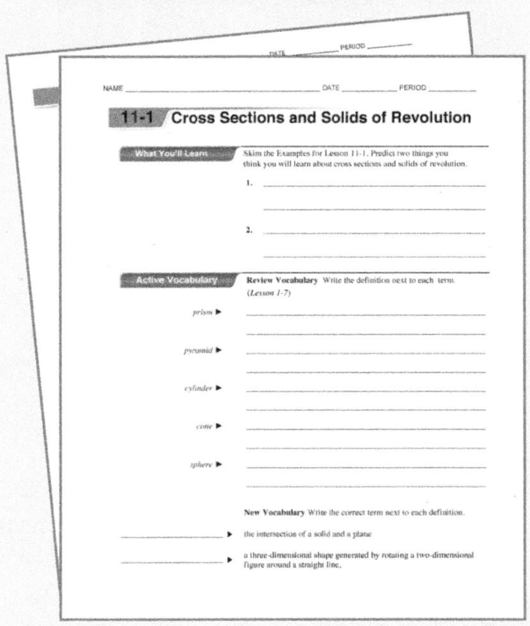

Extension Activities that can be used to extend lesson concepts

Enrichment

OL BL ELL

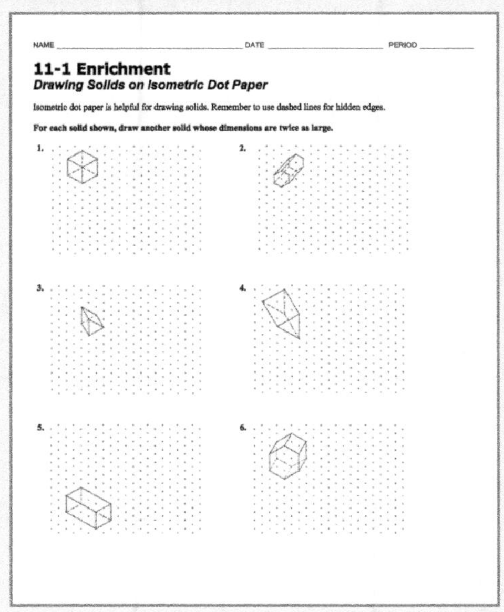

EXPLORE 11-1

Geometry Lab

Solids Formed by Translation

Mathematical Practices
MP 4 Model with mathematics.

We can relate some three-dimensional solids to two-dimensional figures with which we are already familiar. Some three-dimensional solids can be formed by translating a two-dimensional figure along a vector.

A **right solid** has base(s) that are perpendicular to the edges connecting them or connecting the base and the vertex of the solid. Some right solids are formed by translating a two-dimensional figure along a vector that is perpendicular to the plane in which the figure lies.

Activity 1

Identify and sketch the solid formed by translating a horizontal rectangle vertically.

To help visualize the solid formed, let a playing card represent the rectangle and lay it flat on a table so that it is horizontal. To show the translation of the rectangle vertically, stack other cards neatly, one by one, on top of the first.

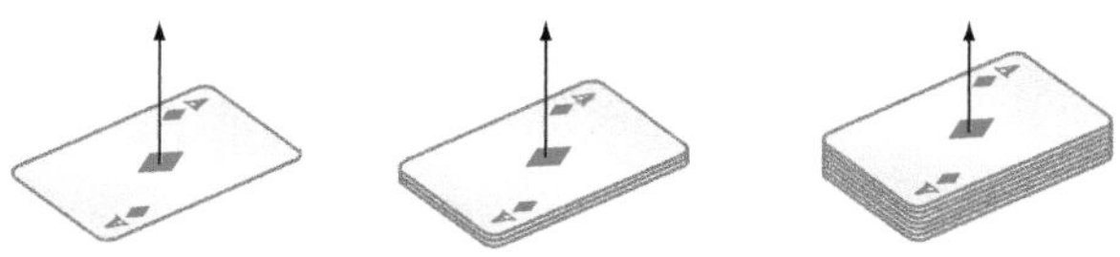

Notice that the solid formed is a right rectangular prism, which has a rectangular base, a translated copy of this base on the opposite side parallel to the base, and four congruent edges connecting the two congruent rectangles. These edges are parallel to each other but perpendicular to the bases. A sketch of the figure is shown.

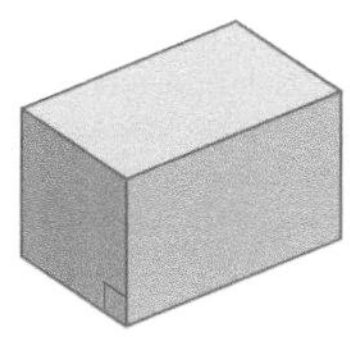

Model and Analyze

1–2. See margin for drawings.

1. Use congruent triangular tangram pieces to identify and sketch the solid formed by translating a horizontal triangle vertically. right triangular prism

2. Use the coins from a roll of quarters to identify and sketch the solid formed by translating a horizontal circle vertically. right cylinder

Identify and sketch the solid formed by translating a vertical two-dimensional figure horizontally. 3–5. See margin for drawings.

3. rectangle

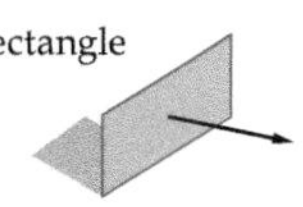

right rectangular prism

4. triangle

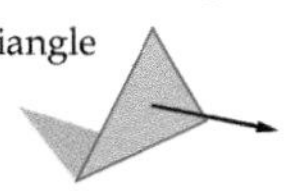

right triangular prism

5. circle

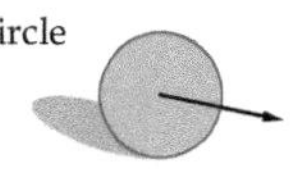

right cylinder

6. MP **REASONING** Are the solids formed in Exercises 3, 4, and 5 right solids? Explain your reasoning. Yes; the edges are perpendicular to the bases.

Launch

Objective Identify and sketch solids formed by translating two-dimensional figures along vectors.

Materials

- playing cards
- triangular tangram pieces
- rolls of quarters or other coins
- ruler

Teaching Tip

Have students predict what solid will result before doing each activity and exercise.

Teach

Working in Cooperative Groups Have students work in mixed ability pairs, taking turns stacking each set of concrete models. Encourage students to use concrete models for Exercises 3–5 as well. ELL

Additional Answers

1.

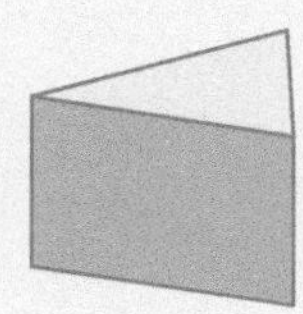

2.

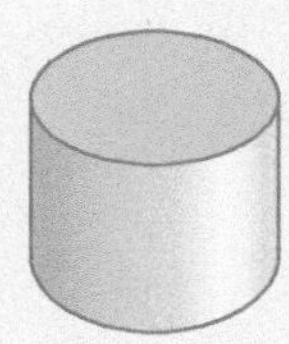

3.

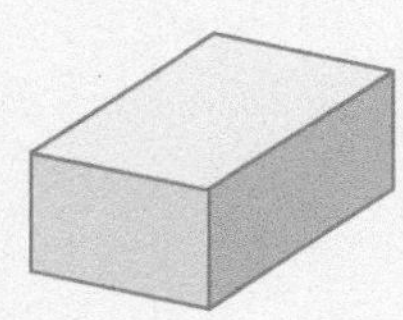

4.

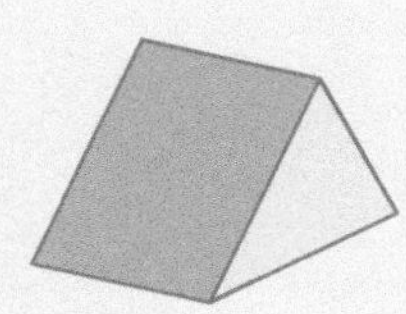

5.

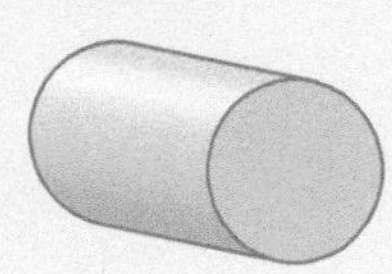

Practice **Have students complete Activities 1 and 2 and Exercises 1–5 and 7–11.**

Assess

Formative Assessment

Use Exercises 6 and 12 to assess each student's understanding of right and oblique solids.

From Concrete to Abstract

Ask students to summarize what they have learned about solids formed by translation and about the difference between right and oblique solids.

Additional Answers

7.

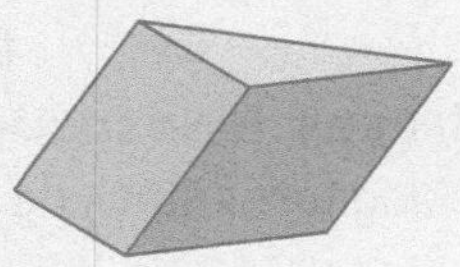

8.

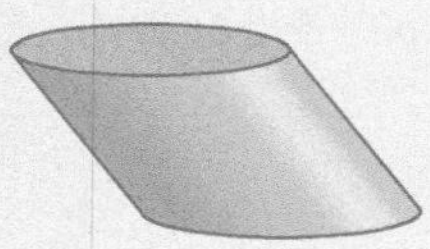

EXPLORE 11-1

Geometry Lab

Solids Formed by Translation *Continued*

An **oblique solid** has base(s) that are not perpendicular to the edges connecting the two bases or vertex. An oblique solid can be formed by translating a two-dimensional figure along an oblique vector that is neither parallel nor perpendicular to the plane in which the two-dimensional figure lies.

Activity 2

Identify and sketch the solid formed by translating a horizontal rectangle along an oblique vector.

Let a playing card represent the rectangle. Lay it flat on a table so that it is horizontal. To show the translation of the rectangle along an oblique line, stack other cards one by one on top of the first so that the cards are shifted from the center of the previous card the same amount each time.

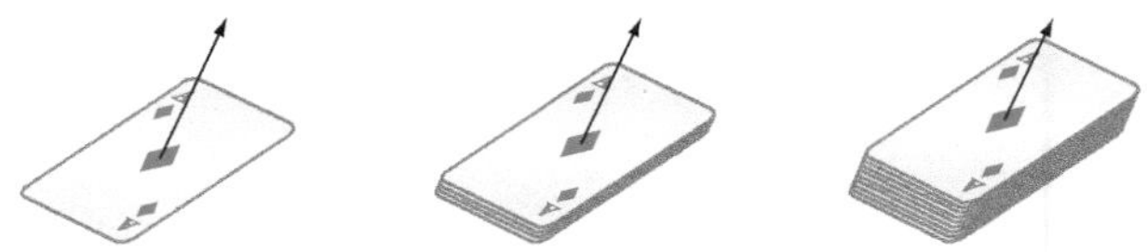

The solid formed is an oblique rectangular prism, which has a rectangular base, a translated copy of this base on the opposite side parallel to the base, and four congruent edges connecting the two congruent rectangles. These edges are parallel to each other but oblique to the bases. A sketch of the figure is shown.

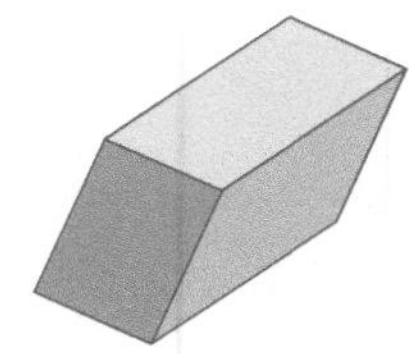

Model and Analyze

Identify and sketch the solid formed by translating each vertical two-dimensional figure along an oblique vector. Use concrete models if needed. 7–8. See margin for drawings.

7. triangle

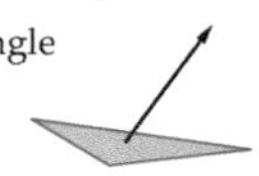

oblique triangular prism

8. circle

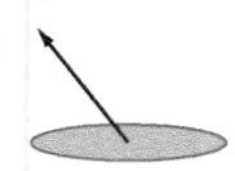

oblique cylinder

Identify each solid as *right*, *oblique*, or *neither*.

9.

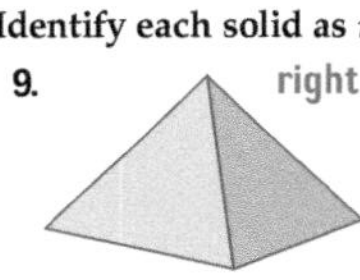

right

10.

neither

11.

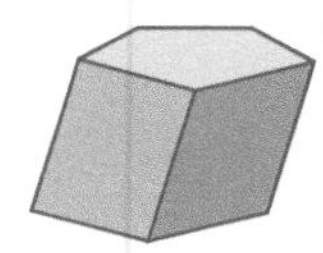

oblique

12. MP **REASONING** Can a pyramid with a square base be formed by translating the base vertically? Explain your reasoning. **No; this translation would result in a square-based rectangular prism.**

LESSON 1

Cross Sections and Solids of Revolution

Then

- You explored area of two-dimensional figures and surface area of three-dimensional solids.

Now

1. Identify cross sections of three-dimensional solids.
2. Identify three-dimensional objects generated by rotations of two-dimensional figures.

Why?

- Video game developers use technology to make the gaming environments appear three-dimensional. As players move within the various video game worlds, objects are realistically shown in 3-D from different perspectives.

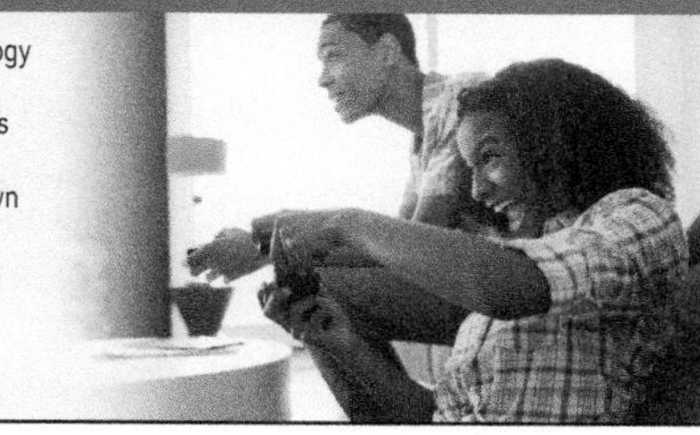

New Vocabulary

cross section
solid of revolution

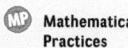

Mathematical Practices

2 Reason abstractly and quantitatively.
4 Model with mathematics.

Content Standards

G.GMD.4 Identify the shapes of two-dimensional cross-sections of three-dimensional objects, and identify three-dimensional objects generated by rotations of two-dimensional objects.

1 Investigate Cross Sections

A **cross section** is the intersection of a solid and a plane. The shape of the cross section depends on the angle of the plane.

G.GMD.4

Example 1 Identify Cross Sections of Solids

Describe each cross section.

a.

When a plane parallel to the base of the pyramid intersects the pyramid, the cross section is a square. When an angled plane passes through opposite faces of the pyramid, the cross section is a trapezoid. When a plane perpendicular to the base of the pyramid passes through the vertex of the pyramid, the cross section is a triangle.

b. sphere, cone, cylinder

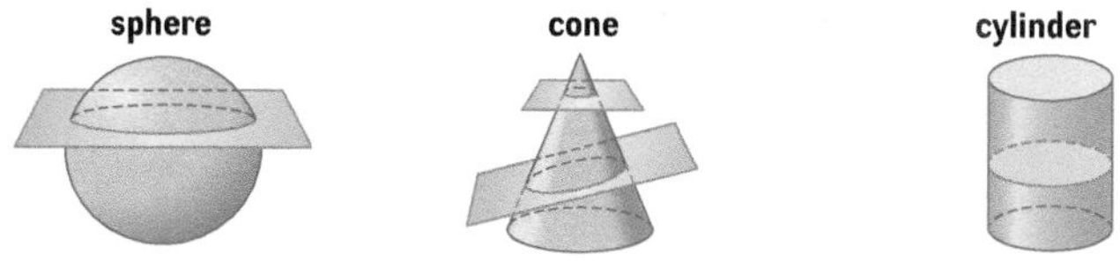

Every cross section of a sphere is a circle. When a plane intersects a cone or cylinder parallel to the base, then the cross section is a circle. When a plane intersects a cone at an angle relative to the base and does not intersect the vertex or base of the cone, then the cross section is an ellipse.

Guided Practice 1A. circle, semicircle 1B. circle, rectangle 1C. triangle, rectangle

1. Determine the shape of each cross section formed by the intersection of two planes with the solid. One plane is parallel to the base of each solid, and one plane is perpendicular to the base of each solid.

A.

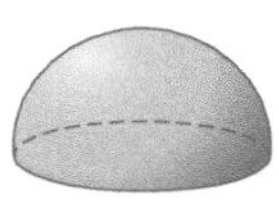

B.

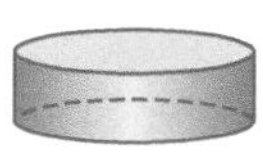

C.

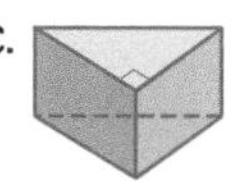

MP Mathematical Practices Strategies

Look for and make use of structure.
Help students visualize complicated structures and recognize relationships between two-dimensional and three-dimensional objects. Ask:

- How can you get more familiar with the properties of three-dimensional figures like pyramids, prisms, and cones? Look at or create drawings; handle and study real objects with those shapes; visualize the intersections of these objects with planes so you can picture cross sections.
- Give two examples of solid figures with curved surfaces that can have cross sections that are polygons. The cross section of a cone sliced vertically through the vertex is a triangle. The cross section of a cylinder sliced perpendicular to the bases is a rectangle.
- What is one characteristic of all three-dimensional figures created by rotating a two-dimensional figure around an axis? They all have curved sides.

Launch

Have students read the Why? section of the lesson.

- Where are other places that represent three-dimensional objects? Sample answer: paintings, television
- When an object on a video game is viewed from only one side, what are some ways that the object can be made to appear three-dimensional? Sample answer: the use of shadow
- How does movement help objects appear three-dimensional? Sample answer: As an object moves, you can see its different sides.

Teach

Ask the scaffolded questions for each example to build conceptual understanding for students at all levels.

1 Investigate Cross Sections

Example 1 Identify Cross Sections of Solid Figures

AL Give an example of a solid and a cross section that would produce a rectangle. Sample answer: a diagonal cut of a cube

OL How could you slice a cone to get a triangle? a cut perpendicular to the base through the vertex of the cone

BL If an angled cut of a cone intersected the base, what would the cross section look like? It would have symmetrical curving sides and a straight side.

Need Another Example?

Prisms A prism is a polyhedron with congruent, parallel bases. If a plane intersects the prism parallel to the base, determine the shape of the cross section. The cross section will be the same shape and size as the base.

Go Online!

Interactive Whiteboard

Use the *eLesson*, *Lesson Presentation*, or *Interactive Classroom* to present this lesson.

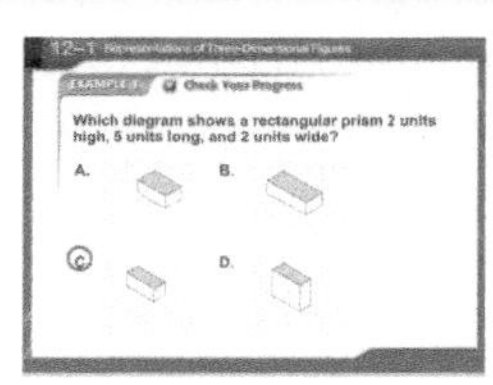

2 Investigate Solids of Revolution

Example 2 Identify Solids of Revolution

AL What solid figure is produced by rotating a quarter circle around an axis? a hemisphere or half of a sphere

OL What kind of solid figure has one curved face and one flat face? cone

BL How could you intersect a right rectangular prism to form a pentagonal cross section? Sample answer: Whenever a plane intersects the face of a solid, it forms the edge of a cross section. To form a pentagonal cross section, I would cut the solid through 5 of its 6 faces.

Need Another Example?
Describe the three-dimensional solid generated by rotating a rectangle 6 feet long and 4 inches wide around an axis that coincides with one of the shorter sides. Sample answer: a large cylinder with a diameter of 12 feet and a thickness of 4 inches.

Teaching Tip
Modeling Look for objects in the classroom that show rotation around an axis. For example, spin a coin or (unbreakable) plate to show a sphere. Open a hinged door to show that a rectangle rotating around an axis sweeps out a cylindrical shape.

MP Teaching the Mathematical Practices
Tools Help students use concrete models of 3-D objects and also find dynamic geometry software and online resources that allow interactive experimenting with cross sections and solids of revolution.

Teaching Tip
Reasoning Help students make sense of the relationships between the sides of a two-dimensional figure and the surfaces of the three-dimensional figure formed by rotating it around an axis. For example, if a right triangle is rotated around an axis through one of the legs, the other leg forms a flat face, and the hypotenuse forms a curved surface.

2 Investigate Solids of Revolution A **solid of revolution** is a solid figure obtained by rotating a plane figure or curve around an axis. The shape of the solid of revolution depends on the location of the axis and the shape of the plane figure or curve being rotated.

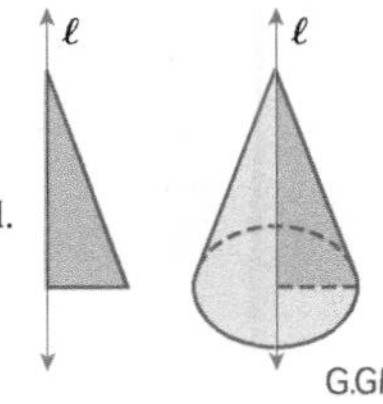

G.GMD.4

Study Tip
MP **Tools** You can use many different tools to help you visualize the solids of revolution. Straws or dowel rods could be used to represent the axis of rotations. Card stock or heavy construction paper can be attached to the straws or dowel rods to represent the two dimensional figures. You could also sketch the figure using dynamic geometry software or graph paper.

Example 2 Identify Solids of Revolution

Describe the three-dimensional solid generated by rotating the circle around the given axis.

As the circle rotates about the axis, a sphere is formed.

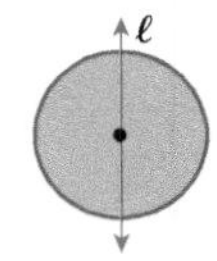

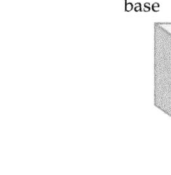

Guided Practice

Describe the three-dimensional solid generated by rotating each two-dimensional shape around the given axis.

2A. Right triangle

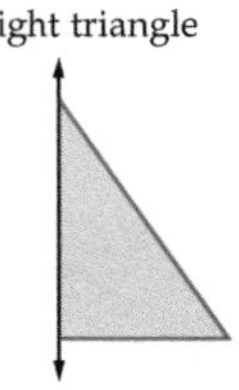

cone

2B. Square

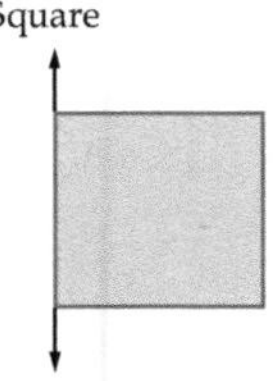

cylinder

2C. Semicircle

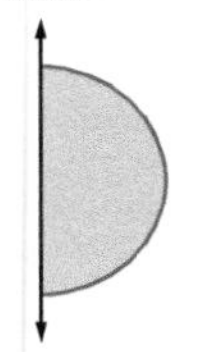

sphere

Check Your Understanding
○ = Step-by-Step Solutions begin on page R13.

Go Online! for a Self-Check Quiz

Example 1 G.GMD.4

Determine the shape of each cross section formed by the intersection of the described plane with the solid.

1. plane perpendicular to the base

rectangle

2. plane parallel to the base

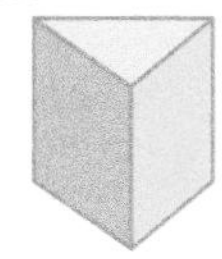

triangle

3. plane at an angle relative to the base through opposite faces

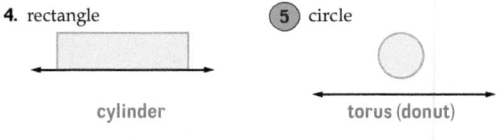

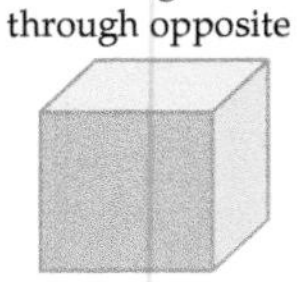

rectangle

Example 2 G.GMD.4

Describe the three-dimensional solid generated by rotating each two-dimensional shape around the given axis.

4. rectangle

cylinder

5. circle

torus (donut)

6. triangle

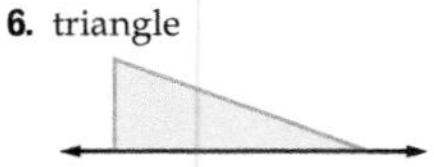

cone

Practice and Problem Solving

Extra Practice is found on page R11.

Example 1 G.GMD.4

Determine the shape of each cross section formed by the intersection of the described plane with the solid.

7. plane at an angle relative to the bases that does not intersect either base

ellipse

8. plane at an angle relative to the base that intersects the base

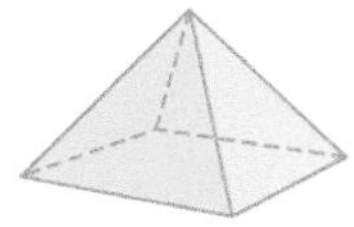

trapezoid

9. angled plane that intersects the sphere

circle

Example 2 G.GMD.4

Describe the three-dimensional solid generated by rotating each two-dimensional shape around the given axis.

10.

bowl shape

11. rectangle

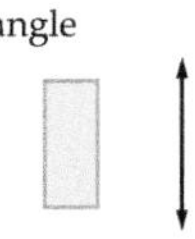

open cylinder (tube)

12. exponential function

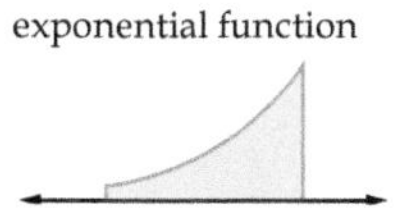

horn shape

B 13. **FOOD** Describe how the cheese at the right can be sliced so that the slices form each shape.

a. rectangle slice perpendicular to the base
b. triangle slice parallel to the base
c. trapezoid slice at an angle

Describe each cross section.

14.

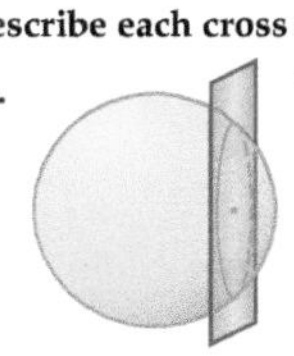

circle

15.

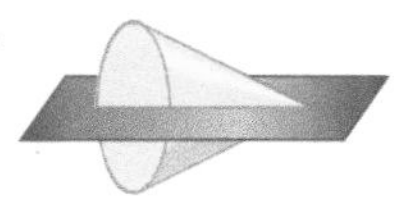

triangle

16. If a plane intersects with a cube at a vertex of the cube, what is the shape of the cross section? Explain your answer. See margin.

17. **UFO** Tanya has a model of a UFO. Sketch a two-dimensional figure that could be rotated around an axis to produce a three-dimensional solid similar to the model. See margin.

C 18. **DESIGN** Describe how you could create a tube with a length of 10 inches, a diameter of 2 inches, and a thickness of $\frac{1}{4}$ inch by rotating a 2-D figure around an axis. Make a sketch and label it. See margin.

19. **POTTERY** A potter creates three-dimensional objects by shaping the clay as it spins on a potter's wheel. Describe the line or curve that could be rotated around a vertical axis to produce the vase shown. See margin.

20. **COOKIES** Michelle is making cookies with a cylindrical roll of cookie dough. Describe how she can cut the cookie dough to make each shape. See margin.

a. circle b. longest rectangle c. oval d. shorter rectangle

Practice

Formative Assessment Use Exercises 1–6 to assess students' understanding of the concepts in the lesson.

The Practice and Problem Solving exercises assess the content taught in the lesson.

Levels of Complexity Chart

The levels of the exercises progress from 1 to 3, with Level 1 indicating the lowest level of complexity.

Exercises	7–12	13–17, 27–38	18–26
C Level 3			●
B Level 2		●	
Level 1	●		

Additional Answers

16. a triangle; Three faces of the cube meet to form the vertex, so the cross section is a two-dimensional figure with three sides.

17. A sample sketch is shown.

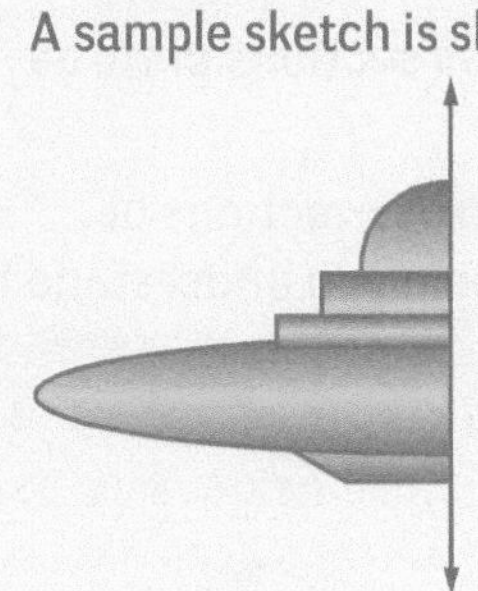

18. Take a rectangle 10 inches long and $\frac{1}{4}$ inch wide and rotate it around a horizontal axis, with the outer edge of the rectangle at a distance of 1 inch from the axis.

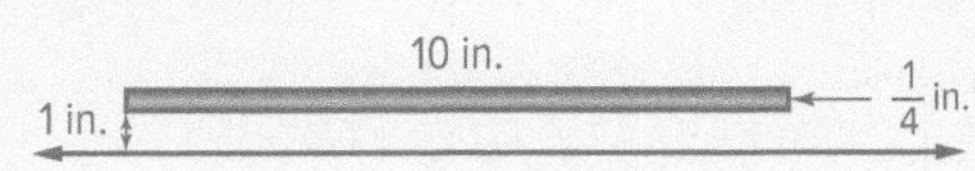

19. Sample answer: The curve would have the same shape as the edge of the vase. The curve would look like the letter *S* stretched vertically.

20a. Make a vertical cut.

20b. Make a horizontal cut through the center of the bases.

20c. Make an angled cut.

20d. Make a horizontal cut not through the center of the bases.

Differentiated Homework Options

Levels	AL Basic	OL Core	BL Advanced
Exercises	7–12, 24, 25, 27–38	7–15 odd, 16–25, 27–38	18–26, (optional: 27–38)
2-Day Option	7–11 odd, 27–38	7–12	
	8–12 even, 24, 25	13–25, 27–38	

You can use ALEKS to provide additional remediation support with personalized instruction and practice.

Go Online! eBook

Interactive Student Guide

Use the *Interactive Student Guide* to deepen conceptual understanding.

- Representations of Three-Dimensional Figures

Extra Practice

See page R11 for extra exercises for students who are approaching level or for on-level students who need additional reinforcement.

Additional Answers

22a. 

22b. 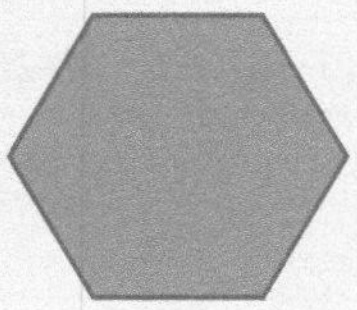

22c. 

Follow-Up

Students have explored cross sections of three-dimensional figures.

Ask: How can studying the cross sections of three-dimensional figures help you understand the properties of the figures? Sample answer: Knowing the formula for the area and perimeter of the two-dimensional cross sections lends insight into the formulas for the volume and surface area of the three-dimensional figures you are studying.

21. **ART** A piece of clay in the shape of a rectangular prism is cut in half as shown at the right.

a. Describe the shape of the cross section. **rectangle**

b. Describe how the clay could be cut to make the cross section a triangle. **Cut off a corner of the clay.**

22. **EARTH SCIENCE** Crystals are solids in which the atoms are arranged in regular geometrical patterns. Sketch a cross section formed by a plane parallel to the base of each crystal. **See margin.**

a. tetragonal **b.** hexagonal **c.** monoclinic

23. Which of the following chess pieces can be created by rotating a two-dimensional figure around a vertical axis? **queen, bishop, rook, pawn**

G.GMD.4

H.O.T. Problems Use Higher-Order Thinking Skills

24. **MP CRITIQUE ARGUMENTS** Ellen says that if you slice a sphere at an angle, you get an elliptical cross section. Is she correct? Explain your answer. **No, the cross section of a sphere is always a circle, not an ellipse.**

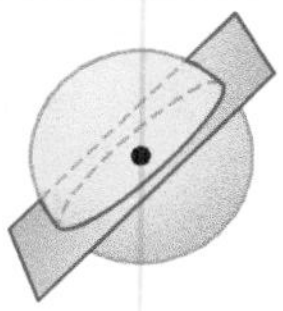

25. **MP REASONING** If you slice off the top of a cone, you are left with a **truncated cone.** What two-dimensional figure could be rotated around the axis to produce a truncated cone? Name and sketch the figure. **a right trapezoid**

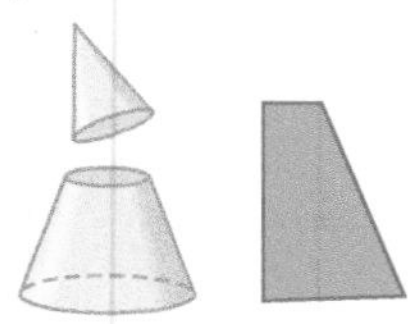

26. **CHALLENGE** If you slice a cone parallel to the base, the cross section is a circle. If the plane cuts at an angle through both sides of the cone, the cross section is an ellipse. What if the plane cuts at an angle through the side of the cone and through the base of the cone? How are such cross sections different from a circle or an ellipse? Research **conic sections** and describe each cross section of a cone in terms of the features of each conic section. **See margin.**

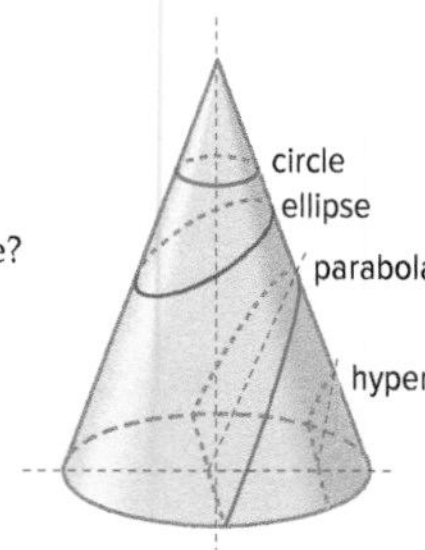

MP Standards for Mathematical Practice

Emphasis On	Exercises
1 Make sense of problems and persevere in solving them.	26, 38
2 Reason abstractly and quantitatively.	16, 25, 32–33, 35–38
3 Construct viable arguments and critique the reasoning of others.	24
4 Model with mathematics.	13, 17–23, 33

Preparing for Assessment

Determine the shape of each cross section. MP 7 G.GMD.4

27.  rectangle

28. 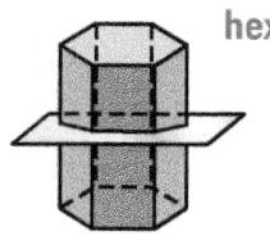 hexagon

29. 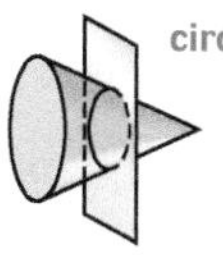 circle

30. 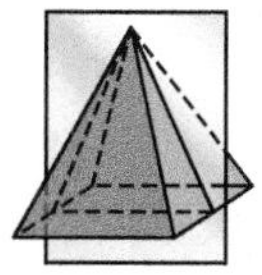 triangle

31. Which of the following three-dimensional solids can be generated by rotating a two-dimensional figure around an axis? MP 4, 7 G.GMD.4 D

- ○ A pyramid
- ○ B banana
- ○ C cube
- ○ D egg

32. Which of the following shapes could not be a cross section of the prism? MP 2 G.GMD.4 A

- ○ A octagon
- ○ B pentagon
- ○ C rectangle
- ○ D triangle

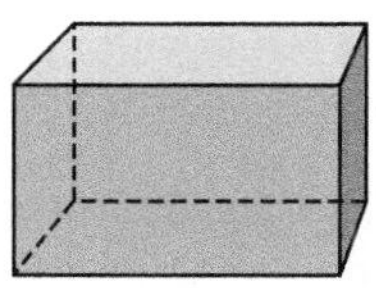

33. Eduardo has a piece of wood in the shape of a square pyramid. The sides of the base are 6 inches long. Eduardo cuts the pyramid with a single straight cut parallel to the base. Which of the following statements about the cross section must be true? MP 2 G.GMD.4 A

- ○ A The cross section is a square with an area less than 36 in^2.
- ○ B The cross section is a square with an area of 36 in^2.
- ○ C The cross section is a triangle with an area less than 36 in^2.
- ○ D The cross section is a triangle with an area of 36 in^2.

34. What shape is generated by rotating a rectangle around an axis parallel to one of its sides? MP 7 G.GMD.4 cylinder

35. Describe how to generate a torus, or donut shape, with an outside radius of 6 inches. MP 2, 4 G.GMD.4 Rotate a circle around an axis. The outer edge of the circle should be 6 inches from the axis.

36. Describe how to generate a tube with the following dimensions: MP 2, 4 G.GMD.4

length = 20 feet

diameter = 8 inches

thickness = $\frac{1}{2}$ inch

Start with a rectangle with $\ell = 20$ feet and $w = 0.5$ inch. Rotate the rectangle about an axis 4 inches from the outer edge of the rectangle.

37. Describe two ways to intersect a solid with a plane to produce a cross section that is a trapezoid. MP 2, 7 G.GMD.4 Sample answer: A plane intersects a square pyramid at an angle through opposite faces. A plane intersects a triangular pyramid at an angle through opposite faces.

38. MULTI-STEP The figure below is a square pyramid with a height of 24 centimeters and a base length of 24 centimeters. MP 1, 2, 4 G.GMD.4

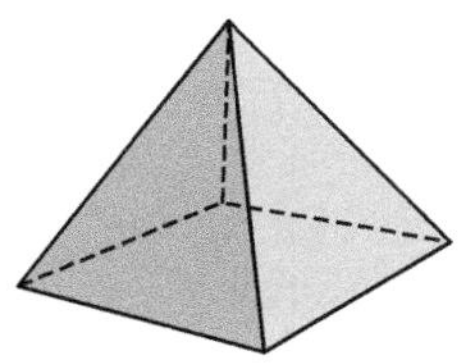

a. The pyramid is intersected by a plane perpendicular to the base of the pyramid and through the vertex. Determine the shape of the cross section. triangle

b. What is the area of the cross section? 288 cm^2

c. A plane parallel to the base of the pyramid intersects the pyramid at a height of 12 centimeters. Determine the shape of the cross section. square

d. What is the area of the cross section? 144 cm^2

e. A third plane intersects the pyramid at an angle. It goes through one face of the pyramid at a height of 12 centimeters, and it intersects the edge of the opposite side of the base. Determine the shape of the cross section. trapezoid

Preparing for Assessment

Exercises 27–38 require students to use the skills they will need on assessments. Each exercise is dual-coded with content standards and mathematical practice standards.

Dual Coding		
Items	Content Standards	MP Mathematical Practices
27–30	G.GMD.4	7
31	G.GMD.4	4, 7
32	G.GMD.4	2
33	G.GMD.4	2
34	G.GMD.4	7
35	G.GMD.4	2, 4
36	G.GMD.4	2, 4
37	G.GMD.4	2, 7
38	G.GMD.4	1, 2, 4

Diagnose Student Errors

Survey student responses for each item. Class trends may indicate common errors and misconceptions.

31.

A	Did not realize that the solid must have a curved surface
B	Did not realize that the solid must be symmetrical
C	Did not realize that the solid must have a curved surface
D	CORRECT

32.

A	CORRECT
B	Did not consider a plane that intersects 5 faces of the prism
C	Did not consider a plane parallel to the bases
D	Did not consider a plane through one corner of the prism

33.

A	CORRECT
B	Did not recognize that the cross section must be a smaller square than the base
C	Thought that a pyramid must be entirely triangular
D	Thought that a pyramid must be entirely triangular

Go Online!

eSolutions Manual

Create worksheets, answer keys, and solutions handouts for your assignments.

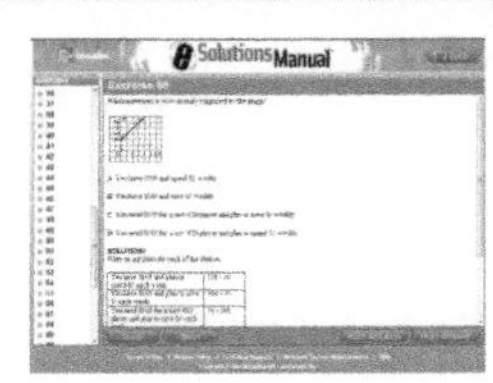

LESSON 11-2

Volumes of Prisms and Cylinders

SUGGESTED PACING (DAYS)

	Instruction	Explore Lab
90 min.	0.5	0.5
45 min.	1.0	1.0

Track Your Progress

Objectives

1 Find volumes of prisms.

2 Find volumes of cylinders.

Mathematical Background

If a prism has a volume of V cubic units, a height of h units, and each base has an area of B square units, then $V = Bh$. Like the volume of a prism, the volume of a cylinder is a product of the area of the base and the height. If a cylinder has a volume of V cubic units, a height of h units, and the bases have radii of r units, then $V = \pi r^2 h$.

Skills Trace

THEN

G.MG.3 Apply geometric methods to solve design problems (e.g., designing an object or structure to satisfy physical constraints or minimize cost; working with typographic grid systems based on ratios).

G.GMD.1 Give an informal argument for the formulas for the circumference of a circle, area of a circle, volume of a cylinder, pyramid, and cone.

NOW

G.GMD.3 Use volume formulas for cylinders, pyramids, cones, and spheres to solve problems.

G.GMD.1 Give an informal argument for the formulas for the circumference of a circle, area of a circle, volume of a cylinder, pyramid, and cone.

G.MG.3 Apply geometric methods to solve design problems

NEXT

G.GMD.1 Give an informal argument for the formulas for the circumference of a circle, area of a circle, volume of a cylinder, pyramid, and cone.

G.GMD.3 Use volume formulas for cylinders, pyramids, cones, and spheres to solve problems.

Go Online! All of these resources and more are available at connectED.mcgraw-hill.com

eLessons utilize the power of your interactive whiteboard in an engaging way. Use **Volume**, Screens 1–5, to introduce the concepts in this lesson.

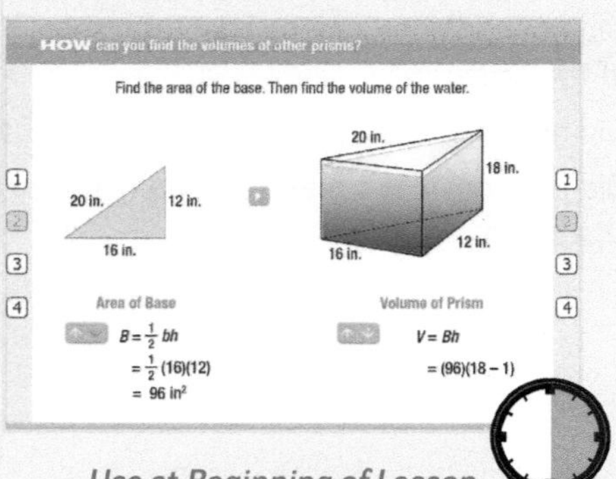

Use at Beginning of Lesson

Personal Tutors (for every example) let students hear real teachers solve problems. Students can pause and repeat as many times as necessary.

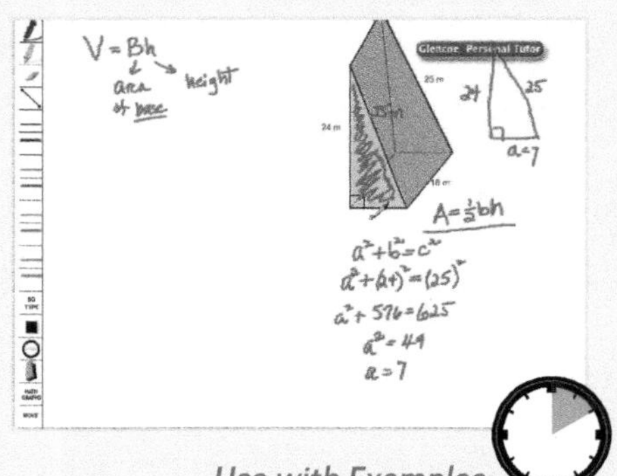

Use with Examples

Use the 3-D Figures tool from eToolkit to explore the volume of different prisms and cylinders.

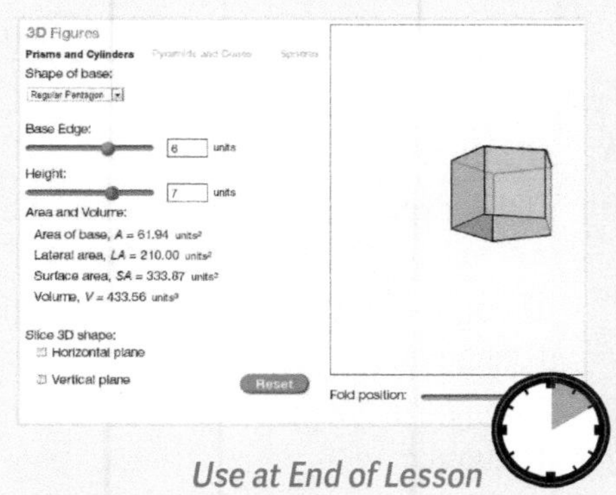

Use at End of Lesson

OER Using Open Educational Resources

Practice Have students review their work on **webmath.com** at **Discovery Education**. They can see the step-by-step solution to problems involving surface area and volume of cylinders. If they make a mistake on a quiz or test they can use this site to see where they went wrong. *Use as homework*

Go Online!

connectED.mcgraw-hill.com

Worksheets

Differentiate Your Resources

Extra Practice Additional practice or homework; Skills Practice is best for approaching-level students and Practice is best for on-level and beyond-level students

Skills Practice

AL OL ELL

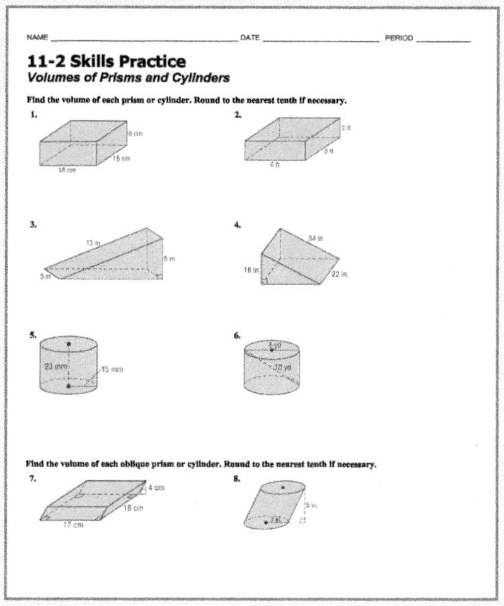

NAME ________ DATE ________ PERIOD ________

11-2 Skills Practice
Volumes of Prisms and Cylinders

Find the volume of each prism or cylinder. Round to the nearest tenth if necessary.

Find the volume of each oblique prism or cylinder. Round to the nearest tenth if necessary.

Practice

AL OL BL ELL

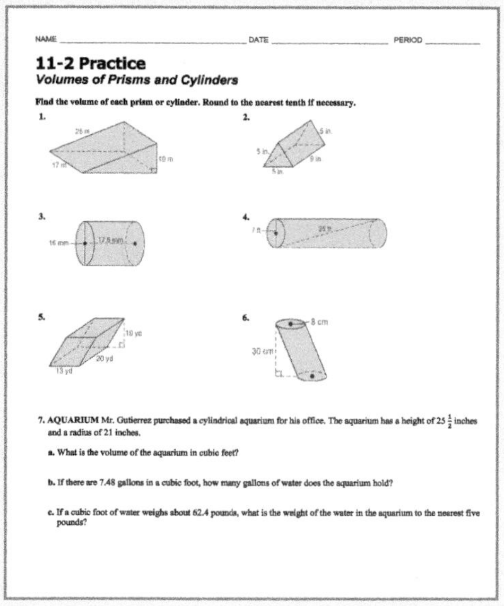

NAME ________ DATE ________ PERIOD ________

11-2 Practice
Volumes of Prisms and Cylinders

Find the volume of each prism or cylinder. Round to the nearest tenth if necessary.

7. AQUARIUM Mr. Gutierrez purchased a cylindrical aquarium for his office. The aquarium has a height of $25\frac{1}{2}$ inches and a radius of 21 inches.

a. What is the volume of the aquarium in cubic feet?

b. If there are 7.48 gallons in a cubic foot, how many gallons of water does the aquarium hold?

c. If a cubic foot of water weighs about 62.4 pounds, what is the weight of the water in the aquarium to the nearest five pounds?

Word Problem Practice

AL OL BL ELL

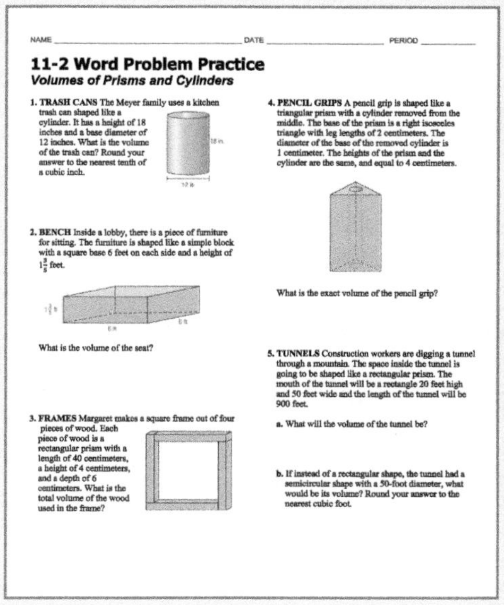

NAME ________ DATE ________ PERIOD ________

11-2 Word Problem Practice
Volumes of Prisms and Cylinders

1. TRASH CANS The Meyer family uses a kitchen trash can shaped like a cylinder. It has a height of 18 inches and a base diameter of 12 inches. What is the volume of the trash can? Round your answer to the nearest tenth of a cubic inch.

2. BENCH Inside a lobby, there is a piece of furniture for sitting. The furniture is shaped like a simple block with a square base 6 feet on each side and a height of $1\frac{1}{2}$ feet.

What is the volume of the seat?

3. FRAMES Margaret makes a square frame out of four pieces of wood. Each piece of wood is a rectangular prism with a length of 40 centimeters, a height of 4 centimeters, and a depth of 6 centimeters. What is the total volume of the wood used in the frame?

4. PENCIL GRIPS A pencil grip is shaped like a triangular prism with a cylinder removed from the middle. The base of the prism is a right isosceles triangle with leg lengths of 2 centimeters. The diameter of the base of the removed cylinder is 1 centimeter. The heights of the prism and the cylinder are the same, and equal to 4 centimeters.

What is the exact volume of the pencil grip?

5. TUNNELS Construction workers are digging a tunnel through a mountain. The space inside the tunnel is going to be shaped like a rectangular prism. The mouth of the tunnel will be a rectangle 20 feet high and 50 feet wide and the length of the tunnel will be 900 feet.

a. What will the volume of the tunnel be?

b. If instead of a rectangular shape, the tunnel had a semicircular shape with a 50-foot diameter, what would be its volume? Round your answer to the nearest cubic foot.

Intervention Reteaching and vocabulary activities that can be used with struggling or absent students and as ELL support

Study Guide and Intervention

AL OL ELL

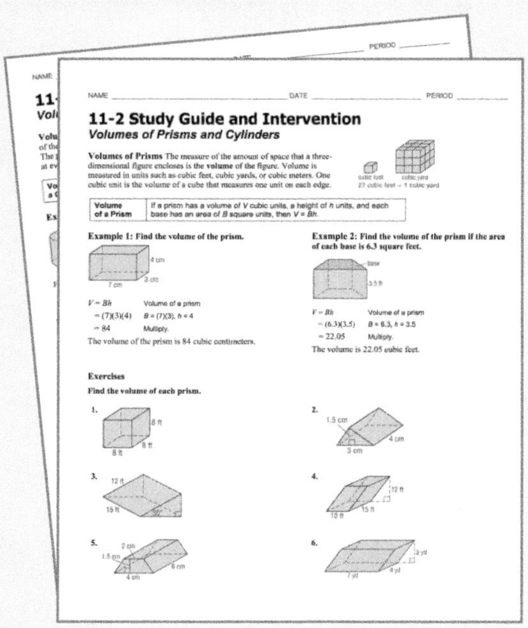

NAME ________ DATE ________ PERIOD ________

11-2 Study Guide and Intervention
Volumes of Prisms and Cylinders

Volumes of Prisms The measure of the amount of space that a three-dimensional figure encloses is the **volume** of the figure. Volume is measured in units such as cubic feet, cubic yards, or cubic meters. One cubic unit is the volume of a cube that measures one unit on each edge.

Volume of a Prism	If a prism has a volume of V cubic units, a height of h units, and each base has an area of B square units, then $V = Bh$.

Example 1: Find the volume of the prism.

$V = Bh$ Volume of a prism
$= (7)(3)(4)$ $B = (7)(3), h = 4$
$= 84$ Multiply.

The volume of the prism is 84 cubic centimeters.

Example 2: Find the volume of the prism if the area of each base is 6.3 square feet.

$V = Bh$ Volume of a prism
$= (6.3)(3.5)$ $B = 6.3, h = 3.5$
$= 22.05$ Multiply.

The volume is 22.05 cubic feet.

Exercises

Find the volume of each prism.

Study Notebook

AL OL BL ELL

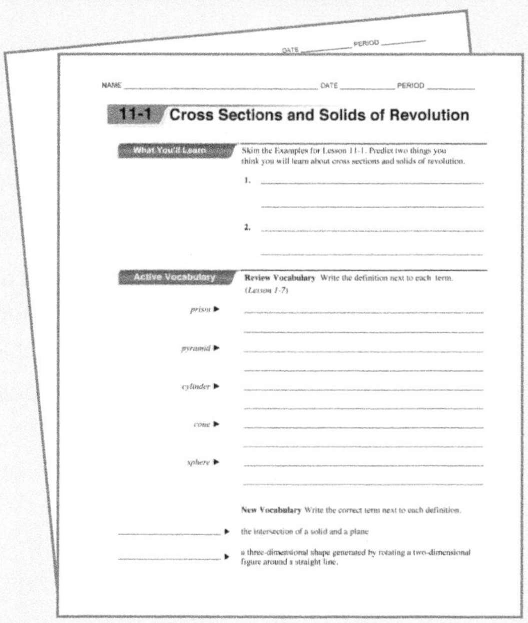

NAME ________ DATE ________ PERIOD ________

11-1 Cross Sections and Solids of Revolution

What You'll Learn: Skim the Examples for Lesson 11-1. Predict two things you think you will learn about cross sections and solids of revolution.

1.

2.

Active Vocabulary: Review Vocabulary Write the definition next to each term. (Lesson 1-7)

prism ▶

pyramid ▶

cylinder ▶

cone ▶

sphere ▶

New Vocabulary Write the correct term next to each definition.

▶ the intersection of a solid and a plane

▶ a three-dimensional shape generated by rotating a two-dimensional figure around a straight line.

Extension Activities that can be used to extend lesson concepts

Enrichment

OL BL ELL

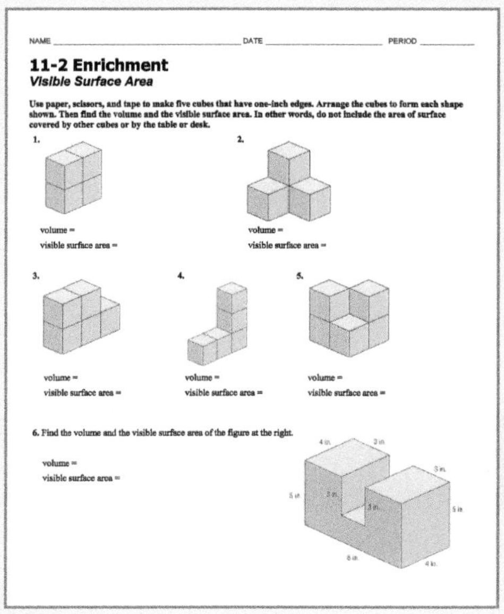

NAME ________ DATE ________ PERIOD ________

11-2 Enrichment
Visible Surface Area

Use paper, scissors, and tape to make five cubes that have one-inch edges. Arrange the cubes to form each shape shown. Then find the volume and the visible surface area. In other words, do not include the area of surface covered by other cubes or by the table or desk.

volume =
visible surface area =

6. Find the volume and the visible surface area of the figure at the right.

volume =
visible surface area =

Launch

Have students read the Why? section of the lesson. Ask:

- Why is the volume of the planter related to the amount of soil needed to fill it? Volume is the amount of space that a solid encloses. The space in the planter is filled with soil.
- What are some other real-world applications of volume? Sample answer: the volume of a cereal box affects the amount of cereal it contains; the volume of a building affects the size of heating or cooling system needed.

Teach

Ask the scaffolded questions for each example to build conceptual understanding for students at all levels.

1 Volume of Prisms

Example 1 Volume of a Prism

AL If the height is changed to 8 centimeters, what is the new volume? 480 cm^3

OL What is the volume of a square prism with side length 7 centimeters and height 4 centimeters? 196 cm^3

BL A right triangular prism has legs 7.5 centimeters and 9 centimeters. If the volume of the prism is 270 cubic centimeters, what is the height of the prism? 8 cm

Need Another Example?

Find the volume of the prism. 1500 cm^3

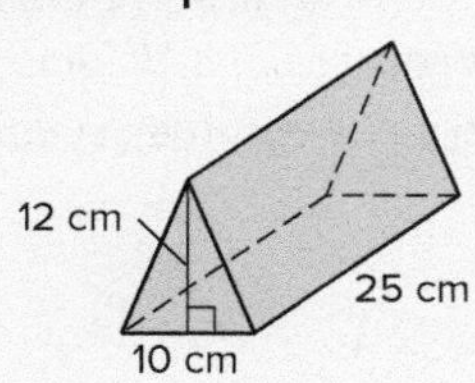

Go Online!

Interactive Whiteboard

Use the *eLesson*, *Lesson Presentation*, or *Interactive Classroom* to present this lesson.

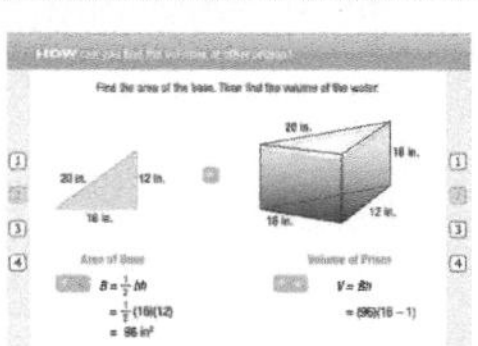

LESSON 2

Volumes of Prisms and Cylinders

Then

- You found surface areas of prisms and cylinders.

Now

1. Find volumes of prisms.
2. Find volumes of cylinder.

Why?

- Planters come in a variety of shapes and sizes. You can approximate the amount of soil needed to fill a planter by finding the volume of the three-dimensional figure that it most resembles.

MP Mathematical Practices

1 Make sense of problems and persevere in solving them.

7 Look for and make use of structure.

Content Standards

G.GMD.1 Give an informal argument for the formulas for the circumference of a circle, area of a circle, volume of a cylinder, pyramid, and cone.

G.GMD.3 Use volume formulas for cylinders, pyramids, cones and spheres to solve problems. ★

1 Volume of Prisms Recall that the volume of a solid is the measure of the amount of space the solid encloses. Volume is measured in cubic units.

The rectangular prism at the right has 6 • 4 or 24 cubic units in the bottom layer. Because there are two layers, the total volume is 24 • 2 or 48 cubic units.

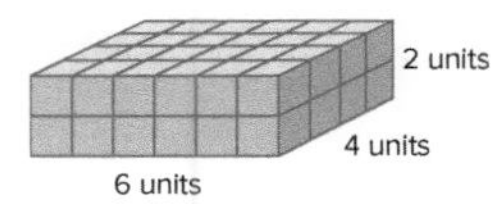

Key Concept Volume of a Prism

Words The volume V of a prism is $V = Bh$, where B is the area of a base and h is the height of the prism.

Symbols $V = Bh$

Model

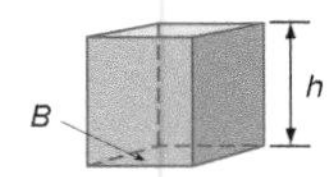

G.GMD.3

Example 1 Volume of a Prism

Find the volume of the prism.

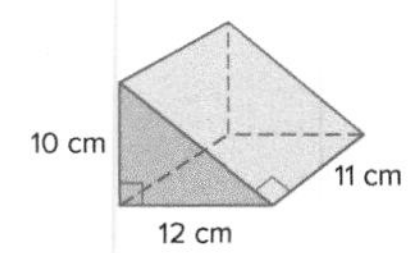

Step 1 Find the area of the base B.

$B = \frac{1}{2}bh$ Area of a triangle

$= \frac{1}{2}(12)(10)$ or 60 $b = 12$ and $h = 10$

Step 2 Find the volume of the prism.

$V = Bh$ Volume of a prism

$= 60(11)$ or 660 $B = 60$ and $h = 11$

The volume of the prism is 660 cubic centimeters.

Guided Practice

1A. 340 mm^3

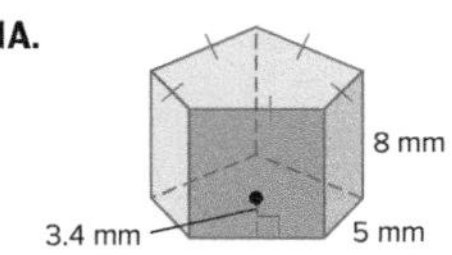

1B. 540 ft^2

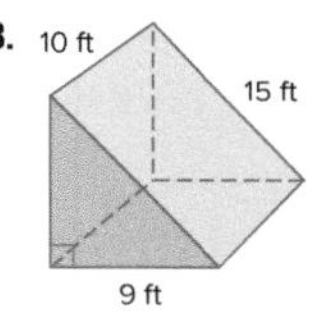

MP Mathematical Practices Strategies

Look for and make use of structure.
Help students understand the structure of prisms and cylinders. For example, ask:

- How can you differentiate the base from the lateral sides of a prism or cylinder? In a prism, the lateral sides are rectangles, but a base can be any polygon; in a cylinder, the lateral surface is curved and the base a circle.
- Once the base is identified, what repeated reasoning is used to calculate volume? Volume is simply multiple layers of the base one unit in thickness.

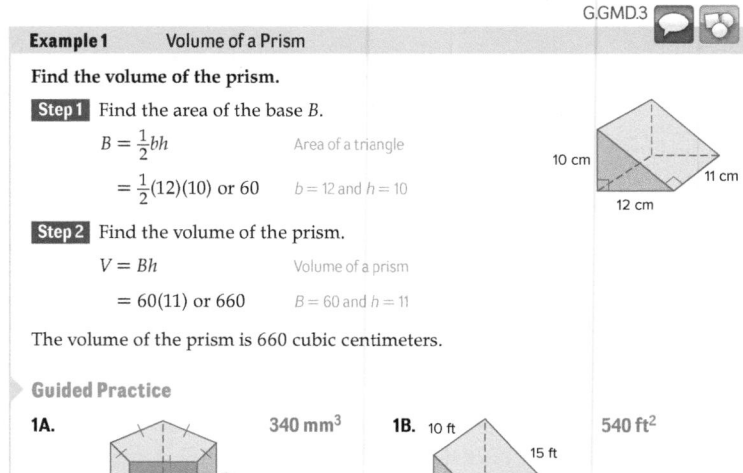

Go Online!

Investigate volumes of prisms and cylinders by using the Geometry Tools in ConnectED.

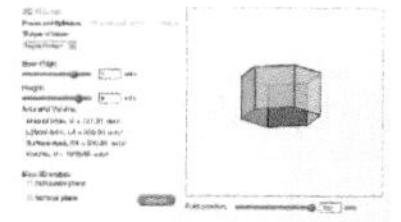

2 Volume of Cylinders

Like a prism, the volume of a cylinder can be thought of as consisting of layers. For a cylinder, these layers are congruent circular discs, similar to the coins in the roll shown. If we interpret the area of the base as the volume of a one-unit-high layer and the height of the cylinder as the number of layers, then the volume of the cylinder is equal to the volume of a layer times the number of layers or the area of the base times the height.

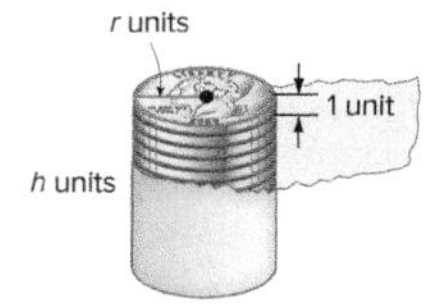

Key Concept Volume of a Cylinder

Words	The volume V of a cylinder is $V = Bh$ or $V = \pi r^2h$, where B is the area of the base, h is the height of the cylinder, and r is the radius of the base.	Model 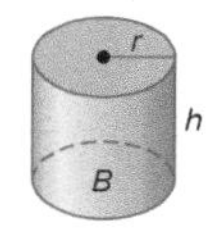
Symbols	$V = Bh$ or $V = \pi r^2h$	

G.GMD.3

Example 2 Volume of a Cylinder

Find the volume of the cylinder at the right.

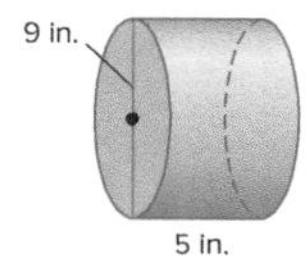

Estimate: $V \approx 3 \cdot 5^2 \cdot 5$ or 375 in^3

$V = \pi r^2h$ — Volume of a cylinder

$= \pi(4.5)^2(5)$ — $r = 4.5$ and $h = 5$

≈ 318.1 — Use a calculator.

The volume of the cylinder is about 318.1 cubic inches. This is fairly close to the estimate, so the answer is reasonable.

Guided Practice

2. Find the volume of a cylinder with a radius of 3 centimeters and a height of 8 centimeters. Round to the nearest tenth. 226.2 cm^2

The first group of books at the right represents a right prism. The second group represents an oblique prism. Both groups have the same number of books. If all the books are the same size, then the volume of both groups is the same.

This demonstrates the following principle, which applies to all solids.

Key Concept Cavalieri's Principle

Words If two solids have the same height h and the same cross-sectional area B at every level, then they have the same volume.

Models

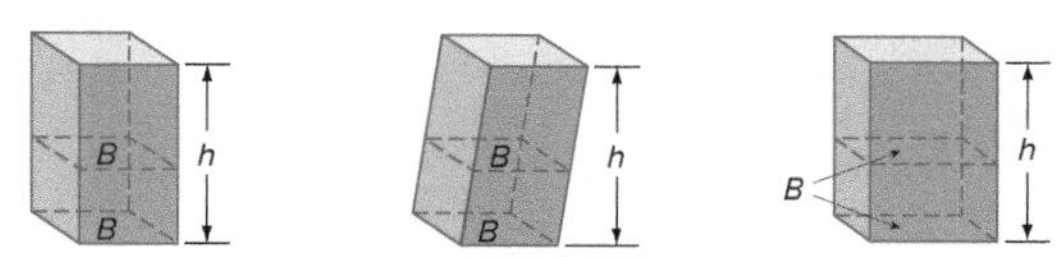

These prisms all have a volume of Bh.

Watch Out

Cross-Sectional Area For solids with the same height to have the same volume, their cross sections must have the same area. The cross sections of the different solids do not have to be congruent polygons.

Differentiated Instruction AL OL BL ELL

Kinesthetic Learners Have students take a tour of the school to find prisms of various shapes and sizes. Have them work with a partner to classify the shapes they find, and then calculate the lateral area and surface area of each prism. ELL

2 Volume of Cylinders

Example 2 Volume of a Cylinder

AL How do we know that the equations $V = Bh$ and $V = \pi r^2h$ are equivalent for a cylinder? Because the base of a cylinder is a circle, and the area of the base B is equal to πr^2 for a circle, we know the two equations are equivalent.

OL If the radius of the cylinder is increased to 6 inches, what is the new volume? 565.5 in^3

BL If the volume of a cylinder with height 8 inches is 308 cubic inches, what is the diameter of the cylinder? about 7 in.

Need Another Example?

Find the volume of the cylinder. Round to the nearest tenth. 18.3 cm^3

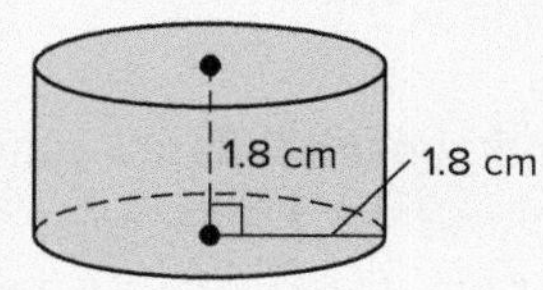

Teaching Tips

Determining Height To help students see the difference between the height of the base of a triangular prism and the height of the prism, have them color the bases of the figures on their papers.

Area of Regular Polygons To review areas of regular polygons, see Lesson 10-4.

Watch Out!

Area and Volume Area is two-dimensional so it is measured in square units. Volume is three-dimensional so it is measured in cubic units.

Example 3 Volume of an Oblique Solid

AL Why is the height outside the prism? This is one way of visualizing the perpendicular height of the prism. If it were drawn from a difference vertex, it could show up inside the prism.

OL If the height of the prism is 8.9 centimeters, what is the volume? about 154 cm^3

BL If the volume of the prism with the same height is 131 cubic centimeters, what is the area of the base of the prism? about 20.5 cm^2

Need Another Example?
Find the volume of an oblique cylinder. Round to the nearest tenth. 17,671.5 ft^3

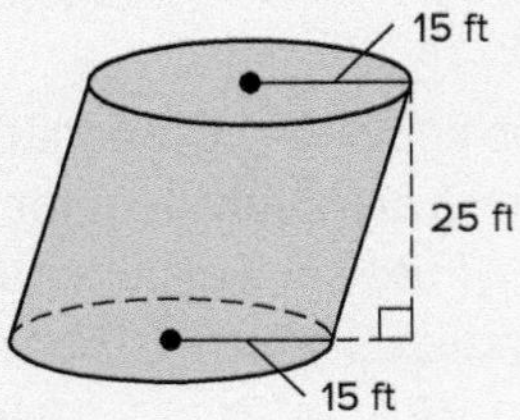

Example 4 Comparing Volumes of Solids

AL How can we check our solution? Sample answer: Use the length to find the volumes of the prisms, then subtract the volume of prism A from the volume of prism B to verify it is 150.

OL Is there another way to solve the problem? Explain. Yes; Sample answer: You can solve for the width of the bases using the difference in height, or $150 = (10 - 7) \cdot 4 \cdot \ell$.

BL Do you think these solids are similar? Explain. Sample answer: No; If they were similar, all of the lengths would increase or decrease by the same scale factor. In this case, the bases are congruent. Only the heights are different.

Need Another Example?
Prisms A and B have the same width and length, but different heights. If the volume of prism B is 128 cubic inches greater than the volume of prism A, what is the height of each prism? B

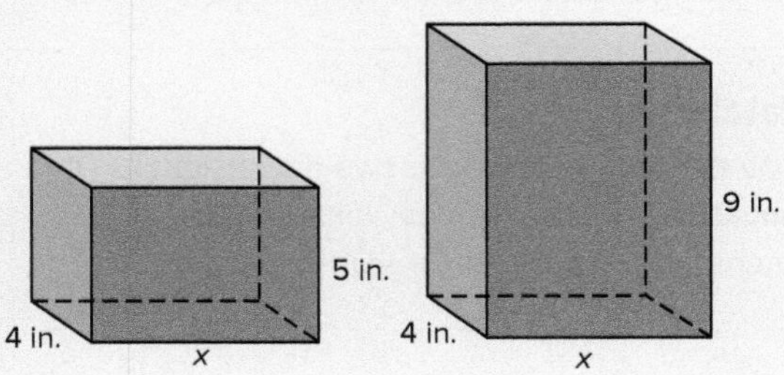

A 12 **C** 4
B 8 **D** 3.5

Problem-Solving Tips
MP Modeling When solving problems involving volume of solids, one way to help you visualize the problem is to make a model of the solid.

G.GMD.3

Example 3 Volume of an Oblique Solid

Find the volume of an oblique hexagonal prism if the height is 6.4 centimeters and the base area is 17.3 square centimeters.

$V = Bh$ — Volume of a prism
$= 17.3(6.4)$ — $B = 17.3$ and $h = 6.4$
$= 110.72$ — Simplify.

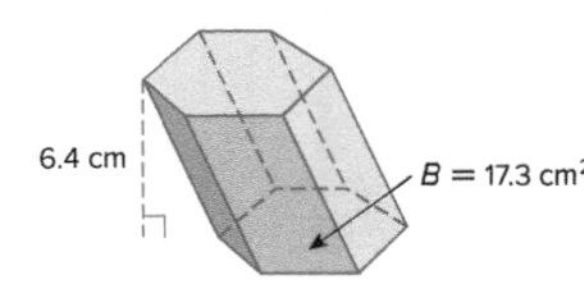

The volume is 110.72 cubic centimeters.

Guided Practice

3. Find the volume of an oblique cylinder that has a radius of 5 feet and a height of 3 feet. Round to the nearest tenth. 235.6 ft^3

G.GMD.3

Example 4 Comparing Volumes of Solids

A manufacturer packages its products in cardboard boxes that have the same length and width, but different heights. If the volume of Box B is 150 cubic inches greater than the volume of Box A, what is the length of each box?

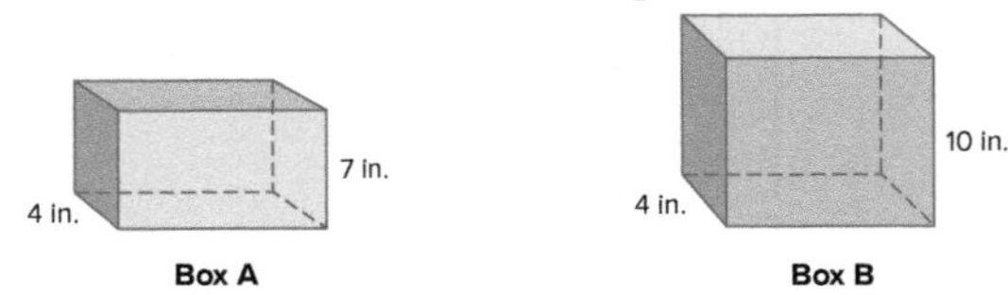

A 10 in. **B** $11\frac{1}{2}$ in. **C** 12 in. **D** $12\frac{1}{2}$ in.

Real-World Career
Architectural Engineer An architectural engineer applies the technical skills of engineering to the design, construction, operation, maintenance, and renovation of buildings.
Architectural engineers are required to have a bachelor's degree in engineering along with specialized coursework. Refer to Exercise 37.

Read the Item

You know two dimensions of each solid and that the difference between their volumes is 150 cubic inches.

Solve the Item

Volume of Box B − Volume of Box A = 150 — Write an equation.
$4\ell \cdot 10 - 4\ell \cdot 7 = 150$ — Use $V = Bh$.
$12\ell = 150$ — Simplify.
$\ell = 12\frac{1}{2}$ — Divide each side by 12.

The length of each box is $12\frac{1}{2}$ inches. The correct answer is D.

Guided Practice

4. The containers at the right are filled with popcorn. About how many times as much popcorn does the larger container hold? G

F 1.6 times as much
G 2.5 times as much
H 3.3 times as much
J 5.0 times as much

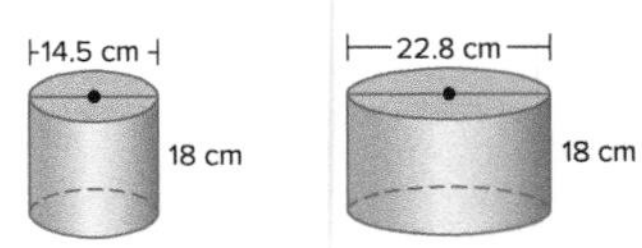

Differentiated Instruction AL OL

Logical Learners Students should reason that an oblique cylinder can also be likened to a stack of circles that has been shifted so that they make an oblique angle with the base. If a line segment is drawn connecting the center of each base (called the axis), then the axis is also an altitude for a right cylinder, but the axis is not an altitude for an oblique cylinder.

Check Your Understanding

◯ = Step-by-Step Solutions begin on page R13.

Go Online! for a Self-Check Quiz.

Examples 1 and 3 G.GMD.3

Find the volume of each prism.

1. $108\ cm^3$

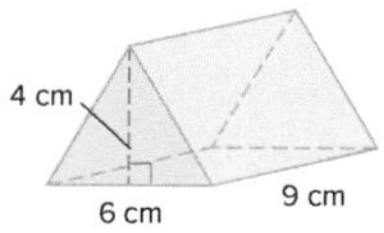

2. $396\ in^3$

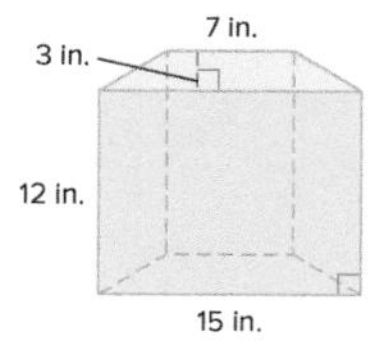

3. the oblique rectangular prism shown at the right $26.95\ m^3$

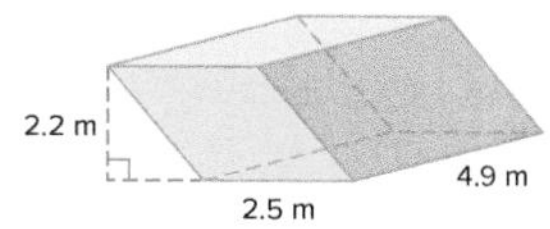

4. an oblique pentagonal prism with a base area of 42 square centimeters and a height of 5.2 centimeters $218.4\ cm^3$

Examples 2–3 G.GMD.3

Find the volume of each cylinder. Round to the nearest tenth.

5. $206.4\ ft^3$

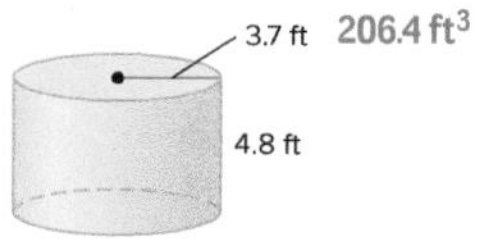

6. $1357.2\ m^3$

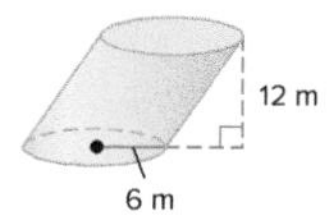

7. a cylinder with a diameter of 16 centimeters and a height of 5.1 centimeters $1025.4\ cm^3$

8. a cylinder with a radius of 4.2 inches and a height of 7.4 inches $410.1\ in^3$

Example 4 G.GMD.3

9. MULTIPLE CHOICE A rectangular lap pool measures 80 feet long by 20 feet wide. If it needs to be filled to four feet deep and each cubic foot holds 7.5 gallons, how many gallons will it take to fill the lap pool? D

A 4000 **B** 6400 **C** 30,000 **D** 48,000

Practice and Problem Solving

Extra Practice is on page R11.

Examples 1 and 3 G.GMD.3

MP STRUCTURE **Find the volume of each prism.**

10. $30\ in^3$

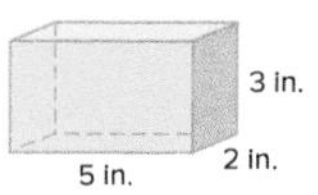

(11) $539\ m^3$

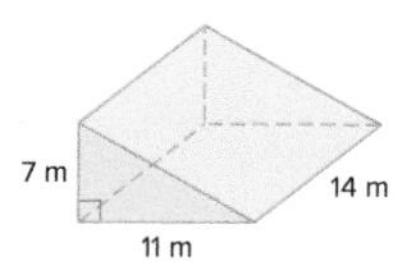

12. $324\ cm^3$

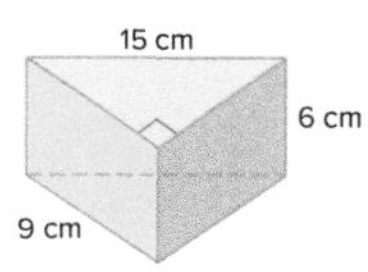

13. $58.14\ ft^3$

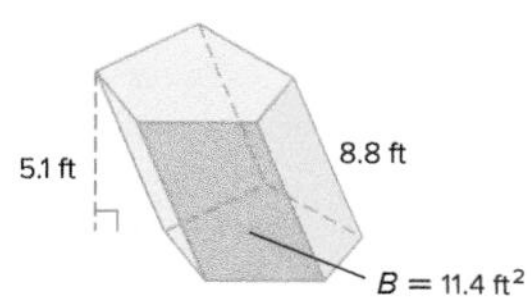

14. an oblique hexagonal prism with a height of 15 centimeters and a base area of 136 square centimeters $2040\ cm^3$

15. a square prism with a base edge of 9.5 inches and a height of 17 inches $1534.25\ in^3$

Practice

Formative Assessment Use Exercises 1–9 to assess students' understanding of the concepts in this lesson.

The Practice and Problem Solving exercises assess the content taught in the lesson. The Preparing for Assessment page is meant to be used as preparation for assessment.

Extra Practice

See page R11 for extra exercises for students who are approaching level or for on-level students who need additional reinforcement.

MP Teaching the Mathematical Practices

Sense-Making Mathematically proficient students consider analogous problems and try simpler forms of the original problem in order to gain insight into its solution. In Exercises 10–13 and 16–19, encourage students to find the area of the base of each solid first.

Levels of Complexity Chart

The levels of the exercises progress from 1 to 3, with Level 1 indicating the lowest level of complexity.

Exercises	10–21	22–38, 48–54	39–47
C Level 3			●
B Level 2		●	
Level 1	●		

Differentiated Homework Options

Levels	AL Basic	OL Core	BL Advanced
Exercises	10–21, 42, 44–54	11–19 odd, 20–25, 27–35 odd, 36–42, 44–54	39–47, (optional: 48–54)
2-Day Option	11–21 odd, 48–54	10–21	
	10–20 even, 42, 44–47	22–42, 44–54	

You can use ALEKS to provide additional remediation support with personalized instruction and practice.

Go Online! eBook

Interactive Student Guide

Use the *Interactive Student Guide* to deepen conceptual understanding.

· Volumes of Prisms and Cylinders

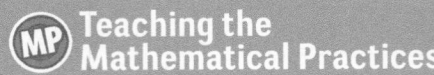

Teaching the Mathematical Practices

Modeling Mathematically proficient students can apply the mathematics they know to solve problems arising in everyday life. In Exercise 24, encourage students to divide the paint tray into rectangular and triangular pyramids.

Additional Answers

22a. The volume is tripled. The surface area only increases by 160π because the area of each base is unaffected by the change in height.

22b. The volume is multiplied by 3^2 or 9. The lateral area is only tripled while the area of each base is multiplied by 9, so the surface area increases by 560π.

22c. The volume is multiplied by 3^3 or 27 and the surface area is multiplied by 3^2 or 9.

22d. The volume and surface area are multiplied by $\frac{8}{5}$.

Examples 2–3 G.GMD.3

STRUCTURE Find the volume of each cylinder. Round to the nearest tenth.

16. 1413.7 yd^3

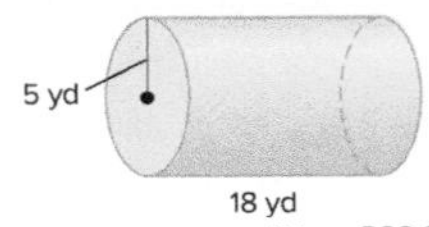

17. 407.2 cm^3

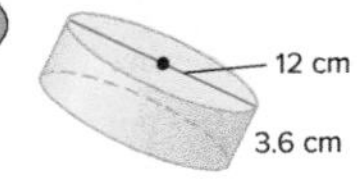

18. 823.0 in^3

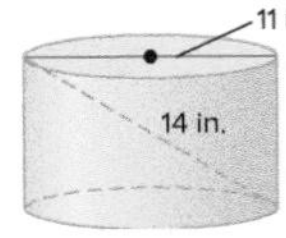

19. 2686.1 mm^3

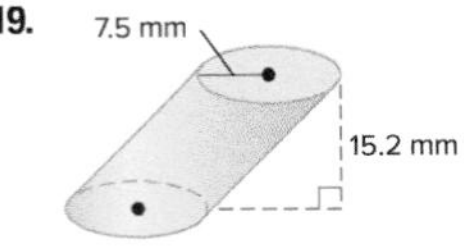

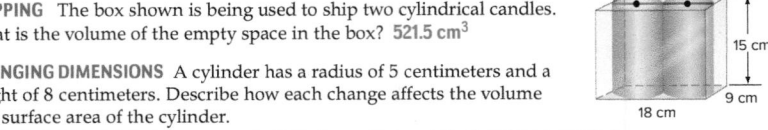

Example 4 G.GMD.3

20. PLANTER A planter is in the shape of a rectangular prism 18 inches long, $14\frac{1}{2}$ inches wide, and 12 inches high. What is the volume of potting soil in the planter if it is filled to $1\frac{1}{2}$ inches below the top? 2740.5 in^3

21. SHIPPING The box shown is being used to ship two cylindrical candles. What is the volume of the empty space in the box? 521.5 cm^3

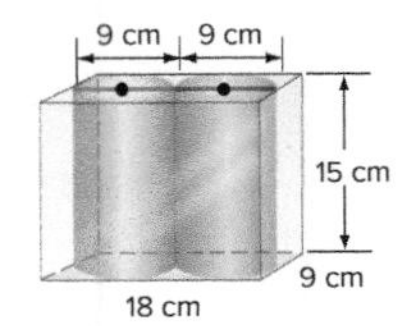

B **22. CHANGING DIMENSIONS** A cylinder has a radius of 5 centimeters and a height of 8 centimeters. Describe how each change affects the volume and surface area of the cylinder.

a. The height is tripled.
b. The radius is tripled.
c. Both the radius and the height are tripled.
d. The dimensions are exchanged.

a–d. See margin.

23. INSULATION The insulated cup holds 16 ounces of liquid. Find the volume of the insulating material rounded to the nearest cubic inch. 31 in^3

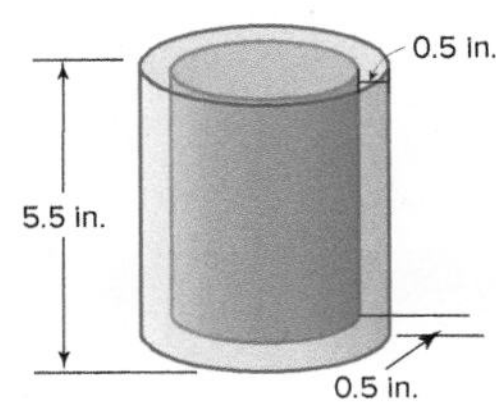

24. MODELING The base of a rectangular paint tray is sloped as shown below. Find the volume of paint it takes to fill the tray. 14,735 cm^3

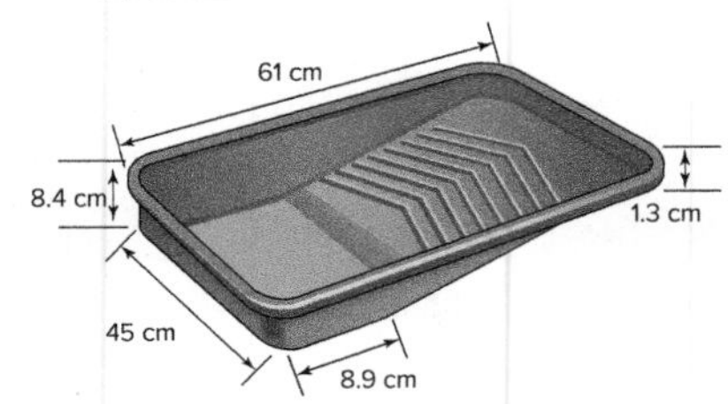

25. CHANGING DIMENSIONS A cereal company wants to increase the volume of each rectangular prism container by 25% without changing the base. Find the height of the new container if the original had a base of 8 inches by 2 inches and a height of 12 inches. What would the height be if the surface area of the container increased by 25%? 15 in.; 15.4 in.

Find the volume of each composite solid. Round to the nearest tenth if necessary.

26. 225 cm^3

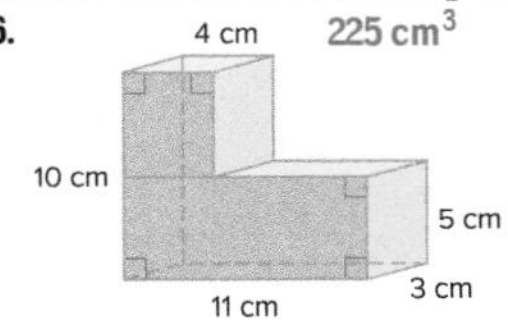

27. 120 m^3

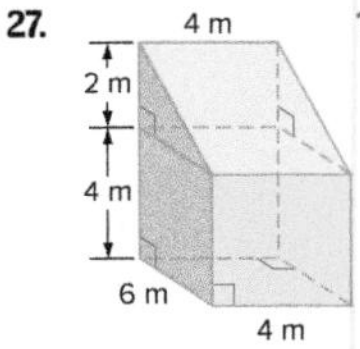

28. 713.1 yd^3

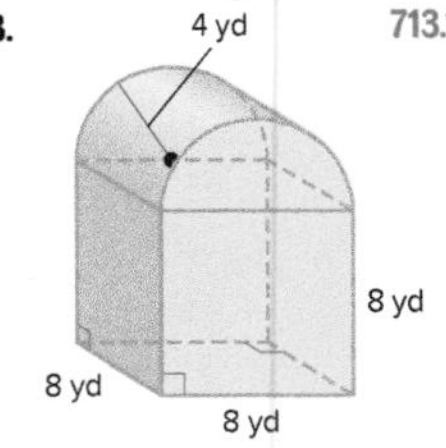

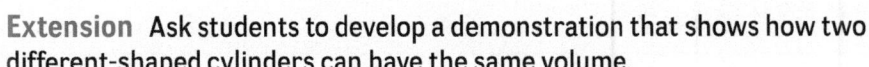

Differentiated Instruction OL BL

Extension Ask students to develop a demonstration that shows how two different-shaped cylinders can have the same volume.

Go Online!

The most up-to-date resources available for your program can be found at connectED.mcgraw-hill.com.

29 **FOOD** A cylindrical can of baked potato chips has a height of 27 centimeters and a radius of 4 centimeters. A new can is advertised as being 30% larger than the regular can. If both cans have the same radius, what is the height of the larger can? 35.1 cm

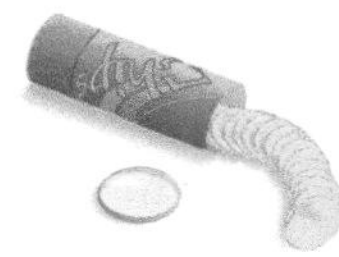

Find each measure to the nearest tenth.

30. A cylindrical can has a volume of 363 cubic centimeters. The diameter of the can is 9 centimeters. What is the height? 5.7 cm

31. A cylinder has a surface area of 144π square inches and a height of 6 inches. What is the volume? 678.6 in^3

32. A rectangular prism has a surface area of 432 square inches, a height of 6 inches, and a width of 12 inches. What is the volume? 576 in^3

Find the volume of the solid formed by each net.

33.

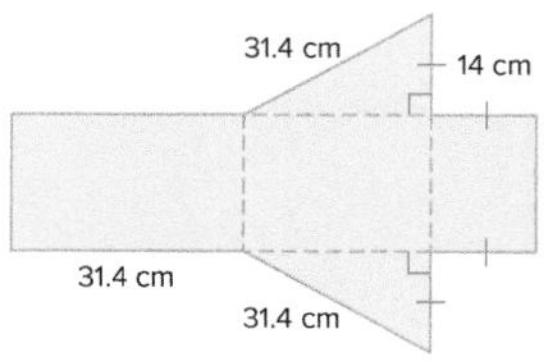

3934.9 cm^3

34. 48.9 m^3

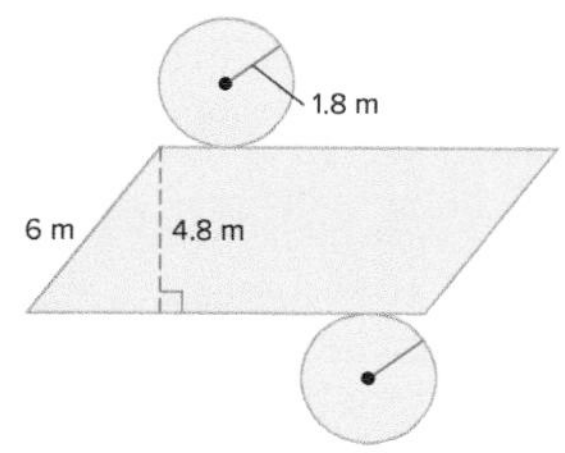

35b. The plant should grow well in this soil since the bulk density of 0.0019 lb/in^3 is close to the desired bulk density of 0.0018 lb/in^3.

35. SOIL A soil scientist wants to determine the bulk density of a potting soil to assess how well a specific plant will grow in it. The density of the soil sample is the ratio of its weight to its volume.

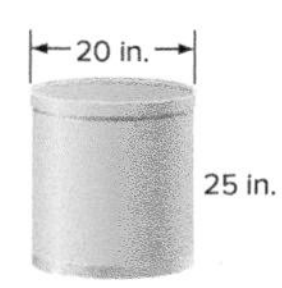

a. If the weight of the container with the soil is 20 pounds and the weight of the container alone is 5 pounds, what is the soil's bulk density? 0.0019 lb/ in^3

b. Assuming that all other factors are favorable, how well should a plant grow in this soil if a bulk density of 0.0018 pound per square inch is desirable for root growth? Explain.

c. If a bag of this soil holds 2.5 cubic feet, what is its weight in pounds? 8.3 lb

36. DESIGN Sketch and label (in inches) three different designs for a dry ingredient measuring cup that holds 1 cup. Be sure to include the dimensions in each drawing. (1 cup $\approx$ 14.4375 in^3) See margin.

37. MP **MODELING** A cylindrical stainless steel column is used to hide a ventilation system in a new building. According to the specifications, the diameter of the column can be between 30 centimeters and 95 centimeters. The height is to be 500 centimeters. What is the difference in volume between the largest and smallest possible column? Round to the nearest tenth. 3,190,680.0 cm^3

38. MULTI-STEP Ryann is planning to build a sand castle. She wants her castle to be 4 feet high, 4 feet wide, and 6 feet deep. She has asked her brother Jack to bring sand over to her building site. They each have a bucket that is 8 inches in diameter and 16 inches tall. Each trip takes Jack about 30 seconds. b–c. See margin.

a. After how long will Ryann have all of the sand she could possibly need to complete her castle? 52 min

b. Describe your solution process.

c. What assumptions did you make?

Follow-Up

Students have explored surface area and volume.

Ask:

- **How can the relationships between two-dimensional and three-dimensional figures help you solve problems?** Sample answer: You can use the formulas and properties for two-dimensional figures that you know to solve problems involving three-dimensional figures. For example, the area of the base of a three-dimensional figure is used to calculate its volume.

MP Teaching the Mathematical Practices

Tools Mathematically proficient students consider the available tools when solving a mathematical problem. In Exercise 37, encourage students to use pencil and paper or dynamic geometry software to draw a diagram of each cylindrical column.

Additional Answers

36. Sample answers:

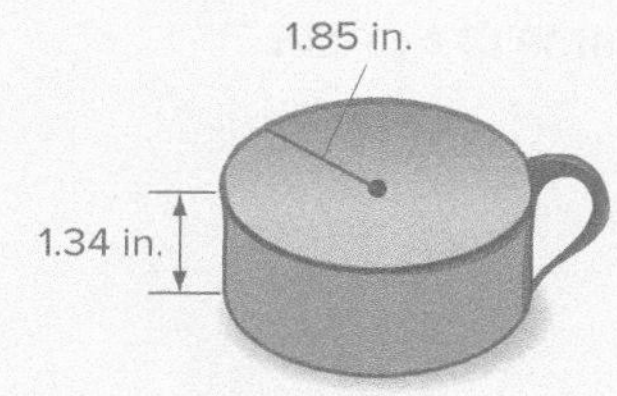

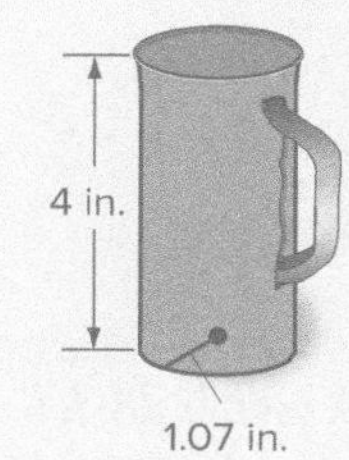

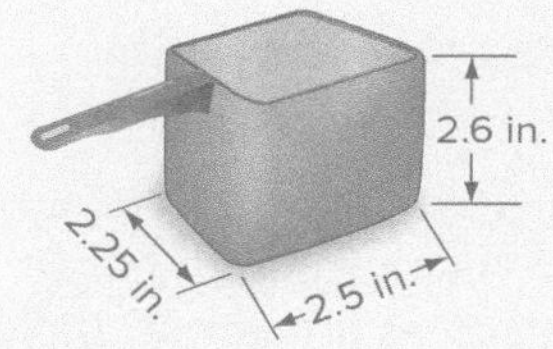

38b. Sample answer: The volume of the bucket is 256π or about 804 in^3. If Jack carries two buckets at a time, then he can carry 1608 in^3. The maximum volume of the castle is 165,888 in^3. Therefore, it would take Jack 104 trips, or 52 minutes, to provide her with the maximum amount of sand that she needs.

38c. Sample answer: The bucket is a cylinder. Ryann's building site had no sand to start with. Jack goes at the same pace for every trip and doesn't take any breaks. Each bucket is filled to the top and not overflowing with sand (or the average bucket-full equals the full capacity of the bucket). Jack uses both buckets at the same time. Ryann never stops to help Jack. Ryann needs enough sand to fill the entire volume.

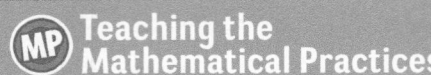

MP Teaching the Mathematical Practices

Construct Arguments Mathematically proficient students can distinguish correct logic from flawed reasoning. In Exercise 42, Valerie incorrectly used $4\sqrt{3}$ as one side of the triangle base.

Assess

Name the Math Have students describe the similarities and differences between the volume of a cylinder and the volume of a prism.

Additional Answers

41a.

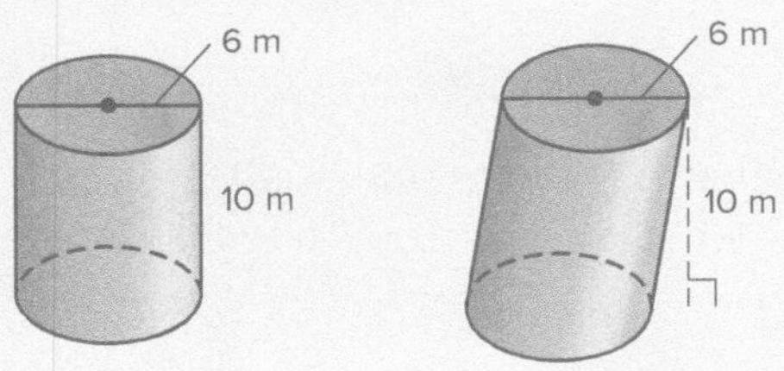

41b. Greater than; a square with a side length of 6 m has an area of 36 m². A circle with a diameter of 6 m has an area of 9π or 28.3 m². Because the heights are the same, the volume of the square prism is greater.

41c. Multiplying the radius by x; since the volume is represented by $\pi r^2 h$, multiplying the height by x makes the volume x times greater. Multiplying the radius by x makes the volume x^2 times greater, assuming $x > 1$.

44. Sample answer: The nursery means a cubic yard, which is 3^3 or 27 cubic feet. Find the volume of your garden in cubic feet and divide by 27 to determine the number of cubic yards of soil needed.

45. Sample answer:

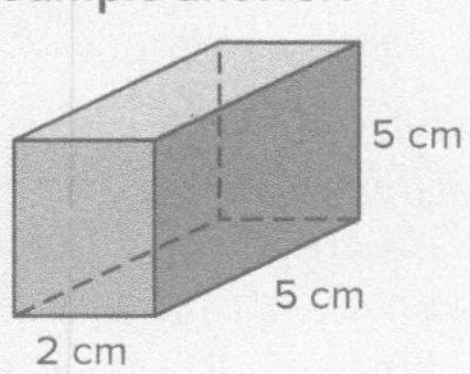

C 39 Find the volume of the regular pentagonal prism at the right by dividing it into five equal triangular prisms. Describe the base area and height of each triangular prism. **1100 cm³; Each triangular prism has a base area of $\frac{1}{2}(8)(5.5)$ or 22 cm² and a height of 10 cm.**

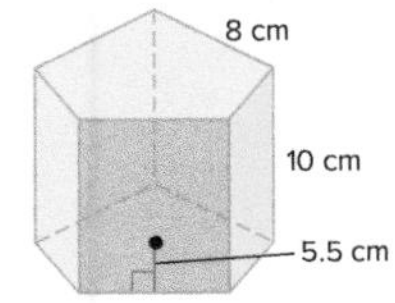

40. Because 2.96 yd³ of concrete are needed, the second contractor is less expensive at $2181.50.

40. PATIOS Mr. Thomas is planning to remove an old patio and install a new rectangular concrete patio 20 feet long, 12 feet wide, and 4 inches thick. One contractor bid $2225 for the project. A second contractor bid $500 per cubic yard for the new patio and $700 for removal of the old patio. Which is the less expensive option? Explain.

41. MULTIPLE REPRESENTATIONS In this problem, you will investigate cylinders. **a–c. See margin.**

a. Geometric Draw a right cylinder and an oblique cylinder with a height of 10 meters and a diameter of 6 meters.

b. Verbal A square prism has a height of 10 meters and a base edge of 6 meters. Is its volume greater than, less than, or equal to the volume of the cylinder? Explain.

c. Analytical Describe which change affects the volume of the cylinder more: multiplying the height by x or multiplying the radius by x. Explain.

42. Francisco; Valerie incorrectly used $4\sqrt{3}$ as the length of one side of the triangular base. Francisco used a different approach, but his solution is correct.

G.GMD.1, G.GMD.3

H.O.T. Problems Use Higher-Order Thinking Skills

42. ERROR ANALYSIS Francisco and Valerie each calculated the volume of an equilateral triangular prism with an apothem of 4 units and height of 5 units. Is either of them correct? Explain your reasoning.

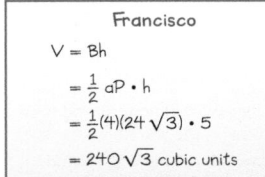

Francisco	Valerie
$V = Bh$ $= \frac{1}{2}aP \cdot h$ $= \frac{1}{2}(4)(24\sqrt{3}) \cdot 5$ $= 240\sqrt{3}$ cubic units	$V = Bh$ $= \frac{\sqrt{3}}{2}s^2 \cdot h$ $= \frac{\sqrt{3}}{2}(4\sqrt{3})^2 \cdot 5$ $= 120\sqrt{3}$ cubic units

43c. base with legs measuring 3 in. and 4 in., height 10π in.

43. CHALLENGE The cylindrical can below is used to fill a container with liquid. It takes three full cans to fill the container. Describe possible dimensions of the container if it is each of the following shapes.

a. rectangular prism **base 3 in. by 5 in., height 4π in.**

b. square prism **base 5 in. per side, height $\frac{12}{5}\pi$ in.**

c. triangular prism with a right triangle as the base

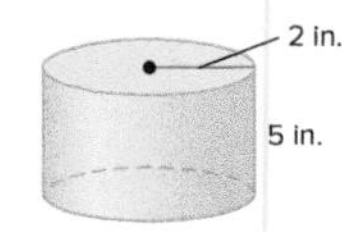

46. True; if two cylinders have the same height and the same lateral area, the circular bases must have the same area. Therefore, $\pi r^2 h$ is the same for each cylinder.

44. WRITING IN MATH Write a helpful response to the following question posted on an Internet gardening forum.
I am new to gardening. The nursery will deliver a truckload of soil, which they say is 4 yards. I know that a yard is 3 feet, but what is a yard of soil? How do I know what to order? **See margin.**

45. OPEN-ENDED Draw and label a prism that has a volume of 50 cubic centimeters. **See margin.**

46. MP CONSTRUCT ARGUMENTS Determine whether the following statement is true or false. Explain.
Two cylinders with the same height and the same lateral area must have the same volume.

47. WRITING IN MATH How are the volume formulas for prisms and cylinders similar? How are they different? **See margin.**

MP Standards for Mathematical Practice

Emphasis On	Exercises
4 Model with mathematics.	20–25, 29, 35–38
7 Look for and make use of structure.	10–13, 16–19

47. Sample answer: Both formulas involve multiplying the area of the base by the height. The base of a prism is a polygon, so the expression representing the area varies, depending on the type of polygon it is. The base of a cylinder is a circle, so its area is πr^2.

Go Online!

eSolutions Manual

Create worksheets, answer keys, and solutions handouts for your assignments.

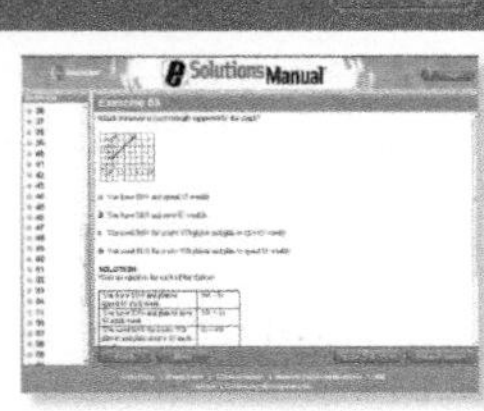

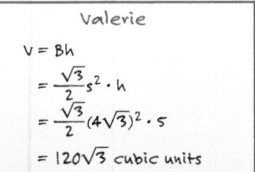

Preparing for Assessment

48. The rectangular prism shown here has a square base and a volume of 132.3 cubic inches.

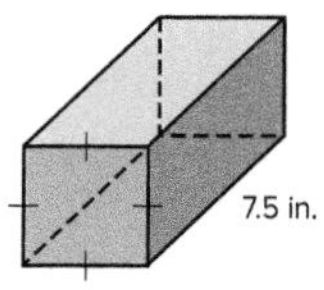

What is the perimeter of the base?
MP 1,7 G.GMD.3 C

- ○ A 30 in.
- ○ B 17.64 in.
- ○ C 16.8 in.
- ○ D 4.2 in.

49. An aquarium is a rectangular prism that is 20 inches long, 1 foot wide, and 15 inches tall. Denise fills the aquarium using a container that holds 400 cubic inches of water. Assuming she always fills the container completely, how many times will Denise need to pour water from the container into the aquarium? MP 1,7 G.GMD.3

[9]

50. Scott adds sand to the cylindrical container shown below so that the surface of the sand is 2 inches below the top of the container.

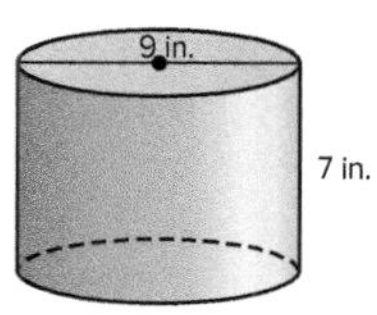

Which of the following is the best estimate of the volume of the sand in the container?
MP 1,7 G.GMD.3 C

- ○ A 127 in^3
- ○ B 269 in^3
- ○ C 318 in^3
- ○ D 445 in^3
- ○ E 1272 in^3

51. A cylindrical tank used for oil storage has a height that is half the length of its radius. If the volume of the tank is 1,122,360 cubic feet, what is the tank's radius in feet? Round to the nearest tenth. MP 1,7 G.GMD.3

[89.4]

52. The cylindrical can of juice shown here has a volume of 300 cubic centimeters. What is the diameter of the can in centimeters? Round to the nearest tenth. MP 1,7 G.GMD.3 A

- ○ A 6.2 cm
- ○ C 9.8 cm
- ○ B 3.1 cm
- ○ D 30 cm

53. A red cube has an edge length of 2 inches. A blue cube has an edge length that is double that of the red cube. What is the volume of the blue cube?
MP 1,7 G.GMD.3

[64 in^3]

54. **MULTI-STEP** Kara has a cylindrical pillar candle that is 4 inches in diameter and 9 inches tall. She melts the candle and pours all of the wax into a square mold that is 4 inches on each side. MP 1,7 G.GMD.3

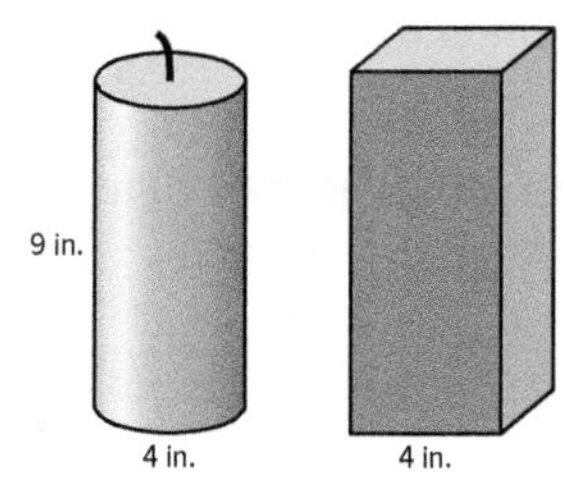

a. To the nearest cubic inch, what is the volume of the pillar candle? 113 in^3

b. Write an equation that makes the volume of the pillar candle equal to the volume of a square candle with 4-inch sides and an unknown height. $113 = 4^2h$

c. Solve the equation to find the height of the square candle. 7 in.

d. If Kara wanted to make the square candle the same height as the cylindrical candle (9 inches), how much more wax would she need? 31 in^3

Differentiated Instruction OL BL

Extension Find the volume of a regular pentagonal prism with a height of 5 feet and a perimeter of 20 feet. $V \approx 137.6$ ft^3

Preparing for Assessment

Exercises 48–54 require students to use the skills they will need on future assessments. Exercises are dual-coded with content standards and mathematical practice standards.

Dual Coding		
Items	Content Standards	MP Mathematical Practices
48	G.GMD.3	1, 7
49	G.GMD.3	1, 7
50	G.GMD.3	1, 7
51	G.GMD.3	1, 7
52	G.GMD.3	1, 7
53	G.GMD.3	1, 7

Diagnose Student Errors

Survey student responses for each item. Class trends may indicate common errors and misconceptions.

48.

A	Calculated $4 \cdot 7.5$
B	Calculated $132.3 \div 7.5$
C	CORRECT
D	Found the length of a side of the base

50.

A	Found volume using $h = 2$ in.
B	Found surface area using $h = 5$ in.
C	CORRECT
D	Found volume using $h = 7$ in.
E	Found volume using $r = 9$ in.

52.

A	CORRECT
B	Found the radius
C	Didn't divide by 10 when solving for radius
D	Didn't divide by π when solving for radius

Go Online!

Quizzes

Students can use *Self-Check Quizzes* to check their understanding of this lesson and have the results sent to you. You can also give *Quiz 2*, which covers the content in Lesson 11-2.

LESSON 11-3

Volumes of Pyramids and Cones

SUGGESTED PACING (DAYS)

	Instruction
90 min.	0.5
45 min.	1.0

Track Your Progress

Objectives

1 Find volumes of pyramids.

2 Find volumes of cones.

Mathematical Background

If a pyramid has a volume V, a height h, and a base with an area B, then $V = \frac{1}{3}Bh$. Similarly, if a cone has a volume V, a height h, and the base has a radius r, then $V = \frac{1}{3}\pi r^2 h$.

Skills Trace

THEN	NOW	NEXT
G.MG.3 Apply geometric methods to solve design problems (e.g., designing an object or structure to satisfy physical constraints or minimize cost; working with typographic grid systems based on ratios). **G.GMD.1** Give an informal argument for the formulas for the circumference of a circle, area of a circle, volume of a cylinder, pyramid, and cone.	**G.GMD.1** Give an informal argument for the formulas for the circumference of a circle, area of a circle, volume of a cylinder, pyramid, and cone. **G.GMD.3** Use volume formulas for cylinders, pyramids, cones, and spheres to solve problems.	**G.GMD.3** Use volume formulas for cylinders, pyramids, cones, and spheres to solve problems. **G.MG.3** Apply geometric methods to solve design problems (e.g., designing an object or structure to satisfy physical constraints or minimize cost; working with typographic grid systems based on ratios).

Go Online! All of these resources and more are available at connectED.mcgraw-hill.com

eLessons utilize the power of your interactive whiteboard in an engaging way. Use **Volume**, Screens 7–9, to introduce the concepts in this lesson.

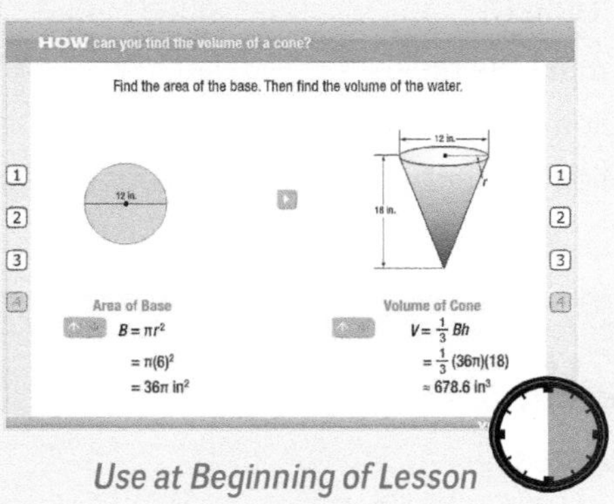

Use at Beginning of Lesson

Use Animations to explore how engineers determine the air condition needs of a building.

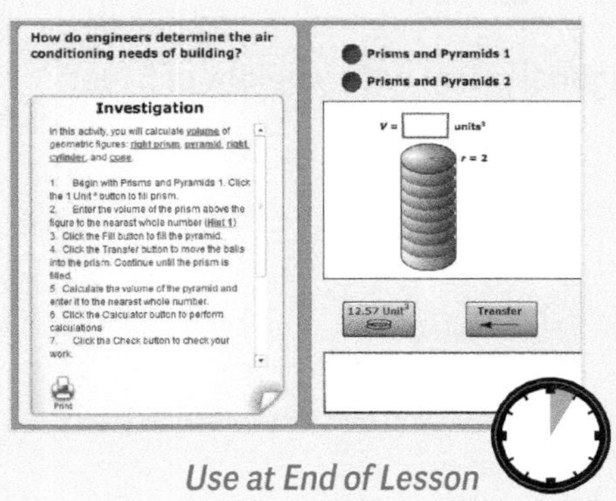

Use at End of Lesson

Use the 3-D Figures tool from eToolkit to explore the volume of different pyramids and cones.

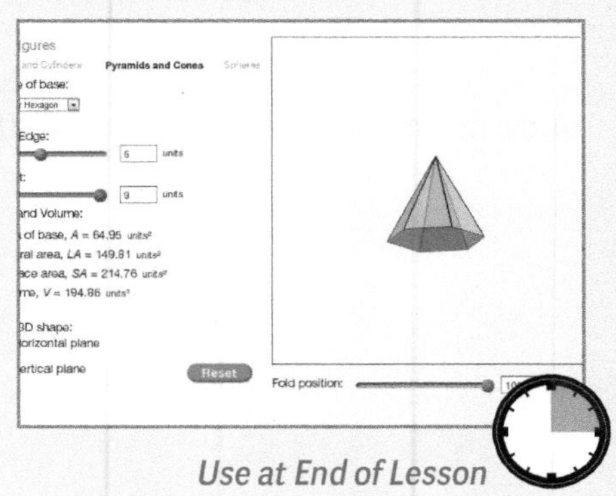

Use at End of Lesson

OER Using Open Educational Resources

Social Networking Students can create a free profile on **Sophia.org** to gain access to free tutorials and tutors. Teachers can join to gain access to free teacher tools including analytic tools that can be used to chart student progress. *Use as professional development*

Go Online!
connectED.mcgraw-hill.com

Worksheets

Differentiate Your Resources

Extra Practice Additional practice or homework; Skills Practice is best for approaching-level students and Practice is best for on-level and beyond-level students

Skills Practice

AL OL ELL

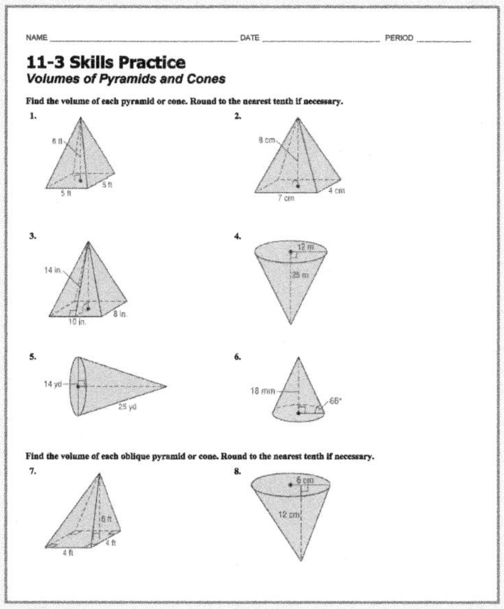
11-3 Skills Practice
Volumes of Pyramids and Cones
Find the volume of each pyramid or cone. Round to the nearest tenth if necessary.
Find the volume of each oblique pyramid or cone. Round to the nearest tenth if necessary.

Practice

AL OL BL ELL

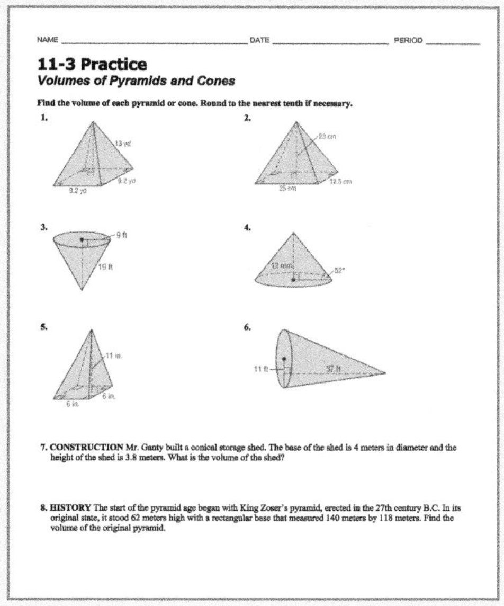
11-3 Practice
Volumes of Pyramids and Cones
Find the volume of each pyramid or cone. Round to the nearest tenth if necessary.

Word Problem Practice

AL OL BL ELL

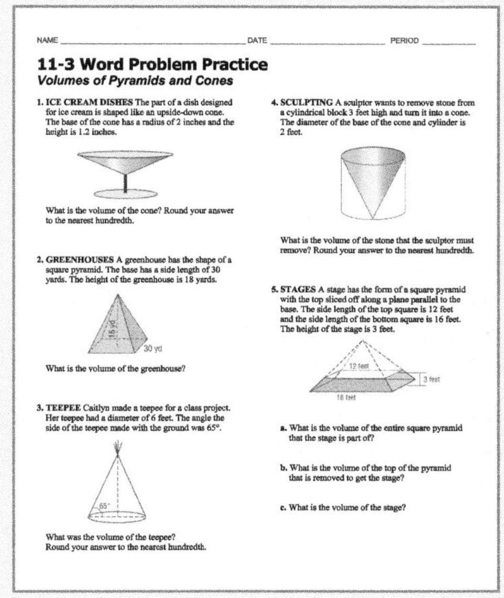
11-3 Word Problem Practice
Volumes of Pyramids and Cones

Intervention Reteaching and vocabulary activities that can be used with struggling or absent students and as ELL support

Study Guide and Intervention

AL OL ELL

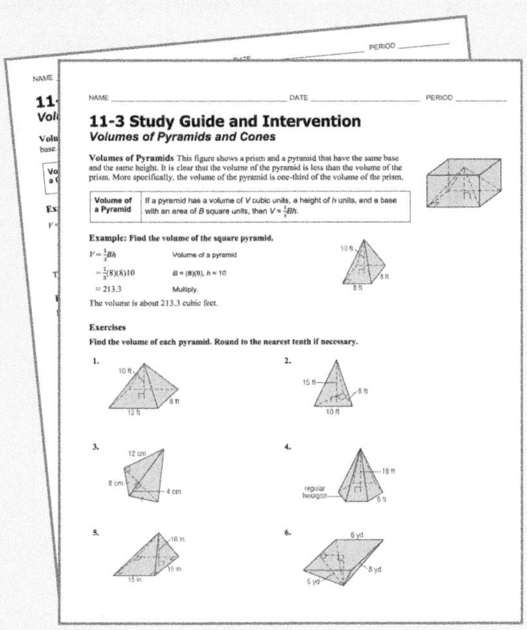
11-3 Study Guide and Intervention
Volumes of Pyramids and Cones

Study Notebook

AL OL BL ELL

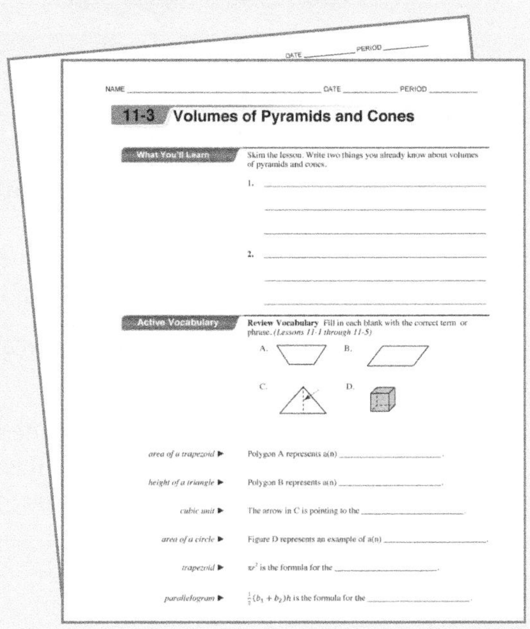
11-3 Volumes of Pyramids and Cones

Extension Activities that can be used to extend lesson concepts

Enrichment

OL BL ELL

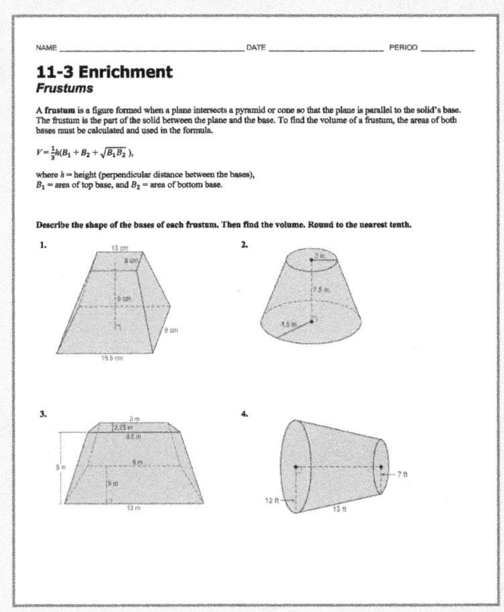
11-3 Enrichment
Frustums

Launch

Have students read the Why? section of the lesson. Ask:

- **Why is determining the volume of the model helpful?** If Marta knows the volume of the model, she knows how much clay she needs to construct it.
- **When have you used the fact that the area of a figure is equal to the sum of the area of its pieces?** Sample answer: when finding the area of a parallelogram

Teach

Ask the scaffolded questions for each example to build conceptual understanding for students at all levels.

1 Volume of Pyramids

Example 1 Volume of a Pyramid

AL **How does the volume of a pyramid compare to the volume of a prism with the same base and height?** The volume of a pyramid is one third of the volume of the prism with the same base and height.

OL **If the width of the base is changed from 8 centimeters to 6 centimeters, what is the new volume?** 171 cm^3

BL **If the length of the base is changed from 9.5 centimeters and the new volume of the pyramid is 185 cubic centimeters, what is the new length?** about 7.7 cm

(continued on the next page)

Go Online!

Interactive Whiteboard

Use the *eLesson*, *Lesson Presentation*, or *Interactive Classroom* to present this lesson.

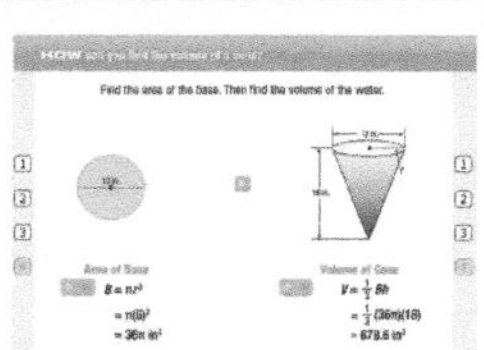

LESSON 3

Volumes of Pyramids and Cones

Then

- You found surface areas of pyramids and cones.

Now

1. Find volumes of pyramids.
2. Find volumes of cones.

Why?

- Marta is studying crystals that grow on rock formations. For a project, she is making a clay model of a crystal with a shape that is a composite of two congruent rectangular pyramids. The base of each pyramid will be 1 by 1.5 inches, and the total height will be 4 inches. Why is determining the volume of the model helpful in this situation?

MP Mathematical Practices

1 Make sense of problems and persevere in solving them.

7 Look for and make use of structure.

Content Standards

G.GMD.1 Give an informal argument for the formulas for the circumference of a circle, area of a circle, volume of a cylinder, pyramid, and cone.

G.GMD.3 Use volume formulas for cylinders, pyramids, cones, and spheres to solve problems. ★

1 Volume of Pyramids A triangular prism can be separated into three triangular pyramids as shown. Because all faces of a triangular pyramid are triangles, any face can be considered a base of the pyramid.

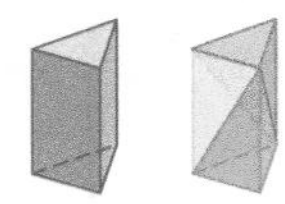

The yellow and orange pyramids have base area B_1 and height h_1. Therefore, by Cavalieri's Principle, they have the same volume. Likewise, the yellow and green pyramids have base area B_2 and height h_2, so they have the same volume.

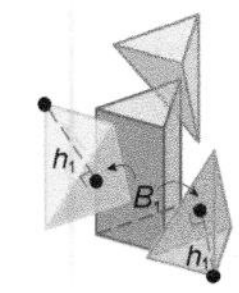

Because the orange and green pyramids have the same volume as the yellow pyramid, it follows that the volumes of all three pyramids are the same. Therefore, each pyramid has one third the volume of the prism with the same base area and height. This is true for a pyramid with any shape base.

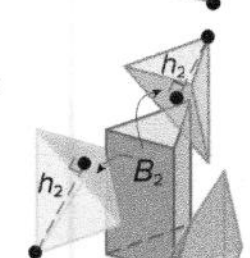

Key Concept Volume of a Pyramid

Words The volume of a pyramid is $V = \frac{1}{3}Bh$, where B is the area of the base and h is the height of the pyramid.

Symbols $V = \frac{1}{3}Bh$

Models

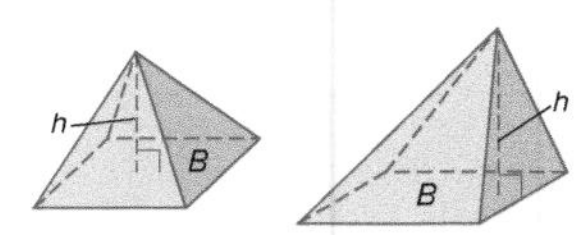

G.GMD.3

Example 1 Volume of a Pyramid

Find the volume of the pyramid.

$V = \frac{1}{3}Bh$ — Volume of a pyramid

$= \frac{1}{3}(9.5 \cdot 8)(9)$ — $B = 9.5 \cdot 8$ and $h = 9$

$= 228$ — Simplify.

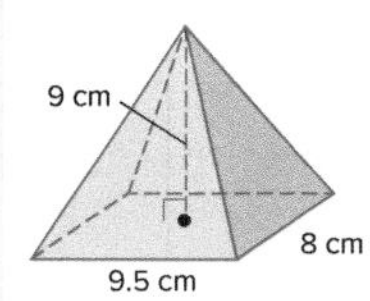

The volume of the pyramid is 228 cubic centimeters.

MP Mathematical Practices Strategies

Look for and make use of structure.
Help students understand the structure of pyramids and cones. For example, ask:

- **How are prisms and pyramids different?** A prism has two bases that are congruent; a pyramid has one base and a vertex.
- **How can you identify the base of a pyramid or cone?** The base is the side opposite the vertex.
- **What relationship between the volume of a prism and a pyramid that have congruent bases and the same height is used to calculate volume of a pyramid?** The volume of a pyramid is $\frac{1}{3}$ the volume of the related prism.

Go Online!

Watch an animation and answer questions to see how the volumes of pyramids and cones apply to architecture.

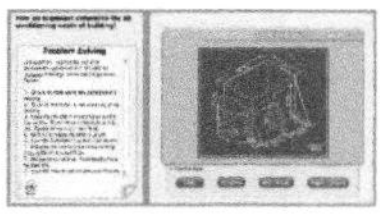

Guided Practice

1A. 36.7 cm^3

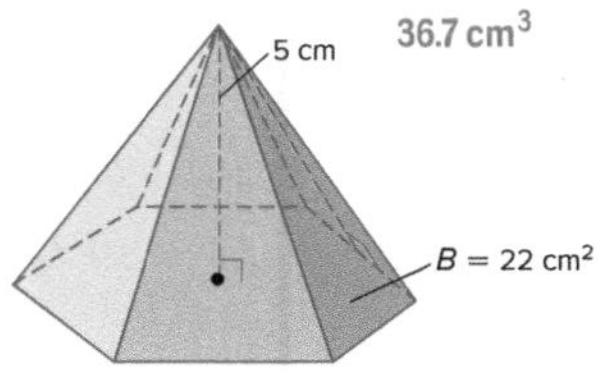

1B. 210 ft^3

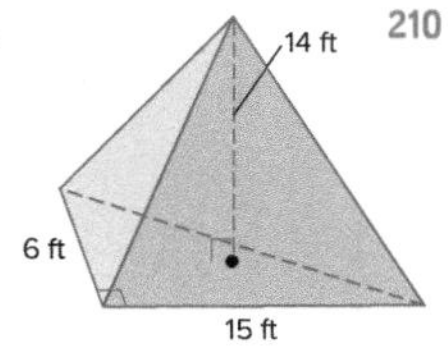

2 Volume of Cones

The pyramid and prism shown have the same base area B and height h as the cylinder and cone. Because the volume of the pyramid is one third the volume of the prism, then by Cavalieri's Principle, the volume of the cone must be one third the volume of the cylinder.

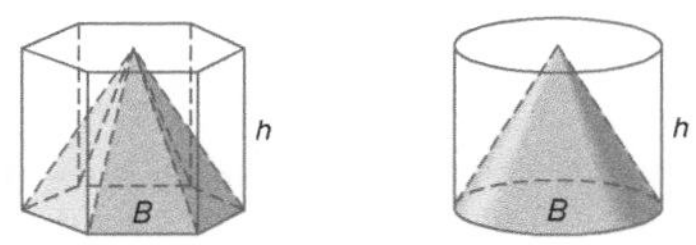

Watch Out!

Volumes of Cones The formula for the surface area of a cone only applies to right cones. However, the formula for volume applies to oblique cones as well as right cones.

Key Concept Volume of a Cone

Words The volume of a circular cone is $V = \frac{1}{3}Bh$, or $V = \frac{1}{3}\pi r^2 h$, where B is the area of the base, h is the height of the cone, and r is the radius of the base.

Models

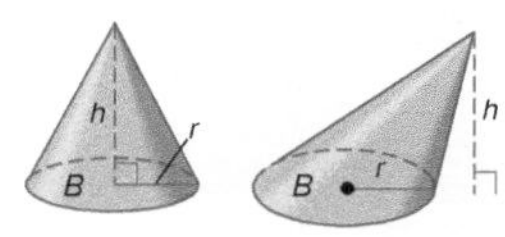

Symbols $V = \frac{1}{3}Bh$ or $V = \frac{1}{3}\pi r^2 h$

G.GMD.3

Example 2 Volume of a Cone

a. Find the volume of the cone. Round to the nearest tenth.

$V = \frac{1}{3}\pi r^2 h$ — Volume of a cone

$\approx \frac{1}{3}\pi(3.2)^2(5.8)$ — $r = 3.2$ and $h = 5.8$

≈ 62.2 — Use a calculator.

The volume of the cone is approximately 62.2 cubic meters.

b. Find the volume of the cone. Round to the nearest tenth.

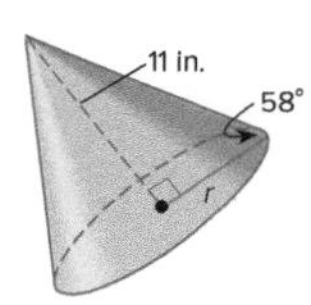

Step 1 Use trigonometry to find the radius.

$\tan 58° = \frac{11}{r}$ — $\tan\theta = \frac{\text{opp}}{\text{adj}}$

$r = \frac{11}{\tan 58°}$ — Solve for r.

$r \approx 6.9$ — Use a calculator.

Need Another Example?

Find the volume of the pyramid. 21 in^3

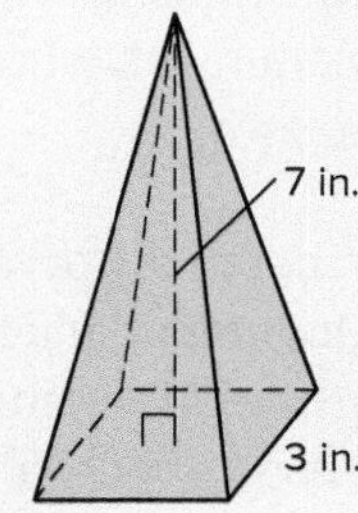

2 Volume of Cones

Example 2 Volume of a Cone

AL What kind of cone is the cone in part **a**? oblique

OL If the radius of the cone in part **a** is increased to 4.5 meters, what would the new volume be? about 123 cm^3

BL The angle formed by the slant height of a cone with the diameter is 45°. If the volume of the cone is 67 cubic inches, what are the height and radius of the cone? height = 4 in.; radius = 4 in.

Need Another Example?

Find the volume of each cone. Round to the nearest tenth.

a. 2168.0 ft^3

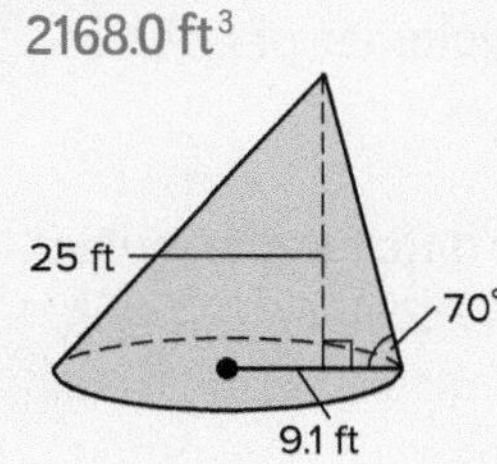

b. 314.2 in^3

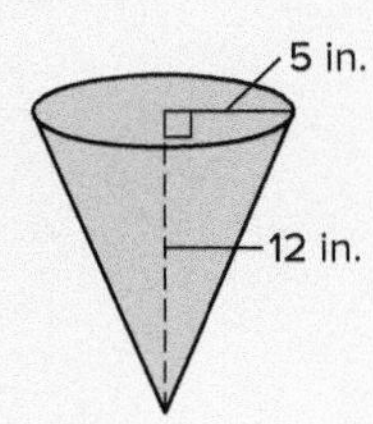

Example 3 Find Real-World Volumes

AL If we built a scale model of the top of the Washington Monument, what shape should the base be? square

OL If we built a model of the pyramidion on the Washington Monument and the model has base side lengths of 41.4 inches and a height of 62.5 inches, is our model a scale model of the actual figure? Explain. No; If we set up proportions, the ratio of the base of the model to the base of the monument and the height of the model to the height of the monument are not the same.

BL A scale model of the pyramidion on the Washington Monument has base side lengths of 41.4 inches and a volume of about 38,050 cubic inches. What is the height of the model? What is the scale factor? 66.6 in.; 1:10

Need Another Example?

Sculpture At the top of a stone tower is a pyramidion in the shape of a square pyramid. This pyramid has a height of 52.5 centimeters and the base edges are 36 centimeters. What is the volume of the pyramidion? Round to the nearest tenth. 22,680 cm^3

Follow-Up

Students have explored the volumes of prisms, cylinders, pyramids, and cones.

Ask: Why is it helpful to have different formulas when finding volume? Sample answer: It may be easier to remember the formulas by using those involving base and height. However, depending upon which measures are known, it may be easier to use one formula instead of another.

Step 2 Find the volume.

$V = \frac{1}{3}\pi r^2 h$ — Volume of a cone

$\approx \frac{1}{3}\pi(6.9)^2(11)$ — $r \approx 6.9$ and $h = 11$

≈ 548.4 — Use a calculator.

The volume of the cone is approximately 548.4 cubic inches.

Guided Practice

2A. 66.0 ft^3
2B. 1005.3 cm^3
2C. 392.7 cm^3

2A.

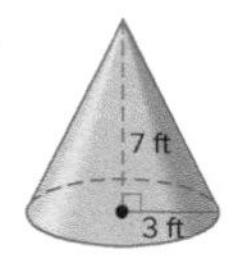

2B.

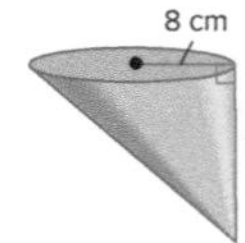

2C.

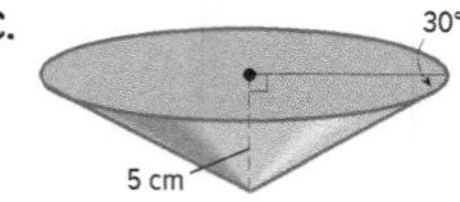

Real-World Link

The Washington Monument is the largest masonry structure in the world. By law, no other building in D.C. is allowed to be taller than the 555-foot-tall structure.

Source: Enchanted Learning

G.GMD.3

Real-World Example 3 Find Real-World Volumes

ARCHITECTURE At the top of the Washington Monument is a square pyramid, called a *pyramidion*. This pyramid has a height of 55.5 feet with base edges of approximately 34.5 feet. What is the volume of the pyramidion? Round to the nearest tenth.

Sketch and label the pyramid.

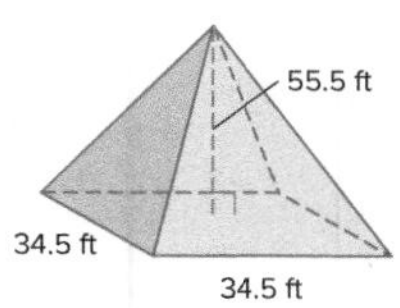

$V = \frac{1}{3}Bh$ — Volume of a pyramid

$= \frac{1}{3}(34.5 \cdot 34.5)(55.5)$ — $B = 34.5 \cdot 34.5$, $h = 55.5$

$\approx 22{,}019.6$ — Simplify.

The volume of the pyramidion atop the Washington Monument is about 22,019.6 cubic feet.

Guided Practice

3. ARCHAEOLOGY A pyramidion that was discovered in Saqqara, Egypt, in 1992 has a rectangular base 53 centimeters by 37 centimeters. It is 46 centimeters high. What is the volume of this pyramidion? Round to the nearest tenth. 30,068.7 cm^3

The formulas for the volumes of solids are summarized below.

Concept Summary Volumes of Solids

Solid	prism	cylinder	pyramid	cone
Model	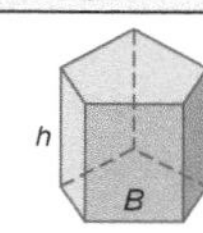	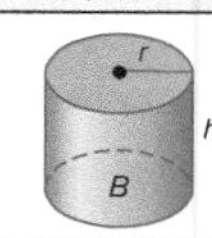	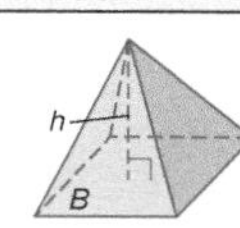	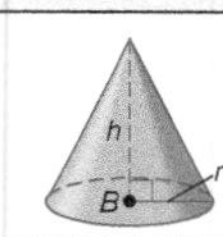
Volume	$V = Bh$	$V = Bh$ or $V = \pi r^2 h$	$V = \frac{1}{3}Bh$	$V = \frac{1}{3}Bh$ or $V = \frac{1}{3}\pi r^2 h$

Differentiated Instruction AL OL BL

Visual/Spatial Learners When you discuss cones and pyramids, show students that three cones fit into a cylinder with the same corresponding base and height by filling a cone with water, rice, or beans and pouring it into the corresponding cylinder or pyramid. This same relationship is true for three pyramids fitting in a prism with a corresponding base and height.

Go Online!

The most up-to-date resources available for your program can be found at connectED.mcgraw-hill.com.

Check Your Understanding

◯ = Step-by-Step Solutions begin on page R13.

Go Online! for a Self-Check Quiz

Example 1 G.GMD.3

Find the volume of each pyramid.

1. 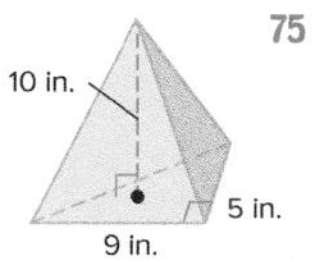

75 in^3

2. 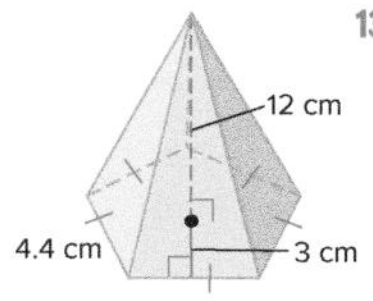

132 cm^3

3. a rectangular pyramid with a height of 5.2 meters and a base 8 meters by 4.5 meters 62.4 m^3
4. a square pyramid with a height of 14 meters and a base with 8-meter side lengths 298.7 m^3

Example 2 G.GMD.3

Find the volume of each cone. Round to the nearest tenth.

5. 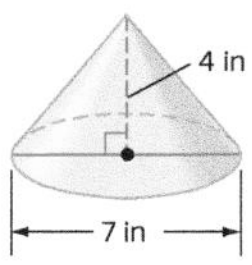

51.3 in^3

6. 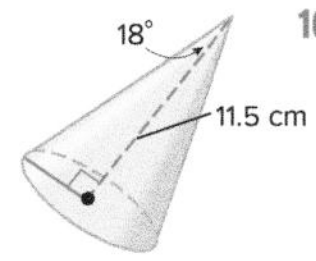

168.1 cm^3

7. an oblique cone with a height of 10.5 millimeters and a radius of 1.6 millimeters 28.1 mm^3
8. a cone with a slant height of 25 meters and a radius of 15 meters 4712.4 m^3

Example 3 G.GMD.3

9. **HUTS** The Caddo Indians lived in tall cone-shaped grass huts made of wooden pole frames with long prairie grasses dried and threaded through the poles in layers. These houses normally measured 40 feet tall. Suppose the diameter is also 40 feet. What is the volume inside the hut? about 16,755 ft^3

Practice and Problem Solving

Extra Practice is on page R11.

Example 1 G.GMD.3

MP **STRUCTURE** Find the volume of each pyramid. Round to the nearest tenth.

10. 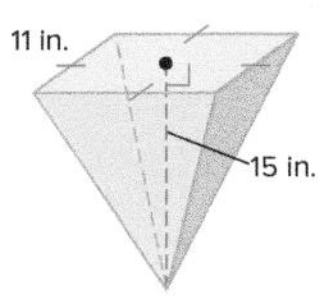

605 in^3

(11) 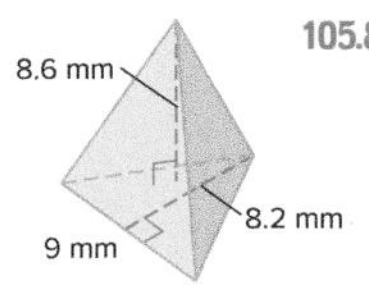

105.8 mm^3

12. 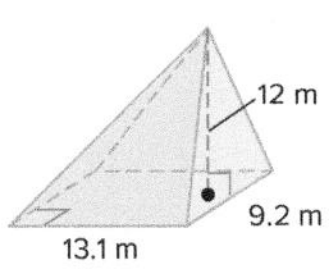

482.1 m^3

13. 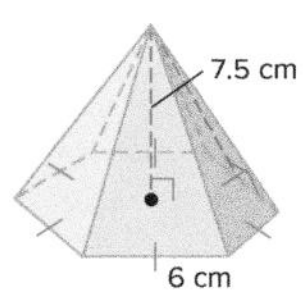

233.8 cm^3

14. a pentagonal pyramid with a base area of 590 square feet and an altitude of 7 feet 1376.7 ft^3
15. a triangular pyramid with a height of 4.8 centimeters and a right triangle base with a leg 5 centimeters and hypotenuse 10.2 centimeters 35.6 cm^3
16. A triangular pyramid with a right triangle base with a leg 8 centimeters and hypotenuse 10 centimeters has a volume of 144 cubic centimeters. Find the height. 18 cm

Practice

Formative Assessment Use Exercises 1–9 to assess students' understanding of the concepts in this lesson.

The Practice and Problem Solving exercises assess the content taught in the lesson. The Preparing for Assessment page is meant to be used as preparation for assessment.

Extra Practice

See page R11 for extra exercises for students who are approaching level or for on-level students who need additional reinforcement

MP Teaching the Mathematical Practices

Sense-Making Mathematically proficient students consider analogous problems and try simpler forms of the original problem in order to gain insight into its solution. In Exercises 10–13, encourage students to find the area of the base of each pyramid first.

Levels of Complexity Chart

The levels of the exercises progress from 1 to 3, with Level 1 indicating the lowest level of complexity.

Exercises	10–24	25–30, 41–46	31–40
Level 3			●
Level 2		●	
Level 1	●		

Differentiated Homework Options

Levels	AL Basic	OL Core	BL Advanced
Exercises	10–24, 36, 37, 39–46	11–23 odd, 24, 25, 27, 29–37, 39–46	31–40, (optional: 41–46)
2-Day Option	11–23 odd, 41–46	10–24	
	10–24 even, 36, 37, 39, 40	25–37, 39–46	

You can use ALEKS to provide additional remediation support with personalized instruction and practice.

Go Online! eBook

Interactive Student Guide

Use the *Interactive Student Guide* to deepen conceptual understanding.

· Volumes of Pyramids and Cones

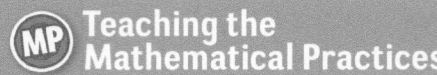

(MP) Teaching the Mathematical Practices

Modeling Mathematically proficient students can apply the mathematics they know to solve problems arising in everyday life. In Exercise 24, encourage students to draw a diagram.

Additional Answers

35a. Sample answer:

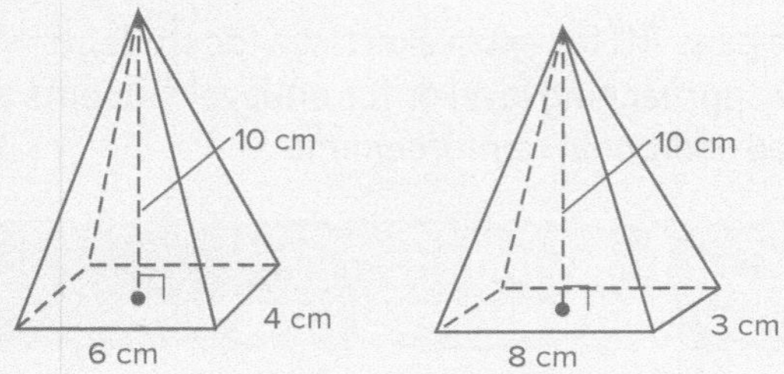

35b. The volumes are the same. The volume of a pyramid equals one third times the base area times the height. So, if the base areas of two pyramids are equal and their heights are equal, then their volumes are equal.

35c. If the base area is multiplied by 5, the volume is multiplied by 5. If the height is multiplied by 5, the volume is multiplied by 5. If both the base area and the height are multiplied by 5, the volume is multiplied by 5 • 5 or 25.

36. Sometimes; the statement is true if the base area of the cone is 3 times as great as the base area of the prism. For example, if the base of the prism has an area of 10 square units, then its volume is $10h$ cubic units. So, the cone must have a base area of 30 square units so that its volume is $\frac{1}{3}(30)h$ or $10h$ cubic units.

Example 2 G.GMD.3

Find the volume of each cone. Round to the nearest tenth.

17. 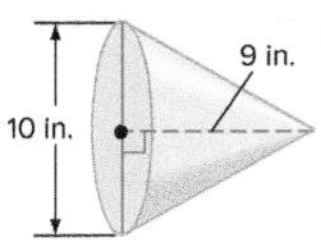

235.6 in^3

18. 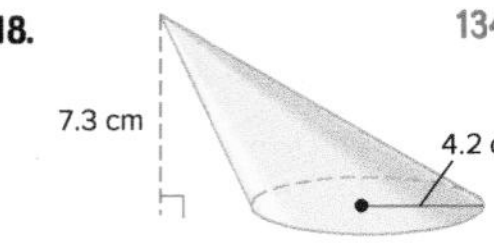

134.8 cm^3

19. 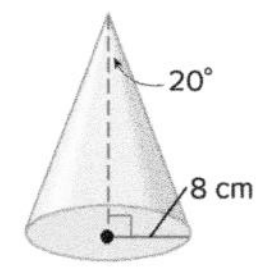

1473.1 cm^3

20. 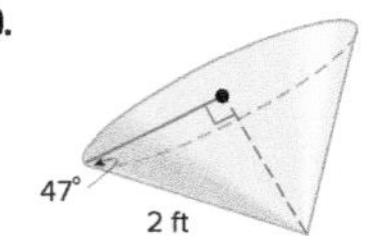

2.8 ft^3

21. an oblique cone with a diameter of 16 inches and an altitude of 16 inches 1072.3 in^3

22. a right cone with a slant height of 5.6 centimeters and a radius of 1 centimeter 5.8 cm^3

Example 3 G.GMD.3

23 **SNACKS** Approximately how many cubic centimeters of roasted peanuts will completely fill a paper cone that is 14 centimeters high and has a base diameter of 8 centimeters? Round to the nearest tenth. 234.6 cm^3

24. (MP) **MODELING** A pyramid-shaped building in Memphis, Tennessee is approximately 350 feet tall, and its square base is 600 feet wide. Find the volume of this pyramid. 42,000,000 ft^3

B

25. **GARDENING** The greenhouse at the right is a regular octagonal pyramid with a height of 5 feet. The base has side lengths of 2 feet. What is the volume of the greenhouse? 32.2 ft^3

Find the volume of each solid. Round to the nearest tenth.

26. 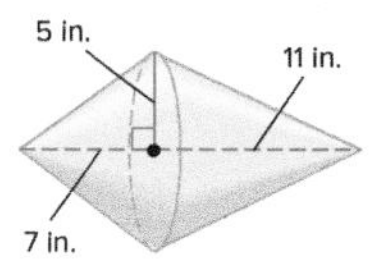

471.2 in^3

27. 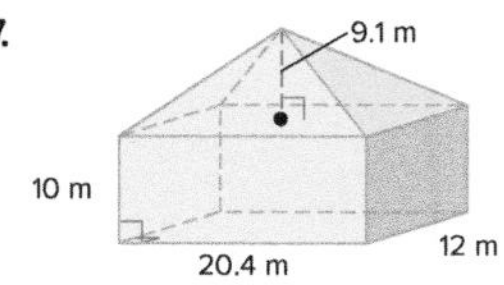

3190.6 m^3

28. 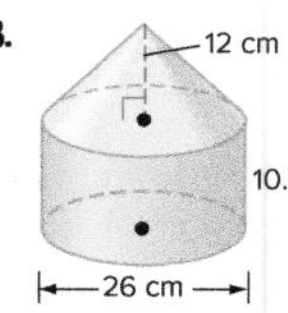

7698.5 cm^3

29. **HEATING** Sam is building an art studio in her backyard. To buy a heating unit for the space, she needs to determine the BTUs (British Thermal Units) required to heat the building. For new construction with good insulation, there should be 2 BTUs per cubic foot. What size unit does Sam need to purchase? about 13,333 BTUs

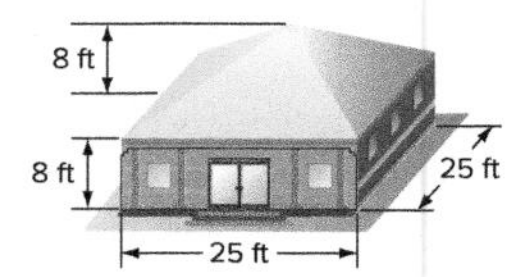

30. **SCIENCE** Refer to page 810. Determine the volume of the crystal model that Marta is making. Explain why knowing the volume is helpful in this situation.

30. 2 in^3; It tells Marta how much clay is needed to make the model.

Differentiated Instruction OL BL

Extension Have students find dimensions for a square pyramid and a cone that have the same height and approximately the same volume. Sample answer: cone with radius 6 cm and height 8 cm and square pyramid with base edge length 10.63 cm and height 8 cm

31. CHANGING DIMENSIONS A cone has a radius of 4 centimeters and a height of 9 centimeters. Describe how each change affects the volume of the cone.

a. The height is doubled. The volume is doubled.

b. The radius is doubled. The volume is multiplied by 2^2 or 4.

c. Both the radius and the height are doubled. The volume is multiplied by 2^3 or 8.

Find each measure. Round to the nearest tenth if necessary.

32. A square pyramid has a volume of 862.5 cubic centimeters and a height of 11.5 centimeters. Find the side length of the base. 15 cm

33. The volume of a cone is 196π cubic inches and the height is 12 inches. What is the diameter? 14 in.

34. The lateral area of a cone is 71.6 square millimeters and the slant height is 6 millimeters. What is the volume of the cone? 70.2 mm^3

35. MULTIPLE REPRESENTATIONS In this problem, you will investigate rectangular pyramids. a–c. See margin.

a. **Geometric** Draw two pyramids with different bases that have a height of 10 centimeters and a base area of 24 square centimeters.

b. **Verbal** What is true about the volumes of the two pyramids? Explain.

c. **Analytical** Explain how multiplying the base area and/or the height of the pyramid by 5 affects the volume of the pyramid.

G.GMD.1, G.GMD.3

H.O.T. Problems Use **H**igher-**O**rder **T**hinking Skills

36. MP **CONSTRUCT ARGUMENTS** Determine whether the following statement is *always*, *sometimes*, or *never* true. Justify your reasoning. See margin.

The volume of a cone with radius r and height h equals the volume of a prism with height h.

37. ERROR ANALYSIS Alexandra and Cornelio are calculating the volume of the cone at the right. Is either of them correct? Explain your answer. See margin.

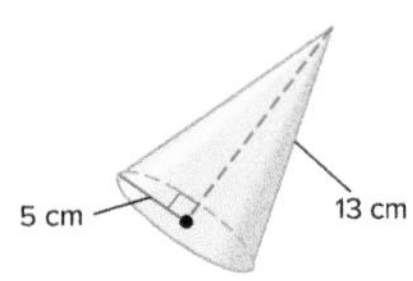

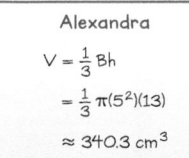

Alexandra	Cornelio
$V = \frac{1}{3}Bh$	$5^2 + 12^2 = 13^2$
$= \frac{1}{3}\pi(5^2)(13)$	$V = \frac{1}{3}Bh$
$\approx 340.3\ cm^3$	$= \frac{1}{3}\pi(5^2)(12)$
	$\approx 314.2\ cm^3$

38. CHALLENGE A cone has a volume of 568 cubic centimeters. What is the volume of a cylinder that has the same radius and height as the cone? Explain your reasoning. See margin.

39. MP **REASONING** Give an example of a pyramid and a prism that have the same base and the same volume. Explain your reasoning. See margin.

40. WRITING IN MATH Compare and contrast finding volumes of pyramids and cones with finding volumes of prisms and cylinders.

40. To find the volume of each solid, you must know the area of the base and the height. The volume of a pyramid is one third the volume of a prism that has the same height and base area. The volume of a cone is one third the volume of a cylinder that has the same height and base area.

MP Standards for Mathematical Practice

Emphasis On	Exercises
2 Reason abstractly and quantitatively.	39
3 Construct viable arguments and critique the reasoning of others.	36
4 Model with mathematics.	9, 23–25, 29–31
7 Look for and make use of structure.	10–13

MP Teaching the Mathematical Practices

Construct Arguments Mathematically proficient students understand and use stated assumptions and definitions in constructing arguments. In Exercise 36, encourage students to calculate and compare the volumes of a cone and prism with the same radius and height.

Watch Out!

Error Analysis In Exercise 37, students should recognize the difference between the height of the cone and the slant height. Alexandra used the slant height instead of the height in the formula.

Assess

Ticket Out the Door Ask students to list all the volume formulas they have learned thus far, along with an example of how to find each. Have students turn in their statements before they leave the classroom.

Additional Answers

37. Cornelio; Alexandra incorrectly used the slant height.

38. 1704 cm^3; The volume of a cylinder is three times as much as the volume of a cone with the same radius and height.

39. Sample answer: A square pyramid with a base area of 16 and a height of 12, a prism with a square base area of 16 and a height of 4; if a pyramid and prism have the same base, then in order to have the same volume, the height of the pyramid must be 3 times as great as the height of the prism.

Go Online!

eSolutions Manual

Create worksheets, answer keys, and solutions handouts for your assignments.

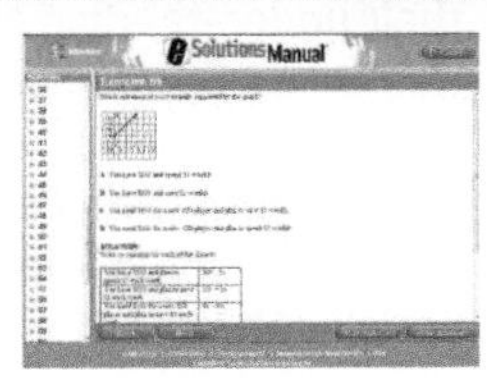

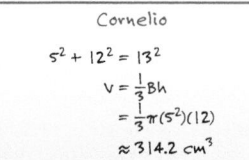

Preparing for Assessment

Exercises 41–46 require students to use the skills they will need on future assessments. Exercises are dual-coded with content standards and mathematical practice standards.

Dual Coding		
Items	Content Standards	MP Mathematical Practices
41–46	G.GMD.3	1, 7

Diagnose Student Errors

Survey student responses for each item. Class trends may indicate common errors and misconceptions.

41.

A	Forgot to multiply by $\frac{1}{3}$
B	Took $\frac{1}{3}$ of the volume
C	CORRECT
D	Found the diagonal of the base

42.

A	Used the diameter of the votive instead of the radius when calculating the volume
B	CORRECT
C	Estimated that the volume of each votive is 1 cubic inch
D	Used the diameter of the candle mold instead of the radius when calculating the volume
E	Found the volume of the candle mold

44.

A	CORRECT
B	Used slant height instead of height
C	Multiplied slant height by height instead of squaring the radius
D	Used slant height for the radius

Go Online!

Quizzes

Students can use *Self-Check Quizzes* to check their understanding of this lesson and have the results sent to you. You can also give *Quiz 3*, which covers the content in Lessons 11-3 and 11-4.

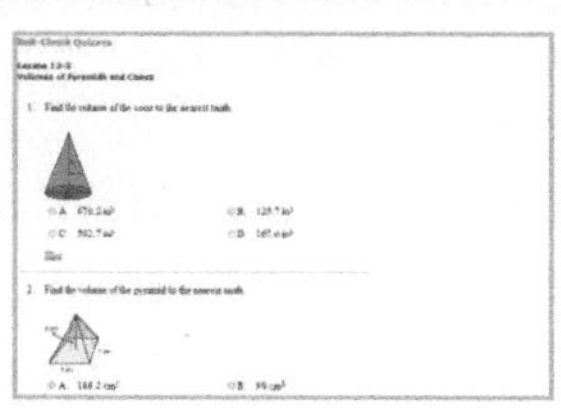

Preparing for Assessment

41. Cullen is buying a tent that is in the shape of a rectangular pyramid.

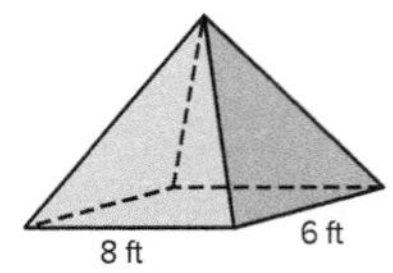

If the tent holds 88 cubic feet of air, how tall is the tent? MP 1, 7 G.GMD.3 **C**

- A $1\frac{5}{6}$ ft
- B $\frac{11}{18}$ ft
- C $5\frac{1}{2}$ ft
- D 10 ft

42. Tara has a cylindrical candle mold that is 8 inches high with a diameter of 3 inches. She would like to melt votive candles and reuse the wax. Each votive candle is a cylinder with a height of 1.5 inches and a radius of 0.5 inch. How many votive candles are needed to fill the candle mold? MP 1, 7 G.GMD.3 **B**

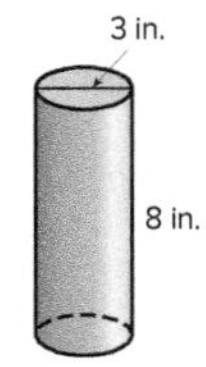

- A 12
- B 48
- C 57
- D 192
- E 226

43. A right circular cone has a height of 10 centimeters and a volume of 32 cubic centimeters. What is the radius of the cone? MP 1, 7 G.GMD.3 **B**

- A 0.5 cm
- B 1.75 cm
- C 2.25 cm
- D 2.75 cm

44. A conical sand toy has the dimensions shown. How many cubic centimeters of sand will it hold when it is filled to the top? MP 1, 7 G.GMD.3 **A**

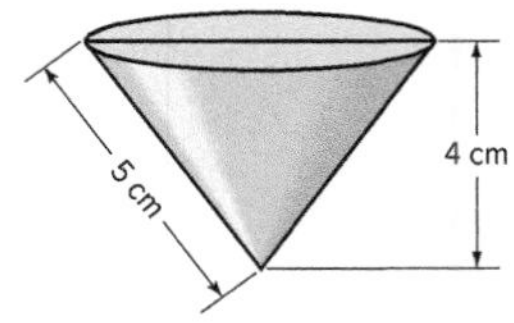

- A 12π
- B 15π
- C $\frac{80}{3}\pi$
- D $\frac{100}{3}\pi$

45. **MULTI-STEP** The figure shows a cone with a cylindrical hole cut out. What is the volume of this solid? MP 1, 7 G.GMD.3 **891π cm^3**

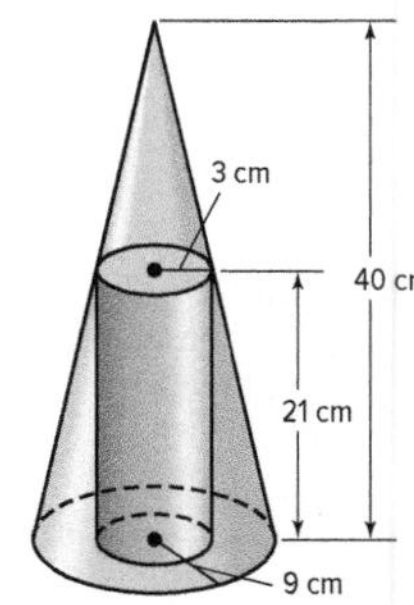

46. What is the height of the pyramid if the volume is 210 cubic feet and the base is 70 square feet? MP 1, 7 G.GMD.3 **9 ft**

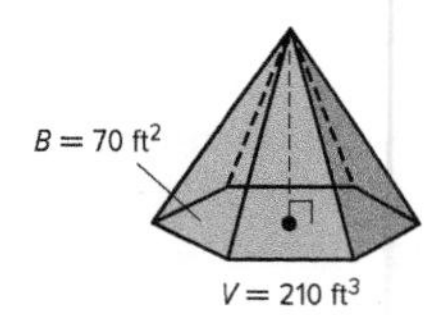

CHAPTER 11
Mid-Chapter Quiz
Lessons 11-1 through 11-3

Sketch each cross section formed by the intersection of the plane and solid. (Lesson 11-1) See Ch. 11 Answer Appendix.

1.
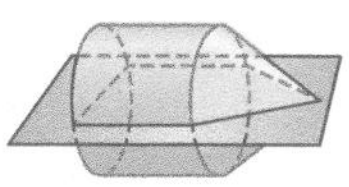

2.
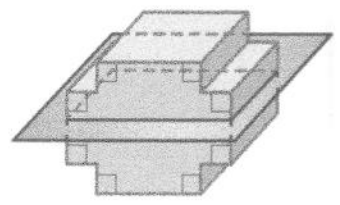

Describe the shape of the cross section. (Lesson 11-1)

3.
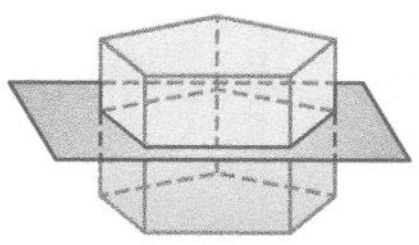
pentagon

4.
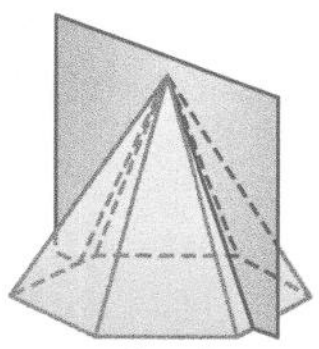
triangle

Identify the three-dimensional shape generated by rotating each two-dimensional shape around the given axis. (Lesson 11-1)

5.
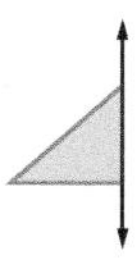
cone

6.
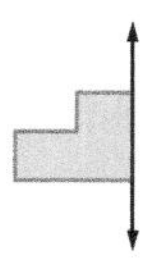
two stacked cylinders

Find the volume of each prism or cylinder. Round to the nearest tenth if necessary. (Lesson 11-2)

7.
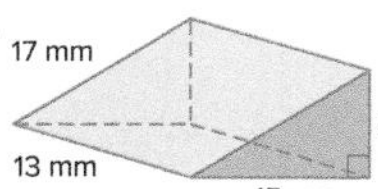

780 mm^3

8.
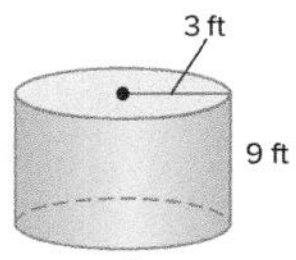

254.5 ft^3

9.
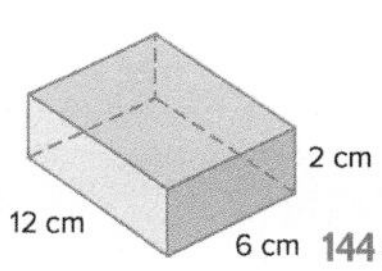

144 cm^3

10.
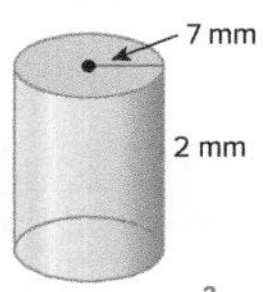

307.9 mm^3

11.
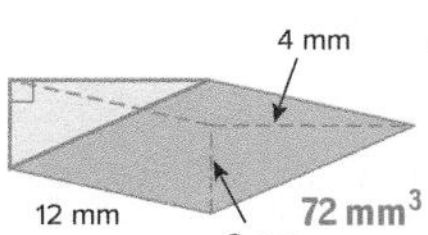

72 mm^3

12.
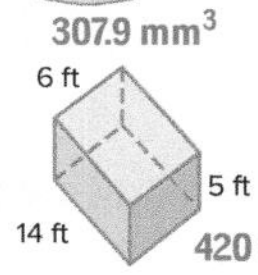

420 ft^3

13. **METEOROLOGY** The TIROS weather satellites were a series of weather satellites that carried television and infrared cameras and were covered by solar cells. The cylinder-shaped body of a TIROS had a diameter of 42 inches and a height of 19 inches. (Lesson 11-2)
   a. What was the volume available for carrying instruments and cameras? Round to the nearest tenth. 26,323.4 in^3
   b. MP What mathematical practice did you use to solve this problem? See students' work.

Find the volume of each pyramid or cone. Round to the nearest tenth if necessary. (Lesson 11-3)

14.
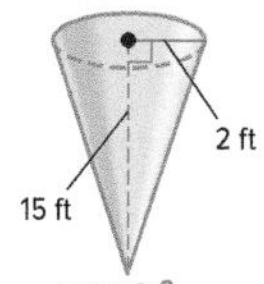

62.8 ft^3

15.
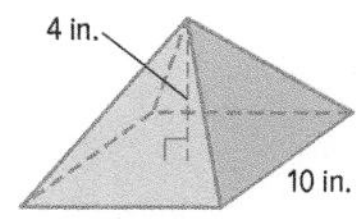

133.3 in^3

16.
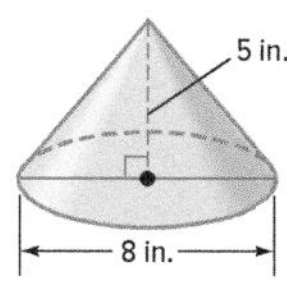

83.8 in^3

17.
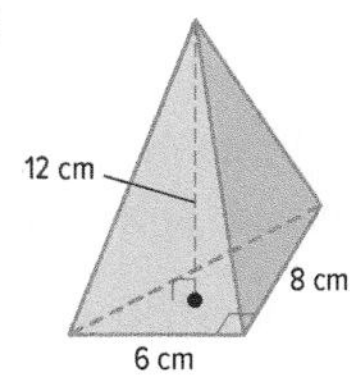

96 cm^3

18.
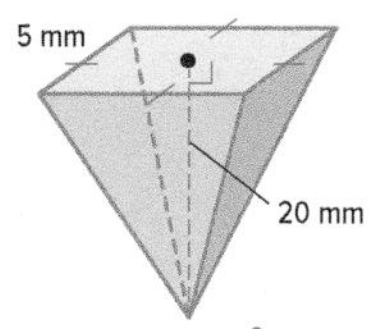

166.7 mm^3

19.
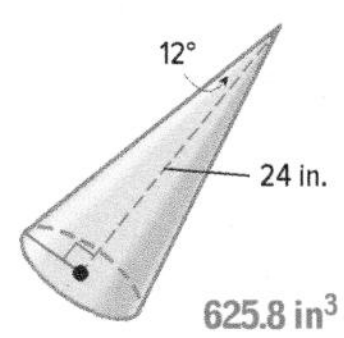

625.8 in^3

20. **PLAYHOUSE** Mary Anne is helping her dad make a playhouse for her little sister. The playhouse is a square pyramid on top of a cube. The pyramid's base is 5 feet and its height is 6 feet. Find the playhouse's volume in cubic feet. (Lesson 11-3) 175 ft^3

21. **COLLECTIONS** Soledad collects unique salt and pepper shakers. She inherited a pair of shakers in the shape of regular square pyramids. Each edge of the base measures 3 centimeters and the height is 4 centimeters. Find the volume of one shaker. (Lesson 11-3) 12 cm^3

Foldables Study Organizer

Dinah Zike's FOLDABLES®

Before students complete the Mid-Chapter Quiz, encourage them to review the information for Lessons 11-1 through 11-3 in their Foldables. Ask students to share the items they have added to their Foldables that have been helpful as they study Chapter 11.

ALEKS can be used as a formative assessment tool to target learning gaps for those who are struggling, while providing enhanced learning for those who have mastered the concepts.

RtI Response to Intervention

Use the Intervention Planner to help you determine your Response to Intervention.

Intervention Planner

TIER 1 On Level OL

IF students miss 25% of the exercises or less,

THEN choose a resource:

SE Lessons 11-1, 11-2, and 11-3

Go Online!
- Skills Practice
- Chapter Project
- Self-Check Quizzes

TIER 2 Strategic Intervention AL
Approaching grade level

IF students miss 50% of the exercises,

THEN choose a resource:

Quick Review Math Handbook

Go Online!
- Study Guide and Intervention
- Extra Examples
- Personal Tutors
- Homework Help

TIER 3 Intensive Intervention
2 or more grades below level

IF students miss 75% of the exercises,

THEN choose a resource:

Use *Math Triumphs, Geometry*

Go Online!
- Extra Examples
- Personal Tutors
- Homework Help
- Review Vocabulary

Go Online!

eAssessment

You can use the premade Mid-Chapter Test to assess students' progress in the first half of the chapter. Customize and create multiple versions of your Mid-Chapter Quiz and answer keys that align to your standards. Tests can be delivered on paper or online.

LESSON 11-4

Spheres

SUGGESTED PACING (DAYS)

	Instruction		Extend Lab
90 min.	0.5	0.5	
45 min.	1.0		0.5

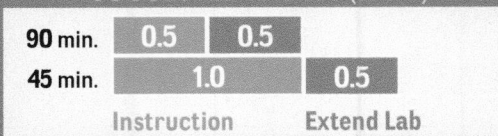

Track Your Progress

Objectives

1 Find surface areas of spheres.

2 Find volumes of spheres.

Mathematical Background

A sphere is the locus of all points that are a given distance from a given point called its center. If a sphere has a surface area of S square units and a radius of r units, then $S = 4\pi r^2$. If a sphere has a volume of V cubic units and a radius of r units, then $V = \frac{4}{3}\pi r^3$.

Skills Trace

THEN	NOW	NEXT
G.GMD.4 Identify the shapes of two-dimensional cross-sections of three-dimensional objects, and identify three-dimensional objects generated by rotations of two-dimensional objects.	**G.GMD.3** Use volume formulas for cylinders, pyramids, cones, and spheres to solve problems. **G.MG.3** Apply geometric methods to solve design problems (e.g., designing an object or structure to satisfy physical constraints or minimize cost; working with typographic grid systems based on ratios).	**G.GMD.1** Give an informal argument for the formulas for the circumference of a circle, area of a circle, and the volume of a cylinder, pyramid, and cone.

Go Online! All of these resources and more are available at connectED.mcgraw-hill.com

eLessons utilize the power of your interactive whiteboard in an engaging way. Use **Volume**, Screens 10–11, to introduce the concepts in this lesson.

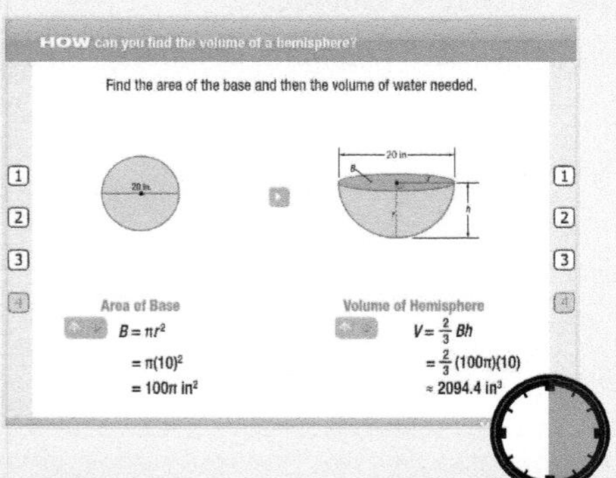

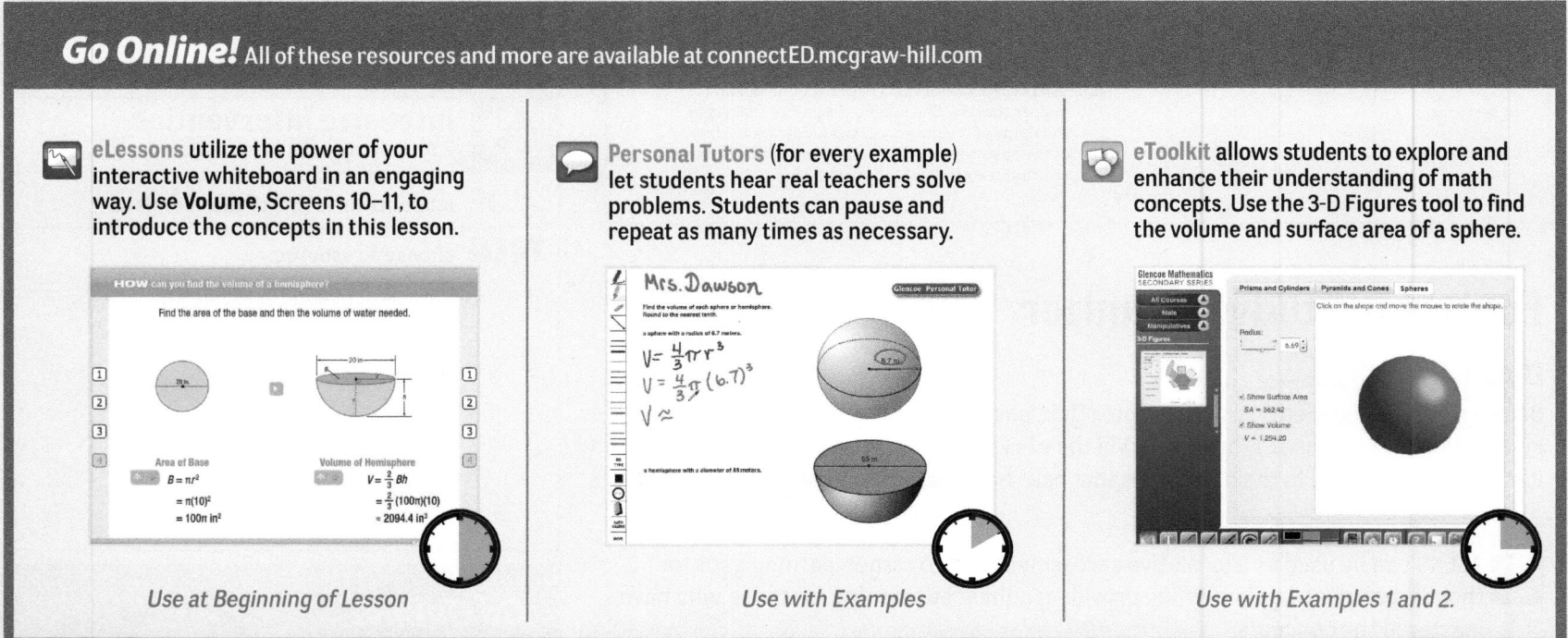

Use at Beginning of Lesson

Personal Tutors (for every example) let students hear real teachers solve problems. Students can pause and repeat as many times as necessary.

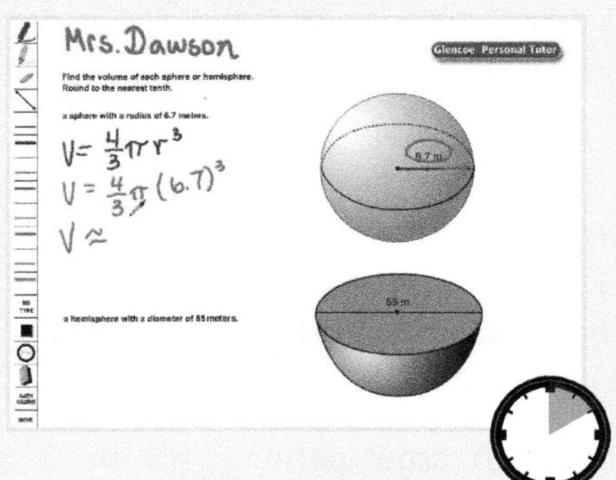

Use with Examples

eToolkit allows students to explore and enhance their understanding of math concepts. Use the 3-D Figures tool to find the volume and surface area of a sphere.

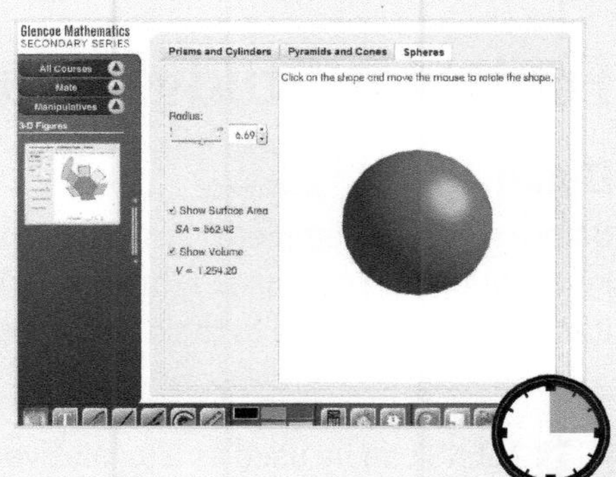

Use with Examples 1 and 2.

OER Using Open Educational Resources

Quiz Have students take the *Geometry Volume/Surface Area* quiz on **thatquiz** to review surface area and volume. Students can receive feedback on their performance and there is a timer option. *Use as review*

Differentiate Your Resources

Extra Practice Additional practice or homework; Skills Practice is best for approaching-level students and Practice is best for on-level and beyond-level students

Skills Practice

AL OL ELL

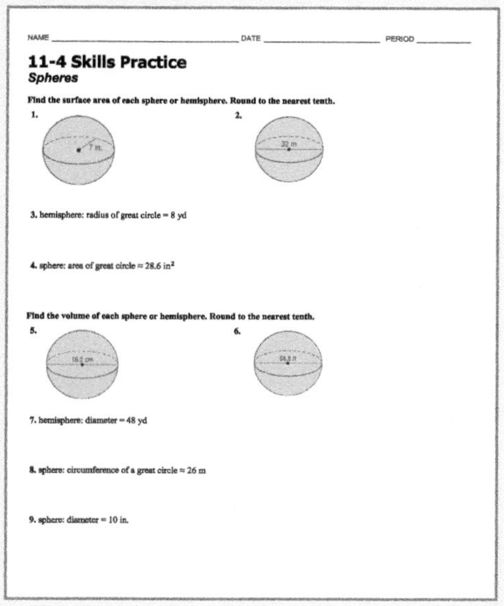
NAME ______ DATE ______ PERIOD ______

11-4 Skills Practice
Spheres

Find the surface area of each sphere or hemisphere. Round to the nearest tenth.

1. 2.

3. hemisphere: radius of great circle = 8 yd

4. sphere: area of great circle ≈ 28.6 in²

Find the volume of each sphere or hemisphere. Round to the nearest tenth.

5. 6.

7. hemisphere: diameter = 48 yd

8. sphere: circumference of a great circle ≈ 26 m

9. sphere: diameter = 10 in.

Practice

AL OL BL ELL

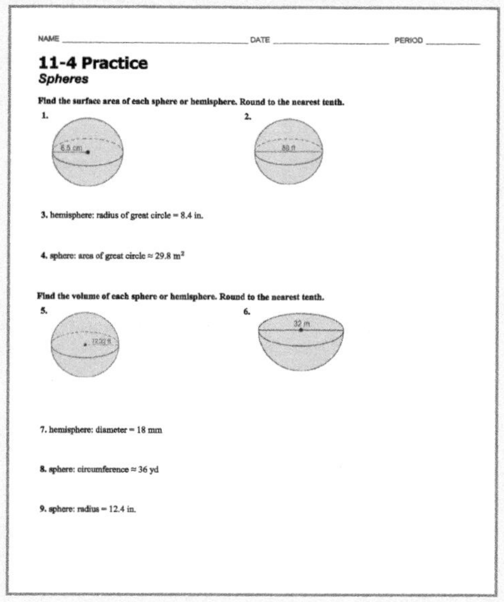
NAME ______ DATE ______ PERIOD ______

11-4 Practice
Spheres

Find the surface area of each sphere or hemisphere. Round to the nearest tenth.

1. 2.

3. hemisphere: radius of great circle = 8.4 in.

4. sphere: area of great circle ≈ 29.8 m²

Find the volume of each sphere or hemisphere. Round to the nearest tenth.

5. 6.

7. hemisphere: diameter = 18 mm

8. sphere: circumference ≈ 36 yd

9. sphere: radius = 12.4 in.

Word Problem Practice

AL OL BL ELL

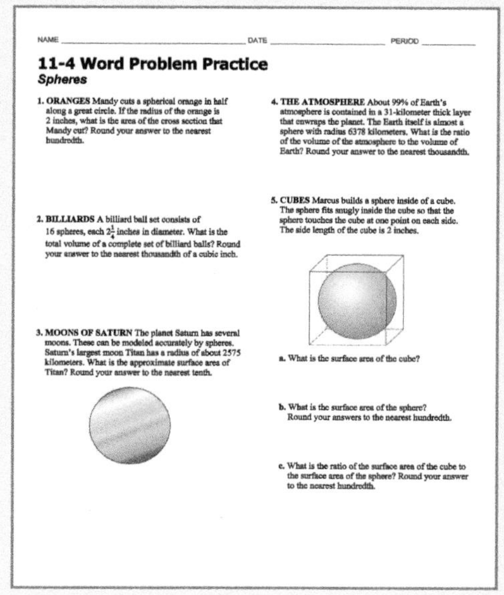
NAME ______ DATE ______ PERIOD ______

11-4 Word Problem Practice
Spheres

1. **ORANGES** Mandy cuts a spherical orange in half along a great circle. If the radius of the orange is 2 inches, what is the area of the cross section that Mandy cut? Round your answer to the nearest hundredth.

2. **BILLIARDS** A billiard ball set consists of 16 spheres, each $2\frac{1}{4}$ inches in diameter. What is the total volume of a complete set of billiard balls? Round your answer to the nearest thousandth of a cubic inch.

3. **MOONS OF SATURN** The planet Saturn has several moons. These can be modeled accurately by spheres. Saturn's largest moon Titan has a radius of about 2575 kilometers. What is the approximate surface area of Titan? Round your answer to the nearest tenth.

4. **THE ATMOSPHERE** About 99% of Earth's atmosphere is contained in a 31-kilometer thick layer that enwraps the planet. The Earth itself is almost a sphere with radius 6378 kilometers. What is the ratio of the volume of the atmosphere to the volume of Earth? Round your answer to the nearest thousandth.

5. **CUBES** Marcus builds a sphere inside of a cube. The sphere fits snugly inside the cube so that the sphere touches the cube at one point on each side. The side length of the cube is 2 inches.

a. What is the surface area of the cube?

b. What is the surface area of the sphere? Round your answers to the nearest hundredth.

c. What is the ratio of the surface area of the cube to the surface area of the sphere? Round your answer to the nearest hundredth.

Intervention Reteaching and vocabulary activities that can be used with struggling or absent students and as ELL support

Study Guide and Intervention

AL OL ELL

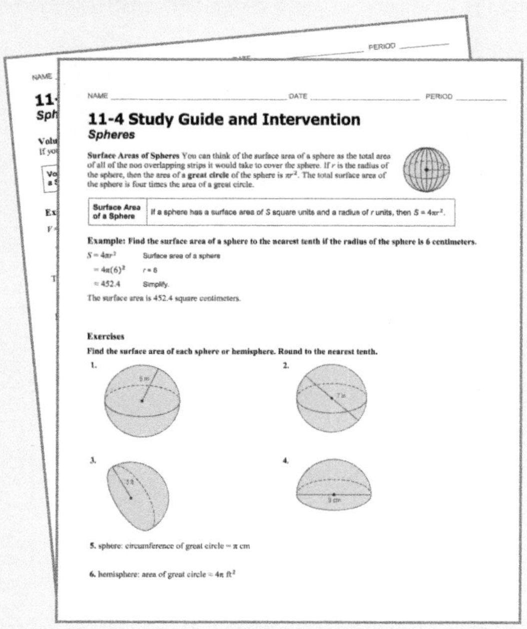
NAME ______ DATE ______ PERIOD ______

11-4 Study Guide and Intervention
Spheres

Surface Areas of Spheres You can think of the surface area of a sphere as the total area of all of the non overlapping strips it would take to cover the sphere. If r is the radius of the sphere, then the area of a **great circle** of the sphere is πr^2. The total surface area of the sphere is four times the area of a great circle.

Surface Area of a Sphere	If a sphere has a surface area of S square units and a radius of r units, then $S = 4\pi r^2$.

Example: Find the surface area of a sphere to the nearest tenth if the radius of the sphere is 6 centimeters.

$S = 4\pi r^2$ Surface area of a sphere
$= 4\pi(6)^2$ $r = 6$
≈ 452.4 Simplify.

The surface area is 452.4 square centimeters.

Exercises

Find the surface area of each sphere or hemisphere. Round to the nearest tenth.

1. 2. 3. 4.

5. sphere: circumference of great circle = π cm

6. hemisphere: area of great circle = 4π ft²

Study Notebook

AL OL BL ELL

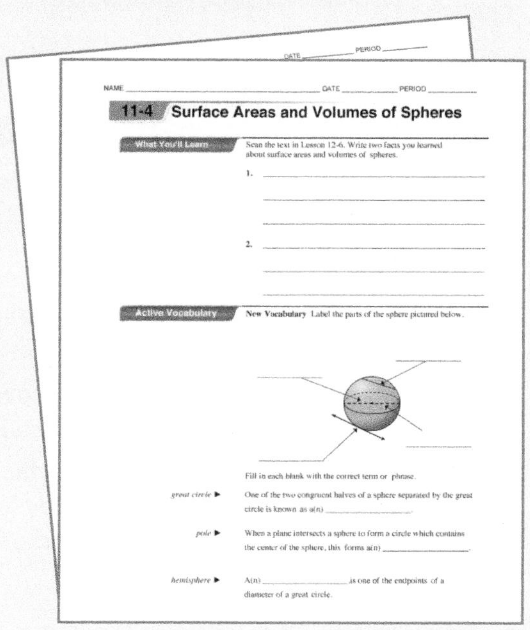
NAME ______ DATE ______ PERIOD ______

11-4 Surface Areas and Volumes of Spheres

What You'll Learn Scan the text in Lesson 12-6. Write two facts you learned about surface areas and volumes of spheres.

1. ______

2. ______

Active Vocabulary New Vocabulary Label the parts of the sphere pictured below.

Fill in each blank with the correct term or phrase.

great circle ▶ One of the two congruent halves of a sphere separated by the great circle is known as a(n) ______.

pole ▶ When a plane intersects a sphere to form a circle which contains the center of the sphere, this forms a(n) ______.

hemisphere ▶ A(n) ______ is one of the endpoints of a diameter of a great circle.

Extension Activities that can be used to extend lesson concepts

Enrichment

OL BL ELL

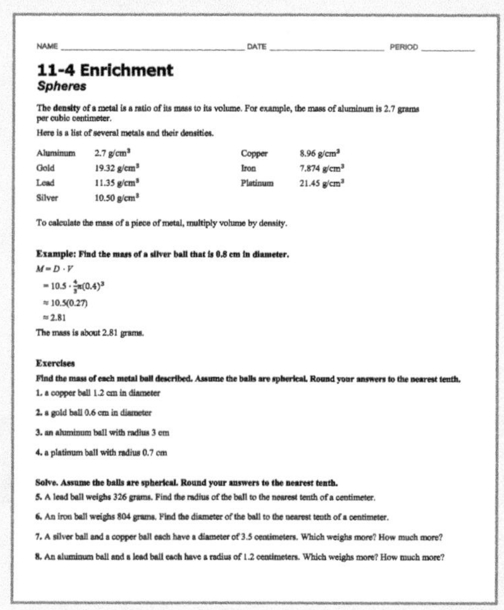
NAME ______ DATE ______ PERIOD ______

11-4 Enrichment
Spheres

The **density** of a metal is a ratio of its mass to its volume. For example, the mass of aluminum is 2.7 grams per cubic centimeter.
Here is a list of several metals and their densities.

Aluminum	2.7 g/cm³	Copper	8.96 g/cm³
Gold	19.32 g/cm³	Iron	7.874 g/cm³
Lead	11.35 g/cm³	Platinum	21.45 g/cm³
Silver	10.50 g/cm³		

To calculate the mass of a piece of metal, multiply volume by density.

Example: Find the mass of a silver ball that is 0.8 cm in diameter.

$M = D \cdot V$
$= 10.5 \cdot \frac{4}{3}\pi(0.4)^3$
$\approx 10.5(0.27)$
≈ 2.81

The mass is about 2.81 grams.

Exercises

Find the mass of each metal ball described. Assume the balls are spherical. Round your answers to the nearest tenth.

1. a copper ball 1.2 cm in diameter
2. a gold ball 0.6 cm in diameter
3. an aluminum ball with radius 3 cm
4. a platinum ball with radius 0.7 cm

Solve. Assume the balls are spherical. Round your answers to the nearest tenth.

5. A lead ball weighs 326 grams. Find the radius of the ball to the nearest tenth of a centimeter.
6. An iron ball weighs 804 grams. Find the diameter of the ball to the nearest tenth of a centimeter.
7. A silver ball and a copper ball each have a diameter of 3.5 centimeters. Which weighs more? How much more?
8. An aluminum ball and a lead ball each have a radius of 1.2 centimeters. Which weighs more? How much more?

Launch

Have students read the Why? section of the lesson. Ask:

- What is a cross section in any direction of a sphere? a circle
- What measurement do you think would be needed to find the volume of a sphere? Sample answer: the radius

LESSON 4

Spheres

Then	Now	Why?
You found surface areas of prisms and cylinders.	1 Find surface areas of spheres. 2 Find volumes of spheres.	When you blow bubbles, soapy liquid surrounds a volume of air. Because of surface tension, the liquid maintains a shape that minimizes the surface area surrounding the air. The shape that minimizes surface area per unit of volume is a sphere.

New Vocabulary
great circle
pole
hemisphere

Mathematical Practices
1 Make sense of problems and persevere in solving them.
6 Attend to precision.

Content Standards
G.GMD.3 Use volume formulas for cylinders, pyramids, cones, and spheres to solve problems.
G.MG.3 Apply geometric methods to solve problems (e.g., designing an object or structure to satisfy physical constraints or minimize cost; working with typographic grid systems based on ratios).

1 Surface Area of Spheres Recall that a *sphere* is the locus of all points in space that are a given distance from a given point called the *center* of the sphere.

- A *radius* of a sphere is a segment from the center to a point on the sphere.
- A *chord* of a sphere is a segment that connects any two points on the sphere.
- A *diameter* of a sphere is a chord that contains the center.
- A *tangent* to a sphere is a line that intersects the sphere in exactly one point.

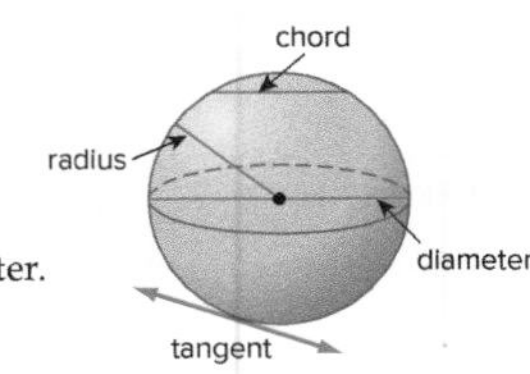

To develop a formula for the surface area of a sphere, consider a tennis ball. The covering of this sphere is comprised of two congruent dumbell-shaped pieces, each of which can be approximated by two congruent circles with radii equal to that of the sphere. So, the entire covering consists of approximately four congruent circles. The sum of these areas approximates the surface area of the sphere.

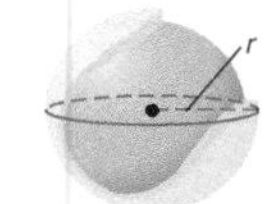

$S \approx 4A$ Sum of circles with area A

$\approx 4(\pi r^2)$ or $4\pi r^2$ $A = \pi r^2$

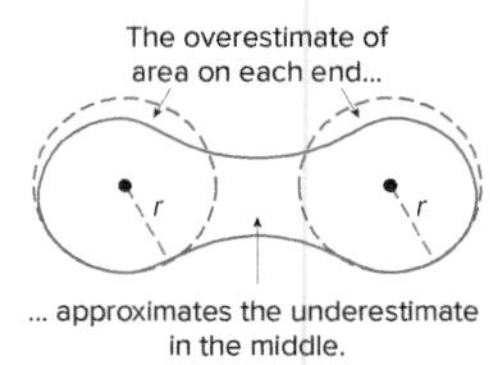

While its derivation is beyond the scope of this course, the exact formula is in fact $S = 4\pi r^2$.

Key Concept Surface Area of a Sphere

Words The surface area S of a sphere is $S = 4\pi r^2$, where r is the radius.

Symbols $S = 4\pi r^2$

Model

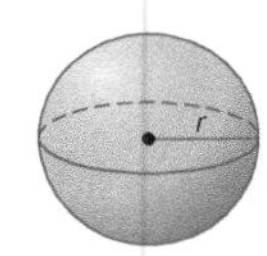

Mathematical Practices Strategies

Make sense of problems and persevere in solving them.
Help students express and use formulas for the surface area and volume of a sphere. For example, ask:

- What is the relationship between the volume of a hemisphere and the volume of a sphere? The volume of a hemisphere is half the volume of a sphere.
- Given the surface area of a sphere, how would you find its volume? You would find its radius and then, using the radius, you would find the volume.
- How do you find the volume and surface area of a sphere given its diameter? You would first need to find the radius by first dividing the diameter by two, and then you would substitute the radius in the formulas.

Go Online!

Interactive Whiteboard
Use the *eLesson, Lesson Presentation,* or *Interactive Classroom* to present this lesson.

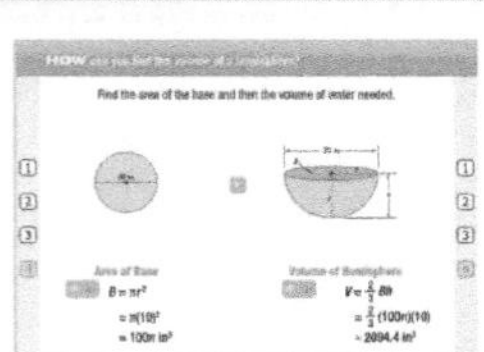

G.GMD.3

Example 1 Surface Area of a Sphere

Find the surface area of the sphere to the nearest tenth.

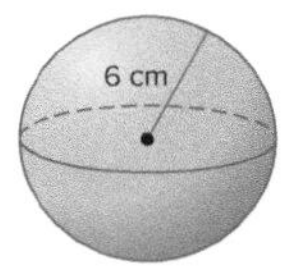

$S = 4\pi r^2$ Surface area of a sphere

$= 4\pi(6)^2$ Replace r with 6.

≈ 452.4 Use a calculator.

The surface area is about 452.4 square centimeters.

Guided Practice

1A. 633.5 mm²

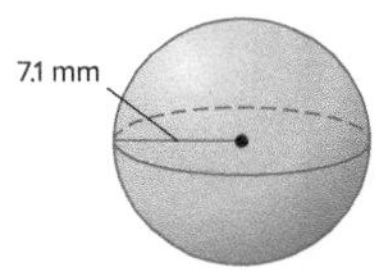

1B. 1520.5 ft²

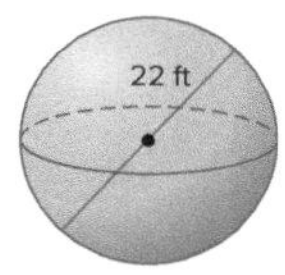

Study Tip
Great Circles A sphere has an infinite number of great circles.

Recall that lateral area is defined as the sum of the area of the lateral faces of a solid. Because a sphere has no lateral faces, the surface area of a sphere is calculated.

A plane can intersect a sphere in a point or in a circle. If the circle contains the center of the sphere, the intersection is called a **great circle**. The endpoints of a diameter of a great circle are called **poles**.

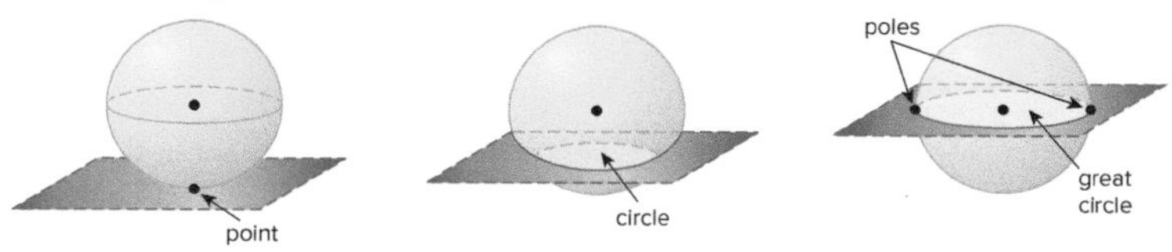

Because a great circle has the same center as the sphere and its radii are also radii of the sphere, it is the largest circle that can be drawn on a sphere. A great circle separates a sphere into two congruent halves, called **hemispheres**.

WatchOut!
Area of Hemisphere When finding the surface area of a hemisphere, do not forget to include the area of the great circle.

G.GMD.3

Example 2 Use Great Circles to Find Surface Area

a. Find the surface area of the hemisphere.

Find half the area of a sphere with a radius of 2.8 centimeters. Then add the area of the great circle.

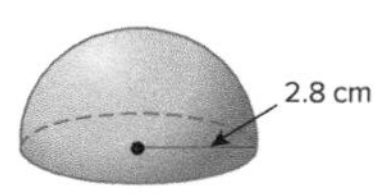

$S = \frac{1}{2}(4\pi r^2) + \pi r^2$ Surface area of a hemisphere

$= \frac{1}{2}[4\pi(2.8)^2] + \pi(2.8)^2$ Replace r with 2.8.

$\approx 73.9 \text{ cm}^2$ Use a calculator.

b. Find the surface area of a sphere if the circumference of the great circle is 5π meters.

First, find the radius. The circumference of a great circle is $2\pi r$. So, $2\pi r = 5\pi$ or $r = 2.5$.

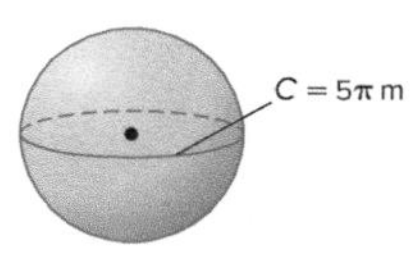

$S = 4\pi r^2$ Surface area of a sphere

$= 4\pi(2.5)^2$ Replace r with 2.5.

$\approx 78.5 \text{ m}^2$ Use a calculator.

Teach

Ask the scaffolded questions for each example to build conceptual understanding for students at all levels.

1 Surface Area of Spheres

Example 1 Surface Area of a Sphere

AL If the radius of the sphere is 3 centimeters, what is the surface area? 113.1 cm²

OL If the surface area of a sphere is 804 square inches, what is the radius of the sphere? about 8 in.

BL The radius of one sphere is three times greater than the radius of the second sphere. How much greater is the surface area of the first sphere than the surface area of the second? 9

Need Another Example?

Find the surface area of the sphere. Round to the nearest tenth.

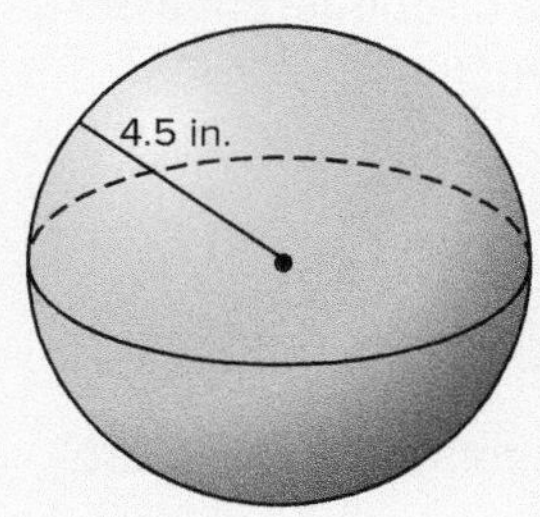

254.5 in²

Need Another Example?

a. Find the surface area of the hemisphere. 129 mm²

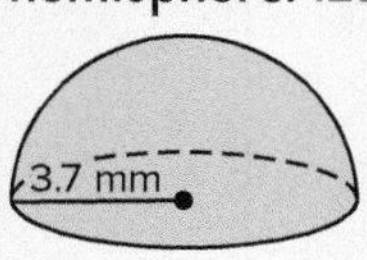

b. Find the surface area of a sphere if the circumference of the great circle is 10π feet. 314.2 ft²

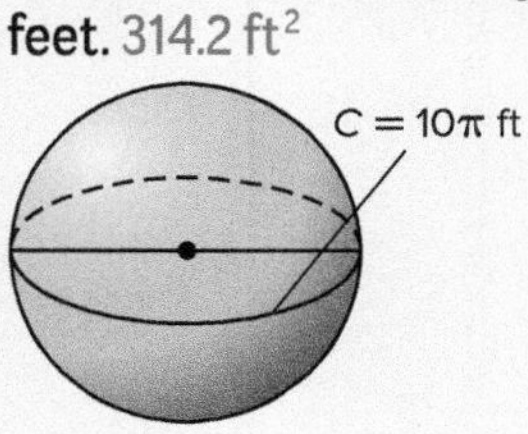

c. Find the surface area of a sphere if the area of the great circle is approximately 220 square meters. 880 m²

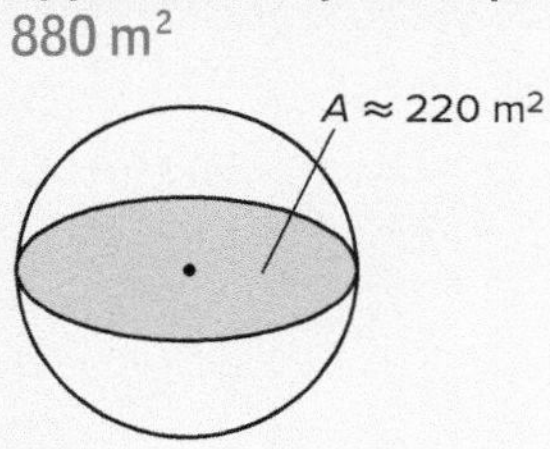

Example 2 Use Great Circles to Find Surface Area

AL How is the surface area of a hemisphere different from half of the surface area of a sphere of the same radius? To find the surface area of a hemisphere, you have to add the area of the great circle that forms the hemisphere.

OL If the area of a great circle is about 113 cm², what is the surface area of the sphere? about 452 cm²

BL What is the relationship between the area of the great circle of a sphere and the surface area of the sphere? The surface area of the sphere is 4 times the area of the great circle.

Watch Out!

Rounding In Example 2c, you could have also replaced πr^2 in the formula with 130. The answer may have been slightly different because of rounding.

2 Volume of Spheres

Example 3 Volumes of Spheres and Hemispheres

AL Why don't we have to calculate the volume of the great circle when we find the volume of a hemisphere? A great circle is two-dimensional, so it does not have volume.

OL What is the volume of a hemisphere with diameter 15 centimeters? 883.6 cm^3

BL What is the radius of a sphere with a volume of 180 cubic centimeters? about 3.5 cm

Need Another Example?

Find the volume of each sphere or hemisphere. Round to the nearest tenth.

a. a sphere with a great circle circumference of 30π centimeters 14,137.2 cm^3

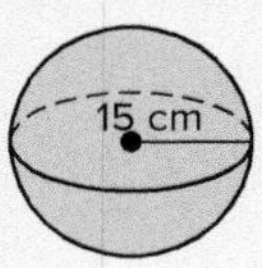

b. a hemisphere with a diameter of 6 feet 56.5 ft^3

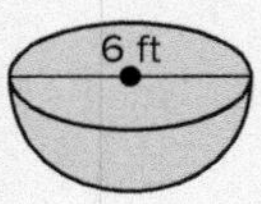

MP Teaching the Mathematical Practices

Precision Mathematically proficient students are careful about specifying units of measure. They calculate accurately and efficiently. Encourage students to check their work to make sure that the units are correct.

---

c. **Find the surface area of a sphere if the area of the great circle is approximately 130 square inches.**

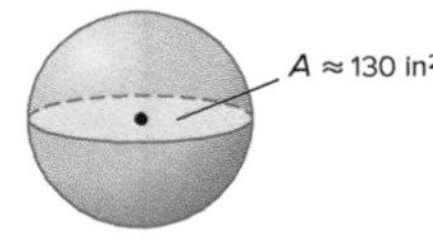

First, find the radius. The area of a great circle is πr^2. So, $\pi r^2 = 130$ or $r \approx 6.4$.

$S = 4\pi r^2$ — Surface area of a sphere

$\approx 4\pi(6.4)^2$ or about 514.7 in^2 — Replace r with 6.4. Use a calculator.

Guided Practice

Find the surface area of each figure. Round to the nearest tenth if necessary.

2A. sphere: circumference of great circle = 16.2π ft 824.5 ft^2

2B. hemisphere: area of great circle ≈ 94 mm^2 282 mm^2

2C. hemisphere: circumference of great circle = 36π cm 3053.6 cm^2

Go Online!

How do you find the surface area and volume of a sphere? Investigate by using the Geometry Tools in ConnectED. Discuss your findings with a partner. Ask for clarification as you need it.

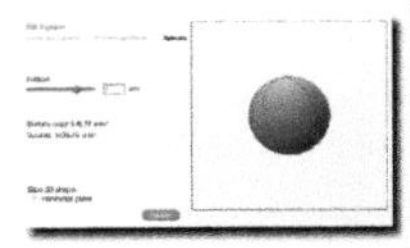

2 Volume of Spheres Suppose a sphere with radius r contains infinitely many pyramids with vertices at the center of the sphere. Each pyramid has height r and base area B. The sum of the volumes of all the pyramids equals the volume of the sphere.

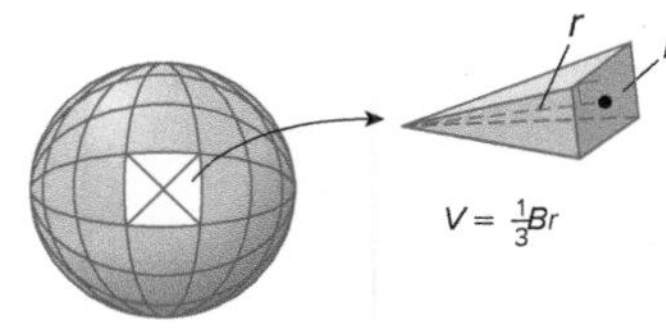

$V = \frac{1}{3}B_1r_1 + \frac{1}{3}B_2r_2 + \ldots + \frac{1}{3}B_nr_n$ — Sum of volumes of pyramids

$= \frac{1}{3}r(B_1 + B_2 + \ldots + B_n)$ — Distributive Property

$= \frac{1}{3}r(4\pi r^2)$ — The sum of the pyramid base areas equals the surface area of the sphere.

$= \frac{4}{3}\pi r^3$ — Simplify.

Study Tip

MP Modeling When solving problems involving volumes of solids, it is helpful to draw and label a diagram when no diagram is provided.

Key Concept Volume of a Sphere

Words	The volume V of a sphere is $V = \frac{4}{3}\pi r^3$, where r is the radius of the sphere.	Model
Symbols	$V = \frac{4}{3}\pi r^3$	

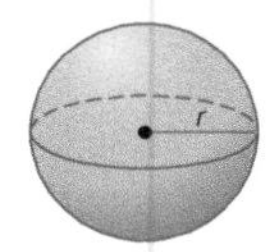

G.GMD.3

Example 3 Volumes of Spheres and Hemispheres

Find the volume of each sphere or hemisphere. Round to the nearest tenth.

a. **a hemisphere with a radius of 6 meters**

Estimate: $V \approx \frac{1}{2}\cdot\frac{4}{3}\cdot 3\cdot 6^3$ or 432 m^3

$V = \frac{1}{2}\left(\frac{4}{3}\pi r^3\right)$ — Volume of a hemisphere

$= \frac{2}{3}\pi(6)^3$ or about 452.4 m^3 — Replace r with 6. Use a calculator.

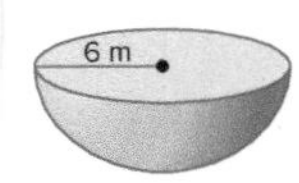

The volume of the hemisphere is about 452.4 cubic meters. This is close to the estimate, so the answer is reasonable.

Study Tip

MP Precision Remember to use the correct units when giving your answers. As with other solids, the surface area of a sphere is measured in square units, and volume is measured in cubic units.

b. a sphere with a great circle circumference of 18π centimeters

Step 1 Find the radius of the sphere.

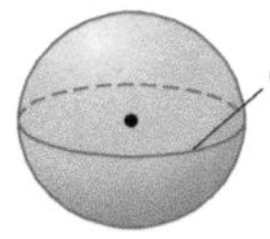

$C = 2\pi r$ Circumference of a circle

$18\pi = 2\pi r$ Replace C with 18π.

$r = 9$ Solve for r.

Step 2 Find the volume.

$V = \frac{4}{3}\pi r^3$ Volume of a sphere

$= \frac{4}{3}\pi(9)^3$ or about $3053.6\ cm^3$ Replace r with 9. Use a calculator.

Guided Practice

3A. sphere: diameter = 7.4 in. $212.2\ in^3$

3B. hemisphere: area of great circle $\approx 249\ mm^2$ $1477.9\ mm^3$

G.GMD.3

Real-World Example 4 Solve Problems Involving Solids

LACROSSE **A regulation lacrosse ball is made of solid rubber. It takes up approximately 8.65 cubic inches. What is the circumference of the lacrosse ball? Round to the nearest tenth.**

Understand Assume that the lacrosse ball is a sphere. You know that the volume is approximately 8.65 cubic inches. The circumference of the lacrosse ball is the circumference of the great circle.

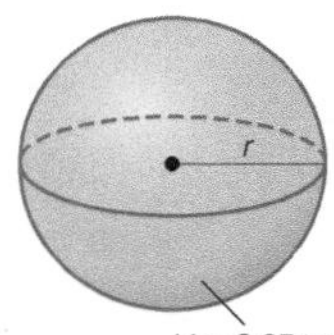

Plan First use the volume formula to find the radius. Then find the circumference of the great circle.

Solve

$V = \frac{4}{3}\pi r^3$ Volume of a sphere

$8.65 \approx \frac{4}{3}\pi r^3$ Replace V with 8.65.

$2.06 \approx r^3$ Divide each side by $\frac{4}{3}\pi$.

Use a calculator to find $\sqrt[3]{2.06}$.

The radius of the sphere is approximately 1.3 inches. So, the circumference is $2\pi r = 2\pi(1.3)$ or approximately 8.2 inches.

Check You can work backward to check the solution.

If $C \approx 8.2$, then $r \approx 1.3$. If $r \approx 1.3$, then $V \approx \frac{4}{3}\pi \cdot 1.3^3$ or about 8.65 cubic inches. The solution is correct. ✓

Assuming that the lacrosse ball was a sphere allows use of the formula for the volume of a sphere to find a solution that closely approximates the actual circumference.

Real-World Link

Starting with the 2014 season, all lacrosse balls must meet the standard specifications. Balls are to weigh between 140 and 147 grams. Rebound is tested as well. They should bounce 70% from the falling point.

Source: NCAA

Guided Practice

4. SNOW CONES Ren makes a snow cone in a conical cup that is 3.5 inches tall with an opening 2.5 inches wide. He fills the cup to the top and then adds a hemispherical scoop that exactly covers the top of the cone. What is the volume of ice used to make the snow cone? Round to the nearest tenth. $9.8\ in^3$

Example 4 Solve Problems Involving Solids

AL If the volume of a ball is 33.5 cubic inches, what is the radius of the ball? about 2 in.

OL The volume of a regulation baseball is about 14.1 cubic inches. What is the diameter of a regulation baseball? about 3 in.

BL The diameter of a softball is about 25% longer than the diameter of a baseball. If a regulation baseball has a volume of 14.1 cubic inches, what is the volume of a softball? about $27.5\ in^3$

Need Another Example?

Archeology The stone spheres of Costa Rica were made by forming granodiorite boulders into spheres. One of the stone spheres has a volume of about $36{,}000\pi$ cubic inches. What is the diameter of the stone sphere? 60 in.

Differentiated Instruction OL BL

Naturalist Learners One way to compare moons is by their approximate diameters. Ask students to describe how to find the surface area of a moon. To find the surface area, determine the radius from the diameter. Then substitute the radius into the formula 4 π times the square of the radius.

Practice

Formative Assessment Use Exercises 1–9 to assess students' understanding of the concepts in this lesson.

The Practice and Problem Solving exercises assess the content taught in the lesson. The Preparing for Assessment page is meant to be used as preparation for assessment.

Extra Practice

See page R11 for extra exercises for students who are approaching level or for on-level students who need additional reinforcement.

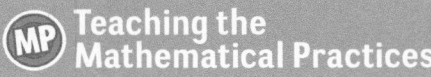

MP Teaching the Mathematical Practices

Precision Mathematically proficient students are careful about specifying units of measure. In Exercises 18–25, encourage students to check the units carefully.

Levels of Complexity Chart

The levels of the exercises progress from 1 to 3, with Level 1 indicating the lowest level of complexity.

Exercises	10–27	28–38, 49–55	39–48
C Level 3			●
B Level 2		●	
Level 1	●		

Check Your Understanding

○ = Step-by-Step Solutions begin on page R13.

Go Online! for a Self-Check Quiz

Examples 1–2 G.GMD.3 **Find the surface area of each sphere or hemisphere. Round to the nearest tenth.**

1. 1017.9 m²

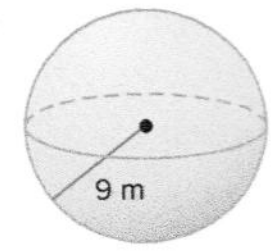

2. 461.8 in²

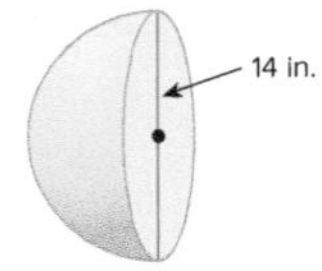

3. sphere: area of great circle = 36π yd² 452.4 yd²
4. hemisphere: circumference of great circle ≈ 26 cm 161.4 cm²

Example 3 G.GMD.3 **Find the volume of each sphere or hemisphere. Round to the nearest tenth.**

5. sphere: radius = 10 ft 4188.8 ft³
6. hemisphere: diameter = 16 cm 1072.3 cm³
7. hemisphere: circumference of great circle = 24π m 3619.1 m³
8. sphere: area of great circle = 55π in² 1708.6 in³

Example 4 G.GMD.3

9. **BASKETBALL** Basketballs used in professional games must have a circumference of $29\frac{1}{2}$ inches. What is the surface area of a basketball used in a professional game? 277.0 in²

Practice and Problem Solving

Extra Practice is on page R11.

Examples 1–2 G.GMD.3 **Find the surface area of each sphere or hemisphere. Round to the nearest tenth.**

10. 50.3 ft²
11. 113.1 cm²
12. 109.0 mm²
13. 680.9 in²

10.

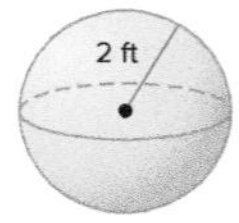

11.

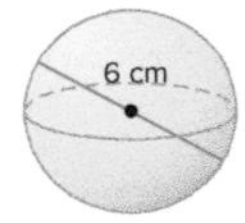

12.

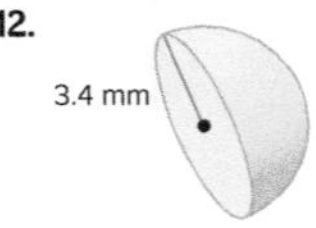

13.

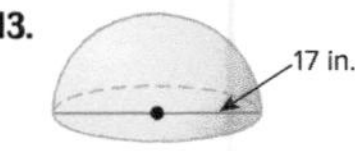

14. sphere: circumference of great circle = 2π cm 12.6 cm²
15. sphere: area of great circle ≈ 32 ft² 128 ft²
16. hemisphere: area of great circle ≈ 40 in² 120 in²
17. hemisphere: circumference of great circle = 15π mm 530.1 mm²

Example 3 G.GMD.3 MP **PRECISION** Find the volume of each sphere or hemisphere. Round to the nearest tenth.

18. 261.8 ft³

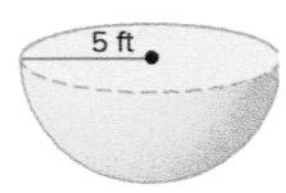

19. 4.2 cm³

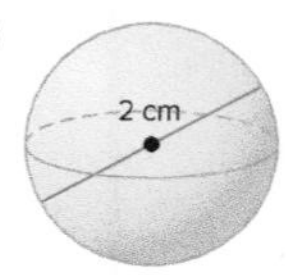

20. sphere: radius = 1.4 yd 11.5 yd³
21. hemisphere: diameter = 21.8 cm 2712.3 cm³
22. sphere: area of great circle = 49π m² 1436.8 m³
23. sphere: circumference of great circle ≈ 22 in. 179.8 in³
24. hemisphere: circumference of great circle ≈ 18 ft 49.2 ft³
25. hemisphere: area of great circle ≈ 35 m² 77.9 m³

Differentiated Homework Options

Levels	AL Basic	OL Core	BL Advanced
Exercises	10–27, 45, 46, 48–55	11–27 odd, 28, 29, 31, 32, 33–37 odd, 38, 39, 41, 43, 44–46, 48–55	39–48, (optional: 49–55)
2-Day Option	11–27 odd, 49–55	10–27	
	10–26 even, 45, 46, 48	28–46, 48–55	

You can use ALEKS to provide additional remediation support with personalized instruction and practice.

Go Online! eBook

Interactive Student Guide

Use the *Interactive Student Guide* to deepen conceptual understanding.
- Volumes of Spheres

Example 4
G.GMD.3

26. **FISH** A *puffer fish* is able to "puff up" when threatened by gulping water and inflating its body. The puffer fish at the right is approximately a sphere with a diameter of 5 inches. Its surface area when inflated is about 1.5 times its normal surface area. What is the surface area of the fish when it is *not* puffed up? **about 52.4 in^2**

27. **ARCHITECTURE** The Reunion Tower in Dallas, Texas, is topped by a spherical dome that has a surface area of approximately $13{,}924\pi$ square feet. What is the volume of the dome? Round to the nearest tenth. **860,289.5 ft^3**

B **28.** **TREE HOUSE** The spherical tree house, or *tree sphere,* shown at the right has a diameter of 10.5 feet. Its volume is 1.8 times the volume of the first tree sphere that was built. What was the diameter of the first tree sphere? Round to the nearest foot. **9 ft**

MP **PERSEVERANCE** Find the surface area and the volume of each solid. Round to the nearest tenth.

29. **276.5 in^2; 385.4 in^3**

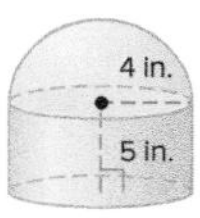

30. **798.5 cm^2; 1038.2 cm^3**

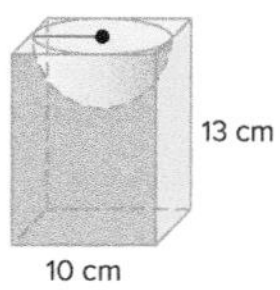

31. **TOYS** The spinning top at the right is a composite of a cone and a hemisphere.

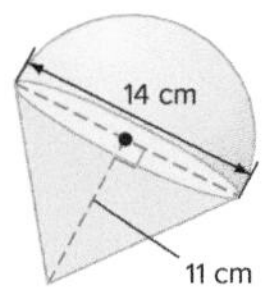

a. Find the surface area and the volume of the top. Round to the nearest tenth. **594.6 cm^2; 1282.8 cm^3**

b. If the manufacturer of the top makes another model with dimensions that are one half of the dimensions of this top, what are its surface area and volume? **148.7 cm^2; 160.4 cm^3**

32. **BALLOONS** A spherical helium-filled balloon with a diameter of 30 centimeters can lift a 14-gram object. Find the size of a balloon that could lift a person who weighs 65 kilograms. Round to the nearest tenth. **The balloon would have to have a diameter of approximately 139,286 cm.**

Use sphere *S* to name each of the following.

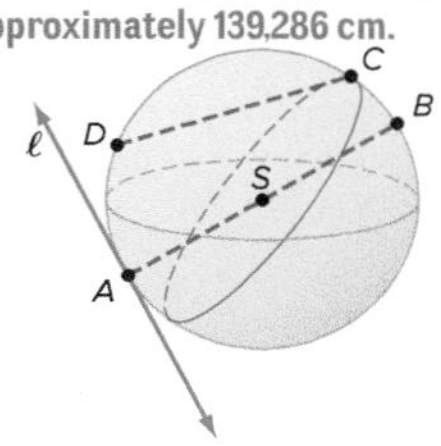

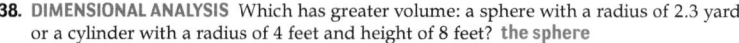

33. a chord $\overline{DC}$

34. a radius **Sample answer: $\overline{SA}$**

35. a diameter $\overline{AB}$

36. a tangent **line ℓ**

37. a great circle **⊙*S***

38. **DIMENSIONAL ANALYSIS** Which has greater volume: a sphere with a radius of 2.3 yards or a cylinder with a radius of 4 feet and height of 8 feet? **the sphere**

MP Teaching the Mathematical Practices

Sense-Making Mathematically proficient students start by explaining the meaning of a problem to themselves and looking for entry points to its solution. They plan a solution pathway rather than simply jumping into a solution attempt. In Exercises 29–30, encourage students to make a plan to solve each problem first.

Differentiated Instruction BL

Extension Ask students, based on their knowledge of plane geometry, to develop definitions for a polyhedron inscribed in a sphere and a polyhedron circumscribed about a sphere. A polyhedron inscribed in a sphere touches the sphere with all of its vertices. A polyhedron circumscribed about a sphere has faces that are all tangent (intersect at one point) to the sphere.

Assess

Name the Math Ask students to describe how to find the surface area of a basketball that is sized by its circumference (usually 30 inches).

Additional Answers

39a. $\sqrt{r^2 - x^2}$

39c. The volume of the disc from the cylinder is $\pi r^2 y$ or $\pi y r^2$. The volume of the disc from the two cones is $\pi x^2 y$ or $\pi y x^2$. Subtract the volumes of the discs from the cylinder and cone to get $\pi y r^2 - \pi y x^2$, which is the expression for the volume of the disc from the sphere at height x.

39d. Cavalieri's Principle

39e. The volume of the cylinder is $\pi r^2(2r)$ or $2\pi r^3$. The volume of one cone is $\frac{1}{3}\pi r^2(r)$ or $\frac{1}{3}\pi r^3$, so the volume of the double napped cone is $2 \cdot \frac{1}{3}\pi r^3$ or $\frac{2}{3}\pi r^3$. Therefore, the volume of the hollowed out cylinder, and thus the sphere, is $2\pi r^3 - \frac{2}{3}\pi r^3$ or $\frac{4}{3}\pi r^3$.

40. There are infinitely many planes that produce reflectional symmetry as long as they pass through the center. Any angle of rotation will produce rotational symmetry.

41. There are infinitely many planes that produce reflectional symmetry as long as they are vertical planes that pass through the center. Only rotation about an axis through the center perpendicular to the base will produce rotational symmetry through infinitely many angles.

42. The surface area is multiplied by 4^2 or 16. The volume is multiplied by 4^3 or 64.

43. The surface area is divided by 3^2 or 9. The volume is divided by 3^3 or 27.

Go Online!

eSolutions Manual

Create worksheets, answer keys, and solutions handouts for your assignments.

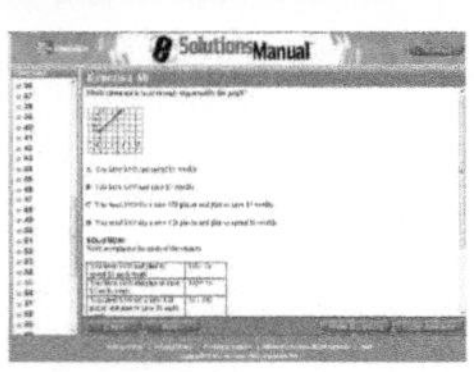

39. INFORMAL PROOF A sphere with radius r can be thought of as being made up of a large number of discs or thin cylinders. Consider the disc shown that is x units above or below the center of the sphere. Also consider a cylinder with radius r and height $2r$ that is hollowed out by two cones of height and radius r.

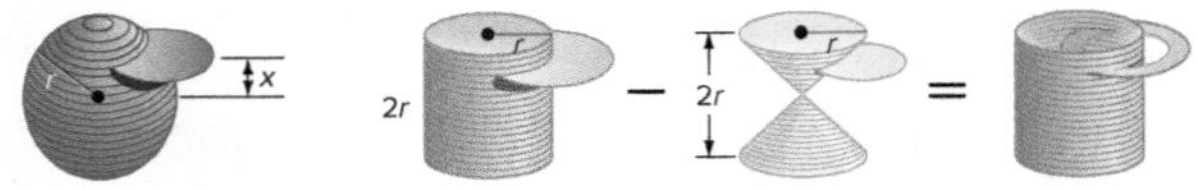

a. Find the radius of the disc from the sphere in terms of its distance x above the sphere's center. (*Hint:* Use the Pythagorean Theorem.) **a, c–e. See margin.**

b. If the disc from the sphere has a thickness of y units, find its volume in terms of x and y. $\pi(\sqrt{r^2 - x^2})^2 \cdot y$ or $\pi y r^2 - \pi y x^2$

c. Show that this volume is the same as that of the hollowed-out disc with thickness of y units that is x units above the center of the cylinder and cone.

d. Since the expressions for the discs at the same height are the same, what guarantees that the hollowed-out cylinder and sphere have the same volume?

e. Use the formulas for the volumes of a cylinder and a cone to derive the formula for the volume of the hollowed-out cylinder and thus, the sphere.

MP PERSEVERANCE Describe the number and types of planes that produce reflectional symmetry in each solid. Then describe the angles of rotation that produce rotational symmetry in each solid.

40. sphere **See margin.**

41. hemisphere **See margin.**

CHANGING DIMENSIONS A sphere has a radius of 12 centimeters. Describe how each change affects the surface area and the volume of the sphere. **42–43. See margin.**

42. The radius is multiplied by 4.

43. The radius is divided by 3.

44. DESIGN A standard juice box holds 8 fluid ounces.

a. Sketch designs for three different juice containers that will each hold 8 fluid ounces. Label dimensions in centimeters. At least one container should be cylindrical. (*Hint:* 1 fl oz ≈ 29.57353 cm³) **a–b. See Ch. 11 Answer Appendix.**

b. For each container in part **a**, calculate the surface area to volume (cm² per fl oz) ratio. Use these ratios to decide which of your containers can be made for the lowest materials cost. What shape container would minimize this ratio, and would this container be the cheapest to produce? Explain your reasoning.

G.GMD.1, G.GMD.3, G.MG.3

H.O.T. Problems Use **H**igher-**O**rder **T**hinking Skills

45. MP MODELING A cube has a volume of 216 cubic inches. Find the volume of a sphere that is circumscribed about the cube. Round to the nearest tenth. **587.7 in³**

46. ERROR ANALYSIS Diego says that the lateral area of a basketball is 29.5 square inches. Rodney says that you cannot calculate the lateral area of a sphere. Who is correct? Explain your reasoning.

46. Rodney is correct. Since a sphere has no lateral faces, you can only calculate its surface area.

47. CHALLENGE Sketch a sphere showing two examples of great circles. Sketch another sphere showing two examples of circles formed by planes intersecting the sphere that are *not* great circles. **See margin.**

48. WRITING IN MATH Write a ratio comparing the volume of a sphere with radius r to the volume of a cylinder with radius r and height $2r$. Then describe what the ratio means. **See margin.**

MP Standards for Mathematical Practice

Emphasis On	Exercises
1 Make sense of problems and persevere in solving them.	1–25, 53, 54
2 Reason abstractly and quantitatively.	47, 48
3 Construct viable arguments and critique the reasoning of others.	38, 46
4 Model with mathematics.	26–28, 31, 32, 44, 49, 51
6 Attend to precision.	29, 30
7 Look for and make use of structure.	33–37, 50, 52
8 Look for and express regularity in repeated reasoning.	42, 43

Preparing for Assessment

49. An artist is planning an exhibit in a hemispherical building with a diameter of 40 feet. The artist wants to cover the inside of the hemisphere (floor and ceiling) with black paint. Which of the following is the best estimate of the surface area that will be painted? MP 4 G.GMD.3 **B**

- ○ **A** 2513 ft^2
- ○ **B** 3770 ft^2
- ○ **C** 5027 ft^2
- ○ **D** 15,080 ft^2
- ○ **E** 16,755 ft^2

50. What is the circumference of a sphere that has a volume of 288π cubic meters? MP 7 G.GMD.3 **C**

- ○ **A** 144π m
- ○ **B** 36π m
- ○ **C** 12π m
- ○ **D** 6π m

51. Adam has a spherical candle with a radius of 2 inches. He melts the candle completely and pours the soft wax into a mold in the shape of a rectangular prism. The dimensions of the mold are shown here.

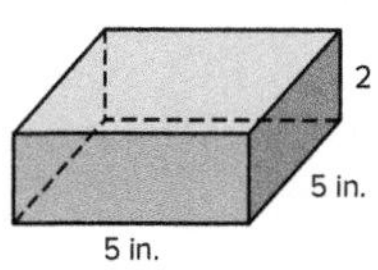

Which of the following best describes how the melted wax will fill the mold? MP 4 G.GMD.3 **B**

- ○ **A** The wax will fill slightly more than $\frac{1}{3}$ of the mold.
- ○ **B** The wax will fill the mold more than halfway.
- ○ **C** The wax will fill the mold almost perfectly.
- ○ **D** The wax will fill the mold, and there will be a lot of leftover wax.

52. A spherical disco ball has a surface area of 169π square centimeters. MP 7 G.GMD.3

a. Find the radius of the ball. $\frac{13}{2}$ cm

b. Find the volume of the ball. $\frac{2197\pi}{6}$ cm^3

53. **MULTI-STEP** Alice bought two spherical ornaments with radii of 2 centimeters and 4 centimeters. Find the following. MP 1 G.GMD.3

a. the volume of the first ornament $\frac{32\pi}{3}$ cm^3

b. the volume of the second ornament $\frac{256\pi}{3}$ cm^3

c. the surface area of the first ornament 16π cm^2

d. the surface area of the second ornament 64π cm^2

e. the ratio of the volume of the first ornament to the volume of the second ornament $\frac{1}{8}$

f. the ratio of the surface area of the first ornament to the surface area of the second ornament $\frac{1}{4}$

54. A ball has a diameter of 18 centimeters. A cylinder holds the ball exactly. What is the volume of the cylinder? MP 1 G.GMD.3 1458π

55. **MULTI-STEP** The length of the equator on a globe is 44 inches. Answer the following questions, rounding to the nearest tenth. MP 1 G.GMD.3

a. What is the diameter of the globe? 14.0 in.

b. What is the radius of the globe? 7.0 in.

c. What is the surface area of the globe? 616.2 in^2

d. What is the volume of the globe? 1438.5 in^3

Additional Answers

47. Sample answer:

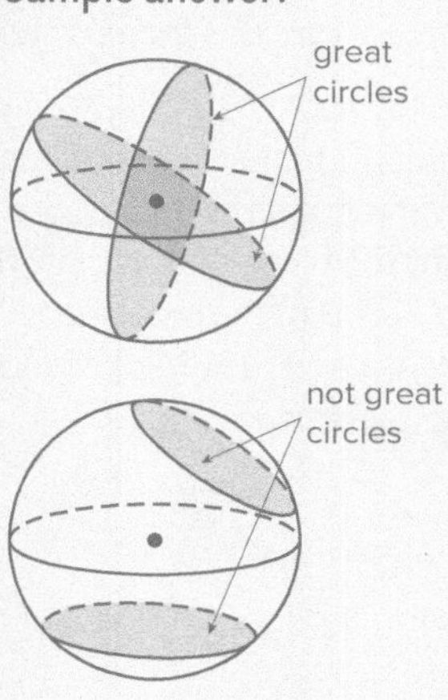

48. $\frac{2}{3}$; The volume of the sphere is two thirds the volume of the cylinder.

Preparing for Assessment

Exercises 49–55 require students to use the skills they will need on future assessments. Exercises are dual-coded with content standards and mathematical practice standards.

Dual Coding		
Items	Content Standards	MP Mathematical Practices
49	G.GMD.3	4
50	G.GMD.3	7
51	G.GMD.3	4
52	G.GMD.3	7
53	G.GMD.3	1
54	G.GMD.3	1
55	G.GMD.3	1

Diagnose Student Errors

Survey student responses for each item. Class trends may indicate common errors and misconceptions.

49.

A	Did not include floor when calculating surface to be painted
B	CORRECT
C	Found surface area of whole sphere
D	Used $r = 40$ ft
E	Found volume of hemisphere

50.

A	Found surface area
B	Found the area of a great circle
C	CORRECT
D	Omitted factor of 2 in circumference formula

51.

A	Used surface area of mold rather than volume
B	CORRECT
C	Used surface area of candle rather than volume
D	Used $4\pi r^3$ for volume of candle

Go Online!

Quizzes

Students can use *Self-Check Quizzes* to check their understanding of this lesson and have the results sent to you. You can also give *Quiz 3*, which covers the content in Lessons 11-3 and 11-4.

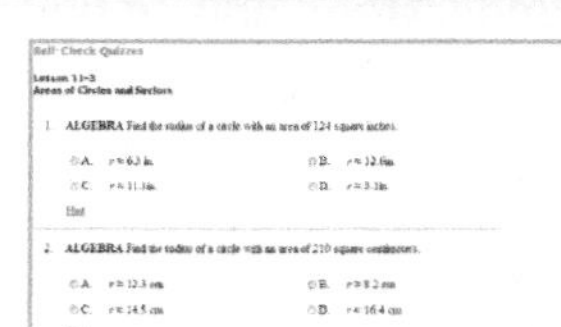

Launch

Objective Find the locus of points a given distance from the endpoints of a segment.

Materials
- ruler
- compass

Teaching Tips
Make sure students are clear that the points a given distance from the endpoint of a segment are points in space, and that they form the surface of a sphere.

Teach

Working in Cooperative Groups Arrange students in groups of 2, mixing abilities. Have students do the experiments and discussion questions. ELL

Activity 1

Ask:
- How could you demonstrate the points that are equidistant from the endpoint of a segment using a pencil or straw? Check students' work.

Practice Have students complete Exercises 1–4.

Activity 2

Ask:
- What is the difference between a circle and a sphere, as they relate to a locus of points? A circle is a locus of points on a plane, and a sphere is a locus of points in space.

Practice Have students complete Exercises 5–8.

Assess

Formative Assessment
Use Exercises 1–8 to assess whether students understand how to find the locus of points a given distance from the endpoints of a segment.

From Concrete to Abstract
Ask students what the locus of three or more coplanar points could be.

EXTEND 11-4
Geometry Lab
Locus and Spheres

Spheres are defined in terms of a locus of points in space. The definition of a sphere is the set of all points that are a given distance from a given point.

Mathematical Practices
1 Make sense of problems and persevere in solving them.
6 Attend to precision.

Content Standards
G.GMD.3 Use the volume formulas for cylinders, pyramids, cones, and spheres to solve problems.

Activity 1 Locus of Points a Given Distance from Endpoints

Work cooperatively. Find the locus of all points that are equidistant from a segment.

Collect the Data
- Draw a given line segment with endpoints J and K.

- Create a set of points that are equidistant from the segment.

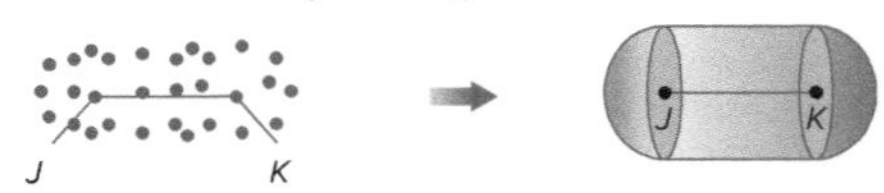

Analyze
1. Draw a figure and describe the locus of points in space that are 8 units from a segment that is 30 units long. See margin.
2. What three-dimensional shapes form the figure? two hemispheres and a cylinder
3. What are the radii and diameters of each hemisphere? 8 units; 16 units.
4. What are the diameter and the height of the cylinder? 16 units; 30 units.

Activity 2 Spheres That Intersect

Work cooperatively. Find the locus of all points that are equidistant from the centers of two intersecting spheres with the same radius.

Collect the Data
- Draw a line segment.
- Draw congruent overlapping spheres, with the centers at the endpoints of the given line segment.

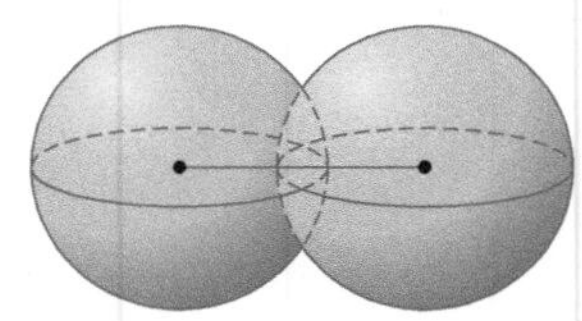

Analyze
5. What is the shape of the intersection of the upper hemispheres? semicircle
6. Can this be described as a locus of points in space or on a plane? Explain. See margin.
7. Describe this intersection as a locus. See margin.
8. FIREWORKS What is the locus of points that describes how particles from a fireworks explosion will disperse in an explosion at 400 feet above ground level if the expected distance a particle could travel is 200 feet? a sphere with radius 200 ft

Additional Answers

1. 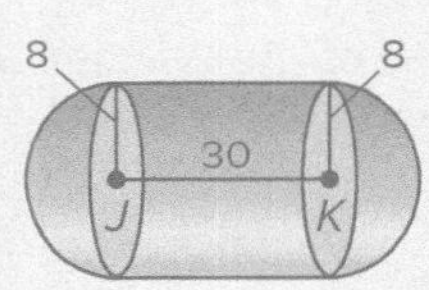

The locus of all points in space at a specific distance from a given point is a sphere. Thus, for this problem, the locus of points is a cylinder with height 30 units with hemispheres of radius 8 units on each end.

6. A semicircle is half of a locus of points on a plane.
7. The intersection is the set of all points located in the upper hemispheres and equidistant from the midpoint of the given line segment in the plane containing the perpendicular bisector of the given line segment.

LESSON 11-5

Spherical Geometry

SUGGESTED PACING (DAYS)

	Instruction		Extend Lab
90 min.	0.5	.25	
45 min.	1.0		0.5

Track Your Progress

Objectives

1 Describe sets of points on a sphere.

2 Compare and contrast Euclidean and spherical geometries.

Mathematical Background

In *spherical geometry* a plane is the surface of a sphere. Lines in spherical geometry are great circles. Some, but not all, of the properties of Euclidean geometry apply to spherical geometry.

Skills Trace

THEN	NOW	NEXT
G.GMD.3 Use volume formulas for cylinders, pyramids, cones, and spheres to solve problems.	**G.MG.3** Apply geometric methods to solve design problems (e.g., designing an object or structure to satisfy physical constraints or minimize cost; working with typographic grid systems based on ratios).	**G.GMD.1** Give an informal argument for the formulas for the circumference of a circle, area of a circle, volume of a cylinder, pyramid, and cone.

Go Online! All of these resources and more are available at connectED.mcgraw-hill.com

Use a Self-Check Quiz to assess students' understanding of spherical geometry and the differences between Euclidean and non-Euclidean geometry.

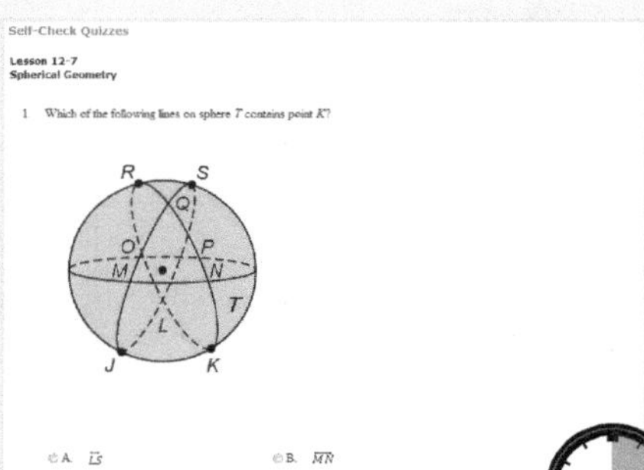

Use at End of Lesson

Personal Tutors (for every example) let students hear real teachers solve problems. Students can pause and repeat as many times as necessary.

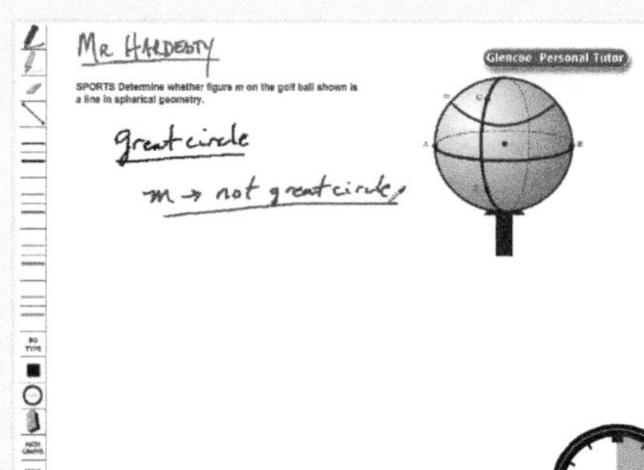

Use with Examples

Use the eGlossary to define Euclidean geometry, spherical geometry, and non-Euclidean geometry.

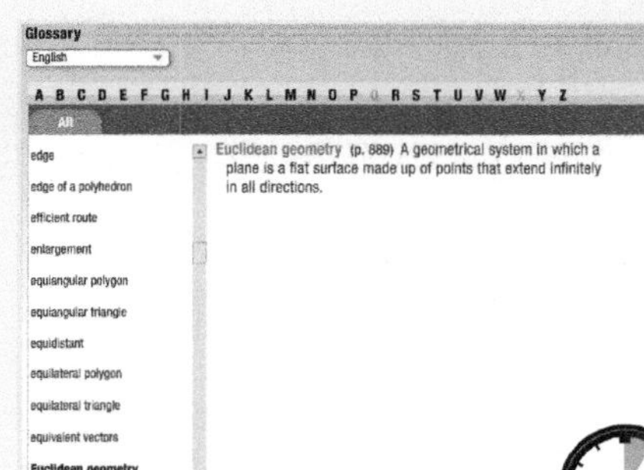

Use at Beginning of Lesson

OER Using Open Educational Resources

Video Sharing Have students work in groups to create a video lesson on **Muvee Cloud** explaining the difference between Euclidean geometry and spherical geometry. Then post students' videos online so students can review them before taking the assessment. *Use as homework*

Go Online!
connectED.mcgraw-hill.com

Worksheets

Differentiate Your Resources

Extra Practice Additional practice or homework; Skills Practice is best for approaching-level students and Practice is best for on-level and beyond-level students

Skills Practice

AL OL ELL

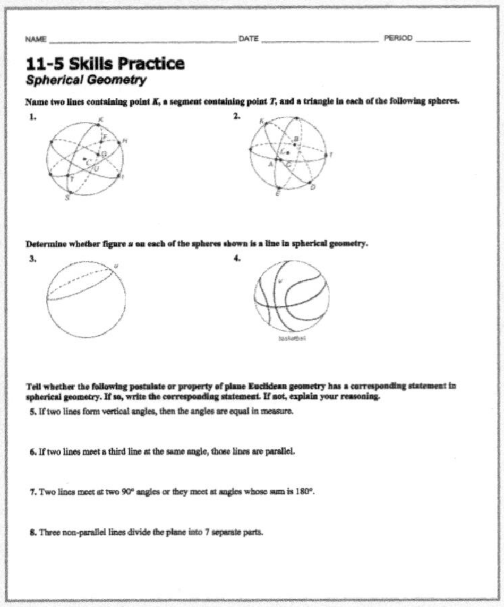

11-5 Skills Practice
Spherical Geometry

Practice

AL OL BL ELL

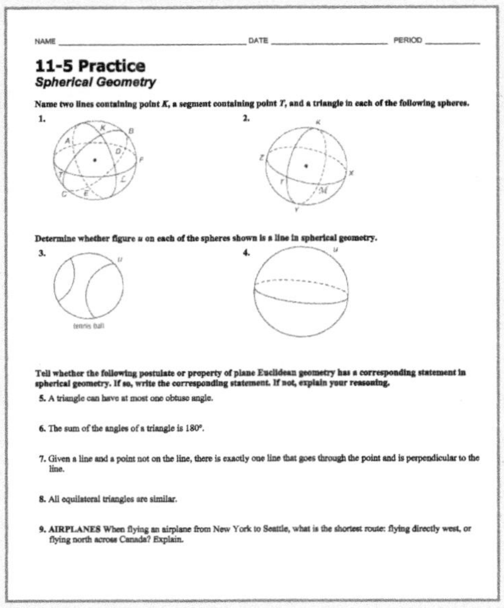

11-5 Practice
Spherical Geometry

Word Problem Practice

AL OL BL ELL

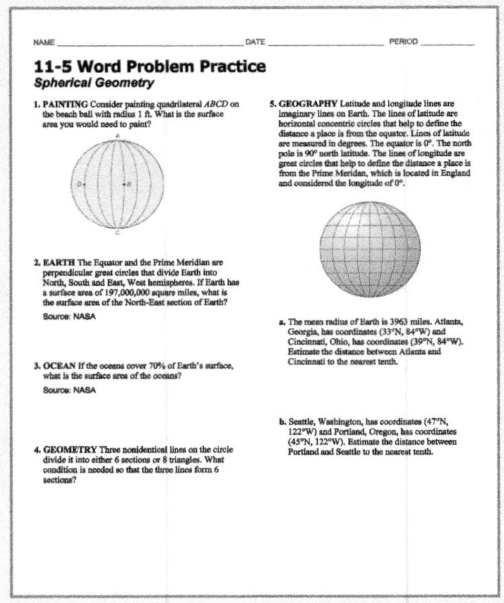

11-5 Word Problem Practice
Spherical Geometry

Intervention Reteaching and vocabulary activities that can be used with struggling or absent students and as ELL support

Study Guide and Intervention

AL OL ELL

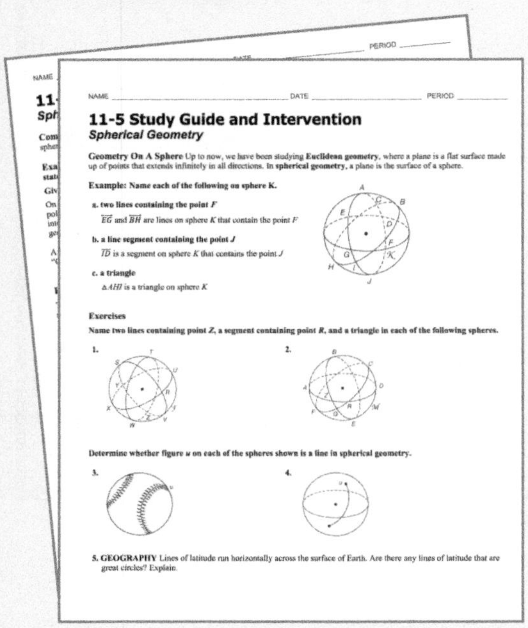

11-5 Study Guide and Intervention
Spherical Geometry

Study Notebook

AL OL BL ELL

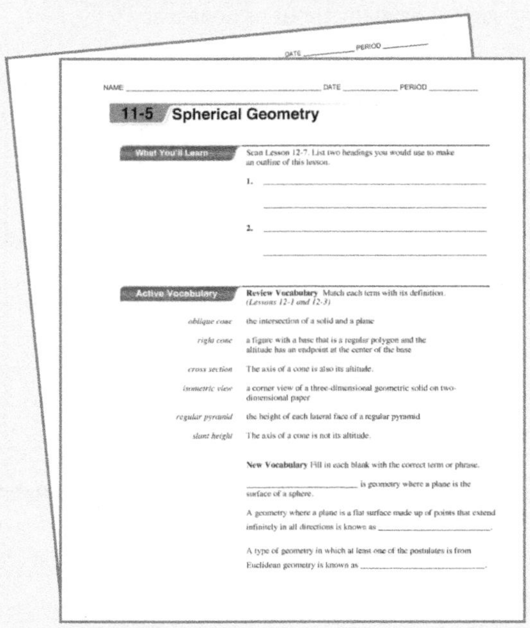

11-5 Spherical Geometry

Extension Activities that can be used to extend lesson concepts

Enrichment

OL BL ELL

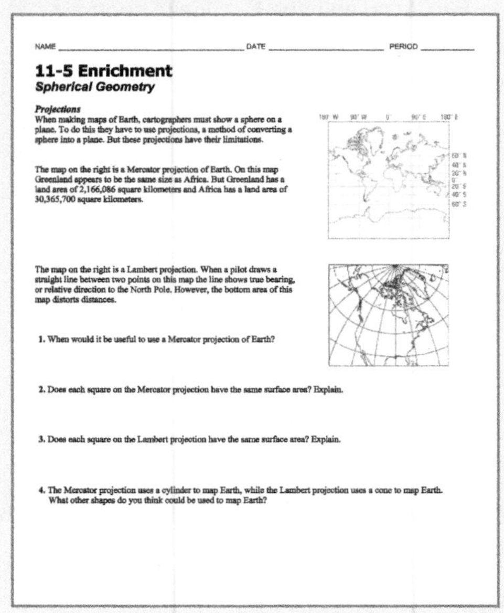

11-5 Enrichment
Spherical Geometry

LESSON 5

Spherical Geometry

Then

- You identified basic properties of spheres.

Now

- **1** Describe sets of points on a sphere.
- **2** Compare and contrast Euclidean and spherical geometries.

Why?

- Because Earth has a curved instead of a flat surface, the shortest path between two points on Earth is described by an arc of a great circle instead of a straight line.

New Vocabulary

Euclidean geometry
spherical geometry
non-Euclidean geometry

Mathematical Practices

3 Construct viable arguments and critique the reasoning of others.

1 Geometry on a Sphere In this text, we have studied **Euclidean geometry**, either in the plane or in space. In plane Euclidean geometry, a *plane* is a flat surface made up of points that extend infinitely in all directions. In **spherical geometry**, or geometry on a sphere, a plane is the surface of a sphere.

Lines are also defined differently in spherical geometry.

Key Concept Lines in Plane and Spherical Geometry

Plane Euclidean Geometry	Spherical Geometry
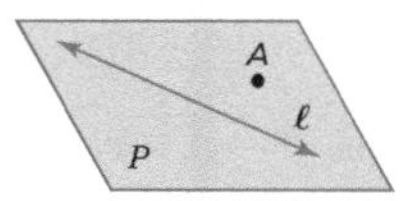	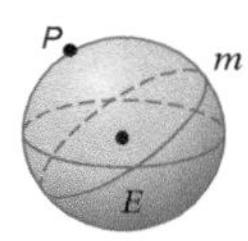
Plane *P* contains line ℓ and point *A* not on line ℓ.	Sphere *E* contains great circle *m* and point *p* not on *m*. Great circle *m* is a line on sphere *E*.

Example 1 Describe Sets of Points on a Sphere

Name each of the following on sphere *F*.

a. two lines containing point *R*

$\overleftrightarrow{GP}$ and $\overleftrightarrow{MQ}$ are lines on sphere *F* that contain point *R*.

b. a segment containing point *K*

$\overline{PS}$ is a segment on sphere *F* that contains point *K*.

c. a triangle

$\triangle RQP$ is a triangle on sphere *F*.

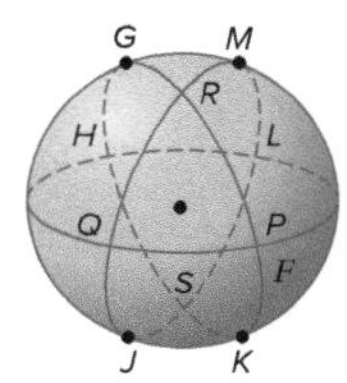

Guided Practice

Name each of the following on sphere *F* above.

1A. two lines containing point *P* $\overleftrightarrow{RK}$, $\overleftrightarrow{QP}$

1B. a segment containing point *Q* $\overline{PH}$

1C. a triangle $\triangle QSP$

Launch

Have students read the Why? section of the lesson. Ask:

- What is the shortest path between two points on a sphere? an arc
- What is the line around the center of the earth that divides it into two equal parts? the equator
- When might it be important to know that the shortest distance between two points on the earth is not a straight line? Sample answer: when planning a flight path for a plane

Teach

Ask the scaffolded questions for each example to build conceptual understanding for students at all levels.

1 Geometry on a Sphere

Example 1 Describe Sets of Points on a Sphere

AL What is the shape of a line in spherical geometry? a circle

OL What is a segment that contains point *J*? Sample answer: $\overline{QS}$

BL In part **c**, what is another triangle on sphere *F*? $\triangle SHL$

Need Another Example?

Name each of the following on sphere *S*.

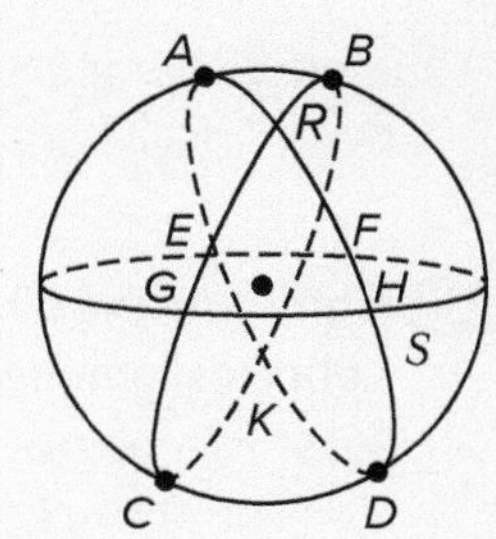

a. two lines containing point *R* $\overleftrightarrow{AD}$ and $\overleftrightarrow{BC}$
b. a segment containing point *C* $\overline{GK}$
c. a triangle $\triangle KGH$

MP Mathematical Practices Strategies

Reason abstractly and quantitatively.
Help students express and use conjectures about spherical geometry. For example, ask:

- When two lines intersect on a sphere, how many angles are formed? eight angles
- The sum of the measures of the angles on a spherical triangle can be at most how many degrees? 540°
- True or false: A line in spherical geometry has infinite length. false

Go Online!

Interactive Whiteboard

Use the *eLesson*, *Lesson Presentation*, or *Interactive Classroom* to present this lesson.

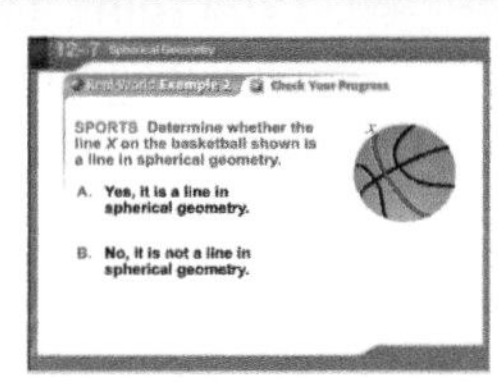

Example 2 Identify Lines in Spherical Geometry

AL What must be true about a line in spherical geometry? The line must pass through two poles of the sphere.

OL Can a sphere contain more than one line in spherical geometry? Explain. Yes; Sample answer: As long as the line passes through two points that are on a straight line through the sphere that intersect the center, it is a line.

BL How many lines do you think a sphere can contain in spherical geometry? Sample answer: infinitely many

Need Another Example?

Sports Determine whether the line *h* on the basketball shown is a line in spherical geometry. Explain.

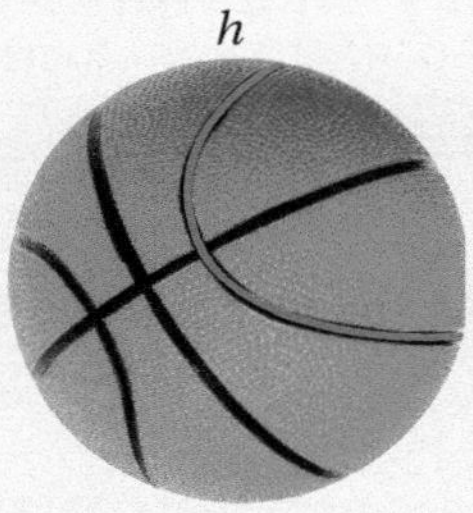

No; it is not a great circle.

2 Comparing Euclidean and Spherical Geometries

Example 3 Compare Plane Euclidean and Spherical Geometries

AL Compare and contrast lines in Euclidian and spherical geometries. They both contain at least two points. A line in Euclidian geometry does not have endpoints. A line in spherical geometry forms a circle.

OL Compare and contrast segments in Euclidian and spherical geometries. They both have endpoints. In Euclidian geometry, segments are straight. In spherical geometry, segments have curvature.

BL Do you think a quadrilateral can exist in spherical geometry? Explain. Yes; Sample answer: I think four intersecting lines or segments in spherical geometry would form a quadrilateral, in the manner that three intersecting lines or segments form triangles.

2. Yes; *p* is a line because it goes through opposite poles of the sphere.

Real-World Example 2 Identify Lines in Spherical Geometry

ENTERTAINMENT Determine whether *m* is a line in spherical geometry.

Notice that *m* does not go through two poles of the sphere. Therefore *m* is not a great circle and so not a line in spherical geometry.

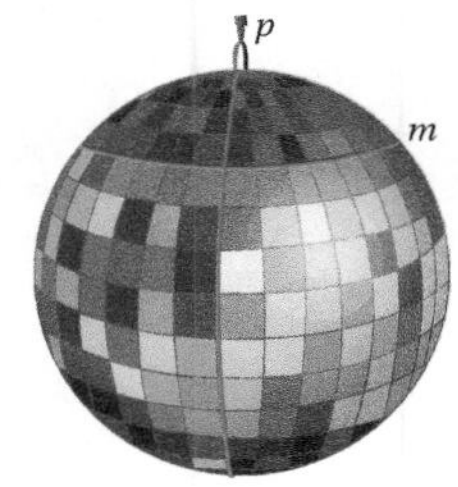

Guided Practice

2. Determine whether *p* on the mirror ball shown is a line in spherical geometry.

Math History Link

Georg F.B. Riemann (1826–1866) Spherical geometry is sometimes called *Riemann geometry*, after Georg Riemann, a German mathematician responsible for the Riemannian Postulate, which states that through a point not on a line, there are no lines parallel to the given line.

2 Comparing Euclidean and Spherical Geometries While some postulates and properties of Euclidean geometry are true in spherical geometry, others are not, or they are true only under certain circumstances. A **non-Euclidean geometry** is a geometry in which at least one of the postulates from Euclidean geometry fails.

Example 3 Compare Plane Euclidean and Spherical Geometries

Determine whether the following postulate or property of plane Euclidean geometry has a corresponding statement in spherical geometry. If so, write the corresponding statement. If not, explain your reasoning.

a. Through any two points, there is exactly one line.

In the figure, there is more than one great circle (line) through polar points *A* and *B*. However, there is only one great circle through nonpolar points *C* and *D*. Therefore, a corresponding statement is that through any two nonpolar points, there is exactly one great circle (line).

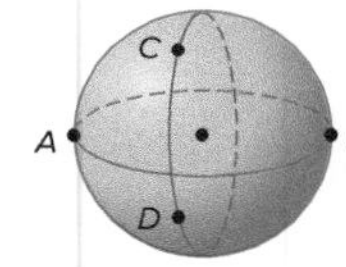

Study Tip

Sense-Making Notice in Example 3b that the Parallel Postulate does not hold true on a sphere. Lines, or great circles, cannot be parallel in spherical geometry. Therefore, spherical geometry is non-Euclidean.

b. If given a line and a point not on the line, there exists exactly one line through the point that is parallel to the given line.

In the figure, notice that every great circle (line) containing point *A* will intersect line ℓ. Thus there exists no great circle through point *A* that is parallel to line ℓ.

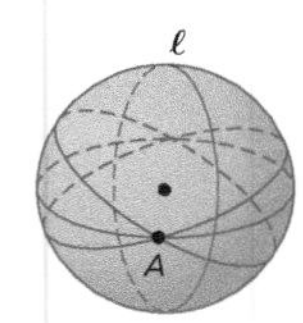

Study Tip

Angle Measures In Exercise 22, you will show that this is true for all triangles on a sphere in Spherical Geometry.

c. The sum of the measures of a triangle is 180.

In the figure, ∠*M* and ∠*J* are both right angles. Thus, the sum of the measures of this triangle is greater than 180.

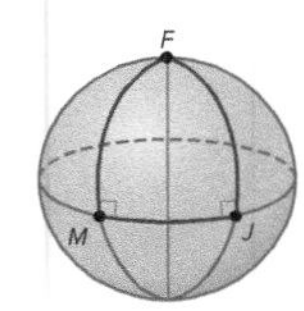

Guided Practice 3A–3B. See margin.

3A. A line segment is the shortest path between two points.

3B. Through any two points, there is exactly one segment.

Differentiated Instruction AL OL BL

Visual/Spatial Learners Have students create a map on a sheet of paper with lines indicating the shortest distance between two points. Wrap the map around a ball or globe, and use a piece of string to compare the original lines with the arcs connecting the points.

Additional Answers (Guided Practice)

3A. An arc of a great circle is the shortest path between two points.

3B. Through any two points on a great circle, there are two segments—the major and minor arcs of the great circle determined by those points.

Check Your Understanding

○ = Step-by-Step Solutions begin on page R13.

Go Online! for a Self-Check Quiz

Example 1 **Name each of the following on sphere B.**

1. two lines containing point Q $\overleftrightarrow{DH}$, $\overleftrightarrow{FJ}$
2. a segment containing point L $\overline{HM}$
3. a triangle $\triangle JKQ$, $\triangle LMP$
4. two segments on the same great circle $\overline{LG}$ and $\overline{FJ}$

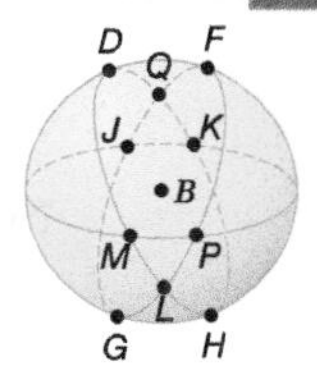

Example 2 **SPORTS Determine whether X on each of the spheres shown is a line in spherical geometry.**

5. no

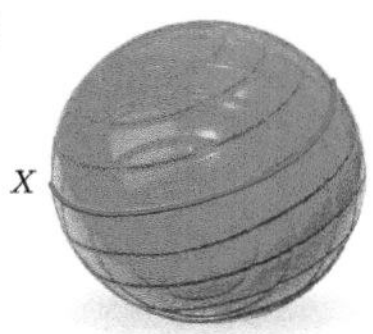

6. yes

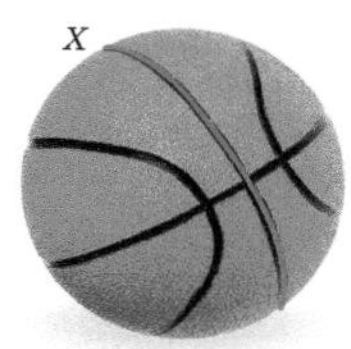

Example 3 **PERSEVERANCE Determine whether the following postulate or property of plane Euclidean geometry has a corresponding statement in spherical geometry. If so, write the corresponding statement. If not, explain your reasoning.**

7. The points on any line or line segment can be put into one-to-one correspondence with real numbers. 7. The points on any great circle or arc of a great circle can be put into one-to-one correspondence with real numbers.
8. Perpendicular lines intersect at one point. Perpendicular great circles intersect at two points.

Practice and Problem Solving

Extra Practice is on page R11.

Example 1 **Name two lines containing point M, a segment containing point S, and a triangle in each of the following spheres.**

9. Sample answers: $\overleftrightarrow{WZ}$ and $\overleftrightarrow{XY}$, $\overline{RY}$ or $\overline{TZ}$, $\triangle RST$ or $\triangle MPL$

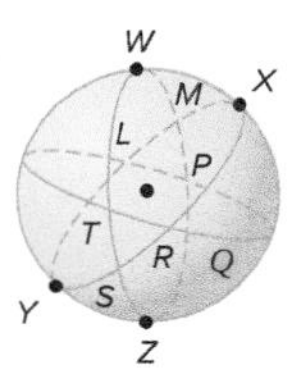

10. Sample answers: $\overleftrightarrow{FB}$ and $\overleftrightarrow{QJ}$, $\overline{CB}$ and $\overline{GL}$, $\triangle FJM$

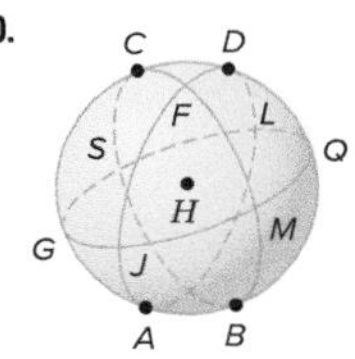

11. SOCCER Name each of the following on the soccer ball shown.
   a. two lines containing point B $\overleftrightarrow{AD}$ and $\overleftrightarrow{FC}$
   b. a segment containing point F Sample answers: $\overline{BG}$ and $\overline{AH}$
   c. a triangle Sample answers: $\triangle BCD$ and $\triangle ABF$
   d. a segment containing point C $\overline{QD}$ and $\overline{BL}$
   e. a line $\overleftrightarrow{MJ}$
   f. two lines containing point A $\overleftrightarrow{MB}$ and $\overleftrightarrow{KF}$

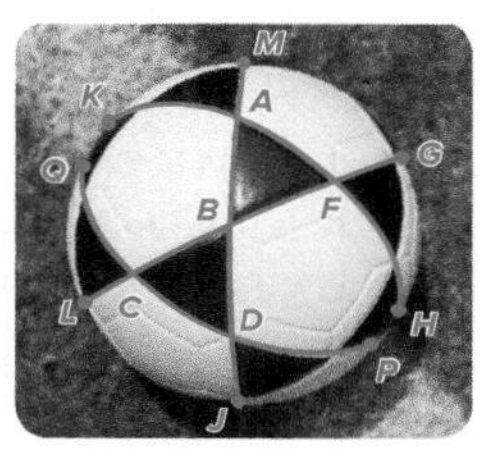

Differentiated Homework Options

Levels	AL Basic	OL Core	BL Advanced
Exercises	9–18, 24, 27–36	9–19 odd, 21–24, 27–36	22–30, (optional: 31–36)
2-Day Option	9–17 odd, 31–36	9–18	
	10–18 even, 24, 27–30	19–24, 27–36	

You can use ALEKS to provide additional remediation support with personalized instruction and practice.

Need Another Example?

Tell whether the following postulate or property of plane Euclidean geometry has a corresponding statement in spherical geometry. If so, write the corresponding statement. If not, explain your reasoning.

a. If two lines are parallel, they never intersect. True: Given a line, the only line on a sphere that is always the same distance from the line is the line itself.

b. Any two distinct lines are parallel or intersect once. False: Two distinct lines on a sphere intersect twice.

Practice

Formative Assessment Use Exercises 1–8 to assess students' understanding of the concepts in this lesson.

The Practice and Problem Solving exercises assess the content taught in the lesson. The Preparing for Assessment page is meant to be used as preparation for assessment.

Extra Practice

See page R11 for extra exercises for students who are approaching level or for on-level students who need additional reinforcement.

MP Teaching the Mathematical Practices

Reasoning Mathematically proficient students make sense of quantities and their relationships in problem situations. In Exercises 7–8, students compare Euclidean geometry to spherical geometry.

Levels of Complexity Chart

The levels of the exercises progress from 1 to 3, with Level 1 indicating the lowest level of complexity.

Exercises	9–18	19–21, 31–36	22–30
Level 3			●
Level 2		●	
Level 1	●		

Go Online! eBook

Interactive Student Guide

Use the *Interactive Student Guide* to deepen conceptual understanding.

· Spherical Geometry

MP Teaching the Mathematical Practices

Modeling Mathematically proficient students can apply the mathematics they know to solve problems arising in everyday life. In Exercise 14, encourage students to review the definition of *great circle*.

Example 2 **ARCHITECTURE** Determine whether *w* on each of the spheres shown is a line in spherical geometry.

12. 

yes

13. 

no

14. MP **MODELING** Lines of latitude and longitude are used to describe positions on the Earth's surface. By convention, lines of longitude divide Earth vertically, while lines of latitude divide it horizontally.

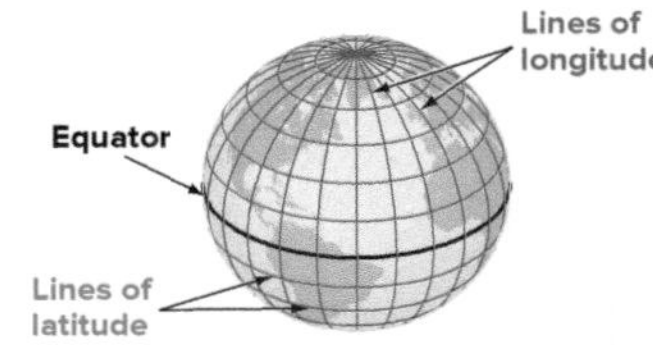

a. Are lines of longitude great circles? Explain.

b. Are lines of latitude great circles? Explain.

14a. Yes; Sample answer: Since lines of longitude pass through poles of the sphere, they form great circles.

14b. No; Sample answer: Of the lines of latitude, only the equator is a great circle. It passes through opposite poles of the sphere. Other latitude lines do not pass through opposite poles of the sphere, so they cannot be great circles.

Example 3 **Determine whether the following postulate or property of plane Euclidean geometry has a corresponding statement in spherical geometry. If so, write the corresponding statement. If not, explain your reasoning.** **15–18. See margin.**

15 A line goes on infinitely in two directions.

16. Perpendicular lines form four 90° angles.

17. If three points are collinear, exactly one is between the other two.

18. If M is the midpoint of $\overline{AB}$, then $\overline{AM} \cong \overline{MB}$.

B **On a sphere, there are two distances that can be measured between two points. Use each figure and the information given to determine the distance between points J and K on each sphere. Round to the nearest tenth. Justify your answer.**

19. 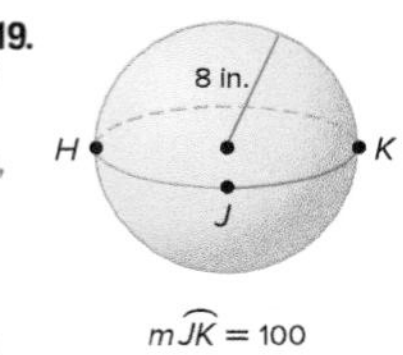

See margin.

20. 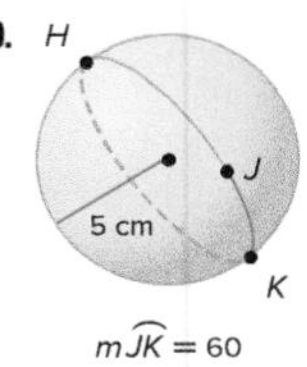

See margin.

21. **GEOGRAPHY** The location of Phoenix, Arizona, is 112° W longitude, 33.4° N latitude, and the location of Helena, Montana, is 112° W longitude, 46.6° N latitude. West indicates the location in terms of the prime meridian, and north indicates the location in terms of the equator. The mean radius of Earth is about 3960 miles. **21a–d. See margin.**

a. Estimate the distance between Phoenix and Helena. Explain your reasoning.

b. Is there another way to express the distance between these two cities? Explain.

c. Can the distance between Washington, D.C., and Lisbon, Portugal, which lie on approximately the same lines of latitude, be calculated in the same way? Explain your reasoning.

d. How many other locations are there that are the same distance from Phoenix as Wichita is? Explain.

Additional Answers

15. No; a great circle is finite and returns to its original starting point.

16. Yes; perpendicular great circles form eight 90° angles.

17. Yes; if three points are collinear, any one of the three points is between the other two.

18. Yes; if M is the midpoint of $\overline{AB}$ on a great circle, then $\overline{AM} \cong \overline{MB}$.

19. 14.0 in.; because 100 degrees is $\frac{5}{18}$ of 360 degrees, $\frac{5}{18} \times$ circumference of great circle ≈ 14.0.

20. 5.2 cm.; because 60 degrees is $\frac{1}{6}$ of 360 degrees, $\frac{1}{6} \times$ circumference of great circle ≈ 5.2.

21a. about 912 mi; The cities are 13.2° apart on the same great circle, so $\frac{13.2}{360} \times 2\pi \times 3960$ gives the distance between them.

21b. Yes; sample answer: Because the cities lie on a great circle, the distance between the cities can be expressed as the major arc or the minor arc. The sum of the two values is the circumference of Earth.

21c. No; Sample answer: Because lines of latitude do not go through opposite poles of the sphere, they are not great circles. Therefore, the distance cannot be calculated in the same way.

21d. Sample answer: infinite locations; If Phoenix were a point on the sphere, then there are infinite points that are equidistant from that point.

22b.

Triangle	$m\angle 1$	$m\angle 2$	$m\angle 3$	Sum
1	90	90	90	270
2	100	106	114	320
3	75	80	30	185

22c. Sample answer: The sum of the measures of the angles of a triangle in spherical geometry is greater than 180°.

23a. No; if $\overline{CD}$ was perpendicular to $\overline{DA}$, then $\overline{DA}$ would be parallel to $\overline{CB}$. This is not possible, because there are no parallel lines in spherical geometry.

24. Sample answer: Points, lines, and planes exist in both Euclidean and spherical geometries. In Euclidean geometry, lines and planes extend infinitely in two dimensions. In spherical geometry, lines occur as great circles and a plane is the surface of a sphere. In Euclidean geometry, two perpendicular lines intersect to form four 90° angles. In spherical geometry, two perpendicular lines intersect to form eight 90° angles. Spherical geometry is non-Euclidean because the parallel postulate is invalid.

25. Sample answer: In plane geometry, the sum of the measures of the angles of a triangle is 180. In spherical geometry, the sum of the measures of the angles of a triangle is greater than 180. In hyperbolic geometry, the sum of the measures of the angles of a triangle is less than 180.

26.

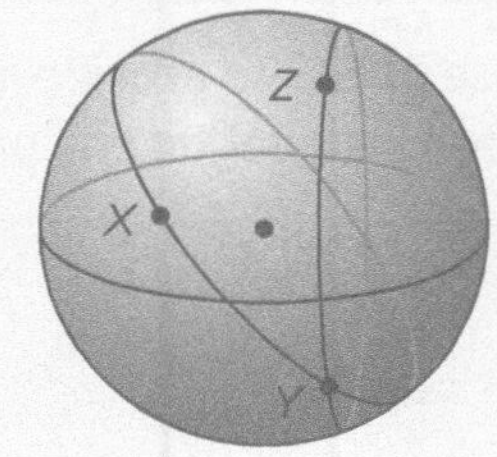

22. **MULTIPLE REPRESENTATIONS** In this problem, you will investigate triangles in spherical geometry. **22b–c. See margin.**

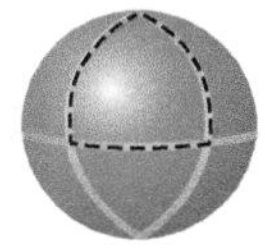

a. **Concrete** Use masking tape on a ball to mark three great circles. At least one of the three great circles should go through different poles than the other two. The great circles will form a triangle. Use a protractor to estimate the measure of each angle of the triangle. **See students' work.**

b. **Tabular** Tabulate the measure of each angle of the triangle formed. Remove the tape and repeat the process two times so that you have tabulated the measure of three different triangles. Record the sum of the measures of each triangle.

c. **Verbal** Make a conjecture about the sum of the measures of a triangle in spherical geometry.

23. **QUADRILATERALS** Consider quadrilateral *ABCD* on sphere *P*. It has four sides with $\overline{DC} \perp \overline{CB}$, $\overline{AB} \perp \overline{CB}$, and $\overline{DC} \cong \overline{AB}$.

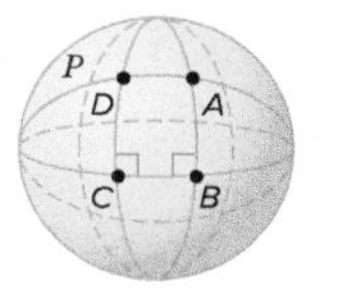

a. Is $\overline{CD} \perp \overline{DA}$? Explain your reasoning. **See margin.**

b. How does *DA* compare to *CB*? **$DA < CB$**

c. Can a rectangle, as defined in Euclidean geometry, exist in non-Euclidean geometry? Explain your reasoning. **No; the sides are not parallel.**

H.O.T. Problems — Use Higher-Order Thinking Skills

24. **WRITING IN MATH** Compare and contrast Euclidean and spherical geometries. Be sure to include a discussion of planes and lines, including parallel and perpendicular lines, in both geometries. **See margin.**

25. **CHALLENGE** Geometries can be defined on curved surfaces other than spheres. Another type of non-Euclidean geometry is *hyperbolic geometry*. This geometry is defined on a curved saddle-like surface. Compare the sum of the angle measures of a triangle in hyperbolic, spherical, and Euclidean geometries. **See margin.**

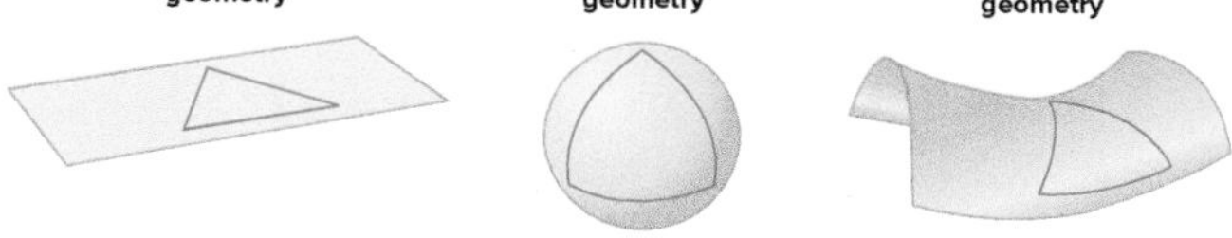

26. **CHALLENGE** Sketch a sphere with three points so that two of the points lie on a great circle and two of the points do not lie on a great circle. **See margin.**

27. **CONSTRUCT ARGUMENTS** A *small circle* of a sphere intersects at least two points, but does not go through opposite poles. Points *A* and *B* lie on a small circle of sphere *Q*. Will two small circles *sometimes*, *always*, or *never* be parallel? Draw a sketch and explain your reasoning. **See margin.**

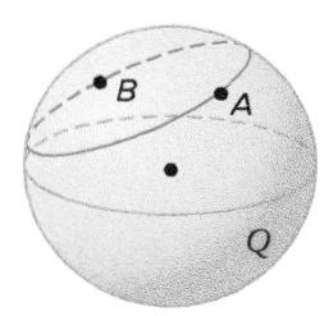

28. **WRITING IN MATH** Do similar or congruent triangles exist in spherical geometry? Explain your reasoning. **See margin.**

29. **REASONING** Is the statement *Spherical geometry is a subset of Euclidean geometry* true or false? Explain your reasoning. **See margin.**

30. **CONSTRUCT ARGUMENTS** Two planes are equidistant from the center of a sphere and intersect the sphere. What is true of the circles? Are they lines in spherical geometry? **See Ch. 11 Answer Appendix.**

Standards for Mathematical Practice

Emphasis On	Exercises
1 Make sense of problems and persevere in solving them.	7, 8, 33, 36
2 Reason abstractly and quantitatively.	1–6, 9, 10, 29
3 Construct viable arguments and critique the reasoning of others.	15–18, 27
4 Model with mathematics.	11–14, 21
5 Use appropriate tools strategically.	26
6 Attend to precision.	19, 20
7 Look for and make use of structure.	22, 23
8 Look for and express regularity in repeated reasoning.	28, 31–32, 34, 35

Exercise Alert

Tape, Ball, and Protractor Exercise 22 requires the use of masking tape, a ball, and a protractor.

Teaching the Mathematical Practices

Construct Arguments Mathematically proficient students understand and use stated assumptions and definitions in constructing arguments. They make conjectures and build a logical progression of statements to explore the truth of their conjectures. In Exercise 27, point out to students that small circles on a sphere do not go through opposite poles.

Assess

Ticket Out the Door Have students write a short summary of how spherical geometry is different from Euclidean geometry.

Additional Answers

27. Sometimes; Sample answer: Since small circles cannot go through opposite poles, it is possible for them to be parallel, such as lines of latitude. It is also possible for them to intersect when two small circles can be drawn through three points, where they have one point in common and two points that occur on one small circle and not the other.

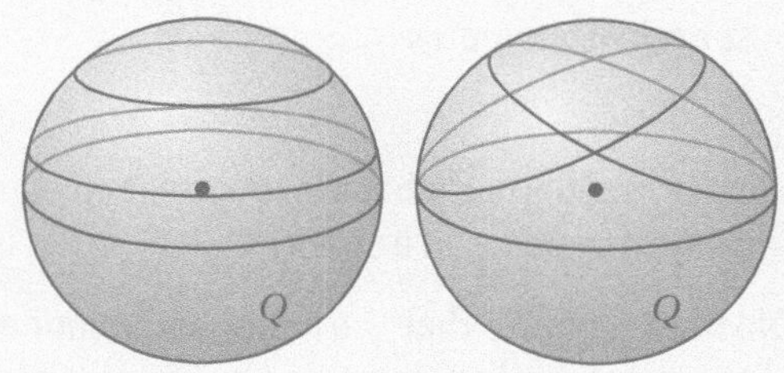

28. Sample answer: Congruent triangles exist, because three great circles that form a triangle will form identical triangles on opposite sides of the sphere. Similar triangles do not exist because the sum of the measures of the angles of a triangle is not constant. If two triangles in spherical geometry have the same angle measures, they are congruent.

29. False; Sample answer: Spherical geometry is non-Euclidean, so it cannot be a subset of Euclidean geometry.

Go Online!

eSolutions Manual

Create worksheets, answer keys, and solutions handouts for your assignments.

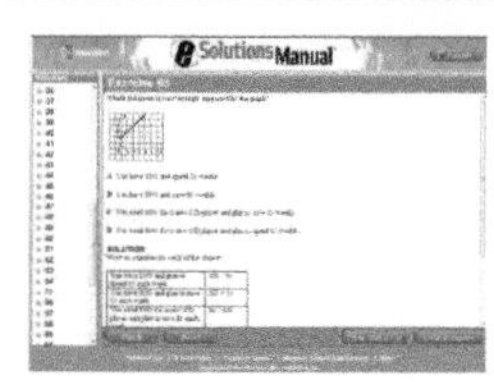

Preparing for Assessment

Exercises 31–36 require students to use the skills they will need on future assessments. Exercises are dual-coded with content standards and mathematical practice standards.

Dual Coding		
Items	Content Standards	MP Mathematical Practices
31	G.MG.3	8
32	G.MG.3	8
33	G.MG.3	1
34	G.MG.3	8
35	G.MG.3	8
36	G.MG.3	1

Diagnose Student Errors

Survey student responses for each item. Class trends may indicate common errors and misconceptions.

31.

A	Did not recognize that a great circle through point *S* need not pass through point *T*
B	CORRECT
C	Did not recognize that there are no parallel lines in spherical geometry
D	Did not recognize the major and minor arcs of the great circle determined by the points
E	Did not recognize that there are no parallel lines in spherical geometry

32.

A	Did not recognize that there is a great circle through any point on a sphere
B	Did not recognize that the major and minor arcs of the great circle determined by the given points are line segments
C	Did not recognize that on a sphere a triangle is formed by arcs of great circles
D	CORRECT

Go Online!

Quizzes

Students can use *Self-Check Quizzes* to check their understanding of this lesson and have the results sent to you. You can also give *Quiz 4*, which covers the content in Lessons 11-5 and 11-6.

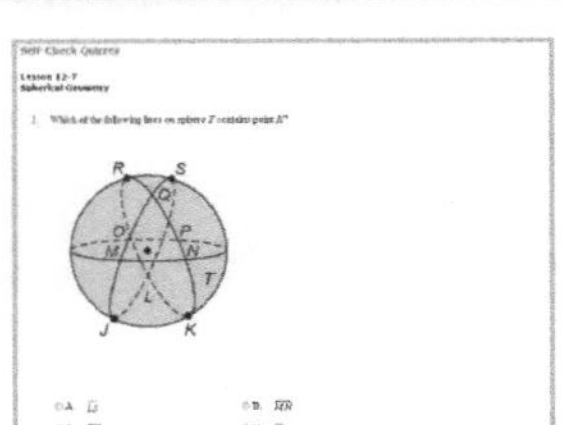

Preparing for Assessment

31. Use spherical geometry to determine which of the following is a true statement about the figure. MP 8 G.MG.3 B

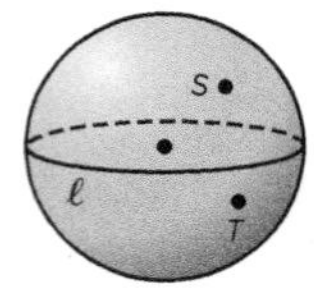

- A All lines through point S pass through point T.
- B All lines through point S intersect line ℓ.
- C All lines through point T are parallel to line ℓ.
- D There is exactly one line segment that has points S and T as endpoints.
- E There is a line through point S and a line through point T that do not intersect.

32. Jared wrote a statement in his math journal. His teacher read the statement and said, "That statement is true in Euclidean geometry but not in spherical geometry." Which of the following could be the statement Jared wrote? MP 8 G.MG.3 D

- A Through any point, there is at least one line.
- B Given any two points, you can draw a line segment that has the points as endpoints.
- C Any three noncollinear points can be used as the vertices of a triangle.
- D If two lines intersect, then they intersect at exactly one point.

33. James is trying to shoot three balls of different sizes consecutively through a hoop with a diameter of 18 inches. The balls have volumes of 850π, 900π, and 950π cubic inches. How many of the balls will fit through the hoop? MP 1 G.MG.3 3

34. Use spherical geometry and the figure shown here to determine which of the following statements is false. MP 8 G.MG.3 C

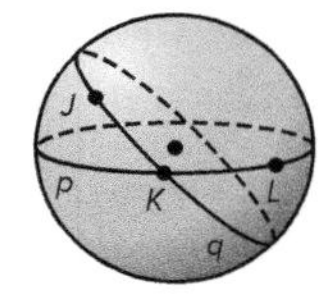

- A The figure shows two lines that intersect at point K.
- B There is exactly one line through points J and K.
- C It is possible to draw a line through point J that is parallel to $\overleftrightarrow{KL}$.
- D Every line through point L intersects $\overleftrightarrow{KL}$.

35. Which statement about spheres is not true? MP 8 G.MG.3 D

- A There is only one great circle through any two points on a sphere that are not poles of the sphere.
- B A great circle is the intersection of a sphere and a plane that goes through the center of the sphere.
- C The shortest path between two points on a sphere is an arc of a great circle.
- D Two lines that are perpendicular to the same line on a sphere are parallel to each other.

36. **MULTI-STEP** Consider a sphere with a radius of 4 units. MP 1 G.MG.3

a. Calculate the length of a great circle in a sphere with radius 4. 8π

b. Calculate the length of a small circle in the same sphere if the center of the small circle is one unit away from the center of the sphere. $2\pi\sqrt{15}$

c. If a small circle on the same sphere has a length of 4π, how many units is its center from the center of the sphere? $2\sqrt{3}$

Differentiated Instruction OL BL

Extension Using a graphing program with three-dimensional capabilities, have students investigate similar triangles drawn on a sphere. Is it possible for two spherical triangles to be similar without being congruent?

EXTEND 11-5

Geometry Lab

Navigational Coordinates

A grid system of imaginary lines on Earth is used for locating places and navigation. Imaginary vertical lines drawn around Earth through the North and South Poles are called **meridians**, and they determine the measure of **longitude**. Imaginary horizontal lines parallel to the equator are called **parallels**, and they determine the measure of **latitude**.

The basic units for measurements are degrees, minutes, and seconds.
1 degree (°) = 60 minutes (′), and 60 minutes = 60 seconds (″).

Mathematical Practices

MP 5 Use appropriate tools strategically.

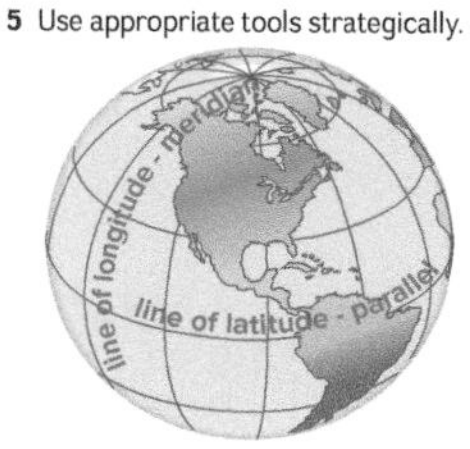

	Location of 0°	Direction	Maximum Degrees
Latitude (parallels)	equator	In northern hemisphere, all are degrees north. In southern hemisphere, all are degrees south.	90° at each pole
Longitude (meridians)	Prime Meridian through Greenwich, England	In eastern hemisphere, all are degrees east. In western hemisphere, all are degrees west.	180° at international dateline

1. City A: northern; City B: southern; City C: northern
2. City A: Lexington, Kentucky; City B: Adelaide, Australia; City C: Reykjavik, Iceland

Activity Investigate Latitude and Longitude

Work cooperatively. The table shows the latitude and longitude of three cities.

City	Latitude	Longitude
A	37°59′N	84°28′W
B	34°55′S	138°36′E
C	64°4′N	21°58′W

1. In which hemisphere is each city located?
2. Use a globe or map to name each city.
3. Earth is approximately a sphere with a radius of 3960 miles. The equator and all meridians are great circles. The circumference of a great circle is equal to the length of the equator or any meridian. Find the length of a great circle on Earth in miles. about 24,881.4 mi
4. Notice that the distance between each line of latitude is about the same. The distance from the equator to the North Pole is $\frac{1}{4}$ of the circumference of Earth, and each degree of latitude is $\frac{1}{90}$ of that distance. Estimate the distance between one pair of latitude lines in miles. about 69.1 mi

5. City F: southern; City G: northern; City H: southern
6. City F: Belem, Brazil; City G: Bangkok, Thailand; City H: Wellington, New Zealand
7. about 64 miles between meridians

Analyze

Work cooperatively. The table shows the latitude and longitude of three cities.

City	Latitude	Longitude
F	1°28′S	48°29′W
G	13°45′N	100°30′E
H	41°17′S	174°47′E

5. Name the hemisphere in which each city is located.
6. MP TOOLS Use a globe or map to name each city.
7. Find the approximate distance between meridians at latitude of about 22° N. The direct distance between the two cities at the right is about 1646 miles.

Calcutta, India	22°34′N	88°24′E
Hong Kong, China	22°20′N	114°11′E

Launch

Objective

- Understand navigational coordinates.
- Find distances by using measurements of navigational coordinates.

Materials for Each Group

- world globe or map

Teaching Tip

Explain that the total number of degrees for latitude is 180° and that the northern and southern hemisphere each consist of 90°. The total number of degrees of longitude is 360° and the eastern and western hemisphere each consist of 180°.

Teach

Working in Cooperative Groups Organize students in pairs, mixing abilities. Have pairs help each other to complete the Activity and Exercises 1–4. ELL

Practice Have students complete Exercises 5–7.

Assess

Formative Assessment

Use Exercises 5–7 to assess whether students understand navigational coordinates.

From Concrete to Abstract

Ask students to describe the similarities and differences between meridians and parallels.

Go Online!

The most up-to-date resources available for your program can be found at connectED.mcgraw-hill.com.

LESSON 11-6

Volume and Nonrigid Transformations

SUGGESTED PACING (DAYS)

	Instruction
90 min.	0.5
45 min.	1.0

Track Your Progress

Objectives

1. Identify congruent or similar solids and scale factor.
2. Use properties of similar solids.

Mathematical Background

Dilation is a nonrigid transformation that enlarges or reduces the original image, making the two images similar but not congruent. The measure of two similar figures is a ratio called the *scale factor*. The surface areas of two similar figures are proportional to the square of the scale factor between them. The volumes of two similar figures are proportional to the cube of the scale factor between them.

THEN	NOW	NEXT
G.GMD.3 Use volume formulas for cylinders, pyramids, cones, and spheres to solve problems.	**G.GMD.1** Give an informal argument for the formulas for the circumference of a circle, area of a circle, volume of cylinder, pyramid, and cone.	**G.GMD.2** Give an informal argument using Cavalieri's principle for the formulas for the volume of a sphere and other solid figures.

Go Online! All of these resources and more are available at connectED.mcgraw-hill.com

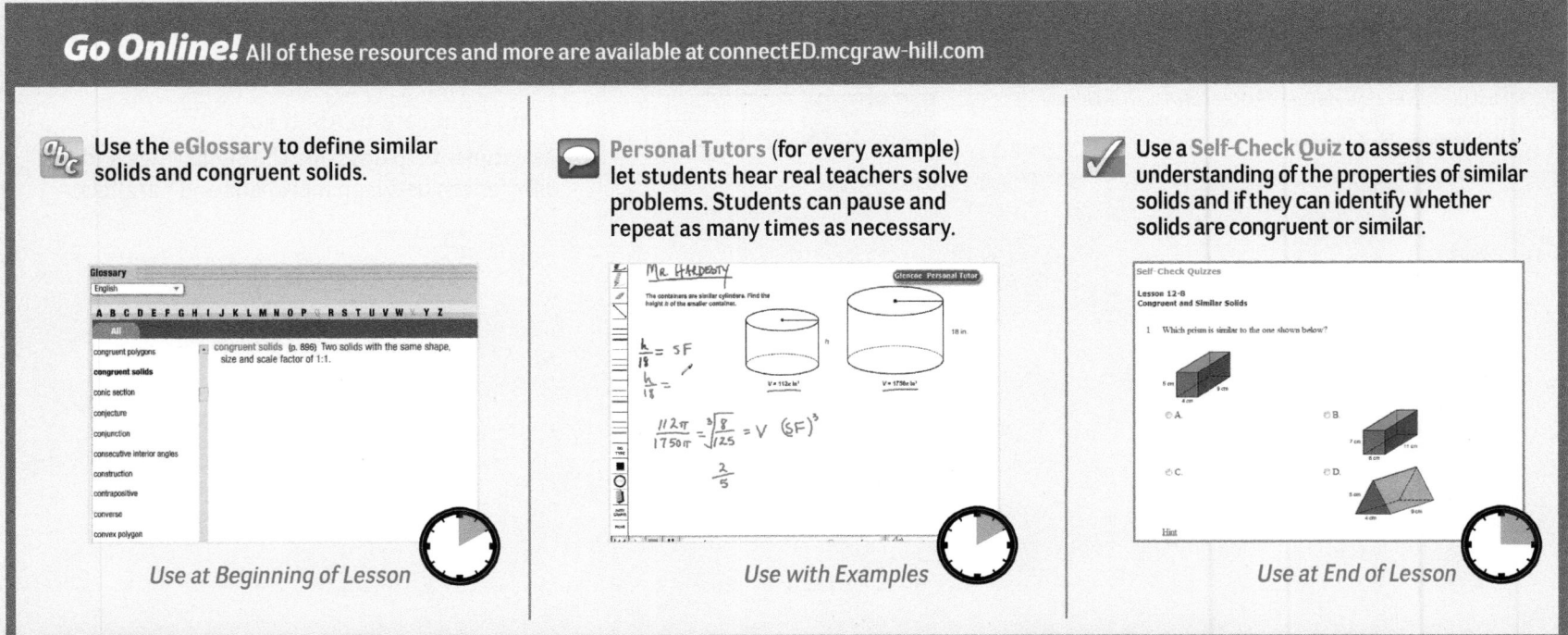

Use the eGlossary to define similar solids and congruent solids.

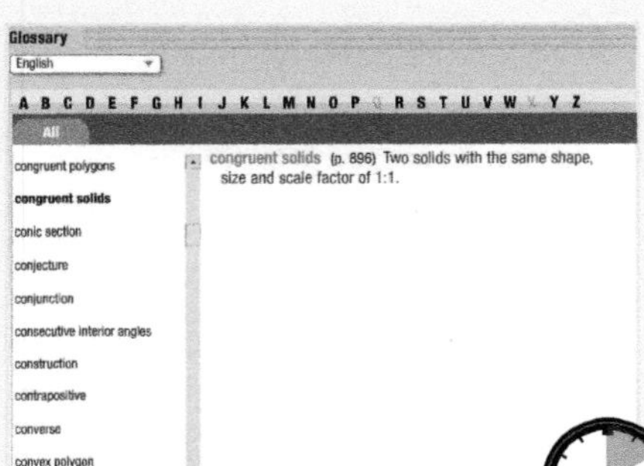

Use at Beginning of Lesson

Personal Tutors (for every example) let students hear real teachers solve problems. Students can pause and repeat as many times as necessary.

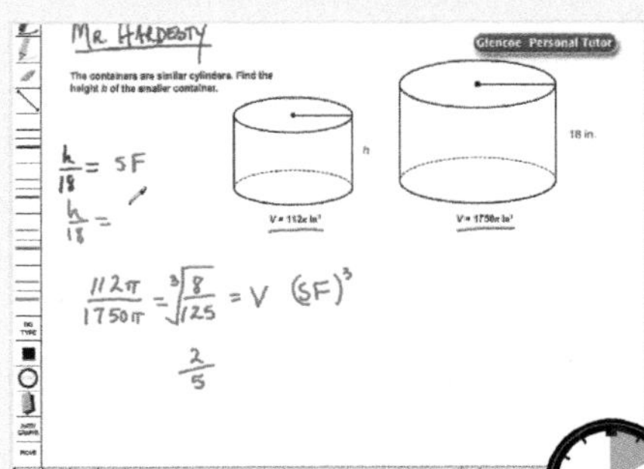

Use with Examples

Use a Self-Check Quiz to assess students' understanding of the properties of similar solids and if they can identify whether solids are congruent or similar.

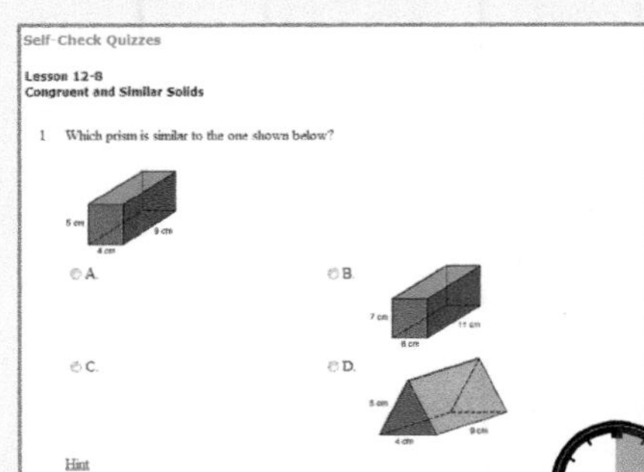

Use at End of Lesson

OER Using Open Educational Resources

Class Management Using **Study Shuffle**, you can move homework online where students can complete and submit their work. You can track their progress and update class material whenever you like. *Use as professional development*

Differentiate Your Resources

Extra Practice Additional practice or homework; Skills Practice is best for approaching-level students and Practice is best for on-level and beyond-level students

Skills Practice

AL OL ELL

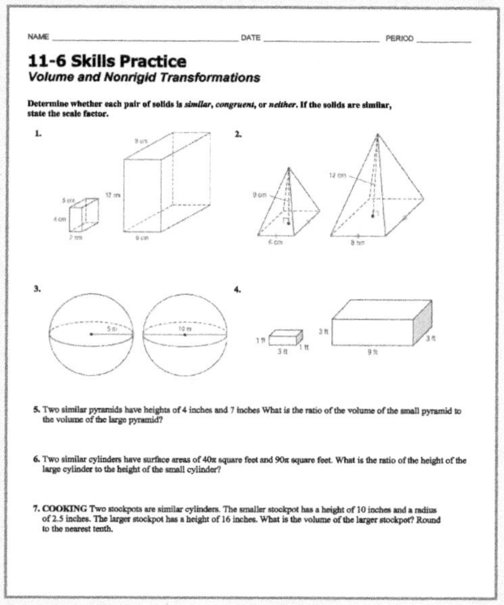
11-6 Skills Practice
Volume and Nonrigid Transformations

Practice

AL OL BL ELL

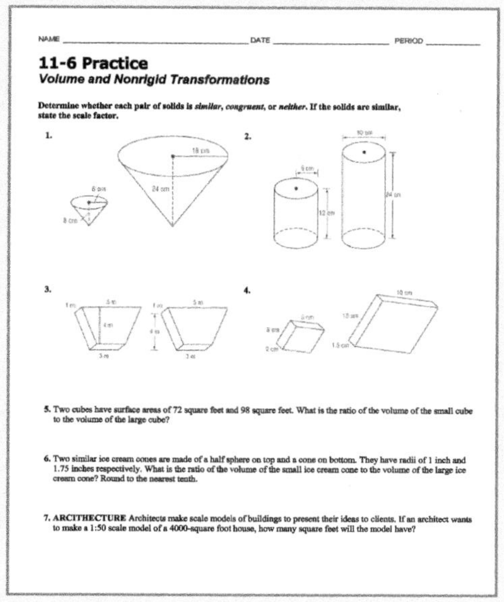
11-6 Practice
Volume and Nonrigid Transformations

Word Problem Practice

AL OL BL ELL

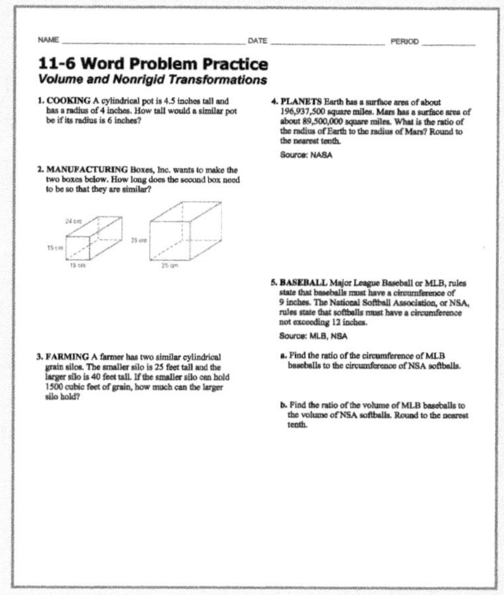
11-6 Word Problem Practice
Volume and Nonrigid Transformations

Intervention Reteaching and vocabulary activities that can be used with struggling or absent students and as ELL support

Study Guide and Intervention

AL OL ELL

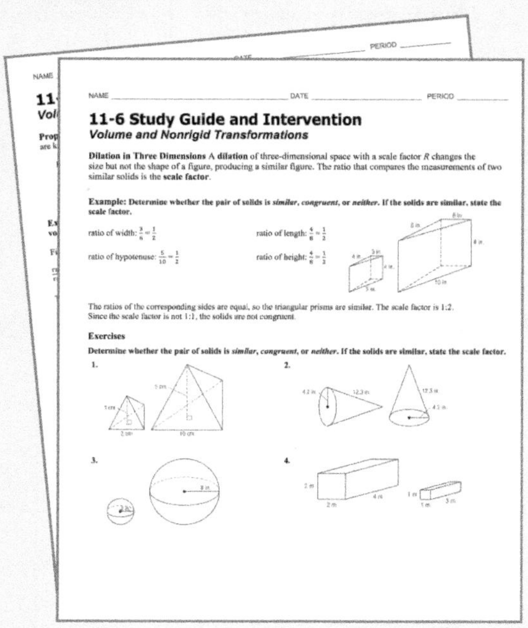
11-6 Study Guide and Intervention
Volume and Nonrigid Transformations

Study Notebook

AL OL BL ELL

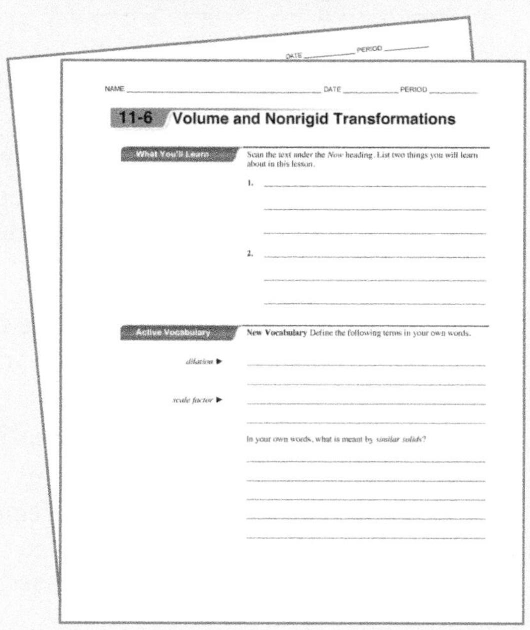
11-6 Volume and Nonrigid Transformations

Extension Activities that can be used to extend lesson concepts

Enrichment

OL BL ELL

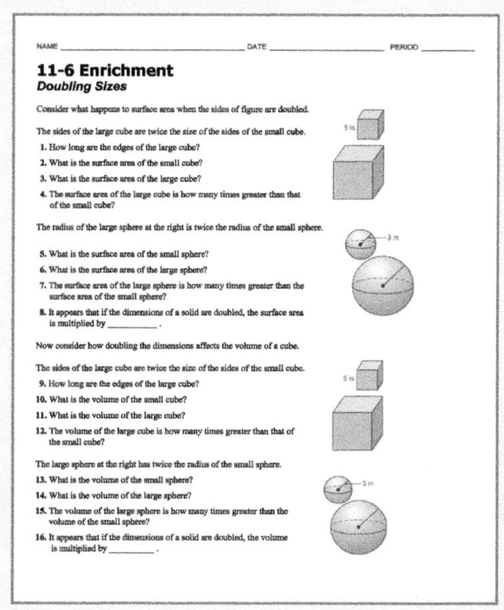
11-6 Enrichment
Doubling Sizes

Launch

Have students read the Why? section of the lesson. Ask:

- **What number relates the side lengths of three-dimensional similar figures?** the scale factor
- **Does the color of the gemstones determine whether they are similar?** Sample answer: No; it matters only whether they are exactly the same shape.

Teach

Ask the scaffolded questions for each example to build conceptual understanding for students at all levels.

1 Dilation in Three Dimensions

Example 1 Identify Similar and Congruent Solids

AL **What measures of length would you compare to determine if a pair of cylinders are similar?** the radius or diameter and the height

OL **How many pyramids exist that are similar to the smaller pyramid?** There are an infinite number of pyramids similar to the smaller pyramid. You can choose any number as a scale factor.

BL **What measure(s) would you use to determine if two spheres are similar?** All spheres are similar.

LESSON 6

Volume and Nonrigid Transformations

Then

- You compared surface areas and volumes of spheres.

Now

1. Identify scale factor by using dilation.
2. Find surface areas and volumes of similar solids by using scale factors.

Why?

- The gemstones at the right are cut in exactly the same shape, but their sizes are different. Their shapes are similar.

New Vocabulary
similar solid
congruent solid

Mathematical Practices
8 Look for and express regularity in repeated reasoning.

Content Standards
G.GMD.1 Give an informal argument for the formulas for the circumference of a circle, area of a circle, volume of cylinder, pyramid, and cone.

1 Dilation in Three Dimensions In Chapter 7, you learned that a nonrigid transformation changes the size but not the shape of a figure, producing a similar figure. **Similar solids** have exactly the same shape but not necessarily the same size. All spheres are similar and all cubes are similar. In similar solids, the corresponding linear measures, such as height and radius, have equal ratios. The common ratio is called the *scale factor*. **Congruent solids** have exactly the same shape and the same size. Congruent solids are similar solids that have a scale factor of 1:1.

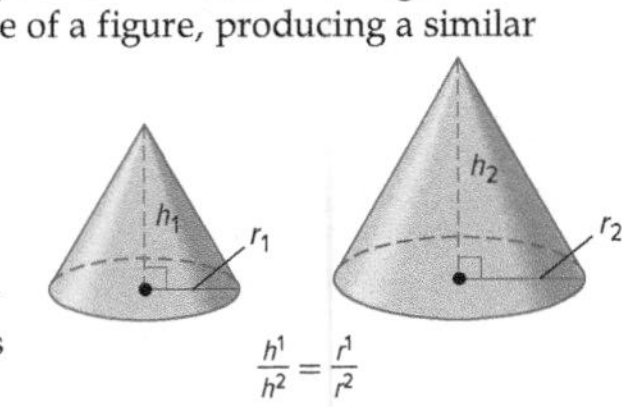

G.GMD.2

Example 1 Identify Similar and Congruent Solids

Determine whether the square pyramids are *similar*, *congruent*, or *neither*. If the pyramids are similar, state the scale factor.

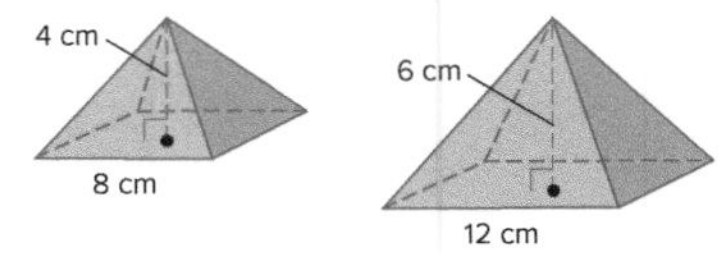

ratio of heights: $\frac{4}{6} = \frac{2}{3}$

ratio of base edges: $\frac{8}{12} = \frac{2}{3}$

The ratios of the corresponding measures are equal, so the pyramids are similar. The scale factor is 2:3. Because the scale factor is not 1:1, the solids are not congruent.

Guided Practice

1A.

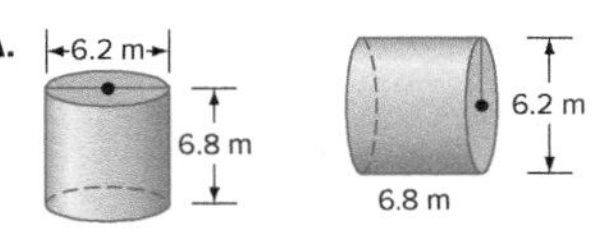

1B.

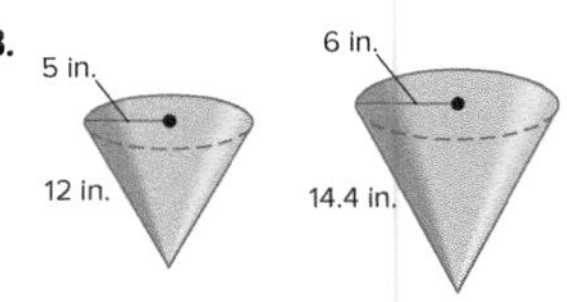

1A. congruent and similar; 1:1
1B. similar; 5:6

2 Properties of Similar Solids The cubes at the right are similar solids with a scale factor of 3:2.

ratio of surface areas: 54 : 24 or 9 : 4
ratio of volumes: 27 : 8

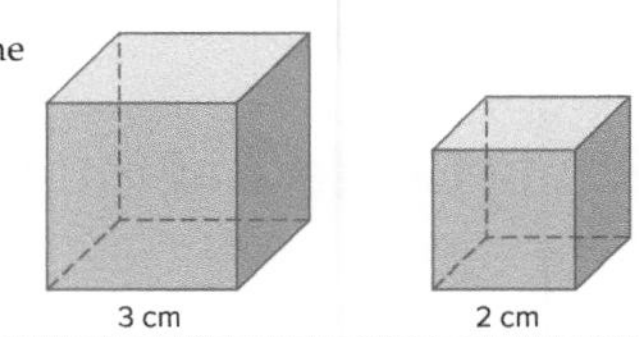

MP Mathematical Practices Strategies

Look for and express regularity in repeated reasoning.
Help students look for regularity in relationships between solids and their surface areas and volumes. For example, ask:

- **How can you determine whether two solids are similar?** Similar solids are solids that have the same shapes and their corresponding measurements are proportional.
- **Are all cubes similar? Why or why not?** Yes, because they have the same shape and their corresponding linear measures are proportional.
- **How can you find a missing measurement on one of two similar figures?** Use the scale factor to write an equation, and then use corresponding sides with known lengths to solve for the missing measurement.

Go Online!

Interactive Whiteboard

Use the *eLesson, Lesson Presentation,* or *Interactive Classroom* to present this lesson.

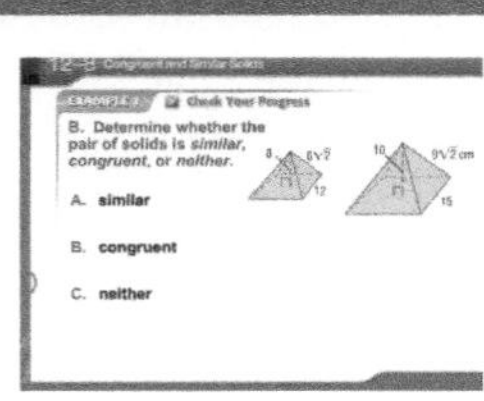

Notice that the ratio of surface areas, 9 : 4, can be written as $3^2 : 2^2$. The ratio of volumes, 27 : 8, can be written as $3^3 : 2^3$. This suggests the following theorem.

Theorem 11.1

Words If two similar solids have a scale factor of $a : b$, then the surface areas have a ratio of $a^2 : b^2$, and the volumes have a ratio of $a^3 : b^3$.

Models

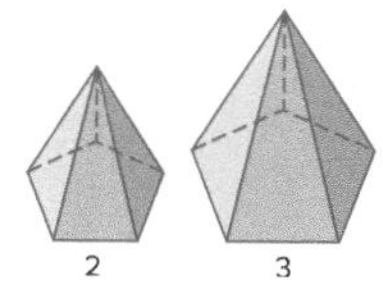

Example

scale factor	2:3
ratio of surface area	4:9
ratio of volumes	8:27

Figures must be similar for Theorem 11.1 to apply.

Study Tip
Similar Solids and Area If two solids are similar, then the ratio of any corresponding areas is $a^2 : b^2$.

G.GMD.1

Example 2 Use Similar Solids to Solve Problems

The edge of a small cube measures 4 centimeters. If the scale factor between the small cube and a larger cube is $\frac{1}{3}$, what is the surface area of the larger cube?

First, find the surface area of the small cube.

$S = 6s$ Surface area of a cube

$= 6(4)^2$ Substitute.

$= 96$ Simplify.

The surface area of the small cube is 96 cm².

$\frac{\text{surface area of large cube}}{\text{surface area of small cube}} = \frac{3^2}{1^2}$ Use proportion.

$\frac{\text{surface area of large cube}}{96} = \frac{9}{1}$ Substitute.

surface area of large cube $= 9 \cdot 96$ or 864 Simplify.

The surface area of the large cube is 864 square centimeters.

Go Online!

Watch Personal Tutor videos to hear descriptions of solving problems involving congruent and similar solids. Try describing how to solve a problem for a partner. Have them ask you questions to help your understanding. ELL

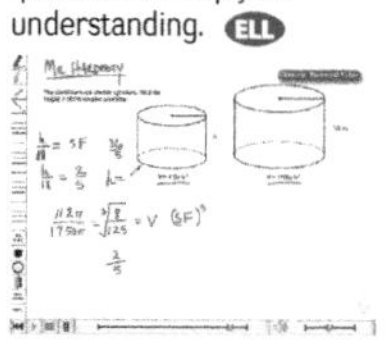

Guided Practice 2. ≈ 15.4 cm

2. Two similar rectangular prisms with square bases have surface areas of 98 square centimeters and 18 square centimeters. If one base edge of the larger rectangular prism measures 9 centimeters, what is the perimeter of one base of the smaller prism?

G.GMD.1

Example 3 Find the Volume of Similar Solids by Using Scale Factor

Rectangular prism A and rectangular prism B are similar. Find the volume of rectangular prism B.

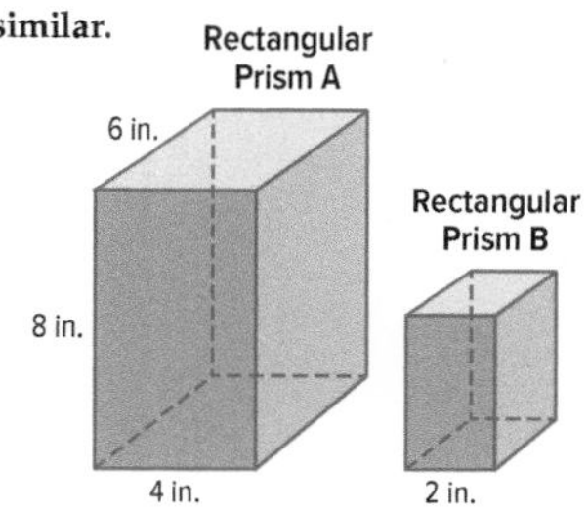

First find the scale factor.

$\frac{\text{length of the rectangular prism A}}{\text{length of the rectangular prism B}} = \frac{4}{2}$ or 2.

The scale factor is 2.

Find the volume of rectangular prism A.

Volume of rectangular prism

A = length × width × height

$V_A = 4 \times 6 \times 8$ Substitute.

$= 192$ Simplify.

The volume of rectangular prism A is 192 in³.

Study Tip
Similar Solids and Volume If two solids are similar, then the ratio of any corresponding volume is $a^3 : b^3$.

Need Another Example?

Determine whether the pair of rectangular prisms is *similar*, *congruent*, or *neither*. If the prisms are similar, state the scale factor. Because the ratios of corresponding measures are not equal, the prisms are neither congruent nor similar.

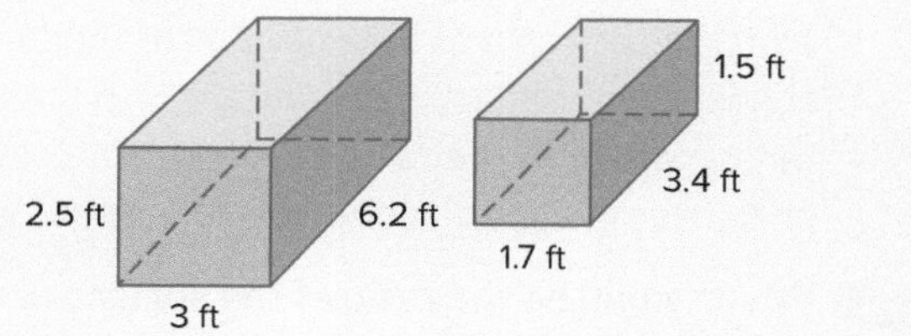

2 Properties of Congruent and Similar Solids

Example 2 Use Similar Solids to Solve Problems

AL What is the relationship between the ratio of surface areas of similar solids and the scale factor between similar solids. The ratio of surface areas in similar solids is the square of the scale factor between them.

OL Why do we need to square the scale factor to find the ratio of the surface areas? Because surface area is a square unit, we need to square the scale factor, which applies only to units of length.

BL How can the relationship between two solids be used to find missing measures? There is a proportional relationship between the scale factor, ratio of the surface areas, and ratio of the volumes of similar solids. By solving proportional relationships, you can find missing values.

Need Another Example?

The surface area of a small pyramid is 40 square centimeters. If the scale factor between the small pyramid and a larger pyramid is $\frac{1}{3}$, what is the surface area of the larger pyramid? 360 cm²

Watch Out!

Writing Ratios When finding the ratio of the surface area of solid A to the surface area of solid B, be sure to write ratio as $\frac{\text{surface area of solid A}}{\text{surface area of solid B}} = k^2$.

Example 3 Find the Volume of Similar Solids by Using Scale Factor

AL What is the relationship between the scale factor between similar solids and their volumes? The ratio of the volumes of two similar solids is the cube of the scale factor.

OL How can you use this relationship to find the volumes of similar solids? Set up an equation relating the cube of the scale factor to the ratio of the volumes. Solve for the missing volume.

BL When the scale factor between two similar rectangular prisms is 2:1, how does the volume change? The volume of the large rectangular prism is 8 times the volume of the small rectangular prism.

Need Another Example?

Circular cone A and circular cone B are similar. The cones have radii of 10 millimeters and 15 millimeters, respectively. The volume of cone A is approximately 1047.2 cubic millimeters. Find the volume of cone B. ≈ 3534.5 mm³

Example 4 Use Similar Solids to Find the Unknown Values

AL **Why did you express the ratio of the volumes as the ratio of two cubed numbers to find the scale factor for the cylinders?** The cube of the scale factor between two similar solids is equal to the ratio of the volumes of the two solids. So, to find the scale factor, you must determine how the ratio of the volumes can be expressed as the cube of two numbers.

OL **What would be the ratio of the surface area of the smaller cylinder to the larger cylinder?** $\frac{9}{16}$

BL **The ratio of the volumes of two similar cones is $\frac{8}{125}$. If the volume of the larger cone is about 785.4 cubic inches, and the height of the smaller cone is 4 inches, what is the diameter of the larger cone?** 17.3 in.

Need Another Example?

Softballs **The softballs below are similar spheres. If the radius of the larger softball is 1.9 inches, find the radius of the smaller softball.**

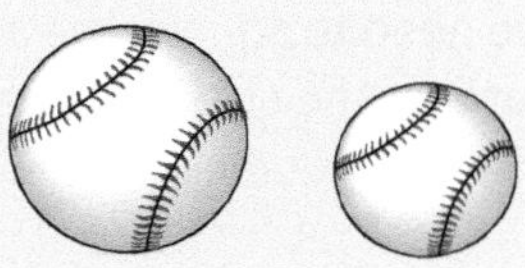

$V = 9.15\pi$ in³ $V = 4.06\pi$ in³

≈1.45 in.

Follow-up

How can you use a scale factor to find the ratio of surface areas and volumes for similar solids? Use the properties of similar solids to find the ratio of the surface area and volume. Then use the proportional relationship to find the unknown value.

$$\frac{\text{Volume of rectangular prism A}}{\text{Volume of rectangular prism B}} = \frac{a^3}{b^3} \quad \text{Write formulas.}$$

$$\frac{192}{\text{Volume of rectangular prism B}} = \frac{2^3}{1^3} \quad \text{Substitute.}$$

$$\text{Volume of rectangular prism B} = \frac{192}{8} \quad \text{Use proportion.}$$

$$= 24 \quad \text{Simplify.}$$

The volume of rectangular prism B is 24 in³.

Guided Practice

3. Two circular cylinders are similar. The ratio of the radii is 3:2. The volume of the smaller cylinder is 60 cubic inches. Find the volume of the larger cylinder. 202.5 in³

G.GMD.1

Real-World Example 4 Use Similar Solids to Find Unknown Values

CONTAINERS **The containers at the right are similar cylinders. Find the height h of the smaller container.**

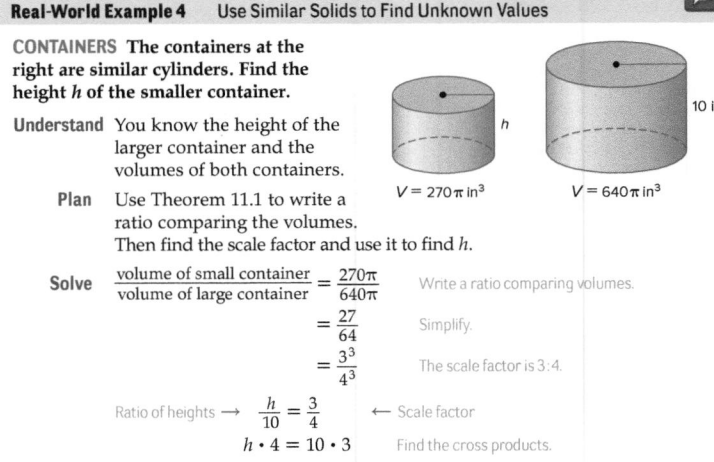

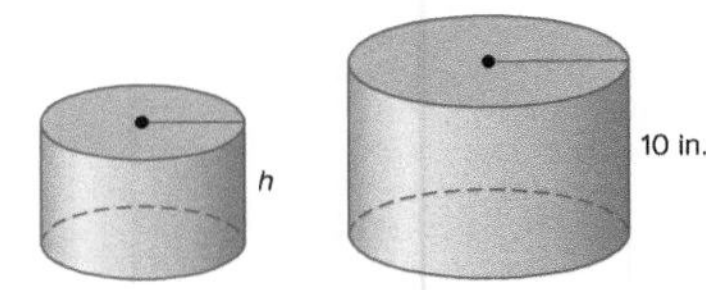

Understand You know the height of the larger container and the volumes of both containers.

Plan Use Theorem 11.1 to write a ratio comparing the volumes. Then find the scale factor and use it to find h.

Solve

$$\frac{\text{volume of small container}}{\text{volume of large container}} = \frac{270\pi}{640\pi} \quad \text{Write a ratio comparing volumes.}$$

$$= \frac{27}{64} \quad \text{Simplify.}$$

$$= \frac{3^3}{4^3} \quad \text{The scale factor is 3:4.}$$

Ratio of heights → $\frac{h}{10} = \frac{3}{4}$ ← Scale factor

$h \cdot 4 = 10 \cdot 3$ Find the cross products.

$h = 7.5$ Solve for h.

Check Because $\frac{7.5}{10} = 0.75 = \frac{3}{4}$, the solution is correct. ✓

For the two cylinders to be similar, all corresponding measurements must have the same scale factor.

Study Tip

MP Precision After finding the missing measure of similar solids, work backward to check your solutions.

Guided Practice

4. **PUZZLES** The world's largest puzzle cube has an edge length of 1.57 meters. The ratio of edge length of the largest puzzle cube to a regular puzzle cube is approximately $\frac{27.5}{1}$. Find the surface area of a regular puzzle cube rounded to the nearest hundredth. 0.02 m²

Differentiated Instruction AL OL BL

Verbal/Linguistic Learners Tell students that for the two-dimensional measurement of surface area, the ratio involves the power of two. For the three-dimensional measurement of volume, the ratio involves the power of three.

Check Your Understanding

◯ = Step-by-Step Solutions begin on page R13.

Go Online! for a Self-Check Quiz

Example 1 G.GMD.2

Determine whether each pair of solids is *similar*, *congruent*, or *neither*. If the solids are similar, state the scale factor.

1. similar; 4:3
2. neither

1.

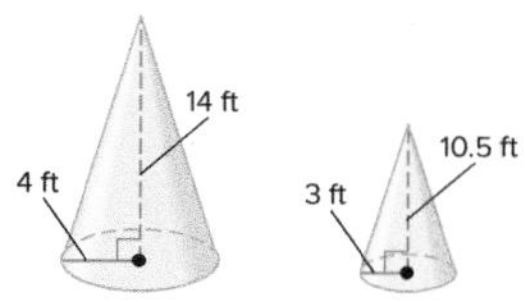

2.

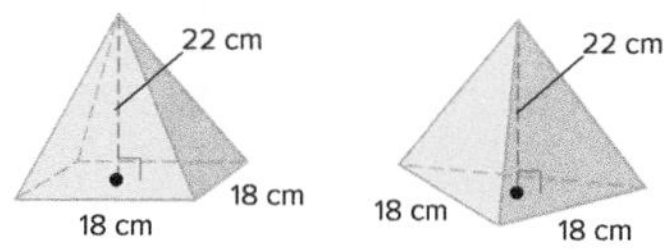

Example 2 G.GMD.1

3. Two similar cylinders have radii of 15 inches and 6 inches. If the surface area of the first cylinder is 2592 square inches, what is the surface area of the second cylinder? 414.7 in^2

Example 3 G.GMD.1

4. Two similar rectangular prisms have surface areas of 83.2 square feet and 20.8 square feet, respectively. If the volume of the first prism is 46.5 cubic feet, what is the volume of the second prism rounded to the nearest tenth? 5.8 ft^3

Example 3 G.GMD.1

5. **EXERCISE BALLS** A company sells two different sizes of exercise balls. The ratio of the diameters is 15 : 11. If the diameter of the smaller ball is 55 centimeters, what is the volume of the larger ball? Round to the nearest tenth. $220{,}893.2 \text{ cm}^3$

Practice and Problem Solving

Extra Practice is on page R11.

Example 1 G.GMD.2

MP **REGULARITY** **Determine whether each pair of solids is *similar*, *congruent*, or *neither*. If the solids are similar, state the scale factor.**

6. similar; 9:8
7. neither
8. neither
9. similar; 6:5

6.

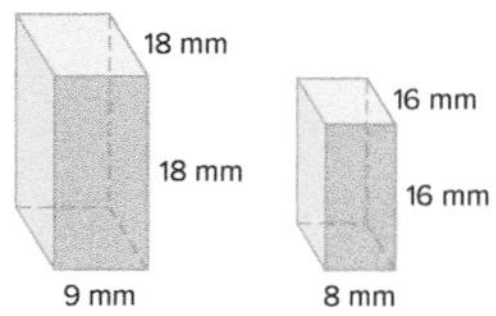

7.

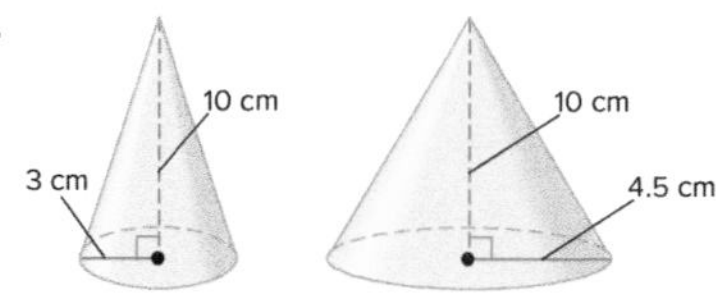

8.

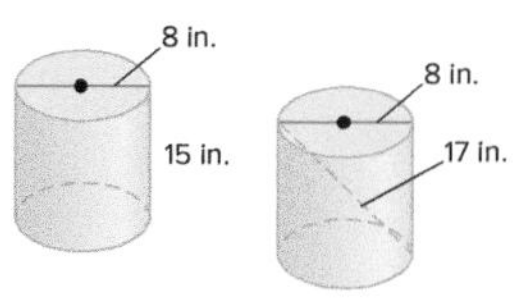

9.

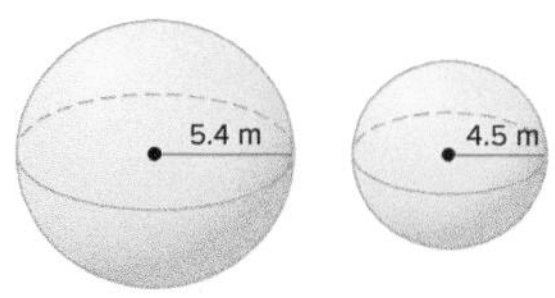

Example 2 G.GMD.1

10. Two similar pyramids have slant heights of 6 inches and 12 inches. If the volume of the large pyramid is 548 cubic inches, what is the volume of the small pyramid? 68.5 in^3

Example 3 G.GMD.1

(11) Two similar cylinders have heights of 35 meters and 25 meters. The volume of the shorter cylinder is 125π. What is the volume of the taller cylinder? 343 m^3

12. Two spheres have surface areas of 100π square centimeters and 16π square centimeters. What is the ratio of the volume of the large sphere to the volume of the small sphere? 125 : 8

13. Two similar hexagonal prisms have heights of 15 feet and 3 feet, respectively. If the volume of the first hexagonal prism is 250 cubic feet, what is the volume of the second hexagonal prism? 0.5 ft^3

Example 4 G.GMD.1

14. **ICE CREAM** Two similar ice cream containers have volumes of 270π and 640π cubic inches. If the height of the larger cylinder is 10 inches, what is the area of the base of the smaller cylinder in terms of π? $36\pi \text{ in}^2$

Practice

Formative Assessment Use Exercises 1–5 to assess students' understanding of the concepts in this lesson.

The Practice and Problem Solving exercises assess the content taught in the lesson. The Preparing for Assessment page is meant to be used as preparation for assessment.

MP Teaching the Mathematical Practices

Regularity Mathematically proficient students maintain oversight of the process, while attending to the details. They continually evaluate the reasonableness of their intermediate results. In Exercises 6–9, encourage students to check the reasonableness of their results.

Differentiated Homework Options

Levels	AL Basic	OL Core	BL Advanced
Exercises	6–16, 27, 29–39	7–13 odd, 14–17, 19, 21–27, 29–39	26–32, (optional: 33–39)
2-Day Option	7–15 odd, 33–39	6–16	
	6–16 even, 27, 29–32	17–27, 29–39	

You can use ALEKS to provide additional remediation support with personalized instruction and practice.

Extra Practice

See page R11 for extra exercises for students who are approaching level or for on-level students who need additional reinforcement.

Levels of Complexity Chart

The levels of the exercises progress from 1 to 3, with Level 1 indicating the lowest level of complexity.

Exercises	6–16	17–25, 33–39	26–32
C Level 3			●
B Level 2		●	
Level 1	●		

MP Teaching the Mathematical Practices

Sense-Making Mathematically proficient students start by explaining the meaning of a problem to themselves and looking for entry points to its solution. They plan a solution pathway rather than simply jumping into a solution attempt. In Exercises 20–21, encourage students to make a plan to solve each problem first.

15. **FOOD** A small cylindrical can of tuna has a radius of 4 centimeters and a height of 3.8 centimeters. A larger and similar can of tuna has a radius of 5.2 centimeters.

a. What is the scale factor of the cylinders? 10:13

b. What is the volume of the larger can? Round to the nearest tenth. 419.6 cm^3

16. **SUITCASES** Two suitcases are similar rectangular prisms. The smaller suitcase is 68 centimeters long, 47 centimeters wide, and 27 centimeters deep. The larger suitcase is 85 centimeters long.

a. What is the scale factor of the prisms? 4:5

b. What is the volume of the larger suitcase? Round to the nearest tenth. 168,539.1 cm^3

B **17.** **CLASS RINGS** The 12-foot replica of the Aggie Ring at Haynes Ring Plaza on the Texas A&M campus weighs about 6500 pounds. Suppose that the ring was based on a ring that was 0.75 inch high, what is the scale factor? 192:1

18. The pyramids shown are congruent.

a. What is the perimeter of the base of pyramid A? 24 cm

b. What is the area of the base of pyramid B? 24 cm^2

c. What is the volume of pyramid B? 104 cm^3

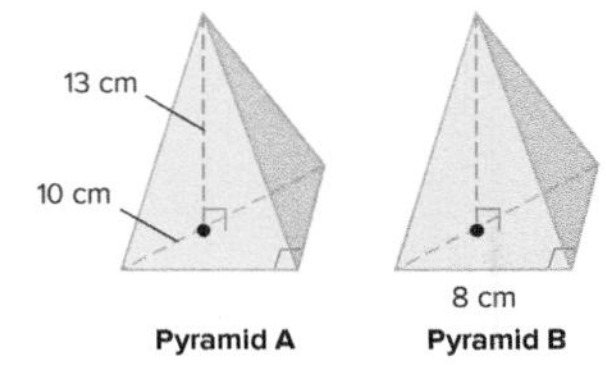

19. **TECHNOLOGY** Jalissa and Mateo each have the same type of digital media player but in different colors. The players are congruent rectangular prisms. The volume of Jalissa's player is 4.92 cubic inches, the width is 2.4 inches, and the depth is 0.5 inch. What is the height of Mateo's player? 4.1 in.

MP **MODELING** **Each pair of solids below is similar.**

20. What is the surface area of the smaller solid shown below? 946.3 cm^2

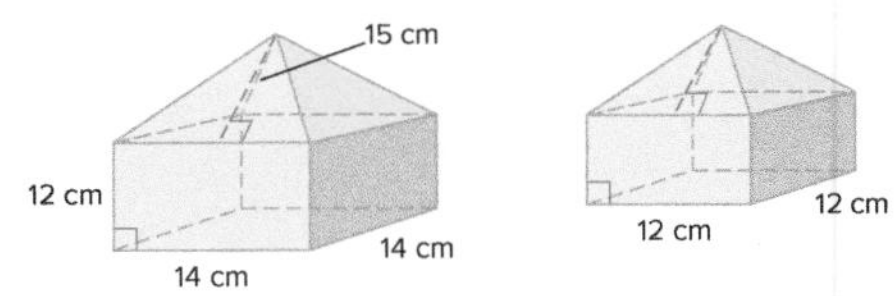

21. What is the volume of the larger solid shown below? 2439.6 cm^3

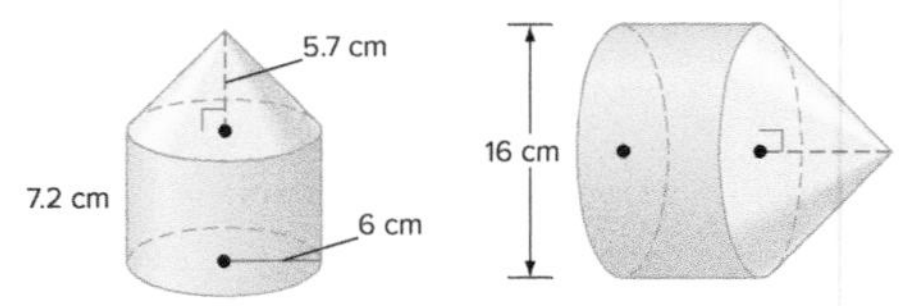

22. **DIMENSIONAL ANALYSIS** Two cylinders are similar. The height of the first cylinder is 23 centimeters, and the height of the other cylinder is 8 inches. If the volume of the first cylinder is 552π cubic centimeters, what is the volume of the other cylinder? Use 2.54 cm = 1 in. 380.65 π cm^3

Differentiated Instruction OL BL

Extension Ask students to explain why food-processing companies might be concerned with maximizing volume for a given surface area of product packaging. Sample answer: The largest possible ratio of volume to ratio of surface area possible minimizes cost for packaging materials.

Go Online!

The most up-to-date resources available for your program can be found at connectED.mcgraw-hill.com.

23. **DIMENSIONAL ANALYSIS** One sphere has a radius of 10 feet. The volume of a second sphere is 0.9 cubic meter. Use 2.54 centimeters = 1 inch to determine the scale factor from the first sphere to the second. **about 5.08 to 1**

24. **ALGEBRA** Two similar cones have volumes of 343π cubic centimeters and 512π cubic centimeters. The height of each cone is equal to 3 times its radius. Find the radius and height of both cones. **smaller cone: $r = 7$ cm, $h = 21$ cm; larger cone: $r = 8$ cm, $h = 24$ cm**

25. **TENTS** Two tents are in the shape of hemispheres with circular floors. The ratio of their floor areas is 9 : 12.25. If the diameter of the smaller tent is 6 feet, what is the volume of the larger tent? Round to the nearest tenth. **89.8 ft^3**

C 26. **MODELING** In this problem, you will investigate similarity. The heights of two similar cylinders are in the ratio 2 to 3. The lateral area of the larger cylinder is 162π square centimeters, and the diameter of the smaller cylinder is 8 centimeters.

a. **Verbal** What is the height of the larger cylinder? Explain your method.

b. **Geometric** Sketch and label the two cylinders. **See margin.**

c. **Analytical** How many times as great is the volume of the larger cylinder as the volume of the smaller cylinder? **3.375 times as great.**

26a. 13.5 cm; The heights are in the ratio 2 to 3, so the scale factor is 2:3. Because $\frac{8}{12} = \frac{2}{3}$, the diameter of the larger cylinder is 12 cm. The lateral area of the large cylinder is 162π cm^2, so the height is $162\pi \div 12\pi$ or 13.5 cm.

G.GMD.1

H.O.T. Problems Use **H**igher-**O**rder **T**hinking Skills

27. MP **CRITIQUE ARGUMENTS** Cylinder X has a diameter of 20 centimeters and a height of 11 centimeters. Cylinder Y has a radius of 30 centimeters and is similar to Cylinder X. Did Laura or Paloma correctly find the height of Cylinder Y? Explain your reasoning. **27. Laura; Laura compared corresponding parts of the similar figures, while Paloma incorrectly compared the diameter of X to the radius of Y.**

Laura	Paloma
Cylinder X: radius 10, height 11	Cylinder X: diameter 20, height 11
Cylinder Y: radius 30, height a	Cylinder Y: diameter 20, height a
$\frac{10}{30} = \frac{11}{a}$, so a = 33.	$\frac{20}{20} = \frac{11}{a}$, so a = 11.

28. 8 : 135; The volume of Cylinder C is 8 times the volume of Cylinder A, and the volume of Cylinder D is 27 times the volume of Cylinder B. If the original ratio of volumes was 1x : 5x, the new ratio is 8x : 135x. So, the ratio of volumes is 8 : 135.

28. **CHALLENGE** The ratio of the volume of Cylinder A to the volume of Cylinder B is 1 : 5. Cylinder A is similar to Cylinder C with a scale factor of 1 : 2, and Cylinder B is similar to Cylinder D with a scale factor of 1 : 3. What is the ratio of the volume of Cylinder C to the volume of Cylinder D? Explain your reasoning.

29. **WRITING IN MATH** Explain how the surface areas and volumes of the similar prisms shown at the right are related. **See margin.**

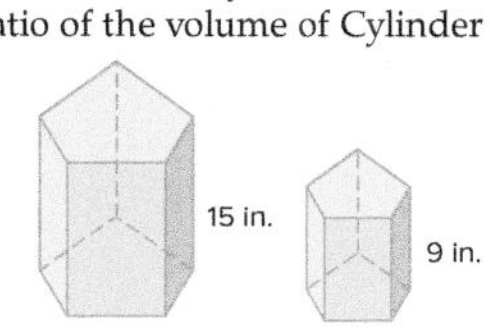

30. **OPEN-ENDED** Describe two nonsimilar triangular pyramids with similar bases. **See margin.**

31. MP **PERSEVERANCE** Plane *P* is parallel to the base of cone *C*, and the volume of the cone above the plane is $\frac{1}{8}$ of the volume of cone *C*. Find the height of cone *C*. **14 cm**

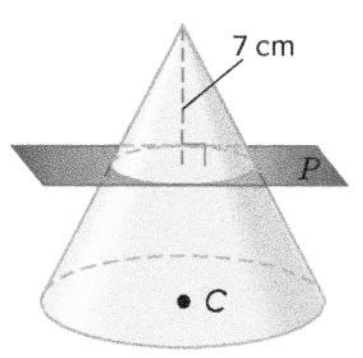

32. **WRITING IN MATH** Explain why all spheres are similar.

32. Sample answer: All spheres are the same shape. The only parameter that can vary is the radius, so all spheres are similar.

e Follow-Up

Students have explored surface area and volume between two similar objects.

Ask:

How are the surface area and volume of similar objects related? If the scale factor between two similar objects is $a : b$, the ratio of the surface area between two objects is $a^2 : b^2$ and the ratio of the volume between two objects is $a^3 : b^3$.

MP Standards for Mathematical Practice

Emphasis On	Exercises
1 Make sense of problems and persevere in solving them.	24, 25, 31
2 Reason abstractly and quantitatively.	22, 23, 34, 35, 38, 39
3 Construct viable arguments and critique the reasoning of others.	27, 35, 36, 39
4 Model with mathematics.	15, 16, 17, 20, 21, 26, 33, 37

Assess

Ticket Out the Door Have students explain how to tell if two solids are congruent. Have students turn in their statements before they leave the classroom.

Watch Out!

Error Analysis For Exercise 27, students should write a proportion to find the height of Cylinder Y. Paloma incorrectly wrote that the diameter of Cylinder Y was 20.

MP Teaching the Mathematical Practices

Perseverance Mathematically proficient students consider analogous problems and try simple forms of the original problem to gain insight into its solution. In Exercise 31, encourage students to write a proportion comparing the two cones.

Additional Answers

26b. Sample answer:

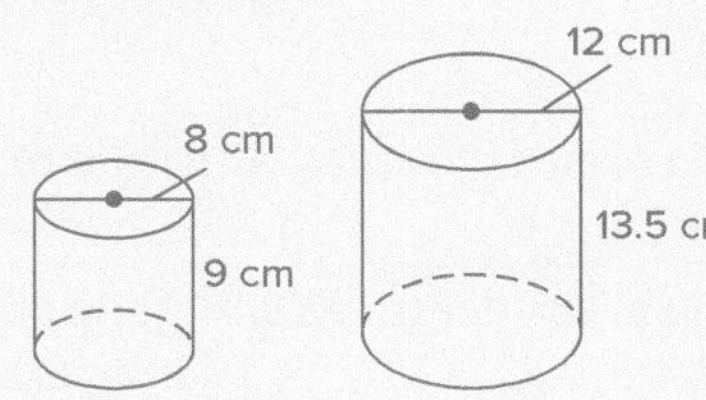

29. Because the scale factor is 15:9 or 5:3, the ratio of the surface areas is 25:9 and the ratio of the volumes is 125:27. So, the surface area of the larger prism is $\frac{25}{9}$ or about 2.8 times the surface area of the smaller prism. The volume of the larger prism is $\frac{125}{27}$ or about 4.6 times the volume of the smaller prism.

30. Sample answer: a pyramid with a right triangle base of 3, 4, and 5 units and a height of 6 units; a pyramid with a right triangle base of 6, 8, and 10 units and a height of 6 units

Go Online!

eSolutions Manual

Create worksheets, answer keys, and solutions handouts for your assignments.

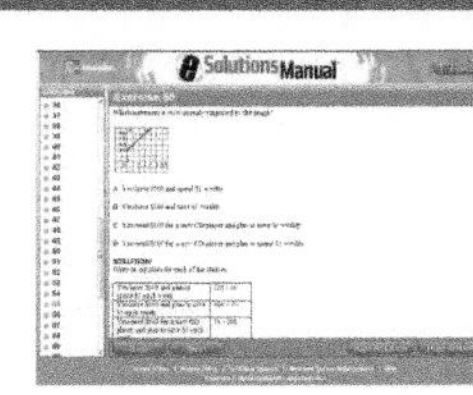

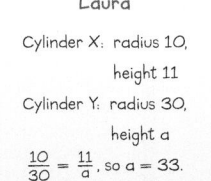

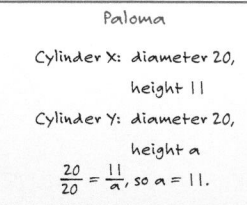

Preparing for Assessment

Exercises 33–39 require students to use the skills they will need on standardized assessments. Each exercise is dualcoded with content standards and mathematical practice standards.

Dual Coding

Items	Content Standards	MP Mathematical Practices
33	G.GMD.1	3, 4
34–36	G.GMD.1	2, 3
37	G.GMD.1	1
38–39	G.GMD.1	2, 3

Diagnose Student Errors

Survey student responses for each item. Class trends may indicate common errors and misconceptions.

33.

A	Assumed ratio of surface areas is same as ratio of side lengths
B	CORRECT
C	Added 420 to the surface area of the smaller prism
D	Assumed ratio of surface areas is same as ratio of volumes

34.

A	CORRECT
B	Confused ratio of surface areas with ratio of volumes
C	Confused ratio of surface areas with ratio of volumes
D	Did not recognize that ratio of circumferences is same as ratio of radii

Preparing for Assessment

33. Two similar rectangular prisms have volumes of 60 cubic meters and 480 cubic meters. The surface area of the smaller prism is 94 square meters. What is the surface area of the larger prism? MP 3 G.GMD.1 **B**

- ○ A 188 m^2
- ○ B 376 m^2
- ○ C 514 m^2
- ○ D 752 m^2

34. Two beach balls have diameters of 8 inches and 20 inches. Which of the following statements must be true? MP 2 G.GMD.1 **A**

- ○ A The ratio of the radii is 2:5.
- ○ B The ratio of the surface areas is 8:125.
- ○ C The ratio of the volumes is 4:25.
- ○ D The ratio of the circumferences is 4:25.

35. The two cones in the figure are similar. The volume of the large cone is 18,000 cubic inches. What is the volume of the small cone? MP 2 G.GMD.1 **C**

- ○ A $18{,}000\text{ in}^3$
- ○ B $83{,}333\text{ in}^3$
- ○ C 3888 in^3
- ○ D 6480 in^3

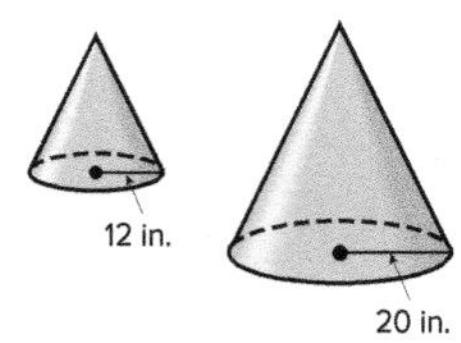

36. There are two square pyramids. One square pyramid has a height of 9 centimeters and base edges measuring 20 centimeters. The second square pyramid has a height of 4.5 centimeters and base edges measuring 10 centimeters. What is the scale factor for the two square pyramids? MP 2 G.GMD.1 **B**

- ○ A 1 to 1
- ○ B 2 to 1
- ○ C 2 to 2
- ○ D 3 to 1
- ○ E 3 to 2

37. The two cylinders shown here are similar. The volume of the small cylinder is 16 cubic feet, and the volume of the large cylinder is 54 cubic feet.

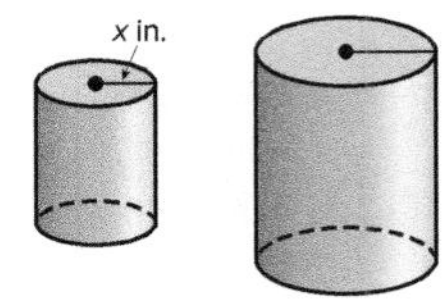

Which expression represents the radius of the large cylinder, in feet? MP 1 G.GMD.1 **C**

- ○ A $\frac{8}{27}x$
- ○ B $\frac{2}{3}x$
- ○ C $\frac{1}{8}x$
- ○ D $\frac{9}{4}x$
- ○ E $\frac{27}{8}x$

38. Two spheres have radii of 20π meters and 6π meters. How many times larger is the surface area of the large sphere compared to the surface area of the small sphere? Round to the nearest tenth. MP 2 G.GMD.1 **11.1**

39. **MULTI-STEP** Triangular prism A and triangular prism B are similar. The scale factor of prism A to prism B is $\frac{2}{5}$. MP 2 G.GMD.1

a. The height of the triangular base of prism A is 4.8 feet. Find the height of the triangular base of prism B. **12 ft**

b. If the length of a side of prism A is 6 feet, what is the length of the corresponding side of prism B? **15 ft**

c. If prism B has a surface area of 80 square feet, what is the surface area of prism A? **12.8 ft^2**

d. If the volume of prism A is 32 cubic feet, what is the volume of prism B? **500 ft^3**

35.

A	Did not recognize that there is a scale factor between two cones
B	Used proportional relationship incorrectly
C	CORRECT
D	Used the ratio of the surface area to find the volume of the small cone

37.

A	Used ratio of volumes rather than scale factor
B	Found correct scale factor, but used reciprocal of correct ratio in expression
C	CORRECT
D	Used ratio of surface areas rather than scale factor
E	Used ratio of volumes rather than scale factor

Go Online!

Quizzes

Students can use *Self-Check Quizzes* to check their understanding of this lesson and have the results sent to you. You can also give *Quiz 4*, which covers the content in Lessons 11-5 and 11-6.

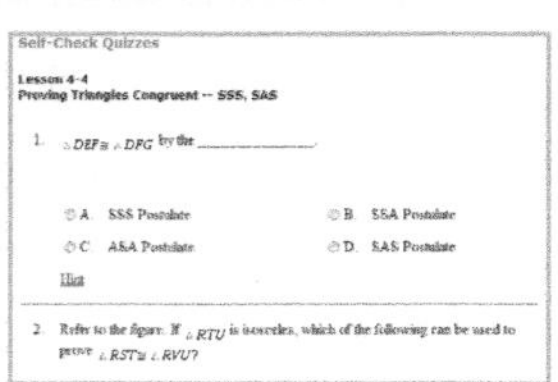

Applying Measurements

SUGGESTED PACING (DAYS)

90 min.	1
45 min.	1.5
	Instruction

Track Your Progress

Objectives

1 Solve real-world problems involving density by using area.

2 Solve real-world problems involving density by using volume.

Mathematical Background

Students have worked extensively with area and volume. Density is an important real-world application of these concepts. Population density is defined as the number of individuals per unit of area. It is typically measured in persons per square mile or persons per square kilometer. Density is defined as the mass of an object per unit of volume. It is often measured in grams per cubic centimeter or kilograms per cubic meter.

THEN	NOW	NEXT
G.GMD.1 Give an informal argument for the formulas for the circumference of a circle, area of a circle, volume of a cylinder, pyramid, and cone.	**G.MG.2** Apply concepts of density based on area and volume in modeling situations (e.g., persons per square mile, BTUs per cubic foot).	**S.CP.1** Describe events as subsets of a sample space (the set of outcomes) using characteristics (or categories) of the outcomes, or as unions, intersections, or complements of other events ("or," "and," "not").

Go Online! All of these resources and more are available at connectED.mcgraw-hill.com

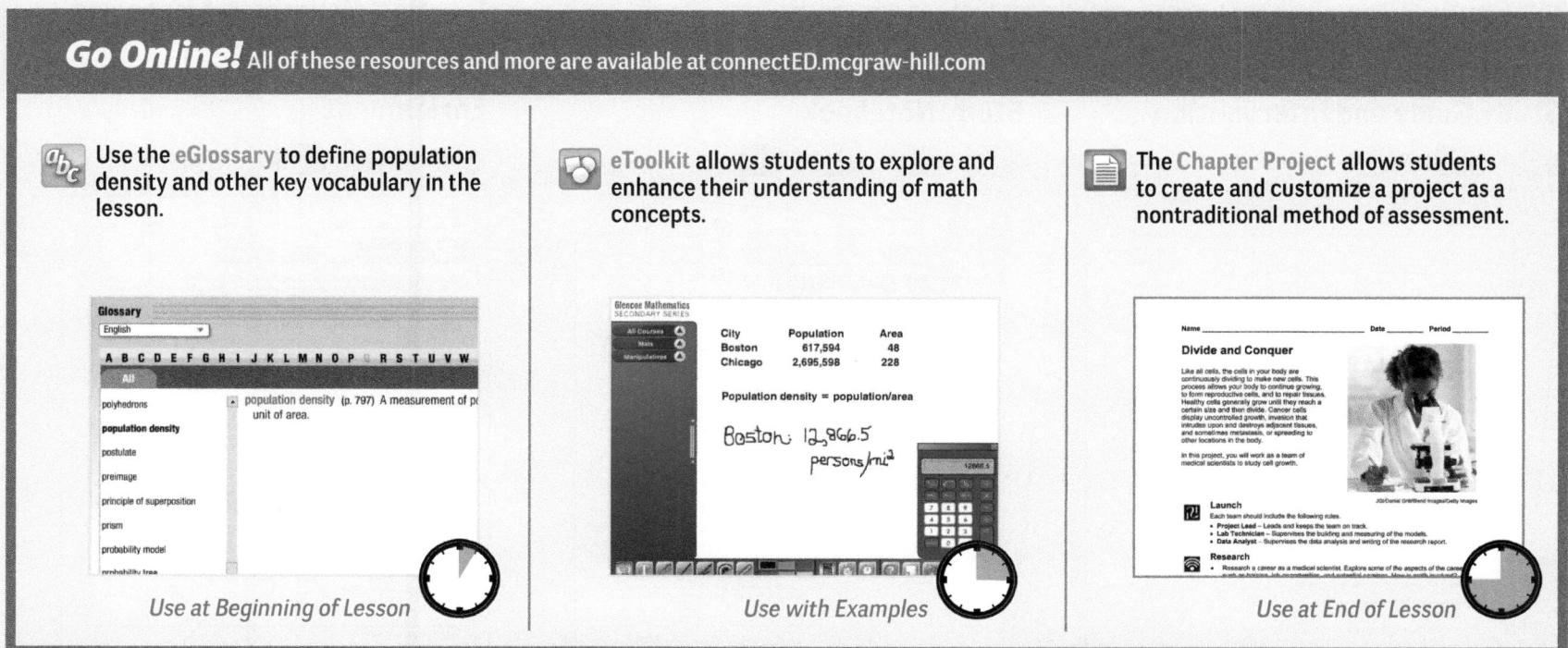

Use the eGlossary to define population density and other key vocabulary in the lesson.

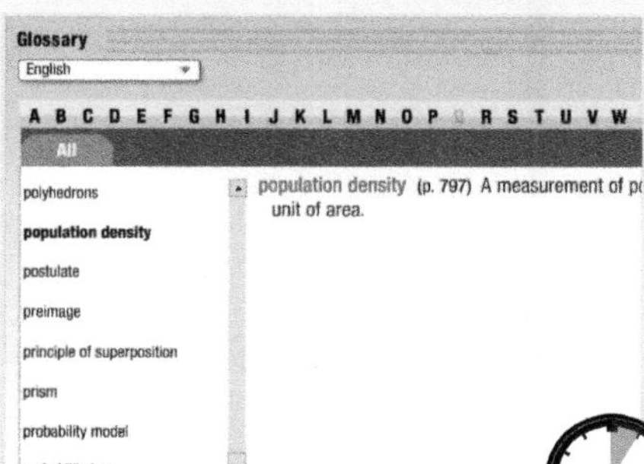

Use at Beginning of Lesson

eToolkit allows students to explore and enhance their understanding of math concepts.

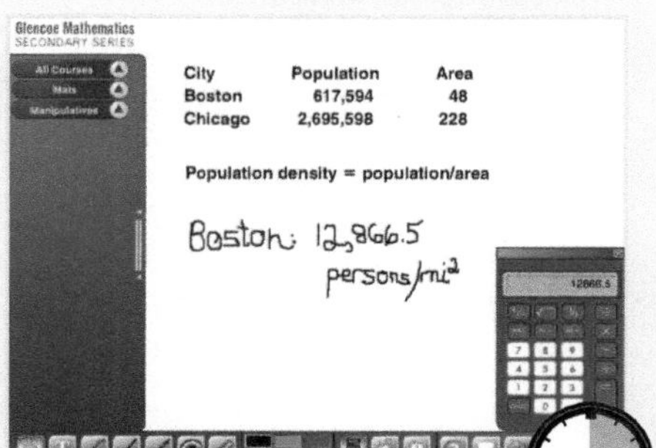

Use with Examples

The Chapter Project allows students to create and customize a project as a nontraditional method of assessment.

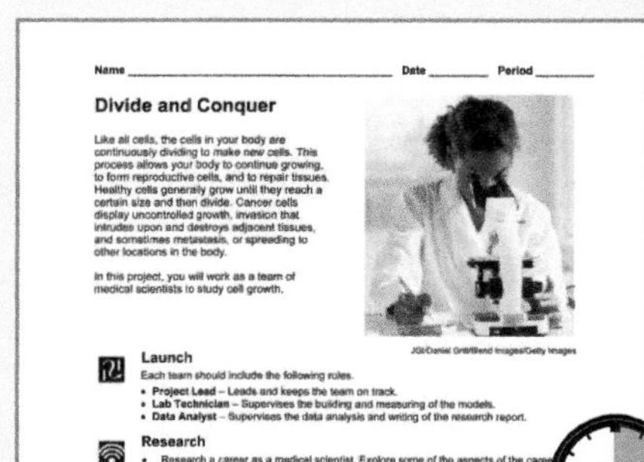

Use at End of Lesson

Using Open Educational Resources

Video Sharing Have students work in groups to record and upload examples on **SchoolTube** about population density and density of three-dimensional solids. Have them watch videos of others for ideas. If you are unable to access **SchoolTube**, try **KidsTube**, **MathATube**, **YouTube**, or **TeacherTube**. *Use as homework*

Differentiate Your Resources

Extra Practice Additional practice or homework; Skills Practice is best for approaching-level students and Practice is best for on-level and beyond-level students

Skills Practice

AL OL ELL

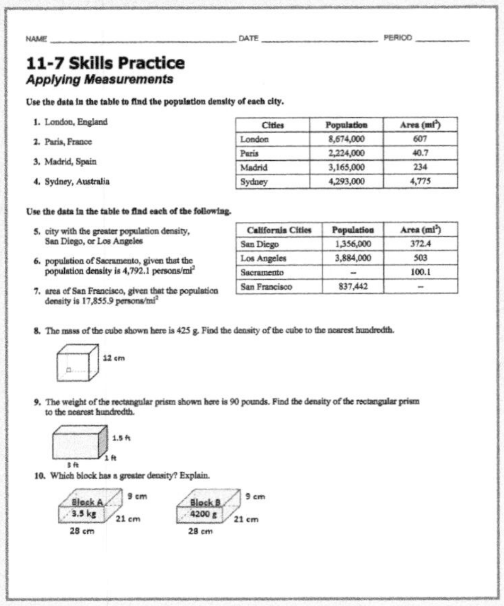

11-7 Skills Practice
Applying Measurements

Practice

AL OL BL ELL

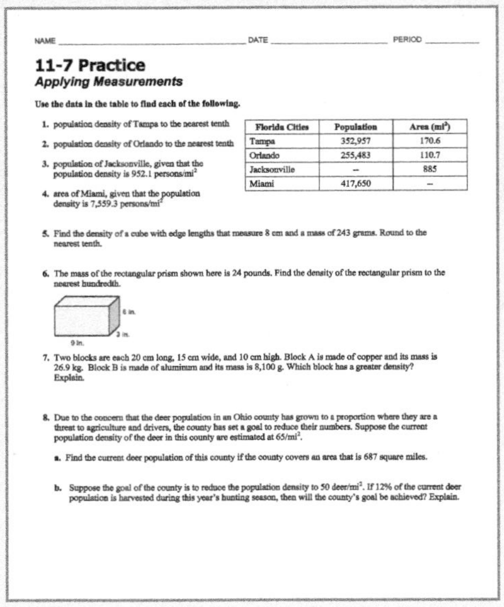

11-7 Practice
Applying Measurements

Word Problem Practice

AL OL BL ELL

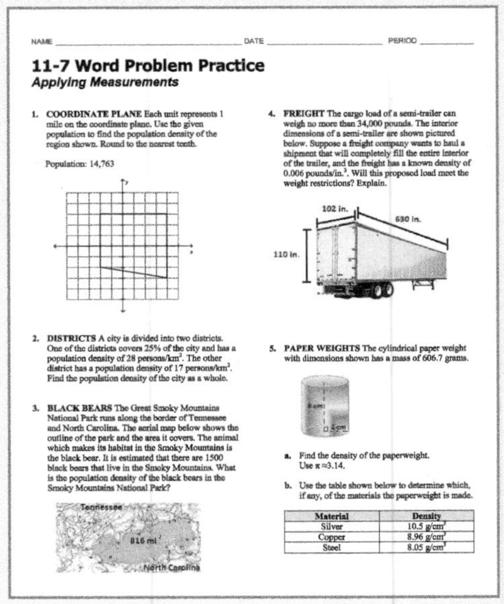

11-7 Word Problem Practice
Applying Measurements

Intervention Reteaching and vocabulary activities that can be used with struggling or absent students and as ELL support

Study Guide and Intervention

AL OL ELL

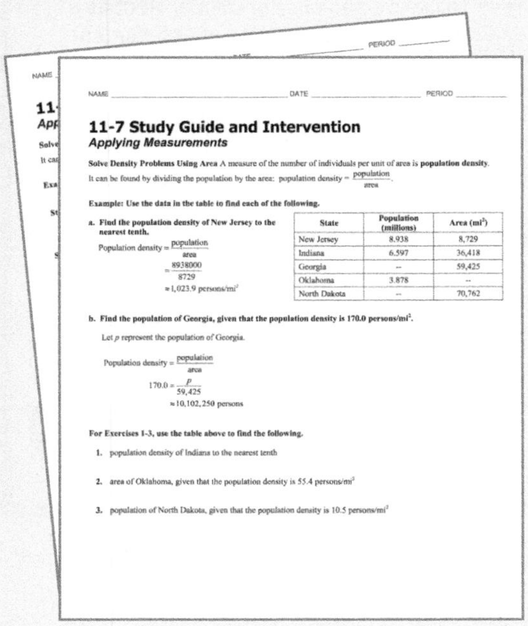

11-7 Study Guide and Intervention
Applying Measurements

Study Notebook

AL OL BL ELL

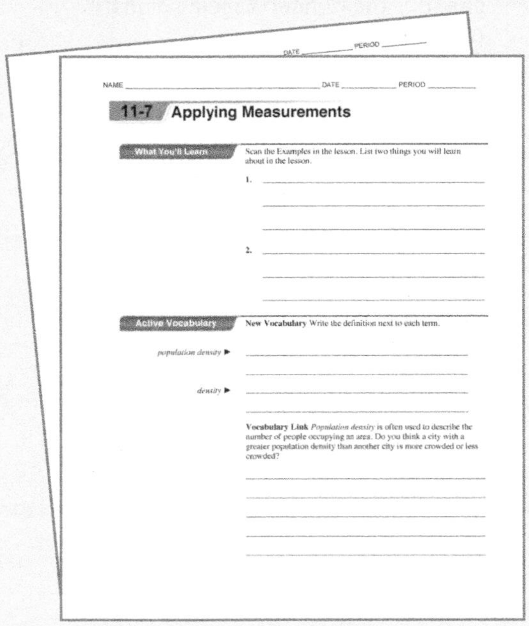

11-7 Applying Measurements

Extension Activities that can be used to extend lesson concepts

Enrichment

OL BL ELL

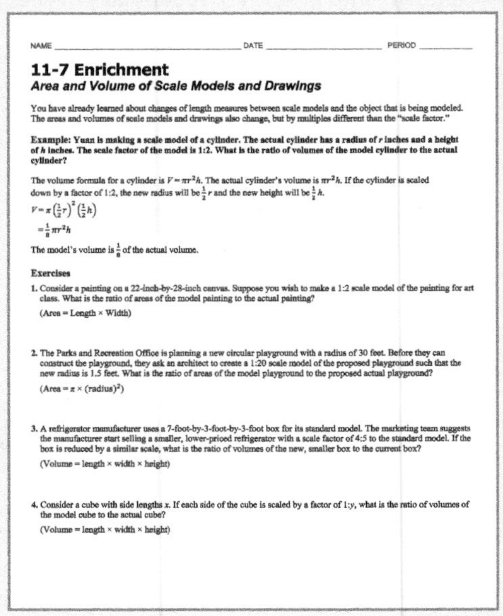

11-7 Enrichment
Area and Volume of Scale Models and Drawings

LESSON 7

Applying Measurements

Then

- You found areas of geometric figures and volumes of solids.

Now

- **1** Solve real-world problems involving density by using area.
- **2** Solve real-world problems involving density by using volume.

Why?

- Cities are more crowded than other areas. In a city, there are more people that live and work in an area of a given size. This means that the population density of a city is higher than other areas.

New Vocabulary

density
population density

Mathematical Practices

1 Make sense of problems and persevere in solving them.
4 Model with mathematics.
5 Use appropriate tools strategically.

Content Standards

G.MG.2 Apply concepts of density based on area and volume in modeling situations (e.g., person per square mile, BTUs per cubic foot).

1 Solve Density Problems Using Area

Density is a measure of the quantity of some physical property per unit of length, area, or volume. One example of density is **population density,** which is the measurement of population per unit of area. Population density is calculated for states, major cities, or other areas, based on data collected from the U.S. Census.

Key Concept Density Based on Area

Words: Density is the ratio of objects to area.

Symbols: $\text{density} = \frac{\text{number of objects}}{\text{area}}$

G.MG.2

Real-World Example 1 Find Population Densities

CITIES **Use the data in the table to find each of the following.**

City	Population	Area (mi^2)
Boston, MA	617,594	48
Chicago, IL	2,695,598	228
Los Angeles, CA	?	469
New York, NY	8,175,133	?

a. Find the population density of Boston to the nearest tenth.

$$\text{Population density} = \frac{\text{population}}{\text{land area}}$$
$$= \frac{617{,}594}{48}$$
$$\approx 12{,}866.5 \text{ persons/mi}^2$$

b. Find the population of Los Angeles, given that the population density is 8086.6 persons per square mile.

Let p represent the population of Los Angeles.

$$\text{Population density} = \frac{\text{population}}{\text{land area}}$$
$$8086.6 = \frac{p}{469}$$
$$469(8086.6) = p$$
$$3{,}792{,}615 \approx p$$

Guided Practice

1A. Find the population density of Chicago to the nearest tenth. 11,822.8 persons/mi^2

1B. Find the area of New York, given that the population density is 26,980.6 persons per square mile. 303 mi^2

MP Mathematical Practices Strategies

Model with mathematics.
Help students understand how to use models to understand and solve density problems. For example, ask:

- What steps would you use to model the population density of cows in a pasture? Determine the shape of the pasture and the dimensions of the pasture; find its area; count how many cows are in the pasture; divide the population of cows by the area.
- In general, how can you interpret a population density that you calculate? Sample answer: A large population density means there are many individuals in a small area; a small population density means there are few individuals in a large area.
- What are some formulas you might need when solving a real-world problem about population density? Sample answer: area of a square, area of a rectangle, area of a circle, and so on.
- What are some formulas you might need when solving a real-world problem about the density of a three-dimensional object? Sample answer: volume of a sphere, volume of a prism, and so on.

Launch

Have students read the Why? section of the lesson. Ask:

- What are the two factors that determine the population density of an area? the population and the size of the area
- Why do you think it might be important to calculate population densities? Sample answer: It helps governments determine services for a specific area, resources, etc.

Teach

Ask the scaffolded questions for each example to build conceptual understanding for students at all levels.

1 Solve Density Problems Using Area

Example 1 Find Population Densities

AL How many people live in Boston? What is the area of Boston? How do you find the population density? 617,594 persons; 48 mi^2; divide the population by the area

OL What will happen to the population density of Boston if the population increases, but the area of the city stays the same? It will increase.

BL What can you say about New York, knowing that it is the most densely populated city? It has the most people in a very small area.

Need Another Example?

State	Population	Area (mi^2)
Rhode Island	1,056,298	1,212
Delaware	—	2,491

a. Find the population density of Rhode Island to the nearest tenth. 871.5 persons/mi^2

b. Find the population of Delaware, given that the population density is 379.7 persons per square mile. 945,833

Teaching Tip

Precision Be sure students understand that density is generally measured using compound units such as grams per cubic centimeter or pounds per cubic foot. If a student reports a population density as 4.5 persons, remind them that the unit should have the form of persons per some unit of area (persons/mi², persons/km², etc.).

MP Teaching the Mathematical Practices

Reasoning Mathematically proficient students make generalizations about the meaning of a population density. They recognize that population density in a given area will change as the population increases or decreases. Have students give examples of U.S. cities whose areas remain the same but whose populations change over time.

Example 2 Apply Population Density

AL What is the area of Yellowstone National Park? 3472 mi²

OL How do you convert acres to square miles? Multiply the number of acres by 0.0015625.

BL How many wolves would need to be found in the park in order for them not to build the campground? 6944

Need Another Example?

A rectangular state park with a length of 2.7 miles and a width of 2.5 miles has a duck population of 2500 ducks. The park rangers want to build a new playground, but can only build the playground if the duck population density is greater than 420 ducks per square mile. Does the population density allow for the playground to be built? No; the duck population density is 370.4 ducks per square mile, so the park rangers cannot build the new playground.

G.MG.2

Real-World Example 2 Apply Population Density

NATIONAL PARKS **Looking at a proposal to establish a new campground at Yellowstone National Park, there is a concern about the number of wolves in the area. At last report, there were 98 wolves in the park. The new campground will be accepted if there are fewer than 2 wolves in the area that the campground would occupy. Use the data in the table to determine whether the campground can be established.**

Location	Area
Entire park	3472 mi²
Proposed campground	10 acres

Step 1 Find the population density of wolves in the park.

$$\frac{\text{population}}{\text{land area}} = \frac{2 \text{ wolves}}{3472 \text{ mi}^2}$$
$$\approx 0.028 \text{ wolves/mi}^2$$

Step 2 Find the population of wolves in the proposed campground. Convert the size of the campground from acres to square miles.

1 acre = 0.0015625 mi²
10 acres = 0.015625 mi²

The potential number of wolves in the proposed site is 0.015625 × 0.028 = 0.0004375 wolf.

Because 0.0004375 is less than 2, the proposed campground can be established.

Watch Out!

Dimensional Analysis In some cases, it may be necessary to use dimensional analysis to convert between units of measurement. To convert from one unit to another, use a numerical quantity known as a conversion factor.

Guided Practice No; an area of 75 mi² would have approximately 1388 alligators.

2. There are about 1.25 million alligators in Florida, which has an area of about 67,555 square miles. The state wants to build a new park with an area of 75 square miles, but the park cannot be built if there are more than 1000 alligators in the area. Should the state build the park? Explain.

2 Solve Density Problems Using Volume

Density is the measure of the quantity of some physical property per unit of length, area, or volume. If two objects have the same volume but different masses, the object with the greater mass will be denser. Density is often measured in grams per cubic centimeter (g/cm³) or kilograms per cubic meter (kg/m³).

Key Concept Density Based on Volume

Words	Density is the ratio of mass to volume.
Symbols	$\text{density} = \frac{\text{mass}}{\text{volume}}$

The figure shows the densities of some common materials.

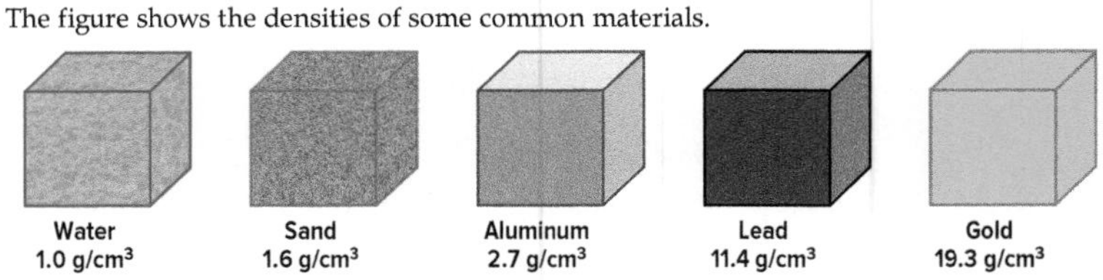

G.MG.2

Example 3 Find the Density of a Solid

The mass of the cube shown here is 275 grams. Find the density of the cube to the nearest tenth.

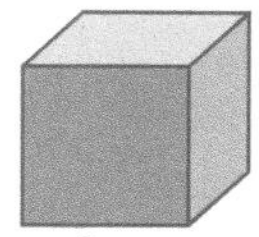

6 cm

Step 1 Find the volume of the cube.

$V = s^3$ — Volume of a cube

$= 6^3$ or 216 cm^3 — Substitution, $s = 6$

Step 2 Find the density of the cube.

$\text{density} = \frac{\text{mass}}{\text{volume}}$

$= \frac{275}{216} \approx 1.3\text{ g/cm}^3$

Guided Practice

3. Find the density of a rectangular prism that is 6 inches by 2 inches by 4 inches with a mass of 16 ounces. Round to the nearest tenth. 0.3 oz/in^3

When you calculate and compare densities in real-world problems, be sure you are using units consistently. You may need to convert units before calculating densities.

G.MG.2

Real-World Example 4 Compare Densities

DRIVEWAYS **The Ramirez family wants to redo the driveway of their home. They have to choose between using asphalt or concrete, and they must make sure that whichever material they use has a density of less than 50 pounds per cubic foot because if the driveway is too heavy, it will sink. The driveway is 192 inches wide, 32 feet long, and 3 inches deep, and it will require about 9.5 tons of concrete or 5700 pounds of asphalt. Which material should the Ramirez family use?**

> **Study Tip**
> **MP Sense-Making** Before starting to solve the problem, look at all of the given units and decide which units will be most convenient to use for comparing densities.

Step 1 Convert units in order to solve the problem using feet and pounds.

Convert 192 inches to feet: $\frac{192}{12} = 16$ ft Convert 3 inches to feet: $\frac{3}{12} = 0.25$ ft

Convert 9.5 tons to pounds: $9.5 \times 2000 = 19{,}000$ lb

Step 2 Find the volume of the driveway.

$V = \ell \times w \times h$

$= 32 \times 16 \times 0.25 = 128\text{ ft}^3$

Step 3 Calculate the density of each material.

$\text{density of asphalt} = \frac{\text{mass}}{\text{volume}} = \frac{5700}{128} \approx 44.5\text{ lb/ft}^3$

$\text{density of concrete} = \frac{\text{mass}}{\text{volume}} = \frac{19{,}000}{128} \approx 148.4\text{ lb/ft}^3$

The Ramirez family should use asphalt.

Guided Practice 4. Block B; the density of Block A is 0.71 g/cm^3, and the density of Block B is 0.79 g/cm^3.

4. Two blocks are each 110 centimeters long, 100 millimeters wide, and 6 centimeters high. Block A is made of zinc, and its mass is 4.7 kilograms. Block B is made of iron, and its mass is 5200 grams. Which block has a greater density? Explain.

Differentiated Instruction OL BL

IF students are successful with the concepts of population density and three-dimensional density,

THEN have them work in small groups to write their own density problems. For example, ask students to write a density problem that has an answer of 5.6 lb/ft^3. Have students exchange and solve each other's problems, and offer feedback for improvements. Remind students to pay careful attention to units and rounding.

2 Solve Density Problems Using Volume

Example 3 Find the Density of a Solid

AL **What do you know about the sides and edges of a cube?** The sides are all squares with the same area; the edges all have the same length.

OL **What information is necessary to find the volume of the cube?** You need to know the length of one of the edges.

BL **How could you change the edge length to get a cube with a density of 1 gram per cubic centimeter?** Change the edge length to $\sqrt[3]{275}$ centimeters

Need Another Example?

A sphere has a radius of 3 feet. Its mass is 550 grams. Find the density of the sphere to the nearest tenth. 4.9 g/cm^3

Example 4 Compare Densities

AL **What information is needed to find the volume of the driveway?** length, width, and depth

OL **How do you convert inches to feet? How do you convert tons to pounds?** Divide the number of inches by 12; multiply the number of tons by 2000.

BL **If you have equal amounts of concrete and asphalt, which material will be heavier? about how many times heavier?** Concrete; it is about 3.3 times heavier than asphalt.

Need Another Example?

An artist is making a sculpture in the shape of a rectangular prism that is 3 meters long, 180 centimeters wide, and 0.5 meter tall. She wants to be sure that the finished sculpture has a density less than 1.5 grams per cubic centimeter. If she makes the sculpture with clay, it will have a mass of 3780 kilograms. If she makes the sculpture with glass, it will have a mass of 6,480,000 grams. Which material should she use? clay

Teaching Tip

Sense-Making Encourage students to plan a solution pathway before they begin the details of solving a density problem. For example, students might outline the main steps as follows: determine the key units of the problem; determine the dimensions of the solid and convert units as needed; find the volume of the solid; find the mass of the solid; find the ratio of mass to volume. Students can check off the steps as they work through the problem.

Practice

Formative Assessment Use Exercises 1–6 to assess students' understanding of the concepts in the lesson.

The Practice and Problem Solving exercises assess the content taught in the lesson. The Preparing for Assessment page is meant to be used as preparation for end-of-course assessments.

Extra Practice

See page R11 for extra exercises for students who are approaching level or for on-level students who need additional reinforcement.

Check Your Understanding

◯ = Step-by-Step Solutions begin on page R13.

Go Online! for a Self-Check Quiz

Example 1 G.MG.2

1. A rectangular pen with length of 32 feet and width of 13 feet holds 56 rabbits. Find the population density of rabbits to the nearest hundredth. **0.13 rabbits/ft^2**

2. There are 13,000 flowers in a square field. The population density of the flowers is 0.9 flower per square foot. Find the side length of the field to the nearest foot. **120 ft**

Example 2 G.MG.2

3. **OWLS** The population density of the burrowing owl in Cape Coral, Florida, is 8.3 pairs per square mile. A new golf course is planned for a 2.4-square mile site where the owl population is estimated to be 17 pairs. Would Lee County approve the proposed club if their policy is to decline expansion when the estimated population density of owls is below the average density? Explain. **No; the population density is about 7.1 pairs/mi^2.**

Example 3 G.MG.2

4. A rectangular prism has a length of 15 centimeters, a width of 4.2 centimeters, and a height of 2 centimeters. The mass of the prism is 755 grams. Find the density of the prism to the nearest tenth. **6.0 g/cm^3**

5. A cube has an edge that is 12 feet long. The mass of the cube is 18,000 pounds. Find the density of the cube to the nearest tenth. **10.4 lb/ft^3**

Example 4 G.MG.2

6. **ART** A cylindrical sculpture has a radius of 50 millimeters and height of 15 centimeters. The mass of the sculpture is 3.7 kilograms. A sculpture in the shape of a rectangular prism has a length of 62 millimeters, width of 40 millimeters, and height of 12 centimeters. Its mass is 1250 grams. Which sculpture has a greater density? Explain. **Rectangular prism; its density is ≈ 4.2 g/cm^3 compared to ≈ 3.1 g/cm^3 for the cylinder.**

Practice and Problem Solving

Extra Practice is found on page R11.

Example 1 G.MG.2

Find the missing value in each row of the table. When necessary, round populations and areas to the nearest whole number and densities to the nearest tenth.

	Country	Population	Area (km^2)	Density (persons/km^2)	
7.	Australia	?	7,682,300	2.5	**19,205,750**
8.	Japan	126,550,976	?	374	**338,372 km^2**
9.	Monaco	31,693	2	?	**15,846.5 persons/km^2**
10.	Mongolia	?	1,553,556	1.7	**2,641,045**
11.	United States	275,562,673	9,147,593	?	**30.1 persons/km^2**

Example 2 G.MG.2

12. **CATTLE RANCHING** The Jackson family owns a ranch that covers 49,747 acres (1 acre = 0.0015625 square mile), but they do not use the entire ranch for cows. According to the USDA, ranches are required to have a minimum of 1.5 acres per cow.

a. The Jackson family has 26,667 cows on the ranch, with a population density of 348.6 cows per square mile. How many square miles do they use for cows? **76.5 mi^2**

b. If the family used the entire ranch for cows, what would be the maximum number of cows that they could have? What would the population density be in cows per square mile? **33,164 cows; 426.7 cows/mi^2**

Example 3 G.MG.2

13. A sphere has a radius of 14 centimeters and a mass of 36,249 grams. Find the density of the sphere to the nearest tenth. **3.2 g/cm^3**

14. A large metal cube measures 5 meters on each edge. Its mass is 537.5 kilograms. What is the density of the cube? **4.3 kg/m^3**

Example 4 G.MG.2

15. **WOOD** Will has two blocks of wood. Block A is 2 feet long, 4 inches wide, and 2 inches tall. Block B is 1.5 feet long, 0.5 feet wide, and 3 inches tall. Block A has a mass of 3.8 pounds, and Block B has a mass of 120 ounces. Which block of wood has a greater density? Explain. **Block B; its density is 40 lb/ft^3 compared to 34.2 lb/ft^3 for Block A.**

Differentiated Homework Options

Levels	AL Basic	OL Core	BL Advanced
Exercises	7–15, 23, 24, 26–34	7–21 odd, 22–24, 26–34	22–27, (optional: 28–34)
2-Day Option	7–15 odd, 28–34	7–15	
	8–14 even, 23, 24, 26, 27	16–24, 26–34	

You can use ALEKS to provide additional remediation support with personalized instruction and practice.

Go Online! eBook

Interactive Student Guide

Use the *Interactive Student Guide* to deepen conceptual understanding.

· Modeling: Three-Dimensional Figures

B **The table shows the densities of some common materials. Use the table and the given information to determine the most likely material that each solid is made of.**

Material	Density (g/cm^3)
Cardboard	0.7
Chalk	2.5
Copper	8.9
Iron	7.2
Rubber	1.5

16. A rectangular prism is 12 cm long, 8.2 cm wide, and 3.3 cm tall. Its mass is 2.89 kg. copper

17. A sphere has a radius of 44 mm. Its mass is 535 kg. rubber

18. A cylinder has a radius of 67 mm and a height of 12 cm. Its mass is 4230 g. chalk

19. A cube has edges that are 0.1 m long. Its mass is 0.7 kg. cardboard

Each unit represents 1 kilometer on the coordinate plane. Use the given population to find the population density of the region shown. Round to the nearest tenth.

20. population: 2358. 64.6 persons/km^2

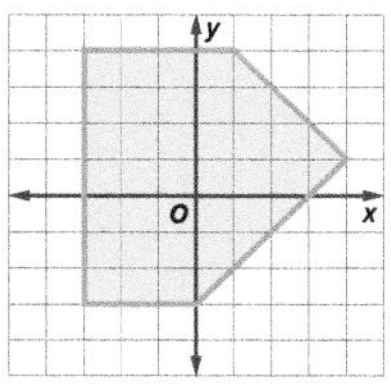

21 population: 55,323 1177.1 persons/km^2

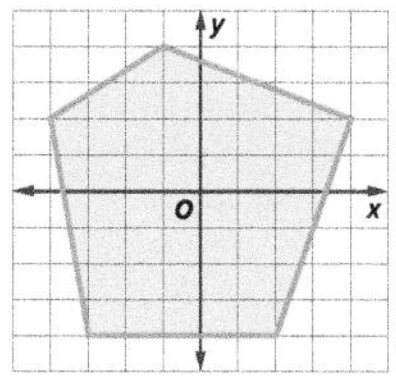

C **22.** **EXERCISE** Saanvi uses a foam exercise roller to help her stretch after workouts. The more dense the roller, the more intense the stretching regimen is. The mass of the roller she is currently using is 436 grams.

a. What is the density of the foam roller? 0.047 g/cm^3

b. If Saanvi uses an exercise roller that has a density of about 0.096 gram per cubic centimeter and is the same shape as the original roller, what is the mass of her new roller rounded to the nearest whole gram? 888 g

24. Cylinder; if the radius of the cylinder is r, then its volume is πr^3 and the volume of the sphere is $\frac{4}{3}\pi r^3$. This means the sphere has a greater volume. Since the masses of the solids are the same, the ratio $\frac{\text{mass}}{\text{volume}}$ is greater for the cylinder.

H.O.T. Problems Use Higher-Order Thinking Skills

23. **ERROR ANALYSIS** India has a population of 1.282 billion people and an area of 3.29 million square kilometers. Jane says the population density of India is 0.003 persons per square kilometer. Is Jane correct? Explain why or why not. No; she found the ratio of area to population rather than the ratio of population to area; 389.7 persons/km^2

24. **MP REASONING** A cylinder and a sphere have the same mass. The height of the cylinder is equal to its radius. The radius of the sphere is equal to the radius of the cylinder. Which solid has a greater density? Explain.

25. **CHALLENGE** A rectangular prism has a length of 5 meters, a width of x meters, and a height of $(x + 2)$ meters. Its density is 1 kilogram per cubic meter, and its mass is 120 cubic meters. Find the value of x. 4

26. **MP CRITIQUE ARGUMENTS** An object will float in water if its density is less than 1 gram per cubic centimeter. Will a block of wood with a mass of 10 kilograms and dimensions 30 centimeters by 40 centimeters by 8 centimeters float in water? Explain.

26. No; the mass is 10,000g, and the volume is 9600 cm^3, so the density is $\frac{10{,}000}{9600} \approx$ 1.04 g/cm^3, which is greater than 1 g/cm^3.

27. **WRITING IN MATH** A student said that steel is heavier than plastic. Use density to explain what the student meant. Sample answer: Steel has a greater density than plastic; this means that if a piece of steel and a piece of plastic have the same volume (i.e., the same size), the piece of steel will have a greater mass than the piece of plastic.

MP Teaching the Mathematical Practices

Modeling Mathematically proficient students can apply the mathematics they know to solve problems arising in everyday life and in society. Population density plays a role in how governments create services, how communities are planned, how traffic lights are timed, when trash is picked up, and where new schools are built. Encourage students to think of other examples of how population density might play a role in their city or town.

Follow-Up

Students have explored density of three-dimensional solids. Have students explain density in their own words. Sample answer: Density is the amount of material in an object per unit of volume.

Assess

Ticket Out the Door Make several copies of different cards or papers that each give a mass and a volume. Give one card or paper to each student. As students leave the room, ask them to estimate the density, using appropriate units.

Levels of Complexity Chart

The levels of the exercises progress from 1 to 3, with Level 1 indicating the lowest level of complexity.

Exercises	7–15	16–21, 28–34	22–27
C Level 3			●
B Level 2		●	
Level 1	●		

MP Standards for Mathematical Practice

Emphasis On	Exercises
1 Make sense of problems and persevere in solving them.	28–32, 34
2 Reason abstractly and quantitatively.	24, 25, 29, 30, 33
3 Construct viable arguments and critique the reasoning of others.	26
4 Model with mathematics.	3, 6, 12, 15, 31, 32

Preparing for Assessment

Exercises 28–34 require students to use the skills they will need on standardized assessments. Each exercise is dual-coded with content standards and mathematical practice standards.

Dual Coding		
Items	Content Standards	MP Mathematical Practices
28	G.MG.2	1
29	G.MG.2	1, 2
30	G.MG.2	1, 2
31	G.MG.2	1, 4
32	G.MG.2	1, 4
33	G.MG.2	2
34	G.MG.2	1, 3

Preparing for Assessment

28. There are 64,288,000 gaming system owners in the United States. The area of the United States is 3,794,083 square miles. What is the population density of gaming system owners? MP 1 G.MG.2 D

- ○ A 0.1 owner/mi²
- ○ B 1.7 owners/mi²
- ○ C 15 owners/mi²
- ○ D 16.9 owners/mi²
- ○ E 17.3 owners/mi²

29. An object has a density of 4.6 grams per cubic centimeter. What is the volume of the object if its mass is 2773.8 grams? MP 1, 2 G.MG.2 B

- ○ A 0.002 cm³
- ○ B 603 cm³
- ○ C 2769.2 cm³
- ○ D 12,759.5 cm³

30. Five pounds of flour completely fills a container that measures $6\frac{3}{4}$ inches by $6\frac{3}{4}$ inches by 6 inches. What is the density of the flour in ounces per cubic inch? MP 1, 2 G.MG.2 B

- ○ A 0.02 oz/in³
- ○ B 0.29 oz/in³
- ○ C 3.42 oz/in³
- ○ D 54.68 oz/in³

31. Kenisha is going to plant 1000 seeds in a flower bed. For which of the following shapes of the flower bed will the density of seeds be greater than 50 seeds per square foot? MP 1, 4 G.MG.2 A, E, F

- ☐ A a rectangle 6 ft long and 3 ft wide
- ☐ B a circle with a radius of 3 ft
- ☐ C a square with sides 5 ft long
- ☐ D a rectangle 5 ft long and 4 ft wide
- ☐ E a circle with a diameter of 2 ft
- ☐ F a square with sides 24 in. long
- ☐ G a circle with a radius of 1.5 ft

32. The population density of polar bears in a region of Canada is 5.1 bears per 1000 square kilometers. Which of the following is the best estimate of the number of polar bears that would be found in a national park within this region if the national park has an area of 26,500 square kilometers? MP 1, 4 G.MG.2 B

- ○ A 5
- ○ B 135
- ○ C 5196
- ○ D 135,150
- ○ E 175,221

33. The rectangular prism shown here has a mass of m grams. Which expression can be used to find the density of the rectangular prism in grams per cubic centimeter? MP 2 G.MG.2 D

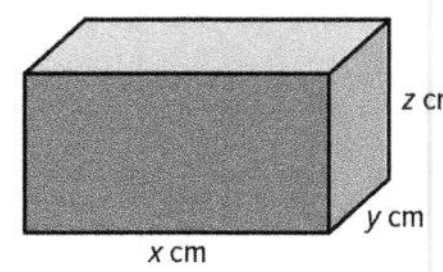

- ○ A $\frac{2xy + 2xz + 2yz}{m}$
- ○ B $\frac{m}{2xy + 2xz + 2yz}$
- ○ C $\frac{xyz}{m}$
- ○ D $\frac{m}{xyz}$

34. MULTI-STEP A cylinder has a diameter of 12 feet and a height of 18 feet. The mass of the cylinder is 6.2 tons. MP 1, 3 G.MG.2

a. What is the density of the cylinder in pounds per cubic foot? Round to the nearest tenth. 6.1 lb/ft³

b. Suppose the mass of the cylinder increases while its dimensions stay the same. How does this affect the density of the cylinder? Justify your answer.

c. What should the mass of the cylinder be, in tons, if the dimensions stay the same and the density changes to 10 pounds per cubic foot? Round to the nearest tenth. 10.2 tons

34b. The density increases because the numerator of the ratio $\frac{\text{mass}}{\text{volume}}$ increases while the denominator remains constant.

Diagnose Student Errors

Survey student responses for each item. Class trends may indicate common errors and misconceptions.

28.

A	Divided area by the number of owners
B	Used 6,428,800 as the value for the number of owners
C	Rounded the number of owners and the area
D	CORRECT
E	Rounded the number of owners and the area

29.

A	Divided density by mass
B	CORRECT
C	Subtracted density from mass
D	Multiplied density and mass

30.

A	Did not convert mass to ounces
B	CORRECT
C	Divided volume by mass
D	Did not convert mass to ounces and divided volume by mass

31.

A	CORRECT
B	Calculated area of circle incorrectly
C	Calculated area of square incorrectly
D	Chose a density equal to 50 seeds/ft²
E	CORRECT
E	CORRECT
G	CORRECT

32.

A	Divided 26.5 by 5
B	CORRECT
C	Divided 26,500 by 5.1
D	Multiplied 5.1 times 26,500

33.

A	Found the ratio of surface area to mass
B	Found the ratio of mass to surface area
C	Found the ratio of volume to mass
D	CORRECT

Go Online!

Quizzes

Students can use *Self-Check Quizzes* to check their understanding of this lesson and have the results sent to you. You can also give *Quiz 5*, which covers the content in Lesson 11-7.

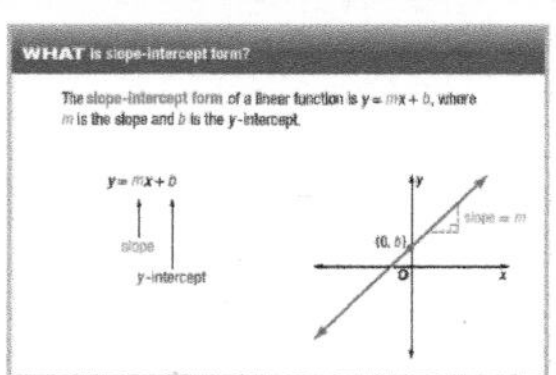

CHAPTER 11

Study Guide and Review

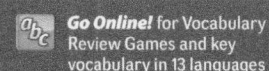

Go Online! for Vocabulary Review Games and key vocabulary in 13 languages

Study Guide

Key Concepts

Cross Sections and Solids of Revolution (Lesson 11-1)

- A cross section is the intersection of a solid and a plane.
- Rotations of two-dimensional objects produce three-dimensional objects.

Volumes of Prisms and Cylinders (Lesson 11-2)

- Volume of prism or cylinder: $V = Bh$

Volumes of Pyramids and Cones (Lesson 11-3)

- Volume of a pyramid: $V = \frac{1}{3}Bh$
- Volume of a cone: $V = \frac{1}{3}\pi r^2 h$

Spheres (Lesson 11-4)

- Surface area of a sphere: $S = 4\pi r^2$
- Volume of a sphere: $V = \frac{4}{3}\pi r^3$

Spherical Geometry (Lesson 11-5)

- Spherical geometry is geometry on a sphere.

Volume and Nonrigid Transformations (Lesson 11-6)

- If two solids are similar, then their volumes are proportional to the cube of the scale factor between them.

Applying Measurements (Lesson 11-7)

- Population density is the measurement of population per unit of area.

9. If two solids are similar, then their volumes are proportional to the cube of the scale factor between them.

FOLDABLES® Study Organizer

Use your Foldable to review the chapter. Working with a partner can be helpful. Ask for clarification of concepts as needed.

Key Vocabulary

cross section (p. 797)	oblique solid (p. 796)
density (p. 842)	pole (p. 819)
Euclidean geometry (p. 827)	population density (p. 841)
great circle (p. 819)	right solid (p. 795)
hemisphere (p. 819)	solid of revolution (p. 798)
non-Euclidean geometry (p. 828)	spherical geometry (p. 827)

Vocabulary Check

State whether each sentence is *true* or *false*. If *false*, replace the underlined term to make a true sentence.

1. Euclidean geometry deals with a system of points, great circles (lines), and spheres (planes). false, spherical geometry
2. Similar solids have exactly the same shape but not necessarily the same size. true
3. A cross section is the intersection of a solid and a plane. true
4. A great circle separates a sphere into two congruent hemispheres. true
5. The perpendicular distance from the base of a geometric figure to the opposite vertex, parallel side, or parallel surface is the altitude. true
6. Population density is the population per unit of area. true
7. A(n) oblique solid has a base that is not perpendicular to the edges. true
8. A composite solid is a three-dimensional figure that is composed of simpler figures. true

Concept Check

9. Explain how the volumes of two similar solids are related.
10. Define non-Euclidean geometry in terms of Euclidean geometry. See margin.
11. Explain how to find the volume of a composite solid. See margin.

FOLDABLES® Study Organizer

A completed Foldable for this chapter should include the Key Concepts related to surface area and volume.

Key Vocabulary ELL

The page reference after each word denotes where that term was first introduced. If students have difficulty answering questions 1–7, remind them that they can use these page references to refresh their memories about the vocabulary terms.

Have students work in pairs to discuss each term in the Key Vocabulary list as they complete the Vocabulary Check. Encourage students to review using their notes and the text.

You can use the detailed reports in ALEKS to automatically monitor students' progress and pinpoint remediation needs prior to the chapter test.

10. Non-Euclidean geometries assume that at least one of the postulates from Euclidean geometry fails.
11. The volume of the composite solid is the sum of the volumes of each of the simpler solids that make up the composite solid.

Answering the Essential Question

Before answering the Essential Question, have students review their answers to the *Building on the Essential Question* exercises found throughout the chapter.

- How can studying the cross sections of three-dimensional figures help you understand the properties of the figures? (p. 800)
- How can the relationships between two-dimensional and three-dimensional figures help you solve problems? (p. 807)
- Why is it helpful to have different formulas when finding volume? (p. 812)

Go Online!

Vocabulary Review

Students can use the *Vocabulary Review Games* to check their understanding of the vocabulary terms in this chapter. Students should refer to the *Student-Built Glossary* they have created as they went through the chapter to review important terms. You can also give a *Vocabulary Test* over the content of this chapter.

Lesson-by-Lesson Review

Intervention If the given examples are not sufficient to review the topics covered by the questions, remind students that the lesson references tell them where to review that topic in their textbook.

Two-Day Option Have students complete the Lesson-by-Lesson Review. Then you can use McGraw-Hill eAssessment to customize another review worksheet that practices all the objectives of this chapter or only the objectives on which your students need more help.

CHAPTER 11

Study Guide and Review *Continued*

Lesson-by-Lesson Review

11-1 Cross Sections and Solids of Revolution

G.GMD.4

Describe each cross section.

12. 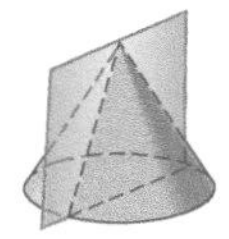 triangle

13. 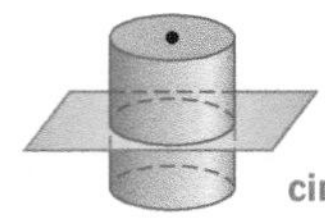 circle

14. **CAKE** The cake shown is cut in half. Describe the cross section of the cake. **rectangle**

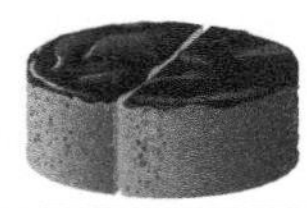

Example 1

Describe the cross sections formed when a plane parallel to the base and a plane perpendicular to the base intersect the solid.

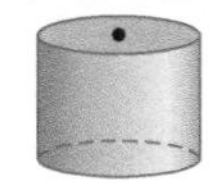

When a plane perpendicular to the base intersects the solid, the cross section is a rectangle.
When a plane parallel to the base intersects the solid, the cross section is a circle.

11-2 Volumes of Prisms and Cylinders

G.GMD.1, G.GMD.3, G.MG.3

15. The volume of a cylinder is 770 cm^3. It has a height of 5 centimeters. Find its radius. **7 cm**

16. Find the volume of the triangular prism. **972 cm^3**

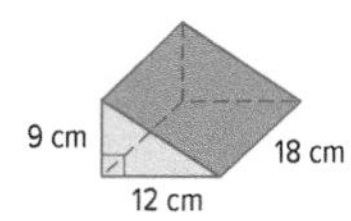

17. **TRAILERS** A semitruck trailer is basically a rectangular prism. A typical height for the inside of these trailers is 108 inches. If the trailer is 8 feet wide and 20 feet long, what is the volume of the trailer? **1440 ft^3**

Example 2

Find the volume of the cylinder.

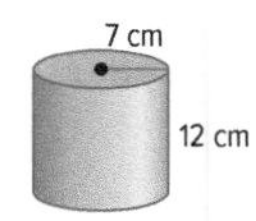

$V = \pi r^2 h$ — Volume of a cylinder

$= \pi(7)^2(12)$ — $r = 7$ and $h = 12$

≈ 1847.5 — Use a calculator.

The volume is approximately 1847.5 cubic centimeters.

11-3 Volumes of Pyramids and Cones

G.GMD.1, G.GMD.3

18. Find the volume of a cone that has a radius of 1 centimeter and a height of 3.4 centimeters. **3.6 cm^3**

19. Find the volume of the regular pyramid. **18 cm^3**

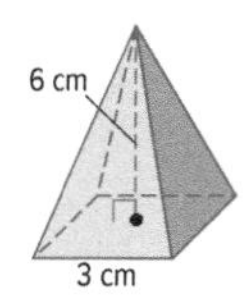

20. **ARCHITECTURE** The Great Pyramid measures 756 feet on each side of the base and the height is 481 feet. Find the volume of the pyramid. **91,636,272 ft^3**

Example 3

Find the volume of the pyramid.

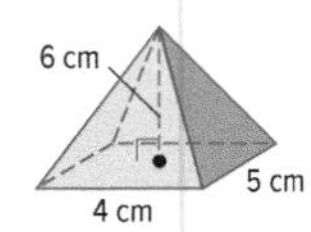

$V = \frac{1}{3}Bh$ — Volume of a pyramid

$= \frac{1}{3}(4 \cdot 5)(6)$ — $B = 4 \cdot 5$ and $h = 6$

$= 40$ — Simplify.

The volume is 40 cubic centimeters.

Go Online!

The most up-to-date resources available for your program can be found at connectED.mcgraw-hill.com.

11-4 Spheres

G.GMD.3, G.MG.3

Find the surface area of each figure.

21. 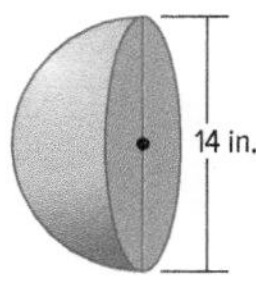

461.8 in^2

22. 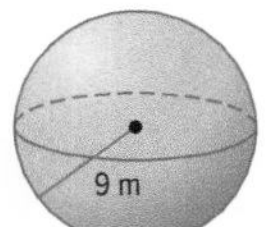

1017.9 m^2

Find the volume of each sphere or hemisphere. Round to the nearest tenth.

23. hemisphere: circumference of great circle = 24π m 3619.1 m^3
24. sphere: area of great circle = 55π in^2 1708.6 in^3
25. **CONSTRUCTION** Cement is poured into a hemisphere that is 6 feet across. What is the volume of cement used? 56.5 ft^3

Example 4

Find the surface area and volume of the sphere. Round to the nearest tenth.

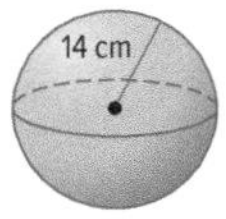

$S = 4\pi r^2$	Surface area of a sphere
$= 4\pi(14)^2$	Substitute.
≈ 2463	Use a calculator.

The surface area is about 2463 square centimeters.

$V = \frac{4}{3}\pi r^3$	Volume of a sphere
$= \frac{4}{3}\pi(14)^3$	Replace r with 14.
$\approx 11{,}494\ cm^3$	Use a calculator.

The volume is about 11,494 cubic centimeters.

11-5 Spherical Geometry

Name each of the following on sphere *A*. 26–31. See margin.

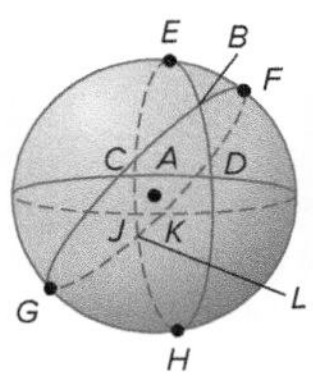

26. two lines containing point *C*
27. a segment containing point *H*
28. a triangle containing point *B*
29. two lines containing point *L*
30. a segment containing point *J*
31. a triangle containing point *K*

32. **MARBLES** Determine whether figure *y* on the sphere shown is a line in spherical geometry. no

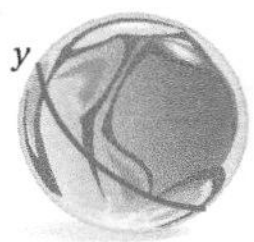

Example 5

Name each of the following on sphere *A*.

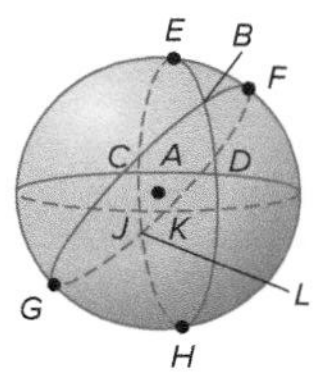

a. two lines containing point *D*
$\overleftrightarrow{EH}$, $\overleftrightarrow{CK}$

b. a segment containing point *E*
$\overline{DJ}$

Additional Answers

26. $\overleftrightarrow{FG}$, $\overleftrightarrow{DJ}$
27. $\overline{DL}$
28. $\triangle CBD$
29. $\overleftrightarrow{HE}$, $\overleftrightarrow{GF}$
30. $\overline{KC}$
31. $\triangle JKL$

Go Online!

Anticipation Guide

Students should complete the *Chapter 11 Anticipation Guide*, and discuss how their responses have changed now that they have completed Chapter 11.

Before the Test

Have students complete the Study Notebook Tie it Together activity to review topics and skills presented in the chapter.

CHAPTER 11

Study Guide and Review *Continued*

11-6 Volume and Nonrigid Transformations

G.GMD.1

Find *x* for each pair of similar solids.

33.

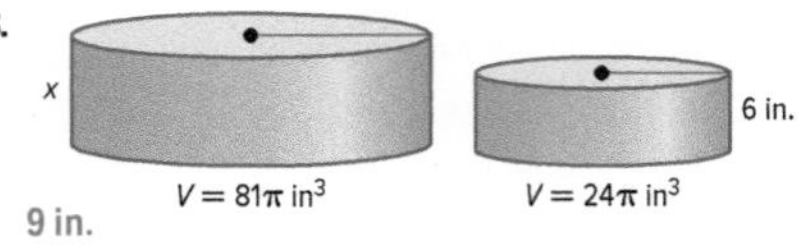

34.

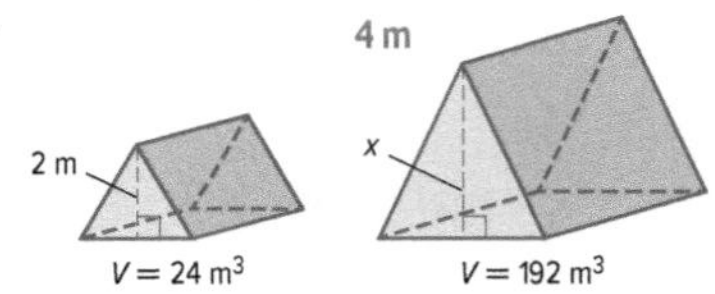

35. **DIMENSIONAL ANALYSIS** Two rectangular prisms are similar. The height of the first prism is 8 inches, and the height of the other prism is 2 feet. If the volume of the first prism is 64 cubic inches, what is the volume of the other prism? **1728 in^3**

Example 6

The rectangular prisms below are similar. Find the height *h* of the smaller prism.

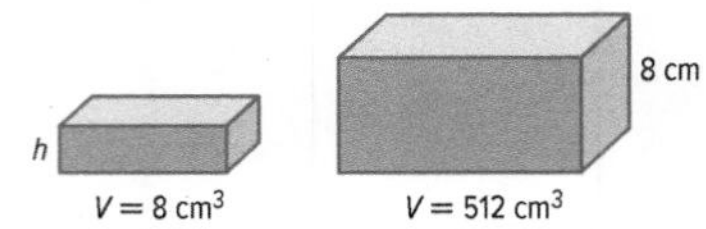

Write a ratio comparing volumes. Then find the scale factor and use it to find *h*.

$\frac{\text{volume of small prism}}{\text{volume of large prism}} = \frac{8}{512}$ Write a ratio comparing volumes.

$= \frac{1}{64}$ Simplify.

$= \frac{1^3}{4^3}$ The scale factor is 1:4.

Ratio of heights → $\frac{h}{8} = \frac{1}{4}$ ← Scale factor

$h = 2$ Solve for *h*.

11-7 Applying Measurements

G.MG.2

36. **DEER** The table below shows the fall deer population and land area for four different counties. Order the counties from greatest to least population density of deer. **C, A, B, D**

County	Deer Population	Land Area (mi^2)
A	9512	232
B	18,720	720
C	55,366	893
D	21,546	1,197

37. Singapore has a population of about 5,535,000 people and a land area of 719 square kilometers. Find the population density. **≈7698 people per km^2**

Example 7

Alaska and New Jersey have the smallest and greatest population density, respectively, of any U.S. state. Determine the population density of each state.

U.S. State	Population	Land Area (mi^2)
Alaska	738,432	570,641
New Jersey	8,958,013	7,354

Calculate population density with the formula population density $= \frac{\text{population}}{\text{land area}}$.

The population density of Alaska is $\frac{738{,}432}{570{,}641}$ or about 1.3 people per square mile.

The population density of New Jersey is $\frac{8{,}958{,}013}{7{,}354}$ or about 1218.1 people per square mile.

Additional Answers (Practice Test)

19. Similar; all of the sides are not equal so the cubes are not congruent. The ratio of the larger cube's side to the smaller cube's side is always 4, so they are similar.

Go Online!

eAssessment

Customize and create multiple versions of chapter tests and answer keys that align to your standards. Tests can be delivered on paper or online.

CHAPTER 11
Practice Test

Go Online! for another Chapter Test

Identify the shape of the cross section.

1. the intersection of a square pyramid and a plane perpendicular to the base and through the vertex triangle
2. the intersection of a cube and a plane parallel to the base square

Identify the solid generated by rotating each two-dimensional shape around the given axis.

3. 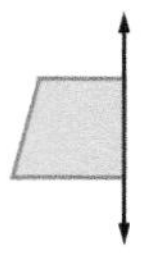
truncated cone

4. 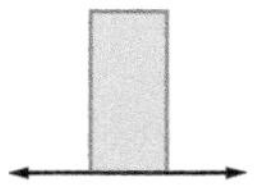
cylinder

5. Describe the cross section. ellipse
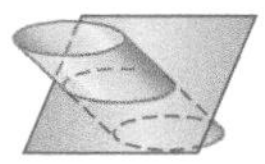

Find the volume of each prism or cylinder. Round to the nearest tenth if necessary.

6. 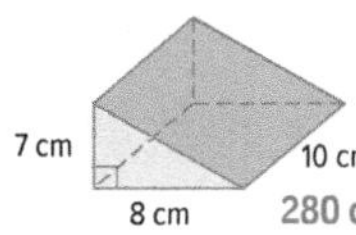

280 cm^3

7. 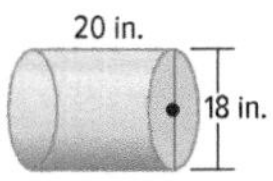

5089.4 in.^{3}

Find the volume of each cone or pyramid. Round to the nearest tenth if necessary.

8. 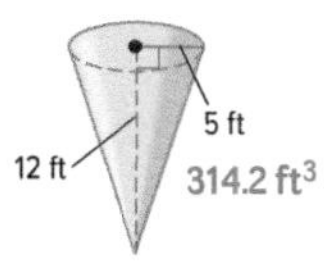

314.2 ft^3

9. 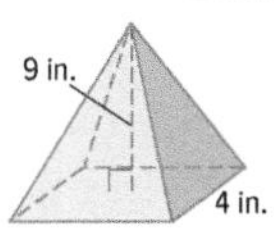

48 in.^{3}

10. **CANDLES** A circular pillar candle is 2.8 inches wide and 6 inches tall. What is the volume of the candle? Round to the nearest tenth if necessary. 36.9 in^3

11. **TEA** A tea bag is shaped like a regular square pyramid. Each edge of the base is 4 centimeters, and the slant height is 5 centimeters. What is the volume of the tea bag in square centimeters? Round to the nearest tenth if necessary. 24.5 cm^3

12. **SOFTBALL** A regulation softball has a circumference of 12 inches. What is the volume of the softball? 29.2 in^3

13. **EARTH** Earth's radius is approximately 6400 kilometers. What are the surface area and volume of the Earth? Round to the nearest whole number. 514,718,540 km^2; 1,098,066,219,444 km^3
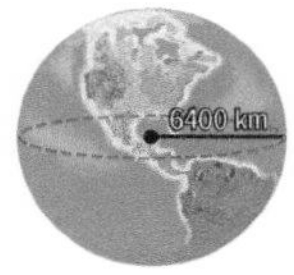

Name each of the following on sphere A.

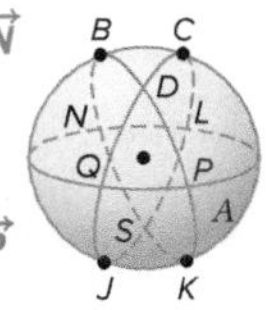

14. two lines containing point S $\overleftrightarrow{JL}$, $\overleftrightarrow{KN}$
15. a segment containing point L $\overline{CS}$
16. a triangle $\triangle DQP$
17. two lines containing point D $\overleftrightarrow{QC}$, $\overleftrightarrow{BP}$
18. a segment containing point P $\overline{DK}$
19. Are these two cubes *similar*, *congruent*, or *neither*? Explain your reasoning. See margin.

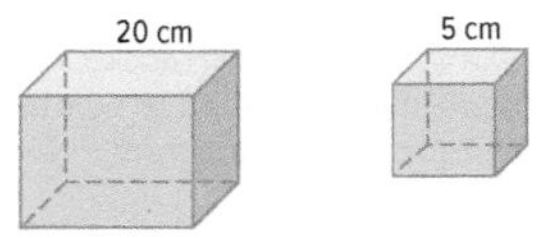

20. Two similar cylinders have heights of 75 centimeters and 25 centimeters. What is the ratio of the volume of the large cylinder to the volume of the small cylinder? 27:1

21. **BAKING** Two spherical pieces of cookie dough have radii of 3 centimeters and 5 centimeters, respectively. The pieces are combined to form one large spherical piece of dough. What is the approximate radius of the new sphere of dough? Round to the nearest tenth. 5.3 cm

22. **ALGEBRA** A rectangular prism has a base with side lengths x and $x + 3$ and height $2x$. Find the volume of the prism. $2x^3 + 6x^2$

23. **TRANSPORTATION** The traffic cone is 19 inches tall and has a radius of 5 inches. Find the volume. 497.4 in^3

24. **CATTLE** In Lewis County, New York, there were 55,509 cattle and calves on 181,741 acres of farmland in 2012. Find the population density of cattle and calves. 0.31 cattle and calves per acre

Go Online!

Chapter Tests

You can use premade leveled *Chapter Tests* to differentiate assessment for your students. Students can also take self-checking *Chapter Tests* to plan and prepare for chapter assessments.

Form	Type	Level
1	MC	AL
2A	MC	OL
2B	FR	OL
2C	FR	OL
3	FR	BL
Vocabulary Test		
Extended-Response Test		

MC = multiple-choice questions
FR = free-response questions

RtI Response to Intervention

Use the Intervention Planner to help you determine your Response to Intervention.

Intervention Planner

TIER 1 On Level OL

IF students miss 25% of the exercises or less,

THEN choose a resource:

SE Lessons 11-1 through 11-7

Go Online!
- Skills Practice
- Chapter Project
- Self-Check Quizzes

TIER 2 Strategic Intervention AL
Approaching grade level

IF students miss 50% of the exercises,

THEN choose a resource:

Quick Review Math Handbook

Go Online!
- Study Guide and Intervention
- Extra Examples
- Personal Tutors
- Homework Help

TIER 3 Intensive Intervention
2 or more grades below level

IF students miss 75% of the exercises,

THEN choose a resource:

Use *Math Triumphs, Geometry*

Go Online!
- Extra Examples
- Personal Tutors
- Homework Help
- Review Vocabulary

Launch

Objective Apply concepts and skills from this chapter in a real-world setting.

Teach

Ask:

- If the smallest candle is 2 inches wide, what is its radius? Sample answer: 1 inch
- How can you find the height, if you are given the volume? Sample answer: Use the formulas for volume and solve for *h*.
- What would the dimensions of the soap be if they added 1 inch to the length? What are the dimensions of the travel soap? Sample answer: The new dimensions would be 4 by 2 by 1. The travel size is 1.5 by 1 by 0.5.
- What do you need to know before you can solve the second problem in Part B? Sample answer: the radius of the smallest sphere of soap
- How many cubic inches are in one bar of soap? How many cubic inches are in 1 pound? Sample answer: 18 in^3; 72 in^3

The Performance Task focuses on the following content standards and standards for mathematical practice.

Dual Coding

Parts	Content Standards	MP Mathematical Practices
A	G.GMD.3	1, 6
B	G.GMD.3	1, 4, 6
C	G.MG.3	1, 4
D	G.MG.2	1, 4, 6

CHAPTER 11
Preparing for Assessment

Performance Task

Provide a clear solution to each part of the task. Be sure to show all of your work, include all relevant drawings, and justify your answers.

APPLY MATH Wax & Suds, Inc. makes a variety of soaps and candles.

Part A

Wax & Suds sells a variety of sizes of candles in metal cylindrical tins. The smallest tin is 3 inches tall and 2 inches wide. The medium tin is 4 inches tall and 3 inches wide. The largest tin is 5 inches tall and 4 inches wide. When pouring the candles, they always leave one half inch of space at the top. Write your answers in terms of π.

1. Determine the volume of wax that will be poured into each size tin. small: 2.5π in^3; medium: 7.875π in^3; large: 18π in^3

Part B

Wax & Suds make a line of speciality candles by pouring candle wax into a variety of molds. They have a cone-shaped mold that is 4 inches wide at the base and has a volume of 8π cubic inches. They also make a 3-inch wide square pyramid with a volume of 15 cubic inches. They have spherical molds in several different sizes.

2. When they pour the cone and pyramid candles, they insert the wick through the height of the figure and leave 1 inch of wick above the top of the wax. Can the employees cut wicks of the same length for use in each candle? Explain. No; the heights are different, the wick for the cone should be 7 in. and 6 in. for the pyramid.
3. The smallest sphere they sell has a volume of 4.5π cubic inches. If Wax & Suds adds 3 inches to the diameter of the spherical candle, determine how much greater the volume will be. Write your answers in terms of π. 31.5π in^3
4. Sometimes, they add a decorative glaze to their candles. Determine the surface area of a spherical candle with a diameter of 4 inches. Write your answer in terms of π. 16π

Part C

Wax & Suds makes bars of soap that are shaped like rectangular prisms in two different sizes. Their regular size is 3 inches long, 2 inches wide, and 1 inch tall. A travel size has dimensions that are exactly half of the larger size.

5. How much greater would the volume of soap be if they added 1 inch to the length of the regular size bar? 2 in^3
6. What is the difference in volume between the travel size bar and the regular bar? 5.25 in^3

Part D

Wax & Suds uses liquid fragrance to scent their candles. They use 2 ounces of scent per 1 pound of soap. One pound of soap makes 4 regular bars of soap.

7. Determine how many cubic inches of soap are used per ounce of scent. 12 in^3 soap per 1 oz scent

Levels of Complexity Chart

Parts	Level 1	Level 2	Level 3
A	●		
B			●
C		●	
D			●

Go Online! eBook

Interactive Student Guide

Refer to *Interactive Student Guide* for an additional Performance Task.

Test-Taking Strategy

Example

Read the question. Then fill in the correct answer on the answer document provided by your teacher or on a sheet of paper.

Luther is building a model rocket for a science fair project. He attaches a nose cone to a cylindrical body to form the rocket's fuselage. The rocket has a diameter of 4 inches and a total height (including the nose cone) of 29 inches. The nose cone is 7 inches tall. What is the surface area of the rocket?

A 333.0 in^2

B 334.7 in^2

C 422.7 in^2

D 694.7 in^2

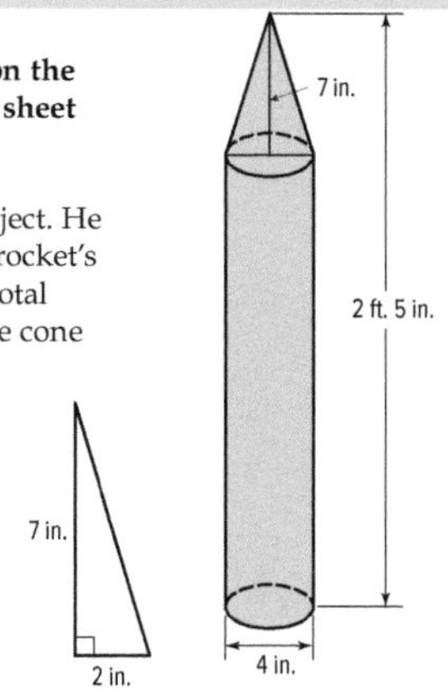

Read the problem statements carefully.

Step 1 **What are you being asked to solve? What information is given?** You are asked to find the surface area of the rocket, which is a composite figure. You are given the total height of the rocket including the nose cone, the height of the nose cone, and the diameter of the rocket.

Step 2 **How can you make your drawing as clear as possible? What can you add to your drawing as you work?**
Label the drawing with all of the information given in the problem. As you make calculations, add the information to the drawing. When the drawing is complete, find the surface area of the cylinder and the surface area of the cone. The surface area of the rocket is the sum of these.

Step 3 **What is the correct answer?**
The correct answer is B.

Test-Taking Tip

Making a Drawing

Making a drawing can be a very helpful way for you to visualize how to solve a problem. Sketch the object and label the measurements that you know as a step in problem solving. The information that is combined in your sketch can then be used to perform calculations.

Apply the Strategy

Read the problem. Identify what you need to know. Then use the information in the problem to solve.

From a single point in her yard, Marti measures and marks distances of 18 feet and 30 feet with stakes for two sides of her garden. How far apart should the two stakes be if the garden will be rectangular shaped? C

A 18 ft

B 30 ft

C 35 ft

D 48 ft

Answer the questions below. See margin.

a. What are you being asked to solve? What information is given?

b. How can you make your drawing as clear as possible? What can you add to your drawing as you work?

c. What is the correct answer?

b. Sample answer: I drew the distances and labeled the right angles. I used the Pythagorean Theorem to find the distance between the stakes and added this to the drawing.

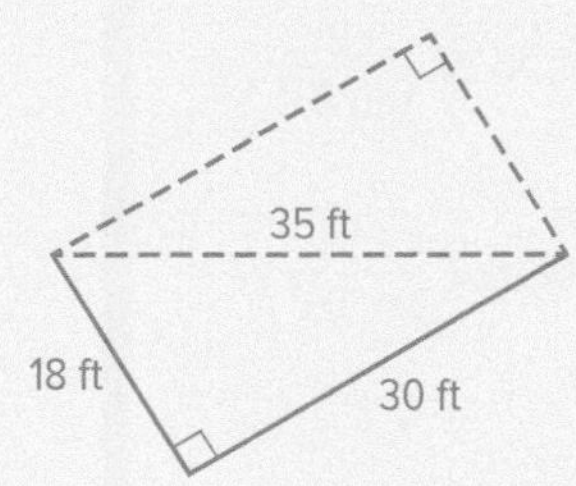

c. C

Test-Taking Strategy

Step 1 Read the problem. Identify what you are being asked to solve and what key information is given. Determine whether a drawing would help visualize the problem.

Step 2 Sketch and label the drawing, adding all information given in the problem. Add any information you gain while performing intermediate calculations.

Step 3 Solve the problem. Check your solution if time permits.

Need Another Example?

A passing boat is 310 feet from the base of a lighthouse. The angle of depression from the top of the lighthouse is 24°. Which of the following is closest to the height of the lighthouse? B

A 126.1 ft

B 138.0 ft

C 283.2 ft

D 696.3 ft

Ask:

a. What are you being asked to solve? What information is given? Would visualizing the scenario help you solve the problem? The height of the lighthouse. Yes, it would help to see what steps to take to solve the problem.

b. How can you make your drawing as clear as possible? What can you add to your drawing as you work? Label the drawing with any information given and add information from intermediate calculations.

c. What is the correct answer? B

Additional Answer (Apply the Strategy)

a. the distance between the two stakes; the distance from a single point that the two stakes are placed and that the first point and the two stakes should be corners of a rectangle.

Go Online!

The most up-to-date resources available for your program can be found at connectED.mcgraw-hill.com.

Diagnose Student Errors

Survey student responses for each item. Class trends may indicate common errors and misconceptions.

3.

A	CORRECT
B	Found surface area of hemisphere
C	Found surface area of entire sphere
D	Found volume of entire sphere

5.

A	Forgot that a line is a great circle
B	Did not draw lines (great circles)
C	CORRECT
D	Did not understand that a counterexample must show two great circles through points

6.

A	Omitted factor of $\frac{1}{3}$
B	Used $\frac{9}{\tan 33°}$ for height rather than 9 tan 33°
C	CORRECT
D	Used 9 sin 33° for height rather than 9 tan 33°

7.

A	CORRECT
B	Did not consider a cut parallel to the base
C	Did not consider a cut perpendicular to the base and not through the vertex
D	Did not consider a cut perpendicular to the base and through the vertex
E	CORRECT

9.

A	Assumed ratio of volumes equals scale factor
B	Added 180 to volume of smaller cylinder
C	Assumed ratio of volumes equals ratio of surface areas
D	CORRECT

CHAPTER 11

Preparing for Assessment

Cumulative Review

Read each question. Then fill in the correct answer on the answer document provided by your teacher or on a sheet of paper.

1. A square pyramid has a base length of 20 meters and a slant height of 14 meters. What is the volume of the pyramid, in cubic meters?

1306.4

2. The bases of the prism are right isosceles triangles.

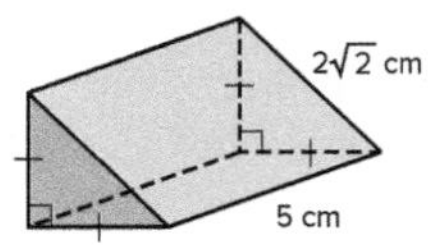

What is the volume of the prism in cubic centimeters?

10

3. The figure shows the dimensions of a tent in the shape of a hemisphere.

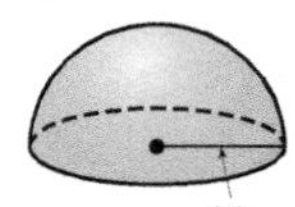

Which is the best estimate of the tent's volume? A

- A 134 ft^3
- B 151 ft^3
- C 201 ft^3
- D 268 ft^3

4. The city of Chicago has a total land area of 227.13 square miles. As of 2010, the number of residents living within the city limits was 2,695,598. What is the population density of Chicago rounded to the nearest whole number?

11,868

5. Kaden said that in spherical geometry, any two points determine a unique line. Which figure is a counterexample to Kaden's statement? C

A
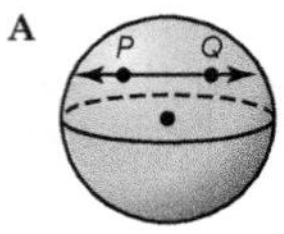

C
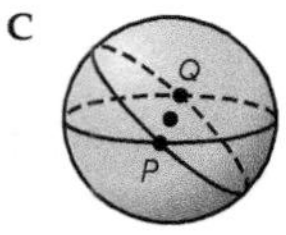

B
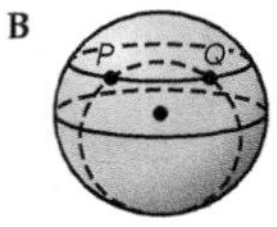

D
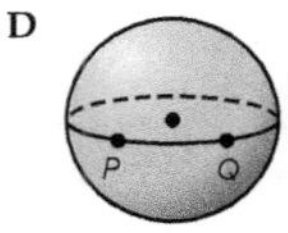

6. The lateral face of a right circular cone makes an angle of 33° with the base of the cone. The cone's radius is 9 inches. Which of the following is closest to the volume of the cone? C

- A 1487 in^3
- B 1176 in^3
- C 496 in^3
- D 416 in^3

7. A café sells frozen yogurt in the shape of a square pyramid. LaTasha uses a knife to make one straight cut through her serving of frozen yogurt. Which of the following is not a possible shape of the resulting cross section? Select all that apply. A, E

- A circle
- B square
- C trapezoid
- D triangle
- E rhombus

Test-Taking Tip

Question 6 Make a sketch of the cone and use a trigonometric ratio to find the height of the cone. Then use the volume formula.

10.

A	Used 2 tan 20° for base instead of $\frac{2}{\tan 20°}$
B	Used $\frac{2}{\cos 20°}$ for base instead of $\frac{2}{\tan 20°}$
C	CORRECT
D	Used $\frac{2}{\sin 20°}$ for base instead of $\frac{2}{\tan 20°}$

11.

A	Used $r = 6$ in.
B	CORRECT
C	Used formula for lateral area instead of volume
D	Used formula for volume of cone instead of cylinder

Go Online!

Standardized Test Practice

Students can take self-checking tests in standardized format to plan and prepare for assessments.

Go Online! for Standardized Test Practice

8. What is the area of the curved surface of a hemisphere with diameter 10 inches? Write your answer in terms of pi. 50π

9. Two similar cylinders have surface areas of 320 square feet and 500 square feet. The volume of the smaller cylinder is 640 cubic feet. What is the volume of the larger cylinder? D

- A 800 ft^3
- B 820 ft^3
- C 1000 ft^3
- D 1250 ft^3

10. The figure shows the side panel of a skateboard ramp.

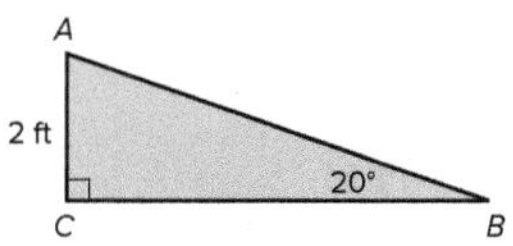

Which of the following is closest to the area of the panel? C

- A 0.7 ft^2
- B 2.1 ft^2
- C 5.5 ft^2
- D 5.8 ft^2

11. The figure shows the dimensions of a cylindrical vase. Anthony wants to pour water into the vase so that the volume of the water is 100 cubic inches.

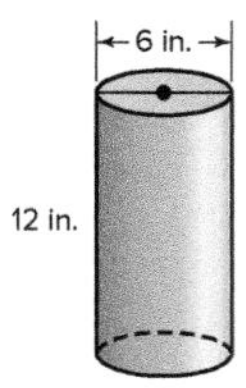

To the nearest tenth of an inch, what should be the height of the water in the vase? B

- A 0.9 in.
- B 3.5 in.
- C 5.3 in.
- D 10.6 in.

12.

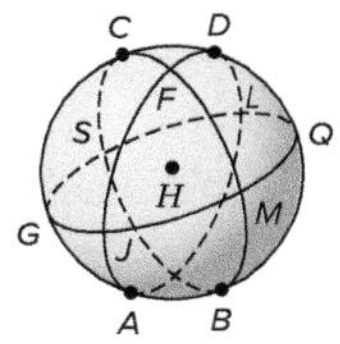

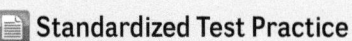

Identify two lines containing point Q, a segment containing point L, and a triangle in the sphere above. Sample answers: lines LM and DB, segment DA, triangle FJM

13. Explain how a plane could intersect a square pyramid to produce the following cross sections. Write *not possible* if the cross section would not be possible.

a. hexagon not possible

b. square parallel to base

c. trapezoid perpendicular to the base but not through the vertex

d. triangle perpendicular to the base and through the vertex

14. **MULTI-STEP** Marilda has a block of modeling clay that is 8 inches by 5 inches by 3 inches. She is experimenting with different shapes that can be made from the clay. Give your answers to the nearest tenth.

a. What is the volume of her clay? 120 in^3

b. What size cube could she make from the clay? 4.9 in.

c. If she rolled the clay into a ball, what would its diameter be? 6.1 in.

d. If she made two balls of the same size, what would their diameter be? 4.9 in.

e. If she rolled a cylinder with a diameter of 3 inches, how long would it be? 17.0 in.

f. If she rolled a cylinder with a diameter of 6 inches, how long would it be? 4.2 in.

g. Suppose Marilda wants to make a square pyramid with a 6×6 in. base. How tall would it be? 10 in.

h. If Marilda made a cone of the same height instead of a pyramid, would the diameter of the base be less than, equal to, or greater than 6 inches? greater than

Need Extra Help?

If you missed Question...	1	2	3	4	5	6	7	8	9	10	11	12	13	14
Go to Lesson...	11-3	11-3	11-4	11-7	11-5	11-3	11-1	11-4	11-2	8-4	11-2	11-5	11-1	11-2, 11-3, 11-4

Exercise Question Types	
Question Type	Exercises
Multiple Choice	3, 5, 6, 9, 10, 11
Multiple Correct Answers	7
Short Response	1, 2, 4, 8, 12, 14
Extended Response	13

Formative Assessment

You can use these pages to benchmark student progress.

Standardized Test Practice

Answer Sheet Practice

Have students simulate taking a standardized test by recording their answers on a practice recording sheet.

Homework Option

Get Ready for Chapter 12 Assign students the exercises on p. 858 as homework to assess whether they possess the prerequisite skills needed for the next chapter.

LEARNSMART®

Use LearnSmart as part of your test-preparation plan to measure student topic retention. You can create a student assignment in LearnSmart for additional practice on these topics.

- Visualize the relation between two-dimensional and three-dimensional objects
- Explain volume formulas and use them to solve problems

Go Online!

eAssessment

Customize and create multiple versions of chapter tests and answer keys that align to your standards. Tests can be delivered on paper or online.

Mid-Chapter Quiz

1. Sample answer:

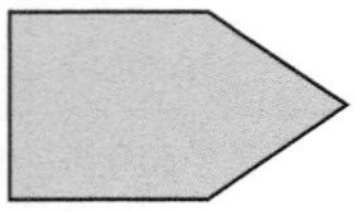

2. Sample answer:

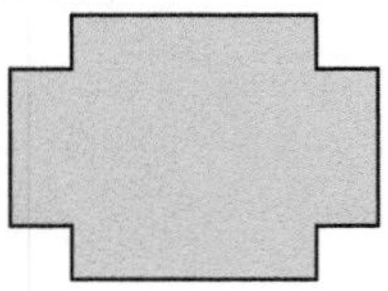

Lesson 11-4

44a. Sample answers:

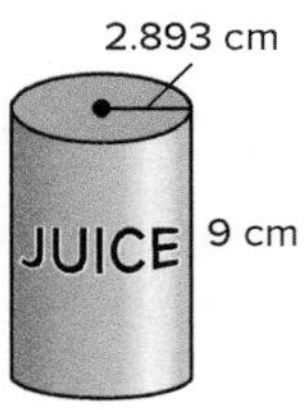

Container A

Container B

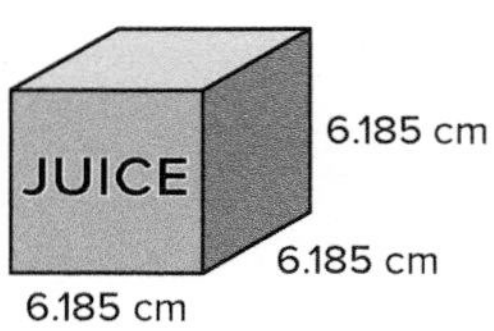

Container C

44b. Sample answers: Container A, ≈27.02 cm^2 per fl oz; Container B, ≈26.48 cm^2 per fl oz; Container C, ≈28.69 cm^2 per fl oz; Of these three, Container B can be made for the lowest materials cost. The lower the surface area to volume ratio, the less packaging used for each fluid ounce of juice it holds. A spherical container with $r = 3.837$ cm would minimize this cost since it would have the least surface area to volume ratio of any shape, ≈ 23.13 cm per fl oz. However, a spherical container would likely be more costly to manufacture than a rectangular container since specially made machinery would be necessary.

Lesson 11-5

30. The circles are congruent. They are not lines in spherical geometry because they are not great circles because they do not have their centers at the center of the sphere.

CHAPTER 12
Probability

SUGGESTED PACING (DAYS)

	Instruction	Review & Assess
7 min.	4	1
9 min.	8	2

Track Your Progress

This chapter focuses on content from the **Conditional Probability and the Rules of Probability** and **Using Probability to Make Decisions** domains

THEN	NOW	NEXT
G.GMD.1 Give an informal argument for the formulas for the circumference of a circle, area of a circle, volume of a cylinder, pyramid, and cone.	**S.CP.1** Describe events as subsets of a sample space using characteristics of the outcomes, or as unions, intersections, or complements of other events.	**S.MD.4** Develop a probability distribution for a random variable defined for a sample space in which probabilities are assigned empirically; find the expected value.
G.GMD.3 Use volume formulas for cylinders, pyramids, cones, and spheres to solve problems.	**S.CP.2** Understand that two events A and B are independent if the probability of A and B occurring together is the product of their probabilities, and use this characterization to determine if they are independent.	**S.MD.5** Weigh the possible outcomes of a decision by assigning probabilities to payoff values and finding expected values.
G.GMD.4 Identify the shapes of two-dimensional cross-sections of three-dimensional objects, and identify three-dimensional objects generated by rotations of two-dimensional objects.	**S.CP.9** Use permutations and combinations to compute probabilities of compound events and solve problems.	**S.MD.6** Use probabilities to make fair decisions.
		S.MD.7 Analyze decisions and strategies using probability concepts.

Standards for Mathematical Practice

All of the Standards for Mathematical Practice will be covered in this chapter. The MP icon notes specific areas of coverage.

MP Teaching the Mathematical Practices

Help students develop the mathematical practices by asking questions like these.

Questioning Strategies As students approach problems in this chapter, help them develop mathematical practices by asking:

Sense-Making
- How can you use permutations with probability?
- How can you use combinations with probability?
- How do you determine truth values of negations, conjunctions, and disjunctions?

Construct Arguments
- How do you find probabilities using length or using area?
- How do you find probabilities of independent and dependent events, of events given the occurrence of other events, or of mutually exclusive events?
- How do you find probabilities of complements?

Modeling
- How do you represent conjunctions and disjunctions using Venn diagrams?
- How would you use a two-way frequency table or contingency table to show the frequencies of data from a survey or experiment classified according to two variables?

Using Tools
- How can you use lists, tables, and tree diagrams to represent sample spaces?
- How do you apply the Fundamental Counting Principle to count outcomes?

Go Online!

StudySync:
SMP Modeling Videos

These demonstrate how to apply the Standards for Mathematical Practice to collaborate, discuss, and solve real-world math problems.

Go Online!

connectED.mcgraw-hill.com

LearnSmart | The Geometer's Sketchpad | Vocabulary | Tutor | Tools | Calculator Resources | Check | Watch

Customize Your Chapter

Use the *Plan & Present*, *Assignment Tracker*, and *Assessment* tools in ConnectED to introduce lesson concepts, assign personalized practice, and diagnose areas of student need.

Differentiated Instruction

Throughout the program, look for the icons to find specialized content designed for your students.

- AL Approaching Level
- OL On Level
- BL Beyond Level
- ELL English Language Learners

Personalize

Differentiated Resources

FOR EVERY CHAPTER	AL	OL	BL	ELL
Chapter Readiness Quizzes	●	●	◐	●
Chapter Tests	●	●	●	●
Standardized Test Practice	●	●	●	●
Vocabulary Review Games	●	●	◐	●
Anticipation Guide (English/Spanish)	●	●	◐	●
Student-Built Glossary	●	●	◐	●
Chapter Project	◐	●	●	●
FOR EVERY LESSON	**AL**	**OL**	**BL**	**ELL**
Personal Tutors (English/Spanish)	●	●	◐	●
Graphing Calculator Personal Tutors	●	●	●	●
Step-by-Step Solutions	●	●	◐	●
Self-Check Quizzes	●	●	●	●
5-Minute Check	●	●	●	●
Study Notebook	●	●	●	●
Study Guide and Intervention	●	●		●
Skills Practice (English/Spanish)	●	◐		●
Practice (English/Spanish)	◐	●	●	●
Word Problem Practice	◐	●	●	◐
Enrichment		●	●	●
Extra Examples	●	◐		◐
Interactive Classroom	●	●	●	●

◐ Aligned to this group ● Designed for this group

Engage

Featured IWB Resources

Animations help students make important connections through motion. *Use with Lesson 12-3.*

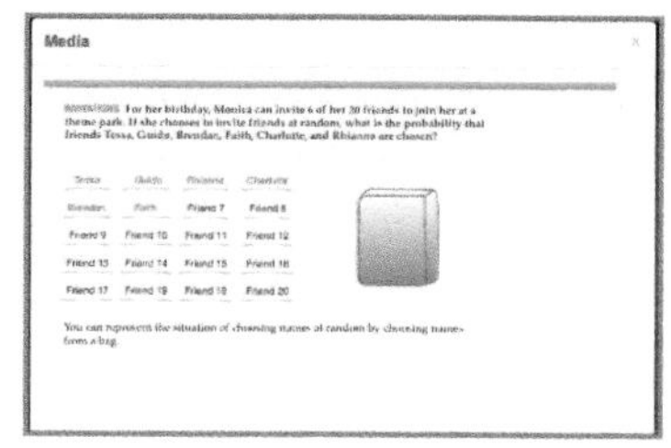

eLessons engage students and help build conceptual understanding of big ideas. *Use with Lessons 12-3 through 12-7.*

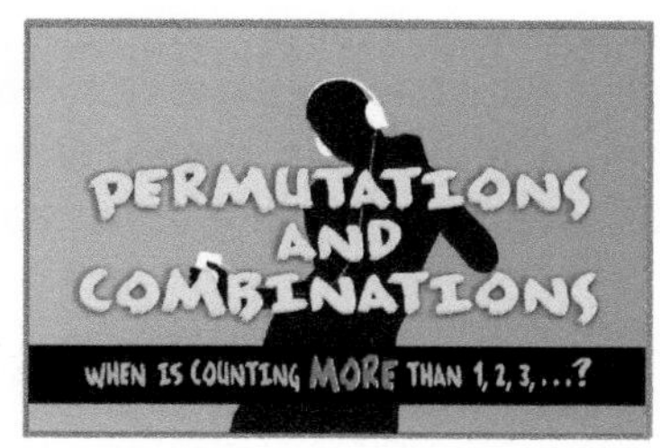

Personal Tutors let you hear a real teacher discuss each step in solving a problem. *Use with Lessons 12-1 through 12-7.*

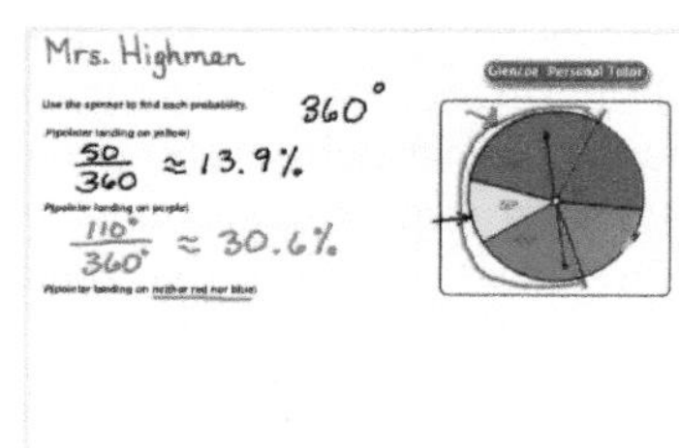

Time Management How long will it take to use these resources? Look for the clock in each lesson interleaf.

Introduce the Chapter

Mathematical Background

A sample space of an experiment is the set of all possible outcomes. The probabilities of independent, dependent, mutually exclusive, not mutually exclusive, and conditional events can be calculated. Geometric probabilities, like the probability of hitting a target, can be calculated using the area. Probability can be determined using the Multiplication Rule the Addition Rule, or two-way frequency tables.

Essential Questions

At the end of this chapter, students should be able to answer the Essential Questions.

- How can we predict the outcomes of events? Sample answers: You can conduct an experiment to determine the chance that the event will occur; you can use the information from previous events; you can use new information that you have gathered.
- How can we quantify predictions? Sample answer: We can calculate or estimate the probability of the outcome occurring.

Apply Math to the Real World

GAMES In this activity, students will use what they already know about probabilities and ratios to explore possible outcomes of games and how this knowledge can help them win. Have students complete this activity individually or in small groups. MP 1

CHAPTER 12

Probability

THEN

You learned about experiments, outcomes, and events. You also found probabilities of simple events.

NOW

In this chapter, you will:

- Represent sample spaces.
- Use permutations and combinations with probability.
- Find probabilities by using length and area.

MP WHY

Games There are many games in which you can increase your chances of winning by being able to draw logical conclusions about which outcomes are most likely.

Use the Mathematical Practices to complete the activity.

1. Sense-Making What are the possible outcomes of a spin or roll?

2. Reasoning If you know the likelihood of all possible outcomes, how can you use that information?

3. Applying Math If you roll a number cube, how often would you predict that you will roll an even number?

4. Use Tools Use the Number Cube tool to roll a number cube 10 times.

5. Discuss Did your prediction match your results? Why or why not?

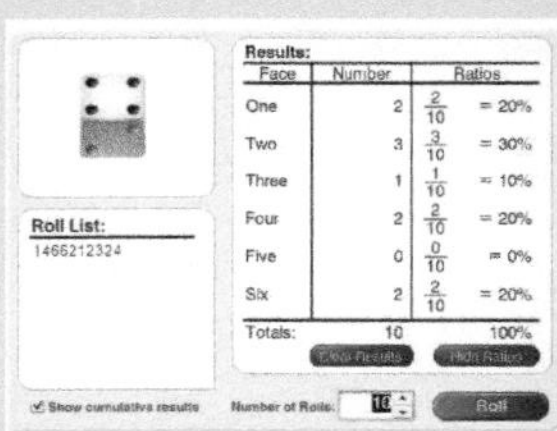

Roll List:
1466212324
Results:
Face
Number
Ratios
One 2 2/10 = 20%
Two 3 3/10 = 30%
Three 1 1/10 = 10%
Four 2 2/10 = 20%
Five 0 0/10 = 0%
Six 2 2/10 = 20%
Totals: 10 100%
Show cumulative results
Number of Rolls:
Roll

Andor Bujdoso/Alamy

Go Online!

Chapter Project

Fair Games Students use what they have learned about probability and expected values to complete a project. This chapter project addresses environmental literacy, as well as several specific skills identified as being essential to student success by the Framework for 21st Century Learning. MP 1, 3, 4

ALEKS®

Your Student Success Tool ALEKS is an adaptive, personalized learning environment that identifies precisely what each student knows and is ready to learn—ensuring student success at all levels.

- Formative Assessment: Dynamic, detailed reports monitor students' progress toward standards mastery.
- Automatic Differentiation: Strengthen prerequisite skills and target individual learning gaps.
- Personalized Instruction: Supplement in-class instruction with personalized assessment and learning opportunities.

Go Online to Guide Your Learning

Explore & Explain

Coin Toss

Use the **Coin Toss** tool to conduct experiments in which you explore probabilities and ratios.

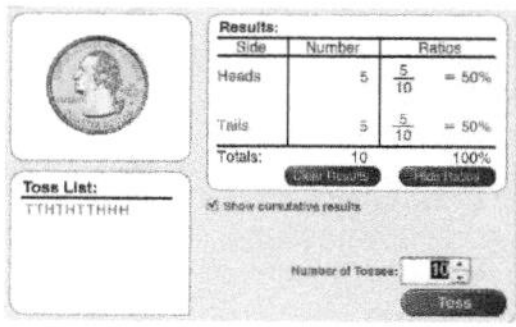

Spinner

Use the **Spinner** tool to explore probability, as discussed in Lesson 12-2.

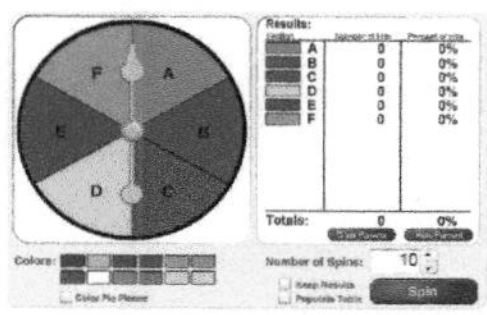

eBook

Interactive Student Guide

Before starting the chapter, answer the **Chapter Focus** preview questions. Check your answers as you complete each lesson. At the end of the chapter, try the **Performance Task**.

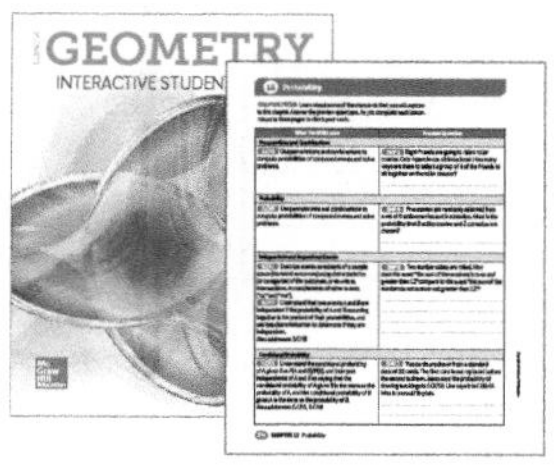

Organize

Foldables

Get organized! Create a **Probability and Measurement Foldable** before you start the chapter to organize your notes about probability.

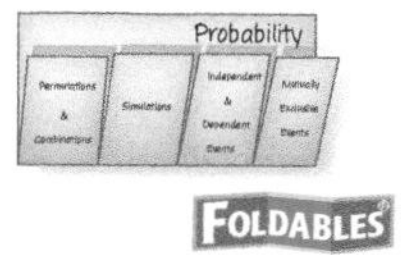

Collaborate

Chapter Project

In the **Fair Games** project, you will use what you have learned about probability and expected values to complete a project that addresses environmental literacy.

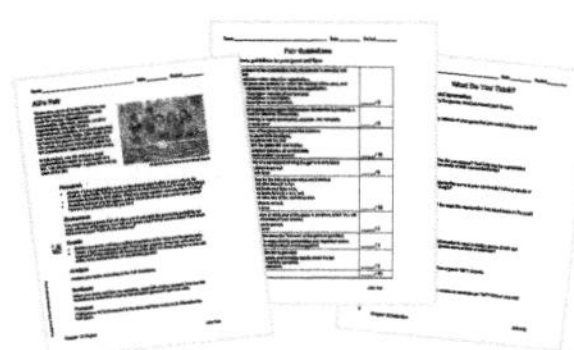

Focus

LEARNSMART

Need help studying? Complete the **Applications of Probability** domain in LearnSmart to review for the chapter test.

ALEKS

You can use the **Polygons and Circles** topic in ALEKS to explore what you know about extending area and what you are ready to learn.*

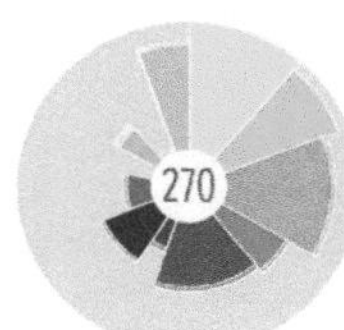

* Ask your teacher if this is part of your program.

Dinah Zike's FOLDABLES

Focus Students write the names of methods of counting and types of probabilities.

Teach After students make their Foldables, have them label the tabs to correspond to the eight lessons in this chapter. Instruct students to take notes while reading each lesson and listening to instruction. They should include definitions of terms and key concepts, as well as diagrams and examples related to the lesson.

When to Use It Use the appropriate tabs as students cover each lesson in this chapter. Students can add to the vocabulary tab during each lesson.

Go Online!

Using VKVs to Support Vocabulary Learning

Practice makes perfect! Find out how to use VKVs to incorporate daily vocabulary practice. MP 5

Get Ready for the Chapter

RtI Response to Intervention

Use the Concept Check results and the Intervention Planner chart to help you determine your Response to Intervention.

Intervention Planner

TIER 1 On Level OL

IF students miss 25% of the exercises or less,

THEN choose a resource:

Go Online!

- Skills Practice, Chapter 1
- Chapter Project
- Self-Check Quizzes

TIER 2 Approaching Level AL

IF students miss 50% of the exercises,

THEN choose a resource:

Go Online!

- Study Guide and Intervention, Ch. 1
- Extra Examples
- Personal Tutors
- Homework Help

Quick Review Math Handbook

TIER 3 Intensive Intervention

IF students miss 75% of the exercises,

THEN use *Math Triumphs, Geometry*

Go Online!

- Extra Examples
- Personal Tutors
- Homework Help
- Review Vocabulary

Get Ready for the Chapter

Go Online! for Vocabulary Review Games and key vocabulary in 13 languages.

Connecting Concepts

Concept Check

Review the concepts used in this chapter by answering each question below.

1. Given $\frac{6}{9} \cdot \frac{1}{2}$, what would be the first step to simplify? **Multiply the numerators and denominators.**
2. Suppose a number cube is rolled. What is the formula to determine the probability of rolling less than a five? **See margin.**
3. If a number cube is rolled, what is the probability that a value greater than 1 will be rolled? $\frac{5}{6}$ **or 83%**
4. If a number cube is rolled, what is the probability that an odd value will be rolled? $\frac{1}{2}$ **or 50%**
5. If a number cube is rolled, what is the probability that a 1 or a 6 will be rolled? $\frac{1}{3}$ **or 33%**
6. The table shows the results of an experiment in which a spinner numbered 1–4 was spun. What is the formula to determine the experimental probability that the spinner will land on 4? **See margin.**

Outcome	Tally	Frequency
1	|||	3
2	~~||||~~ ||	7
3	~~||||~~ |	6
4	||||	4

7. Based on the values in the table, what is the experimental probability that the spinner will land on a 4? $\frac{1}{5}$ **or 20%**
8. Based on the values in the table, what is the experimental probability that the spinner will land on an even number? $\frac{11}{20}$ **or 55%**

Performance Task Preview

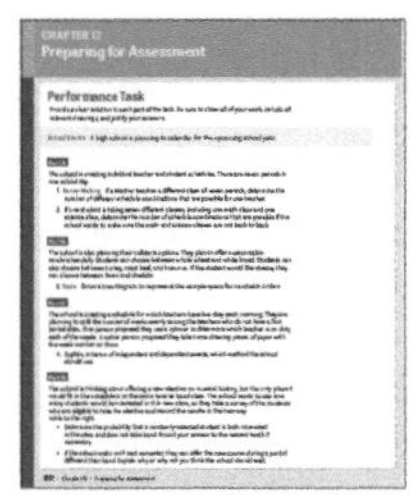

You can use the concepts and skills in the chapter to plan schedules for a school. Understanding probabilities will help you finish the Performance Task at the end of the chapter.

In this Performance Task you will:

- make sense of problems
- construct viable arguments
- model with mathematics
- attend to precision
- look for and express regularity in repeated reasoning

New Vocabulary

English		Español
sample space	p. 859	espacio muestral
tree diagram	p. 859	diagrama de árbol
two-stage experiment	p. 860	experimento de dos pasos
multistage experiment	p. 860	experimentos multietápicos
Fundamental Counting Principle	p. 861	principio fundamental de contar
intersection	p. 866	intersección
complement	p. 867	complemento
permutation	p. 872	permutación
factorial	p. 872	factorial
circular permutation	p. 875	permutación circular
combination	p. 876	combinación
geometric probability	p. 881	probabilidad geométrica
compound event	p. 889	evento compuesto
independent events	p. 889	eventos independientes
dependent events	p. 889	eventos dependientes
mutually exclusive	p. 897	mutuamente exclusivos
conditional probability	p. 903	probabilidad condicional
two-way frequency table	p. 909	tabla de doble enrada o de frecuencias
marginal frequencies	p. 909	frecuencias marginales
joint frequencies	p. 909	frecuencias conjuntas
relative frequency	p. 910	frecuencia relativa

Review Vocabulary

event *evento* one or more outcomes of an experiment

experiment *experimento* a situation involving chance such as flipping a coin or rolling a number cube

Key Vocabulary ELL

Introduce the key vocabulary in the chapter using the routine below.

Define The complement of an event *A* consists of all of the outcomes of a sample space that are not includeed as outcomes of event *A*.

Example If *A* consists of rolling a 1 or a 5 on a die, then the complement of *A* is rolling a 2, 3, 4, or 6.

Ask What is the probability that *A* or its complement occurs? 1

Additional Answers

2. $\dfrac{\text{number of favorable outcomes}}{\text{number of possible outcomes}}$

6. $\dfrac{\text{number of times 4 is spun}}{\text{number of possible outcomes}}$

Representing Sample Spaces

SUGGESTED PACING (DAYS)

90 min.	0.5
45 min.	1.0
	Instruction

Track Your Progress

Objectives

1 Use lists, tables, and tree diagrams to represent sample spaces.

2 Use the Fundamental Counting Principle to count outcomes.

Mathematical Background

The *sample space* of an experiment is the set of all possible outcomes. A sample space can be organized as a list, a table, or a tree diagram. The number of possible outcomes in a sample space can be found by multiplying together the number of possible outcomes at each stage of the event.

THEN	NOW	NEXT
S.CP.9 Use permutations and combinations to compute probabilities of compound events and solve problems.	**S.CP.1** Describe events as subsets of a sample space (the set of outcomes) using characteristics (or categories) of the outcomes, or as unions, intersections, or complements of other events ("or," "and," "not").	**S.CP.2** Understand that two events A and B are independent if the probability of A and B occurring together is the product of their probabilities, and use this characterization to determine if they are independent.

Go Online! All of these resources and more are available at connectED.mcgraw-hill.com

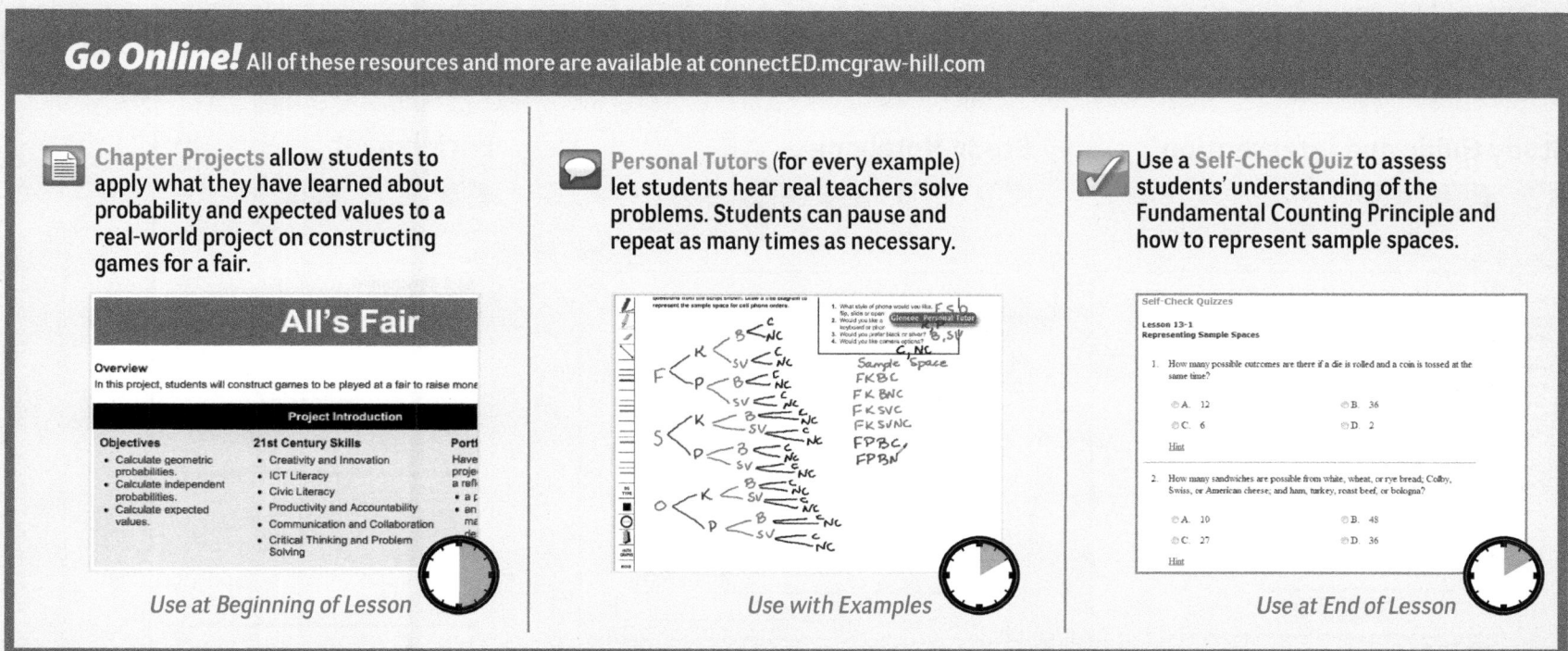

Chapter Projects allow students to apply what they have learned about probability and expected values to a real-world project on constructing games for a fair.

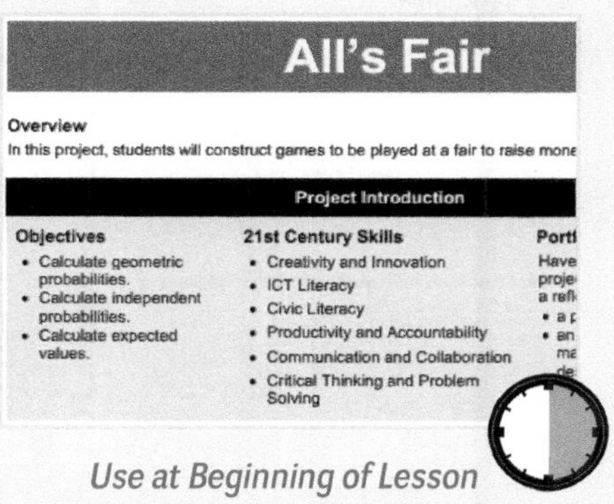

Use at Beginning of Lesson

Personal Tutors (for every example) let students hear real teachers solve problems. Students can pause and repeat as many times as necessary.

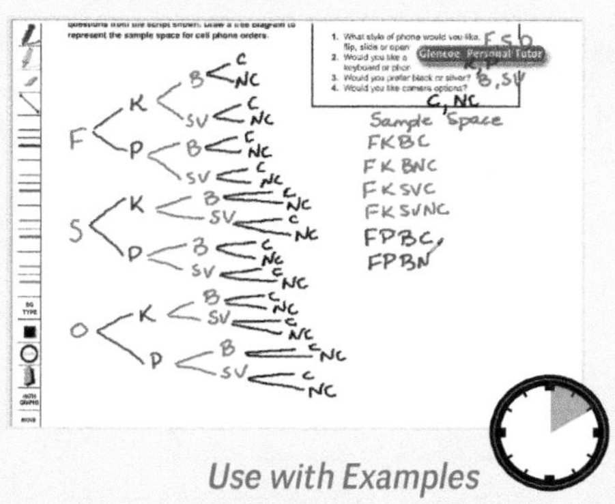

Use with Examples

Use a Self-Check Quiz to assess students' understanding of the Fundamental Counting Principle and how to represent sample spaces.

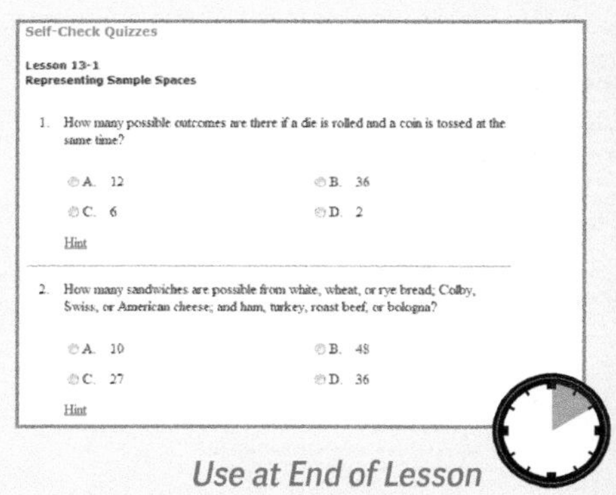

Use at End of Lesson

OER Using Open Educational Resources

Assessment Create your own quizzes using **Yacapaca** or access over 15,000 existing quizzes. Set assignments for your entire class, grade the assignments automatically, and access assessment tools to review your students' progress. *Use a professional development*

Go Online! connectED.mcgraw-hill.com

Worksheets

Differentiate Your Resources

Extra Practice Additional practice or homework; Skills Practice is best for approaching-level students and Practice is best for on-level and beyond-level students

Skills Practice

AL OL ELL

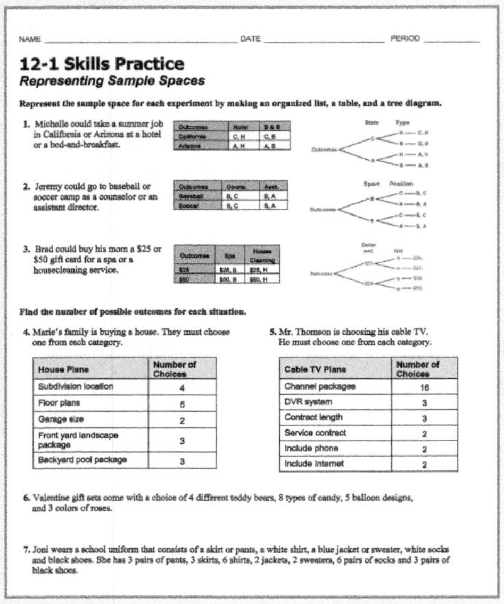
12-1 Skills Practice
Representing Sample Spaces
Represent the sample space for each experiment by making an organized list, a table, and a tree diagram.
Find the number of possible outcomes for each situation.

Practice

AL OL BL ELL

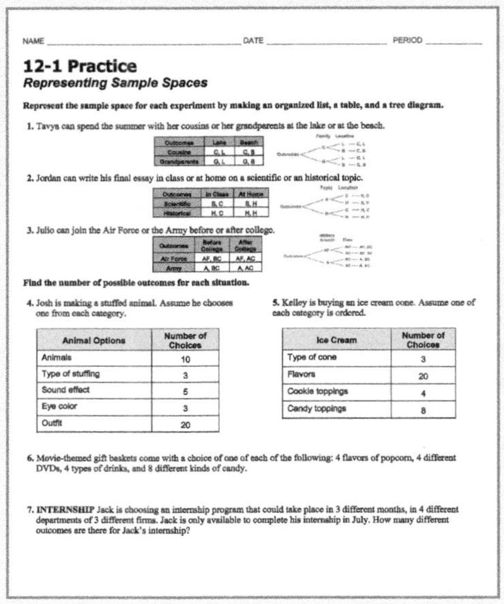
12-1 Practice
Representing Sample Spaces
Represent the sample space for each experiment by making an organized list, a table, and a tree diagram.
Find the number of possible outcomes for each situation.

Word Problem Practice

AL OL BL ELL

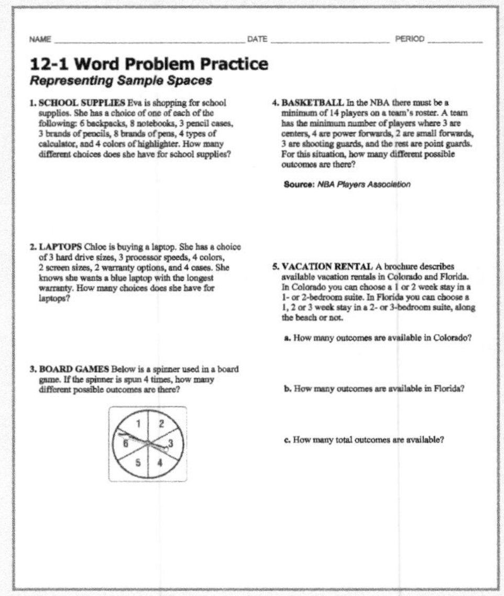
12-1 Word Problem Practice
Representing Sample Spaces

Intervention Reteaching and vocabulary activities that can be used with struggling or absent students and as ELL support

Study Guide and Intervention

AL OL ELL

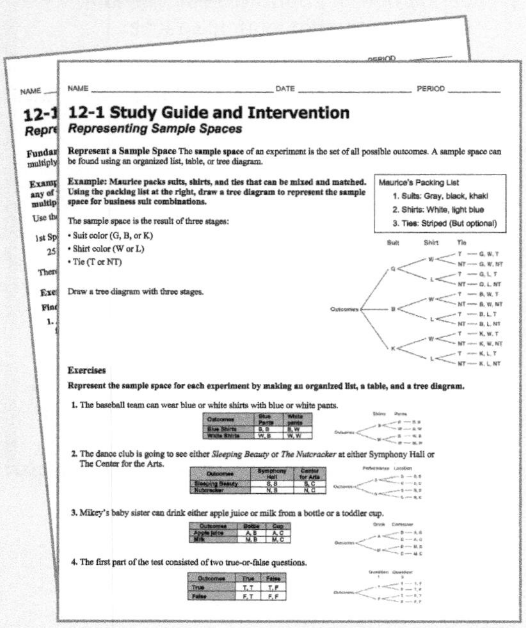
12-1 Study Guide and Intervention
Representing Sample Spaces

Study Notebook

AL OL BL ELL

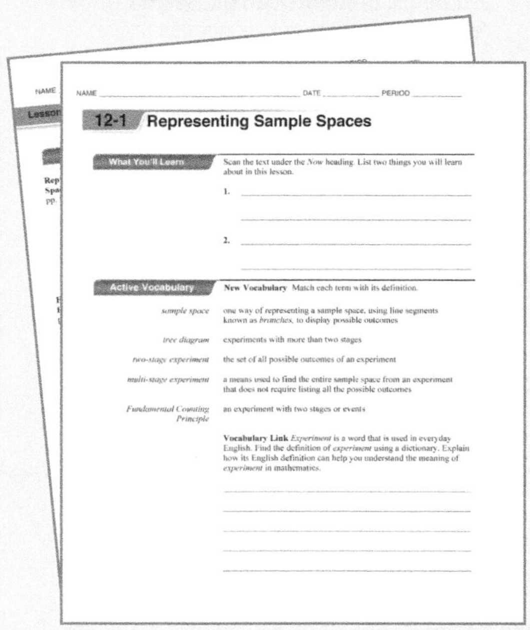
12-1 Representing Sample Spaces

Extension Activities that can be used to extend lesson concepts

Enrichment

OL BL ELL

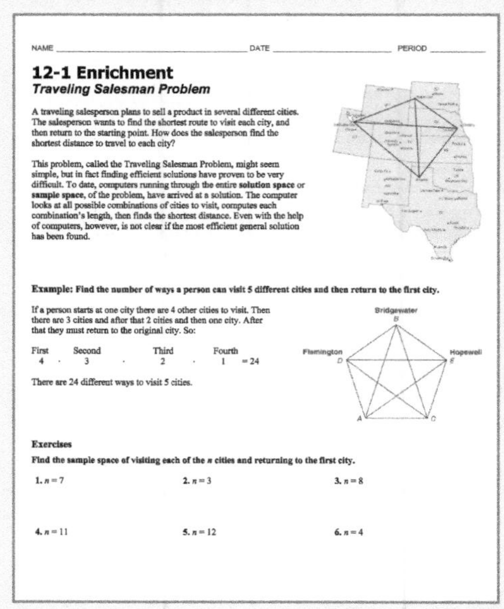
12-1 Enrichment
Traveling Salesman Problem

LESSON 1

Representing Sample Spaces

Then

- You calculated experimental probability.

Now

1. Use lists, tables, and tree diagrams to represent sample spaces.
2. Use the Fundamental Counting Principle to count outcomes.

Why?

- Many sports games start with a coin toss to determine who will start with the possession of the ball. The coin can come up heads or tails.

New Vocabulary
sample space
tree diagram
two-stage experiment
multistage experiment
Fundamental Counting Principle

Mathematical Practices
1 Make sense of problems and persevere in solving them.
2 Reason abstractly and quantitatively.

Content Standards
S.CP.1
Describe events as subsets of a sample space (the set of outcomes) using characteristics (or categories) of the outcomes, or as unions, intersections, or complements of other events ("or," "and," "not").

1 Represent a Sample Space

You have learned the following about experiments, outcomes, and events.

Definition	Example
An *experiment* is a situation involving chance that leads to results called *outcomes*.	In the situation above, the experiment is tossing the coin.
An *outcome* is the result of a single performance or *trial* of an experiment.	The possible outcomes are landing on heads or tails.
An *event* is one or more outcomes of an experiment.	One event of this experiment is the coin landing on tails.

The **sample space** of an experiment is the set of all possible outcomes. You can represent a sample space by using an organized list, a table, or a **tree diagram**.

Prep S.CP.9

Example 1 Represent a Sample Space

A coin is tossed twice. Represent the sample space for this experiment by making an organized list, a table, and a tree diagram.

For each coin toss, there are two possible outcomes, heads H or tails T.

Organized List

Pair each possible outcome from the first toss with the possible outcomes from the second toss.

H, H　　T, T
H, T　　T, H

Table

List the outcomes of the first toss in the left column and those of the second toss in the top row.

Outcomes	Heads	Tails
Heads	H, H	H, T
Tails	T, H	T, T

Tree Diagram

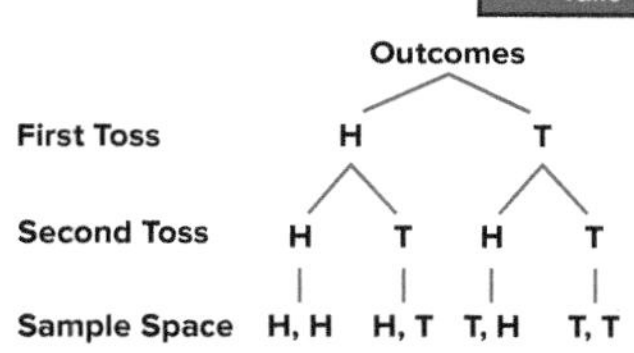

Guided Practice　　**1. See Ch. 12 Answer Appendix.**

1. A coin is tossed and then a number cube is rolled. Represent the sample space for this experiment by making an organized list, a table, and a tree diagram.

MP Mathematical Practices Strategies

Make sense of problems and persevere in solving them.
Help students determine the sample space of an experiment. For example, ask:

- How do we determine the sample space of an experiment? by considering all of the possible outcomes
- When is it not practical to use tree diagrams or lists to describe a sample space? when the number of elements in the sample space is really large
- When an experiment has multiple stages, how do you determine the number of possible outcomes in the sample size? Use the Fundamental Counting Principle.

Launch

Have students read the Why? section of the lesson. Ask:

- What makes a coin fair? There is an equal chance that either side will land faceup.
- How else can you fairly determine who goes first in a game? Sample answers: roll of the die, blind card pick, rock-paper-scissors
- What factor determines a fair outcome? an equal chance for all possible outcomes

Teach

Ask the scaffolded questions for each example to build conceptual understanding for students at all levels.

1 Represent a Sample Space

Example 1 Represent a Sample Space

AL Why are "H, T" and "T, H" not the same outcome? Because the coin is tossed and then tossed again, "H, T" means heads on the first toss and tails on the second toss. "T, H" means tails on the first toss and heads on the second toss.

OL How many outcomes would be in the sample space if a coin were tossed three times? 8

BL How many outcomes would be in the sample space if two coins were tossed at the same time? Explain. 3; If two coins were tossed at the same time, the possible outcomes are: two heads, one heads and one tails, or two tails.

(continued on the next page)

Go Online!

Interactive Whiteboard
Use the *eLesson*, *Lesson Presentation*, or *Interactive Classroom* to present this lesson.

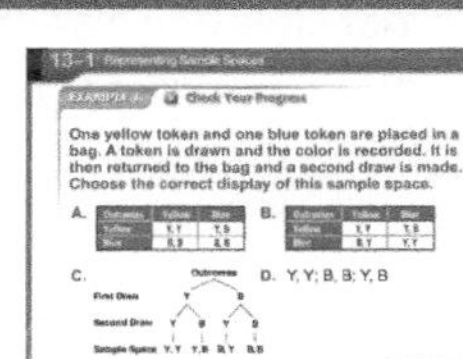

Need Another Example?
One red token and one black token are placed in a bag. A token is drawn, and the color is recorded. It is then returned to the bag, and a second draw is made. Represent the sample space for this experiment by making an organized list, a table, and a tree diagram. Organized List: R,R; B,B; R,B; B,R

Outcomes	Red	Black
Red	R,R	R,B
Black	B,R	B,B

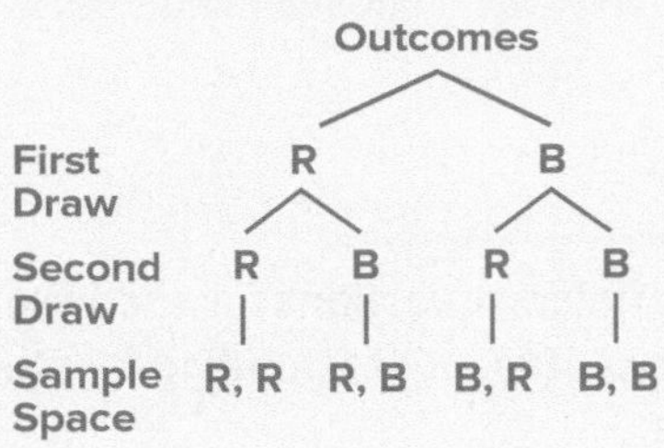

Example 2 Multistage Tree Diagrams

AL **How is this sample space different from the sample space in Example 1?** It has more stages, so there are more possible outcomes.

OL **If the restaurant missed a shipment of tomatoes and had to serve burgers without them, how many hamburger orders would be shown in the sample space?** 12

BL **Is listing the outcomes of a sample space practical for any situation? Explain.** No; Sample answer: If there are a lot of choices and/or multiple stages of an experiment, it would not make sense to list all of the possible outcomes.

Need Another Example?
Chef's Salad A chef's salad at a local restaurant comes with a choice of French, ranch, or blue cheese dressings and optional toppings of cheese, turkey, and eggs. Draw a tree diagram to represent the sample space for salad orders. See students' work.

Watch Out!
Choices For Example 2, remind students that just as choosing an option creates a unique outcome, not choosing also creates a unique outcome that must be included in the sample space.

The experiment in Example 1 is an example of a **two-stage experiment**, which is an experiment with two stages or events. Experiments with more than two stages are called **multistage experiments**.

Prep S.CP.9

Real-World Example 2 Multistage Tree Diagrams

Watch Out!
MP Structure The words *and/or* in Keandra's third question for Example 2 suggest an additional stage in the ordering process. By making separate stages for choosing with or without tomato and with or without pickles, you allow for the possibility of choosing *both* tomato and pickles.

HAMBURGERS To take a hamburger order, Keandra asks each customer the questions from the script shown. Draw a tree diagram to represent the sample space for hamburger orders.

The sample space is the result of four stages.

- burger size (K, R, or L)
- cheese (C or NC)
- tomato (T or NT)
- pickles (P or NP)

Draw a tree diagram with four stages.

Reading Math
Tree Diagram Notation Choose notation for outcomes in your tree diagrams that will eliminate confusion. In Example 2, *C* stands for *cheese*, while *NC* stands for *no cheese*. Likewise, *NT* and *NP* stand for *no tomato* and *no pickles*, respectively.

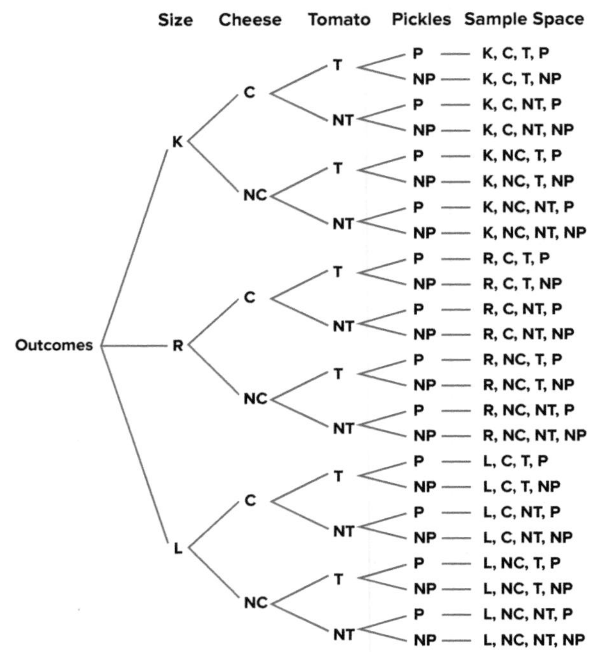

Guided Practice 2. See Ch. 12 Answer Appendix.

2. **MUSIC** Yoki can choose a portable hard drive with 4 or 8 terabytes in black, teal, sage, or red. She can also get a case and/or enhanced data transfer rates to go with it. Make a tree diagram to represent the sample space for this situation.

Differentiated Instruction AL OL BL

Logical Learners Organize students in groups of three or four. Provide each group with a handful of four to six different manipulatives. Challenge each group to make as many unique groups of items as possible. Have students draw and record the total number of unique groups they can make by using one item, two items, three items, and so on. Challenge some groups to find the total number of unique groups if order is important (ABC and BCA are considered two separate groups) and if order is not important (ABC and BCA are considered the same group). Have groups share with the class their drawings and the total number of groups made. ELL

2 Fundamental Counting Principle

2 Fundamental Counting Principle For some two-stage or multistage experiments, listing the entire sample space may not be practical or necessary. To find the *number* of possible outcomes, you can use the **Fundamental Counting Principle**.

Study Tip

Multiplication Rule The Fundamental Counting Principle is sometimes called the *Multiplication Rule for Counting* or the *Counting Principle*.

Key Concept Fundamental Counting Principle

Words The number of possible outcomes in a sample space can be found by multiplying the number of possible outcomes from each stage or event.

Symbols In a k-stage experiment, let

n_1 = the number of possible outcomes for the first stage.

n_2 = the number of possible outcomes for the second stage after the first stage has occurred.

⋮

n_k = the number of possible outcomes for the kth stage after the first $k - 1$ stages have occurred.

Then the total possible outcomes of this k-stage experiment is

$$n_1 \cdot n_2 \cdot n_3 \cdot \ldots \cdot n_k$$

Prep S.CP.9

Real-World Example 3 Use the Fundamental Counting Principle

Real-World Link

Most high school students order a traditional ring style, which includes the name of the school, a stone, and the graduation year.

VStock/Alamy

CLASS RINGS Haley has selected a size and overall style for her class ring. Now she must choose from the ring options shown. How many different rings could Haley create in her chosen style and size?

Ring Options	Number of Choices
metals	10
finishes	2
stone colors	12
stone cuts	5
side 1 activity logos	20
side 2 activity logos	20
band styles	2

Use the Fundamental Counting Principle.

metals		finishes		stone colors		stone cuts		side 1 logos		side 2 logos		band styles		possible outcomes
10	×	2	×	12	×	5	×	20	×	20	×	2	=	960,000

So, Haley could create 960,000 different rings.

Guided Practice

3. Find the number of possible outcomes for each situation.

A. The answer sheet shown is completed. 65,536

B. A dot cube is rolled four times. 1296

C. SHOES A pair of women's shoes comes in whole sizes 5 through 11 in red, navy, brown, or black. They can be leather or suede and are available in three different widths. 168

Answer Sheet

1. Ⓐ Ⓑ Ⓒ Ⓓ
2. Ⓐ Ⓑ Ⓒ Ⓓ
3. Ⓐ Ⓑ Ⓒ Ⓓ
4. Ⓐ Ⓑ Ⓒ Ⓓ
5. Ⓐ Ⓑ Ⓒ Ⓓ
6. Ⓐ Ⓑ Ⓒ Ⓓ
7. Ⓣ Ⓕ
8. Ⓣ Ⓕ
9. Ⓣ Ⓕ
10. Ⓣ Ⓕ

Example 3 Use the Fundamental Counting Principle

AL **Is it practical to represent this situation by drawing the sample space? Explain.** No; there are too many different combinations for it to be practical to write it down.

OL **Next year, three finishes will be offered for class rings. How many possible outcomes will there be?** 1,440,000

BL **At an ice cream store, there are three cone options and five topping options. The total number of possible combinations of cone, ice cream, and a single topping is 270. How many ice cream flavors are offered?** 18

Need Another Example?

Cars New cars are available with a wide selection of options for the consumer. One option is chosen from each category shown. How many different cars could a consumer create in the chosen make and model?

Car Options	Number of Choices
Exterior color	11
Interior color	7
Seat material	5
Engine	3
Computer navigation system	6
Wheels	4
Doors	3

83,160

Teaching Tip

Fundamental Counting Principle The Fundamental Counting Principle can be used to check whether all possible outcomes have been considered in the sample space of a given event.

Differentiated Instruction AL OL BL ELL

Logical Learners Write the following menu choices on the board: 1. What size sundae would you like: small, medium, or large? 2. Would you like chocolate or vanilla ice cream? 3. Would you like caramel sauce, chocolate sauce, or strawberry sauce? 4. Would you like whipped cream? Ask students to create a tree diagram to show all of the possible sundae combinations.

Go Online!

The most up-to-date resources available for your program can be found at connectED.mcgraw-hill.com.

Practice

Formative Assessment Use Exercises 1–5 to assess students' understanding of the concepts in this lesson.

The Practice and Problem Solving exercises assess the content taught in the lesson. The Preparing for Assessment page is meant to be used as preparation for assessment.

MP Teaching the Mathematical Practices

Reasoning Mathematically proficient students make sense of quantities and their relationships in problem situations. In Exercises 6–10, encourage students to list the possible outcomes first.
Sense-Making Mathematically proficient students check their answers to problems using a different method, and they continually ask themselves, "does this make sense?" In Exercises 15–18, encourage students to check their answers for reasonableness.

Levels of Complexity Chart

The levels of the exercises progress from 1 to 3, with Level 1 indicating the lowest level of complexity.

Exercises	6–18	19–21, 31–37	22–30
Level 3			●
Level 2		●	
Level 1	●		

Extra Practice

See page R12 for extra exercises for students who are approaching level or for on-level students who need additional reinforcement.

Additional Answer

1. S, S O, O
S, O O, S

Outcomes	Safe	Out
Safe	S, S	S, O
Out	O, S	O, O

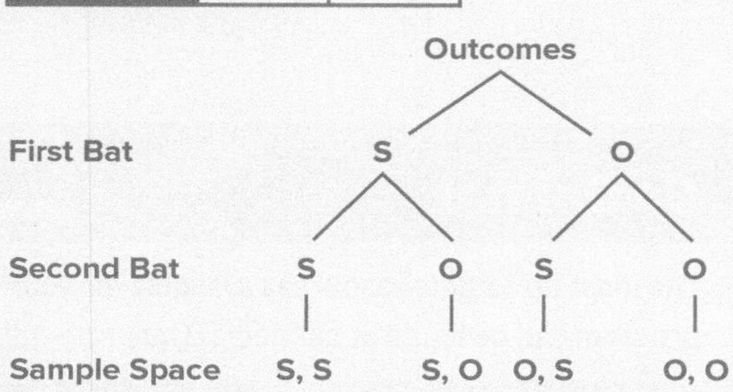

Check Your Understanding

◯ = Step-by-Step Solutions begin on page R13.

Go Online! for a Self-Check Quiz

Example 1 Prep S.CP.9

Represent the sample space for each experiment by making an organized list, a table, and a tree diagram.

1. For each at bat, a player can either get on base or make an out. Suppose a player bats twice. See margin.

2. Quinton sold the most tickets in his school for the annual Autumn Festival. As a reward, he gets to choose twice from a grab bag with tickets that say "free juice" or "free notebook." See Ch. 12 Answer Appendix.

Example 2 Prep S.CP.9

3. **TUXEDOS** Patrick is renting a prom tuxedo from the catalog shown. Draw a tree diagram to represent the sample space for this situation. See Ch. 12 Answer Appendix.

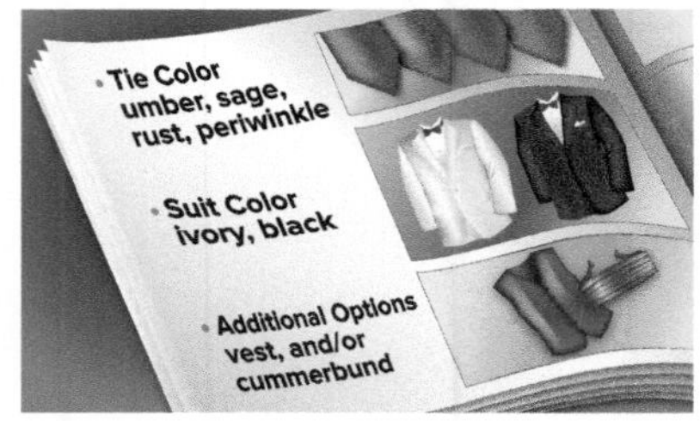

Example 3 Prep S.CP.9

Find the number of possible outcomes for each situation.

4. Desirée is preparing for homecoming and must decide what to wear. Assume one of each is chosen. 1800

Options	Number of Choices
dress	15
shoes	5
purse	3
earrings	4
necklace	2

5. Marcos is creating a new menu for his restaurant. Assume one of each item is ordered. 20,736

Menu Titles	Number of Choices
appetizer	8
soup	4
salad	6
entree	12
dessert	9

Practice and Problem Solving

Extra Practice is on page R13.

Example 1 Prep S.CP.9

MP **STRUCTURE** **Represent the sample space for each experiment by making an organized list, a table, and a tree diagram.** 6–10. See margin.

6. Gina is a junior and has a choice for the next two years of either playing volleyball or basketball during the winter quarter.

7. Two different history classes in New York City are taking a trip to either the Smithsonian or the Museum of Natural History.

8. Simeon has an opportunity to travel abroad as a foreign exchange student during each of his last two years of college. He can choose between Ecuador or Italy.

9. A new club is formed, and a meeting time must be chosen. The possible meeting times are Monday or Thursday at 5:00 or 6:00 P.M.

10. An exam with multiple versions has exercises with triangles. In the first exercise, there is an obtuse triangle or an acute triangle. In the second exercise, there is an isosceles triangle or a scalene triangle.

Differentiated Homework Options

Levels	AL Basic	OL Core	BL Advanced
Exercises	6–18, 25, 27, 28, 30–37	7–11 odd, 12–25, 27, 28, 30–37	22–30, (optional: 31–37)
2-Day Option	7–17 odd, 31–37	6–18	
	6–18 even, 25, 27, 28, 30	19–25, 27, 28, 30–37	

You can use ALEKS to provide additional remediation support with personalized instruction and practice.

11. PAINTING In an art class, students are working on two projects where they can use one of two different types of paints for each project. Represent the sample space for this experiment by making an organized list, a table, and a tree diagram. See margin.

Example 2
Prep S.CP.9

Draw a tree diagram to represent the sample space for each situation.

12. BURRITOS At a burrito stand, customers have the choice of beans, pork, or chicken with rice or no rice, and cheese and/or salsa. See Ch. 12 Answer Appendix.

13. TRANSPORTATION Blake is buying a vehicle and has a choice of sedan, truck, or van with leather or fabric interior, and a GPS and/or sunroof. See Ch. 12 Answer Appendix.

14. TREATS Ping and her friends go to a frozen yogurt parlor which has a sign like the one at the right. Draw a tree diagram for all possible combinations of cones with peanuts and/or sprinkles. See Ch. 12 Answer Appendix.

FROZEN YOGURT
Cones
Flavors
Cake
Sugar
Waffle
Strawberry
Lime
Toppings: Peanuts and Sprinkles

Example 3
Prep S.CP.9

MP MODELING In Exercises 15–18, find the number of possible outcomes for each situation.

15. In the Junior Student Council elections, there are 3 people running for secretary, 4 people running for treasurer, 5 people running for vice president, and 2 people running for class president. 120

16. When signing up for classes during his first semester of college at Texas A&M, Frederico has 4 class spots to fill with a choice of 4 literature classes, 2 math classes, 6 history classes, and 3 film classes. 144

17. Niecy is choosing one each of 6 colleges, 5 majors, 2 minors, and 4 clubs. 240

18. Evita works at a restaurant where she has to wear a white blouse, black pants or skirt, and black shoes. She has 5 blouses, 4 pants, 3 skirts, and 6 pairs of black shoes. 210

B **19. ART** For an art class assignment, Mr. Green gives students their choice of two quadrilaterals to use as a base. One must have sides of equal length, and the other must have at least one set of parallel sides. Represent the sample space by making an organized list, a table, and a tree diagram. See Ch. 12 Answer Appendix.

20. BREAKFAST A hotel restaurant serves omelets with a choice of vegetables, ham, or sausage that come with a side of hash browns, grits, or toast.

a. How many different outcomes of omelet and one side are possible if a vegetable omelet comes with just one vegetable? 18

b. Find the number of possible outcomes for a vegetable omelet if you can get any or all vegetables on any omelet. 45

Omelets
All omelets served with your choice of hash browns, grits, or toast.
Vegetable Omelet
Ham Omelet
Sausage Omelet
Vegetable choices:
green peppers, tomatoes, onions, mushrooms

21. COMPOSITE FIGURES Carlito is calculating the area of the composite figure at the right. List six different ways he can do this. See margin.

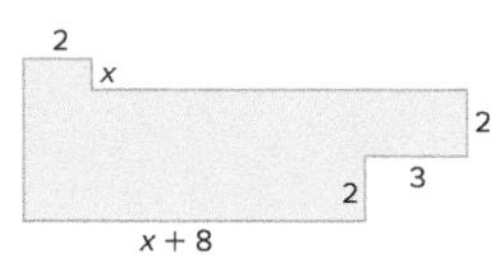

11. O, O A, A O, A A, O

Outcomes	Oil	Acrylic
Oil	O, O	O, A
Acrylic	A, O	A, A

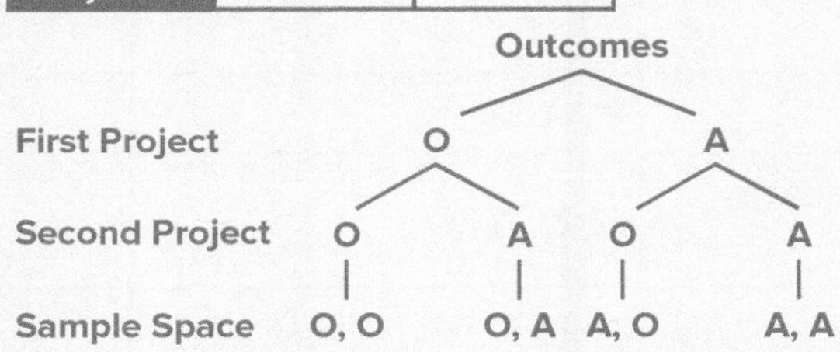

21. Sample answer: 6 different ways: $4(x + 6) + 2(3) + 2(x + 4)$; $2(x + 11) + 2(x + 8) + 2(x)$; $2(x + 4) + 2(x + 9) + 2(x + 6)$; $2(x) + 2(3) + 4(x + 8)$; $2(x) + 2(x + 8) + 2(3) + 2(x + 8)$; $2(x) + 2(3) + 2(4) + 2(x + 6) + 2(x + 6)$

Additional Answers

6. V, V B, B V, B B, V

Outcomes	Volleyball	Basketball
Volleyball	V, V	V, B
Basketball	B, V	B, B

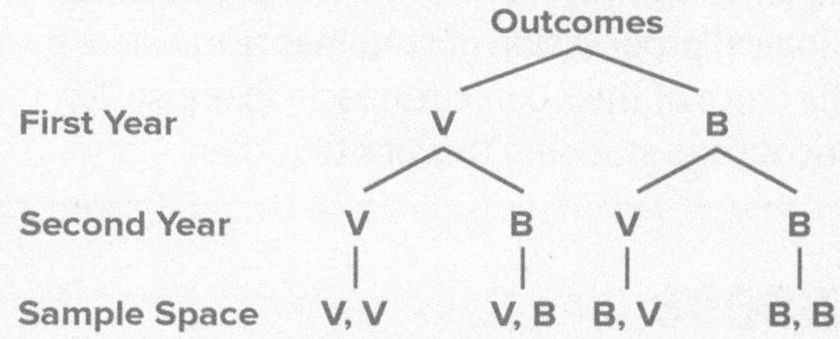

7. S, S N, N S, N N, S

Outcomes	Smithsonian	Natural
Smithsonian	S, S	S, N
Natural	N, S	N, N

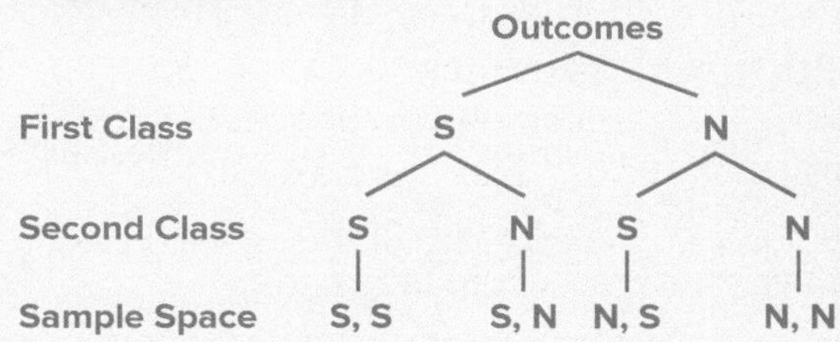

8. E, E I, I E, I I, E

Outcomes	Italy	Ecuador
Italy	I, I	I, E
Ecuador	E, I	E, E

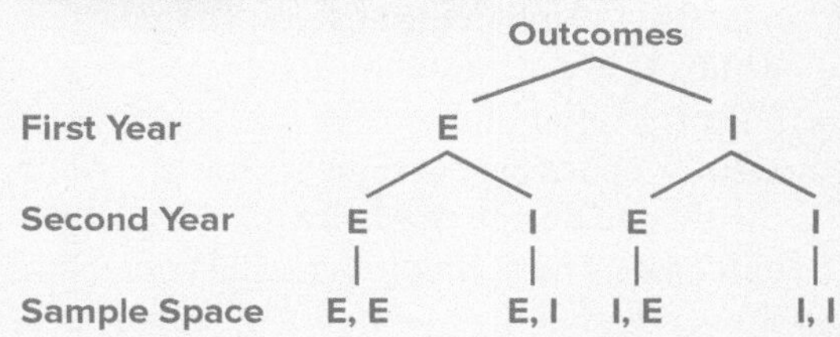

9. M, 5 T, 5 M, 6 T, 6

Outcomes	5	6
Monday	M, 5	M, 6
Thursday	T, 5	T, 6

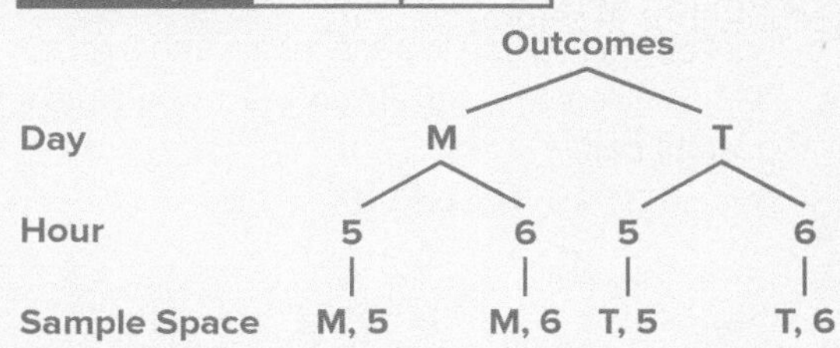

10. A, I A, S O, I O, S

Outcomes	Isosceles	Scalene
Acute	A, I	A, S
Obtuse	O, I	O, S

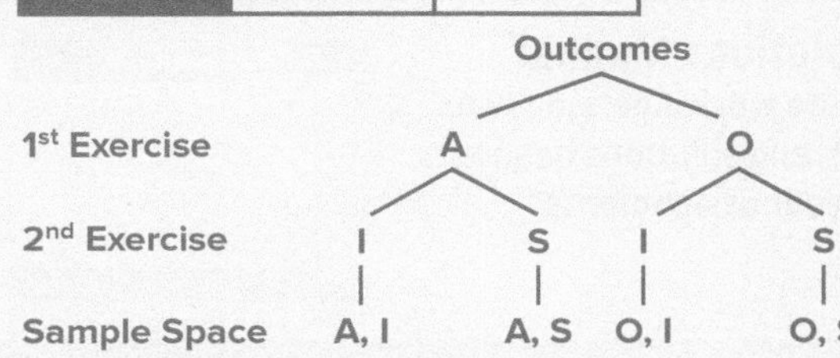

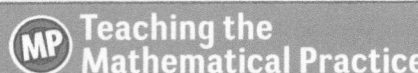

Teaching the Mathematical Practices

Construct Arguments Mathematically proficient students understand and use stated assumptions and definitions in constructing arguments. They make conjectures and build a logical progression of statements to explore the truth of their conjectures. In Exercise 28, encourage students to work together.

Assess

Crystal Ball Have students write about how learning to represent the sample space and to use the Fundamental Counting Principle will connect with permutations and combinations.

Additional Answers

22b. 5040; Sample answer: There are 10 possibilities for the first number in the combination. Because Miranda can use each number only once, there are only 9 possibilities for the second number in the combination, 8 possibilities for the third number in the combination, and 7 possibilities for the fourth number in the combination. The number of possible combinations is $10 \times 9 \times 8 \times 7$ or 5040.

25. $n^3 - 3n^2 + 2n$; Sample answer: There are n objects in the box when you remove the first object, so after you remove one object, there are $n - 1$ possible outcomes. After you remove the second object, there are $n - 2$ possible outcomes. The number of possible outcomes is the product of the number of outcomes of each experiment or $n(n - 1)(n - 2)$.

26. Sample answer: In an experiment, you choose between a blue box and a red box. You then remove a ball from the box that you chose without looking into the box. The blue box contains a red ball, a purple ball, and a green ball. The red box contains a yellow ball and an orange ball.

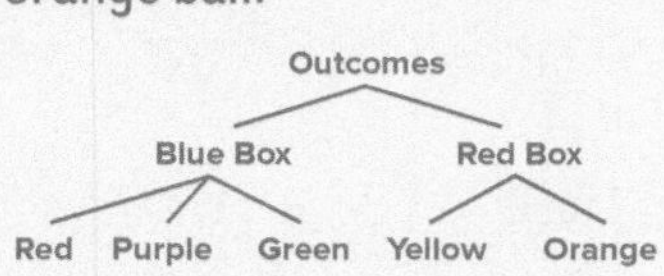

Go Online!

eSolutions Manual
Create worksheets, answer keys, and solutions handouts for your assignments.

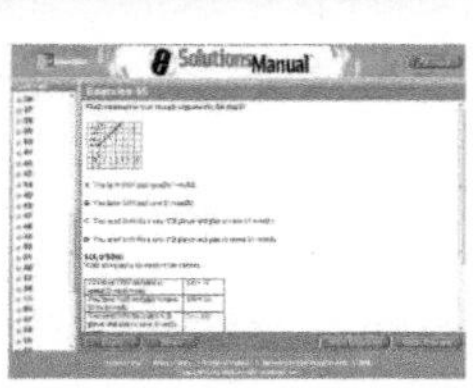

22. TRANSPORTATION Miranda got a new bicycle lock that has a four-number combination. Each number in the combination is from 0 to 9.
  a. How many combinations are possible if there are no restrictions on the number of times Miranda can use each number?
  b. How many combinations are possible if Miranda can use each number only once? Explain.

23. GAMES Cody and Monette are playing a board game in which you roll two dot cubes per turn.
  a. In one turn, how many outcomes result in a sum of 8?
  b. How many outcomes in one turn result in an odd sum?

24. MULTIPLE REPRESENTATIONS In this problem, you will investigate a sequence of events. In the first stage of a two-stage experiment, you spin Spinner 1 below. If the result is red, you flip a coin. If the result is yellow, you roll a dot cube. If the result is green, you roll a number cube. If the result is blue, you spin Spinner 2.

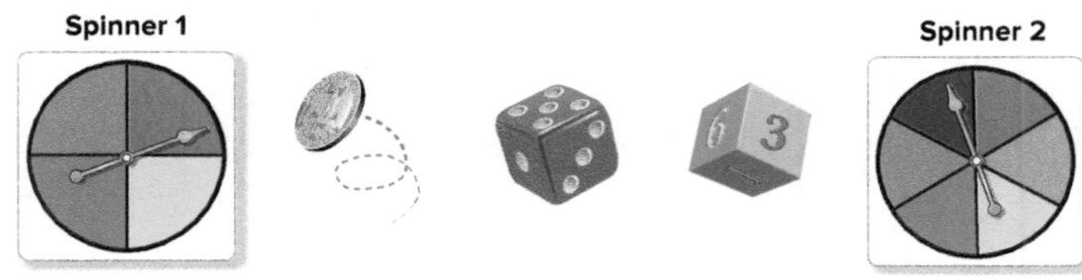

  a. **Geometric** Draw a tree diagram to represent the sample space for the experiment.
  b. **Logical** Draw a Venn diagram to represent the possible outcomes of the experiment.
  c. **Analytical** How many possible outcomes are there?
  d. **Verbal** Could you use the Fundamental Counting Principle to determine the number of outcomes? Explain.

H.O.T. Problems Use Higher-Order Thinking Skills

25. MP CONSTRUCT ARGUMENTS A box contains n different objects. If you remove three objects from the box, one at a time, without putting the previous object back, how many possible outcomes exist? Explain your reasoning.

26. CHALLENGE Sometimes a tree diagram for an experiment is not symmetrical. Describe a two-stage experiment where the tree diagram is asymmetrical. Include a sketch of the tree diagram. Explain.

27. WRITING IN MATH Explain why it is not possible to represent the sample space for a multistage experiment by using a table.

28. MP CONSTRUCT ARGUMENTS Determine if the following statement is *sometimes*, *always*, or *never* true. Explain your reasoning.

When an outcome falls outside the sample space, it is a failure.

29. CHALLENGE A multistage experiment has n possible outcomes at each stage. If the experiment is performed with k stages, write an equation for the total number of possible outcomes P. Explain.

30. WRITING IN MATH Explain when it is necessary to show all of the possible outcomes of an experiment by using a tree diagram and when using the Fundamental Counting Principle is sufficient.

Standards for Mathematical Practice

Emphasis On	Exercises
1 Make sense of problems and persevere in solving them.	1–5, 35–37
2 Reason abstractly and quantitatively.	21, 24, 32
3 Construct viable arguments and critique the reasoning of others.	22, 25, 27, 28
4 Model with mathematics.	11–20, 23
6 Attend to precision.	31, 33, 34
7 Look for and make use of structure.	6–10, 26
8 Look for and express regularity in repeated reasoning.	29, 30

Preparing for Assessment

31. Nathaniel performs an experiment that involves tossing a coin two times. First he plots the point $Q(3, 1)$. Then he tosses a coin. If the coin lands on heads, he translates point Q along $\langle 1, 1\rangle$. If the coin lands on tails, he translates point Q along $\langle -1, -1\rangle$. Then he tosses the coin again and repeats the process on the image of point Q. Nathaniel notes the final image of the point. Which of the following is not in the sample space for this experiment? MP 6 S.CP.9 **B**

- A (5, 3)
- B (4, 2)
- C (3, 1)
- D (1, −1)

32. Brad's password must be five digits long; he must use the numbers 0–9, and the digits must not repeat. What is the maximum number of different passwords that Brad can have? MP 2 S.CP.9

30240

33. Becky performs an experiment that involves tossing a coin three times. First she plots the point $R(-4, 2)$. She tosses a coin and transforms point R according to the rules in the table. Then she tosses the coin again and transforms the image of point R. Then she tosses the coin a third time and transforms the most recent image. Becky notes the final image of the point. Which of the following is not a possible outcome for this experiment? MP 6 S.CP.9 **D**

Result of Toss	Transformation
Heads	$(x, y) \rightarrow (-y, x)$
Tails	$(x, y) \rightarrow (x + 2, y)$

- A (2, 2)
- B (−2, 0)
- C (4, 0)
- D (−2, 2)
- E (0, −2)

34. Amani plots the point $P(2, -1)$. Then she tosses a coin. If the coin lands on heads, she reflects point P in the x-axis. If the coin lands on tails, she reflects point P in the y-axis. Then she tosses the coin again and repeats the process on the image of point P. How many different final images are possible? MP 6 S.CP.9 **B**

- A 1
- B 2
- C 3
- D 4

35. There are 3 trails leading to camp A from your starting position. There are 3 trails from camp A to camp B. How many different routes are there from the starting position to camp B? Draw a tree diagram to illustrate your answer. MP 1 S.CP.9 9

36. Bag A contains 10 marbles of which 2 are red and 8 are black. Bag B contains 12 marbles of which 4 are red and 8 are black. A coin is tossed, and if it comes up heads, a marble is drawn from bag A and its color is noted. If it comes up tails, a marble is drawn from bag B and its color is noted. Find the sample space for this experiment. MP 1 S.CP.9

{(heads, red), (heads, black), (tails, red), (tails, black)}

37. A bag contains four apples and six bananas. A fruit is taken from the bag and eaten. Then another fruit is taken and eaten. This process continues. MP 1 S.CP.9

a. Find the sample space for the following experiments.

i. one fruit is eaten. (apple, banana)

ii. two fruits are eaten.

{(apple, banana), (banana, apple), (apple, apple), (banana, banana)}

iii. three fruits are eaten. See margin.

b. For $n \leq 4$, write an expression for the number of elements in the sample space when n fruits are eaten. 2^n

Preparing for Assessment

Exercises 31–37 require students to use the skills they will need on future assessments. Exercises are dual-coded with content standards and mathematical practice standards.

Dual Coding

Item	Content Standards	MP Mathematical Practices
31	S.CP.9	6
32	S.CP.9	2
33	S.CP.9	6
34	S.CP.9	6
35	S.CP.1	1
36	S.CP.1	1
37	S.CP.1	1

Diagnose Student Errors

Survey student responses for each item. Class trends may indicate common errors and misconceptions.

31.

A	Did not consider the outcome of tossing heads then heads
B	CORRECT
C	Did not consider the outcome of tossing heads then tails or tails then heads
D	Did not consider the outcome of tossing tails then tails

33.

A	Did not consider the outcome of tossing tails then tails then tails
B	Did not consider the outcome of tossing tails then tails then heads
C	Did not consider the outcome of tossing heads then tails then heads
D	CORRECT
E	Did not consider the outcome of tossing tails then heads then tails

Differentiated Instruction OL BL

Extension Have students write a multistage experiment involving marketing, such as mix-and-match outfits, special-of-the-day dinner choices at a restaurant, or pizzas with a selection of toppings. Have students create a table listing all the choice options and then use the Fundamental Counting Principle to determine the number of possible outcomes. Then have students create a tree diagram to identify the sample space. Finally, have students create a marketing flyer highlighting the number of choices available for their product.

Go Online!

Quizzes

Students can use *Self-Check Quizzes* to check their understanding of this lesson and have the results sent to you. You can also give *Quiz 1*, which covers the content in Lesson 12-1.

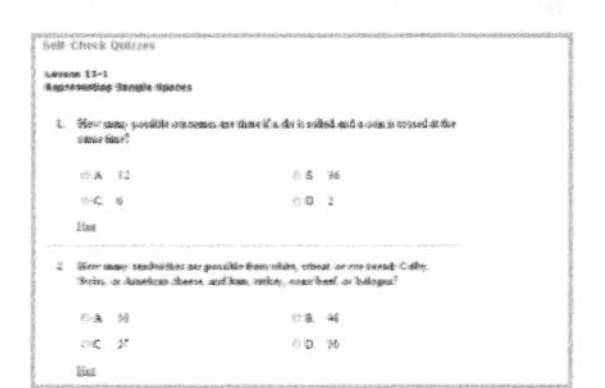

Additional Answer

37 a. iii. {(apple, banana, apple), (apple, banana, banana), (banana, apple, apple), (banana, apple, banana), (apple, apple, apple), (apple, apple, banana), (banana, banana, banana), (banana, banana, apple)}

Probability and Counting

SUGGESTED PACING (DAYS)

	Instruction
90 min.	0.5
45 min.	1.0

Track Your Progress

Objectives

1. Describe events as subsets of sample spaces by using intersections and unions.
2. Find probabilities of complements.

Mathematical Background

An event is a set of outcomes associated with an experiment. An event is a subset of the sample space for the experiment. Two or more events can be joined to form a compound event. A Venn diagram can be used to help calculate the probability of the union, intersection, or complement of events.

THEN

S.C.P.1 Describe events as subsets of a sample space (the set of outcomes) using characteristics (or categories) of the outcomes, or as unions, intersections, or complements of other events ("or," "and," "not").

NOW

S.C.P.1 Describe events as subsets of a sample space (the set of outcomes) using characteristics (or categories) of the outcomes, or as unions, intersections, or complements of other events ("or," "and," "not").

NEXT

S.CP.9 Use permutations and combinations to compute probabilities of compound events and solve problems.

Go Online! All of these resources and more are available at connectED.mcgraw-hill.com

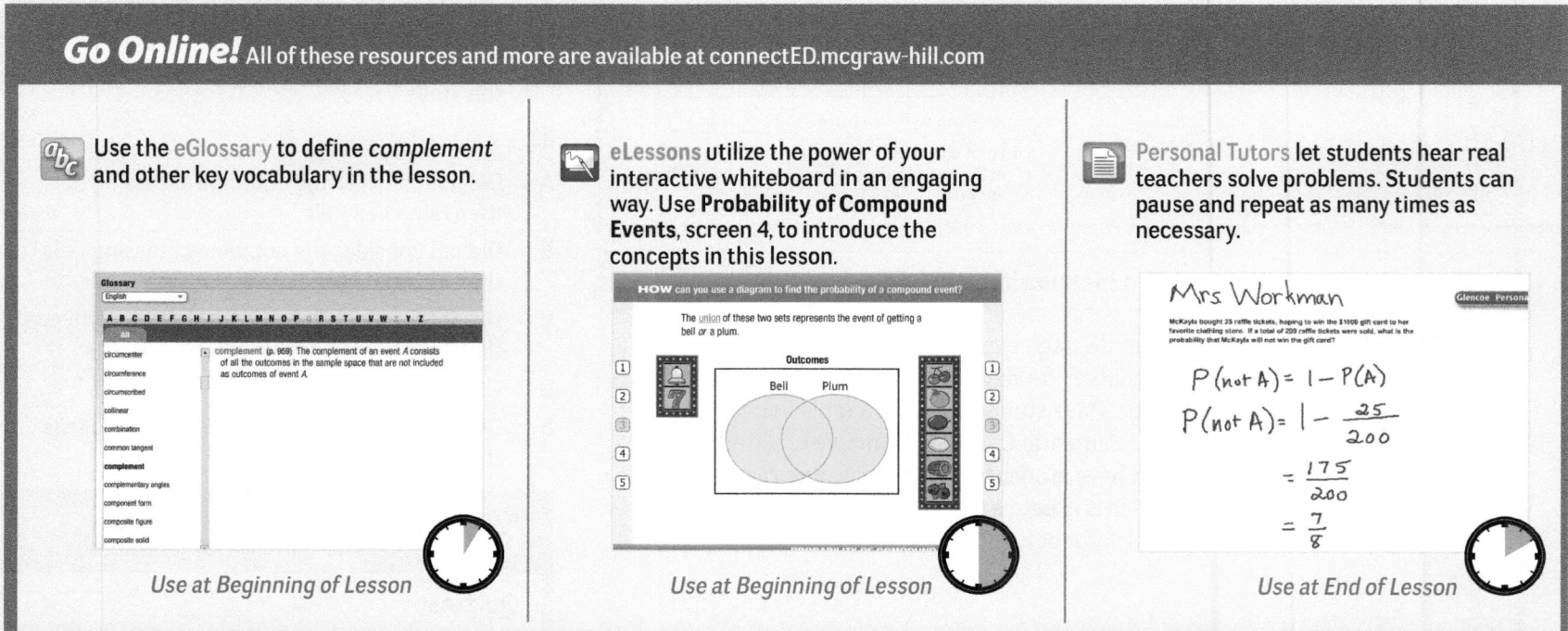

Use the eGlossary to define *complement* and other key vocabulary in the lesson.

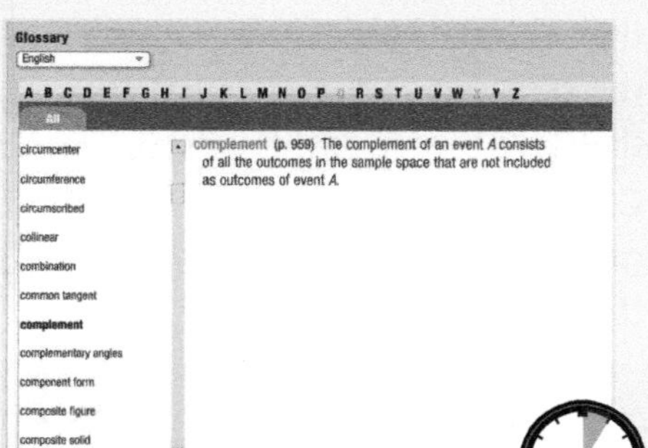

Glossary
English
complement (p. 959) The complement of an event A consists of all the outcomes in the sample space that are not included as outcomes of event A.

Use at Beginning of Lesson

eLessons utilize the power of your interactive whiteboard in an engaging way. Use **Probability of Compound Events**, screen 4, to introduce the concepts in this lesson.

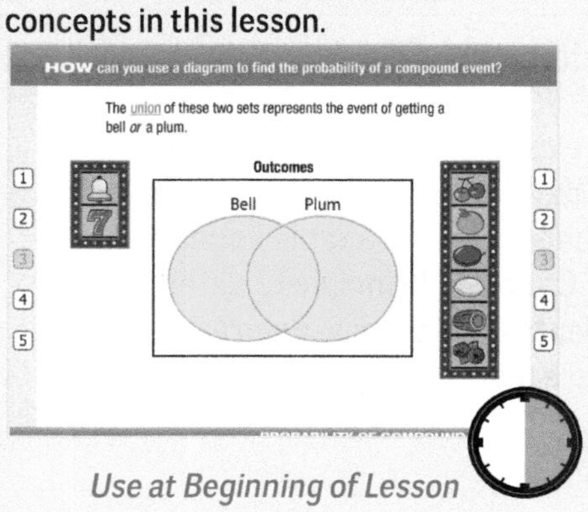

Use at Beginning of Lesson

Personal Tutors let students hear real teachers solve problems. Students can pause and repeat as many times as necessary.

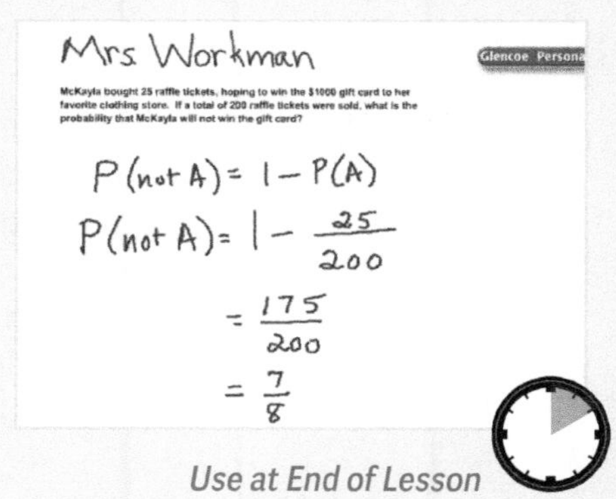

Use at End of Lesson

OER Using Open Educational Resources

Apps Have students access **Google Apps for Education** to collaborate on tips for finding probabilities of unions, intersections, and complements of events. As an educator, the app also offers spreadsheets, calendars, and surveys. You can also try **WhoTeaches** or **TeachAde.** *Use as planning tool*

Go Online!
connectED.mcgraw-hill.com

Worksheets

Differentiate Your Resources

Extra Practice Additional practice or homework; Skills Practice is best for approaching-level students and Practice is best for on-level and beyond-level students

Skills Practice

AL OL ELL

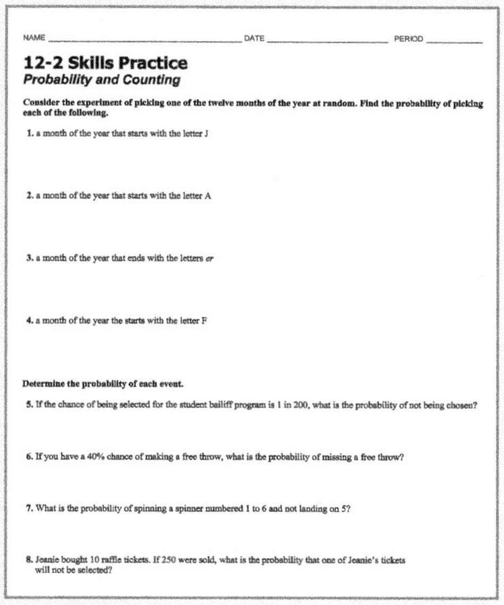
NAME ______ DATE ______ PERIOD ______

12-2 Skills Practice
Probability and Counting

Consider the experiment of picking one of the twelve months of the year at random. Find the probability of picking each of the following.

1. a month of the year that starts with the letter J
2. a month of the year that starts with the letter A
3. a month of the year that ends with the letters *er*
4. a month of the year the starts with the letter F

Determine the probability of each event.

5. If the chance of being selected for the student bailiff program is 1 in 200, what is the probability of not being chosen?
6. If you have a 40% chance of making a free throw, what is the probability of missing a free throw?
7. What is the probability of spinning a spinner numbered 1 to 6 and not landing on 5?
8. Jeanie bought 10 raffle tickets. If 250 were sold, what is the probability that one of Jeanie's tickets will not be selected?

Practice

AL OL BL ELL

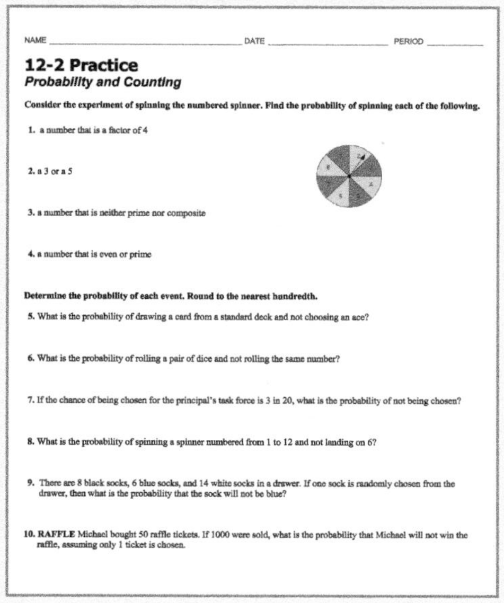
NAME ______ DATE ______ PERIOD ______

12-2 Practice
Probability and Counting

Consider the experiment of spinning the numbered spinner. Find the probability of spinning each of the following.

1. a number that is a factor of 4
2. a 3 or a 5
3. a number that is neither prime nor composite
4. a number that is even or prime

Determine the probability of each event. Round to the nearest hundredth.

5. What is the probability of drawing a card from a standard deck and not choosing an ace?
6. What is the probability of rolling a pair of dice and not rolling the same number?
7. If the chance of being chosen for the principal's task force is 3 in 20, what is the probability of not being chosen?
8. What is the probability of spinning a spinner numbered from 1 to 12 and not landing on 6?
9. There are 8 black socks, 6 blue socks, and 14 white socks in a drawer. If one sock is randomly chosen from the drawer, then what is the probability that the sock will not be blue?
10. **RAFFLE** Michael bought 50 raffle tickets. If 1000 were sold, what is the probability that Michael will not win the raffle, assuming only 1 ticket is chosen.

Word Problem Practice

AL OL BL ELL

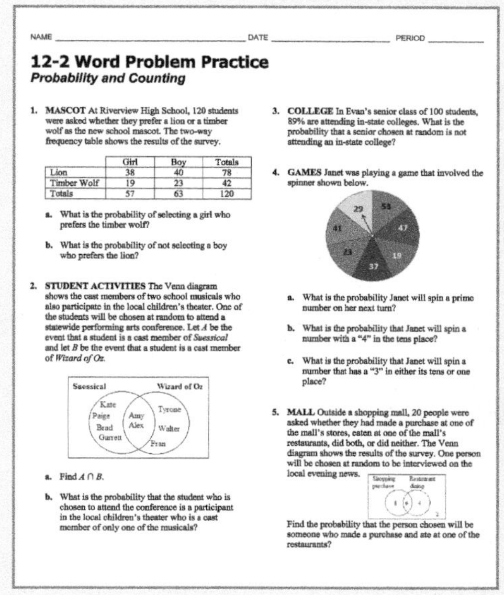
NAME ______ DATE ______ PERIOD ______

12-2 Word Problem Practice
Probability and Counting

1. **MASCOT** At Riverview High School, 120 students were asked whether they prefer a lion or a timber wolf as the new school mascot. The two-way frequency table shows the results of the survey.

	Girl	Boy	Totals
Lion	38	40	78
Timber Wolf	19	23	42
Totals	57	63	120

a. What is the probability of selecting a girl who prefers the timber wolf?
b. What is the probability of not selecting a boy who prefers the lion?

2. **STUDENT ACTIVITIES** The Venn diagram shows the cast members of two school musicals who also participate in the local children's theater. One of the students will be chosen at random to attend a statewide performing arts conference. Let *A* be the event that a student is a cast member of *Seussical* and let *B* be the event that a student is a cast member of *Wizard of Oz*.

a. Find $A \cap B$.
b. What is the probability that the student who is chosen to attend the conference is a participant in the local children's theater who is a cast member of only one of the musicals?

3. **COLLEGE** In Evan's senior class of 100 students, 89% are attending in-state colleges. What is the probability that a senior chosen at random is not attending an in-state college?

4. **GAMES** Janet was playing a game that involved the spinner shown below.

a. What is the probability Janet will spin a prime number on her next turn?
b. What is the probability that Janet will spin a number with a "4" in the tens place?
c. What is the probability that Janet will spin a number that has a "3" in either its tens or one place?

5. **MALL** Outside a shopping mall, 20 people were asked whether they had made a purchase at one of the mall's stores, eaten at one of the mall's restaurants, did both, or did neither. The Venn diagram shows the results of the survey. One person will be chosen at random to be interviewed on the local evening news.

Find the probability that the person chosen will be someone who made a purchase and ate at one of the restaurants?

Intervention Reteaching and vocabulary activities that can be used with struggling or absent students and as ELL support

Study Guide and Intervention

AL OL ELL

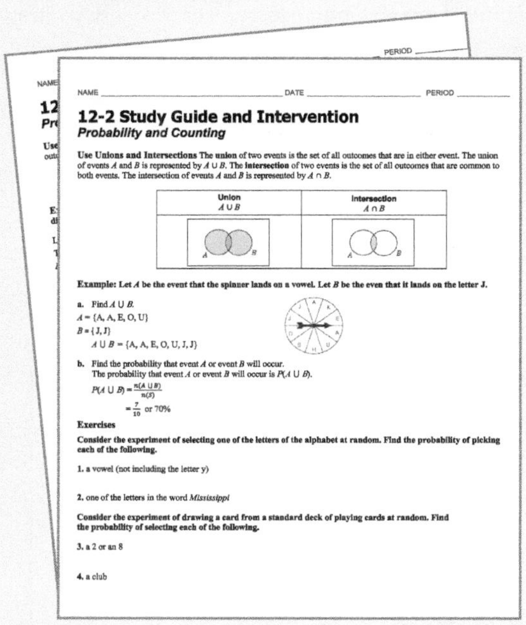
NAME ______ DATE ______ PERIOD ______

12-2 Study Guide and Intervention
Probability and Counting

Use Unions and Intersections The **union** of two events is the set of all outcomes that are in either event. The union of events *A* and *B* is represented by $A \cup B$. The **intersection** of two events is the set of all outcomes that are common to both events. The intersection of events *A* and *B* is represented by $A \cap B$.

Union $A \cup B$	Intersection $A \cap B$

Example: Let *A* be the event that the spinner lands on a vowel. Let *B* be the even that it lands on the letter J.

a. Find $A \cup B$.
$A = \{A, A, E, O, U\}$
$B = \{J, J\}$
$A \cup B = \{A, A, E, O, U, J, J\}$

b. Find the probability that event *A* or event *B* will occur.
The probability that event *A* or event *B* will occur is $P(A \cup B)$.
$P(A \cup B) = \frac{n(A \cup B)}{n(S)}$
$= \frac{7}{10}$ or 70%

Exercises

Consider the experiment of selecting one of the letters of the alphabet at random. Find the probability of picking each of the following.

1. a vowel (not including the letter y)
2. one of the letters in the word *Mississippi*

Consider the experiment of drawing a card from a standard deck of playing cards at random. Find the probability of selecting each of the following.

3. a 2 or an 8
4. a club

Study Notebook

AL OL BL ELL

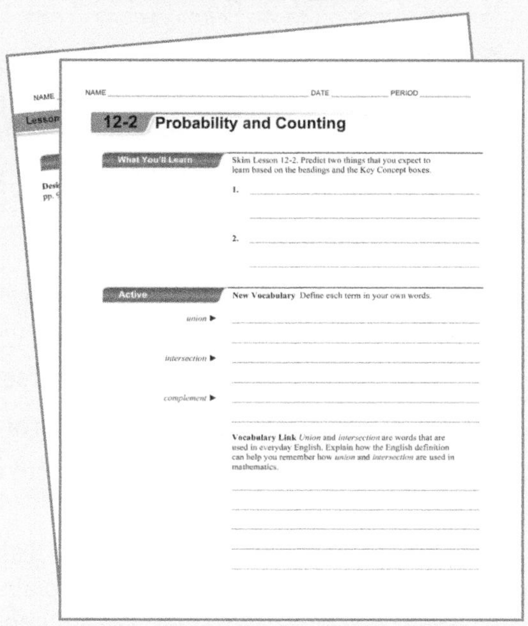
NAME ______ DATE ______ PERIOD ______

12-2 Probability and Counting

What You'll Learn
Skim Lesson 12-2. Predict two things that you expect to learn based on the headings and the Key Concept boxes.
1.
2.

Active
New Vocabulary Define each term in your own words.
union ▶
intersection ▶
complement ▶

Vocabulary Link *Union* and *intersection* are words that are used in everyday English. Explain how the English definition can help you remember how *union* and *intersection* are used in mathematics.

Extension Activities that can be used to extend lesson concepts

Enrichment

OL BL ELL

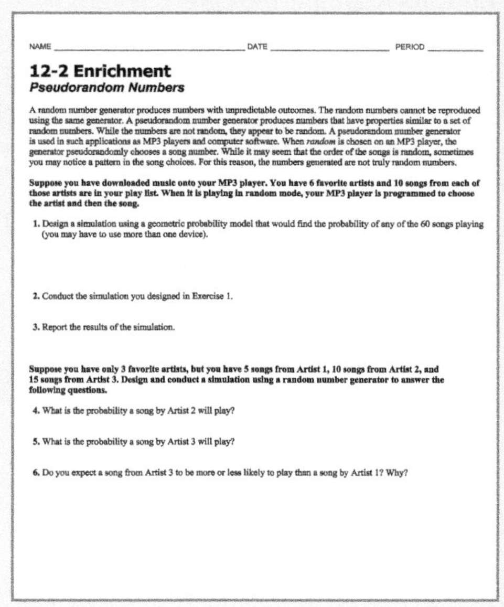
NAME ______ DATE ______ PERIOD ______

12-2 Enrichment
Pseudorandom Numbers

A random number generator produces numbers with unpredictable outcomes. The random numbers cannot be reproduced using the same generator. A pseudorandom number generator produces numbers that have properties similar to a set of random numbers. While the numbers are not random, they appear to be random. A pseudorandom number generator is used in such applications as MP3 players and computer software. When *random* is chosen on an MP3 player, the generator pseudorandomly chooses a song number. While it may seem that the order of the songs is random, sometimes you may notice a pattern in the song choices. For this reason, the numbers generated are not truly random numbers.

Suppose you have downloaded music onto your MP3 player. You have 6 favorite artists and 10 songs from each of those artists are in your play list. When it is playing in random mode, your MP3 player is programmed to choose the artist and then the song.

1. Design a simulation using a geometric probability model that would find the probability of any of the 60 songs playing (you may have to use more than one device).
2. Conduct the simulation you designed in Exercise 1.
3. Report the results of the simulation.

Suppose you have only 3 favorite artists, but you have 5 songs from Artist 1, 10 songs from Artist 2, and 15 songs from Artist 3. Design and conduct a simulation using a random number generator to answer the following questions.

4. What is the probability a song by Artist 2 will play?
5. What is the probability a song by Artist 3 will play?
6. Do you expect a song from Artist 3 to be more or less likely to play than a song by Artist 1? Why?

Launch

Have students read the Why? section of the lesson. Ask:

- **How could you use sets to describe this situation?** Sample answer: Set A = rap songs on the music player; set B = songs on the music player that are longer than 4 minutes
- **Is it possible for a song to be in both of the sets you described? Explain.** Yes; a rap song that is longer than 4 minutes would be in both sets.

Teach

Ask the scaffolded questions for each example to build conceptual understanding for students at all levels.

1 Use Unions and Intersections

Example 1 Find the Union of Events

AL **What is the sample space?** {1, 2, 3, 4, 5, 6, 7, 8}

OL **How would you describe finding the union of two sets in your own words?** Sample answer: Make a new set consisting of all the elements in either of the two given sets.

BL **Suppose event B were the event that the spinner lands on a number between 3 and 8, inclusive. What is $P(A \cup B)$ in this case?** $\frac{7}{8}$

Need Another Example?

A set of 12 cards are numbered 1 through 12. You choose one card at random. Let A be the event that you choose a multiple of 4. Let B be the event that you choose a number less than 3.

a. Find $A \cup B$. {1, 2, 4, 8, 12}

b. Find the probability that event A or event B will occur. $\frac{5}{12}$

LESSON 2

Probability and Counting

Then	Now	Why?
You represented sample spaces using tables, lists, and tree diagrams.	1 Describe events as subsets of sample spaces by using intersections and unions. 2 Find probabilities of complements.	Most music players offer a shuffle feature. When this feature is selected, the probability that the next song you hear is a rap song or a song that is longer than 4 minutes is related to the union of two sets.

New Vocabulary
union
intersection
complement

Mathematical Practices
1 Make sense of problems and persevere in solving them.
2 Reason abstractly and quantitatively.
4 Model with mathematics.

1 Use Unions and Intersections An event is a subset of a sample space, consisting of an outcome or a set of outcomes. You can use unions and intersections to describe events.

Key Concept Union and Intersection of Events

The **union** of two events is the set of all outcomes that are in either event. The union of events A and B is represented by $A \cup B$.

$A \cup B$

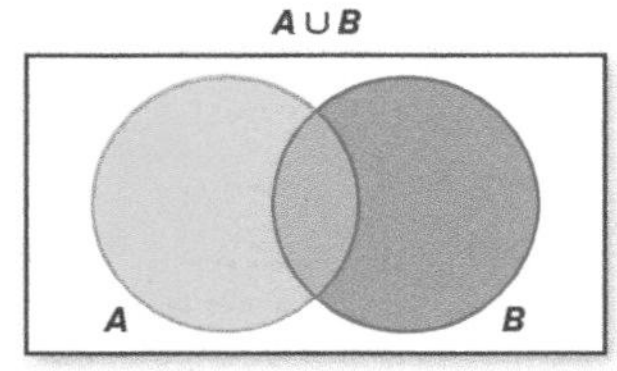

The **intersection** of two events is the set of all outcomes that are common to both events. The intersection of events A and B is represented by $A \cap B$.

$A \cap B$

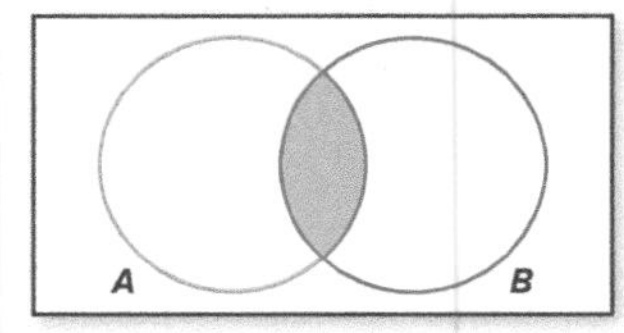

In an experiment with equally likely outcomes, the probability of an event E is the ratio of the number of outcomes in the event to the number of outcomes in the sample space S. You can write this as $P(E) = \frac{n(E)}{n(S)}$, where $P(E)$ is the probability of the event, $n(E)$ is the number of outcomes in the event, and $n(S)$ is the number of outcomes in the sample space.

Example 1 Find the Union of Events

A spinner is divided into 8 equal sections that are numbered 1 through 8 as shown. Let A be the event that the spinner lands on an even number. Let B be the event that it lands on a number between 5 and 8, inclusive.

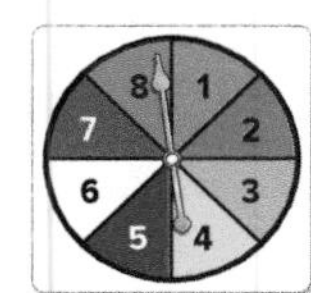

a. Find $A \cup B$.

$A = \{2, 4, 6, 8\}$

$B = \{5, 6, 7, 8\}$

Make a Venn diagram. List the outcomes that are in Event A or in Event B.

$A \cup B = \{2, 4, 5, 6, 7, 8\}$

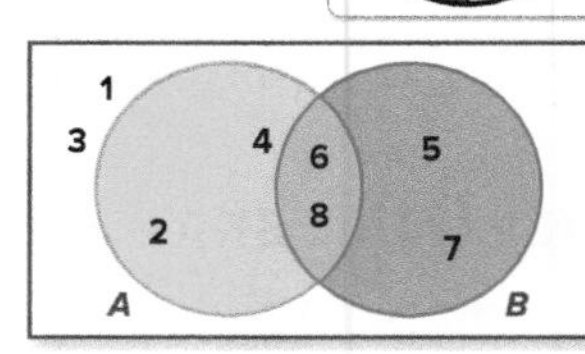

Noel Hendrickson/Blend Images/Getty Images

MP Mathematical Practices Strategies

Reason abstractly and quantitatively.
Help students analyze relationships between two events in a sample space. For example, ask:

- **What are some different ways to represent relationships among events?** Sample answer: Use a Venn diagram, make one or more lists, etc.
- **What word usually indicates an intersection of events?** and
- **What word usually indicates a union of events?** or
- **When should you use the complement of an event?** to find the probability of an event not occurring
- **Given two events A and B, does $A \cup B$ always have more outcomes than either event A alone or event B alone? Explain.** No; for example, if event A is a subset of event B, then $A \cup B$ has the same number of outcomes as event B.

b. Find the probability that event A or event B will occur.

The probability that event A or event B will occur is $P(A \cup B)$.

$$P(A \cup B) = \frac{n(A \cup B)}{n(S)}$$
$$= \frac{6}{8} \quad \text{There are 6 outcomes in } A \cup B \text{ and 8 outcomes in the sample space.}$$
$$= \frac{3}{4}$$

Study Tip

Unions and Intersections The word *or* is a clue that a union of sets may be needed. The word *and* is a clue that an intersection of sets may be needed.

Guided Practice

Let A be the event that the spinner lands on a number less than 4. Let B be the event that it lands on an odd number.

1A. Find $A \cup B$.

1B. Find the probability that event A or event B will occur.

The probability of the intersection of two events is the probability that both events occur.

Example 2 Find the Intersection of Events

The Venn diagram shows members of two school sports teams who serve on the student council. One of the students will be chosen at random to attend a meeting. Let A be the event that a student plays basketball and let B be the event that a student plays tennis.

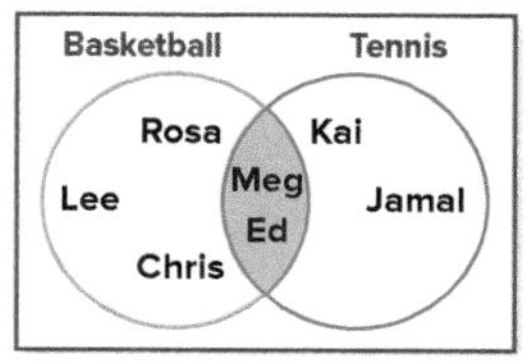

a. Find $A \cap B$.

$A \cap B$ consists of students who play both basketball and tennis.

$A \cap B = \{\text{Meg, Ed}\}$

b. What is the probability that the student who is chosen plays both basketball and tennis?

$$P(A \cap B) = \frac{n(A \cap B)}{n(S)}$$
$$= \frac{2}{7} \quad \text{There are 2 outcomes in } A \cap B \text{ and 7 outcomes in the sample space.}$$

Guided Practice

A standard number cube is rolled. Let A be the event that a number greater than 3 is rolled and let B be the event that an even number is rolled.

2A. Find $A \cap B$.

2B. What is the probability of rolling a number that is greater than 3 and even?

2 Use Complements

The **complement** of an event A consists of all the outcomes in the sample space that are not included as outcomes of event A.

When a standard number cube is rolled, the probability of rolling a 4 is $\frac{1}{6}$. What is the probability of *not* rolling a 4? There are five outcomes for this event: 1, 2, 3, 5, and 6. So, $P(\text{not } 4) = \frac{5}{6}$. Notice that this probability is also $1 - \frac{1}{6}$ or $1 - P(4)$.

Watch Out!

Students often confuse the symbols for the union and intersection of sets and their connection to the words *and* and *or*. Tell students that the intersection symbol, ∩, looks something like a capital A ("and"), while the union symbol, ∪, looks something like a boat that could hold an oar ("or").

MP Teaching the Mathematical Practices

Tools Mathematically proficient students consider the available tools when solving a mathematical problem. These tools include paper and pencil, so students should get in the habit of thinking of a Venn diagram as a problem-solving tool. As students create and interpret Venn diagrams, encourage them to use color coding, shading, or other methods to help make sense of the diagram.

Example 2 Find the Intersection of Events

AL What is the sample space? {Rosa, Lee, Chris, Meg, Ed, Kai, Jamal}

OL What part of the Venn diagram helps solve the problem? the region where the circles intersect

BL If Chris played both basketball and tennis, how would the probability change? $P(A \cap B) = \frac{3}{7}$

Need Another Example?

The Venn diagram shows the employees of a store and the days of the weekend when they work. Let A be the event that an employee works Saturday and let B be the event that an employee works Sunday. An employee is chosen at random to attend a training session.

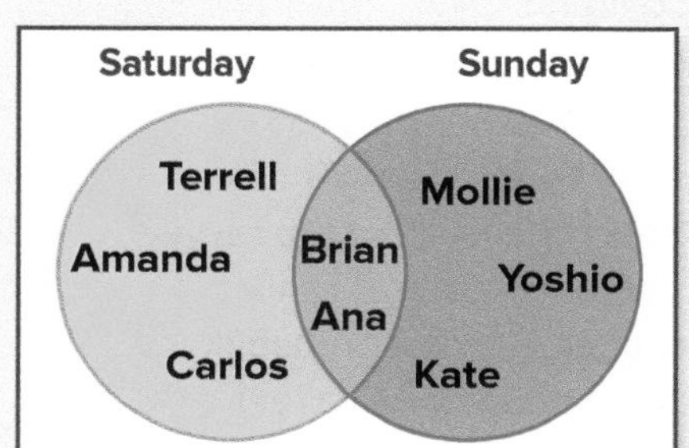

a. Find $A \cap B$. {Brian, Ana}

b. What is the probability that the employee who is chosen works on both Saturday and Sunday? $\frac{1}{4}$

2 Use Complements

Example 3 Use Complementary Events

AL What is the probability of selecting one of Francesca's tickets? $\frac{20}{300}$ or about 6.7%

OL How would you write the expression for $P(\text{not } A)$ if Francesca had bought 5 additional tickets? $1 - \frac{25}{300}$

BL If a total of 200 raffle tickets had been sold, what would be the probability of Francesca not winning? $\frac{9}{10}$ or 90%

Need Another Example?

A box contains 35 red marbles and 120 marbles of other colors. Isaac chooses one of the marbles without looking. What is the probability that he does not choose a red marble? $\frac{24}{31}$ or about 77%

Teaching Tip

Structure Explain that the sum of the probability of an event and the probability of the event not happening must be 1, because all of the outcomes in the sample space are contained in the event or its complement. In other words, $P(A) + P(\text{not } A) = 1$. Solving for $P(\text{not } A)$ shows that $P(\text{not } A) = 1 - P(A)$.

Example 4 Find Probabilities of Events

AL Which part or parts of the diagram represent people who saw a comedy or an action film? the interiors of the two circles

OL How do you find $n(S)$? Add all the numbers in the Venn diagram: $5 + 2 + 2 + 6 = 15$

BL What is the probability that the winner will be someone who saw a comedy film and an action film in the past week? $\frac{2}{15}$ or about 13%

Need Another Example?

Some visitors to an amusement park were surveyed to find out whether they rode the roller coaster or the Ferris wheel. The Venn diagram represents the results of the survey. One respondent will be chosen at random to win a free pass to the park. Find the probability that the winner will be someone who rode the roller coaster and the Ferris wheel. $\frac{3}{20}$ or 15%

Key Concept Probability of the Complement of an Event

Words	The probability that an event will not occur is equal to 1 minus the probability that the event will occur.
Symbols	For an event A, $P(\text{not } A) = 1 - P(A)$.

Reading Math

Complement Everyday use—something that fills up, completes, or makes perfect. Math meaning—all the outcomes in the sample space that are not included in the outcomes of an event. The complement of event A can be written as A^C.

S.CP.1

Example 3 Use Complementary Events

RAFFLE Francesca bought 20 raffle tickets, hoping to win a $100 gift card to her favorite clothing store. If a total of 300 raffle tickets were sold, what is the probability that Francesca will not win the gift card?

Let event A represent selecting one of Francesca's tickets. Then find the probability of the complement of A.

$P(\text{not } A) = 1 - P(A)$ — Probability of a complement

$= 1 - \frac{20}{300}$ — Substitution

$= \frac{280}{300}$ or $\frac{14}{15}$ — Subtract and simplify.

The probability that one of Francesca's tickets will not be selected is $\frac{14}{15}$ or about 93%.

Guided Practice

3. If the chance of rain is 70%, what is the probability that it will not rain? 30%

S.CP.1

Real-World Example 4 Find Probabilities of Events

MOVIES Outside a movie theater, 15 people were asked whether they had seen a comedy film or an action film in the past week. The Venn diagram represents the results of the survey. One respondent will be chosen at random to win a free movie ticket.

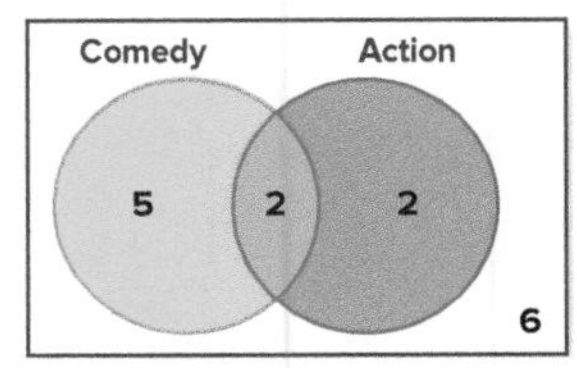

Find the probability that the winner will have seen a comedy film or an action film in the past week.

Add the values in the relevant sections of the Venn diagram to find the number of people who saw a comedy film or an action film: $5 + 2 + 2 = 9$.

$P(\text{comedy} \cup \text{action}) = \frac{n(\text{comedy} \cup \text{action})}{n(S)}$ — Probability of a union

$= \frac{9}{15}$ — Substitution

$= \frac{3}{5}$ or 60% — Simplify.

Guided Practice

4. Find the probability that the winner will be someone who did not see an action film in the past week. $\frac{11}{15}$ or about 73%

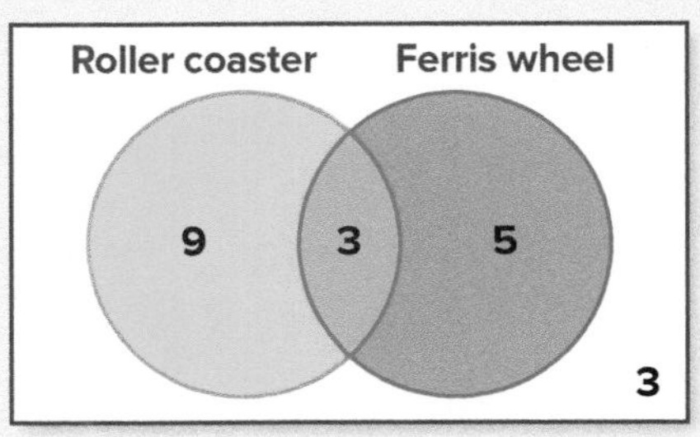

Differentiated Instruction AL OL

IF students have difficulty using intersections and unions of events,

THEN have them work in small groups to model the events using colored slips of paper or sticky notes. Students can write each outcome in event A on slips of one color and each outcome in event B on slips of another color. Then have students sort the slips into groups to represent intersections, unions, and complements.

Check Your Understanding

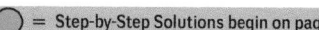

○ = Step-by-Step Solutions begin on page R13.

Go Online! for a Self-Check Quiz

Examples 1–2 S.CP.1

Consider the experiment of rolling a standard number cube. Find the probability of rolling each of the following.

1. a number less than 3 or an even number $\frac{2}{3}$
2. an even number or a number divisible by 4 $\frac{1}{2}$
3. a multiple of 3 and an even number $\frac{1}{6}$
4. an odd number that is a prime $\frac{1}{3}$
5. a 6 or a 4 $\frac{1}{3}$
6. a perfect square and a multiple of 2 $\frac{1}{6}$

Example 3 S.CP.1

7. Consider the experiment of rolling a pair of number cubes. Let A be the event of rolling a sum of 8 or less.
   a. What outcomes are in the complement of event A? 9, 10, 11, 12
   b. Find the probability of the complement of event A. $\frac{5}{18}$
   c. Find the probability of event A. $\frac{13}{18}$

Example 4 S.CP.1

FITNESS A local gym requires new members to fill out a questionnaire about whether they want to lose weight (L) or improve fitness (F). The Venn diagram shows the results. Find the probability of the following events when a new gym member is chosen at random.

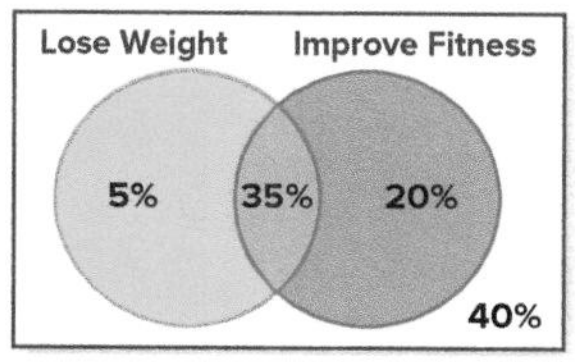

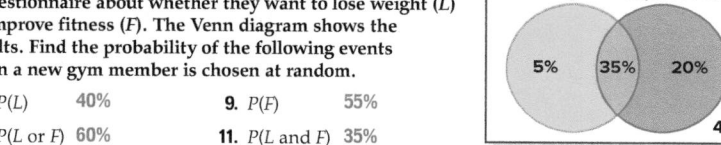

8. $P(L)$ 40%
9. $P(F)$ 55%
10. $P(L$ or $F)$ 60%
11. $P(L$ and $F)$ 35%
12. $P($not $L)$ 60%
13. $P($not $F)$ 45%

Practice and Problem Solving

Extra Practice is on page R12.

Examples 1–2 S.CP.1

Consider the experiment of picking one of the seven days of the week at random. Find the probability of picking each of the following.

14. Friday or a day of the weekend $\frac{3}{7}$
15. a day that starts with the letter T and a day that ends with the letter Y $\frac{2}{7}$
16. a day that contains 8 or more letters and a day that contains the letter D $\frac{3}{7}$

Example 3 S.CP.1

17. **AFTER-SCHOOL PROGRAM** At Crossdale High School, 49 incoming freshmen were asked whether they prefer music or art. Students were then randomly selected to be placed in an after-school program. The two-way frequency table shows the results of the survey.

	Girl	Boy	Totals
Music	12	17	29
Art	9	11	20
Totals	21	28	49

   a. What is the probability of selecting a girl who prefers music? $\frac{12}{49}$
   b. What is the probability of not selecting a girl who prefers music? $\frac{37}{49}$

Example 4 S.CP.1

MARBLES A jar contains 105 marbles. There are 36 red marbles, 44 white marbles, 20 green marbles, and 5 orange marbles. You reach into the jar and choose one marble without looking.

18. Find the probability of choosing an orange or red marble. $\frac{41}{105}$
19. Find the probability of choosing a white or green marble. $\frac{64}{105}$
20. Find the probability of not choosing a green marble. $\frac{17}{21}$
21. Find the probability that the marble you choose is not red and not orange. $\frac{64}{105}$
22. Find the probability that the marble you choose is not red or not orange. 1

Differentiated Homework Options

Levels	AL Basic	OL Core	BL Advanced
Exercises	14–22, 31–42	15–27 odd, 28–42	28–34, (optional: 35–42)
2-Day Option	15–21 odd, 35–42	14–22	
	14–22 even, 31–34	23–42	

You can use ALEKS to provide additional remediation support with personalized instruction and practice.

Practice

Formative Assessment Use Exercises 1–13 to assess students' understanding of the concepts in the lesson.

The Practice and Problem Solving exercises assess the content taught in the lesson. The Preparing for Assessment page is meant to be used as preparation for end-of-course assessment.

Extra Practice

See page R12 for extra exercises for students who are approaching level or for on-level students who need additional reinforcement.

Levels of Complexity Chart

The levels of the exercises progress from 1 to 3, with Level 1 indicating the lowest level of complexity.

Exercises	14–22	23–27, 35–42	28–34
Level 3			●
Level 2		●	
Level 1	●		

MP Teaching the Mathematical Practices

Sense-Making Mathematically proficient students look for entry points to the solution of a problem and plan a solution pathway. For Exercises 28–30, encourage students to think about the given table of data before they begin solving the problems. For instance, ask them to look for patterns in the table and/or describe conclusions that can be drawn from it. Have students explain the structure of the table in their own words. This type of preliminary sense-making can help students solve problems more efficiently and with greater confidence.

Assess

Ticket Out the Door Write several subsets of the numbers 1–10 on the board, such as $A = \{2, 3, 4\}$, $B = \{1, 3, 5, 7, 9\}$, and $C = \{3, 8\}$. Make several copies of probability statements, such as $P(A \cap C)$ and give one probability statement to each student. As students leave the room, ask them to tell you the probability.

B **Consider the experiment of selecting one card at random from a standard deck of 52 playing cards. Find the probability of selecting each of the following.**

23. a card that is not a spade $\frac{3}{4}$

24. a card that is not a 7 $\frac{12}{13}$

25. a card that is a diamond or a 3 $\frac{4}{13}$

26. a card that is neither a king nor a queen $\frac{11}{13}$

27 A sample of 370 magazines was analyzed to determine the types of electronics that were advertised in the magazines. The results are shown in the Venn diagram.

a. What does the 10 represent in the lower right-hand corner of the Venn diagram?

b. If you choose a magazine at random, what is the probability that it will contain an advertisement for a smartphone and a DVR? $\frac{7}{37}$

27a. Ten of the magazines had no advertisements for any of these types of electronics.

Type of Electronics

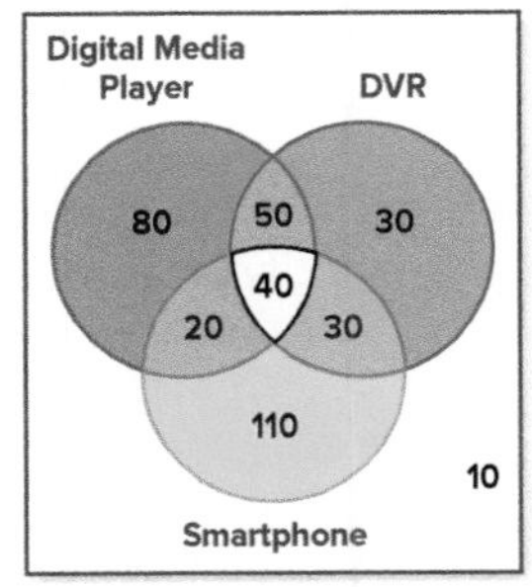

C MP **SENSE-MAKING** **One hundred students were asked how many hours they studied per week and their average test score. The table shows the results.**

31. Sample answer: Rolling a standard number cube with A = rolling a number greater than 1 and B = rolling a number less than 5.

	Less than 70	70–90	Greater than 90	Totals
Studied 8 h or more per week	12	15	37	64
Studied less than 8 h per week	12	16	8	36
Totals	24	31	45	100

28. What is the probability that a student has an average test score greater than 90 and did not study 8 hours or more per week? 8%

29. What is the probability that a student has an average test score between 70 and 90 and studied less than 8 hours per week? 16%

30. What is the probability that a student does not have an average test score greater than 90? 55%

33. No; Latricia did not include the 5 outcomes common to events A and B when she found $P(A)$; Amelie did not calculate $P(A)$ correctly; $P(A)$ should be $\frac{13}{32}$, so $P(\text{not } A)$ is $\frac{19}{32}$.

S.CP.1

H.O.T. Problems Use **H**igher-**O**rder **T**hinking Skills

31. OPEN-ENDED Describe two events A and B such that $P(A \text{ and } B) = \frac{1}{2}$.

32. MP **REASONING** There are n outcomes in a sample space and m outcomes in event E, where $m \le n$. Write an expression for $P(\text{not } E)$. $1 - \frac{m}{n}$

33. ERROR ANALYSIS The Venn diagram shows the number of outcomes in events A and B. Latricia and Amelie were given this information and were asked to find $P(\text{not } A)$. Is either of them correct? Explain your reasoning.

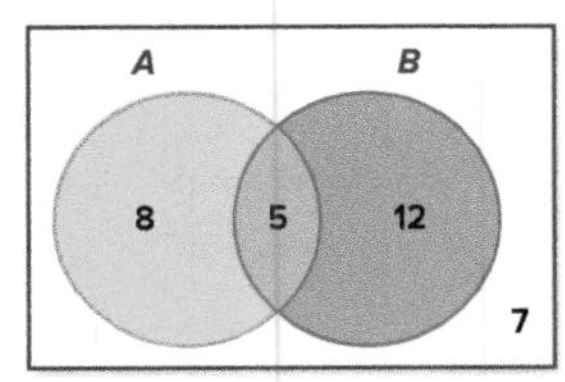

Latricia

$P(\text{not } A) = 1 - P(A)$
$= 1 - \frac{8}{32}$
$= 1 - \frac{1}{4} = \frac{3}{4}$

Amelie

$P(\text{not } A) = 1 - P(A)$
$= 1 - \frac{1}{13}$
$= \frac{12}{13}$

34. Sample answer: In some cases it may be easier to find the probability of the complement of an event because the complement might contain fewer outcomes than the event itself.

34. WRITING IN MATH Explain when you might find the probability of an event by first finding the probability of its complement.

MP Standards for Mathematical Practice

Emphasis On	Exercises
1 Make sense of problems and persevere in solving them.	28–31, 36, 37, 39–42
2 Reason abstractly and quantitatively.	32
4 Model with mathematics.	8–13, 17–22, 27, 37
6 Attend to precision.	31, 35, 38, 39

Go Online!

eSolutions Manual

Create worksheets, answer keys, and solutions handouts for your assignments.

Preparing for Assessment

35. A spinner has 10 equal sections that are labeled 1 through 10. Let *A* be the event that the spinner lands on a prime number and let *B* be the event that the spinner lands on an even number. What is $A \cup B$? MP 6 S.CP.1 C

- ◯ A {2}
- ◯ B {2, 3, 5, 7}
- ◯ C {2, 3, 4, 5, 6, 7, 8, 10}
- ◯ D {2, 4, 6, 8}

36. A jar contains 25 ping pong balls that are numbered 1 through 25. Wei chooses one of the ping pong balls without looking. Let *A* be the event that she chooses an odd number and let *B* be the event that she chooses a multiple of 5. Which of the following outcomes are in the event $A \cap B$? MP 1 S.CP.1 A, D

- ☐ A 5
- ☐ B 7
- ☐ C 10
- ☐ D 15
- ☐ E 19
- ☐ F 20

37. There are 32 students in Mr. Ibarra's class. Nine of the students are in the chess club only, 5 of the students are in the drama club only, and 6 of the students are in both clubs. Mr. Ibarra chooses one student at random. What is the probability that he does not choose a student in the chess club? MP 1, 4 S.CP.1 C

- ◯ A $\frac{9}{32}$
- ◯ B $\frac{15}{32}$
- ◯ C $\frac{17}{32}$
- ◯ D $\frac{21}{32}$

38. There are 8 bottles of juice in a cooler. If 5 of them are apple juice, what is the probability of choosing a bottle at random and not choosing apple juice? Write your answer as a decimal. MP 6 S.CP.1

P(not apple juice) = 0.375

39. What is the sample space for choosing a prime number less than 14 at random? MP 6 S.CP.1 C

- **a.** {1, 2, 3, 5, 7, 11, 13, 14}
- **b.** {2, 3, 5, 7, 11, 13, 14}
- **c.** {2, 3, 5, 7, 11, 13}
- **d.** {1, 3, 5, 7, 9, 11, 13}

40. Stacie surveyed some of her friends to find out whether they had been bowling in the past week (event *A*) or if they had been to the skate park in the past week (event *B*). The Venn diagram shows the results. What is $P(A \cap B)$? MP 1, 4 S.CP.1 B

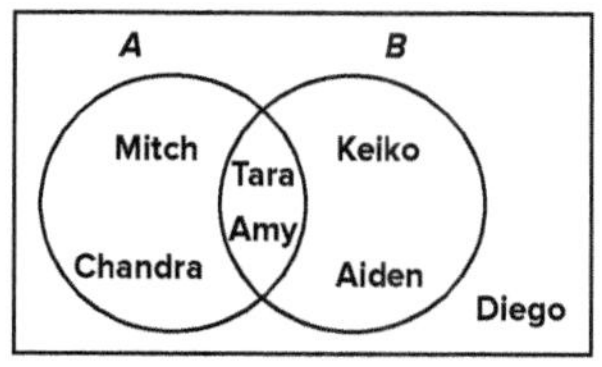

- ◯ A $\frac{1}{7}$
- ◯ B $\frac{2}{7}$
- ◯ C $\frac{4}{7}$
- ◯ D $\frac{6}{7}$

41. Omar has a bag of 26 tiles, each containing a different letter of the alphabet. He reaches into the bag and chooses one tile without looking. What is the best estimate of the probability that he chooses a vowel or the letter Y? MP 1 S.CP.1 C

- ◯ A 4%
- ◯ B 19%
- ◯ C 23%
- ◯ D 81%

42. **MULTI-STEP** Julia has a set of 15 cards that are numbered 1 through 15. She shuffles the cards and chooses one card at random. Let *A* be the event that she chooses a multiple of 3 and let *B* be the event that she chooses an even number. MP 1 S.CP.1

- **a.** Make a Venn diagram to represent the sample space and the two events. List the outcomes in the appropriate sections of the diagram. See margin.
- **b.** What is $A \cup B$? {2, 3, 4, 6, 8, 9, 10, 12, 14, 15}
- **c.** Find $P(A \cup B)$. $\frac{2}{3}$

Preparing for Assessment

Exercises 35–42 require students to use the skills they will need on standardized assessments. Each exercise is dual-coded with content standards and mathematical practice standards.

Dual Coding

Items	Content Standards	MP Mathematical Practices
35	S.CP.1	6
36	S.CP.1	1
37	S.CP.1	1, 4
38	S.CP.1	6
39	S.CP.1	6
40	S.CP.1	1, 4
41	S.CP.1	1
42	S.CP.1	1

Diagnose Student Errors

Survey student responses for each item. Class trends may indicate common errors and misconceptions.

35.

A	Chose $A \cap B$
B	Chose event *A*
C	CORRECT
D	Chose event *B*

36.

A	CORRECT
B	Chose an outcome in $A \cup B$
C	Chose a multiple of 5 that is not odd
D	CORRECT
E	Chose an outcome in $A \cup B$
F	Chose a multiple of 5 that is not odd

37.

A	Found P(chess club only)
B	Found P(chess club)
C	CORRECT
D	Found P(not drama)

40.

A	Found P(Diego)
B	CORRECT
C	Found P(*A*) or P(*B*)
D	Found $P(A \cup B)$

41.

A	Found P(Y)
B	Found P(vowel)
C	CORRECT
D	Found P(not vowel)

Additional Answer

42a.

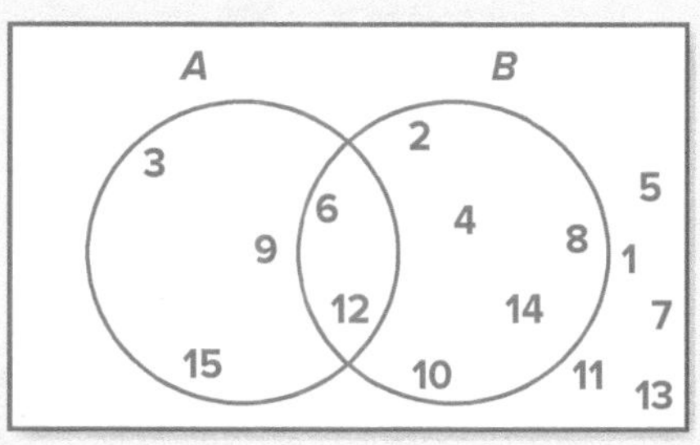

Go Online!

Quizzes

Students can use *Self-Check Quizzes* to check their understanding of this lesson and have the results sent to you. You can also give *Quiz 2*, which covers the content in Lessons 12-2 and 12-3.

LESSON 12-3
Probability with Permutations and Combinations

SUGGESTED PACING (DAYS)

	Instruction
90 min.	0.75
45 min.	1

Track Your Progress

Objectives

1. Use permutations with probability.
2. Use combinations with probability.

Mathematical Background

A *permutation* is a selection of objects where order is important. A *combination* is a selection of objects in which order is not important. Factorials are used to count arrangements of objects.

Skills Trace

THEN	NOW	NEXT
S.CP.1 Describe events as subsets of a sample space (the set of outcomes) using characteristics (or categories) of the outcomes, or as unions, intersections, or complements of other events ("or," "and," "not").	**S.CP.9** Use permutations and combinations to compute probabilities of compound events and solve problems.	**S.MD.7** Analyze decisions and strategies using probability concepts.

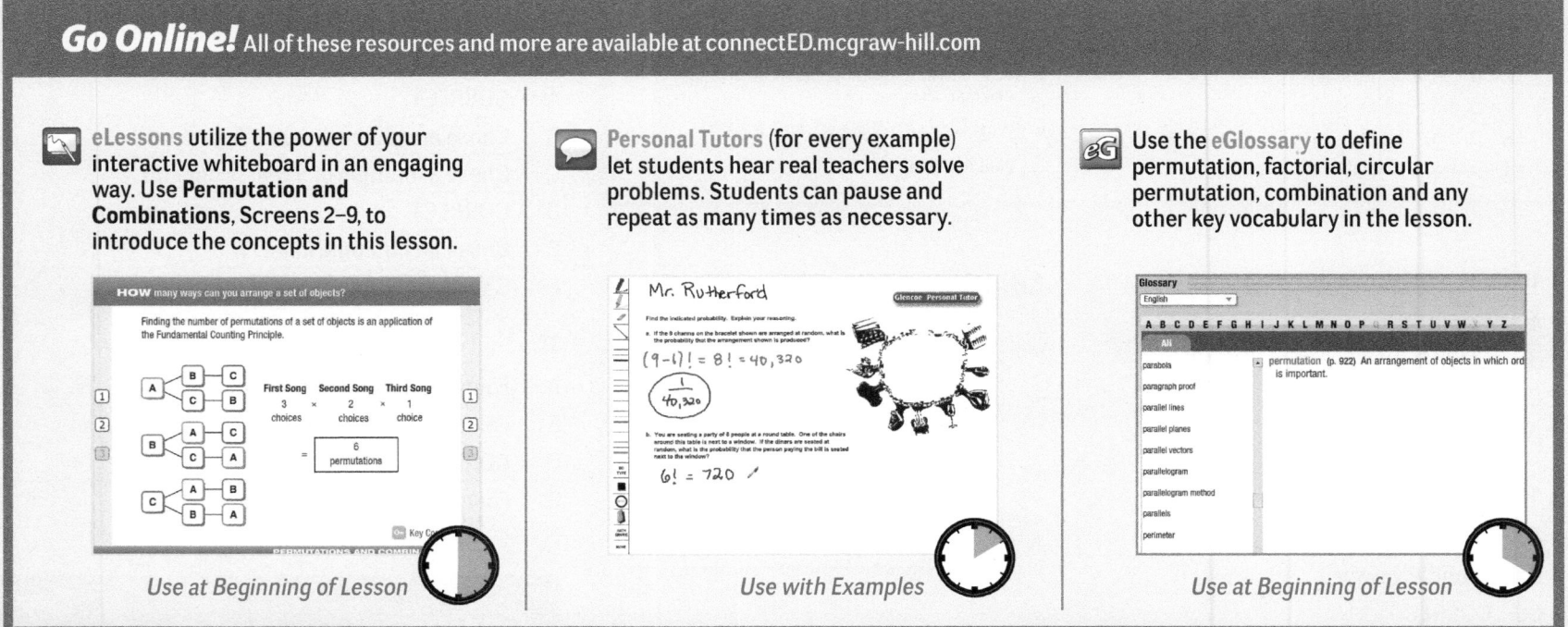

Go Online! All of these resources and more are available at connectED.mcgraw-hill.com

eLessons utilize the power of your interactive whiteboard in an engaging way. Use **Permutation and Combinations**, Screens 2–9, to introduce the concepts in this lesson.

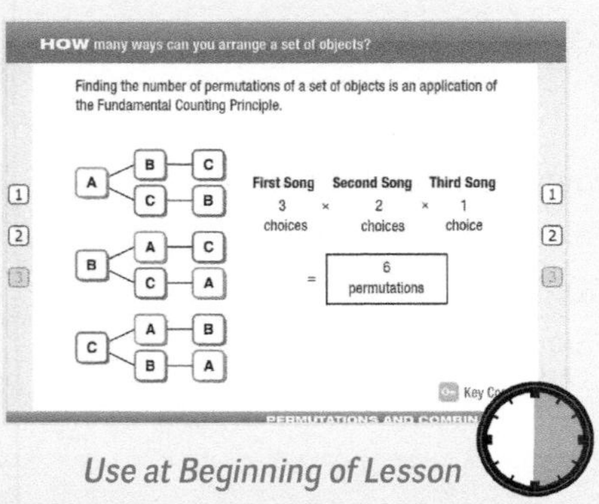

Use at Beginning of Lesson

Personal Tutors (for every example) let students hear real teachers solve problems. Students can pause and repeat as many times as necessary.

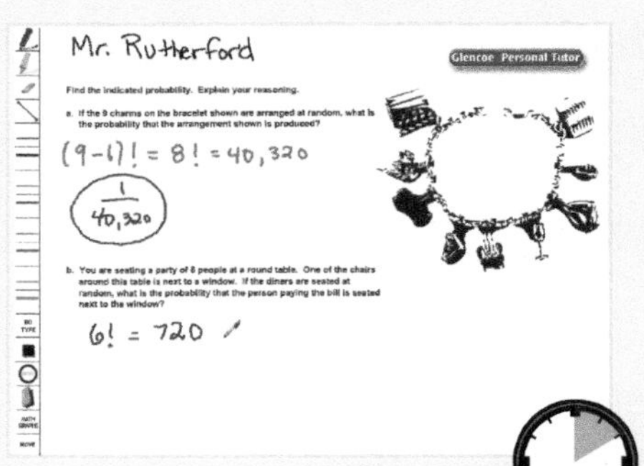

Use with Examples

Use the eGlossary to define permutation, factorial, circular permutation, combination and any other key vocabulary in the lesson.

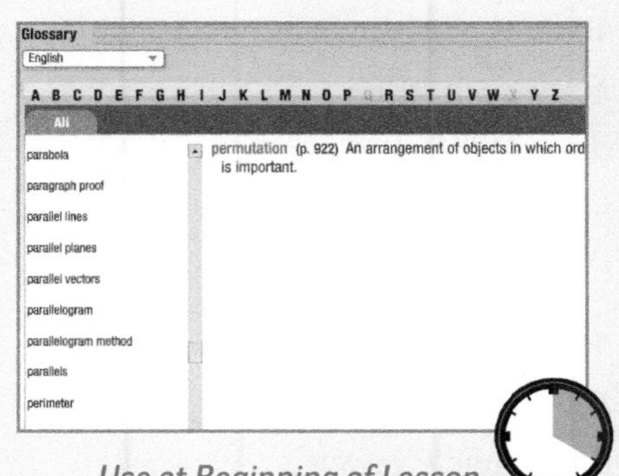

Use at Beginning of Lesson

OER Using Open Educational Resources

Professional Development Probability with permutations and combinations can be a difficult subject to teach. For new ideas visit **Google Classroom Lessons and Resources.** *Use during planning*

Go Online!
connectED.mcgraw-hill.com

Worksheets

Differentiate Your Resources

Extra Practice Additional practice or homework; Skills Practice is best for approaching-level students and Practice is best for on-level and beyond-level students

Skills Practice

AL OL ELL

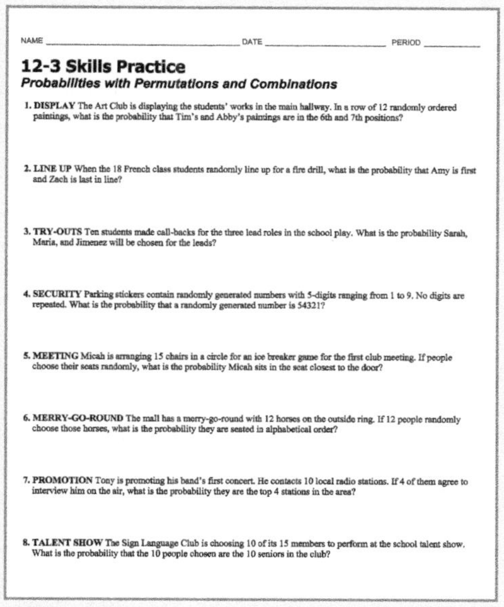
NAME ______ DATE ______ PERIOD ______

12-3 Skills Practice
Probabilities with Permutations and Combinations

1. **DISPLAY** The Art Club is displaying the students' works in the main hallway. In a row of 12 randomly ordered paintings, what is the probability that Tim's and Abby's paintings are in the 6th and 7th positions?
2. **LINE UP** When the 18 French class students randomly line up for a fire drill, what is the probability that Amy is first and Zach is last in line?
3. **TRY-OUTS** Ten students made call-backs for the three lead roles in the school play. What is the probability Sarah, Maria, and Jimenez will be chosen for the leads?
4. **SECURITY** Parking stickers contain randomly generated numbers with 5-digits ranging from 1 to 9. No digits are repeated. What is the probability that a randomly generated number is 54321?
5. **MEETING** Micah is arranging 15 chairs in a circle for an ice breaker game for the first club meeting. If people choose their seats randomly, what is the probability Micah sits in the seat closest to the door?
6. **MERRY-GO-ROUND** The mall has a merry-go-round with 12 horses on the outside ring. If 12 people randomly choose those horses, what is the probability they are seated in alphabetical order?
7. **PROMOTION** Tony is promoting his band's first concert. He contacts 10 local radio stations. If 4 of them agree to interview him on the air, what is the probability they are the top 4 stations in the area?
8. **TALENT SHOW** The Sign Language Club is choosing 10 of its 15 members to perform at the school talent show. What is the probability that the 10 people chosen are the 10 seniors in the club?

Practice

AL OL BL ELL

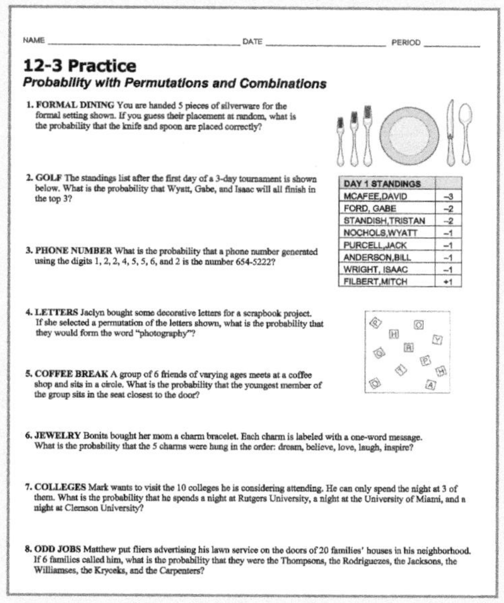
NAME ______ DATE ______ PERIOD ______

12-3 Practice
Probability with Permutations and Combinations

1. **FORMAL DINING** You are handed 5 pieces of silverware for the formal setting shown. If you guess their placement at random, what is the probability that the knife and spoon are placed correctly?
2. **GOLF** The standings list after the first day of a 3-day tournament is shown below. What is the probability that Wyatt, Gabe, and Isaac will all finish in the top 3?

DAY 1 STANDINGS	
MCAFEE,DAVID	−3
FORD, GABE	−2
STANDISH,TRISTAN	−2
NOCHOLS,WYATT	−1
PURCELL,JACK	−1
ANDERSON,BILL	−1
WRIGHT, ISAAC	−1
FILBERT,MITCH	+1

3. **PHONE NUMBER** What is the probability that a phone number generated using the digits 1, 2, 2, 4, 5, 5, 6, and 2 is the number 654-5222?
4. **LETTERS** Jaclyn bought some decorative letters for a scrapbook project. If she selected a permutation of the letters shown, what is the probability that they would form the word "photography"?
5. **COFFEE BREAK** A group of 6 friends of varying ages meets at a coffee shop and sits in a circle. What is the probability that the youngest member of the group sits in the seat closest to the door?
6. **JEWELRY** Bonita bought her mom a charm bracelet. Each charm is labeled with a one-word message. What is the probability that the 5 charms were hung in the order: dream, believe, love, laugh, inspire?
7. **COLLEGES** Mark wants to visit the 10 colleges he is considering attending. He can only spend the night at 3 of them. What is the probability that he spends a night at Rutgers University, a night at the University of Miami, and a night at Clemson University?
8. **ODD JOBS** Matthew put fliers advertising his lawn service on the doors of 20 families' houses in his neighborhood. If 6 families called him, what is the probability that they were the Thompsons, the Rodriguezes, the Jacksons, the Williamses, the Kryceks, and the Carpenters?

Word Problem Practice

AL OL BL ELL

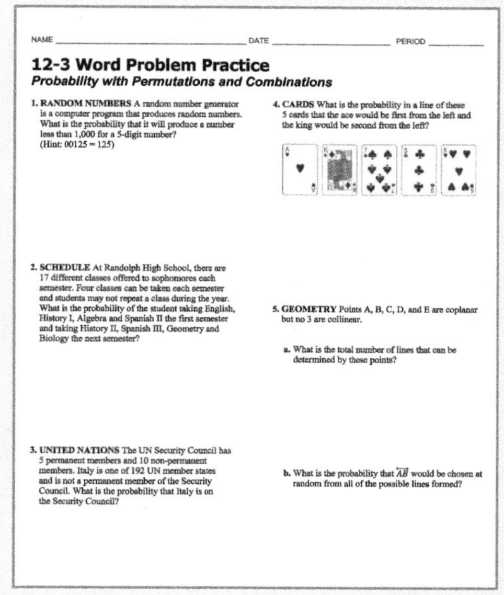
NAME ______ DATE ______ PERIOD ______

12-3 Word Problem Practice
Probability with Permutations and Combinations

1. **RANDOM NUMBERS** A random number generator is a computer program that produces random numbers. What is the probability that it will produce a number less than 1,000 for a 5-digit number? (Hint: 00125 = 125)
2. **SCHEDULE** At Randolph High School, there are 17 different classes offered to sophomores each semester. Four classes can be taken each semester and students may not repeat a class during the year. What is the probability of the student taking English, History I, Algebra and Spanish II the first semester and taking History II, Spanish III, Geometry and Biology the next semester?
3. **UNITED NATIONS** The UN Security Council has 5 permanent members and 10 non-permanent members. Italy is one of 192 UN member states and is not a permanent member of the Security Council. What is the probability that Italy is on the Security Council?
4. **CARDS** What is the probability in a line of these 5 cards that the ace would be first from the left and the king would be second from the left?
5. **GEOMETRY** Points A, B, C, D, and E are coplanar but no 3 are collinear.
   a. What is the total number of lines that can be determined by these points?
   b. What is the probability that $\overleftrightarrow{AB}$ would be chosen at random from all of the possible lines formed?

Intervention Reteaching and vocabulary activities that can be used with struggling or absent students and as ELL support

Study Guide and Intervention

AL OL ELL

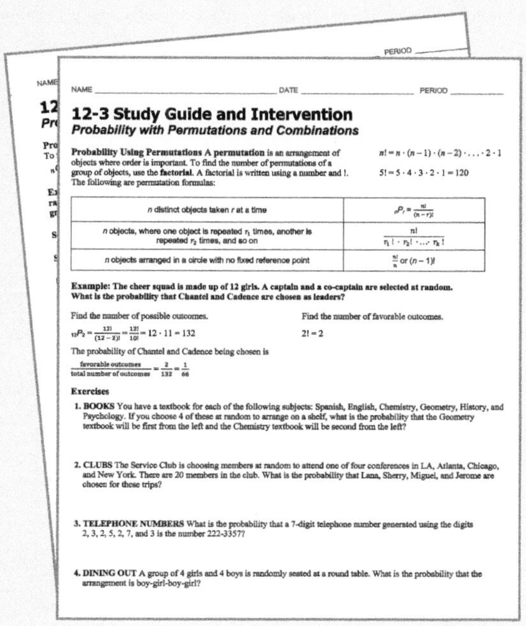
NAME ______ DATE ______ PERIOD ______

12-3 Study Guide and Intervention
Probability with Permutations and Combinations

Probability Using Permutations A **permutation** is an arrangement of objects where order is important. To find the number of permutations of a group of objects, use the **factorial**. A factorial is written using a number and !. The following are permutation formulas:

$n! = n \cdot (n-1) \cdot (n-2) \cdot \ldots \cdot 2 \cdot 1$

$5! = 5 \cdot 4 \cdot 3 \cdot 2 \cdot 1 = 120$

n distinct objects taken r at a time	${}_nP_r = \frac{n!}{(n-r)!}$
n objects, where one object is repeated r_1 times, another is repeated r_2 times, and so on	$\frac{n!}{r_1! \cdot r_2! \cdot \ldots \cdot r_k!}$
n objects arranged in a circle with no fixed reference point	$\frac{n!}{n}$ or $(n-1)!$

Example: The cheer squad is made up of 12 girls. A captain and a co-captain are selected at random. What is the probability that Chantel and Cadence are chosen as leaders?

Find the number of possible outcomes.

${}_{12}P_2 = \frac{12!}{(12-2)!} = \frac{12!}{10!} = 12 \cdot 11 = 132$

Find the number of favorable outcomes.

$2! = 2$

The probability of Chantel and Cadence being chosen is

$\frac{\text{favorable outcomes}}{\text{total number of outcomes}} = \frac{2}{132} = \frac{1}{66}$

Exercises

1. **BOOKS** You have a textbook for each of the following subjects: Spanish, English, Chemistry, Geometry, History, and Psychology. If you choose 4 of these at random to arrange on a shelf, what is the probability that the Geometry textbook will be first from the left and the Chemistry textbook will be second from the left?
2. **CLUBS** The Service Club is choosing members at random to attend one of four conferences in LA, Atlanta, Chicago, and New York. There are 20 members in the club. What is the probability that Lana, Sherry, Miguel, and Jerome are chosen for these trips?
3. **TELEPHONE NUMBERS** What is the probability that a 7-digit telephone number generated using the digits 2, 3, 2, 5, 2, 7, and 3 is the number 222-3357?
4. **DINING OUT** A group of 4 girls and 4 boys is randomly seated at a round table. What is the probability that the arrangement is boy-girl-boy-girl?

Study Notebook

AL OL BL ELL

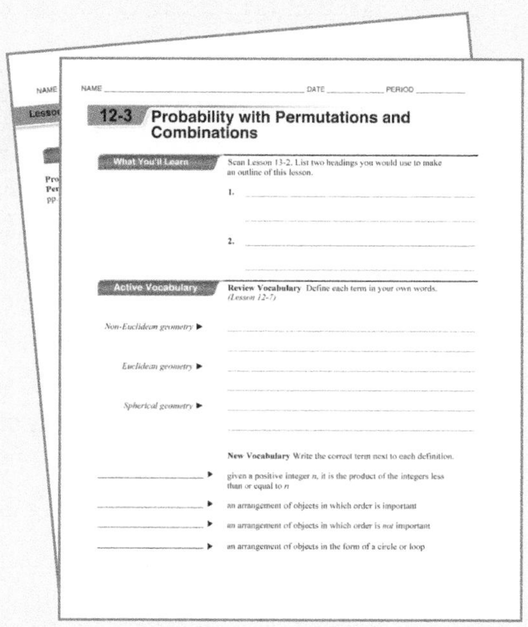
NAME ______ DATE ______ PERIOD ______

12-3 Probability with Permutations and Combinations

What You'll Learn Scan Lesson 13-2. List two headings you would use to make an outline of this lesson.

1. ______
2. ______

Active Vocabulary **Review Vocabulary** Define each term in your own words. *(Lesson 12-7)*

Non-Euclidean geometry ▶ ______

Euclidean geometry ▶ ______

Spherical geometry ▶ ______

New Vocabulary Write the correct term next to each definition.

______ ▶ given a positive integer n, it is the product of the integers less than or equal to n

______ ▶ an arrangement of objects in which order is important

______ ▶ an arrangement of objects in which order is *not* important

______ ▶ an arrangement of objects in the form of a circle or loop

Extension Activities that can be used to extend lesson concepts

Enrichment

OL BL ELL

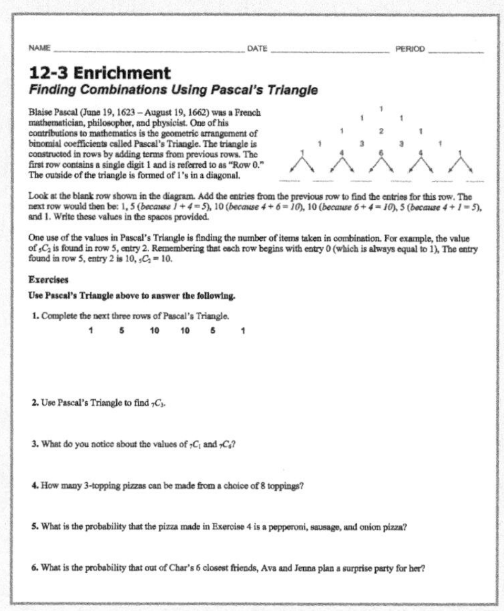
NAME ______ DATE ______ PERIOD ______

12-3 Enrichment
Finding Combinations Using Pascal's Triangle

Blaise Pascal (June 19, 1623 – August 19, 1662) was a French mathematician, philosopher, and physicist. One of his contributions to mathematics is the geometric arrangement of binomial coefficients called Pascal's Triangle. The triangle is constructed in rows by adding terms from previous rows. The first row contains a single digit 1 and is referred to as "Row 0." The outside of the triangle is formed of 1's in a diagonal.

Look at the blank row shown in the diagram. Add the entries from the previous row to find the entries for this row. The next row would then be: 1, 5 (*because 1 + 4 = 5*), 10 (*because 4 + 6 = 10*), 10 (*because 6 + 4 = 10*), 5 (*because 4 + 1 = 5*), and 1. Write these values in the spaces provided.

One use of the values in Pascal's Triangle is finding the number of items taken in combination. For example, the value of ${}_5C_2$ is found in row 5, entry 2. Remembering that each row begins with entry 0 (which is always equal to 1), The entry found in row 5, entry 2 is 10, ${}_5C_2 = 10$.

Exercises

Use Pascal's Triangle above to answer the following.

1. Complete the next three rows of Pascal's Triangle.
   1 5 10 10 5 1
2. Use Pascal's Triangle to find ${}_7C_3$.
3. What do you notice about the values of ${}_7C_1$ and ${}_7C_6$?
4. How many 3-topping pizzas can be made from a choice of 8 toppings?
5. What is the probability that the pizza made in Exercise 4 is a pepperoni, sausage, and onion pizza?
6. What is the probability that out of Char's 6 closest friends, Ava and Jenna plan a surprise party for her?

Launch

Have students read the Why? section of the lesson. Ask:

- Why might order be important in the photograph? Sample answers: height of the people, color of the outfits, who is associated with whom
- In what other situations might the order of objects be important? Sample answer: mixing ingredients in baking
- In what situation might the order of objects not be important? Sample answer: when putting condiments on a hamburger

Teach

Ask the scaffolded questions for each example to build conceptual understanding for students at all levels.

1 Probability Using Permutations

Example 1 Probability and Permutations of *n* Objects

AL What would be the probability that Renee's jersey number will be 1 and Chanise's jersey number will be 2? $\frac{1}{380}$

OL If the team decides to make 5 extra jerseys and randomly assign from all 25 numbers, what is the probability that Chanise's jersey number will be 1 and Renee's jersey number will be 2? $\frac{1}{600}$

BL Chanise and Renee also play volleyball, and each girl is randomly assigned a number based on the number of team members. If the probability that Chanise will be number 1 and Renee will be number 2 is $\frac{1}{132}$, how many players are there on the volleyball team? 12

Go Online!

Interactive Whiteboard

Use the *eLesson, Lesson Presentation*, or *Interactive Classroom* to present this lesson.

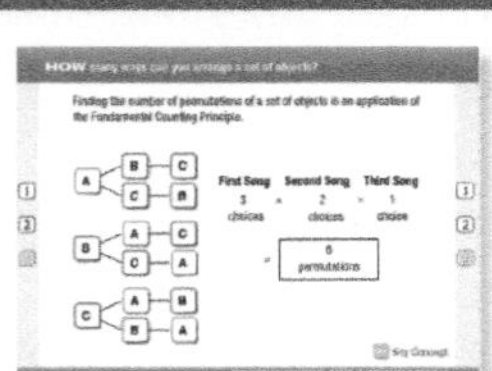

LESSON 3

Probability with Permutations and Combinations

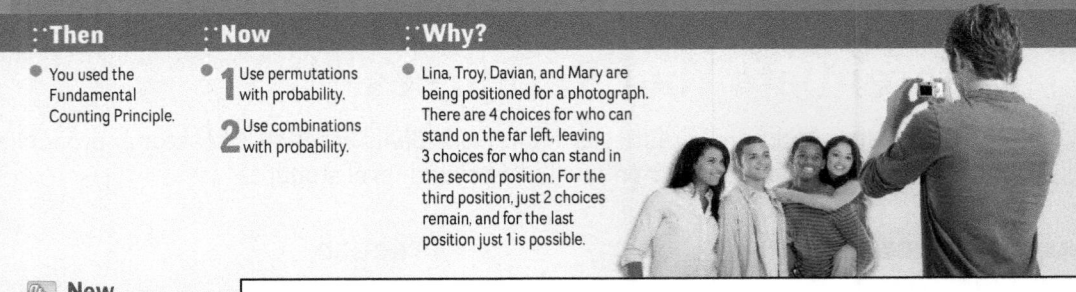

Then

- You used the Fundamental Counting Principle.

Now

1. Use permutations with probability.
2. Use combinations with probability.

Why?

- Lina, Troy, Davian, and Mary are being positioned for a photograph. There are 4 choices for who can stand on the far left, leaving 3 choices for who can stand in the second position. For the third position, just 2 choices remain, and for the last position just 1 is possible.

New Vocabulary
permutation
factorial
circular permutation
combination

Mathematical Practices
1 Make sense of problems and persevere in solving them.
4 Model with mathematics.

Content Standards
S.CP.9 Use permutations and combinations to compute probabilities of compound events and solve problems.

1 Probability Using Permutations A **permutation** is an arrangement of objects in which order is important. One permutation of the four friends above is Troy, Davian, Mary, and then Lina. Using the Fundamental Counting Principle, there are $4 \cdot 3 \cdot 2 \cdot 1$ or 24 possible ordered arrangements of the friends.

The expression $4 \cdot 3 \cdot 2 \cdot 1$ used to calculate the number of permutations of these four friends can be written as 4!, which is read *4 factorial*.

Key Concept Factorial

Words	The **factorial** of a positive integer n, written $n!$, is the product of the positive integers less than or equal to n.
Symbols	$n! = n \cdot (n-1) \cdot (n-2) \cdot \ldots \cdot 2 \cdot 1$, where $0! = 1$

S.CP.9

Example 1 Probability and Permutations of *n* Objects

SPORTS **Chanise and Renee are members of the lacrosse team. If the 20 girls on the team are each assigned a jersey number from 1 to 20 at random, what is the probability that Chanise's jersey number will be 1 and Renee's will be 2?**

Step 1 Find the number of possible outcomes in the sample space. This is the number of permutations of the 20 girls' names, or 20!.

Step 2 Find the number of favorable outcomes. This is the number of permutations of the other girls' names given that Chanise's jersey number is 1 and Renee's is 2: (20 − 2)! or 18!.

Step 3 Calculate the probability.

$P(\text{Chanise 1, Renee 2}) = \frac{18!}{20!}$ ← number of favorable outcomes / ← number of possible outcomes

$= \frac{\overset{1}{\cancel{18!}}}{20 \cdot 19 \cdot \underset{1}{\cancel{18!}}}$ Expand 20! and divide out common factors.

$= \frac{1}{380}$ Simplify.

Guided Practice

1. PHOTOGRAPHY In the opening paragraph, what is the probability that Troy is chosen to stand on the far left and Davian on the far right for the photograph? $\frac{1}{12}$

Digital Vision/Alamy

Mathematical Practices Strategies

Make sense of problems and persevere in solving them.
Help students use formulas to calculate probabilities. For example, ask:

- How do you determine whether to calculate a probability using permutations or combinations? For permutations , the order of the objects matters, and for combinations, the order of the objects does not matter.
- How do you calculate the probability of simple events? Divide the number of favorable outcomes by the number of possible outcomes in the sample space.
- Give an example of a situation where order does not matter. Sample answer: a committee of students

In the opening paragraph, suppose 6 friends were available, but the photographer wanted only 4 people in the picture. Using the Fundamental Counting Principle, the number of permutations of 4 friends taken from a group of 6 friends is 6 • 5 • 4 • 3 or 360.

Another way of describing this situation is the number of permutations of 6 friends taken 4 at a time, denoted $_6P_4$. This number can also be computed using factorials.

$$_6P_4 = 6 \cdot 5 \cdot 4 \cdot 3 = \frac{6 \cdot 5 \cdot 4 \cdot 3 \cdot 2 \cdot 1}{2 \cdot 1} = \frac{6!}{2!} = \frac{6!}{(6-4)!}$$

This suggests the following formula.

Reading Math

Modeling The phrase *distinct objects* means that the objects are distinguishable as being different in some way.

Key Concept Permutations

Symbols The number of permutations of n distinct objects taken r at a time is denoted by $_nP_r$ and given by $_nP_r = \frac{n!}{(n-r)!}$.

Example The number of permutations of 5 objects taken 2 at a time is

$$_5P_2 = \frac{5!}{(5-2)!} = \frac{5 \cdot 4 \cdot \cancel{3!}}{\cancel{3!}} \text{ or } 20.$$

Study Tip

Randomness When outcomes are decided at random, they are equally likely to occur and their probabilities can be calculated using permutations and combinations.

S.CP.9

Example 2 Probability and $_nP_r$

A class is divided into teams each made up of 15 students. Each team is directed to select team members to be officers. If Sam, Valencia, and Deshane are on a team, and the positions are decided at random, what is the probability that they are selected as president, vice president, and secretary, respectively?

Step 1 Because choosing officers is a way of ranking team members, order in this situation is important. The number of possible outcomes in the sample space is the number of permutations of 15 people taken 3 at a time, $_{15}P_3$.

$$_{15}P_3 = \frac{15!}{(15-3)!} = \frac{15 \cdot 14 \cdot 13 \cdot \cancel{12!}}{\cancel{12!}} \text{ or } 2730$$

Step 2 The number of favorable outcomes is the number of permutations of the 3 students in their specific positions. This is 1!, or 1.

Step 3 So the probability of Sam, Valencia, and Deshane being selected as the three officers is $\frac{1}{2730}$.

Guided Practice

2. A student identification card consists of 4 digits selected from 10 possible digits from 0 to 9. Digits cannot be repeated.
   A. How many possible identification numbers are there? 5040
   B. Find the probability that a randomly generated card has the exact number 4213. $\frac{1}{5040}$

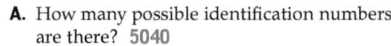

Need Another Example?

Talent Show Eli and Mia, along with 30 other people, sign up to audition for a talent show. Contestants are called at random to perform for the judges. What is the probability that Eli will be called to perform first and Mia will be called second? $\frac{1}{870}$

Example 2 Probability and $_nP_r$

AL Do you think it would be more probable or less probable that Sam, Valencia, and Deshane are all selected as officers, without specifying their offices? Explain. more probable; Sample answer: Because they can be chosen for any of the three offices, there will be more than one positive outcome.

OL What is the probability that Sam is the president, and Valencia and Deshane are selected to either of the remaining offices? $\frac{1}{1365}$

BL What is the probability that Sam, Valencia, and Deshane are selected as officers, regardless of office? $\frac{1}{455}$

Need Another Example?

There are 12 puppies for sale at the local pet shop. Four are brown, four are black, three are spotted, and one is white. What is the probability that all the brown puppies will be sold first? $\frac{1}{495}$

Teaching the Mathematical Practices

Modeling Mathematically proficient students use clear definitions in discussion with others and in their own reasoning. To help students understand permutations, have the class act out the situation in Example 2.

Go Online!

The most up-to-date resources available for your program can be found at connectED.mcgraw-hill.com.

Example 3 Probability and Permutations with Repetition

AL If you have the letters S, S, and O, and you selected a permutation of those letters at random, what is the probability that they would spell SOS? $\frac{1}{3}$

OL Does the probability that we found mean that it is likely the letters would spell Mississippi? Explain. No; Sample answer: There are over 30,000 possible outcomes and only 1 is favorable, so it is not likely at all that the letters would spell the word MISSISSIPPI.

BL What is the probability that the letters would *not* spell the word MISSISSIPPI? $\frac{34649}{34650}$

Need Another Example?

Tiles A box of floor tiles contains 5 blue (bl) tiles, 2 gold (gd) tiles, and 2 green (gr) tiles in random order. The desired pattern is bl, gd, bl, gr, bl, gd, bl, gr, bl. If you selected a permutation of these tiles at random, what is the probability that they would be chosen in the correct sequence? $\frac{1}{756}$

Teaching Tip

Sense-Making Remind students to reread the question they are asked to answer, and to check the reasonableness of their answer. For instance, in Example 3 students may calculate the number of permutations and write an answer of 34,650. If they reread the problem, they will see that the question is asking for the probability of a specific permutation, or $\frac{1}{34{,}650}$.

In a game, you must try to create a word using randomly selected letter tiles. Suppose you select the tiles shown. If you consider the letters O and O to be distinct, then there are 5! or 120 permutations of these letters.

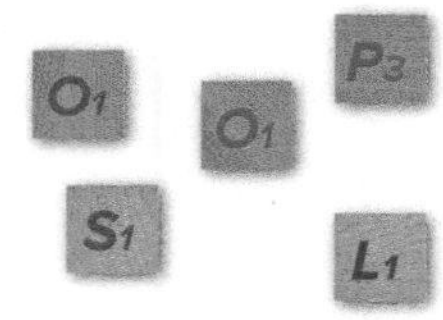

Four of these possible arrangements are listed below.

POOLS POOLS SPOOL SPOOL

Notice that unless the Os are colored, several of these arrangements would look the same. Because there are 2 Os that can be arranged in 2! or 2 ways, the number of permutations of the letters O, P, O, L, and S can be written as $\frac{5!}{2!}$.

Key Concept Permutations with Repetition

The number of distinguishable permutations of n objects in which one object is repeated r_1 times, another is repeated r_2 times, and so on, is $\frac{n!}{r_1! \cdot r_2! \cdot \ldots \cdot r_k!}$.

S.CP9

Example 3 Probability and Permutations with Repetition

Real-World Link

Created in 1956, *The Price is Right* is the longest-running game show in the United States.

Source: IMDB

GAME SHOW On a game show, you are given the following letters and asked to unscramble them to name a U.S. river. If you selected a permutation of these letters at random, what is the probability that they would spell the correct answer of MISSISSIPPI?

Step 1 There is a total of 11 letters. Of these letters, I occurs 4 times, S occurs 4 times, and P occurs 2 times. So, the number of distinguishable permutations of these letters is

$$\frac{11!}{4! \cdot 4! \cdot 2!} = \frac{39{,}916{,}800}{1152} \text{ or } 34{,}650. \quad \text{Use a calculator.}$$

Step 2 There is only 1 favorable arrangement—MISSISSIPPI.

Step 3 The probability that a permutation of these letters selected at random spells Mississippi is $\frac{1}{34{,}650}$.

Guided Practice

3. **TELEPHONE NUMBERS** What is the probability that a 7-digit telephone number with the digits 5, 1, 6, 5, 2, 1, and 5 is the number 556-5211? $\frac{1}{420}$

So far, you have been studying objects that are arranged in *linear* order. Notice that when the spices below are arranged in a line, shifting each spice one position to the right produces a different permutation—curry is now first instead of salt. There are 5! distinct permutations of these spices.

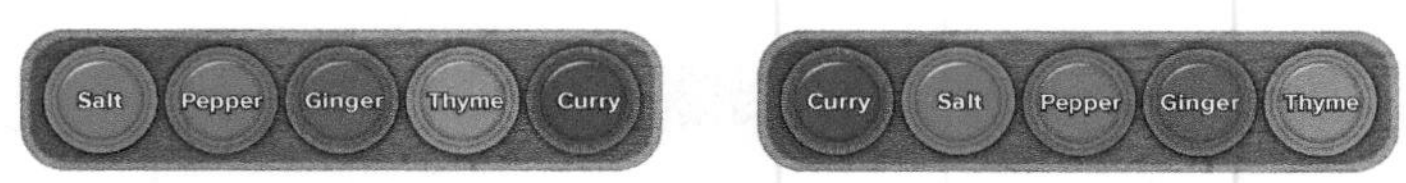

Tomml/iStock/Getty Images

Study Tip

MP Sense-Making If the circular object looks the same when it is turned over, such as a plain key ring, then the number of permutations must be divided by 2.

In a **circular permutation**, objects are arranged in a circle or loop. Consider the arrangements of these spices when placed on a turntable. Notice that rotating the turntable clockwise one position does *not* produce a different permutation—the order of the spices relative to each other remains unchanged.

Because 5 rotations of the turntable will produce the same permutation, the number of distinct permutations on the turntable is $\frac{1}{5}$ of the total number of arrangements when the spices are placed in a line.

$$\frac{1}{5} \cdot 5! = \frac{5 \cdot 4!}{5} \text{ or } 4!, \text{ which is } (5-1)!$$

Key Concept Circular Permutations

The number of distinguishable permutations of n objects arranged in a circle with no fixed reference point is

$$\frac{n!}{n} \text{ or } (n-1)!.$$

If the n objects are arranged relative to a fixed reference point, then the arrangements are treated as linear, making the number of permutations $n!$.

Real-World Career

Statisticians Statisticians collect statistical data for various subject areas, including sports and games. They use computer software to analyze, interpret, and summarize the data. Most statisticians have a master's degree.

S.CP.9

Example 4 Probability and Circular Permutations

Find the indicated probability. Explain your reasoning.

a. JEWELRY **If the 6 charms on the bracelet shown are arranged at random, what is the probability that the arrangement shown is produced?**

Because there is no fixed reference point, this is a circular permutation. So, there are $(6-1)!$ or $5!$ distinguishable permutations of the charms. Thus, the probability that the exact arrangement shown is produced is $\frac{1}{5!}$ or $\frac{1}{120}$.

b. DINING **You are seating a party of 4 people at a round table. One of the chairs around this table is next to a window. If the diners are seated at random, what is the probability that the person paying the bill is seated next to the window?**

Because the people are seated around a table with a fixed reference point, this is a linear permutation. So there are $4!$ or 24 ways in which the people can be seated around the table. The number of favorable outcomes is the number of permutations of the other 3 diners given that the person paying the bill sits next to the window, $3!$ or 6.

So, the probability that the person paying the bill is seated next to the window is $\frac{6}{24}$ or $\frac{1}{4}$.

Example 4 Probability and Circular Permutations

AL When objects are placed in a circle with no fixed reference point instead of a line, why do we need to use a different permutation? Sample answer: When objects are in a line, there is an object at the beginning and one at the end. These objects are only next to each other if there are two choices. When objects are placed in a circle, the first object chosen can fall next to the last object chosen and is indistinguishable from the other objects chosen.

OL In part **a**, if a seventh charm is added, how many possible arrangements are there? 720

BL In part **b**, if it is a party of 6 instead of 4, what is the probability that the person paying the bill is *not* seated by the window? $\frac{5}{6}$

Need Another Example?

Find the indicated probability. Explain your reasoning.

a. Seating If 8 students sit at random in the circle of chairs shown, what is the probability that the students sit in the arrangement shown?

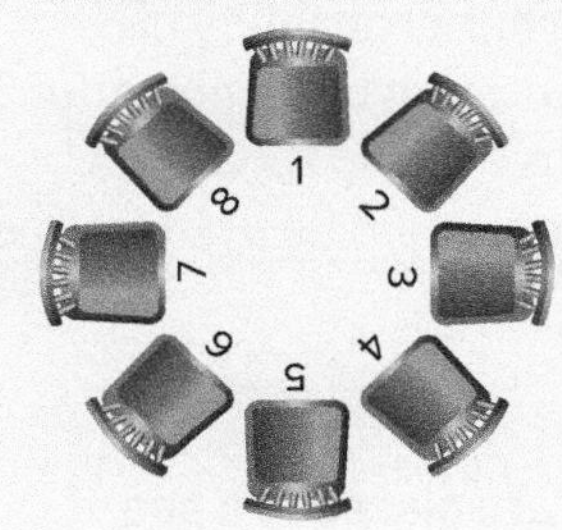

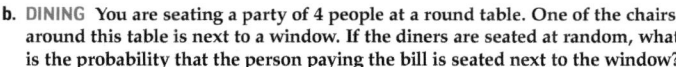

$\frac{1}{5040}$; Because there is no fixed reference point, this is a circular permutation.

b. You purchase a box of 8 crayons. If the crayons are packaged in random order, what is the probability that the crayon on the far left is red? $\frac{1}{8}$; Because the crayons are in a row, this is a linear permutation.

Additional Answer (Guided Practice)

4A. $\frac{1}{10}$; Because there is no fixed reference point, this is a circular permutation. There are $(11-1)!$ or $10!$ distinguishable permutations of the players. The number of favorable outcomes is the permutation of the other 9 players' positions in the huddle, or $9!$. So, the probability that the fullback stands to the right of the quarterback is $\frac{9!}{10!}$ or $\frac{1}{10}$.

2 Probability Using Combinations

Example 5 Probability and ${}_nC_r$

AL How are permutations and combinations different? For permutations, order is important. For combinations, order is not important.

OL If Monica's mom changes her mind and says she can invite 10 friends, what is the probability that her 10 favorites are chosen? $\frac{1}{184{,}756}$

BL If you are drawing marbles from a bag randomly and you want to pull two green marbles and a red marble in three tries, should you calculate your probability of success using a permutation or combination? Explain. Combination; There is no specific order, so a combination would be used for the calculation.

Need Another Example?

A set of alphabet magnets are placed in a bag. If 5 magnets are drawn from the bag at random, what is the probability that they will be the letters *a*, *e*, *i*, *o*, and *u*? $\frac{1}{65{,}780}$

4B. Since the players are huddled next to a fixed reference point, this is a linear permutation. There are 11! ways in which the players can be arranged in the huddle. The number of favorable outcomes is the number of permutations of the other 10 players given that the referee is standing behind the halfback, 10!. So, the probability that the referee stands behind the halfback is $\frac{10!}{11!}$ or $\frac{1}{11}$.

Guided Practice

4. FOOTBALL A team's 11 football players huddle together before a play.

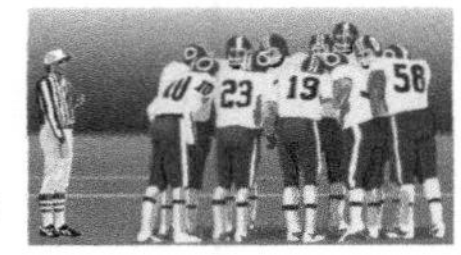

A. What is the probability that the fullback stands to the right of the quarterback if the team huddles together at random? Explain your reasoning. See margin.

B. If a referee stands directly behind the huddle, what is the probability that the referee stands directly behind the halfback? Explain your reasoning.

2 Probability Using Combinations A **combination** is an arrangement of objects in which order is *not* important. Suppose you need to pack 3 of your 8 different pairs of socks for a trip. The order in which the socks are chosen does not matter, so the 3! or 6 groups of socks shown below would *not* be considered different. So, you would use combinations to determine the number of possible different sock choices.

A combination of n objects taken r at a time, or ${}_nC_r$, is calculated by dividing the number of permutations ${}_nP_r$ by the number of arrangements containing the same elements, $r!$.

Study Tip

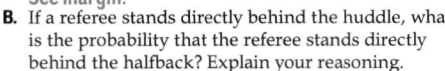

MP Reasoning Use permutations when the order of an arrangement of objects is important and combinations when order is not important.

Key Concept Combinations

Symbols The number of combinations of n distinct objects taken r at a time is denoted by ${}_nC_r$ and is given by ${}_nC_r = \frac{n!}{(n-r)!\,r!}$.

Example The number of combinations of 8 objects taken 3 at a time is

$${}_8C_3 = \frac{8!}{(8-3)!\,3!} = \frac{8!}{5!3!} = \frac{8\cdot7\cdot\cancel{6}\cdot\cancel{5!}}{\cancel{5!}\cdot\cancel{6}} \text{ or } 56.$$

Go Online!

Many students find problems involving permutations and combinations challenging. Watch the Personal Tutor describe how to solve these problems with a partner. Then try describing how to solve a problem for your partner. Have your partner ask questions to help your understanding. ELL

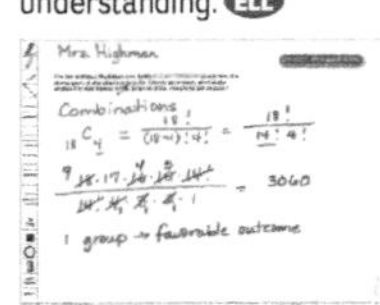

S.CP.9

Example 5 Probability and ${}_nC_r$

INVITATIONS For her birthday, Monica can invite 6 of her 20 friends to join her at a theme park. If she chooses to invite friends at random, what is the probability that friends Tessa, Guido, Brendan, Faith, Charlotte, and Rhianna are chosen?

Step 1 Because the order in which the friends are chosen does not matter, the number of possible outcomes in the sample space is the number of combinations of 20 people taken 6 at a time, ${}_{20}C_6$.

$${}_{20}C_6 = \frac{20!}{(20-6)!\,6!} = \frac{\cancel{20}\cdot19\cdot\cancel{18}\cdot17\cdot\cancel{16}^{8}\cdot15\cdot\cancel{14!}}{\cancel{14!}\cdot\cancel{6}\cdot\cancel{5}\cdot\cancel{4}\cdot\cancel{3}\cdot\cancel{2}} \text{ or } 38{,}760$$

Step 2 There is only 1 favorable outcome—that the six students listed above are chosen. The order in which they are chosen is not important.

Step 3 So the probability of these six friends being chosen is $\frac{1}{38{,}760}$.

Guided Practice

5. GEOMETRY If three points are randomly chosen from those named on the rectangle shown, what is the probability that they all lie on the same line segment? $\frac{1}{14}$

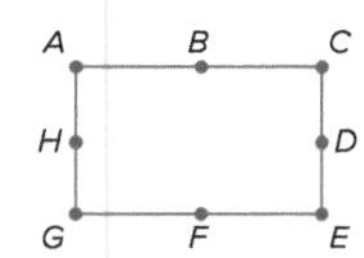

Differentiated Instruction OL BL

Visual/Spatial Learners Organize students in groups of three or four. Provide each group with a handful each of four different objects such as a variety of dry beans, color counters, or plastic beads. Have one group make as many unique combinations of two objects as possible. Have another group complete the same activity for permutations. Other groups can find combinations and permutations for groups of three or four objects. Have each group label a piece of paper and record all the different ways they arranged the objects. Allow groups to share their results with the class. Direct students to pay particular attention to the difference between the number of combinations and permutations made with the same number of objects. ELL

Check Your Understanding

◯ = Step-by-Step Solutions begin on page R13.

Go Online! for a Self-Check Quiz

Example 1 S.CP.9

1. **GEOMETRY** Five students are asked to randomly select and name a polygon from the group shown below. What is the probability that the first two students choose the triangle and quadrilateral, in that order? $\frac{1}{20}$

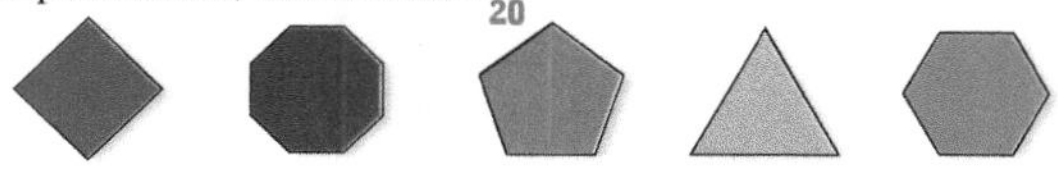

Example 2 S.CP.9

2. **PLAYS** A high school performs a production of *A Raisin in the Sun* with each freshman English class of 18 students. If the three members of the crew are decided at random, what is the probability that Chase is selected for lighting, Jaden is selected for props, and Emelina for spotlighting? $\frac{1}{4896}$

Example 3 S.CP.9

3. **DRIVING** What is the probability that a license plate using the letters C, F, and F and numbers 3, 3, 3, and 1 will be CFF3133? $\frac{1}{420}$

Example 4 S.CP.9

4. **CHEMISTRY** In chemistry lab, you need to test six samples that are randomly arranged on a circular tray.

   a. What is the probability that the arrangement shown at the right is produced? $\frac{1}{120}$
   b. What is the probability that test tube 2 will be in the top middle position? $\frac{1}{6}$

Example 5 S.CP.9

5. Five hundred boys, including Josh and Sokka, entered a drawing for two football game tickets. What is the probability that the tickets were won by Josh and Sokka? $\frac{1}{124,750}$

Practice and Problem Solving

Extra Practice is on page R12.

Example 1 S.CP.9

6. **CONCERTS** Nia and Chad are going to a concert with their high school's key club. If they choose a seat on the row below at random, what is the probability that Chad will be in seat C11 and Nia will be in C12? $\frac{1}{132}$

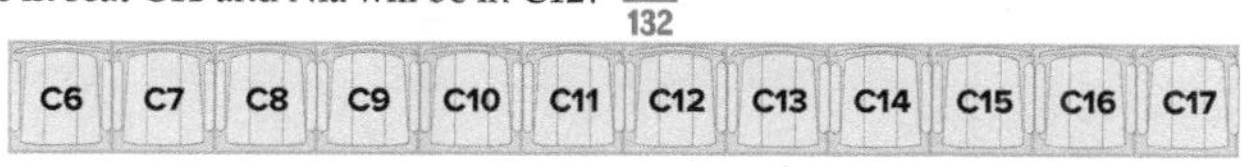

7. **FAIRS** Alfonso and Colin each bought one raffle ticket at the state fair. If 50 tickets were randomly sold, what is the probability that Alfonso got ticket 14 and Colin got ticket 23? $\frac{1}{2450}$

Example 2 S.CP.9

8. **MP MODELING** The table shows the finalists for a floor exercises competition. The order in which they will perform will be chosen randomly.
   a. What is the probability that Cecilia, Annie, and Kimi are the first three gymnasts to perform, in any order? $\frac{1}{35}$
   b. What is the probability that Cecilia is first, Annie is second, and Kimi is third? $\frac{1}{210}$

Floor Exercises Finalists
Eliza Hernandez
Kimi Kanazawa
Cecilia Long
Annie Montgomery
Shenice Malone
Caroline Smith
Jessica Watson

9. **JOBS** A store randomly assigns their employees work identification numbers to track productivity. Each number consists of 5 digits ranging from 1–9. If the digits cannot repeat, find the probability that a randomly generated number is 25,938. $\frac{1}{15,120}$

10. **GROUPS** Two people are chosen randomly from a group of ten. What is the probability that Jimmy was selected first and George second? $\frac{1}{90}$

Differentiated Homework Options

Levels	AL Basic	OL Core	BL Advanced
Exercises	6–16, 23–36	7–19 odd, 20–36	22–28, (optional: 29–36)
2-Day Option	7–15 odd, 29–36	6–16	
	6–16 even, 23–28	17–36	

You can use ALEKS to provide additional remediation support with personalized instruction and practice.

Practice

Formative Assessment Use Exercises 1–5 to assess students' understanding of the concepts in this lesson.

The Practice and Problem Solving exercises assess the content taught in the lesson. The Preparing for Assessment page is meant to be used as preparation for assessment.

MP Teaching the Mathematical Practices

Modeling Mathematically proficient students can apply the mathematics they know to solve problems arising in everyday life. In Exercise 8, students will need to determine the number of favorable outcomes.

Levels of Complexity Chart

The levels of the exercises progress from 1 to 3, with Level 1 indicating the lowest level of complexity.

Exercises	6–16	17–21, 29–36	22–28
Level 3			●
Level 2		●	
Level 1	●		

Extra Practice

See page R12 for extra exercises for students who are approaching level or for on-level students who need additional reinforcement.

Go Online! eBook

Interactive Student Guide

Use the *Interactive Student Guide* to deepen conceptual understanding.

- Permutations and Combinations
- Probability

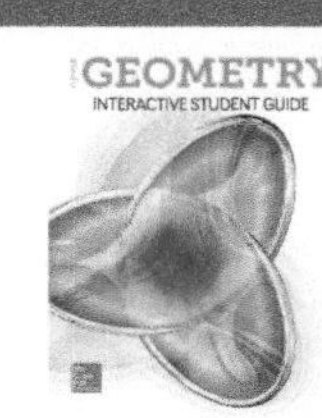

Teaching the Mathematical Practices

Structure Mathematically proficient students start by explaining the meaning of a problem to themselves and looking for entry points to its solution. In Exercise 17, encourage students to determine whether order is important or not.

Additional Answers

22. First, find the probability of winning with each option. There are 10^3 or 1000 three-digit numbers, so there are 1000 possible choices.

    Straight: She has only one chance of winning: $P(\text{straight}) = 1 \div 1000$ or 0.001.

    3-Way Boxed: There are three winning numbers: $P(\text{3-Way}) = 3 \div 1000$ or 0.003.

    6-Way Boxed: There are six winning numbers: $P(\text{6-Way}) = 6 \div 1000$ or 0.006.

    Straight-Box: There are still 6 winning combinations. $P(\text{Straight-Box}) = 6 \div 1000$ or 0.006.

    Because the odds of winning are the same for a 6-Way Boxed and a Straight-Box, Corie should choose either of these options to play.

24. **Sample answer:**

$$r! \cdot {}_nC_r = r! \cdot \frac{n!}{(n-r)!r!}$$
$$= \frac{n!r!}{(n-r)!r!}$$
$$= \frac{n!}{(n-r)!}$$
$$= {}_nP_r$$

${}_nC_r$ and ${}_nP_r$ differ by the factor $r!$ because there are always $r!$ ways to order the groups that are selected. Therefore, there are $r!$ permutations of each combination.

Example 3 S.CP.9

11. **MAGNETS** Santiago bought some letter magnets that he can arrange to form words on his fridge. If he randomly selected a permutation of the letters shown below, what is the probability that they would form the word BASKETBALL? $\frac{1}{453{,}600}$

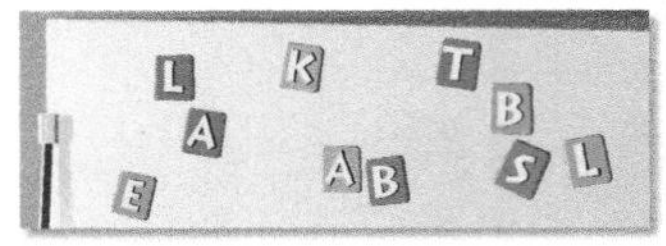

12. **ZIP CODES** What is the probability that a zip code randomly generated from among the digits 3, 7, 3, 9, 5, 7, 2, and 3 is the number 39,372? $\frac{1}{3360}$

Example 4 S.CP.9

13. **GROUPS** Keith is randomly arranging desks into circles for group activities. If there are 7 desks in his circle, what is the probability that Keith will be in the desk closest to the door? $\frac{1}{7}$

14. **AMUSEMENT PARKS** Sylvie is at an amusement park with her friends. They go on a ride that has bucket seats in a circle. If there are 8 seats, what is the probability that Sylvie will be in the seat farthest from the entrance to the ride? $\frac{1}{8}$

Example 5 S.CP.9

15. **PHOTOGRAPHY** If you are randomly placing 24 photos in a photo album and you can place four photos on the first page, what is the probability that you choose the photos at the right? $\frac{1}{10{,}626}$

16. **ROAD TRIPS** Rita is going on a road trip across the United States. She needs to choose from 15 cities where she will stay for one night. If she randomly pulls 3 city brochures from a pile of 15, what is the probability that she chooses Austin, Cheyenne, and Savannah? $\frac{1}{455}$

B 17. **STRUCTURE** Use the figure below. Assume that the balls are aligned at random.

a. What is the probability that in a row of 8 pool balls, the solid 2 and striped 11 would be first and second from the left? $\frac{1}{56}$

b. What is the probability that if the 8 pool balls were mixed up at random, they would end up in the order shown? $\frac{1}{40{,}320}$

c. What is the probability that in a row of seven balls, with three 8-balls, three 9-balls, and one 6-ball, the three 8-balls would be to the left of the 6-ball and the three 9-balls would be on the right? $\frac{1}{140}$

d. If the eight original balls were randomly rearranged and formed a circle, what is the probability that the 6-ball is next to the 7-ball? $\frac{2}{7}$

18. How many lines are determined by 10 randomly selected points, no 3 of which are collinear? Explain your calculation. **45; Sample answer: The number of lines is the combination of 10 objects taken 2 at a time, which is $\frac{10!}{8!2!}$ or 45.**

19. Suppose 7 points on a circle are chosen at random, as shown at the right.

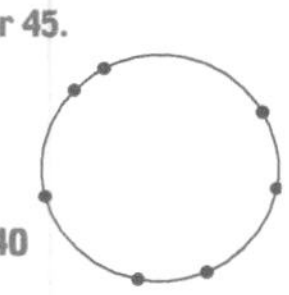

a. Using the letters A through E, how many ways can the points on the circle be named? **720**

b. If one point on the circle is fixed, how many arrangements are possible? **5040**

Differentiated Instruction OL BL

Extension Have students write about how understanding and applying the principles of probability might influence their decision making in some situations. Encourage students to use specific and detailed examples of situations that support their thought processes.

20. RIDES A carousel has 7 horses and one bench seat that will hold two people. One of the horses does not move up or down.

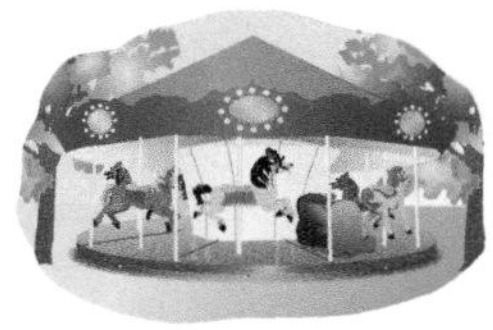

a. How many ways can the seats on the carousel be randomly filled by 9 people? **362,880**

b. If the carousel is filled randomly, what is the probability that you and your friend will end up in the bench seat? $\frac{1}{36}$

c. If 6 of the 9 people randomly filling the carousel are under the age of 8, what is the probability that a person under the age of 8 will end up on the one horse that does not move up or down? $\frac{2}{3}$

21. LICENSES A camera positioned above a traffic light photographs cars that fail to stop at a red light. In one unclear photograph, an officer could see that the first letter of the license plate was a Q, the second letter was an M or an N, and the third letter was a B, P, or D. The first number was a 0, but the last two numbers were blurry. How many possible license plates fit this description? **600**

22. MULTI-STEP Corie is interested in playing a state lottery game in which she needs to choose a certain three-digit number to win. The different game options are shown in the table. Which option should she choose? Explain your solution process. **See margin.**

Option	Requirements	Examples
Straight	Numbers must match in exact order.	431
3-Way Box	Two digits must be identical and order does not matter.	433, 343, 334
6-Way Box	Digits must be unique, and order does not matter.	431, 413, 134, 143, 314, 341
Straight-Box	Can win straight or boxed, and digits must be unique.	431, 413, 134, 143, 314, 341

S.CP.9

H.O.T. Problems Use Higher-Order Thinking Skills

23. MODELING Fifteen boys and fifteen girls entered a drawing for four free movie tickets. What is the probability that all four tickets were won by girls? $\frac{13}{261}$

24. REASONING A student claimed that permutations and combinations were related by $r! \cdot {}_nC_r = {}_nP_r$. Use algebra to show that this is true. Then explain why ${}_nC_r$ and ${}_nP_r$ differ by the factor $r!$. **See margin.**

25. OPEN-ENDED Describe a situation in which the probability is given by $\frac{1}{{}_7C_3}$. **See margin.**

26. CONSTRUCT ARGUMENTS Is the following statement *sometimes*, *always*, or *never* true? Explain.

$${}_nP_r = {}_nC_r$$

Sometimes; sample answer: The statement is true when r is 1.

27. PROOF Prove that $nC_{n-r} = nC_r$. **See margin.**

28. WRITING IN MATH Compare and contrast permutations and combinations. **See margin.**

Standards for Mathematical Practice

Emphasis On	Exercises
1 Make sense of problems and persevere in solving them.	22, 32, 35, 36
2 Reason abstractly and quantitatively.	18, 19, 24, 25, 27
3 Construct viable arguments and critique the reasoning of others.	26
4 Model with mathematics.	1–16, 20, 21, 23
6 Attend to precision.	30, 31, 33, 34
7 Look for and make use of structure.	17
8 Look for and express regularity in repeated reasoning.	28, 29

Teaching the Mathematical Practices

Construct Arguments Mathematically proficient students understand and use stated assumptions and definitions in constructing arguments. They make conjectures and build a logical progression of statements to explore the truth of their conjectures. In Exercise 26, encourage students to analyze the equation for various values of r.

Assess

Name the Math Give students a probability scenario. Have them write the formula they would use to find the probability and state why the formula they chose is the most appropriate for the scenario given. Have students turn in their papers before they leave the classroom.

Additional Answers

25. Sample answer: A bag contains seven marbles that are red, orange, yellow, green, blue, purple, and black. The probability that the orange, blue, and black marbles will be chosen if three marbles are drawn at random can be calculated using a combination.

27.
$$C(n, n-r) \stackrel{?}{=} C(n, r)$$
$$\frac{n!}{[n-(n-r)]!(n-r)!} \stackrel{?}{=} \frac{n!}{(n-r)!r!}$$
$$\frac{n!}{r!(n-r)!} \stackrel{?}{=} \frac{n!}{(n-r)!r!}$$
$$\frac{n!}{(n-r)!r!} = \frac{n!}{(n-r)!r!} \checkmark$$

28. Sample answer: Both permutations and combinations are used to find the number of possible arrangements of a group of objects. The order of the objects is important in permutations but not in combinations.

Go Online!

eSolutions Manual

Create worksheets, answer keys, and solutions handouts for your assignments.

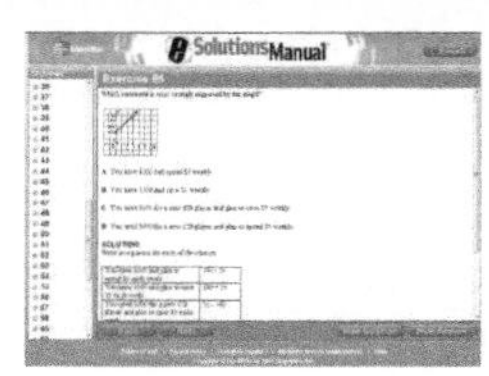

Preparing for Assessment

Exercises 29–36 require students to use the skills they will need on future assessments. Exercises are dual-coded with content standards and mathematical practice standards.

Dual Coding		
Items	Content Standards	MP Mathematical Practices
29	S.CP.9	8
30	S.CP.9	6
31	S.CP.9	6
32	S.CP.9	1
33	S.CP.9	6
34	S.CP.9	6
35	S.CP.9	1
36	S.CP.9	1

Diagnose Student Errors

Survey student responses for each item. Class trends may indicate common errors and misconceptions.

29.

A	Took sample space to have 5 outcomes with 2 favorable outcomes
B	Took sample space to have 5 outcomes with 1 favorable outcome
C	Used ${}_5C_2$ to find number of outcomes in sample space
D	CORRECT

30.

A	Used ${}_5C_2$ to find number of outcomes in sample space
B	CORRECT
C	Used ${}_7P_2$ to find number of outcomes in sample space
D	Used 7! to find the number of outcomes in sample space

Preparing for Assessment

29. Steven, Yasmin, Tyler, Vanessa, and Zack have been nominated to be club officers (president and vice president). Assuming the officers are chosen at random from among the five nominees, what is the probability that Steven is chosen to be the president and Yasmin is chosen to be the vice president? MP 8 S.CP.9 **D**

- ○ A $\frac{2}{5}$
- ○ B $\frac{1}{5}$
- ○ C $\frac{1}{10}$
- ○ D $\frac{1}{20}$

30. Manuel must choose two books from a list of seven to read for book reports in his literature class. How many different pairs of books could he choose? MP 6 S.CP.9 **B**

- ○ A 10
- ○ B 21
- ○ C 42
- ○ D 5040

31. Every student at Shellie's school is assigned a 4-digit PIN to access the school's computers. The first digit of the code is 0 or 1. The remaining digits are chosen from the numbers 2 through 9, and no number may be used more than once in a code. What is the probability that Shellie is assigned the PIN 1234? MP 6 S.CP.9 **D**

- ○ A $\frac{1}{56}$
- ○ B $\frac{1}{112}$
- ○ C $\frac{1}{336}$
- ○ D $\frac{1}{672}$
- ○ E $\frac{1}{5040}$

32. The coach is going to select a team of 5 from among 10 players. Find the probability that John, a particular player, is on the team. MP 1 S.CP.9

[$\frac{1}{2}$]

33. Marsala inserts three $5-bills into 3 of 10 envelopes. The other 7 she leaves empty. She has each of her 10 soccer teammates choose one of the envelopes. How many different ways can the money be won by her teammates? MP 6 S.CP.9 **A**

- ○ A 120
- ○ B 35
- ○ C 720
- ○ D 3,628,800

34. Midori has tiles with the letters *J, K, L, M, N, P,* and *Q*. She chooses three of the tiles at random. What is the probability that the tiles name three collinear points on the coordinate plane shown here? MP 6 S.CP.9 **C**

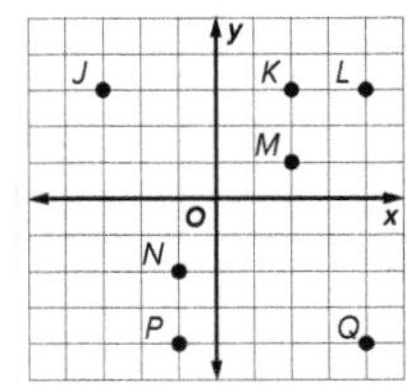

- ○ A $\frac{1}{105}$
- ○ B $\frac{1}{35}$
- ○ C $\frac{2}{35}$
- ○ D $\frac{3}{7}$

35. **MULTI-STEP** Assuming that any arrangement of letters forms a 'word', what is the probability that a 'word' formed from the letters of the word SQUARE: MP 1 S.CP.9

a. starts with E? [$\frac{1}{6}$]

b. starts with E and ends with A? [$\frac{1}{30}$]

36. 15 student council members select a committee of 3 for a project, and then select one of the three to be the liaison for the project. MP 1 S.CP.9

a. In how many ways is this possible?

[1365]

b. What is the probability that Carmen is in the committee?

[$\frac{1}{5}$]

c. What is the probability that Carmen is the liaison for the project?

[$\frac{1}{15}$]

31.

A	Used ${}_8C_3$ to find number of outcomes in sample space
B	Used $2 \times {}_8C_3$ to find number of outcomes in sample space
C	Used ${}_8P_3$ to find number of outcomes in sample space, but did not account for 0 or 1 as first digit
D	CORRECT
E	Used ${}_{10}P_4$ to find number of outcomes in sample space

32.

A	Used 3! to find the number of outcomes in the sample space
B	Used ${}_{10}C_3$ to find the number of outcomes in the sample space
C	CORRECT
D	Used 10! to find the number of outcomes in the sample space

Go Online!

Quizzes

Students can use *Self-Check Quizzes* to check their understanding of this lesson and have the results sent to you. You can also give *Quiz 2*, which covers the content in Lessons 12-2 and 12-3.

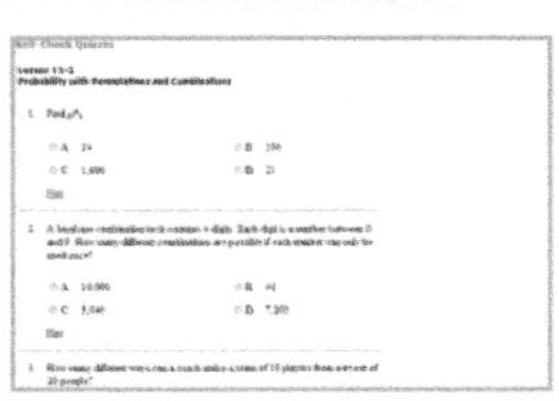

Geometric Probability

SUGGESTED PACING (DAYS)

	Instruction
90 min.	0.5
45 min.	1.0

Track Your Progress

Objectives

1 Find probability using length.

2 Find probability using area.

Mathematical Background

Probability that involves a geometric measure such as length or area is called a *geometric probability.* You can find the probability that a point lies in part of a figure by comparing the length or area of the part to the length or area of the whole figure.

THEN	NOW	NEXT
S.CP.9 Use permutations and combinations to compute probabilities of compound events and solve problems.	**S.MD.7** Analyze decisions and strategies using probability concepts.	**S.CP.2** Understand that two events *A* and *B* are independent if the probability of *A* and *B* occurring together is the product of their probabilities, and use this characterization to determine if they are independent.

Go Online! All of these resources and more are available at connectED.mcgraw-hill.com

Use the Spreadsheet Activity Worksheet to give students the opportunity to extend their skills with geometric probability.

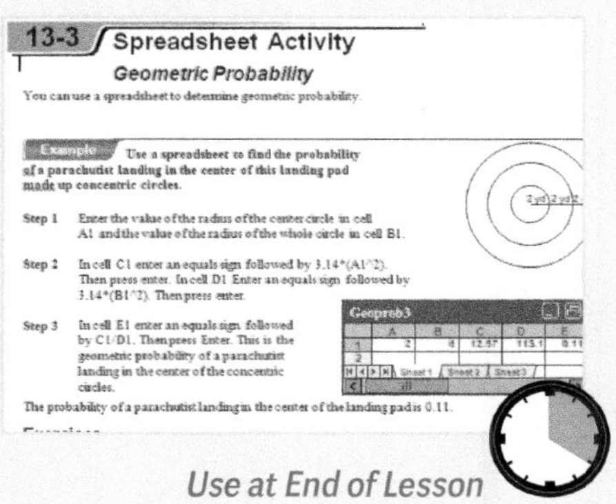

Use at End of Lesson

Personal Tutors (for every example) let students hear real teachers solve problems. Students can pause and repeat as many times as necessary.

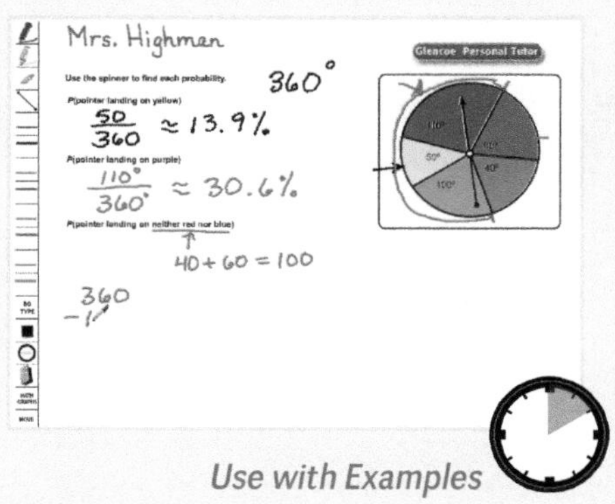

Use with Examples

Use a Self-Check Quiz to assess students' understanding of geometric probability.

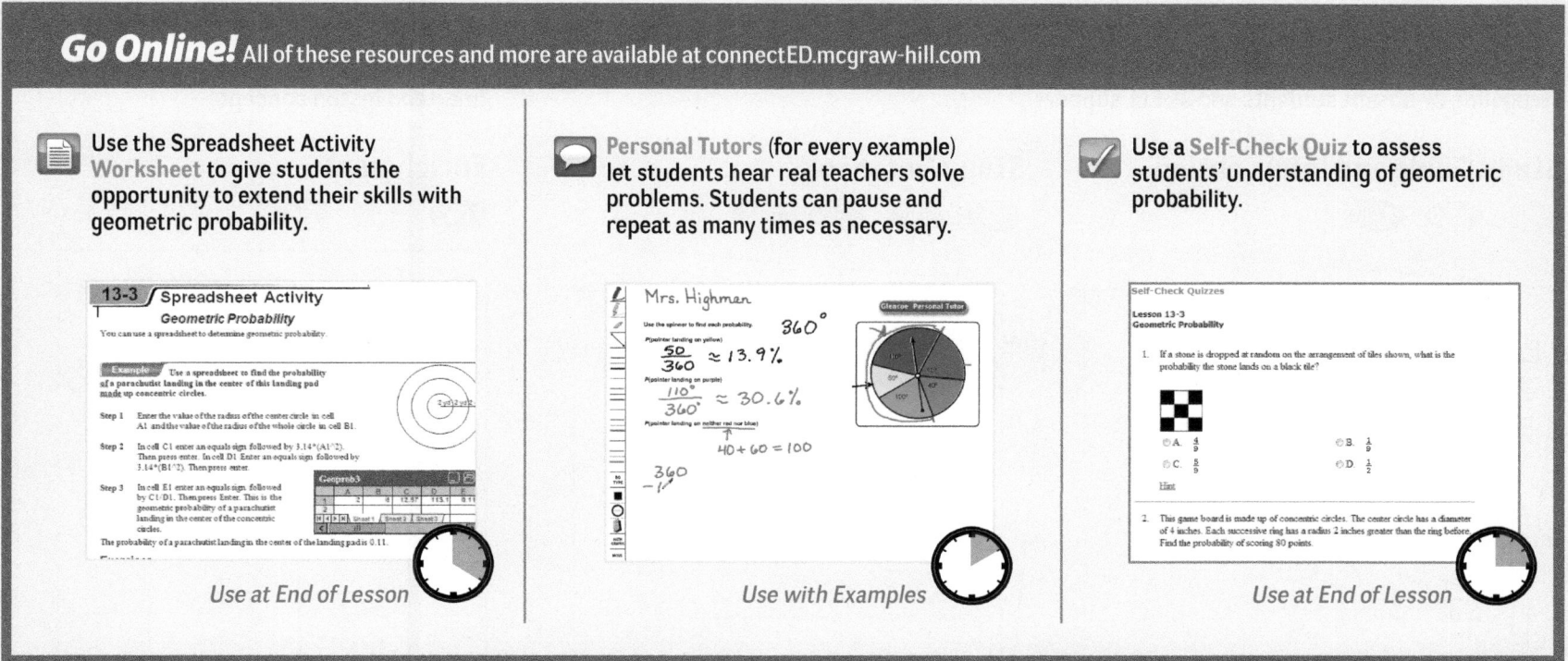

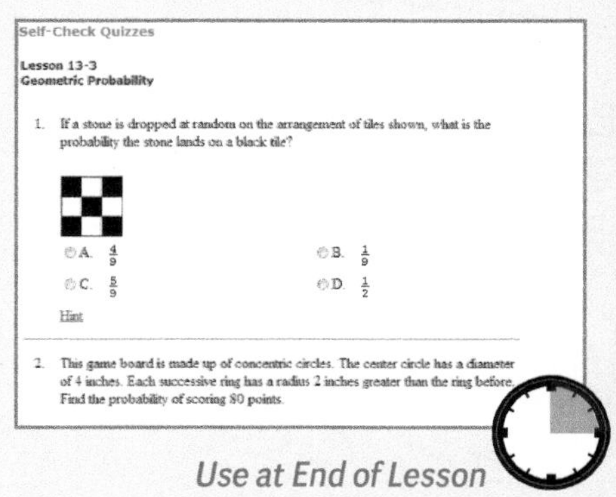

Use at End of Lesson

OER Using Open Educational Resources

Tutorial Have students watch videos on **Study Egg** about geometric probability. Students could watch videos to review important information in this lesson or before the lesson has been presented. *Use as review or as flipped learning*

Go Online!
connectED.mcgraw-hill.com

Worksheets

Differentiate Your Resources

Extra Practice Additional practice or homework; Skills Practice is best for approaching-level students and Practice is best for on-level and beyond-level students

Skills Practice

AL OL ELL

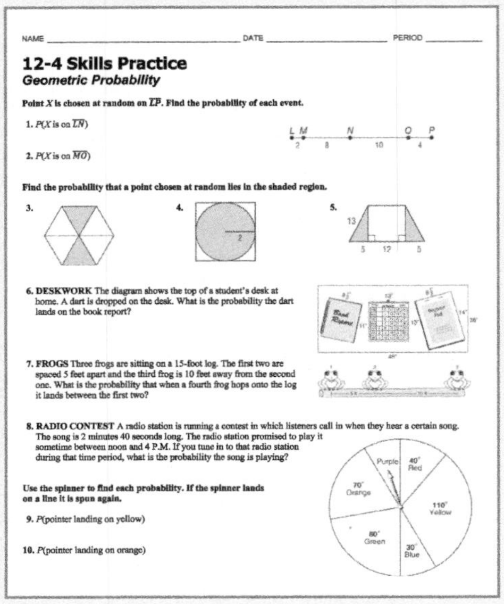
12-4 Skills Practice
Geometric Probability

Practice

AL OL BL ELL

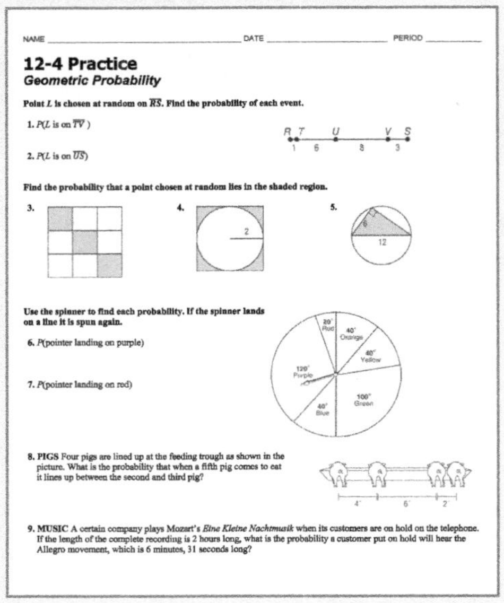
12-4 Practice
Geometric Probability

Word Problem Practice

AL OL BL ELL

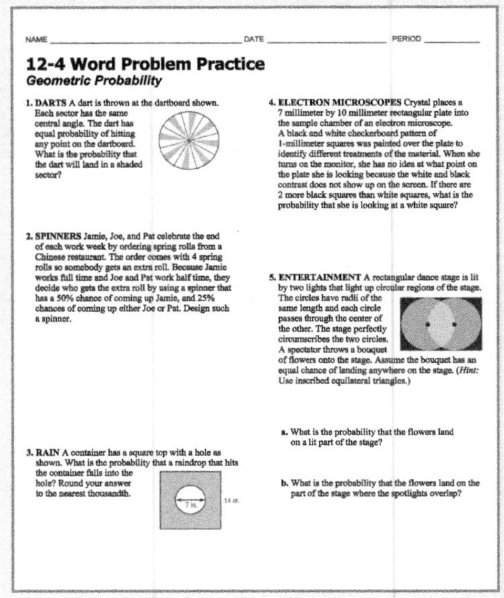
12-4 Word Problem Practice
Geometric Probability

Intervention Reteaching and vocabulary activities that can be used with struggling or absent students and as ELL support

Study Guide and Intervention

AL OL ELL

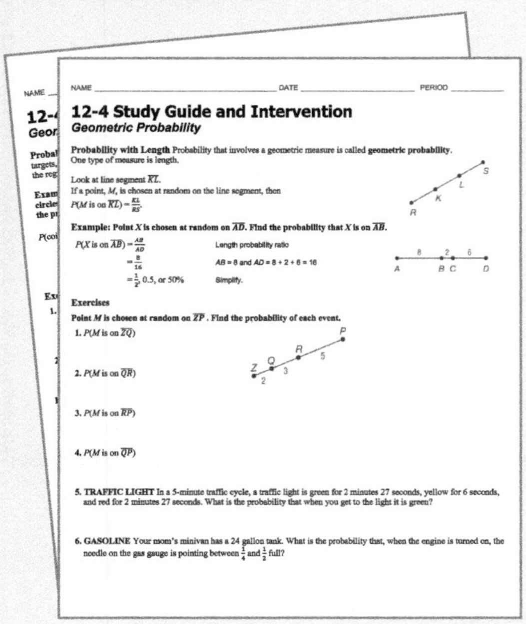
12-4 Study Guide and Intervention
Geometric Probability

Study Notebook

AL OL BL ELL

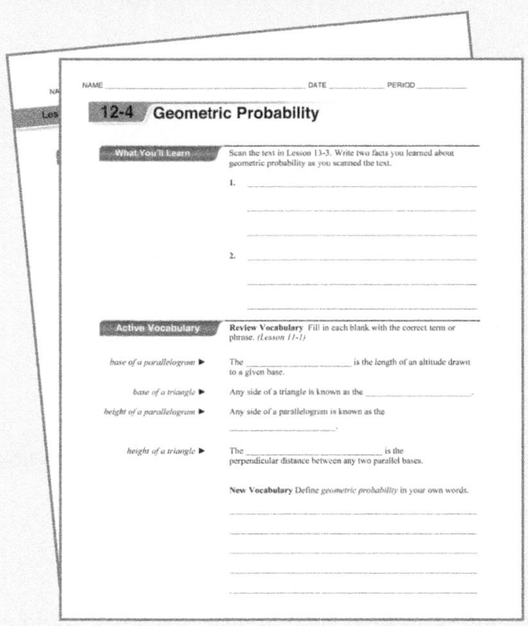
12-4 Geometric Probability

Extension Activities that can be used to extend lesson concepts

Enrichment

OL BL ELL

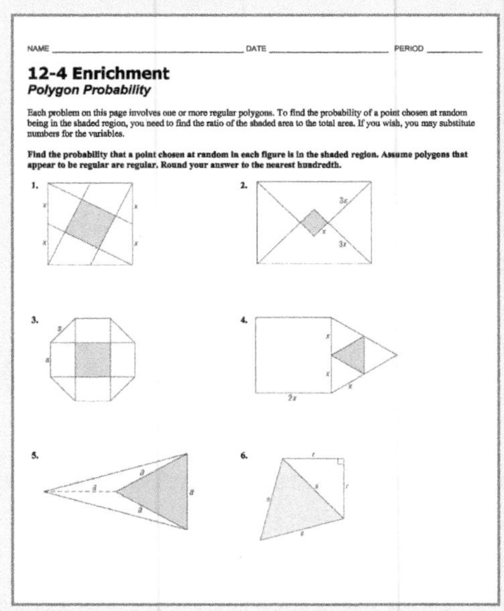
12-4 Enrichment
Polygon Probability

LESSON 4

Geometric Probability

Then

- You found probabilities of simple events.

Now

- **1** Find probabilities by using length.
- **2** Find probabilities by using area.

Why?

- The object of the popular carnival game shown is to collect points by rolling a ball up an incline and into one of several circular target areas. The point value of each area is assigned based on the probability of a person landing a ball in that area.

New Vocabulary
geometric probability

Mathematical Practices
1 Make sense of problems and persevere in solving them.
2 Reason abstractly and quantitatively.

Content Standards
S.MD.7 Analyze decisions and strategies using probability concepts (e.g., product testing, medical testing, pulling a hockey goalie at the end of a game).

1 Probability with Length The probability of winning the carnival game depends on the area of the target. Probability that involves a geometric measure such as length or area is called **geometric probability**.

Key Concept Length Probability Ratio

Words If a line segment (1) contains another segment (2) and a point on segment (1) is chosen at random, then the probability that the point is on segment (2) is

$$\frac{\text{length of segment (2)}}{\text{length of segment (1)}}.$$

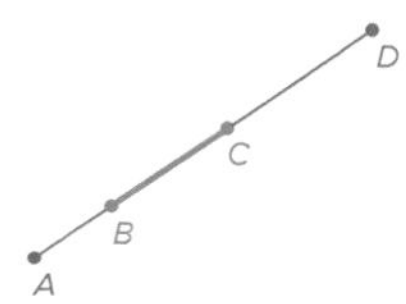

Example If a point E on $\overline{AD}$ is chosen at random, then $P(E \text{ is on } \overline{BC}) = \frac{BC}{AD}$.

S.MD.7

Example 1 Use Lengths to Find Geometric Probability

Point X is chosen at random on $\overline{JM}$. Find the probability that X is on $\overline{KL}$.

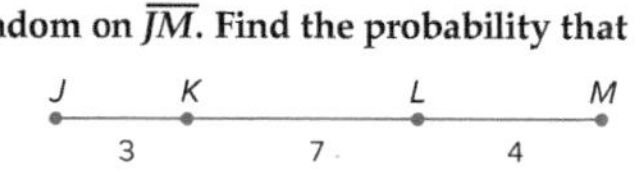

$P(X \text{ is on } \overline{KL}) = \frac{KL}{JM}$ — Length probability ratio

$= \frac{7}{14}$ — $KL = 7$ and $JM = 3 + 7 + 4$ or 14

$= \frac{1}{2}$, 0.5, or 50% — Simplify.

Guided Practice 1A. $\frac{2}{7}$, about 0.29, or about 29%   1B. $\frac{11}{14}$, about 0.79, or about 79%

Point X is chosen at random on $\overline{JM}$. Find the probability of each event.

1A. $P(X \text{ is on } \overline{LM})$ **1B.** $P(X \text{ is on } \overline{KM})$

Geometric probability can be used in many real-world situations that involve an infinite number of outcomes.

fotog/Tetra Images/Getty Images

Mathematical Practices Strategies

Reason abstractly and quantitatively.
Help students use intuition and geometric concepts to find geometric probability. For example, ask:

- What concepts are useful in determining geometric probability? length in one dimension and area in two dimensions
- How do you calculate the geometric probability of simple events? We put the length/area of favorable figure over the length/area of the entire figure.
- Give an example of a situation where geometric probability would use length. Sample answer: landing on a specific line segment on the perimeter of a figure

Launch

Have students read the Why? section of the lesson. Ask:

- Into which circular target area would it be the easiest to roll a ball? the outermost circle
- Into which circular target area would it be the hardest to roll a ball? one of the center circles
- What other factors affect the outcome of the game? Sample answer: the weight, speed, and composition of the ball

Teach

Ask the scaffolded questions for each example to build conceptual understanding for students at all levels.

1 Probability with Length

Example 1 Use Lengths to Find Geometric Probability

AL What is the probability that X is on $\overline{JK}$? $\frac{3}{14}$, about 0.21, or about 21%

OL What is the probability that X is on $\overline{JL}$? $\frac{5}{7}$, about 0.71, or about 71%

BL What is the probability that X is *not* on $\overline{JK}$? $\frac{11}{14}$, about 0.79, or about 79%

Need Another Example?
Point Z is chosen at random on $\overline{AD}$. Find the probability that Z is on $\overline{AB}$.

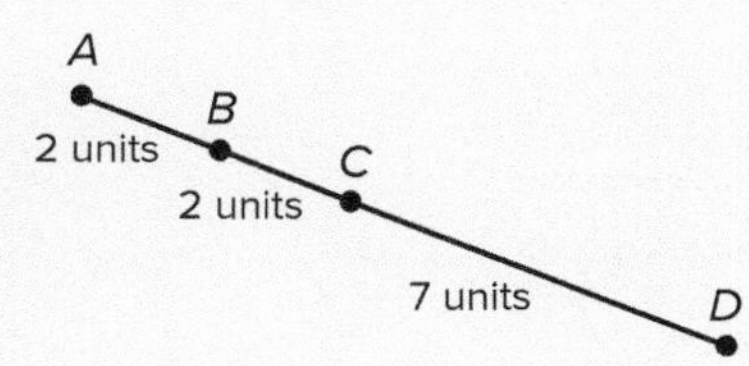

$\frac{2}{11}$, approximately 0.18, or approximately 18%

Go Online!

Interactive Whiteboard
Use the *eLesson*, *Lesson Presentation*, or *Interactive Classroom* to present this lesson.

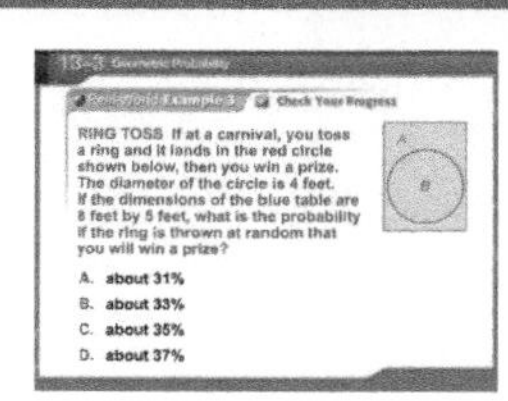

Example 2 Model Real-World Probabilities

AL What is the probability that you will wait less than one minute? $\frac{1}{4}$, or 25%

OL What is the probability that you will wait more than one minute? $\frac{3}{4}$, or 75%

BL What is the probability that you will wait less than one minute or more than three minutes? $\frac{1}{2}$, or 50%

Need Another Example?

Orbits Halley's Comet orbits Earth every 76 years. What is the probability that Halley's Comet will complete an orbit within the next decade? $\frac{5}{38}$, approximately 0.13, or approximately 13%

Watch Out!

Intervals Remind students that the interval of the probability being considered is not necessarily equal to the entire interval of the event. Caution students to use only the units equal to the interval being considered.

Real-World Link

A Chicago Transit Authority train arrives or departs a station like Addison on the Red Line every 15 minutes.

Source: Chicago Transit Authority

Real-World Example 2 Model Real-World Probabilities

TRANSPORTATION Use the information at the left. Assuming that you arrive at Addison on the Red Line at a random time, what is the probability that you will have to wait 3 or more minutes for a train?

We can use a number line to model this situation. Because the trains arrive every 15 minutes, the next train will arrive in 15 minutes or less. On the number line below, the event of waiting 5 or more minutes is modeled by $\overline{BD}$.

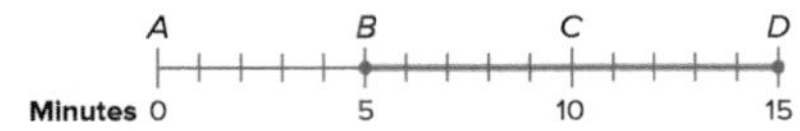

Find the probability of this event.

$P(\text{waiting 3 or more minutes}) = \frac{BD}{AD}$ Length probability ratio

$= \frac{10}{15}$ or $\frac{2}{3}$ $BD = 10$ and $AD = 15$

So, the probability of waiting 5 or more minutes for the next train is $\frac{2}{3}$ or about 67%.

Guided Practice

2. TEA Iced tea at a cafeteria-style restaurant is made in 8-gallon containers. Once the level gets below 2 gallons, the flavor of the tea becomes weak.

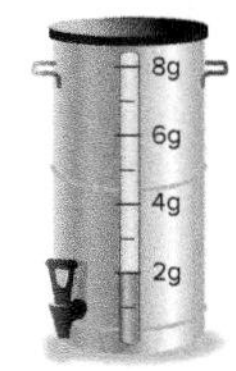

A. What is the probability that when someone tries to pour a glass of tea from the container, it is below 2 gallons?

B. What is the probability that the amount of tea in the container at any time is between 2 and 3 gallons?

2 Probability with Area Geometric probability can also involve area. The ratio for calculating geometric probability involving area is shown below.

Key Concept Area Probability Ratio

Words If a region A contains a region B and a point E in region A is chosen at random, then the probability that point E is in region B is $\frac{\text{area of region } B}{\text{area of region } A}$.

Example If a point E is chosen at random in rectangle A, then $P(\text{point } E \text{ is in circle } B) = \frac{\text{area of region } B}{\text{area of region } A}$.

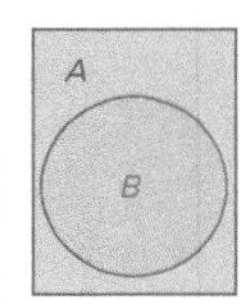

When determining geometric probabilities with targets, we assume

- that the object lands within the target area, and
- it is equally likely that the object will land anywhere in the region.

Go Online!

You can use a spreadsheet to solve probability problems. Learn how with the Spreadsheet Activity Worksheet in ConnectED.

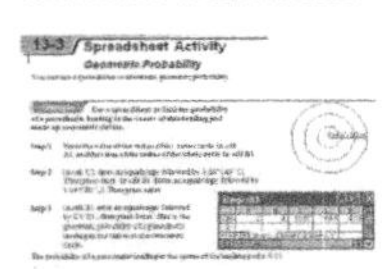

Differentiated Instruction AL OL BL

Logical Learners Have students model simple sample spaces by using geometric probabilities. Each event can be represented by a line segment whose length is proportional to the probability of the event. For example, flipping a coin can be represented by two lines of equal length, and the probability that a point is on either segment is 50%.

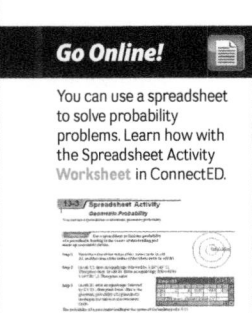

S.MD.7

Real-World Example 3 Use Area to Find Geometric Probability

SKYDIVING Suppose a skydiver must land on a target of three concentric circles. If the diameter of the center circle is 2 yards and the circles are spaced 1 yard apart, what is the probability that the skydiver will land in the red circle?

You need to find the ratio of the area of the red circle to the area of the entire target. The radius of the red circle is 1 yard, while the radius of the entire target is 1 + 1 + 1 or 3 yards.

$P(\text{skydiver lands in red circle}) = \frac{\text{area of red circle}}{\text{area of target}}$ Area probability ratio

$= \frac{\pi(1)^2}{\pi(3)^2}$ $A = \pi r^2$

$= \frac{\pi}{9\pi}$ or $\frac{1}{9}$ Simplify.

The probability that the skydiver will land in the red circle is $\frac{1}{9}$ or about 11%.

Real-World Link

Champion accuracy skydivers routinely land less than two inches away from the center of a target.

Source: *SkyDiving News*

Guided Practice

3. **SKYDIVING** Find each probability using the example above.

A. P(skydiver lands in the blue region) **$\frac{5}{9}$ or about 56%**

B. P(skydiver lands in white region) **$\frac{1}{3}$ or about 33%**

You can also use an angle measure to find geometric probability. The ratio of the area of a sector of a circle to the area of the entire circle is the same as the ratio of the sector's central angle to 360. You will prove this in Exercise 27.

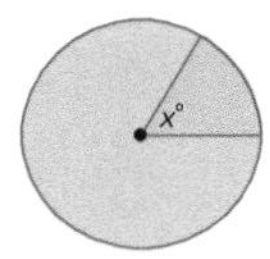

S.MD.7

Example 4 Use Angle Measures to Find Geometric Probability

Use the spinner to find each probability.

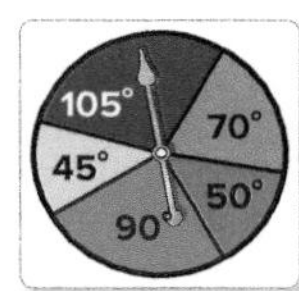

a. P(pointer landing on yellow)

The angle measure of the yellow region is 45.

$P(\text{pointer landing on yellow}) = \frac{45}{360}$ or 12.5%

b. P(pointer landing on purple)

The angle measure of the purple region is 105.

$P(\text{pointer landing on purple}) = \frac{105}{360}$ or about 29%

c. P(pointer landing on neither red nor blue)

The combined angle measures of the red and blue region are 50 + 70 or 120.

$P(\text{pointer landing on neither red nor blue}) = \frac{360 - 120}{360}$ or about 67%

Study Tip

Sense-Making In Example 4b, the area of the purple sector is a little less than $\frac{1}{3}$ or 33% of the spinner. Therefore, an answer of 29% is reasonable.

Guided Practice

4A. P(pointer landing on blue) **4B.** P(pointer not landing on green)

4A. $\frac{7}{36}$ or about 19%

4B. $\frac{3}{4}$ or 75%

2 Probability with Area

Example 3 Use Area to Find Geometric Probability

AL What is the probability that the skydiver will land anywhere inside the yellow and red areas? $\frac{4}{9}$, or about 44%

OL If the radius of the red circle is doubled and the radius of the entire target is 6 yards, do you think the probability of the skydiver landing on the target is the same? Explain. Yes; Sample answer: Because the measures all change proportionally, the probability will be the same.

BL What is the probability that the skydiver will land in the blue area of the target? $\frac{5}{9}$, or about 56%

Need Another Example?

Darts The targets of a dartboard are formed by 3 concentric circles. If the diameter of the center circle is 4 inches and the circles are spread 3 inches apart, what is the probability that a player will throw a dart into the center circle? $\frac{1}{16}$ or approximately 6%

Example 4 Use Angle Measures to Find Geometric Probability

AL What is the probability of the pointer landing on red? $\frac{5}{36}$, or about 14%

OL What is the probability of the pointer not landing on purple or yellow? $\frac{5}{12}$, or about 42%

BL What is the probability of the pointer landing on a multiple of 10 degree measure? $\frac{7}{12}$, or about 58%

Need Another Example?

Use the spinner to find each probability.

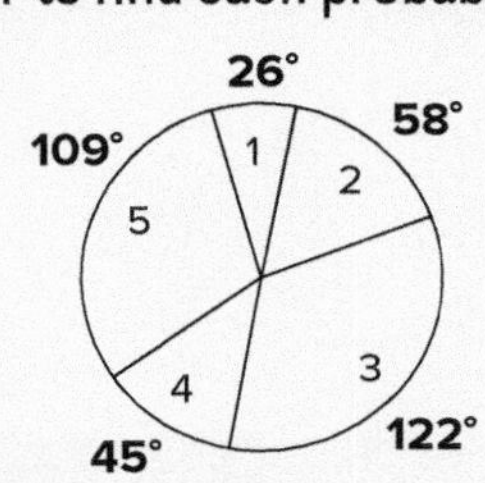

a. P(Pointer landing on section 3) $\frac{122}{360}$ or approximately 34%

b. P(Pointer landing on section 1) $\frac{26}{360}$ or approximately 7%

Practice

Formative Assessment Use Exercises 1–5 to assess students' understanding of the concepts in this lesson.

The Practice and Problem Solving exercises assess the content taught in the lesson. The Preparing for Assessment page is meant to be used as preparation for assessment.

MP Teaching the Mathematical Practices

Tools Mathematically proficient students consider the available tools when solving a mathematical problem. In Exercises 6–9 encourage students to draw a diagram for each exercise.

Levels of Complexity Chart

The levels of the exercises progress from 1 to 3, with Level 1 indicating the lowest level of complexity.

Exercises	6–22	23–27, 40–47	28–39
Level 3			●
Level 2		●	
Level 1	●		

Extra Practice

See page R12 for extra exercises for students who are approaching level or for on-level students who need additional reinforcement.

Check Your Understanding

◯ = Step-by-Step Solutions begin on page R13.

Go Online! for a Self-Check Quiz

Example 1 S.MD.7

Point X is chosen at random on $\overline{AD}$. Find the probability of each event.

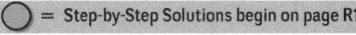

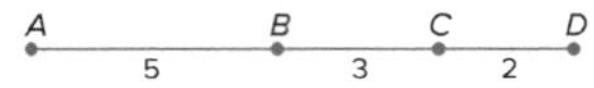

1. $P(X \text{ is on } \overline{BD})$ $\frac{1}{2}$, 0.5, or 50%
2. $P(X \text{ is on } \overline{BC})$ $\frac{3}{10}$, 0.3, or 30%

Example 2 S.MD.7

3. **CARDS** In a game of cards, 43 cards are used, including one joker. Four players are each dealt 10 cards, and the rest are put in a pile. If Greg doesn't have the joker, what is the probability that his partner or the pile has the joker? $\frac{13}{33}$, 0.39, or about 39%

Examples 3–4 S.MD.7

4. **ARCHERY** An archer aims at a target with 10 concentric circles whose diameters decrease by 12.2 centimeters as they get closer to the center. Find the probability that the archer will hit the center. Assume every point on the target is equally likely to be hit. $\frac{1}{100}$, 0.01, or 1%

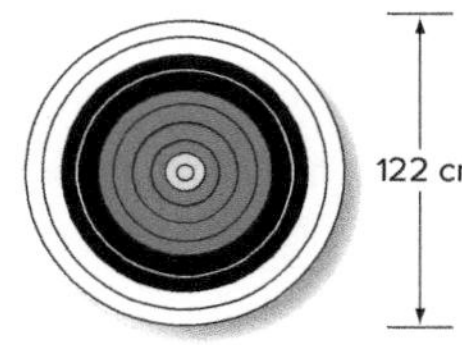

5. **NAVIGATION** A camper lost in the woods points his compass in a random direction. Find the probability that the camper is heading in the NE direction. $\frac{1}{8}$, 0.125, or 12.5%

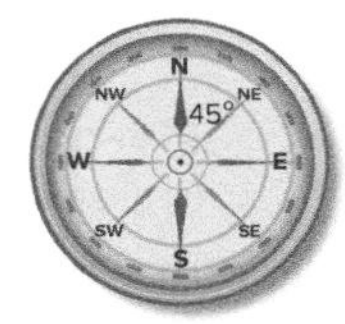

Practice and Problem Solving

Extra Practice is on page R12.

Example 1 S.MD.7

MP TOOLS Point X is chosen at random on $\overline{FK}$. Find the probability of each event.

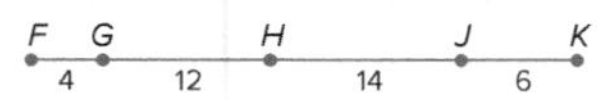

6. $P(X \text{ is on } \overline{FH})$
7. $P(X \text{ is on } \overline{GJ})$
8. $P(X \text{ is on } \overline{HK})$
9. $P(X \text{ is on } \overline{FG})$

6. $\frac{4}{9}$, 0.44, or 44%
7. $\frac{13}{18}$, 0.72, or 72%
8. $\frac{5}{9}$, 0.56, or 56%
9. $\frac{1}{9}$, 0.11, or 11%

10. **BIRDS** Four birds are sitting on a telephone wire. What is the probability that a fifth bird landing at a randomly selected point between birds 1 and 4 will sit at some point between birds 3 and 4? $\frac{1}{3}$, 0.33, or 33%

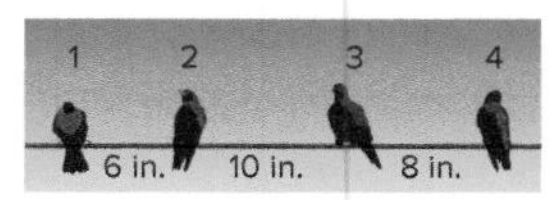

Example 2 S.MD.7

11. **TELEVISION** Julio is watching television and sees an ad for a video game that he knows his friend wants for her birthday. If the ad replays at a random time in each 3-hour interval, what is the probability that he will see the ad again during his favorite 30-minute sitcom the next day? $\frac{1}{6}$, 0.17, or about 17%

Example 3 S.MD.7

Find the probability that a point chosen at random lies in the shaded region. Assume that figures that seem to be regular and congruent are regular and congruent.

12. 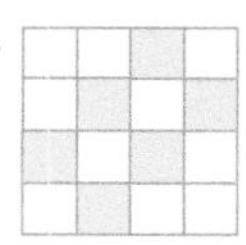
$\frac{3}{8}$, 0.375, or 37.5%

13. 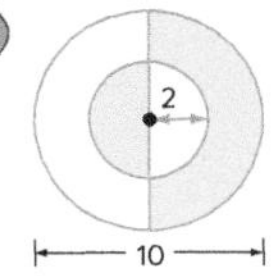

$\frac{1}{2}$, 0.5, or 50%

14. 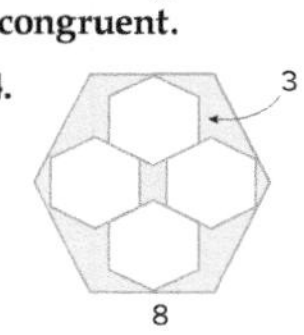

$\frac{7}{16}$, 0.4375, or 43.75%

Differentiated Homework Options

Levels	AL Basic	OL Core	BL Advanced
Exercises	6–22, 35–47	7–25 odd, 26, 27–33 odd, 34–47	28-39, (optional: 40–47)
2-Day Option	7–21 odd, 40–47	6–22	
	6–22 even, 35–39	23–47	

You can use ALEKS to provide additional remediation support with personalized instruction and practice.

Go Online!

The most up-to-date resources available for your program can be found at connectED.mcgraw-hill.com.

Example 4
S.MD.7

Use the spinner to find each probability. If the spinner lands on a line, it is spun again.

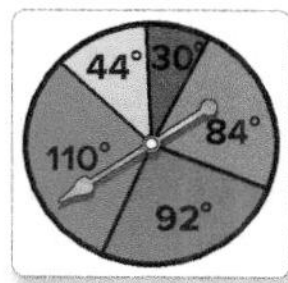

15. P(pointer landing on yellow) 12.2%
16. P(pointer landing on blue) 23.3%
17. P(pointer not landing on green) 69.4%
18. P(pointer landing on red) 25.6%
19. P(pointer landing on neither red nor yellow) 62.2%

Describe an event with a 33% probability for each model.

20. 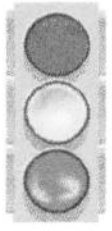 Sample answer: getting a red light

21. 

Sample answer: a point between 10 and 20

22. 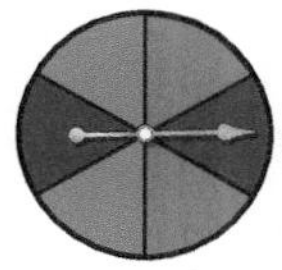 Sample answer: landing on green

Find the probability that a point chosen at random lies in the shaded region.

B

23. 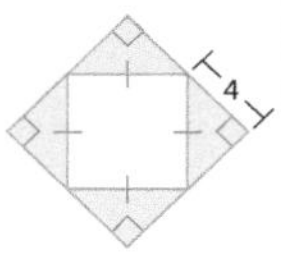

$\frac{1}{2}$, 0.5, or 50%

24. 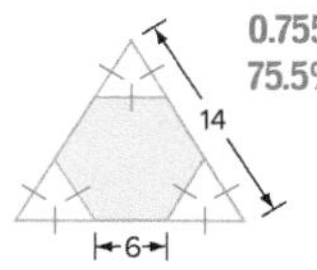

0.755 or 75.5%

25. 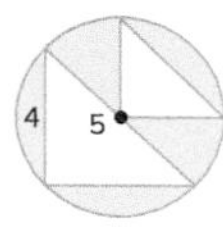

53.5%

26. **FARMING** The layout for a farm is shown with each square representing a plot. Estimate the area of each field to answer each question.

a. What is the approximate combined area of the spinach and corn fields? 67 square units

b. Find the probability that a randomly chosen plot is used to grow soybeans. 0.16 or 16%

27. **ALGEBRA** Prove that the probability that a randomly chosen point in the circle will lie in the shaded region is equal to $\frac{x}{360}$. See margin.

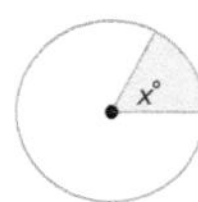

C

28. **COORDINATE GEOMETRY** If a point is chosen at random in the coordinate grid shown at the right, find each probability. Round to the nearest hundredth.

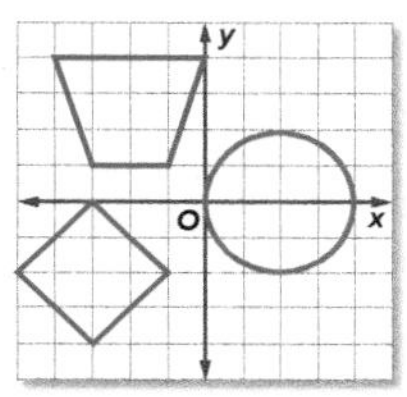

a. P(point inside the circle) $\frac{\pi}{25}$, 0.13, or 13%

b. P(point inside the trapezoid) $\frac{9}{100}$, 0.09, or 9%

c. P(point inside the trapezoid, square, or circle) $\frac{3}{10}$, 0.30, or 30%

MP **STRUCTURE** **Find the probability that a point chosen at random lies in a shaded region.**

29. 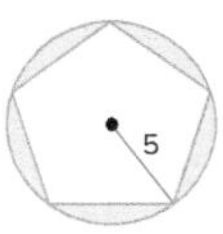

0.24 or 24%

30. 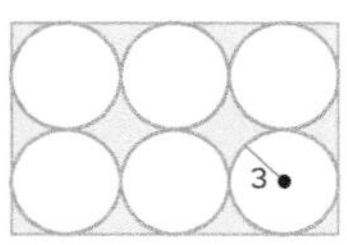

0.21 or 21%

31. 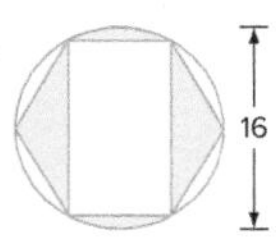

0.33 or 33%

MP Teaching the Mathematical Practices

Structure Mathematically proficient students start by explaining the meaning of a problem to themselves and looking for entry points to its solution. They plan a solution pathway rather than simply jumping into a solution attempt. In Exercises 29–31, encourage students to make a plan to solve each problem first.

Follow-Up

Students have explored geometric probability. Ask:

- How can geometry be used to make predictions? Sample answer: You can find the probability of an event occurring by replacing the variables used for success and failure with measures of length or area. For example, you could find the probability of an event occurring in a specific sector of a circle by finding the ratio of the area of that sector to the area of the entire circle.

Additional Answer

27. Sample answer: The probability that a randomly chosen point will lie in the shaded region is the ratio of the area of the sector to the area of the circle.

P(point lies in sector)

$$= \frac{\text{area of sector}}{\text{area of circle}}$$

$$\frac{x}{360} \stackrel{?}{=} \frac{\frac{x}{360} \cdot \pi r^2}{\pi r^2}$$

$$\frac{x}{360} = \frac{x}{360} \checkmark$$

Differentiated Instruction OL BL ELL

Extension Have students create a game that applies the concepts of probability using area. Students should write clear directions for playing and winning the game. Directions should also include the probability of scoring for all possible events of the game. Allow students to play one another's games, checking to see whether the mathematical probabilities correspond to the experimental probabilities. Have students design games that are fair, very hard to win, or very easy to win.

MP Teaching the Mathematical Practices

Construct Arguments Mathematically proficient students make sense of quantities and their relationships in problem situations. In Exercise 36, encourage students to draw and label a diagram.

Assess

Crystal Ball Have students write a paragraph that explains how the lessons in probability might help them in evaluating simulations.

Additional Answers

37. No; Sample answer: Athletic events should not be considered random because there are other factors involved, such as pressure and ability, that have an impact on the success of the event.

38. Sample answer: The probability that a randomly chosen point on $\overline{AC}$ lies between A and B is 20%.

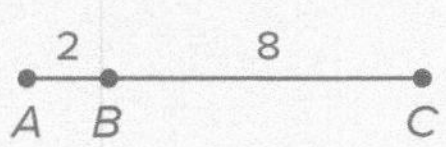

The probability that a randomly chosen point in the circle will lie in the shaded area is 20%.

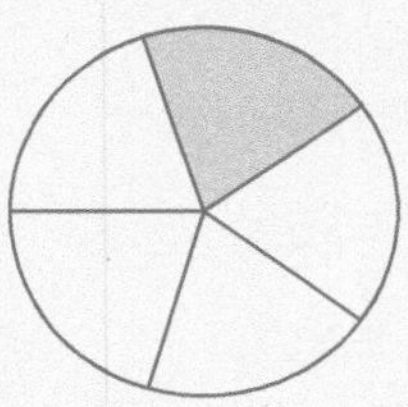

The probability that a randomly chosen point in the square will lie in the unshaded area is 20%.

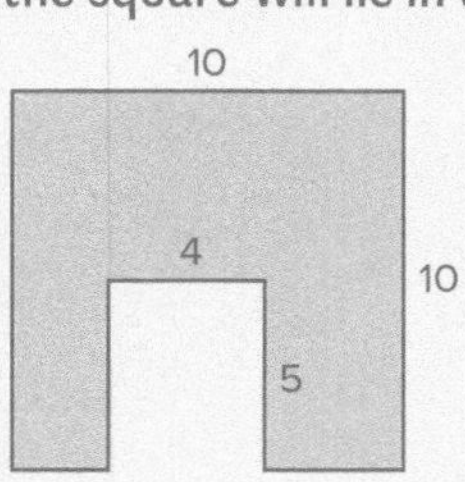

Go Online!

eSolutions Manual

Create worksheets, answer keys, and solutions handouts for your assignments.

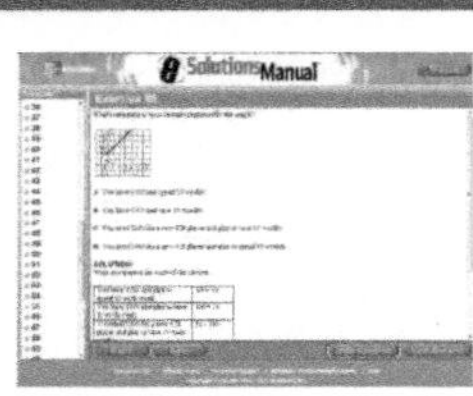

32. **COORDINATE GEOMETRY** Consider a system of inequalities, $1 \leq x \leq 6$, $y \leq x$, and $y \geq 1$. If a point (x, y) in the system is chosen at random, what is the probability that $(x - 1)^2 + (y - 1)^2 \geq 16$? **0.50 or 50%**

33. **VOLUME** The polar bear exhibit at a local zoo has a pool with the side profile shown. If the pool is 20 feet wide, what is the probability that a bear that is equally likely to swim anywhere in the pool will be in the incline region? **0.31 or 31%**

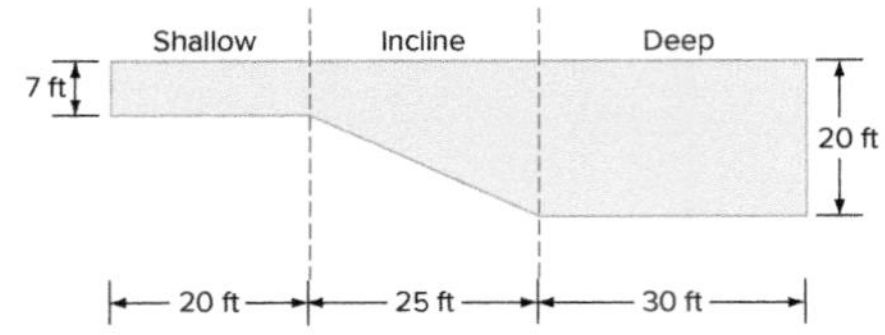

34. **DECISION MAKING** Meleah's flight was delayed, and she is running late to make it to a national science competition. She is planning on renting a car at the airport and prefers car rental company A over car rental company B. The courtesy van for car rental company A arrives every 7 minutes, and the courtesy van for car rental company B arrives every 12 minutes.

a. What is the probability that Meleah will have to wait 5 minutes or less to see each van? Explain your reasoning. (*Hint:* Use an area model.)

b. What is the probability that Meleah will have to wait 5 minutes or less to see one of the vans? Explain your reasoning.

c. Meleah can wait no more than 5 minutes without risking being late for the competition. If the van from company B should arrive first, should she wait for the van from company A or take the van from company B? Explain your reasoning. **34a–c. See Ch. 12 Answer Appendix.**

36. $\frac{1}{7}$; sample answer: Using the Triangle Inequality Theorem, there are 7 isosceles triangles with integer side lengths and a perimeter of 32 centimeters. Of those triangles, only the one with side lengths 10, 10, and 12 has an area of exactly 48 square centimeters. Therefore, the probability is 1 in 7. S.MD.7

H.O.T. Problems Use Higher-Order Thinking Skills

35. **MP MODELING** Find the probability that a point chosen at random would lie in the shaded area of the figure. Round to the nearest tenth of a percent. **14.3%**

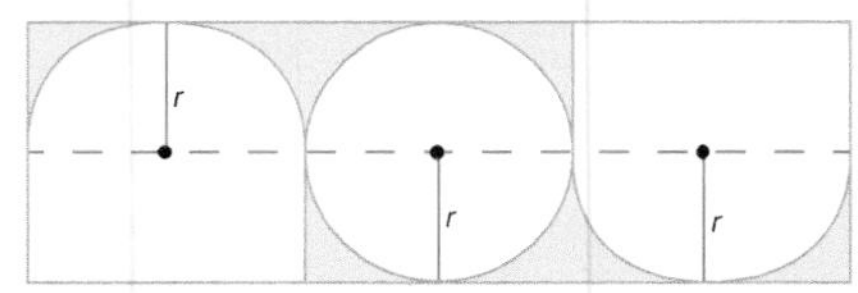

36. **MP CONSTRUCT ARGUMENTS** An isosceles triangle has a perimeter of 32 centimeters. If the lengths of the sides of the triangle are integers, what is the probability that the area of the triangle is exactly 48 square centimeters? Explain.

37. **WRITING IN MATH** Can athletic events be considered random events? Explain. **See margin.**

38. **OPEN-ENDED** Represent a probability of 20% using three different geometric figures. **See margin.**

39. **WRITING IN MATH** Explain why the probability of a randomly chosen point falling in the shaded region of either of the squares shown is the same. **See margin.**

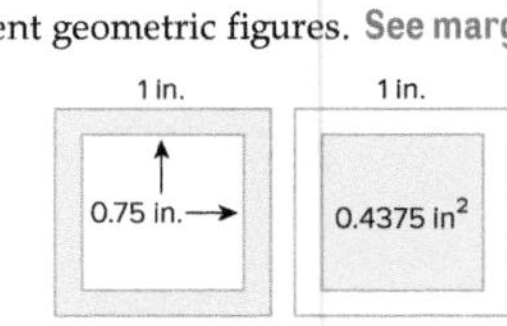

MP Standards for Mathematical Practice

Emphasis On	Exercises
1 Make sense of problems and persevere in solving them.	1–2, 29–31, 43, 46
2 Reason abstractly and quantitatively.	12–14, 23–25, 40, 42, 44, 45, 47
3 Construct viable arguments and critique the reasoning of others.	27, 28, 36
4 Model with mathematics.	3–5, 10, 11, 26, 35
5 Use appropriate tools strategically.	6–9
6 Attend to precision.	15–19, 41

Preparing for Assessment

40. Visitors to a school fair get a chance to use a random number generator to choose coordinates for a point on a square board. They win a prize if the point lies on or in a triangle in the middle of the board, as shown. What is the probability that a visitor wins a prize? Express the probability as a decimal rounded to the nearest hundredth. MP 2 S.MD.7 0.14

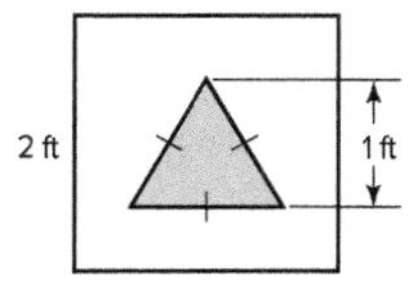

41. Concentric circles have radii of 4 centimeters and 8 centimeters. What is the probability that a grain of rice dropped onto the circles at random lands outside the circle with the 4-centimeter radius and inside the circle with the radius of 8 centimeters? MP 6 S.MD.7 D

- A 4%
- B 25%
- C 50%
- D 75%

42. An archery target consists of a square inscribed in a circle with a radius of 15 inches, as shown. An arrow lands at a random point on the target.

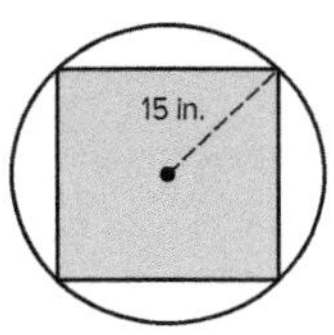

Which expression represents the probability that the arrow lands in the square? MP 2 S.MD.7 C

- A $\frac{15}{\pi}$
- B $\frac{4}{\pi}$
- C $\frac{2}{\pi}$
- D $\frac{1}{\pi}$
- E $\frac{1}{15\pi}$

43. A box contains 7 blue marbles, 6 red marbles, 2 white marbles, and 3 black marbles. If one marble is chosen at random, what is the probability that it will be red? Round to the nearest hundredths. MP 1 S.MD.7 0.33

44. Ashton is designing a dartboard. He wants to paint a circular target on a square piece of wood with the dimensions shown. He assumes darts will hit the piece of wood randomly. What radius should he use for the circle so that the probability of a dart landing in the circle is 60%? Express the answer in feet and round to the nearest hundredth. MP 2 S.MD.7 1.75 feet

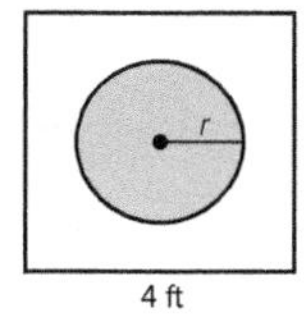

45. A big square has a side length of 24 units, and has a small square within it with area 16 square units. Find the probability of a dart hitting the small square. MP 2 S.MD.7

$\frac{1}{36}$

46. MULTI-STEP A point is chosen at random on $\overline{AD}$.

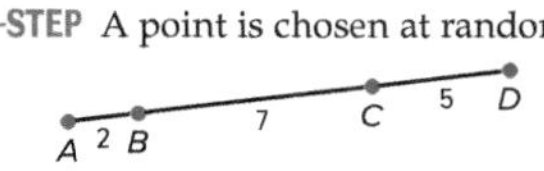

Find the probability: MP 1 S.MD.7

a. that the point is on $\overline{BC}$ $\frac{1}{2}$

b. that the point is not on $\overline{AB}$ $\frac{6}{7}$

47. An archery target is made up of three concentric circles with radii 5, 10 and 20 cm, respectively. MP 2 S.MD.7

a. Find the probability that the arrow lands in the innermost circle.

$\frac{1}{16}$

b. Find the probability that the arrow lands in the outer ring.

$\frac{3}{4}$

c. The radius of the outer circle needs to be changed to make the probability of the arrow landing in the outer ring $\frac{5}{9}$. What is the new radius of the outer circle?

15 cm

39. Sample answer: The probability of a randomly chosen point lying in the shaded region of the square on the left is found by subtracting the area of the unshaded square from the area of the larger square and finding the ratio of the difference of the areas to the area of the larger square. The probability is $\frac{1^2 - 0.75^2}{1^2}$ or 43.75%. The probability of a randomly chosen point lying in the shaded region of the square on the right is the ratio of the area of the shaded square to the area of the larger square, which is $\frac{0.4375}{1}$ or 43.75%. Therefore, the probability of a randomly chosen point lying in the shaded area of either square is the same.

Preparing for Assessment

Exercises 40–47 require students to use the skills they will need on future assessments. Exercises are dual-coded with content standards and mathematical practice standards.

Dual Coding		
Items	Content Standards	MP Mathematical Practices
40	S.MD.7	2
41	S.MD.7	6
42	S.MD.7	2
43	S.MD.7	1
44	S.MD.7	2
45	S.MD.7	2
46	S.MD.7	1
47	S.MD.7	2

Diagnose Student Errors

Survey student responses for each item. Class trends may indicate common errors and misconceptions.

41.

A	Set up ratio as $\frac{\pi \cdot 8^2}{\pi \cdot 4^2}$
B	Found probability of landing inside circle with 4-cm radius
C	Assumed probabilities of landing inside/outside circle with 4-cm radius are equal
D	CORRECT

42.

A	Set up ratio as $\frac{\text{area of square}}{2\pi \cdot 15}$
B	Set up ratio as $\frac{30^2}{\pi \cdot 15^2}$
C	CORRECT
D	Set up ratio as $\frac{15^2}{\pi \cdot 15^2}$
E	Set up ratio as $\frac{15}{\pi \cdot 15^2}$

Go Online!

Quizzes

Students can use *Self-Check Quizzes* to check their understanding of this lesson and have the results sent to you. You can also give *Quiz 3*, which covers the content in Lessons 12-4 and 12-5.

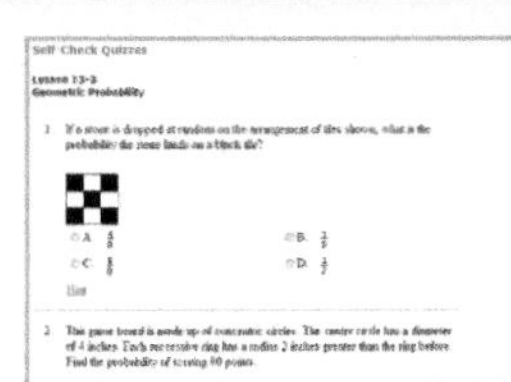

RtI Response to Intervention

Use the Intervention Planner to help you determine your Response to Intervention.

Intervention Planner

TIER 1 On Level OL

IF students miss 25% of the exercises or less,

THEN choose a resource:

SE Lessons 12-1 through 12-4

Go Online!

- Skills Practice
- Chapter Project
- Self-Check Quizzes

TIER 2 Strategic Intervention AL
Approaching grade level

IF students miss 50% of the exercises,

THEN choose a resource:

Quick Review Math Handbook

Go Online!

- Study Guide and Intervention
- Extra Examples
- Personal Tutors
- Homework Help

TIER 3 Intensive Intervention
2 or more grades below level

IF students miss 75% of the exercises,

THEN choose a resource:

Use *Math Triumphs, Geometry*

Go Online!

- Extra Examples
- Personal Tutors
- Homework Help
- Review Vocabulary

Go Online!

eAssessment

You can use the premade Mid-Chapter Test to assess students' progress in the first half of the chapter. Customize and create multiple versions of your Mid-Chapter Quiz and answer keys that align to the your standards. Tests can be delivered on paper or online.

CHAPTER 12

Mid-Chapter Quiz

Lessons 12-1 through 12-4

1. **LUNCH** A deli has a lunch special, which consists of a sandwich, soup, dessert, and a drink for $4.99. The choices are in the table below. (Lesson 12-1)

Sandwich	Soup	Dessert	Drink
chicken salad	tomato	cookie	tea
ham	chicken noodle	pie	coffee
tuna	vegetable		cola
roast beef			diet cola
			milk

   a. How many different lunches can be created from the items shown in the table? **120**

   b. If a soup and two desserts were added, how many different lunches could be created? **320**

2. **FLAGS** How many different signals can be made with 5 flags from 8 flags of different colors? (Lesson 12-1) **6720**

3. **CLOTHING** Marcy has six colors of shirts: red, blue, yellow, green, pink, and orange. She has each color in short-sleeved and long-sleeved styles. Represent the sample space for Marcy's shirt choices by making an organized list, a table, and a tree diagram. (Lesson 12-1) **See Ch. 12 Answer Appendix.**

4. In a class of 26 students, 19 have black hair and 17 have brown eyes. Four students have neither brown hair nor brown eyes. A student is chosen at random from the class. Find the probability that the student has: (Lesson 12-2)

   a. brown eyes $\frac{17}{26}$

   b. has brown eyes and black hair $\frac{7}{13}$

   c. has brown eyes, but not black hair $\frac{3}{26}$

5. A dot cube is rolled and a coin is tossed. Find the probability that: (Lesson 12-2)

   a. the outcome on the dot cube is prime and the coin comes up heads $\frac{1}{4}$

   b. the outcome on the dot cube is prime or the coin comes up heads $\frac{3}{4}$

6. **SPELLING** A bag contains one tile for each letter of the word TRAINS. If you selected a permutation of these letters at random, what is the probability that they would spell TRAINS? (Lesson 12-3) $\frac{1}{720}$

7. **COINS** Ten coins are tossed simultaneously. In how many of the outcomes will the third coin turn up a head? (Lesson 12-3) 2^9

8. A 320-meter-long tightrope is suspended between two poles. Assume that the line has an equal chance of breaking anywhere along its length. (Lesson 12-4)

   a. Determine the probability that a break will occur in the first 50 meters of the tightrope. **about 16%**

   b. Determine the probability that the break will occur within 20 meters of a pole. **about 13%**

Point A is chosen at random on $\overline{BE}$. Find the probability of each event. (Lesson 12-4)

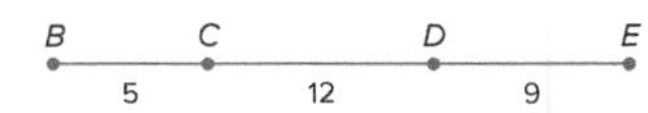

9. $P(A \text{ is on } \overline{CD})$ $\frac{6}{13}$

10. $P(A \text{ is on } \overline{BD})$ $\frac{17}{26}$

11. $P(A \text{ is on } \overline{CE})$ $\frac{21}{26}$

12. $P(A \text{ is on } \overline{DE})$ $\frac{9}{26}$

Use the spinner to find each probability. If the spinner lands on a line, it is spun again. (Lesson 12-4)

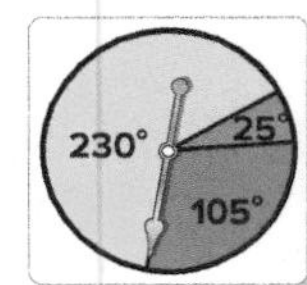

13. P(pointer landing on yellow) **about 64%**

14. P(pointer landing on blue) **about 7%**

15. P(pointer landing on red) **about 29%**

16. **GAMES** At a carnival, the object of a game is to throw a dart at the board and hit region III. (Lesson 12-4)

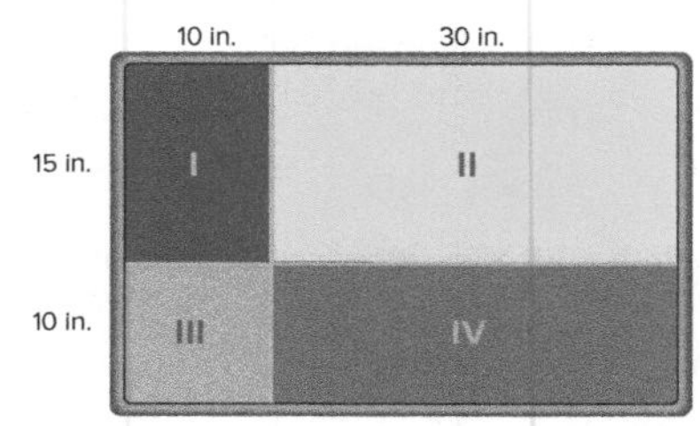

   a. What is the probability that it hits region I? **15%**

   b. What is the probability that it hits region II? **45%**

   c. What is the probability that it hits region III? **10%**

   d. What is the probability that it hits region IV? **30%**

Foldables Study Organizer

Dinah Zike's FOLDABLES®

Before students complete the Mid-Chapter Quiz, encourage them to review the information for Lessons 12-1 through 12-4 in their Foldables. Students may benefit from sharing their Foldable with a partner and taking turns summarizing what they have learned, while the other partner listens carefully. They should seek clarification of any concepts, as needed.

ALEKS can be used as a formative assessment tool to target learning gaps for those who are struggling, while providing enhanced learning for those who have mastered the concepts.

Probability and the Multiplication Rule

SUGGESTED PACING (DAYS)	
90 min.	0.75
45 min.	1.0
	Instruction

Track Your Progress

Objectives

1 Apply the multiplication rule to situations involving independent events.

2 Apply the multiplication rule to situations involving dependent events.

Mathematical Background

A *compound event* consists of two or more simple events. Events *A* and *B* are independent if the occurrence of *A* does not affect the probability that *B* occurs. Events *A* and *B* are dependent if the occurrence of *A* in some way changes the probability that *B* occurs.

THEN

S.MD.7 Analyze decisions and strategies using probability concepts (e.g., product testing, medical testing, pulling a hockey goalie at the end of a game).

S.CP.1 Describe events as subsets of a sample space (the set of outcomes) using characteristics (or categories) of the outcomes, or as unions, intersections, or complements of other events ("or," "and," "not").

NOW

S.CP.2 Understand that two events *A* and *B* are independent if the probability of *A* and *B* occurring together is the product of their probabilities, and use this characterization to determine if they are independent.

S.CP.8 Apply the general Multiplication Rule in a uniform probability model, $P(A \text{ and } B) = P(A)P(B|A) = P(B)P(A|B)$, and interpret the answer in terms of the model.

NEXT

S.CP.7 Apply the Addition Rule, $P(A \text{ or } B) = P(A) + P(B) - P(A \text{ and } B)$, and interpret the answer in terms of the model.

Go Online! All of these resources and more are available at connectED.mcgraw-hill.com

eLessons utilize the power of your interactive whiteboard in an engaging way. Use **Probability of Compound Events**, Screens 2–6, to introduce the concepts in this lesson.

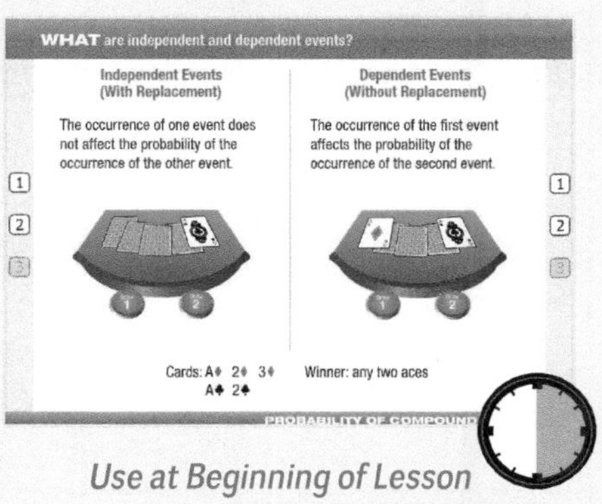

WHAT are independent and dependent events?
Independent Events (With Replacement)
Dependent Events (Without Replacement)
The occurrence of one event does not affect the probability of the occurrence of the other event.
The occurrence of the first event affects the probability of the occurrence of the second event.
Winner: any two aces

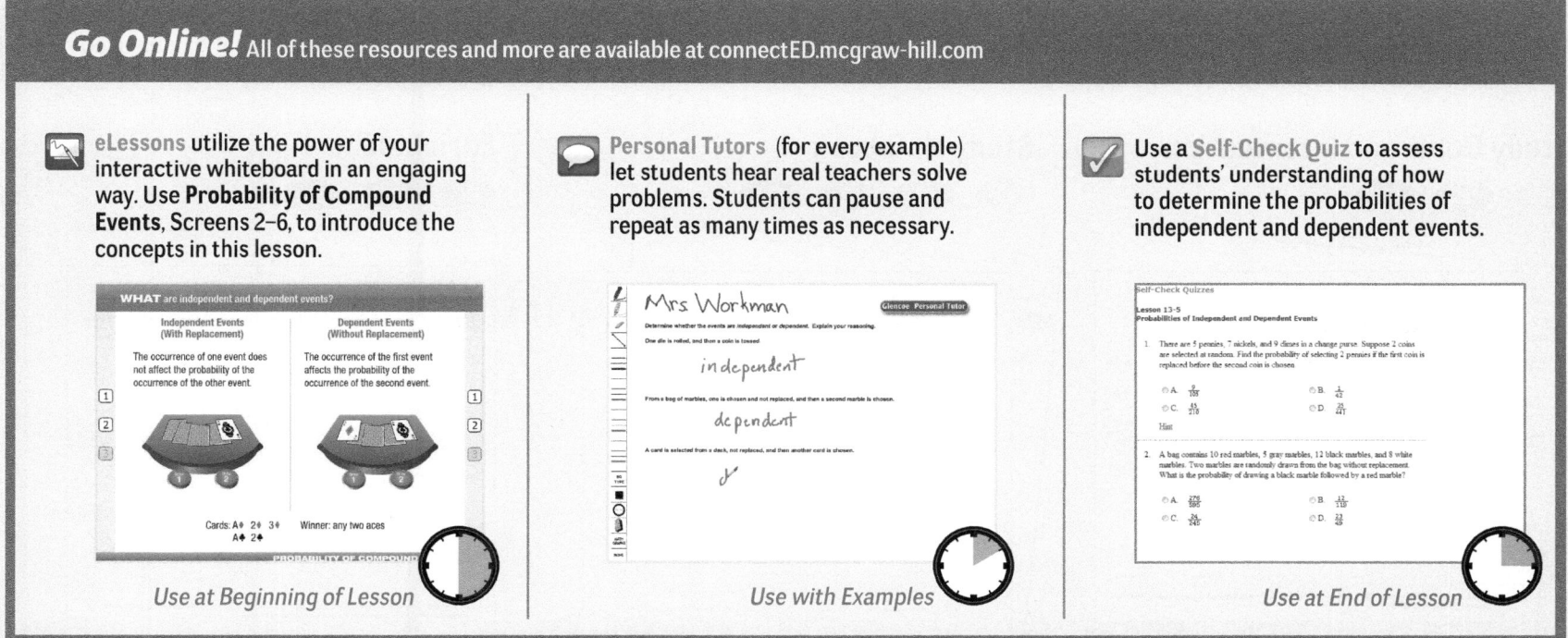

Use at Beginning of Lesson

Personal Tutors (for every example) let students hear real teachers solve problems. Students can pause and repeat as many times as necessary.

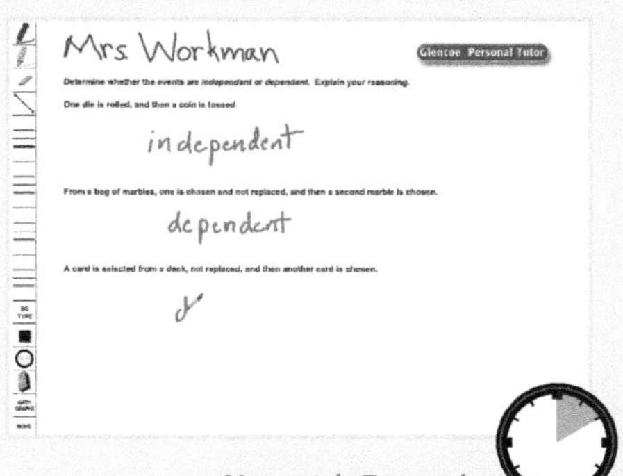

Use with Examples

Use a Self-Check Quiz to assess students' understanding of how to determine the probabilities of independent and dependent events.

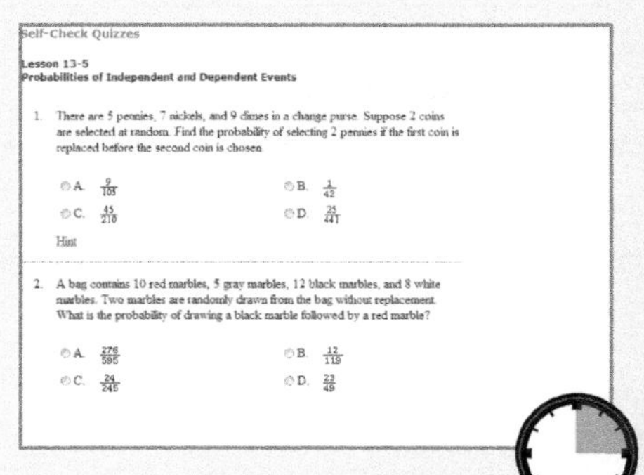

Use at End of Lesson

OER Using Open Educational Resources

Quiz Before beginning this lesson, have students take *Independent or Dependent Events Math Quiz* on **softschools.com** to review these concepts. *Use as introductory activity*

Go Online!
connectED.mcgraw-hill.com

Worksheets

Differentiate Your Resources

Extra Practice Additional practice or homework; Skills Practice is best for approaching-level students and Practice is best for on-level and beyond-level students

Skills Practice

AL OL ELL

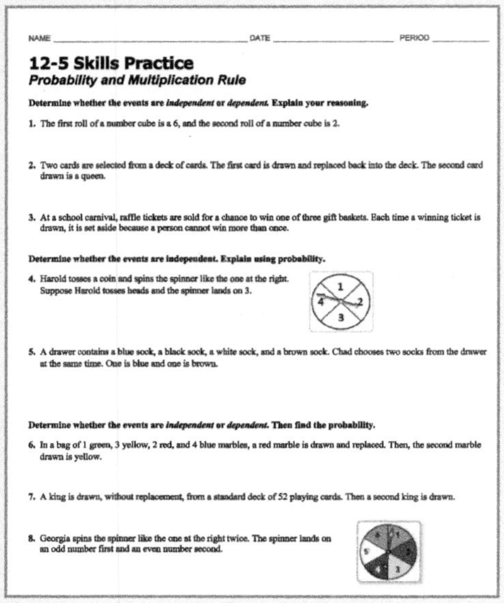
NAME ______ DATE ______ PERIOD ______

12-5 Skills Practice
Probability and Multiplication Rule

Determine whether the events are *independent* or *dependent*. Explain your reasoning.

1. The first roll of a number cube is a 6, and the second roll of a number cube is 2.
2. Two cards are selected from a deck of cards. The first card is drawn and replaced back into the deck. The second card drawn is a queen.
3. At a school carnival, raffle tickets are sold for a chance to win one of three gift baskets. Each time a winning ticket is drawn, it is set aside because a person cannot win more than once.

Determine whether the events are independent. Explain using probability.

4. Harold tosses a coin and spins the spinner like the one at the right. Suppose Harold tosses heads and the spinner lands on 3.
5. A drawer contains a blue sock, a black sock, a white sock, and a brown sock. Chad chooses two socks from the drawer at the same time. One is blue and one is brown.

Determine whether the events are *independent* or *dependent*. Then find the probability.

6. In a bag of 1 green, 3 yellow, 2 red, and 4 blue marbles, a red marble is drawn and replaced. Then, the second marble drawn is yellow.
7. A king is drawn, without replacement, from a standard deck of 52 playing cards. Then a second king is drawn.
8. Georgia spins the spinner like the one at the right twice. The spinner lands on an odd number first and an even number second.

Practice

AL OL BL ELL

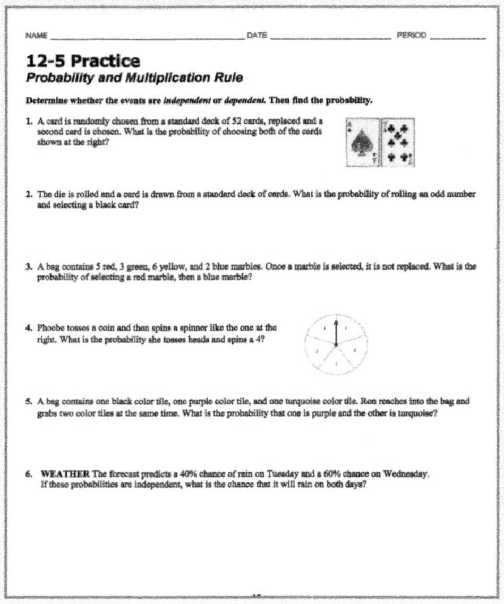
NAME ______ DATE ______ PERIOD ______

12-5 Practice
Probability and Multiplication Rule

Determine whether the events are *independent* or *dependent*. Then find the probability.

1. A card is randomly chosen from a standard deck of 52 cards, replaced and a second card is chosen. What is the probability of choosing both of the cards shown at the right?
2. The die is rolled and a card is drawn from a standard deck of cards. What is the probability of rolling an odd number and selecting a black card?
3. A bag contains 5 red, 3 green, 6 yellow, and 2 blue marbles. Once a marble is selected, it is not replaced. What is the probability of selecting a red marble, then a blue marble?
4. Phoebe tosses a coin and then spins a spinner like the one at the right. What is the probability she tosses heads and spins a 4?
5. A bag contains one black color tile, one purple color tile, and one turquoise color tile. Ron reaches into the bag and grabs two color tiles at the same time. What is the probability that one is purple and the other is turquoise?
6. **WEATHER** The forecast predicts a 40% chance of rain on Tuesday and a 60% chance on Wednesday. If these probabilities are independent, what is the chance that it will rain on both days?

Word Problem Practice

AL OL BL ELL

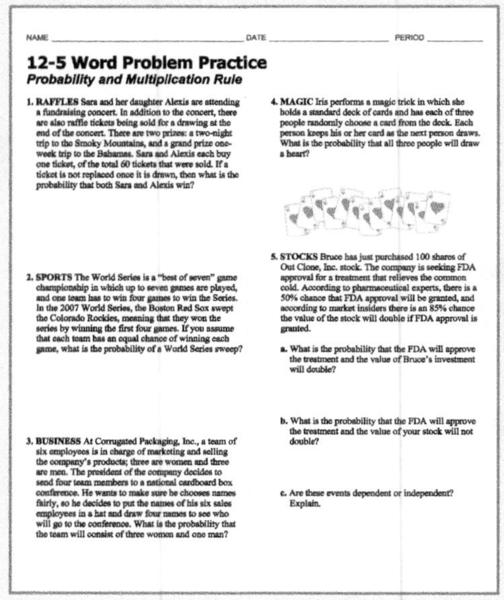
NAME ______ DATE ______ PERIOD ______

12-5 Word Problem Practice
Probability and Multiplication Rule

1. **RAFFLES** Sara and her daughter Alexis are attending a fundraising concert. In addition to the concert, there are also raffle tickets being sold for a drawing at the end of the concert. There are two prizes: a two-night trip to the Smoky Mountains, and a grand prize one-week trip to the Bahamas. Sara and Alexis each buy one ticket, of the total 60 tickets that were sold. If a ticket is not replaced once it is drawn, then what is the probability that both Sara and Alexis win?
2. **SPORTS** The World Series is a "best of seven" game championship in which up to seven games are played, and one team has to win four games to win the Series. In the 2007 World Series, the Boston Red Sox swept the Colorado Rockies, meaning that they won the series by winning the first four games. If you assume that each team has an equal chance of winning each game, what is the probability of a World Series sweep?
3. **BUSINESS** At Corrugated Packaging, Inc., a team of six employees is in charge of marketing and selling the company's products; three are women and three are men. The president of the company decides to send four team members to a national cardboard box conference. He wants to make sure he chooses names fairly, so he decides to put the names of his six sales employees in a hat and draw four names to see who will go to the conference. What is the probability that the team will consist of three women and one man?
4. **MAGIC** Iris performs a magic trick in which she holds a standard deck of cards and has each of three people randomly choose a card from the deck. Each person keeps his or her card as the next person draws. What is the probability that all three people will draw a heart?
5. **STOCKS** Bruce has just purchased 100 shares of Out Cloone, Inc. stock. The company is seeking FDA approval for a treatment that relieves the common cold. According to pharmaceutical experts, there is a 50% chance that FDA approval will be granted, and according to market insiders there is an 85% chance the value of the stock will double if FDA approval is granted.
   a. What is the probability that the FDA will approve the treatment and the value of Bruce's investment will double?
   b. What is the probability that the FDA will approve the treatment and the value of your stock will not double?
   c. Are these events dependent or independent? Explain.

Intervention Reteaching and vocabulary activities that can be used with struggling or absent students and as ELL support

Study Guide and Intervention

AL OL ELL

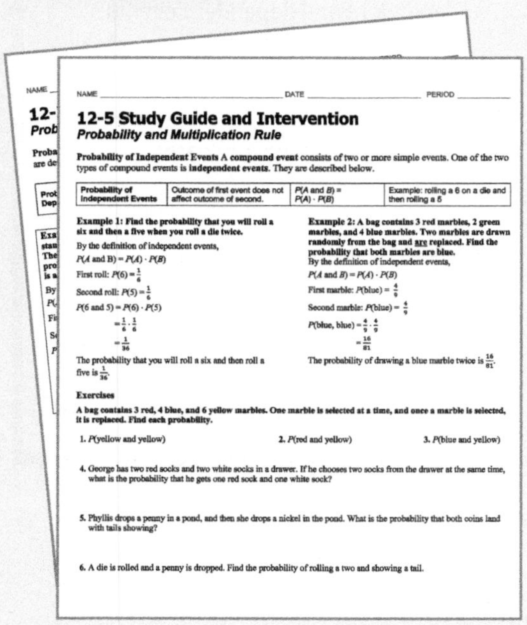
NAME ______ DATE ______ PERIOD ______

12-5 Study Guide and Intervention
Probability and Multiplication Rule

Probability of Independent Events A **compound event** consists of two or more simple events. One of the two types of compound events is **independent events**. They are described below.

Probability of Independent Events	Outcome of first event does not affect outcome of second.	P(A and B) = P(A) · P(B)	Example: rolling a 6 on a die and then rolling a 5

Example 1: Find the probability that you will roll a six and then a five when you roll a die twice.

By the definition of independent events,
$P(A \text{ and } B) = P(A) \cdot P(B)$
First roll: $P(6) = \frac{1}{6}$
Second roll: $P(5) = \frac{1}{6}$
$P(6 \text{ and } 5) = P(6) \cdot P(5) = \frac{1}{6} \cdot \frac{1}{6} = \frac{1}{36}$

The probability that you will roll a six and then roll a five is $\frac{1}{36}$.

Example 2: A bag contains 3 red marbles, 2 green marbles, and 4 blue marbles. Two marbles are drawn randomly from the bag and are replaced. Find the probability that both marbles are blue.

By the definition of independent events,
$P(A \text{ and } B) = P(A) \cdot P(B)$
First marble: $P(\text{blue}) = \frac{4}{9}$
Second marble: $P(\text{blue}) = \frac{4}{9}$
$P(\text{blue, blue}) = \frac{4}{9} \cdot \frac{4}{9} = \frac{16}{81}$

The probability of drawing a blue marble twice is $\frac{16}{81}$.

Exercises

A bag contains 3 red, 4 blue, and 6 yellow marbles. One marble is selected at a time, and once a marble is selected, it is replaced. Find each probability.

1. P(yellow and yellow) 2. P(red and yellow) 3. P(blue and yellow)
4. George has two red socks and two white socks in a drawer. If he chooses two socks from the drawer at the same time, what is the probability that he gets one red sock and one white sock?
5. Phyllis drops a penny in a pond, and then she drops a nickel in the pond. What is the probability that both coins land with tails showing?
6. A die is rolled and a penny is dropped. Find the probability of rolling a two and showing a tail.

Study Notebook

AL OL BL ELL

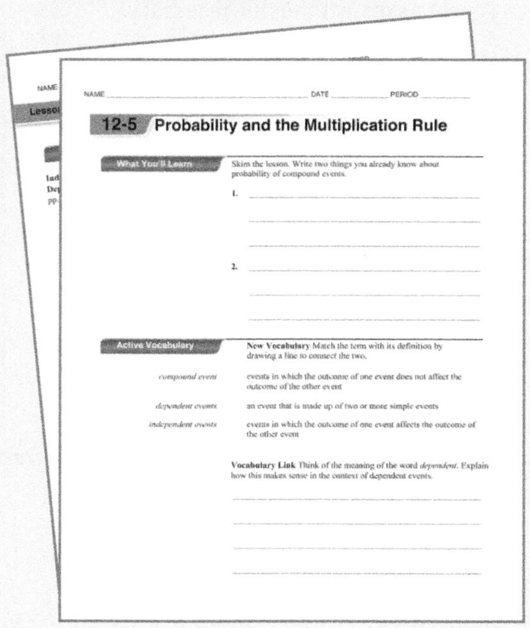
NAME ______ DATE ______ PERIOD ______

12-5 Probability and the Multiplication Rule

What You'll Learn Skim the lesson. Write two things you already know about probability of compound events.

1.
2.

Active Vocabulary **New Vocabulary** Match the term with its definition by drawing a line to connect the two.

compound event — events in which the outcome of one event does not affect the outcome of the other event
dependent events — an event that is made up of two or more simple events
independent events — events in which the outcome of one event affects the outcome of the other event

Vocabulary Link Think of the meaning of the word *dependent*. Explain how this makes sense in the context of dependent events.

Extension Activities that can be used to extend lesson concepts

Enrichment

OL BL ELL

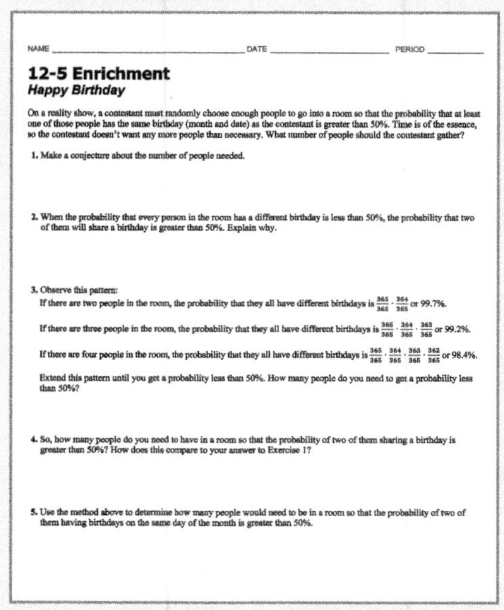
NAME ______ DATE ______ PERIOD ______

12-5 Enrichment
Happy Birthday

On a reality show, a contestant must randomly choose enough people to go into a room so that the probability that at least one of those people has the same birthday (month and date) as the contestant is greater than 50%. Time is of the essence, so the contestant doesn't want any more people than necessary. What number of people should the contestant gather?

1. Make a conjecture about the number of people needed.
2. When the probability that every person in the room has a different birthday is less than 50%, the probability that two of them will share a birthday is greater than 50%. Explain why.
3. Observe this pattern:
   If there are two people in the room, the probability that they all have different birthdays is $\frac{365}{365} \cdot \frac{364}{365}$ or 99.7%.
   If there are three people in the room, the probability that they all have different birthdays is $\frac{365}{365} \cdot \frac{364}{365} \cdot \frac{363}{365}$ or 99.2%.
   If there are four people in the room, the probability that they all have different birthdays is $\frac{365}{365} \cdot \frac{364}{365} \cdot \frac{363}{365} \cdot \frac{362}{365}$ or 98.4%.
   Extend this pattern until you get a probability less than 50%. How many people do you need to get a probability less than 50%?
4. So, how many people do you need to have in a room so that the probability of two of them sharing a birthday is greater than 50%? How does this compare to your answer to Exercise 1?
5. Use the method above to determine how many people would need to be in a room so that the probability of two of them having birthdays on the same day of the month is greater than 50%.

LESSON 5

Probability and the Multiplication Rule

Then

- You found simple probabilities.

Now

1. Apply the multiplication rule to situations involving independent events.
2. Apply the multiplication rule to situations involving dependent events.

Why?

- The 18 students in Mrs. Turner's chemistry class are drawing names to determine who will give his or her presentation first. James is hoping to be chosen first and his friend Arturo wants to be second.

New Vocabulary

compound event
independent events
dependent events

Mathematical Practices

1 Make sense of problems and persevere in solving them.
4 Model with mathematics.

Content Standards

S.CP.1 Describe events as subsets of a sample space (the set of outcomes) using characteristics (or categories) of the outcomes, or as unions, intersections, or complements of other events ("or," "and," "not").

S.CP.2 Understand that two events *A* and *B* are independent if the probability of *A* and *B* occurring together is the product of their probabilities, and use this characterization to determine if they are independent.

S.CP.8 Apply the general Multiplication Rule in a uniform probability model, $P(A \text{ and } B) = P(A)P(B|A) = P(B)P(A|B)$, and interpret the answer in terms of the model.

S.MD.7 Analyze decisions and strategies using probability concepts (e.g., product testing, medical testing, pulling a hockey goalie at the end of a game).

Steve Debenport/E+/Getty Images

1 Probability of Independent Events

A **compound event** or *composite event* consists of two or more simple events. In the example above, James and Arturo being chosen to give their presentations is a compound event. It consists of the event that James is chosen and the event that Arturo is chosen.

Compound events can be independent or dependent.

- Events *A* and *B* are **independent events** if the occurrence of *A* does not affect the probability that *B* occurs.
- Events *A* and *B* are **dependent events** if the occurrence of *A* in some way changes the probability that *B* occurs.

Consider choosing objects one at a time from a group of objects. If you replace the object each time, choosing additional objects are independent events. If you do not replace the object each time, choosing additional objects are dependent events.

S.CP.2

Example 1 Identify Independent and Dependent Events

Determine whether the events are *independent* or *dependent*. Explain your reasoning.

a. A coin lands heads up, and then a second coin lands tails up.

The outcome of the first coin toss in no way affects the outcome of the second coin toss. Therefore, these two events are *independent*.

b. In the class presentation example above, James is chosen first and then Arturo is chosen second.

After James is chosen, his name cannot be selected again. This affects the probability that Arturo is chosen, because the sample space is reduced by one name. Therefore, these two events are *dependent*.

c. Both Wednesday's lottery numbers and Saturday's lottery numbers are 1-2-3-4-5.

The outcome of Wednesday's drawing has no effect on Saturday's drawing. Therefore, these two events are *independent*.

Guided Practice 1A, 1B. See Ch. 12 Answer Appendix.

1A. A red card is selected from a standard deck of cards and put back. Then an ace is selected.

1B. Andrea selects a red shirt from her closet to wear on Monday and then a blue shirt to wear on Tuesday.

Mathematical Practices Strategies

Make sense of problems and persevere in solving them.
Help students to understand the meanings of problems involving compound events and to plan solution pathways. For example, ask:

- When calculating the probability of a compound event, why is it important to first determine whether the simple events within the compound event are independent or dependent? The dependence of the simple events affects the probability of the compound event.
- If you know that the first outcome in a compound event reduces the number of possible outcomes for the second event, are the events independent or dependent? dependent

Launch

Have students read the Why? section of the lesson. Ask:

- What factors affect the probability that James will be chosen first and Arturo will be chosen second? Sample answer: the number of students in the class
- If James is chosen first, what is the probability Arturo will be chosen second? $\frac{1}{17}$
- How does the outcome of the first choice affect the probability that Arturo is chosen second? If Arturo is not chosen first, then his probability of being chosen second increases because there is one less student who could be chosen second.

Teach

Ask the scaffolded questions for each example to build conceptual understanding for students at all levels.

1 Probability of Independent Events

Example 1 Identify Independent and Dependent Events

AL A random number generator produces an even number and then produces an odd number. Are these events independent or dependent? Explain. Independent; the outcome of the first random number generation does not affect the outcome of the second one.

OL Give an example of dependent events. Sample answer: A softball team chooses a player to bat first, and then chooses another player to bat second.

BL Give an example of a series of three independent events. Sample answer: A green marble is chosen from a bag, and then replaced. The experiment is repeated two more times, and each time a green marble is chosen.

(continued on the next page)

Go Online!

Interactive Whiteboard

Use the *eLesson*, *Lesson Presentation*, or *Interactive Classroom* to present this lesson.

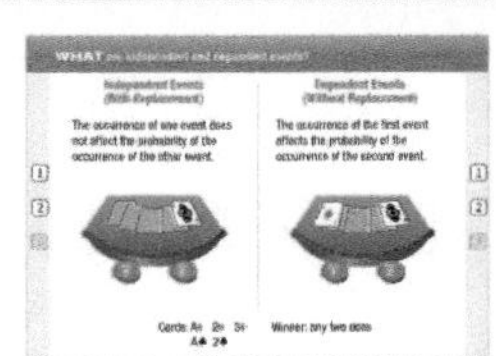

Need Another Example?

Determine whether the events are *independent* or *dependent*. Explain your reasoning.

a. Anna rolls a 6 on one number cube and a 3 on another cube. The two events are independent, because the outcome on the first die does not affect the outcome on the second die.

b. A queen is selected from a standard deck of cards and not put back. Then a king is selected. The two events are dependent because the first card is not put back. This affects the probability that the second card is a king because the sample space is reduced by one.

Example 2 Use Probability to Identify Independent Events

AL How do you find the probability of rolling a 3 on a number cube? There are 6 equally likely outcomes when rolling a number cube, and one of them is a 3; so, the probability is $\frac{1}{6}$.

OL How do you know that the organized list includes *all* of the possible outcomes in the sample space? Each of the 6 possible outcomes on the cube is matched with each of the 3 possible outcomes on the spinner.

BL On Dion's next turn, what is the probability that he will roll an odd number and that the spinner will land on blue? $\frac{1}{6}$ Are these two events independent? Explain using probability.
Yes; $P(\text{odd}) = \frac{1}{2}$, $P(\text{blue}) = \frac{1}{3}$, and $\frac{1}{2} \times \frac{1}{3} = \frac{1}{6}$.

Need Another Example?

A bag contains marbles as described in Guided Practice 2. Andrew selects the white marble, replaces it, and then selects the green marble. Are these events independent? Explain using probability. Yes; the sample space has 16 equally likely outcomes: {WW, WB, WY, WG, BW, BB, BY, BG, YW, YB, YY, YG, GW, GB, GY, GG}.
Therefore, $P(WG) = \frac{1}{16}$.
Also, $P(W) = \frac{1}{4}$, $P(G) = \frac{1}{4}$, and $\frac{1}{4} \times \frac{1}{4} = \frac{1}{16}$; therefore, the two events are independent.

Additional Answer (Guided Practice)

2. No; the sample space has 6 equally likely outcomes: {WB, WY, WG, BY, BG, YG}. Therefore, $P(BY) = \frac{1}{6}$. However, $P(B) = \frac{1}{4}$, $P(Y) = \frac{1}{4}$, and $\frac{1}{4} \times \frac{1}{4} \neq \frac{1}{6}$.

Independent events can also be defined in terms of probability. If the probability of two events occurring together is equal to the product of the probabilities of the individual events, then the events are independent.

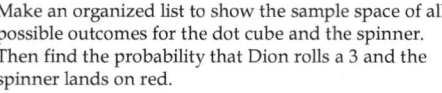

S.CP.1, S.CP.2

Example 2 Use Probability to Identify Independent Events

On each turn of a board game, a player rolls a dot cube and spins a spinner. On Dion's first turn, he rolls a 3 and the spinner lands on red. Are these events independent? Explain using probability.

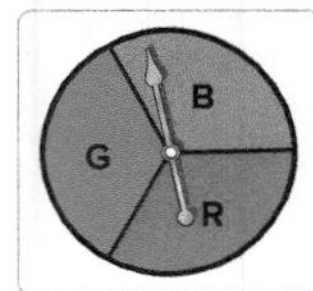

Make an organized list to show the sample space of all possible outcomes for the dot cube and the spinner. Then find the probability that Dion rolls a 3 and the spinner lands on red.

1G	2G	3G	4G	5G	6G
1B	2B	3B	4B	5B	6B
1R	2R	3R	4R	5R	6R

$P(3R) = \frac{1}{18}$ There are 18 equally likely outcomes and 1 successful outcome.

Next, find the individual probabilities.

$P(3) = \frac{1}{6}$ $P(R) = \frac{1}{3}$

The product of the individual probabilities is $\frac{1}{6} \times \frac{1}{3} = \frac{1}{8}$, which is equal to the probability of the two events occurring together. Therefore, the two events—rolling a 3 and the spinner landing on red—are independent.

Guided Practice See margin.

2. A bag contains a white marble, a blue marble, a yellow marble, and a green marble. Naomi chooses 2 marbles from the bag at the same time. One is blue, and one is yellow. Are these events independent? Explain using probability.

The previous example illustrates the first of two Multiplication Rules for Probability.

Key Concept Probability of Independent Events

Words If two events *A* and *B* are independent, then the probability of both events occurring is the product of the probability of *A* and the probability of *B*.

Symbols $P(A \text{ and } B) = P(A) \cdot P(B)$

Model

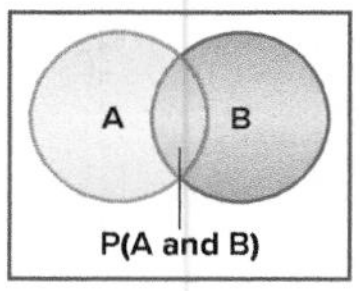

This rule can be extended to any number of events.

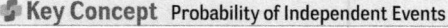

Reading Math ELL
and The word *and* is a key word indicating to multiply probabilities.

MP Teaching the Mathematical Practices

Modeling After students have found the sample spaces in Guided Practice 2 and Additional Example 2, point out that the sample spaces are different, even though both problems involve the same bag of marbles. Discuss this situation with students. As part of the discussion, ask: How are the two problems different? In the Guided Practice problem, Naomi selects two marbles at the same time. The same marble cannot be selected twice, and the possible outcomes involve combinations (the order of the colors does not matter). In the Additional Example problem, Andrew selects the marbles one at a time and replaces the first marble. The same marble *can* be selected twice, and the outcomes involve permutations (the order of the colors *does* matter).

S.CP.8

Real-World Example 3 Probability of Independent Events

TRANSPORTATION **Marisol and her friends are going to a concert. They put the slips of paper shown into a bag. If a person draws a yellow slip, he or she will ride in the van to the concert. A blue slip means he or she will ride in the car.**

Suppose Marisol draws the first slip, puts it back and draws again. What is the probability that on each draw her slip is blue?

These events are independent since Marisol replaced the first slip. Let B represent a blue slip and Y a yellow slip.

Draw 1: $P(B) = \frac{3}{8}$ ← number of blue slips / ← total numbers of slips

Draw 2: $P(B) = \frac{3}{8}$ Because the first slip is replaced, $P(B)$ is the same for the second draw.

	Draw 1		Draw 2	
$P(B \text{ and } B) =$	$P(B)$	$\cdot$	$P(B)$	Probability of independent events
$=$	$\frac{3}{8}$	$\cdot$	$\frac{3}{8}$	$P(B) = \frac{3}{8}$
$=$	$\frac{9}{64}$			Simplify.

So, the probability that Marisol draws two blue slips is $\frac{9}{64}$ or about 14%.

Study Tip

Use an Area Model You can also use the area model shown below to calculate the probability that both slips are blue. The blue region represents the probability of drawing two successive blue slips. The area of this region is $\frac{9}{64}$ of the entire model.

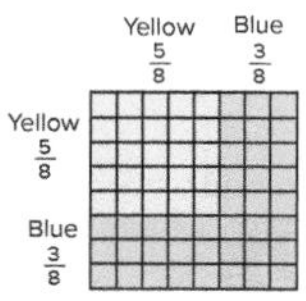

Guided Practice **3A.** $\frac{1}{12}$ **or about 8%** **3B.** $\frac{1}{16}$ **or 6.25%**

Find each probability.

3A. A coin is tossed and a number cube is rolled. What is the probability that the coin lands heads up and the number rolled is a 6?

3B. Suppose you toss a coin four times. What is the probability of getting four tails?

2 Probability of Dependent Events

The second of the Multiplication Rules of Probability addresses the probability of two dependent events.

Key Concept Probability of Dependent Events

Words	If two events A and B are dependent, then the probability of both events occurring is the product of the probability of A and the probability of B after A occurs.
Symbols	$P(A \text{ and } B) = P(A) \cdot P(B \text{ following } A)$

This rule can be extended to any number of events.

Example 3 Probability of Independent Events

AL **Why are the events independent?** Because Marisol replaces the first slip, the outcome of the first draw does not change the probabilities for the second draw.

OL **What is the probability that Marisol's first slip is blue and her second slip is yellow?** $\frac{15}{64}$, or about 23%

BL **What is the probability that on both draws, Marisol's slip is yellow?** $\frac{25}{64}$, or about 39%

Need Another Example?

Eating Out **Michelle and Christina are going out to lunch. They put 5 green slips of paper and 6 red slips of paper into a bag. If a person draws a green slip, she will order a hamburger. If she draws a red slip, she will order pizza. Michelle will draw first and put her slip back. Then Christina will draw. What is the probability that both girls draw green slips?** $\frac{25}{121}$

Differentiated Instruction AL OL ELL

Kinesthetic Learners **Ask students to determine the probability that a number cube rolled five times lands showing 2 each time. Have them use paper, pencils, and manipulatives to solve this problem with a partner. Ask them to explain their reasoning.**

Go Online!

The most up-to-date resources available for your program can be found at connectED.mcgraw-hill.com.

2 Probability of Dependent Events

Example 4 Probability of Dependent Events

AL How many cards are in a standard deck? 52 How many cards of each suit are in a standard deck? 13

OL In part **a**, what is the probability of drawing a diamond on the first draw? 13 out of 52 How many total cards remain after the first card is drawn? 51

BL What information must be considered when finding *P*(heart, 4)? if the first card drawn is the 4 of hearts

Need Another Example?

Games At the school carnival, winners in the ring-toss game are randomly given a prize from a bag that contains 4 sunglasses, 6 hairbrushes, and 5 key chains.

The first three players all win prizes. Find each probability.

a. *P* (sunglasses, hairbrush, key chain) $\frac{4}{91}$

b. *P* (hairbrush, hairbrush, not a hairbrush) $\frac{9}{91}$

Example 5 Use Probability to Analyze Decisions

AL Is Alec likely to win the game? Explain. No; the probability of winning is less than 50%.

OL If the first card is a star, how do you find the probability that the second card is a circle? If the first card is a star, there are 5 cards left, 2 stars and 3 circles. So, the probability that the second card is a circle is $\frac{3}{5}$.

BL How could the rules of the game be changed so that turning over a star and turning over a circle are independent events? Sample answer: After the player turns over the first card, all cards are shuffled and placed facedown again. Then the player turns over a second card.

Need Another Example?

Davina's family will cancel their weekend camping trip if the probability of rain on both Saturday and Sunday is greater than 10%. According to the weather forecast, there is a 30% chance of rain on Saturday and a 20% chance of rain on Sunday. Assuming the two events (rain on Saturday and rain on Sunday) are independent, should Davina's family cancel the trip? Justify your answer using probability. No; $P(\text{Sat and Sun}) = P(\text{Sat}) \cdot P(\text{Sun}) = \frac{3}{10} \cdot \frac{2}{10} = \frac{6}{100}$ or 6%, which is not greater than 10%.

S.CP.8

Example 4 Probability of Dependent Events

CARDS Cynthia randomly draws three cards from a standard deck one at a time without replacing them. Find the probability that the cards are drawn in the given order.

***P*(diamond, spade, diamond)**

The events are dependent because Cynthia does not replace the cards that she draws.

First card: $P(\text{diamond}) = \frac{13}{52}$ or $\frac{1}{4}$ ← number of diamonds / total number of cards

Second card: $P(\text{spade}) = \frac{13}{51}$ ← number of spades / number of cards remaining

Third card: $P(\text{diamond}) = \frac{12}{50}$ or $\frac{6}{25}$ ← number of diamonds remaining / number of cards remaining

$P(\text{diamond, spade, diamond}) = P(\text{diamond}) \cdot P(\text{spade}) \cdot P(\text{diamond})$

$= \frac{1}{4} \cdot \frac{13}{51} \cdot \frac{6}{25}$ or $\frac{13}{850}$ Substitution

The probability is $\frac{13}{850}$ or about 1.5%.

Guided Practice

Find each probability. 4A. $\frac{94}{16{,}575}$ or about 0.6% 4B. $\frac{39}{850}$ or about 5%

4A. *P*(two, five, not a five) **4B.** *P*(heart, not a heart, heart)

S.CP.8, S.MD.7

Real-World Example 5 Use Probability to Analyze Decisions

CARNIVAL GAMES In a carnival game, 3 cards are marked with stars and 3 cards are marked with circles. All 6 cards are placed facedown, and the player turns over 2 cards, one at a time. If the first card is a star and the second card is a circle, the player wins a prize.

Alec decides to play the game only if he has at least a 25% chance of winning. Should he play the game? Justify your answer using probability.

To win, a player must turn over a star followed by a circle. These events are dependent because the first card is removed. Let *S* represent a star and *C* represent a circle.

Card 1 Card 2

$P(S \text{ and } C) = \frac{3}{6} \cdot \frac{3}{5}$ After the first card is turned over, 5 cards remain, and 3 are marked with circles.

$= \frac{9}{30}$ or $\frac{3}{10}$ Simplify.

The probability that Alec will win is $\frac{3}{10}$ or 30%. This probability is at least 25%, so Alec should play the game.

Problem-Solving Tip

Sense-Making Acting out the situation can help you understand the problem. Make a set of cards to model the game described in the problem.

Guided Practice

5. Suppose the rules of the game change so that a player wins a prize only if *both* cards are stars. Should Alec play the game now? Justify your answer using probability. See Ch. 12 Answer Appendix.

Follow-up

Students have explored probability of independent and dependent events.

Ask:

- How can the probabilities of independent and dependent events be used to make predictions? Sample answer: identifying events as dependent or independent can help you calculate the probability of an event's success or failure.

Check Your Understanding

○ = Step-by-Step Solutions begin on page R13.

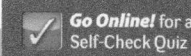

Go Online! for a Self-Check Quiz

Example 1 S.CP.2

Determine whether the events are *independent* or *dependent*. Explain.

1. A number cube is rolled twice, and an odd number is rolled each time. See margin.
2. A bag contains several marbles. Alita selects a black marble, does not replace it, and then selects a yellow marble. See margin.

Tell whether the events are independent. Explain using probability.

Example 2 S.CP.1, S.CP.2

3. José, Pippa, and Raymond are scheduled to give speeches. The order of the speeches is assigned at random. José is assigned to go first, and Raymond is assigned to go second. 3–4. See Ch. 12 Answer Appendix.
4. Sara spins a spinner twice. The spinner has 5 equally sized sections numbered 1 to 5. The spinner lands on an odd number first and an even number second.

Example 3 S.CP.8

5. **CARDS** A card is randomly chosen from a deck of 52 cards, replaced, and a second card is chosen. What is the probability of choosing both of the cards shown at the right in the order shown? $\frac{1}{2704}$ or 3.7×10^{-4}

Example 4 S.CP.8

6. **TRANSPORTATION** Isaiah is getting on the bus after work. It costs $0.50 to ride the bus to his house. If he has 3 quarters, 5 dimes, and 2 nickels in his pocket, find the probability that he will randomly pull out two quarters in a row. Assume that the events are equally likely to occur. $\frac{1}{15}$ or 0.07

Example 5 S.CP.8, S.MD.7

7. **GAMES** A board game has 12 blue cards and 20 red cards. Three of the blue cards are wild cards and 6 of the red cards are wild cards. Maurice may choose two cards at random, one at a time, to add to his hand. For the greatest possible probability of choosing two wild cards, should Maurice choose 2 red cards, 2 blue cards, or 1 red card and 1 blue card? Justify your answer using probability. See Ch. 12 Answer Appendix.

Practice and Problem Solving

Extra Practice is on page R12.

Examples 1–4 S.CP.1, S.CP.2, S.CP.8

MP **REASONING** **Describe whether the events are *independent* or *dependent*. Then find the probability.**

8. In a game, you roll an even number on a number cube and then spin a spinner numbered 1 through 5 and get an odd number. independent; $\frac{3}{10}$ or 30%
9. An ace is drawn, without replacement, from a deck of 52 cards. Then, a second ace is drawn. dependent; $\frac{1}{221}$ or 0.5%
10. In a bag of 3 green and 4 blue marbles, a blue marble is drawn and not replaced. Then, a second blue marble is drawn. dependent; $\frac{2}{7}$ or about 29%
11. You roll two dot cubes and get a 5 each time. independent; $\frac{1}{36}$ or about 3%

Describe whether the events are independent. Explain using probability.

12. A computer program randomly assigns a letter from A to E and a number from 1 to 4 as a user's temporary password. The program assigns C2 as Rebecca's temporary password.
13. A box contains a blueberry muffin, a pumpkin muffin, and a cinnamon muffin. Without looking, Andy takes 2 muffins from the box at the same time. One of Andy's muffins is pumpkin, and the other is cinnamon. 12–13. See Ch. 12 Answer Appendix.

Differentiated Homework Options

Levels	AL Basic	OL Core	BL Advanced
Exercises	8–19, 32–45	9–19 odd, 20, 21, 23, 25–45	27–36, (optional: 37–45)
2-Day Option	9–19 odd, 37–45	8–19	
	8–18 even, 32–36	20–45	

You can use ALEKS to provide additional remediation support with personalized instruction and practice.

Practice

Formative Assessment Use Exercises 1–7 to assess students' understanding of the concepts in this lesson.

The Practice and Problem Solving exercises assess the content taught in the lesson. The Preparing for Assessment page is meant to be used as preparation for end-of-course assessments.

MP Teaching the Mathematical Practices

Reasoning Mathematically proficient students make sense of quantities and their relationships in problem situations. They use the ability to decontextualize—to abstract a given situation and represent it symbolically. In Exercises 8–11, encourage students to determine whether the events are independent or dependent and then apply multiplication rules for probability.

Levels of Complexity Chart

The levels of the exercises progress from 1 to 3, with Level 1 indicating the lowest level of complexity.

Exercises	8–19	20–26, 37–45	27–36
Level 3			●
Level 2		●	
Level 1	●		

Extra Practice

See page R12 for extra exercises for students who are approaching level or for on-level students who need additional reinforcement.

Additional Answers

1. The outcome of the first roll does not affect the probabilities of the outcomes for the second roll. Therefore, these events are *independent.*
2. Because the first marble is not replaced, the outcome of the first selection affects the probabilities of the outcomes for the second selection. Therefore, these events are *dependent.*

Go Online! eBook

Interactive Student Guide

Use the *Interactive Student Guide* to deepen conceptual understanding.

Independent and Dependent Events

Additional Answers

16. $\frac{512}{1000}$ or about 51%

18. No; $P(P \text{ and } P) = P(P) \cdot P(P) = \frac{2}{12} \cdot \frac{2}{12} = \frac{4}{144} = \frac{1}{36}$; Steph's chance of winning a stuffed penguin is $\frac{1}{36}$ or about 3%, which is less than 10%.

19. No; $P(F \text{ and } S) = P(F) \cdot P(S \text{ after } F) = \frac{5}{10} \cdot \frac{7}{10} = \frac{35}{100}$ or 35%; this is less than 50%.

26a. Dependent; sample answer: The assignment of one student as leader affects the probabilities that the other students will be assigned to the other roles.

26b. $\frac{1}{4} \cdot \frac{1}{3} \cdot \frac{1}{2} \cdot \frac{1}{1} = \frac{1}{24}$ or about 4%

26c. There are ${}_4P_4 = 24$ equally likely ways the students could be assigned roles, so each has probability $\frac{1}{24}$ or about 4%; the result is the same using either the multiplication rule for dependent events or permutations.

14. **GAMES** In a game, the spinner at the right is spun and a coin is tossed. What is the probability of getting an even number on the spinner and the coin landing on tails? $\frac{1}{4}$ or 25%

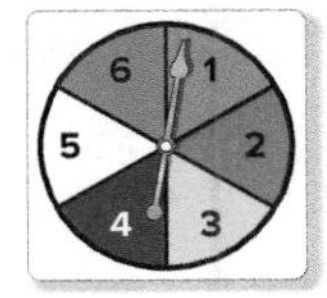

15. **GIFTS** Tisha's class is having a gift exchange. Tisha will draw first, and her friend Brandi will draw second. If there are 18 students participating, what is the probability that Brandi and Tisha draw each other's names? $\frac{1}{306}$ or about 0.3%

16. **VACATION** A work survey found that 8 out of every 10 employees went on vacation last summer. If 3 employees' names are randomly chosen, with replacement, what is the probability that all 3 employees went on vacation last summer? See margin.

17. **CAMPAIGNS** The table shows the number of each color of Student Council campaign buttons Clemente has to give away. If given away at random, what is the probability that the first and second buttons given away are both red? $\frac{20}{161}$ or about 12%

Button Color	Amount
blue	20
white	15
red	25
black	10

Example 5
S.CP.8, S.MD.7

For Exercises 18 and 19, justify your answer using probability.

18. **CARNIVAL GAMES** A carnival game involves a spinner with 12 equally sized sections. Two of the sections are labeled "Penguin." The player spins the spinner twice. If the spinner lands on a "Penguin" section both times, the player wins a stuffed penguin. Steph decides to play the game only if she has at least a 10% chance of winning a stuffed penguin. Should she play the game? See margin.

19. **FESTIVALS** An outdoor music festival is planned for Friday and Saturday. The probability of rain on Friday is 50%. If it rains on Friday, the probability of rain on Saturday is 70%, and if it does not rain on Friday, the probability of rain on Saturday is 40%. The organizer will postpone the festival if the probability of rain on both days is at least 50%. Should the organizer postpone the festival? See margin.

B 20. **CLASSES** The probability that a student takes both geometry and French at Satomi's school is 1.6%. The probability that a student takes French is 8%. If the two events (taking geometry and taking French) are independent, what is the probability that a student takes geometry? 20%

CANDY A box of chocolates contains 10 milk chocolates, 8 dark chocolates, and 12 white chocolates. Sophie randomly chooses a chocolate and eats it and then randomly chooses another chocolate. Find each probability.

21. P(milk and dark) $\frac{8}{87}$ or about 9%

22. P(dark and white) $\frac{16}{145}$ or about 11%

23. P(white and dark) $\frac{16}{145}$ or about 11%

24. P(milk and milk) $\frac{3}{29}$ or about 10%

25. **SOCKS** Damon has 14 white socks, 6 black socks, and 4 blue socks in his drawer. He chooses two socks at random. What is the probability that both socks are white? $\frac{91}{276}$ or about 33%

26. **PROJECTS** Angela, Emery, Rico, and Taylor are working on a class project. Each student is assigned one of the following project roles at random, with no roles repeated: leader, presenter, recorder, and timekeeper. See margin.

 a. Is the assignment of project roles a set of independent events or dependent events? Explain.

 b. Find the probability that Angela is the presenter, Emery is the timekeeper, Rico is the leader, and Taylor is the recorder by using the multiplication rule for independent events or for dependent events.

 c. Find the probability in part **b** by using combinations or permutations. Compare your result to your answer for part **b**.

C 27. **TENNIS** In tennis, the serving player has two chances to land his or her serve in the other player's service box without stepping on or over the service line. A fault occurs when the server fails to do this, and a double fault occurs when the server fails on both attempts. The probability that Kelly's first serve is good is 40%, and the probability that her second serve is good is 70%.

a. What is the probability that Kelly will double fault? **0.18 or 18%**

b. What is the probability that Kelly will fault on her first serve and that her second serve will be good? **0.42 or 42%**

28. **VACATION** A travel website surveyed families to determine their vacation destinations. The results indicated that $P(B) = 0.6$ and $P(M) = 0.3$.

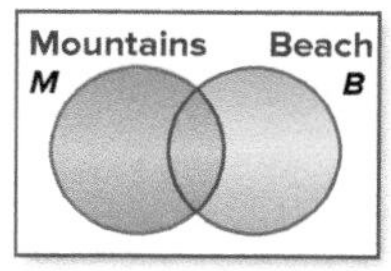

a. What is the probability that a randomly selected family vacations both in the mountains and at the beach? **0.18**

b. What is the probability that a randomly selected family does not vacation at either destination? **0.28**

29. **CANDY** A bag contains 10 red jelly beans, 6 green jelly beans, 7 yellow jelly beans, and 5 orange jelly beans. What is the probability of randomly choosing a red jelly bean, replacing it, randomly choosing another red jelly bean, replacing it, and then randomly choosing an orange jelly bean? $\frac{125}{5488}$ **or about 2%**

30. MP **REASONING** Consider whether the multiplication rule for dependent events can be used to find the probability of independent events. **See margin.**

a. Choose three different pairs of independent events. Find the probability of each pair of events using both multiplication rules. What do you notice?

b. Use mathematical reasoning to explain your observation, and make a conjecture about whether the multiplication rule for dependent events can be used to find the probability of independent events.

31. MP **REASONING** Consider whether the rule for finding the probability of two dependent events A and B, $P(A \text{ and } B) = P(A) \cdot P(B \text{ following } A)$, can also be written as $P(A \text{ and } B) = P(B) \cdot P(A \text{ following } B)$. **See margin.**

a. Suppose that a card is randomly selected from a standard deck and that a second card is selected without replacing the first card. Use both rules given above to find the probability that the first card is a 3 and the second card is an 8. How do the results from the two rules compare?

b. Choose two other pairs of dependent events that do not involve cards. Find the probability of each pair of events using both rules. What do you notice?

c. Make a conjecture about whether the rules are equivalent.

S.CP.1, S.CP.2, S.CP.8, S.MD.7

H.O.T. Problems Use Higher-Order Thinking Skills

32. MP **SENSE-MAKING** In some cases, if one bulb in a string of holiday lights fails to work, the whole string will not light. If each bulb in a set has a 99.5% chance of working, what is the maximum number of lights that can be strung together with at least a 90% chance that the whole string will light? **21**

33. MP **CONSTRUCT ARGUMENTS** There are n different objects in a bag. The probability of drawing object A and then object B without replacement is about 2.4%. What is the value of n? Explain. **See margin.**

34. MP **REASONING** If $P(A \text{ following } B)$ is the same as $P(A)$ and $P(B \text{ following } A)$ is the same as $P(B)$, what can be said about the relationship between events A and B? **A and B are independent events.**

35. **OPEN-ENDED** Describe a pair of independent events and a pair of dependent events. Explain your reasoning. **See Ch. 12 Answer Appendix.**

36. **WRITING IN MATH** Explain how you could determine whether smoking and having a parent who smokes are independent events. **See Ch. 12 Answer Appendix.**

MP Standards for Mathematical Practice

Emphasis On	Exercises
1 Make sense of problems and persevere in solving them.	32, 37–43
2 Reason abstractly and quantitatively.	8–11, 30, 31, 34, 44, 45
3 Construct viable arguments and critique the reasoning of others.	33, 35, 36
4 Model with mathematics.	5–7, 14–29, 39

33. 7; Sample answer: The probability of drawing object A is $\frac{1}{n}$, and the probability of drawing object B when object A is not replaced is $\frac{1}{n-1}$. Since we know that the probability is 2.4%, $\frac{1}{n} \cdot \frac{1}{n-1} = \frac{2.4}{100}$ or 0.024. Solve this equation to determine that n is 7.

MP Teaching the Mathematical Practices

Construct Arguments Mathematically proficient students understand and use stated assumptions and definitions in constructing arguments. They are able to analyze situations by breaking them into cases, and can recognize and use counterexamples. In Exercise 33, encourage students to model this exercise using marbles in a bag.

Assess

Ticket Out the Door Have students write on a piece of paper the difference between independent and dependent events.

Additional Answers

30a. Independent events will vary. Students should notice that both rules give the same result.

30b. The multiplication rule for dependent events can be used for independent events. Sample explanation: When two events A and B are independent, $P(B \text{ following } A) = P(B)$ because A has no effect on the probability of B. Substituting $P(B)$ for $P(B \text{ following } A)$ in the rule for dependent events results in the rule for independent events, $P(A \text{ and } B) = P(A) \cdot P(B)$.

31a. Both rules show that $P(3 \text{ and } 8) = \frac{4}{663}$ or about 0.6%.

31b. Sample answer: A jar contains 5 pennies and 6 dimes. One coin is chosen at random, and then a second coin is chosen without replacing the first. Find the probability that the first coin is a penny and the second coin is a dime. $P(P \text{ and } D) = P(P) \cdot P(D \text{ following } P) = \frac{5}{11} \cdot \frac{6}{10} = \frac{30}{110} = \frac{3}{11}$.
$P(P \text{ and } D) = P(D) \cdot P(P \text{ following } D) = \frac{6}{11} \cdot \frac{5}{10} = \frac{30}{110} = \frac{3}{11}$.

31c. $P(A \text{ and } B) = P(A) \cdot P(B \text{ following } A)$ and $P(A \text{ and } B) = P(B) \cdot P(A \text{ following } B)$ are equivalent.

Go Online!

eSolutions Manual

Create worksheets, answer keys, and solutions handouts for your assignments.

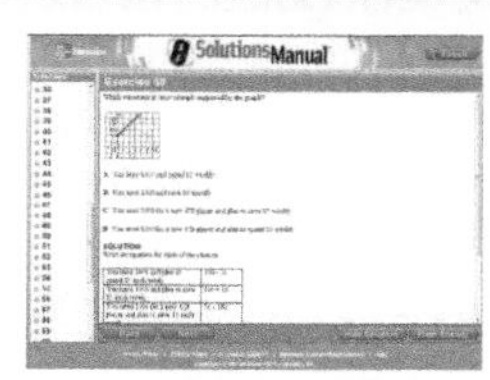

Preparing for Assessment

Exercises 37–45 require students to use the skills they will need on standardized assessments. Exercises are dual-coded with content standards and mathematical practice standards.

Dual Coding		
Items	Content Standards	MP Mathematical Practices
37	S.CP.8	1, 2
38	S.CP.2, S.CP.8	1, 2
39	S.CP.8	1, 2, 4
40	S.CP.2, S.CP.8	1, 2
41	S.CP.8	1, 2
42	S.CP.8, S.MD.7	1, 3
43	S.CP.1, S.CP.2	1, 3, 4
44, 45	S.CP.2	2

Diagnose Student Errors

Survey student responses for each item. Class trends may indicate common errors and misconceptions.

38.

A	Calculated the probability as $\frac{1}{10} \cdot \frac{1}{10}$
B	Calculated the probability without replacement
C	CORRECT
D	Found probability of choosing a single multiple of 3
E	Calculated the probability as $\frac{3}{10} + \frac{3}{10}$

39.

A	Found the probability of choosing two black tiles with replacement
B	Found the probability of choosing two black tiles without replacement
C	Found the probability of choosing two white tiles with replacement
D	CORRECT

Go Online!

Quizzes

Students can use *Self-Check Quizzes* to check their understanding of this lesson and have the results sent to you. You can also give *Quiz 3*, which covers the content in Lessons 13-4 and 13-5.

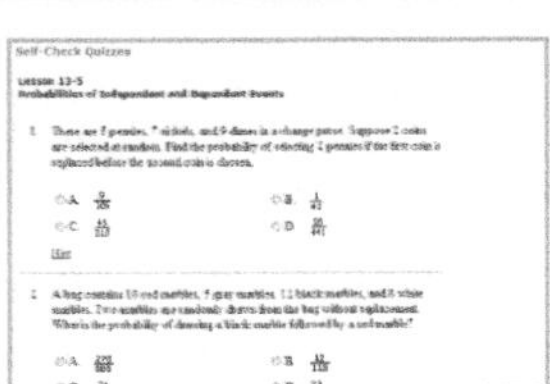

Preparing for Assessment

37. Francisco reaches into the bag shown here and chooses one of the marbles without looking. He puts the marble aside, and then Nevaeh reaches into the bag and chooses a marble without looking. What is the probability that they both choose a black marble? MP 1, 2 S.CP.8 **A**

- ○ A $\frac{1}{12}$
- ○ B $\frac{1}{9}$
- ○ C $\frac{1}{3}$
- ○ D $\frac{7}{12}$

38. Xavier has a deck of 10 cards that are numbered 1 through 10. He chooses a card at random, notes the number on the card, and places it back in the deck. Then he shuffles the deck and chooses another card. What is the probability that both of the cards Xavier chooses are multiples of 3? MP 1, 2 S.CP.2, S.CP.8 **C**

- ○ A $\frac{1}{100}$
- ○ B $\frac{1}{15}$
- ○ C $\frac{9}{100}$
- ○ D $\frac{3}{10}$
- ○ E $\frac{3}{5}$

39. A box contains 4 black tiles and x white tiles. Michelle chooses a tile without looking, puts it aside, and then chooses a second tile. Which expression represents the probability that both of the tiles that Michelle chooses are white? MP 1, 2, 4 S.CP.8 **D**

- ○ A $\frac{4}{x+4} \cdot \frac{4}{x+4}$
- ○ B $\frac{4}{x+4} \cdot \frac{3}{x+3}$
- ○ C $\frac{x}{x+4} \cdot \frac{x}{x+4}$
- ○ D $\frac{x}{x+4} \cdot \frac{x-1}{x+3}$

40. LeBron rolls a number cube three times. The cube's faces are numbered 1 through 6. What is the probability as a decimal that he rolls an odd number on all three rolls? MP 1, 2 S.CP.2, S.CP.8

0.125

41. Lila has a standard deck of cards. She selects 4 cards at random, one at a time without replacing them. Is the probability that she selects 4 aces greater than or less than 1 out of 1 million? MP 1, 2 S.CP.8

greater than

42. At a carnival game, a wading pool contains 50 rubber ducks, and 20 ducks are marked on the bottom with a star. A player selects a duck, does not replace it, and then selects another duck. If both ducks are marked with a star, the player wins a prize. Bella decides to play only if her probability of winning is at least 20%. Should she play the game? Use probability to justify your answer. MP 1, 3 S.CP.8, S.MD.7

See Ch. 12 Answer Appendix.

43. **MULTI-STEP** Calvin rolls two number cubes. MP 1, 3, 4 S.CP.1, S.CP.2

43. a., c. See Ch. 12 Answer Appendix.

a. Make a table or an organized list to represent the sample space.

b. Use your answer to part **a** to find the probability that both numbers rolled are greater than 4. $\frac{1}{9}$ or about 11%

c. Use probability to show that these two events—rolling a number greater than 4 and rolling another number greater than 4—are independent.

44. A box contains 6 white balls and 4 red balls. We randomly (and without replacement) draw two balls from the box. What is the probability that the second ball selected is red? MP 2 S.CP.2

$\frac{2}{5}$

45. Three cards are dealt successively at random and without replacement from a standard deck of 52 playing cards. What is the probability of receiving, in order, a king, a queen, and a jack? MP 2 S.CP.2

$\frac{8}{16{,}575}$

Differentiated Instruction BL

Extension The game show *Let's Make a Deal* has created controversy in the study of probability with the question: Switch or stay? Contestants on the show were asked to choose one door out of three. They were then shown one of the remaining doors that did not contain the one grand prize. The question was then asked, "Do you want to stay with your original choice, or switch to the remaining door?" Students can create a simulation or use an online applet to explore this question. Students should be able to explain why repeating an experiment many times forces the experimental and theoretical probabilities closer together.

Probability and the Addition Rule

SUGGESTED PACING (DAYS)

	Instruction
90 min.	0.5
45 min.	1.0

Track Your Progress

Objectives

1 Apply the Addition Rule to situations involving mutually exclusive events.

2 Apply the Addition Rule to situations involving events that are not mutually exclusive.

Mathematical Background

Mutually exclusive events *A* and *B* cannot occur at the same time. The probability that *A* or *B* occurs is the sum of the probabilities of each individual event. If *A* and *B* are not mutually exclusive, then their probability is the sum of the individual probabilities minus the probability that both *A* and *B* occur.

THEN

S.CP.2 Understand that two events *A* and *B* are independent if the probability of *A* and *B* occurring together is the product of their probabilities, and use this idea to determine if they are independent.

S.CP.8 Apply the general Multiplication Rule in a uniform probability model, $P(A \text{ and } B) = P(A)P(B \mid A) = P(B)P(A \mid B)$, and interpret the answer in terms of the model.

NOW

S.CP.1 Describe events as subsets of a sample space (the set of outcomes) using characteristics (or categories) of the outcomes, or as unions, intersections, or complements of other events ("or," "and," "not").

S.CP.7 Apply the Addition Rule, $P(A \text{ or } B) = P(A) + P(B) - P(A \text{ and } B)$, and interpret the answer in terms of the model.

NEXT

S.CP.3 Understand the conditional probability of *A* given *B* as $P(A \text{ and } B)/P(B)$, and interpret independence of *A* and *B* as saying that the conditional probability of *A* given *B* is the same as the probability of *A*, and the conditional probability of *B* given *A* is the same as the probability of *B*.

S.CP.5 Recognize and explain the concepts of conditional probability and independence in everyday language and everyday situations.

Go Online! All of these resources and more are available at connectED.mcgraw-hill.com

Chapter Projects provide students the opportunity to apply what they have learned about probability and expected values to a real-world project on constructing games for a fair.

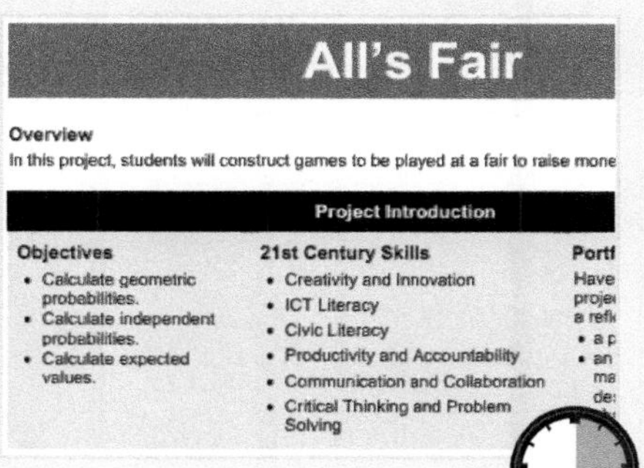

Use at End of Lesson

Personal Tutors (for every example) let students hear real teachers solve problems. Students can pause and repeat as many times as necessary.

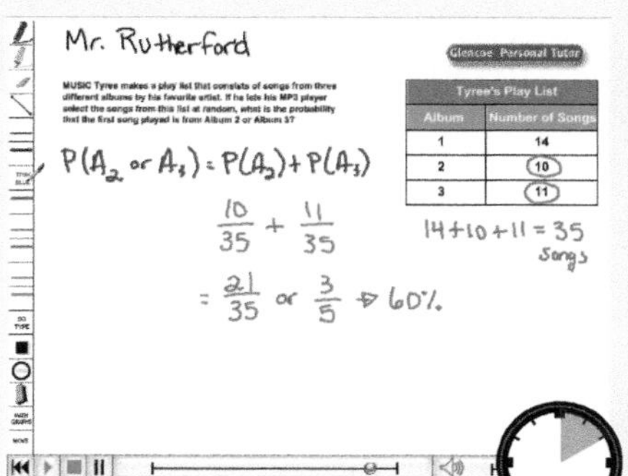

Use with Examples

eLessons utilize the power of your interactive whiteboard in an engaging way. Use **Probability of Compound Events**, Screens 9–10, to introduce the concepts in this lesson.

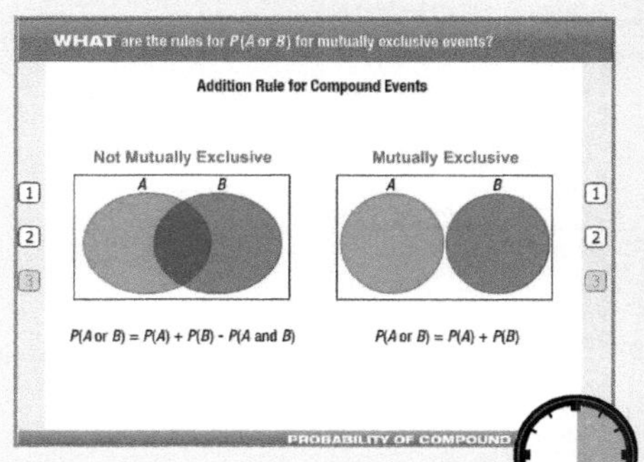

WHAT are the rules for P(A or B) for mutually exclusive events?
Addition Rule for Compound Events
Not Mutually Exclusive
Mutually Exclusive
$P(A \text{ or } B) = P(A) + P(B) - P(A \text{ and } B)$
$P(A \text{ or } B) = P(A) + P(B)$
PROBABILITY OF COMPOUND

Use at Beginning of Lesson

OER Using Open Educational Resources

Publishing Have students work in groups to create a book using **Story Jumper** about probability to reinforce their knowledge of the key concepts in this chapter. *Use as homework*

Go Online!
connectED.mcgraw-hill.com
Worksheets

Differentiate Your Resources

Extra Practice Additional practice or homework; Skills Practice is best for approaching-level students and Practice is best for on-level and beyond-level students

Skills Practice

AL OL ELL

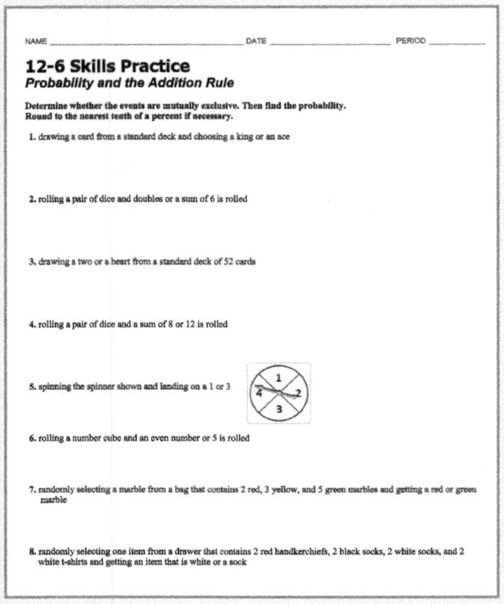
NAME ______ DATE ______ PERIOD ______

12-6 Skills Practice
Probability and the Addition Rule

Determine whether the events are mutually exclusive. Then find the probability. Round to the nearest tenth of a percent if necessary.

1. drawing a card from a standard deck and choosing a king or an ace
2. rolling a pair of dice and doubles or a sum of 6 is rolled
3. drawing a two or a heart from a standard deck of 52 cards
4. rolling a pair of dice and a sum of 8 or 12 is rolled
5. spinning the spinner shown and landing on a 1 or 3
6. rolling a number cube and an even number or 5 is rolled
7. randomly selecting a marble from a bag that contains 2 red, 3 yellow, and 5 green marbles and getting a red or green marble
8. randomly selecting one item from a drawer that contains 2 red handkerchiefs, 2 black socks, 2 white socks, and 2 white t-shirts and getting an item that is white or a sock

Practice

AL OL BL ELL

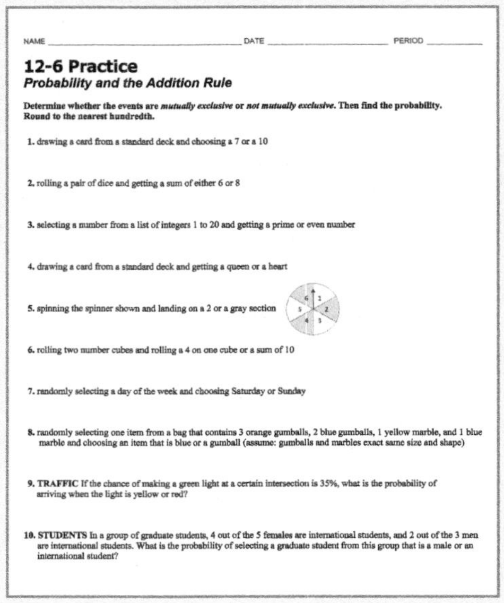
NAME ______ DATE ______ PERIOD ______

12-6 Practice
Probability and the Addition Rule

Determine whether the events are *mutually exclusive* or *not mutually exclusive*. Then find the probability. Round to the nearest hundredth.

1. drawing a card from a standard deck and choosing a 7 or a 10
2. rolling a pair of dice and getting a sum of either 6 or 8
3. selecting a number from a list of integers 1 to 20 and getting a prime or even number
4. drawing a card from a standard deck and getting a queen or a heart
5. spinning the spinner shown and landing on a 2 or a gray section
6. rolling two number cubes and rolling a 4 on one cube or a sum of 10
7. randomly selecting a day of the week and choosing Saturday or Sunday
8. randomly selecting one item from a bag that contains 3 orange gumballs, 2 blue gumballs, 1 yellow marble, and 1 blue marble and choosing an item that is blue or a gumball (assume: gumballs and marbles exact same size and shape)
9. **TRAFFIC** If the chance of making a green light at a certain intersection is 35%, what is the probability of arriving when the light is yellow or red?
10. **STUDENTS** In a group of graduate students, 4 out of the 5 females are international students, and 2 out of the 3 men are international students. What is the probability of selecting a graduate student from this group that is a male or an international student?

Word Problem Practice

AL OL BL ELL

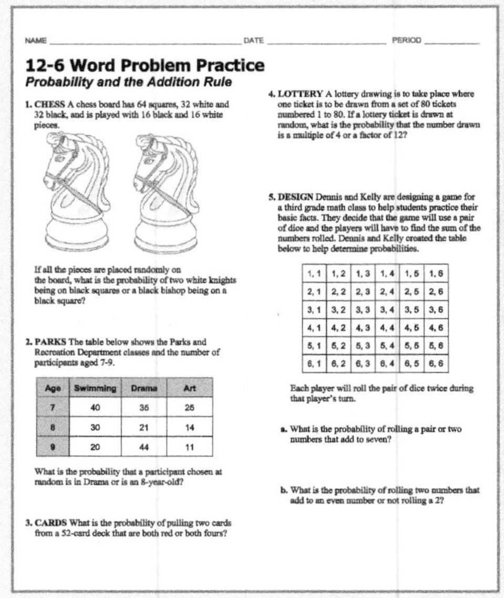
NAME ______ DATE ______ PERIOD ______

12-6 Word Problem Practice
Probability and the Addition Rule

1. **CHESS** A chess board has 64 squares, 32 white and 32 black, and is played with 16 black and 16 white pieces.
If all the pieces are placed randomly on the board, what is the probability of two white knights being on black squares or a black bishop being on a black square?
2. **PARKS** The table below shows the Parks and Recreation Department classes and the number of participants aged 7-9.

Age	Swimming	Drama	Art
7	40	36	25
8	30	21	14
9	20	44	11

What is the probability that a participant chosen at random is in Drama or is an 8-year-old?
3. **CARDS** What is the probability of pulling two cards from a 52-card deck that are both red or both fours?
4. **LOTTERY** A lottery drawing is to take place where one ticket is to be drawn from a set of 80 tickets numbered 1 to 80. If a lottery ticket is drawn at random, what is the probability that the number drawn is a multiple of 4 or a factor of 12?
5. **DESIGN** Dennis and Kelly are designing a game for a third grade math class to help students practice their basic facts. They decide that the game will use a pair of dice and the players will have to find the sum of the numbers rolled. Dennis and Kelly created the table below to help determine probabilities.

1, 1	1, 2	1, 3	1, 4	1, 5	1, 6
2, 1	2, 2	2, 3	2, 4	2, 5	2, 6
3, 1	3, 2	3, 3	3, 4	3, 5	3, 6
4, 1	4, 2	4, 3	4, 4	4, 5	4, 6
5, 1	5, 2	5, 3	5, 4	5, 5	5, 6
6, 1	6, 2	6, 3	6, 4	6, 5	6, 6

Each player will roll the pair of dice twice during that player's turn.
a. What is the probability of rolling a pair or two numbers that add to seven?
b. What is the probability of rolling two numbers that add to an even number or not rolling a 2?

Intervention Reteaching and vocabulary activities that can be used with struggling or absent students and as ELL support

Study Guide and Intervention

AL OL ELL

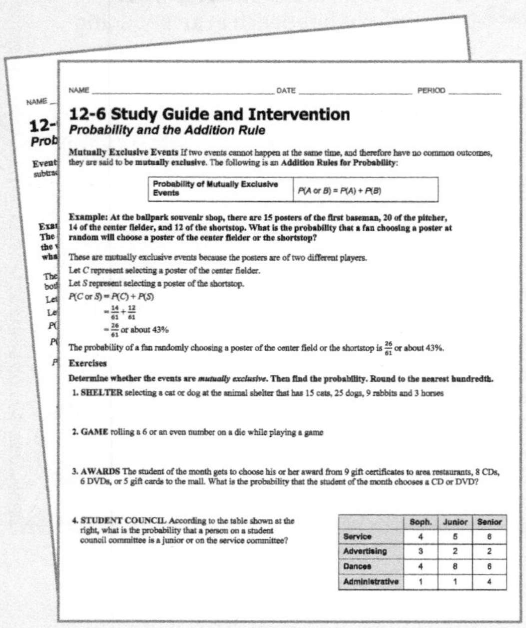
NAME ______ DATE ______ PERIOD ______

12-6 Study Guide and Intervention
Probability and the Addition Rule

Mutually Exclusive Events If two events cannot happen at the same time, and therefore have no common outcomes, they are said to be **mutually exclusive**. The following is an **Addition Rules for Probability**:

Probability of Mutually Exclusive Events	$P(A \text{ or } B) = P(A) + P(B)$

Example: At the ballpark souvenir shop, there are 15 posters of the first baseman, 20 of the pitcher, 14 of the center fielder, and 12 of the shortstop. What is the probability that a fan choosing a poster at random will choose a poster of the center fielder or the shortstop?

These are mutually exclusive events because the posters are of two different players.
Let C represent selecting a poster of the center fielder.
Let S represent selecting a poster of the shortstop.
$P(C \text{ or } S) = P(C) + P(S)$
$= \frac{14}{61} + \frac{12}{61}$
$= \frac{26}{61}$ or about 43%

The probability of a fan randomly choosing a poster of the center field or the shortstop is $\frac{26}{61}$ or about 43%.

Exercises
Determine whether the events are *mutually exclusive*. Then find the probability. Round to the nearest hundredth.

1. **SHELTER** selecting a cat or dog at the animal shelter that has 15 cats, 25 dogs, 9 rabbits and 3 horses
2. **GAME** rolling a 6 or an even number on a die while playing a game
3. **AWARDS** The student of the month gets to choose his or her award from 9 gift certificates to area restaurants, 8 CDs, 6 DVDs, or 5 gift cards to the mall. What is the probability that the student of the month chooses a CD or DVD?
4. **STUDENT COUNCIL** According to the table shown at the right, what is the probability that a person on a student council committee is a junior or on the service committee?

	Soph.	Junior	Senior
Service	4	5	6
Advertising	3	2	2
Dances	4	6	6
Administrative	1	1	4

Study Notebook

AL OL BL ELL

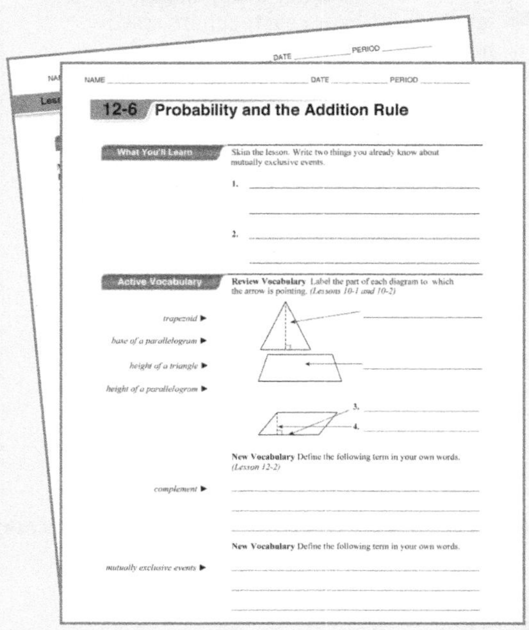
NAME ______ DATE ______ PERIOD ______

12-6 Probability and the Addition Rule

What You'll Learn Skim the lesson. Write two things you already know about mutually exclusive events.
1. ______
2. ______

Active Vocabulary **Review Vocabulary** Label the part of each diagram to which the arrow is pointing. (Lessons 10-1 and 10-2)
trapezoid
base of a parallelogram
height of a triangle
height of a parallelogram

New Vocabulary Define the following term in your own words. (Lesson 12-2)
complement

New Vocabulary Define the following term in your own words.
mutually exclusive events

Extension Activities that can be used to extend lesson concepts

Enrichment

OL BL ELL

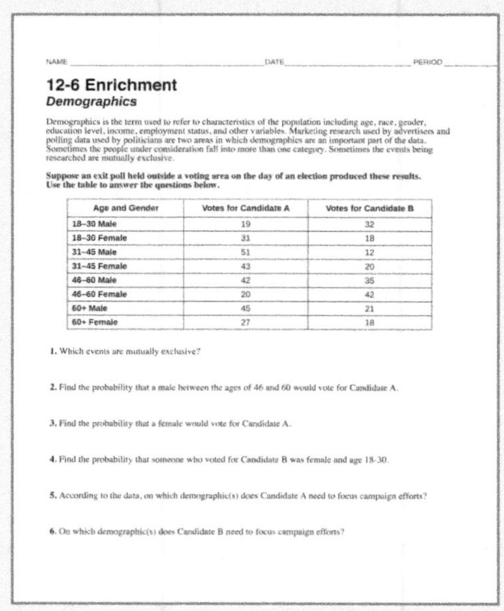
NAME ______ DATE ______ PERIOD ______

12-6 Enrichment
Demographics

Demographics is the term used to refer to characteristics of the population including age, race, gender, education level, income, employment status, and other variables. Marketing research used by advertisers and polling data used by politicians are two areas in which demographics are an important part of the data. Sometimes the people under consideration fall into more than one category. Sometimes the events being researched are mutually exclusive.

Suppose an exit poll held outside a voting area on the day of an election produced these results. Use the table to answer the questions below.

Age and Gender	Votes for Candidate A	Votes for Candidate B
18–30 Male	19	32
18–30 Female	31	18
31–45 Male	51	12
31–45 Female	43	20
46–60 Male	42	35
46–60 Female	20	42
60+ Male	45	21
60+ Female	27	18

1. Which events are mutually exclusive?
2. Find the probability that a male between the ages of 46 and 60 would vote for Candidate A.
3. Find the probability that a female would vote for Candidate A.
4. Find the probability that someone who voted for Candidate B was female and age 18-30.
5. According to the data, on which demographic(s) does Candidate A need to focus campaign efforts?
6. On which demographic(s) does Candidate B need to focus campaign efforts?

LESSON 6

Probability and the Addition Rule

Then

- You found probabilities of independent and dependent events.

Now

- **1** Apply the addition rule to situations involving mutually exclusive events.
- **2** Apply the addition rule to situations involving events that are not mutually exclusive.

Why?

- At Wayside High School, freshmen, sophomores, juniors, and seniors can all run for Student Council president. Dominic wants either a junior or a senior candidate to win the election. Travis wants either a sophomore or a female to win, but says, "If the winner is sophomore Katina Smith, I'll be thrilled!"

New Vocabulary
mutually exclusive

Mathematical Practices
1 Make sense of problems and persevere in solving them.
3 Construct viable arguments and critique the reasoning of others.

Content Standards
S.CP.1 Describe events as subsets of a sample space (the set of outcomes) using characteristics (or categories) of the outcomes, or as unions, intersections, or complements of other events ("or," "and," "not").
S.CP.7 Apply the Addition Rule, *P*(*A* or *B*) = *P*(*A*) + *P*(*B*) − *P*(*A* and *B*), and interpret the answer in terms of the model.

Image Source/Photodisc/Getty Images

1 Mutually Exclusive Events In Lesson 12-5, you examined probabilities involving the intersection of two or more events. In this lesson, you will examine probabilities involving the union of two or more events.

$P(A \text{ and } B)$ — Indicates an intersection of two sample spaces.

$P(A \text{ or } B)$ — Indicates a union of two sample spaces.

To find the probability that one event occurs *or* another event occurs, you must know how the two events are related. If the two events cannot happen at the same time, they are said to be **mutually exclusive**. That is, the two events have no outcomes in common.

S.CP.1

Real-World Example 1 Identify Mutually Exclusive Events

ELECTIONS **Refer to the application above. Determine whether the events are mutually exclusive. Explain your reasoning.**

a. a junior winning the election or a senior winning the election

These events are mutually exclusive. There are no common outcomes—a student cannot be both a junior and a senior.

b. a sophomore winning the election or a female winning the election

These events are not mutually exclusive. A female student who is a sophomore is an outcome that both events have in common.

c. drawing an ace or a club from a standard deck of cards

Because the ace of clubs represents both events, they are not mutually exclusive.

Guided Practice

Determine whether the events are mutually exclusive. Explain your reasoning. **1B. not mutually exclusive**

1A. selecting a number at random from the integers from 1 to 100 and getting a number divisible by 5 or a number divisible by 10 **not mutually exclusive**

1B. drawing a card from a standard deck and getting a 5 or a heart

1C. getting a sum of 6 or 7 when two number cubes are rolled **mutually exclusive**

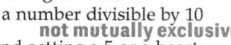

Mathematical Practices Strategies

Construct viable arguments and critique the reasoning of others.
As students determine whether events are mutually exclusive, help them to justify and communicate their reasoning. For example, ask:

- Is the probability of the union of two events greater if the events are mutually exclusive or greater if the events are not mutually exclusive? The probability of the union of two events occurring is greater if the events are mutually exclusive.
- Provide a possible outcome to show that when rolling a 6-sided die, rolling an even number and rolling a prime number are not mutually exclusive. If you roll a 2, you have rolled a number that is both even and prime.

Launch

Have students read the Why? section of the lesson. Ask:

- Why would Travis be thrilled if Katina wins the election? She is a sophomore and female.
- Can a person win the election that both Dominic and Travis want? Yes; if the person is a junior or senior and female.
- Would either Dominic or Travis be happy if freshman Michael Monroe won the election? No; he is a freshman and male.

Teach

Ask the scaffolded questions for each example to build conceptual understanding for students at all levels.

1 Mutually Exclusive Events

Example 1 Identify Mutually Exclusive Events

AL Are rolling a 3 or rolling an odd number on a number cube mutually exclusive events? Explain. No; because 3 is also odd, they are not mutually exclusive.

OL A quadrilateral is drawn, and a rectangle or a square is formed. Are these mutually exclusive events? Explain. No; because squares are also rectangles, the events are not mutually exclusive.

BL Describe a pair of events that are mutually exclusive. Sample answer: I can ride the bus to school, or I can ride in a car to school.

Need Another Example?
Cards Han draws one card from a standard deck. Determine whether the events are mutually exclusive. Explain your reasoning.

a. an ace or a 9 Mutually exclusive; a card cannot be both an ace and a 9.

b. a king or a club Not mutually exclusive; the king of clubs is a common outcome

Go Online!

Interactive Whiteboard
Use the *eLesson*, *Lesson Presentation*, or *Interactive Classroom* to present this lesson.

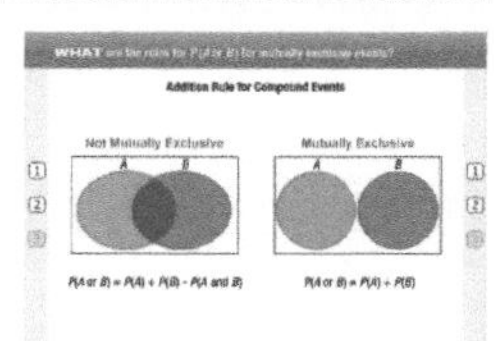

Example 2 Mutually Exclusive Events

AL **If the artist had the same song on two of the albums, would the events still be mutually exclusive? Explain.** No; because at least one of the songs that could be selected could come from more than one album, they would no longer be mutually exclusive.

OL **What is the probability that the first song will be from album 1 or album 3?** $\frac{23}{35}$, or about 66%

BL **What is the probability that the first song will *not* be from album 1?** $\frac{5}{7}$, or about 71%

Need Another Example?

Coins Trevor reaches into a can that contains 30 quarters, 25 dimes, 40 nickels, and 15 pennies. What is the probability that the first coin he picks is a quarter or a penny? $\frac{9}{22}$, or about 41%

Teaching Tip

Reasoning Point out to students that the Venn diagram of two mutually exclusive events does not have overlapping circles. Also show them that the Venn diagrams of two events that are not mutually exclusive will have overlapping circles.

One way of finding the probability of two mutually exclusive events occurring is to examine their sample space.

When a number cube is rolled, what is the probability of getting a 3 or a 4? From the Venn diagram, you can see that there are two outcomes that satisfy this condition, 3 and 4. So,

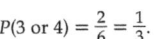

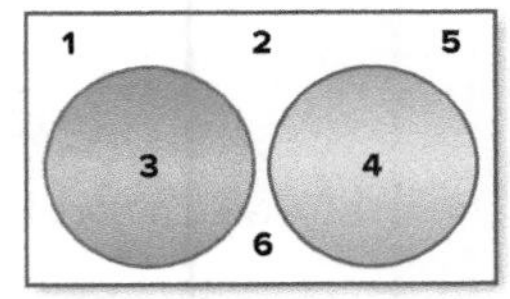

$$P(3 \text{ or } 4) = \frac{2}{6} = \frac{1}{3}.$$

Notice that this same probability can be found by adding the probabilities of each simple event.

$$P(3) = \frac{1}{6} \qquad P(4) = \frac{1}{6} \qquad P(3 \text{ or } 4) = \frac{1}{6} + \frac{1}{6} = \frac{2}{6} \text{ or } \frac{1}{3}$$

This example illustrates the first of two Addition Rules for Probability.

Reading Math ELL
or The word *or* is a key word indicating that at least one of the events occurs. *P*(*A* or *B*) is read as *the probability that A occurs or that B occurs.*

Key Concept Probability of Mutually Exclusive Events

Words If two events *A* and *B* are mutually exclusive, then the probability that *A* or *B* occurs is the sum of the probabilities of each individual event.

Example If two events *A* or *B* are mutually exclusive, then $P(A \text{ or } B) = P(A) + P(B)$.

Math History Link
Leonhard Euler (1707–1783) Euler introduced graph theory in 1736 in a paper titled *Seven Bridges of Königsberg*, a famous solved mathematics problem inspired by an actual place and situation. Also, Euler's formula relating the number of edges, vertices, and faces of a convex polyhedron is the origin of graph theory.

S.CP.1

Real-World Example 2 Mutually Exclusive Events

MUSIC **Ramiro makes a playlist that consists of songs from three different albums by his favorite artist. If he lets his digital media player select the songs from this list at random, what is the probability that the first song played is from album 1 or album 2?**

Ramiro's Playlist

Album	Number of Songs
1	10
2	12
3	13

These are mutually exclusive events, since the songs selected cannot be from both album 1 and album 2.

Let event A1 represent selecting a song from album 1.
Let event A2 represent selecting a song from album 2.
There are a total of 10 + 12 + 13 or 35 songs.

$P(A1 \text{ or } A2) = P(A1) + P(A2)$ Probability of mutually exclusive events

$= \frac{10}{35} + \frac{12}{35}$ $P(A1) = \frac{10}{35}$ and $P(A2) = \frac{12}{35}$

$= \frac{22}{35}$ Add.

So, the probability that the first song played is from album 1 or album 2 is $\frac{22}{35}$ or about 63%.

Guided Practice

2A. Two dice are rolled. What is the probability that doubles are rolled or that the sum is 9? $\frac{5}{18}$ or about 28%

2B. **CARNIVAL GAMES** If you win the ring toss game at a certain carnival, you receive a stuffed animal. If the stuffed animal is selected at random from among 15 puppies, 16 kittens, 14 frogs, 25 snakes, and 10 unicorns, what is the probability that a winner receives a puppy, a kitten, or a unicorn? $\frac{41}{80}$ or about 51%

2 Events That Are Not Mutually Exclusive

When a number cube is rolled, what is the probability of getting a number greater than 2 or an even number? From the Venn diagram, you can see that there are 5 numbers that are either greater than 2 or are an even number: 2, 3, 4, 5, and 6. So,

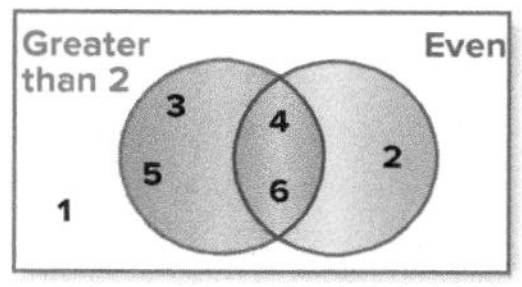

$$P(\text{greater than 2 or even}) = \frac{5}{6}.$$

Because it is possible to roll a number that is greater than 2 *and* an even number, these events are not mutually exclusive. Consider the probabilities of each individual event.

$$P(\text{greater than 2}) = \frac{4}{6} \qquad P(\text{even}) = \frac{3}{6}$$

If these probabilities were added, the probability of two outcomes, 4 and 6, would be counted twice—once for being numbers greater than 2 and once for being even numbers. You must subtract the probability of these common outcomes.

$$P(\text{greater than 2 or even}) = P(\text{greater than 2}) + P(\text{even}) - P(\text{greater than 2 and even})$$

$$= \frac{4}{6} + \frac{3}{6} - \frac{2}{6} \text{ or } \frac{5}{6}$$

This leads to the second of the Addition Rules for Probability.

Key Concept Probability of Events That Are Not Mutually Exclusive

Words If two events *A* and *B* are not mutually exclusive, then the probability that *A* or *B* occurs is the sum of their individual probabilities minus the probability that both *A* and *B* occur.

Symbols If two events A and B are not mutually exclusive, then $P(A \text{ or } B) = P(A) + P(B) - P(A \text{ and } B)$.

S.CP.1, S.CP.7

Real-World Example 3 Events That Are Not Mutually Exclusive

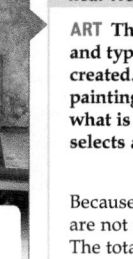

Real-World Link

Juried art shows are shows in which artists are called to submit pieces and a panel of judges decides which art will be shown. They originated in the early 1800s to exhibit the work of current artists and educate the public.

Source: Humanities Web

REALISTIC REFLECTIONS

ART The table shows the number and type of paintings Namiko has created. If she randomly selects a painting to submit to an art contest, what is the probability that she selects a portrait or an oil painting?

Namiko's Paintings			
Media	Still Life	Portrait	Landscape
watercolor	4	5	3
oil	1	3	2
acrylic	3	2	1
pastel	1	0	5

Because some of Namiko's paintings are both portraits and oil paintings, these events are not mutually exclusive. Use the rule for two events that are not mutually exclusive. The total number of paintings from which to choose is 30.

$P(\text{oil or portrait}) = P(\text{oil}) + P(\text{portrait}) - P(\text{oil and portrait})$

$$= \frac{1+3+2}{30} + \frac{5+3+2+0}{30} - \frac{3}{30} \quad \text{Substitution}$$

$$= \frac{6}{30} + \frac{10}{30} - \frac{3}{30} \text{ or } \frac{13}{30} \quad \text{Simplify.}$$

The probability that Namiko selects a portrait or an oil painting is $\frac{13}{30}$ or about 43%.

Guided Practice

3. What is the probability of drawing a king or a diamond from a standard deck of 52 cards? $\frac{4}{13}$ or about 31%

2 Events That Are Not Mutually Exclusive

Example 3 Events That Are Not Mutually Exclusive

AL Why do we subtract the probability that both of the events occur for events that are not mutually exclusive? Sample answer: If we don't account for when both of the events occur, such as oil and portrait in this example, we double count them and the probability is higher than it should be.

OL What is the probability that Namiko will select a landscape or a watercolor? $\frac{2}{3}$, or about 67%

BL What two types of painting are mutually exclusive? portrait and pastel

Need Another Example?

Art Use the table from Example 3. What is the probability that Namiko selects an acrylic or a still life? $\frac{2}{5}$ or 40%

Go Online!

The most up-to-date resources available for your program can be found at connectED.mcgraw-hill.com.

Practice

Formative Assessment Use Exercises 1–6 to assess students' understanding of the concepts in this lesson.

The Practice and Problem Solving exercises assess the content taught in the lesson. The Preparing for Assessment page is meant to be used as preparation for end-of-course assessments.

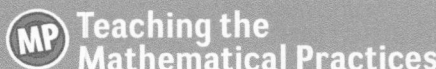

MP Teaching the Mathematical Practices

Modeling Mathematically proficient students can apply the mathematics they know to solve problems arising in everyday life. In Exercise 14, students should first determine whether the events are mutually exclusive or not.

Levels of Complexity Chart

The levels of the exercises progress from 1 to 3, with Level 1 indicating the lowest level of complexity.

Exercises	7–16	17–26, 35–40	27–34
C Level 3			●
B Level 2		●	
Level 1	●		

Extra Practice

See page R12 for extra exercises for students who are approaching level or for on-level students who need additional reinforcement.

Check Your Understanding ◯ = Step-by-Step Solutions begin on page R13.

Go Online! for a Self-Check Quiz

Example 1 S.CP.1

Determine whether the events are mutually exclusive. Explain your reasoning.

1. drawing a card from a standard deck and getting a jack or a club **not mutually exclusive; A jack of clubs is both a jack and a club.**
2. adopting a cat or a dog **mutually exclusive; A cat cannot be a dog, and a dog cannot be a cat.**

Example 2 S.CP.1

3. **JOBS** Adelaide is the employee of the month at her job. Her reward is to select at random from 4 gift cards, 6 coffee mugs, 7 DVDs, 10 picture frames, and 3 gift baskets. What is the probability that Adelaide receives a gift card, coffee mug, or picture frame? $\frac{2}{3}$ **or about 67%**
4. **SPORTS CARDS** Dario owns 145 baseball cards, 102 football cards, and 48 basketball cards. He selects a card at random to give to his brother. What is the probability that he selects a baseball or a football card? $\frac{247}{295}$ **or about 84%**

Example 3 S.CP.1, S.CP.7

5. **CLUBS** According to the table, what is the probability that a student in a club is a junior or on the debate team? $\frac{11}{25}$ **or about 44%**

Club	Soph.	Junior	Senior
Key	12	14	8
Debate	2	6	3
Math	7	4	5
French	11	15	13

6. **KITTENS** Ruby's cat had 8 kittens. The litter included 2 gray females, 3 mixed-color females, 1 gray male, and 2 mixed-color males. Ruby wants to keep one kitten. What is the probability that she randomly chooses a kitten that is female or gray? $\frac{3}{4}$ **or 75%**

Practice and Problem Solving Extra Practice is on page R13.

Examples 1–3 S.CP.1, S.CP.7

Determine whether the events are mutually exclusive. Then find the probability. Round to the nearest tenth of a percent, if necessary.

7. rolling a pair of dice and getting doubles or a sum of 8 **not mutually exclusive;** $\frac{10}{36}$ **or 27.8%**
8. drawing a card from a standard deck and getting a jack or a six **mutually exclusive;** $\frac{2}{13}$ **or 15.4%**
9. selecting a number at random from integers 1 to 20 and getting an even number or a number divisible by 3 **not mutually exclusive;** $\frac{13}{20}$ **or 65%**
10. tossing a coin and getting heads or tails **mutually exclusive; 100%**
11. drawing an ace or a heart from a standard deck of 52 cards **not mutually exclusive;** $\frac{4}{13}$ **or 30.8%**
12. rolling a pair of number cubes and getting a sum of either 6 or 10 **mutually exclusive;** $\frac{2}{9}$ **or about 22.2%**
13. **SPORTS** The table includes all of the programs offered at a sports complex and the number of participants aged 14–16. What is the probability that a player is 14 or plays basketball? **56%**

Graceland Sports Complex			
Age	Soccer	Baseball	Basketball
14	28	36	42
15	30	26	33
16	35	41	29

14. **MP MODELING** An exchange student is moving back to Italy, and her homeroom class wants to get her a going-away present. The teacher takes a survey of the class of 32 students and finds that 10 people choose a card, 12 choose a T-shirt, 6 choose a video, and 4 choose a bracelet. If the teacher randomly selects the present, what is the probability that the exchange student will get a card or a bracelet? $\frac{7}{16}$ **or about 43.8%**
15. Talia is playing a board game where rolling two dice determines the number of spaces she moves. In Talia's current position, she needs to roll at least a sum of 9 to win. What is the probability that Talia will win on her next turn? $\frac{5}{18}$
16. A bag contains six red coins labeled 1 through 6 and six green coins labeled 5 through 10. What is the probability of picking a coin labeled with a 5? $\frac{1}{6}$

Differentiated Homework Options

Levels	AL Basic	OL Core	BL Advanced
Exercises	7–16, 29–40	7–25 odd, 27–40	29–34, (optional: 35–40)
2-Day Option	7–15 odd, 35–40	7–16	
	8–16 even, 29–34	17–40	

You can use ALEKS to provide additional remediation support with personalized instruction and practice.

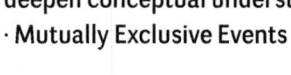

Go Online! eBook

Interactive Student Guide

Use the *Interactive Student Guide* to deepen conceptual understanding.

- Mutually Exclusive Events

B **CARDS** **Suppose you pull a card from a standard 52-card deck. Find the probability of each event.**

17. The card is a 2 or a queen. $\frac{2}{13}$ **or about 15%**
18. The card is a diamond or a heart. $\frac{1}{2}$ **or 50%**
19. The card is a 7 or a club. $\frac{4}{13}$ **or about 31%**
20. The card is a spade or an ace. $\frac{4}{13}$ **or about 31%**
21. The card is a 5 or a prime number. $\frac{4}{13}$ **or about 31%**
22. The card is red or an ace. $\frac{7}{13}$ **or about 54%**

NACHO CHIPS **A restaurant serves red, blue, and yellow tortilla chips. The bowl of chips Gabriel receives has 10 red chips, 8 blue chips, and 12 yellow chips. Gabriel chooses a chip at random. Find each probability.**

23. *P*(red or blue) $\frac{3}{5}$ **or 60%**
24. *P*(blue or yellow) $\frac{2}{3}$ **or about 67%**
25. *P*(yellow or not blue) $\frac{11}{15}$ **or about 73%**
26. *P*(red or not yellow) $\frac{3}{5}$ **or 60%**

C 27. **EDUCATION** Max surveyed 200 students at his school to determine how many nights per week they do homework. His results are shown in the table.

Number of Nights	Number of Students
0	10
1	30
2	50
3	90
4	10
5 or more	10

a. What is the probability that a randomly chosen student does homework at least 3 nights per week? $\frac{11}{20}$ **or 55%**

b. What is the probability that a randomly chosen student does homework no more than 3 nights per week? $\frac{9}{10}$ **or 90%**

28. **TILES** Kirsten and José are playing a game. Kirsten places tiles numbered 1 to 50 in a bag. José selects a tile at random. If he selects a prime number or a number greater than 40, then he wins the game. What is the probability that José will win on his first turn? $\frac{11}{25}$ **or 44%**

S.CP.1, S.CP.7

H.O.T. Problems Use **H**igher-**O**rder **T**hinking Skills

29. **ERROR ANALYSIS** George and Aliyah are determining the probability of randomly choosing a blue or red marble from a bag of 8 blue marbles, 6 red marbles, 8 yellow marbles, and 4 white marbles. Is either of them correct? Explain.

29. Aliyah; to find the probability of blue *or* red, the individual probabilities should be added because the events are mutually exclusive.

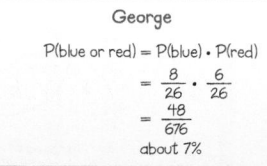

George

$P(\text{blue or red}) = P(\text{blue}) \cdot P(\text{red})$

$= \frac{8}{26} \cdot \frac{6}{26}$

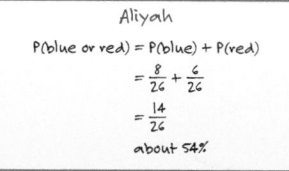

$= \frac{48}{676}$

about 7%

Aliyah

$P(\text{blue or red}) = P(\text{blue}) + P(\text{red})$

$= \frac{8}{26} + \frac{6}{26}$

$= \frac{14}{26}$

about 54%

MP **REASONING** **Determine whether the following are mutually exclusive. Explain.** **30–34. See margin.**

30. choosing a quadrilateral that is a square and a quadrilateral that is a rectangle
31. choosing a triangle that is equilateral and a triangle that is equiangular
32. choosing a complex number and choosing a natural number
33. **OPEN-ENDED** Describe a pair of events that are mutually exclusive and a pair of events that are not mutually exclusive.
34. **WRITING IN MATH** Explain why the sum of the probabilities of two mutually exclusive events is not always 1.

MP Standards for Mathematical Practice

Emphasis On	Exercises
2 Reason abstractly and quantitatively.	27, 30–32, 36–38
3 Construct viable arguments and critique the reasoning of others.	29
4 Model with mathematics.	3–6, 13–28, 35
6 Attend to precision.	39, 40

MP Teaching the Mathematical Practices

Critique Arguments Mathematically proficient students can distinguish correct logic from flawed reasoning. In Exercise 29, George found the probability of randomly choosing a blue marble, replacing it, and then randomly choosing a red marble.

Assess

Name the Math Have students write on a sheet of paper the difference between mutually exclusive and not mutually exclusive events and the probability formula for each.

Additional Answers

30. Not mutually exclusive; sample answer: Because squares are rectangles, but rectangles are not necessarily squares, a quadrilateral can be a square and a rectangle, and a quadrilateral can be a rectangle but not a square.
31. Not mutually exclusive; sample answer: If a triangle is equilateral, it is also equiangular. The two can never be mutually exclusive.
32. Not mutually exclusive; sample answer: A natural number is also a complex number.
33. Sample answer: If you pull a card from a deck, it can be a 3 or a 5. The two events are mutually exclusive. If you pull a card from a deck, it can be a 3 and it can be red. The two events are not mutually exclusive.
34. Sample answer: When two events are mutually exclusive, it means that they can't both happen, but it does not mean that one or the other of the events must happen. The sum of all possible outcomes in a sample space must be 1. For example, if event *A* and event *B* are mutually exclusive, the sample space includes the probability of event *A*, the probability of event *B*, and the probability of neither event *A* nor event *B*, all of which must sum to 1. The sum of the probabilities of event *A* and event *B* may be 1, but not necessarily.

Go Online!

eSolutions Manual

Create worksheets, answer keys, and solutions handouts for your assignments.

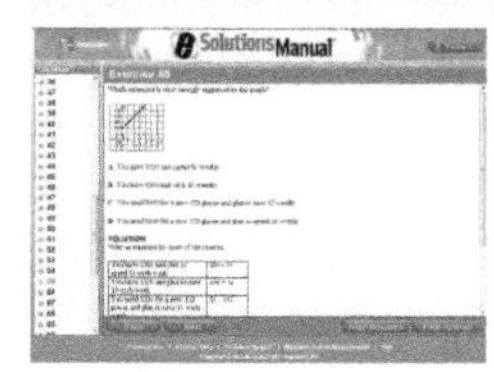

Preparing for Assessment

Exercises 35–40 require students to use the skills they will need on standardized assessments. Exercises are dual-coded with content standards and mathematical practice standards.

Dual Coding

Items	Content Standards	MP Mathematical Practices
35	S.CP.1	4
36	S.CP.1, S.CP.7	1, 2
37	S.CP.1, S.CP.7	1, 2
38	S.CP.1, S.CP.7	1, 2
39	S.CP.1	6
40	S.CP.1, S.CP.7	1, 2, 6

Diagnose Student Errors

Survey student responses for each item. Class trends may indicate common errors and misconceptions.

36.

A	Calculated probability of independent events
B	Calculated P(3 tickets)
C	Calculated P(T-shirt)
D	CORRECT

37.

A	Calculated probability of independent events
B	Used $P(\text{odd and blue}) = \frac{2}{3}$
C	Found $P(\text{odd and blue})$
D	CORRECT
E	Calculated $P(\text{odd}) + P(\text{blue})$

Preparing for Assessment

35. Cindy's bowling records indicate that for any frame, the probability that she will bowl a strike is 30%, a spare 45%, and neither 25%. What is the probability that she will bowl either a spare or a strike for any given frame? MP 4 S.CP.1

$\frac{3}{4}$ or 75%

36. Visitors to a school carnival throw a dart at a rectangular target in order to win prizes. The prizes are determined by the row and column in which the dart lands, as shown in the diagram. Tamiko throws a dart that lands at random on the target. Which is closest to the probability that she wins 3 tickets or a T-shirt? MP 1, 2 S.CP.1, S.CP.7 D

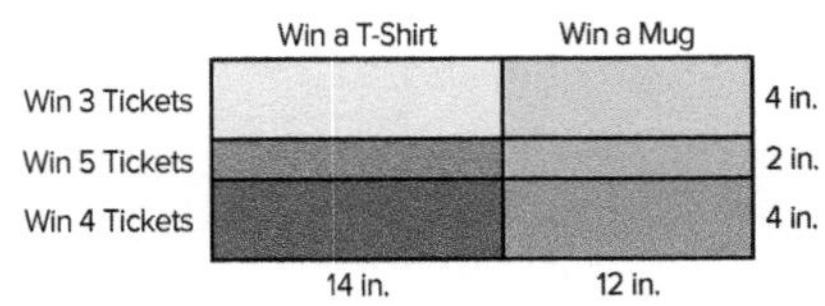

○ A 22%

○ B 40%

○ C 54%

○ D 72%

37. The spinner shown here is divided into 8 equal sectors. Elliott spins the spinner one time. What is the probability that the pointer lands on an odd number or a blue sector? MP 1, 2 S.CP.1, S.CP.7 D

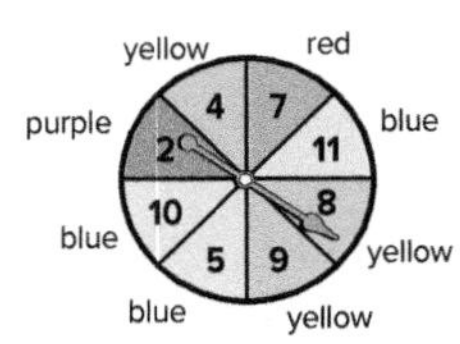

○ A $\frac{3}{16}$

○ B $\frac{5}{24}$

○ C $\frac{1}{4}$

○ D $\frac{5}{8}$

○ E $\frac{7}{8}$

38. Chelsea has a piece of fabric with the dimensions shown below. She spreads out the fabric on a table and then accidentally lets a drop of ink fall onto the fabric.

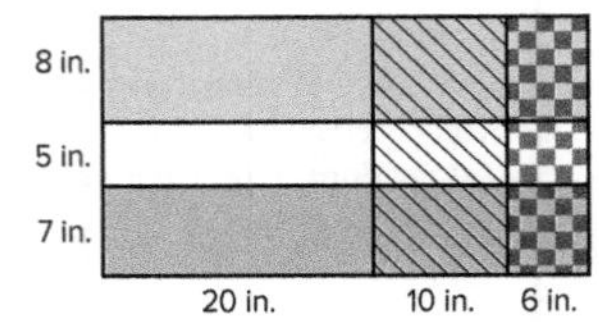

Assuming the ink lands at a random point on the fabric, which is closest to the probability that it lands in the white row or checkerboard column? MP 1, 2 S.CP.1, S.CP.7 B

○ A 42%

○ B 38%

○ C 25%

○ D 4%

39. A single number cube is rolled. Find each probability. MP 6 S.CP.1

a. P(3 or 5) = $\frac{1}{3}$ or about 33%

b. P(at least 4) = $\frac{1}{2}$ or 50%

40. MULTI-STEP The extracurricular activities in which members of the senior class at Valley View High School participate are shown in the Venn diagram. MP 1, 2, 6 S.CP.1, S.CP.7

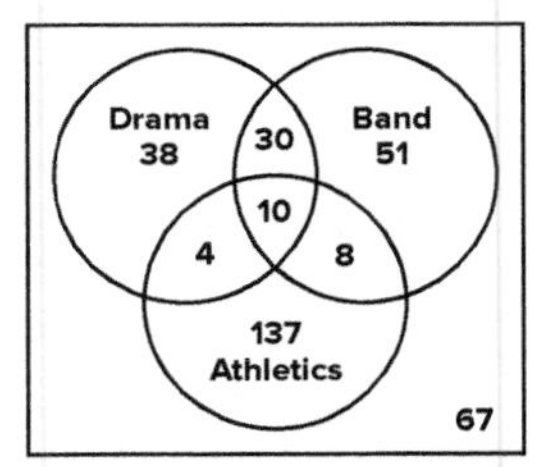

a. How many students are in the senior class? 345

b. How many seniors participate in athletics? 159

c. If a senior is randomly chosen, what is the probability that he or she participates in athletics or drama? $\frac{227}{345}$ or about 66%

d. If a senior is randomly chosen, what is the probability that he or she participates in only drama and band? $\frac{2}{23}$ or about 9%

38.

A	Calculated $P(\text{white}) + P(\text{striped})$
B	CORRECT
C	Calculated $P(\text{white})$
D	Calculated $P(\text{white and striped})$

Go Online!

Quizzes

Students can use *Self-Check Quizzes* to check their understanding of this lesson and have the results sent to you. You can also give *Quiz 4*, which covers the content in Lessons 12-6 and 12-7

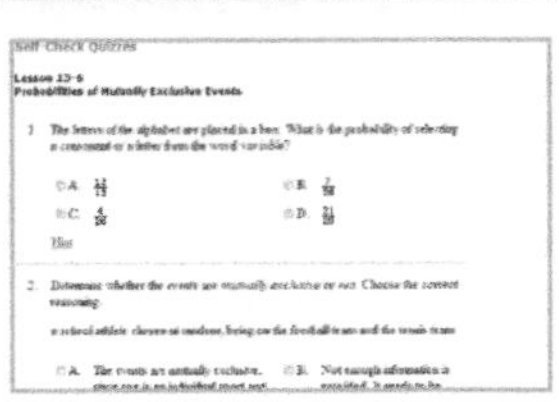

LESSON 12-7

Conditional Probability

SUGGESTED PACING (DAYS)

	Instruction
90 min.	0.75
45 min.	1.0

Track Your Progress

Objectives

1 Find the probability of events given the occurrence of other events.

2 Explain conditional probability and independence of everyday events.

Mathematical Background

Conditional probability is the probability of an event given that another event has already occurred. For independent events A and B, the conditional probability of A given B, written $P(A|B)$, is equal to $P(A)$ because the occurrence of B does not affect $P(A)$. Similarly, $P(B|A) = P(B)$.

THEN

S.CP.1 Describe events as subsets of a sample space (the set of outcomes) using characteristics (or categories) of the outcomes, or as unions, intersections, or complements of other events ("or," "and," "not").

S.CP.7 Apply the Addition Rule, $P(A \text{ or } B) = P(A) + P(B) - P(A \text{ and } B)$, and interpret the answer in terms of the model.

NOW

S.CP.3 Understand the conditional probability of A given B as $\frac{P(A \text{ and } B)}{P(B)}$, and interpret independence of A and B as saying that the conditional probability of A given B is the same as the probability of A, and the conditional probability of B given A is the same as the probability of B.

S.CP.5 Recognize and explain the concepts of conditional probability and independence in everyday language and everyday situations.

NEXT

S.CP.4 Construct and interpret two-way frequency tables of data when two categories are associated with each object being classified. Use the two-way table as a sample space to decide if events are independent and to approximate conditional probabilities.

S.CP.6 Find the conditional probability of A given B as the fraction of B's outcomes that also belong to A, and interpret the answer in terms of the model.

Go Online! All of these resources and more are available at connectED.mcgraw-hill.com

Use the **eGlossary** to define conditional probability and other key vocabulary in the lesson.

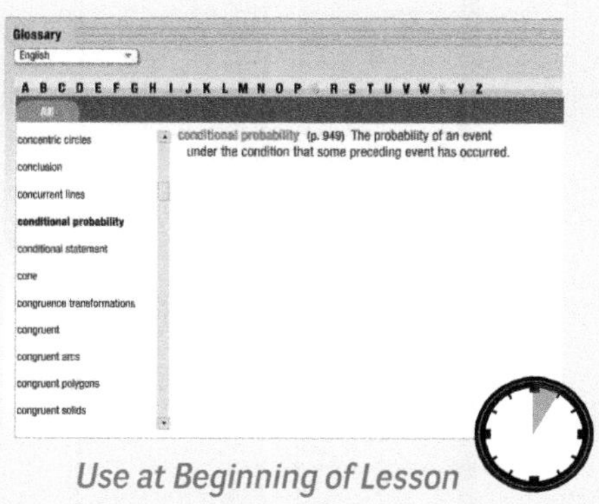

Use at Beginning of Lesson

eLessons utilize the power of your interactive whiteboard in an engaging way. Use **Probability of Compound Events**, screen 18, to introduce the concepts in this lesson.

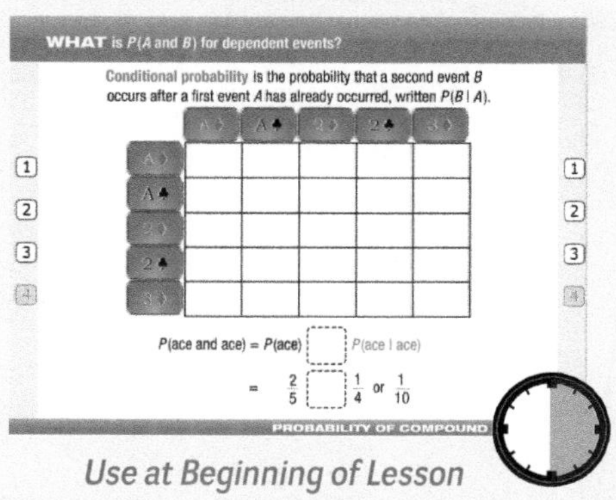

Use at Beginning of Lesson

Personal Tutors let students hear real teachers solve problems. Students can pause and repeat as many times as necessary.

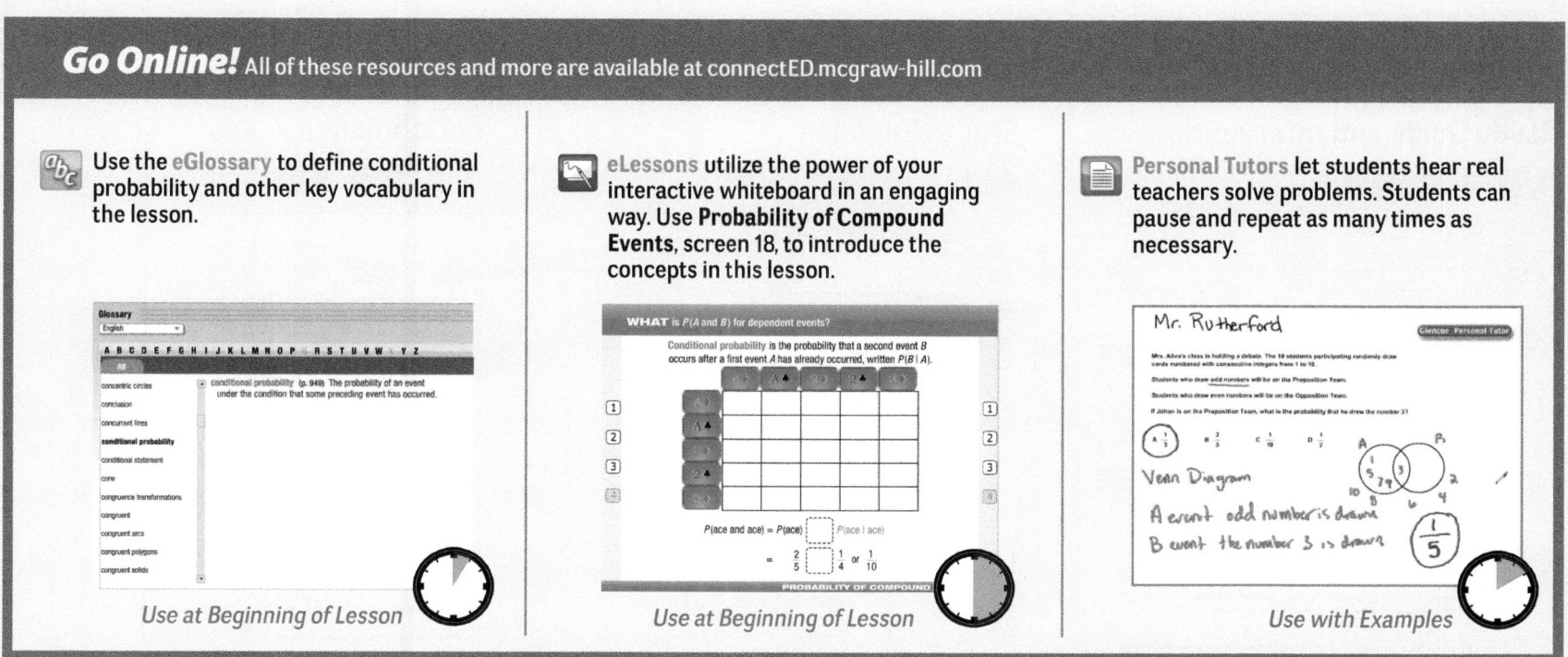

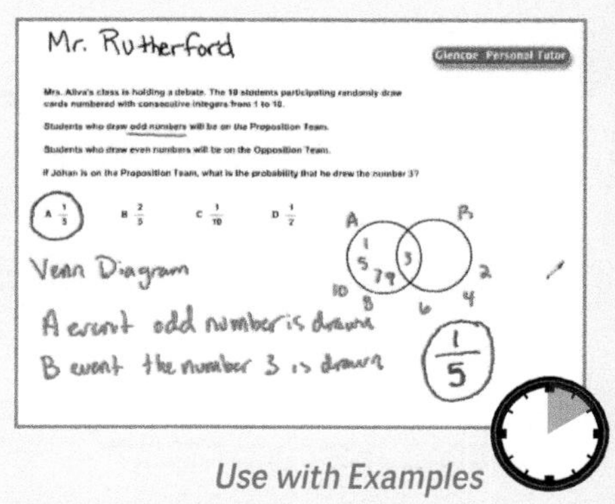

Use with Examples

Using Open Educational Resources

Apps Have students access **Google Apps for Education** to collaborate on tips for finding conditional probabilities. As an educator, it also offers spreadsheets, calendars, and surveys. You can also try **WhoTeaches** or **TeachAde**.

Use as planning tool

Go Online!
connectED.mcgraw-hill.com

Worksheets

Differentiate Your Resources

Extra Practice Additional practice or homework; Skills Practice is best for approaching-level students and Practice is best for on-level and beyond-level students

Skills Practice

AL OL ELL

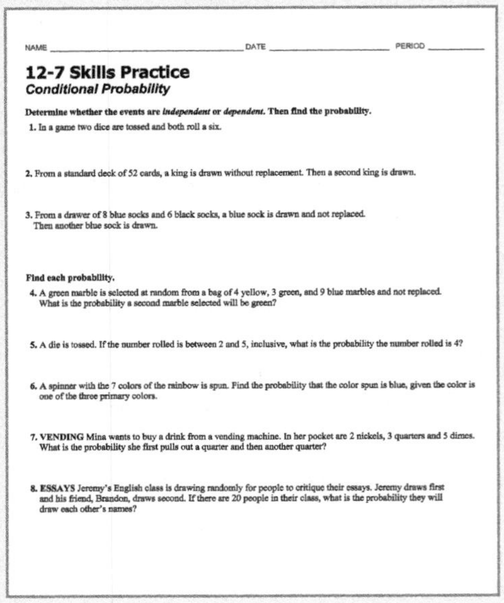
NAME ____ DATE ____ PERIOD ____

12-7 Skills Practice
Conditional Probability

Determine whether the events are *independent* or *dependent*. Then find the probability.

1. In a game two dice are tossed and both roll a six.
2. From a standard deck of 52 cards, a king is drawn without replacement. Then a second king is drawn.
3. From a drawer of 8 blue socks and 6 black socks, a blue sock is drawn and not replaced. Then another blue sock is drawn.

Find each probability.

4. A green marble is selected at random from a bag of 4 yellow, 3 green, and 9 blue marbles and not replaced. What is the probability a second marble selected will be green?
5. A die is tossed. If the number rolled is between 2 and 5, inclusive, what is the probability the number rolled is 4?
6. A spinner with the 7 colors of the rainbow is spun. Find the probability that the color spun is blue, given the color is one of the three primary colors.
7. VENDING Mina wants to buy a drink from a vending machine. In her pocket are 2 nickels, 3 quarters and 5 dimes. What is the probability she first pulls out a quarter and then another quarter?
8. ESSAYS Jeremy's English class is drawing randomly for people to critique their essays. Jeremy draws first and his friend, Brandon, draws second. If there are 20 people in their class, what is the probability they will draw each other's names?

Practice

AL OL BL ELL

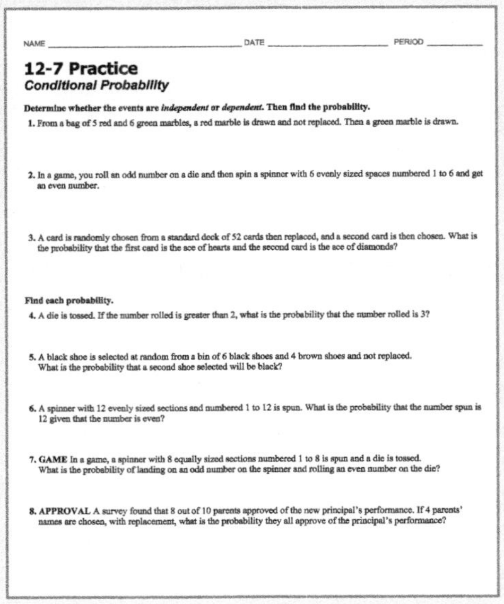
NAME ____ DATE ____ PERIOD ____

12-7 Practice
Conditional Probability

Determine whether the events are *independent* or *dependent*. Then find the probability.

1. From a bag of 5 red and 6 green marbles, a red marble is drawn and not replaced. Then a green marble is drawn.
2. In a game, you roll an odd number on a die and then spin a spinner with 6 evenly sized spaces numbered 1 to 6 and get an even number.
3. A card is randomly chosen from a standard deck of 52 cards then replaced, and a second card is then chosen. What is the probability that the first card is the ace of hearts and the second card is the ace of diamonds?

Find each probability.

4. A die is tossed. If the number rolled is greater than 2, what is the probability that the number rolled is 3?
5. A black shoe is selected at random from a bin of 6 black shoes and 4 brown shoes and not replaced. What is the probability that a second shoe selected will be black?
6. A spinner with 12 evenly sized sections and numbered 1 to 12 is spun. What is the probability that the number spun is 12 given that the number is even?
7. GAME In a game, a spinner with 8 equally sized sections numbered 1 to 8 is spun and a die is tossed. What is the probability of landing on an odd number on the spinner and rolling an even number on the die?
8. APPROVAL A survey found that 8 out of 10 parents approved of the new principal's performance. If 4 parents' names are chosen, with replacement, what is the probability they all approve of the principal's performance?

Word Problem Practice

AL OL BL ELL

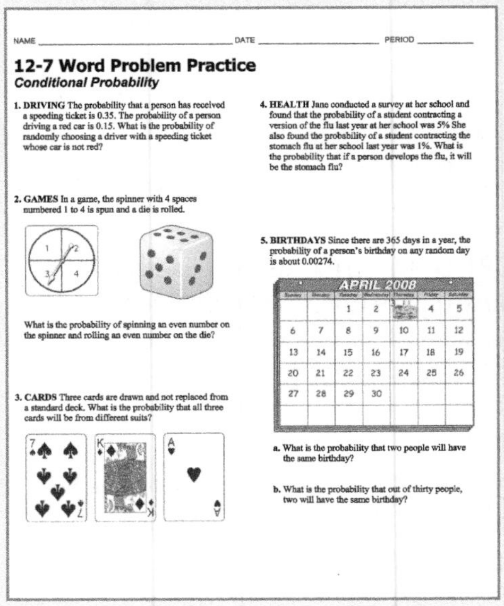
NAME ____ DATE ____ PERIOD ____

12-7 Word Problem Practice
Conditional Probability

1. DRIVING The probability that a person has received a speeding ticket is 0.35. The probability of a person driving a red car is 0.15. What is the probability of randomly choosing a driver with a speeding ticket whose car is not red?
2. GAMES In a game, the spinner with 4 spaces numbered 1 to 4 is spun and a die is rolled. What is the probability of spinning an even number on the spinner and rolling an even number on the die?
3. CARDS Three cards are drawn and not replaced from a standard deck. What is the probability that all three cards will be from different suits?
4. HEALTH Jana conducted a survey at her school and found that the probability of a student contracting a version of the flu last year at her school was 5%. She also found the probability of a student contracting the stomach flu at her school last year was 1%. What is the probability that if a person develops the flu, it will be the stomach flu?
5. BIRTHDAYS Since there are 365 days in a year, the probability of a person's birthday on any random day is about 0.00274.

APRIL 2008

a. What is the probability that two people will have the same birthday?

b. What is the probability that out of thirty people, two will have the same birthday?

Intervention Reteaching and vocabulary activities that can be used with struggling or absent students and as ELL support

Study Guide and Intervention

AL OL ELL

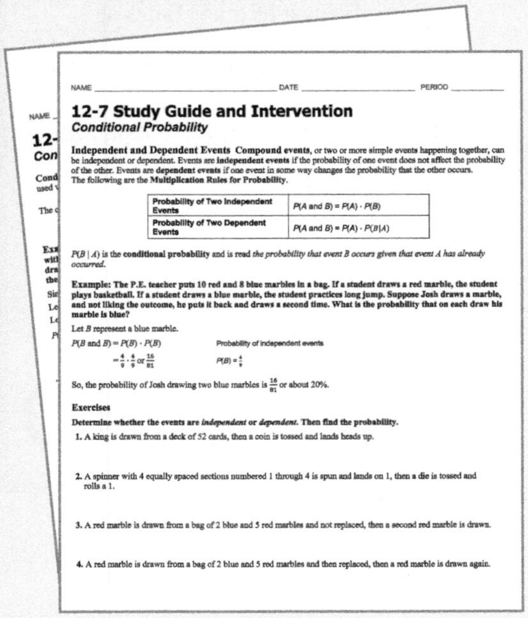
NAME ____ DATE ____ PERIOD ____

12-7 Study Guide and Intervention
Conditional Probability

Independent and Dependent Events **Compound events**, or two or more simple events happening together, can be independent or dependent. Events are **independent events** if the probability of one event does not affect the probability of the other. Events are **dependent events** if one event in some way changes the probability that the other occurs. The following are the **Multiplication Rules for Probability**.

Probability of Two Independent Events	$P(A \text{ and } B) = P(A) \cdot P(B)$
Probability of Two Dependent Events	$P(A \text{ and } B) = P(A) \cdot P(B \mid A)$

$P(B \mid A)$ is the **conditional probability** and is read *the probability that event B occurs given that event A has already occurred.*

Example: The P.E. teacher puts 10 red and 8 blue marbles in a bag. If a student draws a red marble, the student plays basketball. If a student draws a blue marble, the student practices long jump. Suppose Josh draws a marble, and not liking the outcome, he puts it back and draws a second time. What is the probability that on each draw his marble is blue?

Let B represent a blue marble.

$P(B \text{ and } B) = P(B) \cdot P(B)$ Probability of independent events

$= \frac{4}{9} \cdot \frac{4}{9}$ or $\frac{16}{81}$ $P(B) = \frac{4}{9}$

So, the probability of Josh drawing two blue marbles is $\frac{16}{81}$ or about 20%.

Exercises

Determine whether the events are *independent* or *dependent*. Then find the probability.

1. A king is drawn from a deck of 52 cards, then a coin is tossed and lands heads up.
2. A spinner with 4 equally spaced sections numbered 1 through 4 is spun and lands on 1, then a die is tossed and rolls a 1.
3. A red marble is drawn from a bag of 2 blue and 5 red marbles and not replaced, then a second red marble is drawn.
4. A red marble is drawn from a bag of 2 blue and 5 red marbles and then replaced, then a red marble is drawn again.

Study Notebook

AL OL BL ELL

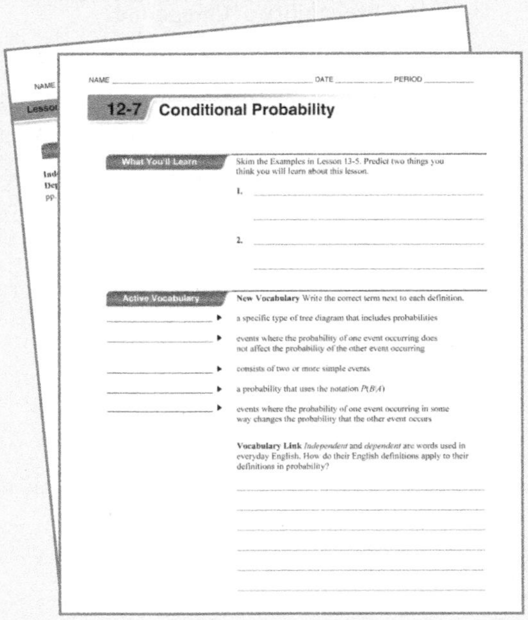
NAME ____ DATE ____ PERIOD ____

12-7 Conditional Probability

What You'll Learn — Skim the Examples in Lesson 13-5. Predict two things you think you will learn about this lesson.

1. ____
2. ____

Active Vocabulary — New Vocabulary Write the correct term next to each definition.

- a specific type of tree diagram that includes probabilities
- events where the probability of one event occurring does not affect the probability of the other event occurring
- consists of two or more simple events
- a probability that uses the notation $P(B|A)$
- events where the probability of one event occurring in some way changes the probability that the other event occurs

Vocabulary Link *Independent* and *dependent* are words used in everyday English. How do their English definitions apply to their definitions in probability?

Extension Activities that can be used to extend lesson concepts

Enrichment

OL BL ELL

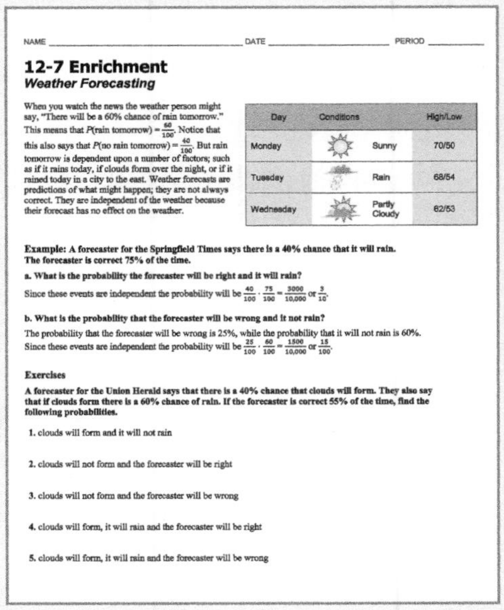
NAME ____ DATE ____ PERIOD ____

12-7 Enrichment
Weather Forecasting

When you watch the news the weather person might say, "There will be a 60% chance of rain tomorrow." This means that $P(\text{rain tomorrow}) = \frac{60}{100}$. Notice that this also says that $P(\text{no rain tomorrow}) = \frac{40}{100}$. But rain tomorrow is dependent upon a number of factors; such as if it rains today, if clouds form over the night, or if it rained today in a city to the east. Weather forecasts are predictions of what might happen; they are not always correct. They are independent of the weather because their forecast has no effect on the weather.

Day	Conditions		High/Low
Monday		Sunny	70/50
Tuesday		Rain	68/54
Wednesday		Partly Cloudy	62/53

Example: A forecaster for the Springfield Times says there is a 40% chance that it will rain. The forecaster is correct 75% of the time.

a. What is the probability the forecaster will be right and it will rain?

Since these events are independent the probability will be $\frac{40}{100} \cdot \frac{75}{100} = \frac{3000}{10{,}000}$ or $\frac{3}{10}$.

b. What is the probability that the forecaster will be wrong and it not rain?

The probability that the forecaster will be wrong is 25%, while the probability that it will not rain is 60%. Since these events are independent the probability will be $\frac{25}{100} \cdot \frac{60}{100} = \frac{1500}{10{,}000}$ or $\frac{15}{100}$.

Exercises

A forecaster for the Union Herald says that there is a 40% chance that clouds will form. They also say that if clouds form there is a 60% chance of rain. If the forecaster is correct 55% of the time, find the following probabilities.

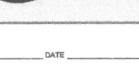

1. clouds will form and it will not rain
2. clouds will not form and the forecaster will be right
3. clouds will not form and the forecaster will be wrong
4. clouds will form, it will rain and the forecaster will be right
5. clouds will form, it will rain and the forecaster will be wrong

LESSON 7

Conditional Probability

∴Then	∴Now	∴Why?
• You applied the addition rule to events that were and were not mutually exclusive.	• **1** Find the probability of events given the occurrence of other events. **2** Explain conditional probability and independence of everyday events.	• An airline reports that 5% of its passengers experience flight delays or lost luggage. Evita's flight from Austin to Honolulu has been delayed. Evita wonders whether the airline is now more likely to lose her luggage, given the delay.

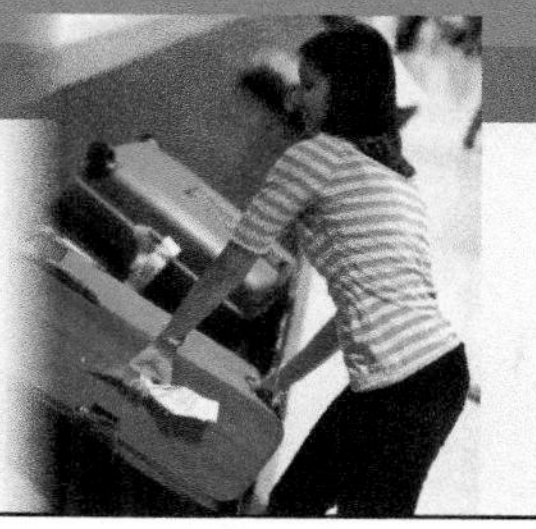

New Vocabulary
conditional probability

Mathematical Practices
2 Reason abstractly and quantitatively.
4 Model with mathematics.

Content Standards
Preparation for S.CP.3 Understand the conditional probability of A given B as $\frac{P(A \text{ and } B)}{P(B)}$, and interpret independence of A and B as saying that the conditional probability of A given B is the same as the probability of A, and the conditional probability of B given A is the same as the probability of B.
S.CP.5 Recognize and explain the concepts of conditional probability and independence in everyday language and everyday situations.

1 Conditional Probability

Conditional probability is the probability of an event given that another event has already occurred. The notation $P(B|A)$ is read *the probability that event B occurs given that event A has already occurred or the probability of B given A.*

Conditional probability can be used when additional information is known about an event. Suppose a dot cube is rolled and it is known that the number rolled is odd. What is the probability that the number rolled is a 5 given that the number rolled is odd?

There are only three odd numbers that can be rolled, so our sample space is reduced from {1, 2, 3, 4, 5, 6} to {1, 3, 5}. So, the probability that the number rolled is a 5 is $P(5|\text{odd}) = \frac{1}{3}$.

S.CP.5

Example 1 Conditional Probability

Ms. Fuentes's class is holding a debate. The 8 students participating randomly draw cards numbered with consecutive integers from 1 to 8.
- **Students who draw odd numbers will be on the Proposition Team.**
- **Students who draw even numbers will be on the Opposition Team.**

If Jonathan is on the Opposition Team, what is the probability that he drew the number 2?

Read the Item

Because Jonathan is on the Opposition Team, he must have drawn an even number. So you need to find the probability that the number drawn was 2 given that the number drawn was even. This is a conditional probability problem.

Solve the Item

Let A be the event that an even number is drawn.
Let B be the event that the number 2 is drawn.

Draw a Venn diagram to represent this situation. There are only four even numbers in the sample space, and only one out of these numbers is a 2. Therefore, the $P(B|A) = \frac{1}{4}$.

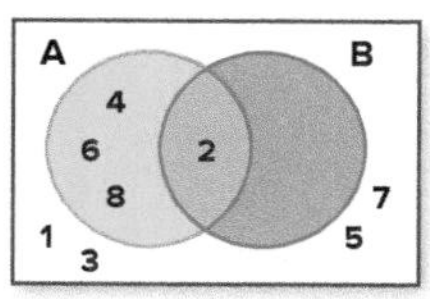

Guided Practice

1. When two dice are rolled, what is the probability that one die is a 4, given that the sum of the two dice is 9? $\frac{1}{2}$

A $\frac{1}{6}$ B $\frac{1}{4}$ C $\frac{1}{3}$ D $\frac{1}{2}$

Go Online!

Use the Venn diagram Tool to help you visualize the relationship between the outcomes of two events.

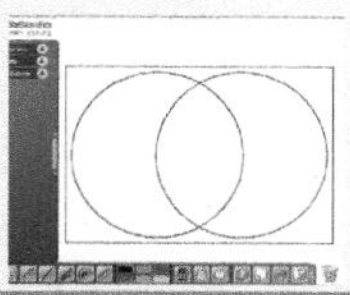

Frith Corey/Getty Images

MP Mathematical Practices Strategies

Reason abstractly and quantitatively.
Help students apply their prior knowledge of sample spaces to understand conditional probability. For example, ask:

- Describe how you can use Venn diagrams to visualize conditional probability. Sample answer: If you want to determine the probability that event *B* occurs given that event *A* has occurred, you can list all possible outcomes for event *A* in one circle of the Venn diagram. Then, list the possible outcomes for event *B* in the second circle. Any outcomes that appear in both circle *A* and circle *B* will fall in the overlap of the two circles.
- If events *A* and *B* are independent, what is the conditional probability that event *B* occurs given that event *A* has already occurred? The conditional probability that event *B* occurs given that event *A* has already occurred is the probability of event *B*.

Launch

Have students read the Why? section of the lesson. Ask:

- What is a *condition*? Sample answers: a circumstance, factor, or occurrence
- What condition may affect whether Evita's luggage is lost? Her flight is delayed.
- Suppose a flight delay does increase the probability of lost luggage. What can you say about the events *delayed flight* and *lost luggage*? The events are dependent.

Teach

Ask the scaffolded questions for each example to build conceptual understanding for students at all levels.

1 Conditional Probability

Example 1 Conditional Probability

AL What other numbers could Jonathan draw? 4, 6, or 8

OL If Jonathan is on the Proposition Team, what is the probability that he drew the number 2? 0

BL If Jonathan is on the Proposition Team, what is the probability that he drew the number 1 or 5? $\frac{1}{2}$, or 50%

Need Another Example?

Mr. Monroe is organizing the gym class into two teams for a game. The 20 students randomly draw cards numbered with consecutive integers from 1 to 20.
- Students who draw odd numbers will be on the Red team.
- Students who draw even numbers will be on the Blue team.

If Monica is on the Blue team, what is the probability that she drew the number 10? B

A $\frac{1}{20}$ **C** $\frac{9}{20}$

B $\frac{1}{10}$ **D** $\frac{1}{2}$

Example 2 Using the Conditional Probability Formula

AL **What decimal represents the probability that the banana is ripe and bruised?** 0.03

OL **How does knowing that the banana is bruised affect the sample space?** Sample answer: The sample space is the bruised bananas, rather than all of the bananas.

BL **Why is the sum of the given percents not equal to 100% of the bananas?** Sample answer: The ripe and bruised bananas are included in the ripe bananas and the bruised bananas, so there is overlap among the percents. Also, the given percents do not include the unripe or unbruised bananas.

Need Another Example?

At a fruit stand, 24% of the grape bags have red grapes, 15% have black grapes, and 3% have both red and black grapes. A customer selects a bag at random.

a. What is the probability that the bag contains red grapes, given that it contains black grapes?

$\frac{1}{5}$ or 20%

b. What is the probability that the bag contains black grapes, given that it contains red grapes?

$\frac{1}{8}$ or 12.5%

Because conditional probability reduces the sample space, the Venn diagram in Example 1 can be simplified as shown, with the intersection of the two events representing those outcomes in *A* and *B*. This suggests the following formula.

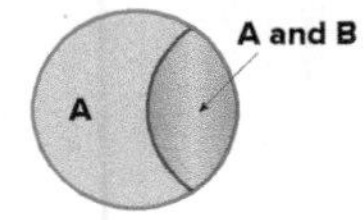

$P(B|A) = \frac{P(A \text{ and } B)}{P(A)}$

Key Concept Conditional Probability

The conditional probability of *B* given *A* is $P(B|A) = \frac{P(A \text{ and } B)}{P(A)}$, where $P(A) \neq 0$.

S.CP.3

Example 2 Using the Conditional Probability Formula

At a grocery store, 32% of the bananas are ripe, 8% of the bananas are bruised, and 3% of the bananas are ripe and bruised. A banana is selected at random. What is the probability that the banana is ripe, given that it is bruised?

$P(\text{ripe}|\text{bruised}) = \frac{P(\text{ripe and bruised})}{P(\text{bruised})}$ Conditional probability formula

$= \frac{0.03}{0.08}$ or $\frac{3}{8}$ or 37.5%

Guided Practice $\frac{3}{32}$ or about 9%

2. What is the probability that a randomly selected banana is bruised, given that it is ripe?

2 Conditional Probability and Independence

Conditional probability can be used to find the probability of dependent events. If *A* and *B* are dependent events, then $P(A \text{ and } B) = P(A) \cdot P(B|A)$.

Recall that if events *A* and *B* are independent, then the occurrence of one does not affect the probability of the other. In other words, the probability of *B* given that *A* has occurred is the same as the probability of *B*, or $P(B|A) = P(B)$. Similarly, $P(A|B) = P(A)$.

Go Online!

The probability rules in this Concept Summary are important to remember. Log into your eStudent Edition to bookmark this page.

Concept Summary Probability Rules

Types of Events	Words	Probability Rule
Independent events	The outcome of a first event *does not affect* the outcome of the second event.	If two events *A* and *B* are independent, then $P(A \text{ and } B) = P(A) \cdot P(B)$.
Dependent events	The outcome of a first event *does affect* the outcome of the other event.	If two events *A* and *B* are dependent, then $P(A \text{ and } B) = P(A) \cdot P(B|A)$.
Conditional	Additional information is known about the probability of an event.	The conditional probability of *A* given *B* is $P(A|B) = \frac{P(A \text{ and } B)}{P(B)}$.
Mutually exclusive events	Events *do not share* common outcomes.	If two events *A* or *B* are mutually exclusive, then $P(A \text{ or } B) = P(A) + P(B)$.
Not mutually exclusive events	Events *do share* common outcomes.	If two events *A* and *B* are not mutually exclusive, then $P(A \text{ or } B) = P(A) + P(B) - P(A \text{ and } B)$.
Complementary events	The outcomes of one event consist of all the outcomes in the sample space that are not outcomes of the other event.	For an event *A*, $P(\text{not } A) = 1 - P(A)$.

Differentiated Instruction AL OL ELL

Verbal/Linguistic Learners Have students discuss the differences between finding probabilities for independent and dependent events and for conditional probabilities. This should include that the formulas for independent and dependent events calculate the probability of two or more events occurring, whereas conditional probability calculates the probability of one event given that another has occurred.

Go Online!

The most up-to-date resources available for your program can be found at connectED.mcgraw-hill.com.

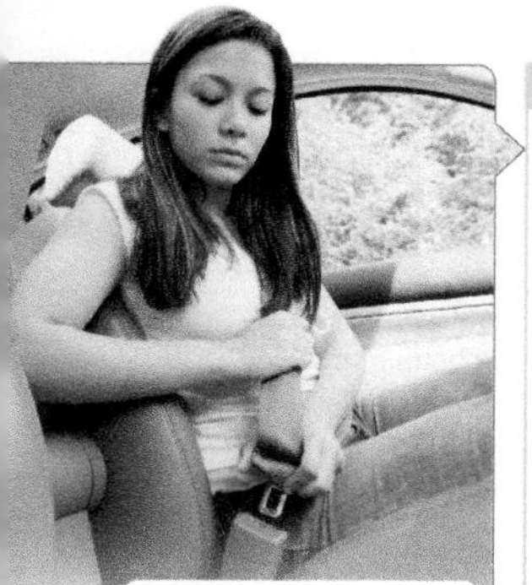

Real-World Link

About 86% of American motorists and their right-front passengers use a seat belt.

Source: National Highway Traffic Safety Administration

S.CP.5

Real-World Example 3 Identify and Use Probability Rules

SEAT BELTS Refer to the information at the left. Suppose two people are chosen at random from a group of 100 American motorists and passengers. If this group mirrors the population, what is the probability that at least one of them does not wear a seat belt?

Understand You know that 86% of Americans *do use* a seat belt. The phrase *at least one* means *one or more*. So, you need to find the probability that either

- the first person chosen does not use a seat belt *or*
- the second person chosen does not use a seat belt *or*
- both people chosen do not use a seat belt.

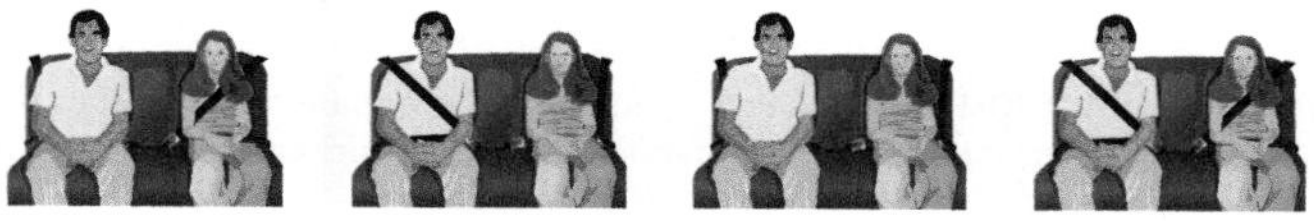

Plan The complement of the event described above is the event that both people chosen *do use* a seat belt. Find the probability of this event, and then find the probability of its complement.

Let event A represent choosing a person who does use a seat belt.

Let event B represent choosing a person who does use a seat belt after the first person has already been chosen.

These are two independent events, because the outcome of the first event does not affect the probability of the outcome of the second event.

Solve

$P(A \text{ and } B) = P(A) \cdot P(B)$	Probability of independent events
$= 0.86 \cdot 0.86$	$P(A) = P(B) = 0.86$
$= 0.7396$	Multiply.
$P[\text{not } (A \text{ and } B)] = 1 - P(A \text{ and } B)$	Probability of a complement
$= 1 - 0.7396$	Substitution
$= 0.2604$	Subtract.

So, the probability that at least one of the passengers does not use a seat belt is about 26%.

Check The probability that one person chosen out of 100 does not wear his or her seat belt is (100 − 86)% or 14%. When you choose two people out of 100, the probability that at least one of them does not wear their seatbelt should be greater than 14%. Because 26% > 14%, the answer is reasonable.

In this example, it is more efficient to calculate the probability of the complement than to calculate the probability of each case in the set of desired outcomes.

Study Tip ELL

Key Probability Words When determining what type of probability you are dealing with in a situation, look for key words and correctly interpret their meaning.

and → independent or dependent events
or → mutually exclusive or not mutually exclusive
not → complementary events
and then → conditional
at least n → *n* or more
at most n → *n* or less

Guided Practice

3. **CELL PHONES** According to an online poll, 35% of American motorists routinely use their cell phones while driving. Three people are chosen at random from a group of 100 motorists. What is the probability that

A. at least two of them use their cell phone while driving? about 28%

B. no more than one use their cell phone while driving? about 72%

2 Conditional Probability and Independence

Example 3 Identify and Use Probability Rules

AL **If we calculated the probability that (1) the first person does not wear a seat belt and the second one does or (2) the first person does wear a seat belt and the second one does not or (3) neither of them wear a seatbelt, would we get the same solution as the example solution? Explain.** Yes; We use the complement because it makes the calculation easier. This situation and the situation in the problem are the same.

OL **What is the probability that one or more passengers wears a seatbelt?** about 0.98 or 98%

BL **What is the probability that *exactly* one person wears a seat belt?** about 0.24 or 24%

Need Another Example?

Pets A survey of Kingston High School students found that 63% of the students had a cat or a dog for a pet. If two students are chosen at random from a group of 100 students, what is the probability that at least one of them does not have a cat or a dog for a pet? ≈ 60%

Differentiated Instruction OL BL

Extension Have students create Venn diagrams to model each of the types of probabilities that they learned about in this chapter. Students should think of a situation to model with that type of probability and create a Venn diagram that models the events.

Practice

Formative Assessment Use Exercises 1–5 to assess students' understanding of the concepts in this lesson.

The Practice and Problem Solving exercises assess the content taught in the lesson. The Preparing for Assessment page is meant to be used as preparation for end-of-course assessments.

MP Teaching the Mathematical Practices

Sense-Making Mathematically proficient students make sense of relationships in problem situations. In Exercises 6–9, encourage students to list the sample space or draw a Venn diagram for each scenario. These representations can help students conceptualize conditional probabilities.

Levels of Complexity Chart

The levels of the exercises progress from 1 to 3, with Level 1 indicating the lowest level of complexity.

Exercises	6–14	15–19, 27–35	20–26
C Level 3			●
B Level 2		●	
Level 1	●		

Extra Practice

See page R12 for extra exercises for students who are approaching level or for on-level students who need additional reinforcement.

Go Online! eBook

Interactive Student Guide

Use the *Interactive Student Guide* to deepen conceptual understanding.

· Conditional Probability

Check Your Understanding ◯ = Step-by-Step Solutions begin on page R13.

Go Online! for a Self-Check Quiz

Example 1 S.CP.5

1. **GAMES** Every Saturday, 10 friends play dodgeball at a local park. To pick teams, they randomly draw cards with consecutive integers from 1 to 10. Odd numbers are on team A, and even numbers are team B. What is the probability that a player on team B has drawn the number 10? **0.20**

Example 2 S.CP.3

2. In a large city, 70% of the residents are adults, 84% of the residents have traveled out of state, and 9% are adults who have not traveled out of state. What is the probability that a randomly selected resident has not traveled out of state, given that the resident is an adult? **$\frac{9}{70}$ or about 13%**

3. **WEATHER** Tomorrow's weather forecast calls for a 25% chance of rain, an 80% chance that the temperature will exceed 80°F, and a 15% chance of both. What is the probability of rain, given that the temperature exceeds 80°F? **$\frac{3}{16}$ or 18.75%**

Example 3 S.CP.5

4. **PROM** In Armando's senior class of 100 students, 91 went to the senior prom. If two people are chosen at random from the entire class, what is the probability that at least one of them did not go to prom? **17.3%**

5. A red marble is selected at random from a bag of 2 blue and 9 red marbles and not replaced. What is the probability that a second marble selected will be red? **$\frac{4}{5}$ or 80%**

Practice and Problem Solving Extra Practice is on page R12.

Example 1 S.CP.5

6. A number cube is rolled and the result is a number greater than 2. What is the probability that the result is a 6? **$\frac{1}{4}$ or 25%**

7. A spinner has 12 equally sized sections numbered 1 through 12. Find the probability that the spinner lands on 11, given that the spinner lands on an odd number. **$\frac{1}{6}$ or about 17%**

8. An eight-sided number cube is rolled and the result is an odd number. Find the probability that the result is 5. **$\frac{1}{4}$ or 25%**

9. The perimeter of a quadrilateral is 12 units, and the length of each side is an odd integer. What is the probability that the quadrilateral is a rhombus? **$\frac{1}{5}$ or 20%**

10. There are 13 players available to play basketball. The players randomly draw cards numbered with consecutive integers from 1 to 13. Players who draw odd numbers are on team A. Players who draw even numbers are on team B.
    a. If Todd is on team A, what is the probability that he drew the number 5? **$\frac{1}{7}$ or about 14%**
    b. If Tyrone is on team B, what is the probability that he drew the number 6? **$\frac{1}{6}$ or about 17%**

Example 2 S.CP.3

B 11. **TECHNOLOGY** At Bell High School, 43% of the students own a smartphone, and 28% own a smartphone and a digital media player. What is the probability that a student owns a digital media player, given that he or she owns a smartphone? **0.65**

12. **CLASSES** The probability that a student takes geometry and French at Satomi's school is 0.064. The probability that a student takes French is 0.45. What is the probability that a student takes geometry if the student takes French? **0.14**

13. **PROOF** Use the formula for the probability of two dependent events $P(A \text{ and } B)$ to derive the conditional probability formula for $P(B|A)$. **See Ch. 12 Answer Appendix.**

14. **TENNIS** A double fault in tennis is when the serving player fails to land his or her serve "in" without stepping on or over the service line in two chances. Kelly's first-serve percentage is 40%, and her second-serve percentage is 70%.
    a. Draw a probability tree that shows each outcome. **See Ch. 12 Answer Appendix.**
    b. What is the probability that Kelly will double-fault? **0.18 or 18%**
    c. Design a simulation using a random number generator that can be used to estimate the probability that Kelly double-faults on her next serve. **See students' work.**

Differentiated Homework Options

Levels	AL Basic	OL Core	BL Advanced
Exercises	6–14, 22–35	7–19 odd, 20–35	20–26, (optional: 27–35)
2-Day Option	7–13 odd, 27–35	6–14	
	6–14 even, 22–26	15–35	

You can use ALEKS to provide additional remediation support with personalized instruction and practice.

15. Of the T-shirts available at a store, 54% are striped, 32% have a logo, and 13% are striped and have a logo.

a. What is the probability that a shirt with a logo is striped? $\frac{13}{32}$ or about 41%

b. What is the probability that a striped shirt has a logo? $\frac{13}{54}$ or about 24%

16. In a large town, 73% of the adults are homeowners, 46% have a college degree, and 38% are homeowners with college degrees.

a. What is the probability that an adult with a college degree owns a home? $\frac{19}{23}$ or about 83%

b. What is the probability that a homeowner has a college degree? $\frac{38}{73}$ or about 52%

17. **SPORTS** At a basketball game, 80% of the fans cheered for the home team. In the same crowd, 20% of the crowd were waving banners and cheering for the home team. What is the probability that a fan who cheered for the home team waved a banner? 25%

Example 3 S.CP.5

18. **JOBS** Of young workers aged 18 to 25, 71% are paid by the hour. If two people are randomly chosen from a group of 100 young workers, what is the probability that exactly one is paid by the hour? 42%

19. **RECYCLING** Suppose 31% of Americans recycle. If two Americans are chosen randomly from a group of 50, what is the probability that at most one of them recycles? about 90.4%

20. **MUSIC** A school carried out a survey of 265 students to see which types of music students prefer to hear at school dances. The results are shown in the Venn diagram. Find each probability.

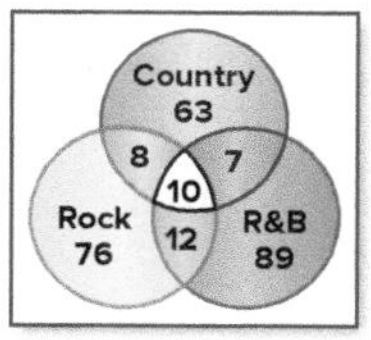

a. P(country or R&B) 71.3%

b. P(rock and country or R&B or rock) 11.3%

c. P(R&B but not rock) 36.2%

d. P(all three) 3.8%

21. **VACATION** A random survey was conducted to determine where families vacationed. The results indicated that $P(B) = 0.6$, $P(B \cap M) = 0.2$, and the probability that a family did not vacation at either destination is 0.1.

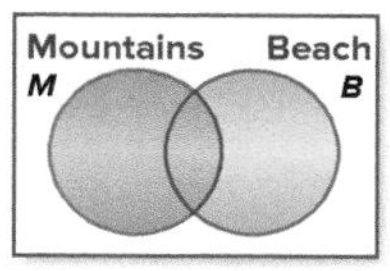

a. What is the probability that a family vacations in the mountains? 0.3

b. What is the probability that a family visiting the beach will also visit the mountains? 0.33

H.O.T. Problems Use Higher-Order Thinking Skills

22. **PROOF** Use the formula for the probability of two dependent events $P(A \text{ and } B)$ to derive the conditional probability formula for $P(B \mid A)$. 22–24. See margin.

23. **PROBLEM SOLVING** You roll 3 number cubes. What is the probability that the outcome on at least two of the cubes will be a number less than or equal to 4? Explain your reasoning.

24. **WRITING IN MATH** Suppose that A and B are mutually exclusive events. What is $P(A \mid B)$ and $P(B \mid A)$? Explain your reasoning.

25. **CONSTRUCT ARGUMENTS** There are n different objects in a bag. The probability of drawing object A and then object B without replacement is about 1.4%. What is the value of n? Explain. See Ch. 12 Answer Appendix.

26. **REASONING** If $P(A|B)$ is the same as $P(A)$, and $P(B|A)$ is the same as $P(B)$, what can be said about the relationship between events A and B? A and B are independent events.

Standards for Mathematical Practice

Emphasis On	Exercises
1 Make sense of problems and persevere in solving them.	6–9, 16, 18, 26
2 Reason abstractly and quantitatively.	1–3, 5, 11–15, 20–24, 26–35
3 Construct viable arguments and critique the reasoning of others.	17, 19, 25
4 Model with mathematics.	4, 10, 13–16

24. Because A and B are mutually exclusive, once either has occurred, the other cannot occur. So $P(A|B) = P(B|A) = 0$.

Extra Practice

See page R12 for extra exercises for students who are approaching level or for on-level students who need additional reinforcement.

Differentiated Instruction BL

Extension The game show *Let's Make a Deal* has created controversy with the question: Switch or Stay? Contestants on the show were asked to choose one door out of three. They were then shown one of the remaining doors that did not contain the one grand prize. The question was then asked, "Do you want to stay with your original choice, or switch to the remaining door?" Students can create a simulation or use an online applet to explore this question. Students should be able to explain why repeating an experiment many times forces the experimental and theoretical probabilities closer together.

Assess

Ticket Out the Door Have the student create a problem that requires the use of conditional probability.

Additional Answers

22. $P(A \text{ and } B) = P(A) \cdot P(B|A)$ Formula for $P(A \text{ and } B)$

$\frac{P(A \text{ and } B)}{P(A)} = P(B|A)$ Divide each side by $P(A)$.

23. $\frac{20}{27}$ or about 74%; The probability that a number cube shows a number less than or equal to 4 is $\frac{4}{6}$. So the probability that the first two number cubes show a number less than or equal to 4 and the last cube does not is $\frac{4}{6} \cdot \frac{4}{6} \cdot \frac{2}{6}$. Because the number greater than 4 can occur on any of the 3 cubes, the probability of a number less than or equal to 4 on exactly two cubes is $3\left(\frac{4}{6} \cdot \frac{4}{6} \cdot \frac{2}{6}\right)$ or $\frac{4}{9}$. The probability of showing a number less than or equal to 4 on all three cubes is $\frac{4}{6} \cdot \frac{4}{6} \cdot \frac{4}{6}$ or $\frac{8}{27}$. Thus the probability of showing a number less than or equal to 4 on two or more cubes is $\frac{4}{9} + \frac{8}{27} = \frac{20}{27}$ or about 74%.

Go Online!

eSolutions Manual

Create worksheets, answer keys, and solutions handouts for your assignments.

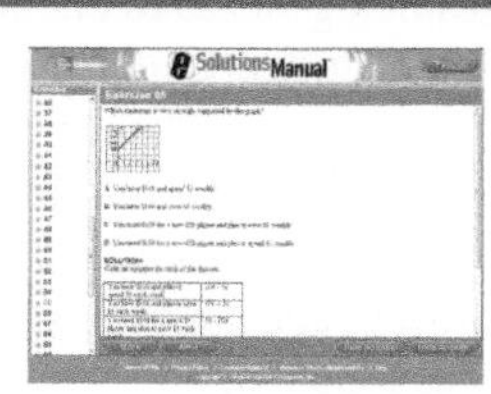

Preparing for Assessment

Exercises 27–35 require students to use the skills they will need on assessments. Exercises are dual-coded with content standards and mathematical practice standards.

Dual Coding		
Items	Content Standards	MP Mathematical Practices
27	S.CP.3	2
28	S.CP.3	2
29	S.CP.3	2
30	S.CP.3	2
31	S.CP.3	2
32	S.CP.3	2
33	S.CP.3, S.CP.5	2
34	S.CP.3	2
35	S.CP.3	1, 2, 4

Diagnose Student Errors

Survey student responses for each item. Class trends may indicate common errors and misconceptions.

27.

A	Calculated $P(5)$ instead of $P(5 \mid \text{multiple of } 5)$
B	Incorrectly counted multiples of 5
C	CORRECT
D	Did not include 10 as a multiple of 5

28.

A	Calculated *P*(both black)
B	Calculated *P*(both black) when first marble is replaced
C	CORRECT
D	Calculated *P*(one black)

Go Online!

Quizzes

Students can use *Self-Check Quizzes* to check their understanding of this lesson and have the results sent to you. You can also give *Quiz 4*, which covers the content in Lessons 12-6 and 12-7.

Preparing for Assessment

27. A deck contains 10 cards that are numbered 1 through 10. Alex chooses a card at random. What is the probability that the number on Alex's card is 5, given that it is a multiple of 5? MP 2 S.CP.3 **C**

○ A $\frac{1}{10}$

○ B $\frac{1}{5}$

○ C $\frac{1}{2}$

○ D $\frac{1}{1}$

28. Leo chooses two marbles at random from the bag shown here. Given that one of Leo's marbles is black, what is the probability that both marbles are black? MP 2 S.CP.3 **C**

○ A $\frac{1}{36}$

○ B $\frac{4}{81}$

○ C $\frac{1}{15}$

○ D $\frac{5}{12}$

29. LeBron rolls a number greater than or equal to 4 on a dot cube. What is the probability that LeBron has rolled a 5? MP 2 S.CP.3

$\frac{1}{3}$

30. At a high school, the probability that a student plays basketball and football is 0.008. The probability that a student only plays football is 0.28. What is the probability that a football player also plays basketball? MP 2 S.CP.3

$\frac{2}{70}$

31. What is the probability that the sum of two dice will be greater than 8, given that the first die is 6? MP 2 S.CP.3

$\frac{2}{3}$

32. What is the probability of drawing two aces from a standard deck of cards, given that the first card is an ace? MP 2 S.CP.3

$\frac{1}{17}$

Mr. Marcos organizes a classroom game for 16 students. Each student is randomly assigned a different number from 1 to 16.

- **Students assigned a multiple of 4 or 9 are on team A.**
- **Students assigned a multiple of 5 or 7 are on team B.**
- **Students assigned any other number are on team C.**

Find each probability.

33. *P*(Maggie was assigned 13 | Maggie is on team C) MP 2 S.CP.3 **C**

○ A $\frac{3}{128}$

○ B $\frac{1}{16}$

○ C $\frac{1}{6}$

○ D $\frac{3}{8}$

34. *P*(Nicole was assigned 7 | Nicole is on team B) MP 2 S.CP.3 **B**

○ A $\frac{1}{16}$

○ B $\frac{1}{5}$

○ C $\frac{5}{16}$

○ D $\frac{3}{8}$

35. MULTI-STEP A certain disease affects 2% of the population. The test for this disease is accurate 90% of the time. The accuracy of a patient's test result is independent of whether the patient has the disease. MP 1, 2, 4 S.CP.3

a. What is the probability that a patient has the disease and receives a positive (accurate) test result? **0.018**

b. What is the probability that a patient does not have the disease and receives a positive (inaccurate) test result? **0.098**

c. What is the probability that a patient receives a positive test result? Explain how you found your answer. **35c–d. See margin.**

d. Jordan receives a positive test result. What is the probability that Jordan has the disease? Show how you found your answer.

33.

A	Calculated *P*(Maggie was assigned 13) · *P*(Maggie is on Team C)
B	Calculated *P*(Maggie was assigned 13)
C	CORRECT
D	Calculated *P*(Maggie is on Team C)

34.

A	Calculated *P*(Nicole was assigned 7)
B	CORRECT
C	Calculated *P*(Nicole is on Team B)
D	Calculated *P*(Nicole was assigned 7) + *P*(Nicole is on Team B)

Additional Answers

35c. Sample answer: A patient who receive positive test result either has the disea or does not have the disease. These are mutually exclusive events, so add the probabilities. From part **a**, *P*(positive te and disease) = 0.018. From part **b**, *P*(positive test and no disease) = 0.098 *P*(positive test) = 0.018 + 0.098 = 0.116

35d. *P*(disease|positive test) =

$$\frac{P(\text{disease and positive test})}{P(\text{positive test})} = \frac{0.018}{0.116} \approx 0$$

LESSON 12-8
Two-Way Frequency Tables

SUGGESTED PACING (DAYS)

	Instruction
90 min.	1
45 min.	1.5

Track Your Progress

Objectives

1. Decide whether events are independent by using two-way frequency tables.
2. Approximate conditional probabilities by using two-way frequency tables.

Mathematical Background

A two-way frequency table is a tool for organizing data from a survey in which the data are classified according to two variables, such as gender and school. Each of the variables must have two or more categories (gender: *male* or *female*; school: *Lincoln High School* or *Chavez High School*). The two-way frequency table can be used to analyze independence of events and conditional probabilities.

THEN

S.CP.3 Understand the conditional probability of *A* given *B* as *P*(*A* and *B*)/*P*(*B*), and interpret independence of *A* and *B* as saying that the conditional probability of *A* given *B* is the same as the probability of *A*, and the conditional probability of *B* given *A* is the same as the probability of *B*.

S.CP.5 Recognize and explain the concepts of conditional probability and independence in everyday language and everyday situations.

NOW

S.CP.4 Construct and interpret two-way frequency tables of data when two categories are associated with each object being classified. Use the two-way table as a sample space to decide if events are independent and to approximate conditional probabilities.

S.CP.6 Find the conditional probability of *A* given *B* as the fraction of *B*'s outcomes that also belong to *A*, and interpret the answer in terms of the model.

NEXT

S.IC.1 Understand statistics as a process for making inferences about population parameters based on a random sample from that population.

Go Online! All of these resources and more are available at connectED.mcgraw-hill.com

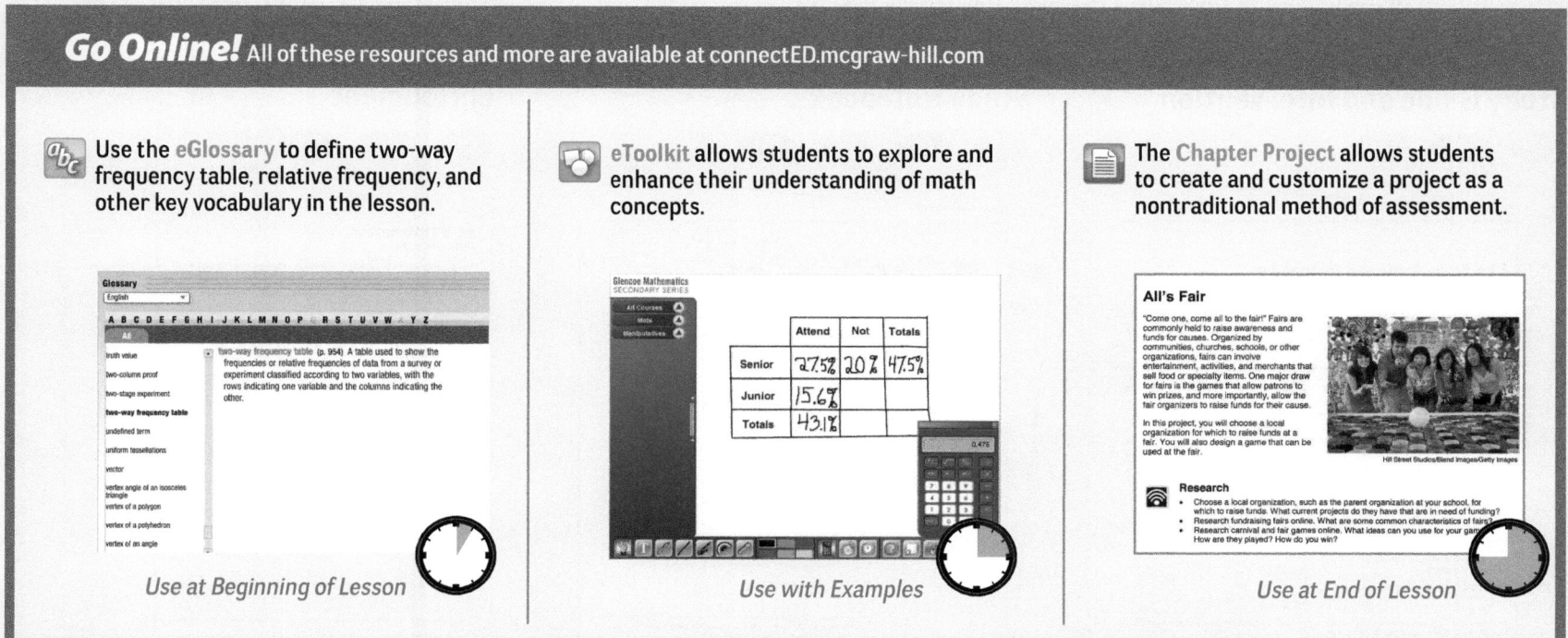

Use the **eGlossary** to define two-way frequency table, relative frequency, and other key vocabulary in the lesson.

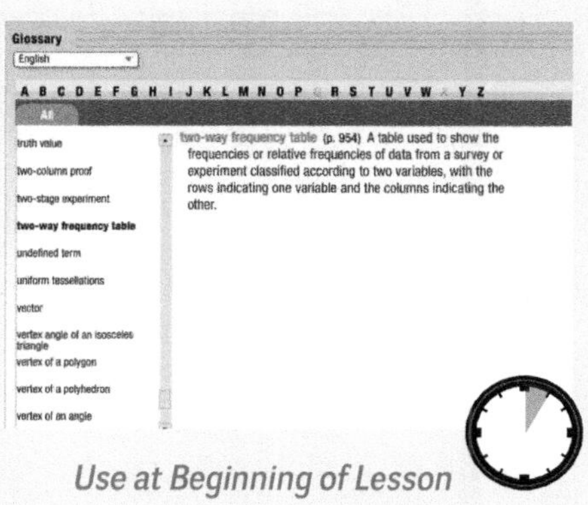

Use at Beginning of Lesson

eToolkit allows students to explore and enhance their understanding of math concepts.

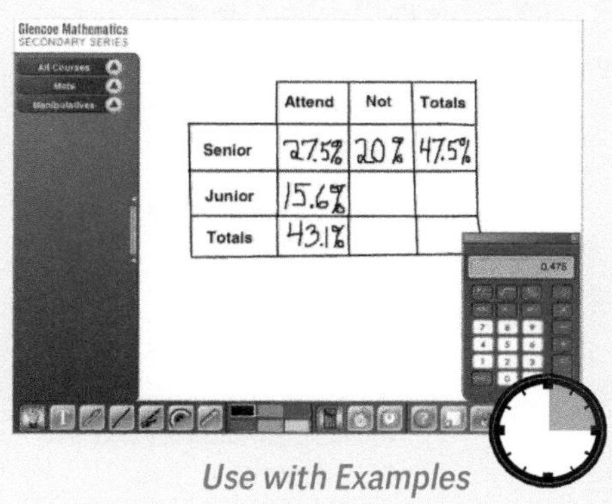

Use with Examples

The **Chapter Project** allows students to create and customize a project as a nontraditional method of assessment.

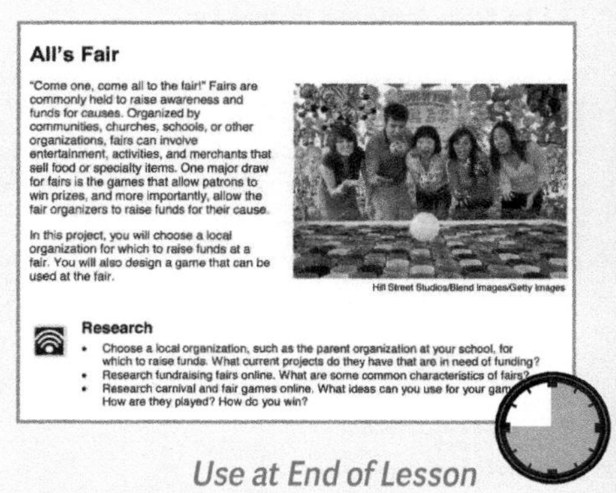

Use at End of Lesson

OER Using Open Educational Resources

Video Sharing Have students work in groups to record and upload examples on **SchoolTube** about how to make and analyze a two-way frequency table. Have them watch videos of others for ideas. If you are unable to access **SchoolTube**, try **KidsTube, MathATube, YouTube**, or **TeacherTube**. *Use as homework*

Go Online!
connectED.mcgraw-hill.com

Worksheets

Differentiate Your Resources

Extra Practice Additional practice or homework; Skills Practice is best for approaching-level students and Practice is best for on-level and beyond-level students

Skills Practice

AL OL ELL

NAME ______ DATE ______ PERIOD ______

12-8 Skills Practice
Two-Way Frequency Tables

Salina surveyed a random sample of students to determine how many take Spanish or French. The data are shown in the two-way frequency table. Answer each question and tell whether you are using a marginal frequency or joint frequency.

	Spanish	French	Total
Girls	75	45	120
Boys	60	20	80
Total	135	65	200

1. How many students are girls and take French?
2. How many students are boys and take Spanish?
3. How many girls were surveyed?
4. How many students that take French were surveyed?

Salina converted the two-way frequency table of data about students that take Spanish or French to a table of relative frequencies.

	Spanish	French	Total
Girls	37.5%	22.5%	60%
Boys	30%	10%	40%
Total	67.5%	32.5%	100%

5. Use the relative frequency table to determine whether gender is independent of taking Spanish or French. Explain.
6. Find the probability that a surveyed student is a girl that they take Spanish.
7. Find the probability that a surveyed student is a boy given that they take French.
8. Find the probability that a surveyed student takes Spanish given that they are a boy.

Practice

AL OL BL ELL

NAME ______ DATE ______ PERIOD ______

12-8 Practice
Two-Way Frequency Tables

Fifty students in middle school were surveyed about after school activities. Four play an instrument and play sports. Sixteen play an instrument and do not play sports. Twenty-four do not play an instrument and play sports. Six do not play an instrument and do not play sports.

1. Make a two-way frequency table to organize the given data.
2. How many students play an instrument and play sports?
3. How many students do not play an instrument and do not play sports?
4. Convert the table from Exercise 1 to a table of relative frequencies.
5. Use the relative frequency table from Exercise 4 to determine whether playing an instrument is independent of playing sports. Explain.
6. Find the probability that a surveyed student does not play sports given that they play an instrument.
7. Find the probability that a surveyed student does not play sports given that they do not play an instrument.
8. Find the probability that a surveyed student plays an instrument given that they play sports.
9. Find the probability that a surveyed student plays an instrument given that they do not play sports.

Word Problem Practice

AL OL BL ELL

NAME ______ DATE ______ PERIOD ______

12-8 Word Problem Practice
Two-Way Frequency Tables

1. **PETS** Nico surveyed 100 students to determine if they prefer a dog or cat as a pet. Of the 55 ninth graders surveyed, 20 preferred a cat. Of the 65 people that preferred a dog, 30 were tenth graders. Make a two-way frequency table of the data.

2. **EXAMS** The data about homework completeness and exam score of the students in Mr. VanWinkle's class are shown in the two-way frequency table. How many students completed their homework and passed the exam? Tell whether you are using a marginal frequency or joint frequency.

	Completed Homework	Did Not Complete Homework	Total
Passed Exam	18	2	20
Did Not Pass Exam	4	2	6
Total	22	4	26

3. **VOTING** A recent poll was taken to determine whether registered voters would vote "yes" or "no" for Issue 1. Of the 250 people that were polled, 130 were females and 120 were males. Of the males that were surveyed, 80 said they would vote "yes" and 40 said they would vote "no" for Issue 1. Of the females that were surveyed, 95 said they would vote "yes" and 35 said they would vote "no" for Issue 1. Make a relative frequency table of the data.

4. **MOVIES** Rachel surveyed 160 people to determine if they preferred Drama or Comedy movies. The relative frequency table shows the data collected from the survey. Determine whether gender is independent of movie type. Explain.

	Drama	Comedy	Total
Males	12.5%	25%	37.5%
Females	46.9%	15.6%	62.5%
Total	59.4%	40.6%	100%

5. **FAVORITE SUBJECT** A poll was taken of students to determine their favorite subject in school. The two-way table shows the results.

	English	Math	History	Total
Girls	30	20	30	80
Boys	10	50	20	100
Total	40	70	50	180

a. Find the probability that a surveyed student is a girl given that the favorite subject is math.
b. Find the probability that a surveyed student is a boy given that the favorite subject is history.
c. Find the probability that a surveyed student's favorite subject is English given that they are a girl.
d. Find the probability that a surveyed student's favorite subject is math given that they are a boy.

Intervention Reteaching and vocabulary activities that can be used with struggling or absent students and as ELL support

Study Guide and Intervention

AL OL ELL

NAME ______ DATE ______ PERIOD ______

12-8 Study Guide and Intervention
Two-Way Frequency Tables

Two-Way Frequency Tables A **two-way frequency table** is used to show the frequencies of data from a survey or experiment in which the data are classified according to two variables. The frequencies reported in the Totals row and Totals column are called **marginal frequencies**, with the bottom rightmost cell reporting the total number of observations. The frequencies reported in the interior of the table are called **joint frequencies**. A **relative frequency** is the ratio of the number of observations in a category to the total number of observations.

Example:
One hundred people were surveyed about the vehicle they drive. The surveyed shows that 15 males and 40 females drive SUVs, while 35 males and 10 females drive trucks. Make a two-way frequency table of the data. Find the number of males surveyed and the number of females that drive a truck. Also, make a relative frequency table.

Step 1 Let the rows represent gender: Male and Female. Let the columns represent vehicle: SUV and Truck. Fill in the cells with the given data.

	SUV	Truck
Males	15	35
Females	40	10

Step 2 Include a Total row and column. Find each sum.
SUV Total: 15 + 40 = 55
Truck Total: 35 + 10 = 45
Males Total: 15 + 35 = 50
Female Total: 40 + 10 = 50

	SUV	Truck	Total
Males	15	35	50
Females	40	10	50
Total	55	45	100

Step 3 Find the number of males surveyed and the number of females that drive a truck.

Look at the Total in the Males row. There were 50 males surveyed. This is a marginal frequency.

Look at the intersection of Females and Truck. There were 10 females that drive a truck. This is a joint frequency.

Step 4 Make a relative frequency table of the data. Divide the frequency in each cell by the Total.

	SUV	Truck	Total
Males	$\frac{15}{100}$ = 15%	$\frac{35}{100}$ = 35%	$\frac{50}{100}$ = 50%
Females	$\frac{40}{100}$ = 40%	$\frac{10}{100}$ = 10%	$\frac{50}{100}$ = 50%
Total	$\frac{55}{100}$ = 55%	$\frac{45}{100}$ = 45%	$\frac{100}{100}$ = 100%

One hundred students were surveyed about whether they like fruit. The surveyed showed that 25 boys and 35 girls like fruit, while 25 boys and 15 girls do not like fruit.

1. Make a two-way frequency table and a relative frequency table of the data.
2. How many girls were surveyed? Is this a marginal or joint frequency?

Study Notebook

AL OL BL ELL

NAME ______ DATE ______ PERIOD ______

12-8 Two-Way Frequency Tables

What You'll Learn Scan the text under the Now heading. List two things you will learn about in this lesson.
1. ______
2. ______

Active Vocabulary **New Vocabulary** Write the correct term next to each definition.
______ ▸ a data display used to show the frequencies of data from a survey or experiment in which the data are classified according to two variables
______ ▸ the frequencies reported in the *Totals* row and *Totals* column of a two-way frequency table
______ ▸ the frequencies reported in the interior of a two-way frequency table
______ ▸ the ratio of the number of observations in a category to the total number of observations in a two-way frequency table

Vocabulary Link Another name for a two-way frequency table is a contingency table. Look up the word contingency. Why is a two-way frequency table also called a contingency table?

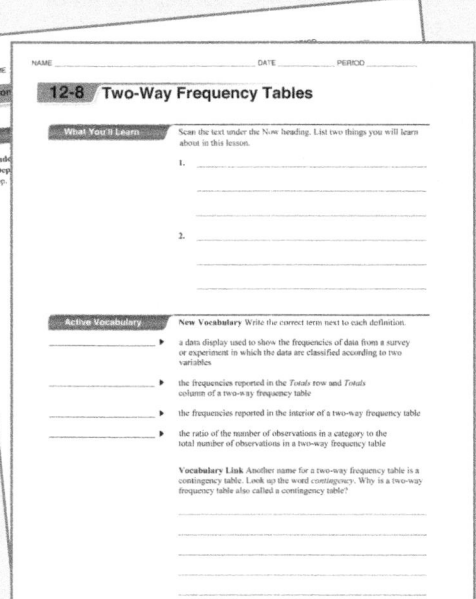

Extension Activities that can be used to extend lesson concepts

Enrichment

OL BL ELL

NAME ______ DATE ______ PERIOD ______

12-8 Enrichment
Demographics

Demographics is the term used to refer to characteristics of the population including age, race, gender, education level, income, employment status, and other variables. Marketing research used by advertisers and polling data used by politicians are two areas in which demographics are an important part of the data. Sometimes the people under consideration fall into more than one category. Sometimes the events being researched are mutually exclusive.

Suppose an exit poll held outside a voting area on the day of an election produced these results. Use the table to answer the questions below.

Age and Gender	Votes for Candidate A	Votes for Candidate B
18–30 Male	19	32
18–30 Female	31	18
31–45 Male	51	12
31–45 Female	43	20
46–60 Male	42	35
46–60 Female	20	42
60+ Male	45	21
60+ Female	27	18

1. Which events are mutually exclusive?
2. Find the probability that a male between the ages of 46 and 60 would vote for Candidate A.
3. Find the probability that a female would vote for Candidate A.
4. Find the probability that someone who voted for Candidate B was female and age 18–30.
5. According to the data, on which demographic(s) does Candidate A need to focus campaign efforts?
6. On which demographic(s) does Candidate B need to focus campaign efforts?

LESSON 8

Two-Way Frequency Tables

Then

- You found conditional probabilities.

Now

- 1 Decide whether events are independent by using two-way frequency tables.
- 2 Approximate conditional probabilities by using two-way frequency tables.

Why?

- Michael surveys students at his school to find out if there is an association between a student's grade level and his or her decision to participate in drama club. Michael can organize and analyze the results in a two-way frequency table.

New Vocabulary

two-way frequency table
marginal frequency
joint frequency
relative frequency

Mathematical Practices

2 Reason abstractly and quantitatively.
4 Model with mathematics.

Content Standards

S.CP.4 Construct and interpret two-way frequency tables of data when two categories are associated with each object being classified.
S.CP.6 Find the conditional probability of *A* given *B* as the fraction of *B*'s outcomes that also belong to *A*, and interpret the answer in terms of the model.

1 Decide Whether Events are Independent

A **two-way frequency table** or contingency table is used to show the frequencies of data from a survey or experiment in which the data are classified according to two variables. The rows of the table indicate one variable and the columns of the table indicate the other.

S.CP.4

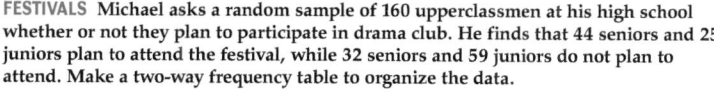

Real-World Example 1 Make a Two-Way Frequency Table

FESTIVALS Michael asks a random sample of 160 upperclassmen at his high school whether or not they plan to participate in drama club. He finds that 44 seniors and 25 juniors plan to attend the festival, while 32 seniors and 59 juniors do not plan to attend. Make a two-way frequency table to organize the data.

Step 1 Identify the variables.

The students surveyed can be classified according to the variables *class* and *participation*. Because the survey included only upperclassmen, the variable *class* has two categories: senior or junior. The variable *participation* also has two categories: participating or not participating.

Step 2 Create a two-way frequency table.

Let the rows of the table represent *class* and let the columns represent *participation*.

	Participating	Not Participating	Totals
Senior	44	32	76
Junior	25	59	84
Totals	69	91	160

Fill in the cells of the table with the given data.

Step 3 Add a *Totals* row and a *Totals* column to the table and fill in these cells with the correct sums.

Guided Practice

1. **PETS** Karima asks a random sample of 50 visitors to a pet store if they prefer cats or dogs. She finds that 18 women and 17 men prefer dogs, while 6 women and 7 men prefer cats. Make a two-way table to organize the data. See margin.

The frequencies reported in the *Totals* row and *Totals* column are called **marginal frequencies**, with the bottom rightmost cell reporting the total number of observations. The frequencies reported in the interior of the table are called **joint frequencies**. These show the frequencies of all possible combinations of the categories for the first variable with the categories for the second variable.

MP Mathematical Practices Strategies

Reason abstractly and quantitatively.
Help students make sense of quantities and their relationships in two-way frequency tables, and help them understand how the quantities relate to the given problem situation. For example, ask:

- Which cells of a two-way frequency table show joint frequencies? The cells in the interior of the table show joint frequencies.
- What information does a joint frequency give you? It tells you the frequency for a combination of one category for the first variable and one category for the second variable.
- Which cells of a two-way frequency table show marginal frequencies? The cells in the *Totals* column show marginal frequencies.
- What information does a marginal frequency give you? It tells you the frequency for one category of one of the variables.
- In a relative frequency table, what must be true about the value in the bottom rightmost cell? It is always 100%.

Launch

Have students read the Why? section of the lesson.

- Why would it be useful to organize the data in a table? The table makes it easy to see the data at a glance and find relationships among the data.
- What do you think are the two variables for Michael's survey? grade level and whether or not the student participates in drama club

Teach

Ask the scaffolded questions for each example to build conceptual understanding for students at all levels.

1 Decide Whether Events Are Independent

Example 1 Make a Two-Way Frequency Table

AL What do you notice about the values in the rows and columns of the table? You can add across the rows to get the values in the *Totals* column; you can add down the columns to get the values in the *Totals* row.

OL How would the table be different if Michael also surveyed freshmen and sophomores? The table would have two additional rows.

BL Is a senior more likely to participate in drama club or not participate in drama club? Explain. 44 out of 76 seniors participate, so seniors are more likely to participate than not participate.

Need Another Example?

Valerie asks a random sample of 70 science teachers and math teachers whether they have been to the town's planetarium. She finds that 25 science teachers have been to the planetarium and 3 have not, while 20 math teachers have been to the planetarium and 22 have not. Make a two-way frequency table to organize the data.

	Has Been to Planetarium	Has Not Been to Planetarium	Totals
Science	25	3	28
Math	20	22	42
Totals	45	25	70

MP Teaching the Mathematical Practices

Modeling Mathematically proficient students apply mathematics to solve problems in everyday life. Ask students what conclusions they might make about the two airlines in Example 2. Ask students which airline they would choose if they wanted the best chance of arriving on time and have them justify their choice.

S.CP.4

Example 2 Use Marginal and Joint Frequencies

Miguel looked at a random sample of flights for two airlines and collected data on whether the flights arrived on time or late. The data are shown in the two-way frequency table. Answer each question and tell whether you are using a marginal frequency or joint frequency.

	On Time	Late	Totals
AirWorld	13	9	22
RedJet	7	11	18
Totals	20	20	40

a. How many RedJet flights arrived on time?

Look at the intersection of the *On Time* column and the *RedJet* row.

The cell shows that 7 RedJet flights arrived on time.

This is a joint frequency.

	On Time	Late	Totals
AirWorld	13	9	22
RedJet	7	11	18
Totals	20	20	40

b. How many flights arrived late?

This includes data from both airlines, so use the total in the *Late* column.

The cell in the *Totals* row shows that 20 flights arrived late.

This is a marginal frequency.

	On Time	Late	Totals
AirWorld	13	9	22
RedJet	7	11	18
Totals	20	20	40

Guided Practice

Answer each question and tell whether you are using a marginal frequency or joint frequency.

2A. How many AirWorld flights are in the sample? 22; marginal frequency

2B. How many AirWorld flights arrived late? 9; joint frequency

A **relative frequency** is the ratio of the number of observations in a category to the total number of observations.

S.CP.4

Example 3 Determine Relative Frequencies

Convert the table from Example 1 to a table of relative frequencies.

Step 1 Divide the frequency reported in each cell by the total number of respondents, 160.

	Attending the Festival	Not Attending the Festival	Totals
Senior	$\frac{44}{160}$	$\frac{32}{160}$	$\frac{76}{160}$
Junior	$\frac{25}{160}$	$\frac{59}{160}$	$\frac{84}{160}$
Totals	$\frac{69}{160}$	$\frac{91}{160}$	$\frac{160}{160}$

Step 2 Write each fraction as a percent rounded to the nearest tenth.

	Attending the Festival	Not Attending the Festival	Totals
Senior	27.5%	20%	47.5%
Junior	15.6%	36.9%	52.5%
Totals	43.1%	56.9%	100%

Study Tip

MP Sense-Making After you convert to relative frequencies, you should still be able to add across rows and down columns to get the percents in the *Totals* cells. This is a good way to check that the percents are correct.

Guided Practice

3. Convert the table from Example 2 to a table of relative frequencies. See margin.

Example 2 Use Marginal and Joint Frequencies

AL For part **a** of the problem, why do you focus on the *RedJet* row? The problem asks for the number of RedJet flights that arrived on time, so only the data in the *RedJet* row is relevant.

OL What can you say about the number of on-time arrivals and late arrivals overall? There were an equal number of on-time arrivals and late arrivals overall.

BL What percent of the RedJet flights arrived on time? 38.9%

Need Another Example?

Deniqua collected data from a random sample of customers at two restaurants to find out if they paid by cash or credit card. The data are shown in the two-way frequency table. Answer each question and tell whether you are using a marginal frequency or joint frequency.

	Joe's Place	Donna's Diner	Totals
Cash	20	8	28
Credit Card	11	11	22
Totals	31	19	50

a. How many customers at Donna's Diner paid by credit card? 11; joint frequency

b. How many customers paid by cash? 28; marginal frequency

Example 3 Determine Relative Frequencies

AL How do you convert the ratios to a percent? Divide to write the ratio as a decimal, and then multiply by 100.

OL What do the relative frequencies tell you about the juniors who were surveyed? Sample answer: They are about twice as likely to not attend the festival as to attend it.

BL What does the value 36.9% in the table tell you? It says that 36.9% of the students surveyed were juniors who are not planning to attend the festival.

Need Another Example?

Convert the table from Additional Example 2 (above) to a table of relative frequencies.

	Joe's Place	Donna's Diner	Totals
Cash	40%	16%	56%
Credit Card	22%	22%	44%
Totals	62%	38%	100%

Variable A is considered to be independent of variable B if $P(A \text{ and } B) = P(A) \cdot P(B)$. In a two-way frequency table, you can test for independence of two variables by comparing the joint relative frequencies with the products of the corresponding marginal relative frequencies.

S.CP.4

Example 4 Decide Whether Events Are Independent

Use the relative frequency table from Example 3 to determine whether attendance at the festival is independent of class. Explain.

Make a new table. Calculate the expected joint frequencies assuming the two variables are independent. Multiply the marginal relative frequencies to find the joint relative frequencies.

Seniors attending:
$(47.5\%)(43.1\%) \approx 20.5\%$

Seniors not attending:
$(47.5\%)(56.9\%) \approx 27\%$

Juniors attending:
$(52.5\%)(43.1\%) \approx 22.6\%$

Juniors not attending: $(52.5\%)(56.9\%) \approx 29.9\%$

	Attending the Festival	Not Attending the Festival	Totals
Senior	20.5%	27%	47.5%
Junior	22.6%	29.9%	52.5%
Totals	43.1%	56.9%	100%

Compare these joint relative frequencies to actual joint relative frequencies in the two-way table in Example 3. Because the expected and actual joint relative frequencies are not the same, attendance at the festival is *not* independent of class.

Guided Practice

4. Use the relative frequency table you made in Guided Practice 3 to determine whether on-time arrivals are independent of airline. Explain.
No; the expected and actual joint relative frequencies are not the same.

2 Approximate Conditional Probabilities

Recall that the conditional probability of event A given that event B has occurred is given by the formula $P(A \mid B) = \frac{P(A \cap B)}{P(B)}$. In a two-way relative frequency table, $P(A \cap B)$ is a joint relative frequency and $P(B)$ is a marginal relative frequency.

S.CP.4, S.CP.6

Example 5 Find a Conditional Probability

Use the relative frequency table from Example 3 to find the probability that a surveyed student plans to attend the festival, given that he or she is a junior.

Use values from the *Junior* row of the table.

$P(\text{attending festival} \mid \text{junior})$

$= \frac{P(\text{attending and junior})}{P(\text{junior})}$

$\approx \frac{0.156}{0.525}$ or 29.7%

	Attending the Festival	Not Attending the Festival	Totals
Senior	27.5%	20%	47.5%
Junior	15.6%	36.9%	52.5%
Totals	43.1%	56.9%	100%

Study Tip
Structure In general, the word *and* corresponds to an intersection or a joint relative frequency. *P*(attending and junior) is found at the intersection of the *Attending* column and the *Junior* row.

Guided Practice

5. Find the probability that a surveyed student is a senior, given that he or she is not planning to attend the festival. 35.1%

Differentiated Instruction OL BL

IF students are successful working with two-way frequency tables and conditional probability,

THEN have small groups develop survey questions with two categories (such as *rides a skateboard* and *does not ride a skateboard*). Have students conduct surveys and organize data in a two-way frequency table. Then have them write conditional probability problems based on the table.

Additional Answer (Guided Practice)

3.

	On Time	Late	Totals
AirWorld	32.5%	22.5%	55%
Red Jet	17.5%	27.5%	45%
Totals	50%	50%	100%

Teaching Tip

Independent Events Remind students of the definition of independent events with which they are already familiar: Two events are independent if the outcome of one event does not affect the probability of the other.

Example 4 Decide Whether Events Are Independent

AL How do you multiply two percents? Convert them to decimals, multiply, then convert back to a percent.

OL How does this table compare to the one in Example 3? The marginal relative frequencies are the same, but the joint relative frequencies are different.

BL What is one conclusion you can make from this table aside from the fact that the variables are not independent? Sample answer: Juniors make up 52.5% of those surveyed, but they do not make up 52.5% of those attending the festival; they are less likely to attend the festival than might be expected.

Need Another Example?
Use the relative frequency table you made in Additional Example 3 to determine whether paying by cash or credit card is independent of the restaurant. Explain. No; the expected and actual joint relative frequencies are not the same.

2 Approximate Conditional Probabilities

Example 5 Find a Conditional Probability

AL Why do you use values from the *Junior* row of the table? The problem says it is given that the student is a junior.

OL Why do you divide 0.156 by 0.525 rather than dividing by 100%? You want to know the probability that a student plans to attend the festival only among the juniors, rather than among all students.

BL What is the probability that a student is a junior, given that he or she plans to attend the festival? 36.2%

Need Another Example?
Use the relative frequency table from Additional Example 3 to find the probability that a customer pays by cash, given that he or she eats at Joe's Place. 64.5%

Practice

Formative Assessment Use Exercises 1–12 to assess students' understanding of the concepts in the lesson.

The Practice and Problem Solving exercises assess the content taught in the lesson. The Preparing for Assessment page is meant to be used as preparation for end-of-course assessments.

Additional Answers

1.

	Breakfast	No Breakfast	Totals
Elementary	38	12	50
High School	22	28	50
Totals	60	40	100

2.

	Amusement Park	Aquarium	Totals
Girls	28	9	37
Boys	34	8	42
Totals	62	17	79

7.

	Car	No Car	Totals
Bus	6.7%	51.7%	58.3%
Train	13.3%	28.3%	41.7%
Totals	20%	80%	100%

13.

	At Least 7 Hours	Less Than 7 Hours	Totals
Doctors	40	35	75
Nurses	24	63	87
Totals	64	98	162

14.

	Photos	Painting	Totals
Film Club	22	9	31
Chess Club	9	9	18
Totals	31	18	49

Check Your Understanding

◯ = Step-by-Step Solutions begin on page R13.

Go Online! for a Self-Check Quiz

Example 1 S.CP.4

Make a two-way frequency table to organize the given data.

1. **MEALS** Students in elementary school and high school were surveyed about eating habits. Thirty-eight students in elementary school ate breakfast, and 12 skipped breakfast. Twenty-two students in high school ate breakfast, and 28 skipped breakfast. **See margin.**

2. **CLASS TRIPS** A random sample of high school seniors was given a survey to determine the location of their class trip. The two choices were an amusement park or an aquarium. The amusement park was the choice of 28 girls and 34 boys. The aquarium was the choice of 9 girls and 8 boys. **See margin.**

Example 2 S.CP.4

Mayumi surveyed a random sample of people who commute to work on a bus or on a train, and she asked them whether or not they own a car. The data are shown in the two-way frequency table. Answer each question and tell whether you are using a marginal frequency or joint frequency.

	Car	No Car	Totals
Bus	8	62	70
Train	16	34	50
Totals	24	96	120

3. How many commuters ride a train and own a car? **16; joint frequency**
4. How many people who commute on a train were surveyed? **50; marginal frequency**
5. How many car owners were surveyed? **24; marginal frequency**
6. How many car owners ride a bus? **8; joint frequency**

Example 3 S.CP.4

7. Convert the two-way frequency table of data about commuters to a table of relative frequencies. **See margin.**

Example 4 S.CP.4

8. Determine whether commuting to work on a bus or train is independent of owning a car. Explain. **No; the expected and actual joint relative frequencies are not the same.**

Example 5 S.CP.4, S.CP.6

Use the two-way frequency table of data about commuters to find each conditional probability.

9. the probability that a commuter rides a bus given that he or she owns a car **33.3%**
10. the probability that a commuter does not own a car given that he or she rides a train **68%**
11. the probability that a car owner rides a train **66.7%**
12. the probability that a train rider owns a car **32%**

Practice and Problem Solving

Extra Practice is on page R12.

Example 1 S.CP.4

Make a two-way frequency table to organize the given data.

13. **SLEEP HABITS** A group of doctors and nurses were surveyed about the number of hours of sleep they get each day. Forty doctors got at least 7 hours of sleep each day, and 35 doctors got less than 7 hours of sleep each day. Among the nurses, 24 got at least 7 hours of sleep each day and 63 got less than 7 hours of sleep each day. **See margin.**

14. **HOBBIES** A random sample of students in the film club and chess club were asked about whether they prefer to take photos or paint. Twenty-two students in the film club chose taking photos, and 9 chose painting. A total of 18 members of the chess club were surveyed, and the results were split evenly between taking photos and painting. **See margin.**

15. **COOKING** Alison surveyed 100 people at a cooking school and asked them whether they prefer to cook on a gas range or an electric range. Fifty-five men participated in the survey, and 21 of them chose a gas range. Of the women who participated, 19 chose an electric range. **See margin.**

Differentiated Homework Options

Levels	AL Basic	OL Core	BL Advanced
Exercises	13–25, 34–36, 38–44	13–25 odd, 26, 27–31 odd, 32–36, 38–44	31–38, (optional: 39–44)
2-Day Option	13–25 odd, 39–44	13–25	
	14–24 even, 34–36, 38	26–36, 38–44	

You can use ALEKS to provide additional remediation support with personalized instruction and practice.

Go Online! eBook

Interactive Student Guide
Use the *Interactive Student Guide* to deepen conceptual understanding.

- Two-Way Frequency Tables

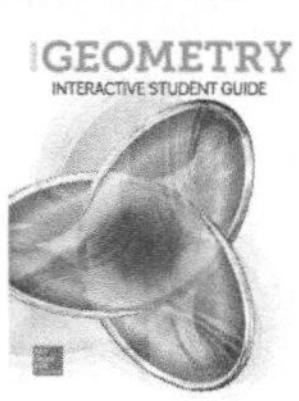

Example 2
S.CP.4

Russell surveyed members of his school's soccer team and softball team to find out whether they prefer to drink water or a sports drink while training. The data are shown in the two-way frequency table. Answer each question and tell whether you are using a marginal frequency or joint frequency.

	Water	Sports Drink	Totals
Soccer	36	24	60
Softball	54	36	90
Totals	90	60	150

16. How many soccer players prefer a sports drink? 24; joint frequency

17. How many members of the softball team were surveyed? 90; marginal frequency

18. How many team members who prefer water are soccer players? 36; joint frequency

19. How many softball players do not prefer a sports drink? 54; joint frequency

Example 3
S.CP.4

20. Convert the two-way frequency table of data about sports teams and beverages to a table of relative frequencies. See margin.

Example 4
S.CP.4

21. Determine whether a team member's beverage preference is independent of his or her team. Explain. Yes; the expected and actual joint relative frequencies are the same.

Example 5
S.CP.4,
S.CP.6

Use the two-way frequency table of data about sports teams and beverages to find each conditional probability.

22. the probability that a team member prefers water, given that he or she is on the soccer team 60%

23. the probability that a team member who prefers a sports drink is on the softball team 60%

24. the probability that a member of the soccer team prefers a sports drink 40%

25. the probability that a team member who prefers water is not on the soccer team 60%

B **26.** **FLOWERS** A florist surveyed a random sample of customers, by asking 20 men and 20 women whether they would rather receive one dozen roses or one dozen tulips. Of the women surveyed, 15 chose one dozen tulips.

a. What is the probability that a customer chose tulips given that she is a woman? 75%

b. What is the joint relative frequency of women who chose roses? 12.5%

c. Can you determine the conditional probability of a customer choosing one dozen roses, given that he is a man? If so, explain how to find the probability. If not, explain why not and describe any additional information you would need.

MP **REASONING** **The two-ways frequency tables show data from a school survey about preferred school colors. Copy and complete each table.**

27.

	Blue	Green	Totals
Boys	40	35	75
Girls	32	18	50
Totals	72	53	125

28.

	Blue	Green	Totals
Seniors	34	12	46
Juniors	36	43	79
Totals	70	55	125

29.

	Red	Yellow	Totals
Teachers	23	7	30
Students	18	33	51
Totals	41	40	81

30.

	Blue	Purple	Totals
Parents	41	44	85
Students	17	15	32
Totals	58	59	117

26c. No; there is not enough information; need to know the number of men in the sample who chose roses or tulips.

MP Teaching the Mathematical Practices

TOOLS Mathematically proficient students consider available tools, including paper and pencil, when solving a problem. Encourage students to think of two-way frequency tables as a tool for problem solving. Exercise 26 does not explicitly require students to make a two-way frequency table, but they will find that making such a table is a helpful first step.

Extra Practice

See page R12 for extra exercises for students who are approaching level or for on-level students who need additional reinforcement.

Levels of Complexity Chart

The levels of the exercises progress from 1 to 3, with Level 1 indicating the lowest level of complexity.

Exercises	13–25	26–30, 39–44	31–38
C Level 3			●
B Level 2		●	
Level 1	●		

Additional Answers

15.

	Gas	Electric	Totals
Men	21	34	55
Women	26	19	45
Totals	47	53	100

20.

	Water	Sports Drink	Totals
Soccer	24%	16%	40%
Softball	36%	24%	60%
Totals	60%	40%	100%

Assess

Ticket Out the Door Make copies of a two-way frequency table and distribute a copy to each student. As students leave the room, ask them to identify a joint frequency or a marginal frequency, or ask them to calculate one or more relative frequencies or conditional probabilities.

Additional Answers

31a.

	AP Classes	No AP Classes	Totals
Senior	40	60	100
Not Senior	110	190	300
Totals	150	250	400

31b.

	AP Classes	No AP Classes	Totals
Senior	10%	15%	25%
Not Senior	27.5%	47.5%	75%
Totals	37.5%	62.5%	100%

33a.

	Bring Lunch	Cafeteria	Go Out	Totals
Men	43	56	23	122
Women	46	52	30	128
Totals	89	108	53	250

34. Sample answer:

	Owns Bike	No Bike	Totals
Male	41	85	126
Female	179	115	294
Totals	220	200	420

44b.

	Crunchy	Smooth	Totals
Vegetarian	10	30	40
Nonvegetarian	15	45	60
Totals	25	75	100%

31d. Not taking advanced placement classes; the marginal relative frequency for *No AP Classes* is 62.5%, which is greater than the marginal relative frequency for *AP Classes.*

C 31. MP **REASONING** In a school with 400 students, 150 students are currently taking advanced placement (AP) classes, and 40 students are seniors taking advanced placement classes. There are 100 seniors in all.

a. Use the given information to create a two-way frequency table. Include the categories *Seniors* and *Not Seniors*, and *AP Classes* and *No AP Classes*. See margin.

b. Convert the table to a table of relative frequencies. See margin.

c. What is the probability that a randomly chosen student at the school is not a senior and not taking advanced placement classes? 47.5%

d. Is a randomly chosen student at the school more likely to be taking advanced placement classes or not taking advanced placement classes? How does your table of relative frequencies show this?

32. **ANIMAL SHELTERS** An employee at an animal shelter collected data on a random sample of cats and dogs as they were brought to the shelter. Copy and complete the table assuming that having fleas is independent of being a cat or a dog.

	Fleas	No Fleas	Totals
Cat	24	56	80
Dog	48	112	160
Totals	72	168	240

33. MP **SENSE-MAKING** Darius surveyed a random sample of 250 employees at the JQP Corporation to find out what the employees do for lunch. Of the 122 men that he surveyed, 43 bring their lunch, 56 eat at the company cafeteria, and the rest go out to get lunch. Of the women that he surveyed, 46 bring their lunch and 30 go out to get lunch.

a. Make a two-way frequency table to organize the data. See margin.

b. What is the probability that a randomly chosen employee is a man, given that the employee eats lunch at the company cafeteria? 51.9%

S.CP.4, S.CP.6

H.O.T. Problems Use Higher-Order Thinking Skills

34. **OPEN-ENDED** Make a two-way frequency table that shows the results of a survey in which 420 people were surveyed and 30% of the people surveyed were male. See margin.

35. **ERROR ANALYSIS** The two-way frequency table shows data about a random sample of apples at a supermarket. Kaci was asked to find the probability that a randomly chosen apple is red, given that it is organic. Her work is shown below. Explain her error and find the correct answer.

	Organic	Not Organic	Totals
Red	18%	42%	60%
Green	12%	28%	40%
Totals	30%	70%	100%

P(red \ Organic) = $\frac{0.18}{0.60}$

= 0.3

= 30%

35. Kaci found the probability that a randomly chosen apple is organic, given that it is red. The correct answer is $\frac{0.18}{0.30} = 60\%$.

36. MP **REASONING** A standard two-way frequency table, in which each variable has two categories, contains 9 cells with numerical values. What is the minimum number of these values that you need to know in order to fill in the rest of the table? 4

37. MP **CHALLENGE** In a two-way relative frequency table in which each variable has two categories, all of the joint relative frequencies are equal. What is the value of the joint relative frequencies? 25%

38. **WRITING IN MATH** Describe the steps for using a two-way frequency table to determine whether two variables are independent of each other.

38. Compare the joint relative frequencies with the products of the corresponding marginal relative frequencies. If these are equal, the variables are independent.

MP Standards for Mathematical Practice

Emphasis On	Exercises
1 Make sense of problems and persevere in solving them.	26, 32, 33
2 Reason abstractly and quantitatively.	27–30, 31, 36, 39, 41, 42, 44
6 Attend to precision.	34, 40
7 Look for and make use of structure.	37, 43

Preparing for Assessment

39. Out of 280 men and women who were surveyed, 95 preferred to watch football rather than soccer, and 40 of those surveyed were women who preferred football. Fifty of those surveyed were men who preferred soccer. What is the relative frequency of men who prefer football? MP 2, 4 S.CP.4 A

- ○ A 19.6%
- ○ B 33.9%
- ○ C 52.4%
- ○ D 57.9%

40. The two-way frequency table shows the results of a survey in which college math majors and history majors were asked whether they prefer to work on a laptop computer or a tablet. What is the probability that a student prefers to work on a tablet given that he or she is a math major? MP 4, 6 S.CP.4, S.CP.6 B

	Math Major	History Major	Totals
Laptop	69	21	90
Tablet	34	61	95
Totals	103	82	185

- ○ A 18.4%
- ○ B 33.0%
- ○ C 35.8%
- ○ D 67.0%

41. Jesse surveys a random sample of 91 adults and children to find out if they prefer a day at the beach or a day in the mountains. He surveys 45 adults and finds that 12 of them prefer a day in the mountains. Twenty-five children prefer a day at the beach. Jesse makes a two-way frequency table of this data. Which of the following values should appear in his table as marginal frequencies? MP 2, 4 S.CP.4 D, E, F

- ☐ A 12
- ☐ B 21
- ☐ C 25
- ☐ D 33
- ☐ E 46
- ☐ F 58

44c. Yes; the expected and actual joint relative frequencies are the same.

42. Kayley surveyed 80 friends to find out whether or not they have a pet dog and whether or not they have a pet cat. She found that 18 friends have a pet dog, 8 friends have a pet cat, and 6 friends have both. What is the probability P that a friend does not have a pet dog, given that he or she has a pet cat? MP 2, 4 S.CP.4, S.CP.6

$P =$ [25%]

43. The manager of a theater asked members of a ballet audience and members of a jazz concert audience whether they would like to learn about upcoming events by a text message or by an email. The variables in the table represent relative frequencies for these data. Which expression can the manager use to find the probability that someone is a member of the ballet audience, given that he or she prefers a text message? MP 4, 7 S.CP.4, S.CP.6 C

	Text	Email	Totals
Ballet	a	b	c
Jazz	d	e	f
Totals	g	h	j

- ○ A $\frac{a}{j}$
- ○ B $\frac{a}{c}$
- ○ C $\frac{a}{g}$
- ○ D $\frac{g}{j}$

44. MULTI-STEP Malik surveyed vegetarians and nonvegetarians about their peanut butter preferences. He recorded some of the data in the two-way frequency table shown. MP 2, 4 S.CP.4

	Crunchy	Smooth	Totals
Vegetarian	8	24	32
Nonvegetarian	12	36	48
Totals	20	60	80

a. Copy and complete the table.

b. Convert the table to a table of relative frequencies. 44b, c. See margin.

c. Determine whether someone's peanut butter preference is independent of whether or not he or she is a vegetarian. Explain.

Preparing for Assessment

Exercises 39–44 require students to use the skills they will need on assessments. Each exercise is dual-coded with content standards and mathematical practice standards.

Dual Coding

Items	Content Standards	MP Mathematical Practices
39	S.CP.4	2, 4
40	S.CP.4, S.CP.6	4, 6
41	S.CP.4	2, 4
42	S.CP.4, S.CP.6	2, 4
43	S.CP.4, S.CP.6	4, 7
44	S.CP.4	2, 4

Diagnose Student Errors

Survey student responses for each item. Class trends may indicate common errors and misconceptions.

39.

A	CORRECT
B	Found the relative frequency of men and women who preferred football
C	Found the probability that someone prefers football given that he is a man
D	Found the probability that someone is a man given that he prefers football

40.

A	Found the probability that a student is a math major and prefers a tablet
B	CORRECT
C	Found the probability that a student is a math major given that he or she prefers a tablet
D	Found the probability that a student prefers a laptop given that he or she is a math major

41.

A	Chose a joint frequency
B	Chose a joint frequency
C	Chose a joint frequency
D	CORRECT
E	CORRECT
F	CORRECT

43.

A	Found the probability that someone is a member of the ballet audience and prefers a text message
B	Found the probability that someone prefers a text message given that he or she is a member of the ballet audience
C	CORRECT
D	Found the probability that someone prefers a text message

Go Online!

Quizzes

Students can use *Self-Check Quizzes* to check their understanding of this lesson and have the results sent to you. You can also give *Quiz 5*, which covers the content in Lesson 12-8.

FOLDABLES Study Organizer

A completed Foldable for this chapter should include the Key Concepts related to probability and measurement.

Key Vocabulary ELL

The page reference after each word denotes where that term was first introduced. If students have difficulty answering questions 1–7, remind them that they can use these page references to refresh their memories about the vocabulary terms.

Have students work together to determine whether each sentence in the Vocabulary Check is true or false. Have students take turns saying each sentence aloud while the other student listens carefully.

You can use the detailed reports in ALEKS to automatically monitor students' progress and pinpoint remediation needs prior to the chapter test.

Additional Answers

8. Permutations would be more appropriate when order is important.
9. The intersection includes events contained in both sample spaces, and the union includes events in either sample space.

CHAPTER 12

Study Guide and Review

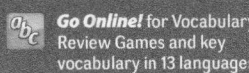

Go Online! for Vocabulary Review Games and key vocabulary in 13 languages

Study Guide

Key Concepts

Representing Sample Spaces (Lesson 12-1 and 12-2)

- The sample space of an experiment is the set of all possible outcomes. It can be determined by using an organized list, a table, or a tree diagram.
- The intersection of two sample spaces includes events contained in both sample spaces.
- The union of two sample spaces includes events contained in either sample space.

Probability with Permutations and Combinations (Lesson 12-3)

- A permutation of n objects taken r at a time is given by $_nP_r = \frac{n!}{(n-r)!}$. Order is important.
- A combination of n objects taken r at a time is given by $_nC_r = \frac{n!}{(n-r)!r!}$. Order is not important.

Geometric Probability (Lesson 12-4)

- If a region A contains a region B and a point E in region A is chosen at random, then the probability that point E is in region B is $\frac{\text{area of region } B}{\text{area of region } A}$.

Probabilities of Compound Events (Lessons 12-5 and 12-6)

- If event A does not affect the outcome of event B, then the events are independent and $P(A \text{ and } B) = P(A) \cdot P(B)$.
- If A and B are dependent, $P(A \text{ and } B) = P(A) \cdot P(B|A)$.
- If two events A and B cannot happen at the same time, they are mutually exclusive and $P(A \text{ or } B) = P(A) + P(B)$.
- If two events A and B are not mutually exclusive, then $P(A \text{ or } B) = P(A) + P(B) - P(A \text{ and } B)$.

Conditional Probability (Lesson 12-7)

- The conditional probability of A given B is $P(A|B) = \frac{P(A \text{ and } B)}{P(B)}$.

Two-Way Frequency Tables (Lesson 12-8)

- Compare expected and actual joint relative frequencies to determine if events are independent.

FOLDABLES Study Organizer

Use your Foldable to review the chapter. Working with a partner can be helpful. Ask for clarification of concepts as needed.

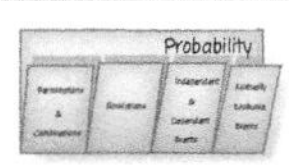

Key Vocabulary

- circular permutation (p. 875)
- combination (p. 876)
- compound events (p. 889)
- conditional probability (p. 891)
- dependent events (p. 889)
- factorial (p. 872)
- Fundamental Counting Principle (p. 861)
- geometric probability (p. 881)
- independent events (p. 889)
- intersection (p. 889)
- joint frequencies (p. 909)
- marginal frequencies (p. 909)
- mutually exclusive (p. 897)
- permutation (p. 872)
- probability tree (p. 891)
- relative frequencies (p. 909)
- sample space (p. 859)
- tree diagram (p. 859)
- two-way frequency table (p. 909)
- union (p. 889)

Vocabulary Check

State whether each sentence is *true* or *false*. If *false*, replace the underlined term to make a true sentence.

1. A <u>tree diagram</u> uses line segments to display possible outcomes. **true**
2. Tossing a coin and then tossing another coin is an example of <u>dependent</u> events. **false, independent**
3. <u>Geometric probability</u> involves a geometric measure such as length or area. **true**
4. $6! = 6 \cdot 5 \cdot 4 \cdot 3 \cdot 2 \cdot 1$ is an example of a <u>factorial</u>. **true**
5. The set of all possible outcomes is the <u>sample space</u>. **true**
6. Combining a coin toss and a roll of a die makes a <u>simple</u> event. **false, compound**
7. Drawing two socks out of a drawer without replacing them is an example of <u>mutually exclusive events</u>. **false, dependent events**

Concept Check

8. Explain when permutations would be more appropriate to use than combinations. **See margin.**
9. Explain the difference between the intersection and the union of two sample spaces. **See margin.**

Answering the Essential Question

Before answering the Essential Question, have students review their answers to the *Building on the Essential Question* exercises found throughout the chapter.

- How can geometry be used to make predictions? (p. 885)
- How can the probabilities of independent and dependent events be used to make predictions? (p. 892)

Go Online!

Vocabulary Review

Students can use the *Vocabulary Review Games* to check their understanding of the vocabulary terms in this chapter. Students should refer to the *Student-Built Glossary* they have created as they went through the chapter to review important terms. You can also give a *Vocabulary Test* over the content of this chapter.

Lesson-by-Lesson Review

12-1 Representing Sample Spaces

Preparation for S.CP.1

10. POPCORN A movie theater sells small (S), medium (M), and large (L) size popcorn with the choice of no butter (NB), butter (B), and extra butter (EB). Represent the sample space for popcorn orders by making an organized list, a table, and a tree diagram. See margin.

11. SHOES A pair of men's shoes comes in whole sizes 5 through 13 in navy, brown, or black. How many different pairs could be selected? 27

Example 1

Three coins are tossed. Represent the sample space for this experiment by making an organized list.

Pair each possible outcome from the first toss with the possible outcomes from the second toss and third toss.

HHH, HHT, HTH, HTT, THH, THT, TTH, TTT

12-2 Probability and Counting

S.CP.1

12. PETS The Venn diagram shows the results of a pet store survey to determine the pets customers owned.

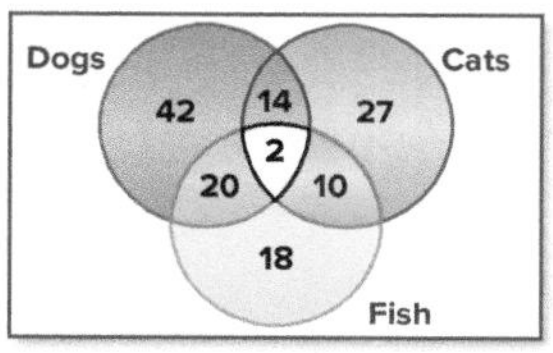

a. How many customers had only fish? 18

b. How many had only cats and dogs? 14

c. How many had dogs as well as fish? 22

Example 2

The Venn diagram shows the number of students who plan to join the soccer or baseball teams.

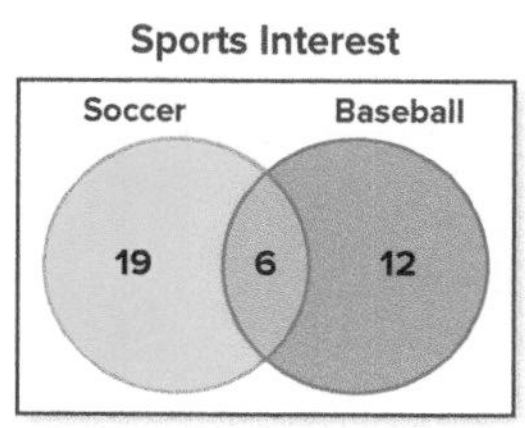

a. How many students plan on joining the soccer or baseball teams?

The students who plan on joining the soccer or baseball teams are represented by the union of the two sets. There are 19 + 6 + 12 = 37 students who plan on joining either team.

b. How many students plan on joining both the soccer and baseball teams?

The students who plan on joining both the soccer and baseball teams are represented by the intersection of the two sets. There are 6 students who plan on joining both teams.

12-3 Probability with Permutations and Combinations

S.CP.9

13. DINING Three boys and three girls go out to eat together. The restaurant only has round tables. Fred does not want any girl next to him and Gena does not want any boy next to her. How many arrangements are possible? 4

14. DANCE The dance committee consisted of 10 students. The committee will select three officers at random. What is the probability that Alice, David, and Carlene are selected? $\frac{1}{120}$

15. COMPETITION From 32 students, 4 are to be randomly chosen for an academic challenge team. In how many ways can this be done? 35,960

Example 3

For a party, Lucita needs to seat four people at a round table. How many combinations are possible?

Because there is no fixed reference point, this is a circular permutation.

$P_n = (n - 1)!$ Formula for circular permutation

$P_4 = (4 - 1)!$ $n = 4$

$= 3!$ or 6 Simplify.

So, there are 6 ways for Lucita to seat four people at a round table.

Lesson-by-Lesson Review

Intervention If the given examples are not sufficient to review the topics covered by the questions, remind students that the lesson references tell them where to review that topic in their textbook.

Two-Day Option Have students complete the Lesson-by-Lesson Review. Then you can use McGraw-Hill eAssessment to customize another review worksheet that practices all the objectives of this chapter or only the objectives on which your students need more help.

Additional Answer

10. S, NB; S, B; S, EB; M, NB; M, B; M, EB; L, NB; L, LB; L, EB

Outcomes	No Butter	Butter	Extra Butter
Small	S, NB	S, B	S, EB
Medium	M, NB	M, B	M, EB
Large	L, NB	L, B	L, EB

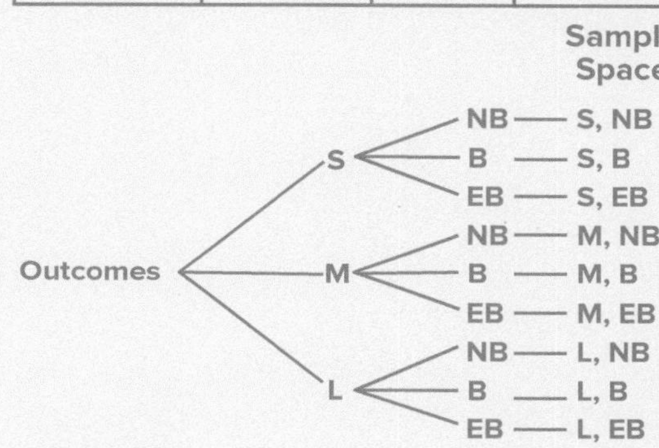

Go Online!

Anticipation Guide

Students should complete the *Chapter 12 Anticipation Guide* and discuss how their responses have changed now that they have completed Chapter 12.

Before the Test

Have students complete the Study Notebook Tie it Together activity to review topics and skills presented in the chapter.

CHAPTER 12

Study Guide and Review *Continued*

12-4 Geometric Probability S.MD.7

16. GAMES Measurements for a beanbag game are shown. What is the probability of each event?

a. P(hole) 2.45%

b. P(no hole) 97.5%

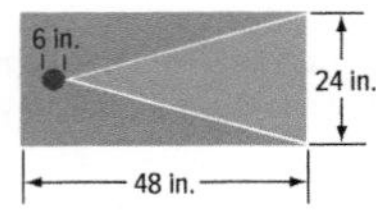

17. POOL Morgan, Phil, Callie, and Tyreese are sitting on the side of a pool in that order. Morgan is 2 feet from Phil. Phil is 4 feet from Callie. Callie is 3 feet from Tyreese. Oscar joins them.

a. Find the probability that Oscar sits between Morgan and Phil. $\frac{2}{9}$

b. Find the probability that Oscar sits between Phil and Tyreese. $\frac{7}{9}$

Example 4

A carnival game is shown.

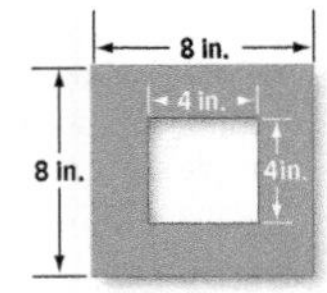

a. If Khianna threw 10 beanbags at the board, what is the probability that the beanbag went in the hole?

Area of hole $= 4 \cdot 4 = 16$

Area of board $= (8 \cdot 8) - 16 = 64 - 16$ or 48

$P(\text{hole}) = \frac{16}{64}$ or about 25%

b. What is the probability that the beanbag did not go in the hole?

$P(\text{no hole}) = \frac{48}{64}$ or about 75%

12-5 Probability and the Multiplication Rule S.CP.1, S.CP.2, S.CP.8, S.MD.7

18. MARBLES A box contains 3 white marbles and 4 black marbles. What is the probability of drawing 2 black marbles and 1 white marble in a row without replacing any marbles? $\frac{6}{35}$

19. CARDS Two cards are randomly chosen from a standard deck of cards with replacement. What is the probability of successfully drawing, in order, a three and then a queen? $\frac{1}{169}$

20. PIZZA A nationwide survey found that 72% of people in the United States like pizza. If 3 people are randomly selected, what is the probability that all three like pizza? 37%

Example 5

A bag contains 3 red, 2 white, and 6 blue marbles. What is the probability of drawing, in order, 1 red and 1 blue marble without replacement?

Because the marbles are not being replaced, the events are dependent events. Apply the multiplication rule for dependent events.

$P(\text{red, red, blue}) = P(\text{red}) \cdot P(\text{blue}|\text{red})$

$= \frac{3}{11} \cdot \frac{6}{10}$

$= \frac{9}{55}$ or about 16.4%

Go Online!

eAssessment

Customize and create multiple versions of chapter tests and answer keys that align to your standards. Tests can be delivered on paper or online.

12-6 Probability and the Addition Rule

S.CP.1, S.CP.7

21. **ROLLING CUBES** Two dot cubes are rolled. What is the probability that the sum of the numbers is 7 or 11? $\frac{2}{9}$

22. **CARDS** A card is drawn from a deck of cards. Find the probability of drawing a 10 or a diamond. $\frac{4}{13}$

23. **RAFFLE** A bag contains 40 raffle tickets numbered 1 through 40.

    a. What is the probability that a ticket chosen is an even number or less than 5? $\frac{11}{20}$

    b. What is the probability that a ticket chosen is greater than 30 or less than 10? $\frac{19}{40}$

Example 6

Two number cubes are rolled. What is the probability that the sum is 6 or doubles are rolled?

These are not mutually exclusive events because the sum of doubles can equal 6. Apply the addition rule for events that are not mutually exclusive.

$P(\text{sum is 6 or doubles}) = P(\text{sum is 6}) + P(\text{doubles}) - P(\text{sum is 6 and doubles})$

$= \frac{5}{36} + \frac{6}{36} - \frac{1}{36}$

$= \frac{5}{18}$ or about 27.8%

12-7 Conditional Probability

S.CP.3, S.CP.5

24. **CARDS** A card is drawn from a deck of cards. If the card is a king, find the probability that it is a red card. $\frac{1}{2}$ or 50%

25. **MARBLES** A blue marble is selected at random from a bag of 4 blue and 9 green marbles and not replaced. What is the probability that a second marble selected will be green? $\frac{3}{4}$ or 75%

26. **TRANSPORTATION** The probability that a city bus arrives late is 0.24. The probability that the bus arrives late and it is raining is 0.02. What is the probability that it is raining given that the bus arrives late? ≈ 0.083

27. What is the probability that the sum of two dice will be at least 9, given that the first die is 5? $\frac{1}{2}$

28. Eileen took two tests. The probability of her passing both tests is 0.6. The probability of her passing the first test is 0.8. What is the probability of her passing the second test given that she has passed the first test? 0.75

Example 7

A card is drawn from a deck of cards.

a. If the card is a diamond card, find the probability that it is an ace.

There are 13 cards in the sample space, and only one out of these cards is the ace. Therefore, $P(\text{ace}|\text{diamond}) = \frac{1}{13}$.

b. If the card is an ace, find the probability that it is a diamond card.

There are 4 cards in the sample space, and only one out of these cards is a diamond. Therefore, $P(\text{diamond}|\text{ace}) = \frac{1}{4}$.

Additional Answer

29c. Not independent; 46.8% of respondents are in the 18-24 age group and 34.2% of respondents were planning on voting, so one would expect 46.8% • 34.2% or about 16% of respondents in the 18-24 age group to plan on voting. The expected joint relative frequency of 16% and the actual joint relative frequency of 21.6% are not the same, so planning to vote is not independent of age group.

CHAPTER 12

Study Guide and Review *Continued*

12-8 Two-Way Frequency Tables

S.CP.4, S.CP.6

29. VOTING A political science group conducts a survey of 18–24-year-olds and 25–34-year-olds, asking whether or not they are planning on voting in the next election. The relative frequency table below shows the results.

Age Group	Planning to Vote	Not Planning to Vote	Totals
18–24	21.6%	25.2%	46.8%
25–34	12.6%	40.6%	53.2%
Totals	34.2%	65.8%	100%

a. Find the probability that a survey respondent is planning to vote, given that he or she is in the 18–24 age group. 46.2%

b. Find the probability that a survey respondent is in the 18–24 age group, given that he or she is planning to vote. 63.2%

c. Determine whether planning to vote is independent of age group. **See margin.**

30. The two-way table shows the gender and hair color of the students in a class.

	Brown Hair	Blonde Hair	Red Hair
Girl	3	6	3
Boy	5	4	1

a. Find the total number of students in the class. 22

b. A student is chosen at random from the class. Find the probability that the student

(i) is a girl $\frac{6}{11}$

(ii) has blonde hair $\frac{5}{11}$

(iii) is a girl or has red hair $\frac{13}{22}$

Example 8

An art teacher conducts a survey of the junior and senior classes to see whether students are interested in a photography seminar. The two-way relative frequency table below shows the results. Determine whether interest in the photography seminar is independent of class.

Class	Interested	Not Interested	Totals
Junior	41.2%	15.6%	56.8%
Senior	24.9%	18.3%	43.2%
Totals	66.1%	33.9%	100%

56.8% of respondents were juniors, and 66.1% of respondents were interested in the photography seminar, so one would expect 56.8% · 66.1% or about 37.5% of respondents to be interested juniors.

Because the expected and actual joint relative frequencies are not the same, interest in the photography seminar is not independent of class.

CHAPTER 12

Practice Test

Go Online! for another Chapter Test

Point X is chosen at random on $\overline{AE}$. Find the probability of each event. 1–2. See margin.

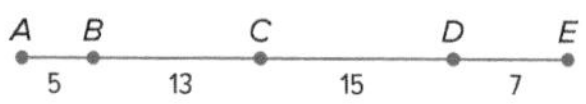

1. $P(X \text{ is on } \overline{AC})$
2. $P(X \text{ is on } \overline{CD})$
3. **BASEBALL** A baseball team fields 9 players. How many possible batting orders are there for the 9 players? 362,880
4. **TRAVEL** A traveling salesperson needs to visit four cities in her territory. How many distinct itineraries are there for visiting each city once? 24

Represent the sample space for each experiment by making an organized list, a table, and a tree diagram.

5. A box has 1 red ball, 1 green ball, and 1 blue ball. Two balls are drawn from the box one after the other, without replacement. See Ch. 12 Answer Appendix.
6. Shinsuke wants to adopt a pet and goes to his local humane society to find a dog or cat. While he is there, he decides to adopt two pets. See Ch. 12 Answer Appendix.
7. **ENGINEERING** An engineer is analyzing three factors that affect the quality of semiconductors: temperature, humidity, and material selection. There are 6 possible temperature settings, 4 possible humidity settings, and 6 choices of materials. How many combinations of settings are there? 144
8. A number cube is rolled. If the number rolled is less than 4, find the probability that it is a 1. $\frac{1}{3}$ or $33\frac{1}{3}\%$
9. **PAINTBALL** Cordell is shooting a paintball gun at the target. What is the probability that he will shoot the shaded region? 0.16 or $\frac{4}{25}$

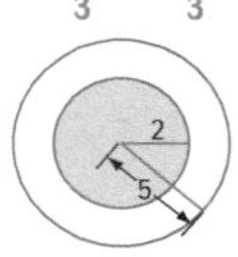

10. What is the probability that a phone number using the numbers 7, 7, 7, 2, 2, 2, and 6 will be 622-2777? $\frac{1}{140}$
11. **TICKETS** Fifteen people entered the drawing at the right. What is the probability that Jodi, Dan, and Pilar all won the tickets? $\frac{1}{455}$

Movie Ticket
Giveaway!
Enter for a chance to win 3 tickets!

Determine whether the events are *independent* or *dependent*. Then find the probability.

12. A deck of cards has 5 yellow, 5 pink, and 5 orange cards. Two cards are chosen from the deck with replacement. Find P(the first card is pink and the second card is pink). independent, $\frac{1}{9}$
13. There are 6 green, 2 red, 2 brown, 4 navy, and 2 purple marbles in a hat. Sadie picks 2 marbles from the hat without replacement. What is the probability that the first marble is brown and the second marble is not purple? dependent, $\frac{13}{120}$
14. **SPORTS** Refer to the Venn diagram that represents the sports students chose to play at South High School last year.

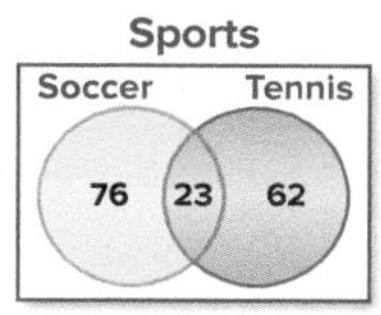

   a. Describe the sports that the students in the nonintersecting portion of the tennis region chose. These students only played tennis.
   b. How many students played soccer and tennis? 23

15. not mutually exclusive, $\frac{7}{13}$

Determine whether the events are *mutually exclusive* or *not mutually exclusive*. Then determine the probability.

15. A card is drawn from a deck of cards. Find the probability of drawing an ace or a red card.
16. Two number cubes are rolled. Find the probability of getting a sum of 10 or 12. mutually exclusive, $\frac{1}{9}$
17. If the chance of snow is 0.05, what is the probability that it will not snow? 95%
18. **HOUSING** A real estate agent conducts a survey of men and women on whether they own a home or rent. Of the 50 men in the survey, 12 responded that they own a home. Of the 75 women in the survey, 18 responded that they own a home. a–d. See Ch. 12 Answer Appendix.
   a. Create a two-way frequency table and relative frequency table.
   b. Find the probability that a survey respondent is a woman given that the respondent owns a home.
   c. Find the probability that a survey respondent owns a home given that the respondent is a woman.
   d. Determine whether owning a home is independent of gender. Explain your reasoning.

Go Online!

Chapter Tests

You can use premade leveled *Chapter Tests* to differentiate assessment for your students. Students can also take self-checking *Chapter Tests* to plan and prepare for chapter assessments.

Form	Type	Level
1	MC	AL
2A	MC	OL
2B	FR	OL
2C	FR	OL
3	FR	BL
Vocabulary Test		
Extended-Response Test		

MC = multiple-choice questions
FR = free-response questions

RtI Response to Intervention

Use the Intervention Planner to help you determine your Response to Intervention.

Intervention Planner

TIER 1 On Level OL

IF students miss 25% of the exercises or less,

THEN choose a resource:

SE Lessons 12-1 through 12-8

Go Online!

- Skills Practice
- Chapter Project
- Self-Check Quizzes

TIER 2 Strategic Intervention AL
Approaching grade level

IF students miss 50% of the exercises,

THEN choose a resource:

Quick Review Math Handbook

Go Online!

- Study Guide and Intervention
- Extra Examples
- Personal Tutors
- Homework Help

TIER 3 Intensive Intervention
2 or more grades below level

IF students miss 75% of the exercises,

THEN choose a resource:

Use *Math Triumphs, Geometry*

Go Online!

- Extra Examples
- Personal Tutors
- Homework Help
- Review Vocabulary

Additional Answer (Practice Test)

1. $\frac{9}{20}$, 0.45, or 45%
2. $\frac{3}{8}$, 0.375, or 37.5%

Launch

Objective Apply concepts and skills from this chapter in a real-world setting.

Teach

Ask:

- **Do you need a combination or a permutation in each situation?** Sample answer: A combination for the first part and a permutation for the second.
- **If a spinner is used, could a teacher end up getting more than his or her fair share? What would happen if they draw pieces of paper?** Sample answer: If they use a spinner, a teacher might get more than 4 weeks of bus duty, while others might get less. If they take turns drawing pieces of paper, each teacher should get exactly 4 weeks of bus duty.

The Performance Task focuses on the following content standards and standards for mathematical practice.

Dual Coding

Parts	Content Standards	MP Mathematical Practices
A	S.CP.9	1, 6
B	S.MD.6	1, 4
C	S.MD.7	3, 8
D	S.MD.6	1, 6
E	S.MD.6	1, 3, 6

Go Online! eBook

Interactive Student Guide

Refer to *Interactive Student Guide* for an additional Performance Task.

CHAPTER 12

Preparing for Assessment

Performance Task

Provide a clear solution to each part of the task. Be sure to show all of your work, include all relevant drawings, and justify your answers.

School Events A high school is planning its calendar for the upcoming school year.

Part A

The school is creating individual teacher and student schedules. There are seven periods in one school day.

1. **Sense-Making** If a teacher teaches a different class all seven periods, determine the number of different schedule combinations that are possible for one teacher.
2. If one student is taking seven different classes, including one math class and one science class, determine the number of schedule combinations that are possible if the school wants to make sure that the math and science classes are not back-to-back.

Part B

The school is also planning their cafeteria options. They plan to offer customizable sandwiches daily. Students can choose between whole wheat and white bread. Students can also choose between turkey, roast beef, and hummus. If the student would like cheese, he or she can choose between Swiss and cheddar.

3. **Tools** Draw a tree diagram to represent the sample space for sandwich orders.

Part C

The school is creating a schedule for which teachers have bus duty each morning. They are planning to split the number of weeks evenly among the teachers who do not have a first-period class. One person proposed they use a spinner to determine which teacher is on duty each of the weeks. Another person proposed they take turns drawing pieces of paper with the week number on them.

4. Explain, in terms of independent and dependent events, which method the school should use.

Part D

The school is thinking about offering a new elective on musical history, but the only place it would fit in the schedule is at the same time as band class. The school wants to see how many students would be interested in this new class, so they take a survey of the students who are eligible to take the elective and record the results in the two-way table to the right.

- Determine the probability that a randomly selected student is both interested in the class and does not take band. Round your answer to the nearest tenth, if necessary.
- If the school waits until next semester, they can offer the new course during a period different than band. Explain why you think the school should or should not wait.

Levels of Complexity Chart

Parts	Level 1	Level 2	Level 3
A		●	
B	●		
C		●	
D			●
E		●	

Part A

1. 5040
2. 3600

Test-Taking Strategy

Example

Read the problem. Identify what you need to know. Then use the information in the problem to solve it.

Of the students who speak a foreign language at Marie's school, 18 speak Spanish, 14 speak French, and 16 speak German. There are 8 students who only speak Spanish, 7 who speak only German, 3 who speak Spanish and French, 2 who speak French and German, and 4 who speak all three languages. If a student is selected at random, what is the probability that he or she speaks Spanish or German, but not French?

A $\frac{7}{12}$ B $\frac{9}{16}$ C $\frac{2}{5}$ D $\frac{5}{18}$

Step 1 **Does the problem contain data? What would be the best display to use to organize the data? Why?**
Yes. A Venn diagram would be best because there are some students who speak more than one language.

Step 2 **How can you make your display as organized as possible? What can you add to your display as you work?**
I can label the display with all of the information given in the problem. After I see what is missing, I'll make any calculations I can to fill in the missing information.

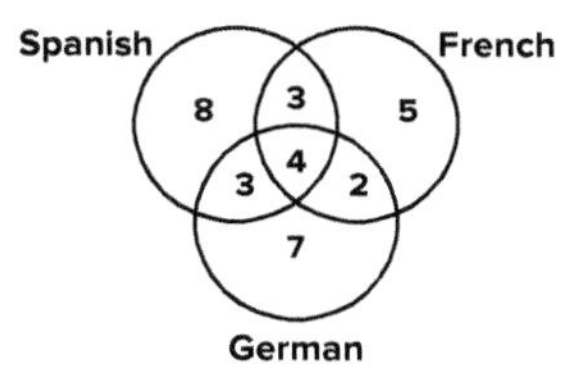

Step 3 **What is the correct answer?**
The correct answer is B.

Test-Taking Tip

Organizing Data Sometimes you may be given a set of data that you need to analyze in order to solve items on a standardized test. Use this section to practice organizing data and to help you solve problems.

Apply the Strategy

Read the problem. Identify what you need to know. Then use the information in the problem to solve it.

There are 10 sophomore, 8 junior, and 9 senior members on the student council. Each member is assigned to help plan one school activity during the year. There are 4 sophomores working on the field day and 6 working on the pep rally. Of the juniors, 2 are working on the field day and 5 are working on the school dance. There are 2 seniors working on the pep rally. If each activity has a total of 9 students helping to plan it, what is the probability that a randomly selected student council member is a junior or is working on the field day?

A $\frac{1}{5}$ B $\frac{4}{18}$ C $\frac{5}{9}$ D $\frac{2}{3}$

Answer the questions below.

a. Does the problem contain data? What would be the best display to use to organize the data? **yes; a two-way table**

b. How can you make your display as organized as possible? What can you add to your display as you work? **I'll fill in the data in the table. Then, once I see what's missing, I'll use the data to make the necessary calculations to fill in the missing data.**

c. What is the correct answer? **C**

Part B

3.

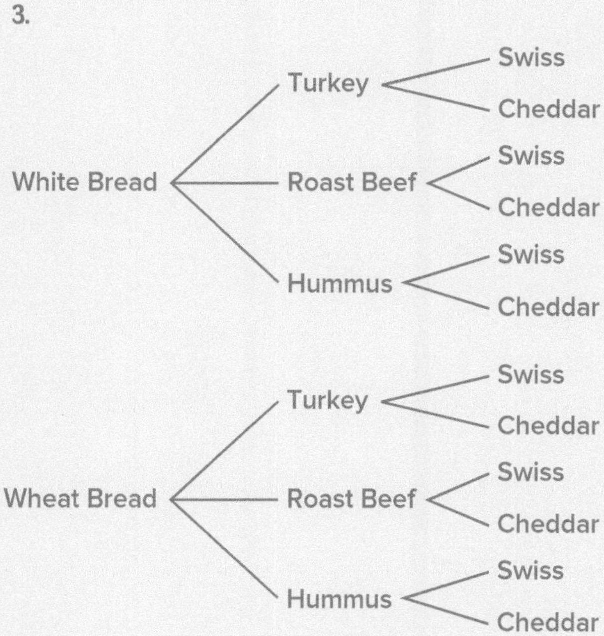

Part C

4. The school should have the teachers take turns drawing week numbers. If they use a spinner, the probability of one event is totally independent of another, which means a teacher could end up getting more than 4 weeks. But if they use the pieces of paper, the probability of an event is dependent on what was drawn before.

Part D

5. 18.5%

6. The school should wait, because less than a third of the students interested in the class would be able to take it this semester.

Test-Taking Strategy

Step 1 Read the problem. If the problem contains data, determine the best display to use to organize the data, such as a table, graph, Venn diagram, box-and-whisker plot, etc.

Step 2 Sketch the display, filling in any data from the problem. Evaluate what data is still needed to solve the problem and make any necessary calculations, filling in new data as you calculate it.

Step 3 Solve the problem. Check your solution if time permits.

Need Another Example?

Of the students in Robert's class who have pets, 13 have dogs, 9 have cats, and 7 have fish. There are 6 students who have a dog and a cat, 5 students who have a dog and fish, 3 students who have a cat and fish, and 2 students who have all three pets. If a student is chosen at random, what is the probability that he or she has a cat or a fish, but not a dog? B

A $\frac{1}{17}$

B $\frac{4}{17}$

C $\frac{6}{17}$

D $\frac{11}{17}$

a. Does the problem contain data? What would be the best display to use to organize the data? Yes; a Venn diagram

b. How can you make your display as organized as possible? What can you add to your display as you work? I'll fill in the data in the table. Then, once I see what's missing, I'll use the data to make the necessary calculations to fill in the missing data.

c. What is the correct answer? B

Go Online!

The most up-to-date resources available for your program can be found at connectED.mcgraw-hill.com.

Diagnose Student Errors

Survey student responses for each item. Class trends may indicate common errors and misconceptions.

5.	A	Used ${}_{10}P_3$ to find number of outcomes in sample space
	B	CORRECT
	C	Calculated the probability as $\frac{3}{{}_{10}C_3}$
	D	Calculated the probability as the ratio of the number of cards chosen to the number of cards in the deck
6.	A	Doubled the probability of choosing a red marble
	B	Found the probability of choosing red both times without replacement
	C	Found the probability of choosing blue both times
	D	CORRECT
9.	A	Reversed the point values for the regions
	B	Averaged the point values
	C	Only included the probability of landing in the blue region on the left
	D	CORRECT
10.	A	Calculated P(grass and Miller)
	B	Calculated P(Miller)
	C	CORRECT
	D	Calculated P(grass) + P(Miller)

Go Online!

Standardized Test Practice

Students can take self-checking tests in standardized format to plan and prepare for assessments.

CHAPTER 12

Preparing for Assessment

Cumulative Review

Read each question. Then fill in the correct answer on the answer document provided by your teacher or on a sheet of paper.

1. Kathleen goes on a business trip and takes with her 4 shirts, 3 pairs of slacks, 2 blazers, and 2 pairs of shoes. Assuming she wears one of each at a time, how many different combinations are possible?

48

2. A target for a penny toss consists of a square board that is 20 inches on each side with a painted square, as shown.

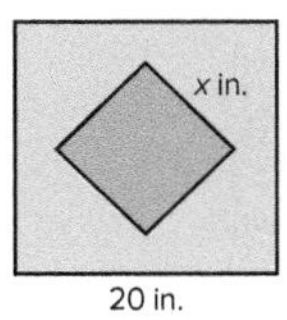

Assume pennies land on the board at random. What should be the value of x so that the probability of a penny landing in the painted square is 50%? Round to the nearest tenth. 14.1

3. Mark each of the following events as *independent* or *dependent*.

a. A child rolls a number cube three times. What is the probability that she will roll at 6 all three times? independent

b. A woman has a male baby. What is the probability that her second child will be female? independent

c. A man does a load of laundry containing 14 socks, 2 of which are black. He pulls out two socks, one after the other. What is the probability that both will be black? dependent

d. A woman accidentally places 4 used batteries with her 12 new batteries. She removes a battery, plugs it into her remote, and realizes it was a used battery. She puts it aside and removes another battery. What is the probability that it will be a used battery? dependent

4. Point D is located on segment AC below, such that the probability of a random point being on BD is $\frac{1}{3}$ and the probability of the point being on AD is $\frac{3}{4}$. Plot point D on the number line.

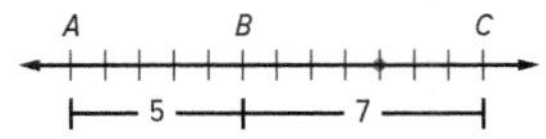

5. Megan has a deck of 10 cards that are numbered 0 through 9. She shuffles the deck and chooses 3 cards at random without replacement. What is the probability that she chooses the cards numbered 7, 8, and 9? B

○ A $\frac{1}{720}$

○ B $\frac{1}{120}$

○ C $\frac{1}{40}$

○ D $\frac{3}{10}$

Test-Taking Tip

Question 5 The order in which the cards are chosen does not matter, so you should use combinations rather than permutations to solve the problem.

6. A bag has b blue marbles and r red marbles. Enrique chooses a marble from the bag without looking, notes the color, and then replaces it. Then he chooses another marble from the bag. Which expression represents the probability that he chooses a red marble both times? D

○ A $\frac{2r}{b+r}$

○ B $\frac{r}{b+r} \cdot \frac{r-1}{b+r-1}$

○ C $\frac{b}{b+r} \cdot \frac{b}{b+r}$

○ D $\frac{r}{b+r} \cdot \frac{r}{b+r}$

7. A die is rolled and a coin is tossed. What is the probability that the die shows a 5 and the coin comes up heads? $\frac{1}{12}$

Go Online! for Standardized Test Practice

8. Determine whether each of the events below is *mutually* exclusive or not *mutually exclusive*. Explain your reasoning. Then find the probability of the event occurring. Round your answer to the nearest tenth.

   a. drawing a card from a standard deck and getting an ace or a spade **not mutually exclusive; A card can be both an ace and a spade; 30.8%.**

   b. drawing a card from a standard deck and getting a king or a queen **mutually exclusive; a card can't be a king and a queen; 15.4%.**

9. Serena throws a dart at the rectangular target, and it hits the target at random. Serena gets 20 points if the dart lands in the blue region and 35 points if the dart lands in the red region.

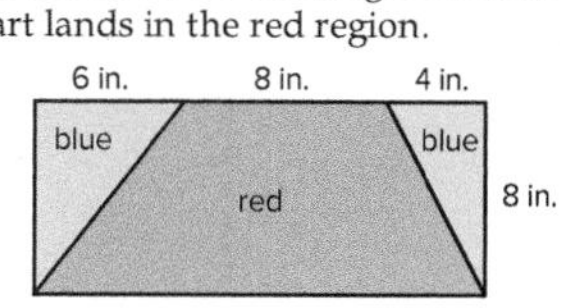

   What is the probability that the dart will land in the red region, given that it hits the target? **D**

   ◯ A 16.7% ◯ C 52.2%

   ◯ B 27.8% ◯ D 72.2%

10. A skydiver plans to land at a random point within a rectangular target. Part of the target is covered in grass, and part is covered in gravel. Also, a county line passes through the target, as shown.

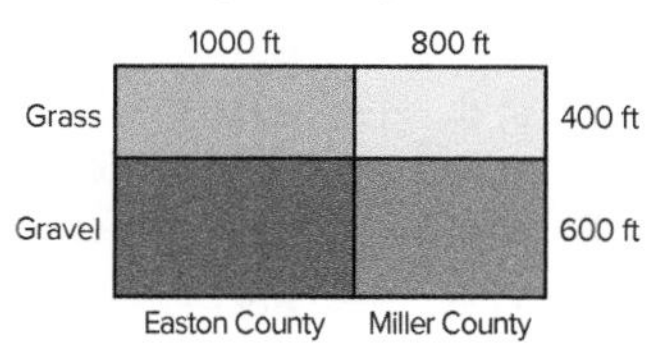

   Which is closest to the probability that the skydiver lands on grass or in Miller County? **C**

   ◯ A 18% ◯ C 67%

   ◯ B 44% ◯ D 84%

11. A news reporter is covering a state election. She asks 42 women whether they are supporting candidate A or B. Exactly three sevenths of the women say they support candidate A and the rest support candidate B. The reporter asks 35 men who they are supporting. Three fifths are supporting candidate A and the rest are supporting candidate B.

   Complete the two-way table below with the data given in the problem. Then answer the question that follows.

	Supports Candidate A	Supports Candidate B	Totals
Women	18	24	42
Men	21	14	35
Totals	39	38	77

   What is the probability that a surveyed respondent is male, given that the respondent supports candidate A? Round your answer to the nearest tenth.

   53.8%

12. Felicity asked 100 students how they came to school one day. Each student walked, came by bicycle, or came by car. 49 of the 100 students are girls. 10 of the girls came by car. 16 boys walked. 21 of the 41 students who came by bicycle are boys.

   a. Find the total number of students who walked to school. **35**

   b. What is the probability that a student walked to school, given that the student is a girl?

   $\frac{19}{49}$

Need Extra Help?

If you missed Question...	1	2	3	4	5	6	7	8	9	10	11	12
Go to Lesson...	12-1	12-4	12-5	12-4	12-3	12-4	12-4	12-6	12-4	12-4	12-8	12-8

Formative Assessment

You can use these pages to benchmark student progress.

Standardized Test Practice

Test Item Formats

In the Cumulative Assessment, students will encounter different formats for assessment questions to prepare them for standardized tests.

Question Type	Exercises
Multiple Choice	5, 6, 9, 10
Short Response	1, 2, 3, 4, 7, 11, 12
Extended Response	8

Answer Sheet Practice

Have students simulate taking a standardized test by recording their answers on a practice recording sheet.

LEARNSMART®

Use LearnSmart as part of your test-preparation plan to measure student topic retention. You can create a student assignment in LearnSmart to additional practice on these topics.

- Understand independence and conditional probability and use them to interpret data.
- Use the rules of probability to compute probabilities of compound events in a uniform probability model.
- Use probability to evaluate outcomes of decisions.

Go Online!

eAssessment

Customize and create multiple versions of chapter tests and answer keys that align to the standards. Tests can be delivered on paper or online.

Lesson 12-1 (Guided Practice)

1. H, 1; T, 1; H, 2; T, 2; H, 3; T, 3; H, 4; T, 4; H, 5; T, 5; H, 6; T, 6

Outcomes	1	2	3	4	5	6
Heads	H, 1	H, 2	H, 3	H, 4	H, 5	H, 6
Tails	T, 1	T, 2	T, 3	T, 4	T, 5	T, 6

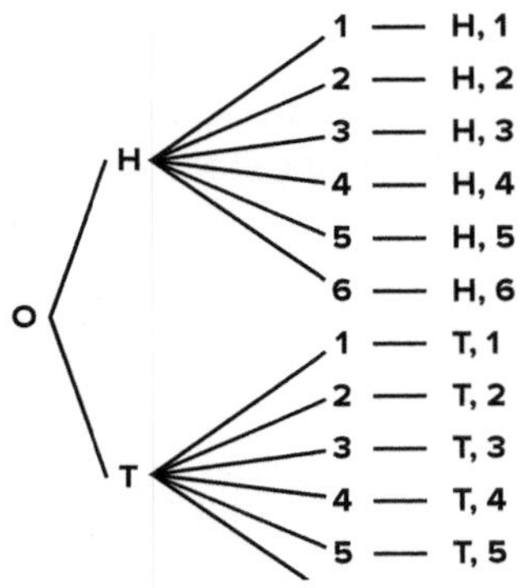

2.

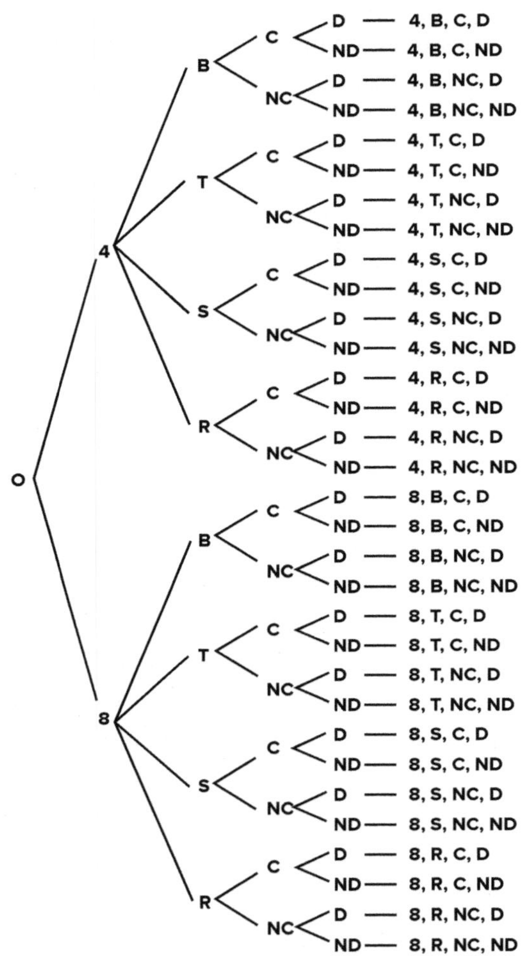

Lesson 12-1

2. J, J N, N
J, N N, J

Outcomes	Juice	Notebook
Juice	J, J	J, N
Notebook	N, J	N, N

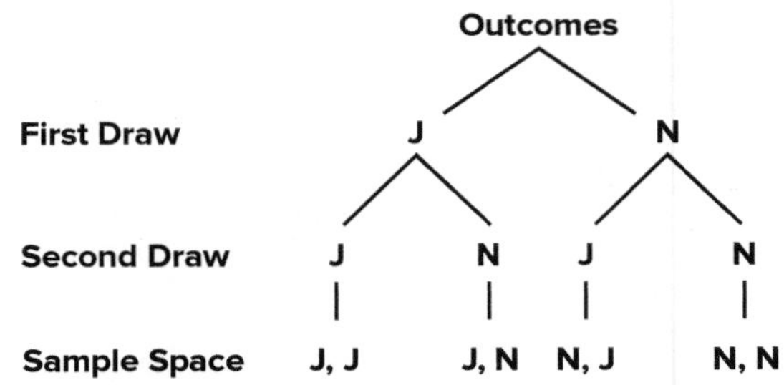

3.

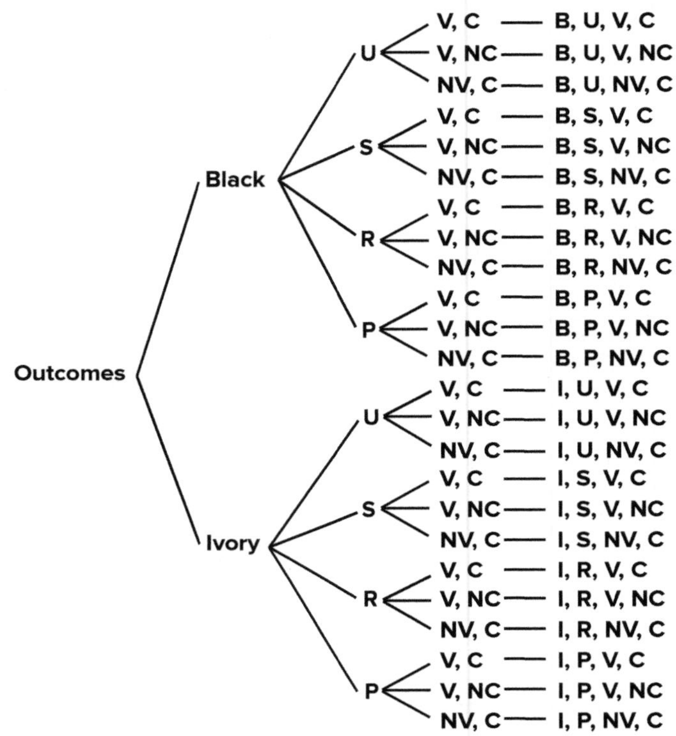

12. B = beans, P = pork, K = chicken, R = rice, NR = no rice, C = cheese, NC = no cheese, S = salsa, and NS = no salsa

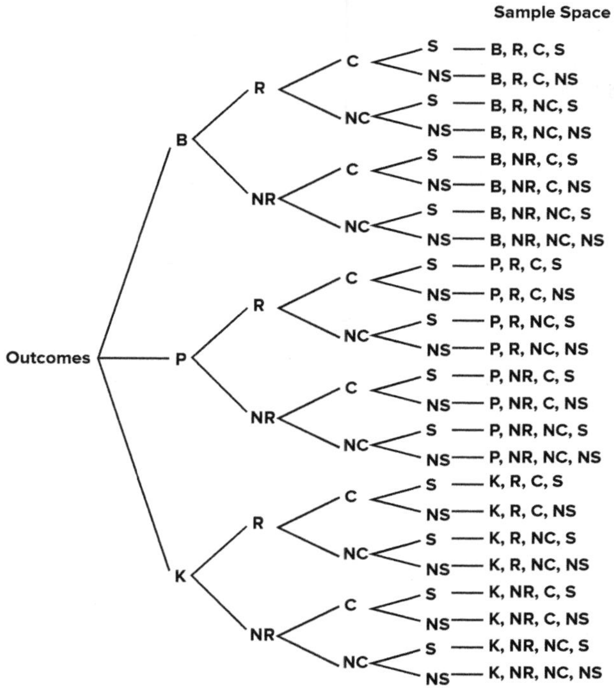

13. S = sedan, T = truck, V = van, L = leather, F = fabric, G = GPS, NG = no GPS, R = sunroof, NR = no sunroof

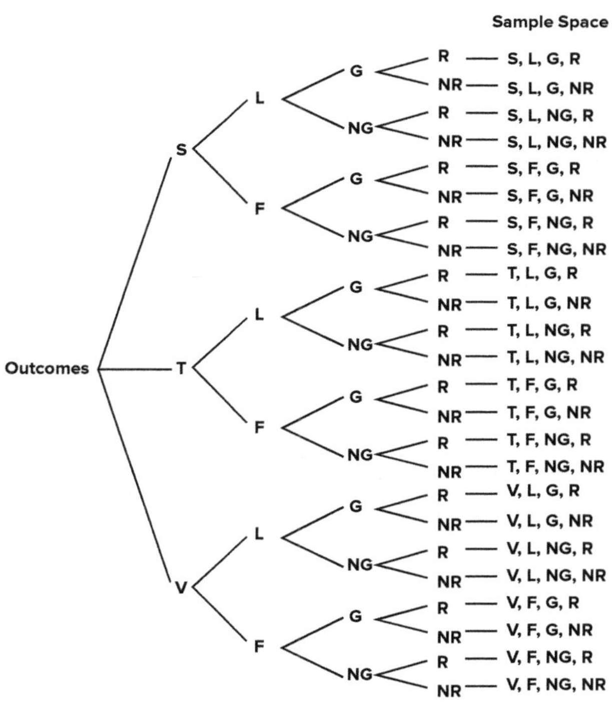

14. C = cake cone, G = sugar cone, W = waffle cone, S = strawberry, L = lime, P = peanuts, NP = no peanuts, K = sprinkles, NK = no sprinkles

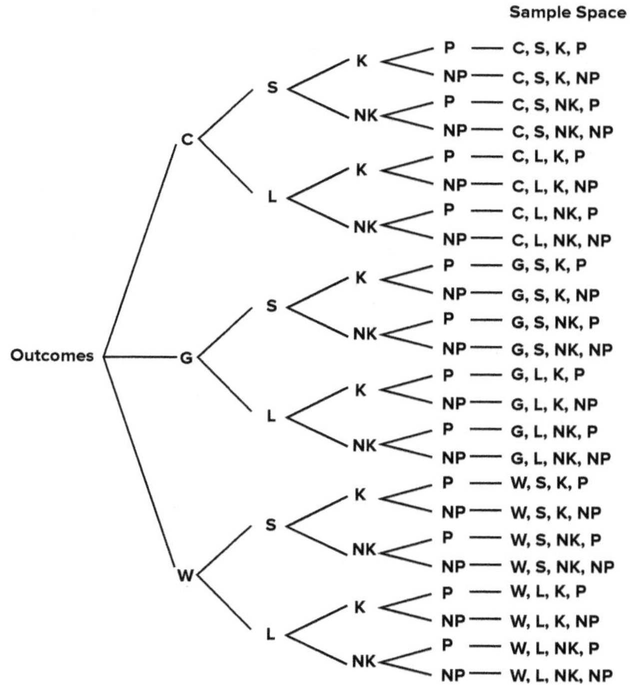

19. H = rhombus, P = parallelogram, R = rectangle, S = square, T = trapezoid; H, P; H, R; H, S; H, T; H, H; S, P; S, R; S, S; S, T; S, H

Outcomes	Rhombus	Square
parallelogram	H, P	S, P
rectangle	H, R	S, R
square	H, S	S, S
trapezoid	H, T	S, T
rhombus	H, H	S, H

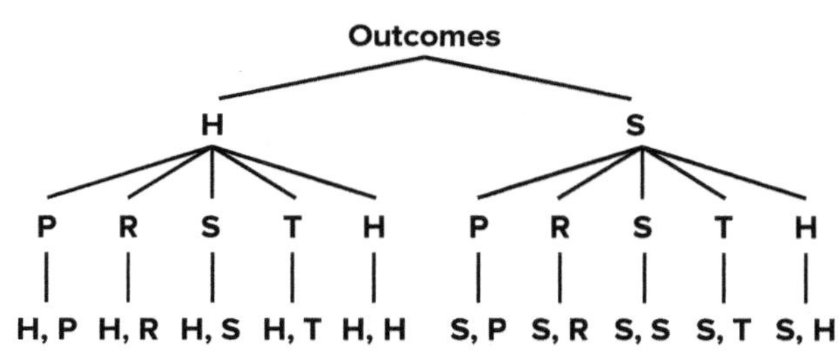

24a.

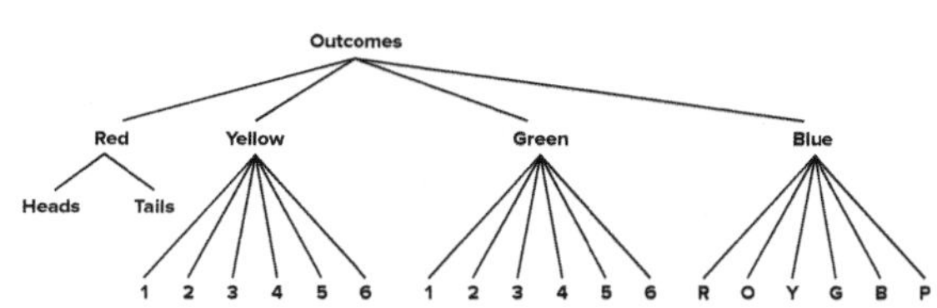

24b.

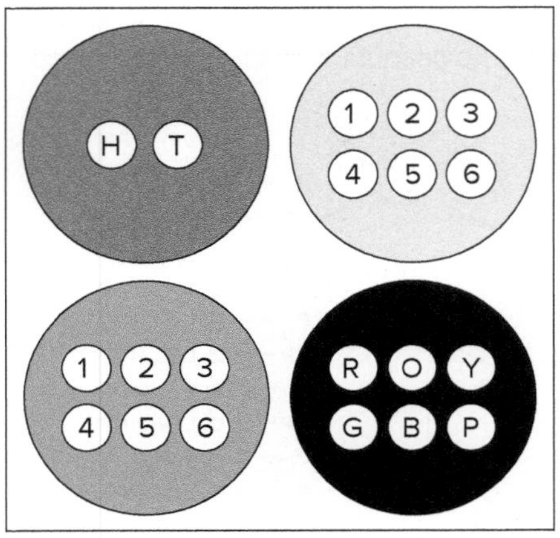

27. Sample answer: You can list the possible outcomes for one stage of an experiment in the columns and the possible outcomes for the other stage of the experiment in the rows. Because a table is two dimensional, it would be impossible to list the possible outcomes for three or more stages of an experiment. Therefore, tables can only be used to represent the sample space for a two-stage experiment.

28. Sample answer: Never; the sample space is the set of all possible outcomes. An outcome cannot fall outside the sample space. A failure occurs when the outcome is in the sample space, but is not a favorable outcome.

29. $P = n^k$; Sample answer: The total number of possible outcomes is the product of the number of outcomes for each of the stages 1 through k. Because there are k stages, you are multiplying n by itself k times which is n^k."

30. Sample answer: Drawing a tree diagram is necessary if you want to show the sample space for an experiment or if you want to know the number of times a certain outcome occurs. Using the Fundamental Counting Principle only tells you how many possible outcomes there are, so it is only useful when you want to know how many outcomes there are.

Lesson 12-4

34a. On a coordinate plane, graph $x = 7$ and shade between this line and the y-axis to represent the possible waiting times for the company A van. Graph $y = 12$ and shade between this line and the x-axis to represent the possible waiting times for the company B van. The area of the rectangle formed by the intersection is 84 units². Then graph $x = 5$ and $y = 5$ and shade the region bounded by these lines and the axes to represent the possible waiting times of 5 minutes or less for both vans. The area of the square is 25 square units. So the geometric probability is $\frac{25}{84}$ or about 30%.

34b. On a coordinate plane, graph the lines $x = 7$ and $y = 12$ and shade as before. The area of this rectangle is 84 units². Then graph $x = 7$ and $y = 5$. Shade the region bounded by the lines $y = 5$, $x = 7$, and the axes to represent the possible waiting times of 5 minutes or less for the company A van. The area of this rectangle is 35 units². Shade the region bounded by the lines $x = 5$, $y = 12$, and the axes to represent the possible waiting times of 5 minutes or less for the company B van. The area of this rectangle is 60 units². In each of these rectangles, the waiting time of 5 minutes or less for both vans has been counted twice. So the geometric probability is $\frac{60}{84} + \frac{35}{84} - \frac{25}{84} = \frac{70}{84}$, or about 83%.

34c. Sample answer: Because the chance of Meleah waiting 5 minutes or less to see the vans from both company A and B is only 30%, Meleah should take the van from company B.

Mid-Chapter Quiz

3. R, S; R, L; B, S; B, L; Y, S; Y, L; G, S; G, L; P, S; P, L; O, S; O, L

Outcomes	Red	Blue	Yellow	Green	Pink	Orange
Short-sleeved	R, S	B, S	Y, S	G, S	P, S	O, S
Long-sleeved	R, L	B, L	Y, L	G, L	P, L	O, L

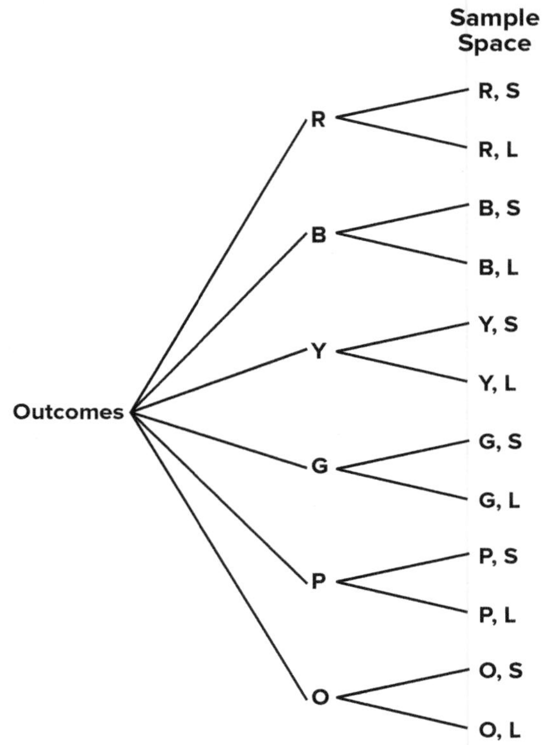

Lesson 12-5 (Guided Practice)

1A. Independent; because the first card is replaced, its selection in no way affects the outcome of the second card's selection.

1B. Dependent; because the first shirt is not put back, the sample space is reduced by one shirt choice.

5. No; $P(S \text{ and } S) = \frac{3}{6} \times \frac{2}{5} = \frac{6}{30}$ or $\frac{1}{5}$ or 20%, which is less than 25%.

Lesson 12-5

3. The events are not independent. The sample space has 6 equally likely outcomes: {JPR, JRP, PJR, PRJ, RJP, RPJ}. So $P(\text{J 1st and R 2nd}) = \frac{1}{6}$, $P(\text{J 1st}) = \frac{1}{3}$, and $P(\text{R 2nd}) = \frac{1}{3}$, but $\frac{1}{3} \times \frac{1}{3} \neq \frac{1}{6}$.

4. The events are independent. The sample space has 25 equally likely outcomes: {(1, 1), (1, 2), (1, 3), (1, 4), (1, 5), (2, 1), (2, 2), (2, 3), (2, 4), (2, 5), (3, 1), (3, 2), (3, 3), (3, 4), (3, 5), (4, 1), (4, 2), (4, 3), (4, 4), (4, 5), (5, 1), (5, 2), (5, 3), (5, 4), (5, 5)}. So $P(\text{odd and even}) = \frac{6}{25}$, $P(\text{odd}) = \frac{3}{5}$, $P(\text{even}) = \frac{2}{5}$, and $\frac{3}{5} \times \frac{2}{5} = \frac{6}{25}$.

7. Maurice should select two blue cards. Let R represent selecting a wild card from the red deck and B represent selecting a wild card from the blue deck. Then $P(R \text{ and } R) = \frac{3}{12} \times \frac{2}{11} = \frac{1}{22} \approx 4.5\%$;
$P(B \text{ and } B) = \frac{6}{20} \times \frac{5}{19} = \frac{3}{38} \approx 7.9\%$; and
$P(B \text{ and } R) = \frac{3}{12} \times \frac{6}{20} = \frac{3}{40} = 7.5\%$.

12. The events are independent. The sample space has 20 equally likely outcomes: {A1, A2, A3, A4, B1, B2, B3, B4, C1, C2, C3, C4, D1, D2, D3, D4, E1, E2, E3, E4}. So $P(\text{C2}) = \frac{1}{20}$, $P(\text{C}) = \frac{1}{5}$, $P(2) = \frac{1}{4}$, and $\frac{1}{5} \times \frac{1}{4} = \frac{1}{20}$.

13. The events are not independent. The sample space has 3 equally likely outcomes: {BP, BC, PC}. So $P(\text{PC}) = \frac{1}{3}$, $P(\text{P}) = \frac{1}{3}$, and $P(\text{C}) = \frac{1}{3}$, but $\frac{1}{3} \times \frac{1}{3} \neq \frac{1}{3}$.

35. Sample answer: The results of two coin flips represent a pair of independent events. Regardless of the outcome of the first flip, the probability of getting heads or tails on the second flip does not change. Drawing two colored marbles out of a bag without replacing the first marble represents a pair of dependent events. Based on the color of the first marble, the probability that the second marble will be a specific color will change.

36. In order for the events to be independent, the probability that a person smokes and has a parent who smokes must be equal to the product of the probability that a person smokes and the probability that a person has a parent who smokes.

42. No; let S represent a duck with a star. $P(S \text{ and } S) = \frac{20}{50} \times \frac{19}{49} = \frac{380}{2450}$ or $\frac{38}{245}$ or about 16%, which is less than 20%.

43a. Sample answer: {(1, 1), (1, 2), (1, 3), (1, 4), (1, 5), (1, 6), (2, 1), (2, 2), (2, 3), (2, 4), (2, 5), (2, 6), (3, 1), (3, 2), (3, 3), (3, 4), (3, 5), (3, 6), (4, 1), (4, 2), (4, 3), (4, 4), (4, 5), (4, 6), (5, 1), (5, 2), (5, 3), (5, 4), (5, 5), (5, 6), (6, 1), (6, 2), (6, 3), (6, 4), (6, 5), (6, 6)}

43c. $P(> 4 \text{ and } > 4) = \frac{1}{9}$; $P(> 4) = \frac{1}{3}$; $P(> 4) = \frac{1}{3}$; $\frac{1}{3} \times \frac{1}{3} = \frac{1}{9}$

Lesson 12-7

13. $P(A \text{ and } B) = P(A) \cdot P(B|A)$ Formula for $P(A \text{ and } B)$

$\frac{P(A \text{ and } B)}{P(A)} = P(B|A)$ Divide each side by $P(A)$.

14a.

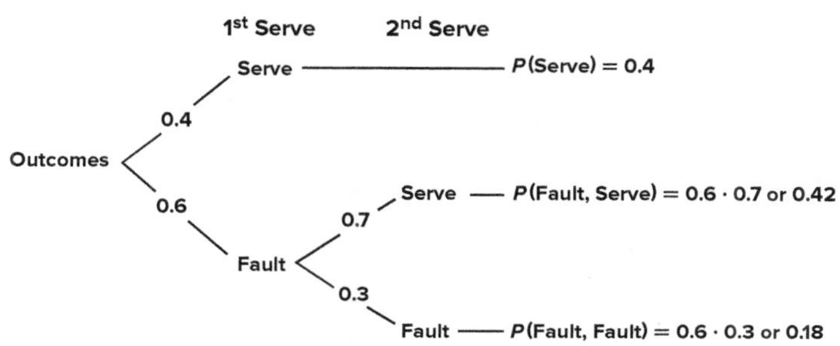

25. 9; Sample answer: The probability of drawing object A is $\frac{1}{n}$, and the probability of drawing object B when object A is not replaced is $\frac{1}{n-1}$. Since we know that the probability is about 1.4%, $\frac{1}{n} \cdot \frac{1}{n-1} \approx \frac{1.4}{100}$. Solve this equation to determine that n is 9.

Lesson 12-8 (Guided Practice)

1.

	Prefer Dogs	Prefer Cats	Totals
Women	18	6	24
Men	17	7	26
Totals	37	13	50

Practice Test

5. R, G; R, B; G, R; G, B; B, R; B, G;

Outcomes	Red	Green	Blue
Red		R, G	R, B
Green	G, R		G, B
Blue	B, R	B, G	

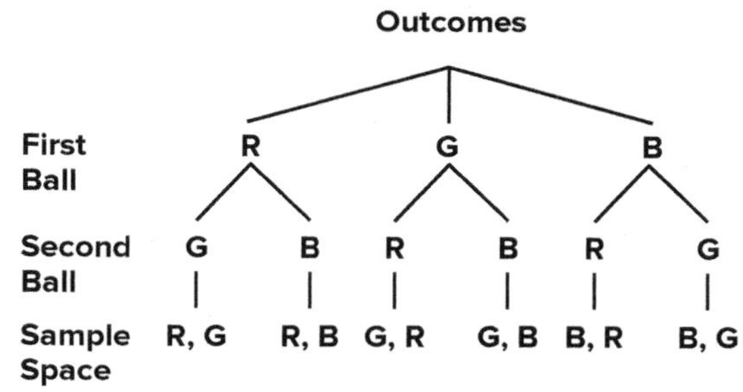

6. D, D; D, C; C, D; C, C;

Outcome	Dog	Cat
Dog	D, D	D, C
Cat	C, D	C, C

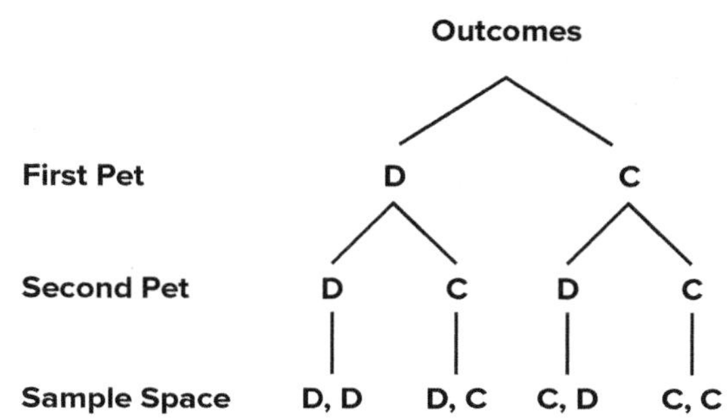

18a.

Gender	Own	Rent	Totals
Men	12	38	50
Women	18	57	75
Totals	30	90	125

Gender	Own	Rent	Totals
Men	9.6%	30.4%	40.0%
Women	14.4%	45.6%	60.0%
Totals	24.0%	76.0%	100%

18b. 60%

18c. 24%

18d. Owning a home is independent of gender; 40% of respondents are men and 24% of respondents own a home, so one would expect 40% · 24% or about 9.6% of respondents to be men and own a home. Because the expected and actual joint relative frequencies are the same, owning a home is independent of gender.

Student Handbook

This **Student Handbook** can help you answer these questions.

What if I Need More Practice?

Extra Practice **R1**

The **Extra Practice** section provides additional problems for each lesson so you have ample opportunity to practice new skills.

See Teacher Edition Volume 1 for Chapters 1–6; see Volume 2 for Chapters 7–12.

What if I Need to Check a Homework Answer?

Selected Answers and Solutions **R13**

The answers to odd-numbered problems are included in **Selected Answers and Solutions**.

See Teacher Edition Volume 1 for Chapters 1–6; see Volume 2 for Chapters 7–12.

What if I Forget a Vocabulary Word?

Glossary/Glosario **R111**

The **English-Spanish Glossary** provides definitions and page numbers of important or difficult words used throughout the textbook.

What if I Need to Find Something Quickly?

Index **R140**

The **Index** alphabetically lists the subjects covered throughout the entire textbook and the pages on which each subject can be found.

What if I Forget a Formula?

Formulas and Measures, Symbols and Properties **Inside Back Cover**

Inside the back cover of your math book is a list of **Formulas and Symbols** that are used in the book.

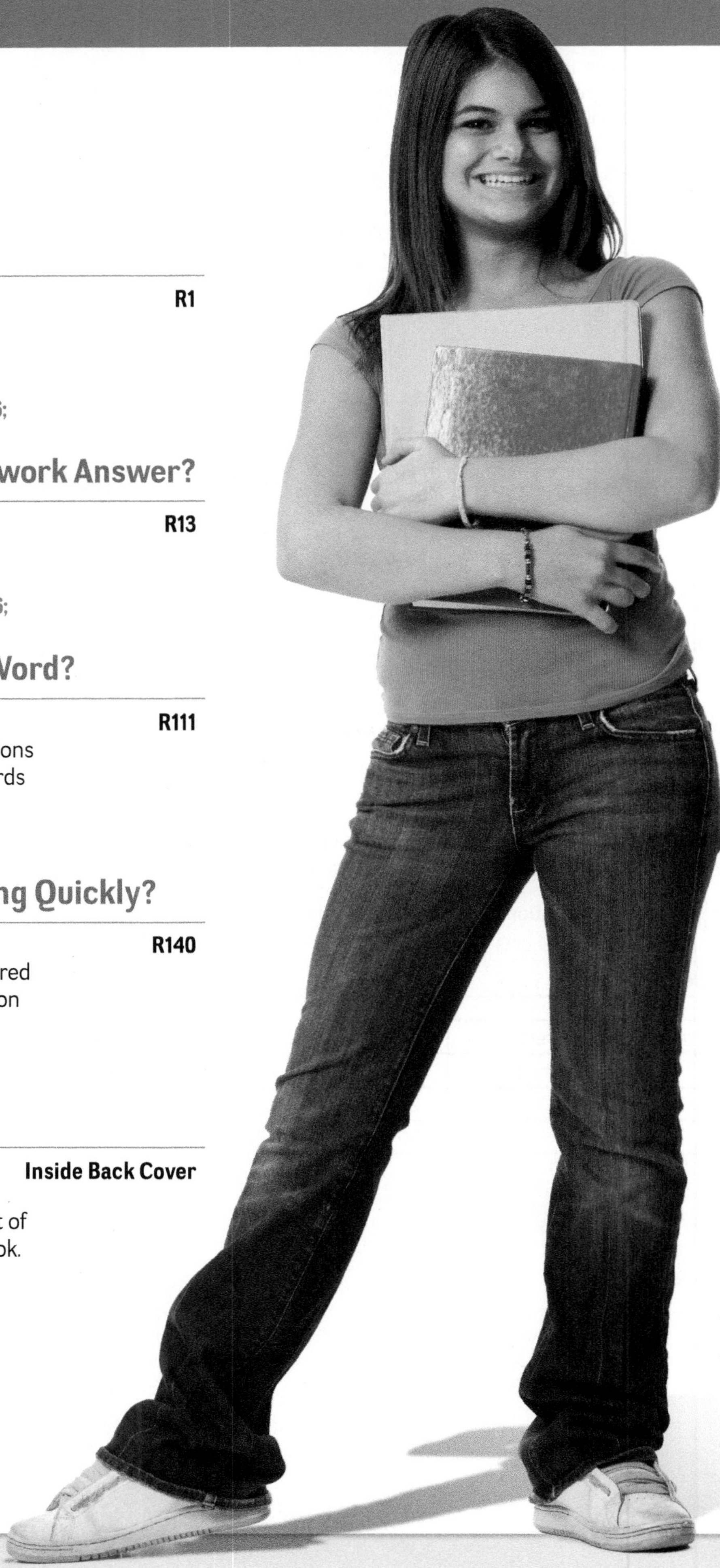

rubberball/Getty Images

CHAPTER 7 Similarity

1. **NATURE** The diameter of a snowflake is 2 millimeters. If the diameter appears to be 3 centimeters when viewed under a microscope, what magnification setting (scale factor) was used? (Lesson 7-1) **15**

2–3. See Extra Practice Answer Appendix.

Graph the image of each polygon with the given vertices after a dilation centered at the origin with the given scale factor. (Lesson 7-1)

2. $A(-5, -4)$, $B(-2, -3)$, $C(-1, -6)$, $D(-4, -8)$; $k = \frac{1}{2}$

3. $X(2, 4)$, $Y(4, 0)$, $Z(5, 5)$; $k = 1.5$

Determine whether each pair of figures is similar. If so, write the similarity statement and scale factor. If not, explain your reasoning. (Lesson 7-2)

4.

5.

4–5. See Extra Practice Answer Appendix.

Each pair of polygons is similar. Find the value of x. (Lesson 7-3) **6. 5** **7. 8.8**

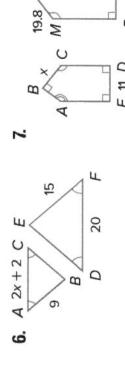

6.

7.

8. **FOOSBALL** Jason wants to determine if his foosball table is similar to his school's soccer field. Both the field and the table are rectangular. The dimensions of the table are 30 inches by $55\frac{1}{2}$ inches, and the dimensions of the field are 60 yards by 110 yards. Are the table and the field similar? Explain. (Lesson 7-2)
See Extra Practice Answer Appendix.

9. **HEIGHT** When Rachel stands next to her cousin, Rachel's shadow is 2 feet long and her cousin's shadow is 1 foot long. If Rachel is 5 feet 6 inches tall, how tall is her cousin? (Lesson 7-3)
2 ft 9 in.

Determine whether the triangles are similar. If so, write a similarity statement. Explain your reasoning. (Lessons 7-3 and 7-4)
10–13. See Extra Practice Answer Appendix.

10. 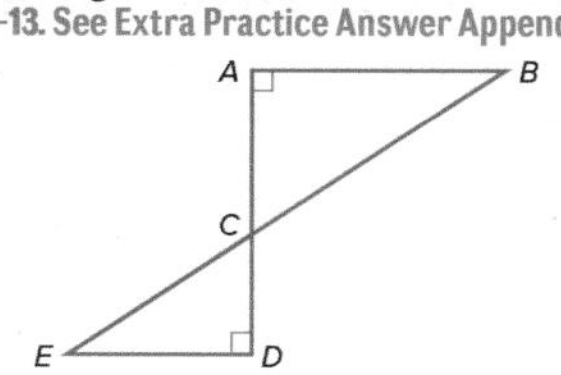

11. 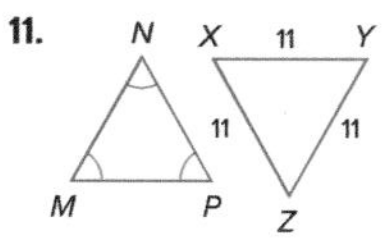

12. 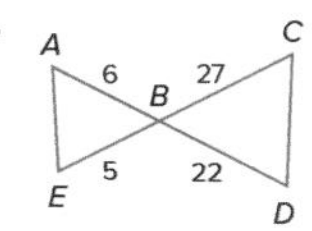

13. 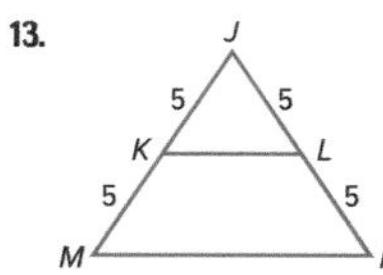

Determine whether the polygons with the given vertices are similar. Explain. (Lesson 7-4)

14. $A(0, -2)$, $B(-1, 3)$, $C(3, -2)$; $X(0, -6)$, $Y(-3, 9)$, $Z(9, -6)$

15. $D(-6, 6)$, $E(6, 2)$, $F(-2, -4)$; $M(-3, 3)$, $N(3, 1)$, $P(-1, -2)$

14–15. See Extra Practice Answer Appendix.

Refer to the figure shown. (Lesson 7-5)

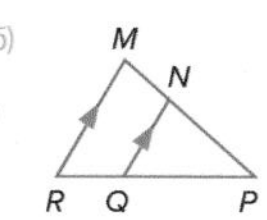

16. If $PN = 4$, $NM = 1$, and $PQ = 5$, find PR. **6.25**

17. If $PR = 13$, $PQ = 9$, and $NM = 3$, find PN. **6.75**

$\overline{DE}$, $\overline{EF}$, and $\overline{FD}$ are midsegments of $\triangle ABC$. Find the value of x. (Lesson 7-5)

18. 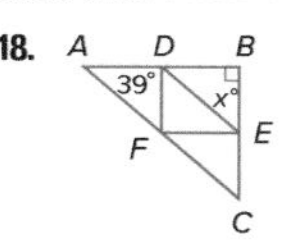

51

19. 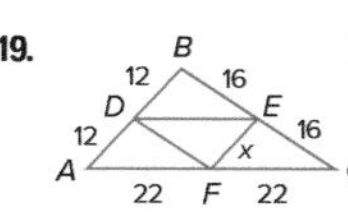

12

Find x. (Lesson 7-6)

20. 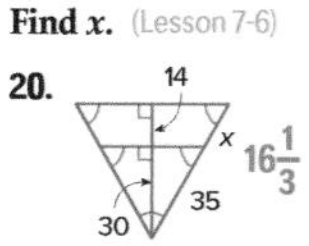

$16\frac{1}{3}$

21. 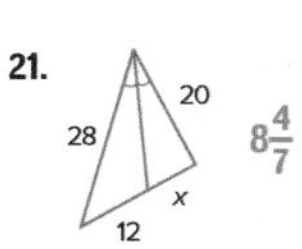

$8\frac{4}{7}$

Extra Practice

Extra Practice

connectED.mcgraw-hill.com R7

CHAPTER 8 Right Triangles and Trigonometry

Find the geometric mean between each pair of numbers. (Lesson 8-1)

1. 7 and 12 $2\sqrt{21}$
2. 8 and 36 $12\sqrt{2}$

3. $x = 9\sqrt{5} \approx 20.1$, $y = 18\sqrt{5} \approx 40.2$, $z = 18$

Find *x*, *y*, and *z*. (Lesson 8-1)

3. 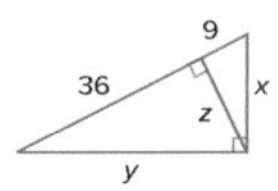

4. 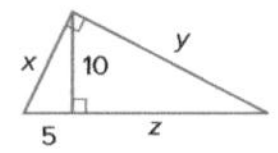

4. $x = 5\sqrt{5} \approx 11.2$, $y = 10\sqrt{5} \approx 22.4$, $z = 20$

Find *x*. (Lesson 8-2)

5. 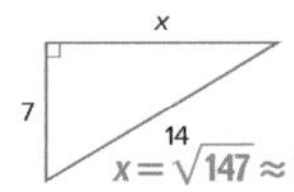

$x = \sqrt{147} \approx 12.1$

6. 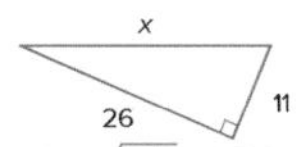

$x = \sqrt{797} \approx 28.2$

Determine whether each set of numbers can be the measures of the sides of a triangle. If so, classify the triangle as *acute*, *obtuse*, or *right*. Justify your answer. (Lesson 8-2)

7. 24, 32, 41
8. 17.5, 60, 62.5

7–8. See Extra Practice Answer Appendix.

Find *x*. (Lesson 8-3)

9. 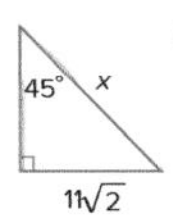

22

10. 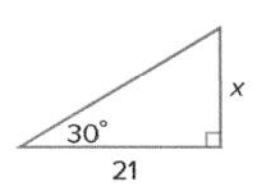

$7\sqrt{3}$

11. 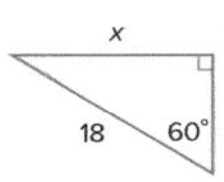

$9\sqrt{3}$

12. 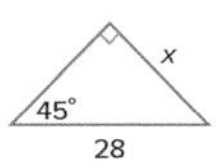

$14\sqrt{2}$

Find *x*. Round to the nearest tenth, if necessary. (Lesson 8-4)

13. 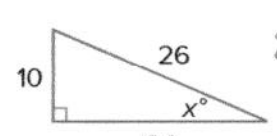

22.6

14. 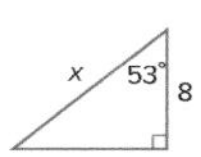

13.3

15. **SKATEBOARDING** Lindsey is building a skateboard ramp. She wants the ramp to be 1 foot tall at the end and she wants it to make a 15° angle with the ground. What length of board should she buy for the ramp itself? Round to the nearest foot. (Lesson 8-4) 4 ft

16. **BUILDINGS** Kara is standing about 50 feet from the base of her apartment building, looking up at it with an angle of elevation of 75°. What is the approximate height of Kara's building? (Lesson 8-5) about 187 ft

17. **ROLLER COASTERS** Evan is looking down the hill of a roller coaster from a height of 75 feet with an angle of depression of about 70°. What is the approximate horizontal distance from the top of the hill to the bottom of the hill? (Lesson 8-5) about 27.3 ft

18. **MOVIES** Kim is sitting in the row behind her friend Somi at the movies. Kim is looking at the screen with an angle of elevation of about 27° and Somi's angle of elevation is about 29°. If there are 3 feet between each row of seats, about how tall is the movie screen? (Lesson 8-5) about 19 ft

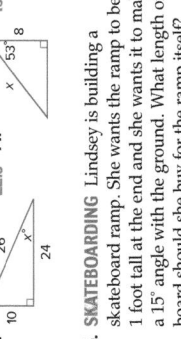

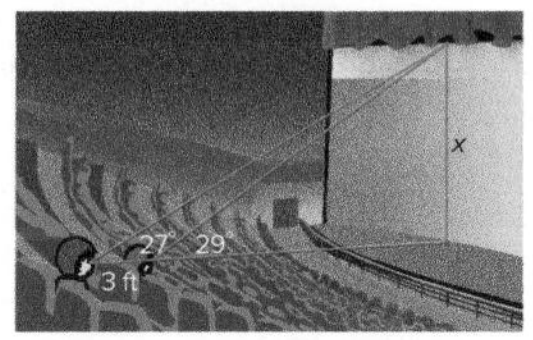

Solve each triangle. Round side lengths to the nearest tenth and angle measures to the nearest degree. (Lesson 8-6)

$B = 88°$, $a \approx 8.8$, $b \approx 10.5$ $\quad Y = 94°$, $x \approx 7.3$, $y \approx 10.4$

19. 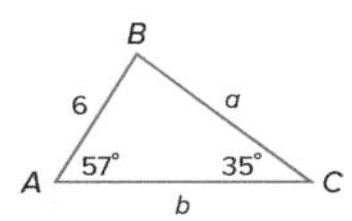

20. 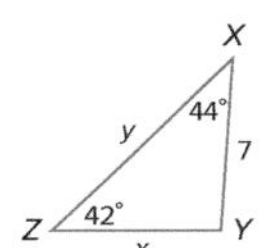

Solve each triangle. Round side lengths to the nearest tenth and angle measures to the nearest degree. (Lesson 8-7)

21. 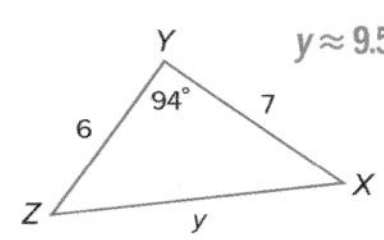

$y \approx 9.5$, $X \approx 39°$, $Z \approx 47°$

22. 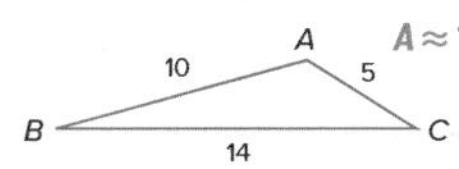

$A \approx 135°$, $B \approx 15°$, $C \approx 30°$

CHAPTER 9 Circles

The diameter of the smaller circle centered at *A* is 3 inches, and the diameter of the larger circle centered at *A* is 9 inches. The diameter of ⊙*D* is 11 inches. Find each measure. (Lesson 9-1)

1. *BC* 3 in.
2. *CD* 2.5 in.

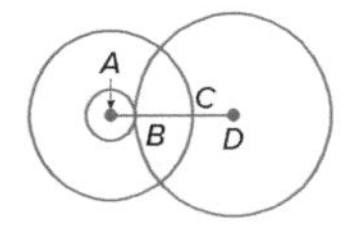

3. **DECORATIONS** To decorate for homecoming, Brittany estimates that she will need to purchase enough streamers to go around the school's circular fountain twice. If the diameter of the fountain is 88 inches, about how many feet of streamers should she buy? (Lesson 9-1) about 46 ft

Use ⊙*C* to find the length of each arc. Round to the nearest hundredth. (Lesson 9-2)

4. $\widehat{XY}$, if the radius is 5 feet 7.85 ft
5. $\widehat{YZ}$, if the diameter is 8 meters 3.84 m

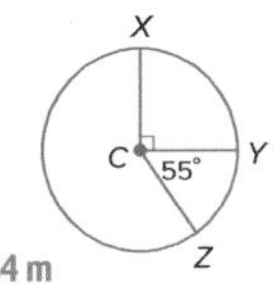

6. **TRANSPORTATION** The graph shows the results of a survey in which students at a high school were asked how they get to school. (Lesson 9-2)

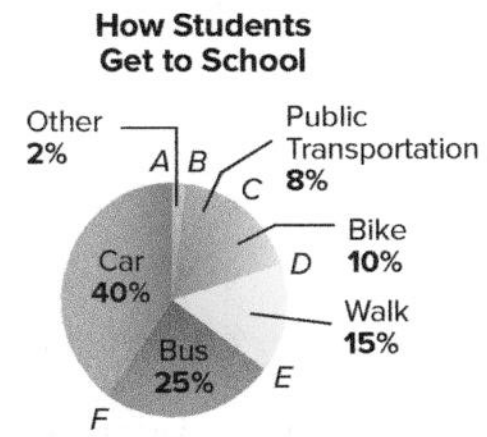

a. Find $m\widehat{CD}$. 36
b. Find $m\widehat{BC}$. 28.8

Find the value of *x*. (Lesson 9-3)

7. 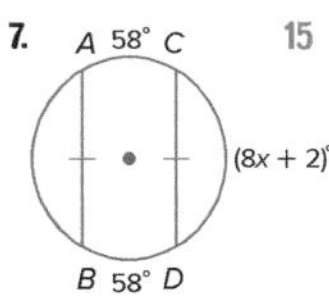

15

8. 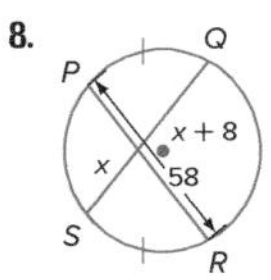

25

In ⊙*M*, *MZ* = 12 and *WY* = 20. Find each measure. Round to the nearest hundredth. (Lesson 9-3)

9. *CM* 6.63
10. *XC* 5.37

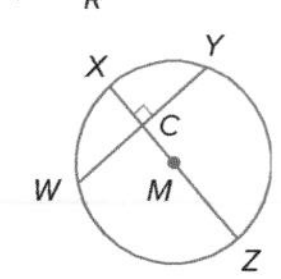

Find each measure. (Lesson 9-4)

11. *m*∠*N* 59

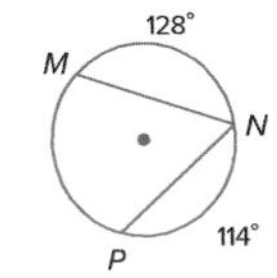

12. *m*∠*B* 34

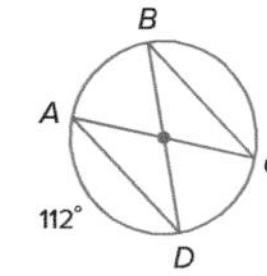

13. Find *x*. Assume that segments that appear to be tangent are tangent. (Lesson 9-5) 15

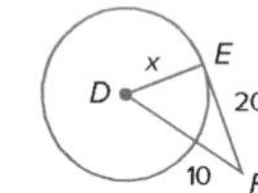

14. Quadrilateral *ABCD* is circumscribed about ⊙*H*. Find *m*. (Lesson 9-5) 33 mm

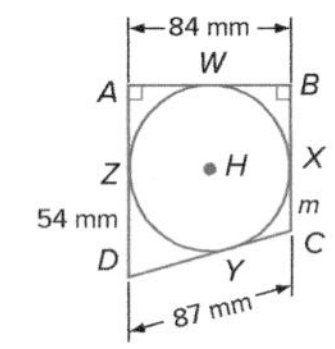

Find each measure. Assume that segments that appear to be tangent are tangent. (Lesson 9-6)

15. $m\widehat{XYZ}$ 140

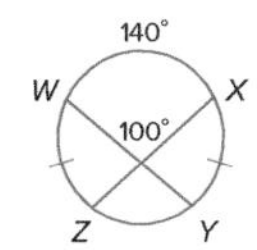

16. $\widehat{MP}$ 40

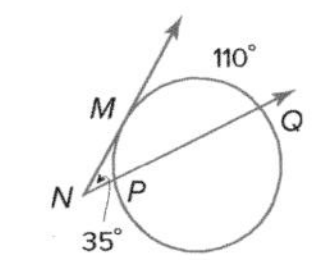

17a. $x^2 + y^2 = 225$

17. **CELL PHONES** A cell phone tower covers a circular area with a radius of 15 miles. (Lesson 9-7)

a. If the tower is located at the origin, write an equation for this circular area of coverage.

b. Will a person 11 miles west and 12 miles south of the tower have coverage? Explain.

17b–18. See Extra Practice Answer Appendix.

18. Write an equation of a circle that contains points *A*(−1, 5), *B*(−5, 9), and *C*(−9, 5). Then graph the equation. (Lesson 9-7)

19. Write an equation of the parabola with focus (0, 2) and directrix $y = -2$. (Lesson 9-8) $x^2 = 8y$

20. Write an equation of the parabola with focus (4, −3) and vertex (1, −3). (Lesson 9-8) $(y + 3)^2 = 12(x - 1)$

CHAPTER 10 Extending Area

Find the perimeter and area of each figure. Round to the nearest tenth if necessary. (Lesson 10-1)

1. 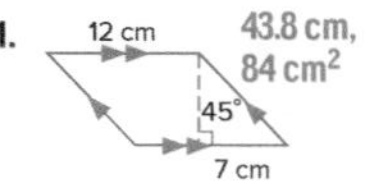

43.8 cm, 84 cm²

2. 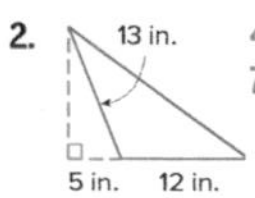

45.8 in., 72 in²

3. The height of a parallelogram is three times its base. If the area of the parallelogram is 108 square meters, find its base and height. (Lesson 10-1) 6 m; 18 m

4. The height of a triangle is three feet less than its base. If the area of the triangle is 275 square feet, find its base and height. (Lesson 10-1) 25 ft; 22 ft

Find the area of each trapezoid, rhombus, or kite. (Lesson 10-2)

5. 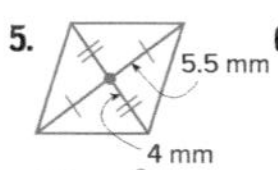

44 mm²

6. 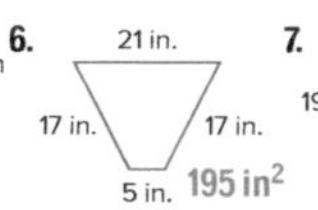

195 in²

7. 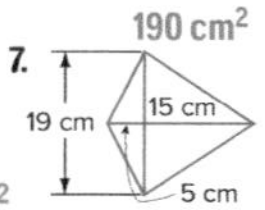

190 cm²

8. **MODELS** Joni is designing a mural for the side of a building. The wall is 15 feet high and 50 feet long. If she covers the wall with a kite as shown, what is the area of the kite? (Lesson 10-2) 375 ft²

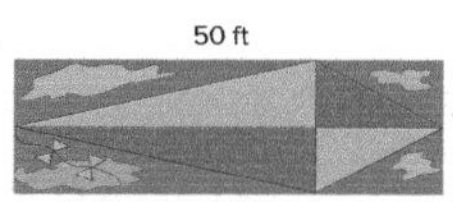

9. A trapezoid has a height of 12 inches, a base length of 9 inches, and an area of 150 square inches. What is the length of the other base? (Lesson 10-2) 16 in.

Find the indicated measure. Round to the nearest tenth. (Lesson 10-3)

10. The area of a circle is 201 square meters. Find the radius. 8 m

11. Find the diameter of a circle with an area of 79 square feet. 10 ft

Find the area of each shaded sector. Round to the nearest tenth if necessary. (Lesson 10-3)

12. 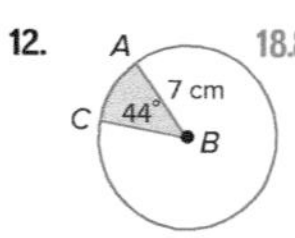

18.8 cm²

13. 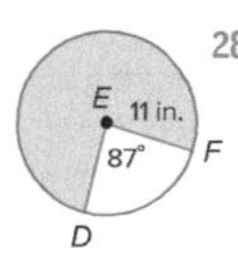

288.3 in²

14. **GRAPHS** Len created a circle graph using the survey results shown in the table. (Lesson 10-3)

Preferred Type of Exercise	
treadmill	62%
stationary bike	8%
swimming	7%
aerobics	12%
other	11%

a. What is the angle measure of the sector representing swimming? 25.2

b. If the graph has a 3-inch diameter, what is the area of the sector representing treadmill? about 4.4 in²

Find the area of each regular polygon. Round to the nearest tenth if necessary. (Lesson 10-4)

15. 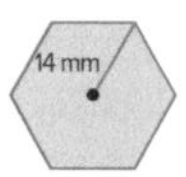

509.2 mm²

16. 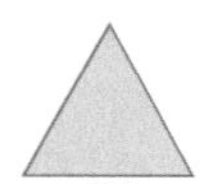

110.9 ft²

17. 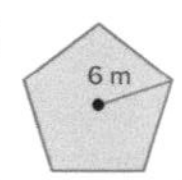

85.6 m²

Find the area of each figure. Round to the nearest tenth if necessary. (Lesson 10-4)

18. 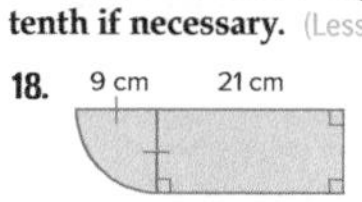

252.6 cm²

19. 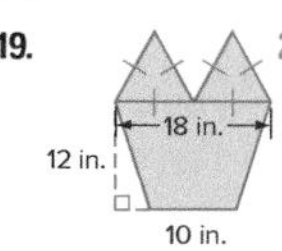

238.1 in²

For each pair of similar figures, find the area of the green figure. (Lesson 10-5)

20. 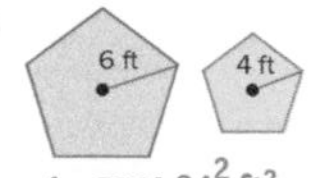

$34\frac{2}{3}$ ft²

21. 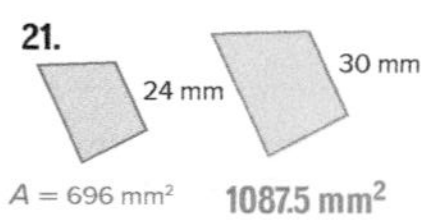

1087.5 mm²

For each pair of similar figures, use the given areas to find the scale factor from the blue to the green figure. Then find *x*. (Lesson 10-5)

22. 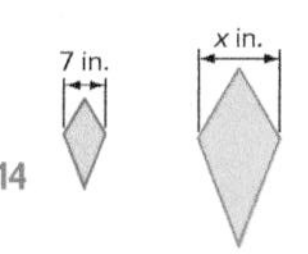

$\frac{1}{2}$; 14

23. 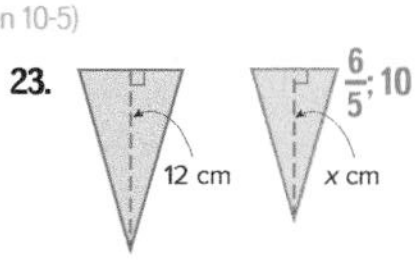

$\frac{6}{5}$; 10

24. **PACKAGING** A shoebox in the shape of a rectangular prism is 15 inches long, 8 inches wide, and 5 inches tall. What is the surface area of the shoebox? (Lesson 10-6) 470 in²

CHAPTER 11 Extending Volume

Determine the shape of each cross section of the solids. (Lesson 11-1)

1. plane parallel to a base

square

2. plane through the vertex and perpendicular to the base
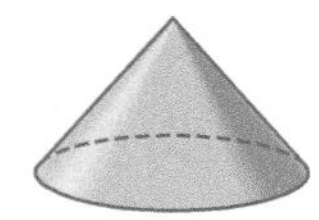
isosceles triangle

Describe the three-dimensional solid generated by rotating each two-dimensional shape around the given axis. (Lesson 11-1)

3. rectangle
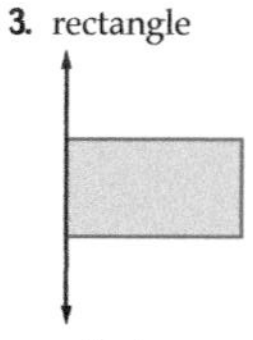
cylinder

4. circle
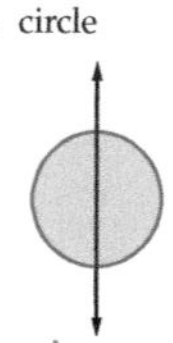
sphere

Find the volume of each solid. Round to the nearest tenth if necessary. (Lesson 11-2)

5. 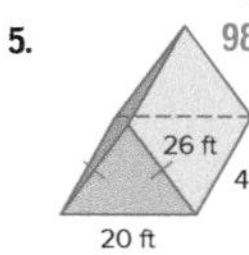

9840 ft³

6. 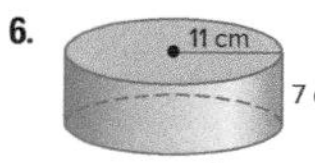

2660.9 cm³

7. **ADVERTISING** A company advertises that their juice boxes contain 20% more juice than their competitor's. If the base dimensions of the boxes are the same, how much taller are the larger boxes? (Lesson 11-2) 0.8 in.

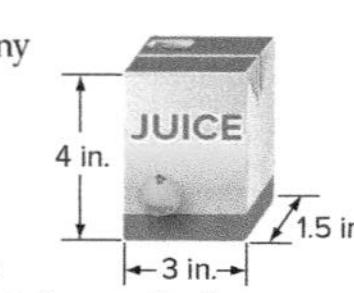

Find the volume of each solid. Round to the nearest tenth if necessary. (Lesson 11-3)

8. 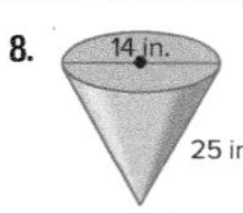

1231.5 in³

9. 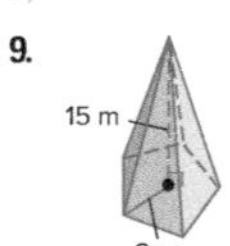

760.8 m³

Find the surface area and volume of each sphere or hemisphere. Round to the nearest tenth. (Lesson 11-4)

10. 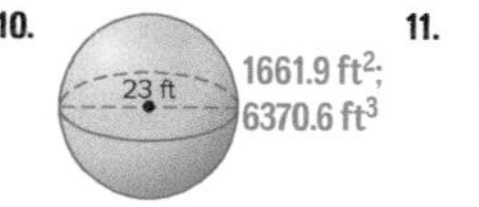

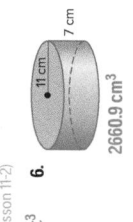

1661.9 ft²; 6370.6 ft³

11. 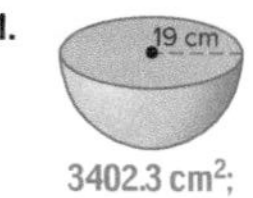

3402.3 cm²; 14,365.5 cm³

12. **SPORTS** The diameter of a tennis ball is 2.7 inches, and the diameter of a baseball is 2.9 inches. How many times as great is the volume of the baseball as the volume of the tennis ball? (Lesson 11-4) 1.24

Name each of the following on sphere *A*. (Lesson 11-5)

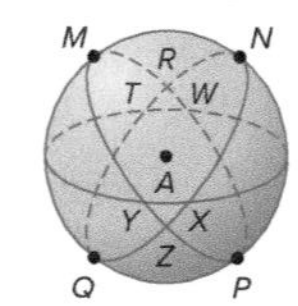

13. a triangle Sample answer: △YXZ

14. two segments on the same great circle Sample answer: $\overline{MZ}$ and $\overline{ZP}$

Determine whether each pair of solids is *similar*, *congruent*, or *neither*. If the solids are similar, state the scale factor. (Lesson 11-6)

15. 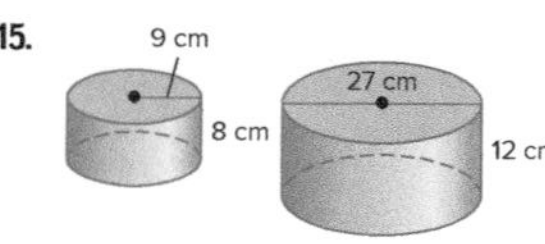

similar; $\frac{2}{3}$

16. 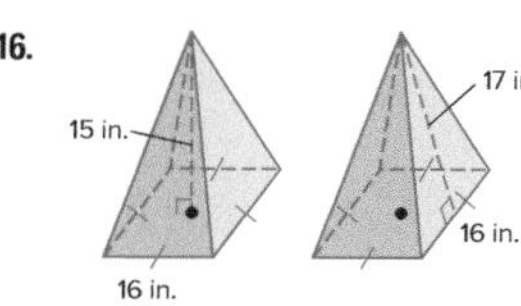

congruent

17. A cube has edges that are each 11 centimeters long. The mass of the cube is 564 grams. Find the density of the cube to the nearest hundredth. (Lesson 11-7) 0.42 g/cm³

CHAPTER 12 Probability

1. **FITNESS** Laura wants to go to a fitness class tomorrow. She can choose a 5:00 or a 7:30 class and spin or water aerobics. Represent the sample space for the situation by making an organized list, a table, and a tree diagram. (Lesson 12-1) **See Extra Practice Answer Appendix.**
2. **SCHOOL UNIFORMS** Susan's school dress code allows her to wear a polo shirt or an oxford shirt and a skirt or a pair of pants. She also has a sweater that she can wear if she chooses. Draw a tree diagram to represent the sample space for Susan's uniform. (Lesson 12-1) **See Extra Practice Answer Appendix.**
3. **CONSTRUCTION** Bert's family is building a house in a new neighborhood, and they must choose one option listed below for each feature. What is the number of possible outcomes for the situation? (Lesson 12-1) **108**

Feature	Options
floor plan	elevation 1, elevation 2
counters	formica, granite
cabinets	French antique glazed, oak, cherry
basement	unfinished, partially finished, finished
garage	none, one car, two car

4. A spinner is divided into 12 equal sections that are numbered 1 through 12. Let A be the event that the spinner lands on a number greater than 8. Let B be the event that it lands on an odd number. Find $P(A \text{ or } B)$. (Lesson 12-2) $\frac{2}{3}$
5. **NUMBERS** Charlie's phone number is 555-3703. If he places each of the digits in a bowl and randomly selects one number at a time without replacement, what is the probability that he will choose his phone number? (Lesson 12-3) $\frac{1}{420}$
6. **RAFFLES** Participants in a raffle received tickets 1101 through 1125. If four winners are chosen, what is the probability that the winning tickets are 1103, 1111, 1118, and 1122? (Lesson 12-3) $\frac{1}{12{,}650}$
7. Point X is chosen at random on $\overline{AE}$. Find the probability that X is on $\overline{CE}$. (Lesson 12-4) **about 0.54 or 54%**

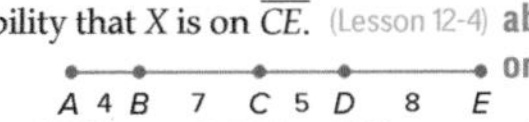

8. ≈ 0.553 or 55.3% **9.** 0.75 or 75% **10.** $\frac{5}{12}$ or about 41.7%

Find the probability that a point chosen at random lies in the shaded region. (Lesson 12-4)

8.
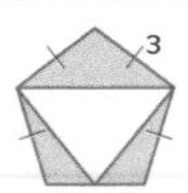

9.
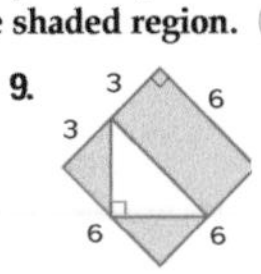

10.
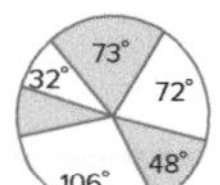

11. A die is rolled twice. What is the probability that the first number rolled is a 3 and the second number rolled is a 5? (Lesson 12-5) $\frac{1}{36}$
12. Three cards are randomly chosen from a deck of 52 cards without replacement. What is the probability that they will all be red? (Lesson 12-5) **about 0.118 or 11.8%**
13. A spinner numbered 1 through 6 is spun. Find the probability that the number spun is a 3 given that it was less than 4. (Lesson 12-5) $\frac{1}{3}$

BOOKS The table shows the number and type of books that Sarah owns. Find each probability. (Lesson 12-6)

Medium	Classic	Mystery	Biography
print	29	8	32
audio	3	6	10
electronic	8	3	43

14. A randomly chosen title is a print or audio book. **about 0.62 or 62%**
15. A randomly chosen title is not a biography. **about 0.401 or 40.1%**
16. **DOGS** The table shows the ages and genders of the dogs at an animal shelter. What is the probability that a randomly chosen dog is a female or over 5 years old? (Lesson 12-6) **0.68 or 68%**

Age	Male	Female
under 1 year	6	5
1–5 years	8	7
6–10 years	4	6
over 10 years	3	5

17. At Marco's school, 41% of the students take advanced placement (AP) classes, 12% of the students play an instrument, and 9% of the students take AP classes and play an instrument. A student is selected at random. What is the probability that the student takes AP classes given that he or she plays an instrument? (Lesson 12-7) **75%**

YOGURT The owner of a frozen yogurt shop asks a random sample of 150 customers whether they would prefer peach or banana yogurt as a new flavor. She finds that 33 men and 28 women prefer peach, while 42 men and 47 women prefer banana. (Lesson 12-8)

18–19. See Extra Practice Answer Appendix.

18. Make a two-way frequency table of the data.
19. Convert the table to relative frequencies.
20. Find the probability that a surveyed customer prefers banana given that the customer is a man. **20. 56%**

Chapter 7

2.

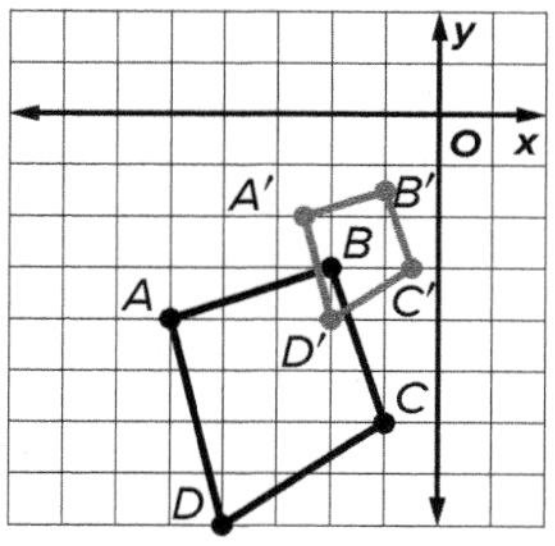

3.

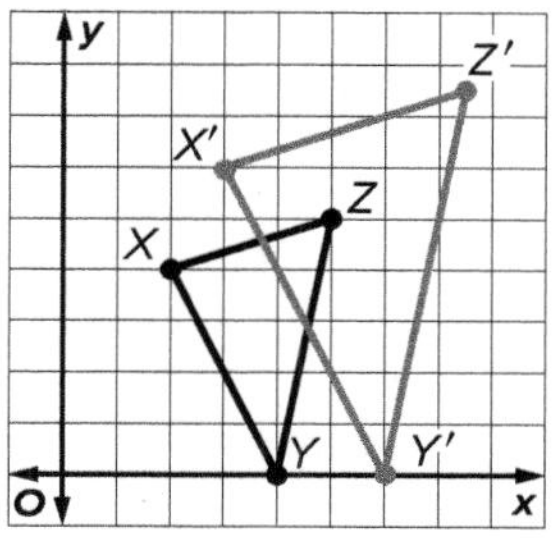

4. No; sample answer: The measures of the angles of $\triangle ABC$ are 37, 53, and 90. The measures of the angles of $\triangle DEF$ are 41, 49, and 90. Because the corresponding angles of the figures are not congruent, the figures are not similar.

5. Yes; sample answer: $MNPQ \sim XWZY$ with a scale factor of $\frac{2}{3}$.

8. No; sample answer: Because $\frac{30}{60} \neq \frac{55.5}{110}$, the table is not similar to the field.

10. Similar; $\triangle ABC \sim \triangle EDC$; $\angle ACB \cong \angle DEC$ because they are vertical angles, so the triangles have two pairs of congruent angles; the triangles are similar by AA Similarity.

11. Similar; sample answer: $\triangle MNP \sim \triangle XYZ$; $\triangle XYZ$ is equilateral. Equilateral triangles are also equiangular. So $\triangle XYZ$ is equiangular. $\triangle MNP$ is also equiangular. All three angles in equiangular triangles measure 60. Therefore, $m\angle N = m\angle P = m\angle Y = m\angle Z = 60$, which means $\angle N \cong \angle Y$ and $\angle P \cong \angle Z$. So $\triangle MNP \sim \triangle XYZ$ by AA Similarity.

12. Not similar; sample answer: We know that the vertical angles are congruent, so we would need to show that the sides that include the angle are proportional. Because $\frac{6}{22} \neq \frac{5}{27}$, the triangles are not similar.

13. Similar; $\triangle JKL \sim \triangle JMN$; $\angle J \cong \angle J$ and $\frac{JM}{JK} = \frac{JN}{JL} = \frac{10}{5}$; the triangles are similar by SAS Similarity.

14.

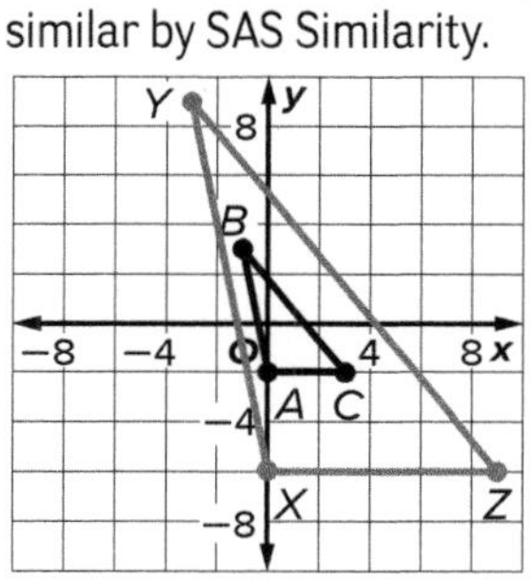

Because $\frac{AB}{XY} = \frac{\sqrt{26}}{3\sqrt{26}} = \frac{1}{3}$, $\frac{BC}{YZ} = \frac{\sqrt{41}}{3\sqrt{41}} = \frac{1}{3}$, and $\frac{AC}{XZ} = \frac{3}{9} = \frac{1}{3}$, the triangles are similar by SSS.

15.

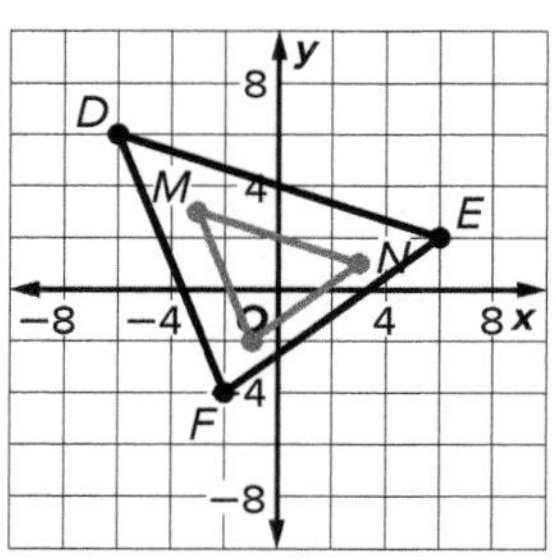

Because $\frac{DE}{MN} = \frac{4\sqrt{10}}{2\sqrt{10}} = 2$, $\frac{EF}{NP} = \frac{10}{5} = 2$, and $\frac{DF}{MP} = \frac{2\sqrt{29}}{\sqrt{29}} = 2$, the triangles are similar by SSS.

Chapter 8

7. yes; obtuse

$41^2 \stackrel{?}{=} 24^2 + 32^2$

$1681 \stackrel{?}{=} 576 + 1024$

$1681 > 1600$

8. yes; right

$62.5^2 \stackrel{?}{=} 17.52^2 + 60^2$

$3906.25 \stackrel{?}{=} 306.25 + 3600$

$3906.25 = 3906.25$

Chapter 9

17b. No; this location is $\sqrt{11^2 + 12^2}$ or about 16.3 mi from the tower, which is greater than the 15-mi radius of coverage.

18. $(x + 5)^2 + (y - 5)^2 = 16$

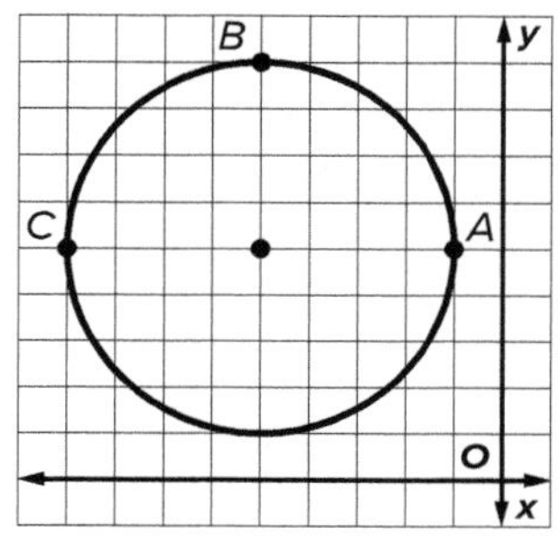

Chapter 12

1. 5:00, spin class
5:00, water aerobics
7:30, spin class
7:30, water aerobics

Outcomes	Spin class	Water aerobics
5:00	5:00, spin class	5:00, water aerobics
7:30	7:30, spin class	7:30, water aerobics

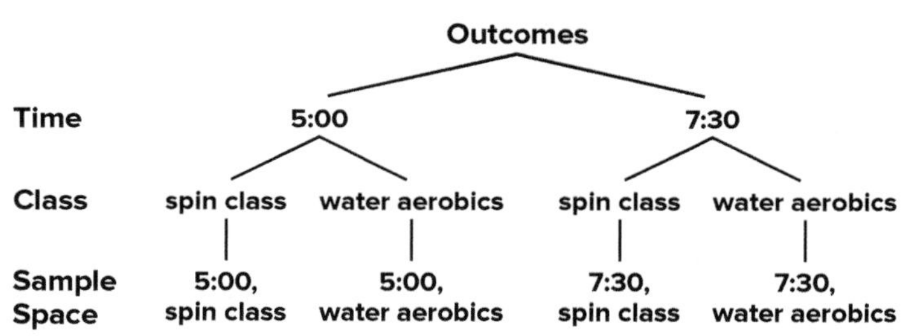

2.

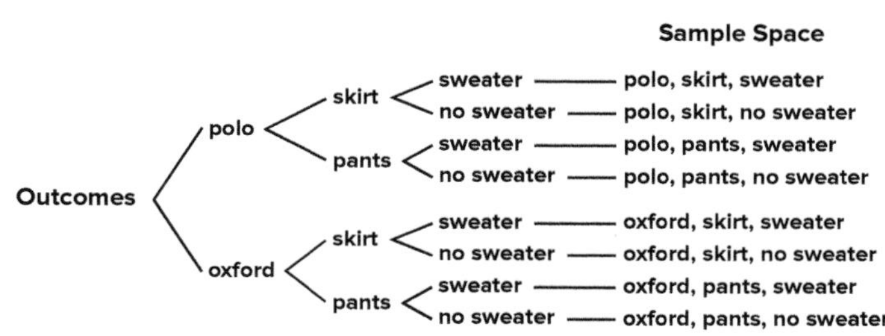

18.

	Peach	Banana	Totals
Men	33	42	75
Women	28	47	75
Totals	61	89	150

19.

	Peach	Banana	Totals
Men	22%	28%	50%
Women	18.7%	31.3%	50%
Totals	40.7%	59.3%	100%

CHAPTER 7

Similarity

Chapter 7 Concept Check

1. cross-multiplication **3.** $m\angle SQR$ is twice $m\angle TQR$. **5.** substitution **7.** The value of x is known and value of $m\angle TQR$ in terms of x is known. Substitute and solve.

Lesson 7-1

1.

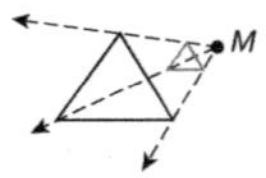

3 The figure increases in size from B to B', so it is an enlargement.

$$\frac{\text{image length}}{\text{preimage length}} = \frac{QB'}{QB} = \frac{8}{6} \text{ or } \frac{4}{3}$$

$QB + BB' = QB'$
$6 + x = 8$
$x = 2$

5.

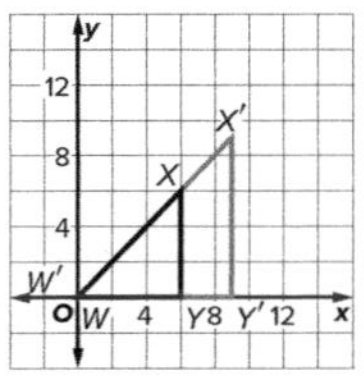

7.

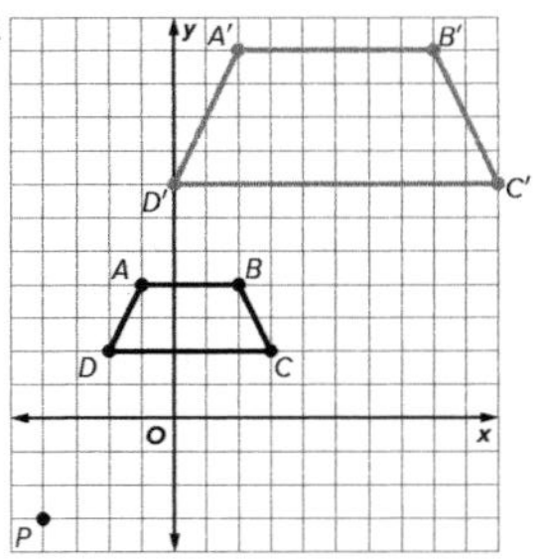

9.

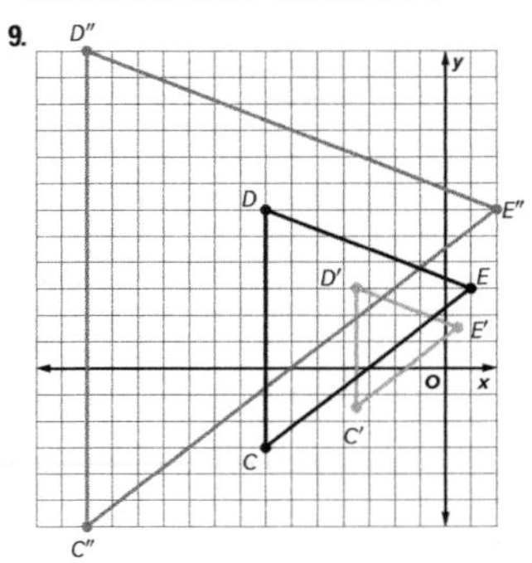

11.

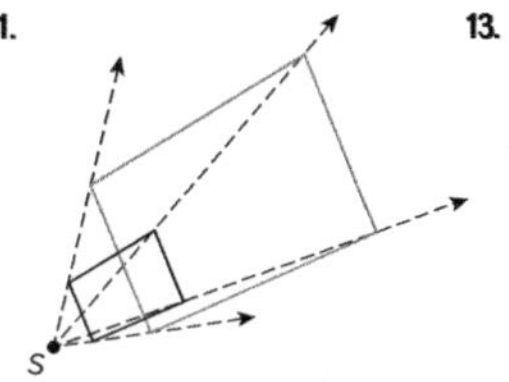

13.

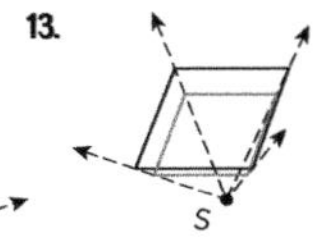

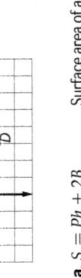

15. enlargement; 2; 4.5 **17.** reduction; $\frac{3}{4}$; 3.5

19. 15×; The insect's image length in millimeters is 3.75 • 10 or 37.5 mm. The scale factor of the dilation is $\frac{37.5}{2.5}$ or 15.

21 Multiply the x- and y-coordinates of each vertex by the scale factor, 0.5.

(x, y)	→	$(0.5x, 0.5y)$
$J(-8, 0)$	→	$J'(-4, 0)$
$K(-4, 4)$	→	$K'(-2, 2)$
$L(-2, 0)$	→	$L'(-1, 0)$

Graph JKL and its image $J'K'L'$.

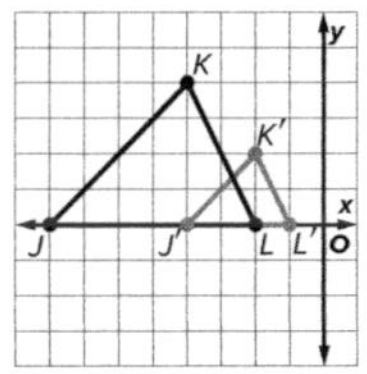

23.

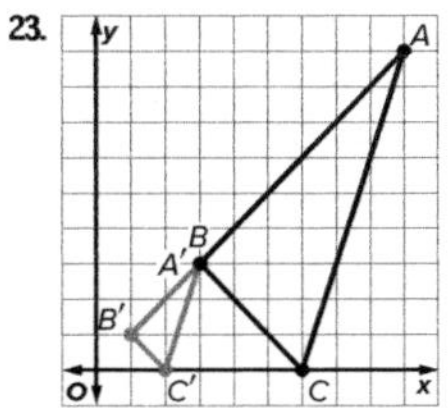

25.

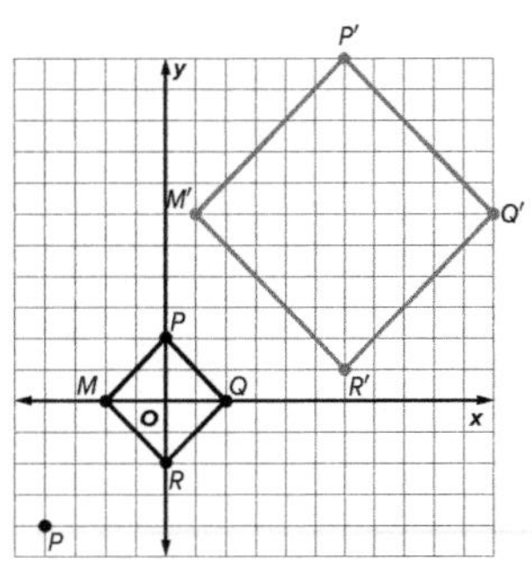

27.

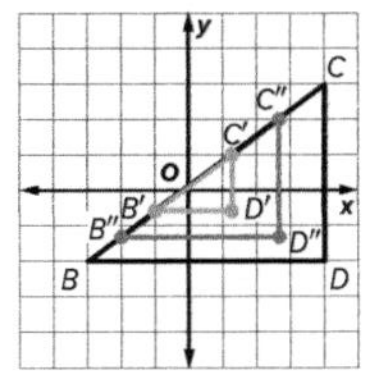

29.

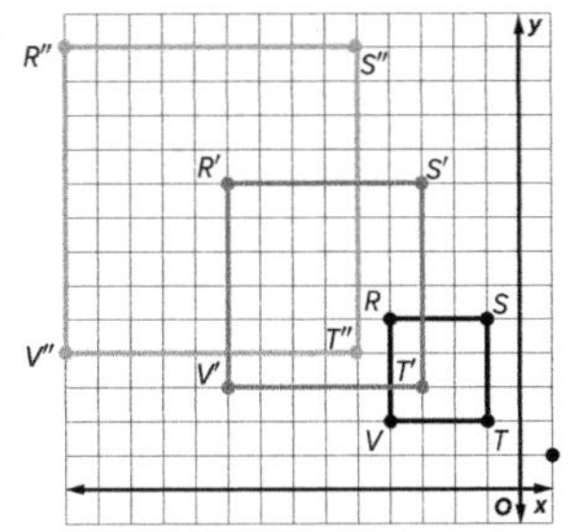

31.

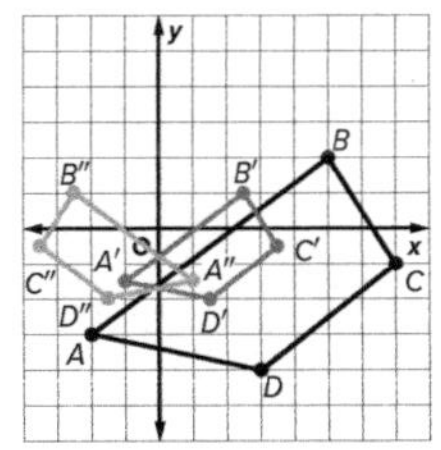

33 **a.** $S = Ph + 2B$ Surface area of a prism
$= (16)(4) + 2(12)$ $P = 16$ cm, $h = 4$ cm, $B = 12$ cm^2
$= 88$ cm^2 Simplify.

$V = Bh$ Volume of a prism
$= (12)(4)$ $B = 12$ cm^2, $h = 4$ cm
$= 48$ cm^3 Simplify.

b. Multiply the dimensions by the scale factor 2: length = 6 • 2 or 12 cm, width = 2 • 2 or 4 cm, height = 4 • 2 or 8 cm.

$S = Ph + 2B$ Surface area of a prism
$= (32)(8) + 2(48)$ $P = 32$ cm, $h = 8$ cm, $B = 48$ cm^2
$= 352$ cm^2 Simplify.

$V = Bh$ Volume of a prism
$= (48)(8)$ $B = 48$ cm^2, $h = 8$ cm
$= 384$ cm^3 Simplify.

c. Multiply the dimensions by the scale factor $\frac{1}{2}$: length = $6 \cdot \frac{1}{2}$ or 3 cm, width = $2 \cdot \frac{1}{2}$ or 1 cm, height = $4 \cdot \frac{1}{2}$ or 2 cm.

$S = Ph + 2B$ Surface area of a prism
$= (8)(2) + 2(3)$ $P = 8$ cm, $h = 2$ cm, $B = 3$ cm^2
$= 22$ cm^2 Simplify.

$V = Bh$ Volume of a prism
$= (3)(2)$ $B = 3$ cm^2, $h = 2$ cm
$= 6$ cm^3 Simplify.

d. surface area of preimage: 88 cm^2
surface area of image with scale factor 2: 352 cm^2 or (88 • 4) cm^2
surface area of image with scale factor $\frac{1}{2}$: 22 cm^2 or $\left(88 \cdot \frac{1}{4}\right)$ cm^2
The surface area is 4 times greater after dilation with scale factor 2, $\frac{1}{4}$ as great after dilation with scale factor $\frac{1}{2}$.

volume of preimage: 48 cm^3
volume of image with scale factor 2: 384 cm^3 or (48 • 8) cm^3
volume of image with scale factor $\frac{1}{2}$: 6 cm^3 or $\left(48 \cdot \frac{1}{8}\right)$ cm^2
The volume is 8 times greater after dilation with scale factor 2; $\frac{1}{8}$ as great after dilation with scale factor $\frac{1}{2}$.

e. The surface area of the preimage would be multiplied by r^2. The volume of the preimage would be multiplied by r^3.

35a.

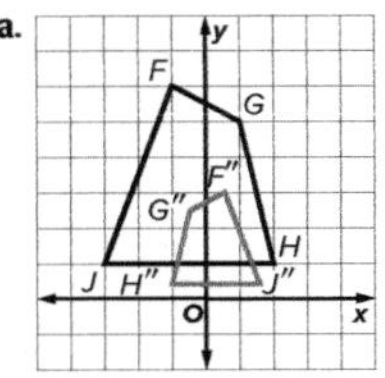

35b.

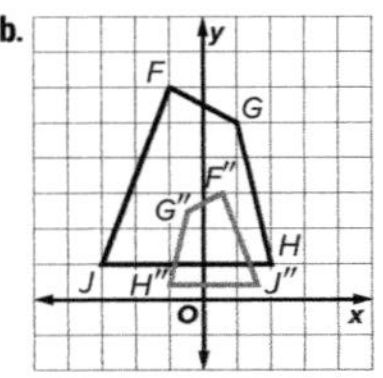

35c. no **35d.** Sometimes; sample answer: For the order of a composition of a dilation centered at the origin and a reflection to be unimportant, the line of reflection must contain the origin, or must be of the form $y = mx$.

37 **a.** $k = \frac{\text{diameter of image}}{\text{diameter of preimage}}$
$= \frac{2 \text{ mm}}{1.5 \text{ mm}}$

$= \frac{2}{1\frac{1}{2}}$

$= 2 \cdot \frac{2}{3}$

$= \frac{4}{3}$ or $1\frac{1}{3}$

b. $A = \pi r^2$ — Area of a circle

$= \pi(0.75)^2$ — $r = 1.5 \div 2$ or 0.75

≈ 1.77 mm^2 — Use a calculator.

$A = \pi r^2$ — Area of a circle

$= \pi(1)^2$ — $r = 2 \div 2$ or 1

≈ 3.14 mm^2 — Use a calculator.

39. $\frac{11}{5}$

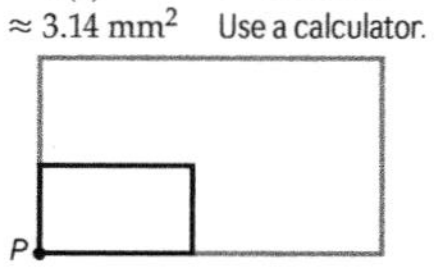

41 The submitted image is distorted because it was not reduced proportionally. Divide the width of the submitted photo by the width of the original photo to determine that the scale factor is 0.6. Multiply the original height of the photo by the scale factor to find the height of the image that should be submitted is 2.7 in. Becca should submit an image sized to 1.8 in. by 2.7 in.

43. ≈23.1

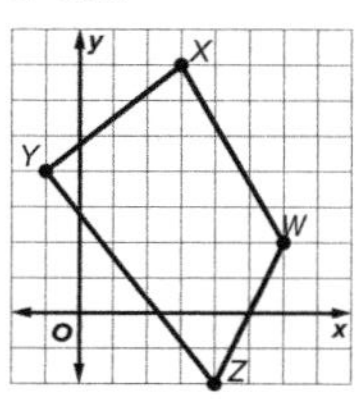

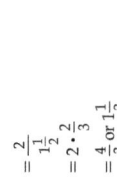

45. $y = 4x - 3$ **47a.** Always; sample answer: Because a dilation of 1 maps an image onto itself, all four vertices will remain invariant under the dilation. **47b.** Always; sample answer: Because the rotation is centered at *B*, point *B* will always remain invariant under the rotation. **47c.** Sometimes: sample answer: If one of the vertices is on the *x*-axis, then that point will remain invariant under reflection. If two vertices are on the *x*-axis, then the two vertices located on the *x*-axis will remain invariant under reflection. **47d.** Never; when a figure is translated, all points move an equal distance. Therefore, no points can remain invariant under translation.
47e. Sometimes; sample answer: If one of the vertices of the triangle is located at the origin, then that vertex would remain invariant under the dilation. If none of the points on $\triangle XYZ$ are located at the origin, then no points will remain invariant under the dilation.
49. Sample answer: Translations, reflections, and rotations produce congruent figures because the sides and angles of the preimage are congruent to the corresponding sides and angles of the image. Dilations produce similar figures, because the angles of the preimage and the image are congruent and the sides of the preimage are proportional to the corresponding sides of the image. A dilation with a scale factor of 1 produces an equal figure because the image is mapped onto its corresponding parts in the preimage.
51. B **53.** A

Lesson 7-2

1. Yes; map *DEFG* to *JKLM* using a dilation centered at the origin with scale factor 3 followed by a translation along (6, 0). **3.** $\angle A \cong \angle Z$, $\angle B \cong \angle Y$, $\angle C \cong \angle X$; $\frac{AC}{ZX} = \frac{BC}{YX} = \frac{AB}{ZY}$ **5.** no; $\frac{NQ}{WZ} \neq \frac{QR}{WX}$ **7.** 6 **9.** 22 ft
11. Yes; map *PQRS* to *WXYZ* using a dilation centered at the origin with scale factor 0.5 followed by a translation along (13, 2). **13.** $\angle J \cong \angle P$, $\angle F \cong \angle S$, $\angle M \cong \angle T$, $\angle H \cong \angle Q$; $\frac{PQ}{JH}, \frac{TS}{MF}, \frac{SQ}{FH} = \frac{TP}{MJ}$; **15** Yes; $\triangle LTK \cong \triangle MTK$ because $\triangle LTK \cong \triangle MTK$; scale factor: 1. **17.** Yes; sample answer: The ratio of the longer dimensions of the screens is approximately 1.1 and the ratio of the shorter dimensions of the screens is approximately 1.1.

19

$\frac{SB}{JH} = \frac{BP}{HT}$	Similarity proportion
$\frac{2}{3} = \frac{x+3}{2x+2}$	$SB = 2$, $JH = 3$, $BP = x + 3$, $HT = 2x + 2$
$2(2x + 2) = 3(x + 3)$	Cross Products Property
$4x + 4 = 3x + 9$	Distributive Property
$x + 4 = 9$	Subtract 3x from each side.
$x = 5$	Subtract 4 from each side.

21. 3 **23.** 10.8 **25.** 18.9 **27.** 40 m

29. Given: $\triangle ABC \sim \triangle DEF$ and $\frac{AB}{DE} = \frac{m}{n}$

Prove: $\frac{\text{perimeter of } \triangle ABC}{\text{perimeter of } \triangle DEF} = \frac{m}{n}$

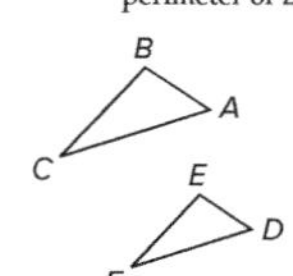

Proof: Because $\triangle ABC \sim \triangle DEF$, $\frac{AB}{DE} = \frac{BC}{EF} = \frac{AC}{DF}$.

So $\frac{AB}{DE} = \frac{BC}{EF} = \frac{AC}{DF} = \frac{m}{n}$. Cross products yield $AB = DE\left(\frac{m}{n}\right)$, $BC = EF\left(\frac{m}{n}\right)$, and $AC = DF\left(\frac{m}{n}\right)$.

Using substitution, the perimeter of $\triangle ABC =$

$DE\left(\frac{m}{n}\right) + EF\left(\frac{m}{n}\right) + DF\left(\frac{m}{n}\right)$, or $\frac{m}{n}(DE + EF + DF)$.

The ratio of the two perimeters $= \frac{\frac{m}{n}(DE + EF + DF)}{DE + EF + DF}$ or $\frac{m}{n}$.

31 **a.** The ratio of the areas is the square of the ratio of the sides. $\left(\frac{4}{1}\right)^2 = \frac{16}{1}$ so the ratio of the areas is 16:1. **b.** Because both rectangles had all sides tripled, the ratio is 3(4):3(1) = 12:1 which is equal to 4:1. The ratio of the sides doesn't change. **c.** The ratio of the areas is the square of the ratio of the sides. $\left(\frac{4}{1}\right)^2 = \frac{16}{1}$, so the ratio of the areas is 16:1. **d.** Because both rectangles corresponding sides are doubled, the ratio is the same, 4:1.

33a. Sample answer:

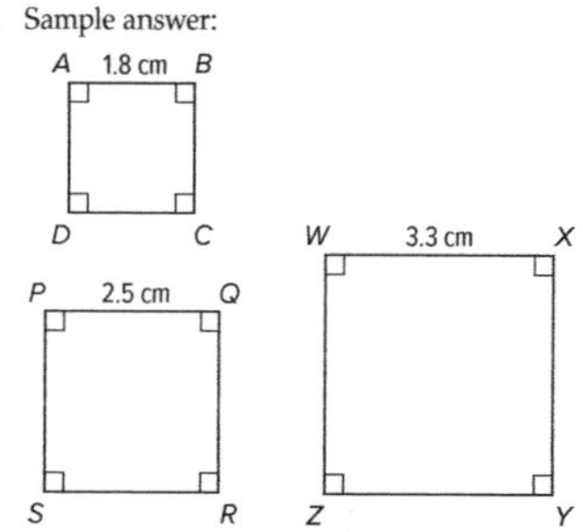

33b.

ABCD and PQRS		PQRS and WXYZ		WXYZ and ABCD	
AB:PQ	0.72	PQ:WX	0.76	WX:AB	1.8
BC:QR	0.72	QR:XY	0.76	XY:BC	1.8
CD:RS	0.72	RS:YZ	0.76	YZ:CD	1.8
AD:SP	0.72	SP:ZW	0.76	ZW:DA	1.8

ABCD is similar to *PQRS*; *PQRS* is similar to *WXYZ*; *WXYZ* is similar to *ABCD*.

33c. Sample answer: All squares are similar.

35. Sample answer:

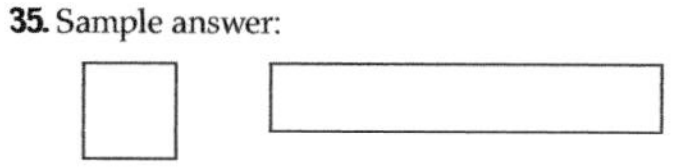

37. Sample answer: The figures could be described as congruent if they are the same size and shape, similar if their corresponding angles are congruent and their corresponding sides are proportional, and equal if they are the same exact figure. **39.** D **41.** 39
43a. Map *DEFG* to *HJKL* using a dilation centered at the origin with scale factor 0.5 followed by a translation along <6, 5>. **43b.** $DEFG \cong HJKL$
43c. $\frac{DE}{HJ} = \frac{EF}{JK} = \frac{FG}{KL} = \frac{GD}{LH}$ **43d.** 3.1 cm; because the scale factor of the dilation is 0.5, the perimeter of *HJKL* is 0.5 times the perimeter of *DEFG*.

Lesson 7-3

1. Yes; $\triangle YXZ \sim \triangle VWZ$ by AA Similarity. **3.** No; the angles are not congruent. **5.** C **7.** $\triangle QVS \sim \triangle RTS$; 20
9. Yes; $\triangle ACE \sim \triangle BCD$ by AA Similarity.
11 Yes; $\angle WVX$ and $\angle VTU$ are both right angles, so they are congruent. $\angle WXV$ and $\angle VUT$ are marked congruent. So, the triangles are similar by AA Similarity. **13.** No; not enough information is given to determine that the triangles are similar.
15. Reflect or rotate one triangle about the shared vertex at *B*, then dilate one triangle to show the triangles are similar.

17 Because $\overline{RS} \parallel \overline{PT}$, $\angle QRS \cong \angle QPT$ and $\angle QSR \cong \angle QTP$ because they are corresponding angles. By AA Similarity, $\triangle QRS \sim \triangle QPT$.

$\frac{RS}{PT} = \frac{QS}{QT}$	Definition of similar polygons
$\frac{12}{16} = \frac{x}{20}$	$RS = 12$, $PT = 16$, $QS = x$, $QT = 20$
$12 \cdot 20 = 16 \cdot x$	Cross Products Property
$240 = 16x$	Simplify.
$15 = x$	Divide each side by 16.

Because $QS + ST = 20$ and $QS = 15$, $ST = 5$.
19. $\triangle HJK \sim \triangle NQP$; 15, 10 **21.** $\triangle GHJ \sim \triangle GDH$; 14, 20
23. 12.8 ft

25. **Reflexive Property of Similarity**

Given: $\triangle ABC$

Prove: $\triangle ABC \sim \triangle ABC$

Proof: Statements (Reasons)

1. $\triangle ABC$ (Given)
2. $\angle A \cong \angle A$, $\angle B \cong \angle B$ (**Refl. Prop.**)
3. $\triangle ABC \sim \triangle ABC$ (**AA Similarity**)

Symmetric Property of Similarity

Given: $\triangle ABC \sim \triangle DEF$

Prove: $\triangle DEF \sim \triangle ABC$

Proof: Statements (Reasons)

1. $\triangle ABC \sim \triangle DEF$ (Given)
2. $\angle A \cong \angle D$, $\angle B \cong \angle E$ (**Def. of ~ polygons**)
3. $\angle D \cong \angle A$, $\angle E \cong \angle B$ (**Symm. Prop.**)
4. $\triangle DEF \sim \triangle ABC$ (**AA Similarity**)

Transitive Property of Similarity

Given: $\triangle ABC \sim \triangle DEF$ and $\triangle DEF \sim \triangle GHI$

Prove: $\triangle ABC \sim \triangle GHI$

Proof: Statements (Reasons)

1. $\triangle ABC \sim \triangle DEF$, $\triangle DEF \sim \triangle GHI$ (**Given**)
2. $\angle A \cong \angle D$, $\angle B \cong \angle E$, $\angle D \cong \angle G$, $\angle E \cong \angle H$ (**Def. of ~ polygons**)
3. $\angle A \cong \angle G$, $\angle B \cong \angle H$ (**Trans. Prop.**)
4. $\triangle ABC \sim \triangle GHI$ (**AA Similarity**)

27. Given: $\triangle XYZ$ and $\triangle ABC$ are right triangles; $\angle Z \cong \angle C$

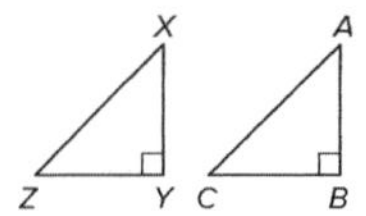

Prove: $\triangle YXZ \sim \triangle BAC$

Proof:

Statements (Reasons)

1. $\triangle XYZ$ and $\triangle ABC$ are right triangles. (Given)
2. $\angle XYZ$ and $\angle ABC$ are right angles. (Def. of rt. $\triangle$)
3. $\angle XYZ \cong \angle ABC$ (All rt. $\angle$s are $\cong$.)
4. $\angle Z \cong \angle C$ (Given)
5. $\triangle YXZ \sim \triangle BAC$ (AA Similarity)

29

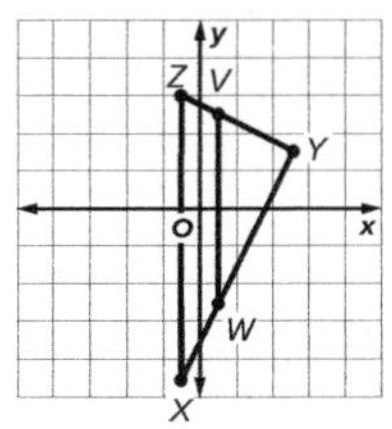

$XY = \sqrt{12^2 + 6^2} = \sqrt{180}$ or $6\sqrt{5}$;

$YZ = \sqrt{3^2 + (-6)^2} = \sqrt{45}$ or $3\sqrt{5}$;

$ZX = 6 - (-9) = 15$; $VW = 5 - (-5) = 10$;

$WY = \sqrt{8^2 + 4^2} = \sqrt{80}$ or $4\sqrt{5}$;

$YV = \sqrt{2^2 + (-4)^2} = \sqrt{20} = 2\sqrt{5}$.

$\frac{XY}{WY} = \frac{6\sqrt{5}}{4\sqrt{5}}$ or $\frac{3}{2}$, $\frac{YZ}{YV} = \frac{3\sqrt{5}}{2\sqrt{5}}$ or $\frac{3}{2}$,

$\frac{ZX}{VW} = \frac{15}{10}$ or $\frac{3}{2}$. Because $\frac{XY}{WY} = \frac{YZ}{YV} = \frac{ZX}{VW} = \frac{3}{2}$,

$\triangle XYZ \sim \triangle WYV$ by SSS Similarity.

31. about 61 in.

33a. The scale factor from $\triangle ABC$ to $\triangle JKL$ is $\frac{1}{2}$. So $JK = \frac{1}{2}AB$, $KL = \frac{1}{2}BC$, and $JL = \frac{1}{2}AC$. Thus the perimeter of $\triangle JKL$ is $\frac{1}{2}AB + \frac{1}{2}BC + \frac{1}{2}AC = \frac{1}{2}$(perimeter of $\triangle ABC$) $= \frac{1}{2}$(40 in.) or 20 in. The ratio of the areas is $\frac{1}{2}$, which is the scale factor.

b. The scale factor from $\triangle ABC$ to $\triangle JKL$ is $\frac{1}{3}$. So $JK = \frac{1}{3}AB$, $KL = \frac{1}{3}BC$, and $JL = \frac{1}{3}AC$. Thus the perimeter of $\triangle JKL$ is $\frac{1}{3}AB + \frac{1}{3}BC + \frac{1}{3}AC = \frac{1}{3}$(perimeter of $\triangle ABC$) $= \frac{1}{3}$(21 in.) or 7 in. The ratio of the areas is $\frac{1}{3}$, which is the scale factor.

35a. Sample answer:

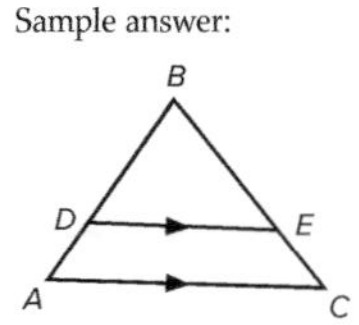

35b. Sample answer:

Lengths		Ratios	
AD	0.9 cm	$\frac{AD}{DB}$	$\frac{1}{2}$
DB	1.8 cm		
CE	1.1 cm	$\frac{CE}{EB}$	$\frac{1}{2}$
EB	2.2 cm		

35c. Sample answer: The segments created by a line $\parallel$ to one side of a $\triangle$ and intersecting the other two sides are proportional. **37.** Yes; Because it is an altitude, $\overline{YW} \perp \overline{XZ}$. So $\angle XWY$ and $\angle ZWY$ are right angles. It is given that $\angle XYZ$ is a right angle. Thus $\angle XWY \cong \angle XYZ$ and $\angle XYZ \cong \angle ZWY$ because all right angles are congruent. $\angle WXY \cong \angle YXZ$ by the Reflexive property. So $\triangle WXY \sim \triangle YXZ$ by AA Similarity. $\angle XZY \cong \angle WZY$ by the Reflexive property. So $\triangle YXZ \sim \triangle WYZ$ by AA Similarity. Therefore $\triangle WXY \sim \triangle WYZ$ by the Transitive property.

39. Sample answer:

$\triangle A'B'C' \sim \triangle ABC$ because the measures of each side have a scale factor of 0.5 and the measures of corresponding angles are equal.

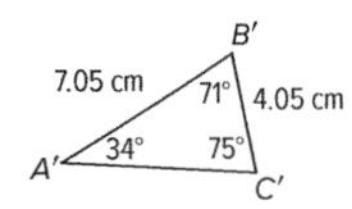

41. 6 **43a.** D **43b.** C

Lesson 7-4

1. Yes; $\triangle LMN \sim \triangle OPN$ by SAS Similarity. **3.** No; corresponding sides are not proportional. **5.** $\triangle LMN$ is not similar to $\triangle PQR$. **7a.** No; need congruent included angles. **7b.** Yes; SSS Similarity. **7c.** Yes; SSS Similarity. **7d.** No; need congruent included angles. **9.** Yes; $\triangle XUZ \sim \triangle WUY$ by SSS Similarity. **11.** Yes; $\triangle CBA \sim \triangle DBF$ by SAS Similarity. **13.** No; not enough information to determine. If $JH = 3$ or $WY = 24$, then $\triangle JHK \sim \triangle XWY$ by SSS Similarity. **15.** Yes; $\triangle JLK \sim \triangle PLM$ by AA Similarity.

17 No; there is not enough information to determine. If sides $\overline{AF}$ and $\overline{DF}$ were known to be proportional, the triangles would be congruent by SAS Similarity. If either $\angle C$ and $\angle B$ or $\angle A$ and $\angle D$ were congruent, the triangles would be congruent by AA Similarity.

19. $\triangle DEF \sim \triangle GHT$ by SSS Similarity because $\frac{DE}{GH} = \frac{EF}{HI} = \frac{DF}{GI} = \frac{1}{3}$. **21.** $\triangle JKL \sim \triangle MNO$ by SSS Similarity because $\frac{JK}{MN} = \frac{KL}{NO} = \frac{JL}{MO} = 4$

23. $\triangle FGH \sim \triangle FJK$ by SAS Similarity because $\angle GFH \cong \angle JFK$ and $\frac{FG}{FJ} = \frac{FH}{FK} = 3$ **25.** $\triangle MNP \nsim \triangle MRT$

27. Proof:

Statements (Reasons)

1. $\triangle XYZ$ and $\triangle ABC$ are right triangles. (Given)
2. $\angle XYZ$ and $\angle ABC$ are right angles. (Def. of rt. $\triangle$)
3. $\angle XYZ \cong \angle ABC$ (All rt. $\angle$s are $\cong$.)
4. $\frac{XY}{AB} = \frac{YZ}{BC}$ (Given)
5. $\triangle YXZ \sim \triangle BAC$ (SAS Similarity)

29 We are given than $\angle X \cong \angle J$. $m\angle Y = 52$ and $m\angle K = 52$, so $m\angle Y = m\angle K$ by substitution. $\angle Y \cong \angle K$ by the definition of congruent angles. Thus $\triangle XYZ \sim \triangle JKL$ by AA Similarity.

$\frac{XY}{JK} = \frac{YZ}{KL}$

$\frac{5}{4} = \frac{15}{x}$

$5x = 60$

$x = 12$

31. Proof:

Statements (Reasons)

1. $\triangle ABC$ and $\triangle DEF$ are right triangles. (Given)
2. $\angle B$ and $\angle E$ are right angles. (Def. of rt. triangle)
3. $\angle B \cong \angle E$ (All rt. angles are congruent.)
4. $DE = \frac{2}{3}AB$, $EF = \frac{2}{3}BC$ (Given)
5. $\frac{DE}{AB} = \frac{2}{3}$, $\frac{EF}{BC} = \frac{2}{3}$ (Div. Prop. of =)
6. $\frac{DE}{AB} = \frac{EF}{BC}$ (Substitution)
7. $\triangle ABC \sim \triangle DEF$ (SAS Similarity Theorem)
8. $\frac{DF}{AC} = \frac{DE}{AB}$ (Corr. sides of $\sim$ $\triangle$s are proportional.)

33a.

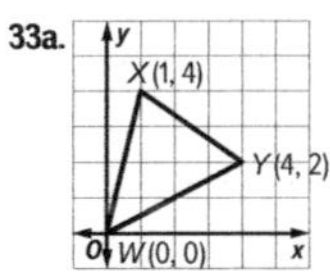

33b. $W'(0, 0)$, $X'(2, 8)$, and $Y'(8, 4)$ **33c.** Use the Distance Formula to find the side lengths of the preimage triangle and of the image triangle. Then find the ratio of the side lengths for each pair of corresponding sides. Use coordinates $W'(0, 0)$, $X'(2, 8)$, and $Y'(8, 4)$ for the image triangle.

$WX = \sqrt{(1-0)^2 + (4-0)^2} = \sqrt{17}$

$W'X' = \sqrt{(2-0)^2 + (8-0)^2} = 2\sqrt{17}$

So, $\frac{W'X'}{WX} = \frac{2\sqrt{17}}{\sqrt{17}}$ or 2.

$XY = \sqrt{(4-1)^2 + (2-4)^2} = \sqrt{13}$

$X'Y' = \sqrt{(8-2)^2 + (4-8)^2} = 2\sqrt{13}$

So, $\frac{X'Y'}{XY} = \frac{2\sqrt{13}}{\sqrt{13}}$ or 2.

$WX = \sqrt{(2-0)^2 + (4-0)^2} = 2\sqrt{5}$

$W'X' = \sqrt{(4-0)^2 + (8-0)^2} = 4\sqrt{5}$

So, $\frac{X'Z'}{XZ} = \frac{4\sqrt{5}}{2\sqrt{5}}$ or 2.

Because all three pairs of corresponding sides have a ratio of 2 to 1, the triangles are similar by the SSS Similarity Theorem.

35a. 10 in^2; The ratio of the areas is the square of the scale factor. **35b.** 7 in^2; The ratio of the areas is the square of the scale factor.

37a.

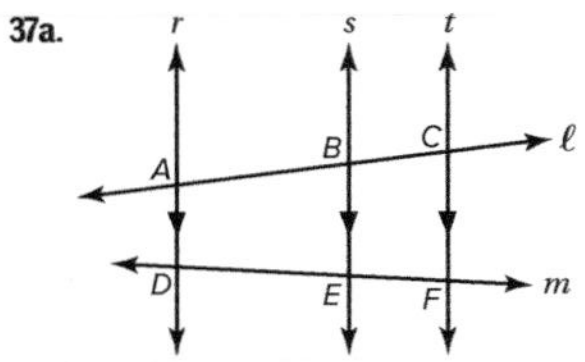

37b. Sample answer:

Lengths		Ratios	
AB	13 mm	$\frac{AB}{BC}$	1.625
BC	8 mm		
DE	12 mm	$\frac{DE}{EF}$	1.714
EF	7 mm		

37c. Sample answer: If three parallel lines intersect two transversals, then they divide the transversals proportionally. **39.** Sample answer: $\triangle EFG$ and $\triangle DBC$ are right triangles. Use the Pythagorean Theorem to find EG, or 6, and DB, or $2\sqrt{2}$. $\angle EFG \cong \angle DBC$ because all right angles are congruent and $\frac{EF}{DB} = \frac{FG}{BC} = \frac{3}{2}$. So $\triangle EFG \sim \triangle DBC$ by the SAS Similarity Theorem.

41. Sample answer:

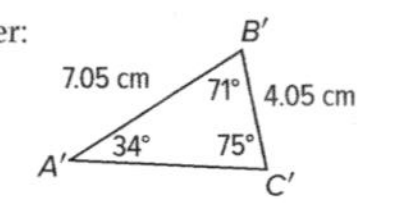

43. Sample answer: Because one pair of corresponding angles are congruent, compare the ratios of the sides for which the angle is the included angle, or $\frac{KM}{ON} = \frac{30}{25}$ or $\frac{6}{5}$, $\frac{LM}{PN} = \frac{36}{30}$ or $\frac{6}{5}$. Because $\frac{KM}{ON} = \frac{LM}{PN}$, the SAS Similarity Theorem applies. To find KL, solve the proportion $\frac{KL}{OP} = \frac{6}{5}$. $\frac{KL}{OP} = \frac{6}{5}$, $\frac{4x}{3x+2} = \frac{6}{5}$; $x = 6$; Thus $KL = 24$, and $OP = 20$. **45a.** C **45b.** D **45c.** B, D, E **47.** D

Lesson 7-5

1. 10 **3.** Yes; $\frac{AD}{DC} = \frac{BE}{EC} = \frac{2}{3}$, so $\overline{DE} \parallel \overline{AB}$. **5.** 11 **7.** 2360.3 ft **9.** $x = 20$; $y = 2$

11 If $AB = 12$ and $AC = 16$, then $BC = 4$.

$\frac{AB}{BC} = \frac{AE}{ED}$	Triangle Proportionality Theorem
$\frac{12}{4} = \frac{AE}{5}$	Substitute.
$12 \cdot 5 = 4 \cdot AE$	Cross Products Property
$60 = 4AE$	Multiply.
$15 = AE$	Divide each side by 4.

13. 10 **15.** yes; $\frac{ZV}{VX} = \frac{WY}{YX} = \frac{11}{5}$ **17.** no; $\frac{ZV}{VX} \neq \frac{WY}{YX}$

19

$m\angle PHM + m\angle PHJ + m\angle JHL = 180$	Definition of a straight angle
$44 + m\angle PHJ + 76 = 180$	Substitution
$120 + m\angle PHJ = 180$	Simplify.

$m\angle PHJ = 60$ Subtract 120 from each side.

By the Triangle Midsegment Theorem, $\overline{PH} \parallel \overline{KL}$.

$\angle PHJ \cong \angle JHL$ Alternate Interior Angles Theorem

$m\angle PHJ = m\angle JHL$ Definition of congruence

$60 = x$ Substitution

21. 1.35 **23.** 1.2 in. **25.** $x = 18; y = 3$ **27.** $x = 48; y = 72$

29. Given: $\overline{AD} \parallel \overline{BE} \parallel \overline{CF}$, $\overline{AB} \cong \overline{BC}$
Prove: $\overline{DE} \cong \overline{EF}$

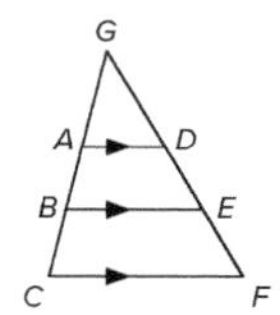

Proof:
From Corollary 7.1, $\frac{AB}{BC} = \frac{DE}{EF}$.
Because $\overline{AB} \cong \overline{BC}$, $AB = BC$ by definition of congruence.
Therefore, $\frac{AB}{BC} = 1$.
By substitution, $1 = \frac{DE}{EF}$. Thus, $DE = EF$. By definition of congruence, $\overline{DE} \cong \overline{EF}$.

31. Given: $\frac{DB}{AD} = \frac{EC}{AE}$
Prove: $\overline{DE} \parallel \overline{BC}$

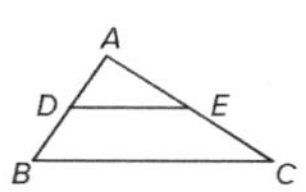

Proof:
Statements (Reasons)
1. $\frac{DB}{AD} = \frac{EC}{AE}$ (Given)
2. $\frac{AD}{AD} + \frac{DB}{AD} = \frac{AE}{AE} + \frac{EC}{AE}$ (Add. Prop.)
3. $\frac{AD + DB}{AD} = \frac{AE + EC}{AE}$ (Subst.)
4. $AB = AD + DB$, $AC = AE + EC$ (Seg. Add. Post.)
5. $\frac{AB}{AD} = \frac{AC}{AE}$ (Subst.)
6. $\angle A \cong \angle A$ (Refl. Prop.)
7. $\triangle ADE \sim \triangle ABC$ (SAS Similarity)
8. $\angle ADE \cong \angle ABC$ (Def. of $\sim$ polygons)
9. $\overline{DE} \parallel \overline{BC}$ (If corr. ∡ are ≅, then the lines are ∥.)

33. 9

(35) If $CA = 10$ and $CD = 2$, then $DA = 8$.

$\frac{CE}{EB} = \frac{CD}{DA}$	Triangle Proportionality Theorem
$\frac{t-2}{t+1} = \frac{2}{8}$	Substitute.
$(t-2)(8) = (t+1)(2)$	Cross Products Property
$8t - 16 = 2t + 2$	Distributive Property
$6t - 16 = 2$	Subtract $2t$ from each side.
$6t = 18$	Add 16 to each side.
$t = 3$	Divide each side by 6.

If $t = 3$, then $CE = 3 - 2$ or 1.

37. 8, 7.5 **39.** Because $\overline{FD} \parallel \overline{AC}$, $\angle EFD \cong \angle EAC$. By the Reflexive Property of Congruence, $\angle AEC \cong \angle AEC$. Therefore, $\triangle EFD \sim \triangle EAC$ by the AA Similarity Postulate. By the Triangle Proportionality Theorem, ED is proportional to EC. Because the segments stay parallel as the gauge is repositioned, ED remains proportional to EC. **41.** 6

(43) All the triangles are isosceles. Segment EH is the midsegment of triangle ABC. Therefore, segment EH is half of the length of AC, which is $35 \div 2$ or 17.5 feet. Similarly, FG is the midsegment of triangle BEH, so $FG = 17.5 \div 2$ or 8.75 feet. To find DJ, use the vertical altitude which is 12 feet. Let the altitude from B to the segment AC meet the segment DJ at K. Find BC using the Pythagorean Theorem.

$BC^2 = BK^2 + KC^2$
$BC^2 = 12^2 + 17.5^2$
$BC = \sqrt{12^2 + 17.5^2}$
$BC \approx 21.22$ ft

Because the width of each piece of siding is the same, $BJ = \frac{3}{4}BC$, which is about $\frac{3}{4}(21.22)$ or 15.92 ft. Now, use the Triangle Proportionality Theorem.

$\frac{AC}{BC} = \frac{DJ}{BJ}$
$\frac{35}{21.22} = \frac{DJ}{15.92}$
$21.22(DJ) = (15.92)(35)$
$21.22(DJ) = 557.2$
$DJ \approx 26.25$ ft

45. Sample answer:

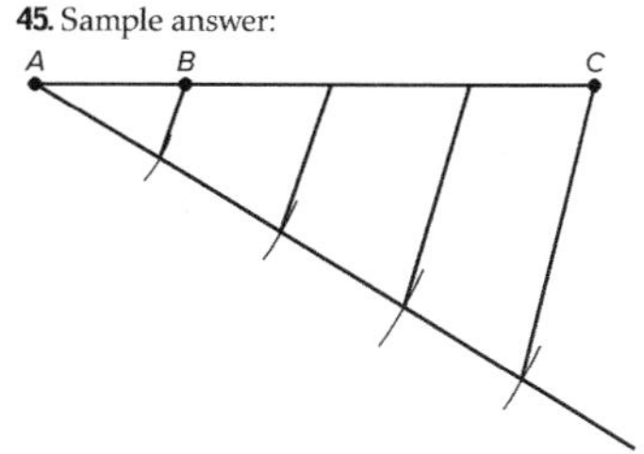

47a. Sample answer:

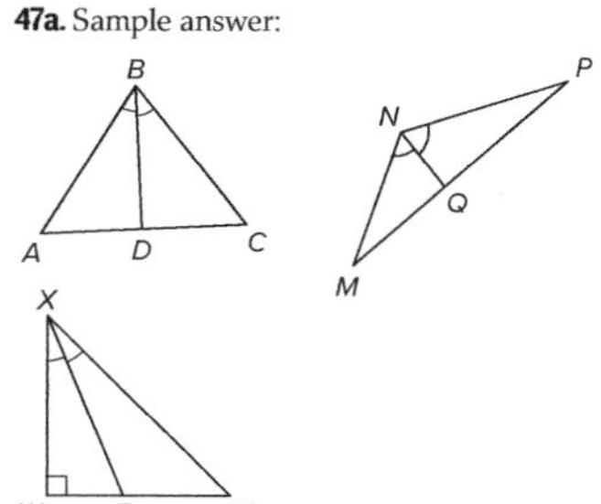

47b.

Triangle	Length		Ratio	
ABC	AD	1.1 cm	$\frac{AD}{CD}$	1.0
	CD	1.1 cm		
	AB	2.0 cm	$\frac{AB}{CB}$	1.0
	CB	2.0 cm		
MNP	MQ	1.4 cm	$\frac{MQ}{PQ}$	0.8
	PQ	1.7 cm		
	MN	1.6 cm	$\frac{MN}{PN}$	0.8
	PN	2.0 cm		
WXY	WZ	0.8 cm	$\frac{WZ}{YZ}$	0.7
	YZ	1.2 cm		
	WX	2.0 cm	$\frac{WX}{YX}$	0.7
	YX	2.9 cm		

47c. Sample answer: The proportion of the segments created by the angle bisector of a triangle is equal to the proportion of their respective consecutive sides.
49. Always; sample answer: $\overline{FH}$ is a midsegment. Let $BC = x$, then $FH = \frac{1}{2}x$. $FHCB$ is a trapezoid, so $DE = \frac{1}{2}(BC + FH) = \frac{1}{2}\left(x + \frac{1}{2}x\right) = \frac{1}{2}x + \frac{1}{4}x = \frac{3}{4}x$.
Therefore, $DE = \frac{3}{4}BC$.

51.

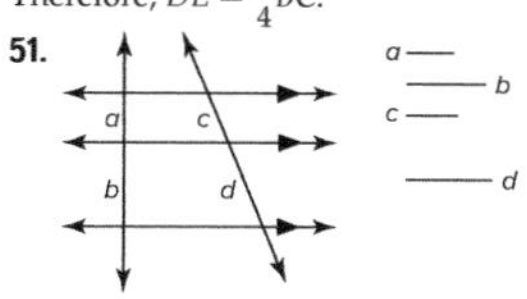

By Corollary 7.1, $\frac{a}{b} = \frac{c}{d}$.

53. B **55.** C **57.** 50 **59.** $\frac{20}{3}$

Lesson 7-6

(1) The triangles are similar by AA Similarity.

$\frac{x}{10} = \frac{12}{15}$	$\sim\triangle$s have corr. medians proportional to the corr. sides.
$x \cdot 15 = 10 \cdot 12$	Cross Products Property
$15x = 120$	Simplify.
$x = 8$	Divide each side by 15.

3. 35.7 in. **5.** 20 **7.** 8.5 **9.** 18

(11)

$\frac{15}{27} = \frac{28 - b}{b}$	Triangle Angle Bisector Theorem
$15 \cdot b = 27(28 - b)$	Cross Products Property
$15b = 756 - 27b$	Multiply.
$42b = 756$	Add $27b$ to each side.
$b = 18$	Divide each side by 42.

13. 15

(15)

$\frac{AB}{JK} = \frac{AD}{JM}$	$\sim\triangle$s have corr. altitudes proportional to the corr. sides.
$\frac{9}{21} = \frac{4x - 8}{5x + 3}$	Substitute.
$9(5x + 3) = 21(4x - 8)$	Cross Products Property
$45x + 27 = 84x - 168$	Distributive Property
$27 = 39x - 168$	Subtract $45x$ from each side.
$195 = 39x$	Add 168 to each side.
$5 = x$	Divide each side by 39.

17. 4
19. Given: $\triangle ABC \sim \triangle RST$
$\overline{AD}$ is a median of $\triangle ABC$.
$\overline{RU}$ is a median of $\triangle RST$.
Prove: $\frac{AD}{RU} = \frac{AB}{RS}$

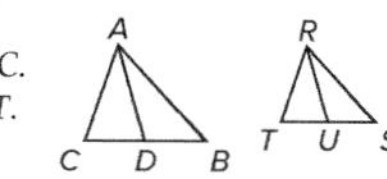

Proof:
Statements (Reasons)
1. $\triangle ABC \sim \triangle RST$; $\overline{AD}$ is a median of $\triangle ABC$; $\overline{RU}$ is a median of $\triangle RST$. (Given)
2. $CD = DB$; $TU = US$ (Def. of median)
3. $\frac{AB}{RS} = \frac{CB}{TS}$ (Def. of $\sim\triangle$s)
4. $CB = CD + DB$; $TS = TU + US$ (Seg. Add. Post.)
5. $\frac{AB}{RS} = \frac{CD + DB}{TU + US}$ (Subst.)
6. $\frac{AB}{RS} = \frac{DB + DB}{US + US}$ or $\frac{2(DB)}{2(US)}$ (Subst.)
7. $\frac{AB}{RS} = \frac{DB}{US}$ (Subst.)
8. $\angle B \cong \angle S$ (Def. of $\sim\triangle$s)
9. $\triangle ABD \sim \triangle RSU$ (SAS Similarity)
10. $\frac{AD}{RU} = \frac{AB}{RS}$ (Def. of $\sim\triangle$s)

21. 3 **23.** 70
25. Given: $\overline{CD}$ bisects $\angle ACB$.
By construction, $\overline{AE} \parallel \overline{CD}$.
Prove: $\frac{AD}{DB} = \frac{AC}{BC}$

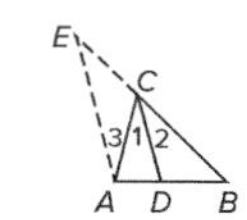

Proof:
Statements (Reasons)
1. $\overline{CD}$ bisects $\angle ACB$; By construction, $\overline{AE} \parallel \overline{CD}$. (Given)
2. $\frac{AD}{DB} = \frac{EC}{BC}$ (△ Prop. Thm.)
3. $\angle 1 \cong \angle 2$ (Def. of ∠ Bisector)
4. $\angle 3 \cong \angle 1$ (Alt. Int. ∡ Thm.)
5. $\angle 2 \cong \angle E$ (Corr. ∡ Post.)
6. $\angle 3 \cong \angle E$ (Trans. Prop.)
7. $\overline{EC} \cong \overline{AC}$ (Converse of Isos. △ Thm.)
8. $EC = AC$ (Def. of ≅ segs.)
9. $\frac{AD}{DB} = \frac{AC}{BC}$ (Subst.)

27. Given: $\triangle QTS \sim \triangle XWZ$,
$\overline{TR}$, $\overline{WY}$ are ∠ bisectors.
Prove: $\frac{TR}{WY} = \frac{QT}{XW}$

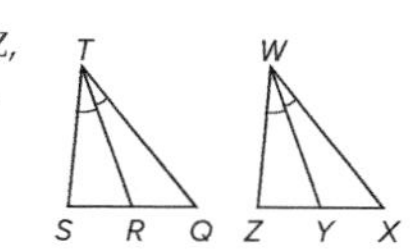

Proof:
Statements (Reasons)
1. $\triangle QTS \sim \triangle XWZ$, $\overline{TR}$ and $\overline{WY}$ are angle bisectors. (Given)
2. $\angle QTS \cong \angle XWZ$, $\angle Q \cong \angle X$ (Def of $\sim\triangle$s)
3. $\angle STR \cong \angle QTR$, $\angle ZWY \cong \angle XWY$ (Def. ∠ bisector)
4. $m\angle STQ = m\angle STR + m\angle QTR$, $m\angle ZWX = m\angle ZWY + m\angle XWY$ (∠ Add. Post.)

5. $m\angle STQ = 2m\angle QTR$, $m\angle ZWX = 2m\angle XWY$ (Subst.)
6. $2m\angle QTR = 2m\angle XWY$ (Subst.)
7. $m\angle QTR = m\angle XWY$ (Div. Prop.)
8. $\angle QTR \cong \angle XWY$ (Def. of $\cong$ Angles)
9. $\triangle QTR \sim \triangle XWY$ (AA Similarity)
10. $\frac{TR}{WY} = \frac{QT}{XW}$ (Def. of $\sim \triangle$s)

29 Because the segment from Trevor to Ricardo is an angle bisector, the segments from Ricardo to Craig and from Ricardo to Eli are proportional to the segments from Trevor to Craig and from Trevor to Eli. Because Craig is closer to Trevor than Eli is, Craig is also closer to Ricardo than Eli is. So, Craig will reach Ricardo first.

31. Chun; by the Angle Bisector Theorem, the correct proportion is $\frac{5}{8} = \frac{15}{x}$. **33.** $PS = 18.4$, $RS = 24$ **35.** Both theorems have a segment that bisects an angle and have proportionate ratios. The Triangle Angle Bisector Theorem pertains to one triangle, while Theorem 7.9 pertains to similar triangles. Unlike the Triangle Angle Bisector Theorem, which separates the opposite side into segments that have the same ratio as the other two sides, Theorem 7.9 relates the angle bisector to the measures of the sides. **37.** D **39.** 36

Chapter 7 Study Guide and Review

1. f; midsegment. **3.** g; dilation **5.** i; reduction **7.** j; Transitive Property of Similarity **9.** The line segment must be parallel to the third side and its length is one half the length of the third side. **11.** reduction; 0.45; 8.25 **13.** Yes, the rectangles are similar because all of the corresponding angles are congruent and the corresponding sides are proportional in a 3:2 ratio. **15.** The triangles are not similar. **17.** 34.2 ft **19.** Yes, $\triangle IJK \sim \triangle HFG$ by the SSS ~ Thm. **21.** 22.5 **23.** 6 **25.** 633 mi

CHAPTER 8

Right Triangles and Trigonometry

Chapter 8 Concept Check

1. Multiply by $\frac{\sqrt{3}}{\sqrt{3}}$. **3.** $a^2 + b^2 = c^2$ **5.** Take the positive square root of each side. **7.** 68.8 in. **9.** Plot points A and B and then connect the plotted points.

Lesson 8-1

1. 10 **3.** $10\sqrt{6}$ or 24.5 **5.** $x = 6$; $y = 3\sqrt{5} \approx 6.7$; $z = 6\sqrt{5} \approx 13.4$ **7.** 18 ft 11 in.

9
$x = \sqrt{ab}$ — Definition of geometric mean
$= \sqrt{16 \cdot 25}$ — $a = 16$ and $b = 25$
$= \sqrt{(4 \cdot 4) \cdot (5 \cdot 5)}$ — Factor.
$= 4 \cdot 5$ or 20 — Simplify.

11. $12\sqrt{6} \approx 29.4$ **13.** $3\sqrt{3} \approx 5.2$ **15.** $\triangle WXY \sim \triangle XZY \sim \triangle WZX$ **17.** $\triangle HGF \sim \triangle HIG \sim \triangle GIF$

19
$17 = \sqrt{6 \cdot (y - 6)}$ — Geometric Mean (Altitude) Theorem
$289 = 6 \cdot (y - 6)$ — Square each side.
$\frac{289}{6} = y - 6$ — Divide each side by 6.
$54\frac{1}{6} = y$ — Add 6 to each side.
$54.2 \approx y$ — Write as a decimal.
$x = \sqrt{6 \cdot y}$ — Geometric Mean (Leg) Theorem
$= \sqrt{6 \cdot 54\frac{1}{6}}$ — $y = 54\frac{1}{6}$
$= \sqrt{325}$ — Multiply.
$= 5\sqrt{13}$ — Simplify.
≈ 18.0 — Use a calculator.
$z = \sqrt{(y - 6) \cdot y}$ — Geometric Mean (Leg) Theorem
$= \sqrt{\left(54\frac{1}{6} - 6\right) \cdot 54\frac{1}{6}}$ — $y = 54\frac{1}{6}$
$= \sqrt{48\frac{1}{6} \cdot 54\frac{1}{6}}$ — Subtract.
≈ 51.1 — Use a calculator.

21. $x \approx 4.7$; $y \approx 1.8$; $z \approx 13.1$ **23.** $x = 24\sqrt{2} \approx 33.9$; $y = 8\sqrt{2} \approx 11.3$; $z = 32$ **25.** 161.8 ft **27.** $\frac{\sqrt{30}}{7}$ or 0.8 **29.** $x = \frac{3\sqrt{3}}{2} \approx 2.6$; $y = \frac{3}{2}$; $z = 3$ **31.** 11 **33.** 3.5 ft **35.** 5 **37.** 4

39. Given: $\angle PQR$ is a right angle. $\overline{QS}$ is an altitude of $\triangle PQR$.
Prove: $\triangle PSQ \sim \triangle PQR$
$\triangle PQR \sim \triangle QSR$
$\triangle PSQ \sim \triangle QSR$

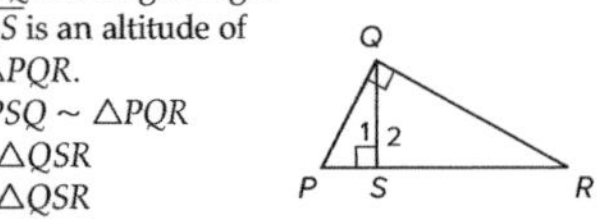

Proof:
Statements (Reasons)
1. $\angle PQR$ is a right angle. $\overline{QS}$ is an altitude of $\triangle PQR$. (Given)
2. $\overline{QS} \perp \overline{RP}$ (Definition of altitude)
3. $\angle 1$ and $\angle 2$ are right angles. (Definition of perpendicular lines)
4. $\angle 1 \cong \angle PQR$, $\angle 2 \cong \angle PQR$ (All right $\angle$s are $\cong$.)
5. $\angle P \cong \angle P$, $\angle R \cong \angle R$ (Congruence of angles is reflexive.)
6. $\triangle PSQ \sim \triangle PQR$, $\triangle PQR \sim \triangle QSR$ (AA Similarity Statements 4 and 5)
7. $\triangle PSQ \sim \triangle QSR$ (Similarity of triangles is transitive.)

41. Given: $\angle ADC$ is a right angle. $\overline{DB}$ is an altitude of $\triangle ADC$.
Prove: $\frac{AB}{AD} = \frac{AD}{AC}$
$\frac{BC}{DC} = \frac{DC}{AC}$

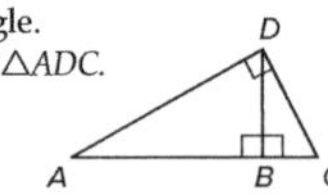

Proof:
Statements (Reasons)
1. $\angle ADC$ is a right angle. $\overline{DB}$ is an altitude of $\triangle ADC$. (Given)
2. $\triangle ADC$ is a right triangle. (Definition of right triangle)
3. $\triangle ABD \sim \triangle ADC$, $\triangle DBC \sim \triangle ADC$ (If the altitude is drawn from the vertex of the rt. $\angle$ to the hypotenuse of a rt. $\triangle$, then the 2 $\triangle$s formed are similar to the given $\triangle$ and to each other.)
4. $\frac{AB}{AD} = \frac{AD}{AC}$, $\frac{BC}{DC} = \frac{DC}{AC}$ (Def. of similar triangles)

43
$x = \sqrt{ab}$ — Definition of geometric mean
$= \sqrt{7 \cdot 12}$ — $a = 7$ and $b = 12$
$= \sqrt{84}$ — Multiply.
≈ 9 — Simplify.

The average rate of return is about 9%.

45 Sample answer: The geometric mean of two consecutive integers is $\sqrt{x(x+1)}$ and the average of two consecutive integers is $\frac{x + (x+1)}{2}$.

$\sqrt{x(x+1)} \stackrel{?}{=} \frac{x + (x+1)}{2}$
$\sqrt{x^2 + x} \stackrel{?}{=} \frac{2x+1}{2}$
$\sqrt{x^2 + x} \stackrel{?}{=} x + \frac{1}{2}$
$x^2 + x \stackrel{?}{=} \left(x + \frac{1}{2}\right)^2$
$x^2 + x \stackrel{?}{=} x^2 + x + \frac{1}{4}$
$0 \neq \frac{1}{4}$

If you set the two expressions equal to each other, the equation has no solution. So, the statement is never true.

47. Sometimes; sample answer: When the product of the two integers is a perfect square, the geometric mean will be a positive integer. **49.** Neither; sample answer: On the similar triangles created by the altitude, the leg that is x units long on the smaller triangle corresponds with the leg that is 8 units long on the larger triangle, so the correct proportion is $\frac{4}{x} = \frac{x}{8}$ and x is about 5.7. **51.** Sample answer: 9 and 4, 8 and 8; In order for two whole numbers to result in a whole-number geometric mean, their product must be a perfect square. **53.** Sample answer: Both the arithmetic and the geometric mean calculate a value between two given numbers. The arithmetic mean of two numbers a and b is $\frac{a+b}{2}$, and the geometric mean of two numbers a and b is $\sqrt{ab}$. The two means will be equal when $a = b$.

Justification:

$\frac{a+b}{2} = \sqrt{ab}$

$\left(\frac{a+b}{2}\right)^2 = ab$

$\frac{(a+b)^2}{4} = ab$

$(a+b)^2 = 4ab$

$a^2 + 2ab + b^2 = 4ab$

$a^2 - 2ab + b^2 = 0$

$(a-b)^2 = 0$

$a - b = 0$

$a = b$

55. C **57.** D **59a.** 2:3 **59b.** 28, 63

Lesson 8-2

1. 12

(3) The side opposite the right angle is the hypotenuse, so $c = 16$.

$a^2 + b^2 = c^2$	Pythagorean Theorem
$4^2 + x^2 = 16^2$	$a = 4$ and $b = x$
$16 + x^2 = 256$	Simplify.
$x^2 = 240$	Subtract 16 from each side.
$x = \sqrt{240}$	Take the positive square root of each side.
$x = 4\sqrt{15}$	Simplify.
$x \approx 15.5$	Use a calculator.

5. D **7.** yes; obtuse **9.** 20 **11.** $\sqrt{21} \approx 4.6$

$26^2 \stackrel{?}{=} 16^2 + 18^2$

$676 > 256 + 324$

13. $\frac{\sqrt{10}}{5} \approx 0.6$

(15) 16 and 30 are both multiples of 2: $16 = 2 \cdot 8$ and $30 = 2 \cdot 15$. Because 8, 15, 17 is a Pythagorean triple, the missing hypotenuse is $2 \cdot 17$ or 34.

17. 70 **19.** about 3 ft

21. yes; obtuse

$21^2 \stackrel{?}{=} 7^2 + 15^2$

$441 > 49 + 225$

23. yes; right

$20.5^2 \stackrel{?}{=} 4.5^2 + 20^2$

$420.25 = 20.25 + 400$

25. yes; acute

$7.6^2 \stackrel{?}{=} 4.2^2 + 6.4^2$

$57.76 < 17.64 + 40.96$

27. 15 **29.** $4\sqrt{6} \approx 9.8$

31. acute; $XY = \sqrt{29}$, $YZ = \sqrt{20}$, $XZ = \sqrt{13}$; $(\sqrt{29})^2 < (\sqrt{20})^2 + (\sqrt{13})^2$ **33.** right; $XY = 6$, $YZ = 10$, $XZ = 8$; $6^2 + 8^2 = 10^2$

35. Given: $\triangle ABC$ with sides of measure a, b, and c, where $c^2 = a^2 + b^2$

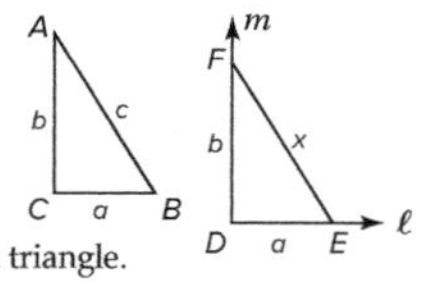

Prove: $\triangle ABC$ is a right triangle.

Proof:

Draw $\overline{DE}$ on line ℓ with measure equal to a. At D, draw line $m \perp \overline{DE}$. Locate point F on m so that $DF = b$. Draw $\overline{FE}$ and call its measure x. Because $\triangle FED$ is a right triangle, $a^2 + b^2 = x^2$. But $a^2 + b^2 = c^2$, so $x^2 = c^2$ or $x = c$. Thus, $\triangle ABC \cong \triangle FED$ by SSS. This means $\angle C \cong \angle D$. Therefore, $\angle C$ must be a right angle, making $\triangle ABC$ a right triangle.

37. Given: In $\triangle ABC$, $c^2 > a^2 + b^2$ where c is the length of the longest side.

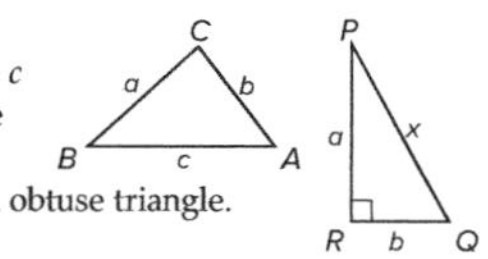

Prove: $\triangle ABC$ is an obtuse triangle.

Proof:

Statements (Reasons)

1. In $\triangle ABC$, $c^2 > a^2 + b^2$ where c is the length of the longest side. In $\triangle PQR$, $\angle R$ is a right angle. (Given)

2. $a^2 + b^2 = x^2$ (Pythagorean Theorem)

3. $c^2 > x^2$ (Substitution Property)

4. $c > x$ (A property of square roots)

5. $m\angle R = 90$ (Definition of a right angle)

6. $m\angle C > m\angle R$ (Converse of the Hinge Theorem)

7. $m\angle C > 90$ (Substitution Property of Equality)

8. $\angle C$ is an obtuse angle. (Definition of an obtuse angle)

9. $\triangle ABC$ is an obtuse triangle. (Definition of an obtuse triangle)

39. $P = 36$ units; $A = 60$ square units^2 **41.** 15

(43)

Scale	Width to Length	
	$\frac{16}{9} = \frac{41 \text{ in.}}{x \text{ in.}}$	Write a proportion.
	$16 \cdot x = 9 \cdot 41$	Cross Product Property
	$16x = 369$	Simplify.
	$x = \frac{369}{16}$	Divide each side by 16.

The length of the television is about 23 inches.

$a^2 + b^2 = c^2$	Pythagorean Theorem
$\left(\frac{369}{16}\right)^2 + 41^2 = c^2$	$a = \frac{369}{16}$ and $b = 41$
$\sqrt{\left(\frac{369}{16}\right)^2 + 41^2} = c$	Take the positive square root of each side.
$47.0 \approx c$	Use a calculator.

The screen size is about 47 inches.

(45) The side opposite the right angle is the hypotenuse, so $c = x$.

$a^2 + b^2 = c^2$	Pythagorean Theorem
$8^2 + (x-4)^2 = x^2$	$a = 8$ and $b = x - 4$
$64 + x^2 - 8x + 16 = x^2$	Find 8^2 and $(x-4)^2$.
$-8x + 80 = 0$	Simplify.
$80 = 8x$	Add $8x$ to each side.
$10 = x$	Divide each side by 8.

47. $\frac{1}{2}$ **49.** 5.4 **51.** Right; sample answer: If you double or halve the side lengths, all three sides of the new triangles are proportional to the sides of the original triangle. Using the Side-Side-Side Similarity Theorem, you know that both of the new triangles are similar to the original triangle, so they are both right.

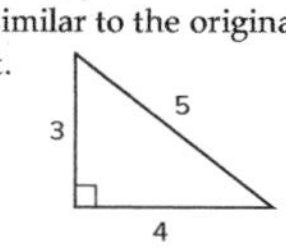

53. C **55.** 85 **57.** B

Lesson 8-3

1. $5\sqrt{2}$ **3.** 22 **5.** $x = 14$; $y = 7\sqrt{3}$ **7.** Yes; sample answer: The height of the triangle is about $3\frac{1}{2}$ in., so because the height of the plaque is less than the diameter of the opening, it will fit. **9.** $\frac{15\sqrt{2}}{2}$ or $7.5\sqrt{2}$

(11) In a 45°-45°-90° triangle, the length of the hypotenuse is $\sqrt{2}$ times the length of a leg.

$h = x\sqrt{2}$	Theorem 8.8
$= 18\sqrt{3} \cdot \sqrt{2}$	Substitution
$= 18\sqrt{6}$	$\sqrt{3} \cdot \sqrt{2} = \sqrt{6}$

13. $20\sqrt{2}$ **15.** $\frac{11\sqrt{2}}{2}$ **17.** $8\sqrt{2}$ or 11.3 cm **19.** $x = 10$; $y = 20$ **21.** $x = \frac{17\sqrt{3}}{2}$; $y = \frac{17}{2}$ **23.** $x = \frac{14\sqrt{3}}{3}$; $y = \frac{28\sqrt{3}}{3}$ **25.** $16\sqrt{3}$ or 27.7 ft **27.** 22.6 ft

(29) In a 45°-45°-90° triangle, the length of the hypotenuse is 2 times the length of a leg.

$h = x\sqrt{2}$	Theorem 8.8
$6 = x\sqrt{2}$	Substitution
$\frac{6}{\sqrt{2}} = x$	Divide each side by $\sqrt{2}$.
$\frac{6}{\sqrt{2}} \cdot \frac{\sqrt{2}}{\sqrt{2}} = x$	Rationalize the denominator.
$\frac{6 \cdot \sqrt{2}}{\sqrt{2} \cdot \sqrt{2}} = x$	Multiply.
$\frac{6\sqrt{2}}{2} = x$	$\sqrt{2} \cdot \sqrt{2} = 2$
$3\sqrt{2} = x$	Simplify.
$h = x\sqrt{2}$	Theorem 8.8
$y = 6\sqrt{2}$	Substitution

31. $x = 5$; $y = 10$ **33.** $x = 45$; $y = 12\sqrt{2}$

(35) In a 30°-60°-90° triangle, the length of the hypotenuse is 2 times the length of the shorter leg.

$h = 2s$	Theorem 8.9
$= 2(25)$ or 50	Substitution

The zip line's length is 50 feet.

37. $x = 9\sqrt{2}$; $y = 6\sqrt{3}$; $z = 12\sqrt{3}$

39. 7.5 ft; 10.6 ft; 13.0 ft **41.** (6, 9) **43.** (4, −2)

(45) **a.**

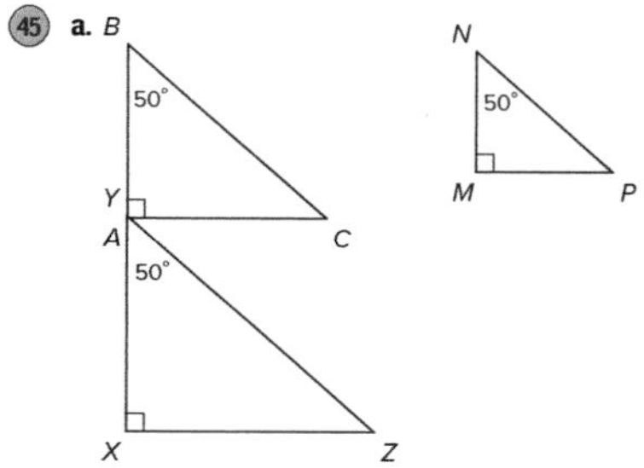

b. Measure the sides of the triangles to the nearest tenth of a centimeter. Find the ratios to the nearest tenth of a centimeter. Sample answer:

Triangle	Length				Ratio	
ABC	AC	2.4 cm	BC	3.2 cm	$\frac{BC}{AC}$	1.3
MNP	MP	1.7 cm	NP	2.2 cm	$\frac{NP}{MP}$	1.3
XYZ	XZ	3.0 cm	YZ	3.9 cm	$\frac{YZ}{XZ}$	1.3

c. Sample answer: In a right triangle with a 50° angle, the ratio of the leg opposite the 50° angle to the hypotenuse will always be the same, 1.3.

47. Sample answer: Let ℓ represent the length. $\ell^2 + w^2 = (2w)^2$; $\ell^2 = 3w^2$; $\ell = w\sqrt{3}$.

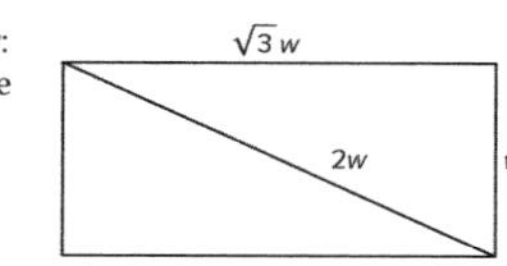

49. 37.9 **51.** C **53.** $20\sqrt{2}$ units **55.** C **57a.** $6\sqrt{2}$ **57b.** $4\sqrt{3}$ **59.** 12

Lesson 8-4

1. $\frac{16}{20} = 0.80$ **3.** $\frac{12}{20} = 0.60$ **5.** $\frac{16}{20} = 0.80$ **7.** $\frac{\sqrt{3}}{2} \approx 0.87$ **9.** 27.44 **11.** about 1.2 ft **13.** 44.4 **15.** $RS \approx 6.7$; $m\angle R \approx 42$; $m\angle T \approx 48$

(17) $\sin J = \frac{\text{opp}}{\text{hyp}} = \frac{56}{65} \approx 0.86$

$\cos J = \frac{\text{adj}}{\text{hyp}} = \frac{33}{65} \approx 0.51$

$\tan J = \frac{\text{opp}}{\text{adj}}$ $\qquad \sin L = \frac{\text{opp}}{\text{hyp}}$
$= \frac{56}{33}$ $\qquad = \frac{33}{65}$
≈ 1.70 $\qquad \approx 0.51$
$\cos L = \frac{\text{adj}}{\text{hyp}}$ $\qquad \tan L = \frac{\text{opp}}{\text{adj}}$
$= \frac{56}{65}$ $\qquad = \frac{33}{56}$
≈ 0.86 $\qquad \approx 0.59$

19. $\frac{84}{85} = 0.99$; $\frac{13}{85} = 0.15$; $\frac{84}{13} = 6.46$; $\frac{13}{85} = 0.15$; $\frac{84}{85} = 0.99$; $\frac{13}{84} = 0.15$ **21.** $\frac{\sqrt{3}}{2} = 0.87$; $\frac{2\sqrt{2}}{4\sqrt{2}} = 0.50$; $\frac{2\sqrt{6}}{2\sqrt{2}} = \sqrt{3} = 1.73$; $\frac{2\sqrt{2}}{4\sqrt{2}} = 0.50$; $\frac{\sqrt{3}}{2} = 0.87$; $\frac{\sqrt{3}}{3} = 0.58$
23. $\frac{\sqrt{3}}{2} \approx 0.87$ **25.** $\frac{1}{2}$ or 0.5 **27.** $\frac{1}{2}$ or 0.5 **29.** 28.7
31. 57.2 **33.** 17.4

35 Let $m\angle A = 55$ and let x be the height of the roller coaster.

$\sin A = \frac{\text{opp}}{\text{hyp}}$	Definition of sine ratio
$\sin 55 = \frac{x}{98}$	Substitution
$98 \cdot \sin 55 = x$	Multiply each side by 98.
$80 \approx x$	Use a calculator.

The height of the roller coaster is about 80 feet.

37. 61.4 **39.** 28.5 **41.** 21.8 **43.** $WX = 15.1$; $XZ = 9.8$; $m\angle W = 33$ **45.** $ST = 30.6$; $m\angle R = 58$; $m\angle T = 32$

47 $JL = \sqrt{[-2-(-2)]^2 + [4-(-3)]^2} = 7$
$KJ = \sqrt{[-2-(-7)]^2 + [-3-(-3)]^2} = 5$

$\tan K = \frac{\text{opp}}{\text{adj}}$	Definition of tangent ratio
$= \frac{7}{5}$	Substitution
$m\angle K = \tan^{-1}\left(\frac{7}{5}\right) \approx 54.5$	Use a calculator.

49. 51.3 **51.** 13.83 in.; 7.51 in^2 **53.** 8.45 ft; 3.06 ft^2
55. 0.92

57 The triangle is isosceles, so two sides measure 32 and the two smaller triangles each have a side that measures x. Let $m\angle A = 54$.

$\cos A = \frac{\text{adj}}{\text{hyp}}$	Definition of cosine ratio
$\cos 54 = \frac{x}{32}$	Substitution
$32 \cdot \cos 54 = x$	Multiply each side by 32.
$18.8 \approx x$	Simplify.
$\sin A = \frac{\text{opp}}{\text{hyp}}$	Definition of sine ratio
$\sin 54 = \frac{y}{32}$	Substitution
$32 \cdot \sin 54 = y$	Multiply each side by 32.
$25.9 \approx y$	Simplify.

59. $x = 9.2$; $y = 11.7$

61a.

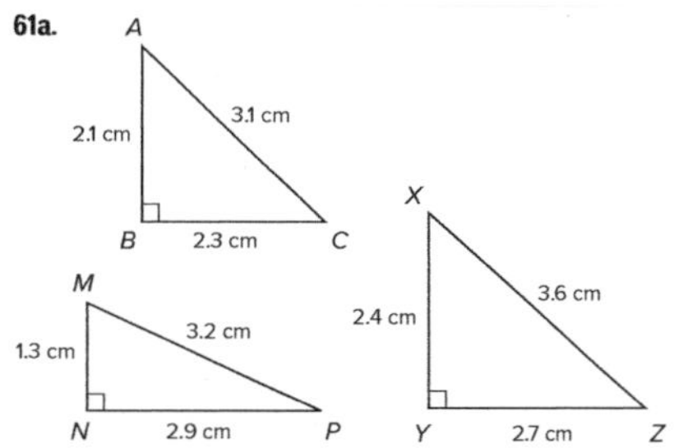

61b. Sample answer:

Triangle	Trigonometric Ratios				Sum of Ratios Squared	
ABC	cos A	0.677	sin A	0.742	$(\cos A)^2 + (\sin A)^2$	1
	cos C	0.742	sin C	0.677	$(\cos C)^2 + (\sin C)^2$	1
MNP	cos M	0.406	sin M	0.906	$(\cos M)^2 + (\sin M)^2$	1
	cos P	0.906	sin P	0.406	$(\cos P)^2 + (\sin P)^2$	1
XYZ	cos X	0.667	sin X	0.75	$(\cos X)^2 + (\sin X)^2$	1
	cos Z	0.75	sin Z	0.667	$(\cos Z)^2 + (\sin Z)^2$	1

61c. Sample answer: The sum of the cosine squared and the sine squared of an acute angle of a right triangle is 1.
61d. $(\sin X)^2 + (\cos X)^2 = 1$
61e. Sample answer:

$(\sin A)^2 + (\cos A)^2 \stackrel{?}{=} 1$	Conjecture
$\left(\frac{y}{r}\right)^2 + \left(\frac{x}{r}\right)^2 \stackrel{?}{=} 1$	$\sin A = \frac{y}{r}$, $\cos A = \frac{x}{r}$
$\frac{y^2}{r^2} + \frac{x^2}{r^2} \stackrel{?}{=} 1$	Simplify.
$\frac{y^2 + x^2}{r^2} \stackrel{?}{=} 1$	Combine fractions with like denominators.
$\frac{r^2}{r^2} \stackrel{?}{=} 1$	Pythagorean Theorem
$1 = 1$	Simplify.

63. Sample answer: Yes; because the values of sine and cosine are both calculated by dividing one of the legs of a right triangle by the hypotenuse, and the hypotenuse is always the longest side of a right triangle, the values will always be less than 1. You will always be dividing the smaller number by the larger number. **65.** Sample answer: To find the measure of an acute angle of a right triangle, you can find the ratio of the leg opposite the angle to the hypotenuse and use a calculator to find the inverse sine of the ratio, you can find the ratio of the leg adjacent to the angle to the hypotenuse and use a calculator to find the inverse cosine of the ratio, or you can find the ratio of the leg opposite the angle to the leg adjacent to the angle and use a calculator to find the inverse tangent of the ratio. **67a.** 47 **67b.** 1 **69.** A **71.** C

73a. $\frac{5\sqrt{29}}{29}$ **73b.** $\frac{2\sqrt{29}}{29}$ **73c.** $\frac{2\sqrt{29}}{29}$ **73d.** $\frac{5\sqrt{29}}{29}$ **73e.** 1

Lesson 8-5

1. 27.5 ft **3.** 14.2 ft

5 Make a sketch.

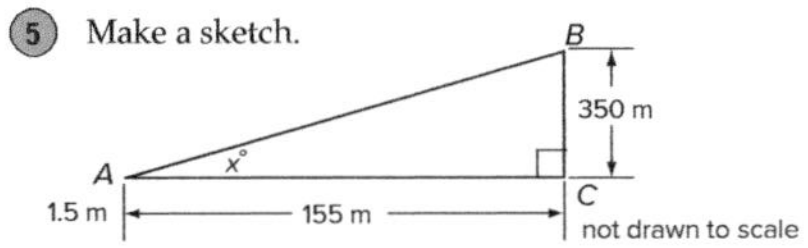

$\tan A = \frac{BC}{AC}$	$\tan = \frac{\text{opposite}}{\text{adjacent}}$
$\tan x° = \frac{348.5}{155}$	$m\angle A = x$, $BC = 350 - 1.5$ or 348.5, $AC = 155$
$x = \tan^{-1}\left(\frac{348.5}{155}\right)$	Solve for x.
$x \approx 66.0$	Use a calculator.

The angle of elevation is about 66°.

7. 14.8°

9 Make a sketch.

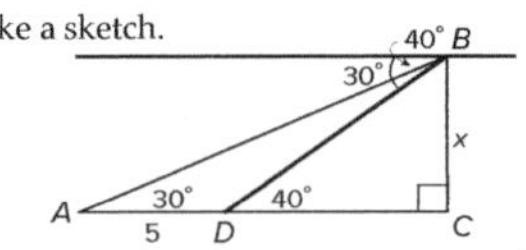

$\tan 30 = \frac{x}{5} + DC$	$\tan = \frac{\text{opposite}}{\text{adjacent}}$
$(5 + DC)\tan 30 = x$	Solve for x.
$\tan 40 = \frac{x}{DC}$	$\tan = \frac{\text{opposite}}{\text{adjacent}}$
$DC \tan 40 = x$	Solve for x.
$DC \tan 40 = (5 + DC) \tan 30$	Substitution
$DC \tan 40 = 5 \tan 30 + DC \tan 30$	Distributive Property
$DC \tan 40 - DC \tan 30 = 5 \tan 30$	Subtract $DC \tan 30$ from each side.
$DC(\tan 40 - \tan 30) = 5 \tan 30$	Factor DC.
$DC = \frac{5 \tan 30}{\tan 40 - \tan 30}$	Divide each side by tan 40 − tan 30.
$DC \approx 11.0$	Use a calculator.
$\tan A = \frac{BC}{AC}$	$\tan = \frac{\text{opposite}}{\text{adjacent}}$
$\tan 30 = \frac{x}{16.0}$	$A = 30$, $BC = x$, $AC = 5 + 11.0$ or 16.0
$16.0 \tan 30 = x$	Multiply each side by 16.0.
$9.3 \approx x$	Use a calculator.

The platform is about 9.3 feet high.

11. about 1309 ft **13.** 16.6° **15a.** about 2.17 ft
15b. Sample answer: The overhang is used to keep sunlight out of the windows in the summer, but allow the sunlight in during the winter. He would want the overhang to be long enough to block all of the sunlight on the longest day when the Sun is at the greatest elevation. For El Paso, this angle is 81.2°. The overhang begins 2 feet above the windows, so it will need to cover 14 feet. The length of the overhang is $L = \frac{14}{\tan 81.2}$ or about 2.17 feet. If the overhang is any longer, then less sunlight will get into the house in the winter.

17 Make a sketch.

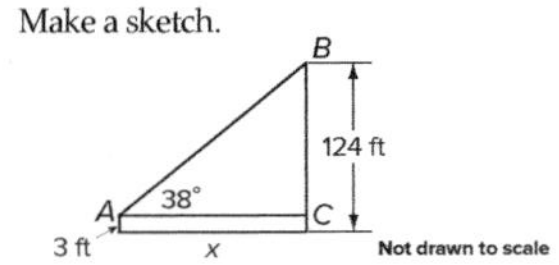

$\tan A = \frac{BC}{AC}$	$\tan = \frac{\text{opposite}}{\text{adjacent}}$
$\tan 38° = \frac{121}{x}$	$m\angle A = 38$, $BC = 124 - 3$ or 121, $AC = x$
$x = \frac{121}{\tan 38°}$	Solve for x.
$x \approx 154.9$	Use a calculator.

You should place the tripod about 154.9 feet from the monument.

19a. ≈65.4° **19b.** ≈110.1 m

21 Make two sketches.

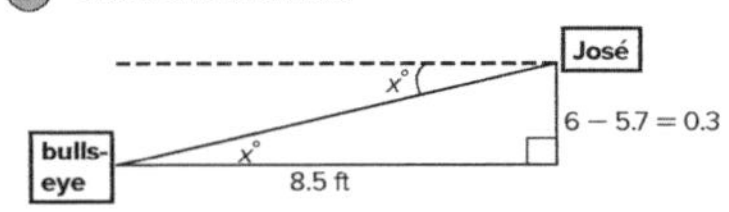

$\tan x° = \frac{0.3}{8.5}$	$\tan = \frac{\text{opp}}{\text{adj}}$
$x = \tan^{-1}\left(\frac{0.3}{8.5}\right)$	Solve for x.
$x \approx 2.02$	Use a calculator.

José throws at an angle of depression of 2.02°.

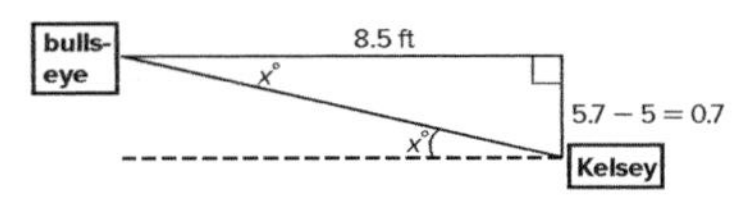

$\tan x° = \frac{0.7}{8.5}$	$\tan = \frac{\text{opp}}{\text{adj}}$
$x = \tan^{-1}\left(\frac{0.7}{8.5}\right)$	Solve for x.
$x \approx 4.71$	Use a calculator.

Kelsey throws at an angle of elevation of 4.71°.

23. Rodrigo; sample answer: Because your horizontal line of sight is parallel to the other person's horizontal line of sight, the angles of elevation and depression are congruent according to the Alternate Interior Angles Theorem.
25. True; sample answer: As a person moves closer to an object, the horizontal distance decreases, but the height of the object is constant. The tangent ratio will increase, and therefore the measure of the angle also increases.
27. Sample answer: If you sight something with a 45° angle of elevation, you don't have to use trigonometry to determine the height of the object. Because the legs of a 45°-45°-90° are congruent, the height of the object will be the same as your horizontal distance from the object.
29. $\frac{70\sqrt{3}}{3}$ ft **31.** D **33.** 66.7 **35.** 56 ft

Selected Answers and Solutions
Selected Answers and Solutions

Lesson 8-6

1. 27.9 mm^2

(3) Area $= \frac{1}{2}bc \sin A$ — Area Formula

$= \frac{1}{2}(11)(6) \sin 40°$ — Substitution

≈ 21.2 cm^2 — Simplify.

5. $E = 107°, d \approx 7.9, f \approx 7.0$ **7.** $F = 60°, f \approx 12.3, h \approx 9.1$ **9.** no solution **11.** one; $B = 90°, C = 60°, c \approx 5.2$ **13.** 10.6 km^2 **15.** 36.8 m^2 **17.** 5.9 ft^2 **19.** 65.2 m^2 **21.** $C = 30°, b \approx 11.1, c \approx 5.8$ **23.** $L = 74°, m \approx 4.9, n \approx 3.1$

(25) $m\angle K = 180 - (53 + 20)$ or $107°$

$\frac{\sin H}{h} = \frac{\sin J}{j}$ — Law of Sines

$\frac{\sin 53°}{31} = \frac{\sin 20°}{j}$ — Substitution

$j = \frac{31 \sin 20°}{\sin 53°}$ — Solve for j.

$j \approx 13.3$ — Use a calculator.

$\frac{\sin H}{h} = \frac{\sin K}{k}$ — Law of Sines

$\frac{\sin 53°}{31} = \frac{\sin 107°}{k}$ — Substitution

$k = \frac{31 \sin 107°}{\sin 53°}$ — Solve for k.

$k \approx 37.1$ — Use a calculator.

27. $B = 63°, b \approx 2.9, c \approx 3.0$ **29.** one; $B \approx 25°, C \approx 55°, c \approx 5.8$ **31.** one; $B \approx 32°, C \approx 110°, c \approx 32.1$ **33.** two; $B \approx 53°, C \approx 85°, c \approx 7.4$; $B \approx 127°, C \approx 11°, c \approx 1.4$ **35.** no solution **37.** about 28°

(39)

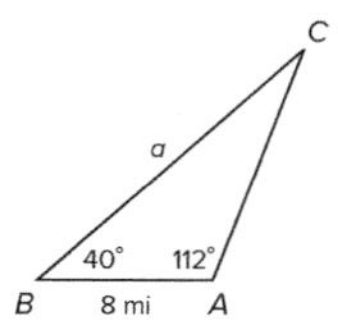

$m\angle C = 180 - (40 + 112)$ or $28°$

$\frac{\sin A}{a} = \frac{\sin C}{c}$ — Law of Sines

$\frac{\sin 112°}{a} = \frac{\sin 28°}{8}$ — Substitution

$a = \frac{8 \sin 112°}{\sin 28°}$ — Solve for a.

$a \approx 15.8$ — Use a calculator.

Sirens B and C are about 15.8 miles apart.

41a. Sample answer:

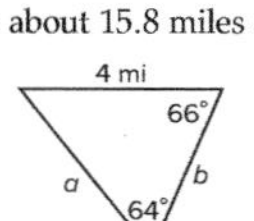

41b. Sample answer: $\frac{\sin 66°}{a} = \frac{\sin 64°}{4}$; $\frac{\sin 50°}{b} = \frac{\sin 64°}{4}$

41c. about 11.5 mi **43.** Cameron; R is acute and $r > t$, so there is one solution.

45. Sample answer:

$\sin A = \frac{opposite}{hypotenuse}$ — Definition of sine

$\sin A = \frac{h}{c}$ — h = opposite side, c = hypotenuse

$c \sin A = h$ — Multiply both sides by c.

area $= \frac{1}{2} \cdot$ base $\cdot$ height — Area of a triangle

area $= \frac{1}{2}bh$ — b = base, h = height

area $= \frac{1}{2}bc \sin A$ — Substitution

47. Sample answer: In the triangle, $B = 115°$. Using the Law of Sines, $\frac{\sin 50°}{a} = \frac{\sin 115°}{b}$. This equation cannot be solved because there are two unknowns. To solve a triangle using the Law of Sines, two sides and an angle must be given or two angles and a side opposite one of the angles must be given.
49. 6 cm^2 **51.** C, F

53a.

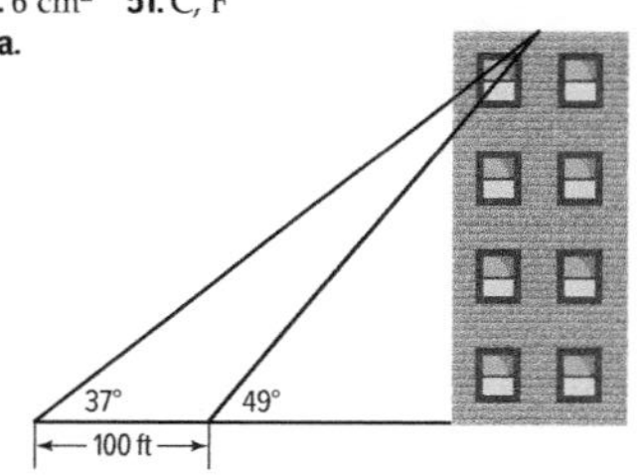

53b. 289.9 ft **53c.** 218.5 ft

Lesson 8-7

1. $A \approx 36°, C \approx 52°, b \approx 5.1$ **3.** $A \approx 18°, B \approx 29°, C \approx 133°$ **5.** Sines; $B \approx 40°, C \approx 33°, c \approx 6.9$

(7) Because the lengths of two sides and the measure of the included angle are known, first use the Law of Cosines to find the missing side length.

$r^2 = s^2 + t^2 - 2st \cos R$ — Law of Cosines

$r^2 = 16^2 + 9^2 - 2(16)(9) \cos 35°$ — $s = 16, t = 9, R = 35°$

$r^2 \approx 101.1$ — Use a calculator.

$r \approx 10.1$ — Take the positive square root of each side.

$\frac{\sin R}{r} = \frac{\sin T}{t}$ — Law of Sines

$\frac{\sin 35°}{10.1} = \frac{\sin T}{9}$ — Substitution

$\frac{9 \sin 35°}{10.1} = \sin T$ — Multiply each side by 9.

$31° \approx T$ — Use the $\sin^{-1}$ function.

$m\angle S = 180 - (35° + 31°)$ or $114°$

9. $A \approx 70°, B \approx 40°, c \approx 3.0$ **11.** $A \approx 31°, B \approx 108°, C \approx 41°$ **13.** $a \approx 6.9, B \approx 41°, C \approx 23°$ **15.** $F \approx 65°, G \approx 94°, H \approx 21°$ **17.** Sines; $C \approx 45°, A \approx 85°, a \approx 18.2$ **19.** Cosines; $A \approx 27°, B \approx 115°, C \approx 38°$

21. Sines; $A \approx 17°, B \approx 79°, b \approx 6.9$

(23) $d^2 = 338^2 + 520^2 - 2(338)(520) \cos 70°$

$d^2 \approx 264{,}417.1$

$d \approx 514.2$ m

25. 81°, 36°, 63° **27.** about 13,148 yd^2

29a. Sample answer:

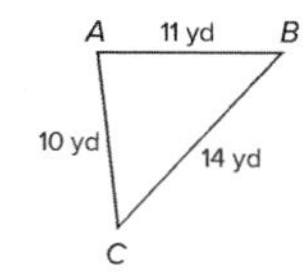

29b. Sample answer: Use the Law of Cosines to find the measure of $\angle A$. Then use the formula Area $= \frac{1}{2}bc \sin A$. **29c.** 54.6 yd^2

(31) $\frac{\sin A}{a} = \frac{\sin B}{b}$ — Law of Sines

$\frac{\sin 104°}{12.4} = \frac{\sin B}{8.1}$ — Substitution

$\frac{8.1 \sin 104°}{12.4} = \sin B$ — Multiply each side by 8.1.

$39° \approx B$ — Use the $\sin^{-1}$ function.

$m\angle C \approx 180 - (39° + 104°)$ or $37°$

$\frac{\sin A}{a} = \frac{\sin C}{c}$ — Law of Sines

$\frac{\sin 104°}{12.4} = \frac{\sin 37°}{c}$ — Substitution

$c = \frac{12.4 \sin 37°}{\sin 104°}$ — Solve for c.

$c \approx 7.7$ — Use a calculator.

33. $F \approx 42°, G \approx 72°, H \approx 66°$ **35.** The longest side is 14.5 centimeters. Use the Law of Cosines to find the measure of the angle opposite the longest side; 102°.
37. When two angles and a side are given or when two sides and an angle opposite one of the sides are given, you can use the Law of Sines to solve a triangle. When two sides and an included angle are given or when three sides are given, you can use the Law of Cosines to solve a triangle. **39.** A **41.** 43 **43a.** 95 degrees **43b.** 9.0 **43c.** 15.6 **43d.** 36.6 **45.** 2

Chapter 8 Study Guide and Review

1. false, geometric **3.** false, sum **5.** false, Law of Cosines **7.** The angle of elevation is equal to the angle of depression. **9.** 6 **11.** $\frac{8}{3}$ **13.** 50 ft **15.** $9\sqrt{3} \approx 15.6$
17. yes; acute

$16^2 \stackrel{?}{=} 13^2 + 15^2$

$256 < 169 + 225$

19. 18.4 m **21.** $x = 4\sqrt{2}, y = 45°$ **23.** $\frac{5}{13}$, 0.38 **25.** $\frac{12}{13}$, 0.92 **27.** $\frac{5}{12}$, 0.42 **29.** 32.2 **31.** 63.4° and 26.6° **33.** 86.6 feet **35.** two solutions; first solution; $C = 30°, B = 125°, b = 29.1$; second solution; $C = 150°, B = 5°, b = 3.1$ **37.** 98.9 ft **39.** Sines; $B \approx 52°, C \approx 48°, c \approx 11.3$ **41.** Sines; $B \approx 75°, C \approx 63°, c \approx 12.0$ or $B \approx 105°, C \approx 33°, c \approx 7.3$ **43.** about 750.5 ft
45. 226 ft

Selected Answers and Solutions

CHAPTER 9

Circles

Chapter 9 Concept Check

1. Change 26% to a decimal. **3.** isosceles right triangle

5. Pythagorean Theorem $x^2 + x^2 = 20^2$ **7.** completing the square

Lesson 9-1

1. $\odot N$ **3.** 8 cm **5.** 14 in. **7.** 22 ft; 138.23 ft **9.** $4\pi\sqrt{13}$ cm **11.** $\overline{SU}$ **13.** 8.1 cm

15 $d = 2r$ — Diameter formula
$= 2(14)$ or 28 in. — Substitute and simplify.

17. 3.7 cm **19.** 14.6 **21.** 30.6 **23.** 13 in.; 81.68 in. **25.** 39.47 ft; 19.74 ft **27.** 830.23 m; 415.12 m

29 $a^2 + b^2 = c^2$ — Pythagorean Theorem
$(6\sqrt{2})^2 + (6\sqrt{2})^2 = c^2$ — Substitution
$144 = c^2$ — Simplify.
$12 = c$ — Take the positive square root of each side.

The diameter is 12π feet.
$C = \pi d$ — Circumference formula
$= \pi(12)$ — Substitution
$= 12\pi$ ft — Simplify.

31. 10π in. **33.** 14π yd **35a.** 31.42 ft **35b.** 4 ft **37.** 22.80 ft; 71.63 ft **39.** $0.25x$; $0.79x$ **41.** neither

43 The radius is 3 units, or $3 \cdot 25 = 75$ feet.
$C = 2\pi r$ — Circumference formula
$= 2\pi(75)$ — Substitution
$= 150\pi$ — Simplify.
≈ 471.2 ft — Use a calculator.

45a. Sample answer:

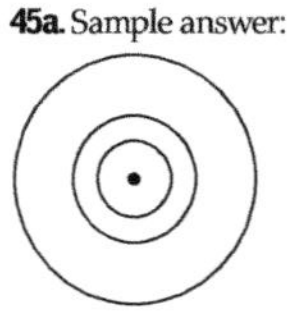

45b.

Circle Radius (cm)	Circumference (cm)
0.5	3.14
1	6.28
2	12.57

45c. They all have the same shape–circular.
45d. The ratio of their circumferences is also 2.
45e. $(C_B) = \frac{b}{a}(C_A)$ **45f.** 4 in.

47 **a.** $C = 2\pi r$ — Circumference formula
$= 2\pi(30)$ — Substitution
$= 60\pi$ — Simplify.
$C = 2\pi r$ — Circumference formula
$= 2\pi(5)$ — Substitution
$= 10\pi$ — Simplify.
$60\pi - 10\pi = 50\pi \approx 157.1$ mi

b. If $r = 5$, $C = 10\pi$; if $r = 10$, $C = 20\pi$; if $r = 15$, $C = 30\pi$, and so on. So, as r increases by 5, C increases by 10π or by about 31.4 miles.

49a. $8r$ and $6r$; Twice the radius of the circle, $2r$ is the side length of the square, so the perimeter of the square is $4(2r)$ or $8r$. The regular hexagon is made up of six equilateral triangles with side length r, so the perimeter of the hexagon is $6(r)$ or $6r$. **49b.** less; greater; $6r < C < 8r$ **49c.** $3d < C < 4d$; The circumference of the circle is between 3 and 4 times its diameter. **49d.** These limits will approach a value of πd, implying that $C = \pi d$.
51. Always; a radius is a segment drawn between the center of the circle and a point on the circle. A segment drawn from the center to a point inside the circle will always have a length less than the radius of the circle.
53. $\frac{8\pi}{\sqrt{3}}$ or $\frac{8\pi\sqrt{3}}{3}$ in. **55.** 25.13 **57.** 50.27 **59a.** circle M **59b.** $\widehat{MJ}$ or $\widehat{ML}$ **59c.** 6π

Lesson 9-2

1. 170 **3.** major arc; 270 **5.** semicircle; 180 **7.** 147 **9.** 123 **11.** 13.74 cm **13.** 3.14 cm

15 $65 + 70 + x = 360$ — Sum of central angles
$135 + x = 360$ — Simplify.
$x = 225$ — Subtract 135 from each side.

17. 40 **19.** major arc; 125 **21.** major arc; 305 **23.** semicircle; 180 **25.** major arc; 270 **27a.** 90; 100.8 **27b.** minor; minor **27c.** No; no categories share the same percentage of the circle. **29.** 60 **31.** 300 **33.** 180 **35.** 220 **37.** 120

39 $\ell = \frac{x}{360} \cdot 2\pi r$ — Arc length equation
$= \frac{112}{360} \cdot 2\pi(4.5)$ — Substitution.
≈ 8.80 cm — Use a calculator.

41. 17.02 in. **43.** 12.04 m **45.** The length of the arc would double. **47.** 40.83 in. **49.** 9.50 ft **51.** 142

53 **a.** $m\widehat{AB} = m\angle ACB$ — $\widehat{AB}$ is a minor arc.
$= 180 - (22 + 22)$ — Angle Addition Postulate
$= 180 - 44$ or 136 — Simplify.
b. $\ell = \frac{x}{360} \cdot 2\pi r$ — Arc length equation
$= \frac{136}{360} \cdot 2\pi(62)$ — Substitution.
≈ 147.17 ft — Use a calculator.

55 **a.**

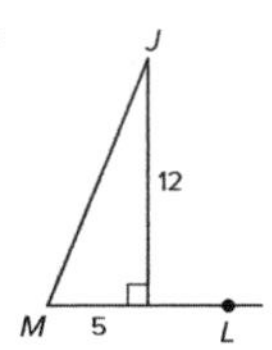

$\tan \angle JML = \frac{12}{5}$
$m\angle JML = \tan^{-1}\left(\frac{12}{5}\right)$
$\approx 67.4°$
$m\widehat{JL} = m\angle JML \approx 67.4°$

b.

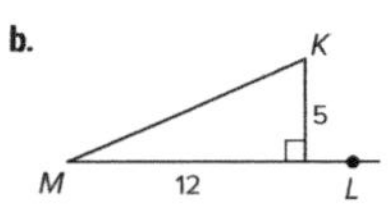

$\tan \angle KML = \frac{5}{12}$
$m\angle KML = \tan^{-1}\left(\frac{5}{12}\right)$
$\approx 22.6°$
$m\widehat{KL} = m\angle KML \approx 22.6°$

c. $m\angle JMK = m\angle JML - m\angle KML$
$\approx 67.4 - 22.6$
$\approx 44.8°$
$m\widehat{JK} = m\angle JMK \approx 44.8°$

d. $r = \sqrt{(x_2 - x_1)^2 + (y_2 - y_1)^2}$ — Distance Formula
$= \sqrt{(5 - 0)^2 + (12 - 0)^2}$ — $(x_1, y_1) = (0, 0)$ and $(x_2, y_2) = (5, 12)$
$= 13$ — Simplify.
$\ell = \frac{x}{360} \cdot 2\pi r$ — Arc length equation
$= \frac{67.4}{360} \cdot 2\pi(13)$ — Substitution
≈ 15.29 units — Use a calculator.

e. $\ell = \frac{x}{360} \cdot 2\pi r$ — Arc length equation
$= \frac{44.8}{360} \cdot 2\pi(13)$ — Substitution
≈ 10.16 units — Use a calculator.

57. Selena; the circles are not congruent because they do not have congruent radii. So, the arcs are not congruent. **59.** Never; obtuse angles intersect arcs that measure between 90° and 180° **61.** $m\widehat{LM} = 150$, $m\widehat{MN} = 90$, $m\widehat{NL} = 120$ **63.** 175 **65.** C **67.** 51 **69.** C

Lesson 9-3

1 $\widehat{ST}$ is a minor arc, so $m\widehat{ST} = 93$. $\overline{RS}$ and $\overline{ST}$ are congruent chords, so the corresponding arcs $\widehat{RS}$ and $\widehat{ST}$ are congruent.
$\widehat{RS} \cong \widehat{ST}$ — Corresponding arcs are congruent.
$m\widehat{RS} = m\widehat{ST}$ — Definition of congruent arcs
$x = 93$ — Substitution

3. 3 **5.** 3.32 **7.** 21 **9.** 127 **11.** 7

13 $\overline{KL}$ and $\overline{AJ}$ are congruent chords in congruent circles, so the corresponding arcs $\widehat{KL}$ and $\widehat{AJ}$ are congruent.
$\widehat{KL} \cong \widehat{AJ}$ — Corresponding arcs are congruent.
$m\widehat{KL} = m\widehat{AJ}$ — Definition of congruent arcs
$5x = 3x + 54$ — Substitution
$2x = 54$ — Subtract $3x$ from each side.
$x = 27$ — Divide each side by 2.

15. 122.5° **17.** 5.34 **19.** 6.71

21 $DE + EC = DC$ — Segment Addition Postulate
$15 + EC = 88$ — Substitution
$EC = 73$ — Subtract 15 from each side.
$EC^2 + EB^2 = CB^2$ — Pythagorean Theorem
$73^2 + EB^2 = 88^2$ — Substitution
$EB^2 = 2415$ — Subtract 73^2 from each side.
$EB \approx 49.14$ — The positive square root of each side
$EB = \frac{1}{2}AB$ — $\overline{DC} \perp \overline{AB}$, so $\overline{DC}$ bisects $\overline{AB}$.
$2EB = AB$ — Multiply each side by 2.
$2(49.14) \approx AB$ — Substitution
$98.3 \approx AB$ — Simplify.

23. 4

25. Proof:
Because all radii are congruent, $\overline{QP} \cong \overline{PR} \cong \overline{SP} \cong \overline{PT}$. You are given that $\overline{QR} \cong \overline{ST}$, so $\triangle PQR \cong \triangle PST$ by SSS. Thus, $\angle QPR \cong \angle SPT$ by CPCTC. Because the central angles have the same measure, their intercepted arcs have the same measure and are therefore congruent. Thus, $\widehat{QR} \cong \widehat{ST}$.

27. Each arc is 90°, and each chord is 2.12 ft.

29. Given: $\odot L$, $\overline{LX} \perp \overline{FG}$, $\overline{LY} \perp \overline{JH}$, $\overline{LX} \cong \overline{LY}$
Prove: $\overline{FG} \cong \overline{JH}$

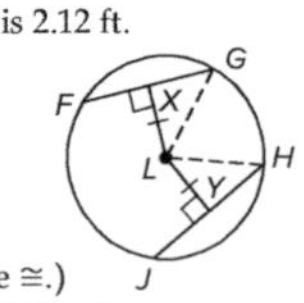

Proof:
Statements (Reasons)
1. $\overline{LG} \cong \overline{LH}$ (All radii of a $\odot$ are $\cong$.)
2. $\overline{LX} \perp \overline{FG}$, $\overline{LY} \perp \overline{JH}$, $\overline{LX} \cong \overline{LY}$ (Given)
3. $\angle LXG$ and $\angle LYH$ are right $\angle$s. (Def. of $\perp$ lines)
4. $\triangle XGL \cong \triangle YHL$ (HL)
5. $\overline{XG} \cong \overline{YH}$ (CPCTC)
6. $XG = YH$ (Def. of $\cong$ segments)
7. $2(XG) = 2(YH)$ (Multiplication Property)
8. $\overline{LX}$ bisects $\overline{FG}$; $\overline{LY}$ bisects $\overline{JH}$. (A radius $\perp$ to a chord bisects the chord.)
9. $FG = 2(XG)$, $JH = 2(YH)$ (Def. of seg. bisector)
10. $FG = JH$ (Substitution)
11. $\overline{FG} \cong \overline{JH}$ (Def. of $\cong$ segments)

31 Because $\overline{AB} \perp \overline{CE}$ and $\overline{DF} \perp \overline{CE}$, $\overline{CE}$ bisects $\overline{AB}$ and $\overline{DF}$.
Because $\overline{AB} \cong \overline{DF}$, $AB = DF$.
$CB = \frac{1}{2}AB$ — Definition of bisector
$CB = \frac{1}{2}DF$ — Substitution
$CB = DE$ — Definition of bisector
$9x = 2x + 14$ — Substitution
$7x = 14$ — Subtract $2x$ from each side.
$x = 2$ — Divide each side by 7.

33. 5 **35.** About 17.3; P and Q are equidistant from the endpoints of $\overline{AB}$, so they lie on the perpendicular bisector of $\overline{AB}$; so, $\overline{PQ}$ is the perpendicular bisector of $\overline{AB}$. Hence, both segments of $\overline{AB}$ are 5. Because $\overline{PS}$ is perpendicular to chord $\overline{AB}$, $\angle PSA$ is a right angle. So, $\triangle PSA$ is a right triangle.
By the Pythagorean Theorem, $PS = \sqrt{(PA)^2 - (AS)^2}$.
By substitution, $PS = \sqrt{11^2 - 5^2}$ or $\sqrt{96}$.
Similarly, $\triangle ASQ$ is a right triangle with $SQ = \sqrt{(AQ)^2 - (AS)^2} = \sqrt{9^2 - 5^2}$ or $\sqrt{56}$.
Because $PQ = PS + SQ$, $PQ = \sqrt{96} + \sqrt{56}$ or about 17.3.

37a. Given: $\overline{CD}$ is the perpendicular bisector of chord $\overline{AB}$ in $\odot X$.
Prove: $\overline{CD}$ contains point X.

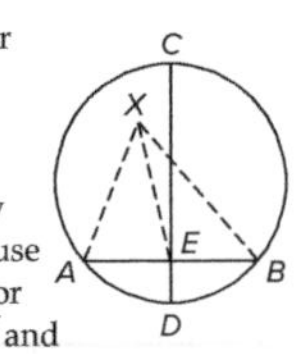

Proof:
Suppose X is not on $\overline{CD}$. Draw $\overline{XE}$ and radii $\overline{XA}$ and $\overline{XB}$. Because $\overline{CD}$ is the perpendicular bisector of $\overline{AB}$, E is the midpoint of $\overline{AB}$ and

$\overline{AE} \cong \overline{EB}$. Also, $\overline{XA} \cong \overline{XB}$, because all radii of a ⊙ are ≅. $\overline{XE} \cong \overline{XE}$ by the Reflexive Property. So, $\triangle AXE \cong \triangle BXE$ by SSS. By CPCTC, $\angle XEA \cong \angle XEB$. Because they also form a linear pair $\angle XEA$ and $\angle XEB$ are right angles. So, $\overline{XE} \perp \overline{AB}$. By definition $\overline{XE}$ is the perpendicular bisector of $\overline{AB}$. But $\overline{CD}$ is also the perpendicular bisector of $\overline{AB}$. This contradicts the uniqueness of a perpendicular bisector of a segment. Thus, the assumption is false, and center X must be on $\overline{CD}$.

37b. Given: In ⊙X, X is on $\overline{CD}$ and $\overline{FG}$ bisects $\overline{CD}$ at O.
Prove: Point O is point X.
Proof:
Because point X is on $\overline{CD}$ and C and D are on ⊙X, $\overline{CD}$ is a diameter of ⊙X. Because $\overline{FG}$ bisects $\overline{CD}$ at O, O is the midpoint of $\overline{CD}$. Because the midpoint of a diameter is the center of a circle, O is the center of the circle. Therefore, point O is point X.

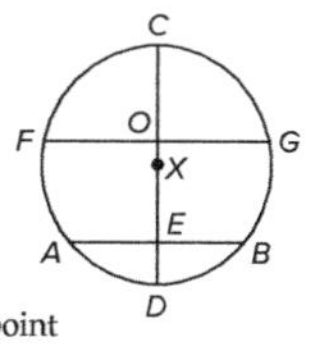

39. No; sample answer: In a circle with a radius of 12, an arc with a measure of 60 determines a chord of length 12. (the triangle related to a central angle of 60 is equilateral.) If the measure of the arc is tripled to 180, then the chord determined by the arc is a diameter and has a lenth of 2(12) or 24, which is not three times as long as the original chord. **41.** D **43a.** $\triangle JLM$ or $\triangle JLK$ **43b.** $\overline{LM}$ is $\frac{1}{2}$ of 24 feet, or 12 feet; the chord is bisected because it is perpendicular to the diameter. $\overline{JM}$ is the radius, which is $\frac{1}{2}$ the diameter of 36 feet, or 18 feet. **43c.** $JL^2 + 12^2 = 18^2$ **43d.** $6\sqrt{5}$ ft
45. B

Lesson 9-4

1. 30 **3.** 66 **5.** 54
7. Given: $\overline{RT}$ bisects $\overline{SU}$.
Prove: $\triangle RVS \cong \triangle UVT$
Proof:
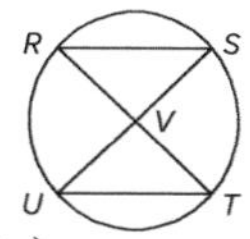
Statements (Reasons)
1. $\overline{RT}$ bisects $\overline{SU}$. (Given)
2. $\overline{SV} \cong \overline{VU}$ (Def. of segment bisector)
3. $\angle SRT$ intercepts $\widehat{ST}$. $\angle SUT$ intercepts $\widehat{ST}$. (Def. of intercepted arc)
4. $\angle SRT \cong \angle SUT$ (Inscribed ∠s of same arc are ≅.)
5. $\angle RVS \cong \angle UVT$ (Vertical ∠s are ≅.)
6. $\triangle RVS \cong \triangle UVT$ (AAS)

9. 25 **11.** 162

13 $m\widehat{NP} + m\widehat{PQ} + m\widehat{QN} = 360$ Addition Theorem
$120 + 100 + m\widehat{QN} = 360$ Substitution
$220 + m\widehat{QN} = 360$ Simplify.
$m\angle \widehat{QN} = 140$ Subtract 220 from each side.
$m\angle P = \frac{1}{2}m\widehat{QN}$ $\angle P$ intercepts $\widehat{QN}$.
$= \frac{1}{2}(140)$ or 70 Substitution

15. 140 **17.** 32 **19.** 20
21. Given: $m\angle T = \frac{1}{2}m\angle S$
Prove: $m\widehat{TUR} = 2m\widehat{URS}$
Proof:
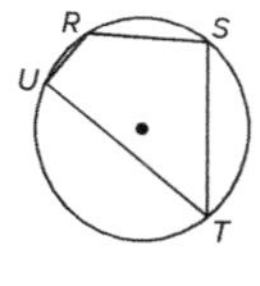
$m\angle T = \frac{1}{2}m\angle S$ means that $m\angle S = 2m\angle T$. Because $m\angle S = \frac{1}{2}m\widehat{TUR}$ and $m\angle T = \frac{1}{2}m\widehat{URS}$, the equation becomes $\frac{1}{2}m\widehat{TUR} = 2\left(\frac{1}{2}m\widehat{URS}\right)$. Multiplying each side of the equation by 2 results in $m\widehat{TUR} = 2m\widehat{URS}$.

23. 30 **25.** 12.75 **27.** 135 **29.** 106
31. Given: Quadrilateral $ABCD$ is inscribed in ⊙O.
Prove: $\angle A$ and $\angle C$ are supplementary. $\angle B$ and $\angle D$ are supplementary.
Proof: By arc addition and the definitions of arc measure and the sum of central angles, $m\widehat{DCB} + m\widehat{DAB} = 360$. Because by Theorem 9.6, $m\angle C = \frac{1}{2}m\widehat{DAB}$ and $m\angle A = \frac{1}{2}m\widehat{DCB}$, $m\angle C + m\angle A = \frac{1}{2}(m\widehat{DCB} + m\widehat{DAB})$, but $m\widehat{DCB} + m\widehat{DAB} = 360$, so $m\angle C + m\angle A = \frac{1}{2}(360)$ or 180. This makes $\angle C$ and $\angle A$ supplementary. Because the sum of the measures of the interior angles of a quadrilateral is 360, $m\angle A + m\angle C + m\angle B + m\angle D = 360$. But $m\angle A + m\angle C = 180$, so $m\angle B + m\angle D = 180$, making them supplementary also.

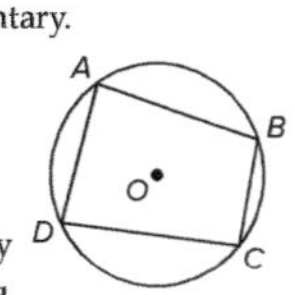

33 Because all the sides of the sign are congruent, all the corresponding arcs are congruent.
$8m\widehat{QR} = 360$, so $m\widehat{QR} = \frac{360}{8}$ or 45.
$m\angle RLQ = \frac{1}{2}m\widehat{QR}$
$= \frac{1}{2}(45)$ or 22.5

35. 135
37. Proof:
Statements (Reasons)
1. $m\angle ABC = m\angle ABD + m\angle DBC$ (∠ Addition Postulate)
2. $m\angle ABD = \frac{1}{2}m\widehat{AD}$
$m\angle DBC = \frac{1}{2}m\widehat{DC}$ (The measure of an inscribed ∠ whose side is a diameter is half the measure of the intercepted arc (Case 1).)
3. $m\angle ABC = \frac{1}{2}m\widehat{AD} + \frac{1}{2}m\widehat{DC}$ (Substitution)
4. $m\angle ABC = \frac{1}{2}(m\widehat{AD} + m\widehat{DC})$ (Factor)
5. $m\widehat{AD} + m\widehat{DC} = m\widehat{AC}$ (Arc Addition Postulate)
6. $m\angle ABC = \frac{1}{2}m\widehat{AC}$ (Substitution)

39 Use the Inscribed Angle Theorem to find the measures of $\angle FAE$ and $\angle CBD$. Then use the definition of congruent arcs and the Multiplication Property of Equality to help prove that the angles are congruent.

Given: $\angle FAE$ and $\angle CBD$ are inscribed; $\widehat{EF} \cong \widehat{DC}$
Prove: $\angle FAE = \angle CBD$
Proof:
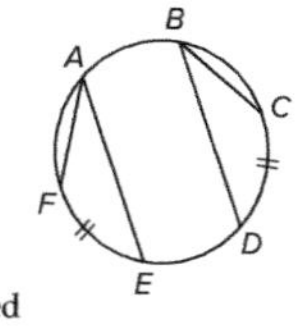
Statements (Reasons)
1. $\angle FAE$ and $\angle CBD$ are inscribed; $\widehat{EF} \cong \widehat{DC}$ (Given)
2. $m\angle FAE = \frac{1}{2}m\widehat{EF}$; $m\angle CBD = \frac{1}{2}m\widehat{DC}$ (Measure of an inscribed ∠ = half measure of intercepted arc.)
3. $m\widehat{EF} = m\widehat{DC}$ (Def. of ≅ arcs)
4. $\frac{1}{2}m\widehat{EF} = \frac{1}{2}m\widehat{DC}$ (Mult. Prop.)
5. $m\angle FAE = m\angle CBD$ (Substitution)
6. $\angle FAE \cong \angle CBD$ (Def. of ≅ ∠s)

41a.
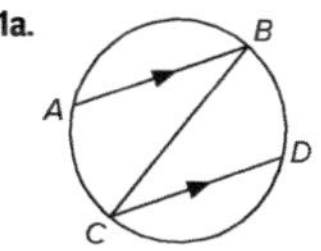
41b. Sample answer: $m\angle A = 30$, $m\angle D = 30$; $m\widehat{AC} = 60$, $m\widehat{BD} = 60$; The arcs are congruent because they have equal measures.
41c. Sample answer: In a circle, two parallel chords cut congruent arcs. **41d.** 70; 70
43. Always; rectangles have right angles at each vertex, therefore each pair of opposite angles will be supplementary and inscribed in a circle. **45.** Sometimes; a rhombus can be inscribed in a circle as long as it is a square. Because the opposite angles of rhombi that are not squares are not supplementary, they can not be inscribed in a circle. **47.** $\frac{\pi}{2}$ **51.** 108 **53.** D

Lesson 9-5

1. no common tangent
3 $FG^2 + GE^2 \stackrel{?}{=} FE^2$
$36^2 + 15^2 \stackrel{?}{=} (24 + 15)^2$
$1521 = 1521$
$\triangle EFG$ is a right triangle with right angle EGF. So $\overline{FG}$ is perpendicular to radius $\overline{EG}$ at point G. Therefore, by Theorem 10.10, $\overline{FG}$ is tangent to ⊙E.

5. 16 **7.** $x = 4$; $y = 15$
9.
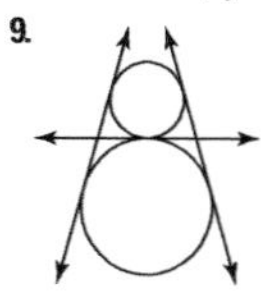
11.
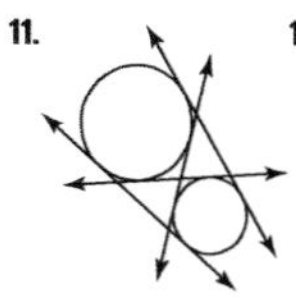
13. yes; 625 = 625

15 $XY^2 + YZ^2 \stackrel{?}{=} XZ^2$
$8^2 + 5^2 \stackrel{?}{=} (3 + 5)^2$
$89 \neq 64$
Because $\triangle XYZ$ is not a right triangle, $\overline{XY}$ is not perpendicular to radius $\overline{YZ}$. So, $\overline{XY}$ is not tangent to ⊙Z.

17 $\overrightarrow{QP}$ is tangent to ⊙N at P. So, $\overrightarrow{QP} \perp \overline{PN}$ and $\triangle PQN$ is a right triangle.
$QP^2 + PN^2 = QN^2$ Pythagorean Theorem
$24^2 + 10^2 = x^2$ $QP = 24$, $PN = 10$, and $QN = x$
$576 + 100 = x^2$ Multiply.
$676 = x^2$ Simplify.
$26 = x$ Take the positive square root of each side.

19. 9 **21.** 4 **23a.** 37.95 in. **23b.** 37.95 in. **25.** 8; 52 cm
27. 8.06
29. Given: Quadrilateral $ABCD$ is circumscribed about ⊙P.
Prove: $AB + CD = AD + BC$
Statements (Reasons)
1. Quadrilateral $ABCD$ is circumscribed about ⊙P. (Given)
2. Sides $\overline{AB}$, $\overline{BC}$, $\overline{CD}$, and $\overline{DA}$ are tangent to ⊙P at points H, G, F, and E, respectively. (Def. of circumscribed)
3. $\overline{EA} \cong \overline{AH}$; $\overline{HB} \cong \overline{BG}$; $\overline{GC} \cong \overline{CF}$; $\overline{FD} \cong \overline{DE}$ (Two segments tangent to a circle from the same exterior point are ≅.)
4. $AB = AH + HB$, $BC = BG + GC$, $CD = CF + FD$, $DA = DE + EA$ (Segment Addition)
5. $AB + CD = AH + HB + CF + FD$; $DA + BC = DE + EA + BG + GC$ (Substitution)
6. $AB + CD = AH + BG + GC + FD$; $DA + BC = FD + AH + BG + GC$ (Substitution)
7. $AB + CD = FD + AH + BG + GC$ (Commutative Prop. of Add.)
8. $AB + CD = DA + BC$ (Substitution)

31
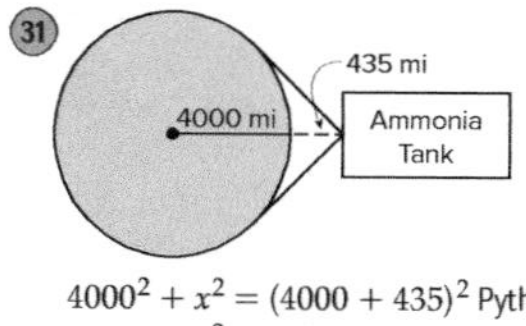

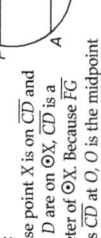

$4000^2 + x^2 = (4000 + 435)^2$ Pythagorean Theorem
$x^2 = 3{,}669{,}225$ Subtract 4000^2 from each side.
$x \approx 1916$ mi Take the positive square root of each side.

33. Proof: Assume that ℓ is not tangent to ⊙S. Because ℓ intersects ⊙S at T, it must intersect the circle in another place. Call this point Q. Then $ST = SQ$. $\triangle STQ$ is isosceles, so $\angle T \cong \angle Q$. Because $\overline{ST} \perp$ ℓ, $\angle T$ and $\angle Q$ are right angles. This contradicts that a triangle can only have one right angle. Therefore, ℓ is tangent to ⊙S.

35. Sample answer: Using the Pythagorean Theorem, $2^2 + x^2 = 10^2$, so $x \approx 9.8$. Because $PQST$ is a rectangle, $PQ = x = 9.8$.
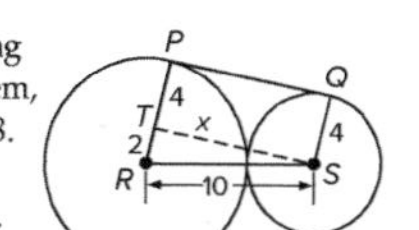

37. Sample answer:

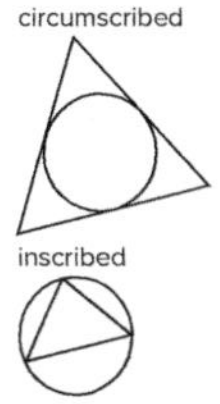

39. No; sample answer: From a point outside the circle, two tangents can be drawn. From a point on the circle, one tangent can be drawn. From a point inside the circle, no tangents can be drawn because a line would intersect the circle in two points.

41. 8.5 in. **43.** C

Lesson 9-6

1. 110 **3.** 73 **5.** 248

7 Draw and label a diagram.

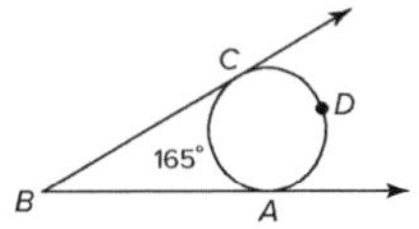

$m\angle B = \frac{1}{2}(m\widehat{CDA} - m\widehat{CA})$	Theorem 10.14
$= \frac{1}{2}[(360 - 165) - 165]$	Substitution
$= \frac{1}{2}(195 - 165)$ or 15	Simplify.

9. 71.5

11 $51 = \frac{1}{2}(m\widehat{RQ} + m\widehat{NP})$	Theorem 10.12
$51 = \frac{1}{2}(m\widehat{RQ} + 74)$	Substitution
$102 = m\widehat{RQ} + 74$	Multiply each side by 2.
$28 = m\widehat{RQ}$	Subtract 74 from each side.

13. 144 **15.** 125 **17a.** 100 **17b.** 20 **19.** 74 **21.** 185 **23.** 22 **25.** 168

27 $3 = \frac{1}{2}[(5x - 6) - (4x + 8)]$	Theorem 10.14
$6 = (5x - 6) - (4x + 8)$	Multiply each side by 2.
$6 = x - 14$	Simplify.
$20 = x$	Add 14 to each side.

29a. 145 **29b.** 30

31. Statements (Reasons)

1. $\overleftrightarrow{FM}$ is a tangent to the circle and $\overrightarrow{FL}$ is a secant to the circle. (Given)
2. $m\angle FLH = \frac{1}{2}m\widehat{HG}$, $m\angle LHM = \frac{1}{2}m\widehat{LH}$ (The meas. of an inscribed $\angle = \frac{1}{2}$ the measure of its intercepted arc.)
3. $m\angle LHM = m\angle FLH + m\angle F$ (Exterior $\angle$ Th.)
4. $\frac{1}{2}m\widehat{LH} = \frac{1}{2}m\widehat{HG} + m\angle F$ (Substitution)
5. $\frac{1}{2}m\widehat{LH} - \frac{1}{2}m\widehat{HG} = m\angle F$ (Subtraction Prop.)
6. $\frac{1}{2}(m\widehat{LH} - m\widehat{HG}) = m\angle F$ (Distributive Prop.)

33a. Proof: By Theorem 9.10, $\overline{OA} \perp \overline{AB}$. So, $\angle FAE$ is a right $\angle$ with measure 90, and $\widehat{FCA}$ is a semicircle with measure of 180. Because $\angle CAE$ is acute, C is in the interior of $\angle FAE$. By the Angle and Arc Addition Postulates, $m\angle FAE = m\angle FAC + m\angle CAE$ and $m\widehat{FCA} = m\widehat{FC} + m\widehat{CA}$. By substitution, $90 = m\angle FAC + m\angle CAE$ and $180 = m\widehat{FC} + m\widehat{CA}$. So, $90 = \frac{1}{2}m\widehat{FC} + \frac{1}{2}m\widehat{CA}$ by Division Prop., and $m\angle FAC + m\angle CAE = \frac{1}{2}m\widehat{FC} + \frac{1}{2}m\widehat{CA}$ by substitution. $m\angle FAC = \frac{1}{2}m\widehat{FC}$ because $\angle FAC$ is inscribed, so substitution yields $\frac{1}{2}m\widehat{FC} + m\angle CAE = \frac{1}{2}m\widehat{FC} + \frac{1}{2}m\widehat{CA}$. By Subt. Prop., $m\angle CAE = \frac{1}{2}m\widehat{CA}$.

33b. Given: $\angle CAB$ is obtuse.
Prove: $m\angle CAB = \frac{1}{2}m\,\widehat{CDA}$

Proof: Using the Angle and Arc Addition Postulates, $m\angle CAB = m\angle CAF + m\angle FAB$ and $m\widehat{CDA} = m\widehat{CF} + m\widehat{FDA}$. Because $\overline{OA} \perp \overline{AB}$ and $\overline{FA}$ is a diameter, $\angle FAB$ is a right angle with a measure of 90 and $\widehat{FDA}$ is a semicircle with a measure of 180. By substitution, $m\angle CAB = m\angle CAF + 90$ and $m\widehat{CDA} = m\widehat{CF} + 180$. Because $\angle CAF$ is inscribed, $m\angle CAF = \frac{1}{2}m\widehat{CF}$ and by substitution, $m\angle CAB = \frac{1}{2}m\widehat{CF} + 90$. Using the Division and Subtraction Properties on the Arc Addition equation yields $\frac{1}{2}m\widehat{CDA} - \frac{1}{2}m\widehat{CF} = 90$. By substituting for 90, $m\angle CAB = \frac{1}{2}m\widehat{CF} + \frac{1}{2}m\widehat{CDA} - \frac{1}{2}m\widehat{CF}$. By subtraction, $m\angle CAB = \frac{1}{2}m\widehat{CDA}$.

35 **a.** Sample answer:

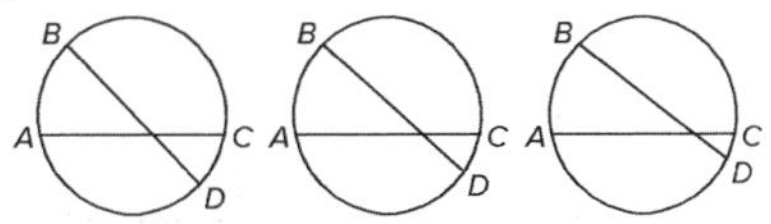

b. Sample answer:

	Circle 1	Circle 2	Circle 3
$\widehat{CD}$	25	15	5
$\widehat{AB}$	50	50	50
x	37.5	32.5	27.5

c. As the measure of $\widehat{CD}$ gets closer to 0, the measure of x approaches half of $m\widehat{AB}$; $\angle AEB$ becomes an inscribed angle.

d. Theorem 10.12 states that if two chords intersect in the interior of a circle, then the measure of an angle formed is one half the sum of the measure of the arcs intercepted by the angle and its vertical angle. Use this theorem to write an equation relating x, $m\widehat{AB}$, and $m\widehat{CD}$. Then let $m\widehat{CD} = 0$ and simplify. The result is Theorem 9.6, the Inscribed Angle Theorem.

$x = \frac{1}{2}(m\widehat{AB} + m\widehat{CD})$

$x = \frac{1}{2}(m\widehat{AB} + 0)$

$x = \frac{1}{2}m\widehat{AB}$

37. 15 **39a.** $m\angle G \le 90$; $m\angle G < 90$ for all values except when $\overleftrightarrow{JG} \perp \overleftrightarrow{GH}$ at G, then $m\angle G = 90$. **39b.** $m\widehat{KH} = 56$; $m\widehat{HJ} = 124$; Because a diameter is involved, the intercepted arcs measure $(180 - x)$ and x degrees. Hence, solving $\frac{180 - x - x}{2} = 34$ leads to the answer.

41. Sample answer: Using Theorem 9.14, $60° = \frac{1}{2}[(360° - x) - x]$ or 120°; repeat for 50° to get 130°. The third arc can be found by adding 50° and 60° and subtracting from 360° to get 110°. **43.** 35 **45.** A

Lesson 9-7

1. $(x - 9)^2 + y^2 = 25$

3 $r = \sqrt{(x_2 - x_1)^2 + (y_2 - y_1)^2}$	Distance Formula
$= \sqrt{(2 - 0)^2 + (2 - 0)^2}$	$(x_1, y_1) = (0, 0)$ and $(x_2, y_2) = (2, 2)$
$= \sqrt{8}$	Simplify.
$(x - h)^2 + (y - k)^2 = r^2$	Equation of a circle
$(x - 0)^2 + (y - 0)^2 = (\sqrt{8})^2$	$h = 0, k = 0$, and $r = \sqrt{8}$
$x^2 + y^2 = 8$	Simplify.

5. $(x - 2)^2 + (y - 1)^2 = 4$

7. $(3, -2)$; 4

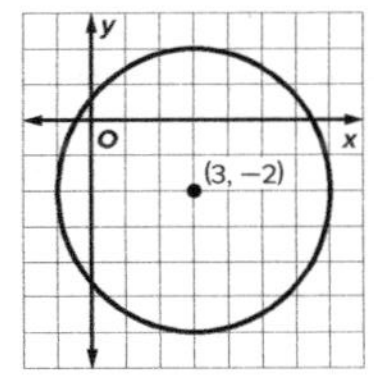

9. $(2, -1)$; $(x - 2)^2 + (y + 1)^2 = 40$

11. $(1, 2), (-1, 0)$

13. $x^2 + y^2 = 16$

15. $(x + 2)^2 + y^2 = 64$

17. $(x + 3)^2 + (y - 6)^2 = 9$

19. $(x + 5)^2 + (y + 1)^2 = 9$

21 The third ring has a radius of 15 + 15 + 15 or 45 miles.

$(x - h)^2 + (y - k)^2 = r^2$	Equation of a circle
$(x - 0)^2 + (y - 0)^2 = 45^2$	$h = 0, k = 0$, and $r = 45$
$x^2 + y^2 = 2025$	Simplify.

23. (0, 0); 6

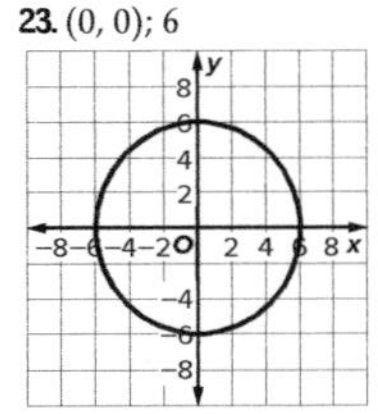

25 Write equation in standard form.

$x^2 + y^2 + 8x - 4y = -4$	Original equation
$x^2 + 8x + y^2 - 4y = -4$	Isolate and group like terms.
$x^2 + 8x + 16 + y^2 - 4y + 4 = -4 + 20$	Complete the squares.
$(x + 4)^2 + (y - 2)^2 = 16$	Factor and simplify.
$[x - (-4)]^2 + (y - 2)^2 = 4^2$	Write +4 as −(−4) and 16 as 4^2.

So $h = -4$, $k = 2$, and $r = 4$. The center is at $(-4, 2)$ and the radius is 4.

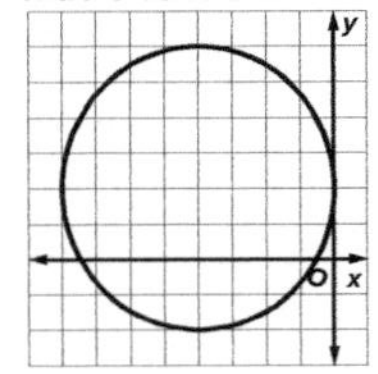

27. $(x - 3)^2 + (y - 3)^2 = 13$

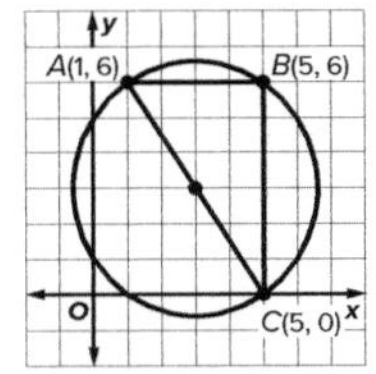

29. $(-2, -1), (2, 1)$

31. $(-2, -4), (2, 0)$

33. $\left(\frac{\sqrt{2}}{2}, \frac{3\sqrt{2}}{2}\right)$, $\left(-\frac{\sqrt{2}}{2}, -\frac{3\sqrt{2}}{2}\right)$

35. $(x - 3)^2 + y^2 = 25$

37a. $x^2 + y^2 = 810{,}000$ **37b.** 3000 ft

39a. No, her friend's house is outside the free delivery area.

39b. I used a coordinate grid with Consuela's house at (0, 0), and the pizza restaurant at (−4, 5). By the Pythagorean Theorem, Consuela's house is $\sqrt{41}$, or approximately 6.4 miles away from the pizza place. The equation of the circle for free delivery is $(x + 4)^2 + (y - 5)^2 = 41$. Consuela's friend's house is at (−1, −1). Substitute this ordered pair into the equation of the circle for free delivery.

$(x + 4)^2 + (y - 5)^2 = 41$	Equation of circle for free delivery
$(-1 + 4)^2 + (-1 - 5)^2 \stackrel{?}{=} 41$	Substitute (−1, −1) for (x, y).
$3^2 + (-6)^2 \stackrel{?}{=} 41$	Simplify.
$9 + 36 \stackrel{?}{=} 41$	Square each term.
$45 > 41$	Compare.

This means that Consuela's friend's house is farther away from the pizza place than Consuela's house. Because Consuela's house is at the edge of the free-delivery area, her friend's house is outside of the free-delivery area.

41 The radius of a circle centered at the origin and containing the point (0, −3) is 3 units. Therefore, the equation of the circle is $(x - 0)^2 + (y - 0)^2 = 3^2$ or $x^2 + y^2 = 9$. The point $(1, 2\sqrt{2})$ lies on the circle, because evaluating $x^2 + y^2 = 9$ for $x = 1$ and $y = 2\sqrt{2}$ results in a true equation.

$1^2 + (2\sqrt{2})^2 = 9$
$1 + 8 = 9$
$9 = 9$ ✓

43. $x^2 + y^2 = 16$ **43a.** outside **43b.** on **43c.** inside **43d.** on **45.** $(x + 5)^2 + (y - 2)^2 = 36$ **47.** $(x - 8)^2 + (y - 2)^2 = 16$; the first circle has its center at (5, −7). If the circle is shifted 3 units right and 9 units up, the new center is at (8, 2), so the new equation becomes $(x - 8)^2 + (y - 2)^2 = 16$. **49a.** 4 **49b–c.** Method 1: Draw a circle of radius 200 miles centered on each station. Method 2: Use the Pythagorean Theorem to identify pairs of stations that are more than 200 miles apart. Using Method 2, plot the points representing the stations on a graph. Stations that are more than 4 units apart on the graph will be more than 200 miles apart and will thus be able to use the same frequency. Assign station A to the first frequency. Station B is within 4 units of station A, so it must be assigned the second frequency. Station C is within 4 units of stations A and B, so it must be assigned a third frequency. Station D is also within 4 units of stations A, B, and C, so it must be assigned a fourth frequency. Station E is $\sqrt{29}$, or about 5.4 units away from station A, so it can share the first frequency. Station F is $\sqrt{29}$, or about 5.4 units away from station B, so it can share the second frequency. Station G is $\sqrt{32}$, or about 5.7 units away from station C, so it can share the third frequency. Therefore, the least number of frequencies that can be assigned is 4. **51.** (−6.4, 4.8) **53.** A **55.** C

Lesson 9-8

1. $x^2 = 24y$ **3.** $y^2 = -8x$ **5.** $\left(x, \frac{9}{16}\right)^2 = 8(y - 1)$
7. Sample answer: $x^2 = 7.2y$

9.

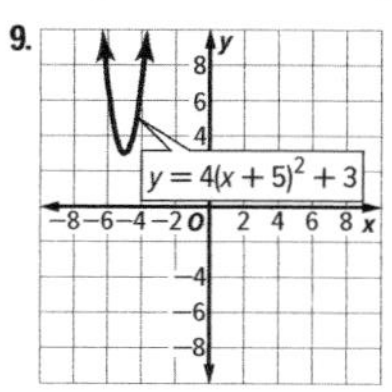

11

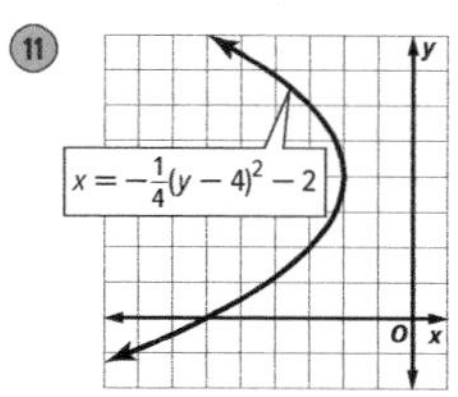

13. $x^2 = -7y$ **15.** $x^2 = -40y$ **17.** $(x - 2)^2 = -8(y - 1)$
19. $(y + 1)^2 = -8(x - 6)$ **21.** $y^2 = -12x$
23. $(x - 1)2 = -8(y + 1)$ **25.** $(y - 1)2 = 4(x + 3)$
27. $y^2 = -20(x + 7)$

29.

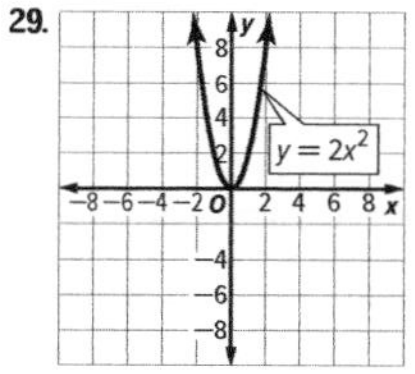

31.

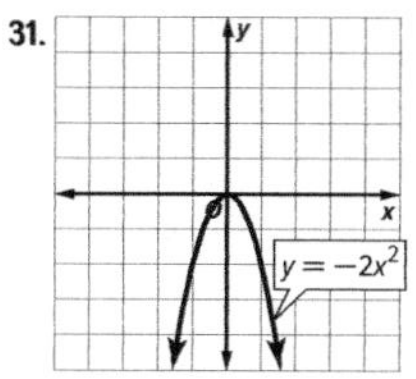

33.

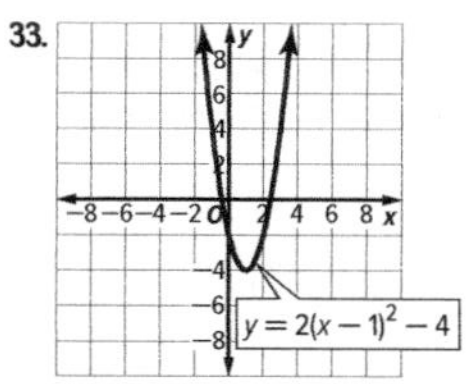

35.

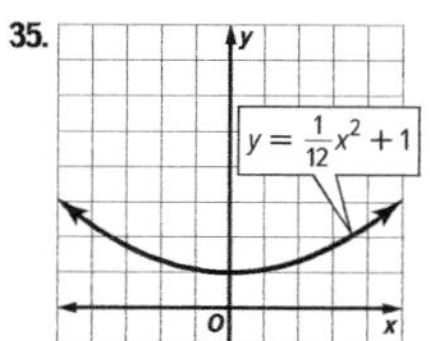

37.

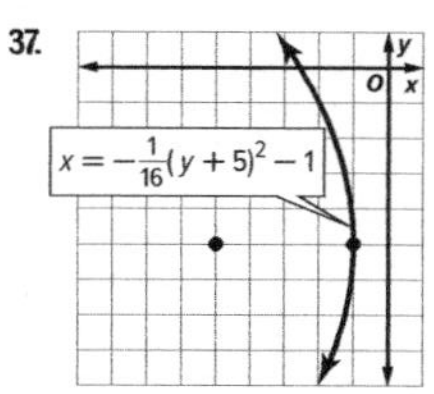

39.

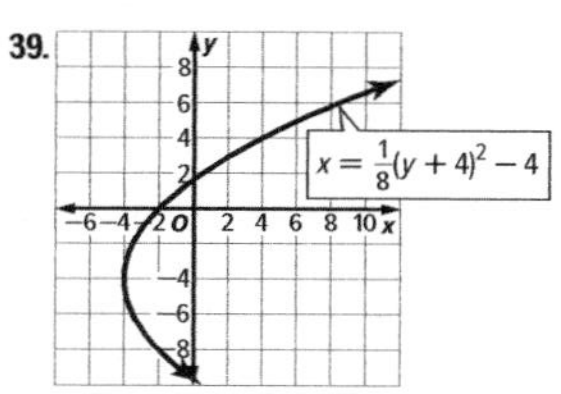

41. $F(-2, 5)$, $y = 1$
43. $F(3, 1)$, $x = -9$
45. $y^2 = 6x$
47. $x^2 = \frac{22}{3}y$
49. $y^2 = 16x$

51. Conjecture: The equation of the new parabola is $(y - 2)^2 = 16(x - 3)$. The graph verifies that $(y - 2)^2 = 16(x - 3)$ is a translation of $y^2 - 16x = 0$ by 3 units to the right and 2 units up.

53. $x^2 = 28y$ **55.** $6\left(x - \frac{3}{4}\right) = (y + 2)^2$

57. vertex: (4, −2), focus: $\left(4\frac{1}{48}, -2\right)$; directrix: $x = 3\frac{47}{48}$

59. vertex: (4, −6), focus: $\left(4\frac{1}{4}, -6\right)$; directrix: $x = 3\frac{3}{4}$

61. vertex: (0, 4), focus: $\left(0, 4\frac{1}{4}\right)$; directrix: $y = 3\frac{3}{4}$

63a. Sample answer: (0, 4), (2, 0) **63b.** $x = 0$ or $x = 2$ **63c.** $y = 4$ or $y = 0$ **63d.** (0, 4), (2, 0); They are the same as the intersection points.

65a.

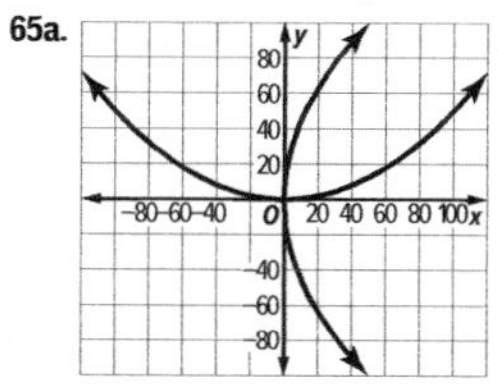

65b. $y^2 = 200x$; $x^2 = 200y$ **65c.** No. The depth of the antenna is the same for both sketches. It is equal to the distance between the focus and the vertex, 50 inches.

67. Sample answer: If you rewrite the equation of the parabola as $y^2 = \frac{1}{4}x$, it is of the form $y^2 = 4px$. Therefore, $4p = \frac{1}{4}$, and $p = \frac{1}{16}$. The value of p represents the distance from the focus to the vertex and from the vertex to the directrix. So, the distance from the focus to the directrix must be $2p$, or $\frac{1}{8}$ in this case.

69. Sample answer: Make a sketch of the parabola by graphing the vertex and focus. Since they are on the same horizontal line and the focus is to the right of the vertex, the parabola opens to the right and will be of the form $(y - k)^2 = 4p(x - h)$ with vertex (h, k). So, $h = 3$ and $k = -2$. The distance between the focus and the vertex is the value of p, or 3. Substitute the values into $(y - k)^2 = 4p(x - h)$ to get the equation, $(y + 2)^2 = 4(3)(x - 3)$, or $(y + 2)^2 = 12(x - 3)$.

71a. Top half of a parabola that has vertex (0, 0) and is open to the right

71b. Domain: $x \geq 0$; Range: $y \geq 0$

71c. Sample answer: If you square both sides of $y = \sqrt{x}$, you get $y^2 = x$. This is related to $y^2 = 4px$ because the coefficient of x in $y^2 = 4px$ is $4p$. So they are part of the same family of parabolas $y^2 = x$. If $p = \frac{1}{4}$, then the equations are identical.

71d. Sample answer: Make a list of values for p, including values less than 1, and then use the calculator to graph the family of functions of the form $y = \sqrt{4px}$ and $y = -\sqrt{4px}$ to see the complete parabolas.
73. Sample answer: As p increases, the focus gets further away from the vertex of the graph of $y^2 = 4px$, and the distance between the focus and directrix increases. As p decreases, the focus gets closer to the vertex of the graph of $y^2 = 4px$, and the distance between the focus and directrix decreases. This is verified by graphing.
75. Sample answer: Graph the three points to see that they are located on a parabola with vertex (0, 0) that is opening downward. Because the vertex is (0, 0), substitute the coordinates into $x^2 = 4py$, and solve for p. If p is the same for both points, then the points are solutions to the same parabola. The parabola containing (−8, 4) has $p = -4$. The parabola containing $\left(-2\sqrt{2}, -\frac{\sqrt{2}}{8}\right)$ has $p = -\frac{16}{\sqrt{2}}$. Because the value of p is different for each point, the points are not on the same parabola. **77a.** $(x + 4)^2 = 12(y - 2)$ **77b.** A **77c.** A, D, E **77d.** A **77e.** The vertex is translated 4 units left and 2 units up. **79a.** (−5, 1) **79b.** (−7, 1) **79c.** $x = -3$ **81.** $x^2 = 34y$ or $y^2 = 34x$

Chapter 9 Study Guide and Review

1. false; chord **3.** true **5.** true **7.** false; congruent
9. A tangent line intersects the circle at exactly one point, while a secant line intersects the circle at exactly two points. **11.** $\overline{DM}$ or $\overline{DP}$ **13.** 13.69 cm; 6.84 cm **15.** 34.54 ft; 17.27 ft **17.** 163 **19a.** 100.8 **19b.** 18 **19c.** minor arc **21.** 131 **23.** 50.4 **25.** 56
27.

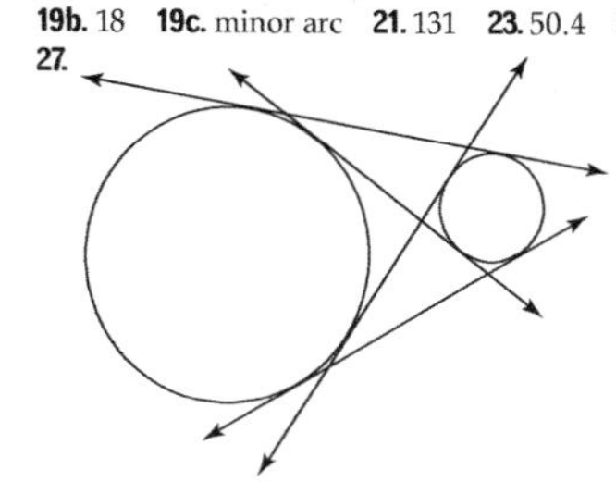

29. 97
31. 214
33. $(x - 1)^2 + (y - 2)^2 = 49$
35. (1, −5); $r = 2$
37. (3, 1); $r = 3$
39. (−8, −2); $r = 7$
41. (3, 3), (−2, −2)
43. $x^2 + y^2 = 1156$
45. $y^2 = 16x$
47. $(y + 3)^2 = 12(x - 1)$

Selected Answers and Solutions

CHAPTER 10

Extending Area

Chapter 10 Concept Check

1. $A = \ell \times w$ **3.** substitution **5.** hypotenuse
7. 45°-45°-90° triangle

Lesson 10-1

1. 56 in., 180 in^2 **3.** 64 cm, 207.8 cm^2

5. 43.5 in., 20 in^2

7. 32.5 in., 33.8 in^2 **9.** $15 + \sqrt{65}$ or about 23.1 units; 20 units^2

11 perimeter = 21 + 17 + 21 + 17 or 76 ft
Use the Pythagorean Theorem to find the height.
$8^2 + h^2 = 17^2$ Pythagorean Theorem
$64 + h^2 = 289$ Simplify.
$h^2 = 225$ Subtract 64 from each side.
$h = 15$ Take the positive square root of each side.
$A = bh$ Area of a parallelogram
$= 21(15)$ or 315 ft^2 $b = 21$ and $h = 15$

13. 69.9 m, 129.9 m^2 **15.** 174.4 m, 1520 m^2 **17.** 727.5 ft^2

19. 338.4 cm^2 **21.** 480 m^2

23

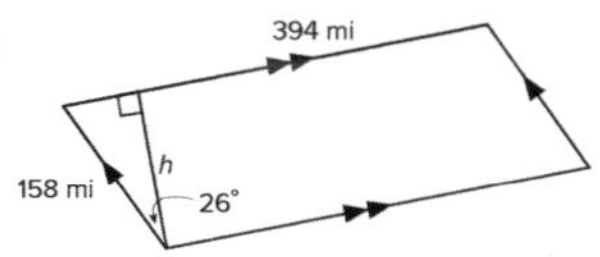

$\cos 26° = \frac{h}{158}$ $\cos = \frac{\text{adjacent}}{\text{hypotenuse}}$
$158 \cos 26° = h$ Multiply each side by 158.
$142 \approx h$ Use a calculator.

$A = bh$ Area of a parallelogram
$\approx 394(142)$ or 55,948 mi^2 $b = 394$ and $h = 142$

25. $6 + 5\sqrt{2} + \sqrt{26}$ or about 18.2 units; 15 units^2

27 Graph the parallelogram, then measure the length of the base and the height and calculate the perimeter and area.

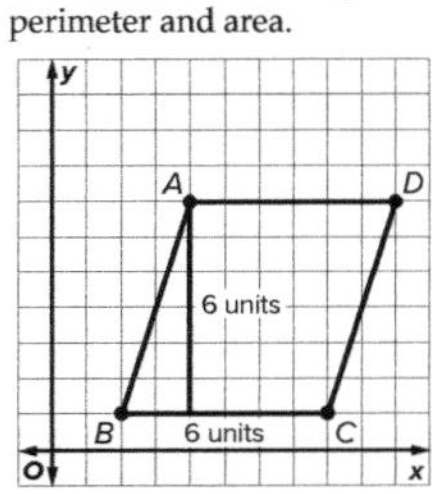

$P = AB + BC + CD + AD$
$= 2\sqrt{10} + 6 + 2\sqrt{10} + 6$
$= 12 + 4\sqrt{10}$ or about 24.6 units

$A = bh$ Area of a parallelogram
$\approx 6(6)$ or 36 units^2 $b = 6$ and $h = 6$

29a. yellow: 1 gal, 1 qt, and 3 8-oz bottles; blue: 2 qt; red: 3 8-oz bottles; purple: 1 8-oz bottle **29b.** Sample answer: I created two tables to organize the information provided and my calculations. The first table shows the relationship between each size paint container and the amount of area each will cover.

Size	8 oz	1 qt (32 oz in a qt)	1 gal (4 qt in a gal)
Cost ($)	3.75	14	30
Area covered (ft²)	21.875	87.5	350

The second table shows the relationship between the paint color, the area to be covered, and the possible purchase options and cost.

Color	Area (ft²)	Area to Paint (ft²)	Possible Purchase	Cost ($)
Red	$A_R = \frac{1}{2}(5)(6) = 15$	(15)(3) = 45	• 3 8-oz bottles	• 11.25
Purple	$A_P = (1)(4) = 4$	(4)(3) = 12	• 1 8-oz bottle	• 3.75
Blue	$A_B = (12)(5) - 4 = 56$	(56)(3) = 168	• 1 qt + 4 8-oz bottles • 2 quarts	• 29 • 28
Yellow	$A_Y = (12)(20) - (56 + 4 + 15) = 165$	(165)(3) = 495	• 2 gal • 1 gal + 2 qt • 1 gal + 1 qt + 3 8-oz bottles	• 60 • 58 • 55.25

Madison should buy 3 8-oz bottles of red paint, 1 8-oz bottle of purple paint, 2 qts of blue paint, and 1 gal, 1 qt, and 3 8-oz bottles of yellow paint.
31. 9.19 in.; 4.79 in^2 **33.** $b = 14$ ft; $h = 7$ ft

35a. 10.9 units^2

35b. $\sqrt{s(s-a)(s-b)(s-c)} \stackrel{?}{=} \frac{1}{2}bh$
$\sqrt{15(15-5)(15-12)(15-13)} \stackrel{?}{=} \frac{1}{2}(5)(12)$
$\sqrt{15(10)(3)(2)} \stackrel{?}{=} 30$
$\sqrt{900} \stackrel{?}{=} 30$
$30 = 30$

37. 15 units^2; Sample answer: I inscribed the triangle in a 6-by-6 square. I found the area of the square and subtracted the areas of the three right triangles inside the square that were positioned around the given triangle. The area of the given triangle is the difference, or 15 units^2. **39.** Sample answer: The area will not change as *K* moves along line *p*. Because lines *m* and *p* are parallel, the perpendicular distance between them is constant. That means that no matter where *K* is on line *p*, the perpendicular distance to line *p*, or the height of the triangle, is always the same. Because points *J* and *L* are not moving, the distance between them, or the length of the base, is constant. Because the height of the triangle and the base of the triangle are both constant, the area will always be the same. **41.** Sample answer: To find the area of the parallelogram, you can measure the height $\overline{PT}$ and then measure one of the bases $\overline{PQ}$ or $\overline{SR}$ and multiply the height by the base to get the area. You can also measure the height $\overline{SW}$ and measure one of the bases $\overline{QR}$ or $\overline{PS}$ and then multiply the height by the base to get the area. It doesn't matter which side you choose to use as the base, as long as you use the height that is perpendicular to that base to calculate the area. **43.** A **45.** D **47.** 18 **49a.** $6h^2$ **49b.** $12h$ **49c.** 216 **49d.** 72

Lesson 10-2

1. 132 ft^2 **3.** 178.5 m^2 **5.** 8 cm **7.** 6.3 ft **9.** 678.5 ft^2
11. 136 in^2 **13.** 137.5 ft^2

15 $A = \frac{1}{2}d_1d_2$ Area of a kite
$= \frac{1}{2}(4.8)(10.2)$ $d_1 = 4.8$ and $d_2 = 10.2$
$= 24.48$ Simplify.
The area is about 24.5 square microns.

17. 784 ft^2

19 Let x represent the length of one diagonal. Then the length of the other diagonal is $3x$.
$A = \frac{1}{2}d_1d_2$ Area of a rhombus
$168 = \frac{1}{2}(x)(3x)$ $A = 168$, $d_1 = x$, and $d_2 = 3x$
$168 = \frac{3}{2}x^2$ Simplify.
$112 = x^2$ Multiply each side by $\frac{2}{3}$.
$\sqrt{112} = x$ Take the positive square root of each side.
So the lengths of the diagonals are $\sqrt{112}$ or about 10.6 centimeters and $3(\sqrt{112})$ or about 31.7 centimeters.

21. 4 m **23.** The area of $\triangle HJF = \frac{1}{2}d_1\left(\frac{1}{2}d_2\right)$ and the area of $\triangle HGF = \frac{1}{2}d_1\left(\frac{1}{2}d_2\right)$. Therefore, the area of $\triangle HJF = \frac{1}{4}d_1d_2$, and the area of $\triangle HGF = \frac{1}{4}d_1d_2$. The area of kite *FGHJ* is equal to the area of $\triangle HJF$ + the area of $\triangle HGF$ or $\frac{1}{4}d_1d_2 + \frac{1}{4}d_1d_2$. After simplification, the area of kite *FGHJ* is equal to $\frac{1}{2}d_1d_2$. **25a.** 24 in^2 each of yellow, red, orange, green, and blue; 20 in^2 of purple **25b.** Yes; her kite has an area of 140 in^2, which is less than 200 in^2. **27.** 18 sq. units **29.** The area of a trapezoid is $\frac{1}{2}h(b_1 + b_2)$. So, $A = \frac{1}{2}(x + y)(x + y)$ or $\frac{1}{2}(x^2 + xy + y^2)$. The area of $\Delta 1 = \frac{1}{2}(y)(x)$, $\Delta 2 = \frac{1}{2}(z)(z)$, and $\Delta 3 = \frac{1}{2}(x)(y)$. The area of $\Delta 1 + \Delta 2 + \Delta 3 = \frac{1}{2}xy + \frac{1}{2}z^2 + \frac{1}{2}xy$. Set the area of the trapezoid equal to the combined areas of the triangles to get $\frac{1}{2}(x^2 + 2xy + y^2) = \frac{1}{2}xy + \frac{1}{2}z^2 + \frac{1}{2}xy$. Multiply by 2 on each side: $x^2 + 2xy + y^2 = 2xy + z^2$. When simplified, $x^2 + y^2 = z^2$.

31 The length of the base of the triangle is $\frac{12-8}{2}$ or 2.
Use trigonometry to find the height of the triangle (and trapezoid).
$\tan 30 = \frac{\text{opposite}}{\text{adjacent}}$
$\frac{\sqrt{3}}{3} = \frac{2}{h}$
$\sqrt{3}h = 6$
$h = \frac{6}{\sqrt{3}}$
$h = 2\sqrt{3}$

Use the Pythagorean Theorem to find the hypotenuse of the triangle.
$a^2 + b^2 = c^2$
$2^2 + (2\sqrt{3})^2 = c^2$
$4 + 12 = c^2$
$16 = c^2$
$4 = c$

Find the perimeter and area of the trapezoid.
perimeter = 12 + 8 + 4 + 4
= 28 in.
$= \frac{28}{12}$ ft
≈ 2.3 ft

area $= \frac{1}{2}(b_1 + b_2)h$
$= \frac{1}{2}(8 + 12)(2\sqrt{3})$
$= 20\sqrt{3}\text{in}^2$
$= 20\sqrt{3}\text{in}^2 \cdot \frac{1 \text{ ft}}{12 \text{ in.}} \cdot \frac{1 \text{ ft}}{12 \text{ in.}}$
$= \frac{20\sqrt{3}}{144}$ ft^2
≈ 0.2 ft^2

33a.

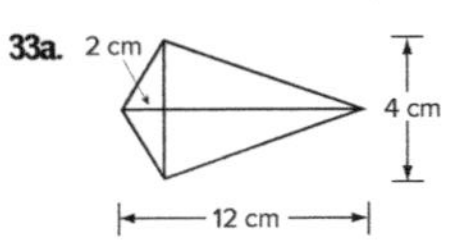

33b.

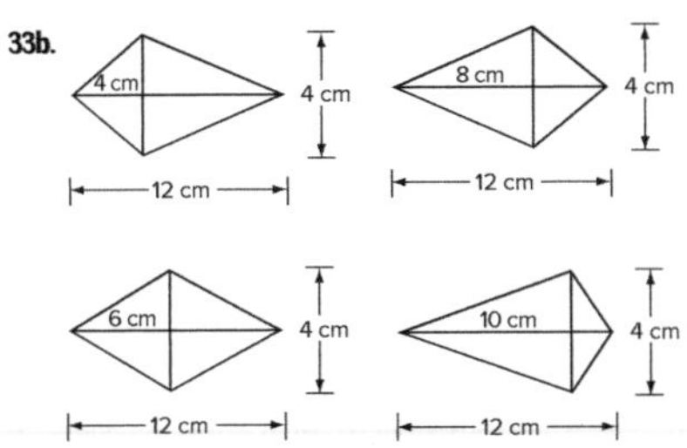

33c.

x	P
2 cm	26.1 cm
4 cm	25.4 cm
6 cm	25.3 cm
8 cm	25.4 cm
10 cm	26.1 cm

33d.

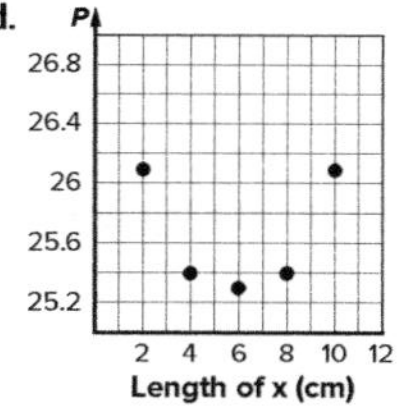

33e. Sample answer: Based on the graph, the perimeter will be minimized when $x = 6$. This value is significant because when $x = 6$, the figure is a rhombus. **35.** 7.2 **37.** Sometimes; sample answer: If the areas are equal, it means that the products of the diagonals are equal. The only time that the perimeters will be equal is when the diagonals are also equal, or when the two rhombi are congruent. **39.** D **41.** 12 m and 48 m **43.** C

Lesson 10-3

1. 1385.4 yd^2

(3)
$A = \pi r^2$ Area of a circle
$74 = \pi r^2$ $A = 74$
$23.55 \approx r^2$ Divide each side by π.
$4.85 \approx r$ Take the positive square root of each side.
So, the diameter is $2 \cdot 4.85$ or about 9.7 millimeters.

5. 4.5 in^2 **7a.** 10.6 in^2 **7b.** \$48 **9.** 78.5 yd^2
11. 14.2 in^2 **13.** 78.5 ft^2 **15.** 10.9 mm **17.** 8.1 ft

(19)
$A = \frac{x}{360} \cdot \pi r^2$ Area of a sector
$= \frac{72}{360} \cdot \pi(8)^2$ $x = 72$ and $r = 8$
≈ 40.2 cm^2 Use a calculator.

21. 322 m^2 **23.** 284 in^2 **25a.** 1.7 cm^2 **25b.** about 319.4 mg
27. 13 **29.** 9.8

(31) **a.** $C = \pi d$ Circumference of a circle
$36 = \pi d$ $C = 36$
$11.5 \text{ ft} \approx d$ Divide each side by π.
b. age = diameter • growth factor
$= 11.5 \cdot 130$ or 1495 yrs

33. 53.5 m^2 **35.** 10.7 cm^2 **37.** 7.9 in^2 **39.** 30 mm^2

(41) The area equals the area of the large semicircle with a radius of 6 in. plus the area of a small semicircle minus 2 times the area of a small semicircle. The radius of each small semicircle is 2 in.
$A = \frac{1}{2}\pi(6)^2 + \frac{1}{2}\pi(2)^2 - 2\left[\frac{1}{2}\pi(2)^2\right]$
$= 18\pi + 2\pi - 4\pi$
$= 16\pi$
≈ 50.3 in^2

43a. $A = \frac{x\pi r^2}{360} - r^2\left[\sin\left(\frac{x}{2}\right)\cos\left(\frac{x}{2}\right)\right]$

43b.

x	A
10	0.1
20	0.5
30	1.7
40	4.0
45	5.6
50	7.7
60	13.0
70	20.3
80	29.6
90	41.1

43c.

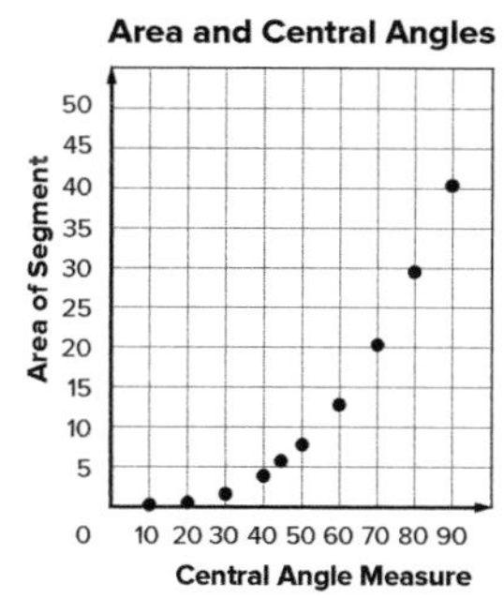

43d. Sample answer: From the graph, it looks like the area would be about 15.5 when x is 63°. Using the formula, the area is 15.0 when x is 63°. The values are very close because I used the formula to create the graph. **45.** 449.0 cm^2 **47.** Sample answer: You can find the shaded area of the circle by subtracting x from 360° and using the resulting measure in the formula for the area of a sector. You could also find the shaded area by finding the area of the entire circle, finding the area of the unshaded sector using the formula for the area of a sector, and subtracting the area of the unshaded sector from the area of the entire circle. The method in which you find the ratio of the area of a sector to the area of the whole circle is more efficient. It requires fewer steps, is faster, and there is a lower probability for error. **49.** Sample answer: If the radius of the circle doubles, the area will not double. If the radius of the circle doubles, the area will be four times as great. Because the radius is squared, if you multiply the radius by 2, you multiply the area by 2^2, or 4. If the arc length of a sector is doubled, the area of the sector is doubled. Because the arc length is not raised to a power, if the arc length is doubled, the area would also be twice as large. **51.** B **53.** A **55.** C
57a. 8 in. **57b.** 33.5 in^2 **57c.** 27.7 in^2 **57d.** 5.8 in^2

Lesson 10-4

1. center: point P, radius: $\overline{PC}$, apothem: $\overline{PR}$, central angle: $\angle BPC$, ≈51.4 **3.** 162 in^2 **5.** 120 ft^2

(7) **a.** The blue area equals the area of the center circle with a radius of 3 ft plus 2 times the quantity of the area a rectangle 19 ft by 12 ft minus the area of a semicircle with a radius of 6 ft.
Area
= Area of circle + 2 • Area of rectangle – Area of semicircle
$= \pi r^2 + 2 \cdot \left(\ell w - \frac{1}{2}\pi r^2\right)$
$= \pi(3)^2 + 2\left[(19(12) - \frac{1}{2}\pi(6)^2\right]$
$= 9\pi + 2(228 - 18\pi)$
$= 9\pi + 456 - 36\pi$
$= 456 - 27\pi$
≈ 371 ft^2

b. The red area equals the area of the center circle with a radius of 6 ft minus the center circle with a radius of 3 ft plus 2 times the area of a circle with a radius of 6 ft.
Area
= Area of large circle – Area of small circle + 2 • Area of circle
$= \pi r^2 - \pi r^2 + 2 \cdot \pi r^2$
$= \pi(6)^2 - \pi(3)^2 + 2\pi(6)^2$
$= 36\pi - 9\pi + 72\pi$
$= 99\pi$
≈ 311 ft^2

9. center: point R, radius: $\overline{RO}$, apothem: $\overline{RT}$, central angle: $\angle ORN$, 45 **11.** 59.4 cm^2 **13.** 584.2 in^2

(15) The figure can be separated into a rectangle with a length of 12 cm and a width of 10 cm and a triangle with a base of 12 cm and a height of 16 cm – 10 cm or 6 cm.
Area of figure = Area of rectangle + Area of triangle
$= \ell w + \frac{1}{2}bh$
$= 12(10) + \frac{1}{2}(12)(6)$
$= 120 + 36$ or 156 cm^2

17. 55.6 in^2 **19a.** 29.7 in., 52.3 in^2 **19b.** 16
21. ≈354 ft^2 **23.** 1.9 in^2 **25a.** 50.9 ft^2 **25b.** 4 boxes
27. 58.1 mm; 232.4 mm^2

(29) To find the area of the shaded region, find the area of the rectangle 8 units by 4 units minus the area of the semicircle with a radius of 2 units minus the area of the trapezoid with bases 4 units and 2 units and height 2 units.
Area of figure
= Area of rectangle – Area of semicircle – Area of trapezoid
$= \ell w - \frac{1}{2}\pi r^2 - \frac{1}{2}h(b_1 + b_2)$
$= 8(4) - \frac{1}{2}\pi(2)^2 - \frac{1}{2}(2)(4 + 2)$
$= 32 - 2\pi - 6$
$= 26 - 2\pi$
≈ 19.7 $units^2$

31. 24 $units^2$ **33.** 0.43 in^2; 0.56 in^2; 0.62 in^2; 0.65 in^2; Sample answer: When the perimeter of a regular polygon is constant, as the number of sides increases, the area of the polygon increases.
35. Chloe; sample answer: The measure of each angle of a regular hexagon is 120°, so the segments from the center to each vertex form 60° angles. The triangles formed by the segments from the center to each vertex are equilateral, so each side of the hexagon is 11 in. The perimeter of the hexagon is 66 in. Using trigonometry, the length of the apothem is about 9.5 in. Putting the values into the formula for the area of a regular polygon and simplifying, the area is about 313.5 in^2.

37. Sample answer:

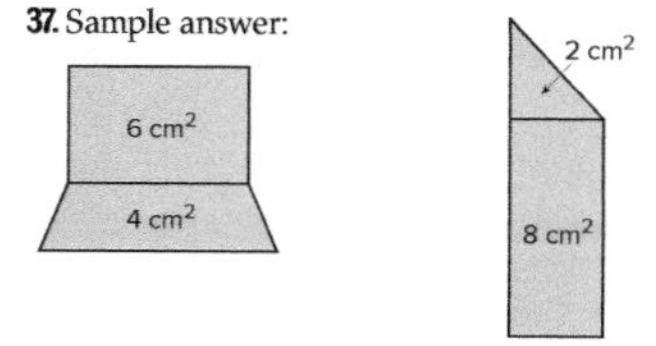

39. Sample answer: You can decompose the figure into shapes for which you know the area formulas. Then, you can sum all of the areas to find the total area of the figure. **41.** A **43.** 84.3 square inches **45.** B **47.** 30.9 square inches

Lesson 10-5

1. 9 yd^2 **3.** $\frac{5}{3}$; 35 **5.** 5.28 in^2

(7) The scale factor between the parallelograms is $\frac{7.5}{15}$ or $\frac{1}{2}$, so the ratio of their areas is $\left(\frac{1}{2}\right)^2$ or $\frac{1}{4}$.
$\frac{\text{area of small figure}}{\text{area of large figure}} = \frac{1}{4}$ Write a proportion.
$\frac{60}{\text{area of large figure}} = \frac{1}{4}$ Substitution
$60 \cdot 4 = \text{area of large figure} \cdot 1$ Cross multiply.
$240 = \text{area of large figure}$ Simplify.
So the area of the large parallelogram is 240 ft^2.

9. 672 cm^2 **11.** $\frac{4}{5}$; 17.5 **13.** $\frac{3}{2}$; 36 **15a.** If the area is doubled, the radius changes from 24 in. to 33.9 in. **15b.** If the area is tripled, the radius changes from 24 in. to 41.6 in. **15c.** If the area changes by a factor of x, then the radius changes from 24 in. to $24\sqrt{x}$ in. **17a.** 4 in. **17b.** Larger; sample answer: The area of a circular pie pan with an 8 in. diameter is about 50 in^2. The area of the larger pan is 52.6 in^2, and the area of the smaller pan is 41.6 in^2. The area of the larger pan is closer to the area of the circle, so Kaitlyn should choose the larger pan to make the recipe.

(19) Area of $\triangle JKL = \frac{1}{2}bh$
$= \frac{1}{2}(5)(6)$ or 15 square units
The scale factor between the triangles is $\frac{5}{3}$, so the ratio of their areas is $\left(\frac{5}{3}\right)^2$ or $\frac{25}{9}$.
$\frac{\text{area of } \triangle JKL}{\text{area of } \triangle J'K'L'} = \frac{25}{9}$ Write a proportion.
$\frac{15}{\triangle J'K'L'} = \frac{25}{9}$ Area of $\triangle JKL = 15$
$15 \cdot 9 = \text{area of } \triangle J'K'L' \cdot 25$ Cross multiply.
$5.4 = \text{area of } \triangle J'K'L'$ Divide each side by 25.
So the area of $\triangle J'K'L'$ is 5.4 $units^2$.

21. area of $ABCD = 18$; area of $A'B'C'D' \approx 56.2$

Selected Answers and Solutions

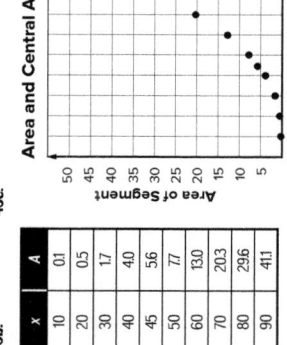

(23) **a.** Sample answer: The graph is misleading because the tennis balls used to illustrate the number of participants are similar circles. When the diameter of the tennis ball increases, the area of the tennis ball also increases. For example, the diameter of the tennis ball representing 1995 is about 2.6 and the diameter of the tennis ball representing 2000 is about 3. So, the rate of increase in the diameters is $\frac{3 - 2.6}{2000 - 1995}$ or about 8%. The area of the circle representing 1995 is $\pi(1.3)^2$ and the area of the circle representing 2000 is $\pi(1.5)^2$. So, the rate of increase in the areas is $\frac{2.25\pi - 1.69\pi}{2000 - 1995}$ or about 35%. The area of the tennis ball increases at a greater rate than the diameter of the tennis ball, so it looks like the number of participants in high school tennis is increasing more than it actually is.

b. Sample answer: If you use a figure with a constant width to represent the participation in each year and only change the height, the graph would not be misleading. For example, use rectangles of equal width and height that varies.

25. Neither; sample answer: In order to find the area of the enlarged circle, you can multiply the radius by the scale factor and substitute it into the area formula, or you can multiply the area formula by the scale factor squared. The formula for the area of the enlargment is $A = \pi(kr)^2$ or $A = k^2\pi r^2$. **27.** $P_{enlarged} = Q\sqrt{R}$ **29.** Sample answer: If you know the area of the original polygon and the scale factor of the enlargement, you can find the area of the enlarged polygon by multiplying the original area by the scale factor squared. **31.** A **33.** scale factor: $\frac{4}{3}$; $x = 12$ **35a.** $\frac{14}{11}$ **35b.** $\frac{\text{area of } KLMN}{\text{area of } FGHJ} = \left(\frac{14}{11}\right)^2$ **35c.** area of $KLMN = \frac{196}{121} \cdot 200 \approx 324$; the area of $KLMN$ is about 324 mm^2.

Lesson 10-6

1. 640 cm^2 **3.** ≈ 571.9 cm^2 **5.** 336 ft^2 **7.** ≈ 571.8 in^2 **9.** 840 ft^2

(11) $S = L + 2B$

Find the missing edge length x of the base.

$3^2 + 4^2 = x^2$ by the Pythagorean Theorem.

$25 = x^2$, so $x = 5$ ft

B is the area of a base. The area of a right triangle is $\frac{1}{2}bh$. For the base, $b = 3$ and $h = 4$.

$B = \frac{1}{2}bh = \frac{1}{2}(3)(4) = 6$

L is the total area of the three lateral faces.

$L = 2 \cdot 3 + 2 \cdot 4 + 2 \cdot 5 = 6 + 8 + 10 = 24$

$S = L + 2B = 24 + 2(6) = 36$ ft^2

13. ≈32.8 cm^2 **15.** ≈236.6 ft^2 **17.** ≈43.8 cm^2 **19.** ≈255 mm^2 **21.** ≈256.4 in^2 **23.** ≈339.3 mm^2 **25.** ≈311.2 ft^2 **27.** ≈427.6 in^2 **29.** ≈8.4 km^2

(31) The lateral area of a regular pyramid is $L = \frac{1}{2}P\ell$. The base of the pyramid is a square, so $P = 4(165) = 660$ yd.

To find the slant height ℓ, find the length of the hypotenuse of a right triangle with legs of length 20 yd and $\frac{1}{2}(165) = 82.5$ yd.

$\ell^2 = 20^2 = 82.5^2$

$\ell^2 = 7206.25$

$\ell \approx 84.8896$

$L = \frac{1}{2}(660)(84.8896) \approx 28{,}013.6$ yd^2

33. about 380.1 ft^2 **35a.** about 12 ft **35b.** Sample answer: First, find the sum of the surface areas of each individual section. The rectangular section of the front and back is $2 \times 20 \times g$ or $40g$ ft^2. The sides cover $2 \times 40 \times g$ or $80g$ ft^2. The triangular tops of the front and back of the greenhouse cover $2(0.5)(4)(20)$ or 80 ft^2. The slant of the roof is $\sqrt{116} \approx 10.77$. Thus, the roof covers $2(40)(10.77)$ or 861 ft^2. The total surface area is $861 + 80 + 120g$ ft^2. Hector can use up to $60{,}000 \div 25$ or 2400 ft^2. Therefore, g is approximately 12.1. Rounding down, we get a height of 12 ft. **35c.** Sample answer: Hector used the entire available plot. There was no glass used for the base. The entrance was made of glass. The top of the roof ran along the 40-ft length of the greenhouse.

(37) The composite figure has trapezoid bases. The trapezoids have bases 20 cm and 13 cm and a height of 21 cm. To find the length of the fourth side of the trapezoid x, use the Pythagorean Theorem.

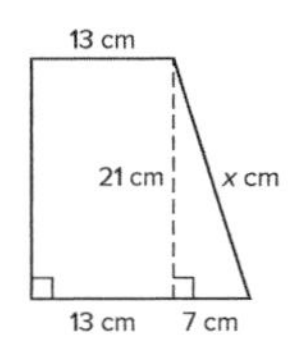

$x^2 = 21^2 + 7^2$	Pythagorean Theorem
$x^2 = 490$	Simplify.
$x \approx 22.136$	Take the square root of each side.

$S = Ph + 2B$	Surface area of a prism
$\approx (21 + 13 + 22.136 + 20)(28) + 2\left[\frac{1}{2}(21)(20 + 13)\right]$	Substitution
$\approx 2131.8 + 693$ or 2824.8 cm^2	Simplify.

39. 4524.8 ft^2 **41.** about 299.1 cm^2 **43.** They are not equal. The slant height of the cone is $\frac{2\sqrt{\pi}}{\pi}$ or about 1.13 times greater than the slant height of the square pyramid. 45. Always; if the heights and radii are the same, the surface area of the cylinder will be greater because it has two circular bases and additional lateral area.

47. $\frac{\sqrt{3}}{2}\ell^2 + 3\ell h$; the area of the equilateral triangle of side ℓ is $\frac{\sqrt{3}}{4}\ell^2$ and the perimeter of the triangle is 3ℓ. So, the total surface area is $\frac{\sqrt{3}}{2}\ell^2 + 3\ell h$.

49. D **51.** C **53.** B

Chapter 10 Study Guide and Review

1. false; height **3.** false; radius **5.** true **7.** true **9.** If two polygons are similar, then their areas are proportional to the square of the scale factor between them. **11.** $P = 50$ cm; $A = 60$ cm^2 **13.** $P = 13.2$ mm; $A = 6$ mm^2 **15.** 132 ft^2 **17.** 96 cm^2 **19.** 336 cm^2 **21.** 1.5 m^2 **23.** 59 in^2 **25.** 166.3 ft^2 **27.** 65.0 m^2 **29.** 7.66 cm^2 **31.** $\frac{1}{2}$; 8 **33.** area of $\triangle RST = 18$ square units; area of $\triangle R'S'T' = 4.5$ square units **35.** 75 mi^2 **37.** Sample answer: 160 ft^2; 202 ft^2 **39.** 113.1 cm^2; 169.6 cm^2 **41.** 354.4 cm^2; 432.9 cm^2

CHAPTER 11

Extending Volume

Chapter 11 Concept Check

1a. Take one-half the product of the lengths of the diagonals. **1b.** 176 in^2 **3.** 64π **5.** Evaluate the exponents.

Lesson 11-1

1. rectangle **3.** rectangle

5 As the circle rotates around the horizontal axis, it sweeps out a three-dimensional shape with a circular cross section and an empty space in the center. This shape resembles a donut, or torus.

7. ellipse **9.** circle

11 As the rectangle rotates around the vertical axis, it sweeps out a three-dimensional shape with a rectangular cross section and an empty space in the center. This shape resembles a tube, or open cylinder.

13a. slice perpendicular to the base **13b.** slice parallel to the base **13c.** slice at an angle **15.** triangle

17. A sample sketch is shown.

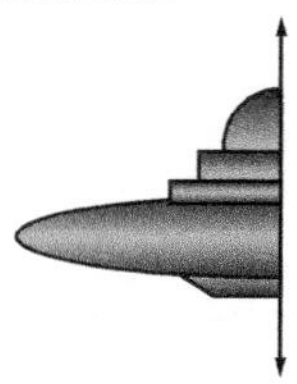

19. Sample answer: The curve would have the same shape as the edge of the vase. The curve would look like the letter *S* stretched vertically.

21a. rectangle **21b.** Cut off a corner of the clay.

23. queen, bishop, rook, pawn **25.** a right trapezoid **27.** rectangle **29.** circle

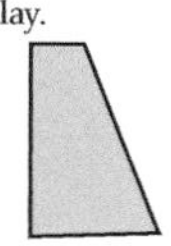

31. D **33.** A **35.** Rotate a circle around an axis. The outer edge of the circle should be 6 inches from the axis. **37.** Sample answer: A plane intersects a square pyramid at an angle through opposite faces. A plane intersects a triangular pyramid at an angle through opposite faces.

Lesson 11-2

1. 108 cm^3 **3.** 26.95 m^3 **5.** 206.4 ft^3 **7.** 1025.4 cm^3 **9.** D

11 $V = Bh$ Volume of a prism

$= 38.5(14)$ $B = \frac{1}{2}(11)(7)$ or 38.5, $h = 14$

$= 539$ m^3 Simplify.

13. 58.14 ft^3 **15.** 1534.25 in^3

17 $V = \pi r^2 h$ Volume of a cylinder

$= \pi(6)^2(3.6)$ Replace r with $12 \div 2$ or 6 and h with 3.6.

≈ 407.2 cm^3 Use a calculator.

19. 2686.1 mm^3 **21.** 521.5 cm^3 **23.** 31 in^3 **25.** 15 in.; 15.4 in. **27.** 120 m^3

29 Find the volume of the original cylinder.

$V = \pi r^2 h$ Volume of a cylinder

$V = \pi(16)(27)$ $r = 4, h = 27$

$V = 432\pi$ Multiply.

The new cylinder is 30% larger than the original. Find 30% of the volume and add to the original.

new volume $= 0.30(432\pi) + 432\pi$ or 561.6π

Because the new can has the same radius as the original, use the volume formula to find the height.

$V = \pi r^2 h$ Volume of a cylinder

$561.6\pi = 16\pi h$ Substitution

$35.1 = h$ Divide.

The height of the larger can is 35.1 cm.

31. 678.6 in^3 **33.** 3934.9 cm^3 **35a.** 0.0019 lb/in^3

35b. The plant should grow well in this soil because the bulk density of 0.0019 lb/in^3 is close to the desired bulk density of 0.0018 lb/in^3. **35c.** 8.3 lb

37. 3,190,680.0 cm^3

39

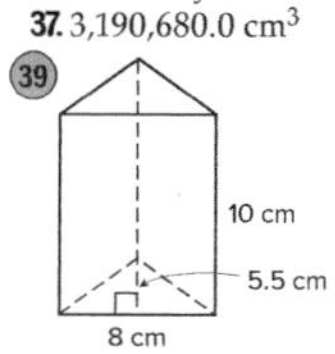

Each triangular prism has a base area of $\frac{1}{2}(8)(5.5)$ or 22 cm^2 and a height of 10 cm. The volume of each triangular prism is $22 \cdot 10$ or 220 cm^3. So, the volume of five triangular prisms is $220 \cdot 5$ or 1100 cm^3.

41a.

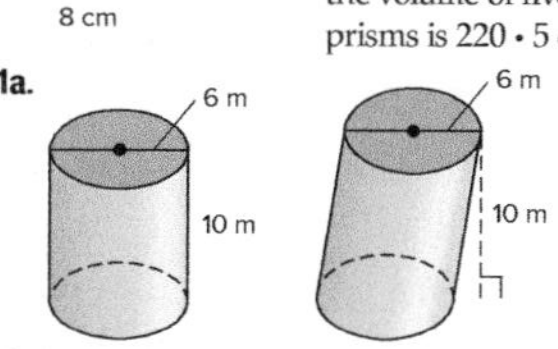

41b. Greater than; a square with a side length of 6 m has an area of 36 m^2. A circle with a diameter of 6 m has an area of 9π or 28.3 m^2. Because the heights are the same, the volume of the square prism is greater.

41c. Multiplying the radius by x; because the volume is represented by $\pi r^2 h$, multiplying the height by x makes the volume x times greater. Multiplying the radius by x makes the volume x^2 times greater, assuming $x > 1$. **43a.** base 3 in. by 5 in., height 4π in.

43b. base 5 in. per side, height $\frac{12}{5}\pi$ in. **43c.** base with legs measuring 3 in. and 4 in., height 10π in.

45. Sample answer:

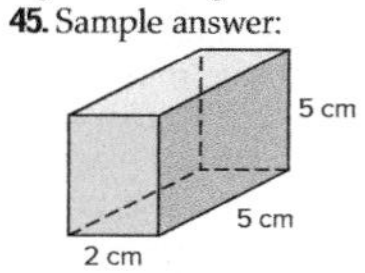

47. Sample answer: Both formulas involve multiplying the area of the base by the height. The base of a prism is polygon, so the expression representing the area varies, depending on the type of polygon it is. The base of a cylinder is a circle, so its area is πr^2. **49.** 9

51. 89.4 **53.** 64 in^3

Lesson 11-3

1. 75 in^3 **3.** 62.4 m^3 **5.** 51.3 in^3 **7.** 28.1 mm^3

9. about 16,755 ft^3

11 $V = \frac{1}{3}Bh$ Volume of a pyramid

$= \frac{1}{3}(36.9)(8.6)$ $B = \frac{1}{2} \cdot 9 \cdot 8.2$ or 36.9, $h = 8.6$

≈ 105.8 mm^3 Simplify.

13. 233.8 cm^3 **15.** 35.6 cm^3 **17.** 235.6 in^3

19. 1473.1 cm^3 **21.** 1072.3 in^3

23 $V = \frac{1}{3}\pi r^2 h$ Volume of a cone

$= \frac{1}{3}\pi(4)^2(14)$ Replace r with $\frac{8}{2}$ or 4 and h with 14.

≈ 234.6 cm^3 Use a calculator.

25. 32.2 ft^3 **27.** 3190.6 m^3 **29.** about 13,333 BTUs

31a. The volume is doubled. **31b.** The volume is multiplied by 2^2 or 4. **31c.** The volume is multiplied by 2^3 or 8.

33 $V = \frac{1}{3}\pi r^2 h$ Volume of a cone

$196\pi = \frac{1}{3}\pi r^2(12)$ Replace V with 196π and h with 12.

$196\pi = 4\pi r^2$ Simplify.

$49 = r^2$ Divide each side by 4π.

$7 = r$ Take the square root of each side.

The radius of the cone is 7 inches, so the diameter is $7 \cdot 2$ or 14 inches.

35a. Sample answer:

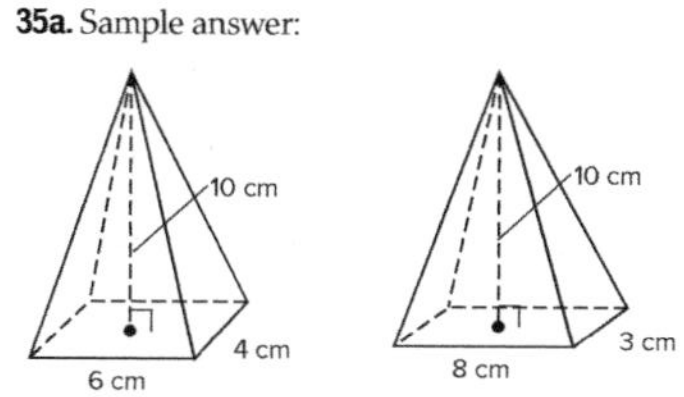

35b. The volumes are the same. The volume of a pyramid equals one third times the base area times the height. So, if the base areas of two pyramids are equal and their heights are equal, then their volumes are equal. **35c.** If the base area is multiplied by 5, the volume is multiplied by 5. If the height is multiplied by 5, the volume is multiplied by 5. If both the base area and the height are multiplied by 5, the volume is multiplied by $5 \cdot 5$ or 25. **37.** Cornelio; Alexandra incorrectly used the slant height. **39.** Sample answer: a square pyramid with a base area of 16 and a height of 12, a prism with a square base of area 16 and height of 4; if a pyramid and prism have the same base, then in order to have the same volume, the height of the pyramid must be 3 times as great as the height of the prism. **41.** C **43.** B **45.** 891π cm^3

Lesson 11-4

1. 1017.9 m^2 **3.** 452.4 yd^2 **5.** 4188.8 ft^3 **7.** 3619.1 m^3

9. 277.0 in^2 **11.** 113.1 cm^2 **13.** 680.9 in^2 **15.** 128 ft^2

17. 530.1 mm^2

19 $V = \frac{4}{3}\pi r^3$ Volume of a sphere

$= \frac{4}{3}\pi(1)^3$ $r = \frac{2}{2}$ or 1

≈ 4.2 cm^3 Use a calculator.

21. 2712.3 cm^3 **23.** 179.8 in^3 **25.** 77.9 m^3

27. 860,289.5 ft^3

29 Surface area $= \frac{1}{2} \cdot$ Area of sphere + Lateral area of cylinder + Area of circle

$= \frac{1}{2}(4\pi r^2) + 2\pi rh + \pi r^2$

$= \frac{1}{2}(4\pi)(4)^2 + 2\pi(4)(5) + \pi(4)^2$

≈ 276.5 in^2

Volume = Volume of hemisphere + Volume of cylinder

$= \frac{1}{2}\left(\frac{4}{3}\pi r^3\right) + \pi r^2 h$

$= \frac{1}{2}\left(\frac{4}{3}\pi \cdot 4^3\right) + \pi(4)^2(5)$

≈ 385.4 in^3

31a. 594.6 cm^2; 1282.8 cm^3 **31b.** 148.7 cm^2; 160.4 cm^3 **33.** $\overline{DC}$ **35.** $\overline{AB}$ **37.** $\odot S$

39a. $\sqrt{r^2 - x^2}$ **39b.** $\pi\left(\sqrt{r^2 - x^2}\right)^2 \cdot y$ or $\pi yr^2 - \pi yx^2$

39c. The volume of the disc from the cylinder is $\pi r^2 y$ or πyr^2. The volume of the disc from the two cones is $\pi x^2 y$ or πyx^2. Subtract the volumes of the discs from the cylinder and cone to get $\pi yr^2 - \pi yx^2$, which is the expression for the volume of the disc from the sphere at height x. **39d.** Cavalieri's Principle **39e.** The volume of the cylinder is $\pi r^2(2r)$ or $2\pi r^3$. The volume of one cone is $\frac{1}{3}\pi r^2(r)$ or $\frac{1}{3}\pi r^3$, so the volume of the double-napped cone is $2 \cdot \frac{1}{3}\pi r^3$ or $\frac{2}{3}\pi r^3$. Therefore, the volume of the hollowed-out cylinder–and thus the sphere–is $2\pi r^3 - \frac{2}{3}\pi r^3$ or $\frac{4}{3}\pi r^3$.

41. Vertical: There is an infinite number of vertical planes that produce reflection symmetry. When any vertical plane intersects the hemisphere through a diameter, both sides of the hemisphere are mirror images. Horizontal: There are no horizontal planes that produce reflection symmetry. When any horizontal plane intersects the hemisphere, the part on top will always be slightly smaller than the bottom. Rotation: There is an infinite number of angles of rotation. When the axis of rotation passes through the center of the sphere perpendicular to its base, the hemisphere can be mapped onto itself by a rotation of any angle between 0° and 360° in the axis.

(43) The surface area is divided by 3^2 or 9. The volume is divided by 3^3 or 27. **45.** 587.7 in^3

47.

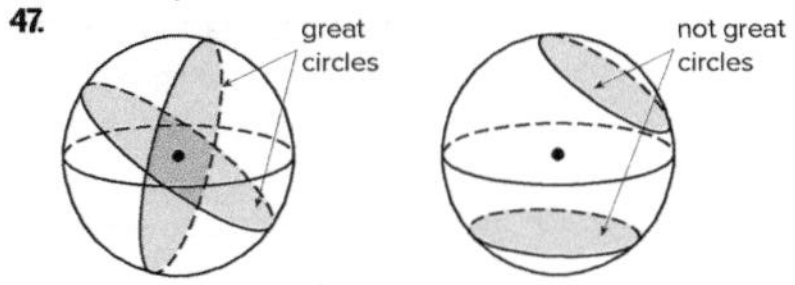

49. B **51.** B **53a.** $\frac{32\pi}{3}$ cm^3 **53b.** $\frac{256\pi}{3}$ cm^3 **53c.** 16π cm^2 **53d.** 64π cm^2 **53e.** $\frac{1}{8}$ **53f.** $\frac{1}{4}$ **55a.** 14.0 in. **55b.** 7.0 in. **55c.** 616.2 in^2 **55d.** 1438.5 in^3

Lesson 11-5

1. $\overleftrightarrow{DH}$, $\overleftrightarrow{FJ}$ **3.** $\triangle JKQ$, $\triangle LMP$

(5) Figure *x* does not go through the poles of the sphere. So, figure *X* is not a great circle and not a line in spherical geometry.

7. The points on any great circle or arc of a great circle can be put into one-to-one correspondence with real numbers. **9.** Sample answers: $\overleftrightarrow{WZ}$ and $\overleftrightarrow{XY}$, $\overline{RY}$ or $\overline{TZ}$, $\triangle RST$ or $\triangle MPL$ **11a.** $\overleftrightarrow{AD}$ and $\overleftrightarrow{FC}$ **11b.** Sample answers: $\overline{BG}$ and $\overline{AH}$ **11c.** Sample answers: $\triangle BCD$ and $\triangle ABF$ **11d.** $\overline{QD}$ and $\overline{BL}$ **11e.** $\overleftrightarrow{MJ}$ **11f.** $\overleftrightarrow{MB}$ and $\overleftrightarrow{KF}$ **13.** no

(15) Every great circle (line) is finite and returns to its original starting point. Thus, there exists no great circle that goes on infinitely in two directions.

17. Yes; if three points are collinear, any one of the three points is between the other two. **19.** 14.0 in.; because 100 degrees is $\frac{5}{18}$ of 360 degrees, $\frac{5}{18}$ × circumference of the great circle ≈ 14.0.

21a. about 912 mi; The cities are 13.2° apart on the same great circle, so $\frac{13.2}{360} \times 2\pi \times 3963$ gives the distance between them. **21b.** Yes; sample answer: Because the cities lie on a great circle, the distance between the cities can be expressed as the major arc or the minor arc. The sum of the two values is the circumference of Earth. **21c.** No; sample answer: Because lines of latitude do not go through opposite poles of the sphere, they are not great circles. Therefore, the distance cannot be calculated in the same way. **21d.** Sample answer: infinite locations; If Phoenix were a point on the sphere, then there are infinite points that are equidistant from that point.

(23) **a.** No; if $\overline{CD}$ were perpendicular to $\overline{DA}$, then $\overline{DA}$ would be parallel to $\overline{CB}$. This is not possible, because there are no parallel lines in spherical geometry. **b.** $DA < CB$ because $\overline{CB}$ appears to lie on a great circle. **c.** No; because there are no parallel lines in spherical geometry, the sides of a figure cannot be parallel. So, a rectangle, as defined in Euclidean geometry, cannot exist in non-Euclidean geometry.

25. Sample answer: In plane geometry, the sum of the measures of the angles of a triangle is 180. In spherical geometry, the sum of the measures of the angles of a triangle is greater than 180. In hyperbolic geometry, the sum of the measures of the angles of a triangle is less than 180. **27.** Sometimes; sample answer: Because small circles cannot go through opposite poles, it is possible for them to be parallel, such as lines of latitude. It is also possible for them to intersect when two small circles can be drawn through three points, where they have one point in common and two points that occur on one small circle and not the other.

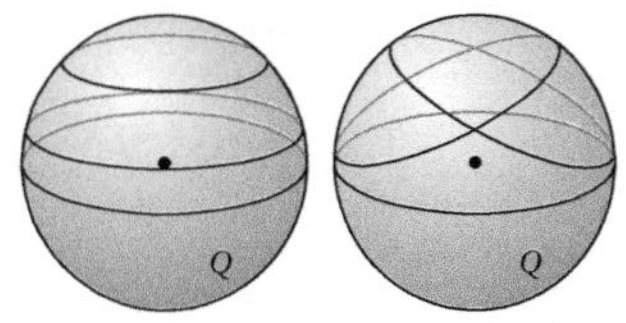

29. False; sample answer: Spherical geometry is non-Euclidean, so it cannot be a subset of Euclidean geometry. **31.** B **33.** 3 **35.** D

Lesson 11-6

1. similar; 4:3 **3.** 414.7 in^2 **5.** 220,893.2 cm^3 **7.** neither **9.** similar; 6:5

(11) $\frac{\text{height of large cylinder}}{\text{height of small cylinder}} = \frac{35}{25}$ or $\frac{7}{5}$

The scale factor is $\frac{7}{5}$. If the scale factor is $\frac{a}{b}$, then the ratio of volumes is $\frac{a^3}{b^3} = \frac{7^3}{5^3} = \frac{x}{125}$. So, by calculating the cross products, you find that $x = 343$ in^3.

13. 0.5 ft^3 **15a.** 10:13 **15b.** 419.6 cm^3

17. scale factor $= \frac{12 \text{ ft}}{0.75 \text{ in.}}$ Write a ratio comparing the lengths.

$= \frac{144 \text{ in.}}{0.75 \text{ in.}}$ 12 ft = 12 • 12 or 144 in.

$= \frac{192}{1}$ Simplify.

The scale factor is 192:1.

19. 4.1 in. **21.** 2439.6 cm^3 **23.** about 5.08 to 1

(25) $\frac{\text{area of smaller tent}}{\text{area of larger tent}} = \frac{9}{12.25}$ Write a ratio comparing the floor areas.

$= \frac{3^2}{3.5^2}$ Write as $\frac{a^2}{b^2}$.

The scale factor is 3:3.5.

ratio of diameters → $\frac{6}{d} = \frac{3}{3.5}$ ← scale factor

$6 \cdot 3.5 = d \cdot 3$ Find the cross products.

$7 = d$ Solve for *d*.

So, the diameter of the larger tent is 7 feet.

$V = \frac{1}{2}\left(\frac{4}{3}\pi r^3\right)$ Volume of a hemisphere

$= \frac{1}{2}\left(\frac{4}{3}\pi \cdot 3.5^3\right)$ Radius $= \frac{7}{2}$ or 3.5

≈ 89.8 Use a calculator.

The volume of the larger tent is about 89.8 ft^3.

27. Laura; Laura compared corresponding parts of the similar figures, while Paloma incorrectly compared the diameter of X to the radius of Y. **29.** Because the scale factor is 15:9 or 5 : 3, the ratio of the surface areas is 25:9 and the ratio of the volumes is 125:27. So, the surface area of the larger prism is $\frac{25}{9}$ or about 2.8 times the surface area of the smaller prism. The volume of the larger prism is $\frac{125}{27}$ or about 4.6 times the volume the smaller prism. **31.** 14 cm **33.** B **35.** C **37.** C **39a.** 12 ft **39b.** 15 ft **39c.** 12.8 ft^2 **39d.** 500 ft^3

Lesson 11-7

1. 0.13 rabbits/ft^2

(3) To find the density, divide the population by the area. 17 ÷ 2.4 = 7.08. No, they will not approve the club. The population density is about 7.1 pairs/mi^2, which is below the average density of 8.3 pairs/mi^2.

5. 10.4 lb/ft^3 **7.** 19,205,750 **9.** 15,846.5 persons/km^2 **11.** 30.1 persons/km^2 **13.** 3.2 g/cm^3 **15.** Block B has density 40 lb/ft^3 compared to 34.2 lb/ft^3 for Block A. **17.** rubber **19.** cardboard

(21) To find the area, find the smallest rectangle/square that surrounds the pentagon, and then subtract the areas of the triangular areas that are not shaded. The area of the square is 64 km^2. There are four triangles in the corners with areas 3 km^2, 3 km^2, 5 km^2, and 6 km^2. The area of the shaded pentagon is 64 km^2 − 3 km^2 − 3 km^2 − 5 km^2 − 6 km^2 = 47 km^2. To find population density, divide the population by the area: 55,323 ÷ 47 ≈ 1177.1 persons/km^2.

23. No; she found the ratio of area to population rather than the ratio of population to area; 389.7 persons/km^2 **25.** 4 **27.** Sample answer: Steel has a greater density than plastic; this means that if a piece of steel and a piece of plastic have the same volume (i.e. the same size), the piece of steel will have a greater mass than the piece of plastic. **29.** B **31.** A, E, F **33.** D

Chapter 11 Study Guide and Review

1. false; spherical geometry **3.** true **5.** true **7.** true **9.** If two solids are similar, then their volumes are proportional to the cube of the scale factor between them. **11.** The volume of the composite solid is the sum of the volumes of each of the simpler solids that make up the composite solid. **13.** circle **15.** 7 cm **17.** 1440 ft^3 **19.** 18 cm^3 **21.** 461.8 in^2 **23.** 3619.1 m^3 **25.** 56.5 cm^3 **27.** $\overline{DL}$ **29.** $\overleftrightarrow{HE}$, $\overleftrightarrow{GF}$ **31.** $\triangle JKL$ **33.** 9 in. **35.** 1728 in^3 **37.** approximately 7698 people per km^2

CHAPTER 12

Probability

Chapter 12 Concept Check

1. Multiply the numerators and the denominators.
3. $\frac{5}{6}$ or 83% **5.** $\frac{1}{3}$ or 33% **7.** $\frac{1}{5}$ or 20%

Lesson 12-1

1. S, S O, O
S, O O, S

Outcomes	Safe	Out
Safe	S, S	S, O
Out	O, S	O, O

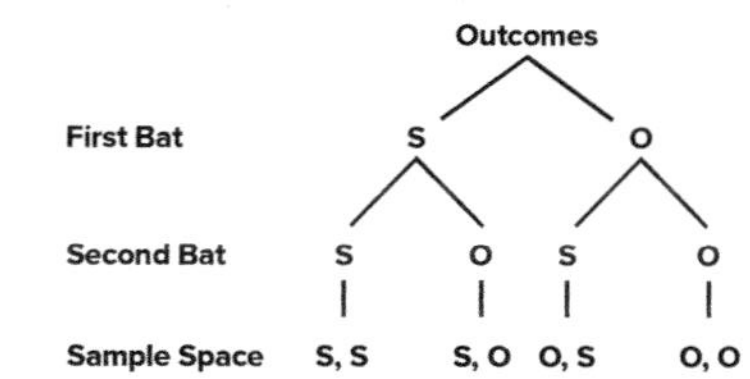

3.

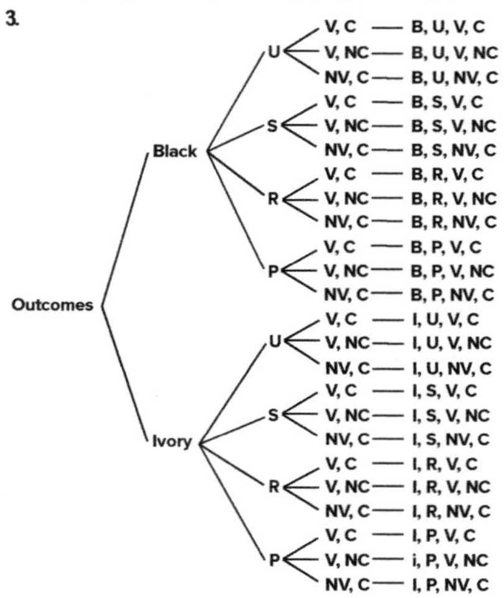

5 Possible Outcomes
= Appetizers × Soups × Salads × Entrees × Desserts
= 8 × 4 × 6 × 12 × 9 or 20,736

7. S, S N, N
S, N N, S

Outcomes	Smithsonian	Natural
Smithsonian	S, S	S, N
Natural	N, S	N, N

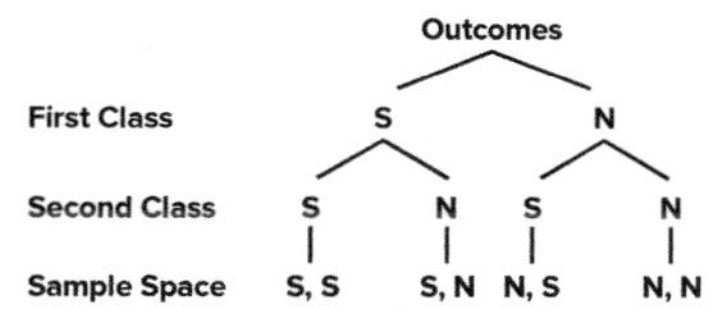

9. M, 5 T, 5
M, 6 T, 6

Outcomes	5	6
Monday	M, 5	M, 6
Thursday	T, 5	T, 6

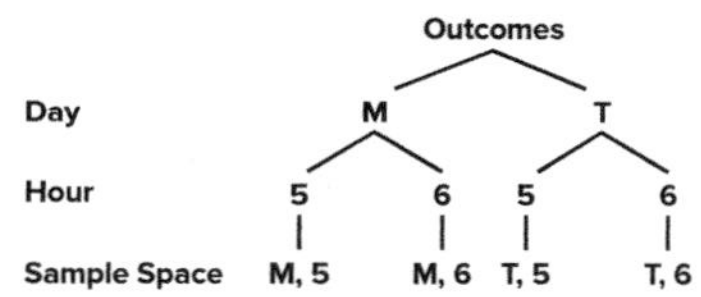

11. O, O A, A
O, A A, O

Outcomes	Oil	Acrylic
Oil	O, O	O, A
Acrylic	A, O	A, A

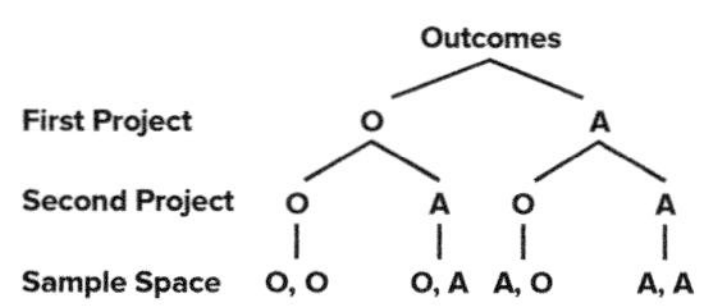

13. S = sedan, T = truck, V = van, L = leather,
F = fabric, G = GPS, NG = no GPS, R = sunroof,
NR = no sunroof

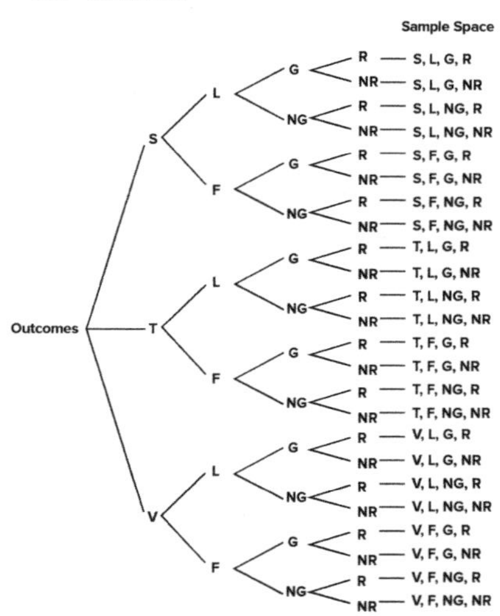

15 Possible Outcomes = Secretary × Treasurer × Vice President × President
= 3 × 4 × 5 × 2 or 120

17. 240 **19.** H = rhombus, P = parallelogram, R = rectangle, S = square, T = trapezoid; H, P; H, R; H, S; H, T; H, H; S, P; S, R; S, S; S, T; S, H

Outcomes	Rhombus	Square
Parallelogram	H, P	S, P
Rectangle	H, R	S, R
Square	H, S	S, S
Trapezoid	H, T	S, T
Rhombus	H, H	S, H

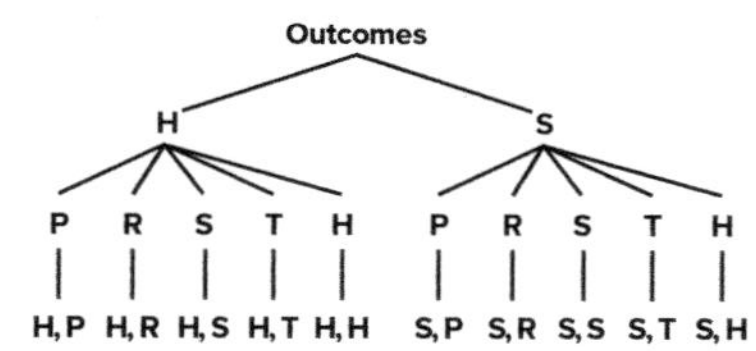

21. Sample answer: 6 different ways:
$4(x + 6) + 2(3) + 2(x + 4)$;
$2(x + 11) + 2(x + 8) + 2(x)$;
$2(x + 4) + 2(x + 9) + 2(x + 6)$;
$2(x) + 2(3) + 4(x + 8)$;
$2(x) + 2(x + 8) + 2(3) + 2(x + 8)$;
$2(x) + 2(3) + 2(4) + 2(x + 6) + 2(x + 6)$

23 **a.** The rolls that result in a sum of 8 are 2 and 6, 3 and 5, 4 and 4, 5 and 3, 6 and 2. So, there are 5 outcomes.
b. The rolls that result in an odd sum are shown.

1, 2	1, 4	1, 6
2, 1	2, 3	2, 5
3, 2	3, 4	3, 6
4, 1	4, 3	4, 5
5, 2	5, 4	5, 6
6, 1	6, 3	6, 5

So, there are 18 outcomes.

25. $n^3 - 3n^2 + 2n$; Sample answer: There are n objects in the box when you remove the first object, so after you remove one object, there are $n - 1$ possible outcomes. After you remove the second object, there are $n - 2$ possible outcomes. The number of possible outcomes is the product of the number of outcomes of each experiment or $n(n - 1)(n - 2)$.

27. Sample answer: You can list the possible outcomes for one stage of an experiment in the columns and the possible outcomes for the other stage of the experiment in the rows. Since a table is two-dimensional, it would be impossible to list the possible outcomes for three or more stages of an experiment. Therefore, tables can only be used to represent the sample space for a two-stage experiment.

29. $P = n^k$; Sample answer: The total number of possible outcomes is the product of the number of outcomes for each of the stages 1 through k. Since there are k stages, you are multiplying n by itself k times, which is n^k. **31.** B **33.** D **35.** 9

Lesson 12-2

1. $\frac{2}{3}$ **3.** $\frac{1}{6}$ **5.** $\frac{1}{3}$ **7a.** 9, 10, 11, 12 **7b.** $\frac{5}{18}$ **7c.** $\frac{13}{18}$
9. 55% **11.** 35% **13.** 45% **15.** $\frac{2}{7}$

17 **a.** The intersection of the column for Girl and the row for Music shows 12. The total number of students is 49. The probability of selecting a girl who prefers music is $\frac{12}{49}$. **b.** The number of girls who do not prefer music is the total number of students minus the number of girls who prefer music: 49 − 12 = 37. The probability of selecting a girl who does not prefer music is $\frac{37}{49}$. **19.** $\frac{64}{105}$ **21.** $\frac{64}{105}$ **23.** $\frac{3}{4}$ **25.** $\frac{4}{13}$

27 **a.** The number 10 is outside of the regions representing advertisements for specific kinds of electronics. So, 10 of the magazines had no advertisements for any of these types of electronics.
b. The circle for smartphones and the circle for DVRs overlap in a region that contains the numbers 30 and 40. So there were advertisements for both a smartphone and a DVR in 30 + 40 = 70 magazines. The total number of magazines is 370. The probability is $\frac{70}{370} = \frac{7}{37}$. **29.** 16% **31.** Sample answer: Rolling a standard number cube with A = rolling a number greater than 1 and B = rolling a number less than 5.
33. No; Latricia did not include the 5 outcomes common to events A and B when she found $P(A)$; Amelie did not calculate $P(A)$ correctly; $P(A)$ should be $\frac{13}{32}$, so $P(\text{not } A) = \frac{19}{32}$. **35.** C **37.** C **39.** C **41.** C

Lesson 12-3

1. $\frac{1}{20}$ **3.** $\frac{1}{420}$ **5.** $\frac{1}{124{,}750}$

7 The number of possible outcomes is 50!. The number of favorable outcomes is (50 − 2)! or 48!.
P(Alfonso 14, Colin 23)

$= \frac{48!}{50!}$ — $\frac{\text{Number of favorable outcomes}}{\text{Number of possible outcomes}}$

$= \frac{\cancel{48!}^{1}}{50 \cdot 49 \cdot \cancel{48!}_{1}}$ — Expand 48! and divide out common factors.

$= \frac{1}{2450}$ — Simplify.

9. $\frac{1}{15{,}120}$

(11) There is a total of 10 letters. Of these letters, B occurs 2 times, A occurs 2 times, and L occurs 2 times. So, the number of distinguishable permutations of these letters is

$\frac{10!}{2! \cdot 2! \cdot 2!} = \frac{3,628,800}{8}$ or 453,600 Use a calculator.

There is only 1 favorable arrangement– BASKETBALL. So, the probability that a permutation of these letters selected at random spells basketball is $\frac{1}{453,600}$.

13. $\frac{1}{7}$ **15.** $\frac{1}{10,626}$ **17a.** $\frac{1}{56}$ **17b.** $\frac{1}{40,320}$ **17c.** $\frac{1}{140}$ **17d.** $\frac{2}{7}$ **19a.** 720 **19b.** 5040

(21) Find the number of ways to choose the second letter times the number of ways to choose the third letter times the number of ways to choose the last two numbers.

possible license plates $= {}_2C_1 \cdot {}_3C_1 \cdot {}_{10}C_1 \cdot {}_{10}C_1$
$= 2 \cdot 3 \cdot 10 \cdot 10$ or 600

23. $\frac{13}{261}$ **25.** Sample answer: A bag contains seven marbles that are red, orange, yellow, green, blue, purple, and black. The probability that the orange, blue, and black marbles will be chosen if three marbles are drawn at random can be calculated using a combination.

27. $C(n, n-r) \stackrel{?}{=} C(n, r)$

$\frac{n!}{[n-(n-r)]!(n-r)!} \stackrel{?}{=} \frac{n!}{(n-r)!r!}$

$\frac{n!}{r!(n-r)!} \stackrel{?}{=} \frac{n!}{(n-r)!r!}$

$\frac{n!}{(n-r)!r!} = \frac{n!}{(n-r)!r!}$ ✓

29. D **31.** D **33.** A **35a.** $\frac{1}{6}$ **35b.** $\frac{1}{30}$

Lesson 12-4

1. $\frac{1}{2}$, 0.5, or 50% **3.** $\frac{13}{33}$, 0.39, or about 39% **5.** $\frac{1}{8}$, 0.125, or 12.5% **7.** $\frac{13}{18}$, 0.72, or 72% **9.** $\frac{1}{9}$, 0.11, or 11% **11.** $\frac{1}{6}$, 0.17, or about 17%

(13) You need to find the ratio of the area of the shaded region to the area of the entire region. The area of shaded region equals the area of the large semicircle minus the area of the small semicircle plus the area of the small semicircle. So, the area of the shaded region equals the area of the large semicircle. Since the area of the large semicircle equals half the total area, P(landing in shaded region) $= \frac{1}{2}$, 0.5, or 50%.

(15) P(pointer landing on yellow) $= \frac{44}{360}$ or about 12.2%

17. 69.4% **19.** 62.2% **21.** Sample answer: a point between 10 and 20 **23.** $\frac{1}{2}$, 0.5, or 50% **25.** 53.5%

27. Sample answer: The probability that a randomly chosen point will lie in the shaded region is ratio of the area of the sector to the area of the circle.

P(point lies in sector) $= \frac{\text{area of sector}}{\text{area of circle}}$

$\frac{x}{360} \stackrel{?}{=} \frac{\frac{x}{360} \cdot \pi r^2}{\pi r^2}$

$\frac{x}{360} = \frac{x}{360}$ ✓

29. 0.24 or 24% **31.** 0.33 or 33%

(33) volume of shallow region $= Bh = (7 \cdot 20) \cdot 20$ or 2800 ft^3

volume of incline region $= Bh = \frac{1}{2}(25)(7+20) \cdot 20$ or 6750 ft^3

volume of deep region $= Bh = (20 \cdot 30) \cdot 20$ or 12,000 ft^3

P(bear swims in the incline region)

$= \frac{\text{volume of incline region}}{\text{volume of pool}}$

$= \frac{6750}{2800 + 6750 + 12,000}$

≈ 0.31 or 31%

35. 14.3% **37.** No; sample answer: Athletic events should not be considered random because there are other factors involved, such as pressure and ability, that have an impact on the success of the event. **39.** Sample answer: The probability of a randomly chosen point lying in the shaded region of the square on the left is found by subtracting the area of the unshaded square from the area of the larger square and finding the ratio of the difference of the areas to the area of the larger square. The probability is $\frac{1^2 - 0.75^2}{1^2}$ or 43.75%. The probability of a randomly chosen point lying in the shaded region of the square on the right is the ratio of the area of the shaded square to the area of the larger square, which is $\frac{0.4375}{1}$ or 43.75%. Therefore, the probability of a randomly chosen point lying in the shaded area of either square is the same. **41.** D **43.** 0.33 **45.** $\frac{1}{36}$ **47a.** $\frac{1}{16}$ **47b.** $\frac{3}{4}$ **47c.** 15 cm

Lesson 12-5

1. The outcome of the first roll does not affect the probabilities of the outcomes for the second roll. Therefore, these events are independent. **3.** The events are not independent. The sample space has 6 equally likely outcomes: {JPR, JRP, PJR, PRJ, RJP, RPJ}. So P(J 1st and R 2nd) $= \frac{1}{6}$, P(J 1st) $= \frac{1}{3}$, and P(R 2nd) $= \frac{1}{3}$, but $\frac{1}{3} \cdot \frac{1}{3} \neq \frac{1}{6}$. **5.** $\frac{1}{2704}$ or 3.7×10^{-4}

7. Maurice should select two blue cards. Let R represent selecting a wild card from the red deck and B represent selecting a wild card from the blue deck. Then P(R and R) $= \frac{3}{12} \cdot \frac{2}{11} = \frac{1}{22} \approx 45\%$;

P(B and B) $= \frac{6}{20} \cdot \frac{5}{9} = \frac{3}{38} \approx 7.9\%$; and

P(B and R) $= \frac{3}{12} \cdot \frac{6}{20} = \frac{3}{40} \approx 7.5\%$.

(9) Since the card is not replaced, the events are dependent. P(Ace) $= \frac{4}{12}$. After that ace is removed, there are only 51 cards left to choose from, 3 of which are aces, so the P(another Ace) $= \frac{3}{51}$. So, P(Ace and Ace) $= \frac{4}{52} \cdot \frac{3}{51} = \frac{1}{221}$, or about 0.005, which is 0.5%.

11. independent; $\frac{1}{36}$ or about 3%. **13.** The events are not independent. The sample space has 3 equally likely outcomes: {BP, BC, PC}. So P(PC) $= \frac{1}{3}$, P(P) $= \frac{1}{3}$, and P(C) $= \frac{1}{3}$, but $\frac{1}{3} \cdot \frac{1}{3} \neq \frac{1}{3}$. **15.** $\frac{1}{306}$ or about 0.3% **17.** $\frac{20}{161}$ or about 12% **19.** No; P(F and S) = P(F) • P(S after F) $= \frac{5}{10} \cdot \frac{7}{10} = \frac{35}{100}$ or 35%; this is less than 50%. **21.** $\frac{8}{87}$ or about 9% **23.** $\frac{16}{145}$ or about 11%

(25) P(1st white) $= \frac{14}{24}$; P(2nd white) $= \frac{13}{23}$; P(white, then white) $= \frac{14}{24} \cdot \frac{13}{23} = \frac{182}{552} = \frac{91}{276}$ or about 33%

(27) **a.** P(1st good) = 40% or 0.4, so P(1st fault) = 0.6. P(2nd good) = 70% or 0.7, so P(2nd fault) = 0.3. P(double fault) = P(1st fault, then 2nd fault) = $0.6 \cdot 0.3 = 0.18$ or 18% **27b.** P(1st fault, then 2nd good) $= 0.6 \cdot 0.7 = 0.42$ or 42% **29.** $\frac{125}{5488}$ or about 2%

31a. Both rules show that P(3 and 8) $= \frac{4}{663}$ or about 0.6%. **31b.** Sample answer: A jar contains 5 pennies and 6 dimes. One coin is chosen at random, and then a second coin is chosen without replacing the first. Find the probability that the first coin is a penny and the second coin is a dime. P(P and D) = P(P) • P(D following P) $= \frac{5}{11} \cdot \frac{6}{10} = \frac{30}{110} = \frac{3}{11}$. P(P and D) = P(D) • P(P following D) $= \frac{6}{11} \cdot \frac{5}{10} = \frac{30}{110} = \frac{3}{11}$.

31c. P(A and B) = P(A) • P(B following A) and P(A and B) = P(B) • P(A following B) are equivalent. **33.** 7; Sample answer: The probability of drawing object A is $\frac{1}{n}$, and the probability of drawing object B when object A is not replaced is $\frac{1}{n-1}$. Since we know that the probability is 2.4%, $\frac{1}{n} \cdot \frac{1}{n-1} = \frac{2.4}{100}$ or 0.024. Solve this equation to determine that n is 7. **35.** Sample answer: The results of two coin flips represent a pair of independent events. Regardless of the outcome of the first flip, the probability of getting heads or tails on the second flip does not change. Drawing two colored marbles out of a bag without replacing the first marble represents a pair of dependent events. Based on the color of the first marble, the probability that the second marble will be a specific color will change. **37.** A **39.** D **41.** greater than **43a.** Sample answer: {(1, 1), (1, 2), (1, 3), (1, 4), (1, 5), (1, 6), (2, 1), (2, 2), (2, 3), (2, 4), (2, 5), (2, 6), (3, 1), (3, 2), (3, 3), (3, 4), (3, 5), (3, 6), (4, 1), (4, 2), (4, 3), (4, 4), (4, 5), (4, 6), (5, 1), (5, 2), (5, 3), (5, 4), (5, 5), (5, 6), (6, 1), (6, 2), (6, 3), (6, 4), (6, 5), (6, 6)} **43b.** $\frac{1}{9}$ or about 11% **43c.** P(> 4 and > 4) $= \frac{1}{9}$; P(> 4) $= \frac{1}{3}$; P(> 4) $= \frac{1}{3}$; $\frac{1}{3} \cdot \frac{1}{3} = \frac{1}{9}$ **45.** $\frac{1}{16,575}$

Lesson 12-6

1. not mutually exclusive; A jack of clubs is both a jack and a club. **3.** $\frac{2}{3}$ or about 67% **5.** $\frac{11}{35}$ or about 44%

(7) Since rolling two fours is both getting doubles and getting a sum of 8, the events are not mutually exclusive.

P(doubles or a sum of 8)

= P(doubles) + P(a sum of 8) − P(doubles and a sum of 8)

$= \frac{6}{36} + \frac{5}{36} - \frac{1}{36}$

$= \frac{10}{36}$ or about 27.8%

9. Not mutually exclusive; $\frac{13}{20}$ or 65% **11.** not mutually exclusive $\frac{4}{13}$ or 30.8% **13.** 56% **15.** $\frac{5}{18}$ or about 28%

(17) There are four 2s in a deck and 4 queens in a deck. There are 52 total cards. A card cannot be both a 2 and a queen, so the events are mutually exclusive. Add the probabilities of the individual events. $\frac{4}{52} + \frac{4}{52} = \frac{8}{52} = \frac{2}{13}$ or about 15% **19.** $\frac{4}{13}$ or about 31% **21.** $\frac{4}{13}$ or about 31% **23.** $\frac{3}{5}$ or 60% **25.** $\frac{11}{15}$ or about 73%

27a. $\frac{11}{20}$ or 55% **27b.** $\frac{9}{10}$ or 90% **29.** Aliyah; to find the probability of blue or red, the individual probabilities should be added because the events are mutually exclusive. **31.** Not mutually exclusive; sample answer: If a triangle is equilateral, it is also equiangular. The two can never be mutually exclusive. **33.** Sample answer: If you pull a card from a deck, it can be either a 3 or a 5. The two events are mutually exclusive. If you pull a card from a deck, it can be a 3 and it can be red. The two events are not mutually exclusive. **35.** $\frac{3}{4}$ or 75% **37.** D **39a.** 1/3 or about 33% **39b.** $\frac{1}{2}$ or 50%

Lesson 12-7

1. 0.20 **3.** $\frac{3}{16}$ or 18.75% **5.** $\frac{4}{5}$ or 80% **7.** $\frac{1}{6}$ or 17% **9.** $\frac{1}{5}$ or 20%

11 P(own digital media player | own smartphone)

$= \frac{P(\text{own digital media player and smartphone})}{P(\text{own smartphone})}$

$= \frac{0.28}{0.43}$

≈ 0.65

13. $P(A \text{ and } B) = P(A) \cdot P(B \mid A)$ Formula for $P(A$ and $B)$.

$\frac{P(A \text{ and } B)}{P(A)} = P(B \mid A)$ Divide each side by $P(A)$.

15a. $\frac{13}{32}$ or about 41% **15b.** $\frac{13}{54}$ or about 24%

17 $P(\text{banner} \mid \text{home team}) = \frac{P(\text{banner and home team})}{P(\text{home team})}$

$= \frac{0.2}{0.8} = \frac{1}{4}$ or 25%

19. About 90.4% **21a.** 0.3 **21b.** 0.33 **23.** $\frac{20}{27}$ or about 74%; Sample answer: The probability that a number cube shows a number less than or equal to 4 is $\frac{4}{6}$. So the probability that the first two number cubes show a number less than or equal to 4 and the last cube does not is $\frac{4}{6} \cdot \frac{4}{6} \cdot \frac{2}{6}$. Because the number greater than 4 can occur on any of the 3 cubes, the probability of a number less than or equal to 4 on exactly two cubes is $3\left(\frac{4}{6} \cdot \frac{4}{6} \cdot \frac{2}{6}\right)$ or $\frac{4}{9}$. The probability of showing a number less than or equal to 4 on all three cubes is $\frac{4}{6} \cdot \frac{4}{6} \cdot \frac{4}{6}$ or $\frac{8}{27}$. Thus the probability of showing a number less than or equal to 4 on two or more cubes is $\frac{4}{9} + \frac{8}{27} = \frac{20}{27}$ or about 74%. **25.** 7; Sample answer: The probability of drawing object A is $\frac{1}{n}$, and the probability of drawing object B when A is not replaced is $\frac{1}{n-1}$. Since we know that the probability is about 1.4%, $\frac{1}{n} \cdot \frac{1}{n-1} \approx \frac{1.4}{100}$. Solve this equation to determine that n is 9.

27. C **29.** $\frac{1}{3}$ **31.** $\frac{2}{3}$ **33.** C **35a.** 0.018 **35b.** 0.098

35c. Sample answer: A patient who receives a positive test result either has the disease or does not have the disease. These are mutually exclusive events, so add the probabilities. From part **a**, P(positive test and disease) = 0.018. From part **b**, P(positive test and no disease) = 0.098. So P(positive test) = 0.018 + 0.098 = 0.116.

35d. P(disease | positive test)

$= \frac{P(\text{disease and positive test})}{P(\text{positive test})}$

$= \frac{0.018}{0.116} \approx 0.155.$

Lesson 12-8

1.

	Breakfast	No Breakfast	Totals
Elementary	38	12	50
High School	22	28	50
Totals	60	40	100

3. 16; joint frequency **5.** 24; marginal frequency

7.

	Car	No Car	Totals
Bus	6.7%	51.7%	58.3%
Train	13.3%	28.3%	41.7%
Totals	20%	80%	100%

9. 33.3% **11.** 66.7%

13.

	At Least 7 Hours	Less Than 7 Hours	Totals
Doctors	40	35	75
Nurses	24	63	87
Totals	64	98	162

15. Make rows: Men, Women, and Totals. Make columns: Gas, Electric, Totals. In the bottom right cell, enter 100 for the total number of people surveyed. Enter 55 in the total column and row for Men. Enter 21 in the column for Gas and row for Men. Enter 19 in the column for Electric and row for Women. The number of men who chose a gas range is 55 − 21 = 34. The total number of women is 100 − 55 = 45. The number of women who chose a gas range is 45 − 19 = 26. Add the men and women who chose a gas range: 21 + 26 = 47. Add the men and women who chose an electric range: 34 + 19 = 53.

	Gas	Electric	Totals
Men	21	34	55
Women	26	19	45
Totals	47	53	100

17. 90; marginal frequency **19.** 54; joint frequency **21.** Yes; the expected and actual joint relative frequencies are the same. **23.** 60% **25.** 60%

27

	Blue	Green	Totals
Boys	40	35	75
Girls	32	18	50
Totals	72	53	125

Boys who chose green: 75 − 40 = 35
Girls who chose blue: 50 − 18 = 32
Total Blue: 40 + 32 = 72
Total Green: 35 + 18 = 53
Total: 72 + 53 = 75 + 50 = 125

29.

	Red	Yellow	Totals
Teachers	23	7	30
Students	18	33	51
Totals	41	40	81

31a.

	AP Classes	No AP Classes	Totals
Senior	40	60	100
Not Senior	110	190	300
Totals	150	250	400

Total: 400
Total AP Classes: 150
Seniors taking AP Classes: 40
Total seniors: 100
Seniors not taking AP: 100 − 40 = 60
Not seniors taking AP: 150 − 40 = 110
Total not seniors: 400 − 100 = 300
Not seniors not taking AP: 300 − 110 = 190
Total not taking AP: 60 + 190 = 250

31b.

	AP Classes	No AP Classes	Totals
Senior	10%	15%	25%
Not Senior	27.5%	47.5%	75%
Totals	37.5%	62.5%	100%

Divide each value from the table in part a by the total number of students, 400. Write the quotient as a percent.

31c. The intersection of the row for students who are not seniors and the column for students not taking AP classes is 47.5%.

31d. There are 250 students not taking AP Classes and 150 students taking AP classes, so it is more likely that a student is not taking advanced-placement classes. The marginal relative frequency for *No AP Classes* is 62.5%, which is greater than the marginal relative frequency for *AP Classes.*

33a.

	Bring Lunch	Cafeteria	Go Out	Totals
Men	43	56	23	122
Women	46	52	30	128
Totals	89	108	53	250

33b. 51.9% **35.** Kaci found the probability that a randomly-chosen apple is organic, given that it is red. The correct answer is $\frac{0.18}{0.30} = 60\%$. **37.** 25%

39. A **41.** D, E, F **43.** C

Chapter 12 Study Guide and Review

1. true **3.** true **5.** true **7.** false; dependent events **9.** The intersection includes events contained in both sample spaces, while the union includes events in either sample space. **11.** 27 **13.** 4 **15.** 35,960 **17a.** $\frac{2}{9}$ **17b.** $\frac{7}{9}$ **19.** $\frac{1}{169}$ **21.** $\frac{2}{9}$ **23a.** $\frac{11}{20}$ **23b.** $\frac{19}{40}$ **25.** $\frac{3}{4}$ or 75% **27.** $\frac{1}{2}$ **29a.** 46.2% **29b.** 63.2%

29c. Not independent; 46.8% of respondents are in the 18-24 age group and 34.2% of respondents were planning on voting, so one would expect 46.8% • 34.2% or about 16% of respondents in the 18–24 age group to plan on voting. The expected joint relative frequency of 16% and the actual joint relative frequency of 21.6% are not the same, so planning to vote is not independent of age group.

Glossary/Glosario

Multilingual eGlossary

Go to connectED.mcgraw-hill.com for a glossary of terms in these additional languages:

Arabic	Chinese	Hmong	Spanish	Vietnamese
Bengali	English	Korean	Tagalog	
Brazilian Portuguese	Haitian Creole	Russian	Urdu	

English / Español

A

absolute error (p. 91) The absolute error of a measurement is equal to one half the unit of measure.

error absoluto El error absoluto de una medida es igual a un medio de la unidad de medida.

accuracy (p. 92) The closeness of a measurement to its true value.

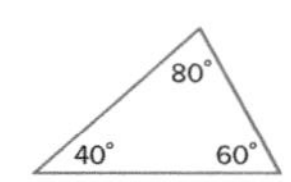

three acute angles

exactitud La cercanía de una medida a su valor verdadero.

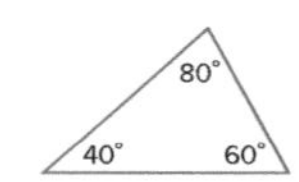

tres ángulos agudos

acute angle (p. 38) An angle with a degree measure less than 90.

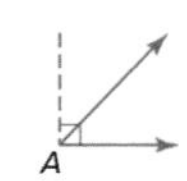

$0 < m\angle A < 90$

ángulo agudo Ángulo cuya medida en grados es menos de 90.

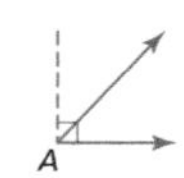

$0 < m\angle A < 90$

adjacent angles (p. 46) Two angles that lie in the same plane and have a common vertex and a common side, but no common interior points.

ángulos adyacentes Dos ángulos que yacen sobre el mismo plano, tienen el mismo vértice y un lado en común, pero ningún punto interior en común.

adjacent arcs (p. 654) Arcs in a circle that have exactly one point in common.

arcos adyacentes Arcos en un círculo que tienen un solo punto en común.

algebraic proof (p. 143) A proof that is made up of a series of algebraic statements. The properties of equality provide justification for many statements in algebraic proofs.

demostración algebraica Demostración que se realiza con una serie de enunciados algebraicos. Las propiedades de la igualdad proveen justificación para muchas enunciados en demostraciones algebraicas.

alternate exterior angles (p. 169) In the figure, transversal t intersects lines ℓ and m. $\angle 5$ and $\angle 3$, and $\angle 6$ and $\angle 4$ are alternate exterior angles.

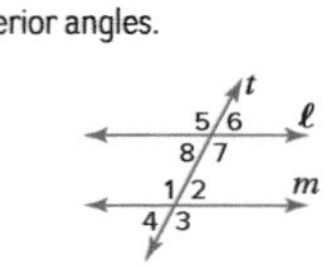

ángulos alternos externos En la figura, la transversal t interseca las rectas ℓ y m. $\angle 5$ y $\angle 3$, y $\angle 6$ y $\angle 4$ son ángulos alternos externos.

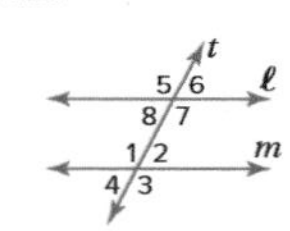

alternate interior angles (p. 169) In the figure for alternate exterior angles, transversal t intersects lines ℓ and m. $\angle 1$ and $\angle 7$, and $\angle 2$ and $\angle 8$ are alternate interior angles.

altitude **1.** (p. 367) In a triangle, a segment from a vertex of the triangle to the line containing the opposite side and perpendicular to that side. **2.** (p. 770) In a prism or cylinder, a segment perpendicular to the bases with an endpoint in each plane. **3.** (pp. 773, 775) In a pyramid or cone, the segment that has the vertex as one endpoint and is perpendicular to the base.

ambiguous case (p. 618) A situation in which more than one solution for a triangle exists.

ambiguous case of the Law of Sines (p. 816) Given the measures of two sides and a nonincluded angle, there exist two possible triangles.

angle (p. 36) The intersection of two noncollinear rays at a common endpoint. The rays are called *sides* and the common endpoint is called the *vertex*.

angle bisector (p. 39) A ray that divides an angle into two congruent angles.

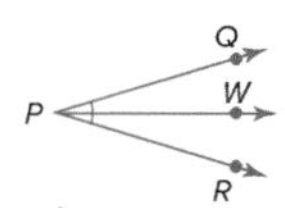

$\overrightarrow{PW}$ is the bisector of $\angle P$.

angle of depression (p. 608) The angle between the line of sight and the horizontal when an observer looks downward.

angle of elevation (p. 608) The angle between the line of sight and the horizontal when an observer looks upward.

angle of rotation (p. 240) The angle through which a preimage is rotated to form the image.

apothem (pp. 751, 752) A segment that is drawn from the center of a regular polygon perpendicular to a side of the polygon.

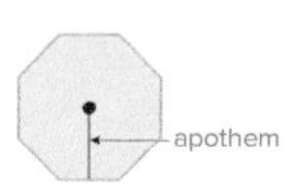

arc (p. 652) A part of a circle that is defined by two endpoints.

arc length (p. 654) The distance between the endpoints along an arc, measured in linear units.

ángulos alternos internos En la figura anterior, la transversal t interseca las rectas ℓ y m. $\angle 1$ y $\angle 7$, y $\angle 2$ y $\angle 8$ son ángulos alternos internos.

altura **1.** En un triángulo, segmento trazado desde uno de los vértices del triángulo hasta el lado opuesto y que es perpendicular a dicho lado. **2.** En un prisma o un cilindro, segmento perpendicular a las bases con un extremo en cada plano. **3.** En una pirámide o un cono, segmento que tiene un extremo en el vértice y que es perpendicular a la base.

caso ambiguo Una situación en la que existe más de una solución para un triángulo.

caso ambiguo de la ley de los senos Dadas las medidas de dos lados y de un ángulo no incluido, existen dos triángulos posibles.

ángulo La intersección de dos rayos no colineales en un extremo común. Las rayos se llaman *lados* y el punto común se llama *vértice*.

bisectriz de un ángulo Rayo que divide un ángulo en dos ángulos congruentes.

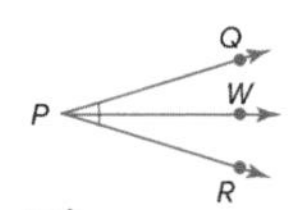

$\overrightarrow{PW}$ es la bisectriz del $\angle P$.

ángulo de depresión Ángulo formado por la horizontal y la línea de visión de un observador que mira hacia abajo.

ángulo de elevación Ángulo formado por la horizontal y la línea de visión de un observador que mira hacia arriba.

ángulo de rotación Ángulo a través del cual se rota una preimagen para formar la imagen.

apotema Segmento trazado desde el centro de un polígono regular hasta uno de sus lados y que es perpendicular a dicho lado.

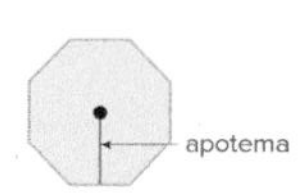

arco Parte d e un círculo definida por dos extremos.

longitud del arco La distancia entre los extremos de un arco, medida en unidades lineales.

area (p. 58) The number of square units needed to cover a surface.

auxiliary line (p. 282) An extra line or segment drawn in a figure to help complete a proof.

axiom (p. 141) A statement that is accepted as true.

axis **1.** (p. 771) In a cylinder, the segment with endpoints that are the centers of the bases. **2.** (p. 856) In a cone, the segment with endpoints that are the vertex and the center of the base.

área Número de unidades cuadradas para cubrir una superficie.

línea auxiliar Recta o segmento de recta adicional que es traza en una figura para ayudar a completar una demostración.

axioma Enunciado que se acepta como verdadero.

eje **1.** En un cilindro, el segmento cuyos extremos son el centro de las bases. **2.** En un cono, el segmento cuyos extremos son el vértice y el centro de la base.

B

base angle of an isosceles triangle (p. 325) See *isosceles triangle* and *isosceles trapezoid.*

base angle of a trapezoid (p. 469) Angles of a trapezoid that are formed by the base and one of the legs.

base edges (p. 770) The intersection of the lateral faces and bases in a solid figure.

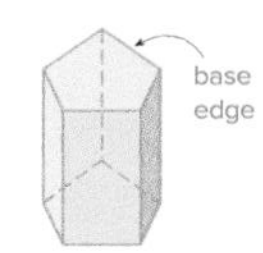

base of a parallelogram (p. 725) Any side of a parallelogram.

base of a polyhedron (p. 76) The two parallel congruent faces of a polyhedron.

base of a trapezoid (p. 469) The two parallel sides of a trapezoid.

base of a triangle (p. 727) Any side of a triangle.

between (p. 14) For any two points A and B on a line, there is another point C between A and B if and only if A, B, and C are collinear and $AC + CB = AB$.

betweenness of points (p. 14) See *between.*

biconditional (p. 124) The conjunction of a conditional statement and its converse.

ángulo de la base de un triángulo isósceles Ver *triángulo isósceles* y *trapecio isósceles.*

ángulo de la base de un trapecio Los ángulos de un trapecio que están formados por la base y uno de los catetos.

aristas de las bases Intersección de las base con las caras laterales en una figura sólida.

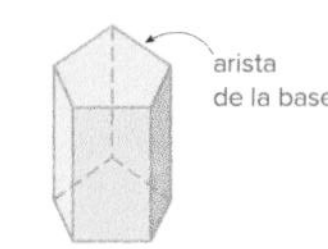

base de un paralelogramo Cualquier lado de un paralelogramo.

base de poliedro Las dos caras paralelas y congruentes de un poliedro.

base de un trapecio Los dos lados paralelos de un trapecio.

base de un triángulo Cualquier lado de un triángulo.

entre Para cualquier par de puntos A y B de una recta, existe un punto C ubicado entre A y B si y sólo si A, B y C son colineales y $AC + CB = AB$.

intermediación de puntos Ver *entre.*

bicondicional Conjunción entre un enunciado condicional y su recíproco.

C

center of a circle (p. 643) The central point where radii form a locus of points called a circle.

center of dilation (p. 492) The center point from which dilations are performed.

center of a regular polygon (p. 752) The center of the circle that circumscribes the polygon.

center of rotation (p. 240) A fixed point around which shapes move in a circular motion to a new position.

center of symmetry (p. 260) The point in the center of a figure about which the figure can be mapped onto itself by a rotation.

central angle (p. 652) An angle that intersects a circle in two points and has its vertex at the center of the circle.

central angle of a regular polygon (p. 752) An angle that has its vertex at the center of a polygon and with sides that pass through consecutive vertices of the polygon.

centroid (p. 365) The point of concurrency of the medians of a triangle.

chord 1. (p. 643) For a given circle, a segment with endpoints that are on the circle. 2. (p. 880) For a given sphere, a segment with endpoints that are on the sphere.

circle (p. 643) The locus of all points in a plane equidistant from a given point called the *center* of the circle.

P is the center of the circle.

circular permutation (p. 875) A permutation of objects that are arranged in a circle or loop.

circumcenter (p. 355) The point of concurrency of the perpendicular bisectors of a triangle.

circumference (pp. 58, 645) The distance around a circle.

circumscribed (p. 646) A circle is circumscribed about a polygon if the circle contains all the vertices of the polygon.

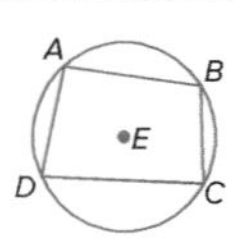

⊙*E* is circumscribed about quadrilateral *ABCD*.

centro de un círculo Punto central desde el cual los radios forman un lugar geométrico de puntos llamado círculo.

centro de la homotecia Punto fijo en torno al cual se realizan las homotecias.

centro de un polígono regular El centro del círculo que circunscribe el polígono.

centro de rotación Punto fijo alrededor del cual gira una figura hasta alcanzar una posición dada.

centro de la simetría Vea *el punto de simetría.*

ángulo central Ángulo que interseca un círculo en dos puntos y cuyo vértice está en el centro del círculo.

ángulo central de un polígono regular Ángulo cuyo vértice esta en el centro del polígono y cuyos lados pasan por vértices consecutivas del polígono.

baricentro Punto de intersección de las medianas de un triángulo.

cuerda 1. Para cualquier círculo, segmento cuyos extremos están en el círculo. 2. Para cualquier esfera, segmento cuyos extremos están en la esfera.

círculo Lugar geométrico formado por todos los puntos en un plano, equidistantes de un punto dado llamado *centro* del círculo.

P es el centro del círculo.

permutación circular Permutación de objetos que se arreglan en un círculo o un bucle.

circuncentro Punto de intersección de las mediatrices de un triángulo.

circunferencia Distancia alrededor de un círculo.

circunscrito Un polígono está circunscrito a un círculo si todos sus vértices están contenidos en el círculo.

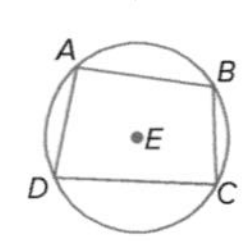

⊙*E* está circunscrito al cuadrilátero *ABCD*.

collinear (p. 5) Points that lie on the same line.

P, *Q*, and *R* are collinear.

combination (p. 876) An arrangement or listing in which order is not important.

common tangent (p. 678) A line or segment that is tangent to two circles in the same plane.

complement (p. 867) The complement of an event *A* consists of all the outcomes in the sample space that are not included as outcomes of event *A*.

complementary angles (p. 47) Two angles with measures that have a sum of 90.

component form (p. 233) A vector expressed as an ordered pair, (change in *x*, change in *y*).

composite figure (p. 754) A figure that can be separated into regions that are basic figures.

composite solid (p. 778) A three-dimensional figure that is composed of simpler figures.

composition of transformations (p. 249) The resulting transformation when a transformation is applied to a figure and then another transformation is applied to its image.

compound event (p. 889) An event that consists of two or more simple events.

compound statement (p. 119) A statement formed by joining two or more statements.

concave polygon (p. 56) A polygon for which there is a line containing a side of the polygon that also contains a point in the interior of the polygon.

concentric circles (p. 644) Coplanar circles with the same center.

conclusion (p. 121) In a conditional statement, the statement that immediately follows the word *then*.

concurrent lines (p. 355) Three or more lines that intersect at a common point.

conditional probability (p. 903) The probability of an event under the condition that some preceding event has occurred.

conditional statement (p. 121) A statement that can be written in *if-then* form.

colineal Puntos que yacen sobre la misma recta.

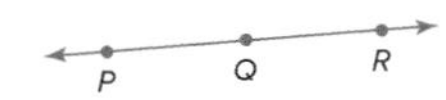

P, *Q* y *R* son colineales.

combinación Arreglo o lista en que el orden no es importante.

tangente común Recta o segmento de recta tangente a dos círculos en el mismo plano.

complemento El complemento de un evento *A* consiste en todos los resultados en el espacio muestral que no se incluyen como resultados del evento *A*.

ángulos complementarios Dos ángulos cuyas medidas suman 90.

componente Vector expresado en forma de par ordenado, (cambio en *x*, cambio en *y*).

figura compuesta Figura que se puede separar en regiones formas de figuras básicas.

solido compuesto Figura tridimensional formada por figuras más simples.

composición de transformaciones Transformación que resulta cuando se aplica una transformación a una figura y luego se le aplica otra transformación a su imagen.

evento compuesto Evento que consiste de dos o más eventos simples.

enunciado compuesto Enunciado formado por la unión de dos o más enunciados.

polígono cóncavo Polígono para el cual existe una recta que contiene un lado del polígono y un punto en el interior del polígono.

círculos concéntricos Círculos coplanarios con el mismo centro.

conclusión Parte de un enunciado condicional que está escrito justo después de la palabra *entonces*.

rectas concurrentes Tres o más rectas que se intersecan en un punto común.

probabilidad condicional La probabilidad de un acontecimiento bajo condición que ha ocurrido un cierto acontecimiento precedente.

enunciado condicional Enunciado escrito en la forma *si-entonces*.

cone (p. 76) A solid with a circular base, a vertex not contained in the same plane as the base, and a lateral surface area composed of all points in the segments connecting the vertex to the edge of the base.

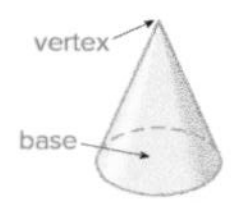

cono Sólido de base circular cuyo vértice no yace en el mismo plano que la base y cuya área de superficie lateral está formada por todos los puntos en los segmentos que conectan el vértice con el bonde de la base.

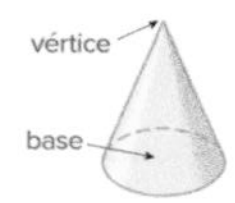

congruence transformations (p. 67) A mapping for which a geometric figure and its image are congruent.

transformaciones de congruencia Aplicación en la cual una figura geométrica y su imagen son congruentes.

congruent (p. 15) Having the same measure.

congruente Que tienen la misma medida.

congruent arcs (p. 653) Arcs in the same circle or in congruent circles that have the same measure.

arcos congruentes Arcos que tienen la misma medida y que pertenecen al mismo círculo o a círculos congruentes.

congruent polygons (p. 291) Polygons in which all matching parts are congruent.

polígonos congruentes Polígonos cuyas partes correspondientes son todas congruentes.

congruent segments (p. 15) Two segments with the same measure.

segmentos congruentes Dos segmentos que tienen la misma medida.

congruent solids (p. 835) Two solids with the same shape, size, and scale factor of 1:1.

sólidos congruentes Dos sólidos con la misma forma, tamaño y factor de escala de 1:1.

conjecture (p. 111) An educated guess based on known information.

conjetura Juicio basado en información conocida.

conjunction (p. 119) A compound statement formed by joining two or more statements with the word *and*.

conjunción Enunciado compuesto que se obtiene al unir dos o más enunciados con la palabra *y*.

consecutive interior angles (p. 169) In the figure, transversal t intersects lines ℓ and m. There are two pairs of consecutive interior angles: $\angle 8$ and $\angle 1$, and $\angle 7$ and $\angle 2$.

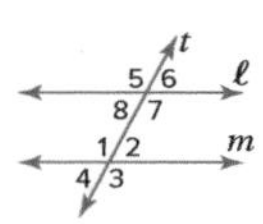

ángulos internos consecutivos En la figura, la transversal t interseca las rectas ℓ y m. La figura presenta dos pares de ángulos internos consecutivos; $\angle 8$ y $\angle 1$; y $\angle 7$ y $\angle 2$.

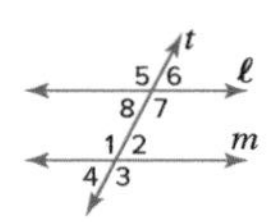

constructions (p. 16) A method of creating geometric figures without the benefit of measuring tools. Generally, only a pencil, straightedge, and compass are used.

construcción Método para dibujar figuras geométricas sin el uso de instrumentos de medición. En general, sólo requiere de un lápiz, una regla y un compás.

contrapositive (p. 122) The statement formed by negating both the hypothesis and conclusion of the converse of a conditional statement.

antítesis Enunciado formado por la negación tanto de la hipótesis como de la conclusión del recíproco de un enunciado condicional.

converse (p. 122) The statement formed by exchanging the hypothesis and conclusion of a conditional statement.

recíproco Enunciado que se obtiene al intercambiar la hipótesis y la conclusión de un enunciado condicional dado.

convex polygon (p. 56) A polygon for which there is no line that contains both a side of the polygon and a point in the interior of the polygon.

polígono convexo Polígono para el cual no existe recta alguna que contenga un lado del polígono y un punto en el interior del polígono.

coordinate proofs (p. 334) Proofs that use figures in the coordinate plane and algebra to prove geometric concepts.

demostraciones en coordinadas Demostraciones que usan figuras en el plano de coordinados y álgebra para demostrar conceptos geométricos.

coplanar (p. 5) Points that lie in the same plane.

coplanar Puntos que yacen en el mismo plano.

corner view (p. 84) The view from a corner of a three-dimensional figure, also called the *isometric view*.

vista de esquina Vista desde una de las esquinas de una figura tridimensional. También se conoce como *vista en perspectiva*.

corollary (p. 285) A statement that can be easily proved using a theorem is called a corollary of that theorem.

corolario Un enunciado que se puede demostrar fácilmente usando un teorema se conoce como corolario de dicho teorema.

corresponding angles (p. 169) In the figure, transversal t intersects lines ℓ and m. There are four pairs of corresponding angles: $\angle 5$ and $\angle 1$, $\angle 8$ and $\angle 4$, $\angle 6$ and $\angle 2$, and $\angle 7$ and $\angle 3$.

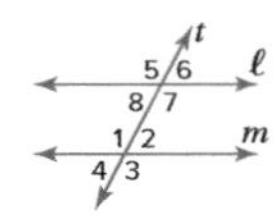

ángulos correspondientes En la figura, la transversal t interseca las rectas ℓ y m. La figura muestra cuatro pares de ángulos correspondientes: $\angle 5$ y $\angle 1$, $\angle 8$ y $\angle 4$, $\angle 6$ y $\angle 2$; y $\angle 7$ y $\angle 3$.

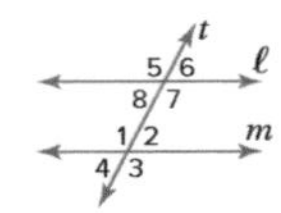

corresponding parts (p. 291) Matching parts of congruent polygons.

partes correspondientes Partes que coinciden de polígonos congruentes.

cosecant (p. 606) The reciprocal of the sine of an angle in a right triangle.

cosecante Recíproco del seno de un ángulo en un triángulo rectangulo.

cosine (p. 596) For an acute angle of a right triangle, the ratio of the measure of the leg adjacent to the acute angle to the measure of the hypotenuse.

coseno Para cualquier ángulo agudo de un triángulo rectángulo, razón de la medida del cateto adyacente al ángulo agudo a la medida de la hipotenusa.

cotangent (p. 606) For an acute angle of a right triangle, the ratio of the adjacent to the opposite side of a right triangle.

cotangente Razón de la medida del cateto adyacente a la medida de cateto opuesto de un triángulo rectángulo.

counterexample (p. 114) An example used to show that a given statement is not always true.

contraejemplo Ejemplo que se usa para demostrar que un enunciado dado no siempre es verdadero.

cross section (p. 797) The intersection of a solid and a plane.

sección transversal Intersección de un sólido con un plano.

cylinder (p. 76) A figure with bases that are formed by congruent circles in parallel planes.

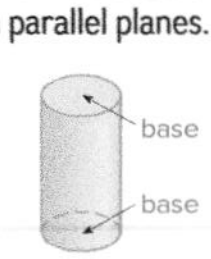

cilindro Figura cuyas bases son círculos congruentes ubicados en planos paralelos.

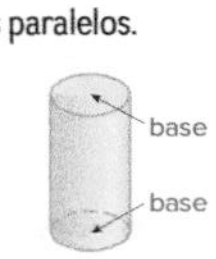

D

deductive argument (p. 143) A proof formed by a group of algebraic steps used to solve a problem.

deductive reasoning (p. 131) A system of reasoning that uses facts, rules, definitions, or properties to reach logical conclusions.

degree (p. 37) A unit of measure used in measuring angles and arcs. An arc of a circle with a measure of 1° is $\frac{1}{360}$ of the entire circle.

density (p. 842) The mass of an object per unit of volume.

dependent events (p. 889) Two or more events in which the outcome of one event affects the outcome of the other events.

diagonal (p. 423) In a polygon, a segment that connects nonconsecutive vertices of the polygon.

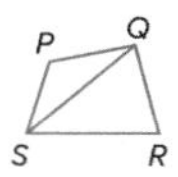

$\overline{SQ}$ is a diagonal.

diameter **1.** (p. 643) In a circle, a chord that passes through the center of the circle. **2.** (p. 818) In a sphere, a segment that contains the center of the sphere, and has endpoints that are on the sphere.

dilation (p. 834) A transformation that enlarges or reduces the original figure proportionally. A dilation with center C and positive scale factor k, $k \neq 1$, is a function that maps a point P in a figure to its image such that

- if point P and C coincide, then the image and preimage are the same point, or
- if point P is not the center of dilation, then P' lies on $\overrightarrow{CP}$ and $CP' = k(CP)$.

If $k < 0$, P' is the point on the ray opposite $\overrightarrow{CP}$ such that $CP' = |k|(CP)$.

direct isometry (p. 69) An isometry in which the image of a figure is found by moving the figure intact within the plane.

directrix (p. 703) The fixed line in a parabola that is equidistant from the locus of all points in a plane.

disjunction (p. 120) A compound statement formed by joining two or more statements with the word *or*.

distance between two points (p. 16) The length of the segment between two points.

argumento deductivo Demostración que consta de un conjunto de pasos algebraicos que se usan para resolver un problema.

razonamiento deductivo Sistema de razonamiento que emplea hechos, reglas, definiciones o propiedades para obtener conclusiones lógicas.

grado Unidad de medida que se usa para medir ángulos y arcos. El arco de un círculo que mide 1° equivale a $\frac{1}{360}$ del círculo completo.

densidad La masa de un objeto por unidad de volumen.

eventos dependientes Dos o más eventos en que el resultado de un evento afecta el resultado de los otros eventos.

diagonal Recta que conecta vértices no consecutivos de un polígono.

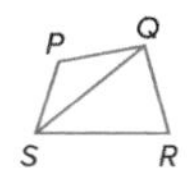

$\overline{SQ}$ es una diagonal.

diámetro **1.** En un círculo cuerda que pasa por el centro. **2.** En una estera segmento que incluye el centro de la esfera y cuyos extremos están ubicados en la esfera.

homotecia Transformación que amplía o disminuye proporcionalmente el tamaño de una figura. Una homotecia con centro C y factor de escala positivo k, $k \neq 1$, es una función que aplica un punto P a su imagen, de modo que si el punto P coincide con el punto C, entonces la imagen y la preimagen son el mismo punto, o si el punto P no es el centro de la homotecia, entonces P' yace sobre $\overrightarrow{CP}$ y $CP' = k(CP)$. Si $k < 0$, P' es el punto sobre el rayo opuesto a $\overrightarrow{CP}$, tal que $CP' = |k|(CP)$.

isometría directa Isometría en la cual se obtiene la imagen de una figura, al mover la figura intacta dentro del plano.

directriz Línea fija en una parábola que está equidistante del lugar geométrico de todos los puntos en un plano.

disyunción Enunciado compuesto que se forma al unir dos o más enunciados con la palabra *o*.

distancia entre dos puntos Longitud del segmento entre dos puntos.

E

edge (p. 76) A line that connects two nodes in a network.

edge of a polyhedron (p. 76) A line segment where the faces of a polyhedron intersect.

elimination (p. P18) The use of addition or subtraction in combination with multiplication or division to eliminate one variable and solve a system of equations.

equiangular polygon (p. 57) A polygon with all congruent angles.

equiangular triangle (p. 326) A triangle with all angles congruent.

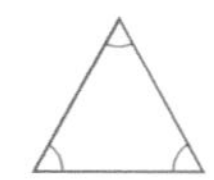

equidistant (p. 197) The distance between two lines measured along a perpendicular line is always the same.

equilateral polygon (p. 57) A polygon with all congruent sides.

equilateral triangle (p. 326) A triangle with all sides congruent.

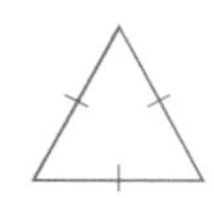

Euclidean geometry (p. 827) A geometrical system in which a plane is a flat surface made up of points that extend infinitely in all directions.

event (p. P8) A specific outcome or type of outcome.

experiment (p. P8) A situation involving chance such as flipping a coin or rolling a die.

experimental probability (p. P9) The ratio of the number of positive outcomes to the total number of events or trials in a probability experiment.

exterior (p. 36) A point is in the exterior of an angle if it is neither on the angle nor in the interior of the angle.

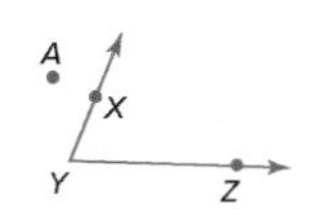

A is in the exterior of ∠*XYZ*.

arista Recta que conecta dos nodos en una red.

arista de un poliedro Segmento de recta donde se intersecan las caras de un poliedro.

eliminación El uso de la suma o la resta en combinación con la multiplicación o la división para eliminar una variable y resolver un sistema de ecuaciones.

polígono equiangular Polígono cuyos ángulos son todos congruentes.

triángulo equiangular Triángulo cuyos ángulos son todos congruentes.

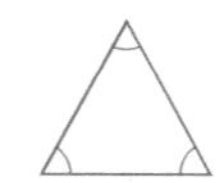

equidistante La distancia entre dos rectas que siempre permanece constante cuando se mide a lo largo de una perpendicular.

polígono equilátero Polígono cuyos lados son todos congruentes.

triángulo equilátero Triángulo cuyos lados son todos congruentes.

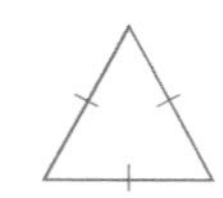

geometría euclidiana Sistema en el cual un plano es una superficie plana formada por puntos que se extienden infinitamente en todas las direcciones.

suceso Un resultado o tipo de resultado específico.

experimento Una situación que involucra la probabilidad, como lanzar una moneda o un dado.

probabilidad experimental La razón de la cantidad de resultados positivos a la cantidad total de sucesos o pruebas en un experimento de probabilidad.

exterior Un punto yace en el exterior de un ángulo si no se ubica ni en el ángulo ni en el interior del ángulo.

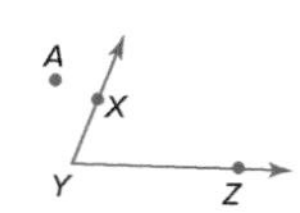

A está en el exterior del ∠*XYZ*.

exterior angle (p. 169) An angle formed by one side of a triangle and the extension of another side.

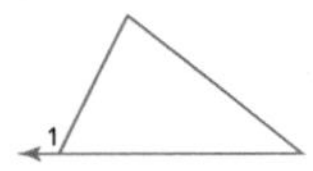

∠1 is an exterior angle.

exterior angle (p. 284) An angle that lies in the region that is not between two transversals that intersect the same line.

F

face of a polyhedron (p. 76) A flat surface of a polyhedron.

factorial (p. 872) The product of the integers less than or equal to a positive integer *n*, written as *n*!

finite plane (p. 10) A plane that has boundaries or does not extend indefinitely.

flow proof (pp. 144, 284) A proof that organizes statements in logical order, starting with the given statements. Each statement is written in a box with the reason verifying the statement written below the box. Arrows are used to indicate the order of the statements.

focus (p. 703) The fixed point in a parabola that is equidistant from the locus of all points in a plane.

fractal (p. 552) A figure generated by repeating a special sequence of steps infinitely often. Fractals often exhibit self-similarity.

Fundamental Counting Principle (p. 861) A method used to determine the number of possible outcomes in a sample space by multiplying the number of possible outcomes from each stage or event.

G

geometric mean (p. 565) For any positive numbers *a* and *b*, the positive number *x* such that $\frac{a}{x} = \frac{x}{b}$.

geometric probability (p. 881) Using the principles of length and area to find the probability of an event.

glide reflection (p. 249) The composition of a translation followed by a reflection in a line parallel to the translation vector.

great circle (p. 819) A circle formed when a plane intersects a sphere with its center at the center of the sphere.

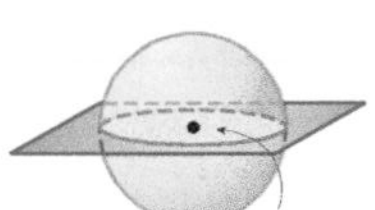

ángulo externo Ángulo formado por un lado de un triángulo y la prolongación de otro de sus lados.

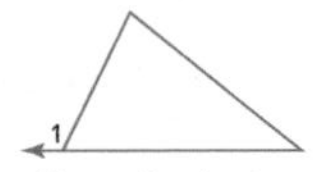

∠1 es un ángulo externo.

ángulo externo Un ángulo que está en la región que no está entre dos transversals que cruzan la misma línea.

cara de un poliedro Superficie plana de un poliedro.

factorial Producto de los enteros menores o iguales a un número positivo *n*, escrito como *n*!

plano finito Plano que tiene límites o que no se extiende indefinidamente.

demostración de flujo Demostración que organiza los enunciados en orden lógico, comenzando con los enunciados dados. Cada enunciado se escribe en una casilla y debajo de cada casilla se escribe el argumento que verifica dicho enunciado. El orden de los enunciados se indica con flechas.

foco Punto fijo en una parábola que está equidistante del lugar geométrico de todos los puntos en un plano.

fractal Figura que se obtiene mediante la repetición infinita de una sucesión particular de pasos. Los fractales a menudo exhiben autosemejanza.

principio fundamental de contar Método para determinar el número de resultados posibles en un espacio muestral multiplicando el número de resultados posibles de cada etapa o evento.

media geométrica Para todo número positivo *a* y *b*, existe un número positivo *x* tal que $\frac{a}{x} = \frac{x}{b}$.

probabilidad geométrica Uso de los principios de longitud y área para calcular la probabilidad de un evento.

reflexión del deslizamiento Composición de una traslación seguida por una reflexión en una recta paralela al vector de la traslación.

círculo mayor Círculo que se forma cuando un plano interseca una esfera y cuyo centro es el mismo que el centro de la esfera.

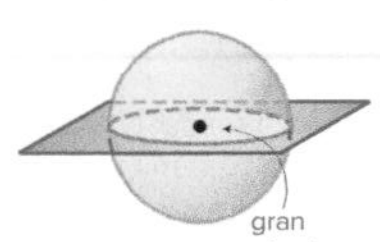

H

height of a parallelogram (p. 725) The length of an altitude of a parallelogram.

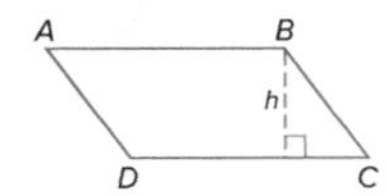

h is the height of parallelogram *ABCD*.

height of a solid figure (p. 770) The height is the length of the altitude.

height of a trapezoid (p. 735) The perpendicular distance between the bases of a trapezoid.

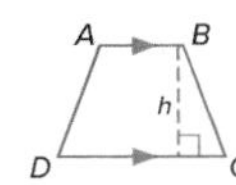

h is the height of trapezoid *ABCD*.

height of a triangle (p. 727) The length of an altitude drawn to a given base of a triangle.

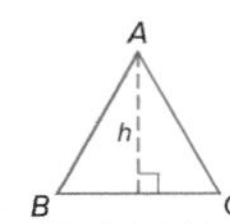

h is the height of triangle *ABC*.

hemisphere (p. 819) One of the two congruent parts into which a great circle separates a sphere.

hypothesis (p. 121) In a conditional statement, the statement that immediately follows the word *if*.

I

if-then statement (p. 121) A compound statement of the form "if *p*, then *q*," where *p* and *q* are statements.

image (p. 67) A figure that results from the transformation of a geometric figure.

incenter (p. 358) The point of concurrency of the angle bisectors of a triangle.

included angle (p. 302) In a triangle, the angle formed by two sides is the included angle for those two sides.

altura de un paralelogramo Longitud del segmento perpendicular que va desde la base hasta el vértice opuesto a ella.

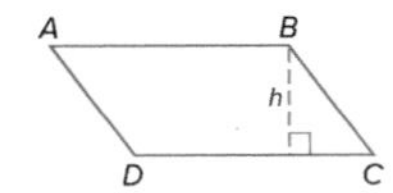

h es la altura del paralelogramo *ABCD*.

altura de un cuerpo geométrico La altura es la longitud de la altitud.

altura de un trapecio Distancia perpendicular entre las bases de un trapecio.

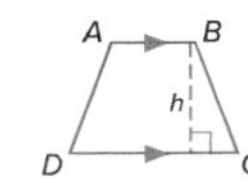

h es la altura del trapecio *ABCD*.

altura de un triángulo Longitud de una altura trazada a una base dada de un triángulo.

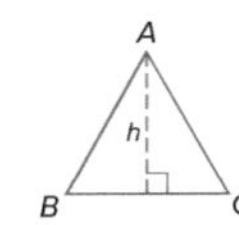

h es la altura de triángulo *ABC*.

hemisferio Una de las dos partes congruentes en las cuales un círculo mayor divide una esfera.

hipótesis Enunciado escrito inmediatamente después de la palabra *si* en un enunciado condicional.

enunciado si-entonces Enunciado compuesto de la forma "si *p*, entonces *q*," donde *p* y *q* son enunciados.

imagen Figura que resulta de la transformación de una figura geométrica.

incentro Punto de intersección de las bisectrices interiores de un triángulo.

ángulo incluido En un triángulo, el ángulo formado por dos lados es el ángulo incluido de esos dos lados.

Glossary/Glosario

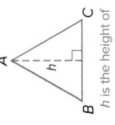

included side (p. 311) The side of a polygon that is a side of each of two angles.

independent events (p. 889) Two or more events in which the outcome of one event does not affect the outcome of the other events.

indirect isometry (p. 69) An isometry that cannot be performed by maintaining the orientation of the points, as in a direct isometry.

indirect proof (p. 385) In an indirect proof, one assumes that the statement to be proved is false. One then uses logical reasoning to deduce that a statement contradicts a postulate, theorem, or one of the assumptions. Once a contradiction is obtained, one concludes that the statement assumed false must in fact be true.

indirect reasoning (p. 385) Reasoning that assumes that the conclusion is false and then shows that this assumption leads to a contradiction of the hypothesis like a postulate, theorem, or corollary. Then, since the assumption has been proved false, the conclusion must be true.

inductive reasoning (p. 111) Reasoning that uses a number of specific examples to arrive at a plausible generalization or prediction. Conclusions arrived at by inductive reasoning lack the logical certainty of those arrived at by deductive reasoning.

inscribed (p. 646) A polygon is inscribed in a circle if each of its vertices lie on the circle.

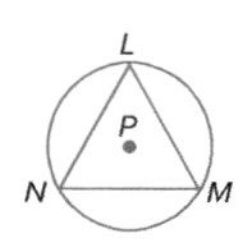

$\triangle LMN$ is inscribed in $\odot P$.

inscribed angle (p. 669) An angle that has a vertex on a circle and sides that contain chords of the circle.

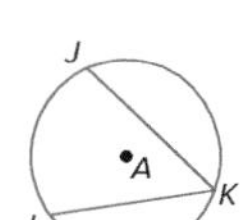

In $\odot A$, $\angle JKL$ is an inscribed angle.

intercepted arc (p. 669) An angle intercepts an arc if and only if each of the following conditions are met.
1. The endpoints of the arc lie on the angle.
2. All points of the arc except the endpoints are in the interior of the circle.
3. Each side of the angle has an endpoint on the arc.

lado incluido Lado de un polígono común a dos de sus ángulos.

eventos independientes El resultado de un evento no afecta el resultado del otro evento.

isometría indirecta Tipo de isometría que no se puede obtener manteniendo la orientación de los puntos, como ocurre con la isometría directa.

demostración indirecta En una demostración indirecta, se supone que el enunciado a demostrar es falso. Después, se deduce lógicamente que existe un enunciado que contradice un postulado, un teorema o una de las conjeturas. Una vez hallada una contradicción, se concluye que el enunciado que se suponía falso debe ser, en realidad, verdadero.

razonamiento indirecto Razonamiento en que primero se supone que la conclusión es falsa y luego se demuestra que esta conjetura lleva a una contradicción de la hipótesis como un postulado, un teorema o un corolario. Finalmente, como se ha demostrado que la conjetura es falsa, la conclusión debe ser verdadera.

razonamiento inductivo Razonamiento que usa varios ejemplos específicos para lograr una generalización o una predicción pausible. Las conclusiones obtenidas por razonamiento inductivo carecen de la certeza lógica de aquellas obtenidas por razonamiento deductivo.

inscrito Un polígono está inscrito en un círculo si todos sus vértices yacen en el círculo.

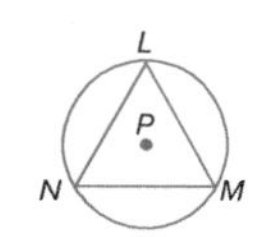

$\triangle LMN$ está inscrito en $\odot P$.

ángulo inscrito Ángulo cuyo vértice esté en un círculo y cuyos lados contienen cuerdas del círculo.

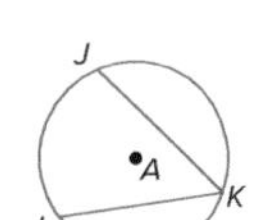

En $\odot A$, $\angle JKL$ es un ángulo inscrito.

arco intersecado Un ángulo interseca un arco si y sólo si se cumple cada una de las siguientes condiciones.
1. Los extremos del arco yacen en el ángulo.
2. Todos los puntos del arco, excepto los extremos, yacen en el interior del círculo.
3. Cada lado del ángulo tiene un extremo del arco.

interior (p. 36) A point is in the interior of an angle if it does not lie on the angle itself and it lies on a segment with endpoints that are on the sides of the angle.

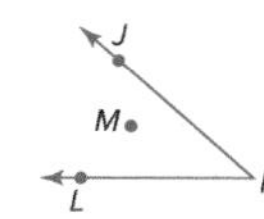

M is in the interior of $\angle JKL$.

interior angles (p. 169) Angles that lie between two transversals that intersect the same line.

intersection 1. (p. 6) A set of points common to two or more geometric figures. 2. (p. 866) For the intersection of event A and event B, the set of all outcomes that are common to both events; represented by $A \cap B$.

inverse (p. 122) The statement formed by negating both the hypothesis and conclusion of a conditional statement.

inverse cosine (p. 599) The inverse function of cosine, or $\cos^{-1}$. If the cosine of an acute $\angle A$ is equal to x, then $\cos^{-1} x$ is equal to the measure of $\angle A$.

inverse sine (p. 599) The inverse function of sine, or $\sin^{-1}$. If the sine of an acute $\angle A$ is equal to x, then $\sin^{-1} x$ is equal to the measure of $\angle A$.

inverse tangent (p. 599) The inverse function of tangent, or $\tan^{-1}$. If the tangent of an acute $\angle A$ is equal to x, then $\tan^{-1} x$ is equal to the measure of $\angle A$.

irrational number (p. 17) A number that cannot be expressed as a terminating or repeating decimal.

irregular figure (p. 57) A polygon with sides and angles that are not all congruent.

isometry (p. 67) A mapping for which the original figure and its image are congruent.

isosceles trapezoid (p. 469) A trapezoid in which the legs are congruent, both pairs of base angles are congruent, and the diagonals are congruent.

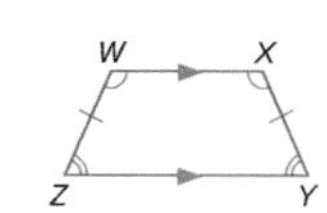

interior Un punto se encuenta en el interior de un ángulo si no yace en el ángulo como tal y si está en un segmento cuyos extremos están en los lados del ángulo.

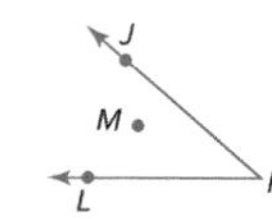

M está en el interior del $\angle JKL$.

ángulos interiores Ángulos que yacen entre dos transversales que intersecan la misma recta.

intersección 1. Conjunto de puntos comunes a dos o más figuras geométricas. 2. Para la intersección del suceso A y el suceso B, el conjunto de todos los resultados que son comunes a ambos sucesos; se representa con $A \cap B$.

inverso Enunciado que se obtiene al negar tanto la hipótesis como la conclusión de un enunciado condicional.

inverso del coseno Función inversa del coseno, o $\cos^{-1}$. Si el coseno de un $\angle A$ agudo es igual a x, entonces $\cos^{-1} x$ es igual a la medida del $\angle A$.

inverso del seno Función inversa del seno, o $\sin^{-1}$. Si el seno de un $\angle A$ agudo es igual a x, entonces $\sin^{-1} x$ es igual a la medida del A.

inverse del tangente Función inversa de la tangente, o $\tan^{-1}$. Si la tangente de un $\angle A$ agudo es igual a x, entonces $\tan^{-1} x$ es igual a la medida del $\angle A$.

número irracional Número que no se puede expresar como un decimal terminal o periódico.

figura irregular Polígono cuyos lados y ángulos no son todo congruentes.

isometría Aplicación en la cual la figura original y su imagen son congruentes.

trapecio isósceles Trapecio cuyos catetos son congruentes, ambos pares de ángulos de las bases son congruentes y las diagonales son congruentes.

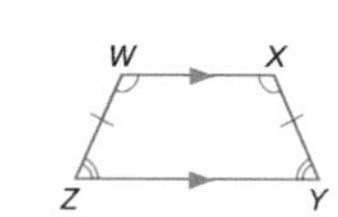

isosceles triangle (p. 325) A triangle with at least two sides congruent. The congruent sides are called *legs*. The angles opposite the legs are *base angles*. The angle formed by the two legs is the *vertex angle*. The side opposite the vertex angle is the *base*.

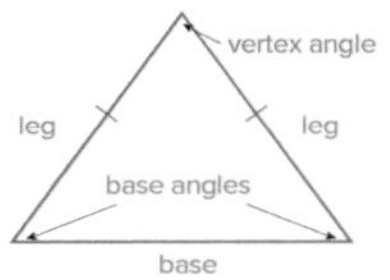

triángulo isósceles Triángulo que tiene por lo menos dos lados congruentes. Los lados congruentes se llaman *catetos*. Los ángulos opuestos a los catetos son los *ángulos de la base*. El ángulo formado por los dos catetos es el *ángulo del vértice*. El lado opuesto al ángulo del vértice es la *base*.

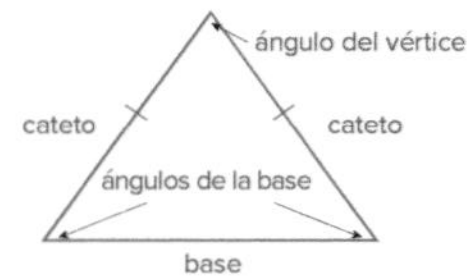

iteration (p. 552) A process of repeating the same procedure over and over again.

iteración Proceso de repetir el mismo procedimiento una y otra vez.

J

joint frequencies (p. 909) In a two-way frequency table, the frequencies reported in the cells in the interior of the table.

frecuencias conjuntas En una tabla de double entrada o de frecuencias, las frecuencias reportadas en las celdas en el interior de la tabla.

K

kite (p. 472) A quadrilateral with exactly two distinct pairs of adjacent congruent sides.

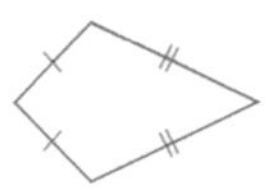

cometa Cuadrilátero que tiene exactamente dos pares differentes de lados congruentes y adyacentes.

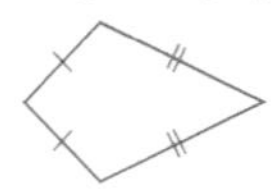

L

lateral area (p. 770) For prisms, pyramids, cylinders, and cones, the area of the faces of the figure not including the bases.

área lateral En prismas, pirámides, cilindros y conos, es el área de la caras de la figura sin incluir el área de las bases.

lateral edges (p. 770) In a prism, the intersection of two adjacent lateral faces. In a pyramid, lateral edges are the edges of the lateral faces that join the vertex to vertices of the base.

aristas laterales En un prisma, la intersección de dos caras laterales adyacentes. En una pirámide, las aristas de las caras laterales que unen el vértice de la pirámide con los vértices de la base.

lateral faces (p. 770) In a prism, the faces that are not bases. In a pyramid, faces that intersect at the vertex.

caras laterales En un prisma, las caras que no forman las bases. En una pirámide, las caras que se intersecan en el vértice.

latitude (p. 833) A measure of distance north or south of the equator.

latitud Medida de la distancia al norte o al sur del ecuador.

Law of Cosines (p. 624) Let $\triangle ABC$ be any triangle with *a*, *b*, and *c* representing the measures of sides opposite the angles with measures *A*, *B*, and *C*, respectively. Then the following equations are true.

$a^2 = b^2 + c^2 - 2bc \cos A$

$b^2 = a^2 + c^2 - 2ac \cos B$

$c^2 = a^2 + b^2 - 2ab \cos C$

ley de los cosenos Sea $\triangle ABC$ cualquier triángulo donde *a*, *b* y *c* son las medidas de los lados opuestos a los ángulos que miden *A*, *B* y *C*, respectivamente. Entonces las siguientes ecuaciones son verdaderas.

$a^2 = b^2 + c^2 - 2bc \cos A$

$b^2 = a^2 + c^2 - 2ac \cos B$

$c^2 = a^2 + b^2 - 2ab \cos C$

Law of Detachment (p. 131) If $p \rightarrow q$ is a true conditional and *p* is true, then *q* is also true.

ley de indiferencia Si $p \rightarrow q$ es un enunciado condicional verdadero y *p* es verdadero, entonces *q* también es verdadero.

Law of Sines (p. 617) Let $\triangle ABC$ be any triangle with *a*, *b*, and *c* representing the measures of sides opposite the angles with measures *A*, *B*, and *C*, respectively.

Then, $\frac{\sin A}{a} = \frac{\sin B}{b} = \frac{\sin C}{c}$.

ley de los senos Sea $\triangle ABC$ cualquier triángulo donde *a*, *b* y *c* representan las medidas de los lados opuestos a los ángulos que miden *A*, *B* y *C*, respectivamente.

Entonces, $\frac{\text{scn } A}{a} = \frac{\text{scn } B}{b} = \frac{\text{scn } C}{c}$.

Law of Syllogism (p. 133) If $p \rightarrow q$ and $q \rightarrow r$ are true conditionals, then $p \rightarrow r$ is also true.

ley del silogismo Si $p \rightarrow q$ y $q \rightarrow r$ son enunciados condicionales verdaderos, entonces $p \rightarrow r$ también es verdadero.

legs of an isosceles triangle (p. 325) The two congruent sides of an isosceles triangle.

catetos de un triángulo isósceles Las dos lados congruentes de un triángulo isósceles.

legs of a trapezoid (p. 469) The nonparallel sides of a trapezoid.

catetos de un trapecio Los lados no paralelos de un trapecio.

line (p. 5) A basic undefined term of geometry. A line is made up of points and has no thickness or width. In a figure, a line is shown with an arrowhead at each end. Lines are usually named by lowercase script letters or by writing capital letters for two points on the line, with a double arrow over the pair of letters.

recta Término geometrico basico no definido. Una recta está formada por puntos y carece de grosor o ancho. En una figura, una recta se representa con una flecha en cada extremo. Generalmente se designan con letras minúsculas o con las dos letras mayúsculas de dos puntos sobre la recta y una flecha doble sobre el par de letras.

line of reflection (p. 221) A line in which each point on the preimage and its corresponding point on the image are the same distance from this line.

línea de reflexión Una línea en la cual cada punto en el preimage y el su corresponder senalañ en la imagen es la misma distancia de esta línea.

line of symmetry (p. 259) A line that can be drawn through a plane figure so that the figure on one side is the reflection image of the figure on the opposite side.

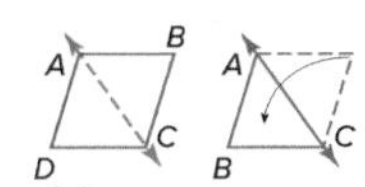

$\overleftrightarrow{AC}$ is a line of symmetry.

eje de simetría Recta que se traza a través de una figura plana, de modo que un lado de la figura es la imagen reflejada del lado opuesto.

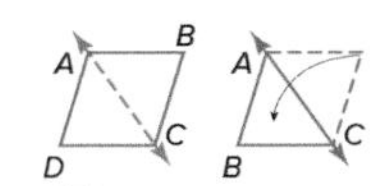

$\overleftrightarrow{AC}$ es un eje de simetría.

line segment (p. 14) A measurable part of a line that consists of two points, called endpoints, and all of the points between them.

segmento de recta Sección medible de una recta que consta de dos puntos, llamados extremos, y todos los puntos entre ellos.

line symmetry (p. 259) If a figure can be mapped onto itself by a reflection in a line, the figure has reflectional symmetry or line symmetry.

línea de simetría Si doblamos una figura a lo largo de una recta y las dos partes coinciden, entonces la figura tiene simetría reflexiva o simetría axial.

linear pair (p. 46) A pair of adjacent angles whose noncommon sides are opposite rays.

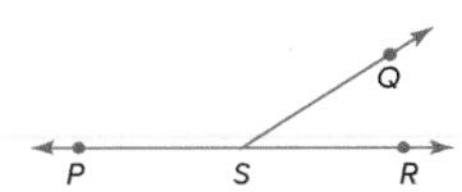

$\angle PSQ$ and $\angle QSR$ are a linear pair.

par lineal Par de ángulos adyacentes cuyos lados no comunes forman rayos opuestos.

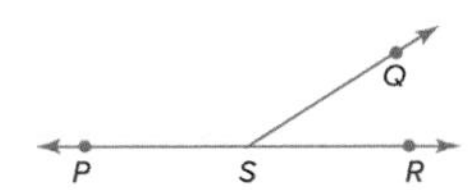

$\angle PSQ$ y $\angle QSR$ forman un par lineal.

Glossary/Glosario

Glossary/Glosario

locus (p. 11) The set of points that satisfy a given condition.

logically equivalent (p. 123) Statements that have the same truth values.

longitude (p. 833) A measure of distance east or west of the Prime Meridian.

M

magnitude of symmetry (p. 260) The smallest angle through which a figure can be rotated so that it maps onto itself.

major arc (p. 653) An arc with a measure greater than 180. $\widehat{ACB}$ is a major arc.

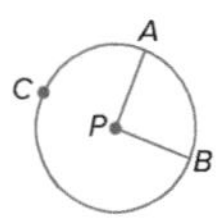

marginal frequencies (p. 909) In a two-way frequency table, the accumulated frequencies reported in the Totals row and Totals column.

matrix logic (p. 383) A rectangular array in which learned clues are recorded in order to solve a logic or reasoning problem.

median (p. 365) In a triangle, a line segment with endpoints that are a vertex of a triangle and the midpoint of the side opposite the vertex.

meridians (p. 833) Imaginary vertical lines drawn around the Earth through the North and South Poles.

midpoint (p. 26) The point on a segment exactly halfway between the endpoints of the segment.

midsegment of a trapezoid (p. 471) A segment that connects the midpoints of the legs of a trapezoid.

midsegment of a triangle (p. 535) A segment with endpoints that are the midpoints of two sides of a triangle.

minor arc (p. 653) An arc with a measure less than 180. $\widehat{AB}$ is a minor arc.

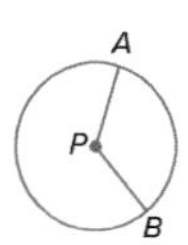

lugar geométrico Conjunto de puntos que satisfacen una condición dada.

lógicamente equivalentes Enunciados que poseen los mismos valores verdaderos.

longitud Medida de la distancia del este o al oeste del Primer Meridiano.

magnitud de la simetria El angulo mas pequeno con el cual una figura puede serrotada de modo que traz sobre si mismo.

arco mayor Arco que mide más de 180. $\widehat{ACB}$ es un arco mayor.

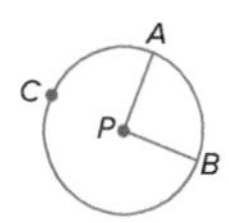

frecuencias marginales En una tabla de double entrada o de frecuencias, las frecuencias acumuladas que se reportan en la hilera de los totales y en la columna de los totales.

lógica matricial Arreglo rectangular en que las claves aprendidas se escriben en orden para resolver un problema de lógica o razonamiento.

mediana En un triángulo, Segmento de recta de cuyos extremos son un vértice del triángulo y el punto medio del lado opuesto a dicho vértice.

meridianos Líneas verticales imaginarias dibujadas alrededor de la Tierra que von del polo norte al polo sur.

punto medio Punto en un segmento que yace exactamente en la mitad, entre los extremos del segmento.

segmento medio de un trapecio Segmento que conecta los puntos medios de los catetos de un trapecio.

segmento medio de un triángulo Segmento cuyas extremos son los puntos medianos de dos lados de un triángulo.

arco menor Arco que mide menos de 180. $\widehat{AB}$ es un arco menor.

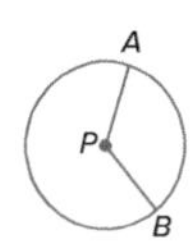

multistage experiments (p. 860) Experiments with more than two stages.

mutually exclusive (p. 897) Two events that have no outcomes in common.

N

negation (p. 119) If a statement is represented by *p*, then *not p* is the negation of the statement.

net (p. 85) A two-dimensional figure that when folded forms the surfaces of a three-dimensional object.

***n*-gon** (p. 57) A polygon with *n* sides.

non-Euclidean geometry (p. 828) The study of geometrical systems that are not in accordance with the Parallel Postulate of Euclidean geometry.

O

oblique cone (p. 775) A cone that is not a right cone.

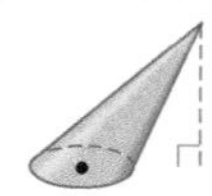

oblique cylinder (p. 772) A cylinder that is not a right cylinder.

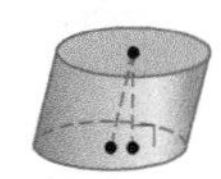

oblique prism (p. 770) A prism in which the lateral edges are not perpendicular to the bases.

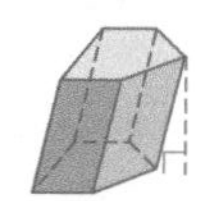

oblique solid (p. 796) A solid with base(s) that are not perpendicular to the edges connecting the two bases or vertex.

obtuse angle (p. 38) An angle with degree measure greater than 90 and less than 180.

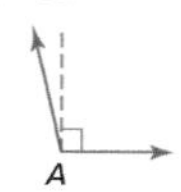

$90 < m\angle A < 180$

experimentos multietápicos Experimentos con más de dos etapas.

mutuamente exclusivos Eventos que no tienen resultados en común.

negación Si *p* representa un enunciado, entonces *no p* es la negación del enunciado.

red Figura bidimensional que al ser plegada forma las superficies de un objeto tridimensional.

enágono Polígono con *n* lados.

geometría no euclidiana El estudio de sistemas geométricos que no satisfacen el postulado de las paralelas de la geometría euclidiana.

cono oblicuo Cono que no es un cono recto.

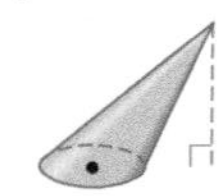

cilindro oblicuo Cilindro que no es un cilindro recto.

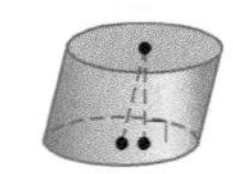

prisma oblicuo Prisma cuyas aristas laterales no son perpendiculares a las bases.

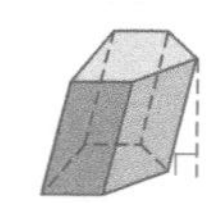

sólido oblicuo Sólido con base o bases que no son perpendiculares a las aristas, las cuales conectan las dos bases o vértice.

ángulo obtuso Ángulo que mide más de 90 y menos de 180.

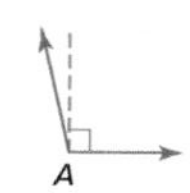

$90 < m\angle A < 180$

opposite rays (p. 36) Two rays $\overrightarrow{BA}$ and $\overrightarrow{BC}$ such that B is between A and C.

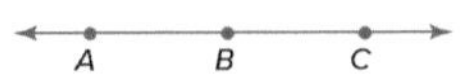

order of symmetry (p. 260) The number of times a figure can map onto itself as it rotates from 0° to 360°.

ordered pairs (p. P15) A pair of numbers used to locate a point in the coordinate plane or the solution of an equation in two variables. An ordered pair is written in the form (*x*-coordinate, *y*-coordinate).

ordered triple (p. 584) Three numbers given in a specific order used to locate points in space.

origin (p. P15) The point (0, 0) in a coordinate plane where the *x*-axis and the *y*-axis intersect.

orthocenter (p. 367) The point of concurrency of the altitudes of a triangle.

orthographic drawing (p. 84) The two-dimensional top view, left view, front view, and right view of a three-dimensional object.

outcome (p. P8) One possible result of a probability event. Example: 4 is an outcome when a number cube is rolled.

P

parabola (p. 703) The graph of a quadratic function. The set of all points in a plane that are the same distance from a given point, called the focus, and a given line, called the directrix.

paragraph proof (p. 145) An informal proof written in the form of a paragraph that explains why a conjecture for a given situation is true.

parallel lines (p. 170) Coplanar lines that do not intersect.

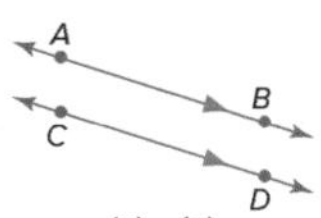

$\overleftrightarrow{AB} \parallel \overleftrightarrow{CD}$

rayos opuestos Dos rayos $\overrightarrow{BA}$ y $\overrightarrow{BC}$ donde B esta entre A y C.

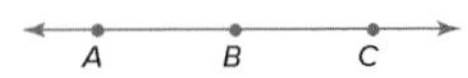

orden de la simetría Número de veces que una figura se puede aplicar sobre sí misma mientras gira de 0° a 360°.

pares ordenados Un par de números que se usa para ubicar un punto en el plano de coordenadas o la solución de una ecuación con dos variables. Un par ordenado se escribe en la forma (coordenada *x*, coordenada *y*).

triple ordenado Tres números dados en un orden específico que sirven para ubicar puntos en el espacio.

origen El punto (0, 0) en un plano de coordinadas, donde se intersecan el eje *x* y el eje *y*.

ortocentro Punto de intersección de las alturas de un triángulo.

proyección ortogonal Vista bidimensional superior, del lado izquierda, frontal y del lado derecho de un objeto tridimensionl.

resultado Una consecuencia posible de un suceso de probabilidad. Ejemplo: 4 es un resultado cuando se lanza un cubo numérico.

parábola La grafica de una funcion cuadratica. Conjunto de todos los puntos de un plano que estan a la misma distancia de un punto dado, llamado foco, y de una recta dada, llamada directriz.

demostración de párrafo Demostración informal escrita en párrafo que explica por qué una conjetura para una situación dada es verdadera.

rectas paralelas Rectas coplanares que no se intersecan.

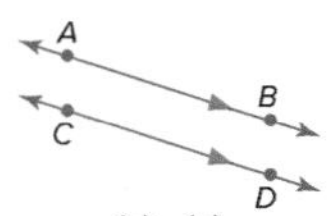

$\overleftrightarrow{AB} \parallel \overleftrightarrow{CD}$

parallel planes (p. 169) Planes that do not intersect.

parallelogram (p. 433) A quadrilateral with parallel opposite sides. Any side of a parallelogram may be called a *base*.

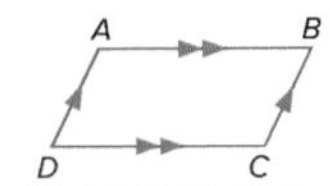

$\overline{AB} \parallel \overline{DC}$; $\overline{AD} \parallel \overline{BC}$

parallels (p. 833) Imaginary horizontal lines parallel to the equator.

perimeter (p. 58) The sum of the lengths of the sides of a polygon.

permutation (p. 872) An arrangement of objects in which order is important.

perpendicular bisector (p. 354) In a triangle, a line, segment, or ray that passes through the midpoint of a side and is perpendicular to that side.

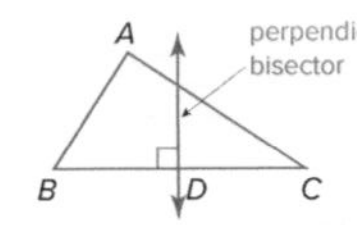

D is the midpoint of $\overline{BC}$.

perpendicular lines (p. 48) Lines that form right angles.

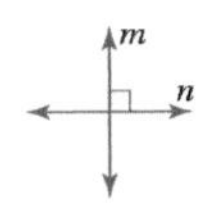

line $m \perp$ line n

pi (π) (p. 645) An irrational number represented by the ratio of the circumference of a circle to the diameter of the circle.

plane (p. 5) A basic undefined term of geometry. A plane is a flat surface made up of points that has no depth and extends indefinitely in all directions. In a figure, a plane is often represented by a shaded, slanted four-sided figure. Planes are usually named by a capital script letter or by three noncollinear points on the plane.

Platonic solids (p. 77) The five regular polyhedra: tetrahedron, hexahedron, octahedron, dodecahedron, or icosahedron.

point (p. 5) A basic undefined term of geometry. A point is a location. In a figure, points are represented by a dot. Points are named by capital letters.

planos paralelos Planos que no se intersecan.

paralelogramo Cuadrilátero cuyos lados opuestos son paralelos y cuya *base* puede ser cualquier de sus lados.

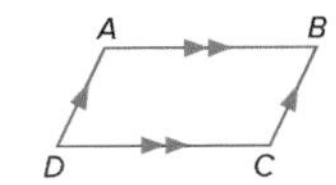

$\overline{AB} \parallel \overline{DC}$; $\overline{AD} \parallel \overline{BC}$

paralelos Rectas horizontales imaginarias paralelas al ecuador.

perímetro Suma de la longitud de los lados de un polígono.

permutación Disposicion de objetos en la cual el orden es importante.

mediatriz Recta, segmento de recta o rayo perpendicular que corta un lado del triángulo en su punto medio.

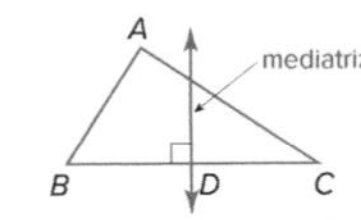

D es el punto medio de $\overline{BC}$.

rectas perpendiculares Rectas que forman ángulos rectos.

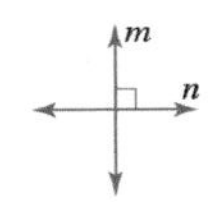

recta $m \perp$ recta n

pi (π) Número irracional representado por la razón de la circunferencia de un círculo al diámetro del mismo.

plano Término geométrico básico no definido. Superficie plana sin espesor formada por puntos y que se extiende hasta el infinito en todas direcciones. En una figura, los planos a menudo se representan con una figura inclinada y sombreada y se designan con una letra mayúscula o con tres puntos no colineales del plano.

sólidos platónicos Los cinco poliedros regulares siguientes: tetraedro, hexaedro, octaedro, dodecaedro e icosaedro.

punto Término geométrico básico no definido. Un punto representa un lugar o ubicación. En una figura, se representa con una marca puntual y se designan con letras mayúsculas.

point of concurrency (p. 355) The point of intersection of concurrent lines.

point of symmetry (p. 260) A figure that can be mapped onto itself by a rotation of 180°.

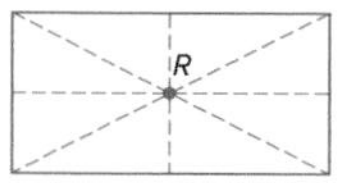

R is a point of symmetry.

point of tangency (p. 678) For a line that intersects a circle in only one point, the point at which they intersect.

point-slope form (p. 179) An equation of the form $y - y_1 = m(x - x_1)$, where (x_1, y_1) are the coordinates of any point on the line and m is the slope of the line.

poles (p. 819) The endpoints of the diameter of a great circle.

polygon (p. 56) A closed figure formed by a finite number of coplanar segments called *sides* such that the following conditions are met:

1. The sides that have a common endpoint are noncollinear.
2. Each side intersects exactly two other sides, but only at their endpoints, called the *vertices*.

polyhedrons (p. 76) Closed three-dimensional figures made up of flat polygonal regions. The flat regions formed by the polygons and their interiors are called *faces*. Pairs of faces intersect in segments called *edges*. Points where three or more edges intersect are called *vertices*.

population density (p. 841) A measurement of population per unit of area.

postulate (p. 141) A statement that describes a fundamental relationship between the basic terms of geometry. Postulates are accepted as true without proof.

precision (p. 91) The preciseness of a measurement depends on the unit of measure. The smaller the unit, the more precise the measurement.

preimage (p. 67) The graph of an object before a transformation.

principle of superposition (p. 291) Two figures are congruent if and only if there is a rigid motion or a series of rigid motions that maps one figure exactly onto the other.

prism (p. 76) A solid with the following characteristics:

1. Two faces, called *bases*, are formed by congruent polygons that lie in parallel planes.

punto de concurrencia Punto de intersección de rectas concurrentes.

punto de simetría Una figura que se puede traz sobre sí mismo por una rotación de 180°.

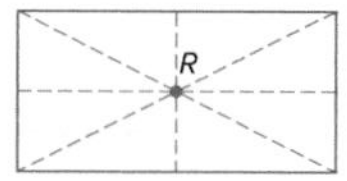

R es un punto de simetría.

punto de tangencia Punto de intersección de una recta en un círculo en un solo punto.

forma punto-pendiente Ecuación de la forma $y - y_1 = m(x - x_1)$, donde (x_1, y_1) representan las coordenadas de un punto cualquiera sobre la recta y m representa la pendiente de la recta.

postes Las extremos del diámetro de un círculo mayor.

polígono Figura cerrada formada por un número finito de segmentos coplanares llamados *lados*, tal que satisface las siguientes condiciones:

1. Los lados que tienen un extremo común son no colineales.
2. Cada lado interseca exactamente dos lados mas, pero sólo en sus extremos, llamados *vértices*.

poliedros Figuras tridimensionales cerrada formadas por regiones poligonales planas. Las regiones planas definidas por un polígono y sus interiores se llaman *caras*. Cada intersección entre dos caras se llama *arista*. Los puntos donde se intersecan tres o más aristas se llaman *vértices*.

densidad demográfica Medida de la población por unidad de área.

postulado Enunciado que describe una relación fundamental entre los términos geométricos básicos. Los postulados se aceptan como verdaderos sin necesidad de demostración.

precisión La precisión de una medida depende de la unidad de medida. Cuanto más pequeña es la unidad, más precisa es la medida.

preimagen Gráfica de una figura antes de una transformación.

principio de superposición Dos figuras son congruentes si y sólo si existe un movimiento rígido o una serie de movimientos rígidos que aplican una de las figuras exactamente sobre la otra.

prisma Sólido con las siguientes características:

1. Dos caras llamadas *bases*, formadas por polígonos congruentes que yacen en planos paralelos.

2. The faces that are not bases, called *lateral faces*, are formed by parallelograms.
3. The intersections of two adjacent lateral faces are called *lateral edges* and are parallel segments.

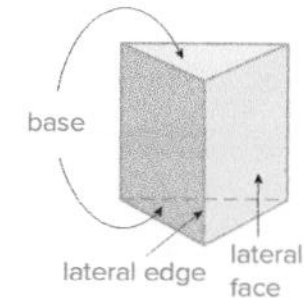

triangular prism

probability (p. P8) The ratio of the number of favorable outcomes for an event to the number of possible outcomes of the event. P(a) = Number of favorable outcomes/total number of possible outcomes

proof (p. 143) A logical argument in which each statement you make is supported by a statement that is accepted as true.

proof by contradiction (p. 385) An indirect proof in which one assumes that the statement to be proved is false. One then uses logical reasoning to deduce a statement that contradicts a postulate, theorem, or one of the assumptions. Once a contradiction is obtained, one concludes that the statement assumed false must in fact be true.

proportion An equation of the form $\frac{a}{b} = \frac{c}{d}$ that states that two ratios are equal.

pyramid (p. 76) A solid with the following characteristics:

1. All of the faces, except one face, intersect at a point called the *vertex*.
2. The face that does not contain the vertex is called the *base* and is a polygonal region.
3. The faces meeting at the vertex are called *lateral faces* and are triangular regions.

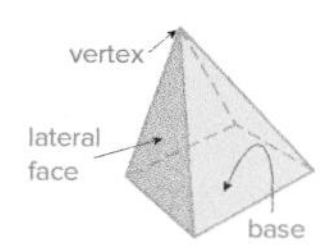

rectangular pyramid

2. Las caras que no son las bases, llamadas *caras laterales*, son paralelogramos.
3. Las intersecciones de dos caras laterales adyacentes se llaman *aristas laterales* y son segmentos paralelos.

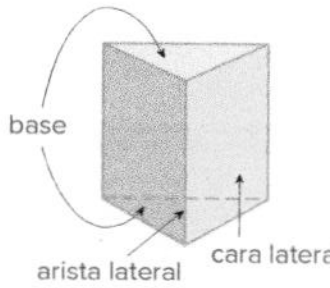

prisma triangular

probabilidad La razón de la cantidad de resultados favorables de un suceso a la cantidad de resultados posibles de ese suceso. P(a) = Cantidad total de resultados favorables/cantidad total de resultados posibles

demostración Argumento lógico en el cual cada enunciado que se hace está respaldado por un enunciado que se acepta como verdadero.

demostración por contradicción Demostración indirecta en la cual se supone que el enunciado a demostrarse es falso. Luego, se usa el razonamiento lógico para inferir un enunciado que contradiga el postulado, teorema o una de las conjeturas. Una vez que se obtiene una contradicción, se concluye que el enunciado que se supuso falso es, en realidad, verdadero.

proporción Ecuación de la forma $\frac{a}{b} = \frac{c}{d}$ que establece que dos razones son iguales.

pirámide Sólido con las siguientes características:

1. Todas las caras, excepto una, se intersecan en un punto llamado *vértice*.
2. La cara sin el vértice se llama *base* y es una región poligonal.
3. Las caras que se encuentran en los vértices se llaman *caras laterales* y son regiones triangulares.

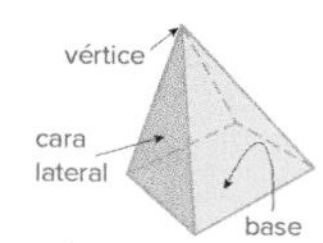

pirámide rectangular

Pythagorean triple (p. 576) A group of three whole numbers that satisfies the equation $a^2 + b^2 = c^2$, where c is the greatest number.

Q

quadrant (p. P15) One of four regions into which the x- and y-axes separate the coordinate plane.

R

radian measure (p. 655) The radian measure, θ, of a central angle is the ratio of the arc length to the radius of the circle: $\theta = \frac{\ell}{r}$ radians.

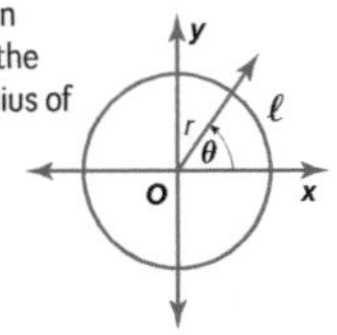

$\theta = \frac{\ell}{r}$ radians

radius **1.** (p. 643) In a circle, any segment with endpoints that are the center of the circle and a point on the circle. **2.** (p. 880) In a sphere, any segment with endpoints that are the center and a point on the sphere.

radius of a regular polygon (p. 752) The radius of a circle circumscribed about a polygon.

rate of change (p. 178) Describes how a quantity is changing over time.

ratio A comparison of two quantities using division.

ray (p. 36) $\overrightarrow{PQ}$ is a ray if it is the set of points consisting of $\overline{PQ}$ and all points S for which Q is between P and S.

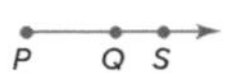

rectangle (p. 453) A quadrilateral with four right angles.

reduction (p. 493) An image that is smaller than the original figure.

reflection (p. 67) A transformation representing the flip of a figure over a point, line, or plane. A reflection in a line is a function that maps a point to its image such that

- if the point is on the line, then the image and preimage are the same point, or
- if the point is not on the line, then the line is the perpendicular bisector of the segment joining the two points.

regular polygon (p. 57) A convex polygon in which all of the sides are congruent and all of the angles are congruent.

triplete pitágorico Grupo de tres números enteros que satisfacen la ecuación $a^2 + b^2 = c^2$, donde c es el número mayor.

cuadrante Una de las cuatro regiones en las que los ejes x e y dividen el plano de coordenadas.

medida del radián La medida en radianes de un ángulo central es igual a la proporción entre la longitud del arco y el radio del círculo: $\theta = \frac{\ell}{r}$ rad.

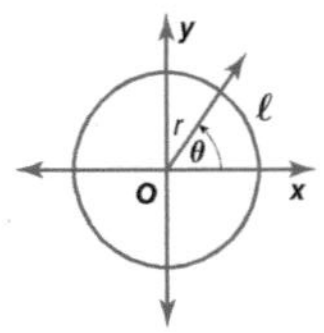

$\theta = \frac{\ell}{r}$ radianes

radio **1.** En un círculo, cualquier segmento cuyos extremos son en el centro y un punto del círculo. **2.** En una esfera, cualquier segmento cuyos extremos son el centro y un punto de la esfera.

radio de un polígono regular Radio de un círculo circunscrito alrededor de un polígono.

tasa de cambio Describe cómo cambia una cantidad a través del tiempo.

razón Comparación de dos cantidades mediante división.

rayo $\overrightarrow{PQ}$ es un rayo si se el conjunto de puntos formado por $\overline{PQ}$ y todos los puntos S para los cuales Q se ubica entre P y S.

rectángulo Cuadrilátero con cuatro ángulos rectos.

reducción Imagen más pequeña que la figura original.

reflexión Transformación en la cual una figura se "voltea" a través de un punto, una recta o un plano. Una reflexión en una recta es una función que aplica un punto a su imagen, de modo que si el punto yace sobre la recta, entonces la imagen y la preimagen son el mismo punto, o si el punto no yace sobre la recta, la recta es la mediatriz del segmento que une los dos puntos.

polígono regular Polígono convexo cuyos los lados y ángulos son congruentes.

regular polyhedron (p. 77) A polyhedron in which all of the faces are regular congruent polygons.

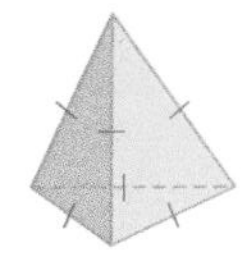

regular pyramid (p. 773) A pyramid with a base that is a regular polygon.

related conditionals (p. 122) Statements that are based on a given conditional statement.

relative error (p. 92) The ratio of the absolute error to the expected measure.

relative frequency (p. 910) In a frequency table, the ratio of the number of observations in a category to the total number of observations.

remote interior angles (p. 284) The angles of a triangle that are not adjacent to a given exterior angle.

rhombus (p. 460) A quadrilateral with all four sides congruent.

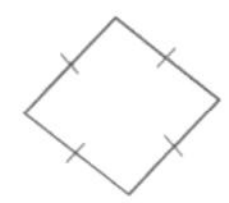

right angle (p. 38) An angle with a degree measure of 90.

right cone (p. 775) A cone with an axis that is also an altitude.

right cylinder (p. 772) A cylinder with an axis that is also an altitude.

right prism (p. 770) A prism with lateral edges that are also altitudes.

right solid (p. 795) A solid with base(s) that are perpendicular to the edges connecting them or connecting the base and the vertex of the solid.

right triangle (p. 319) A triangle with a right angle. The side opposite the right angle is called the *hypotenuse*. The other two sides are called *legs*.

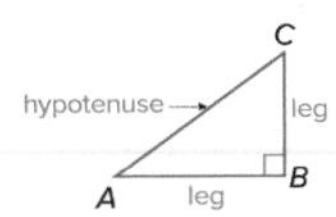

rigid transformation (pp. 15, 67) A transformation in which the position of the image may differ from that of the preimage, but the two figures remain congruent.

poliedro regular Poliedro cuyas caras son polígonos regulares congruentes.

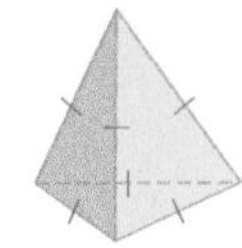

pirámide regular Pirámide cuya base es un polígono regular.

condicionales relacionados Enunciados que se basan en un enunciado condicional dado.

error relativo La razón del error absoluto a la medida esperada.

frecuencia relativa En una tabla de frecuencias, la razón del número de observaciones en una categoría al número total de observaciones.

ángulos internos no adyacentes Ángulos de un triángulo que no son adyacentes a un ángulo exterior dado.

rombo Cuadrilátero con cuatro lados congruentes.

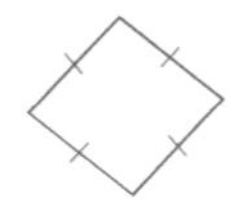

ángulo recto Ángulo que mide 90.

cono recto Cono cuyo eje es también su altura.

cilindro recto Cilindro cuyo eje es también su altura.

prisma recto Prisma cuyas aristas laterales también son su altura.

sólido recto Sólido con base o bases perpendiculares a las aristas, conectándolas entre sí o conectando la base y el vértice del sólido.

triángulo rectángulo Triángulo con un ángulo recto. El lado opuesto al ángulo recto se conoce como *hipotenusa*. Los otros dos lados se llaman *catetos*.

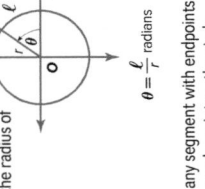

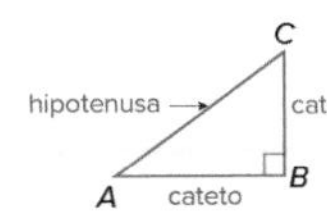

transformación rígida Es la transformación en que la posición de una imagen puede diferir con la posición de la imagen previa, pero las dos figuras siguen siendo congruentes.

Glossary/Glosario

rotation (pp. 67, 239) A transformation that turns every point of a preimage through a specified angle and direction about a fixed point, called the *center of rotation.* A rotation about a fixed point through an angle of $x°$ is a function that maps a point to its image such that

- if the point is the center of rotation, then the image and preimage are the same point, or
- if the point is not the center of rotation, then the image and preimage are the same distance from the center of rotation and the measure of the angle of rotation formed by the preimage, center of rotation, and image points is x.

rotational symmetry (p. 260) If a figure can be rotated less than 360° about a point so that the image and the preimage are indistinguishable, then the figure has rotational symmetry.

rotación Transformación en la cual se hace girar cada punto de la preimagen a través de un ángulo y una dirección determinadas alrededor de un punto llamado *centro de rotación.* La rotación de $x°$ es una función que aplica un punto a su imagen, de modo que si el punto es el centro de rotación, entonces la imagen y la preimagen están a la misma distancia del centro de rotación y la medida del ángulo formado por los puntos de la preimagen, centro de rotación e imagen es x.

simetría rotacional Si una imagen se puede girar menos de 360° alrededor de un punto, de modo que la imagen y la preimagen sean idénticas, entonces la figura tiene simetría rotacional.

S

sample space (p. 859) The set of all possible outcomes of an experiment.

scale factor (pp. 504, 834) The ratio of corresponding measurements of two similar figures.

scale factor of dilation (p. 504) The ratio of a length on an image to a corresponding length on the preimage.

secant (pp. 606, 687) Any line that intersects a circle in exactly two points.

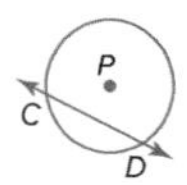

$\overleftrightarrow{CD}$ is a secant of⊙P.

sector of a circle (p. 744) A region of a circle bounded by a central angle and its intercepted arc.

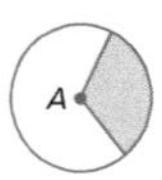

The shaded region is a sector of⊙A.

segment (p. 14) See *line segment.*

segment bisector (p. 27) A segment, line, or plane that intersects a segment at its midpoint.

espacio muestral El conjunto de todos los resultados posibles de un experimento.

factor de escala La razón de las medidas correspondientes de dos figuras semejantes.

factor de escala de homotecia Razon de una longitud en la imagen a una longitud correspondiente en la preimagen.

secante Cualquier recta que interseca un círculo exactamente en dos puntos.

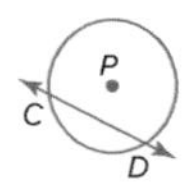

$\overleftrightarrow{CD}$ es una secante de⊙P.

sector circular Región de un círculo limitada por un ángulo central y su arco de intersección.

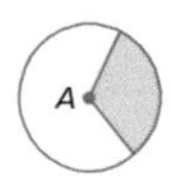

La región sombreada es un sector de⊙A.

segmento Ver *segmento de recta.*

bisector del segmento Segmento, recta o plano que interseca un segmento en su punto medio.

segment of a circle (p. 748) The region of a circle bounded by an arc and a chord.

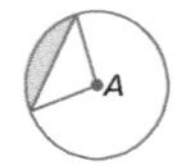

The shaded region is a segment of⊙A.

self-similar (p. 552) If any parts of a fractal image are replicas of the entire image, the image is self-similar.

semicircle (p. 653) An arc that measures 180.

sides of an angle (p. 36) The rays of an angle.

Sierpinski Triangle (p. 552) A self-similar fractal described by Waclaw Sierpinski. The figure was named for him.

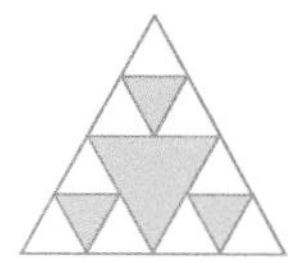

significant digits (p. 92) All of the digits of a measurement that are known to be accurate, plus one estimated digit.

similar polygons (p. 502) Polygons that have the same shape, but not necessarily the same size.

similar solids (p. 834) Solids that have exactly the same shape, but not necessarily the same size.

similarity ratio (p. 504) The scale factor between two similar polygons.

similarity transformation (p. 502) When a figure and its transformation image are similar.

sine (p. 596) For an acute angle of a right triangle, the ratio of the measure of the leg opposite the acute angle to the measure of the hypotenuse.

skew lines (p. 170) Lines that do not intersect and are not coplanar.

slant height (p. 773) The height of the lateral side of a pyramid or cone.

slope (p. 178) For a (nonvertical) line containing two points (x_1, y_1) and (x_2, y_2), the number m given by the formula $m = \frac{y_2 - y_1}{x_2 - x_1}$ where $x_2 \neq x_1$.

segmento de un círculo Región de un círculo limitada por un arco y una cuerda.

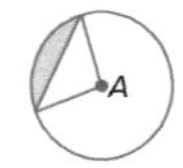

La región sombreada es un segmento de⊙A.

autosemejante Si cualquier parte de una imagen fractal es una réplica de la imagen completa, entonces la imagen es autosemejante.

semicírculo Arco que mide 180.

lados de un ángulo Los rayos de un ángulo.

triángulo de Sierpinski Fractal autosemejante descrito por el matemático Waclaw Sierpinski. La figura se nombró en su honor.

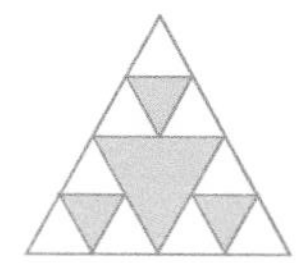

dígitos significativos Todos los dígitos de una medida que se sabe que son exactos más un dígito estimado.

polígonos semejantes Polígonos que tienen la misma forma, pero no necesariamente el mismo tamaño.

sólidos semejantes Sólidos que tienen exactamente la misma forma, pero no necesariamente el mismo tamaño.

razón de semejanza Factor de escala entre dos polígonos semejantes.

transformación de semejanza cuando una figura y su imagen transformada son semejantes.

seno Para un ángulo agudo de un triángulo rectángulo, razón entre la medida del cateto opuesto al ángulo agudo a la medida de la hipotenusa.

rectas alabeadas Rectas que no se intersecan y que no son coplanares.

altura oblicua Altura de la cara lateral de una pirámide o un cono.

pendiente Para una recta (no vertical) que contiene dos puntos (x_1, y_1) y (x_2, y_2), tel número m viene dado por la fórmula $m = \frac{y_2 - y_1}{x_2 - x_1}$ donde $x_2 \neq x_1$.

slope-intercept form (p. 179) A linear equation of the form $y = mx + b$. The graph of such an equation has slope m and y-intercept b.

solid of revolution (p. 798) A three-dimensional figure obtained by rotating a plane figure about a line.

solving a triangle (p. 617) Finding the measures of all of the angles and sides of a triangle.

space (p. 7) A boundless three-dimensional set of all points.

sphere (p. 76) In space, the set of all points that are a given distance from a given point, called the *center*.

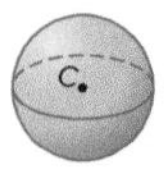

C is the center of the sphere.

spherical geometry (p. 827) The branch of geometry that deals with a system of points, great circles (lines), and spheres (planes).

square (p. 461) A quadrilateral with four right angles and four congruent sides.

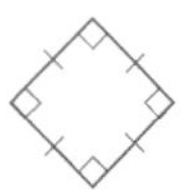

statement (p. 119) Any sentence that is either true or false, but not both.

substitution (p. P17) The process of solving one equation for a variable and substituting the resulting expression for that variable in another equation to solve a system of equations.

supplementary angles (p. 47) Two angles with measures that have a sum of 180.

surface area (p. 78) The sum of the areas of all faces and side surfaces of a three-dimensional figure.

symmetry (p. 259) A figure has symmetry if there exists a rigid motion—reflection, translation, rotation, or glide reflection—that maps the figure onto itself.

system of equations (p. P17) A set of two or more equations with the same variables.

forma pendiente-intersección Ecuación lineal de la forma $y = mx + b$ donde, la pendiente es m y la intersección y es b.

sólido de revolución Figura tridimensional que se obtiene al rotar una figura plana alrededor de una recta.

resolver un triángulo Calcular las medidas de todos los ángulos y todos los lados de un triángulo.

espacio Conjunto tridimensional no acotado de todos los puntos.

esfera En el espacio, conjunto de todos los puntos a cierta distancia de un punto dado llamado *centro*.

C es el centro de la esfera.

geometría esférica Rama de la geometría que estudia los sistemas de puntos, los círculos mayores (rectas) y las esferas (planos).

cuadrado Cuadrilátero con cuatro ángulos rectos y cuatro lados congruentes.

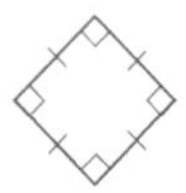

enunciado Cualquier suposición que puede ser falsa o verdadera, pero no ambas.

sustitución El proceso de resolver una ecuación para hallar una variable y sustituir esa variable por la expresión resultante en otra ecuación para resolver un sistema de ecuaciones.

ángulos suplementarios Dos ángulos cuya suma es igual a 180.

área de superficie Suma de las áreas de todas las caras y superficies laterales de una figura tridimensional.

simetría Una figura tiene simetría si existe un movimiento rígido (reflexión, translación, rotación, o reflexión con deslizamiento) que aplica la figura sobre sí misma.

sistema de ecuaciones Un conjunto de dos o más ecuaciones que tienen las mismas variables.

T

tangent 1. (p. 596) For an acute angle of a right triangle, the ratio of the measure of the leg opposite the acute angle to the measure of the leg adjacent to the acute angle. 2. (p. 678) A line in the plane of a circle that intersects the circle in exactly one point. The point of intersection is called the *point of tangency*. 3. (p. 818) A line that intersects a sphere in exactly one point.

theorem (p. 144) A statement or conjecture that can be proven true by undefined terms, definitions, and postulates.

theoretical probability (p. P9) The ratio of the number of favorable outcomes to the total number of possible outcomes.

transformation (p. 67) In a plane, a mapping for which each point has exactly one image point and each image point has exactly one preimage point.

translation (p. 67) A transformation that moves a figure the same distance in the same direction. A translation is a function that maps each point to its image along a vector such that each segment joining a point and its image has the same length as the vector, and this segment is also parallel to the vector.

translation vector (p. 232) The vector in which a translation maps each point to its image.

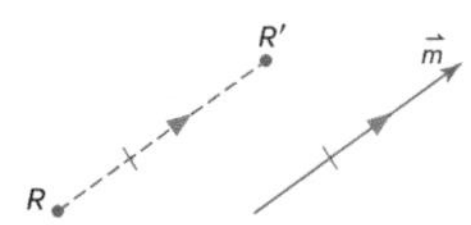

Point R', is a translation of point R along translation vector m.

tangente 1. Para un ángulo agudo de un triángulo rectángulo, razón de la medida del cateto opuesto al ángulo agudo a la medida del cateto adyacente al ángulo agudo. 2. Recta en el plano de un círculo que interseca el círculo en exactamente un punto. El punto de intersección se conoce como *punto de tangencia*. 3. Recta que interseca una esfera en exatamente un punto.

teorema Enunciado o conjetura que se puede demostrar como verdadera mediante términos geométricos básicos, definiciones y postulados.

probabilidad teórica La razón de la cantidad de resultados favorables a la cantidad total de resultados posibles.

transformación En un plano, aplicación para la cual cada punto del plano tiene un único punto de la imagen y cada punto de la imagen tiene un único punto de la preimagen.

traslación Transformación que mueve una figura la misma distancia en la misma dirección. Una traslación es una función que aplica cada punto a su imagen a lo largo de un vector, de modo que cada segmento que une un punto a su imagen tiene la misma longitud que el vector y este segmento es también paralelo al vector.

vector de traslación Vector en el cual una traslación aplica cada punto a su imagen.

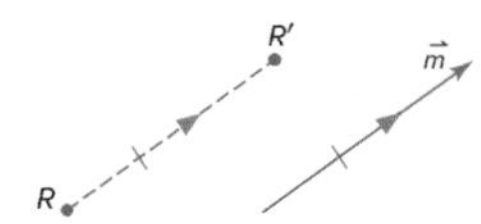

El punta R', es la traslación del punto R a lo largo del vector m de traslación.

transversal (p. 169) A line that intersects two or more lines in a plane at different points.

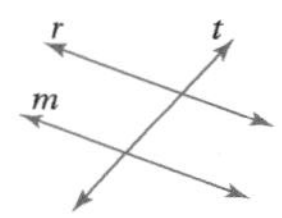

Line *t* is a transversal.

trapezoid (p. 469) A quadrilateral with exactly one pair of parallel sides. The parallel sides of a trapezoid are called *bases*. The nonparallel sides are called *legs*. The pairs of angles with their vertices at the endpoints of the same base are called *base angles*.

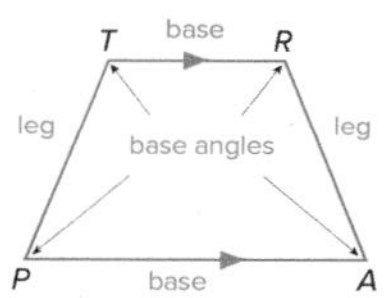

tree diagram (p. 859) An organized table of line segments (branches) that shows possible experiment outcomes.

trial (p. P8) A single performance of an experiment such as rolling a die one time.

trigonometric ratio (p. 596) A ratio of the lengths of sides of a right triangle.

trigonometry (p. 596) The study of the properties of triangles and trigonometric functions and their applications.

truth value (p. 119) The truth or falsity of a statement.

two-column proof (p. 152) A formal proof that contains statements and reasons organized in two columns. Each step is called a *statement*, and the properties that justify each step are called *reasons*.

two-stage experiment (p. 860) An experiment with two stages or events.

two-way frequency table (p. 909) A table that is used to show the frequencies or relative frequencies of data from a survey or experiment classified according to two variables, with the rows indicating one variable and the columns indicating the other.

U

undefined terms (p. 5) Words, usually readily understood, that are not formally explained by means of more basic words and concepts. The basic undefined terms of geometry are *point*, *line*, and *plane*.

transversal Recta que interseca dos o más rectas en el diferentes puntos del mismo plano.

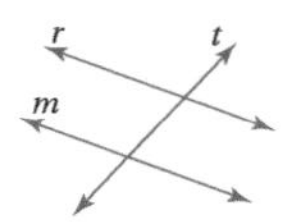

La recta *t* es una transversal.

trapecio Cuadrilátero con sólo un par de lados paralelos. Los lados paralelos del trapecio se llaman *bases*. Los lados no paralelos se llaman *catetos*. Los pares de ángulos cuyos vértices coinciden en los extremos de la misma base son los *ángulos de la base*.

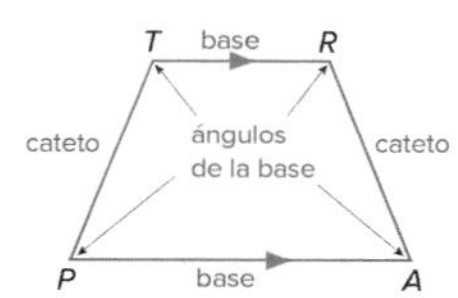

diagrama del árbol Tabla organizada de segmentos de recta (ramas) que muestra los resultados posibles de un experimento.

prueba Una sola realización de un experimento, como lanzar un dado una vez.

razón trigonométrica Razón de las longitudes de los lados de un triángulo rectángulo.

trigonometría Estudio de las propiedades de los triángulos, de las funciones trigonométricas y sus aplicaciones.

valor de verdad Condición de un enunciado de ser verdadero o falso.

demostración de dos columnas Demostración formal que contiene enunciados y razones organizadas en dos columnas. Cada paso se llama *enunciado* y las propiedades que lo justifican son las *razones*.

experimento de dos pasos Experimento que consta de dos pasos o eventos.

tabla de doble entrada o de frecuencias Tabla que se usa para mostrar las frecuencias o frecuencias relativas de los datos de una encuesta o experimento clasificado de acuerdo con dos variables, en la cual las hileras indican una variable y las columnas indican la otra variable.

término geométrico básico no definido Palabras que por lo general se entienden fácilmente y que no se explican formalmente mediante palabras o conceptos más básicos. Los términos geométricos básicos no definidos son el *punto*, la *recta* y el *plano*.

union (p. 866) For the union of event *A* and event *B*, the set of all outcomes in either event; represented by $A \cup B$.

V

vector (p. 600) A directed segment representing a quantity that has both magnitude (length) and direction.

vertex angle of an isosceles triangle (p. 285) See *isosceles triangle*.

vertex of an angle (p. 36) The common endpoint of an angle.

vertex of a polygon (p. 56) The vertex of each angle of a polygon.

vertex of a polyhedron (p. 76) The intersection of three edges of a polyhedron.

vertical angles (p. 46) Two nonadjacent angles formed by two intersecting lines.

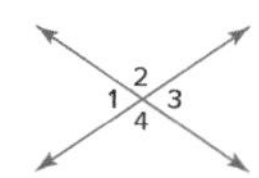

$\angle 1$ and $\angle 3$ are vertical angles.
$\angle 2$ and $\angle 4$ are vertical angles.

volume (p. 78) A measure of the amount of space enclosed by a three-dimensional figure.

X

x-coordinate (p. P15) The first number in an ordered pair.

Y

y-coordinate (p. P15) The second number in an ordered pair.

unión Para la unión del suceso *A* y el suceso *B*, el conjunto de todos los resultados de cualquiera de los dos sucesos; se representa con $A \cup B$.

vector Segmento dirigido que representa una cantidad, la cual posee tanto magnitud (longitud) como dirección.

ángulo del vértice un triángulo isosceles Ver *triángulo isósceles*.

vértice de un ángulo Extremo común de un ángulo.

vertice de un polígono Vértice de cada ángulo de un polígono.

vértice de un poliedro Intersección de las aristas de un poliedro.

ángulos opuestos por el vértice Dos ángulos no adyacentes formados por dos rectas que se intersecan.

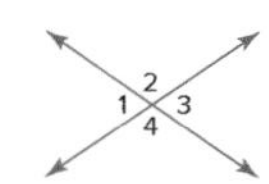

$\angle 1$ y $\angle 3$ son ángulos opuestos por el vértice.
$\angle 2$ y $\angle 4$ son ángulos opuestos por el vértice.

volumen La medida de la cantidad de espacio contiene una figura tridimensional.

coordenada *x* El primer número de un par ordenado.

coordenada *y* El segundo número de un par ordenado.

Index

Index

Index

Index

D

D

Index

Index

G

Index

G

Index

I

Index

H

I

Index

K

L

Index

L

M

M

Index

Index

Index

O

Open Educational Resources

Index

P

Index

Q

R

Index

S

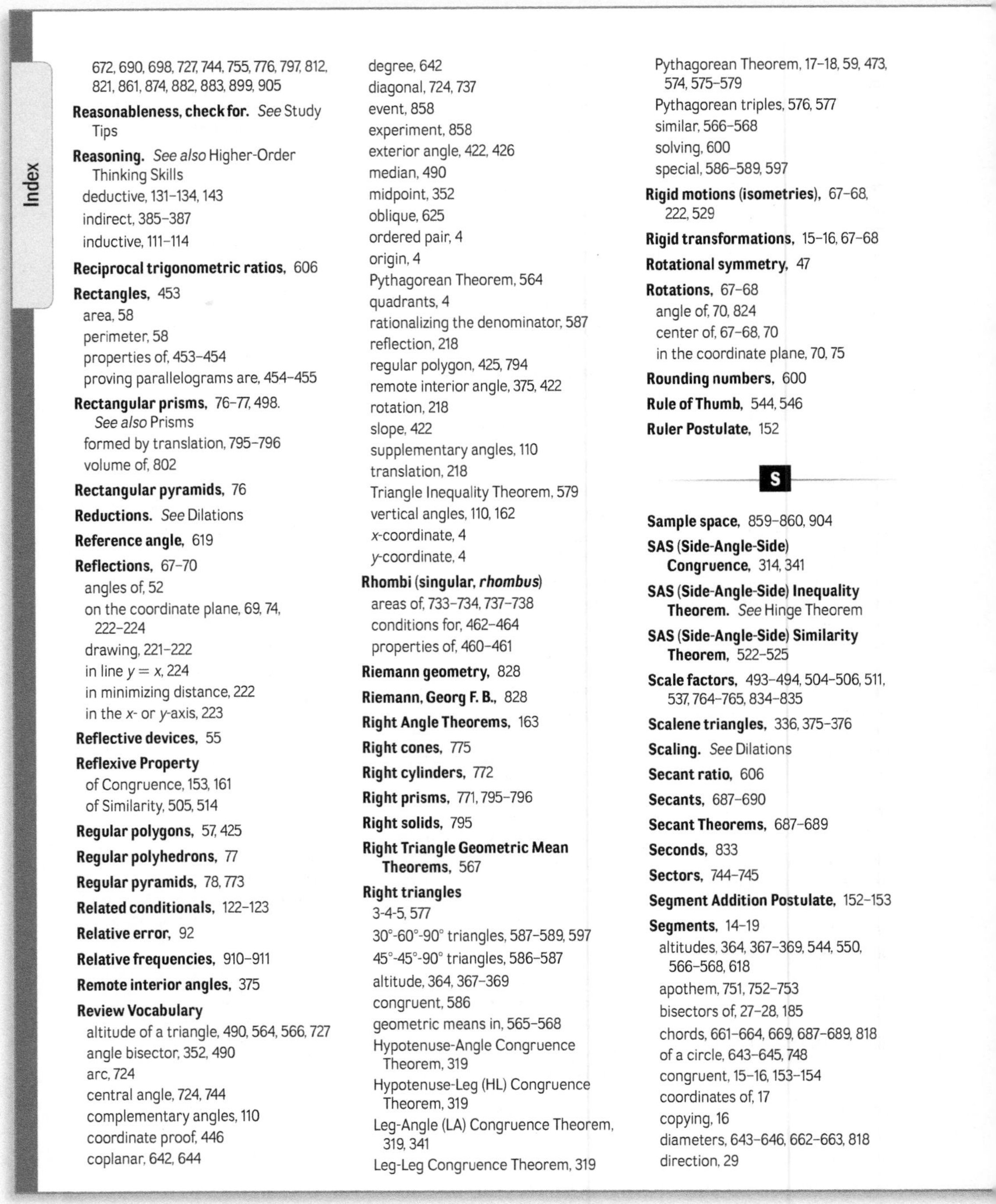
Index

Index

T

Index

T

Index

Index

Index

V

W

Coordinate Geometry

Slope	$m = \frac{y_2 - y_1}{x_2 - x_1}$
Distance on a number line	$d = \|a - b\|$
Distance on a coordinate plane	$d = \sqrt{(x_2 - x_1)^2 + (y_2 - y_1)^2}$
Distance in space	$d = \sqrt{(x_2 - x_1)^2 + (y_2 - y_1)^2 + (z_2 - z_1)^2}$
Arc length	$\ell = \frac{x}{360} \cdot 2\pi r$
Midpoint on a number line	$M = \frac{a + b}{2}$
Midpoint on a coordinate plane	$M = \left(\frac{x_1 + x_2}{2}, \frac{y_1 + y_2}{2}\right)$
Midpoint in space	$M = \left(\frac{x_1 + x_2}{2}, \frac{y_1 + y_2}{2}, \frac{z_1 + z_2}{2}\right)$

Perimeter and Circumference

square	$P = 4s$	**rectangle**	$P = 2\ell + 2w$	**circle**	$C = 2\pi r$ or $C = \pi d$

Area

square	$A = s^2$	**triangle**	$A = \frac{1}{2}bh$
rectangle	$A = \ell w$ or $A = bh$	**regular polygon**	$A = \frac{1}{2}Pa$
parallelogram	$A = bh$	**circle**	$A = \pi r^2$
trapezoid	$A = \frac{1}{2}h(b_1 + b_2)$	**sector of a circle**	$A = \frac{x}{360} \cdot \pi r^2$
rhombus	$A = \frac{1}{2}d_1d_2$ or $A = bh$		

Lateral Surface Area

prism	$L = Ph$	**pyramid**	$L = \frac{1}{2}P\ell$
cylinder	$L = 2\pi rh$	**cone**	$L = \pi r\ell$

Total Surface Area

prism	$S = Ph + 2B$	**cone**	$S = \pi r\ell + \pi r^2$
cylinder	$S = 2\pi rh + 2\pi r^2$	**sphere**	$S = 4\pi r^2$
pyramid	$S = \frac{1}{2}P\ell + B$		

Volume

cube	$V = s^3$	**pyramid**	$V = \frac{1}{3}Bh$
rectangular prism	$V = \ell wh$	**cone**	$V = \frac{1}{3}\pi r^2h$
prism	$V = Bh$	**sphere**	$V = \frac{4}{3}\pi r^3$
cylinder	$V = \pi r^2h$		

Equations for Figures on a Coordinate Plane

slope-intercept form of a line	$y = mx + b$	**circle**	$(x - h)^2 + (y - k)^2 = r^2$
point-slope form of a line	$y - y_1 = m(x - x_1)$		

Trigonometry

Law of Sines	$\frac{\sin A}{a} = \frac{\sin B}{b} = \frac{\sin C}{c}$	**Law of Cosines**	$a^2 = b^2 + c^2 - 2bc \cos A$ $b^2 = a^2 + c^2 - 2ac \cos B$ $c^2 = a^2 + b^2 - 2ab \cos C$
Pythagorean Theorem	$a^2 + b^2 = c^2$		

$\neq$	is not equal to	$\parallel$	is parallel to	$\lvert\overrightarrow{AB}\rvert$	magnitude of the vector from A to B
$\approx$	is approximately equal to	$\nparallel$	is not parallel to	A'	the image of preimage A
$\cong$	is congruent to	$\perp$	is perpendicular to	$\rightarrow$	is mapped onto
$\sim$	is similar to	$\triangle$	triangle	$\odot A$	circle with center A
$\angle$, $\measuredangle$	angle, angles	$>, \geq$	is greater than, is greater than or equal to	π	pi
$m\angle A$	degree measure of $\angle A$	$<, \leq$	is less than, is less than or equal to	$\widehat{AB}$	minor arc with endpoints A and B
$^\circ$	degree	$\square$	parallelogram	$\widehat{ABC}$	major arc with endpoints A and C
$\overleftrightarrow{AB}$	line containing points A and B	n-gon	polygon with n sides	$m\widehat{AB}$	degree measure of arc AB
$\overline{AB}$	segment with endpoints A and B	$a{:}b$	ratio of a to b	$f(x)$	f of x, the value of f at x
$\overrightarrow{AB}$	ray with endpoint A containing B	(x, y)	ordered pair	!	factorial
AB	measure of $\overline{AB}$, distance between points A and B	(x, y, z)	ordered triple	${}_nP_r$	permutation of n objects taken r at a time
$\sim p$	negation of p, not p	$\sin x$	sine of x	${}_nC_r$	combination of n objects taken r at a time
$p \wedge q$	conjunction of p and q	$\cos x$	cosine of x	$P(A)$	probability of A
$p \vee q$	disjunction of p and q	$\tan x$	tangent of x	$P(A\mid B)$	the probability of A given that B has already occurred
$p \longrightarrow q$	conditional statement, if p then q	$\vec{a}$	vector a		
$p \longleftrightarrow q$	biconditional statement, p if and only if q	$\overrightarrow{AB}$	vector from A to B		

Measures

Metric	Customary
Length	
1 kilometer (km) = 1000 meters (m) 1 meter = 100 centimeters (cm) 1 centimeter = 10 millimeters (mm)	1 mile (mi) = 1760 yards (yd) 1 mile = 5280 feet (ft) 1 yard = 3 feet 1 yard = 36 inches (in.) 1 foot = 12 inches
Volume and Capacity	
1 liter (L) = 1000 milliliters (mL) 1 kiloliter (kL) = 1000 liters	1 gallon (gal) = 4 quarts (qt) 1 gallon = 128 fluid ounces (fl oz) 1 quart = 2 pints (pt) 1 pint = 2 cups (c) 1 cup = 8 fluid ounces
Weight and Mass	
1 kilogram (kg) = 1000 grams (g) 1 gram = 1000 milligrams (mg) 1 metric ton (t) = 1000 kilograms	1 ton (T) = 2000 pounds (lb) 1 pound = 16 ounces (oz)